D1087848

THE   ENCYCLOPEDIA   OF   GEOMORPHOLOGY

REINHOLD ONE-VOLUME ENCYCLOPEDIAS

The

ENCYCLOPEDIA

of

GEOMORPHOLOGY

ENCYCLOPEDIA OF EARTH SCIENCES SERIES, VOLUME III

EDITED BY

Rhodes W. Fairbridge

Professor of Geology
Columbia University
New York

REINHOLD BOOK CORPORATION
New York   Amsterdam   London

*"MEN LOVE ABSTRACT REASON-
ING AND NEAT SYSTEMATIZATION
SO MUCH THAT THEY THINK
NOTHING OF DISTORTING THE
TRUTH, CLOSING THEIR EYES AND
EARS TO CONTRARY EVIDENCE TO
PRESERVE THEIR LOGICAL CON-
STRUCTIONS."*
THE UNDERGROUND MAN IN
NOTES FROM UNDERGROUND
—DOSTOEVSKY

ReF
GB
10
.F3

Copyright © 1968 by
REINHOLD BOOK CORPORATION
All rights reserved
Library of Congress Catalog Card Number: 68-58342
Printed in the United States of America

PREFACE

"The Encyclopedia of Geomorphology" appears as the first alphabetic, encyclopedic treatment of the science of Geomorphology—the analytic physiography of the Earth's surface. It is numbered, for convenience in cross-referencing, as Volume III of the "Encyclopedia of Earth Sciences" series that Reinhold is publishing under the present editor. At this time eight volumes either have appeared or are in preparation. Each volume is completely autonomous and runs from A to Z within its own subdisciplines.

It is our plan to bring the subdisciplines of the Earth Sciences together into convenient, coherent "packages," so that the man in search of information need not face a morass of card files, computer banks, or endless library shelves before getting his basic orientation in the subject. This Encyclopedia should first answer general questions. The inquirer should be able to handle the technical language if he has had a reasonable high school education. The specialist may also find this volume an appreciable time-saver. If these pages do not give the last word, then reference may be made to the long bibliographies.

Integration

To the student reader the editor cannot stress emphatically enough the need to keep your reading and training as broad as possible. If your investigations have led you only into geomorphology, without getting a good foundation in the principles of the Earth Sciences, you can *never* become a competent geomorphologist. It is essential in order to appreciate coastal geomorphology, for example, to read about the oceans (see "Encyclopedia of Oceanography," our Volume I, published in 1966). To understand about ice ages in connection with glaciation, one cannot avoid some consideration of meteorology and climatology (see "Encyclopedia of Atmospheric Sciences and Astrogeology," our Volume II, published

in 1967). To appreciate the nature of the history of the atmosphere, one must consider the history of our own planet and other planets (see the astrogeology entries in Volume II). To realize the nature of weathering, rocks, and solution, reference must be made to geochemistry, and so on (see "The Encyclopedia of Geochemistry and Mineralogy," in preparation as Volume IV).

Future volumes also planned or in preparation at the time of writing include:

Volume V	"The Encyclopedia of Geophysics, Structure and Petrology"
Volume VI	"The Encyclopedia of Applied Geology and Sedimentology"
Volume VII	"The Encyclopedia of Stratigraphy and Paleontology"
Volume VIII	"The Encyclopedia of Regional Geology" (including Biographies)

The "Science of Scenery"

Geomorphology is sometimes defined as the study of landscape and of the geologic forces that produce it. Put another way, it is the dynamic geology of the face of the Earth. Little is said, as a rule, about the esthetic appreciation of scenery. Perhaps that is the realm of poets, but at heart many geologists *are* poets; certainly, many are musicians. You should hear them lamenting the ruination of the countryside by garbage dumps, wrecked cars, and advertisement bill-boards . . . ! And the pollution of our rivers and lakes by industrial wastes. . . And our air with smoke and fumes. . . Yet, we of the geological profession are partly responsible for placing the facilities in the hand of Man that have

ALMA COLLEGE
MONTEITH LIBRARY
ALMA, MICHIGAN

helped create this disruption on the face of Mother Earth. We all appreciate the comforts brought by civilization, but we should also share in the burden of trying to conserve and preserve the natural heritage. By learning to know the natural processes of the Earth's scenery and environment, we, both amateurs and professionals, can best serve our fellow residents on this Earth by establishing what the fundamental laws of geomorphology are and then by protesting most vigorously wherever and whenever Man's activity seems to be directed toward destruction and chaos. All morality is not simply a matter of black and white. In the construction of a great water-conservation dam facility, the question must be asked: "Does the benefit derived, e.g. the farms irrigated, the hungry mouths fed, and so on, compensate for the loss of the original landscape? Will the new lake that is created upset nature so much that it will generate unsuspected disequilibria in the local morphology? Will it upset the ecology? Will it introduce new diseases or apply unjustified hardships on the former residents?" The questions can be repeated in countless variations. The geomorphologist in the coming decades faces a considerable social challenge.

Point of View

Articles in an encyclopedia of this sort, written by many different persons, naturally represent many points of view. Needless to say, there is no room for every opinion. Where the individual author's opinions differ from those of the editor, however, no effort has been made at censorship. On the other hand there has been no referee for the editor's own views, except for the excellent collaboration of readers who have been most generous with their time in critically reviewing papers. We have tried to get each paper reviewed at least once, but this does not guarantee either accuracy or balance. To err is human, but in the time and space available we have done our best.

Overlaps and omissions are inevitable. We have purposely allowed many overlaps to come in, because expressed in different language or in a different context the overlap may present an interesting or new viewpoint. What a geologist regards as "Quaternary Stratigraphy," a geographer may call "Morphogenetic History," and an anthropologist may think of as "Archeological Environments." The approach is likely to be different in each case, but it is illuminating to observe the range of viewpoints.

In allocating articles for a particular volume, the editor and his many advisers have had to be guided by two things: (a) the appropriateness and usefulness of a certain grouping of articles, and (b) the limitations of space. We have been criticized already for some of these decisions. For example, "Coral Reefs" was left out of the Oceanography volume (I) and placed under Geomorphology (III); "Ecology" was left out of Oceanography and allocated to Stratigraphy and Paleontology (VII).

References

Several systems of referencing have been used to help the reader go on to the next step:

a) Reference to a related discipline, in another volume, usually noted by volume number only; it is assumed to be one of the "Encyclopedia of Earth Sciences" series (though some are still only in the planning stage), e.g., ICE AGE METEOROLOGY (see Volume II), PALEOGEOGRAPHY (see Volume VII).

b) Reference from the alphabetic listing to a specific article, usually when the name is almost or is entirely synonymous, e.g., ICE SCOUR, *see* GLACIAL SCOUR, OMBILIC *see* CIRQUE.

c) Reference from the body of an article to a subject that is taken up in more detail elsewhere in the volume, e.g., within MOUNTAIN SYSTEMS there is a cross-reference, amongst others, to *Basin-Range Landscape* (q.v.).

d) References to related articles, listed at the end of a given entry, thus **Cross-references:** e.g., at the end of REGOLITH AND SAPROLITE, cross-reference is made to *Head, Solifluction, Weathering,* etc.

e) Under the title **References** there are literature citations. In some instances these are not all mentioned in the text; in others there are many mentions in the text of various papers for which there is no room for full citation. However, a star (asterisk *) usually indicates at least one paper or book containing long bibliographies and thus most of the relevant literature.

No doubt some critics will complain that the editor has monopolized many of the entries in what purports to be a balanced symposium. Let it be noted that this was not his original intention. Literally thousands of invitations were sent out, but geologists are busy people: they are always surveying, exploring, teaching, administering, and writing. Some, alas, in high hopes, did promise to help but later became involved in something else. So in the end, the editor often had to dig into his own files and do his best. Some of these efforts are less than perfect, but the motto has been: get the job done. If we delay, ever seeking perfection, we may still be encyclopedia-less a decade from now. The reference is needed *now*. In a decade or so we can think of another edition.

References to current literature have been stressed throughout the volume. New material is constantly coming in, but often enough the old quotations from G. K. Gilbert, Alexander Agassiz, or Sir Charles Lyell and the other "greats" are as important today as in the past century. If the reader asks how the editor keeps up with it all, the answer is simple: lots of good friends, punch cards, and hard work. This could not be done without the aid of the excellent abstract sources; to each and all

of the diligent workers preparing abstracts, we say "thank you, a thousand times."

The principal research sources are:

1. *Geomorphological Abstracts,* 1960–1965 (edited by Keith M. Clayton, London). From 1966 onwards issued as *Geographical Abstracts.* Every serious student should get a subscription in order to keep abreast of the field.

2. *Bibliography of North American Geology* (now issued monthly by the U.S. Geological Survey; integrated volumes list references back to 1732). The subscription price is extraordinarily modest. This should be a *must* for all English-speaking geologists.

3. *Bibliography of Geology Exclusive of North America* (issued by the Geological Society of America). From 1933 to 1964 this was an invaluable source of information. From 1965 onwards, however, it has been in an expanded form, and the subscription price was raised to such astronomic levels that it can be consulted only in select libraries. Prior to 1933 one may refer to the Geological Society of London, "List of Geological Literature added to the library" (annually).

4. *Current Geographical Publications* (issued monthly by the American Geographical Society, New York City, since 1938.)

5. Foreign-language abstracts and bibliographies are issued in French, German, and Russian. All are of high quality and are to be found in the better geological libraries.

6. Abstracts in cognate fields (Biology, Chemistry, Engineering, Hydrology, Meteorology, Physics, Soils, etc.) are available in professional libraries but generally speaking, are too voluminous and expensive for geological users. Little effort appears to have been made to make their sub-sections useful to specialists. (For example, *Chemical Abstracts* is broken down into fields, so

that geologists can subscribe to the parts that interest them; but these sections carry *no alphabetic author indexes,* so they are largely useless.)

There are three good journals specializing in geomorphology (all foreign, but many of the articles are in English), namely, *Zeitschrift für Geomorphologie* (Berlin), *Revue de Géomorphologie Dynamique* (Paris), *Geografiska Annaler,* Series A (Stockholm). Overseas, geomorphology is usually classed as "physical geography," and accordingly many of the references are to be found in geographical volumes, e.g., the *Geographic Journal* (London). In the United States geomorphology is more integrated into geology, and the best sources are the *Professional Papers of the U.S. Geological Survey, Geological Society of America Bulletin, Journal of Geology,* and the *American Journal of Science.* In Canada, there is in particular the *Geographical Bulletin* of Ottawa, the *Canadian Geographer* of Toronto, and the *Cahiers de Géographie de Quebec.* Specialized journals are also to be found in Australia, New Zealand, India, and elsewhere. For the linguists there are fine journals in Russian (see parts translated in *Soviet Geography* by the American Geographical Society), in Polish (also many articles translated or with western abstracts), Czech, Slovak, Yugoslav, Rumanian, and other languages. (For a thorough listing see the Index, *Geographical Abstracts,* sections A–D).

Spelling and Units

With regard to spelling, style, and terminology, we have been constantly plagued by differences of opinion amongst our various contributors, e.g., groyne and groin, dike and dyke, paleolithic and palaeolithic, aeolian and eolian, gage and gauge, landform and land form, groundwater and ground water, watershed and divide. What does the distracted editorial staff do? We have tried to avoid the dictatorial straight-

jacket. In part, the question is resolved by saying that this Encyclopedia is being published initially in North America (though intended for international use), therefore we shall follow local usage. However, not all Americans agree on Webster's third edition; they may prefer the second edition or the Oxford English Dictionary. Partly, it is a question of discipline: the engineers like "gage"; geologists usually prefer "gauge." It is said that "consistency is the shiboleth of little minds." Whichever way, if the facts are straight (pious hope!), let us say to the spelling controversialists: "A plague on both your houses!"

Many of us in the geological world, as scientists, have been conscious of the superiorities of the metric system since our high school days. It is good to record that in the year of our publication (1968) a) the U.S. Congress voted funds to explore the question of introducing the metric system officially into the United States, and b) Great Britain, even more advanced, has laid out a time-table for its introduction; the Royal Society Conference of Editors (1968) has recommended that all scientific papers give preference to this system. It is not always easy for geomorphologists who have to deal with topographic maps in feet or charts in fathoms; mining and engineering geologists frequently have to deal with non-scientists, while soil specialists may have to work with farmers. In Volume II of this series ("Encyclopedia of Atmospheric Sciences and Astrogeology," 1967) a very long entry was devoted to UNITS, NUMBERS, CONSTANTS AND SYMBOLS; this entry contains conversion tables and data that may prove helpful for geomorphologists and geophysicists.

Abbreviations and Citations

Abbreviations widely used through this volume include the following:

B.P. (Before Present, i.e., before A.D. 1950, in C^{14} dating)

G = Günz
(Nebraskan)
M = Mindel
(Kansan)
R = Riss
(Illinoian)
W = Würm
(Wisconsin, -an)

} The four "standard" Quaternary glacial stages

G/M, M/R, R/W = interglacial stages.

$W_{I,II,III}$ = stadials (cold phases, within a stage).

q.v. = *quod vide* (Latin), used to cross-reference articles.

see pr Vol. . . . = see another volume in "Encyclopedia of Earth Sciences" series, planned for future production.

Abbreviations to *literature citations* follow, in general, the system used by *Chemical Abstracts*.

To Our Friends

The creation of this Encyclopedia, like the others in the series, would not have been possible without the wonderful and whole-hearted cooperation of our numerous contributors. There are 150 of them in this volume and twenty different countries are represented.

We have great pleasure in acknowledging the generous help of many colleagues in reading and constructively criticizing many of the contributions. Alphabetically, the list includes:

Claude Bernard, André Cailleux, Sir Charles Cotton, D. R. Crandell, Willi Czajka, R. R. Dagon, G. H. Dury, Donald P. Elston, Knut Faegri, R. Galon, H. F. Garner, R. P. Goldthwait, Stuart Harris, H. M. Huber, P. B. King, O. K. Leontyev, John Oliver, Erwin Raisz, Erik Rudberg, Stanley Schumm, J. B. Sissons, David Smith, Arthur N. Strahler, S. A. Strelkov, C. R. Twidale, E. M. Van Zinderen Bakker, H. T. Verstappen, Lee Wilson, Herbert Wright.

Appreciation is also due to our indexers: Dolores Fairbridge, Lillian Cavallero, and Marie McMahon. Likewise to our excellent draftsman, Ernest Adelberg. Again, to our copy-editors, Florence Poillon and Alberta Gordon. To our ever-patient and wise publisher, Charles Hutchinson, of Reinhold Book Corporation. Without the constant aid of the Columbia University librarians, notably Beth Fossland, many of our references might never have been found. Finally, we must acknowledge the dedicated loyalty and passionate attention to every detail of the project of our editorial assistant "Dotty" Spiro.

The preface is, of course, the place for the editor to get his revenge on numbers of otherwise unsung heroes amongst the stenographers, typesetters, and just plain literary geniuses. This year's crop of "specials" includes: the "debauched river," "ice-damned lakes," "medical moraines," "cretched pebbles," the "roche mutiny," some "lunatic ripples," "crystalline bounders," "horseshow-like walls," "salacious ooze," "thin-bedded senses," "peneplainsated surface" (obviously fed up with peneplains), island belts that are "accurate" in plan, and finally our trusty old friend "seal level"—which is evidently the surface of the ocean to which seals occasionally come up for a breath of air. Prize phrase of the year: "In North America there was early recognition of ice transport by Peter Dobson in 1826 . . ." Stout fellow, Mr. Dobson! Alas, it must be confessed that the editor was the perpetrator.

RHODES W. FAIRBRIDGE

New York, N.Y.
September, 1968

CONTRIBUTORS

L. C. BEADLE, Dept. of Zoology, The University, Newcastle-on-Tyne, England. *East African Lakes.*

ROBERT P. BECKINSALE, Dept. of Geography, University of Oxford, Oxford, England. *Base Level; Geomorphology, History of.*

Y. K. BENTOR, Dept. of Geology, Hebrew University of Jerusalem, Israel. *Dead Sea.*

ERIC C. F. BIRD, Dept. of Geography, University of Melbourne, Parkville, Victoria, Australia. *Coastal Lagoon Dynamics; Delta Dynamics.*

ERIC H. BROWN, Dept. of Geography, University College, London, England. *Peneplain: Planation Surface.*

PER BRUUN, Dept. of Port and Ocean Engineering, Technical University of Norway, Trondheim, Norway. *Beach Erosion and Coastal Protection; Sediment Transport—Fluvial and Marine; Stream Flow.*

JULIUS BÜDEL, Geographischen Instituts der Universitäts, Würzburg, West Germany. *Geomorphology—Principles.*

WILLIAM B. BULL, Dept. of Geology, College of Mines, University of Arizona, Tucson, Arizona. *Alluvial Fan, Cone.*

R. E. BURNS, U.S. Dept. of Commerce, Environmental Science Services Administration, Joint Oceanographic Research Group, Seattle, Washington. *Island Arcs, General.*

RAYMUNDO J. CHICO, Economic Geology Consultant, 103 Woodlawn Road, Baltimore, Maryland. *Epigene; Mud Cracks; Playa; Soil Cracks (Giant).*

RICHARD CHORLEY, Dept. of Geography, Cambridge University, Cambridge, England. *Base Level; Geomorphology, History of.*

JOHN I. CLARKE, Dept. of Geography, University of Durham, Durham, England. *Altimetric Frequency Curve.*

KEITH M. CLAYTON, Dept. of Geography, University of East Anglia, Norwich, England. *Terraces, Thalassostatic.*

DONALD R. COATES, Dept. of Geology, State University of New York, Binghamton, New York. *Finger Lakes.*

ROBERT E. COHENOUR, Vanguard Exploration Co., Salt Lake City, Utah. *Great Salt Lake.*

JAMES W. COLE, Victoria University, Wellington, New Zealand. *Crater Lakes.*

JAMES M. COLEMAN, Coastal Studies Institute, Louisiana State University, Baton Rouge, Louisiana. *Deltaic Evolution.*

DONALD J. COLQUHOUN, Dept. of Geology, University of South Carolina, Columbia, South Carolina. *Coastal Plains.*

MAURICE E. COOLEY, U.S. Geological Survey, Water Resources Division, Tucson, Arizona. *Canyon Cutting in the Colorado River System.*

CHARLES A. COTTON, Emeritus Professor of Geology, Victoria University of Wellington, New Zealand. *Mountain Glacier Landscapes; Plunging Cliffs; Relict Landforms; Tectonic Landscapes; Volcanic Landscapes.*

DWIGHT R. CRANDELL, U.S. Geological Survey, Engineering Geology Branch, Denver, Colorado. *Avalanche; Mudflow.*

MAX D. CRITTENDEN, Jr., U.S. Geological Survey, Menlo Park, California. *Water Loading and Crustal Response.*

J. L. DAVIES, Dept. of Geography, University of Tasmania, Hobart, Tasmania, Australia. *Beach Ridges.*

EDWARD DERBYSHIRE, Dept. of Geography, University of Keele, Newcastle, Staffordshire, England. *Cirque; Cirque Glacier.*

MAX DERRUAU, Institut de Géographie, Université de Clermont-Ferrand, Carnot, France. *Mountains; Thalweg or Talweg.*

ROBERT S. DIETZ, Environmental Science Services Administration, Institute for Oceanography, Silver Spring, Maryland. *Wave Base.*

L. DRAPER, National Institute of Oceanography, Godalming, Surrey, England. *Rip Current.*

GEORGE H. DURY, Dept. of Geography, University of Sydney, Sydney, New South Wales, Australia. *Dry Valley; Gibber; Glacial Breaching; Streams— Underfit.*

JAN DYLIK, Instytut Geograficzny, Uniwersytetu Lodzkiego, Lodz, Poland. *Thermokarst.*

J. A. ELSON, Dept. of Geological Sciences, McGill University, Montreal, Canada. *Champlain Sea; Glacial Lake Agassiz; Washboard Moraines.*

WILLIAM W. EMMETT, U.S. Geological Survey, Water Resources Division, Washington, D.C. *Gully Erosion.*

ROBERT D. ENZMANN, 29 Adams Street, Lexington, Massachusetts. *Geomorphology—Expanded Theory; Instrument Contour Diagram; Signature Theory.*

ROBERT K. FAHNESTOCK, Dept. of Geology, State University College, Fredonia, New York. *Stream Channel Characteristics.*

RHODES W. FAIRBRIDGE, Dept. of Geology, Columbia University, New York. Principal entries: *Ablation Moraine; Algal Reefs; Aral Sea; Atlantic and Pacific Type Coasts; Badlands; Beach; Col; Colluvium; Cone Karst; Continent; Continents and Oceans; Coral Reefs— Morphology and Theories; Corrosion, Etching; Crater; Cryology, Cryosphere, Cryergy; Cryopedology, Cryonivation, Cryoplanation, Cryoturbation; Cryptodepressions; Deflation; Deglaciation, Recession; Dell; Denudation; Desert Varnish; Drift, Glacial: Drift Theory; Drowned Valley; Earth Pillars or Pyramids; Estuary; Etched Pebbles; Exhumed Landscape; Exogenic Dynamics; Faro; Fault Scarp, Faultline Scarp; Felsenmeer; Fjell; Fjord; Fringing Reef; Gipfelflur; Glacial Geology: Periglacial and Global Effects; Glacial Lakes; Glacial Refuges; Glaciation, Glacierization; Hamada; Head, Eluvium; Holocene; Ice-Thrusting; Induration; Inversion (of Topogra-*

phy, Relief); Islands; Kara-Bogaz Gulf; Kettle; Lagoon (Coral-reef Type); Lake Baikal; Lake Titicaca; Land Mass and Major Landform Classification; Landscape Types; Limestone Coastal Weathering; Littoral Processes—An Introduction; Makatea; Microatoll; Morphogenetic Regions; Morphotectonics; Mountain Systems; Organisms as Geomorphic Agents; Periglacial Eolian Effects; Plateau; Platforms— Wave-cut; Quaternary Period; Regolith and Saprolite; Ria, Rias Coast; Sabkha; Salt Karst; Savanna Landscape; Slipoff Slope; Solution Pits and Pans; Spheroidal Weathering; Steppe Landscape; Suffosion and Tundra Craters; Surell's Laws of Fluvial Erosion; Taiga Landscape; Terraces, Fluvial— Environmental Controls; Terracettes, Lynchets and "Cattle Tracks"; Terrain, Terrane; Texture—Topographic; Volcanic Necks and Diatremes; Volcano-Karst; Warping; Wave Base.

W. R. FARRAND, Dept. of Geology, University of Michigan, Ann Arbor, Michigan. *Isobase; Postglacial Isostatic Rebound.*

SANDRA FELDMAN, Dept. of Geology, University of New Mexico, Albuquerque, New Mexico. *Drainage Patterns.*

N. C. FLEMMING, National Institute of Oceanography, Godalming, Surrey, England. *Submerged Shorelines.*

DEREK C. FORD, Dept. of Geography, McMaster University, Hamilton College, Hamilton, Ontario, Canada. *Stalactite and Stalagmite; Waterfalls.*

OTTO FRÄNZLE, Geographisches Institut der Universität, Bonn, West Germany. *Valley Evolution.*

THEODORE F. FREERS, North Dakota Geological Survey, Grand Forks, North Dakota. *Crevasse.*

IVAN GAMS, Geografski Institut, University of Ljublijana, Yugoslavia. *Blind Valley.*

H. F. GARNER, Dept. of Geology, Rutgers —The State University, Newark, New Jersey. *Climatic Geomorphology;*

Tropical Weathering and Relief.

J. GENTILLI, University of Western Australia, Nedlands, W. A., Australia. *Duricrust; Exfoliation; Landscape, Geographical; Regions, Natural and Geographical.*

I. P. GERASIMOV, Geographic Institute, Academy of Sciences, Moscow, U.S.S.R. *Morphostructure.*

R. GERMAN, Geologisches Institut Universität, Tübingen, West Germany. *Moraines.*

DAVID GILES, Dept. of Geology, University of New Mexico, Albuquerque, New Mexico. *Graben; Horst.*

EDMUND D. GILL, National Museum of Victoria, Melbourne, Australia. *Eustasy.*

RICHARD P. GOLDTHWAIT, Dept. of Geology, Ohio State University, Columbus, Ohio. *Glacial Geology: Introduction.*

W. GRIJM, Rijkswaterstaat Directie Noord-Holland, Den Haag, The Netherlands. *Coastlines: Theoretical Shapes.*

RICHARD F. HADLEY, U.S. Geological Survey, Denver, Colorado. *Ephemeral Streams.*

STUART A. HARRIS, Dept. of Geography, University of Kansas, Lawrence, Kansas. *Cycles, Geomorphic; Drainage Patterns; Gilgai; Grade, Graded Stream; Landscape Analysis; Microrelief; Misfit Stream; Mobility Principle; Nickpoint; Primärrumpf; Process— Structure—Stage; Puys; Tombolo; Treppen Concept; Weathering Unit; Youth—Maturity—Old Age.*

BRUCE C. HEEZEN, Lamont Geological Observatory of Columbia University, Palisades, New York. *Submarine Geomorphology.*

C. G. HIGGINS, Dept. of Geology, University of California, Davis, California. *Beachrock.*

PETER V. HOBBS, Dept. of Atmospheric Sciences, University of Washington, Seattle, Washington. *Snow: Metamorphism of Deposited Snow.*

FRANCIS D. HOLE, Dept. of Soil Science, University of Wisconsin, Madison, Wisconsin. *Erosion.*

DONALD A. HOLM (retired), formerly with Arabian American Oil Co., Dhahran, Saudi Arabia. *Sand Dunes.*

JACK L. HOUGH, Dept. of Meteorology and Oceanography, University of Michigan, Ann Arbor, Michigan. *Great Lakes (North America).*

ALAN D. HOWARD, Dept. of Geography, Johns Hopkins University, Baltimore, Maryland. *General Systems Theory in Geomorphology.*

ARTHUR D. HOWARD, Dept. of Geology, Stanford University, Stanford, California. *Terraces, Fluvial—Introduction; Terraces—Marine.*

JOHN N. HUTCHINSON, Dept. of Civil Engineering, Imperial College of Science and Technology, University of London, London, England. *Mass Movement.*

ALFRED JAHN, Geographical Institute, Wroclaw University, Wroclaw, Poland. *Patterned Ground.*

J. N. JENNINGS, Dept. of Geography, Australian National University, Canberra, A.C.T., Australia. *Tafoni.*

ARTHUR JOHNSON, Dept. Civil Engineering, University of North Dakota, Grand Forks, North Dakota. *Valley (Mountain) Glaciers.*

O. A. JONES, Dept. of Geology, University of Queensland, St. Lucia, Australia. *Great Barrier Reefs.*

C. KIDSON, Dept. of Geography and Anthropology, University College of Wales, Aberystwyth, Wales. *Coastal Geomorphology.*

LESTER C. KING, Dept. of Geology, University of Natal, Durban, South Africa. *Cymatogeny; Geomorphology; Gondwana Landscape; Pediplanation.*

M. V. KLENOVA, Institute of Oceanology, Academy of Sciences, Moscow, U.S.S.R. *Caspian Sea.*

EDWARD R. LaCHAPELLE, Dept. of Atmospheric Sciences, University of Washington, Seattle, Washington. *Snow Avalanches.*

ARTHUR H. LACHENBRUCH, U.S. Geological Survey, Branch of Theoretical

Geophysics, Menlo Park, California. *Permafrost.*

ROBERT G. LaFLEUR, Dept. of Geology, Rensselaer Polytechnic Institute, Troy, New York. *Glacial Lake Albany.*

J. LAGRULA, Institut de Météorologie et de Physique du Globe, Université d'Alger, Algeria. *Hypsographic Curve.*

LAURENCE H. LATTMAN, Dept. of Geology and Geophysics, Pennsylvania State University, University Park, Pennsylvania. *Structural Control in Geomorphology.*

W. R. LAUDER, Dept. of Geology, Victoria University, Wellington, New Zealand. *Stream Capture, Piracy.*

HULBERT A. LEE, Dept. of Mines and Technical Surveys, Geological Survey of Canada, Ottawa, Canada. *Tyrrell Sea.*

BERNARD LE MÉHAUTÉ, Tetra Tech, Inc. Pasadena, California. *Littoral Processes—Quantitative Treatment.*

F. STEARNS MacNEIL, U.S. Geological Survey, Menlo Park, California. *Atolls.*

RUDOLF MARTIN, Rudolf Martin & Associates, Calgary, Alberta, Canada. *Paleogeomorphology.*

BRUCE MASON, Dept. of Geography, University of Adelaide, Adelaide, South Australia, Australia. *Lake Eyre.*

JOHN H. MAXSON (deceased, March, 1966), formerly with the Aerial Exploration Co., Denver, Colorado. *Arid Cycle.*

ALEXANDER R. McBIRNEY, Center for Volcanology, University of Oregon, Eugene, Oregon. *Caldera.*

BRAINERD MEARS, Jr., Dept. of Geology, University of Wyoming, Laramie, Wyoming. *Piping.*

MESCHERIKOV, J. A., Soviet Geophysical Committee, Academy of Sciences, Moscow, U.S.S.R. *Crustal Movements—Contemporary; Morphostructure; Neotectonics; Plains.*

GEORGE W. MOORE, La Jolla Marine Geology Laboratory, U.S. Geological Survey, La Jolla, California. *Arctic Beaches; Limestone Caves; Speleothems.*

MARIE MORISAWA, Dept. of Geology, Antioch College, Yellow Springs, Ohio. *Rivers.*

ROGER B. MORRISON, U.S. Geological Survey, Denver, Colorado. *Pluvial Lakes.*

FRITZ MÜLLER, McGill University, Montreal, Quebec, Canada. *Pingos (Modern).*

J. G. NELSON, Dept. of Geography, University of Calgary, Calgary, Alberta, Canada. *Stagnant Ice Melting.*

A. CONRAD NEUMANN, Institute of Marine Science, University of Miami, Miami, Florida. *Biological Erosion of Limestone Coasts.*

WALTER S. NEWMAN, Dept. of Geology, Queens College of the City University of New York, Flushing, New York. *Coastal Stability.*

CLIFF D. OLLIER, Earth Science Dept., University of Papua and New Guinea, Boroko, T.P.N.G., Australia. *Lava-displaced Drainage and Deep Leads.*

JERRY S. OLSON, Dept. of Biology, University of Tennessee, Knoxville, Tennessee and Oak Ridge National Laboratory, Oak Ridge, Tennessee. *Eolian Transport.*

MÁRTON PÉCSI, Institute of Geography, Hungarian Academy of Science, Budapest, Hungary. *Loess.*

J. M. PERES, Station Marine d'Endoume, Université de Marseille, Marseille, France. *Trottoir.*

GEORGE PETER, U.S. Dept. of Commerce, Environmental Science Services Administration, Atlantic Oceanographic Laboratory, Miami, Florida. *Island Arcs, General.*

THERESE PIPPAN, Geographisches Institut der Universität, Salzburg, Austria. *Watershed.*

A. PISSART, Laboratoire de Géologie et Géographie Physique de l'Université, Liège, Belgium. *Pingos (Pleistocene).*

W. ARMSTRONG PRICE, Consulting Geologist, 1213 Ocean Drive, Corpus Christi, Texas. *Barriers—Beaches and Islands; Bars; Carolina Bays; Clay*

Dunes; Oriented Lakes; Oyster Reefs; Tidal Delta; Tidal Inlet.

R. A. PULLAN, Dept. of Geography, University of Liverpool, Liverpool, England. *Lake Chad.*

JAMES H. QUINN, Dept. of Geology, University of Arkansas, Fayetteville, Arkansas. *Escarpment, Scarp; Prairie Mounds; Terraces, Fluvial— Introduction.*

SAUL E. RANTZ, U.S. Geological Survey, Water Resources Division, Menlo Park, California. *Salton Sea.*

ANDERS RAPP, Dept. Physical Geography, University of Uppsala, Uppsala, Sweden. *Talus Fan or Cone: Scree and Cliff Debris.*

ALFRED C. REDFIELD, Woods Hole Oceanographic Institution, Woods Hole, Massachusetts. *Lake Maracaibo.*

C. C. REEVES, Jr., Dept. of Geosciences, Texas Technological College, Lubbock, Texas. *Maar.*

DALE F. RITTER, Dept. of Geology, Franklin and Marshall College, Lancaster, Pennsylvania. *Continental Erosion.*

BRYAN P. RUXTON, Division of Land Research, Commonwealth Scientific and Industrial Research Organization, Canberra, A.C.T., Australia. *Corrasion; Panplanation; Rock Fan.*

JOHN E. SATER, Arctic Institute of North America, Washington, D.C. *Arctic Regions.*

CARLETON N. SAVAGE, Idaho Bureau of Mines and Geology, and Dept. of Geology, University of Idaho, Moscow, Idaho. *Mass Wasting.*

ADRIAN E. SCHEIDEGGER, Dept. of Mining and Metallurgy, University of Illinois, Urbana, Illinois. *Badlands; Stream Orders.*

THEODORE H. SCHMUDDE, Dept. of Geography, Southern Illinois University, Carbondale, Illinois. *Flood Plain.*

J. C. SCHOFIELD, New Zealand Geological Survey, Dept. of Scientific and Industrial Research, Papatoetoe, New Zealand. *Prograding Shoreline; Retrograding Shoreline.*

DAVID W. SCHOLL, U.S. Geological Survey, Marine Geology and Hydrology, Menlo Park, California. *Mangrove Swamps: Geology and Sedimentology.*

AXEL SCHOU, Dept. of Geography, University of Copenhagen, Copenhagen, Denmark. *Block Diagram.*

STANLEY A. SCHUMM, Dept. of Geology, Colorado State University, Fort Collins, Colorado. *Badlands.*

MAURICE L. SCHWARTZ, Dept. of Geology, Western Washington State College, Bellingham, Washington. *Stream Table Construction and Operation.*

G. SERET, Laboratoire de Géologie et Géographie Physique de l'Université, Liège, Belgium. *Fluvioglacial Processes.*

HENRY S. SHARP (retired), 180 Ames Avenue, Leonia, New Jersey. *Natural Bridges.*

FRANCIS P. SHEPARD, Scripps Institution of Oceanography, La Jolla, California. *Coastal Classification.*

VINCENT C. SHEPPS (deceased, August 25, 1967), formerly with the Pennsylvania Geological Survey, Dept. of Internal Affairs, Harrisburg, Pennsylvania. *Drumlin; Esker; Glacial Deposits; Kame.*

RICHARD SILVESTER, Dept. of Civil Engineering, University of Western Australia, Nedlands, W.A., Australia. *Sediment Transport—Long-term Net Movement.*

DAVID S. SIMONETT, Center for Research in Engineering Science, Dept. of Geography, University of Kansas, Lawrence, Kansas. *Cuesta; Interfluve; Landslides; Selva Landscape; Wind Action.*

ALEC J. SMITH, Dept. of Geology, University College, London, England. *Lakes.*

DAVID SMITH, Lanchester College of Technology, Coventry, England. *Strandline; Tarn; Warping.*

GEOFFREY W. SMITH, Dept. of Geology, Ohio State University, Columbus, Ohio. *Glacial Geology: Introduction.*

RICHARD A. STEIN, Dept. of Geology, Iowa State University, Ames, Iowa. *Bed Load.*

ROBERT E. STEVENSON, U.S. Fish and Wildlife Service, Bureau of Commercial Fisheries, Biological Laboratory, Galveston, Texas. *Lagoon.*

RICHARD STONE, Dept. of Geology, University of Southern California, Los Angeles, California. *Deserts and Desert Landforms.*

DENIS A. ST-ONGE, Geological Survey of Canada, Dept. Energy, Mines and Resources, Ottawa, Ontario, Canada. *Geomorphic Maps.*

ARTHUR N. STRAHLER, Dept. of Geology, Columbia University, New York. *Quantitative Geomorphology; Slope Analysis.*

S. A. STRELKOV, Institute of Geology and Geophysics, Siberian Branch Academy of Sciences, Novosibirsk, U.S.S.R. *Taiga Landscape; Tundra Landscape.*

W. SUGDEN, Dept. of Geology, University of Queensland, Pimlico, Townsville, Australia. *Ventifacts.*

MARJORIE SWEETING, St. Hugh's College, Oxford University, Oxford, England. *Karst.*

WILLIAM F. TANNER, Dept. of Geology, Florida State University, Tallahassee, Florida. *Chute or Cutoff; Equilibrium in Geomorphology; Geomorphology —Statistical Analysis; Levee, Natural; Oxbow Lake; Rivers—Meandering and Braiding.*

MICHAEL F. THOMAS, Dept. of Geography, University of St. Andrews, St. Andrews, Scotland. *Bornhardt; Etchplain; Tor.*

JAMES THORP, Professor Emeritus, Earlham College, Richmond, Indiana. *Alluvium.*

JEAN TRICART, Centre de Géographie Appliquée, Université de Strasbourg, France. *Periglacial Landscapes.*

C. R. TWIDALE, Dept. of Geography, University of Adelaide, Adelaide, S. A., Australia. *Anthropogenic Influences in Geomorphology; Cycles, Geomorphic;*

Glacial Spillways and Proglacial Lakes; Granite Landforms; Inselberg; Lake Eyre; Monadnock; Pediment; Singing Sands; Weathering; Yardang.

H. TH. VERSTAPPEN, International Institute for Aerial Survey and Earth Sciences, Delft, The Netherlands. *Coral Reefs—Wind and Current Growth Control.*

WILLIAM WARNTZ, Laboratory for Computer Graphics and Spatial Analysis, Harvard University, Cambridge, Massachusetts. *Geography: Concept, Growth and Status.*

H. W. WELLMAN, Dept. of Geology, Victoria University of Wellington, Wellington, New Zealand. *Salt Weathering or Fretting.*

SIDNEY E. WHITE, Dept. of Geology, Ohio State University, Columbus, Ohio. *Humid Cycle.*

WILLIAM B. WHITE, Materials Research Laboratory and Dept. of Geochemistry and Mineralogy, Pennsylvania State University, University Park, Pennsylvania. *Speleology.*

P. J. WILLIAMS, Division of Building Research, National Research Council, Ottawa, Ontario, Canada. *Solifluction.*

ALFONSO WILSON, U.S. Geological Survey, Water Resources Division, Tucson, Arizona. *Canyon Cutting in the Colorado River System.*

A. T. WILSON, Dept. of Chemistry, Victoria University of Wellington, Wellington, New Zealand. *Salt Weathering or Fretting.*

LEE WILSON, Dept. of Geology, Columbia University, New York. *Asymmetric Valleys; Dynamic Geomorphology; Frost Action; Land Systems; Morphogenetic Classification; Slopes; Submarine Geomorphology.*

MICHAEL J. WOLDENBERG, Laboratory for Computer Graphics and Spatial Analysis, Harvard University, Cambridge, Massachusetts. *Open Systems— Allometric Growth.*

LEE A. WOODWARD, Dept. of Geology,

University of New Mexico, Albuquerque, New Mexico. *Basin and Range Landscape.*

WARREN YASSO, Dept. of Science Education, Teachers College, Columbia University, New York. *Cuspate Foreland or Spit.*

V. P. ZENKOVICH, Institute of Oceanology, Academy of Sciences, Moscow, U.S.S.R. *Littoral Processes—Field Methods; Littoral Processes in Tideless Seas.*

JAMES H. ZUMBERGE, School of Earth Sciences, University of Arizona, Tucson, Arizona. *Lobes, Lobation.*

A

ABLATION—*See* pr Vol. VI

ABLATION MORAINE, ABLATION TILL

On low-altitude glaciers, e.g., those on the eastern parts of the Southern Alps of New Zealand, the ablation rate is relatively high. Englacial debris is exposed at the ice surface; the resultant cover of boulders and rock debris is termed *ablation moraine* (Cotton, 1942), or, after the ice has gone, *ablation drift* (Flint, 1957). Melting and evaporation are vigorous in such regions, due to high insolation. The presence of dark-colored material on the ice surface reduces the *albedo* (q.v., Vol. II), and hence greatly raises the rate of heat absorption. The ice itself then becomes stagnant and the accumulation of the ablation moraine becomes increasingly rapid. Ablation moraine material is frequently mixed with debris from the surface of lateral, medial and end moraines.

Flint (1957, p. 121) refers to the basal drift (ground moraine) as "lodgment till" to emphasize that it comes to rest more or less in place where the ice stagnates. However, the ablation moraine is lowered *in situ* from the melting ice surface onto the top of the lodgment till; since the latter is accompanied by extensive melting, the *ablation till* is marked by its partial loss of fine constituents to the subglacial streams and the random orientation of the boulders. In contrast, the lodgment till will retain most of its "fines," and both fine material and the boulders may well preserve a fabric orientation, indicative of former ice orientation.

RHODES W. FAIRBRIDGE

References

Cotton, C. A., 1942, "Climatic Accidents in Landscape-making," Christchurch, N.Z., Whitcombe and Tombs, 354pp.
Flint, R. F., 1957, "Glacial and Pleistocene Geology," New York, John Wiley & Sons, 553pp.

Cross-references: *Glacial Deposits*; *Moraine*. Vol. II: *Albedo and Reflectivity*. pr. Vol. VI: *Ablation*; *Glacier Geophysics*; *Glaciers—Introduction*.

ABRASION

Abrasion is the physical process of rubbing, scouring, or scraping whereby particles of rock (usually microscopic) are eroded away by friction. Thornbury (1954, p. 47) indicates that all the four principal agencies of erosion may involve abrasion: (a) running water, (b) waves and currents, (c) wind, and (d) glaciers. The term *corrasion* (as distinct from corrosion: chemical weathering) is really a synonym for abrasion, but only with respect to running water for the deepening of valley floors. Nevertheless Holmes (1965) uses "corrasion" for mechanical wear by waves and rivers, and "abrasion" for similar wear by wind. Webster's dictionary specifically refers to "corrasion" by wind-borne sands.

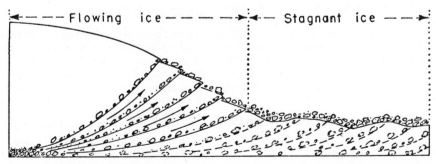

FIG. 1. Ideal radial section through terminal part of a glacier, showing transfer of load from basal to superglacial position by ice movement along upward-directed surfaces of thrusting. As ablation thins marginal part of glacier beyond the minimum required for movement, marginal ice becomes stagnant, and its thrust surfaces (broken lines) become inactive; ablation drift accumulates on its surface (Flint, 1957). (By permission of John Wiley & Sons, N.Y.)

FIG. 1. Example of abrasion (or "*corrasion*," q.v.) by wind-borne particles at Djadokhta, Mongolia; cliffs of massive red sandstones of Cretaceous age (Berkey and Morris, 1927). (Courtesy of the American Museum of Natural History.)

It should be stressed that in every case, the moving agency, water, wind or ice, must be "armed" with rock particles or fragments with which to carry out the abrasion. The agency without the "arming" would be like sandpaper without sand. The abrasion of the transported particles is called *attrition* (q.v.).

The product of abrasion is "rock flour" (silt and clay material) which in water is largely scattered and carried away in turbulent suspension, likewise by wind, but in moving ice is locked up in the glacier until it reaches the snout and melts out in the terminal moraine. The rock flour of hydraulic abrasion is largely modified by chemical erosion (see *Corrosion*), but wind and glacier abraded material is derived under essentially arid, nonaqueous conditions and therefore the "flour" is less modified chemically; as loess or desert "clay" it often is much richer in $CaCO_3$ and other unstable components than is waterborne clay-size particulate matter.

The surface texture of the abraded surface in nature is generally smooth and polished, in striking contrast to the corroded surface which is jagged and sharp. Water abrasion tends to form rounded surfaces, pot holes in the country rock and rounded boulders. Sand abrasion is very commonly observed in deserts. Walther (1924) noted that although desert sandstorms involved dust that rose thousands of feet in the air, the sand moved close to the ground (by saltation) and hence abraded pedestal rocks and Pharonic monuments only near the base.

RHODES W. FAIRBRIDGE

References

Berkey, C. P. and Morris, F. K., 1927, "Geology of Mongolia," New York, Am. Mus. Nat. Hist.
Bryan, K., and Albritton, C. C., Jr., 1942, "Wind-polished rocks in the Trans-Pecos region, Texas and New Mexico," *Bull. Geol. Soc. Am.*, **53**, 1403–1416.

Cailleux, A., 1942, "Les actions éoliennes périglaciaires en Europe," *Mém. Soc. Géol. France*, No. 46.
Cloos, H., 1911, "Geologische Beobachtungen in Süd-afrika. I. Wind und Wüste im Deutschen Namalande," *Neues Jahrb. Mineral. Geol. Paleontol. Beil.*, 32.
Hillefors, Å., 1961, "On wind-eroded boulders and stones in horizons in the Dösebacka Buildings, near Gothenburg," Göteborgs Universitets Geogr. Inst.
Holmes, A., 1965, "Principles of Physical Geology," Second ed., London, Nelson; N.Y., Ronald, 1288pp.
Kuenen, P. H., 1928, "Experiments on the formation of wind-worn pebbles," *Leidsche Geol. Mededeel.*, **3**.
Kuenen, P. H., 1960, "Experimental abrasion 4: Eolian action," *J. Geol.*, **68**, 427–449.
Mattsson, A., 1958, "Windgeschliffenes Gestein im Südlichsten Schweden und auf Bornholm," Lund Studies in Geogr., Ser. A, No. 11, 49–68.
Powers, W. E., 1936, "The evidences of wind abrasion," *J. Geol.*, **44**, 214–219.
Sindowski, K. H., 1956, "Korngrössen- und Korn-formen-Auslese beim Sandtransport durch Wind," *Geol. Jahrb.*, **71**.
Thornbury, W. D., 1954, "Principles of Geomorphology," New York, John Wiley & Sons, 618 pp.
Thoulet, J., 1887, "Expériences synthétiques sur l'abrasion des roches," *Compt. Rend. Acad. Sci.*, **104**.
Walther, J., 1924, "Das Gesetz der Wüstenbildung," Fourth ed., Leipzig, Quelle & Meyer, 421 pp.

Cross-references: *Attrition; Corrasion; Corrosion; Loess; Striae, Striated Pavement; Wind Action.* Vol. IV: *Abrasion pH.* pr. Vol. VI: *Parna.*

ABSTRACTION—*See* STREAM CAPTURE

ACCELERATED EROSION—*See* GULLY EROSION

ACTUALISM—*See* pr Vol. VI

AEOLIAN PROCESSES—*See* ARID CYCLE; SAND DUNES; WIND ACTION

AGASSIZ, LAKE—*See* GLACIAL LAKE AGASSIZ

AGGRADATION

A process of physical geology, aggradation means to fill up with sediment (first used by Salisbury in the last century, 1893, p. 103; see Fig. 1). It is thus the opposite of *degradation* (q.v.). Aggradation may occur along a river valley (see *Alluvium*), at the foot of a slope, in a lake basin, bolson depression, on a desert, or in the ocean.

W. M. Davis (1899) applied the term in a more specialized way to the talweg and valley of a river; where the erosional or degradational sector ends, the sedimentational or aggradation stage begins.

Mackin (1948), however, points out that the usual state of a stream is that of "grade" (as first proposed by Davis), and thus "degrading" or "aggrading" are both special cases where the equilibrium

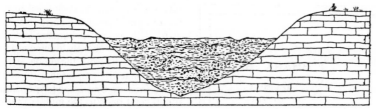

FIG. 1. Diagrammatic cross section of an aggraded valley in which the stream shifted its course many times in the process of aggradation, as depositing streams are known to do. The coarser materials in the various positions, from below upward, represent the successive sites of the channel, two channels being represented in the last stage. In nature, the shiftings of the channel are much more frequent than represented here, so that the coarse materials marking the temporary sites of the channels do not remain so distinctly separated from each other (from Salisbury, 1893, p. 104).

is shifting. "Regrading" refers to a simultaneous alteration in both senses in different sectors (Johnson, 1932). Short-term changes (scour and fill) should not be included in these terms, which refer to the general regime.

An "aggraded valley floor" (according to Cotton, 1952, p. 193) is a broad alluvial flat that is thicker than the depth of the stream channel.

RHODES W. FAIRBRIDGE

References

Cotton, C. A., 1952, "Geomorphology," sixth ed., New York, John Wiley & Sons, 505pp.

Davis, W. M., 1899, "The geographical cycle," *Geograph. J.,* **14,** 481–504 (also "Geographical Essays," New York, Dover, reprint, 1954).

Johnson, D. W., 1932, "Rock planes of arid regions," *Geograph. Rev.,* **22,** 656–665.

Mackin, J. H., 1948, "Concept of the graded river," *Bull. Geol. Soc. Am.,* **59,** 463–512.

Moody, A. E., 1907, "Aggradation and degradation of valleys," *Ohio Nat.,* **8,** 191–197.

Salisbury, R. D., 1893, Annual Report (for 1892), "Surface geology," *New Jersey Geol. Surv.,* 37–166.

Cross-references: *Alluvium*; *Base Level*; *Degradation*; *Equilibrium*; *Rivers*; *Thalweg or Talweg*.

ALBANY, LAKE—*See* GLACIAL LAKE ALBANY

ALGAL REEFS

Algal reefs are organic rocky structures found in the ocean and certain carbonate-rich lakes. In the warmer oceans they may contribute to the complex of *coral reefs* (q.v.) or, on a small scale, may form independent "bioherms" (organic hillocks). In the geological past, algal reefs were considerably more important than at present and fossil algal platforms can be found in Precambrian rocks dating back to over two billion years. Primitive algal reefs are known collectively as *Stromatolites*.

The nature of the reef-forming algae, or the related organisms that simply favor the precipitation of lime-muds or provide hairy mats for their entrapment is treated in another volume (pr Vol. VII); suffice it to say here that the calcareous algae frequently inhabit an ecologic niche around about the intertidal belt in warm latitudes where conditions are not quite right for corals. Thus the algal reefs or platforms are found today in parts of Florida (Ginsburg, 1960) and the Mediterranean where winter temperatures are too cold for coral; or on the mid-Queensland coast where heavy rains during the monsoon render the salinity too low and the turbidity too high for corals; or in Shark Bay, Western Australia, where the salinity and temperature are at times too high for corals (Logan, 1961). Algal reefs are also found inland, in salt-water lakes, such as Great Salt Lake, Utah (Cohenour, 1966).

Three characteristic forms of algal reefs are most important:

(1) *"Cabbage-head bioherms"* (Logan, 1961) form rocky hummocks 30–100 cm in height, sometimes in isolated patches (Figs. 1 and 3), sometimes filled

FIG. 1. "Cabbage-head bioherms" (of Logan, 1961), also known sometimes as "cauliflower heads," typical living algal reefs, in the intertidal belt, in Hamelin Pool, Shark Bay, Western Australia. (Photo courtesy of Brian Logan.)

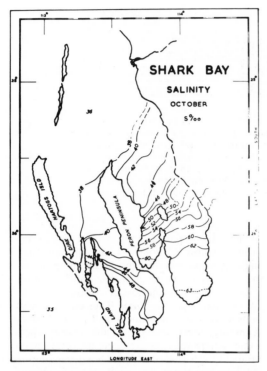

FIG. 2. Bottom isohalines at Shark Bay, Western Australia, latitude about 26°S, during October, 1957. (Courtesy of Brian Logan.)

in with sediment to form a massive continuous reef. The salinity conditions at the south end of Shark Bay, where outstanding examples occur, are illustrated in Fig. 2.

(2) *Algal mat platforms* (Ginsburg, 1960) are characteristically exposed along the shores of the Florida Keys, where they form a thick veneer over the erosion platforms of older limestones, preventing further erosion and protecting the shore. Cut

into vertical sections such algal mat structures are found to be disposed in curious domes, convex upward, with concentric banding and with intradomal limbs pointing sharply downward; this structure seems to result from the mode of reproduction of the algal mats, by simple binary fission. As structures of *Collenia* or *Cryptozoon* type, similar forms are found right back to the middle Precambrian.

(3) *Algal rims* or *ridges* (Wentworth, 1939; Ladd, 1950; Newell *et al.*, 1957) form on exposed outer and upper parts of existing coral reefs, typically in the Pacific and Indian Oceans where they were classically described by Charles Darwin (1842) as the *lithothamnion rim*; the rim is often formed of *Porolithon* and other genera, so that the term "*algal rim*" (q.v.) is most often preferred nowadays. Since the rim of living algae can survive under merely splash and breaker-spray conditions, the rim often grows up well above the limit of coral growth, developing a slightly raised rampart-like ridge around the outer margin of any exposed reef. Sometimes they form a series of rimmed pools like *sinter terraces. Lithothamnion* and some other encrusting algae also form coatings over rock surfaces down to great depths in cold oceans or independent small limestone concretionary structures, but these features are of such small scale that they cannot be classified as geomorphic structures. Small algal discs (about 10-cm diameter) known as "algal biscuits" have been described by Sir Douglas Mawson in the super-saline coastal lagoons of South Australia.

It is a peculiarity of many modern coral reefs that a large fraction of their intertidal surfaces is covered by a thin veneer of encrusting algae. Traces of older, dead and truncated coral colonies may often be recognized. During mid-Holocene times there were periods when sea level was somewhat (0.5–3 meters) higher than today, and these reefs (2000–5000 years old) are now truncated by erosion to present low-tide level. Because of the algal veneer, Setchell (1926)

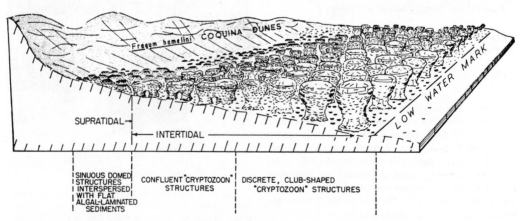

FIG. 3. Idealized form zonation in stromatolite reef at Flint Cliff, Hamelin Pool, in Shark Bay, Western Australia (Logan, B. W., 1961).

and some other authors became erroneously convinced that modern reefs were largely algal rather than coral. If this veneer is continuous, it is known as an *algal pavement* (Ladd, 1930).

An important geochemical aspect of algal reefs is that they usually consist of calcite with a large fraction (up to nearly 30 %) of $MgCO_3$ in solid solution; this unstable arrangement renders algal reef material particularly liable to subsequent dolomitization.

RHODES W. FAIRBRIDGE

References

Cohenour, R. E., 1966, "Industrial potential and development of Great Salt Lake," *Utah Geol. Soc. Guidebook*, **20**, 153–163.

Darwin, C., 1842, "The Structure and Distribution of Coral Reefs," London, 214pp.

Fairbridge, Rhodes W., 1950, "Recent and Pleistocene coral reefs of Australia," *J. Geol.*, **58**, 330–401.

Ginsburg, R. N., 1960, "Ancient analogues of recent stromatolites," *Rept. Intern. Geol. Congr., 21st, Norden*, Pt. 22, 26–35.

Ladd, H. S., 1930, "Vatu Lele, an elevated submarine bank," *Am. J. Sci.*, **19**, Ser. 5, 435–450.

Ladd, H. S., 1950, "Recent reefs", *Bull. Am. Assoc. Petrol. Geologists*, **34**, 203–214.

Logan, B. W., 1961, "*Cryptozoon* and associated stromatolites from the Recent, Shark Bay, Western Australia," *J. Geol.*, **69**, 517–533.

Newell, N. D., and Rigby, J. K., 1957, "Geological studies on the Great Bahama Bank" in (LeBlanc and Breeding, editors), "Regional aspects of carbonate deposition—a symposium," *Soc. Econ. Pal. and Min. Spec. Publ.* No. 5, 15–72; errata, *J. Sediment Petrol.*, **28**(1), 111, Mar., 1958.

Setchell, W. A., 1926, "Nullipore versus coral in reef-formation," *Proc. Am. Phil. Soc.*, **65**, 136–140.

Wentworth, C. K., 1939, "Marine bench-forming processes II. Solution benching," *J. Geomorphol.*, **2**, 3–25.

Cross-references: *Algal Rim; Coral Reefs; Fringing Reef; Great Salt Lake; Holocene; Organisms as Geomorphic Agents;* pr Vol. VII: *Stromatolites*.

ALGAL RIMS, TERRACES AND LEDGES

Early voyagers to the Pacific were often struck by the fact that coral reefs frequently possessed a slightly raised rim, or crestal ridge, especially on the seaward side, which tended to protect the reef surface from the action of the surf and at low tide was often dry enough for investigators to walk on or paddle around freely. Charles Darwin (1842) observed that the rim was not built of coral but largely of encrusting calcareous algae such as *Lithothamnion*. In some areas, the rim builders are predominately *Porolithon*.

In microcosm, the rim is observed also around *microatolls* (q.v.), where in addition to algae, the rim may be built of encrusting gastropod tubes, *Vermetus*, the pelecypods *Mytilus* or *Brachyodontes* and so on.

FIG. 1. Algal rim on the margin of a platform cut in eolian calcarenite ("Coastal Limestone") at Garden Island, Western Australia. Note that at low tide the platform has only about 10 cm of water over it. The shape of the former dune is shown in the background by the calcrete duricrust capping.

If one breaks the rim apart, it is sometimes found to have a core of reefrock, either coral or, in non-coral areas, eolian calcarenite (see Figs. 1 and 2). The organic rim material evidently acts as a protective plaster. Small changes of sea level (± 3m over the last 6000 years) are thought to have occurred in such regions (see *Mean Sea Level—Long-term Changes*, Vol. I). Accordingly, the rims often contain traces of eroded rocks appropriate to other sea levels as well as beachrocks, paleosols and accumulations of superficial character (Fairbridge, 1950, p. 51).

The important biological role of the algal rim is that it occurs where the waves habitually break. Most hermatypic corals will not grow above about mean low-tide limit; nor are they particularly resistant to the hydraulic action of surf. But the calcareous algae form a dense plaster that fills in gaps in the dead coral and coats all in a highly resistant

FIG. 2. Algal rim about 50 cm high and 2 meters broad, bordering an inner pool not far from the site of Fig. 1. Breakers on the outer rim may be seen in the distance. In the lower right-hand corner, a fracture, up which the water surges, is also lined by an algal rim.

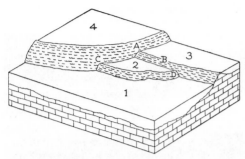

FIG. 3. Diagram illustrating the stepped nature of algal rims, where terraced pools are formed. The highest pool is 4, dropping either directly or in steps (3, 2) to level 1 over a trickle zone. The latter is constantly wet regardless of its height (A, B, C, D; sketch from Kuenen, 1933).

FIG. 5. Algal rimmed terraces cut into eolian calcarenite ("Coastal Limestone") at the west end of Rottnest Island, Western Australia.

veneer 10–100 cm or more in thickness. This plaster is astoundingly resistant to wave action. In heavy weather, the breakers send spray 100 meters into the air and the constant roar may be heard for miles across the placid lagoon. Yet the *Lithothamnion* or *Porolithon* coating hardly ever seems to be damaged, unless the entire coral foundation is broken away. Because the calcareous algae can withstand exposure during low-tide conditions and can even survive entirely on spray moistening, the height of the algal rim is dictated by the degree of exposure to maximum oceanic swell, in favored areas reaching several meters above the general reef level and extending 100–200 meters in width (Fig. 3).

In protected lagoon areas, one may find an algal rim that is a mere 10 cm high and 50 cm wide (see photographs of the lagoon in the Houtmans Abrolhos Islands, in the Indian Ocean off Western Australia: Fairbridge, 1948). In the more protected waters of the Mediterranean, the rim may be built of successive layers of *Vermetus, Lithophyllum* and *Tenarea* (Molinier and Picard, 1953; Termier and Termier, 1963). (See Fig. 4.)

Algal Terraces

In areas of particularly vigorous wave action which leads to constant heavy spray, the algae tend to build low-rimmed terraces analogous to the (inorganic) sinter terraces of volcanic hot-spring areas, e.g., those of Yellowstone Park, Wyoming, or the once celebrated pink terraces of Rotomahana, New Zealand, that were destroyed during an eruption and earthquake in 1886. These algal-rimmed terraces are magnificently displayed along the south coast of Tongatabu in the Tonga Islands (see Lister, 1891) and have been illustrated from numbers of Pacific Islands.

Figure 5 shows an example of algal terracing on eolian calcarenite near the west end of Rottnest I. off Western Australia. An interesting aspect of these rims is that if they are locally damaged or breached, the flow of water through the opening will permit the algae to make a rapid repair of the damage, so that the "dam" is constantly maintained.

Organic Ledge or Corniche

Around parts of the Mediterranean coasts (particularly southern France, Corsica, Sardinia, Algeria, Italy, Yugoslavia and Greece), there are ancient (Mesozoic) limestones that plunge precipitously from coastal cliffs to appreciable depths, without the intertidal reefs so commonly associated with the tropical coral islands and eolian calcarenites of the

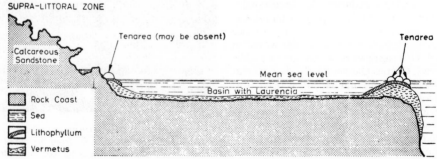

FIG. 4. Section across the littoral Vermetus Platform at Torre del Isola, Sicily (after Molinier and Picard, 1953).

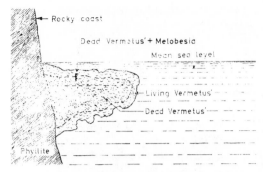

FIG. 6. The "corniche," or organic ledge, at Centurei, Corsica (after Molinier, 1955).

subtropics. Here, encrusting organisms form intertidal ledges. Even non-carbonate cliffs may sometimes offer a foundation for crusting organic growths. In such steep-to situations, the organisms tend to form a ledge or corniche, growing out horizontally 50 cm to 2 meters. The principal corniche builders are *Vermetus*, *Melobesia* and *Tenarea*; the corniche generally reaches up to about mean sea level, while the base of the corniche is about 1 or 2 meters lower (Fig. 6).

RHODES W. FAIRBRIDGE

References

Darwin, C., 1842, "The Structure and Distribution of Coral Reefs," First ed., London, 214pp.

Fairbridge, R. W., 1948, "Notes on the geomorphology of the Pelsart Group of the Houtman's Abrolhos Islands," *J. Roy. Soc. W. Australia*, **33** (1946–47), 1–43.

Fairbridge, R. W., 1950, "The geology and geomorphology of Point Peron, Western Australia," *J. Roy. Soc. W. Australia*, **34**, 35–72.

Kuenen, P. H., 1933, "Geology of coral reefs," in "The Snellius Expedition," Vol. 5, No. 2, Utrecht, Kemink en Zoon, 126pp.

Lister, J. J., 1891, "Notes on the geology of the Tonga Islands," *Quart. J. Geol. Soc. London*, **47**, 590–617.

Molinier, R., 1955, "Les plate-formes et corniches récifales de Vermets (*Vermetus cristatus* Biondi) en Méditerranée occidentale," *Compt. Rend. Acad. Sci.*, **240**, 361–363.

Molinier, R., and Picard, J., 1953, "Notes biologiques à propos d'un voyage d'étude sur les côtes de Sicile," *Ann. Inst. Océanogr.*, **28**, fasc. 4, 163–188.

Pérès, J. M., and Picard, J., 1952, "Les corniches calcaires d'origine biologique en Méditerranée occidentale," *Trav. Station Marine d'Endoume, Fac. Sci. Marseille*, fasc. 4, No. 1.

Termier, H., and Termier. G., 1963. "Erosion and Sedimentation," London and Princeton, N.J., D. Van Nostrand Co., 433pp. (translated by D. W. and E. E. Humphries).

Cross-references: *Coral Reefs*; *Microatoll*; *Organisms as Geomorphic Agents*. Vol. I: *Mean Sea Level*.

ALKALI FLATS—*See* **PLAYA**; also Vol. IV, **EVAPORITE MINERALS**

ALLUVIAL FAN, CONE

An alluvial fan is a body of stream deposits whose surface approximates a segment of a cone that radiates downslope from the point where the stream leaves a mountainous area. Alluvial fans have greatly diverse sizes, slopes, types of deposits and source-area characteristics. They are most widespread in the drier parts of the world but have been studied also in humid regions such as Japan, the Himalaya Mountains (Drew, 1873), and Canada (Winder, 1965), and in the Arctic regions (Hoppe and Ekman, 1964; Legget and others, 1966). [*Talus cone* is sometimes taken to be steeper than *talus fan* (see *Talus Fan or Cone*). The same distinction is sometimes made with alluvial fan and cone. (editor)]

Deposition on Alluvial Fans

Flow on alluvial fans varies from clear water to viscous mud. Water-laid sediments occur chiefly as sheets of sediments deposited by a network of braided streams, and as stream-channel deposits. The discharge per unit of time Q is equal to the product of the width w, the mean depth d, and the velocity of flow $v(Q = w\,dv)$. When flow reaches the end of a channel, it spreads out. The increase in width is accompanied by a decrease in depth and velocity, causing deposition of sediment (Bull, 1964a, p. 17). The discharge Q does not remain constant when flowing over highly permeable deposits. Such deposits may act as a "... sieve by permitting water to pass while holding back the coarse material in transport" (Hooke, 1965, p. 8). This results in deposition of lobate masses called "sieve deposits."

Mudflows are poorly sorted, have lobate tongues extending from sheetlike deposits, have abrupt, well-defined margins, and are capable of carrying boulders weighing many tons. Factors that promote mudflows are abundant water, steep slopes having insufficient vegetative protection and source material that provides a matrix of mud. Because of their high viscosity, mudflows are deposited mainly on the upper parts of fans.

Areas of a fan not receiving deposits are eroded and weathered. A good discussion of gullying and development of desert pavements is given by Denny (1965).

Mountain ranges in semiarid regions commonly are bordered by many coalescing alluvial fans. In the southwestern United States, the surface of such a piedmont plain is often called a *bajada* (sometimes anglicized to bahada)—a Spanish word for detrital slope. A bajada is shown in Fig. 1.

FIG. 1. Alluvial fans in an arid region. Aerial view looking east over a fault scarp in the northern Panamint Range, California. (Courtesy John Maxson).

Fan Morphology

The areas, slopes and histories of deposition of alluvial fans reflect a tendency toward a state of equilibrium among a complex set of controlling factors which include the area, lithology, mean slope and vegetative cover of the drainage basin; slope of the stream channel; discharge; climatic and tectonic environment; and geometry of the adjacent fans and the basin of deposition. Changes in one or more of these factors will tend to cause a readjustment of the fan morphology.

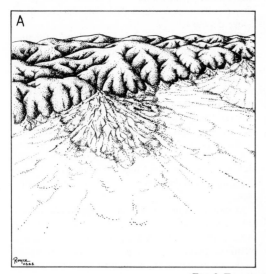
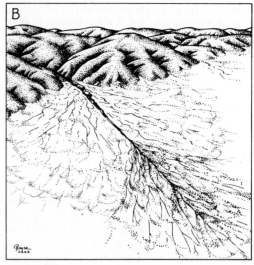

FIG. 2. Two types of alluvial fans.

Alluvial fans are characteristic of tectonically active regions, and most fans occur in one of two tectonic settings (Bull, 1964b, p. 105): (1) fans whose area of maximum deposition has remained close to the mountain front, and (2) fans whose area of deposition has moved downfan. If uplift of the mountain front exceeds stream downcutting, the fanhead will not be deeply trenched by the stream, and deposition will continue to occur close to the mountain front [Fig. 2(A)]. If stream downcutting exceeds uplift of the mountain front, the stream channel will become entrenched into the fan, and deposition will occur on the lower part of the fan [Fig. 2(B)].

Fan Area. Fan area A_f is in part a function of drainage basin area A_d. A general relation can be expressed by the equation $A_f = cA_d^n$. In Fig. 3, the slopes of the plots, n, average about 0.9; n generally is less than unity, partly because the discharge per square mile of a given frequency is higher in small drainages than in large ones (Hooke, 1965, pp. 110–118). The coefficient c varies considerably, ranging from 0.15–2.1, because of independent variables other than drainage basin area, such as drainage basin lithology, climate, tectonic history and the amount of available space in which fans can be deposited. Within a given basin of deposition, such as the San Joaquin Valley, California, fans derived from mudstone source areas are about twice as large as those derived from sandstone source areas of comparable size (Bull, 1964b, pp. 94, 95). This is shown by the coefficients of the equations for lines 1 and 2 in Fig. 3. Hooke (1965, p. 119) and Denny

(1965, p. 38) found a separation of lines of plots for fans in Death Valley, California, because of the differing effects of tectonic history. Fan area-fan volume relations can affect the coefficient also. For example, the two types of fans shown in Fig. 2 would have different fan area-fan volume relations, because in Fig. 2(A) deposition is concentrated near the mountain front, and in Fig. 2(B) deposition is spread out to a greater extent. See Lustig (1965, p. 134) for further discussion of fan area and fan volume.

Fan Slope. Maps and cross-fan profiles show that fans resemble parts of gently sloping cones. The fan-shaped area shown by a map is the result of the stream emerging at an apex and migrating from one side of the fan to the other as the fan is aggraded. The cause of conical aspect is in part revealed by the predominance of stream channels within 30° of the medial radial lines on fans, which implies that deposition occurs more frequently there than in areas farther from the medial position (Bull, 1964b, p. 114).

Many factors affect the slopes of fans, but the relative importance of the factors has yet to be determined. Hooke (1965) concluded from laboratory and field studies that fans produced by lower discharges had steeper slopes, that fans composed largely of mudflows or sieve deposits were steeper than fans composed of other types of fluvial deposits, and that the more coarse grained the deposit, the steeper would the slope be (also see Blissenbach, 1954, p. 182). Bull (1964b, pp. 94, 95) concluded that fans that had large volumes of deposits per unit drainage basin area were steeper than fans that had small volumes per unit drainage basin area.

Bull (1964b) suggested that a balance existed between the slope of the fan in the area of deposition and the stream-channel gradient upstream from the area of deposition (Fig. 4). He showed that changes in stream-channel gradient, resulting from

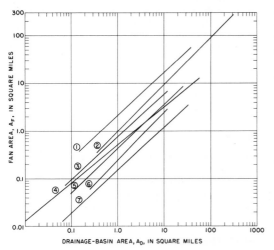

FIG. 3. Relation of fan area to drainage basin area for groups of fans in California and Nevada. The equations and sources of data are as follows: (1, 2) $A_f = 2 \cdot 1 A_d^{0.91}$, $A_f = 0 \cdot 96 A_d^{0.98}$, least squares revisions from Bull (1964b); (3) $A_f = 0 \cdot 74 A_d^{0.89}$, (Hawley and Wilson, 1966); (4) $A_f = 0 \cdot 5 A_d^{0.8}$, depositional parts of fans (Denny, 1965); (5, 6, 7) $A_f = 0 \cdot 42 A_d^{0.94}$, $A_f = 0 \cdot 24 A_d^{1.01}$, $A_f = 0 \cdot 15 A_d^{0.90}$ (Hooke, 1965).

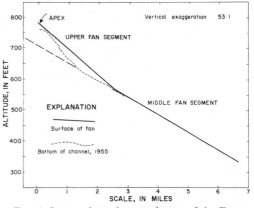

FIG. 4. Stream-channel entrenchment of the Tumey Gulch fan, western Fresno County, California. The heavy dashed line represents a projection of the slope of the middle fan segment.

9

tectonic or climatic events, cause changes in the depositional slope. Slope changes may be observed in radial topographic profiles of many fans. The radial profiles are not smooth curves, but instead comprise three or four straight-line, or less commonly, concave, segments. The surfaces represented by these segments form bands of approximately uniform slope that are concentric about the fan apex. Part of a radial profile is shown in Fig. 4. Examples of segmented alluvial fans are shown in Fig. 2. Figure 2(A) represents the situation where the stream channel has been steepened by intermittent uplift of the mountain front, resulting in deposition of a new segment of steeper slope on the upper part of the preexisting fan. Figure 2(B) represents a situation where climatic changes have caused accelerated downcutting of the stream channel into the fan, resulting in a rapid downfan shift of the end of the stream channel and the locus of deposition. The new segment is deposited at a lower gradient downfan from the preexisting area of deposition.

Stream Channels. Entrenchment of the main stream channel on a fan is common and controls the locus, and to some extent the mode (Bull, 1964a, p. 36), of deposition. The trenching may be of long duration and result in channel bottoms being more than 100 feet below the fan surface. Other fanhead trenches appear to be temporary, being less than 50 feet deep, and having been entrenched and back-filled one or more times before the present trenching.

Channels can be entrenched as a result of changes in rainfall intensity (Bull, 1964b, pp. 122–125). A temporary channel entrenchment of this type is shown in Fig. 4. The channel ends at the downslope end of a fan segment and has, in part, established a gradient that is the same as the adjacent lower fan segment. Not all incised streams intersect the fan surface at fan-segment boundaries.

Fanhead entrenchment has been the subject of much discussion. Denny (1965, p. 55) believes that ". . . the gradient and cross section of a desert wash are probably adjusted to the available discharge and load." Eckis (1928, pp. 237, 238) suggests that a stream will ultimately dissect the upper part of the fan it has constructed, because of continuing downcutting of the stream within the mountains. Beaty (1963, pp. 527–528) says that mudflows may plug an incised channel and cause channel diversion. Lustig (1965, p. 165) relates estimated tractive forces to channel trenching, using the expression $r = \gamma \, dS$ (r is the tractive force; γ the specific weight of the transporting medium; d, the depth of flow estimated from maximum particle sizes; S, the slope of the energy gradient derived from the local fan slope). Lustig (p. 184) believes that the channel cutting fluid was more viscous than the fluids that deposited the surficial fan material. He postulates a climatic change that resulted in a greater prevalence of mudflows, which entrenched the channel because of their greater tractive force. In contrast, Hooke

(pp. 138–141) believes that mudflows deposit material near the fanhead when they exceed the depth of the incised channel. He attributes fanhead entrenchment to subsequent water flows which are capable of transporting, on a lower slope, much of the material deposited by mudflows.

W. B. Bull

References

*Beaty, C. B., 1963, "Origin of alluvial fans, White Mountains, California and Nevada," *Ann. Assoc. Am. Geographers*, **53**, 516–535.

Blissenbach, Erich, 1954, "Geology of alluvial fans in semiarid regions," *Bull. Geol. Soc. Am.*, **65**, 175–189.

Bull, W. B., 1964a, "Alluvial fans and near-surface subsidence in western Fresno County, California," *U.S. Geol. Surv. Profess. Paper* **437-A**, 71pp.

Bull, W. B., 1964b, "Geomorphology of segmented alluvial fans in western Fresno County, California," *U.S. Geol. Surv. Profess. Paper* **352-E**, 89–129.

Denny, C. S., 1965, "Alluvial fans in the Death Valley region, California and Nevada," *U.S. Geol. Surv. Profess. Paper* **466**, 62pp.

Drew, Frederick, 1873, "Alluvial and lacustrine deposits and glacial records of the upper Indus basin," *Quart. J. Geol. Soc. London*, **29**, 441–471.

Eckis, Rollin, 1928, "Alluvial fans in the Cucamonga district, southern California," *J. Geol.*, **36**, 224–247.

Hawley, J. W., and Wilson, W. E., 1966, "Quaternary geology of the Winnemucca area, Nevada," *Nevada Univ., Desert Research Inst., Tech. Rept. No. 5*, 66pp.

Hooke, R. LeB., 1965, "Alluvial Fans," *Ph.D. thesis*, California Institute of Technology, Pasadena, 192pp.

Hoppe, Gunnar, and Ekman, Stig-Rune, 1964, "A note on the alluvial fans of Ladtjovagge, Swedish Lapland," *Geografiska Annaler*, **46**, 338–342.

Legget, R. F., Brown, R. J. E., and Johnston, G. H., 1966, "Alluvial fan formation near Aklavik, Northwest Territories, Canada," *Bull. Geol. Soc. Am.*, **77**, 15–30.

Lustig, L. K., 1965, "Clastic sedimentation in Deep Springs Valley, California," *U.S. Geol. Surv. Profess. Paper* **352-F**, 131–192.

Winder, C. G., 1965, "Alluvial cone construction by alpine mudflow in a humid temperate region," *Can. J. Earth Sci.* **2**, 270–277.

* Additional bibliographic references may be found in this work.

Cross-references: *Alluvium*; *Bajada, Bahada*; *Braided Streams*; *Climatic Geomorphology*; *Drainage Basins*; *Equilibrium in Geomorphology*; *Grade, Graded Stream*; *Gully Erosion*; *Mass Wasting*; *Mudflow*; *Slopes*; *Stream Channel Characteristics*; *Talus*.

ALLUVIUM

Definition

Alluvium (from the Latin word for "flood") is a more or less stratified deposit of gravel, sand, silt, clay, or other debris, moved by streams from higher to lower ground (Howell *et al.*, 1957). It is usually distinguished by its mode of deposition from lacustrine and marine sediments, deposited, respectively, by the waters of lakes and seas, but the three classes of deposits merge imperceptibly where they meet. In the seventeenth century, the term included all water-laid deposits (Stamp, 1961), but Lyell in 1830 restricted it to material brought down "by rivers, floods, or other causes...." However, in the mid-nineteenth century, Naumann, the German geologist, applied it to all sediments that were non-eolian. The term "Alluvium" was widely used in Central Europe for the Holocene stage, as distinct from "Diluvium" (Pleistocene).

Land Forms

Alluvial flood plains receive new alluvium with each flood, and the coarser sediments usually are more abundant close to the main stream channels. Alluvium takes the form of *cones* or *fans* where steeply graded streams of highlands flow into more gently sloping land. *Deltas* are low, essentially level plains of alluvium formed where streams enter lakes or seas. The alluvium of deltas merges imperceptibly with adjacent lacustrine or marine sediments. During different stages of erosion-deposition cycles, the alluvium of many stream valleys is cut into a series of *alluvial terraces* arranged at different levels along the sides of the valleys.

Meltwater floods from glaciers deposit alluvium with a number of geomorphic features that differ in detail from those of ordinary streams. Glacial alluvium takes the following forms: (1) Broad *outwash plains*, some of which are *pitted plains*; (2) narrower *valley trains*, lying between valley walls, and frequently terraced; (3) *kames* and *kame terraces*, formed where alluvium was laid in depressions of the glacier age or in contact with the ice of glacier margins; and (4) *eskers*—sinuous gravel and sandy ridge of alluvium, laid originally in ice-walled tunnels and exposed when the glacier melted.

Alluvial Soils

In the technical sense, *alluvial soils* are recent deposits of alluvium, usually subject to floods, that have been affected only slightly by soil-forming processes such as the incorporation of humus and the development of mottled colors owing to poor drainage (U.S. Dept. of Agriculture, 1957). Alluvial soils may be very fertile and productive, or almost sterile, depending on their texture (particle-size distribution) and their chemical and mineralogical composition. Stagnant ground water can render sterile some otherwise desirable alluvial soils. Good agricultural alluvial soils are those with medium to moderately clayey textures, medium-acid to moderately alkaline reaction (pH 5.6–7.8), good supply of organic matter, and a wide variety of minerals. Most of the alluvium of these soils is derived from large drainage basins with a great variety of rocks and soils, and a large proportion of it has a significant component eroded from limestone and calcareous shales. Alluvial soils

support some of the world's most dense populations, as on the flood plains and deltas of the Yangtze, Hwai, Huang and Chu rivers in China, the Mekong river in Vietnam, the Indo-Gangetic Plain of India, the delta of the Nile, and the flood plains and deltas of the Mississippi, Colorado and Sacramento rivers in the United States. Some otherwise rich alluvial soils of dry regions have been made barren by the accumulation of soluble salts and alkali in irrigated areas, as in Mesopotamia, Pakistan, southwestern United States, and in many other dry regions. Many salty and alkali soils can be reclaimed for agriculture.

Much of the alluvium of stream terraces, no longer subject to flood, has been converted to true soils which, to degrees corresponding to the length of time they have been exposed, give expression to the effects of the environmental factors of soil formation. Such soils may resemble the genetically well-developed soils of the adjacent stable uplands, and may no longer be classed as *alluvial soils*.

JAMES THORP

References

Howell, J. V., *et al.*, 1957, "Glossary of Geology and Related Sciences," p. 8, American Geological Institute, National Academy of Science—National Research Council, Washington, D.C.

Stamp, L. D., 1961, "A Glossary of Geographical Terms," London, Longmans, 539pp.

Suggate, R. P., 1963, "The fan surfaces of the central Canterbury Plain," *New Zealand J. Geol. Geophys.*, **6**, 281–287.

U.S. Dept. of Agriculture, 1957, "Soil," Yearbook of Agriculture, p. 751, 1957.

Cross-references: *Alluvial Fan, Cone; Deltaic Evolution; Esker; Floodplain; Grade, Graded Stream; Kame; Outwash Plain, Fan; Sediment Transport; Terraces—Lacustrine; Terraces—Marine.* pr. Vol. VI: *Groundwater; Soil Genesis.*

ALPINE LANDSCAPE—*See* MOUNTAIN GLACIER LANDSCAPE

ALTIMETRIC FREQUENCY CURVE

The altimetric frequency curve depicts at successive altitudes either the frequency of certain levels (spot heights, highest points in grid squares, summit heights) or the areas or lengths of flats (summits, shoulders, benches, cols). The various methods involve sampling with differing degrees of objectivity, but all are designed to demonstrate the existence of erosion surfaces or levels and to correlate levels from area to area.

Frequencies, areas or lengths (as totals or percentages) are generally plotted on the horizontal axis and altitudinal groups on the vertical. Refinement is possible by subdividing the frequency columns, so as

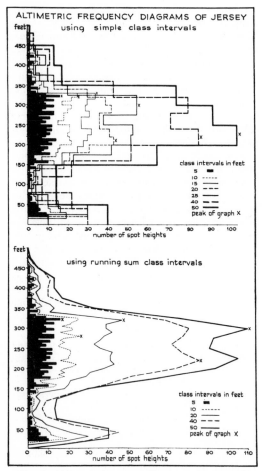

FIG. 1. Altimetric frequency diagrams of Jersey using simple and running sum class intervals. The effects of the grouping of data are clearly seen. Note the shifts in the peaks (X) of the graphs.

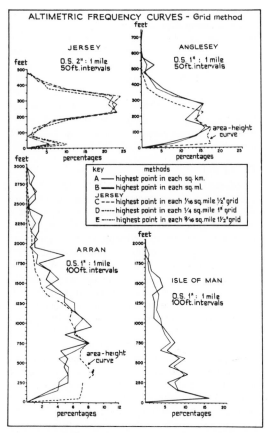

FIG. 2. Altimetric frequency curves of Jersey, Anglesey, Arran and the Isle of Man demonstrating how variation in grid size affects data. Area-height curves of Anglesey and Arran are included for comparison.

to illustrate the dimensions and lithologies of flats. Interpretation of results varies with the altitudinal class intervals, which themselves are dependent upon the contour intervals of maps. Figure 1 shows how running sum class intervals merely smooth out some of the irregularities of simple class frequencies, just as large intervals smooth out the irregularities of small class frequencies.

Frequency of Spot Heights. First used by Baulig (1926), this method assumes that spot heights are sufficiently numerous and uniformly distributed. However, surveyors by the choice of spot heights introduce a considerable element of subjectivity into the range of data, which do not provide random samples. Many spot heights have little morphometric significance, and flat surfaces, in particular, tend to be poorly represented, but the introduction of summit levels which are not marked by spot heights is permissible. In small areas, spot heights

are rarely numerous enough to constitute a valid statistical sample.

Highest Points in Grid Squares. In order to overcome some of the deficiencies of the spot height method, Baulig (1935, 1939) superimposed a grid on the topographic map and derived a frequency distribution of the highest points of grid squares. One difficulty arises over the size of the grid. Obviously it should be small enough to permit a large total of observations, yet if it is too small it lowers the altitude of the frequency maxima. Indeed, the grid could be so reduced in size that the results would conform to those of an area-height curve. With a coarse grid, the highest points in individual squares are likely to be summits, but with a fine grid they are likely to occur on slopes and may even lie on valley bottoms. On the other hand, several planation features in a large square might have to be represented by a single value or be neglected altogether in favor of a highest point of no erosional significance. Figure 2 shows how variation in the size of grid used on four islands of widely differing reliefs influences altimetric frequency curves.

Baulig (International Geographical Union, 1948b) has insisted that this grid method is valuable only when a concordant series of two or more erosion periods has operated and that it is not valid in regions affected by widespread uplifts or characterized by horizontal structure. This view has been disputed by Fourmarier and Macar (International Geographical Union, 1948a) who point out that as cyclical elements are generally concave, high points of squares are often on slopes rather than flats. They advocate plotting the lowest point in each square. The problem is that arbitrary point sampling cannot be relied upon to portray the various heights of particular facets of relief.

Frequency of Summits. On the assumption that accordant summits may be remnants of erosion platforms or peneplains, Thompson (1936) ascertained summit frequencies in a study of the Hudson Gorge. Closed contours are used, and each summit is given a unitary value regardless of dimension. Some geomorphologists have counted only summits considered relevant to the study of platforms, and some have stressed that the method is only suitable for maturely dissected plateaus. In this case, the scope of the method is severely limited.

Figure 3 compares the altimetric frequency

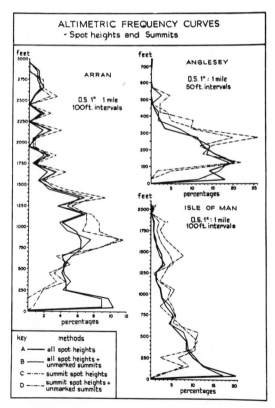

FIG. 3. Four different altimetric frequency curves of Arran, Anglesey and the Isle of Man using spot heights and summits.

methods so far discussed for the three islands, Anglesey, Arran and the Isle of Man. It is evident that there are substantial discrepancies in the frequencies, and other workers confirm this.

Areas of Summits. The calculation by Thompson (1941) of areas of summits in the Appalachians overcomes one criticism of summit frequencies, namely that they are overdependent upon degree of dissection. However, it is often difficult to delimit a summit with precision, as the closed contour may give an inadequate indication of summit area.

Areas of Bench Units. Aware that the previous methods incorporate much data of little geomorphological significance, Macar (1938, 1955) calculated the altimetric frequency of bench units (*unités de replat*) in the Ardennes, a unit being finally defined as an area of 10 hectares in which amplitude of relief does not exceed 5 meters, i.e., where the slope is no more than 2.5%. This technique is preferable to the previous methods or to hypsometric analysis in the study of benches, but large-scale maps with small contour intervals are required for delimitation of benches, and the complications of interpretation of the frequency distribution increase with the size of the area examined. Moreover, many so-called benches are merely the lower parts of slopes.

For a large area, the curve of bench units bears a fairly close resemblance to the hypsometric curve, with the highest flats almost always represented poorly because of their small size. Consequently, De Smet (1954) proposed the calculation of a relative frequency curve of bench units showing the areas of bench units as percentages of intercontour areas.

Shoulder, Summit and Col Method. Geyl's (1961) shoulder, summit and col method is essentially an elaboration of Macar's method, involving the analysis of 1 : 50,000 or 1 : 63,360 maps and the allocation of points for unit areas of summits and lengths of shoulders or cols. These are plotted separately (Fig. 4), and often the frequency maxima of shoulders and cols occur at one contour below that of summits. Although there would be difficulties in calculating the areas of shoulders and cols, the wisdom of using lengths is not obvious, especially as it gives enhanced values to narrow but fairly horizontal ridges devoid of flats. Furthermore, the utility of col data is difficult to establish, and for interpretation Geyl relies primarily on shoulder data and secondarily on summit data.

Recent methods of construction of altimetric frequency curves are increasingly subjective. The earlier methods equal hypsometric and clinographic curves in objectivity, but lose accuracy through their dependence upon point sampling which may give neither a true synthesis of area-height relationships nor a good indication of erosion platforms. Sometimes they merely demonstrate the obvious. The methods of Macar and Geyl are more concerned with the analysis of flats, but they also incorporate

13

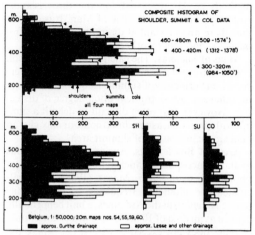

FIG. 4. Two ways of depicting shoulder, summit and col data and altimetric frequency diagrams. The upper diagram is a composite histogram of the three lower graphs, which distinguish the Ourthe drainage basin from the Lesse and other drainage on four Belgian maps (after Geyl).

data of doubtful utility. In particular, they do not readily identify the gentle slopes characteristic of erosion surfaces. As yet, there is no method of altimetric frequency analysis indispensable to the analysis of erosion surfaces.

JOHN I. CLARKE

References

Baulig, H., 1926, "Sur une méthode altimétrique d'analyse morphologique appliquée à la Bretagne Péninsulaire," *Bull. Assoc. Géogr. Français*, **10**, 7–9.

Baulig, H., 1935, "The changing sea-level," *Inst. Brit. Geographers*, Publ. No. 3.

Baulig, H., 1939, "Deux méthodes d'analyse morphologique appliquées à la haute Belgique," *Bull. Soc. Belge d'Études Géogr.*, **9**, 165–184.

Clarke, J. I., 1966, "Morphometry from Maps," in (Dury, G. H., editor) "Essays in Geomorphology," pp. 235–274, London, Heinemann.

Geyl, W. F., 1961, "Morphometric analysis and the world-wide occurrence of stepped erosion surfaces," *J. Geol.*, **69**, 388–416.

International Geographical Union, 1948a, "Problèmes des terrasses," Sixième Rapport de la Commission pour l'Étude des Terrasses Pliocènes et Pleistocènes, Paris, A. Colin.

International Geographical Union, 1948b, "Problèmes des terrasses, éclaircissements et répliques," Paris, A. Colin.

Macar, P., 1937–38, "Contribution à l'étude géomorphologique de l'Ardenne," *Ann. Soc. Géol. Belg.*, **61**, 224–237.

Macar, P., 1955, "Appalachian and Ardennes levels of erosion compared," *J. Geol.*, **63**, 253–267.

Smet, R. de, 1954, "Courbe hypsographique et profil moyen de l'Ardenne," *Bull. Soc. Belge d'Études Géogr.*, **23**, 146–167.

Thompson, H. D., 1936, "Hudson Gorge in the Highlands," *Bull. Geol. Soc. Am.*, **47**, 1831–1848.

Thompson, H. D., 1941, "Topographic analysis of the Monterey, Staunton and Harrisonburg Quadrangles," *J. Geol.*, **49**, 521–549.

Cross-references: *Hypsometric Analysis*; *Quantitative Geomorphology*. Vol. II: *"Iso"-Terms*.

ALTIPLANATION, EQUIPLANATION, CRYOPLANATION

Altiplanation is the name proposed by Eakin (1916) on the basis of work in Alaska, for the formation of a subhorizontal land form at relatively high altitudes by solifluction and related processes of freeze and thaw in subpolar latitudes or high elevations. An *altiplanation terrace* is one forming on a slope. Evidently no former base level is involved, as would be the case in marine, lacustrine or fluvial terraces. Cairnes (1912) used the term *equiplanation* for the same concept, and Bryan (1946) preferred *cryoplanation* as a more general form. In each case, a reduction and flattening of the landscape by solifluction processes is implied.

RHODES W. FAIRBRIDGE

References

Bryan, K., 1946, "Cyropedology—The study of frozen ground and intensive frost-action with suggestions of nomenclature," *Am. J. Sci.*, **244**, 622–642.

Cairnes, D. D., 1912, "Differential erosion and equiplanation in portions of Yukon and Alaska," *Bull. Geol. Soc. Am.*, **23**, 333–348.

Demek, J., 1964, "Altiplanation terraces in Czechoslovakia and their origin," *J. Czech. Geogr. Soc.*, *Suppl. for I.G.U.*, 55–65.

Iakim (-Eakin), H. M., 1916, "The Yukon-Koyukuk region, Alaska," *Bull. U.S. Geol. Surv.*, **631**, 67–82.

Richter, H., Haase, G., and Barthel, H., 1963, "Die Golezterrassen," *Peterm. Geogr. Mitt. Jg.*, **107**, 183–192.

Rudberg, S., 1965–66, "Reconstruction of polycyclic relief in Scandinavia," *Norsk Geogr. Tidsskr.*, **20**, 65–73.

Cross-references: *Base Level*; *Cryopedology*; *Frost Action*; *Solifluction*; *Terraces*: *Terracettes*.

AMPHITHEATER VALLEY HEADS

Semicircular valley heads of non-glacial origin are known as amphitheaters or amphitheater valley heads. Glacial valleys of this sort are *cirques* (q.v.), and Freeman (1925) has called the non-glacial amphitheaters "pseudo-cirques," but this has not found favor (Hinds, 1925). The nature of glacial cirque erosion ("plucking," etc.) is quite different from fluvial action. Some periglacial activity is involved in amphitheater development at high altitudes in the mid- and low latitudes.

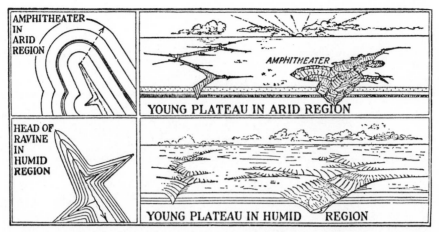

FIG. 1. Young plateaus in arid and humid regions showing contrast between valley heads. Amphitheaters can occur locally in humid regions (Lobeck, 1939). (By permission of McGraw-Hill Book Co.)

Structural conditions most favorable to amphitheater building include:

(1) Horizontal or gently dipping formations; they may be sediments or lava flows with ash layers;

(2) Resistant layers (capstones) underlain by easily weathered beds; the capstone in semiarid country may be a duricrust (paleosol) of calcrete (caliche), silcrete (quartzite) or ferricrete (laterite).

Amphitheaters develop characteristically as a secondary attribute of canyon cutting in flat-lying rocks. Deep canyon dissection is followed by secondary headward erosion of smaller tributaries. Headward sapping leads to undercuts and landslides, which maintain precipitous slopes in the amphitheater. Excellent examples are seen in the Grand Canyon of the Colorado and its principal branches. They are well developed also along the southwest side of the Kaiparowitz Plateau of Utah and in the Sierra Ancha of Arizona. "Nested amphitheaters" occur where several hard horizons are separated by weak formations of appreciable thickness. Some magnificent amphitheaters are also seen in the dissected lava domes of Hawaii.

RHODES W. FAIRBRIDGE

References

Freeman, O. W., 1925, "The origin of the Swimming Woman Canyon, Big Snowy Mountains, Montana, an example of a pseudocirque formed by landslide sapping," *J. Geol.*, **23**, 75–79.

Hinds, N. E. A., 1925, "Amphitheater valley heads," *J. Geol.*, **33**, 816–818.

Lobeck, A. K., 1939, "Geomorphology, An Introduction to the Study of Landscapes," New York, McGraw-Hill Book Co., 731 pp.

Cross-references: *Canyon Cutting; Cirques; Slopes.*

ANABRANCH—*See* **BRAIDED STREAMS**

ANASTOMOSIS, ANASTOMOSING CHANNELS—*See* **BRAIDED STREAMS; TROPICAL WEATHERING**

ANTARCTICA, GLACIOLOGY and GLACIAL GEOLOGY—*See* pr Vol. VI

ANTECEDENT VALLEY, STREAM—*See* **STRUCTURAL CONTROL IN GEOMORPHOLOGY**

ANTHROPOGENIC INFLUENCES IN GEO-MORPHOLOGY

Since man spread over the earth's surface, he has extensively modified his environment. Some of the changes effected have caused new land forms to develop, so much so that late in the last century, a Russian geographer wrote that he "cannot conceive physiography from which Man has been excluded" (Krapotkin, 1893, p. 355). Deforestation, introduction of exotic plants and animals, the use of agricultural machinery, the use and building of tracks and roads, and overgrazing of pastures have all, singly and in combination, altered the preexisting quasi-equilibrium of the environment and caused accelerated erosion and deposition to occur. So significant is this physiographic activity initiated by man that many workers consider a new, anthropogenic, epicycle of erosion to be in progress.

The clearance of woodland for agricultural purposes has various and complex repercussions. Forest and bushfires may achieve similar results. The soil surface is exposed to direct raindrop impact, a measure of the significance of which is that during a heavy rainstorm 100 tons of soil per acre may be blasted into the air. The removal of timber can cause a rise in the water table, and with it salts, causing destruction of vegetation at the sur-

FIG. 1. Primary gullying of a devegetated slope, product of a single storm (in February 1955, near Hawker, South Australia). (Photo: C. R. Twidale.)

face and hence exposure to erosion. Removal of plant litter causes loss of soil structure and particularly of porosity: hence runoff is increased. Runoff from a bare soil surface is many times that from a sward or woodland area. Vegetation has a binding influence upon the surface soil, and its loss promotes erosion. Overgrazing has similar effects, and the introduction of animal pests such as the rabbit also has a deleterious influence.

The removal or reduction of vegetation also renders the land surface susceptible to wind action. The voracious nibbling of the goats of nomadic herdsmen has, in several areas on the southern margin of the Sahara, intensified and extended the desert. It has been said that in some areas the Arab is not so much the son of the desert, but its father. Similarly, on the southern edge of the Kalahari and in the Australian desert and semi-

FIG. 2. Advanced dendritic gullying (near Yankalilla, South Australia). (Photo: C. R. Twidale.)

FIG. 3. Cirque-like head of gully in Quaternary silty clays (near Hawker, South Australia). (Photo: C. R. Twidale.)

desert areas, overgrazing has caused dunes which were fixed by vegetation to be reactivated.

The changes wrought by man are of course widespread and well-known, and they require no elaboration here, but it is less commonly realized that the introduction of new species of plants (either deliberately or accidentally) may also change the environmental equilibrium. Exotic species may not, for instance, withstand climatic extremes of a new environment as well as the natives. For example, in the southern Flinders Ranges of Australia, introduced annual herbs and grasses quickly replaced the native perennial ground cover following white settlement of the area in the mid-nineteenth century. The annuals do not stand up to summer heat and drought as well as the native grasses, and

FIG. 4. Landslip and slumping in deforested Permian clays (near Normanville, South Australia). (Photo: C. R. Twidale.)

consequently at the end of the dry season the soil surface is usually quite bare and thus susceptible to wash and to gullying.

Tracks and roads are ready-made channels for runoff and are moreover devoid of vegetation and impermeable because of compaction: hence, they are readily washed away. No water permeates through the surface of sealed roads but the precipitation that falls upon them drains off the road margins which are usually bare and (where there are no gutters and drains) vulnerable to erosion.

Such anthropogenic works render the soil surface susceptible to erosion by runoff and particularly by heavy and rapid runoff associated with torrential downpours. Many of the gullies in South Australia can be dated to a particular storm, and the recency of the erosion is evidenced by buried fenceposts and other anthropogenic or anthropogenically introduced features such as the bones of the horse. Man's activities themselves do not directly cause serious erosion and deposition, but they do render the land surface vulnerable to climatic accidents. The relative roles of man and climate have long been argued in relation to the arroyos of the American High Plains and South West, but it now seems generally considered that man has played a decisive part in their initiation.

Gullies are perhaps the best known and most obvious manifestation of the new epicycle of erosion and deposition. They are presently found in many parts of the world, and there is evidence that in some long-settled areas like western Europe where gullies are not now a prominent feature of the landscape, they were more prevalent in past times. Though not so obvious as gullies, sheet erosion is perhaps quantitatively more significant and has influenced not merely narrow areas but extensive tracts of the land surface. Its importance is suggested by accumulations of detritus at fences, at the foot of slopes and by the exposure of tree roots and former areas of subsurface weathering, resulting in the revelation of minor caverns and pedestal forms at the surface.

On a very much more limited scale, man has influenced the morphology of bedrock slopes. At one archaeological site in South Australia, it can be shown that periods of occupation and desertion of the site have caused changes in the relative rates of erosion and burial of the backwall and have, in effect, caused the formation of a stepped bedrock surface. Man's mining activities have also caused local subsidence of the earth's surface, and waste heaps are also prominent in some localities.

Principally, however, human occupation of the land surface has resulted in an acceleration of erosion and the loss of valuable soil.

The distinction between anthropogenic and paleoclimatic forces is not always easy. Through the Mediterranean and North Africa, after the Roman occupation, there was a general desiccation of the climate; there was also overpopulation, overgrazing by goats and camels, and the breakdown of many organized controls. Hillsides were eroded and valleys became heavily silted. Was man's role purely secondary to the climatic change?

C. R. Twidale

References

Jacks, G. V., and White, R. O., 1939, "The Rape of the Earth: A World Survey of Soil Erosion," London, 313pp.

Krapotkin, P. A., 1893, "On the teaching of physiography," *Geogr. J.,* **2**, 350–359.

Sharpe, C. F. S., 1941, "Geomorphic aspects of normal and accelerated erosion," *Trans. Am. Geophys. Union,* Pt. 2, 236–240.

Strahler, A. N., 1956, "The Nature of Induced Erosion and Aggradation," in (Thomas, W. L., Jr., editor) "Man's Role in Changing the Face of the Earth," pp. 621–638, Chicago, Univ. of Chicago Press 1193pp.

UNESCO Symposium on changes of climate, with special reference to the arid zone, 1961, Rome.

Vogt, J., 1953, "Erosion des sols et techniques de culture en climat tempéré maritime de transition (France et Allemagne), *Rev. Géomorph. Dynam.,* No. 4, 157–183.

Wallwork, K. L., 1956, "Subsidence in the mid-Cheshire industrial area," *Geograph. J.,* **122**, 40–53.

Cross-references: *Gully Erosion*; *Sheet Erosion, Sheetwash, Rainwash, Sheetflood*; *Slopes.* Vol. II: *Paleoclimatology—Astronomic Cycles.* pr Vol. VII: *Paleoclimatology—Geologic Synthesis.*

ANTHROPOMORPHISM—*See* pr Vol. VI

ANTICLINAL RIDGES, VALLEYS—*See* **STRUCTURAL CONTROL IN GEOMORPHOLOGY**

ARAL SEA

Situated in Kazakstan, USSR (in Asia, about 45°N, 60°E) some 400 km east of the Caspian Sea, the broad shallow Aral Sea is the world's fourth largest lake, in terms of area (following the Caspian, Lake Superior and Lake Victoria). It is of considerable geological interest on account of its salts, sediments and evolutionary history. It is situated at only 52 meters above mean sea level and 80 meters above the Caspian. Its dimensions are 428 by 284 km, area 66,458 km^2 (incl. 2345 km^2 of islands), and volume about 970 km^3. The mean depth is only 16.2 meters with a maximum depth of 67 meters on the west side. The area of the entire catchment basin is 940,000 km^2. There is a row of islands extending NNE-SSW in the western quarter of the sea, fault controlled and making a rather deep narrow trough near the west shore; near the north end, a large island

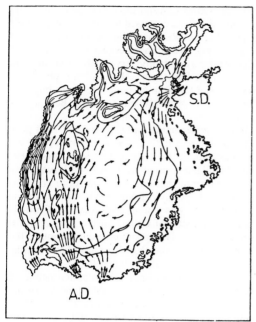

FIG. 1. Bathymetric sketch map of the Aral Sea (Nikolsky, 1940). Currents indicated by arrows (Kulichenko, 1944; from Zenkevitch, 1963). Abbreviations: A.D. = Amu Darya (Oxus) Delta; S.D. = Syr Darya (Iaxartes) Delta. Maximum length of sea: 428 km.

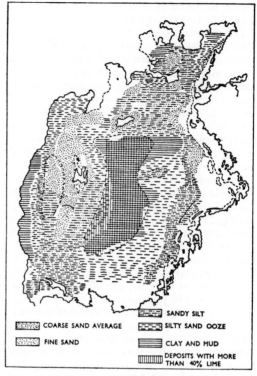

COARSE SAND AVERAGE	SANDY SILT
FINE SAND	SILTY SAND OOZE
	CLAY AND MUD
	DEPOSITS WITH MORE THAN 40% LIME

FIG. 2. Distribution of the sediments of the Aral Sea (Kulichenko, 1944; from Zenkevitch, 1963).

Kugaral (Kurch-Aral) almost isolates a large bay Maloie More (the "little sea" in Russian).

The Aral Sea was first mapped and described by A. Butakov in 1848–49, then studied by the Aral-Caspian Expedition of 1874 (worked up by N. Andrussov and others), but it was most extensively investigated on several trips by L. Berg from 1900–06, resulting in an important monograph (1908). The establishment of the Aral Fishery Station in 1929 led to detailed hydrologic and biologic studies (summarized in Zenkevitch, 1963).

The *water balance* in the Aral is maintained largely by inflow of rivers (in the south and northeast) with 53.7 km^3/yr, plus 5.63 km^3 from rainfall, as against 58.09 km^3 lost by evaporation, plus 1.27 km^3 by seepage into underground aquifers (total budget 59.36 km^3/yr). Evaporation is thus 10 times the local rainfall.

The *sediments* are predominantly a gray mud, capped by a thin brown oxidized layer. Calcareous oolites are common in the shallows, just as in Great Salt Lake, Utah. Black mud, marked by colloidal ferrous hydroxide, plus H$_2$S, occurs in the deep western trough where there is a continuous mat of rotting filamentous algae. Extensive sands occur along the north, east and southern coasts to a depth of 10 meters. Generally the sediments are quite low in organic matter with the C/N ratio 6:10. In the south is the delta of the Amu Darya (Oxus) and in

the northeast that of the Syr Darya (Iaxartes), which drains the northern Tian Shan (Zenkevitch, 1963). These are two classical examples of deltas discharging into a shallow depression. The eastern coast is very interesting: it was called the "*Aral-type*" *coast* by Berg (1908) and is marked by parallel dunes; a rise of water level has led to an invasion of the swales between them, giving a very sinuous coast; the exposed dune shores are now being slowly eroded down by wave action. The western shore is almost straight, with a steep rocky escarpment (*chink*) up to 190 meters high; it is of faulted origin and marked by landslides (Lymarev, 1957). The north shore consists mainly of parallel belts of loose Quaternary deposits. Because of the absence of sediment in suspension, the sea is remarkably transparent, with the Secchi disk visible to 24 meters. Organisms are poor in species and few in number, the principal plankton being diatoms. There are twenty species of fish; the annual commercial catch is about 35,000 tons (sazan, ship, bream).

Temperatures in the western part of the sea at the surface range from 1°C in February to 24.2°C in August; in the central part from 0.7–23.7°C, with very similar temperatures at all depths except in the west where there is a marked thermocline at about 25 meters; thus at 50–60 meters, the temperature ranges from −0.2°C in summer to 4.0°C in winter. Ice forms in midwinter (Nov.–April), but the middle part remains ice free.

The *currents* display a miniature North Atlantic gyre, thus clockwise motion, being largely in response to the wind patterns, aided by the Amu Darya influx setting north on the west side and the Syr Darya setting south on the east. Such clockwise motion is in contrast to most other Asiatic inland waters. Like that other large, shallow sea, Lake Erie, there is a very long-period seiche in the Aral Sea (1365 minutes). There is also one of 500-minute period and 24-cm amplitude, but wind-driven changes in water level are much more important.

As to *salinity*, the Aral is even more distinct from the ocean type than the *Caspian* (q.v.), the average salinity being 10–11 parts per thousand: NaCl 54%, $MgSO_4$ 26%, $CaSO_4$ 15%. Nevertheless, it is in a completely distinct class from Lake Superior which is low in NaCl but rich in $CaCO_3$. According to L. Blinov (1956), the annual salt budget is as follows: brought in by rivers, 12,850,000 tons; brought in by atmosphere, 64,800 tons; carried away by wind, 101,120 tons. The accumulated salt total in the Aral is over 1.05×10^9 tons. Blinov calculated that if the water level drops by 10 meters, salinity will rise to 23 parts per thousand. In spite of the H_2S-rich sediments in the west, the oxygen content is never below 83% and the basin is entirely oxidizing. The pH range is small (7.2–7.8). Phosphates, nitrate and silica are all very low.

Geological History

The Aral Sea appears to represent a relict basin, the closing stage, or at least a near-equilibrium stage, of an autogeosyncline that was formerly marine, having been connected in Tertiary times with the great Mediterranean–Black Sea–Caspian epicontinental marine belt (the "Sarmatian Sea" a branch of the old Tethys, see Hutchinson, 1957, p. 5). During Quaternary glacial stages, a huge meltwater lake extended over the West Siberian Lowland at up to 125 meters above mean sea level, connecting with the Aral basin via the Ubagan-Turgai trough. The old basin has been subdivided by extensive epeirogenic warping, with minor faulting, during the Quaternary period. Today the Aral forms the collecting area for one of the broad endorheic basins of central Asia. The present fauna suggests a gradual cutting off of the Mediterranean countries from east to west, so that both fauna and flora are quite poor in varieties.

The Amu Darya (Oxus) which rises in the Hindu Kush and Pamirs apparently changed its course at several stages of the Pleistocene and switched its discharge (through the Uzboi Channel) from the Caspian to the Aral, the last time as recently as 1559 A.D., probably due to dune blocking in the Kara Kum Desert. According to Ellsworth Huntington (1907) this extended into early historical times, and about the time of Alexander the Great, between 500 and 300 B.C., an enormous "*Oxian Lake*" (Lake Oxus) existed, as discussed by Strabo, Marco Polo and William of Rubrouck, but the details have been argued by several authorities (e.g., Gregory, 1914). The Aral was certainly very much larger at some stages of the Pleistocene. Huntington claimed very high pluvial levels up till quite late times, but these terraces are probably much older. Berg (1950) pointed out that the adapted marine pelecypod *Cardium edule* marked all Caspian and Aral postglacial shores and these did not normally exceed 5 meters above the present Aral level. Kes (1958) noted similar terraces along the Adschi Darya*. Neotectonic warping has raised this terrace to 11 meters in the north (A. L. Yanshin, 1953). The maximum transgression was about 5000 B.P. for Cardium beds rest on sites of Celtaminarian people; in the southern Aral, a late maximum is dated about 2700–3000 B.P. Kes found that there have been fluctuations up to 8 meters since 5000 B.P.

The Amu Darya responds to summer melting in the Pamirs, so it is to be expected that the Aral water level oscillation, like Lake Balkhash, is in phase with world ocean (eustatic) levels and out of phase with the Volga-Caspian system (controlled by the strength of westerly circulation). Data are sparse, but there is evidence that the Aral rose 2 meters in 1885–1911, at a time of Caspian drop (Berg, 1934, 1950).

[Grateful acknowledgment is due to Prof. Sergei Strelkov, USSR Academy of Sciences, for checking this manuscript, and supplying additional notes.]

RHODES W. FAIRBRIDGE

References

Andrussov, N., 1897, "Der Adschi-darja oder Kara-bugaz Busen," *Peterm. Mitt,* **43,** 25–34.

Berg, L., 1908, "Der Aralsee. Versuch einer physisch-geographischen Monographie," *Mitt. Turkestan. Abteil. Kaiserl. Russ. Geogr. Gesellsch,* **5,** (in Russian).

Berg, L., 1950, "Natural Regions of U.S.S.R.," New York, The Macmillan Co., 436pp. (translated by G. A. Titelbaum from the second Russian ed., 1938; editors T. A. Morrison and C. C. Nikiforoff).

Blinov, L., 1956, "The Hydrochemistry of the Aral Sea," Leningrad (in Russian).

Brodskaya, N. G., 1952, *Trudy Akad. Nauk SSR,* Inst. Geol. **115,** Geol. Ser. 57, 106pp.

Gregory, J. W., 1914, "Is the earth drying up?", *Geogr. J.,* **43,** 148–172, 293–313.

Huntington, E., 1907, "The Pulse of Asia," Boston, Houghton Mifflin Company, 415pp.

Hutchinson, G. E., 1957, "A Treatise on Limnology," vol. 1, New York, John Wiley & Sons, 1015pp.

Kes, A. S., 1958, "Fluctuations of the Aral Sea level" (in Russian), *Priroda,* **1,** 95–99 (translated in *Intern. Geol. Rev.,* **2,** 623–627, 1960).

Lymarev, V., 1957, "The type of the coasts in Aral Sea," *Tr. Okeanogr. Komis. Akad. Nauk SSSR,* **2** (in Russian).

* Note: see *Kara-Bogaz Gulf.*

Yanshin, A. L., 1953, "Geologiya severnogo Priaralya," *Mater. Poznaniyu Geol. Stroeniya SSSR,* new ser. **15**(19), 736pp.

Zenkevitch, L. 1963, "Biology of the Seas of the U.S.S.R.," New York, Interscience Publishers, 955 pp. (translated by S. Botcharskaya).

Cross-references: *Caspian Sea*; *Great Lakes* (*N. America*); *Great Salt Lake*; *Lakes*; *Lake Baikal*; *Lake Balkhash*; *Pluvial Lakes*; *Quaternary*. Vol. I: *Seiche*; *Transparency*.

ARCTIC BEACHES

The major difference between beach processes in the arctic and elsewhere in the world is the cessation of wave action during extensive periods when the sea is covered by ice. Processes related to freezing affect only the uppermost part of an arctic beach, so evidence for such processes is rarely preserved in the geologic record. Disruption of the beach sediment by wind-blown and current-driven pack ice tends to be rather superficial. A shelf of sea ice freezes to the bottom along the shore (Fig. 1), and usually this shelf stops any landward movement of the ice. Where part of an ice floe may be driven onto the land, it generally rides up over the shelf of fast ice and builds a spectacular and chaotic pile on the frozen beach behind but does not disturb its sediment greatly. An aerial inspection of the arctic coast of Alaska in the spring of 1960 revealed that such piles of ice occurred along about 10% of the shore.

Northern beaches are generally low-energy beaches. This is partly a geographic accident— many of the seas around the Arctic Ocean are small, and their fetch is consequently limited. The persistent ice cover of an arctic region also restricts the places where a strong surf can develop along its shore. Although sand beaches are locally common in the arctic, an increase in the effectiveness of physical weathering over chemical weathering in cold climates makes gravel beaches more abundant there than elsewhere.

A characteristic feature of arctic beaches in the winter is a flat rampart of alternating layers of beach sediment and ice called a *kaimoo* (Fig. 1).

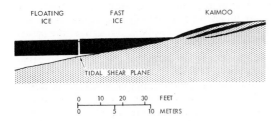

FIG. 1. On arctic beaches in the fall, before winter temperatures stop wave action, a kaimoo forms from interbedded layers of beach sediment and ice. Directly offshore from the kaimoo, sea ice frozen fast to the bottom helps protect the beach from disruption by moving ice floes.

It is extensively used by Eskimos as a convenient sled trail. Kaimoos are built in the fall when the air temperature is below freezing but before formation of continuous sea ice. Each wave, as it slides up over a cold beach, leaves a thin layer of ice, usually followed by a layer of sediment. Ultimately, the progradation of the ice and clastic layers forms a flat upper surface, the height of which is controlled by the height to which the waves run.

In the early summer, when wave action begins, fragments of kaimoos containing layers of sand and gravel may float far out to sea before melting. Rafting by kaimoo fragments is probably the chief mechanism for supplying rounded pebbles to offshore sedimentary basins of the arctic.

The melting out of ice from a kaimoo during early summer results in a rough beach surface that may persist throughout much of the remainder of the summer. During some years, this microrelief lasts into mid-August on beaches as far south as the Seward Peninsula of Alaska and makes landings with a light airplane difficult. The first major storm, however, obliterates all traces of this characteristic roughness.

Where a beach-ridge plain is building out toward the sea, permafrost forms in the sediment as it becomes separated from the relatively warm seawater. Vertical ice wedges then grow in contraction cracks within the frozen sediment. In well-sorted beach sand and gravel, the ice wedges appear at the top of the layer of seasonal thaw as widely spaced straight ditches that almost seem to be man made.

Coasts cut into perennially frozen loess have some unique features. When the ice melts from these deposits of wind-blown silt, the shore line often retreats rapidly. As the permafrost thaws to depth, the coast subsides, causing a submergence that might well be falsely ascribed to tectonic subsidence or to a general rise of sea level.

Where a beach is backed either by loess or till, large quantities of silt usually flow onto its upper surface during the summer thaw. This silt may harden and persist as a continuous sheet until it is finally removed by storm waves.

Beach deposits in undeformed and unglaciated parts of the arctic are useful indicators of post-Pleistocene geologic history. Beachridge plains on the Lisburne Peninsula of Alaska provide an extensive record of sea level change that may be compared to the history recorded in other stable parts of the world. On such a plain at Cape Krusenstern, Alaska (67° 07′ N, 163° 44′ W), a unique record of fossil-wind direction also appears to be preserved (Fig. 2). Deposition has alternated from the west to the south side of Cape Krusenstern, as indicated by unconformities that cut the beach ridges. Six reversals in effective wind direction are recorded over approximately the last 5000 years. The reversals may be related to changes in the average position of the polar front, and such changes

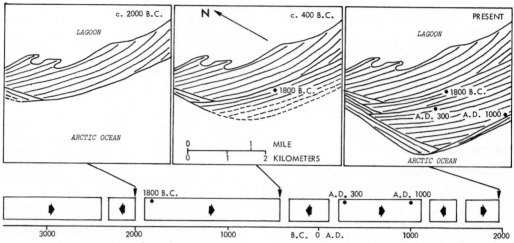

Fig. 2. Maps of a beach-ridge plain at Cape Krusenstern, Alaska, show successive stages of its growth. Certain beach ridges have been dated at archeological sites studied by J. L. Giddings, and sites with radiocarbon-age determinations are marked by dots. These sites, like modern Eskimo homes, are inferred to have been next to the shore when occupied, because the ground around them is littered with marine-mammal bones. The beach ridges are cut by numerous unconformities, and sawtoothed intersections of the unconformities record six reversals in the direction of net beach-sediment transport over approximately the last 5000 years. As the sediment-transport direction (arrows on the time scale) is controlled by the wave-generating wind, a record of past arctic air circulation is preserved on the beach-ridge plain.

in arctic air circulation would have a broad influence on the climate of the northern hemisphere.

At present, and for approximately the last 400 years, deposition has predominated on the south side of Cape Krusenstern, and deposition there occurs when the average effective wave-generating wind is from the northwest. A northwest wind in Alaska is associated with a more southerly position of the polar front, which in turn is normally associated in temperate latitudes with cooler temperatures and heavier precipitation. Hence, the paleoclimatic record from this arctic beach might correlate with contemporaneous records preserved to the south at mountain glaciers and pluvial lakes.

GEORGE W. MOORE

References

Hume, J. D., and Schalk, M., 1967, "Shoreline processes near Barrow, Alaska: A comparison of the normal and the catastrophic," *Arctic,* **20,** 86–103.

Moore, G. W., 1966, "Arctic Beach Sedimentation," in (Wilimovsky, N. J., and Wolfe, J. N., editors) "Environment of the Cape Thompson Region, Alaska," pp. 587–608, Oak Ridge, Tenn., U.S. Atomic Energy Commission Rept. PNE-481.

Moore, G. W., and Giddings, J. L., 1962, "Record of 5000 years of Arctic wind direction recorded by Alaskan beach ridges," *Geol. Soc. Am. Spec. Paper* **68,** 232.

Cross-references: *Beach; Frost Action; Holocene; Ice Thrusting; Pluvial Lakes; Valley (Mountain) Glacier.* Vol. I: *Arctic Ocean; Beaufort Sea; East Siberian Sea; Fetch; Kara Sea; Laptev Sea.* Vol. II: *Climatic Variation (Historical Record).* pr Vol. VII: *Paleoclimatology.*

ARCTIC REGIONS

The Arctic Regions are usually thought of as remote and forbidding by those who have not encountered them, as well as by some who have. Actually, this idea stems from the thinking and experience of those who were brought up in temperate regions and who had neither reason nor need to delve into the circumstances or conditions of the Arctic. Today, with a better understanding of nature and our environment, plus an appreciable mastery of a material technology, the Arctic is being fathomed and its processes are being acknowledged and understood. Generally, the region is no different now than it has been throughout the period of man's experience with it. It is still formidable and challenging to temperate man who is still no better equipped physiologically to cope with its demands, but the proficiency of man's undertakings is greater than in the past and his needs are more pressing. As a consequence, some members of today's society are modifying their temperate-oriented patterns and are settling and developing this little known region (for dimensions see Table 1 and Table 2).

One of the confusing matters pertaining to the region, which will probably never be fully resolved,

TABLE 1. APPROXIMATE AREAS OF ARCTIC AND SUBARCTIC (from S. Haden-Guest, in Kimble and Good, 1955)

	Areas (sq miles)		
	North America (including Greenland)	Eurasia (including Iceland)	Total
Arctic			
Ice desert	750,000	170,000	920,000
Rock and tundra	750,000	680,000	1,430,000
All land	1,500,000	850,000	2,350,000
Sea area[a]			5,500,000
Subarctic			
Marginal and alpine tundra	350,000	600,000	950,000
Transitional forest	750,000	2,000,000	2,750,000
Boreal and other forest	1,300,000	3,000,000	4,300,000
All land	2,400,000	5,600,000	8,000,000

[a] Adjoining arctic lands, but not equivalent to arctic zone of marine environment.

is defining it to everyone's satisfaction. Because of its size, diversity, complexity, and the random and scattered manner in which man has experienced it, the terms used to describe it have become part of our language without a precise recognition of their meaning. Also, men concerned with the Arctic, whose backgrounds and purposes vary, have different meanings for the same word. Hence, arctic Norway is warmer than subarctic Greenland, and fish which live in temperate waters are now found off Greenland. For the layman, the most meaningful definition is the most common one—the area lying north of the Arctic Circle. For the specialist, however, greater care must be used since some areas north of the Circle are not Arctic in all senses of the word, while some areas south of it are (see

TABLE 2. CANADIAN ARCTIC ARCHIPELAGO: APPROXIMATE AREAS OF MAIN ISLANDS (from P. D. Baird, in Kimble and Good, 1955)

	sq. miles
Baffin	200,000
Victoria	79,000
Ellesmere	73,000
Banks	26,000
Devon	20,000
Melville	16,000
Prince of Wales	14,000
Axel Heiberg	13,000
Somerset	9,500
Bathurst	6,500
Prince Patrick	6,500
King William	5,000
Bylot	4,500
Ellef Ringnes	4,000
Remaining small isles	23,000
	500,000

Figs. 1 and 2). From the climatic viewpoint, it is convenient to define Arctic as the region where the warmest monthly mean temperature does not exceed 50°F (10°C) and the coldest is below 32°F (0°C). Subarctic covers the belt where the mean monthly temperatures do not exceed 50°F for more than 4 months, and the coldest temperatures are below 32°F.

Geological Character

Geologically and geomorphically, the region is basically an extension of the areas south of it. The rock types and evolutionary events through geologic time are comparable to those found elsewhere on the globe, with temperate or even tropical indications; glacial conditions are relatively recent characteristics of this region. Fossil remains indicate that the climate and the geography of the region we call the Arctic have changed considerably during geologic time. It has been only since the onset of the last great ice age, the Pleistocene (one to two million years ago), that the region has taken on most of its present characteristics. It is these characteristics which now help to make the Arctic unique with respect to the lower latitudes. The region today is only partly glaciated; the present time is intermediate between an interglacial and a full glacial period. The area involved in the last glacial maximum is indicated in Table 3. As a result of gradual deglaciation since about 15,000 years B.P., much of the region has recently become isostatically upwarped, as evidenced by numerous raised beaches, up to 1000 feet above present sea level.

Climatic Features

Broadly taken, the Arctic differs from more temperate regions by virtue of a cold climate, a varying day-night cycle, and magnetic and ionospheric

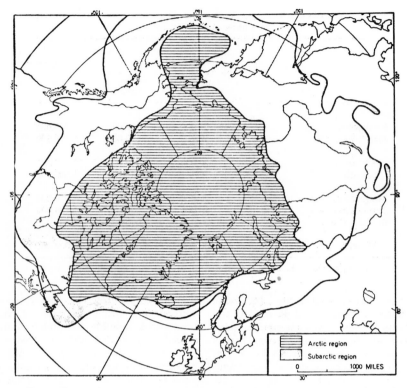

FIG. 1. The Arctic and subarctic according to the definitions adopted by Kimble and Good (1955). (By permission of the American Geographical Soc.)

TABLE 3. ESTIMATED AREAS COVERED BY GLACIERS AT THE MAXIMUM WISCONSIN OR FOURTH GLACIAL AGE (modified from R. F. Flint by Kimble and Good, 1955)

Continents	Principal Glaciated Areas	Extent of Glaciers (sq miles)
North America	Laurentide Ice Sheet	4,840,000
	Cordilleran glacier ice (coalescent)	875,000
	Greenland Ice Sheet	835,000
Europe	Scandinavian Ice Sheet	1,650,000
	Glaciers of British origin	143,000
	The Faroes	4,000
	Iceland and Jan Mayen Island	45,000
	Svalbard	60,000
Asia	Siberian Ice Sheet	836,000
	Franz Josef Land	20,000
	New Siberian Islands and Wrangell Island	35,000
	Northeastern Siberia (coalescent glaciers)	360,000
	Koryak Mountains	38,000
	Kamchatka Peninsula	19,000
	Transbaykal Highlands (coalescent glaciers)	54,000
	Other separate areas in Siberia	8,000
	Altay Highlands	125,000
	Coalescent glaciers in Central Asia, including Himalaya Mountains	335,000

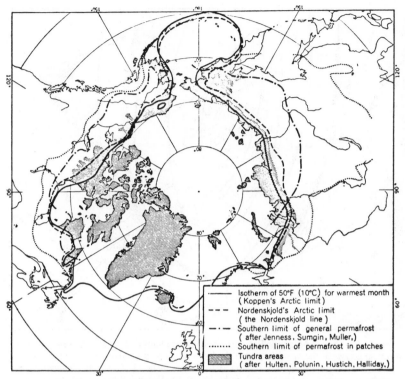

FIG. 2. Some significant boundaries in the Arctic lands (Kimble and Good, 1955).
(By permission of the American Geographical Soc.)

peculiarities. Generally the region is a heat sink. Not as much solar energy falls on it as is lost to space, or as falls on more southerly regions. Mean temperatures are considerably lower than near the equator so that plant life, especially agriculture, is more limited. This lack of plant life accounts for much of its "bleakness." The occurrence of the midnight sun during summer and the absence of sun during midwinter pose psychological problems for man which, together with the more severe climate, make the region even more "formidable." The presence of the magnetic dip-pole and geomagnetic pole add scientifically complex problems to understanding its nature and have a direct influence on conditions to the south. For navigation on land, sea or air, the use of the sun compass or gyro is necessary within a broad area (see Fig. 3).

Regionally, the Arctic is dominated by an ocean in its center. Although the Arctic Ocean is smaller than the other oceans (5.4 million square miles, 14 million km^2)—it is no larger than some seas— it is nonetheless deep and the structure of its basin appears in part to be truly oceanic in character. Distributed, but not balanced, around it are the land masses of the Eurasian and North American continents. Near the 180th meridian, the two continents are only 48 miles apart; north of the Atlantic Ocean they are over 2000 miles apart. However, much of this latter space is taken up with islands of the Canadian Archipelago, Greenland, Iceland, Svalbard, and others. As a result of being almost an inland ocean situated over the North Pole, the Arctic Ocean is unique in that over 80% of its surface remains ice covered throughout the year and it is essentially entirely frozen over from November to June. This fact profoundly influences the climate of the region.

Physiographic Regions (Fig. 4)

Those parts of the North American continent, including Greenland, which fall within the Arctic are divided into three sections: the Canadian Shield, the Plains, and the Cordillera. The largest of the three by far is the Canadian Shield which lies in the arc from 60–120° W longitude. Generally it resembles a large saucer with the peaks of the Torngat Mountains on the east and a pronounced scarp on the west where it borders the Mackenzie plains. The rim area is made up of igneous rocks which form the major relief, while the central depression is composed of largely young, flat-lying, sedimentary rocks. Greenland too is a saucer which is filled with ice—an ice sheet in places as much as 10,000 feet deep. Its saucer shape is believed to be an important factor in delaying its melting. The mountains of the eastern portion of

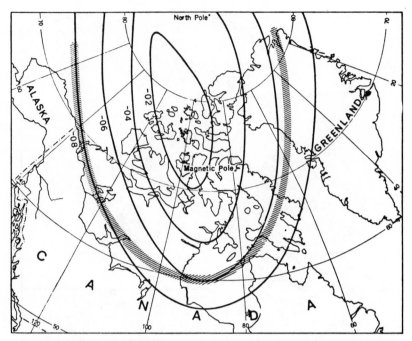

FIG. 3. The North Magnetic Pole and approximate lines of equal horizontal magnetic force, in gauss. In the area within the shaded boundary, it is advisable to use the directional gyro for maintaining direction (based on a map in *Arctic Air Navigation* by Squadron Leader K. R. Greenaway, published by the Defense Research Board, Ottawa; from Kimble and Good, 1955). *Note*: There is a secular shift of the magnetic pole, at present in a northwesterly direction.

the Canadian Shield (e.g., Baffin Island) are rugged and support many glaciers and some ice caps. The coasts are abrupt and deeply fiorded. The western portion of the shield and the western islands of the Canadian Arctic Archipelago are gently rolling and contain vast numbers of lakes.

West of the Canadian Shield is the Plains Province which is the northward extension of the Great Plains. In Canada, it comprises the Mackenzie lowlands and in Alaska the Arctic Slope. Both portions are low-lying, flat, monotonous regions filled with lakes and meandering rivers. West and south of these is the Cordilleran province which in its entirety reaches along the western shore of both the North and South American continents. In Canada, the Rocky Mountain system continues in the Richardson Mountains which then curve west into the Brooks Range of northern Alaska. Although rugged and still relatively high, these two chains support glaciers only in the eastern portions of the Brooks Range.

In Eurasia, these three groups of physical land forms are also evidenced. There are two shields (the Baltic and the Angara), extensive plains provinces along almost all of the Russian and Siberian coasts, and mountain provinces in the Urals and in northeastern Siberia.

Geomorphically, these regions are set apart from those to the south by two circumstances, *permafrost* (q.v.) and the *lack of precipitation* and running water to carry out the more common processes of mass wasting. Permafrost may be defined as permanently frozen ground, and as a result of the generally low temperatures in the Arctic, much of the earth's surface there remains in this condition throughout the year. Depending on the latitude, the vegetative cover, and the make-up of the soil, as much as three feet of the surface material may thaw during the summer. However, as much as 1000 feet below this thaw zone, the temperature remains below freezing at all times. The result of this phenomenon is that the water cycle is quite different from that of other areas. Surface waters cannot percolate into the soils so they run off and form lakes or fill the rivers. The number of temperate plants which have adapted to this condition is small, and those that have adapted are stunted. There are numerous species of plants in the Arctic but all are small in stature. In relation to man's activities, permafrost is of importance because of the part it plays in construction. It cannot be disregarded or ignored, or it will ruin almost any structure set on it. It is only when adequate allowance is made for it that success is achieved.

As a result of the low precipitation and the extent

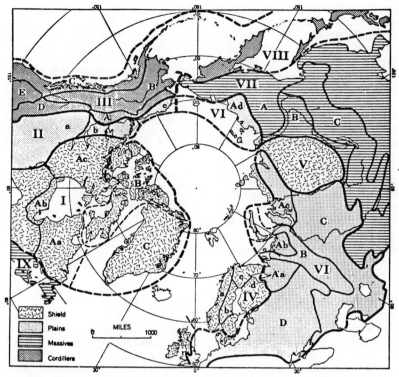

FIG. 4. Physiographic regions of the Arctic lands, numbered according to the following plan. I. Canadian Shield Division. A, Laurentian Upland Province (a, Ungava Section; b, Hudson Bay Coastal Plain Section; c, Keewatin Section); B, Arctic Archipelago Province; C, Greenland Province. II. Interior Plains Division of North America, Great Plains Province (a, Alberta Plains Section; b, Mackenzie Lowlands Section; c, Arctic Plains Section). III. North American Cordillera Division: A, Arctic and Mackenzie Mountain Province; B, Interior Uplands and Plateaus Province; C, Coastal Mountains and Troughs Province; D, Rocky Mountains Province; E, Columbia Plateau Province. IV. Baltic Shield Division (a, Norwegian Highlands Section; b, Swedish Highlands Section; c, Lapland Plateau Section; d, Finnish Massif Section). V. Angara Shield Division. VI. Eurasian Northern Plains Division: A, Arctic Plains Province (a, Severnaya Dvina Plain Section; b, Pechora Plain Section; c, Ob' Delta-Northern Siberian Plain Section; d, Lena-Yana-Indigirka-Kolyma Delta Plain Section); B, Uralian Province; C, West Siberian Lowland Province; D, The Great Central Plain. VII. Central Massives Division: A, Highland Province; B, Corridor Province; C, Central Asiatic Block Mountains Province. VIII. Alpine Folded Division. IX. Appalachian Highlands Division (mainly after Lobeck, with additions from Berg, Bostock, Cooke, Ebbely, and *Great Soviet World Atlas*; from Kimble and Good, 1955). (By permission of the American Geographical Soc.)

of the freezing period, the wasting away of rock and soils and the formation of soils differs from nonpolar regions. In the Arctic, weathering is accomplished primarily by frost action and by physical means rather than chemical ones. Therefore, the breakdown is often less complete. Low precipitation and the behavior of permafrost cause soils to erode through mass slippage or *solifluction* (q.v.) Particle size and the duration of freezing mean that soils are very poorly developed, lack many minerals, and generally have a low organic content.

Environmentally, the region is described, oddly enough, not on the basis of how cold it is but on the basis of its summer temperatures. As mentioned earlier, using the system developed by Köppen, the Arctic is that area where the mean temperature for the warmest month is below 50°F and the average temperature for the coldest month is below 32°F. This definition is of considerable importance because it generally describes the northern *limit of trees*. However, in no way is it close to the Arctic Circle. In terms of temperature, almost all of the region has experienced −40°F during the winter, although only in eastern Siberia does the average January temperature reach this extreme. Except for the interior of Greenland, the summer temperatures usually are above freezing and may reach into the sixties.

The ice cover on the ocean and the retention of soil moisture in the permafrost are the principal causes of the low precipitation in the region. Exact figures are not known because of the difficulty in measuring snowfall. It is generally assumed that the region is essentially a desert in that it receives less than 15 inches (400 mm) of rain per year. Even in areas where lakes abound, the moisture available to plants is such that many temperate species would die of thirst. Hence, new species must be developed if man is to utilize the Arctic for agriculture. Despite the low precipitation, some parts of the Arctic are faced with the problem of poor visibility due to blowing snow during the winter months. The lack of trees and the dryness of the snow make the snow easily transported to the extent that visibility is reduced to less than one-half mile during much of the time. This causes problems with all types of transportation.

Man himself will only fully adapt to the region when he has not only understood the processes and conditions which occur there but taught himself to adjust to them. It is far easier and more likely that man will simply transport his temperate environment into the Arctic for the great majority of his activities, such as residence and most occupations, and will encounter the elements only on a limited scale. It is not known how readily temperate man can acclimatize himself to cold, if he can at all. It may require many generations before such a change could take place, and probably technology would advance simultaneously so that there would be no need to acclimatize. Regardless of which happens, he must learn to adapt to the isolation, which will presumably lessen in the future, and to the changing day-night cycle. While it has been shown that he can do this, not many have yet chosen to do so. That he will eventually do so is almost a foregone conclusion at a time when the need for natural resources and land for population expansion is increasing algebraically. Not even the tropic desert regions are as sparsely populated or as little explored. Much of man's present commerce and communication now leads him over the North Pole. It is difficult to imagine that he will not fill in the voids and gaps which the Arctic represents in his knowledge and accomplishments.

JOHN E. SATER

References

Baird, P. D., 1964, "The Polar World," London, Longmans, Green and Co., 328pp.
Bird, J. B., 1967, "The Physiography of Arctic Canada," Baltimore, Johns Hopkins Press.
Kimble, G. H. T., and Good, Dorothy, (editors), 1955, "Geography of the Northlands," New York, Am. Geogr. Soc. Spec. Publ. 32.

Pantenburg, Vitalis, 1964, "Die Arktis ruft," Stuttgart, Spectrum Verlag.
Proceedings of the Alberta Association of Petroleum Geologists, 1961, "Geology of the Arctic," Toronto, University of Toronto Press.
*Sater, John E., (editor), 1963, "The Arctic Basin," Arctic Institute of North America, Centerville, Md., Tidewater Publishing Co.
U.S. Army, 1961, "Atlas of Arctic Environment," Headquarters Quartermaster Research and Engineering Command, Environmental Protection Research Section, Research Study Report No. RER-33, Natick, Mass.

* Additional bibliographic references may be found in this work.

Cross-references: Permafrost; Pingos; Solifluction. Vol. I: Arctic Ocean. Vol. II: Arctic Meteorology. Vol. VI: Zonation of Terrestrial Ecologic Belts.

ARÊTE—See BERGSCHRUND

ARID CYCLE

The arid geographic cycle or geomorphic cycle is that sequential system of landforms developed in an arid climate, i.e., in a region of relatively little rainfall and consequently sparse plant growth, as compared with heavy rainfall and lush vegetation in a humid climate. It involves an orderly evolution of landscape features with the passage of time through stages of youth, maturity, and old age. It was conceived by its originator, W. M. Davis, to be a variation of the usual or "normal" humid cycle. Utilizing the "structure, process, and stage" basic factors in the cycle concept ("structure" in its comprehensive Davisian or geomorphic sense includes not only geologic structure but also rock character and distribution, original regional morphology, etc.), it was devised to explain progressive desert land forms as the results of special, arid combinations of erosional processes. The aridity itself was envisioned as an abnormality or "climatic accident." It was recognized that a continuous gradation from the normal humid to the accidental arid cycle was feasible, that intermediate "semiarid" distribution of emphasis on erosional processes precluded any sharp line of demarcation, and that as a result of control of rainfall by altitude, land forms characteristic of both cycles might coexist in a single mountainous area.

The Davisian arid cycle was based on a provincial type of initial "structure," the fault block topography of the arid Great Basin of the southwestern United States. With this initial "structure" characterizing the first or youthful stage of the arid cycle, isolated mountain masses and independent, intermediate basins set the topographic pattern. Maximum relief prevailed at this initial stage in the arid cycle instead of at maturity as postulated for the

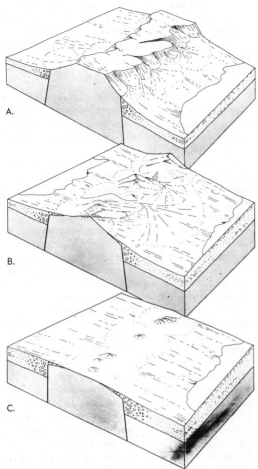

FIG. 1. Block diagrams illustrating stages in the arid cycle of erosion. (A) Youth; relief is at a maximum; dissection of mountains begins; alluvial fans and playas occur. (B) Maturity; mountain masses are intricately dissected; pediments are developed and alluvium encroaches progressively inward upon the mountain mass. (C) Old Age; a few inselbergs remain above the surrounding pediment and alluvial (bajada) surface (from "Physical Geology Laboratory Manual," p. 75 by W. K. Hamblin and J. D. Howard, Minneapolis, Minn., Burgess Publishing Co.)

humid cycle. Progression to maturity in the arid cycle involved reduction of the mountain masses and alluvial filling of the intermediate basins, with extension of an integrated drainage system for all the basins. The stage of old age was characterized by a cut-and-fill surface of low relief (as distinguished from the cut surface of low relief, peneplain, in the humid cycle), but increasing wind erosion and deflation caused development of hollows and disintegration of the drainage system (see Fig. 1).

In his later embellishment of the arid cycle concept, Davis recognized the essential nature of the

pediment of W J McGee, and of Kirk Bryan, developed as an expanding rock floor from youth to old age. He followed the concept of A. C. Lawson of mountain front retreat with maintenance of steep frontal slope and development of a "suballuvial bench." Acknowledging lateral planation by mountain-debouching streams as a factor in pediment formation, he rejected it as the major factor. He considered that the suballuvial bench might be partially exposed as a pediment by "rock-floor robbing by sheetfloods." Elaboration of desert geomorphology has led to widespread recognition of rock-cut surfaces formed by pediplanation, i.e., planation along the foot of a mountain, essentially mountain front or slope retreat. Some of these are elevated and dissected, others are being eroded and extended actively at the present time. As a practical matter, most of the desert surfaces of low relief are composite cut-and-fill surfaces, coalescing alluvial fans, alluvial mantle, and pediments, i.e., pediplains. Although the pediplain is a surface of low relief, it is not, like the peneplain, related only to the old-age stage in its cycle; it is a land form which may develop in youth and continue to expand through maturity and old age.

The majority of the desert areas of the world do not fit well in a cyclical scheme. Many of them do have erosion residuals, inselbergs, bornhardts, etc., which appear to be subject to reduction in area by pediplanation and slope retreat, a change in surface progressive with time. A significant new emphasis on regional and local warping in the development of initial land surfaces and in modification and interruption of cycles in progress is changing the analysis of land forms. If regarded as an inflexible sequential system, the arid cycle concept has lost its claim to universal validity. If used as a tool in organizing loosely interrelated geomorphic data of infinite variability into generalized and easily understandable groupings, the cycle concept may be helpful to geologists for many years to come.

JOHN H. MAXSON

References

Cotton, C. A., 1942, "Climatic Accidents," Section I, "Dry and Dry-Seasonal Climatic Landscape Types," Wellington, Whitcombe and Tombs, Ltd.

Davis, W. M., 1905, "The geographical cycle in an arid climate." *J. Geol.*, **13**, 381–407.

*Thornbury, William D., 1954, "Principles of Geomorphology," pp. 276–298, New York, John Wiley & Sons, Inc.

* Additional bibliographic references may be found in this work.

Cross-references: *Alluvial Fan*; *Bajada*; *Bornhardt*; *Cycles—Geomorphic*; *Deserts and Desert Landforms*; *Duricrust*; *Exfoliation*; *Inselberg*; *Landscape Analysis*;

ARROYO CUTTING—*See* GULLY EROSION

ASTROBLEME—*See* Vol. II

ASYMMETRIC VALLEYS

Asymmetric valleys are those in which opposing sides have markedly different inclinations (Fig. 1). A method of indicating this disparity is the *symmetry index* (Emery, 1947) which is the ratio of the average inclination (in degrees) of the left side of the valley to the inclination of the right side of the valley, where *left* and *right* sides are relative to an observer facing *downstream*. If a valley is perfectly symmetrical, the index will be 1.0; if the left wall is steeper, the index will be greater than 1.0; if the right wall is steeper, the index will be less than 1.0. This index has not been widely used, perhaps because it involves large integers as well as small fractions. An alternative would be to subtract the average inclination of the right valley side from the average inclination of the left valley side. If the left side is steeper, the valley will have a *"positive asymmetry"*; if the right side is steeper, the valley will have a *"negative asymmetry"*; if the valley sides have identical slopes, the valley will have 0° asymmetry, i.e., it is symmetrical (see Fig. 1 for example of the use of this index). A third method would be to indicate the side of the steepest slope by speaking of "dextral asymmetry" or "sinistral asymmetry."

According to Thornbury (1954, p. 111), "recognition of the causes of asymmetry is essential to a proper interpretation of valley history." A great number and variety of explanations have been suggested and have been discussed by Emery (1947) and Thornbury (1954). Some examples are given below.

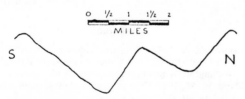

Fig. 1. Profile of asymmetric valleys in central Bitterroot Range, Montana (Beaty, 1962, p. 351). Profile is drawn 6 miles from upstream from canyon mouths and looks *upstream*. For the larger canyon the south slope (north facing) has an average inclination of 21°, while the opposite slope averages 35°. The valley has a positive asymmetry of 14°. Alternately one could say the valley has a sinistral asymmetry (i.e., the left-side slope, looking downstream is steepest). Emery's symmetry index gives a value of 35/21 or 5/3.

It is important to note that each of the following explanations is oversimplified in that it is assumed that only the factors mentioned in the explanation are involved in the origin of the asymmetry. However, nature is seldom so straightforward, and often more than one factor is necessary to explain fully the condition.

(1) *Slip-off slopes:* The valley side on the outside of a meander often develops a steep or undercut slope, whereas the opposite valley side, a *slip-off slope* (q.v.), descends more gradually from upland to valley floor.

Melton (1960) has mentioned a comparable case. He related decreasing asymmetry in certain Wyoming valleys to increasing channel gradient; furthermore, he suggested that the entrance of tributaries to a main stream forces the channel to undercut the valley side opposite the channel entrance. The resultant steeper slopes occur only where the main channel is unable to remove all of the debris contributed by the tributary. Where there are steep channels and all of the tributary bed load is removed, asymmetry of valley sides does not occur.

The remaining theories of asymmetry, given below, explain situations in which one valley side is consistently steeper than another, in a given area. Louis (1961) has identified this phenomenon as *systematic asymmetry*.

(2) *Earth rotation* (and thus *Coriolis force*, q.v., Vol. II) is said to produce differential lateral erosion, according to the *theory of Babinet* (1859). Theoretically, in the northern hemisphere earth rotation deflects streams to the right (looking downstream), thereby tending to produce steeper right walls than left walls (negative or dextral asymmetry). Eakin (1910) applied this theory to the valley of the Yukon River. Fairchild (1932) believed the effect of earth rotation to be a minor factor in controlling asymmetry on the south side of Long Island, New York.

(3) *Structural controls:* Asymmetrical profiles develop where there is a regional dip of strata which tends to produce progressive lateral shifting of strike valleys (Fig. 2). Cotton (1942) has used the term *homoclinal shifting* to describe such lateral migration of stream axes with resultant development of asymmetry. Others have called this tendency *uniclinal, monoclinal, isoclinal.* Faults may also be a cause of valley asymmetry (Thornbury, 1954).

(4) *Microclimate and related factors, past or present:* Valley asymmetry may be due to variations in microclimate, paleomicroclimate or slope cover (vegetation, snow). The asymmetry results largely from differential insolation, precipitation or evapotranspiration, which in turn reflects exposure (i.e., azimuth or orientation) of the valley sides relative to the sun or to prevailing rain and wind. No simple generalizations can be made regarding valley asymmetry of this type. However, most observers have claimed that average slope inclination is less on slopes which are being actively eroded (by weather-

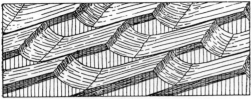

FIG. 2. Homoclinal shifting as illustrated by Cotton (1942). Sequence of diagrams—oldest at back proceeding to youngest in front.

ing, sheetwash, mass-wasting) than on slopes being less actively eroded. On the other hand, if the bedrock is strongly stratified or has a cap rock of *duricrust* (q.v.), as is common in subtropical regions, the slope of most active erosion is the steepest. Erosion in any case is favored under conditions of high surface runoff and hindered by the presence of a protective cover (vegetation, snow).

It seems likely that much valley asymmetry is inherited from Pleistocene cold epochs, when wind systems were appreciably different from those of today and widespread periglacial phenomena developed. The rates of cryergenic mass-wasting were often several orders of magnitude above present-day figures.

A variety of climatic and other factors affect *runoff* (see pr Vol. VI) and protective covering. Thornbury (1954, p. 112), for example, has outlined a general relationship appropriate to a semiarid middle-latitude region. He states that north- and northeast-facing slopes (in North America, for example) generally receive less insolation than south- and southeast- facing slopes. As insolation increases, so also do evaporation, the number of freeze/thaw cycles and the rate of snow melt. As a result of higher temperatures and lower soil moisture on south-facing slopes, there usually will be less vegetation. Hence runoff and denudation will be more rapid, and in homogeneous materials the average slope will be less steep on south-facing slopes than on north-facing ones. Naturally, if there are resistant "ridge-formers," the slope affected by maximum erosion will become quite steep (at least in its upper part).

Melton (1957) has confirmed that for certain drainage basins in the southwestern United States, greater runoff produces relatively gentle valley side slopes. As might be expected, slopes were observed to steepen with increased infiltration capacity and, hence, with amount of subsurface moisture available for vegetation. Relatively bare valley sides with low infiltration capacities have a high runoff intensity and frequency; thus, they erode rapidly and have relatively low slope inclinations.

Studies made in humid, periglacial, glacial and other climates establish many exceptions to the simple relationships outlined above. For instance, as Thornbury points out, where moisture-bearing

winds are prevailingly from one direction, as in the *trade wind* belt (q.v., Vol. II), there may be asymmetry of windward and leeward slopes because of the variation in the amount of rainfall on the two sides of a valley.

On the other hand, in "periglacial" and glacial climates, where slopes have been severely denuded by glacial *abrasion and sapping, nivation, solifluction,* and other cryogenic processes, i.e., those associated with cold climates (see *Frost Action*), the surfaces should for the most part be more rounded and gentler than slopes which are not so affected. Exceptions occur, of course; glacial cirque plucking and some cases of nivation lead to locally steepened slopes. Beaty (1962) found (Fig. 1) that in the Bitterroot Range, Montana, north-facing slopes are more eroded and gentler than south-facing slopes, a relationship opposite to that outlined above. He concluded that under a periglacial and glacial regime like that which characterized the Bitterroots during much of the Quaternary, denudation is favored on slopes with low insolation, i.e., on north-facing valley sides. Protection from insolation facilitates formation of a snow pack, nivation, and eventually development of glaciers. Thus cirques are predominantly found on north- and northeast-facing slopes.

In Lapland, Rapp (1960) found marked frost action and mass-wasting effects on wet west-facing slopes, whereas dry east-facing slopes were relatively inactive. Where snow accumulates most readily, the slopes are wetter, thus aiding frost action processes. Melting snow also promotes avalanching on these slopes, thus greatly increasing the overall rate of erosion.

Taillefer (1950) explained asymmetric valleys of the Northern Pyrenees Piedmont (Fig. 3) as being due to the combined product of Pleistocene frost action and lateral shifting of streams. Much of the relief is inherited from cold Quaternary epochs when frost action appears to have been greatest on east-facing slopes, which in addition to having less insolation, also are areas of maximum snow accumulation because they were in the lee of moist westerly winds. Essentially the same conclusion was reached by Büdel (see his discussion in *Geomorphology*). Thus, in the Pyrenees Piedmont, solifluction has been extremely active in poorly consolidated piedmont fan deposits, materially aiding the shift of stream beds to the right in the north-flowing regimes. Moderate downcutting has kept the right-hand slopes steep or even precipitous.

In high-latitude polar regions, a relationship similar to the semiarid situation may exist. North-facing slopes may be completely covered by snow all year round, and thus protected, while south-facing slopes will be affected by seasonal melting, runoff erosion and mass-wasting. Hence south-facing valley sides may be gentler under a polar climate. In the coldest microclimates, snow cover

TABLE 1. SUMMARY OF CHARACTERISTICS OF OPPOSITE SIDES OF ASYMMETRIC VALLEYS IN THE LITTLE RIVER BASIN, VIRGINIA (FROM HACK AND GOODLETT, 1960)

Characteristics	Northwest- or Southwest-facing Slopes[a]	Northeast- or Southeast-facing Slopes[a]
Declivity	Gentle	Steep
Moistness	Dry	Wet
Surface mantle of stones	Coarse	Fine
Predominant vegetation	Yellow pine forest unit	Oak forest unit
Density of cover	Dense, many shrubs	Open, few shrubs
Drainage density	High	Low
Drainage network	Well developed	Less well developed
Postulated most important process	Slope wash and channel erosion	Creep

[a] Differences between northwest and southeast characteristics are related to the prevailing southeasterly dip of the rock strata. Differences, between northeast and southwest characteristics are related to exposure.

protects the land surface, but in freeze/thaw regimes, it promotes solifluction and other mass movements.

In humid regions, variations in vegetation due to moisture may not always be a controlling factor. For example, relatively high insolation on south-facing slopes may well promote growth of vegetation, especially of shrubs, since on protected north-facing slopes little or no sunlight penetrates to the ground. As with tree-ring interpretation (dendrochronology), it should be noted that in one environ-

TABLE 2. POSSIBLE CAUSES OF VALLEY ASYMMETRY. ASYMMETRY NEED NOT OCCUR IN THE FOLLOWING TYPES OF SITUATIONS, ESPECIALLY WHERE THERE ARE COMPLICATIONS DUE TO VARIABLE STRUCTURE, MICROCLIMATE OR PALEOCLIMATE. THE TABLE MERELY INDICATES SOME OF THE NUMEROUS POSSIBILITIES AND IS RESTRICTED TO THE NORTHERN HEMISPHERE

Type of Situation	Gentler Slope	Cause of Asymmetry
Meandering river	Inside of meander bend	Lateral cutting of meander steepens slope outside of bend (undercut slope), leaves gentle slope inside of bend (slip-off slope)
River valley	Slopes adjacent to vigorous tributary	Tributary supplies more debris than main stream can remove, forcing stream to undercut slopes opposite tributary
River valley	Left slope (looking downstream)	Coriolis force aids lateral cutting to right, steepening right-hand slopes (Vice versa, in southern hemisphere)
Stratified rock (dip less than 45°)	Dip slope (slope parallel to dip of strata)	Slopes directly reflect attitude of strata
Wind and precipitation come from same direction throughout year	Windward slope	Windward slopes have more runoff, more erosion, hence are gentler
Equatorial regions	No asymmetry	Insolation does not vary significantly with azimuth
Middle latitudes	South- or southwest-facing slopes	South slopes have less vegetation (especially grass, shrubs) due to higher insolation and evapotranspiration, storm runoff is higher and erosion greater than on north-facing slopes
Glacial conditions	North- or northeast-facing slopes	Glacial conditions are most intense on shaded slopes; hence, north-facing slopes are most eroded
Periglacial conditions	South-facing slopes (in high latitudes)	Insolation on south-facing slopes promotes freeze-thaw, solifluction
	North-facing slopes (in mid-latitudes)	Greater snow cover on north-facing slopes acts as protector from erosion

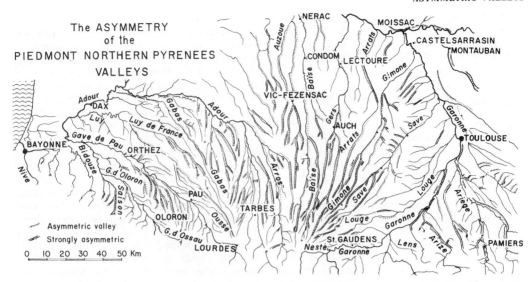

FIG. 3. Asymmetric valleys of the Piedmont Northern Pyrenees valleys of France (after Taillefer, 1950). Valleys show a negative or dextral asymmetry. The east-facing slopes are gentler due to intense erosion by frost action and solifluction during glacial maxima.

ment growth is promoted by warmer temperatures, in another by more moisture, depending on the limiting factors for various types of trees. In such a situation, it is difficult to predict which slopes will be relatively gentle.

An interesting study of slope asymmetry in a humid mid-latitude area is that of Hack and Goodlett (1960). This study illustrates the complexity of climate-slope relationships and is also a reminder that factors such as structural control may combine with climatic effects to produce valley asymmetry. Hack and Goodlett studied the Shenandoah Valley region of Virginia and found that dry (and warm) slopes have a denser cover of vegetation than do wet (and cooler) slopes (Table 1). However, despite a dense vegetative cover on south- and southwest-facing valley sides, runoff and erosion are relatively high and slope inclination is relatively low. On north- and northeast-facing slopes, soil moisture is relatively high and resistance to mass movement is relatively low; hence, denudation on these valley sides is mainly by creep. Complicating the entire situation, a prevailing southeasterly dip of rock strata strongly influences valley asymmetry.

In summary, valley asymmetry may have many causes, most notable among them being stream meandering, earth rotation, structural control and microclimate (see Table 2).

LEE WILSON

References

Babinet, J., 1859, "Influence du mouvement de rotation de la terre sur le cours des rivières," Paris.

Beaty, C. B., 1962, "Asymmetry of stream patterns in the Bitterroot Range, Montana," *J. Geol.*, **70**, 347–354.

Cotton, C. A., 1942, "Geomorphology," Christchurch, Whitcombe & Tombs, Ltd., 505pp.

Eakin, H. M., 1910, "The influence of the earth's rotation upon the lateral erosion of streams," *J. Geol.*, **18**, 435–447.

Emery, K. O., 1947, "Asymmetrical valleys of San Diego County, Calif.," *Bull. S. Calif. Acad. Sci.*, **46**, 61–71.

Fairchild, H. L., 1932, "Earth rotation and river erosion," *Science*, **76**, 423–427.

Hack, J., and Goodlett, J., 1960, "Geomorphology and forest ecology of a mountain region in the central Appalachians," *U.S. Geol. Surv. Profess. Paper* **347**, 66pp.

Louis, H., 1961, "Allgemeine Geomorphologie," Berlin, de Gruyter & Co., 355pp.

Melton, M. A., 1957, "An analysis of the relations among elements of climate, surface properties, and geomorphology," *Tech. Rept. 11*, ONR, Columbia University, New York.

Melton, M. A., 1960, "Intravalley variation in slope angles related to microclimate and erosional environment," *Bull. Geol. Soc. Am.*, **71**, 133–144.

Rapp, A., 1960, "Recent developments of mountain slopes in Kärkevagge and surroundings, northern Scandinavia," *Geogr. Ann.*, **42**, (2–3) 71–200.

Taillefer, E., 1950, "Le versant atlantique des Pyrénées et son avantpays," *Rev. Geomorph. Dyn.*, **1**, 101–122.

Thornbury, W. D., 1954, "Principles of Geomorphology," New York, John Wiley & Sons, 618pp.

Cross-references: *Abrasion*; *Baer–Babinet Law*; *Cirques*; *Cryology, Cryosphere, Cryergy*; *Denudation*; *Drainage Patterns*; *Duricrust*; *Frost Action*; *Geomorphology*; *Mass Wasting*; *Nivation*; *Periglacial Landscapes*; *Quaternary Period*; *Rivers*; *Sheet Erosion, Sheetwash, Rainwash, Sheetflood*; *Slip-off Slope*; *Slope Analysis*; *Slopes*; *Solifluction*; *Valley Evolution*; *Weathering*. Vol. II: *Coriolis Force*; *Earth's Rotation*; *Evaporation*; *Evapotranspiration*; *Insolation*; *Microclimates*; *Middle*

Latitude Climates; *Precipitation*; *Trade Winds*; *Tree-ring Analysis* (*Dendroclimatology*). pr Vol. VI: *Runoff*; *Snow*; *Vegetation Markers and Landscapes*. pr Vol. VII: *Dendrochronology*; *Paleoclimatology*; *Pleistocene*.

ATLANTIC AND PACIFIC TYPE COASTS

In 1885 (p. 6), Edward Suess recognized that there was a fundamental geotectonic control in the orientation of the continental coastlines of the world. There are modifying controls due to rock material, climatic factors, local tectonics, and eustasy (see *Coastal Classification*), and the emphasis placed upon emergence or submergence by the W. M. Davis school of geomorphology has tended to divert attention from the fundamental characteristic recognized by Suess.

Since most continental coasts (excepting those of epicontinental seas, like the Baltic or Persian Gulf) are, in broad outlines, subparallel to the outer margins of their accompanying continental shelves, the coastal trend must be related to the pattern of the continent itself. If, in any particular stage of geologic history, the eustatic phase is high, the coast will be far "inland" from the shelf break, but if it is low, the coastline may closely approximate the continental margin. The higher the eustatic phase, the more transgressive the sea, and the greater the opportunity for modifying factors, local tectonics, rock materials, reefs, mangrove swamps, etc., to control the coastal pattern.

Suess recognized two basic divisions in this fundamental control. He labeled them with the names of two great oceans where they are respectively best developed, but did not imply for a moment that such coastal types were exclusively so distributed.

The types are:

(a) *Atlantic Type:* coasts which truncate the geologic grain of the hinterland, seen ideally in Ireland, Brittany, northwest Spain, Newfoundland, and parts of the Precambrian Atlantic coasts of South America and Africa. In addition, many sectors of the Precambrian hinterlands of the Indian Ocean (former *Gondwanaland*, see pr Vol. VII), are also of the Atlantic type.

(b) *Pacific Type:* coasts which parallel the geologic grain of the continent, to be seen ideally around the margins of the Pacific, e.g., the West Coast cordillera of North America, the Andes, the island arcs of the western Pacific, from the Aleutians to New Guinea and New Zealand. The same "Pacific type" is represented in the Indian Ocean in the orogenic belt that runs from Burma (Arakan Yoma), through the Sunda Arc (Sumatra–Java) to the lesser Sunda Islands and Banda Arc. A shore sector is also represented by the Makran coast of Iran and Baluchistan (West Pakistan). In the Mediterranean, the island of Crete and the "Magreb" coast of Morocco and Algeria are "Pacific".

The year after Suess presented his fundamental division, Von Richthofen (1886) recognized some modified classes, proposing a different terminology:

(a) *Longitudinal coasts*, parallel to the structural grain (i.e., synonymous with "Pacific" type). Supan, the German geographer, preferred to call these *concordant*.

(b) *Transverse coasts*, cross-cutting the grain (i.e., "Atlantic" type). Supan (1930, p. 467) named this type *discordant*.

(c) *Collapsed basin coasts*, those bordering basins that have recently subsided, e.g., Western Mediterranean, Tyrrhenian Sea, Pacific marginal basins (see below: Gregory's "Secondary Pacific").

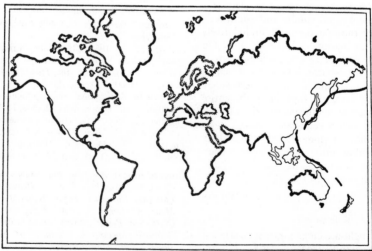

FIG. 1. Atlantic (discordant) notched, and Pacific (concordant) straight (from Von Engeln, 1942). (By permission of The Macmillan Co., N.Y.)

(d) *Block coasts*, marking the edges of plateaus, as those of Central and South Africa, and Brazil. These plateaus are essentially Precambrian peneplains, while the type "c" have variegated Mesozoic-Tertiary hinterlands. This class is clearly in the "Atlantic" category.

(e) *Alluvial coasts*, characterized by recent sedimentary accumulations, i.e., unconsolidated materials.

A beginning was thus made to a comprehensive classification, considering geotectonics, geomorphology and sedimentology that ultimately led to the Shepard type of *coastal classification* (q.v.), but it tended to obscure the gross geotectonic subdivision. Only the category "c" belongs to these major types, and Gregory (1912) suggested it be called "Secondary Pacific".

Gregory pointed out that there were some confusing cases in the Pacific. Along the "quasi-cratonic" belt of marginal seas within the island arcs of the western Pacific (Bering Sea to Tasman Sea), the continental coasts were often very strongly cut off by faults, yet the geotectonic grain of the old rocks usually paralleled the coastline. This is well seen in eastern Australia, where late Tertiary-Quaternary ("Kosciusko Phase") epeirogeny and faulting has elevated the hinterland to 2000 meters, dropping down the coastal plain, Tasman Sea and Coral Sea basins, in places to give a total vertical contrast of 7–8 km.

"Secondary" Pacific type coasts are rather widespread, as in many parts of the western Mediterranean and in parts of the Caribbean, and indeed many of the more mature "classic" Pacific coasts (e.g., in California, Japan, New Zealand) show a tremendous amount of secondary faulting. The basic distinction of the two coast types is *trend*, either it is parallel or truncated; the presence of large-scale block-faulting is a secondary characteristic.

The terms "Atlantic" and "Pacific" type have also been adopted to designate *petrographic series* (by Harker, 1896, 1909; and by Becke, 1903). The "Atlantic Type" alkaline lavas are found typically in oceanic (mid-oceanic, in all three oceans) and continental cratonic regions, while the "Pacific Type" are found only in the orthogeosynclinal belts, exemplified today by the island arcs of the circum-Pacific, and also in the Indian Ocean (where there are also Pacific type coasts: Sunda-Banda arcs, Makran), in the Mediterranean (Hellenic arc), and western Atlantic (Antillean arc, Scotia arc).

The terms "Atlantic" and "Pacific" have also been taken up by Stille (1944, 1958) to designate *tectonic style*. "Atlantic" indicates the diastrophic development of semistable cratonic regions, or post orogenic revival of old fold belts, with faulting, regeneration of ocean troughs, etc. In contrast, "Pacific" tectonics are those associated with contemporary orthogeosynclines, island arcs, oceanic trenches and active foredeeps.

We may see, therefore, that Suess identified a fundamental pattern in world geology, that reaches out from geomorphology into petrology and geotectonics.

RHODES W. FAIRBRIDGE

References

Becke, F., 1903, "Die Eruptivgebiete des böhmischen Mittelgebirges und der amerikanischen Andes," *Tschermaks Mineral. Petrog. Mitt.*, **22**, 209–265.
Gregory, J. W., 1912, "The structural and petrographical classification of coast-types," *Scientia*, **2**, 36–63.
Harker, A., 1896, "The natural history of igneous rocks: I. Their geographical and chronological distribution," *Sci. Progr.*, **6**, 12–33.
Harker, A., 1909, "The Natural History of Igneous Rocks," London, Methuen, 384pp.
Richthofen, F. von, 1886, "Führer für Forschungsreisende," Hannover, Jänecke, 734pp.
Schwarz, E. H. L., 1912, "The Atlantic and Pacific types of coast," *Geogr. J.*, **40**, 294–299.
Stille, H., 1958, "Einiges über die Weltozeane und ihre Umrahmungsraume," *Geologie*, **7**, 237–306.
Suess, E., 1885–1909, "Das Antlitz der Erde," Vienna, F. Tempsky, English translation "The Face of the Earth," Oxford, Clarendon, 1904–1924.
Supan, A., 1930, "Grundzüge der physischen Erdkunde," seventh ed., Vol. II, Pt. 1, Berlin, DeGruyter.
Von Engeln, O. D., 1942, "Geomorphology," New York, Macmillan, 655pp.

Cross-references: *Coastal Classification*; *Eustasy*; *Island Arcs*. Vol. I: *Coral Sea*; *Tasman Sea*; *Trenches*. Vol. V: *Geosynclines*; *Geotectonics*; *Petrology*. pr Vol. VII: *Gondwanaland*.

ATOLLS*

An atoll (Maldivian *atolu*) is an annular organic reef enclosing a lagoon. The shape ranges from circular to very irregular. The reef may or may not have gaps or passages. There may be above-tidal islets on the reef. Some islets are accumulations of storm-cast detritus on the reef surface. Other islets are erosional remnants of former and higher extensions of the reef, or a combination of a remnant and detritus.

Reefs are composed of reef limestone or reef rock. Reef rock is *biohermal* if it consists of a growth lattice of interlocking organisms and *detrital* if it consists of fragments of either attached or solitary organisms, or fragments of older consolidated reef rock. Chemical contributions of fine-grained nature help to cement the reef mass, either during sedimentation or at some stage of diagenesis.

Most of the world's atolls are concentrated in the tropical Indo-Pacific region between latitudes

* Publication authorized by the Director, *U.S. Geological Survey*.

25°N and 25°S, although a few are in the Atlantic, off the coast of Brazil.

World sea level has been several feet higher in comparatively recent time (mid-Holocene), so that many reefs, particularly their windward side where growth is fastest, once extended higher than at present. The upper surface of an atoll reef is a nearly flat surface called the reef flat, located at or near low-tide level. The reef flat may be constructed to low-tide level by the upward growth of corals and algae, or it may be planed to low-tide level by the solution of reef limestone that once extended higher. On the windward side of atolls the reef flat is almost always planed behind the seaward growing edge; usually there is a zonation from biohermal reef rock on the seaward side to detrital reef rock on the lagoonward side. Living algae and corals may form a ridge extending to high-tide level or higher along the windward seaward growing edge. On the leeward side of atolls the reef flat may be either constructed or planed. The reef on the leeward side may be incompletely constructed; i.e., long stretches of it may lie below low-tide level and still be in the process of building up to present sea level.

The main source of detritus on an atoll is the organic growth, mainly coralline algae, along the windward seaward margin. Normal wave fragmentation of the growing edge produces detritus that is carried both downward along the submarine slope as talus (Ladd *et al.*, 1950) and lagoonward, where it forms a deltalike sediment apron along the lagoon margin. Owing to the prevailing winds, the latter deposition is much more rapid. Subsidiary amounts of detritus are supplied by segmented algae, corals, and unattached organisms, mainly Foraminifera. Relatively insignificant amounts of detritus are produced on the leeward reef.

Storm waves may disrupt the normal depositional pattern, causing a rearrangement of unconsolidated detrital deposits in the lagoon, on the submarine slope, on the reef flat, and on islets that may be contrary to the sediment pattern due to normally prevailing winds and waves (Wiens, 1962). Powerful currents upwelling in submarine clefts during typhoons (hurricanes) bring coarse detritus and live heads of coral onto the reef flat from the submarine slope.

Boulder ramparts (a type of beach ridge system) may be thrown up on any seaward side of an atoll, their location being controlled by the path of the eye of a typhoon with respect to the atoll and the consequent direction of effective wind and waves. Even the shallower parts of the lagoon are scoured extensively by typhoon-generated waves if there is a sufficient fetch of water. The highest altitude in the Marshall Islands, over 25 feet, is along a beach ridge on the lagoon side of Kabinwor Islet, Likiep Atoll, on the leeward side of the atoll. The materials in this beach ridge are similar to the materials, including the live corals and algae, found on the present adjacent floor of the lagoon from 5–12 fathoms. This ridge is believed to have formed during a typhoon that completely devastated the atoll about 1865; as a consequence, the atoll remained uninhabited for over 30 years.

No two atolls are exactly alike. The greatest similarity is on the windward side. Mid-Pacific atolls have a prominent growth of coralline algae along their windward seaward margin, forming the so-called algal ridge (the "Lithothamnion Rim" of early authors). Passages or "passes" are rare on the windward side of atolls because any preexisting solution clefts are usually filled by growth. A few atolls, for example, those in the East Indies, are perfect rings, without passes. This form is favored by complete seasonal reversal in direction of the monsoon wind.

The largest detrital deposits on atolls are found along the lagoon margin of the windward side. On other sides of atolls the type of reef flat, the existence of passages, the type of coral, the presence or absence of coralline algae, and the presence and distribution of detrital sediments are fortuitous. The local condition depends on the morphology of the foundation, the amount of reef growth, the species of organism growing in a particular location, and the frequency, intensity, and direction of storm-generated waves in the past.

The shape of the reef may be altered by structural weaknesses. Cracks are common on reef flats, and locally great half-moon-shaped segments can be seen to have fallen away, leaving bare cresentic scarps. These curved scarps led Fairbridge (1950a) to suggest that many of the scallop-shaped indentations of reef margins are due to submarine slides, which are particularly common on the conical slopes of submarine volcanoes.

The thickness of the accumulation of reef rock beneath an atoll depends partly on the stability of the foundation. "Shelf atolls" on continental shelves, or in quasicratonic oceanic platform areas (e.g., off Borneo, South China Sea, Indian Ocean, and Coral Sea), may be underlain by relatively thin deposits of reef limestone. "Oceanic atolls" in the mid-Pacific, located on foundered, truncated volcanic cones, cap accumulations of reef rock between 4000 and 5000 feet thick that range in age from early Tertiary at the base to Recent at the surface. At least three stratigraphic breaks have been recognized, however, and immediately below each break the limestone is recrystallized, suggesting subaerial alteration. Land snails have been identified at several levels (Ladd, 1958). The reef rock consists throughout of the remains, or detritus, of shallow-water reef-building organisms. These facts suggest that there has been intermittent and net submergence of the mid-Pacific region since the close of Cretaceous time, the submergence having been slow enough for phototropic reef-building organisms to maintain the growing surface close to sea level.

Chemical alteration of reef rock belongs more properly under the subject of reefs than atolls, although most studies of this nature have been concerned with the reef rock beneath atolls. Dolomite is a common constituent of reef rock, but Schlanger (1963) has shown that its occurrence in known borings is not controlled by stratigraphy, depth or geography. The only consistent relationship seems to be that aragonite and dolomite never occur together, suggesting that aragonite must be converted to calcite before dolomitization can occur. Because aragonite is stable only in seawater, temporary emergences are indicated.

Phosphate is mined commercially on several raised atolls in the Pacific Ocean, Indian Ocean, and West Indies. It occurs as a replacement of the near-surface parts of reef limestones. The source of the phosphate, a hydroxylapatite, is guano, the rock crests having served as sea-bird rookeries for thousands of years. Phosphate of marine origin is usually fluorapatite.

Development of the Annular Reef

The relationship of the annular shape of the atoll to the history and structure of the underlying reef limestone has been one of the most debated aspects of atoll theory. Darwin (1838) concluded, from a study of fringing reefs and barrier reefs around volcanic islands, that atolls were the ultimate result of subsidence, that a reef fringing a volcanic cone grew upwards and outwards, forming first a circular barrier with partial submergence of the cone, and finally an atoll with complete drowning of the cone. Some atolls may well have developed in this way, but this theory does not explain atolls on continental shelves, such as those along eastern Australia, and those on quasicratonic platforms like the Maldive Islands, and it is difficult, in the case of the mid-Pacific atolls, to visualize maintenance of the annular shape through thousands of feet of upward growth and millions of years of time. Furthermore, the subsidence was an intermittent process. Schlanger (1963) has shown that Eniwetok Atoll was partly emergent twice, and possibly three times, during its history, and that it was almost completely planed during each emergence.

During the middle and late nineteenth century, Darwin's "subsidence theory" was criticized by Sir John Murray, who experimented with carbonate reef materials and found them to be soluble in CO_2-rich water, particularly fresh water. His "solution theory" argument that lagoons were dissolved out under contemporary conditions was generally rejected, but the Royal Society of London (David and Sweet, 1904) undertook to test the subsidence theory by putting down a deep bore, selecting Funafuti Atoll in the Gilberts for this purpose. The bore went to 1112 feet without reaching basement, a depth far below the vigorous growth limits of hermatypic corals, so that Darwin's thesis of subsidence was here confirmed. Other Pacific atolls, such as Bikini and Eniwetok, have subsequently been drilled to over 4000 feet, clearly proving subsidence, or it would be better to say "submergence," because it is not known how much sea level has risen and how much the atoll foundations and the whole Pacific basin itself have sunk. On the other hand, boring of atoll reefs on continental shelves shows that there had been relatively little subsidence, and the reef submergence is mostly explained by glacial eustasy.

Numerous other theories have contended that the shape of atoll-type reefs is predetermined either by the type of foundation or by some particular movement of the foundation. Opinion today seems to favor the theory that an atoll is a secondarily modified reef and that a reef can become established on a foundation of any type, whether hard or soft, whether it be an alien rock or a preexisting reef, and regardless of whether the foundation is stable, rising, or subsiding. The only requirements seem to be that the region must be accessible and ecologically favorable for coral colonization, that the foundation must have on it some object *hard* enough to serve as the attachment for the first reef-building organism, even a shell on a mud bottom, and that the foundation must lie within the depth range of phototropic algae and corals. The annular shape of the upper surface of the reef and the enclosed lagoon is a subsequent development resulting from alternating growth and erosion with fluctuating sea level. Sea level may fluctuate as a result of either glacial eustasy, which affected all reefs during the Pleistocene epoch, or tectonic movements that may have intervened locally to change the altitude of a reef with respect to an existing sea level.

Daly (1915) was first to suggest that the annular shape of an atoll is a condition related to postglacial rise of sea level. He stated that glacial eustasy, which permits periods of erosion alternating with periods of upward growth, provides a better explanation for the origin and uniform depth of lagoons, particularly for lagoons having different levels of uniform depth. Without oscillation of sea level, the tops of oceanic reefs would be constructed more uniformly to sea level.

Yabe and Asano in 1942 (Burke, 1951) first suggested that atolls are the result of coralline growth on limestone solution forms. Hoffmeister and Ladd (1945) later observed saucer-shaped forms developed on raised limestone islands in the tropical Pacific. They compared such islands with a similarly shaped block that they had produced by placing a slab of Solenhofen Limestone under a shower of weak acid.

Subsequent studies of limestone solution forms on Okinawa by D. E. Flint *et al.* (1953), revealed

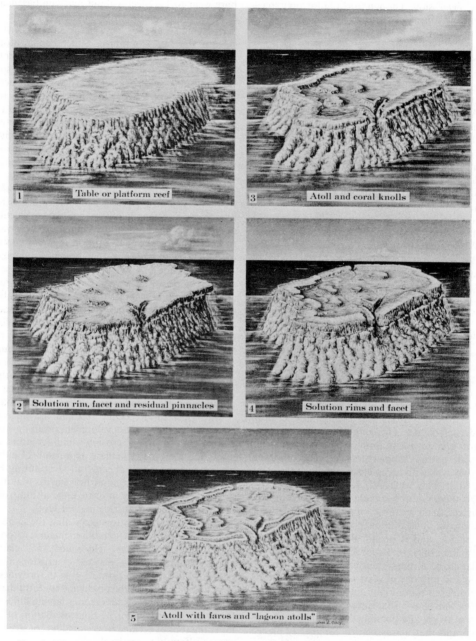

FIG. 1. Diagrams showing supposed development of atolls and faros on subaerial erosion forms. Note that in each sketch the front part is shown as a "cutaway" with the ocean water removed (MacNeil, 1954).

numerous features that with submergence might be modified by coral growth to form most of the physical features of atolls. These facts were elaborated by MacNeil (1954) in an atoll "subaerial solution theory" that ascribed the annular shape of atolls to the growth of reef-forming organisms on the rim of saucer-shaped solution platforms that were formed under subaerial conditions during low-water stages of the Pleistocene Epoch (Fig. 1). Unlike the original Darwinian theory, which ascribed the annular shape to normal growth on a subsiding alien foundation, MacNeil's solution theory denies any relationship between the annular shape and the foundation or, indeed, the growth of the reef

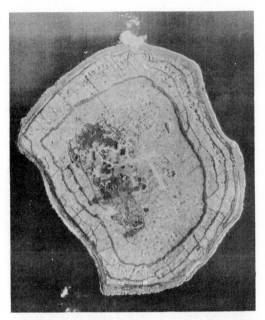

FIG. 2. Vertical air photograph of Minami Daito-jima, a raised atoll (about 5 miles across) situated on a submarine ridge southwest of Japan. Note pock-marked surface, due to karst solution; the terraced rim indicates progressive but irregular emergence. The coral cap grew up from a preexisting reef platform subsequent to a time when it was affected by peripheral landslides (concave segments).

prior to a period of subaerial exposure. Geologically, therefore, atolls are an unusual type of reef, developed under special conditions, almost accidental, related to glacial eustasy. They are common in modern seas because of comparatively recent sea-level fluctuations resulting from glaciations.

Slope, which determines the amount and rate of runoff, is believed to be a prime factor in the predetermination of the shape of atolls by subaerial solution during low-sea-level stages. Two secondary processes are involved: (1) case-hardening of steep bare limestone surfaces by recrystallization due to alternate wetting and drying, causing them to weather into relief as walls or knife edges and (2) continuous subsoil solution on more nearly horizontal surfaces due, probably, to the maintenance of moisture and the presence of humic acids. These secondary processes combine in emerged limestone islands to produce a prominent rim and a bowl-shaped interior. Open drainage, either incised or resulting from the roof collapse of underground streams, develops natural levees or embankments. Any limestone prominence may become accentuated to stand in relief as a residual pinnacle. With submergence, a resumption of algal and coral growth takes place, the fastest growth being on the rim and pinnacles. The annular reef develops along

the marginal rim and fresh detrital deposits accumulate along the margin of the depression or lagoon. Elongate reefs that commonly border forked channels inside the main passages rise from former stream embankments. Coral knolls grow on former residual pinnacles in the lagoon (Fig. 1, 1–3).

Although the subaerial solution theory of atoll development evolved mainly from a study of mid-Pacific atolls, it seems probable that all atolls have been basically controlled by this process, though local modifications vary in different regions. Reef growth on an atoll-shaped platform is fastest on the windward side so that a stage exists when the surface reef is crescent-shaped, concave on the leeward side. Fairbridge (1950b), citing examples on the *Great Barrier Reef* (q.v.), suggested that atolls develop from small table reefs which, under the influence of prevailing winds, assume a crescentic form, then a U-shaped form, and later, by closing the horns on the leeward side, an atoll; subsequent filling of the lagoon results in a large table reef. Fairbridge cites other examples to show that large table reefs develop from small table reefs directly through an intermediate "horse's hoof" form. However, it is probable that all the sea-level reefs on the Great Barrier Reef have been modified by subaerial solution in some way and that the present atolls are growing on reef-rock platforms with marginal rims.

In the Maldive Islands, and less commonly in the East Indies, there are atolls whose main annular reef is composed of small annular reefs called faros. According to the subaerial solution theory, faros might result from a second generation of subaerial weathering, a weathering period long enough to allow the development of a rim along the edges of the main annular reef, but not long enough for the raised reef to be reduced significantly. With submergence the atoll-like growth would be repeated on a similar scale (Fig. 1, 4–5). Kita-Daito-Jima, in the western Pacific, is a raised atoll whose annular reef has developed marginal rims such as are required by this theory. Karst-affected elevated atolls in the South Pacific that have these features are known as "makateas," after a prototype example. In the Houtman's Abrolhos Islands of Western Australia (Fairbridge, 1950b), there is an eroded reef stump (pre-Wisconsin) that has Karst features formed under subaerial conditions during a low-sea-level stage, but new reef growth has not completely obscured the basin-shaped foundation.

Conclusion

The explanation of the atoll is therefore to be found in several theories. Darwin recognized the role of submergence, pointing out that oceanic atolls have volcanic foundations that show considerable subsidence. Numerous transitions may be observed from volcanic islands through barrier-reef islands ("almost atolls") to atolls. Daly showed that the last major submergence was a glacio-eustatic rise of sea level, and that during the last glacial period, many atoll stumps were greatly reduced by erosion. MacNeil demonstrated that this erosion was not by waves, but was subaerial, the result being a limestone island with a wall-like rim and an excavated interior marked by karst features. Former valleys to the exterior became open passes after the postglacial rise of sea level permitted the annular reef ring to grow up on the subaerial rim. In large atolls with many passes, the lagoon has remained almost unfilled, but in others there are progressive stages of infilling from the sides or upgrowth of pinnacles from the floor. Some tectonically raised atolls have the form of limestone islands such as would have appeared during the last glacial emergence.

F. STEARNS MACNEIL

References

Berner, R. A., 1965, "Dolomitization of the Mid-Pacific atolls," *Science*, **147**, 1297–1299.

Burke, H. W., 1951, "Contributions by the Japanese to the Study of Coral Reefs," *U.S. Geol. Surv., Military Geology Branch, Memo for record* (English summaries of papers in Japanese).

Daly, R. A., 1915, "The glacial control theory of coral reefs," *Proc. Am. Acad. Arts Sci.*, **51**, 157–251.

Darwin, Charles, 1838, "On certain areas of elevation and subsidence in the Pacific and Indian Oceans, as deduced from the study of coral formations," *Proc. Geol. Soc., London*, **2**, 552–554.

David, T. W., and Sweet, G., 1904, "The geology of Funafuti," in "The atoll of Funafuti," *Roy. Soc. London, Coral Reef Comm. Rept.*, 61–111 (1904).

Fairbridge, R. W., 1950a, "Landslide patterns on oceanic volcanoes and atolls," *Geograph. J.*, **115**, 84–88.

Fairbridge, R. W., 1950b, "Recent and Pleistocene coral reefs of Australia," *J. Geol.*, **58**, 330–401.

Flint, D. E., Corwin, G., Dings, M. C., Fuller, W. P., MacNeil, F. S., and Saplis, R. A., 1953, "Limestone walls of Okinawa," *Bull. Geol. Soc. Am.*, **64**, 1247–1260.

Hoffmeister, J. E., and Ladd, H. S., 1945, "Solution effects on elevated limestone terraces," *Bull. Geol. Soc. Am.*, **56**, 809–817.

Ladd, H. S., 1958, "Fossil land shells from western Pacific atolls," *J. Paleontol.*, **32**, 183–198.

Ladd, H. S., Tracey, J. I., Jr., Wells, J. W., and Emery, K. O., 1950, "Organic growth and sedimentation on an atoll," *J. Geol.*, **58**, 410–425.

MacNeil, F. S., 1954, "The shape of atolls: an inheritance from subaerial erosion forms," *Am. J. Sci.*, **252**, 402–427.

Schlanger, S. O., 1963, "Subsurface geology of Eniwetok Atoll," *U.S. Geol. Surv. Profess. Paper* **260-BB**, 991–1066.

Wiens, H. J., 1962, "Atoll Environment and Ecology," New Haven and London, Yale University Press.

Cross-References: *Algal Reefs*; *Beach Ridge*; *Coral Reef*; *Eustasy*; *Faro*; *Fringing Reef*; *Great Barrier Reef*; *Holocene*; *Karst*; *Lagoons*; *Makatea*. Vol. IV: *Phosphate Deposits* (*including Guano*). pr Vol. VII: *Foraminifera*.

ATTRITION

Attrition is the act of rubbing things together and thus wearing them down. It is used in physical geology for "the wear and tear that rock particles in transit undergo through mutual rubbing, grinding, . . . , etc., with resulting comminution in size" (Thornbury, 1954, p. 48). It specifically refers to the particles themselves and excludes erosion of the rock floor, which is also involved in the mutual collisions and wear, the latter process being referred to as *abrasion* (q.v.).

The particles involved in attrition, notably sand grains, develop characteristic textures (see pr Vol. VI); for example, wind-worn sands have a distinctive "frosting." However, there are some possibilities of confusion when these particles are examined only under low magnification. Under the electron microscope, however, a unique appearance characterizes the surface texture of every type of grain—eolian, beach, fluvial and glacial (Krinsley and Takahashi, 1962). Under low-energy conditions, desert sands develop a frosting and patina due to chemical etch and redeposition under the action of dew (Kuenen and Perdok, 1962), but this patina, like *desert varnish* (q.v.), may be worn off under vigorous attrition.

The larger particles, pebbles or boulders also develop distinct shapes and textures (Tricart and Schaeffer, 1950). Water-rolled boulders tend to sphericity in ordinary running streams, but on beaches where the erosion is essentially one-sided the boulders become extremely oblate.

Under glacial abrasion, the boulders tend to be held in single positions for long periods, so that they develop flat, striated surfaces—"*faceted boulders.*" Two somewhat rarer processes may also produce faceted boulders: salt and gypsum diapirs and "glaciers" also have a high viscosity and tend to flatten one or more sides of the boulder. *Mudflows* (q.v.), though somewhat less viscous, nevertheless cause the faceting and striation of boulders. The striations of both these types of boulder are less regular than for ice-faceting and have been called *pseudo-glacial faceted boulders* by Kayser (1913).

Under wind conditions, faceting also takes place, but the texture is more fluted and may be deeply scoured; the boulders or pebbles are called *ventifacts* (q.v.), and *dreikanter* or *zweikanter* according to the number of surfaces so affected.

RHODES W. FAIRBRIDGE

References

Kayser, E., 1913, "Lehrbuch der Geologie," Fourth ed., Vol. 1; Stuttgart, Enke.

Krinsley, D., and Takahashi, T., 1962, "Surface textures of sand grains: an application of electron microscopy," *Science*, **135**, 923–925.

Kuenen, P. H. and Perdok, W. G., 1962, "Experimental abrasion: Frosting and defrosting of quartz grains," *J. Geol.*, **70**, 648–658.

Mason, M. A., 1942, "Abrasion of beach sand," Beach Erosion Board, Tech. Memo no. 2.

Thornbury, W. D., 1954, "Principles of Geomorphology," New York, John Wiley & Sons, 618pp.

Tricart, J., and Schaeffer, R., 1950, "The study of erosion systems through the soundness index of pebbles," *Rev. Geomorphol. Dynamique*, 151–179.

Cross-references: *Abrasion; Erosion; Mudflow; Ventifact; Wind Action.* pr Vol. VI: *Attrition; Texture; Sand Surfaces.*

AVALANCHE

An avalanche is a large mass of snow, ice, earth, rock, or other material occurring in swift motion down a mountainside or over a precipice (Webster's Third New International Dictionary). Avalanches can be classified, depending on their content, as *snow* and *ice avalanches* (q.v.), *debris avalanches*, and *rock avalanches*. Debris avalanches originate in incoherent earth materials and generally are wet; rock avalanches are derived directly from lithified bedrock, and although they may be wet, their movement does not depend on moisture. Although debris and rock avalanches are defined here as dynamic geologic processes, the same terms are applied to the deposits of these processes.

(1) *Debris avalanches* are the rapid downslope flowage of masses of incoherent earth material. They are caused most frequently when a sudden influx of water reduces the shear strength of earth material on a steep slope, and they typically accompany cloudbursts in the mountains of the eastern United States (see examples and references in Sharpe, 1938; Hack and Goodlett, 1960). Mobility of these avalanches is due chiefly to water, but may be increased by a fine-grained component of the debris. Debris avalanches also have been triggered by earthquakes; the acceleration of the shock wave increases shear stress on earth materials and reduces their shear strength.

FIG. 1. These rock avalanches on Sherman Glacier, 160 miles southeast of Anchorage, Alaska, originated in rockfalls during an earthquake on March 27, 1964. The largest avalanche dropped more than 2500 feet vertically, and moved at least 3 miles laterally. (Photograph: Austin S. Post, U.S. Geological Survey)

(2) *Rock avalanches* are the very rapid down-slope flowage of segments of bedrock that become shattered and pulverized during movement. Despite fragmentation, the mass moves essentially as a unit. Rock avalanches typically result from very large rockfalls and rockslides, and their manner of movement has led them to be described as rock-fragment flows (Varnes, 1958). Characteristic features of their deposits are a chaotic distribution of large blocks, evidence of flowage-type movement, relative thinness in comparison to large areal extent, little or no abrasion of rock fragments, high porosity, and lobate form (Mudge, 1965; Kent, 1966).

Some rock avalanches have been remarkably mobile, flowing distances of several miles on relatively low gradients, at speeds approaching or even exceeding 100 mph. Although rock avalanches may contain water, their mobility is due primarily to interstitial air which reduces internal friction (Kent, 1966). The manner and distance of flowage of some large, dry avalanches have also been attributed to movement on a cushion of compressed air which prevents the debris from striking the ground (see Crandell and Fahnestock, 1965, and references therein). Because of their tremendous kinetic energy, some rock avalanches have risen hundreds of feet onto obstacles in their paths. In the valley of the Saidmarreh River in southwestern Iran, a prehistoric rock avalanche moved 9 miles laterally after descending nearly 5000 feet. In the course of lateral movement, the avalanche ascended more than 1500 feet as it crossed the end of a mountain range (Harrison and Falcon, 1938).

Well-known rock avalanches caused by rockfalls and rockslides occurred at Elm, Switzerland, in 1881, at Frank in Alberta, Canada, in 1903, and in the Madison River Canyon in southwestern Montana in 1959 (see references in Mudge, 1965). The avalanche in the Madison River Canyon was triggered by a strong earthquake, as also were numerous large rock avalanches in southeastern Alaska in March 1964 (Fig. 1). The high speed of rock avalanches and their long distance of movement create hazards to human life and property; the avalanches at Elm, Frank, and Madison River Canyon took 115, 70, and 26 lives, respectively.

Avalanches of rock debris also result from volcanic eruptions. Glowing avalanches owe their mobility to the buoyant effect of gas emitted from incandescent particles of the erupted material; block-and-ash avalanches are masses of hot, dry, gas-poor rock debris mobilized by entrapped and heated air. Volcanic avalanches are more fully described under *Volcanology* (Vol. V).

DWIGHT R. CRANDELL

References

Crandell, D. R., and Fahnestock, R. K., 1965, "Rockfalls and avalanches from Little Tahoma Peak on Mount Rainier, Washington," *U.S. Geol. Surv. Bull.,* **1221-A,** A1–A30.

Hack, J. T., and Goodlett, J. C., 1960, "Geomorphology and forest ecology of a mountain region in the central Appalachians," *U.S. Geol. Surv. Profess. Paper* **347,** 66 pp.

Harrison, J. V., and Falcon, N. L., 1938, "An ancient landslip at Saidmarreh in southwestern Iran," *J. Geol.,* **46,** 296–309.

Kent, P. E., 1966, "The transport mechanism in catastrophic rock falls," *J. Geol.,* **74,** 79–83.

Mudge, M. R., 1965, "Rockfall-avalanche and rockslide-avalanche deposits at Sawtooth Ridge, Montana," *Bull. Geol. Soc. Am.,* **76,** 1003–1014.

Sharpe, C. F. S., 1938, "Landslides and Related Phenomena," New York, Columbia University Press, 137 pp.

Varnes, D. J., 1958, "Landslide types and processes," pp. 20–47 *in* (Eckel, E. B., editor), "Landslides and engineering practice," *Highway Res. Board, Special Rept.* **29,** 20–47 (232 pp.).

Cross-references: *Landslides; Mass Movement; Mass Wasting; Mudflow; Snow Avalanche.* Vol. V: *Volcanoes and Volcanology.*

B

BADLANDS
(A) Introduction (R.W.F.)

The term "badlands" is derived from a term, employed by the western pioneers, meaning an extremely dissected landscape difficult to cross on horseback and agriculturally useless. There are equivalents in French and Spanish, e.g., *mauvais terres pour traverser*, and these in turn go back to an Indian name of the same intent. (In modern French geomorphology, however, they are *les badlands*.) They are characterized by a very fine drainage network (see Table 1) and short steep slopes with narrow interfluves (Fig. 1–5). The slopes may ter-minate abruptly in pediments on a miniature scale. They are often completely free of vegetation.

(1) Slopes. Badlands develop generally along the face or front of a retreating scarp. Three main slope elements develop: small pediments at the base, steep "cohesion slopes" and, thirdly, the dissected upland areas. The latter may be (a) *rounded* (Mears' "haystack type") found on clay-stones, (b) *knife-edged* (as in South Dakota tuffaceous silty clays), or (c) *castellete* (as in Zion National Park sandstones). The slopes may thus be graded in part under litho-logic control, and further weathered regolith or saprolite may be eroded in patterns distinctive from those of the underlying materials. In clayey for-mations, the role of desiccation cracks is important in opening up rill channels.

(2) Lithology. The underlying soil, regolith or geological formation that favors badland relief is unconsolidated or very poorly cemented material of clay and silt, sometimes with soluble minerals such

FIG. 1. Badlands in South Dakota. (Photo: Sam Falk). Note the typical knife-edged interfluves of the classic badlands, in contrast to the rounded contours of the "haystack type," conditioned by clay instead of silt lithology.

TABLE 1. MEAN TEXTURE RATIOS AND DRAINAGE DENSITY VALUES FOR SEVEN GENERAL AREAS (SMITH, 1958)

Locality	Mean Texture Ratio	Mean Drainage Density
Pennsylvania	2.64	4.08
Verdugo Hills, Calif.	8.65	18.10
Little Tujunga, Calif.	17.83	31.50
Badlands, South Dakota (Chadron formation)	26.90	77.60
Badlands, South Dakota (Brule formation)	69.70	258.00
Petrified Forest, Arizona (Chinle formation)	111.00	230.00
Perth Amboy, N.J. (clay-sand bank fill)	230.00	747.00

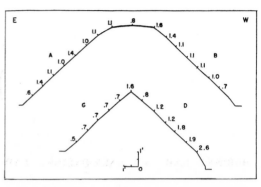

FIG. 3. Typical Perth Amboy slope profiles. Ticks on profiles show position of stakes; numbers indicate depth of erosion in inches that occurred during a 10-week survey period in late summer. Profiles A, B and C are typical of the area; profile D shows a basal convexity (Schumm, 1956a).

as gypsum or halite. The clays may be dominated by montmorillonite which has swelling characteristics; it is an important component in bentonite, a sediment derived from volcanic ash showers. The phenomenon of *piping* (q.v.) occurs where extreme badland conditions are marked by solution effects.

(3) Climate. Badlands are usually formed in regions of strongly marked seasonal contrasts, usually with a fairly long dry season or drought spells. They seem to be absent from either the cool or the hot humid regions that are marked by fairly constant, uniform rainfall. Derruau (1962) remarks that they are most characteristic of Mediterranean climates, wherever the vegetative cover is absent or destroyed for one reason or another. Evidently the essential cause is lack of vegetation, a condition favored by (a) strong seasonality with an extended arid period, and (b) man-made effects such as overgrazing.

It is a feature of the classical Mediterranean that since the Roman era two important convergent factors have been operative:

(a) There has been an oscillating but progressively drier climatic regime reaching its peak about 900 years ago; winter rains were often replaced by brief but heavy summer thunderstorms.

(b) There has been a concomitant tendency toward overpopulation and overgrazing, especially by

goats which have an omnivorous capacity to utilize every last vestige of vegetative nourishment. The result has been deforestation and general baring of the soil. The latter is then stripped from hillsides under summer cloudbursts and accumulates in thick silty alluvium in valleys, itself ideal material for further "badland" development.

(B) Dynamics of Badland Evolution (A.E.S.),

(1) The Problem. Badlands are an example of more general types of drainage basins. Because of the peculiar composition of the ground (very soft material) and the special characteristics of climate, erosion in badlands is very rapid and can be studied in great detail. There is, however, no *fundamental* difference between badlands and drainage basins of

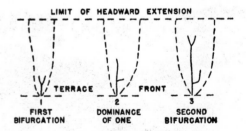

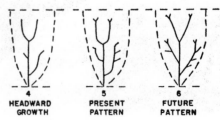

FIG. 4. Suggested evolution of the Perth Amboy drainage pattern (Schumm, 1956a).

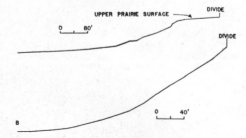

FIG. 2. Two longitudinal stream profiles surveyed in Badlands National Monument, South Dakota. Vertical and horizontal scales are the same (Schumm, 1956a).

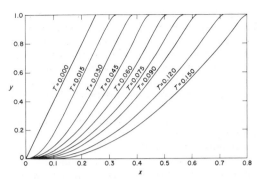

FIG. 6. Graph showing basic slope development (Scheidegger, 1964).

FIG. 5. Advanced soil erosion (man-generated) producing badlands in youthful sediments, near Lumpkin, Georgia. (Oblique air photo.)

a better known type (e.g., in hilly country in a temperate climate). Because of the rapidity by which denudationary processes occur in badlands, the latter provide an excellent example for studying denudation in general.

The evolution of a landscape (in particular of a badland landscape) is the combined result of the evolution of the individual slopes, pediments and channels characterizing the landscape. In badlands, there are no structural controls, no rocky outcrops, etc.; hence the landscape evolution is governed by the denudation of the individual slopes.

Denudation is a combined effect caused by various agents. The primary influence is that of water: little miniature gullies form which become enlarged as time passes, thereby causing destruction of the slope. The first problem in the dynamics of badland evolution is, therefore, to find a suitable model for the destruction of individual slopes.

Eventually, the miniature gullies with which the erosional and denudational processes begin, become deeper and broader. Soon they run into each other and begin to form a *drainage network*. The second problem in the dynamics of badland evolution is, therefore, to explain the observed connections and arrangement of the drainage channels.

Finally, the erosion of its parts produces large-scale changes in the appearance of a badland landscape. The final problem, thus, is to explain these large-scale changes.

(2) Slope Evolution. (*a*) *Basic Model.* The evolution of a slope is an extremely complex process, and it cannot be hoped to elucidate each detail in the recession of a declivity. Although the erosion proceeds by means of the formation and washing-out of individual gullies, it is not possible to follow the physics of this process in detail, and it is therefore necessary to make reasonable assumptions regarding the overall effect of this process.

Of the many attempts that have been made, the following hypothesis seems to have proved acceptable (see Scheidegger, 1961).

Suppose that in rectangular coordinates ($y =$ height above some base; $x =$ horizontal abscissa), the slope profile is given by some function $y = f(x)$. Then, we assume that the action of the water (*i*) is proportional to the declivity $\partial y / \partial x$ of the slope and (*ii*) acts normal to the slope profile. This hypothesis produces the following differential equation for the slope-profile evolution:

$$\frac{\partial y}{\partial T} = -a \sqrt{1 + \left(\frac{\partial y}{\partial x}\right)^2} \frac{\partial y}{\partial x} \quad (1)$$

where a is a constant indicating the erodibility of the badland material and T denotes time. Being nonlinear, this basic differential equation [Eq. (1)] cannot be solved in closed form, but can easily be integrated numerically on a digital computer. A sequence of slope profiles calculated in this manner is shown in Fig. 6.

(*b*) *Mesas.* The basic slope equation can be applied to cases where the lithology changes with depth. In particular, if there is a resistant layer at the top, it can be shown that theory produces features that represent *mesas*. This is done simply by letting the constant a be a function of x in the numerical solution of Eq. (1). The result of a calculation, with a

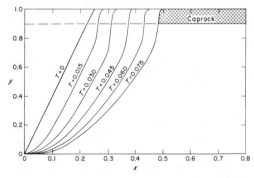

FIG. 7. Graph showing slope with cap rock (Scheidegger, 1964).

being 1/10 as much in the "cap rock" region as below, is shown in Fig. 7 (after Scheidegger, 1964).

(*c*) *Effect of Undercutting Rivers.* Many badland slopes recede primarily because of the effect of river action at their foot. In this instance, essentially a straight slope recession results as governed by the sideways eroding power of the stream at the foot (see Scheidegger, 1961, p. 110).

(*d*) *Hoodoos.* Occasionally, denudation of badland slopes can produce interesting features such as earth pillars and hoodoos with an overhanging "hat" (see *Earth Pillars, Pyramids*). The formation of pillars is explained by the slope-denudation theory given above, but for "hoodoos" with an overhang, an additional physical cause must be postulated. This is the "teapot effect," implying that water can turn a corner and flow on the *underside* (like on the underside of the spout of a teapot or the "hat" of a hoodoo) of a horizontal protrusion. Theoretical calculations have given reasonable values for the possible overhang of the "hat" of the hoodoo (Scheidegger, 1961).

(3) Drainage Net Development. (*a*) *Stream Orders.* The quantitative description of a drainage network, such as seen in badlands, is based on the concept of *stream order*. By definition, streams (or channels) with *no* tributaries are counted as first order; two first-order channels combine to form a channel segment of second order,..., two *N*th order channels form a channel of $N + 1$ order. This system of ordering channels is due to Strahler ("Strahler orders"); Horton previously devised a system in which always *one* of the two lower-order channel segments was renumbered at a junction to the higher order all the way to the headwater ("Horton orders"). Both Horton and Strahler ignore the junctions of *N*th order channels with channels of lower than *N*th order. This produces a certain inconsistency in the orders of streams which can be amended by introducing "consistent" orders (Scheidegger, 1965) defined as follows; Suppose a channel segment of order *N* and a channel segment of order *M* combine to form a channel segment of order *X*. The value of *X* is then:

$$X = \lceil \log(2^N + 2^M) \rceil / \log 2 \qquad (2)$$

Naturally, in the "consistent" scheme of ordering channel segments, order numbers are no longer integers.

(*b*) *Branching Statistics.* In a drainage network, it is possible to count channel segments of order *i*. This gives a function

$$n = n(i)$$

where *n* is the *number* of channel segments of (Strahler) order *i*. The aim is to deduce the "law of stream order numbers" theoretically. This law, due to Horton, states that the numbers of channel segments of subsequent (Strahler or Horton) orders form a geometric sequence.

As with slopes, the individual processes that lead

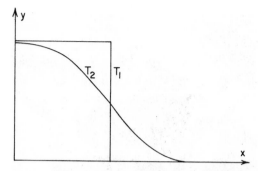

Fig. 8. Decay of a slope bank.

to the junction of stream channels are of extreme complexity. Leopold and Langbein (1962) have recently shown that the best way to deal with such phenomena is to treat them as quasi-stochastic. In this approach, each individual drainage channel performs a "random walk," and will meet and combine with other channels as if by chance.

An alternative method in arriving at an expression for $n = n(i)$ is by considering the combination of channels as a reversed stochastic branching process (Scheidegger, 1966). The latter can be shown to be a Markov process for which the pertinent relationships are well known. In this fashion, one obtains the correct "law of stream order numbers," implying that the bifurcation ratio [defined as $n(i + 1)/n(i)$] is nothing but a branching probability.

(4) Large-scale Evolution of Badlands. (*a*) *Basic Ideas.* It has recently been noted that there is a formal analogy between the transient behavior of temperature in a solid medium and the transient evolution of height (above some base line) in a landscape. Leopold and Langbein (1962) have made this analogy the basis of an interpretation of landscape evolution in which they were able to show that the concept of entropy can be meaningfully introduced. This interpretation of landscape development assumes that the individual and detailed processes in the mass transport are too complex to be followed in detail and that a stochastic model is therefore called for in order to explain the observed phenomena.

(*b*) *Statistical Justification of the Thermodynamic Analogy.* The analogy between temperature in thermodynamics and height in a landscape is, at first, completely heuristic. However, it can be shown that the mass transport in landscape evolution is nothing but a special case of a general class of mass transport in which the individual particle motions are so complex and numerous that they can be treated as quasi-stochastic. In effect, there is a perfect analogy between height in a landscape and energy in the statistical mechanics of gases as formulated long ago by Gibbs (see Scheidegger and Langbein, 1966); under very general statistical assumptions, the height in a landscape corresponds to the Hamiltonian expression for energy in thermodynamics and

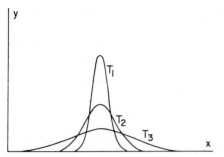

FIG. 9. Decay of a protrusion (Langbein and Scheideger, 1966).

the transient behavior of the landscape is described by some master equation (in the simplest case a diffusivity equation) that depends only on the statistical interaction between various parts of the landscape. On this basis, one can proceed to set up equations for the large-scale "average" behavior of a landscape.

(c) *Application to Badlands.* As noted above, the simplest equation describing landscape evolution is a diffusivity equation. Well-known solutions of this equation are shown in Figs. 8 and 9. Thus, on the average, a slope bank as well as a protrusion must decay. Since this refers only to the large-scale "average" evolution of such features, the theory certainly explains the facts observed in badlands. Details of lithology, etc., will, of course, affect the result in each individual case.

Rates of Erosion (S.A.S.)

Sedimentary rocks which characteristically form badlands are highly erodible, but in addition, vegetational cover must be sparse or absent. For example, badlands form in erodible sediments of humid regions where vegetation has been destroyed by smelter fumes as at Ducktown, Tennessee.

In Wyoming, where the sediments of the White River Group are mantled with vegetation, the sediment produced by small drainage basins averages about 2 acre-ft/square mile/yr, but where vegetation is absent and badlands have formed, the sediment production approaches 30 acre-ft/square mile annually (Hadley and Schumm, 1961). Obviously, with a rate of sediment production of this magnitude, the components of badland topography—hillslopes, channels and pediments—must be passing through their evolutionary stages of development at a rapid rate. The relatively few measurements of hillslope and pediment erosion confirm this conclusion. For example, during ten weeks, hillslope erosion was on the order of 1 inch in the Perth Amboy badlands (Fig. 3). In Badlands National Monument hillslope erosion ranges from 0.4–0.8 in./yr (Schumm, 1956a).

Not only does the absence of vegetation permit erosion by rainwash and mass movement, but the effect of raindrop impact is enhanced. During the winter months, frost action on the bare hillslopes may also be quite important. In badlands developed on the Mancos shale of Western Colorado, the effect of frost action is very important in determining not only the rates of erosion but also the dominant erosive process. During the winter, creep is dominant. The influence of frost action produces rates of creep greatly in excess of those measured in humid regions. Rates of movement of rock fragments on the slopes ranged from 15 mm/yr on a 10° slope to about 70 mm/yr on a 40° slope (Schumm, 1967). The downslope rate of movement of surficial material is greatly in excess of that during the summer months when raindrop impact compacts and seals the surface of the slopes, and rainwash and rilling become dominant. These seasonal changes also exert a major effect on the hydrology of the badland drainage basins. For a given amount of precipitation, spring runoff is significantly less than autumn runoff (Schumm and Lusby, 1963; Schumm, 1964).

Although the high rates of badland erosion often cause sedimentation problems downstream, an important result of rapid hillslope erosion is the frequent exposure of fossils contained within the sediments (Colbert, 1956).

Development and Evolution of Badlands (S.A.S.)

The rapid rates of badland erosion permit at least a partial understanding of the development and evolution of the components of this type of topography.

Measurements of the characteristics of the drainage system of the Perth Amboy badlands reveal that these miniature land forms conform to the laws of drainage composition and that these intricate drainage systems develop in a manner similar to those of large systems. In fact, during a detailed analysis of badland drainage systems it was discovered that a unit drainage area is required for the development and maintenance of a unit of channel length. In the Perth Amboy badlands, about 9 square feet of drainage area was required to provide the runoff necessary to maintain 1 foot of drainage channel. Therefore, although a dendritic drainage pattern may be generated by random walk techniques, the spacing of the channels and their distribution throughout a landscape is closely related to the erodibility of the material in which the channels are developing and to the runoff produced by a unit area of the system.

The drainage channels incise rapidly into the erodible sediments, and a channel is present at the base of each of the steep, newly formed hillslopes. Later as the hillslopes retreat from the channels, miniature pediments are formed. These pediments develop as a result of the retreat of the hillslopes. Although they lie at the base of the steep, rapidly evolving hillslopes, they too are eroded, as the water

A

B

FIG. 10. (A) The cycle of slope development on the Brule formation, (runoff dominant). (B) The cycle of slope development on the Chadron formation (creep dominant). (Schumm, 1956a; by permission of *American Journal of Science*, New Haven, Conn.)

and sediment moving down from the hillslopes passes over them. The junction of hillslope and pediment is abrupt and the sharp junction appears to be maintained by the ability of the runoff to sweep sediment away from the base of the slope and across the upper part of the pediment (Schumm, 1962). Apparently, the abrupt decrease in slope is compensated for by an equally abrupt change in surface roughness from that of the irregular hillslope to that of the smooth pediment, and velocity remains constant.

Badlands are very different depending upon the dominant erosion process in operation. At Perth Amboy and on the badlands of the Brule formation in South Dakota, erosion occurs as a result of the movement of runoff down the slopes. The result is a parallel retreat of the steep, straight slopes. On the Chadron formation in South Dakota and on the Mancos shale of Western Colorado, the predominant erosion process is creep owing to the high infiltration capacity of the hillslope materials and the effects of frost action. In these areas, the hillslopes decline as they retreat, and the broadly convex summits of these slopes join with a straight midportion of the slope or a basal convexity (Fig. 1). Figure 10 shows the cycles of hillslope evolution when runoff and creep are dominant.

In badland areas where lithologic differences occur, the regularity of the slope is disturbed, and often miniature cliffs form below the resistant layers. In fact, sod can act as a cap rock when overlying highly erodible sediments. These miniature scarps retreat leaving behind a well-developed pediment surface.

Many aspects of large-scale land forms are reproduced in miniature in badlands. Further studies of the rates and mechanics of badland erosion may provide preliminary information which will lead to a better understanding of the more slowly developing portions of the landscape.

ADRIAN E. SCHEIDEGGER

STANLEY A. SCHUMM

RHODES W. FAIRBRIDGE

References

Colbert, E. H., 1956, "Rates of erosion in the Chinle formation," *Plateau*, **28,** 73–76.

Derruau, M., 1962, "Précis de Géomorphologie," Third ed., Paris, Masson et Cie, 413pp.

Hadley, R. F., and Schumm, S. A., 1961, "Sediment sources and drainage basin characteristics in the Upper Cheyenne River Basin," *U.S. Geol. Surv. Water Supply Paper* **1531-B,** 137–198.

Leopold, L. B., and Langbein, W. B., 1962, "The concept of entropy in landscape evolution," *U.S. Geol. Surv. Profess. Paper* **500A.**

Scheidegger, A. E., 1961, "Theoretical Geomorphology," Englewood Cliffs, N.J., Prentice-Hall, 333pp.

Scheidegger, A. E., 1964, "Lithologic variations in slope development theory," *U.S. Geol. Surv. Circ.* **485**

Scheidegger, A. E., 1965, "The algebra of stream order numbers," *U.S. Geol. Surv. Profess. Paper* **525B,** B187-9.

Scheidegger, A. E., 1966, "Stochastic branching processes and the law of stream order numbers," *Water Resources Research*, **2**(2), 199–203.

Scheidegger, A. E., and Langbein, W. B., 1966, "Probability concepts in geomorphology," *U.S. Geol. Surv. Profess. Paper* **500C.**

Schumm, S. A., 1956a, "The role of creep and rainwash on the retreat of badland slopes," *Am. J. Sci.*, **254,** 693–706.

Schumm, S. A., 1956b, "Evolution of drainage systems and slopes in badlands at Perth Amboy, N.J.," *Bull. Geol. Soc. Am.*, **67,** 597–646.

Schumm, S. A., 1962, "Erosion on miniature pediments in Badlands National Monument, South Dakota," *Bull. Geol. Soc. Am.*, **75,** 719–724.

Schumm, S. A., 1964, "Seasonal variations of erosion rates and processes on hillslopes in Western Colorado," *Z. Geomorphol.*, Supplementband 5, 215–238.

Schumm, S. A., 1967, "Rates of surficial rock creep on hillslopes in Western Colorado," *Science*, **155,** 560–561.

Schumm, S. A., and Lusby, G. C., 1963, "Seasonal variations of infiltration capacity and runoff on hillslopes in Western Colorado," *J. Geophys. Res.*, **68,** 3655–3666.

Smith, K. G., 1958, "Erosional processes and landforms in Badlands National Monument, South Dakota," *Bull. Geol. Soc. Am.*, **69,** 975–1007.

Strahler, A. N., 1956, "Quantitative slope analysis," *Bull. Geol. Soc. Am.*, **67,** 571–596.

Cross-references: *Alluvium*; *Denudation*; *Earth Pillars or Pyramids*; *Frost Action*; *Gully Erosion*; *Interfluve*; *Law of Declivities, etc.*; *Mesa and Butte*; *Organisms as Geomorphic Agents*; *Pediment*; *Piping*; *Quantitative Geomorphology*; *Regolith and Saprolite*; *Slopes*; *Soil Creep*; *Stream Orders.*

BAER–BABINET LAW

What is sometimes called the Law of Baer was actually arrived at as a result of work pursued independently by both Baer and Babinet. Babinet (1859) published first, but the quantitative study of von Baer (1860) was more definite. The joint name is therefore justified, although considerable controversy developed among the various proponents. It was believed that the rotation of the earth influenced the course of river development, i.e., under the *Coriolis force* (q.v., Vol. I) all moving particles in the northern hemisphere tend to bear right, and correspondingly those in the southern hemisphere bear left. The river banks on the stressed side would tend to recede faster than on the other. The question of whether the stream is oriented in a meridional direction is quite secondary and may be neglected (Günther, 1882; the early literature has been reviewed by Némenyi, 1952).

Gilbert (1884) computed that a stream such as the lower Mississippi would erode its right bank about 9% more than the left, and this should indeed lead to a right-handed displacement (in the northern hemisphere), all other things being equal.

The Baer–Babinet Law was criticized by W. Schmidt (1926), whose experiments suggested an opposite effect. Nevertheless, field observations on many rivers, e.g., the Danube, at first sight seem to justify the theory, though wind, sedimentation and tectonics may all play a role. Schmidt concluded that the wind effect (also moving under Coriolis stress) was more likely the actual cause of the stream deflection. Schmidt's experiments were criticized as being too small in scale to be acceptable (Exner, 1927).

It was the celebrated physicist Albert Einstein (1926) who considered the Baer–Babinet Law most effectively. He believed that it operates on much the same principles as meander formation. He assumes on a slight curve a sudden increase in the stage of the flow (such wavelike acceleration and deceleration are now well recognized). Particles of water nearest the bottom will be subject to friction, while nearer the surface centrifugal force will be dominant. A secondary crosscurrent component is thus generated and the greatest velocity will be generated on the concave bank, causing scour. Thus, from a gentle curve, a meander evolves. If one substitutes for the inertial force engendered by the initial curvature, the Coriolis force, omnipresent on a rotating earth, except just at the equator, the same result is achieved.

The Baer-Babinet Law has also been invoked to explain some erosional effects of ice motion. The asymmetry of drumlins in the Rhine valley was quoted by Schmidt (1932, p. 364) as a possible example, but the general consensus seems to favor rather a change of ice flow during melting (Charlesworth, 1957, p. 395).

In the opinion of most modern writers (e.g., Bryan and Mason, 1932) the systematic asymmetry of valleys may be more convincingly explained by climatic effects (solifluction, sedimentation, prevailing winds or even paleowinds).

RHODES W. FAIRBRIDGE

References

Babinet, J., 1859, "Influence du mouvement de rotation de la terre sur le cours des rivières," *Compt. Rend.*, **49,** 638–641.

Baer, K. E. von, 1860, *Bull. Acad. Sci., St. Petersbourg*, **2,** 1, 218, 353.

Brunhes, B., and J., 1904, "Les analogies des tourbillon atmospheriques et des turbillon des cours d'eau et la question de la déviation des rivières vers la droite," *Ann. Géogr.*, **13,** 1–20.

Bryan, K., and Mason, S. L., 1932, "Asymmetric valleys and climatic boundaries," *Science*, **75,** 215–216.

Charlesworth, J. K., 1957, "The Quaternary Era," London, Ed. Arnold, 2 vols.

Eakin, H. M., 1910, "The influence of the earth's rotation upon the lateral erosion of streams," *J. Geol.*, **18,** 435–447.

Einstein, A., 1926, "Üeber die Ursachen der Mäanderbildung der Flusse und des Baer'schen Gesetzes," *Naturwissenschaften*, **14,** 223–225.

Exner, F. M., 1927, "Zur Wirkung der Erddrehung auf Flusslauge," *Geogr. Ann.*, **9,** 173–180.

Fairchild, H. L., 1932, "Earth rotation and river erosion," *Science*, **76,** 423–427.

Gilbert, G. K., 1884, "The sufficiency of terrestrial rotation for the deflection of streams," *Am. J. Sci.*, Ser. 3, **27,** 427–432.

Günther, S., 1882, "Die sichtbaren und fühlbaren Wirkungen der Erdrotation," *Humboldt*, **1,** 328–333, 359–368.

Némenyi, P. F., 1952, "Annotated and illustrated bibliographic material on the morphology of rivers," *Bull. Geol. Soc. Am.*, **63,** 595–644.

Quaraishy, M. S., 1943, "River meandering and the earth's rotation," *Current Sci.*, **12,** 278.

Schmidt, W., 1926, "Modellversuche zur Wirkung der Erddrehung auf Flusslaufe," *Festuchr. Zentralanstalt Meteor. Geodynamik* (*Wien*), 187–195.

Schmidt, W., 1932, "Die Drumlinhügel des diluvialen Rheingletschers," *Fortschr. Geol. Pal.*, **11,** 341–375.

Tolmachoff, I. P., 1933, "The history of Baer's Law," *Science*, **76,** 516.

Cross-references: *Asymmetric Valleys; Rivers—Meandering and Braiding*. Vol. I: *Coriolis Force*.

BAJADA, BAHADA (PROLUVIUM)

A Spanish term *bajada*, often anglicized to *bahada*, which stems from the semiarid southwestern United States, is applied to broad slopes of detrital alluvial outwash, which is often in the form of multiple coalescing *alluvial fans* or *cones* (q.v.). King (1942) uses *piedmont* (q.v.) as a synonym. It is thus in contrast to rock-cut surface *pediments* (q.v.), i.e., bajadas are aggradational features, not degradational. They are characteristic of the bolsons or

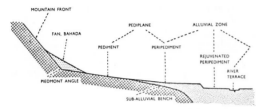

FIG. 1. Elements in the piedmont profile (Balchin and Pye, 1956).

basin regions at the foot of the mountains in the basin-range country (see air photo, from Death Valley, California, in Von Engeln, 1942, p. 410).

Tolman (1909) introduced the term into geomorphological literature to distinguish such features clearly from detrital accumulations in the mountains, being "the flanking detrital slopes, built up by terrestrial deposition, the aggradational equivalent of the active erosion above."

The usual form of deposition is during and immediately following flash floods which normally result from summer thunderstorms in the mountains. The torrent emerges from a canyon or gulch at the mountain front; the gradient becomes gentler and the floodwaters are dispersed over the fan. Numerous fans along the mountain front coalesce to become a general apron. The mountain front retreats, according to Davis, and as worked out in detail by Lawson (1915), by "back-wearing" of a pediment, overlapped up to the mountain foot by the bajada; as the one retreats, the other accumulates.

Blackwelder (1931) has called the bajadas "compound fans," which is one of his "desert plains" (along with pediments, playas, dip slopes, graded river flood plains and aggraded river flood plains). He claims that a bajada is induced by diastrophic movement, e.g., the development of the basin-range structure (horst and graben complexes), or by climatic change; both cases involve a disturbance of some sort in the existing equilibrium profile.

The superficial appearance of the bajada and the pediment make it necessary to look for a profile, as in a gully, where the feature can be seen in section. The pediment is strictly degradational, the slope cutting across the bedding of older formations, with only a thin veneer of gravelly debris; in contrast, the bajada is a three-dimensional prism, stratified parallel to the slope, and underlain by poorly sorted gravels and detritus, torrent and mudflow deposits, Series of dry distributaries fan out over every unit of the confluent aprons. The slope is concave up, ranging from 10° or more at the mountain angle, to near zero in the valley floor or playa. As one travels along the apron sequence of bajadas parallel to the mountain foot, one may notice a scarcely perceptible undulation, a rise and fall as one passes over each fan unit. Fans, however,

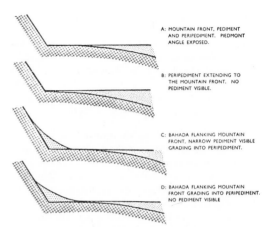

FIG. 2. Profiles in the piedmont zone (Balchin and Pye, 1956).

are much less uniform in gradient than pediments.

Another important difference between the bajada and the pediment is that at the mountain front, the gradient of the former passes imperceptibly out into the plain, while the latter passes out with an abrupt change in slope at the "piedmont angle" (Figs. 1 and 2). Blackwelder considered that the mountain front is practically always controlled by faulting, especially when the bajadas are several thousand feet thick.

Complex or composite pediment-bajada combinations are known in the Basin-Range Province: normal pediment surfaces capped by 50–200 feet of bajada-type deposits, termed by Blackwelder "fan-topped pediments" (1931, p. 139). In contrast, he believes that some bajadas have been reduced by erosion to pediments.

In its outer parts, the bajada may die out and pass into a bare pediment or it may merge into the finer sediments of the alluvial zone or playa depression (*bolson*, q.v.). The pediment that truncates older bajada deposits was termed *peripediment* by Howard (1942). As Balchin and Pye (1956) indicated, all combinations of these features may occur, giving a wide variety of forms to the piedmont profile (Figs. 1 and 2). In the U.S.S.R., the whole bajada-peripediment complex is known as *proluvium*.

RHODES W. FAIRBRIDGE

References

Balchin, W. G. V., and Pye, N., 1956, "Piedmont profiles in the arid cycle," *Proc. Geologists Assoc. Engl.*, **66**, 167–181.

Blackwelder, E., 1931, "Desert plains," *J. Geol.*, **39**, 133–140.

Cotton, C. A., 1942, "Climatic Accidents," Christchurch, Whitcombe and Tombs, 354pp.

Howard, A. D., 1942, "Pediments and the pediment pass problem," *J. Geomorphol.*, **5**, 3–31, 95–136.

King, L. C., 1942, "South African Scenery," Edinburgh, Oliver & Boyd (Second ed., 1951).

Lawson, A. C., 1915, "Epigene profiles of the desert," *Univ. Calif. Publ. Bull. Dept. Geol.*, **9**, 23–48.

Tolman, C. F., 1909, "Erosion and deposition in southern Arizona bolson region," *J. Geol.*, **17**, 136–163.

Von Engeln, O. D., 1942, "Geomorphology," New York, The Macmillan Co., 655pp.

Cross-references: *Alluvial Fan, Cone*; *Alluvium*; *Arid Cycle*; *Basin and Range Landscape*; *Bolson*; *Pediment*; *Slopes*.

BARBED DRAINAGE—*See* DRAINAGE PATTERNS

BARCHAN—*See* CLAY DUNE; SAND DUNE

BARRIER REEF—*See* GREAT BARRIER REEF

BARRIERS—BEACHES AND ISLANDS

A barrier is a partly emergent bar-like ridge of sand or coarser sediment lying off a shore or shoal and usually subparallel to the shore, projecting from the flank of a headland or connecting two headlands. A barrier is usually cut by one or more tidal inlets, forming a barrier chain—a succession of barrier peninsulas and barrier islands or simple, narrow beaches. A partly emergent sand spit is a barrier spit. Barriers are commonly connected below water by tidal deltas. Where inlets migrate, the makeup of a chain is changeable. The barrier (coastal) lagoon is a succession of shallow troughs or basins set off by widenings of the islands (Price, 1947; Rusnak, 1960, Figs. 4, 5). There are baymouth, midbay and bayhead barriers.

Barriers have been called "sand banks," "off-shore bars" and "barrier bars." Related forms include: sand key or cay (off a shore line or oceanic shoal), sand atoll (Marquesas Islands, Florida) and dwip (closed crescentic sand key, Ganges delta, India: Bates, 1953, Fig. 21). Barriers are narrow near headlands of changeable shore line positions and on the up-drift sides of migrating inlets, where they grow longitudinally. They begin at first with a single water-laid beach ridge, commonly vegetated. Elevated by eolian sand, this becomes an eolian beach ridge. If hummocky, it is a foredune or foredune chain. Addition of *beach ridges* (q.v.) takes place to seaward (a "prograding" shore), which eventually forms a beach plain. Small wave deltas and larger washover fans develop lagoonward from overwash flood channels, scalloping the lagoonal shore line. Blow-out fans form downwind from eolian blowouts in the foredune chain. On and from the two types of fans, fields of bare dunes develop, migrating until checked by

FIG. 1. Barrier complex, Central Padre Island, south Texas. Foredune chain, bluffed facing the beach, is cut by overwash channels, the mouths of which are closed by beach growth. Channels led to washover fans which discharged, in flood, to the first clear lane back of foredune. Dark channels are ponds. Three ranks of clear lanes alternate with seif dune fields back of foredune chain, having reworked the washover fans. Low, vegetated dune remnants dot and rib the clear lanes. Dark tones in clear lanes include vegetated areas, ponds and moist, dark-bottomed, depressions. The Central (wind-tide) Mud Flats of Laguna Madre fill the lagoon back of the dune fields. Marsh buggy tracks crisscross in southwest corner of photograph. Shore-line trend N 16°W. Photo is centered at 26°N and is 5 by 6 miles on a side. North is at the top.

vegetation, or moving into the lagoon over tidal flats. Dune migration leaves behind a corrugated, baseleveled and vegetated plain. These various additions convert a simple barrier beach into a barrier complex (Fig. 1). A barrier tied to a low headland usually continues in front of it as a beach ridge with no break between.

Barriers are common and well developed along coastal plain shore lines (Fig. 2), except where coarse-grained sediment is scarce or absent (chenier plains and some marsh plains), wave activity is weak, or the tidal range exceeds about 8–9 feet. Barriers are usually short and scarce on rocky coasts, with their steep continental shelves. Barrier shore lines are well aligned from unit to unit where wave energy is large, poorly aligned where it is medium (Mississippi Sound: Price, 1954). Barriers deteriorate to series of short islands (broken barrier) where the tidal range and the sand supply approach the critical values (western

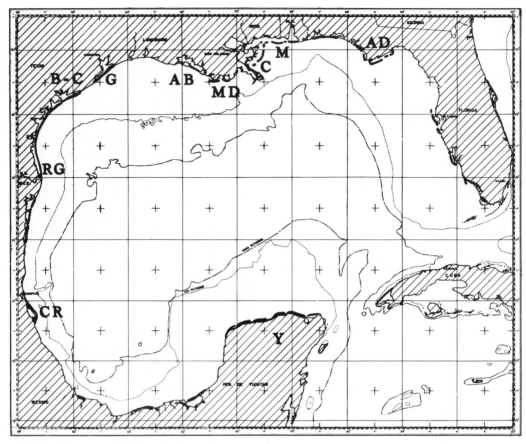

FIG. 2. Barriers of Gulf of Mexico. Long, well-aligned chains flank the Rio Grande delta (RG) and connect the Rio Grande and Brazos-Colorado (B-C) deltas. Poorly aligned chains enclose Chandeleur (C) and Mississippi (M) sounds and border the north coast of the Yucatan peninsula (Y). Baymouth barriers and chains, some poorly aligned, enclose Galveston Bay (G), indentations of the western flank of the Mississippi delta (MD) and bays of western Florida and southern Mexico. Large cuspate forelands occur on the Apalachicola delta (AD) and Cabo Rojo (CR), the latter reportedly built on a limestone shoal. Rocky headlands are associated with barriers of the peninsulas of Florida and Yucatan, and some other Mexican coastal sectors. Emergent coralline reefs fringe southern Florida and the Laguna Colorados of western Cuba. A 25-mile oyster reef, elevated by shell detritus, spans the mouth of Atchafalaya Bay (AB). The 2° latitude and longitude quadrangles measure 119 miles along each latitude line, 135.6 miles along each longitude line.

Mississippi Sound; West to East Frisian Islands, North Sea). Poorly aligned barriers are usually eroded on up-current ends and prograde on the other ends (Mississippi Sound; Yucatan Peninsula, north coast). New barriers may form on deltaic cuspate forelands (Price, 1962), Fig. 3, and, in small units, along poorly aligned chains (Shepard, 1960, Fig. 11; 1963, Fig. 88). Revisions of barrier shore lines and trend directions occur adjacent to retreating or advancing headlands.

Barrier plains may stand 3–10 feet above MSL (Mean Sea Level), and the barrier toe may lie as deep as −50 to −60 feet. A sector of a barrier that has retreated may be perched on its lagoonal sediments (Fig. 4). Barriers are equilibrium structures and are not predestined to retreat and destruction

(as suggested by Johnson's 1919 hypothesis). The large barriers of today seem to have formed at or toward the end of the Flandrian transgression, the major volume of sand having come from the grading of the nearshore bottom, with progradation continuing for a few centuries until a dynamic equilibrium was effected. These conclusions are supported by the dating of shells from the bases of barriers which show that they were built up and seaward in late Flandrian time (Fisk, 1959, Figs. 12, 13; Shepard, 1960, p. 212). Net progradation has been rare in historic time, except as previously noted (see Fig. 3, and Shepard 1960, 1963).

Closely timed before-and-after observations (at the Brazos delta, Texas) with detailed instrumental control show that a barrier may begin to

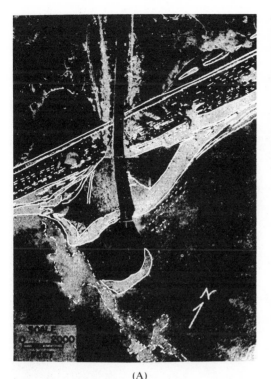

(A)

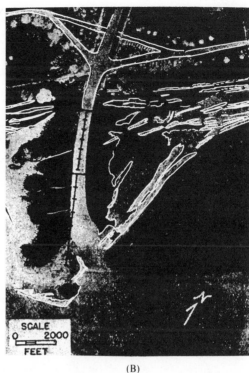

(B)

Fig. 3. Barrier building on small cuspate foreland, Brazos Delta, Texas. Some 40 successive barriers built in the outgrowth of the delta after 1928 had recognizable fragments in 1962, including beach-ridge extensions and the active barrier chain. The delta formed after the river mouth was shifted 6 miles west, past the town of Freeport. (A) the delta in 1938; (B) in 1949, showing maximum subsequent gulfward growth, since which time the delta has been held in check gulfward by erosion but has been widened at the base by lateral growths. Intracoastal canal and locks lie back of delta. Growth of natural levees shown in B by dark marsh vegetation. Maximum heights of active barriers 2.5–3.0 feet MSL. Older ridges vegetated and partly eolian, rising to 6 feet. Scale drawn along river has same point of origin in A and B. Intervals are river widths (from Bates, 1953, Fig. 20).

form on a progradational coastal sector as a longshore bar of an elevated storm-surge sea level, the bar emerging soon afterward at normal high-tide levels (Price, 1962). Also, without storminess, a longshore bar of the high-tide season of the Brazos delta emerged during the following low-tide season (Marmer, 1951, Figs. 24–29). It was then built up by swash and remained emergent as a barrier during the following season of high tides. Nevertheless, over the next few years it was only emergent at low tides. Thus the idea of tide-facilitated barrier-building remains unproven. These new barriers of the Brazos delta were low barrier beaches of fine-grained sand with gently sloping flanks; they have persisted unvegetated and with very slight shell content until fronted by a later barrier or beach ridge (Fig. 3).

Longshore bars have been shown by long series of observations (Evans, 1942; Keulegan, 1948; Shepard, 1950) to be held down to stillwater (half-wave) level by the plunge of the breakers if the water level remains constant. A miniature bar, sometimes emerging a few inches just off the beach,

(Johnson, 1919, p. 388), and made in a wave tank by McKee and Sterrett (1961), would seem to form under a local slight rise of stillwater level when backwash and advancing wave waters meet. Such bars disappear under storm breakers and do not seem to form a nucleus for barrier building.* Barrier building by processes other than those described remain hypothetical and unsupported by controlled observations.

W. Armstrong Price

References

Bates, C. C., 1953, "Rational theory of delta formation," *Bull. Am. Assoc. Petrol. Geologists,* **37,** 2119–2162.

Evans, O. F., 1942, "The origin of spits, bars and related structures," *J. Geol.,* **50,** 846–865.

Fisk, H. N., 1959, "Padre Island and the Laguna Madre flats, coastal south Texas," in (Russell, R. J.,

* Information not previously published is from current research of Price.

FIG. 4. Oblique air photograph of Mitchell River, Gulf of Carpentaria, Queensland, Australia, crossing Pleistocene barrier and lagoon terrace and building Holocene deltaic cuspate foreland barrier, with tide marsh lagoon. Distributaries diverge into Quaternary lagoons forming deltaic cusps along shore, three seen in upper part of view. Meandering foreground distributary branches and beach ridges of Holocene barrier fan out toward another cusp just out of view at bottom. Looking southward from above 15°10′S, 141°35′E.

editor) Coastal Geogr. Conf., 2nd, pp. 103–151, Office of Naval Research.

Johnson, D. W., 1919, "Shore Processes and Shoreline Development," New York, John Wiley & Sons, xvi + 584pp.

Keulegan, G. H., 1948, "An experimental study of submarine sand bars," *U.S. Beach Erosion Board Tech. Rept. 3*, vii + 40pp.

Marmer, H. A., 1951, "Tidal datum planes," *U.S. Coast & Geodetic Survey, Spec. Publ. 135*, revised ed., vii + 142pp.

McKee, E. D., and Sterrett, T. S., 1961, "Laboratory experiments on form and structure of longshore bars and beaches," in (Peterson, A. A., and Osmond, J. C., editors) "Geometry of sandstone bodies," *Am. Assoc. Petrol. Geologists*, 13–28.

Price, W. A., 1947, "Equilibrium of form and forces in tidal basins of coast of Texas and Louisiana,"

Bull. Am. Assoc. Petrol. Geologists, **31,** 1619–1663.

Price, W. A., 1954, "Dynamic environments—reconnaissance mapping, geologic and geomorphic, of continental shelf of Gulf of Mexico," *Gulf Coast Assoc. Geol. Socs., Trans.,* **4,** 75–107.

Price, W. A., 1962, "Origin of barrier chain and beach ridge," *Geol. Soc. Am. Abs. for 1962,* 219.

Rusnak, G. A., 1960, "Sediments of Laguna Madre, Texas," in (Shepard, F. P., *et al.,* editors) "Recent Sediments, Northwest Gulf of Mexico," 153–196, Am. Assoc. Petrol. Geologists.

Shepard, F. P., 1950, "Longshore bars and longshore troughs," *U.S. Beach Erosion Board Tech. Mem. 15,* 31pp.

Shepard, F. P., 1960, "Gulf Coast barriers," in (Shepard, F. P., *et al.,* editors) "Recent Sediments, Northwest Gulf of Mexico," 197–220, Am. Assoc. Petrol. Geologists.

Shepard, F. P., 1963, "Submarine Geology," second ed., New York, Harper & Row, xviii + 557pp.

Cross-references: *Bars; Beach; Beach Ridge; Cuspate Foreland or Spit; Deltaic Evolution; Lagoon; Littoral Processes—An Introduction; Sand Dunes; Swash, Swash Mark.* Vol. I: *Mean Sea Level.*

BARS

Submerged ridges of detrital sediments which are larger and less regularly spaced than ripple marks are termed *bars.* Formed typically in shallow epicontinental or shelf waters by waves and currents, they are found singly or together, and internally laminated. Active quartzitic sand and calcareous sand bars are typically unconsolidated, shallow-based and highly mutable with changes in environmental factors (Fig. 1). The laminae show the directions of the formative currents, and cross-beds aid in determining directions of bar migration. Some bar-like accumulations of carbonate sand (Rusnak, Bowman and Ostland, 1964) show superficial encrustation dated from less than 200–1000 years ago.

Bars may be classified as *longitudinal* or *transverse* to a dominant current or to an associated shore line. The underwater extensions of sand spits are bar-like. Long, narrow, highly stable, bar-like ridges lying in parallel series in shelf waters beyond the surf zone have been called "tidal current ridges" by Off (1963) and occur where tidal ranges are 10 feet or more. Similar large, broad, submerged accumulations of sand with surfaces singly or

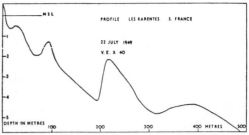

FIG. 2. Profile of a barred tideless beach on the Mediterranean (after Shepard).

numerously ridged, and related to bars, are given names such as subaqueous dunes, barchans, sand waves and sand bores (cf. Vol. I, *Subaqueous Sand Dunes*). So-called giant ripple-marks of carbonate sands on Bahamian platform shoals are so regular in their spacing and parallelism as to suggest that they are formed by somewhat the same process as normal ripple marks (Newell and Rigby, 1957).

Bars longitudinal to confined currents include stream channel bars and some bars of river mouths, funnel estuaries, straits and tidal inlets. River

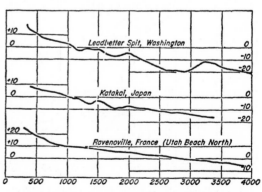

FIG. 3. Profiles of the Scripps beach in California to show bars and their removal (after Shepard).

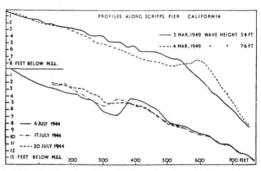

FIG. 1. Circulation of water in surf as steep waves transform dashed profile to solid profile by moving sand from berm to bar (Bascom, 1964). (By permission of Doubleday & Co., N.Y.)

FIG. 4. Profiles of flat beaches. Note the three bars on the beach at Leadbetter Spit (slope exaggerated 1:5; Bascom, 1964). (By permission of Doubleday & Co., N.Y.)

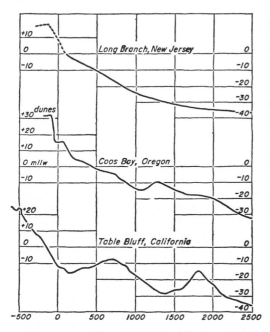

FIG. 5. Intermediate slope beaches. Contrast the bar-less beach profile at Long Branch with the two huge bars at Table Bluff (slope exaggerated 1:5; Bascom, 1964). (By permission of Doubleday & Co., N.Y.)

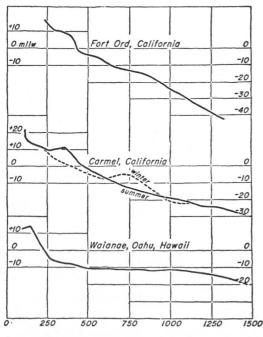

FIG. 6. Profiles of steep beaches. At Waianae only the beach face is sand. The flat area is a coral reef over which great breakers form and where the surfing is excellent (for an expert) (exaggerated 1:2.5; Bascom, 1964). (By permission of Doubleday & Co., N.Y.)

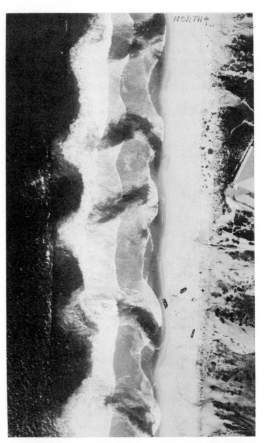

FIG. 7. Rip channels cutting a "terrace-like" bar, Fort Ord, California. Bar and ocean (dark) at left, beach (white) and vegetated land (dark) at right, with trough between. (Bascom, 1964). (By permission of Doubleday & Co., N.Y.)

channel bars may become channel islands at lowered stream stages. Off (1963) considers his "tidal current ridges" to be longitudinal to the dominant currents. Smaller ridges of similar nature on coasts with smaller tidal ranges—e.g., off the Rio Grande delta, Texas, and the coast of Georgia—are diagonal to the nearby shore lines. The huge Bahamian "sand bores" and giant subaqueous barchans of calcareous sands seem to be longitudinal to the dominant current. They may have small bars and aqueous dunes on their surfaces.

Bars transverse to confined currents include crescentic bars of some river mouths and tidal inlet channels. There are sand waves and aqueous dunes which are transverse to the current.

Longshore Bars

Longshore bars occurring singly or in parallel series of 2 or 3 off sandy beaches are formed in the surf zone along the seaward flanks of plunge troughs excavated by the swirling motion of breakers (Figs.

FIG. 8. Oblique air photograph of the Bahama Banks, showing patterns of huge calcareous sand bars at shallow depth beneath the water. (Courtesy F. Goro and *Science*.)

2–7). The excavated sands rise in the turbulent water, some accumulating as a series of bars along the seaward flanks of troughs, while the rest is carried shoreward in the rush of the solitary wave (*wave of translation*) formed by the water from the tops of the breakers (see *Beach*). Currents from both flanks later build up the longshore bar, both trough and bars being affected also by longshore currents, and the troughs are scoured by water escaping laterally behind the bars from the beach zone and longshore drift-currents bringing sand.

Longshore bars—straight or looped—are not built up above stillwater (half-wave) level because the breakers plunge on and over them, keeping their summits planed down. The building of these bars up to emergence is described in the article *Barriers*. In some experiments these bars are topped at low tide level, in others at half-wave height.

The term bar is only appropriate to features below swash limits. The criterion of submergence at normal high tide advocated by Price (1951) and Shepard (1952) eliminates from the category *bar* such proposed emergent forms as the swash "bar," bay "bar," marsh "bar," "flying bar" and "offshore bar" (the term formerly used for "*barrier*" q.v.). The terms *swash ridge, bay barrier, marsh beach ridge* and *flying spit* may be employed in such cases, while a true *offshore bar* should be kept for any bar lying well offshore.

The above definition does not embrace shallow, bar-like sedimentary structures of large size, the emergent parts of which are not regarded here as bars. Such structures include "distributary-mouth bars," "bar fingers" of the Mississippi River mouth (Fisk, 1961, p. 30, Fig. 2) and "point bars" of the inner side of river meanders which are composed of a crescentic beach plain, a true current bar and a "point" beach. "Barrier bar" is also used by some for a buried barrier or the submerged parts of an existing barrier.

W. Armstrong Price

References

True Bars

Bascom, W., 1964, "Waves and Beaches; The Dynamics of the Ocean Surface," pp. 191–204, Pls. 18, 19, Figs. 60–62, Garden City, N.Y., Anchor Books, Doubleday & Co., 267pp.

Evans, O. F., 1942, "Origin of spits, bars and related structures," *J. Geol.*, **50**, 846–865. (The "low and ball" of Evans and certain British writers are the longshore trough and bar of present usage.)

Guilcher, A., 1958, "Coastal and Submarine Morphology," London, Methuen; New York, John Wiley & Sons, 274pp. (translated by B. W. Sparks and R. H. W. Kneese).

Keulegan, G. H., 1948, "An experimental study of submarine sand bars," *Beach Erosion Board, Chief of Engineers, U.S. Army, Tech. Rept. 3*, 40pp.

McKee, E. D., and Sterrett, T. S., 1961, "Laboratory Experiments on Form and Structure of Longshore Bars and Beaches," in (Peterson, J. A., and Osmond, J. C., editors) "Geometry of Sandstone Bodies," pp. 13–28, American Association of Petroleum Geologists.

Price, W. A., 1951, "Barrier island, not 'offshore bar'," *Science*, **113**, 487–488.

Shepard, F. P., 1950, "Longshore bars and longshore troughs," *Tech. Mem. 15, Beach Erosion Board, Chief of Engineers, U.S. Army*, 31pp.

Shepard, F. P., 1952, "Revised nomenclature for depositional coastal features," *Bull. Am. Assoc. Petrol. Geologists*, **36**, 1902–1912.

Bar-like Ridges and Larger Bar-like Sand Bodies

McManus, D. A., and Creager, J. S., 1963, "Physical and sedimentary environments on a large spitlike shoal," *J. Geol.*, **71**, 498–512.

Newell, N. D., and Rigby, J. K., 1957, "Geological studies on the Great Bahama Bank," in (LeBlanc, R. J., and Breeding, J. G., editors) "Regional aspects of carbonate sand bodies," *Soc. Econ. Paleontologists Mineralogists, Spec. Publ.*, **5**, 15–79 (see pp. 56, 57 and Pls. 10, 11, 13).

Off, T., 1963, "Rhythmic linear sand bodies caused by tidal currents," *Bull. Am. Assoc. Petrol. Geologists*, **47**, 324–341.

Rich, J. L., 1948, "Submarine sedimentary features on Bahama Banks and their bearing on the distribution patterns of lenticular oil sands," *Bull. Am. Assoc. Petrol. Geologists*, **32**, 767–779.

Rusnak, G. A., Bowman, A. L., and Ostlund, H. G., 1964, "Miami natural radiocarbon measurements III," *Radiocarbon*, **6**, 208–214.

Stratigraphic "Bars"

Fisk, H. N., 1961, "Bar-finger sands of Mississippi Delta," in (Peterson, J. A., and Osmond, J. C., editors) "Geometry of Sandstone Bodies," pp. 29–52, American Association of Petroleum Geologists.

Frazier, D. E., and Osanik, A., 1961, "Point-bar deposits. Old River locksite, Louisiana," *Trans. Gulf Coast Assoc. Geol. Soc.*, **11**, 121–137.

Cross-references: *Barriers*; *Beach*; *Cuspate Foreland or Spit*; *Sand Dunes*; *Swash, Swash Mark*; *Tidal Inlet*. Vol. 1: *Subaqueous Sand Dunes*.

BASE LEVEL

The concept of the existence of an effective lower limit to erosional processes and the susceptibility of landmasses to be worn down to sea level were recognised both by Leonardo da Vinci and by James Hutton, the latter writing "The heights of our land are thus levelled with the shores..." (Chorley, Dunn and Beckinsale, 1964, pp. 7 and 40).

The first formal statement and naming of the concept was by J. W. Powell in 1875, who wrote "We may consider the level of the sea to be a grand base level, below which the dry lands cannot be eroded; but we may also have, for local and temporary purposes, other base levels of erosion, which are the levels of the beds of the principal streams which carry away the products of erosion. (I take some liberty in using the term "level" in this connection, as the action of a running stream in wearing its channel ceases, for all practical purposes, before its bed has quite reached the level of the lower end of the stream. What I have called the base level would, in fact, be an imaginary surface, inclining slightly in all its parts toward the lower end of the principal stream draining the area through which the level is supposed to extend, or having the inclination of its parts varied in direction as determined by tributary streams.) Where such a stream crosses a series of rocks in its course, some of which are hard, and others soft, the harder beds form a series of temporary dams, above which the corrasion of the channel through the softer beds is checked, and thus we may have a series of base levels of erosion, below which the rocks on either side of the river, though exceedingly friable, cannot be degraded." (Powell, 1875; Chorley *et al.*, 1964, pp. 529–531).

Much of the subsequent confusion regarding the definition springs from the number of different meanings employed by Powell (Malott, 1928) and other late-nineteenth-century geologists. The different meanings in use in 1902 were analyzed and criticized by W. M. Davis (1902). The chief meanings then were, "an imaginary level surface in extension of that of the ocean (the convex geoid surface); an imaginary mathematical plane; an imaginary surface sloping with the mature or old streams of its area; the lowest slope to which rivers can reduce a land surface; a level not much above that of the sea; ... a condition in which rivers cannot corrade or in which they are balanced between erosion and deposition; a certain stage in the history of rivers when vertical cutting ceases and their slope approximates a parabolic curve; an ultimate planation; and a plain of degradation" (Davis, 1902, pp. 386–387).

Today the main interpretations may be grouped into:

(1) Grand base level: The plane surface forming the extension of sea level under the lands. This usage was supported by Davis (1902) and D. W. Johnson (1929), being termed "ultimate base level" by Malott (1928).

(2) Temporary base level: A limit to downward erosion of an ephemeral character imposed headward of a resistant outcrop. This is sometimes termed a "structural base level," with reference to which "graded" stream reaches or stripped surfaces may develop.

(3) Base-leveled surface: An ultimate or penultimate topographic surface. Much of the terminological confusion is related to this usage, for Powell's "surface, inclined slightly in all its parts..." presents certain features of the peneplain. In addition, by analogy with the stable *terminant* longitudinal profile of Philippson (Chorley *et al.*, 1964, p. 609),

this concept has presented considerable overlap with the idea of *grade*—at least, as the latter term was applied during much of the first half of the twentieth century.

(4) Local base level: This term, which has often been used in the same sense as "temporary base level," has commonly been employed in at least two other contexts. First, Davis (1905) used the term in connection with areas of interior drainage under an arid cycle; second, others used it as implying that "the level of every point on a river may be regarded as a local base-level for the river above that point with all its tributaries" (Cotton, 1948). This second usage, which was foreshadowed by Playfair's Law of Accordant Junctions (Chorley, *et al.*, 1964, pp. 61–63), has presented great difficulty. Besides introducing a confusion with the graded condition, it implies the ability of erosional processes (independent of lithological control) to produce extensive surfaces of low relief without reference to grand base level or, in some instances, to the rivers whose profiles have been developed with reference to grand base level. German workers in the early part of this century based much of their theoretical thinking on this assumption of "leveling without base-leveling," wherein the initiation of local breaks of slope would provide local base level surfaces of low relief. The *piedmont treppen* of W. Penck (1924) were of this character, as were the high-level surfaces in the Peninsular Range of California envisaged by Sauer (1929). Penck's proposals regarding the formation and subsequent erosional exploitation of these breaks of slope, which were in effect local base levels, were severely criticized by Davis (1932).

The concept of a grand base level for the operation of fluvial processes has proved to be a most important ingredient of twentieth-century geomorphological thought, particularly because of the key position which it assumed in the cyclic scheme of W. M. Davis (1909). It was the eustatic theory of Eduard Suess (1888), however, which gave added significance to the concept. His view of earth history as being dominated by synchronous swings of sea level, particularly when reinforced by the glacial eustatic theory, popularized by A. Penck (1894), and by the notion of the widespread production of correlatable erosion surfaces cut with reference to identical base levels, produced what was considered to be a "great unifying generalization" in denudation chronology (Chorley, 1963). This eustatic view of earth history received eminent geological support from T. C. Chamberlin (1909) and later provoked the wide areal generalizations regarding erosional chronology in the writings of Baulig (1928) and Wooldridge and Linton (1939). Yet it is noticeable that W. M. Davis and other American writers such as D. W. Johnson (1931) tended to interpret erosional history in terms of *crustal* instability.

Since the late 1930's the uncomplicated view on

sea-level and base-level changes inherent in the ideas of Suess has become increasingly complicated by increasing knowledge of epeirogenic and isostatic movements, particularly of those connected with the local vertical uplift of orogenic belts. Indeed, in recent years earth scientists have become more and more impressed with the reality of differential local or regional earth movements and more and more sceptical of the occurrence of successive synchronous changes of sea level.

The use of sea level as a grand or ultimate base level itself creates minor problems of definition and exactitude. In the estuaries of powerful streams, erosion by flowing water, fresh and salt, proceeds far below mean sea level (Beckinsale, 1964). Moreover, tidal currents are capable of considerable erosion on the continental shelf. In addition, it is possible that once a land mass has been lowered sufficiently, the ocean might encroach upon it and reduce it to *wave base* or the lower limit of effective wave attack, which is appreciably *below* mean sea level (Dietz, 1963).

Although the concept of base level has been most fruitfully applied to fluvial studies, other types of base level have been suggested. For example, Cvijić (1918) postulated a lower level of cave formation controlled by the lowest level at which water can move laterally after descending from the surface of a karst area. Similarly, the water table has been proposed as exercising the role of a base level for erosion by deflation in arid and semiarid climates.

RICHARD J. CHORLEY
ROBERT P. BECKINSALE

References

Baulig, H., 1928, "Le Plateau Central de la France," Paris, A. Colin, 590 pp.

Beckinsale, R. P., and Richardson, L., 1964, "The Lower Severn Valley," *Geog. J.*, **130**, 87–105 (esp. 103).

Chamberlin, T. C., 1909, "Diastrophism as the ultimate basis of correlation," *J. Geol.*, **17**, 685–693.

Chorley, R. J., 1963, "Diastrophic background to twentieth century geomorphological thought," *Bull. Geol. Soc. Am.*, **74**(8), 953–970.

Chorley, R. J., Dunn, A. J., and Beckinsale, R. P., 1964, "The History of the Study of Landforms," Vol. I, London, Methuen, 678 pp.

Cotton, C. A., 1948, "Landscape," Cambridge, The University Press, 509 pp.

Cvijić, J., 1918. "Hydrographie Souterraine et Évolution Morphologique du Karst," *Rec. Trav. Inst. Geog. Alpine*, **6**, No. 4.

Davis, W. M., 1902, "Base-level, grade, and peneplain," *J. Geol.*, **10**, 77–111.

Davis, W. M., 1905, "The geographical cycle in an arid climate," *J. Geol.*, **13**, 381–401.

Davis, W. M., 1909, "Geographical Essays," New York, Dover reprint, 1954, 777 pp.

Davis, W. M., 1932, "Piedmont benchlands and primärrumpfe," *Bull. Geol. Soc. Am.*, **43**, 399–440.

Dietz, R. S., 1963, "Wave-base, marine profile of equilibrium, and wave-built terraces: A critical appraisal," *Bull. Geol. Soc. Am.*, **74**, 971–990.

Garner, H. F., 1965, "Base level control of erosion surfaces," *Proc. Arkansas Acad. Sci.*, **19**.

Johnson, D. W., 1929, "Baselevel," *J. Geol.*, **37**, 775–782.

Johnson, D. W., 1931, "Stream Sculpture on the Atlantic Slope," New York, Columbia University Press, 142 pp.

Mallott, C. A., 1928, "Base-level and its variations," *Indiana Univ. Studies*, **82**, 37–59.

Penck, A., 1894, "Morphologie der Erdoberfläche," Stuttgart, J. Engelhorn, 2 vols.

Penck, W., 1924, "Die Morphologische Analyse," Stuttgart, J. Engelhorn (also English translation, 1953, "Morphological Analysis of Land Forms," London and New York, St. Martins Press, 429 pp.)

Powell, J. W., 1875, "Exploration of the Colorado River of the West," New York, Dover reprint, 1961.

Sauer, C. O., 1929, "Landforms in the Peninsular Range of California as developed about Warner's Hot Springs," *Univ. Calif. Publ. Geogr.*, **3**, No. 4 (esp. 212–213).

Suess, E., 1888, "Das Antlitz der Erde," Vol. 2, Vienna, Tempsky.

Wooldridge, S. W., and Linton, D. L., 1939, "Structure, surface and drainage in southeast England," *Inst. Brit. Geogr.*, No. 10, 124 pp.

Cross-references: *Degradation*; *Estuary*; *Eustasy*; *Grade*, *Graded Stream*; *Karst*; *Peneplain*; *Planation Surface*; *Slopes*; *Treppen Concept*. Vol. I: *Continental Shelf*; *Mean Sea Level*. Vol. V: *Geoid*; *Isostasy*.

BASIN AND RANGE LANDSCAPE

The Basin and Range physiographic province extends southward from the Columbia Plateaus and is bounded by the Sierra Nevada and Wasatch Ranges, including most of Nevada and parts of Oregon, Idaho, Utah, California, Arizona, and New Mexico (Fenneman, 1931).

Distinctive topographic features of the province are isolated, nearly parallel mountain ranges, commonly trending north, with intervening valleys or basins composed of sediments derived from the mountains. In cross profile the ranges are typically asymmetrical; the steeper slope commonly is fairly straight, but may be somewhat sinuous. Steep slopes may bound both sides of a range, but are generally found on only one side.

Most ranges are bordered by smooth piedmont slopes having low gradients. These slopes typically make a sharp angle with the steeper mountain front and are comprised of two parts, a *pediment* eroded in bedrock adjacent to the range and a *bajada* composed of alluvium toward the basin (Fig. 2). The pediment and bajada usually merge imperceptibly; however, the pediment may be missing in some cases.

Many of the intermontane basins are *bolsons* (having no external drainage) and have *playas*.

The origin of Basin and Range topography involves the structure of the underlying bedrock

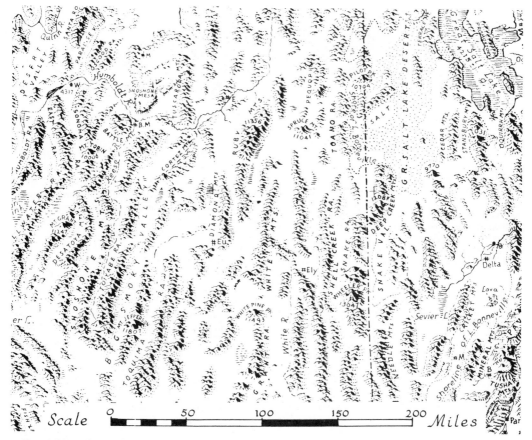

FIG. 1. Map of part of eastern Nevada and western Utah showing linear north-trending ranges (Raisz, 1957).

This problem has been discussed by many geologists including King, Powell, Dutton, Gilbert, Davis and many others (see references in Nolan, 1943).

King (1870) interpreted the ranges as erosional remnants of folds formed by compression. Gilbert (1875) concluded that geomorphic evidence indicated block faulting of the ranges. This view was challenged but was later defended by Davis who presented geomorphic criteria for recognition of range-marginal faults. The origin of Basin and Range topography by Tertiary age fault blocks (taphrogenic "Zwischengebirge") modified by erosion is widely accepted.

Ranges in various stages of erosion are illustrated in Fig. 3 (after Davis, 1925). Section 1 shows a

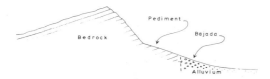

FIG. 2. Suspected relationship of the fault to the mountain front, showing pediment and bajada.

youthful range and section 6 is of an older range with residual hills rising above a pediment.

LEE A. WOODWARD

References

Davis, W. M., 1925, "The Basin Range problem," *Proc. Natl. Acad. Sci.,* **11,** 387–392.

Davis, W. M., 1930, "The Peacock Range, Arizona," *Bull. Geol. Soc. Am.,* **41,** 293–313.

Davis, W. M., 1932, "Basin Range types," *Science,* **76,** 241–245.

*Fenneman, N. M., 1931, "Physiography of Western United States," New York, McGraw-Hill Book Co., 534pp.

Fuller, R. E., and Waters, A. C., 1929, "The nature and origin of the horst and graben structure of southern Oregon," *J. Geol.,* **37,** 204–238.

Gilbert, G. K., 1875, "Report on the geology of portions of Nevada, Utah, California, and Arizona examined in the years 1871 and 1872," *U.S. Geog. and Geol. Surv. W. 100th Mer., Rept.,* **3,** Geology.

Gilbert, G. K., 1928, "Studies of Basin-Range structure," *U.S. Geol. Surv. Profess. Paper* **153**.

Johnson, D. W., 1930, "Geomorphologic aspects of rift

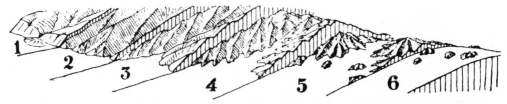

FIG. 3. Evolution from youthful fault scarp to residual hills and general pediment (after Davis, 1925).

valleys," 15th International Geological Congress South Africa 1929, *Compt. Rend.*, **2**, 354–373.

Keyes, C. R., 1924, "Basin range structure in the Great Basin," *Pan-Am. Geol.*, **41**(3), 219–224.

King, C., 1870, *U.S. Geol. Explor. 40th Parallel, Rept.*, **3**, 451–473.

Louderback, G. D., 1926, "Morphologic features of Basin-Range displacements," *Geol. Bull. 16, Univ. of California Publ. Dept.*

*Nolan, T. B., 1943, "The Basin and Range Province in Utah, Nevada, and California," *U.S. Geol. Surv. Profess. Paper* **197-D**, 55pp.

Raisz, E. J., 1957, "Landforms of the United States," 6th ed.

Spurr, J. E., 1901, "Origin and structure of the Basin Ranges," *Bull. Geol. Soc. Am.*, **12**, 217–270.

Thornbury, W. D., 1965, "Regional Geomorphology of the United States," New York, John Wiley & Sons, 609pp.

* Additional bibliographic references may be found in this work.

Cross-references: *Bajada*; *Bolson*; *Fault Scarp*; *Graben*; *Horst*; *Pediment*; *Piedmont Land Forms*; *Playa*. Vol. V: *Zwischengebirge*.

BEACH

A beach is defined as a shore consisting at least partly of unconsolidated material. Most often that material is of sand grade ($2-\frac{1}{16}$ mm), but the sand may be replaced by cobbles or shingle, thus a *boulder beach* or *shingle beach*. Fine-grained argillaceous material provides a mud beach, but the term beach is then generally dropped in favor of "muddy shore."

The *shore* is technically the coastal zone extending from the low tide limit to the maximum *swash line*.

The *coast*, on the other hand, is a loosely defined expression that embraces the shore and adjacent belt of land directly influenced by it. The *coastline* is sometimes taken as the low-water limit and sometimes the high-water limit. Beaches may be just as well formed on lakes or nontidal inland seas, as on ocean coasts (see *Coastal Classification*; *Coastal Geomorphology*; *Coastal Stability*; *Coastlines—Theoretical Shapes*; *Littoral Processes* and in pr Vol. VI: *Coastal Vegetation Types*).

Beach materials tend to be carried up the beach to the limit of *swash* (q.v.), and back with the backwash. Since incoming waves are rarely parallel to shore, in spite of refraction, the locus of sand motion up and down the beach tends to be zigzag, resulting in a net motion *along* the beach (Figs. 1 and 2). This is known as *beach drift*. A second process, *littoral* or *longshore drift*, occurs in the zone of wave turbulence; longshore drift refers also to the water current as well as the sand motion, but the two tend to be taken as one (Fig. 3).

In any incoming wave, the oscillatory motion encounters *effective* friction from the bottom at a depth corresponding to half the wave length. At a depth of about 1.3 times the wave height, the wave breaks; during heavy storms that maximum depth is about 10 m. The wave then begins to break and is converted to one of translation, which travels toward the beach, causing mean sea level to become tilted up in that direction. At the foot of the beach, the wave breaks for a second time, generating a powerful turbulence or gyratory motion at its base. The beach sands (along with gravel, and boulders, if present) are here subjected to vigorous mixing. The finer grains are diffused, moving in part seaward and in part landward. The former forms an offshore bar or is carried laterally by the longshore drift current, while the latter is swept up the beach. There is a tendency therefore for the *grade* of sand

Wind Direction

Direction of Uprush of Oblique Waves

FIG. 1. Diagram to illustrate beach drifting, showing the path along a sloping beach, followed by a pebble under the influence of the uprush and backwash of successive oblique waves during an advancing tide (Holmes, 1965). Actually, the wind direction may vary considerably within any quadrant. (By permission of T. Nelson & Sons, London and Ronald Press Co., N.Y.)

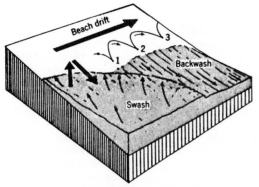

FIG. 2. When waves approach a shore obliquely, the swash and backwash move sand and gravel particles along the beach in a series of arched paths (Strahler, 1960). (By permission of John Wiley & Sons, Inc., N.Y.)

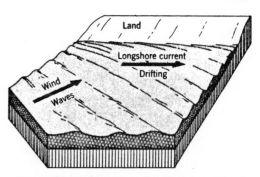

FIG. 3. When waves approach a shore line obliquely, a longshore current is set in motion in the shallow-water zone where waves are breaking (Strahler, 1960). (By permission of John Wiley & Sons, Inc., N.Y.)

to become finer toward the top of the beach forming at any one tide cycle. However, there are day-to-day variations in wave energy, under which coarser materials will be carried higher during storm conditions. As a result, many beaches show multiple lines of material grade sizes, each corresponding to a particular energy peak.

An energy peak of unusual intensity, accompanied by a "meteorologic" high sea-level condition, occurs during a hurricane or storm of exceptional severity; this may lead to the building of a *storm beach* (see also below). Over a longer time span (10–100 years, in some regions an approximation of sunspot cycles of 11–22 years), a small rise and fall of sea level will also lead to the building of successive lines of such beaches, so-called *beach ridges* (q.v.). Change in the general regime, such as a river mouth displacement in a delta system, a man-made disturbance, or a climatic shift in wind patterns may amplify (or reduce) such effects.

Beach Growth

In the long-term sense, the aggradational evolution of a beach is achieved by erosion of headlands,

by feeding from a river mouth bar, or by inward migration from the continental shelf (from old Pleistocene beaches). Here, on the beach itself angular material is reduced to rounded shapes, but boulders are not easily reduced to sand. The bulk of all siliceous beach sands is derived from breakdown of quartz-containing rocks like granite. As quoted by Guilcher (1958, p. 76) after Ferronnière: "The sea is a consumer and not a producer of sand." Once an equilibrium beach is well established on a coast, it protects the hinterland from further erosion. Only the upsetting of that equilibrium will reopen the erosive phase. Such disturbances are mainly due (a) to man, because of disturbance of normal sand movement patterns and (b) to small climatic changes that lead to slight changes in mean sea level or in mean wind directions.

According to old English law (also transferred to the American colonies and other areas), an accretion of land by beach growth that becomes part of the stabilized littoral plain is automatically crown or state land. Land areas lost through coastal erosion are, however, the individual misfortune of the land title-holder. Economically, the state may assume responsibility, if the erosion reaches disaster proportions. Beach erosion is an

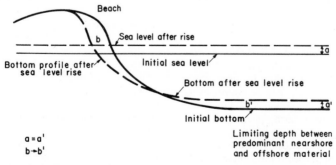

FIG. 4. Beach erosion following a rise in sea level, according to the "Bruun rule."

accepted area of study and action by the U.S. Army Corps of Engineers (see *Beach Erosion*).

The ideal equilibrium profile of a beach is only broadly established and in fact is not long maintained owing to constantly varying sea state and tide height (Fenneman, 1902; Johnson, 1919; Rector, 1954; Watts and Dearduff, 1954; Le Méhauté and Brebner, 1961). Bruun (1962) has developed a theoretical formula to cover the question of beach profiles under either erosion or aggradation. In reality, for any given wave energy situation and sand size range, the profile remains constant. The processes of erosion and aggradation take place under *both* rise and fall of sea level. This has been checked carefully by observations in a wave tank (Schwartz, 1965) as well as by Scuba diving and field measurements. Change of equilibrium is engendered daily by rise and fall of tide, fortnightly by neaps and springs, annually by seasonal oscillation of mean sea level, aperiodically by temporary rise of sea level during storms, and on a long-term basis by eustatic changes of sea level or even by very slow tectonic changes. The causes of equilibrium disturbances are multiple, but the effects on the beach are the same in principle.

The rise of sea level has the effect of raising the ideal equilibrium profile (fixed for any wave energy/ grain size situation). Thus there results erosion of the upper beach and deposition in the foreshore and offshore. The fall of sea level produces erosion in the foreshore and offshore, and aggradation in the upper beach (Fig. 4). Naturally a storm condition changes the equilibrium profile additionally, but does not invalidate what may be called *Bruun's Rule*.

The tidal and longer-term cycles of beach cut and fill are sometimes known as the *Beach Cycle*.

The motion of individual sand grains on beaches may be followed out, by various techniques (see pr Vol. VI, *Tracer Techniques*): fluorescent dyes, synthetic introduction of radioactive materials or, in suitable regions, the case of natural diagnostic minerals or mineral suites (Neiheisel, 1965) or naturally occurring radioactive minerals (Byerly, 1963a and b).

Beach Dimensions

The beach may be narrow and steep, or immensely wide, with every intermediate size. The vertical parameters are controlled by grain size, wave energy and the tidal range or water level, which may vary from a few centimeters in lakes and inland seas (often related to atmospheric pressure, rather than lunar–solar effects) to 15 m or more in places like the Bay of Fundy. Because of this enormous variation in vertical limits, there is also a range of beach width from a few meters to several kilometers.

Major Features of Beach

The beach is normally subdivided into zones, usually subparallel to the coast, which range from the outermost limits at lower low spring tides, to the highest swash limit of the "once-a-century" storm. Because of the daily, fortnightly and annual variations of the *tides* (q.v., Vol. I), and *mean sea level* (q.v., Vol. I), and the incidence of storms of great intensity, but of less predictable periodicity, the net limits of day-to-day wave action on any particular coast are necessarily random, but over extended periods they are largely within the range of the neap tides. Nevertheless, since mean sea level is elevated during storms, because of low atmospheric pressure and mass buildup of water volume due to onshore winds, the zone of most vigorous abrasion is likely to be in the upper half of the tidal range. We have, therefore, the expression "*storm beach*" implying the belt that is activated only at these aperiodic episodes of relatively brief but violent agitation. A certain school of geologists (Douglas Johnson and others) was quite convinced that storm waves cut a specific rock platform at $1\frac{1}{2}$–3 m above low tide level, but C^{14} dating of associated shell beaches have proved these to be either of mid-Holocene (about 5000–3000 B.P.) or pre-Wisconsin age. There seems little doubt however that the base level for maximum erosion of rock-cut platforms is about mean low spring tide (see *Platforms*). The loose sand of a contemporary "storm beach" may certainly cover and uncover such platforms, and further abrasion of the old platform then takes place, so that the certain recognition of ancient and modern features requires very careful study in every instance.

It should be stressed that all major features of the beach are in dynamic equilibrium and thus liable to effacement under severe storm conditions, but with the return of normal condition they will be reestablished once more.

A classification of the littoral belt widely adopted in the United States, including the Corps of Engineers, Shepard (1963) and others, recognizes the following zones (Fig. 7):

(1) *Offshore:* from low tide level to the breaker zone, often featuring longshore bars and troughs;

(2) *Foreshore:* from low tide level to high tide storm swash limit (berm crest);

(3) *Backshore:* from the berm crest to the cliff foot, dune or first vegetated *beach ridge* (q.v.).

Following Guilcher (1958, p. 78), especially for the French equivalents, the major subdivisions of the beach are:

(a) The *Offshore or Sublittoral Zone* (French *Avant-côte*; German *Sublitoral*) which extends from mean lower low spring tide level to about −10 m; it constitutes essentially the "feeding reserve" of the beach since this is the zone of offshore bars, vigorous vertical wave-break turbulence, and longshore drift.

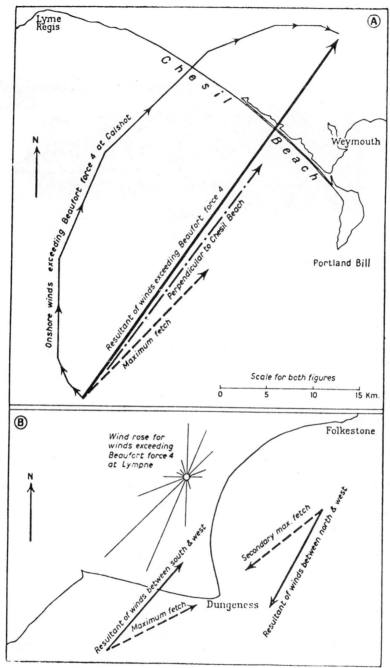

FIG. 5. Relation of wind vectors and fetch to the orientation of beaches: (A) Chesil beach, (B) Dungeness (Southern England) (after Lewis; from Guilcher, 1958). (By permission of John Wiley & Sons, Inc., N.Y.)

(b) The *Foreshore Step* or *Low Tide Terrace* (French, *Basse plage*; German, *nasser Strand*) which is a slope of very low angle, generally less than 1 in 100 extending from the level of about low neap tides to the mean lower low spring tide mark. The outer part may, in regions of large tidal range, be subdivided again into low *ridges and swales* ("incipient bars") connected here and there to the offshore zone by cross channels; at lowest tides and in calm weather, *pools* are often trapped in these swales or

FIG. 6. A cemented beachrock of late Quaternary, at present suffering wave destruction, illustrating maximum range of grain size for beach detrital components (0.1 mm to 2 meters). Example photographed near Cape Naturaliste, Western Australia. (Photo: Rhodes W. Fairbridge.)

runnels. The surface of the foreshore is frequently marked by a variety of *ripple marks* (q.v., pr Vol. VI and below). Many authors, (e.g., Johnson, King) extend the "foreshore" up to the berm, or upper swash limit at any particular period; however, this introduces a sliding scale and merges two normally distinct gradient zones. Guilcher's system is here considered more precise.

(c) The *Upper Beach* (French *cordon littoral*) rises to a height corresponding to the maximum storm or hurricane wave swash limit of recent history (*berm crest*) and includes the beach face, various berms and the backshore. The beach face may terminate in a beach scarp (as shown in Fig. 7), but this is only seen on an eroding beach. The normal profile is shown in Fig. 8, the beach face being usually separated by an abrupt *break in slope* which is a change in gradient from the lower foreshore step or low tide terrace (order of 1:100) to the beach face (order of 1:10). The precise gradient of the latter varies considerably from beach to beach, dependent on such parameters as grain size, wind and swell incidence, and wave energy. The upper beach is usually marked by one or more broad steps or *berms* (French, *gradins de plage*) separated by abrupt

FIG. 7. The principal subdivisions of beaches and of the adjacent shallow water area (Shepard, 1963). (By permission of Harper & Row, N.Y.)

beach scarps, which represent the limits of recent wave (storm) building.

In the case of coarse cobble or shingle beaches, there may be five or six of these ridges which are particularly stable; in the Chesil Beach of Dorset in southern England, owing to considerable wave fetch and maximum exposure to severe storms, the crest of the shingle banks reaches 13 m, although tidal range is only about 3 m (Fig. 3). This case nicely exemplifies the "*Lewis Law*" (beaches tend to orient themselves perpendicular to the dominant waves). Schou (1945) by constructing wind *hodographs* (q.v., Vol. I) obtained a vectoral resultant that demonstrates that the controlling direction is obtainable from winds exceeding 4 on the Beaufort scale (18 mph, 8 m/sec). The calculation is made by multiplying the frequency, or sum of the periods of duration, by the Beaufort number or velocity, adding them vectorially (as indicated on Fig. 5), and joining the first and last points. Williams concluded that it was better still to add the cube of the velocities multiplied by the frequency.

Studying the upper beach slope, Bascom (1951) selected a reference point at mid-tide and found that on the Pacific coast of the United States, a rather constant relationship of slope to grain size existed; e.g., a fairly fine sand of 0.17-mm median diameter gave a beach of 1 : 40 slope, while a coarse sand of 0.65-mm mean size gave a 1 : 8 beach slope. Eroding beaches flatten, while building beaches steepen. Thus protected beaches are steeper for any given sand size than exposed beaches.

Minor Features of Beach

Many of the structural features of the beach are

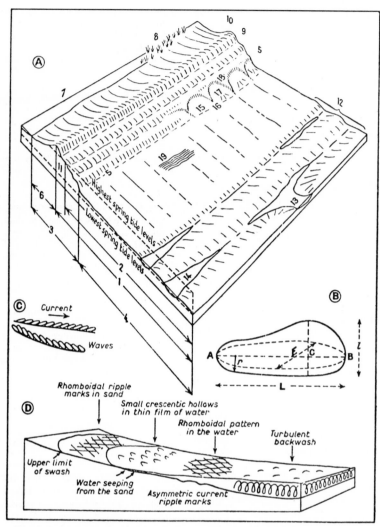

FIG. 8. Beach terminology (from Guilcher, 1958). A: (1) Beach, (2) shore, (3) upper beach (cordon littoral), (4) foreshore, (5) break of slope between upper beach and foreshore, (6) inner side of beach ridge, (7) lagoon, (8) marsh, (9) berms, (10) storm beach, (11) coastline, (12) ridges and runnels on the foreshore, (13) channel on foreshore, (14) pool in runnel on foreshore, (15) beach cusp, (16) apex of cusp, (17) bay of cusp, (18) horn of cusp, (19) ripple marks. B: Dimensions of a pebble: L = length; l = width; E = thickness; r = least radius of curvature in the principal plane (after Cailleux, Berthois and Tricart). C: Ways in which pebbles may overlap under the influence of waves and currents (after Twenhofel). D: Formation of rhomboidal ripple marks (after Demarest). (By permission of John Wiley & Sons, Inc., N.Y.)

found in fossil form (Thompson, 1937) and since they are strictly oriented with respect to the center of the earth ("geopetality") and to the original beach orientation and wave characteristics, they are exceptionally useful for paleogeographic reconstructions (see pr Vol. VI. *Ripple Marks*; *Sedimentary Structures—Primary*; *Cross-bedding*, etc.). Recently cemented beaches (Fig. 6) also contain many of these structures (see *Beach Rock*).

The minor features (see Fig. 7), commonly observed on modern beaches include:

(a) *Ripple Marks*. Of the several varieties, *oscillatory* (symmetric) ripples, are rare, being characteristic of standing water. Most common are *translational* ripples (asymmetric), which develop normal to the current direction, and *rhomboid* ripple marks (interference type).

(b) *Low and Ball*. These are mega-ripples or incipient bars, commonly built over wide foreshores, with large tidal ranges. They migrate slowly as a rule (see *Bars*).

(c) *Beach Cusps* (French, *Croissants de Plage*): Developing parallel to wave motion, these evolve as a series of U-shaped undulations along the upper beach, with intermediate "horns" directed seaward. They range in height from a few centimeters to several meters. Guilcher reported that the wavelength also varies, 5 to 77 m (see also Jefferson, 1899; Russell and McIntire, 1965).

Mineral deposits concentrated in beaches by wave action are known as "heavy sands," "beach ores" and "beach placers" (see *Placers*, Vol. IV).

RHODES W. FAIRBRIDGE

References

Bascom, W. N., 1951, "The relationship between sand size and beach-face slope," *Trans. Am. Geophys. Union*, **32**, 866–874.

Bascom, W., 1964, "Waves and Beaches," New York, Anchor Books, Doubleday & Co., 267pp.

Bruun, P., 1962, "Sea level rise as a cause of shore erosion," *J. Waterways Harbors Div., Am. Soc. Civil Engrs*, **88**, 117–130.

Byerly, J. R., 1963a, "Naturally occurring radioactive minerals as littoral tracers," *Shore and Beach*, **31**, No. 1.

Byerly, J. R., 1963b, "The relationship between watershed geology and beach radioactivity," *Beach Erosion Board Tech. Memo. 135*.

Fenneman, N. M., 1902, "Development of the profile of equilibrium of the subaqueous shore terrace," *J. Geol.*, **10**, 1–32.

Guilcher, A., 1958, "Coastal and Submarine Morphology," London, Methuen & Co., Ltd., 274pp.

Holmes, A., 1965, "Principles of Physical Geology," Second edition, New York, Ronald Press Co., 1288 pp.

Jefferson, M. S. W., 1899, "Beach cusps," *J. Geol.*, **7**, 237–246.

Johnson, D. W., 1919, "Shore Processes and Shoreline Development," New York, John Wiley & Sons, 583pp.

King, C. A. M., 1959, "Beaches and Coasts," London, E. Arnold Ltd., 402pp.

Le Méhauté, B., and Brebner, A., 1961, "An introduction to coastal morphology and littoral processes." Kingston, Ontario, Queen's Univ., *Civil Eng. Research Rept.* No. 14, 46pp.

Lewis, W. V., 1931, "The effect of wave incidence on the configuration of a shingle beach," *Geograph. J.*, **78**, 129–148.

Lewis, W. V., 1938, "The evolution of shoreline curves," *Proc. Geol. Assoc.*, **49**, 107–127.

Neiheisel, J., 1965, "Source and distribution of sediments at Brunswick Harbor and vicinity, Georgia," *Coastal Engineering Res. Cent., Tech Memo.* 12, 49pp.

Rector, R. L., 1954, "Laboratory study of equilibrium profiles of beaches," *Beach Erosion Board Tech. Memo*, No. 41, 38pp.

Russell, R. J., and McIntire, W. G., 1965, "Beach cusps," *Bull. Geol. Soc. Am.*, **76**, 307–320.

Schou, A., 1945, "Det Marine forland," *Folia Geogr. Danica*, **4**, 1–236.

Schwartz, M., 1965, "Laboratory study of sea-level rise as a cause of shore erosion," *J. Geol.*, **73**, No. 3, 528–534.

Shepard, F. P., 1963, "Submarine Geology" Second edition, New York, Harper & Row, 557 pp.

Smith, E. R., 1945, "Sand," *Proc. Ind. Acad. Sci.*, **55**, 121–143.

Strahler, A. N., 1960, "Physical Geography," Second edition, New York, John Wiley & Sons, Inc., 534 pp.

Thompson, W. O., 1937, "Original structures of beaches, bars, and dunes," *Bull. Geol. Soc. Am.*, **48**, 723–751.

Watts, G. M., 1954, "Laboratory study of effect of varying wave periods on beach profiles," *Beach Erosion Board Tech. Memo.*, No. 53, 19pp.

Watts, G. M., and Dearduff, R. F., 1954, "Laboratory study of effect of tidal action on wave-formed beach profiles," *Beach Erosion Board Tech. Memo.*, No. 52, 21pp.

Cross-references: *Bars*; *Beach Erosion*; *Beach Ridge*; *Beachrock*; *Coastal Classification*; *Coastal Geomorphology*; *Coastal Stability*; *Coastlines—Theoretical Shapes*; *Littoral Processes*; *Platforms*; *Swash, Swash Mark*. Vol. I: *Hodograph*; *Mean Sea Level*; *Tides*; *Waves*. Vol. II: *Wind*. Vol. IV: *Placer Deposits*. pr Vol. VI: *Coastal Vegetation*; *Cross-bedding*; *Ripple Marks*; *Sedimentary Structures*; *Tracer Techniques in Sediment Transport*.

BEACH EROSION AND COASTAL PROTECTION

Beach erosion starts when more material is eroded from a beach than is deposited. An eroding beach has an appearance of devastation and often presents a tragic aftermath of destroyed groins and seawalls. In many areas of the United States shores suffer from erosion by waves and currents, e.g., the New England shores, particularly parts of Cape Cod and Long Island, New Jersey, the North and South Carolina shores, and many shores in the southern part of Florida on the Atlantic, as well as on the Gulf. Shoreline recessions may range from a few feet up to 30 ft/yr in certain areas. The Outer Banks of North Carolina have, at some places, eroded so severely that natural dunes do not have time to build up as replacement for dunes washed away, and breakthroughs of the barriers occur as a result of every major storm or hurricane as e.g., in 1962 and 1963.

Beach erosion is classified as "natural" or as "man-made" (Bruun, 1962, 1963). Natural erosion is usually a relatively slow geological process by which equilibrium conditions between acting forces of waves and currents and land masses are sought. In the long-range time scale, the slightly rising sea level undoubtedly shares a considerable responsibility for this development. According to Fairbridge (1961), since the Roman Era, 1500–2000 years ago, the general rise in sea level has been approximately 2 meters (7 feet) or an average of 1.2 mm/yr. The mean annual rise from 1900–50 was still 1.2 mm, but the entire eastern seaboard of North America shows an irregularly high apparent rise of sea level. The decade showing the most rapid rise was 1946–56, with 5.5 mm/yr as recorded on the Florida East Coast. The rise varies from year to year depending upon meteorological conditions, winds and barometric pressures. The responsibility for the rise may lie in glacial changes and finally in variation in solar energy submitted to the earth (Fairbridge, 1961). An appreciable component in the extra rapid rise on the East Coast is possibly due to deceleration of the Gulf Stream, which, because of the earth's rotation, will raise the water level on the left side (United States East Coast) and lower it on the right side (The Bahamas). As explained by Bruun (1962), the rise in sea level may be responsible for shoreline recessions of 1–3 ft/yr on the Florida East Coast, the actual magnitude depending upon the configuration and steepness of the offshore bottom profile.

Man-made erosion is caused by man's interference with natural shoreline processes. Sand is drifting along the shore because of the action by waves and currents. The direction of this so-called littoral drift depends upon the variation in wave and longshore current activity (Bruun, 1963). But, there will almost always be one predominant direction of drift as, e.g., on the shores of the Carolinas, Georgia, and East Florida, where the predominant drift, because of the strong northeast winds, goes towards the South (Bruun, Morgan and Purpura, 1962). If the littoral drift current meets an obstacle, e.g., a jetty, a groin (short jetty), or a dredged channel for an inlet (Fig. 1), sand will accumulate on the updrift side of the obstacle, and erosion will start on the downdrift side (Bruun and Manohar, 1963).

It is not a matter of coincidence that most beach erosion in Florida occurs where the most concentrated development along the shores has taken place. Man's interference with natural shore processes is the major cause of the increased erosion in some of the highly populated areas on the lower

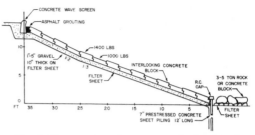

FIG. 2. Cross section of revetment at Jupiter Island.

East Coast and lower Gulf Coast of Florida (Bruun, Morgan and Purpura, 1962). Groins have caused severe leeside erosion problems in many areas along the Florida shores, and have, unfortunately, often done considerably more harm than good, although this conclusion shall not be generalized. In numerous cases, seawalls have protected valuable property or dune faces, but when built as vertical bulkheads, they have, in fully as many cases, caused a lowering and increased erosion of the beach itself, giving rise to heavy water turbulence by waves colliding with the wall at high tides.

Modern adequate coastal protection, as explained by Bruun and Manohar (1963) includes structural as well as replenishment measures. Groins may be used in certain cases to hold an artificial (replenishment) fill, but inasmuch as they include the unfortunate leeside erosion effect, they should only be used with great care. Seawalls should, generally speaking, be of the energy-absorbing type whether in the form of a rubble mound or as an energy-absorbing revetment of interlocking concrete blocks resting on filter layers. Figure 2 shows cross section of such modern revetment built at Jupiter Island, Florida (Bruun and Manohar, 1963).

The artificial nourishment of beaches or replenishment of eroded material is now generally recognized as being the "atomic weapon" against beach erosion (Beach Erosion Board, 1952, 1961, Bruun and Manohar, 1963). Artificial nourishment includes dredging of material in bays and waterways, e.g., navigation inlets and spilling of this material on eroding beaches. It also includes bypassing of sand from one side of an inlet to the other, thereby reestablishing natural shore processes. Numerous nourishment projects have been undertaken, using bay or lagoon sources for suitable beach material, and several bypassing sand plants have been built, e.g., at Virginia Beach, Virginia, Palm Beach, and Boynton Beach, Florida. The difficulty involved in this new method is the lack of proper and ample sources of material suitable for nourishment. The offshore sea bottom seems to be the future source, and the offshore dredge, which is able to stay in the open sea and pump material to shore, is now being developed and practical tests are starting. A fully developed artificial replenish-

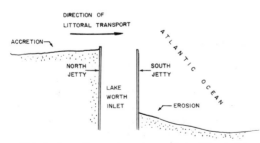

FIG. 1. Accretion and erosion at Lake Worth Inlet, Florida.

ment technique may change future coastal protection radically.

With respect to emergency actions on acute cases of erosion, the reader is referred to Bruun and Purpura (1963).

PER BRUUN

References

Beach Erosion Board, Corps of Engineers, 1952, "Artificially nourished and constructed beaches," *Technical Memorandum No. 29.*

Beach Erosion Board, Corps of Engineers, 1961, *Technical Report No. 4.*

Bruun, P., 1962, "Sea-level rise as cause of shore erosion," *Proc. Am. Soc. Civil Engrs., J. Waterways Harbors Div.,* **WW1.**

Bruun, P., 1963, "Longshore currents and longshore troughs," *J. Geophys. Res.,* **68,** No. 4.

Bruun, P., and Manohar, M., 1963, "Coastal protection." *Florida Eng. Ind. Expt. Sta.*

Bruun, P., Morgan, W. H., and Purpura, J. A., 1962, "Review of beach erosion and storm tide conditions in Florida 1961–1962," *Florida Eng. Ind. Expt. Sta.*

Bruun, P., and Purpura, J. A., 1963, "Emergency actions against beach erosion," *Florida Eng. Ind. Expt. Sta.*

Fairbridge, R. W., 1961, "Eustatic Changes in Sea Level," in "Physics and Chemistry of the Earth," Vol. 4, New York, Pergamon Press.

Cross-references: *Littoral Processes; Sand Dunes.* Vol. I: *Gulf Stream; Tides.* Vol. II: *Earth's Rotation; Solar Energy; Tropical Cyclones; Wind—Principles.*

BEACH RIDGES

These are subparallel ridges of sand, shell or pebble, varying in amplitude from a few inches to many feet and varying also in the distance between them. The depressions between them are known as *swales.* The number of ridges may vary from two or three to over a hundred. They are located behind the present shore and are to be distinguished from the ridge and runnel features occurring between tidemarks. Where, as in deltaic environments, the ridges are perched on a muddy substratum they are called "*cheniers,*" so-named from belts of oak trees (in Louisiana French) that mark their distribution in the Mississippi delta region.

Each ridge marks the position of a pre-existing shore line. They are common constituents of prograding constructional shore features such as barrier beaches and cuspate forelands, and by extrapolation from old ridges, the history of the development of such features can sometimes be deduced. Radiocarbon dating may be obtained from pockets of beach shells or vegetation from the swales. While most ridges are probably postglacial in age, others originated in the Pleistocene.

Beach ridges are built where the beach face angle appropriate to the beach material and most signi-

ficant wave type is steeper than the overall shore profile (Savage, 1959). Since beach faces are steeper with coarser material and lower waves, ridge building will be favored by either of these conditions. According to Johnson (1919), multiple ridges arise through continued shallowing of the offshore profile, usually because of abundant sediment supply. Shallowing of the offshore profile may also arise from a fall in sea level, and radiocarbon dating has suggested the association of some ridge systems with certain small negative oscillations of sea level during the last 5000 years (Fairbridge, 1961; Schofield, 1961).

Sand beach ridges may contain a proportion of wind-blown material, but this is scarce where successive ridges have been built rapidly or in hot, wet regions where dune building is inhibited. Vegetation may be important in the accretion of the wind-blown component, and it normally acts as a subsequent protection. Because sand beach ridge complexes comprise a large number of fossil beaches, they sometimes contain important concentrations of economically valuable heavy minerals.

See Fig. 1, p. 71.

J. L. DAVIES

References

Davies, J. L., 1957, "The importance of cut and fill in the development of sand beach ridges," *Australian J. Sci.,* **20,** 105–111.

Doeglas, D. J., 1955, "Origin and destruction of beach ridges," *Leidse Geol. Mededel.,* **20,** 34–47.

Fairbridge, R. W., 1961, "Eustatic Changes in Sea Level," in "Physics and Chemistry of the Earth," Vol. 4, pp. 99–185, New York, Pergamon Press.

Guilcher, A., 1954, "Coastal and Submarine Morphology," London, Methuen (translated by B. W. Sparks and R. H. W. Kneese).

Johnson, D. W., 1919, "Shore Processes and Shoreline Development," Ch. 9, New York, John Wiley & Sons.

Savage, R. P., 1959, "Notes on the formation of beach ridges," *Beach Erosion Board Bull.,* No. 13, 31–35.

Schofield, J. C., 1961, "Sea level fluctuations during the last 4000 years as recorded by a chenier plain, Firth of Thames, New Zealand," *New Zealand J. Geol. Geophys.,* **3,** 461–485.

Cross-references: *Barriers; Cuspate Foreland or Spit; Delta; Prograding Shoreline; Quaternary.* Vol. I: *Mean Sea Level Changes.*

BEACHROCK

Beachrock is beach sand consolidated in place by interstitial cement, chiefly calcium carbonate. Although recently-cemented beach sands have been reported from relatively cool coasts such as the North Atlantic (van Straaten, 1957; Russell, 1962, p. 2), typical beachrock seems to be developed best along tropical and subtropical coasts. It was described, in the Indian Ocean, as early as 1835

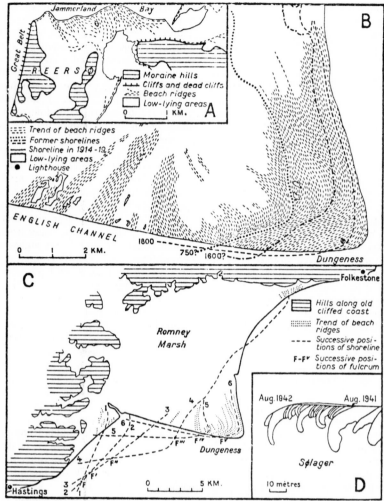

FIG. 1. Coastal features formed by series of beach ridges (from Guilcher, 1954). (A) General features of Reersjo, Zeeland, Denmark (after Schou, 1945). (B and C) The evolution of Dungeness (after Lewis and Balchin, 1932 and 1940). (D) Spit with recurved laterals at Sjolager, Zeeland, Denmark (after Schou, 1945). (By permission of Methuen & Co. Ltd., London, England.)

(Moresby, 1835, p. 400), and since then it has been widely studied, notably in Samoa (Daly, 1924), in Ceylon (Gardiner, 1930), in India (Sewell, 1932), in Indonesia (Kuenen, 1933), in Australia (Fairbridge, 1948, 1950), in Brazil (Branner, 1904), in Florida (Ginsburg, 1953), in the Caribbean and Mediterranean (Russell, 1959, 1962), in the Pacific and eastern Mediterranean (Emery and others, 1956, 1960, 1962, 1963), in Greece (Mistardis, 1956, 1963), in Crete (Boekschoten, 1962, 1963), and in British Honduras (Stoddart and Cann, 1965). Despite so much attention to the subject, however, there is still little agreement about most aspects of it.

No one has yet discovered any undisputable fossil beachrock, but Mistardis (1963, p. 10) has shown that some used in ancient tombs near Athens is older than 3500 years B.P. (before present). On the other hand, Russell (1959, p. 230) and others have shown that some beachrock elsewhere has been cemented since World War II. Many writers have reported fragments of older beachrock incorporated into younger cemented beds. Presumably, then, beachrock has long been forming and is still being formed in some parts of the world, so that theoretically it should be possible to study the actual process and conditions of cementation at such places. Most studies that have been made, however, have been based on already cemented, old beachrock, and these have yielded contradictory results as to its characteristics and origin.

It is difficult to tell exactly where beachrock may be forming, for it is not exposed to view until some time after it has been cemented. Most authors agree that the cementation takes place underground, probably in or near the top of the water-saturated zone of the beach. Hence, beachrock is not visible except where the shore has receded since cementation and the overlying unconsolidated sand has been washed away. Where the shore has retreated only slightly, beachrock generally appears as a flat platform several meters to tens of meters wide fronting the shore and extending along it for tens to hundreds of meters. Where the shore has retreated greatly, beachrock may be left behind as an offshore reef-like ridge; if coral reefs are also present, offshore beachrock ridges, encrusted with algae and other marine life, can easily be (and have often been) mistaken for coral reefs (Branner, 1904). In such areas, the beach sand may be derived almost wholly from calcareous organic remains, and the resulting beachrock is a calcarenite, or cemented clastic limestone. This has led some writers to the assumption that all beachrock is calcareous, but Boekschoten (1962, pp. 3–4) and others have reported beachrock containing relatively little clastic carbonate. Most recent writers agree that beachrock generally has approximately the same composition as nearby or overlying beach sand (Emery and Neev, 1960, p. 3).

In most examples the sand is stratified, with beds dipping gently (less than 15°) seaward; in some instances shoreward dips (Kuenen, 1933, p. 87) and cross-stratification (Boekschoten, 1962, p. 3) have been reported. In some places the sand is pebbly or even cobbly. Generally, differential erosion has etched out the less well cemented beds so that the exposed surface forms a series of asymmetric ridges, or low cuestas in miniature. Some surfaces are very irregular, with pits, basins, channels, and other solutional and abrasional features. Exposed masses may also be broken into blocks, some of which, undermined by the waves, may be steeply tilted or even thrown up onto the beach (Russell, 1959, p. 229).

In what appears to be recently exposed beachrock, the upper surface of the cemented zone appears to be relatively flat, cross-cutting the stratification of the sand at about the level of the water table in the nearby beach (Russell, 1962). The lower surface of the cemented zone has also been reported to be abrupt and flat (Kuenen, 1933, p. 87). Thickness of the zone varies from less than half a meter to nearly three meters (Vaughan, 1914, p. 63). Russell has attributed such variation to differences in tidal ranges (1959, p. 229). Commonly, exposed beachrock surfaces lie close to mean tide level, but some lie several meters above or below it (Vaughan, 1914, p. 63; Mistardis, 1956, p. 146; Russell, 1962, p. 10), presumably indicating

that relative sea level has changed there since the sand was cemented.

Beachrock may be closely associated with cemented dune sand ("eolianite") and a variety of cemented swamp and alluvial deposits, and in some cases it is difficult to distinguish among them. Some writers believe that cementation of all of them results from the same process; others believe they each form in distinct and different ways. This disagreement simply shows that the cementation process—at least of beachrock—is not yet clearly understood.

Most writers agree in suggesting that the cement is precipitated as a result of concentration by one or more factors: evaporation, the effect of temperature rise in the beach, organic activity, and decrease in hydrostatic pressure, but they do not all agree on the source of the water from which the cement is derived. Some have suggested that it is derived from relatively fresh groundwater (Kuenen, 1933, pp. 87–88; Russell, 1962, pp. 6–7); others that it is derived from seawater (Daly, 1924, pp. 139–140; Ginsburg, 1953, pp. 88–91; Emery, 1962, p. 62), and still others, that it is precipitated as a result of the mixing of groundwater and seawater (Gardiner, 1930, p. 16; Boekschoten, 1963, p. 244).

Some of this disagreement stems from dispute about the mineral composition of the cement. It has been identified as calcite by X-ray techniques (Russell, 1962, p. 7) and by staining (Boekschoten, 1962, p. 5), and as aragonite by staining and by petrographic examination (Ginsburg, 1953, p. 88; Rusnak, 1960, p. 167; Stoddart and Cann, 1965). It is widely held, as a result of phase studies by Cloud (1962) and others, that calcium carbonate is precipitated in the form of aragonite rather than calcite in solutions as saline as seawater. Hence the presence of calcite as the cement in beachrock suggests to some authors that it was formed in fresh to moderately brackish water. However, aragonite is metastable and may recrystallize to calcite if removed from its briny environment; significantly, Rusnak (1960, p. 167) found only aragonite cement in fresh beachrock of Texas, but found calcite cement in some older beachrock that had been subjected to subaerial alteration. Stoddart and Cann (1965) speak of "two-stage" beachrock, the calcite belonging to a diagenetic phase. Some other geochemists believe that degree of supersaturation rather than salinity determines whether calcite or aragonite will be precipitated; in this case, beachrock origin cannot be deduced from the nature of the cement.

It is, of course, possible that beachrock has been formed in different ways in different environments and that the arguments about its origin stem largely from overgeneralizations based on particular cases. However, so long as the debate centers on the nature of the cement, which is difficult to identify and apparently subject to relatively rapid metastable phase changes, the origin of beachrock will remain a debatable issue.

C. G. HIGGINS

References

Boekschoten, G. J., 1962, "Beachrock at Limani Chersonisos, Crete," *Geol. Mijnbouw*, **31**, 3–5.

Boekschoten, G. J., 1963, "Some geological observations on the coasts of Crete," *Geol. Mijnbouw*, **42**, 241–247.

Branner, J. C., 1904, "The stone reefs of Brazil," *Harvard Coll. Mus. Comp. Zoöl., Bull.* **44**, 285pp.

Cloud, P. E., Jr. 1962, "Behaviour of calcium carbonate in sea water," *Geochim. Cosmochim. Acta*, **26**, 867–884.

Daly, R. A., 1924, "The geology of American Samoa," *Carnegie Inst. Pub.*, **340**, 95–143.

Emery, K. O., 1962, "Marine geology of Guam," *U.S. Geol. Surv. Profess. Paper* **403-B**, 76pp.

Emery, K. O., and Cox, D. C., 1956, "Beachrock in the Hawaiian Islands," *Pacific Sci.* **11**, 382–402.

Emery, K. O., and George, C. J., 1963, "The shores of Lebanon," *Am. Univ. of Beirut, Misc. Pap. in Nat. Sci.*, No. 1, 10pp.

Emery, K. O., and Neev, D., 1960, "Mediterranean beaches of Israel," *Israel Geol. Surv., Bull.* No. 26, 1–23.

Fairbridge, R. W., 1950, "Recent and Pleistocene coral reefs of Australia," *J. Geol.*, **58**, 330–402.

Fairbridge, R. W., and Teichert, C., 1948, "The Low Isles of the Great Barrier Reef; a new analysis," *Geog. J.*, **111**, 67–88.

Gardiner, J. S., 1930, "Studies in coral reefs," *Harvard Coll. Mus. Comp. Zoöl., Bull.* **71**, 3–16.

Ginsburg, R. N. 1953, "Beachrock in South Florida," *J. Sediment Petrol.*, **23**, 85–92.

Kuenen, Ph. H., 1933, "Geology of Coral Reefs," in "The Snellius-expedition in the Eastern Part of the Netherlands East-Indies, 1929–1930," Vol. 5, Part 2, Leiden, E. J. Brill, 126pp.

Mistardis, G. C., 1956, "Les plages cimentées d'anciennes lignes de rivage," *Quaternaria*, **3**, 145–150.

Mistardis, G. G., 1963, "On the beach rock of southeastern Greece," *Geol. Soc. Greece, Bull.* **5**, 1–19. [Greek, with English Summary, pp. 15–19].

Moresby, [Capt. R. M.], 1835, "Extracts from . . . Report on the Northern Atolls of the Maldivas [sic]," *J. Roy. Geog. Soc. London*, **5**, 398–404.

Rusnak, G. A., 1960, "Sediments of Laguna Madre, Texas," pp. 153–196 in "Recent Sediments, Northwest Gulf of Mexico, 1951–1958," Tulsa, Am. Assoc. Petrol. Geologists.

Russell, R. J., 1959, "Caribbean beach rock observations," *Z. Geomorph., N. F.*, **3**, 227–236.

Russell, R. J., 1962, "Origin of beach rock," *Z. Geomorph., N. F.*, **6**, 1–16.

Sewell, R. B. S., 1932, "The coral coasts of India," *Geog. J.*, **79**, 449–465.

Stoddart, D. R., and Cann, J. R., 1965, "Nature and origin of beach rock," *J. Sediment. Petrol.*, **25**, 243–247.

van Straaten, L. M. J. U., 1957, "Recent sandstones on the coasts of the Netherlands and of the Rhone delta," *Geol. Mijnbouw, N. S.*, **19**, 196–213.

Vaughan, T. W., 1914, "The building of the Marquesas and Tortugas Atolls," *Carnegie Inst. Publ.*, **182**, 55–67.

Cross-references: *Coral Reefs*; *Organisms as Geomorphic Agents*; *Sand Dunes*; *Solution Pits and Pans*. Vol. I: *Sea Water Salinity*. Vol. II: *Evaporation*. Vol. IV: *Aragonite*; *Calcite*; *Calcium Carbonate*. pr Vol. VI: *Diagenesis*; *Groundwater*.

BED FORMS IN ALLUVIAL CHANNELS—*See* pr Vol. VI

BED LOAD

Water flowing in natural waterways is capable of transporting alluvial materials. The mass rate of discharge of solid materials, usually referred to as sediment, transported by the water current is called *total load*. Total load, for convenience, is usually artificially subdivided into categories which are commonly defined as follows (Einstein, 1950):

Washload refers to the very small sediment particles transported by the flow which are not found in significant quantities in the stream bed.

Bed material load refers to the discharge of sediment particles transported by the flow which are found in significant quantities in the stream bed.

Suspended load refers to the discharge of sediment particles which are suspended in the flow current turbulence.

Bed load refers to the discharge of sediment particles which are too heavy to be suspended by the turbulent action of the flow. These particles move by rolling, sliding and skipping ("saltation") along the stream bed.

The definition of bed load appears to be short, clear and precise. However, practically insurmountable problems arise when an accurate measure of bed load is attempted.

First, the elevation above any particular point on the channel bed at which bed load becomes suspended load is difficult to define for bed load measuring purposes. This is complicated by the fact that the gradient of the sediment load can be quite large in this region. Consequently, small errors committed in estimating the separation level between the bed load and the suspended load can have large effects on the measured bed load rate.

Bed load measuring devices are called bed load samplers (Hubbell, 1964). Although some bed load samplers are better designed than others, they all create disturbances in the flow pattern of the stream in their proximity, which in turn modifies the sediment inflow rate to the sampler.

In addition to these difficulties, one must realize that the bed load transport rate at any particular location on the stream bed is highly time dependent. An alluvial bed surface has an ever-shifting geometrical pattern. Our present lack of concrete knowledge about bed load makes an open question of how long a bed load sample (assuming that it can be accurately taken) should be collected (even for the simple case of steady flow) so that the average measured bed load is within a certain percentage of the true average bed load at a given confidence level.

When flow depths are relatively large with respect to the average flow velocity, "dunes" (megaripples: see *Bed Forms in Alluvial Channels*, pr Vol. VI) are generally formed on the channel bed. These dunes propagate downstream. It is observed that the bed material located on the back or upstream face of a given dune rolls and slides over the dune in the direction of flow. Arriving at the dune crest, the major portion of the bed load rolls down the dune front, causing the dune front to advance. Thus a good approximation of bed load could be obtained from considering dune geometry and propagation rates.

As flow velocities increase with respect to the depth, the dunes are washed out. At present, there is no good way to determine bed load when dunes are not present on the stream bed.

The notion of bed load, so simple and intuitive at first sight, leads to unexpected experimental complications which are very difficult to cope with. The amount of experimental work remaining to be done in this field is considerable. Indeed the whole science of flow in alluvial channels is still in its infancy.

RICHARD A. STEIN

References

Colby, B. R., 1964, "Discharge of sands and mean-velocity relationships in sand-bed streams," *U.S. Geol. Surv. Profess. Paper* **462-A**, 47 pp.

Einstein, H. A., 1950, "The bed-load function for sediment transportation in open-channel flows," *U.S. Dept. Agr. Tech. Bull.* **1026**.

Hubbell, D. W., and Sayre, W. W., 1964, "Sand transport studies with radioactive tracers," *Proc. Am. Soc. Civ. Engrs.*, **90**, 39–68.

Ismail, H. M., 1952, "Turbulent transfer mechanism and suspended sediment in closed channels," *Trans. Am. Soc. Civil. Engrs.*, **117**, 409–446.

Meyer-Peter, E., and Muller, R., 1948, "Formulas for bed load transport," *Proc. Intern. Assoc. for Hyd. Research*, **2**, 39–65.

Shulits, S., 1935, "The Schoklitsch bed-load formula," *Engineering* (*London*), 644–687.

Stein, R. A., 1965, "Laboratory studies of total load and apparent bed load," *J. Geophys. Res.*, **70**, 1831–1842.

Cross-references: *Rivers*; *Sand Dunes*; *Sediment Transport*; *Stream Flow*; *Wind Action*. pr Vol. VI: *Bed Forms in Alluvial Channels*; *Fluvial Sediment Transport*.

BEHEADING—*See* STREAM CAPTURE

BERGSCHRUND

The Bergschrund (German, for mountain, plus cleft; *rimaye*, in French) or "Schrund Line" (of Gilbert, 1904) is a term used in geomorphology and glaciology for the crevasse which develops at the head of mountain or corrie glaciers immediately

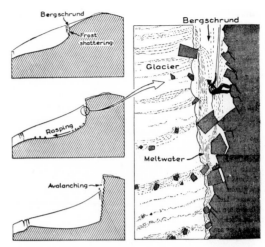

FIG. 1. Progressive stages of erosion at the head of a valley glacier, and detail of the Bergschrund (after W. V. Lewis, 1938; modified by Gilluly *et al.*, 1968, p. 260). (By permission of W. A. Freeman, San Francisco.)

adjacent to the rock wall of the mountain itself. As the glacier ice gradually moves down and away from the wall, a massive plucking or sapping operation takes place, whereby the rock of the mountain is progressively torn away from the mountain wall and eventually transported by ice movement or meltwater to the moraine area. Lewis (1938, 1954) has stressed both the roles of meltwater and pressure release in the bergschrund.

The plucking of the bergschrund is a form of mechanical erosion (the "Bergschrund Theory" of W. D. Johnson, 1904) that is believed to contribute to the development of a characteristic geomorphic feature of mountain glaciation, a semicircular *corrie* (Scottish, Gaelic, a small semicircular hollow on a mountain side, called *kar* in Austria, *cwm* in Wales, and *botn* in Scandinavia), or *cirque* (French). The classic example of a cirque, in the French Pyrenees at Gavarnie, is a huge glacial amphitheater, and in British and American usage, "cirque" is normally restricted to large glacial features of this sort, while in French it is often applied to amphitheaters in

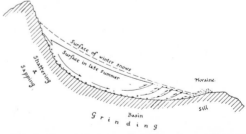

FIG. 2. Contrast between the winter snow surface (A) on a cirque glacier and the summer surface with a well-developed bergschrund. Note the transport of boulders from the latter to the moraine (Lewis, 1949).

semiarid regions, as in the Sahara. One may specify "glacial cirque" to emphasize the first meaning. The minor features, typically developed in periglacial areas and often called cwms or coombes in Britain, may be also referred to as "nivation cirques" according to Flint (1957). The bergschrund theory has received some criticism, and there is little doubt that bergschrund plucking is only one of a number of phenomena involved in cirque erosion (Lewis, 1949).

This process of cirque excavation was first described clearly in English by J. Tyndall (1860), the term for cirque being given as "mountain circus." The Ice Glossary (1958) indicates that an "ice apron" may be associated with the rock wall, but if absent the gap is sometimes called (in German) *Randkluft*. The contrast in the frequently smooth gentle morphology of the mountain (in mature massifs) and the near-vertical plucked and jagged rock wall of the bergschrund is striking. This abrupt angle or scarp at the upper limit of the cirque is known as an *arête* (French) or *Grat* (German); these terms are equally applied to the knife edge caused by the intersection of two adjacent cirque walls or indeed any sharp mountain ridge (Cotton, 1942).

RHODES W. FAIRBRIDGE

References

Armstrong, T. E., and Roberts, B. B., 1956–58, "Illustrated ice glossary," *Polar Record*, **8**, No. 52, 4–12; **9**, No. 59, 90–96, (2nd. ed., 1967.)

Battle, W. R. B., and Lewis, W. V., 1951, "Temperature observations in bergschrunds and their relationship to cirque erosion," *J. Geol.*, **59**, 537–545.

Cotton, C. A., 1942, "Climatic Accidents in Landscape-Making," Christchurch, N.Z., Whitcombe & Tombs.

Flint, R. F., 1957, "Glacial and Pleistocene Geology," New York, J. Wiley, 553pp.

Gilbert, G. K., 1904, "Glaciers and glaciation of Alaska," New York, *Harriman Alaska Exped.*, **3**, 231pp.

Gilluly, J., Waters, A. C., and Woodford, A. O., 1968, "Principles of Geology," Third edition, San Francisco, W. H. Freeman & Co., 687pp.

Johnson, W. D., 1904, "Maturity in Alpine glacial erosion," *J. Geol.*, **12**, 569–578.

Lewis, W. V., 1938, "A meltwater hypothesis of cirque formation," *Geol. Mag.*, **75**, 249–265.

Lewis, W. V., 1949, "The function of meltwater in cirque formation," *Geograph. Rev.*, **30**, 64–83.

Lewis, W. V., 1954, "Pressure release and glacial erosion," *J. Glaciol.*, **2**, 417–422.

Matthes, F. E., 1900, "Glacial sculpture of the Big Horn Mountains," *U.S. Geol. Surv., Ann. Rept.*, **21**(2), 167–190.

Tyndall, J., 1860, "The Glaciers of the Alps," London, J. Murray.

Cross-references: *Cirques*; *Crevasse*; *Glacial Plucking*; *Glacial Scour*; *Moraine*; *Mountain Glacier Landscapes*; *Nivation*; pr Vol. VI: *Glaciology*.

BERM—*See* **BEACH**

BIOHERM—*See* **CORAL REEFS; MICROATOLL**

BIOLOGICAL EROSION OF LIMESTONE COASTS

Coastal Limestones

In many places of the world such as the Straits of Dover, Gibraltar, and much of the Mediterranean, parts of Western Ireland, southern Sweden and in the Canadian Maritime Provinces, ancient limestone meets the sea because crustal movement and erosion have brought the two together. Along tropical coastlines, however, limestone is especially prevalent for another reason. Here, because of the growth of shelled organisms and perhaps chemical precipitation, there is an abundance of calcium carbonate. The absence of rivers along most arid and island coastlines means that rather pure deposits of lime can accumulate unadulterated by terrigenous weathering products. Within the last few hundred thousand years or so, the level of the sea has fluctuated several times by as much as 300 or 400 feet as glaciers grew to continental proportions and melted away. Both deposition and erosion have accompanied these oscillations of sea level and have left a complex record written in and on the coastal limestones. One common rock type deposited is eolianite, formed when sand swept from nearby beaches into dunes is cemented into hard rock by the action of the air and rain. Reef rock, another common type of coastal limestone, is nothing more than an elevated coral reef, e.g., the 100,000-year-old Key Largo limestone of the Florida Keys. The lithified deposits of ancient lagoons, shallow shelves and beaches are also found exposed today along tropical coastlines. Under certain conditions as yet not understood, some beach deposits become cemented very rapidly; thus certain "beachrock" has a modern origin. All of these deposits of varied age and origin may also differ from one another in the degree of chemical and mineral alteration that they have undergone. The differences mean that the rocks may respond quite differently to the various processes of erosion. Often the processes of deposition and erosion go on together with the net result shifting from one to the other. The constructive and destructive processes may be either biological, chemical or mechanical in nature, as exemplified by the growth of coral and its breakdown by boring organisms, the precipitation and solution of calcium carbonate by seawater, and the accumulation of debris originally torn from a reef by storm waves. It would be expected that this complex of many processes acting upon a variety of limestone types at levels changing with time and tide would create a confusion of random and irregular coastal features, yet the intriguing truth is that the gross forms as well as the minor features of

FIG. 1. Echinoids boring (for protection) into reef limestone in the Abrolhos Islands (Western Australia). Width of photo about 80 cm. (Photo: R. W. Fairbridge).

limestone coastlines are more often characterized by similarity than difference.

Coastal Morphology

The present coastline is only a temporary line of contact between land and sea, and therefore the submerged nearshore scenery is equally important to the study of coastal geomorphology as the forms exposed on land. There are submerged terraces, canyons and cliffs. Sometimes the cliffs are notched vertically by canyons or scored laterally by elongate notches. In many areas there are submarine knolls and ridges down to depths of a few hundred feet which may be the eroded remnants of now drowned reef, dune or beach deposits. Intertidal forms are especially complex, both the large-scale and the small-scale features, because here in the vicinity of the atmosphere-ocean contact zone a great variety of processes are brought to bear. Reef fronts are grooved and buttressed by the processes of growth and erosion. The reef edge is often built up in a mound-like ridge by the encrustation of algae and/ or the storm-tossed debris torn from the reef front. In some areas there is a broad reef flat just below or between the level of the tides, then a slightly deeper boat channel and, further, landward, a beach. Even further landward there may be a series of beach ridges, or dunes, or one or more raised wave-cut terraces, or perhaps an old reef deposit now high and dry behind the beach. Instead of a beach there may be a rocky cliff with step-like ledges undercut in elongate nips or notches. These are often within the level of the tides, but they may be submerged or seen well up the cliff face above the present reach of either waves or tide. Features being formed today are often superimposed upon or adjacent to those that have been formed in the past.

It can be seen that the features displayed along a tropical limestone coast represent the net effect of many interacting factors. Important among these are: the nature and structural configuration of the various limestones exposed; the past history of sea level fluctuation; the past history of local crustal movements; the degree of exposure of the coast to the force of waves and currents; the tidal range and periodicity; the significant chemical characteristics of the coastal seawater such as degree of dilution or concentration, plus the chemical behavior of those components involved in calcium carbonate and carbon dioxide reactions; the vertical and horizontal distribution of organisms and their effect—individually and collectively—upon the substrate. As far as the problem of limestone erosion is concerned, in most places the most significant processes

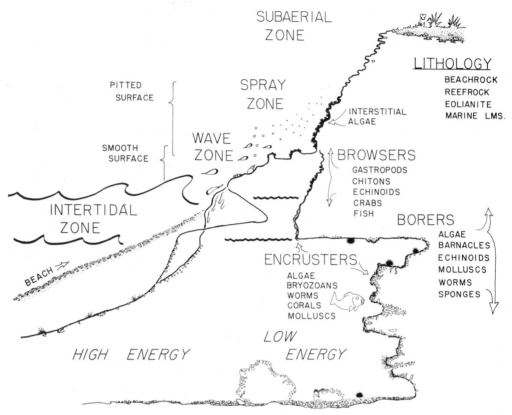

Fig. 2. Some general shore profiles, associated zonation and bioerosive agents observed on the limestone coasts of Bermuda.

acting are the chemical and/or biological ones and yet these are the most incompletely understood. Much more needs to be known about the actual mechanisms by which organisms destroy rocky substrates and about the zonation of rock-destroying organisms and the relationship between these communities and the morphologic features of the coast.

Biochemical and Biophysical Erosion

Recent observation and experiments indicate that biological erosion is a rapid process and can perhaps explain many of the features of limestone coasts which in the past have been relegated to the general categories of "chemical" or "physical" erosion. These terms are vague because organisms of all kinds are so prevalent on rock surfaces bathed by sea spray, washed by the tides, or permanently immersed in the sea that it is difficult to imagine how seawater can act directly by either chemical or physical means upon the substance of the rock. The organisms often intervene, especially in the tropics where limestone substrates are common and the organisms that grow upon them are abundant. The organisms can change the chemical nature of

the surrounding seawater in several ways, e.g. by the generation of carbon dioxide. This biologically produced gas will dissolve in seawater making it capable (when not dissipated) of dissolving more limestone. In tidal pools, this process leads to extreme daily variations due to diurnal photosynthetic activity of algae. Processes that appear to be essentially chemical are often biologically controlled.

In another type of erosion, organisms may grow so closely together that a mat, film or encrustation is formed over the surface of the limestone. Beneath this covering, the organic wastes, or metabolites, may be concentrated with the result that they react with the limestone surface and help to dissolve it. The dissolved material seeps deeper into the rock, and on exposure to the sun's heating, it may precipitate between the grains and thus "caseharden" the upper layer of the limestone. This process, initiated by microscopic boring algae that flourish on and in the surface of the limestone in the inter- and supratidal zones, is often believed to be the cause of both the extremely rough, corroded surface and the case-hardened outer rind that is characteristically developed on limestone in these zones.

TABLE 1. ORGANISMS ASSOCIATED WITH BIOLOGICAL EROSION

Organism	Erosional Process	Biological Mechanism Employed	Features Produced	Habitat
Algae, green, blue-green, and red	Boring	Chemical solution at boring point	Network of fine tubes—may cause rough surface at and above tide level	Supratidal, intertidal and subtidal
Moss	Surface corrosion	Chemical solution by metabolites	Cup-shaped holes	Terrestrial
Algae and lichens	Surface corrosion	Chemical solution by metabolites	Irregular surface, small pits	Terrestrial and marine (algae)
Bacteria	Surficial and interstitial corrosion	Chemical solution by metabolites	(?)	Terrestrial and marine
Fungi	Surficial and interstitial corrosions	Chemical solution by metabolites	Honeycombing of shells, irregular surfaces	Terrestrial and marine
Spermatophytes (general)	Fracturing	Wedging by root growth	Surficial cracks	Terrestrial
Sponges Clionids Spirastrellids	Boring	Chemical and mechanical—process unknown—small particles are excavated	Intensive network of galleries, may penetrate several centimeters	Usually subtidal
Worms Annelids Sipunculids Echuroids	Boring	Chemical solution or mechanical abrasion or both, exact process unknown	Bore holes are long, thin and winding; sometimes closely spaced	Intertidal and subtidal
Arthropods Boring barnacles (*Lithotrya sp.*)	Boring	Mechanical abrasion by peduncle and valves, chemical action may also take place	Circular to oval vertical bore holes, 3–5 cm deep, often closely spaced	Intertidal
Certain crabs	Browsing	Mechanical abrasion by pincers	Sets of several shallow parallel scratches on rock surface	Supratidal and intertidal
Chitons	Browsing and burrowing	Mechanical abrasion by means of a radula reinforced with mineral magnetite	Small oval pits	Intertidal
Gastropods Limpets	Burrowing	Mechanical rasping with the radula and abrasion by the shell	Small oval pits with sharp edges	Intertidal
Snails (many species)	Browsing and burrowing	Mechanical rasping with the radula	Smooth-floored depressions, pits and grooves separated by sharp ridges and pinnacles	Supratidal and intertidal
Pelecypods (many species)	Boring and burrowing	Chemical boring by secretion of solvents, mechanical abrasion by action of valves, or combination of above, exact processes unknown	Features vary from small pits made by some species to long, cylindrical bore holes, often closely spaced	Intertidal and subtidal

TABLE 1—Continued

Organism	Erosional Process	Biological Mechanism Employed	Features Produced	Habitat
Echinoids (several species)	Burrowing and browsing	Mechanical by action of spines and teeth, burrowers also may use some chemical action, exact process unknown	Browsing forms smooth rock surface and leave network of star-shaped scratches, burrowing forms produce deep cup-shaped burrows, circular to oval in plan and variable in cross section	Lower inter-tidal, sub-tidal
Fish (rock browsing types such as trigger fish, parrot fish, etc.)	Browsing	Mechanical, nibbling with specialized teeth	Smoothed surfaces, irregular pattern of short broad scrapes on rock or coral surfaces	Lower inter-tidal, and subtidal

Physical processes may also be strongly affected by biological agencies. When a wave knocks off a piece of limestone it may do so because the limestone was previously weakened by rock-boring organisms. Scuba-diving biologists studying Jamaican reefs have found that large fragments of the deeper reef front can often be dislodged by one hand because the bases of the coral colonies have been weakened by rock-boring sponges. Under other circumstances, encrusting organisms (e.g., *Lithothamnion* and *Porolithon*) protect the rock from physical wear. The biological elements can work vigorously toward either construction or destruction; only in extreme conditions do the physical or chemical factors dominate, and rarely, if ever, do they work without biological help.

Bioerosion

Direct biological erosion usually takes the form of boring, browsing and burrowing. By the latter is meant the excavation of shallow pits, or burrows, in the rock surface. This could be considered either a limited form of boring or a form of browsing concentrated in one spot. Most organisms like sponges, algae, worms, echinoids and pelecypods probably bore into solid mineral material for protection—for a place to live. Other forms, like some gastropods, bore through the shell of other mollusks for purposes of predation. There is little food value in most shell or rock material, so it is unlikely that rock boring is motivated by nutritional needs. On the other hand, the browsers (gastropods, crabs, fish) scrape the rock in order to graze on the surficial organisms. Both intertidal and supratidal limestone surfaces are eroded into a variety of forms and at considerable rates by surface-scraping organisms which feed on the microscopic algae that infiltrate the upper few millimeters of the calcareous rock (Figs. 1–4).

Rock-destroying Organisms

A great number of rock-destroying organisms have been described, and they constitute a considerable cross section of the animal and plant kingdoms. The accompanying table presents a list of most of the general groups of rock-destroying organisms, the methods by which they erode the substrate, the features they produce and the habitat they occupy.

FIG. 3. A dead brain coral, *Diploria strigosa*, bored by sponge *Cliona lampa*, Longbird Bridge, Bermuda, depth about 6 feet.

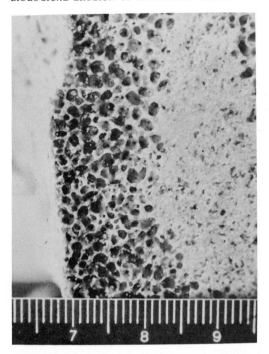

FIG. 4. Outer surface of dense limestone bored by sponge *Cliona lampa*; from 6-foot depth, Longbird Bridge, Bermuda.

It can be seen that biological erosion is performed by a great variety of organisms and can take place anywhere from high mountains to the deep sea. Limestones are more susceptible to this form of erosion because they can be more readily dissolved and because the major mineral component, calcite, is softer than most other common rock-forming minerals. Although the erosive activity of organisms is widespread, it appears to be concentrated along marine coastlines in the intertidal zones as well as the spray zone just above and the shallow subtidal zone below (see Fig. 2). It is also here that the processes of organic erosion have received most attention from both biologists and geologists. It should be noted, however, that the precise mechanisms by which organisms accomplish their rock boring or burrowing are commonly either unknown or only partially understood. In many cases, such as intertidal browsing by gastropods, it is difficult to associate surficial features of the rock with the erosive activity of the organisms because many other processes also work upon the same rock surface. A recent study of beachrock erosion in Barbados (McLean, 1964) has contributed much valuable information on the rates of intertidal biological erosion, the features produced and the zonal association of a variety of limestone-eroding organisms.

Rate of Coastal and Biological Erosion

Some field measurements of the overall rate of limestone erosion are seemingly low when the more rapid rates of individual organisms or groups of organisms are considered. A number of measurements have been made, or estimates calculated, of the rate of intertidal limestone erosion in diverse parts of the world. These values center around 1 mm/yr. Over a long span of time a considerable retreat of the coast could be achieved at this rate. Since sea level has been approximately in its present position for only a few thousand years, during this interval only a few feet of overall erosion could be accomplished at such rates.

In most tropical and subtropical areas in the world, the rates of overall coastal limestone erosion, although not measured directly, must be considerably more rapid because of the nature of the erosional forms produced. The width of erosional reefs calls for a mean rate more like 10 mm/yr. These are not necessarily areas of high physical energy. In Harrington Sound, a quiet lagoon in Bermuda, the surrounding cliff face was found to be extensively undercut below the level of low tide (Neumann, 1966). Subtidal notches with a horizontal depth of 15 feet (5 meters) were measured. The scars of three recent rockfalls and many recently collapsed cliff blocks observed along the coast of this 2-mile-wide lagoon attest to the fact that erosion of the cliffs by subtidal undercutting must be relatively rapid. It was concluded by close observation that several biological agencies, namely the boring of sponges, pelecypods, and worms, plus browsing by echinoids, were probably responsible for the intense subtidal erosion.

Recent studies of the erosion rates of a variety of organisms yield greater values than those determined for overall coastal retreat. Field and laboratory experiments with boring sponges indicate that they are capable of erosion rates as great as 14 mm/yr. Burrowing echinoids have been clocked at 6 mm/yr, and chitons and limpets indicate similarly high values. These values are relatively high because they refer to only one erosional agent and the specific area upon which it acts. In nature, organisms of several types usually work together, and physical removal of weakened rock accompanies biologic attack. The overall rate of erosion, as well as the final forms of the sculpturing, is thus the result of an intricate system of interrelated processes. By separating the elements and studying them singularly, an understanding is emerging of the complexities of the coastal erosion of limestones.

A. CONRAD NEUMANN

References

Fairbridge, R. W., 1952, "Marine erosion," *Seventh Pacific Science Congress*, **3**, 1–11.
Ginsburg, R. N., 1953, "Intertidal erosion on the

Florida keys," *Bull. Marine Sci. Gulf Caribbean,* **3**(1), 55–69.

Kaye, C. A., 1959, "Shoreline features and Quaternary shoreline changes in Puerto Rico. Coastal Geology of Puerto Rico," *U.S. Geol. Surv. Profess. Paper* **317B,** 140 pp.

McLean, R. F., 1964, "Mechanical and Biological Erosion of Beachrock in Barbados, W. I.," unpublished Ph.D. thesis, McGill University, Montreal.

Neumann, A. C., 1966, "Observations on coastal erosion in Bermuda and measurements of the boring sponge, *Cliona lampa,*" *Limnol. Oceanog.,* **11,** 92–108.

Otter, G. W., 1937, "Rock-destroying organisms in relation to coral reefs," *Rept. Great Barrier Reef Comm.,* **1**(12), 324–350.

Cross-references: *Algal Reefs; Coral Reefs; Organisms as Geomorphic Agents; Platforms—Wave-cut; Terraces—Marine.* Vol. I: *Mean Sea Level; Scuba as a Scientific Tool; Tides.* Vol. IV: *Calcium Carbonate Geochemistry.* Vol. VI: *Weathering—Organic.* pr Vol. VII: *Algae; Echinodermata; Gastropoda; Mollusca; Pelecypoda; Porifera; Vermes (Worms).*

BIOLOGICAL REFUGES—*See* GLACIAL REFUGES

BIORHEXISTASY—*See* pr Vol. VI

BLIND VALLEY

A blind valley is a composite surface feature of the karst cycle consisting of a normal river valley in impermeable sediments and its continuation in permeable rocks where the stream (or river and likewise the valley) abruptly ends in a depression or sinkhole. The part of the valley which is on impermeable sediments (shales, sandstones, dolomites; in the Mediterranean karst—flysch, for example) is usually several times longer (up to 20 times or more) than the part on the permeable rocks (usually limestone). In the limestone sector, the bottom is wider and flatter, while the slopes are steeper and form the rim of the amphitheatre. For this reason, the whole valley is called a blind or closed valley (Fig. 1).

The stream or river draining the impermeable sediments sinks at the end of the valley into alluvial swallow holes (see *Sink, Sinkhole, Swallow Hole*), and rarely into the horizontal caves. In the classical Karst (Yugoslavia, north of Trieste; Fig. 2), the best-known caves at the end of the 40-km-long blind valley of the river Notranjska Reka are called Škocjanske Jame (St. Canzian Grottoes). If the *ponors* (sinkholes) are not large enough, the terminal part of the valley is periodically flooded. Because of their depressed shape, the blind valleys are suitable for water storage for various purposes (after suitable practical engineering preparation). Although the largest part of the valley is situated on non-karst sediments, the blind valley is a typical

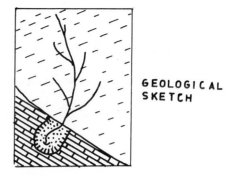

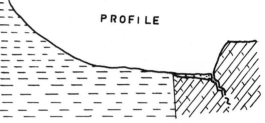

FIG. 1. Geological plan of a blind valley showing headwaters of stream in insoluble rocks, disappearing into blind depression on the limestone; (below) profile of the same.

karst feature as it is genetically linked with ponors. They are most numerous where permeable sediments alternate with impermeable rocks. In the contact area between the karst and non-karst territory, they are a common feature if the water flow is directed toward the karst area. In the Dinaric Karst, blind valleys occur in a series in the Peninsula of Istria and at the foot of the flysch hills called Brkini in Slovenia. Their depth varies from several up to 200 meters.

The main morphogenetic processes in the valley on the impermeable sediments are mechanical and chemical erosion, but in the terminal part of the valley chemical corrosion usually prevails. The lateral corrosion causes the undercutting and retreat of the slopes. In temperate and cold climates, the alluvium is partially permeable so that corrosion also occurs beneath the alluvial mantle ("ground corrosion") and this causes the lowering of the floor.

In the course of geological time, the terminal part of the valley gets wider and the river valley relatively smaller, so that the blind valley becomes a rudimentary form of karst *polje* (q.v.). If the surface flow of the stream or river is reduced by new ponors, the blind valley continues into a *dry valley* (q.v.) with a graded floor between fossil ponors. In the Moravian Karst (Czechoslovakia), blind valleys appear in "fossil" canyons as well. If the impermeable sediments have been eroded, the blind valley is transformed into a dry valley or *uvala* (q.v.).

IVAN GAMS

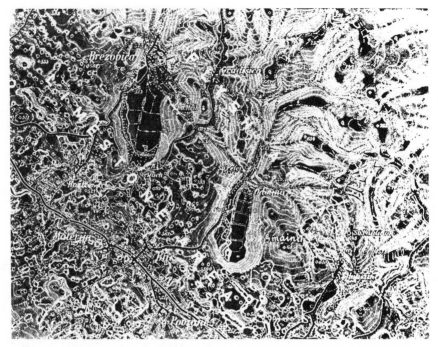

Fig. 2. Two blind valleys on the map of the classical Karst, Yugoslavia (scale, 1.25,000).

References

Cvijić, J., 1893, "Das Karstphänomen," *Penck's Geogr. Abh.*, **5** (3).

Gams, I., 1962, "Blind valleys in Slovenia," *Geografski Sbornik (Ljubljana)*, **7**, 263–306 (in Slovene, with long English summary).

Geikie, J., 1898, "Earth Sculpture or the Origin of Land Forms," London, John Murray.

Rathjens, C., 1960, "Beobachtungen an hochgelegenen Poljen im südlichen Dinarischen Karst. Ein Beitrag zur Frage der Entstehung und Datierung der Poljen," *Z. Geomorphol.*, **2**, 141–151.

von Engeln, O. D., 1942, "Geomorphology," New York, The Macmillan Co., 655pp.

Cross-references: *Dry Valley*; *Karst*; *Polje*; *Sink, Sinkhole, Swallow Hole*; *Uvala*. pr. Vol. VI: *Flysch and Flysch Facies*.

BLOCK DIAGRAM

The block diagram has been invented first and foremost in order to make it possible to illustrate directly the relationship of substratum structure to surface morphology. In all geomorphological descriptions there is a need for a type of illustration that coordinates the information from topographical and geological maps. Phenomena of a three-dimensional nature most easily are demonstrated on spatial landscape models while book illustrations have to be two-dimensional only. As a consequence of this combination of demands the block diagram was constructed and could be defined as a drawing in a two-dimensional plane of a three-dimensional landscape model. This model has to be cut and placed with a tilting that makes it possible to see not only the surface but also two of the lateral faces. When series of block diagrams are constructed in order to show morphogenetic stages in the development of certain type of landscape, time as the fourth dimension is introduced. The three schematic block diagrams in two-point perspective included in Fig. 4 show how successive stages of landform development may be illustrated.

Concerning geometrical construction three different types could be distinguished,

(A) One-point perspective block diagram,

(B) Two-point perspective block diagram,

(C) Isometric block diagram.

Figure 1 is a drawing in one-point perspective. The nearest face being identical with the geological plane section is not drawn in perspective. This type is useful when a description needs an illustration to show for example how the elements of the cliff face are dependent on the geological structure, in this case the stratification of the Upper Cretaceous sedimentary layers. The anvil-shaped cliff profile can thus be shown to be the result of a resistant stratum of Danian limestone with continuous beds of grey flint placed over a nonresistant series of strata consisting of Senonian limestone with clay lenses in the shallow basins in the surface. The existence of a vertical cliff front in the Danian lime-

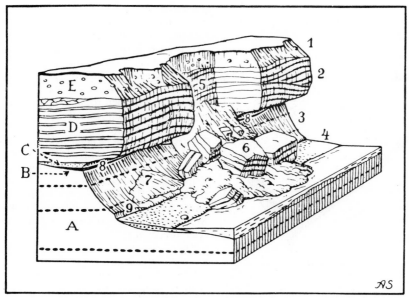

FIG. 1. Block diagram in one-point perspective. Cliff of Senonian and Danian limestone beds overlain by boulder clay (Stevns Klint, east Zealand, Denmark). Block edges, 30 × 70 meters. Direction of front edge west-east. Horizontal and vertical scales equal (from "Atlas of Denmark," Vol. I.).

(A) Senonian limestone with concretions of black flint. (B) ('Fish clay,') laid down in shallow basins in the surface of the Senonian limestone. (C) Cerithium limestone. (D) Danian limestone, with continuous beds of grey flint. Upper stratum locally transformed into breccia by ice pressure. Upper limit a glacier-scratched plane with striae. (E) Boulder clay.

(1) Slope of boulder clay. (2) Precipice of overhanging limestone. (3) Undercutting of cliff by wave action. (4) Beach with flint pebbles. (5) Scar due to fall of limestone. (6) Fallen limestone and boulder clay. (7) Scree washed away below the high-water mark. (8) Bed of ('fish clay.') (9) Wave-cut scar.

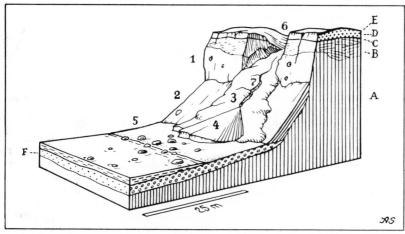

FIG. 2. Block diagram in two-point perspective. Cliff in glacial deposits (Halsnaes, Denmark). Block edges 25 × 75 meters. Horizontal and vertical scales equal (from "Atlas of Denmark," Vol. I).

(A) Boulder clay. (B) Diluvial sand. (C) Humus stratum, old land surface. (D) Blown sand. (E) Recent humus stratum. (F) Marine sediments.

(1) Precipice in clay. (2) Scree. (3) Landslide debris. (4) Scree cone. (5) Beach. (6) Landslide scar. (7) Rain gully.

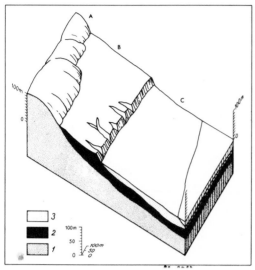

FIG. 3. Isometric block diagram. Elevated shore lines (Vendsyssel, Denmark). Block edges 1 × 2 km. Height scale 3 times exaggerated. The highest, late-glacial shore line is formed in the Würm moraine. The lower elevated shore line from the Flandrian transgression is formed in late glacial clay deposits.

(A) Hummocky moraine landscape. (B) Late-glacial plateau. (C) Litorina coastal plain.

gram often is drawn as a series of transparent planes corresponding to the lines along which the investigation borings have been drilled.

It is possible by purely geometrical construction with pencil and ruler on the plane of the drawing-paper to prepare a block diagram based on information taken from a contour map. The value of the block diagram when completed depends upon the amount of detail shown on the basic map, especially as regards the elevations, i.e., levels and contours. However, there can be no general formula concerning contour intervals, because requirements must vary according to the intensity of relief of the landscape. Thus there must be a greater contour density to represent flat surface forms than is needed for landscapes with marked differences of elevation. Moreover, the map accuracy depends upon what scale is chosen.

The construction of the surface could be done in various ways, either by means of precisely constructed, densely spaced section lines or by using a shading technique by means of hachuring. The tilting of the block can be controlled and a relevant exaggeration of the height scale can be introduced. For detailed instructions, reference could be made to the literature mentioned below.

When the block diagram was invented, aerial photographs were unknown; it has been said that nowadays aerial photographs could replace block diagrams as illustrations in geomorphological papers, but this is not so. When certain objects are to be illustrated, it will frequently be necessary to supplement the information given by the map with, for instance, the shapes of details, obtained by direct observation in the field or from photographs. Indeed many elements that characterize the landscape may be recorded inadequately or not at all on the map. It is obvious that aerial photographs are particularly useful for this purpose. However, those who advocate aerial photographs as direct substitutes for block diagrams should clearly recognize the following differences between the two forms of reproduction. The value of an aerial photograph is of a documentary character; it provides an objective description of great importance, especially for map drawing, but also by combining vivid visual impression and detailed distributional patterns, it provides first-class illustrative material for geographical studies. The block diagram, on the other hand, is a method of schematic representation by which the elements to be illustrated may be emphasized, other details of no interest to the immediate purpose being suppressed. This essential difference should always be borne in mind when drawing block diagrams; the diagrammatic character, which may differ with the nature of the task in hand, should always be retained; for it is not the aim of the block to produce a landscape picture which is true to reality.

AXEL SCHOU

stone section and a sloping upper part in the moraine section can be explained directly by observing the geological profile in the nearest face of the block diagram.

Figure 2 is drawn in two-point perspective, which means that both visible faces are drawn in perspective. This type of block diagram is the only one which is correctly drawn in accordance with the rules of linear perspective. This type could be used in the same way as the one-point block diagram. It is an advantage that it is more attractive because it corresponds to normal sight perception.

Figure 3 shows an isometric block diagram, which is constructed with its opposite faces parallel and of equal length. The height scale is the same at all points of this type of block diagram. The isometric block diagram could be defined as a three-dimensioned model viewed from an infinite distance. It could be compared with a photograph taken with a telephoto lens and is similarly distorted. As blocks are normally viewed at distances corresponding to natural vision, the isometric block is sometimes confusing for persons who are not aware of the construction principles.

The isometric block diagram is mostly used by mining engineers as a highly favored procedure to show structural patterns in three dimensions because the isometric character makes it possible to use the same measuring scale in various vertical planes parallel to the front lateral face. To facilitate the use of this technique, the isometric block dia-

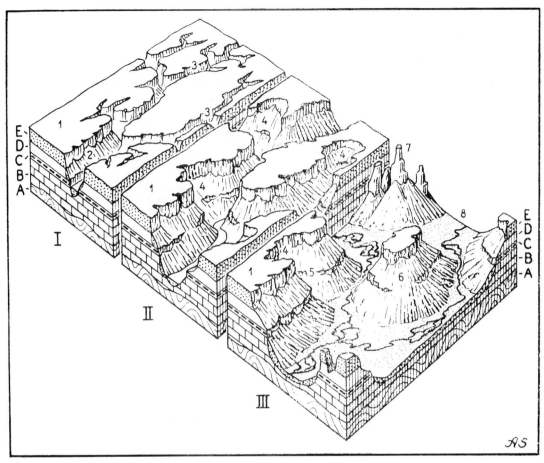

FIG. 4. Three stages in the evolution of a semiarid region of horizontal sedimentary rocks are depicted (Arizona). In diagram I, a plateau has been deeply dissected by streams whose steep-sided valleys meet the plateau surface at a sharp angle. In diagram II, the valleys are wider and the plateau less extensive, and the influence on valley form of the alternations of weak and resistant rocks is seen. In the final diagram (III), the rivers wander over plains of their own deposits between hills whose slopes are covered in rock waste (except where resistant beds outcrop) and whose summits retain small flat remnants of the initial plateau surface.

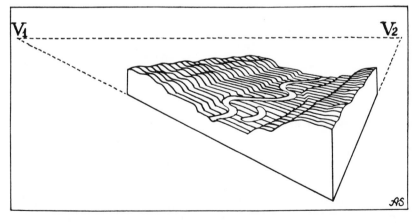

FIG. 5. The surface relief of a valley with terraces, reproduced solely by means of section lines (from Axel Schou, 1962). (By permission of Nelson & Sons, London, England.)

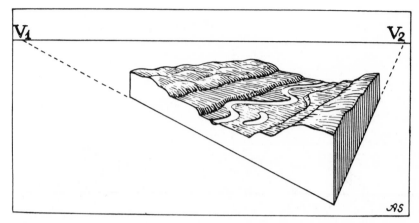

FIG. 6. The surface relief of a valley with terraces (cf. Fig. 5) reproduced by means of ground hachuring (from Axel Schou, 1962). (By permission of Nelson & Sons, London, England.)

Reference

Brown, C. B., and Debenham, F., 1929, "Structure and Surface," London, E. Arnold, 168pp.

Davis, W. M., 1912, "Die beschreibende Erklärung der Landformen," Leipzig-Berlin, Teubner, 565pp.

Frebold, Georg, 1951, "Profil und Blockbild," Braunschweig.

Kunský, Josef, 1955, "Blockdiagram," Geograficzny Wykres Brylowy, Warszawa.

Kunský, Josef, 1954, "Zeměpisný nákres Blokdiagram." Praha.

Lobeck, A. K., 1924, "Block Diagrams," New York, John Wiley & Sons., 206pp.

Nielsen, N. (editor), 1949, "Atlas of Denmark," Vol. 1, "The Landscapes," Copenhagen, H. Hagerup, 32pp.

Schou, Axel, 1962, "The Construction and Drawing of Block Diagrams," London, Nelson & Sons Ltd., 33pp.

Schuster, Matthäus, 1954, "Das Geographische und Geologische Blockbild," Berlin, Akad.-Verlag, 222pp.

Solger, Fr., 1929, "Das Blockdiagramm und das Zeichnen mit Hilfe des perspektivischen Liniennetzes," Glogau.

Cross-references: *Geomorphic Maps*; *Physiographic or Landform Maps*; *Structural Control in Geomorphology*.

BLOCK FIELD—*See* FELSENMEER

BLOCK MOUNTAIN (FAULT-BLOCK MOUNTAIN)

The term "block mountain" was introduced by W. M. Davis; other terms are "fault-block mountain" as given by D. W. Johnson (1903) or simply "fault blocks" of Strahler (1946), for the "initial land forms," i.e., mountains, where geotectonically positive, produced by crustal fracturing. The simple symmetrically bounded positive fault block is known as a *horst* (q.v.), and thus we have "horst mountain" (Geikie, 1914), but the term block mountain may be applied also to tilted fault blocks and complex faulted uplands.

Block mountains are typically developed in the Basin-Range Province of Nevada, Utah and Arizona (see *Basin-Range Landscape*) and may be equally well observed in other parts of the world subject to block faulting. This is the phenomenon of *taphrogeny*, which is analogous to epeirogeny, but involves gross fracturing of the earth's crust. The term taphrogeny was proposed by Krenkel with the great rift valleys of East Africa in mind, and it is now

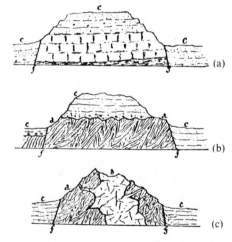

FIG. 1 (a). Block Mountain (Simple). *cc*, Mesozoic strata; *ff*, faults (Geikie, 1914).

(b). Block Mountain (with unconformity). *aa*, Paleozoic strata; *cc*, Mesozoic strata; *ff*, faults (Geikie, 1914).

(c). Block Mountain (complex). *a*, Paleozoic rocks; *b*, igneous rock; *cc*, Mesozoic strata; *ff*, faults (Geikie, 1914).

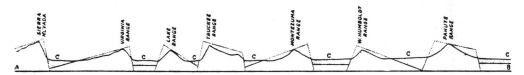

FIG. 2. Parallel ranges of the Great Basin, North America (after Russell Hinman, from Geikie, 1914). A to B = 120 miles; CCC, superficial deposits. Note irregularity of blocks, attributed to crustal stretching.

universally applied to block-faulted tectonics. Analogous areas of intramontane (or *Zwischengebirge*) taphrogeny are seen in the Central Plateau of Mexico, the altiplano (and "puna") areas of Peru and Bolivia and in Hungary, Anatolia, Iran and Tibet (Figs. 3 and 4).

Geomorphic characteristics of block mountains have been summarized by Davis (1901, 1909), and include: more or less rectilinear borders, lack of continuity of formations except from evidence of deep drilling in the adjoining basins, faceted spurs, occasionally seismic revival, rejuvenated relief, and fresh *fault scarps* (q.v.).

The uplifted blocks may have younger covering formations stripped off them, leaving "stripped erosion surfaces" or *relict landforms* (q.v.). Examples of such "upland massifs" are well-known in the Harz and Black Forest of Germany and in the Massif Central of France (Wooldridge and

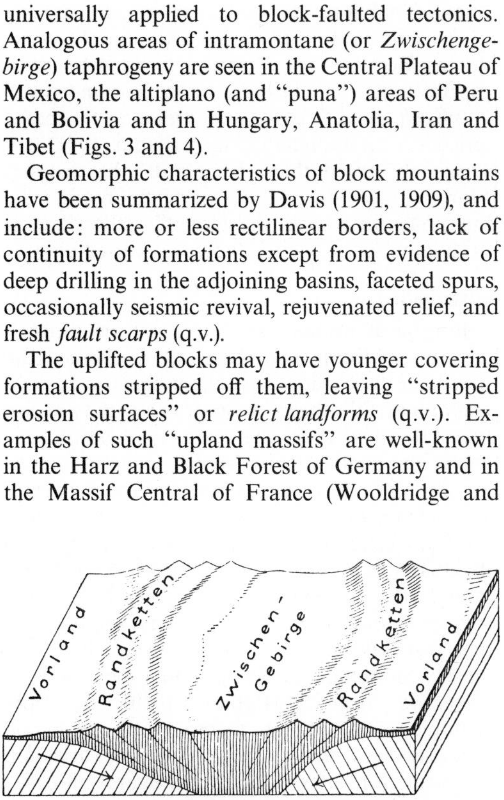

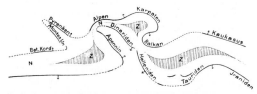

FIG. 3. Idealized sketch of a bilaterally symmetric orogenic belt as visualized by L. Kober (1928), showing position of the *Zwischengebirge* (block mountains of the median mass) between twin fold belts (*Randketten*), underthrust by foreland blocks (*Vorland*), which also develop block mountains in places, e.g., Black Forest, Harz.

FIG. 4. Sketch plan of bilateral symmetry of the Alpine orogenic belt in Europe and the Mediterranean by Kober (1928). Z = principal Zwischengebirge areas. *left*, W. Mediterranean, Corsica, Sardinia; *middle*, Pannonian block, Hungary; *right*, Aegean and Anatolia. Note: Suffix -*iden* in German, given as -*ides* in English.

Morgan, 1937). Such landscapes are often affected by superimposed or antecedent drainage systems (see *Drainage Patterns*).

RHODES W. FAIRBRIDGE

References

Davis, W. M., 1901, "The ranges of the Great Basin: physiographic evidence of faulting," *Science*, **14**, 457–459.

Davis, W. M., 1909, "The Mountain Ranges of the Great Basin," in "Geographical Essays," pp. 725 and 772, Boston (New York, Dover reprint 1954; originally issued 1903, *Bull. Mus. Comp. Zool. Harvard Coll.*, **42**, 129–177).

Geikie, J., 1914, "Mountains, Their Origin, Growth and Decay," Princeton, N.J., D. Van Nostrand Co., 311pp.

Johnson, D. W., 1903, "Block mountains in New Mexico," *Am. Geol.*, **31**, 135–139.

Johnson, D. W., 1930, "Geomorphologic aspects of rift valleys," *Congr. Geol. Intern. Compt. Rend. 15th, South Africa, 1929*, **2**, 354–373.

Kober, L., 1928, "Der Bau der Erde," Second ed., Berlin, Borntraeger, 499pp.

Strahler, A. N., 1946, "Geomorphic terminology and classification of land masses," *J. Geol.*, **54**, 32–42.

Wooldridge, S. W., and Morgan, R. S., 1937, "The Physical Basis of Geography: An Outline of Geomorphology," London, Longmans Green & Co., 445pp.

Cross-references: *Basin and Range Landscape*: *Drainage Patterns*; *Fault Scarp*; *Horst*; *Louderback*; *Mountain Types*; *Relict Landforms*. Vol. V: *Taphrogeny*; *Zwischengebirge*.

BLOWOUTS—*See* DEFLATION

BOG—*See* pr Vol. VI, SWAMP, MARSH, BOG

BOLSON

The geomorphic term *bolson* (from the Spanish word for "purse") is widely used in the southwestern United States and northern Mexico for a depression with centripetal drainage entirely surrounded by hills or mountains. Its lowest part is generally marked by a *playa* (q.v.) or salt pan. If the playa is drained by an ephemeral stream the basin may be termed a *semi-bolson* (Tolman, 1909). The term is also used for the pebble-covered alluvial fans that often surround the central playa, thus *bolson plains* (Tight, 1905).

Bolsons are by definition, therefore, areas of semiarid endorheic drainage. There are three genetic types: (a) deflation hollows (Lobeck, 1939); (b) basin-range type structural grabens; (c) any longitudinal structural depression which has been broken up into isolated segments by irregular alluvial fan building. The fact that most of the world's bolson-type depressions are found in the Basin-Range Province of the Southwest and northern Mexico suggests that types (b) and (c), above, are the important ones; deflation hollows ("blow-outs") are not so common in the area.

Von Engeln (1942, Fig. 238) illustrates the well-watered and volcano-studded central plain of Mexico, south of Mexico City, as a bolson; this seems to stretch the term somewhat beyond its customary usage.

RHODES W. FAIRBRIDGE

References

Lobeck, A. K., 1939, "Geomorphology," New York, McGraw-Hill Book Co., 731pp.

Tight, W. G., 1905, "Bolson plains of the southwest," *Am. Geologist,* **36,** 271–284.

Tolman, C. F., 1909, "Erosion and deposition in the S. Arizona bolson region," *J. Geol.,* **17,** 136–163.

Von Engeln, O. D., 1942, "Geomorphology," New York, The Macmillan Co., 655pp.

Cross-references: *Alluvial Fan, Cone; Arid Cycle; Basin and Range Landscape; Deflation; Deserts and Desert Landforms; Playa.* pr Vol. VIII: *Basin-Range Province.*

BOREAL WOODLAND—*See* TAIGA LANDSCAPE

BORNHARDT

A German geologist of this name first described (1900) certain prominent hills on the East African shield as "inselberge" (island mounts). Subsequently, the term inselberg acquired a wider connotation and Bailey Willis (1936) suggested the term "bornhardt" to describe hills with "bare surfaces, dome-like summits, precipitous sides becoming steeper toward the base, an absence of talus, alluvial cones or soil, a close adjustment of form to internal structure" (Willis, 1936, p. 117). The occurrence of bornhardts, he said, depended upon "one, a terrain composed chiefly of gneiss or schist, intruded by granite and traversed by veins of aplite and quartz; two, vertical or steeply dipping schistosity or jointing, which in general facilitates the decomposition of the rock and which serves to give precipitous faces to more massive or more quartzose bodies; three, a climate characterized by warmth and humidity, favorable to abundant vegetation and the resultant processes of rock decay; four, notable uplift . . ."

(Willis, 1936, p. 120). In early writings, such hills were often called "exfoliation domes."

King (1948) described bornhardts as "granite-gneiss inselbergs"; other authors have called them "domed" or "domical" inselbergs. But the implication that all bornhardts rise as inselbergs from wide plains would exclude many hills of the type described by Willis. In fact, bornhardts occupy a great range of topographic situations, and, describing the sugar loaves of Rio de Janeiro, Birot (1958) wrote "nous n'oublions pas que les pains de sucre bresiliens sont des formes de jeunesse du cycle, et non des inselberg" (p. 24). Thus in so far as *inselberg* is a precise and genetic term, it cannot be equated with *bornhardt* which is based on morphological characteristics. Carl Troll and Dudley Stamp (1961) have separately urged that "bornhardt" be dropped. Many authors do not use the term "bornhardt," but prefer to restrict the term "inselberg" to its original usage or to qualify it as indicated above.

Distribution

Bornhardt domes occur over a wide range of climatic environments. King (1957) claimed that they were "recorded from every climatic environment on earth"; they also occur in a variety of rock types. Bornhardts are characteristic of granite, acid gneiss and migmatite, but similar forms are known in unusually massive sedimentary rocks such as sedimentary quartzite (diagenetic). Ayer's Rock in Central Australia is an example. The margins of individual hills are seldom controlled by petrological boundaries according to King (1948), but jointing frequency may exert a fundamental control over their distribution. Domes occur outside the tropics [Stone Mountain in Georgia and the domes of Yosemite Valley (Matthes, 1930) are good examples], and within the tropics, they occur in both humid and arid environments. Their size varies continuously from a few square yards in area and a few feet in height to hills 1000 feet or more in height (Fig. 1).

No agreement has been reached as to the origins of bornhardts; separately or in combination three mechanisms of dome formation can be listed: (1) Exfoliation due to unloading leads to the shedding of curved sheets; this process is thought by some authors (e.g., Matthes) to account for the domical form; others regard it as a contributory factor only. (2) Some bornhardts are true inselbergs: these have been regarded (e.g., by King, 1948) as residual hills resulting from scarp retreat and pediplanation (some early writers explained the island form literally as a result of marine action; others thought eolian erosion responsible; neither hypothesis is advocated today). (3) Bornhardts commonly occur in areas of known deep chemical weathering; this process is now regarded by many authors as fundamental to dome formation, more susceptible or closely fractured rocks becoming weathered to

FIG. 1. A small bornhardt displaying domical shape, bare rock surface with remnants of exfoliation sheet, absence of talus and sharp junction with plain. Medium-grained biotite granite of Precambrian age, Jos Plateau, Northern Nigeria.

depths in excess of 100 feet, while the resistant and massive rocks become *etched* into relief as bornhardt domes (Fig. 2). Smaller resistant masses become *tors*. Adherents of this theory include Willis (1936), Ollier (1960), Twidale (1964), and Thomas (1965). Sheeting is acknowledged as a factor by most authors, but conflict between exhumation and pediplanation theories remains. If they are weathering residuals, then domes are *azonal* forms resulting from differential etching, but if they are planation residuals, they must generally be *zonal* forms related to erosional stage of the landscape (i.e., inselbergs). Distribution patterns show azonal characteristics in many areas, but claims for zonal patterns have been made. Büdel (1957) recognized

the occurrence of both types, describing azonal domes as "shield inselbergs" and accounting for them by exhumation from deep weathering profiles, while zonal domes resulted from scarp retreat (Fig. 3). It is doubtful if a single hypothesis can account for all occurrences of the bornhardt form, but it may be observed that climatic change has brought many high-latitude locations within subtropical or tropical climates during recent geological time and that deep weathering is a proven phenomenon in such areas.

Bornhardts appear to survive for long periods, the larger more massive hills having grown in height during several cycles. Bornhardts may however degenerate into *koppies* (often called *castle-koppies* after their irregular profile) either as a result of slope retreat (King, 1948) or of subaerial collapse (Thomas, 1965). The term kop or koppie is Afrikaans, formerly *kopje* ("little head").

MICHAEL F. THOMAS

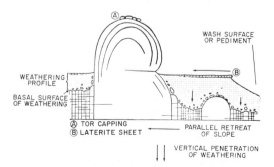

FIG. 2. Bornhardt development by etching and the stripping of weathered material.

FIG. 3. Tropical denudation surfaces with marginal pediment slopes (*Randspülpedimenten*), zonal (outlier) inselberg on the left and azonal "shield" inselbergs in the middle, showing notches of the lower pediment (from Büdel, 1957). Examples: northern Nigeria; southern Somalia.

89

References

Birot, P., 1958, "Les Dômes Crystallins," *Centre Natl. Rech. Sci. (C.N.R.S.), Memoires et Documents,* **6,** 8–34.

Bornhardt, W., 1900, "Zur Oberflächengestaltung und Geologie Deutsch-Ostafrikas," Berlin.

Büdel, J., 1957, "Die Doppelton Einebnungsflächen in den feuchten Tropen," *Z. Geomorphol., N.F.,* **1,** 201–225.

King, L. C., 1948, "A theory of bornhardts," *Geograph. J.,* **112,** 83–87.

King, L. C., 1957, "The uniformitarian nature of hillslopes," *Trans. Edinburgh Geol. Soc.,* **17,** 81–102.

Matthes, F. E., 1930, "The geologic history of the Yosemite Valley," *U.S. Geol. Surv. Profess. Paper* **160.**

Ollier, C. D., 1960, "The inselbergs of Uganda," *Z. Geomorphol. N.F.,* **4,** 43–52.

Stamp, D. L., 1961, "Glossary of Geographical Terms," London, Longmans, 539pp.

Thomas, M. F., 1965, "Some aspects of the geomorphology of domes and tors in Nigeria," *Z. Geomorphol., N.F.,* **9,** 63–81.

Twidale, C. R., 1964, "A contribution to the general theory of domed inselbergs," *Trans. Inst. British Geographers,* **34,** 91–113.

Willis, Bailey, 1936, "East African Plateaus and Rift Valleys," in "Studies in Comparative Seismology," Washington, D.C., Carnegie Institution.

Cross-references: *Denudation*; *Dome Mountains*; *Etchplain*; *Exhumed Landscape*; *Granite Landforms*; *Inselberg*; *Pediplain*; *Relict Landforms*; *Tor.*

BOTN—*See* BERGSCHRUND; CIRQUE

BOULDER—*See* PERCHED BLOCK, BOULDER

BRAIDED STREAMS

A stream or river bed is said to have a braided pattern when the deeper channels form a lacy or reticulate network of divergent and convergent members. This branching or weaving characteristic is properly called *anastomosis* (from the Greek), and the channels may be described as *anastomosing*. (These terms are used in the same sense in many fields: e.g., in botany—veins on a leaf; in anatomy—veins in the bloodstream, "veins" in an insect's wing; also in petrology—"anastomosing dikes and veins"; in volcanology—"anastomosing or braided lava flows", in speleology—"anastomosing caves.")

Most braided streams occur where there are almost no lateral confining banks, as on large alluvial piedmont fans or sandurs, but in certain regions they occur in confined valleys (often "*underfit*"; see *Streams—Underfit*).

Friedkin (1945) after completing experimental studies on stream patterns, wrote:

"Rivers are described as braided when the channel is extremely wide and shallow and the flow passes through

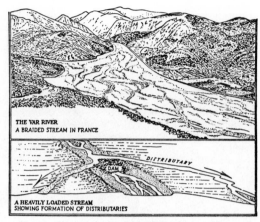

FIG. 1. Two aspects of braided streams: *above*, the loaded seasonal stream leaves the confining valleys of the mountains; *below*, the deposited load of flood time blocks the main channel with a dam of pebbles and boulders (Lobeck, 1939). (By permission of McGraw-Hill Book Co., N.Y.)

a number of small interlaced channels separated by bars. There is little or no erosion of the main banks. The channel as a whole does not meander, although local meandering in minor channels generally occurs . . . braiding results when the banks of a channel are extremely easily eroded."

Environment

Braided streams, active today, are found in three rather contrasting environments:

(a) Semiarid regions of relatively low relief, but with the streams usually receiving the runoff of mountain areas.

(b) A variant of this condition is the *sandur* or glacial outwash plain or valley, where the source is a melting ice front.

(c) Mature streams in mountain areas—arid, temperate or even periglacial. The stream gradient may be remarkably steep.

In each case, the precipitation (or thaw) will be marked by extreme seasonality, or in desert regions it may be quite sporadic, perhaps limited to 50–100 year intervals. As Krigstrom (1962) noted, whereas the semiarid braided valley occasionally becomes totally submerged, this condition does not seem to have been reached over the sandur plains (though possibly in the more confined sandur valleys), even during glacier dam bursts.

Load

The uniting feature of all active braided streams is that the discharge is extremely irregular; through most of the year or longer periods, the river bed is dry or the stream is very much reduced. When precipitation (or snow thaw) does occur in the headwater catchment area, it is usually heavy and relatively brief. It may be in the form of brief summer thunderstorms, in which case heavy flow (a "flash flood" or "freshet") may occur in a single tributary, while the rest of the catchment is dry, or it may be in the form of heavy monsoonal front rains which last for a brief period and are followed by a long, dry period. In the case of sandur braided channels, the glacier thawing is again strictly seasonal.

In each case, the landscape is usually rather bare of vegetation, so that a high runoff with considerable slope wash causes a large sediment load to become entrained. At maximum flood level, the river is frequently very turbid, and where profile is relatively steep, considerable turbulence permits a large suspended bed load to be shifted. Geomorphologists formerly spoke of a stream being "overloaded," but this is scarcely possible and "maximum load" is the condition.

Braiding and Meandering

There is a close but contrasting relationship between braiding and meandering (Leopold *et al.*, 1964), the slope/discharge ratio being always higher for the braided stream (Fig. 2). In general plan, the braided stream is much less sinuous than the meandering stream, although the channels in the former certainly have curves that have a characteristic radius to channel width ratio. At overbank flow the braided river tends to assume a relatively straight course, reverting to highly sinuous trickles at low water.

Lateral Migration

During floods there are major changes in the principal *thalwegs* (q.v.). Indeed, Leopold *et al.* (1964, p. 291) give details of the astonishing shifts of the Kosi River in India. The Kosi rises near Mt. Everest and flows over a flat cone down to the Ganges, gradients on the cone dropping from 0.0009 to 0.0002 over 130 miles. Annual discharge is about 160,000 cfs. In some two centuries, it has

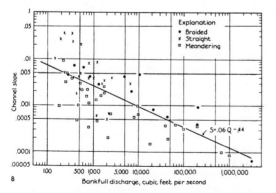

FIG. 2. Relation of discharge to slope and a line which separates data from meandering and braided channels (after Leopold, Wolman, and Miller, 1964). (By permission of W. H. Freeman & Co., San Francisco).

migrated 70 miles in irregular jumps, up to 12 miles in one year.

The enormous shifts of the bed of the Yellow River over the course of history are almost legendary. For many years, however, strenuous efforts have been put into the construction of dikes or levees to maintain some sort of control. A recent summary in English of a Chinese survey of the Yellow River (Huang-Ho) is as follows (Chien Ning *et al.*, 1961):

"The Lower Yellow River in Honan Province is characterized by a wide and shallow bed choked with sand bars. The stream is deflected in all directions into such a diffuse and intricately subdivided cross section that no meanders have ever developed. The river flows in a number of branching and reuniting streamlets with one of them as the main channel. This main river course often shifts its position at an average speed of 10–300 m/day during floods. Three basic types of channel shifting can be distinguished. The main flow often captures another river fork and fills the old channel with sediment. The flow direction is sometimes changed either by the movement of sandbanks or by bank cavings. These local adjustments of bank lines are often associated with changes in flow pattern upstream. The braided stream of the Lower Yellow River is separated intermittently by a sequence of wide and narrow reaches. Whenever the flow pattern varies, its effect will be felt much less downstream of a narrow reach. These reaches are, therefore, called the primary control points of the river. At median and low flows, a number of secondary control points along the river course are noted. They are located where there are high shores or river regulating works on one side, and low sandbanks on the other. The flow here takes a curved path and the concave side coincides with the fixed bank line. If the low sand bank is destroyed by the passage of a larger flood, the control effect is also lost.

"Distinctive features of the Yellow River are: (1) A large amount of sedimentary particles is produced by the basin which fill the channel with fine sediment. (2) The alluvial deposits along the river course are not homogeneous; there are fine sands and silts in Honan Province and more clayey deposits in Shantung Province. (3) The sediment, once deposited, can be easily put into motion again by the flow which moves rather rapidly along a comparatively steep slope. (4) The flood rises and subsides abruptly with a prominent peak. (5) The variation of discharge is large. (6) The sediment concentration varies widely during the same discharge. Among these conditions, the aggradation of the channel and the lack of lateral control are the basic factors which induce the development of the braided channel pattern in Honan Province. Other factors are more responsible in setting up the high frequency and large amplitude of the channel shifting."

Bar Formation

With its steeper gradient/discharge ratio than other streams, the transported material in the braided river tends to be very coarse. The catastrophic nature of the high discharge period means that unsorted coarse material is often swept down, far from the mountain front. With the sudden drop in flow energy, this load is dumped in midstream, setting up the nucleus of a sand bar, while secondary channels develop on either side. At flood time there is often a diagonal flow over these bars from the more obstructed channels to the deeper ones. In such channels, megaripples may develop. The nature of bar formation has been abundantly observed in the field and confirmed in flume experiments.

Braided Stream Lithofacies

In ancient deposits, a characteristic facies and sorting pattern permits recognition of former braided stream environments (Allen, 1965). Experimental work is again helpful in this area. In an abstract of his work, Ore (1964) reports:

"Observations of modern and ancient braided stream deposits supplemented by stream table experiments show certain criteria to be useful in recognizing the deposits in the stratigraphic record. Braiding commonly results where partially incompetent streams form longitudinal bars by depositing coarse elements of bed load which trap finer elements. Transverse bars formed of better-sorted sediment are tabular, wedge-shaped bodies with foreset cross strata. They either may be the only depositional form or may be deposited on downstream ends of longitudinal bars. External geometric criteria are of less use than internal ones. Longitudinal bars exhibit asymmetric inclined surfaces, terraces, and transverse bar wedges on their downstream ends. Transverse channels commonly cut across longitudinal and transverse bar surfaces. Internal geometric features are easily recognizable and yield paleocurrent information. Statistically treated preferred orientations of flat-surface pebbles give population characteristics and allow estimates of stream direction during deposition. Larger pebbles are more reliable indicators of downstream direction. Two types of sediment, separable by sorting characteristics, characterize braided stream deposits. Upstream ends of longitudinal bars have coarser, more poorly sorted sediment than do downstream ends and transverse bars. Sorting characteristics aid in recognizing braided stream deposits. Discontinuous, horizontal stratification is common in the deposits. Foreset cross strata exhibit grading along the inclined laminae, and the sediment is more poorly sorted at the bottoms than at the tops. Foreset, bed roughness and trough-fill cross stratification characterize braided stream deposits. The foreset variety is most abundant, can be a valuable current indicator and has certain high-dispersion population characteristics. Deformed stratification is present locally. Braided stream deposits are commonly found where abundant sediment and high discharges were available during deposition."

Anabranches

Secondary channels in a broad plain of braided channels that maintain semipermanent courses are known as "anabranches" (see Stamp, 1961, for examples and first use: 1834, *J. Roy. Geogr. Soc.*, **4,** 79). Many great river systems of the world have sectors where the gradient flattens over a significant area, having usually a rather remote source of water in distant mountains. The classical area where

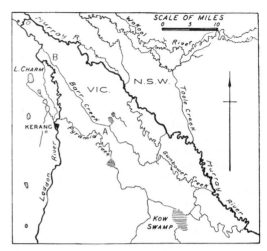

Fig. 3. Map showing portion of the complex system of anabranches and effluents along the Murray and Loddon Rivers in southeastern Australia. At A, the Pyramid and Barr Creeks are prevented from joining by natural levee banks. At B, the Barr Creek is similarly prevented from joining the Loddon (Hills, 1940).

the term anabranch was first applied is in eastern Australia, in the states of Victoria and New South Wales where the Murray and Murrumbidgee rivers spread out on the interior plains of the "Riverina" (Fig. 3). Similar patterns (in a totally different climate) are seen in the Sudd area of the White Nile in Southern Sudan. They occur also in the swampy lands south of Lake Chad. Again, they are seen in the presently jungle areas of Venezuela and Brazil. They occur in the coastal section of the Yellow River of China.

As pointed out by Garner (1967), all of these regions have one common factor. They were areas of semiarid character during repeated cycles of the Pleistocene. Meteorological principles show that in worldwide cooling episodes, the mean world precipitation must have been greatly reduced and recent carbon-14 dating proves that many great rivers almost dried up during glacial stages (Fairbridge, 1964). The result of this general desiccation was the development of widespread braided alluvial plains. Revival of heavy precipitation in the headwater regions during the postglacial epoch has caused many of the rivers to develop a new perennial regime, marked by year-round flow, low sediment load and meandering courses. The evidence, however, is often erroneously interpreted (see, for example, Berry, 1961; with comments by Tricart).

In this way, anabranches are interpreted to represent the relict features of a former morphoclimatic condition, on which there is an "overprint" of a totally different condition. It is scarcely necessary to add that the subject has been surrounded by controversy and it is only with carbon-14 dating that a reasonable chronology is emerging.

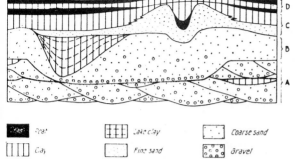

Peat.   Lake clay   Coarse sand

Clay   Fine sand   Gravel

FIG. 4. Scheme of a fluvial sedimentation cycle as observed in the Pliocene and lower Pleistocene of the southeastern Netherlands (Zagwijn, 1963).

(A) Stage of braided river; in part perhaps channel bottom deposits; (B) Stage of large meandering river; (C) Stage of small meandering river, probably strongly branched; (D) Stage of general swamping and peat formation, perhaps only small streamlets left.

Pleistocene Proglacial and Periglacial Streams

For many years it has been known that a vast network of proglacial streams surrounded the southern borders of the Scandinavian Pleistocene ice sheet in central Europe (the "Urstromtäler") and likewise the peripheries of the North American ice sheets. Vast sediment loads and brief melt seasons provided the ideal setting for major braided stream developments. Even in the periglacial areas, braiding developed in streams that were not fed by melting ice, but loaded with copious solifluction debris, rendered highly subject to erosion by the semiarid climate (glacial anticyclones) and sparseness of vegetation (see Fig. 4, from Zagwijn, 1963). The Thames Valley Pleistocene fluvial terraces in southern England thus have long been recognized as "exotic" in the present humid climate (see Embleton and Mountjoy, 1964).

RHODES W. FAIRBRIDGE

References

Allen, J. R. L., 1965, "A review of the origin and characteristics of recent alluvial sediments," *Sedimentology*, **5**, 89–191.
Berry, L., 1961, "Large scale alluvial islands in the White Nile," *Rév. Géomorph. Dyn.*, **12**, 105–109.
Chien Ning *et al.*, 1961, "The characteristics and genetic analysis of the braided stream of the Lower Yellow River," *Acta Geogr. Sinica*, **27**, 1–27 (in Chinese; see *Geomorph. Abs.*, 65/45).
Embleton, C., and Mountjoy, A. B., 1964, "Geomorphology and industry in part of the middle Thames Valley," in (Clayton, K. M., editor) "Guide to London excursions," *Intern. Geogr. Congr., London, 20th*, 88–92.
Fairbridge, R. W., 1964, "African Ice-Age Aridity," in (Nairn, A. E. M., editor), "Problems in Palaeoclimatology," pp. 356–363, New York, Interscience Publishers.
Friedkin, J. F., 1945, "A Laboratory Study of the Meandering of Alluvial Rivers," Vicksburg, U.S. Waterways Expt. Sta., 40pp.
Garner, H. F., 1966, "Derangement of the Rio Caroni, Venezuela," *Rév. Géomorph. Dyn.*, **16**, 54–83.
Garner, H. F., 1967, "Rivers in the making," *Sci. Am.*, **216**, 83–94.
Hills, E. S., 1940, "The Physiography of Victoria," Melbourne, Whitcombe & Tombs, 292pp.
Krigstrom, A., 1962, "Geomorphological studies of sandur plains and their braided rivers in Iceland," *Geogr. Ann.*, **44**, 328–346.
Leopold, L. B., Wolman, M. G. and Miller, J. P., 1964, "Fluvial Processes in Geomorphology," San Francisco, W. H. Freeman & Co., 522pp.
Lobeck, A. K., 1939, "Geomorphology, an Introduction to the Study of Landscapes," New York, McGraw-Hill Book Co., 731pp.
Ore, H. T., 1964, "Some criteria for recognition of braided stream deposits," *Wyoming Univ. Dept. Geology, Contr. Geology*, **3**(1), 1–14.
Stamp, L. D. (editor), 1961, "A Glossary of Geographical Terms," London, Longmans, 539pp.
Zagwijn, W. H., 1963, "Pleistocene stratigraphy in the Netherlands, based on changes in vegetation and climate," *Verhandel, Ned. Geol. Mijnbouwk. Genoot.* **21**(2), 173–196.

Cross-references: *Glacial Spillways and Proglacial Lakes; Outwash Plain, Fan, Terrace, Sandur; Rivers—Meandering and Braiding; Stream Channel Characteristics; Stream Flow; Streams—Underfit; Terraces, Fluvial—Environmental Controls; Thalweg.* Vol. II: *Paleoclimatology.* Vol. VI: *Fluvial Sediment Transport.*

BREACHED ANTICLINE—*See* STRUCTURAL CONTROL IN GEOMORPHOLOGY

BURIED VALLEYS AND CHANNELS

Large numbers of shallow borings, in the peripheral areas of the great Quaternary continental ice sheets, mainly for groundwater search or made in the course of engineering foundation studies, have disclosed the presence of deep valleys cut in the bedrock terrain and today filled largely with alluvium, glacial outwash gravels and sands or with till (Fig. 1). These are known as *buried valleys* or *channels*, a number of classes of which may be identified—partly directly due to ice action, and partly inherited valleys, later modified.

(1) Primary Channels

Two genetic types of the primary class may be recognized: (a) *glacial scour* (q.v.) channels, due to the erosion by ice of softer formations, fault zones, etc., and (b) *glacial spillways and meltwater channels* (q.v.), due to erosion by fluvioglacial streams.

In distribution, the scour channels are restricted to former subglacial areas while spillways tend to be more widespread in the periglacial areas or developed over the ice-retreat terrain. Some overlap is

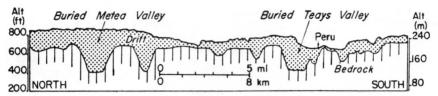

FIG. 1. Buried Teays Valley and its tributary, Metea Valley, at and near Peru in north-central Indiana, defined by subsurface exploration (Thornbury and Deane 1955).

thus possible. In plan, the scours tend toward rectilinear or broad, winding troughs, while the spillways are generally more meandering like mature streams, although in high-velocity spillways with heavily loaded meltwaters the meandering criteria do not apply.

(2) Modified Channels

Two types again may be observed where the valley is an inherited one: (a) an old, established drainage channel, for some reason blocked or diverted, and (b) a valley overdeepened in its lower course due to glacio-eustatic lowering of sea level, and then thalassostatically dammed back and alluviated by postglacial (or interglacial) rise of sea level.

Modified channels can also result from changes in the *climate regime* or from *tectonic activity*. In each case a buried valley can be created by siltation (alluviation).

In North America, the major example of a diverted river system is the Lake Superior–Lake Michigan system that formerly drained through Georgian Bay to near Toronto on Lake Ontario and thence to the proto-St. Lawrence (Fig. 2). Another system was the ancestral Cheyenne–Missouri that drained from the Dakotas northward into the Hudson Bay (Howard, 1958). In Indiana and Ohio the ancestral Teays (pronounced "tayz") took most of the Ohio waters westward into Mohomet Valley of Illinois and thence to the Mississippi (Leverett, 1942; Horberg, 1950; Flint, 1957). This "Deep Stage" was ponded during Kansan time and filled in places to 60-meter depth,

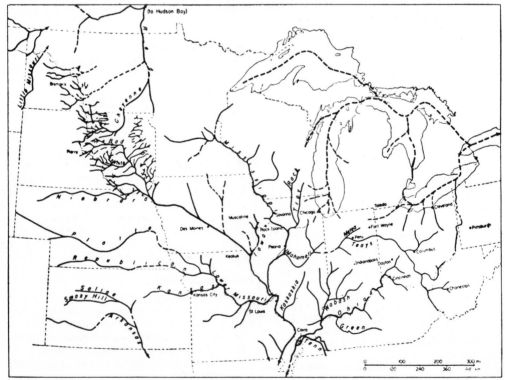

FIG. 2. Stream valleys antedating at least one glaciation in east-central United States. Temporary channels are not included (Flint, 1957). (By permission of John Wiley & Sons, N.Y.)

later coverings of till burying it locally to 120 meters, though subsequent erosion has reexcavated some of the channels.

In northern Europe (Woldstedt, 1954; Charlesworth, 1957), the Saale ice sheet from Scandinavia blocked all the main north-flowing rivers (Vistula, Oder, Elbe), and they were diverted westward to form a valley through the present Straits of Dover to reach the Atlantic west of Brittany. This "Channel River" may still be traced in the gravels beneath the Straits of Dover, where they played an important role in planning the Channel Tunnel.

RHODES W. FAIRBRIDGE

References

Charlesworth, J. K., 1957, "The Quaternary Era," London, Edward Arnold, 2 vols.

Flint, R. F., 1957, "Glacial and Pleistocene Geology," New York, John Wiley & Sons, 553pp.

Horberg, L., 1950, "Bedrock topography of Illinois," *Bull. Illinois Geol. Surv.*, No. 73, 111pp.

Howard, A. D., 1958, "Drainage evolution in northeastern Montana and northwestern North Dakota," *Bull. Geol. Soc. Am.*, **69,** 575–588.

Lee, H. A., 1965, "Buried valleys near Kirkland Lake, Ontario," *Geol. Surv. Canada Pap.* 65–14(2).

Leverett, F., 1942, "Shiftings of the Mississippi River in relation to glaciation," *Bull. Geol. Soc. Am.*, **53,** 1283–1298.

Lumsden, J. I. and Davies, A., 1965, "The buried channel of the River Nith and its marked change in level across the Southern Upland Fault," *Scottish J. Geol.*, **1**(2), 134–143.

Thornbury, W. D., and Deane, H. L., 1955, "The geology of Miami County, Indiana," *J. Geol.*, **48,** 449–475.

Woldstedt, P., 1954–58, "Das Eiszeitalter," Stuttgart, Enke Verlag, second ed., 2 vols.

Cross-references: *Glacial Scour; Glacial Spillways and Proglacial Lakes; Glacial Valleys; Quaternary.* Vol. I: *Mean Sea Level Changes.*

BUTTE—*See* **MESA AND BUTTE**

C

CALDERA

According to the widely accepted definition of Williams (1941), "calderas are large volcanic depressions, more or less circular or cirque-like in form, the diameter of which are many times greater than those of the included vents." The name was first used as a morphological term by Leopold von Buch who applied it to the summit depression of La Palma volcano in the Canary Islands. The name was taken from "caldeira," the Portuguese word for kettle or caldron, which had been used for a depression at the summit of the central volcano of Fayal Island in the Azores.

Calderas are distinguished from craters both by size and origin. Most craters result from ejection of solid and gaseous material from a vent, and few exceed a mile in diameter. Calderas are believed to result primarily from subsidence or collapse which may or may not be related to explosive eruptions. The maximum dimension of explosion craters, about 1 mile, provides an arbitrary but convenient lower limit for the diameter of calderas. Smaller depres-

sions formed by collapse are referred to as *pit craters* or *sinks*. Certain large depressions, though associated with regional volcanic activity, have subsided along fractures controlled by tectonic features or regional fault patterns; these have been called *volcano-tectonic depressions*.

The name caldera is also applied to cirque-like depressions produced by erosion of the central area of large volcanoes, but these *erosion calderas* have little if any direct genetic relation to true calderas (see discussion under *Crater*).

Many classifications of calderas have been proposed, but in recent years two principal types have been recognized as most important. These have been referred to as the Glen Coe type and Krakatoa type;

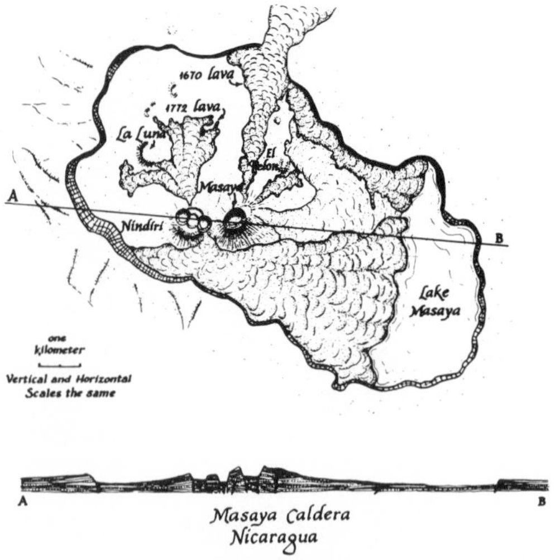

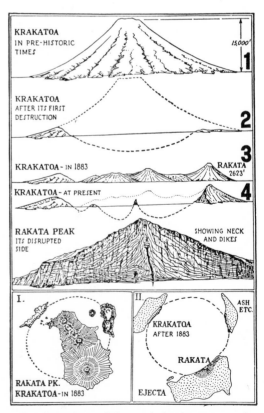

FIG. 1. The Masaya caldera of Nicaragua is a splendid example of a caldera of the Glen Coe type formed by piecemeal passive subsidence unrelated to explosive eruptions. It is a broad, shallow structure with low rims of irregular shape. Several youthful vents on the floor have erupted basaltic lavas of uniform composition.

FIG. 2. Krakatoa, before and after its great eruption in 1883 (from Lobeck, 1939; after Royal Society Report). (By permission of McGraw-Hill Book Co., N.Y.)

FIG. 3. Beginning of the collapse of the crater wall (note semicircular ring fault), on White Island, north of New Zealand. (Photo: S. N. Beatus, New Zealand Geological Survey).

the distinction between them is morphological, structural, and genetic.

The *Glen Coe-type caldera*, named for a deeply eroded structure of Devonian age in Scotland, is formed by passive subsidence along ring-fractures into an underlying magma reservoir. Modern examples are characterized by a broad shallow depression, the floor of which is usually relatively flat and flooded by lavas. The rims of some calderas of this type have been overflowed by lavas, and some are made up of arcuate or scalloped scarps produced by successive subsidences of interlocking circular areas. Steeply dipping dikes intrude the marginal fracture systems in many deeply eroded calderas of this type. Basaltic lavas greatly predominate among the products of eruption, although rhyolite, granophyre, or other acid differentiates may appear during late stages, especially as dikes. Pyroclastic ejecta are very subordinate.

An excellent example of the Glen Coe type still active today is the Masaya caldera of Nicaragua (Fig. 1). Many of the large summit calderas of Hawaii and the Galápagos Islands are also of this type.

Krakatoan calderas are more common, especially in the Circum-Pacific region and in island arcs where they are found on andesitic volcanoes forming large summit depressions with high steep walls that commonly enclose lakes. The caldera of Krakatoa itself was formed in 1883, and several others have been formed during historic times by sudden collapse following colossal eruptions of pumice and other pyroclastic debris (Fig. 2). Explosion mechanisms have clearly played an important role in their origin; nevertheless, the volume of fragmental ejecta derived from the former tops of the volcanoes is far less than the volumes of the depressions. Hence, calderas can only have been formed in part by explosive removal of the mountain tops. The volume discrepancy can be accounted for by assuming that much of the material collapsed into space evacuated by rapid outpouring of magmatic material from the subterranean reservoir below the summit (Fig. 3).

Crater Lake, Oregon, is probably the finest example of a Krakatoa-type caldera (Fig. 4). Other examples are Hakone and Aso calderas in Japan, Santorin caldera in the Grecian archipelago (Fig. 5),

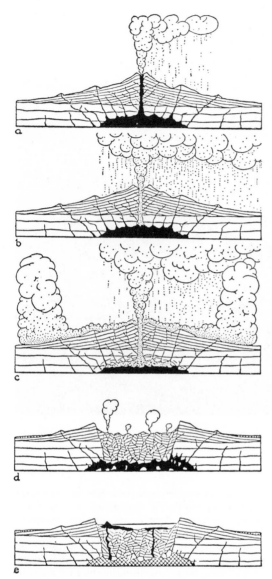

FIG. 4. Evolution and representation of a caldera, based on the example of the 5-mile wide Crater Lake, Oregon (Williams, 1942).

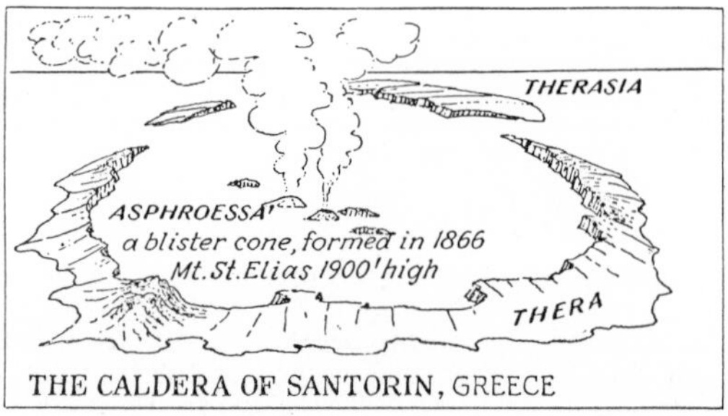

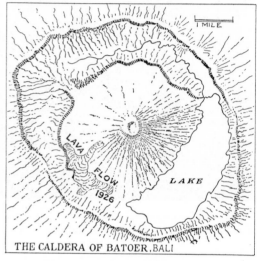

THE CALDERA OF SANTORIN, GREECE

FIG. 5. Partly drowned caldera of Santorin, Greece (Lobeck, 1939). (By permission of McGraw-Hill Book Co., N.Y.)

THE CALDERA OF BATOER, BALI

FIG. 6. Sketch map of the Caldera and new cone of Batoer (or Batur in the new spelling) on Bali (Lobeck, 1939). (By permission of McGraw-Hill Book Co., N.Y.)

Batoer on the island of Bali (Fig. 6), and the caldera of Monte Somma, produced by the great eruption of Vesuvius in A.D. 79.

ALEXANDER R. MCBIRNEY

References

Cotton, C. A., 1952, "Volcanoes as Landscape Forms," pp. 295–337, New York, John Wiley & Sons.
Lobeck, A. K., 1939, "Geomorphology, an Introduction to the Study of Landscapes," New York, McGraw-Hill Book Co., 731pp.
Williams, H., 1941, "Calderas and their origin," *Univ. Calif. Publ. Geol. Sci.*, **25,** 239–346.
Williams, H., 1942, "The geology of Crater Lake National Park, Oregon," *Carnegie Inst. Wash. Publ.*, **540,** 162pp.

Cross-references: *Crater; Volcanic Landscapes; Volcanic Necks and Diaremes.* Vol. II: *Explosion Craters.*

CALICHE, CALCRETE—*See* **INDURATION; DURICRUST;** *also* pr Vol. VI

CANYON CUTTING IN THE COLORADO RIVER SYSTEM

On and along the borders of the Colorado Plateaus, the Colorado River and its main tributaries—the Green, San Juan, Little Colorado and Gila Rivers—have carved the most spectacular network of canyons in North America. The Colorado River

FIG. 1. Marble Canyon, a branch of the Colorado River system, exposing Permian and Carboniferous rocks.

is the trunk stream for the drainage system of the western slope of the Southern Rocky Mountains province, all the Colorado Plateaus province, and much of the eastern part of the Basin and Range province. The canyons were first studied by Powell and later by Blackwelder, Davis, Dutton, Gilbert, Lee, Longwell, Gregory and Hunt (see references in Hunt, 1956; Heindl, 1962; Richmond, 1962; Kottlowski *et al.*, 1965).

Factors Influencing Cutting

Canyon formation in much of the Colorado River system has not been a simple process of continuous downcutting. Instead, it has occurred in pulses controlled mainly by recurrent structural and volcanic activity during Tertiary time, and by climatic fluctuations, structural warping and minor volcanism during Quaternary time. In the Colorado Plateaus province, where structural and volcanic activity was slight, stream entrenchment and canyon cutting were more continuous than in the Basin and Range province. In that province, as exemplified in the Gila River drainage area, the development of drainage and cutting has been complex because of the recurrent differential uplift or subsidence, faulting, and the volcanic activity.

There is evidence of a marked influence of climatic conditions on the general entrenchment of streams in the Colorado River system only during Pleistocene time. Climatic changes producing at times glacial and periglacial activity caused alternating episodes of accelerated erosion and deposition and widespread terracing to modify the downcutting pattern of many streams. For example, seven prom-

FIG. 3. Canyon de Chelly, near Chinle, Arizona. Cut in Triassic and Permian sandstone, the valley is partly filled with late Pleistocene and Recent alluvium, up to 90 meters thick. (Photo: R. W. Fairbridge.)

FIG. 2. Canyon of the Little Colorado, exposing Permian and Carboniferous rocks, as in Fig. 1.

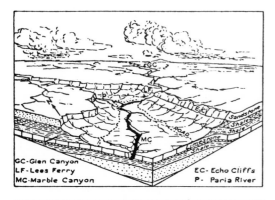

GC-Glen Canyon
LF-Lees Ferry
MC-Marble Canyon

EC- Echo Cliffs
P- Paria River

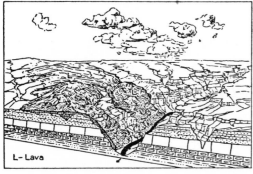

L- Lava

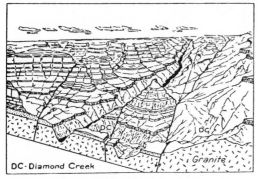

DC-Diamond Creek

Granite

FIG. 4. Block diagrams of Colorado canyons. The uppermost figure shows erosion of soft strata between Glen and Marble Canyons. The middle figure shows invasion of Grand Canyon by lava from the plateau above, near the Toroweap fault. The lowest figure shows faulted area near Diamond Creek. The river does not follow the faults (Birdseye and Moore, 1924).

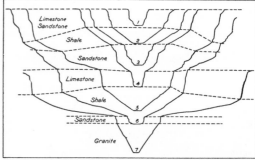

Limestone
Sandstone
Shale
Sandstone
Limestone
Shale
Sandstone
Granite

1. Upper Marble Canyon, three miles below Paria R
2. Upper Marble Canyon, at mouth of Soap Creek
3. Upper Marble Canyon, twenty miles below Paria R.
4. Middle Marble Canyon, below Vaseys Paradise
5. Lower Marble Canyon, at mouth of Kwagunt Cr.
6. Three miles below mouth of Little Colorado R.
7. Granite Gorge above Bright Angel Creek.

FIG. 5. Profiles of Marble and Grand Canyons showing the manner in which the topography and the width of the canyons are controlled by the character of the rocks (Birdseye and Moore, 1924).

Amount and Time of Cutting

Early investigators postulated that the development and entrenchment of the Colorado River system on the Colorado Plateaus occurred during two general periods of erosion. The first, generally considered to be of Tertiary age, was referred to by Dutton (1882) as the "Great Denudation," and Davis (1901) termed it the "Plateau Cycle." The latter one, of Quaternary age, was referred to as the "Canyon Cycle" by these investigators. Recent investigations have indicated that regional downcutting and entrenchment of the Colorado River system was generally continuous throughout late Cenozoic time and that it was, perhaps, interrupted by only one period of deposition during the Pliocene and by episodes of terracing during the Quaternary. However, the initial cutting of most canyons occupied by the Colorado River and its principal tributaries occurred in late Tertiary time, although the beginning of the canyon cutting differs from drainage to drainage and along reaches of the same drainage.

Other canyons, generally older than those occupied by the Colorado River, were trenched in Tertiary time. Among these are the Unaweep Canyon of western Colorado, abandoned by the Colorado River probably during the Tertiary, and several canyons in the southwestern border region of the Colorado Plateaus in Arizona. The original depth of some of these canyons of the plateaus border region is more than 300 meters (1000 feet); some were filled by sediments that were partly removed, and the canyons were deepened by renewed canyon cutting beginning in late Tertiary time.

Canyon cutting in the part of the Basin and Range province drained by the Colorado River system took place mainly in the mountainous areas along the margins of the Colorado Plateaus and in the mountain ranges that surrounded the closed basins.

inent terrace levels record interruptions in the cutting of Glen Canyon by the Colorado River. The terraces are capped by gravel; the capping along many streams in the Colorado River system is more than 30 meters (100 feet) thick. The gravel that caps some of the terraces in the Colorado and in the nearby Rio Grande system has been traced upstream into the glacial outwash, which was deposited in the mountainous headwater regions.

TABLE 1. DEPTH OF RIVER DOWNCUTTING AT SELECTED POINTS IN THE COLORADO RIVER SYSTEM

River	Approximate Depth of River Downcutting					
	Since Beginning of Middle Quaternary (post-Blancan Time)		Since Beginning of Early Quaternary		Since Beginning of Late Tertiary (Late Miocene and Younger)	
	meters	feet	meters	feet	meters	feet
Colorado River						
North of La Sal Mountains	?		250	800[a]	600 +	2000 +
Confluence with San Juan River	200	650	300	1000	1500 +	4900 +
Boulder Reservoir	175 +	575 +	?		?	
Little Colorado River						
Near St. Johns	60	200	130	425	800±	2600±
Near Holbrook	100	325	150	400	1000±	3300±
Near Cameron at head of canyon	110	350	175	575	1000 +	3300 +
Gila River						
Safford basin	270	900[b]	?		?	
Florence	50	175	?		?	
Painted Rock Dam	100	325	?		?	
Salt River						
Salt River Canyon	100–150?	330–500?	?		1000 +	3300 +
Santa Cruz River near Tucson	150±	500±	?		?	

[a] Richmond (1962, p. 94).
[b] Written communication (1966), E. S. Davidson, U.S. Geological Survey.

Canyon erosion in the closed basin systems was principally a headward extension of canyon reaches of streams that drained basinward. As the basins were integrated during late Tertiary and Quaternary time, through-flowing drainage was established generally in a downstream direction from the headwater areas. Concurrent with the establishment of through drainage, canyon cutting was accelerated in the mountainous areas, particularly in the ranges bordering the previously closed basins. The newly formed canyons, however, are not of the same age. Excavation of Salt River Canyon probably began in Pliocene time, but the establishment of the through-flowing Gila River with the resulting accelerated canyon cutting across the mountain chains downstream from Safford basin did not occur until after early Pleistocene time. As a result of regional downwarping accompanied by recurrent faulting and tilting and in places by volcanism, canyon cutting was interrupted; alluvial deposits, locally many hundreds of meters thick, were laid down in the basins also during late Tertiary and early Quaternary time. Some of the deposits were sufficiently widespread to extend into the mountainous areas and partly fill many canyons.

During late Quaternary time when climatic influences were at a maximum, downcutting accompanied by extensive terracing took place along most drainages of the Colorado River system (Table 1). Terraces owing their origin to climatic influences are best recognized along streams draining high mountainous areas that receive considerable precipitation. The greatest amount of downcutting occurred in parts of southeastern Arizona and southwestern New Mexico and on the Colorado Plateaus, as a result of climatic influences and also of regional upwarping. Conversely, the least was in southwestern Arizona and southeastern California, where climatic influences and regional upwarping have been at a minimum.

Most canyons and valleys in the Colorado River system probably had attained essentially their present maximum depths by late Pleistocene or not later than early Recent time. Thereafter, the canyons were progressively, but intermittently, aggraded until renewed cutting, beginning mainly during the late part of the last century, terminated deposition. The thickness of the alluvium differs considerably and in many places is as much as 60 meters.

MAURICE E. COOLEY
ALFONSO WILSON

References

Birdseye, C. H., and Moore, R. C., 1924, "A boat voyage through the Grand Canyon of the Colorado," *Geogr. Rev.*, **14**, 177–196.

Davis, W. M., 1901, "An excursion to the Grand Canyon of the Colorado," *Harvard Coll. Mus. Zoology Bull.*, **38**, 107–201.

Dutton, C. E., 1882, "Tertiary history of the Grand Canyon district, with atlas," *U.S. Geol. Surv. Mon.*, **2**, 264pp.

Heindl, L. A. (editor), 1962, "Cenozoic geology of

Arizona—a symposium," *Arizona Geol. Soc. Digest*, **5**, 130pp.

Hunt, C. B., 1956, "Cenozoic geology of the Colorado Plateau," *U.S. Geol. Surv. Profess. Paper* **279**, 99pp.

Kottlowski, F. E., Cooley, M. E., and Ruhe, R. V., 1965, "Quaternary Geology of the Southwest," in (Wright, H. E., Jr., and Frey, D. G., editors) "The Quaternary of the United States," pp. 287–298, Princeton, N.J., Princeton University Press.

Richmond, G. M., 1962, "Quaternary stratigraphy of the La Sal Mountains, Utah," *U.S. Geol. Surv. Profess. Paper* **324**, 135pp.

Cross-references: *Amphitheater Valley Heads*; *Alluvium*; *Basin and Range Landscape*; *Climatic Geomorphology*; *Denudation*; *Drainage Patterns*; *Quaternary Period*; *Rivers*; *Sediment Transport*; *Stream Flow*; *Structural Control in Geomorphology*; *Terraces—Fluvial*;*Valley Evolution*. pr Vol. VIII: *Basin and Range Province*.

CAPTURE—STREAM, RIVER—*See* STREAM CAPTURE, PIRACY

CAROLINA BAYS

These *oriented lakes* (q.v.) are sharply outlined, elliptical, white-rimmed, forest-bound features that are widespread along the Atlantic coastal plain of the United States from Maryland to northern Florida (Fig. 1). They elicited wide interest when they were first described from aerial photographs with the suggestion that they might be the craters of a giant swarm of meteorites (Melton and Schriever, 1933). A large literature on the "Bays" has resulted, and by 1949 a total of a dozen or more other genetic hypotheses had been proposed (Table 1) all of which have been found to be untenable (Tables 2 and 3).

Bay trees are abundant around the shores of most "Bay" lakes and thus gave the name to their geomorphic form and the assemblage of marsh plants common to them. The aboriginal name *pocosin* has been used by some writers.

The Bays region stretches 700 miles along the coast, its greatest width being 200 miles in southern Georgia. There may be as many as a half-million Bays (Prouty, 1952). They have been most fully studied in the Carolinas where they are most thickly distributed. In some places, they occupy more than half the area, with innumerable intersections and bay-in-bay forms.

The Bays are oriented northwest-southeast, with a small angular shift to the south from Maryland to Florida (Johnson, 1942, Figs. 27, 28). They are limited to the Quaternery coastal plain (Fig. 1) and occur in two coastwise belts (Price, 1958, pp. 62–69, 72, 73). In a belt extending inland some 50 miles, the Bays lie along the beach plains of each of the Pleistocene terraces (Cooke, 1954) with the associated deltaic cuspate forelands. The Bays are here aligned in parallel series along their short axes (see Johnson, 1942, Fig. 7), which conform to the lineation of the beach plains (Fig. 2).

Interior to the coastal belt is a broad belt of Bays, 150 miles wide, in southern Georgia. In this belt, the

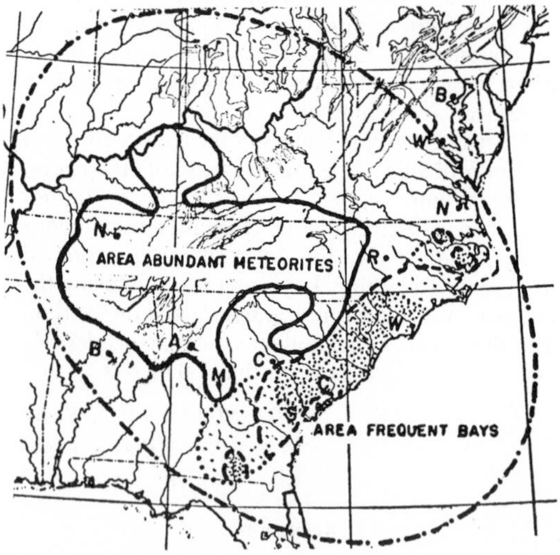

Fig. 1. Distribution of Carolina "Bays," forested humid Atlantic coastal plain of southeastern United States (modified after Prouty, 1952, Fig. 1). Zone of Bays now known to extend northeastward into Virginia and Maryland. Coastal terrace belt and interior sand dune field belt (approximately divided along broken line) distinguished by lateral and longitudinal alignments, respectively (some terrace alignments northwest of line). Longitudinal dune field remnants known in Brandywine area, just east of Washington (W).

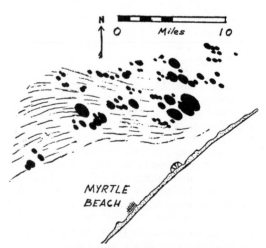

Fig. 2. Bays more than 1000 feet long aligned (along short axes) with pattern of marshy inter-ridge swales of coastwise cuspate deltaic foreland of Pee Dee River. Sandy ridges (dashed lines) diverge toward river. Present mainland beach stippled. Bays shorter than 600 feet occur in area, a part of Horry County, South Carolina, near Myrtle Beach (modified after Prouty, 1952, Fig. 21; Johnson, 1942, Fig. 7).

TABLE 1. GENETIC SUGGESTIONS AND HYPOTHESES[a]

(1) Spring basins (Toumey, 1848, pp. 143, 144).

(2) Sand bar dams of drowned valleys (Glenn, 1895).

(3) Depressions dammed by giant sand ripples (Glenn, 1895, alternative).

(4) Craters of meteor swarm (Melton and Schriever, 1933). Supported by Prouty (1952) and associates, holding that weak magnetic anomalies showed buried magnetic meteorites southeast of individual Bays. Supported also by Wells and Boyce (1953). Peat in crater fill was burned out by Indians.

(5) Submarine scour by eddies, currents or undertow (Melton, 1934; alternative to No. 4).

(6) Segmentation of lagoons and formation of crescentic keys (Cooke, 1934). Original hollows at the foot of marine terraces and between dunes (Cooke, 1954, p. 195).

(7) Lakes in sand elongated in direction of maximum wind velocity (Raisz, 1934).

(8) Solution depressions, with wind-drift sand forming the "rims" (Johnson, 1936).

(9) Solution depressions, with magnetic highs near Bays due to redeposition of iron compounds leached from basins (Lobeck, 1939, pp. 714, 715).

(10) Basins scoured out by confined gyroscopic eddies (Cooke, 1940, 1954). Schriever finds the hypothesis mathematically and physically insupportable (Schriever, 1955; Jones, 1956).

(11) Solution basins of artesian springs, with lee dunes. Johnson's (1942) "complex artesian-solution-lacustrine-aeolian" hypothesis.

(12) Fish nests made by giant schools of fish waving their fins in unison over submarine artesian springs (Grant, 1945).

(13) Eolian (deflation) blowouts, reported by Prouty (1952) as suggested "by a number of scientists" (unnamed, see No. 15).

(14) Bays are sinks over limestone solution areas, streamlined by groundwater (Le Grand, 1953; Shockley *et al.*, 1956). A modification of Johnson (1942, pp. 247–274) and Prouty (1952, pp. 194, 195).

(15) Oriented lakes of stabilized grassland inter-ridge swales of former beach plains and longitudinal dune fields, with some formed from basins in Pleistocene lagoons (Price, 1951, 1958). This is an elaboration of No. 13, here modified following Carson and Hussey's (1960, 1962) principle of orientation by wind waves of opposed wind systems. The basins are now in humid forest phase of Quaternary climatic oscillations and thus extinct, with the few having lakes now being senescent or nearly so.

[a] After Prouty (1952) with additions.

Bays are aligned in parallel series with their long axes along the lineation of the now vaguely outlined field or fields of longitudinal dunes in which they lie (Price, 1958; see also Figs. 3, 4 and 5). Here, the Bays are widespread over the alluvial deltaic plain of the Citronelle formation (Doering, 1960) and occur also on river terraces, valley slopes and the higher parts of some river flood plains (Prouty, 1952), and on deltaic parts of some higher coastwise terraces. In the dune field areas, the secondary upland drainage preserves the parallel pattern of the inter-ridge swales in spite of Bay interferences

TABLE 2. OBJECTIONS TO HYPOTHESES
(See Nos. 1–3, 5–14 of Table 1)

(a) Patterns of subaerial barriers and dune fields within which all the Bays lie would not have survived marine invasions and did not form under water (except beach ridges) as required by submarine hypotheses (Nos. 2, 3, 5, 6 and 12).

(b) Under solution-geared hypotheses (Nos. 8, 9, 11 and 14) as recognized by Melton (1950), the characteristic lenticularity of Quaternary terrace and delta strata would have prevented the existing uniformity of Bay size range and orientation and the highly selective distribution.

(c) Eolian erosion, appealed to in No. 13 is a part of the activities under No. 15, here advocated.

(d) Burning of peat in Bays by aborigines could have altered outline of lakes within bays and changed the rates of sedimentary filling, but solves no other Bays problems (see Wells and Boyce's modification of No. 4).

(e) Spring crater basins (Nos. 1 and 11) and limestone sinks (No. 14) would have had to be too numerous and too selectively distributed to have produced the Bays. Artesian springs emanating in the midst of areas of precipitation intake over an extensive plain would not be consistent. Recognized by Melton (1950).

(f) Schriever (1955) showed (1) that water does not sustain gyroscopic eddies in open basins, (2) that eddies in lakes the sizes of the bays would not be sufficiently erosive to have shaped them, and (3) that the long axis directions of typical Bays do not conform to the rigid earth-axis control of orientation demanded by Cooke's hypothesis (No. 10). Still less would the hypothesis apply to the world distribution of oriented lakes.

(g) Objections to No. 4, meteor crater origin, will be discussed on a later page and in Table 3.

TABLE 3. GENETIC CRITERIA OF "BAYS" AND METEOR CRATERS COMPARED

Craters	Bays
(A) Criteria of Craters Not Found in Bays	
(1) Meteoritic material abundant about the crater.	The two meteorites found so far have no genetic relation to Bays. (Henderson 1965; Henderson and Cooke 1942).
(2) Ejecta breccia covers an elevated structural rim.	Rims are of sorted beach and eolian sand. No structural disturbances reported in or near Bays.
(B) Criteria of "Bays" Not Found in Meteor Craters	
(1) Largest known group of craters, at Campo del Cielo, Argentina has 9 craters in a NE-SW zone 17.5 × 1.0 km in area. (Cassidy *et al.*, 1965).	Hundreds of thousands of "Bays" in regional spread of 700 × 200 miles.
(2) No terrain selectivity. Craters preserved longest in hard rocks.	Highly selective distribution in Quaternary deposits, along preexisting inter-ridge swales of sandy land.
(C) Contrast Not Critical if Craters had been Long Modified by Lake Development	
(1) Most craters rounded and deep.	Bays elliptical, and shallow for their widths.

(Price, 1958; Hack, 1955, Pl. 1; see also Fig. 3). The normal drainage pattern of the region is dendritic. Cooke's (1934) idea that the Bays originated in coastwise lagoons is not borne out by the published photographs, but seems to apply to some of the oriented lakes of arctic Alaska (Black and Barksdale, 1949, Pl. 4B).

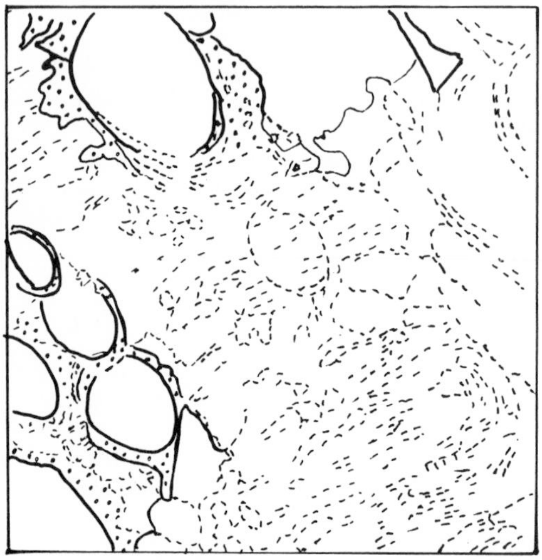

In their occurrence in the two coastwise belts, the Bays show a high degree of distributional selectivity for specific geomorphic forms and terrain types— beach ridges and dune fields. This selectivity is emphasized by the alignments of the basins in parallel series along the lineation of the ridges and inter-ridge swales of sandy land. This selectivity rules out all other hypotheses of their origin.

The Bays occur in two nearly elliptical forms: One is slightly bulged, mostly at the southeast, and the other is tapered at one end, also usually toward the south. Axial ratios range from 1:1.2 to 1:1.7, with a mean of about 1.5. Most simple Bays are 1–3 miles long, but one is reportedly 7 miles long (Prouty, 1952). The Bays are largely sediment filled; a few have residual lakes mostly in their southern parts which are filled by precipitation or, in a few reported cases, maintained by artesian springs. The filled areas are grassy glades or forested peaty marsh with cypresses along their shore lines. The maximum water depth reported is 12 feet and the depth of fill is up to about 25 feet (Glenn, 1895; Frey, 1954). Most Bays are partly or wholly rimmed by narrow beach ridges of gray or white bleached sand (Fig. 4). They may be multiple, forming narrow beach plains (Fig. 5), or widened by sand drifting, some having U-dunes (Prouty, 1952, Pl. 4, Fig. 2) and some transversely grooved by wind (Johnson, 1942, Fig. 14).

Rim-ridge development is greatest at the east and southeast parts of a Bay. The beach slopes gently offshore with an equilibrium profile in sand. The opposite peaty shore usually has a jagged, caving shore line, with as much as 4 feet of water just offshore (Frey, 1954). Beach plain development, where multiple, has crowded the lake to the west (see

FIG. 3. Marshy and sand-filled bays aligned on long axes along swales between stabilized sandy dune ridges (dashed pattern). Beach ridges of Bays, white in nature (stippled). Dashed lines show pattern of transverse deflationary grooving indicating recent reworking by southwest wind. During earlier period, storm waves drove against eastern, southeastern and southern shores and Bays were oriented by bimodal (flank) wind waves from the northeast and southwest. Bladen and Sampson counties, North Carolina (from Prouty, 1952, Pl. 6, Fig. 2; air photograph). North is at top (scale in miles).

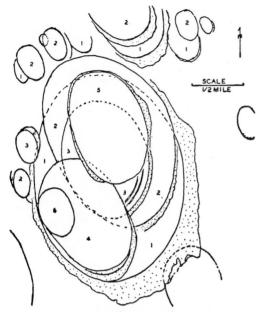

SCALE
1/2 MILE

FIG. 4. Bay-in-bay shrinkage pattern showing retrograde westward migration and progressive shift of axis. Basin age succession 1-6 as numbered by Prouty. In interior longitudinal dune field belt, Cumberland County, North Carolina. Beach ridges stippled; Bay outlines in broken line inferred (Prouty, 1952, Fig. 14A).

Johnson, 1942, Fig. 36), successive shore lines showing moderate westward migration (Fig. 4). Vegetational histories show late alternations of moderate shrinkage and enlargement, the latter characterizing at least the last 500 years (Frey, 1954). However, the pattern of rims and former shore lines show that shrinkage has been the major trend in their late history.

Bay-fill surfaces (Portsmouth soil of Hardison, 1915) are peaty or have 8–15 inches of black organic sand underlain by loose white or light-gray sand, with a compact brown layer a few inches thick and about 20 inches down. The beach ridge sand (St. Lucie soil) is white to a depth of 3 feet or more. The ridges are as high as 10–30 feet. Stabilized dune ridges (Norfolk sand; Fig. 5) are yellow with a grayish surface layer. They are commonly transversely grooved southwest-northeast by recent southwest sand-moving winds (Johnson, 1942, pp. 314–316). Near the coast, Pleistocene terrace beach ridges, as exposed along estuarine bluffs, are brown, somewhat consolidated sand with columnar jointing below a gray or white surface zone. In the southeast, surface sands that are normally yellow to light brown are bleached gray or white in lows. In the Bays, bleaching goes deeper than elsewhere. The white "rims" are sand reworked from the Portsmouth soil of the Bays. The dune-field belt of Bays lies in the zone of Pleistocene eolian sands shown on the United States Eolian Map (1952).

Borings into Bay fill to 25-foot depth show silt with some clay and two thin organic layers below the surficial peat and black sand. The lowest organic zone is more than 40,000 years old, roughly the age of the 15-foot Princess Anne terrace (Hoyt *et al.*, 1965). The organic layers represent interstadial or interglacial humid hardwood forest, and the silts record cold glacials. Full-glacial vegetation had very widely spaced red or jack pines on coarse sand ridges with shrubs and herbs, while spruce and other trees occurred elsewhere (Frey, 1953, 1955; Whitehead, 1965).

The sea has invaded some Bays of the Silver Bluff 2–10 foot terrace in Maryland (Cooke, 1954, Pls. 41–43). Marine erosion, at a higher level than today, is thought to have obliterated a zone of Bays near Myrtle Beach, South Carolina (Prouty, 1952, p. 192, Fig. 19). This information, with the dates of Bay fill obtained, suggests one or more late Pleistocene periods of Bay development and possibly some coastal warping.

Among all the genetic hypotheses of Tables 1 and 2, only the lacustrine wind-and-wave erosion process (Price, 1958), as here described, explains the high degree of terrain selectivity of the Carolina Bays and other oriented lakes of ridged sandy land not controlled by fault-block slumping (Plafka, 1964). However, many, probably most, of the Alaskan coastal plain permafrost lakes may have had beach ridge and dune field swale control (Black and Barksdale 1949, pl. 3B).

Modern and Analogous Lakes

Forms intermediate between the Bays and the initial swale ponds of today's beach plains (Prouty, 1952, Pl. 3, Fig. 2) occur in the Bays region (Figs. 2 and 3), as well as on the Pleistocene Ingleside barrier of Texas and other old barriers.

The closest counterparts of the mature Bays, among oriented lakes, are the shallow, 60-foot-deep series of unfilled elliptical playa basins of the former longitudinal dune field of the Llano Estacado plateau (southern High Plains of New Mexico and Texas) (Price, 1958). The oriented Alaskan coastal plain lakes are similar, though the elongated form produced in permafrost has no counterpart in the Bays region.

Wind Conditions

To predict the form of an oriented lake from the wind spread, or, conversely, to infer a wind regime from lake form, may be attempted by the use of analytical wind diagrams, or "wind roses" (see Vol. II), as in Fig. 6.

The effectiveness of wind on sand and in producing water waves is an exponential value of velocity, the cube being used for sand transport. The square has been used as a comparative value for wave erosion (Price, 1933, Fig. 9), although the cube may be better. Long-period effects require that the

FIG. 5. Short-axis alignments of Bays follow pattern of deltaic cuspate foreland of Pee Dee River, west of canal and Myrtle Beach, South Carolina. Bay "rims" white to gray. Wider, downweathered beach ridges gray, mostly cultivated. Dark areas marshy, some forested. Several Bays are too faint to show clearly. Shore line trends N45°E (part of area shown by Prouty, 1952, Fig. 21; Johnson, 1942, Fig. 7).

exponential velocity value be multiplied by duration, or the number of hourly observations. The frequently used rose based on the first power of velocity gives erroneous comparative values. However, the use of an exponential value will not appreciably change the relative values of opposing winds of approximately equal velocities. Using the cube, the following form has been developed, based on the work by Bagnold (1941):

$$S = (V - v)^3 D$$

where S is the comparative wind strength, V is all wind velocities (prevailing wind), v the velocities of light winds below threshold value, and D the

duration, or number, of observations [Price, 1958 (Fig. 8), 1963]. An error which is insignificant in morphological analysis is introduced when average values are cubed or squared (sum of cubes not equal to cube of sums). Time (age) is also a factor in morphological analysis.

In lake development, the values of fetch diameter) and depth may determine the range of velocities which are effective for winds blowing across the lake. The degree to which a protective forest may reduce the effectiveness of wind has not been determined. It may be that only storm winds have been effective, after forestation.

A sub-uniform distribution of wind tends to

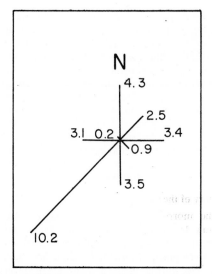

FIG. 6. Wind rose showing comparative wind "strengths" for Wilmington, North Carolina. Weather Bureau, climatic summaries, period before 1942 (data from Johnson, 1942, pp. 292, 294; see Table IV). "Strength" (directed toward center of graph) figures are from V^3D column. V includes all winds in miles per hour. (By permission of Columbia University Press, N.Y.)

produce round lakes. Sub-equally opposed resultants of two flank wind systems develop an elongated lake form with the orientation axis perpendicular to the mean direction of opposition of the flank resultants (Carson and Hussey, 1960, 1962).

A slight departure from equality of flank wind opposition should produce only a slight departure from ellipticity or elongate-oval form, as in the Bays and the Arctic Coastal Plain lakes of Alaska (Black and Barksdale, 1949). However, when an

exponential wind rose is constructed from the prevailing winds for the Bays region (see Fig. 6 and Table 4), the opposed resultants are too unequal to explain the small lack of symmetry of the Bays. This supports the conclusion from other conditions that the Bays were shaped before the coming of the forest and the present wind regime.

In grassy prairie free from forest, a present angle of around 160° between opposing flank resultant vectors seems to agree with the present heart-shaped and clam-shaped forms of the wedge-shaped playa lake basins of the south Texas coastal plain (Johnson, 1942, Fig. 46; Price, 1958, Figs. 8, 18). They now trend east-west but lie in interdune swale depressions that trend northwest-southeast. In tundra, tapered Alaskan coastal plain lakes are explained by Carson and Hussey (1962, Fig. 14) as shaped by a present seasonal asymmetry in the opposition of flank resultants.

Magnetic Surveys and the Meteor Crater Hypothesis

Prouty concluded from widely scattered, small-area magnetometer surveys which yielded both large and small, weak anomalies that he had located buried meteoritic materials lying roughly southeast of certain large Bays. However, when studying such small anomalies where large, strong ones are also present, it is standard practice to map large surrounding areas to determine the patterns of anomaly occurrence, especially desirable here, where the Bays occur in definite alignments. Large-area surveys were not made and Prouty did not find simple relationships between the large Bays and their supposedly related small anomalies. The looked-for relationship was based on a diagonal penetration hypothesis. Nevertheless, Prouty attempted by various involved interpretations of a subjective nature to relate small anomalies to specific large Bays. As late as 1965 (Henderson,

TABLE 4. WIND-STRENGTH ROSE FOR WILMINGTON, N.C. FROM CLIMATIC SUMMARIES, U.S. WEATHER BUREAU[a]

Direction from which wind blew;	Annual mean average hourly velocity, V	V^3	1/100 of total hours for year (each wind), D	Wind strengths (relative),[b] V^3D
W	6.3	250	16.56	3150
SW	8.0	512	19.90	10240
S	6.9	393	8.82	3537
N	6.6	287	14.59	4305
NE	6.1	227	10.73	2497
E	7.2	373	9.14	3394
NW	3.7	51	3.65	182
SE	6.3	250	3.93	982

[a] Data from D. W. Johnson (1942, pp. 292, 294). Period not given.
[b] There is an error in the final column (the sum of the cubes is not equal to the cube of the sums). However, the errors are too small to affect the morphological conclusions.

1965), no meteoritic materials are reported to have been found in association with any Bay.

Limestone Sinks in Bays Region

Limestone sinks occur in the Bays region where the rock is at or near the surface, but there is no similarity in distribution patterns between Bays and sinks. The sinks have no common orientation (Johnson, 1942, Fig. 41), although where there are lakes in the sinks, beach ridges have formed along their shores (Johnson, 1942, pp. 256, 266). Shockley and associates (1956) illustrated lakes which they interpreted as solution basins and sinks, but which lack the orientation and alignment patterns of the Bays. LeGrand (1953) advocated limestone solution as the origin of the Bays, but shows no examples of solution basins or sinks with Bay-distribution patterns. Johnson (1942, Fig. 44) illustrates alignments of a few oval lakes of Florida along what seem to be parallel fractures, but the geology of the occurrence has not been described. The writer knows of no large assemblies of oriented lakes in limestone nor whether this occurrence is in a dune field.

The oriented playa basins of the Llano Estacado, once described by the writer as forming a "caliche karst," in the main do not penetrate the thin, impure caliche beds, and those that do so seem to have had a deflation-lacustrine origin not materially influenced in shape by leaching of the caliche.

Bays Senescent in Forest

The Carolina Bays are all filled or nearly filled with sediment. Johnson (1942) names ten Bays with lakes and says that many others have at least seasonal lakes. These must have very shallow basins. Thus, the percentage of Bays with lakes of appreciable depth is very small. According to Wells and Boyce (1953) peat fires, especially during the period of human occupation, have made depressions in basins formerly filled. Fire may have had a part in the "modest" expansion of Bay lakes during the past 500 or more years recognized by Frey (1954).

Oriented lakes, as a class, lie mostly in open treeless plains of warm or cold arid and semiarid climates. Most of the oriented squarish lakes of the Beni Basin fracture network in Bolivia (Plafka, 1964) lie in subhumid marshy savanna. The Carolina Bays are the only large assembly in a humid hardwood forest, but river-course tongues and a narrow marginal zone of the Beni Basin lakes are enclosed in forest. Many of the Beni Basin lakes in the open savanna have developed oval elongations on the northeast-southwest axis. In the narrow belts of forest, however, the map shows only two of the squarish lakes so elongated, these lying in the margin of the forest which may well be a late expansion enclosing lakes already having oval elongations.

Associated Dunes are Grassland Forms

The longitudinal dune fields of the interior belt of the Bays and *oriented lakes* (q.v.) of the Llano Estacado required semiarid grassland for their stabilization into the period of lake orientation. It is most likely that the dunes are of the hairpin and wind drift varieties, the ridges being formed as lag accumulations of a migrating spot blowout. It is probable that the Bays attained mature elliptical forms in the grassland stage, or in successive grassland stages. The filling required prolonged lake stages. Today, they seem to be oscillating between stages of "modest" expansion and contraction (Frey, 1954), but the present expansion may have been aided by peat fires (Wells and Boyce, 1953).

History of the Bays

The morphology of the Bay region and the organic layers representing former humid forests in the Bay fill suggest the following hypothesis of Bay development. Longitudinal dune field building took place during one or more events of glaciation and lowered sea level, the fields extending down the alluviated surfaces of major river valleys to and beyond the present shore line (e.g. Savannah River, Georgia). Bays developed to maturity of form along the inter-ridge swales and on beach plains of the terraces. For reasons unknown, the sandy beach plains were not reworked into longitudinal dunes. Bay development occurred just before the Princess Anne (15-foot) shore line period and after the Silver Bluff (2–10 foot) shore line.

Filling of the Bays, with shrinkage morphology, took place during humid forest periods. A change in wind regime between grassland and forest conditions is indicated by the offshore movement of sand during the dune building and the present northeasterly movement of sand eroded from Bay rims. A similar wind change is recorded for the oriented lakes of the Llano Estacado between the period of dune building and lake enlargement (sand movement to the southeast) and the present period, during which sand is moved dominantly to the north-northeast and north-northwest. In both regions, present eolian activity is considerably less than during the dune building stage.

W. Armstrong Price

References

Bagnold, R. A., 1941, "The Physics of Blown Sand and Desert Dunes," First ed., London, Methuen & Co., 265pp.

Black, R. F., and Barksdale, W. L., 1949, "Oriented lakes of northern Alaska," *J. Geol.*, **57**, 105–118.

Carson, C. E., and Hussey, K. M., 1960, "Hydrodynamics in three arctic lakes," *J. Geol.*, **68**, 585–600.

Carson, C. E., and Hussey, K. M., 1962, "The oriented lakes of arctic Alaska," *J. Geol.*, **70**, 417–439.

Cassidy, W. A., *et al.*, 1965, "Meteorites and craters of Campo del Cielo, Argentina," *Science*, **149**, 1055–1064.

Cooke, C. W., 1934, "Discussion of the origin of the

supposed meteorite scars of South Carolina," *J. Geol.*, **42**, 88–96.

Cooke, C. W., 1940, "Elliptical bays in South Carolina and the shape of eddies," *J. Geol.*, **48**, 205–211.

Cooke, C. W., 1954, "Carolina Bays and the shapes of eddies," *U.S. Geol. Survey Profess. Paper* **254-I**, 195–204.

Doering, J. A., 1960, "Quaternary surface formations of southern part of Atlantic coastal plain," *J. Geol.*, **68**, 182–202.

Frey, D. G., 1953, "Regional aspects of the late-glacial and post-glacial pollen succession of southeastern North Carolina," *Ecol. Monog.*, **23**, 289–313.

Frey, D. G., 1954, "Evidence for the recent enlargement of the "Bay" lakes of North Carolina," *Ecology*, **35**, 78–88.

Frey, D. G., 1955, "A time revision of the Pleistocene pollen chronology of southeastern North Carolina," *Ecology*, **36**, 762–763.

Glenn, L. C., 1895, "Some notes on Darlington, South Carolina bays," *Science*, **2**, 472–475.

Grant, Chapman, 1945, "A biological explanation of the Carolina Bays," *Sci. Monthly*, **61**, 443–450.

Hack, J. T., 1955, "Geology of the Brandywine area and origin of the upland of southern Maryland," *U.S. Geol. Surv. Profess. Paper* **267-A**, 43pp., maps.

Hardison, R. B., *et al.*, 1915, "Soil survey of Bladen County, North Carolina," U.S. Bureau of Soils, Field Operations 1914, 35pp., map.

Henderson, E. P., 1965, Letter to W. A. Price.

Henderson, E. P., and Cooke, C. W., 1942, "The Sardis (Ga.) meteorite; a nickle-rich ataxite," *U.S. Nat. Mus. Proc.*, **92**, 21–23.

Hoyt, J. H., Weimer, R. J., and Henry, V. J., 1965, "Age of late Pleistocene shoreline deposits, coastal Georgia," *Abstracts Int. Assoc. Quaternary Res. (INQUA)*, *VII Congres, Gen. Sess., Boulder and Denver, Colorado* (Aug. 30–Sept. 5, 1965).

Johnson, D. W., 1936, "Origin of the supposed meteorite scars of Carolina," *Science*, **48**, 15–18.

Johnson, D. W., 1942, "The Origin of the Carolina Bays," New York, Columbia University Press, 341pp.

Jones, V. L., 1956, "Discussion of 'Were the Carolina bays oriented by gyroscopic action?' by W. Schriever," *Trans. Am. Geophys. Union*, **37**, 112–117.

Le Grand, H. E., 1953, "Streamlining of the Carolina Bays," *J. Geol.*, **61**, 263–274.

Lobeck, A. K., 1939, "Geomorphology, An Introduction To the Study of Landscapes," New York, McGraw-Hill Book Co., 731pp.

Melton, F. A., 1934, "Reply to Cooke (1934)," *J. Geol.*, **42**, 97–104.

Melton, F. A., 1950, "The Carolina bays," *J. Geol.*, **58**, 128–134.

Melton, F. A., and Schriever, W., 1933, "The Carolina 'bays'—are they meteorite scars?," *J. Geol.*, **41**, 52–66.

Plafka, Geo., 1964, "Oriented lakes and lineaments of northeastern Bolivia," *Bull. Geol. Soc. Am.*, **75**, 503–522.

Price, W. A., 1933, "Role of diastrophism in topography of Corpus Christi area, south Texas," *Bull. Am. Assoc. Petrol. Geologists*, **17**, 907–962.

Price, W. A., 1951, "Winds caused pattern," *Science News-Letter*, 327 (Nov. 24, 1951).

Price, W. A., 1958, "Sedimentology and Quaternary geomorphology of south Texas," *Trans. Gulf Coast Assoc. Geol. Soc.*, **8**, 41–75.

Price, W. A., 1963, "The oriented lakes of Arctic Alaska: a discussion," *J. Geol.*, **71**, 530, 531.

Prouty, W. F., 1952, "Carolina Bays and their origin," *Bull. Geol. Soc. Am.*, **63**, 167–224.

Raisz, E. J., 1934, "Rounded lakes and lagoons of the coastal plains of Massachussets," *J. Geol.*, **42**, 839–848.

Robertson, E. C., 1962, "The Carolina Bays and emergence of the coastal plain of the Carolinas and Georgia," *U.S. Geol. Surv. Profess. Paper* **450-C**, 87–90.

Schriever, William, 1955, "Were the Carolina Bays oriented by gyroscopic action?" *Trans. Am. Geophys. Union*, **36**, 465–469 (discussion by Shockley, Kolb, and Steinreide, *ibid.*, **37**, 112).

Shockley, W. G., Kolb, C. R., and Steinreide, W. B., 1956, "Discussion of 'Were the Carolina Bays oriented by gyroscopic action?' by W. Schriever," *Trans. Am. Geophys. Union*, **37**, 112–115.

Tuomey, Michael, 1848, "Report on the geology of South Carolina," *Geol. Surv. So. Car.*, 293pp.

U.S. Eolian Map, 1952, "Pleistocene eolian deposits of the United States, Alaska and parts of Canada," *Geol. Soc. Am.*, Scale 1 : 2,500,000, 2 sheets.

Wells, B. W., and Boyce, S. G., 1953, "Carolina bays: additional data on their origin, age and history," *J. Elisha Mitchell Sci. Soc.*, **69**, 119–141.

Whitehead, D. R., 1965, "Palynology and Pleistocene phytogeography of unglaciated eastern North America," in (Wright, H. E., Jr., and Frey, D. G., editors) "The Quaternary of the United States," Pt. I, Geology, pp. 417–432, Princeton, N.J., Princeton University Press, 922pp.

Cross-references: *Beach; Beach Ridge; Coastal Geomorphology; Coastal Plain; Littoral Processes; Oriented Lakes;* Vol. I: *Fetch;* Vol. II: *Astroblemes and Meteorite Craters; Explosion Craters; Wind Measurement, Wind Roses.*

CARTOGRAPHY—*See* pr Vol. VI

CASE HARDENING—*See* INDURATION

CASPIAN SEA

Dimensions and Shape

The Caspian Sea is the greatest saline lake in the world. Its area is 436,000 km^2, and its volume is 77,000 km^3 (average depth 180 m). The sea is 1200 km long from north to south. The coasts are slightly indented. Connected to it, there are the almost closed Gulf of Karabogaz(gol) (18,000 km^2) and a series of small bays: Gurguyanian Bay, Tourkmen Bay, Krasnovodsky Bay, Baku Bay and others. Apart from the Volga Delta, there are a few islands: Tiuleny, Chechen, Artem, Giloy, Ogurchinsky, and Koulaly, and also some small islands in the Baku and Apsheron archipelagos. Most of the inflow into the Caspian Sea is carried by the following rivers from the north and west: the Ural,

TABLE 1.

River	Volume Delivered (km³)	Proportion of Whole Delivery (%)
Volga	270.83	76.3
Kura	17.22	4.9
Ural	13.17	3.7
Terek	11.31	3.2
Others	42.65	11.9
	355.18	100

Volga, Terek, Sulak, Samur, Kura; from the south, Sefidrud, Gurguen and Atrek rivers. Table 1 shows volumes and percentages (from Zenkevitch, 1963).

Climate

The climate of the Caspian Sea is complex. In the north, the frost reaches as low as $-38°C$, while in the south, the January temperatures are $+5$ to $+9°C$. The climate is arid on the northern and eastern coasts. The mountainous coasts in the west, southwest and south have humid warm climates. The precipitation in the south and southwest is 1500 mm, but at Krasnovodsk on the east coast, it is only 120 mm. The entire Caspian drainage area is enormous (3.7×10^6 km²). The inflow (Table 1) is increased to 451 km³ by direct rainfall. Evaporation accounts for 86.6 cm annually.

A monsoon-type regime with the dominant northeast winds is characteristic for the Caspian Sea in winter, particularly for its northern part. The monsoon character diminishes in summer when land breezes prevail.

The Bottom Relief

The Caspian Sea is divided in three roughly equal parts according to bottom morphology. In the north part, the depth is no more than 20 m (Fig. 1). The middle part has a maximum depth of 790 m and is bordered by a sill from the southern part with a depth not less than 170 m (Apsheron sill). The South Caspian, with depths down to 980 m, has a very complex relief in the west and a broad flat shelf in the east. The maximum depth in the Gulf of Karabogaz(gol) is 10 m (*Gol* = Gulf in the Turkmen language).

Hydrological Features

The north Caspian freezes in winter. In summer, the mean surface temperature is 22–25°C; near the east coast, it is 27–30°C. The bottom temperature in the basins is always constant at 5–6°C.

The salinity is 0.3‰ in the north Caspian, with the freshening effect of the Volga River, and rises southward gradually to 14‰ (southeast). In the Gulf of Karabogaz(gol), the salinity is 300‰, a classic evaporating basin.

Due to the great difference in conditions in the northern and southern parts of the sea, a vertical circulation is provided in summer by the heating and evaporation and in winter by the outflow of cold waters from the north Caspian into the middle and south basins. Oxygen is still present even at the maximum depths. Some H_2S contamination occurs locally but only for a short time.

The currents are formed by the winds and by density differences between fresh northern waters and more saline southern ones. The general Caspian water movement is cyclonic (Fig. 2). Two circulations develop at a depth of 300 m and more in the middle and southern basins. A coastal current moves along the western shore from the Volga delta southward, and northward along the eastern shore.

A steady current into the Karabogaz(gol) partly compensates for the evaporation from the gulf surface. Nevertheless evaporation (500.7 km³) prevails over the water inflow (422.4 km³); this leads to permanent precipitation of salts.

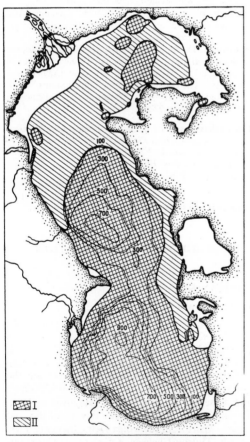

FIG. 1. Bathymetric map of the Caspian Sea (Knipovich, 1936) with main sediment classes: (I) fine-grained, (II) coarse-grained (Klenova: sketch-map from Zenkevitch, 1963). (By permission of George Allen & Unwin, London, England)

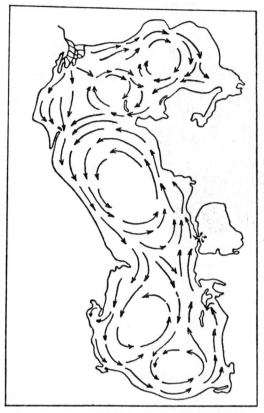

FIG. 2. Current systems of the Caspian Sea (A. Mikhalevsky, 1931; from Zenkevitch, 1963). (By permission of George Allen & Unwin, London, England).

On the shallow northern coasts there are wind-generated tides.

Caspian Sea Level Oscillations

The instability of the sea level is a characteristic feature of the Caspian Sea. Many serious falls took place in the past; at the present time, a fall has been proceeding since 1930. Over this period, the sea level has been lowered by more than 2 m

and in 1952 was 27.6 m below ocean level. Decline in the water level has changed coastal shapes, mostly in the northern part. Many bays disappeared and islands increased. Some islands changed into peninsulas, e.g., Cheleken and Sara islands, etc. The Emba River does not flow into the sea any more. The area of the Volga Delta has increased very much owing to the emergence of the bar. Oscillations for the period 1886–1936 are shown in Fig. 3; documentation exists to indicate major oscillations over many centuries.

Geological Structure

The Caspian Sea is situated in a broad tectonic depression of heterogeneous origin. Its northern part belongs to the southeast margin of the Russian Platform. A buried folded system of Paleozoics trends from the Mangyshlak peninsula to the Volga Delta. The southwest part of the Caspian has a geosynclinal origin. The boundary between the platform and the geosynclinal parts of the sea floor strikes from the Terek River to Krasnovodsk. The bottom, south of the Terek mouth, continues the structure of the Caucasian foredeep.

The Apsheron sill at the boundary of middle and south Caspian, between the Apsheron and Krasnovodsk peninsula is a complex geologic structure. The Tertiary Caucasus folding, the southern edge of the Krasnovodsk platform, and the Tertiary folding of the northern border of the Turkmen depression all converge here.

The south Caspian between the Kura and Turkmen depressions is an area of subsidence and continuous sedimentation from Paleozoic time, and possibly earlier. Geophysical investigations show that in the south Caspian depression the granite layer is absent, (i.e., oceanic type crust).

Geological History

As on the Russian Platform, it is possible to see the alternation of more or less north–south and east–west movements in the geological history of the Caspian Sea. The Caspian has been united frequently with the Black Sea and, through it, connected to the World Ocean at the times of east–west

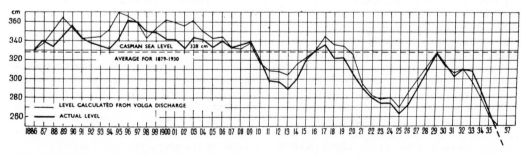

FIG. 3. Fluctuations in the Caspian Sea level 1886–1936 (Brujevitch, 1938; from Zenkevitch, 1963). (By permission of George Allen & Unwin, London, England.)

warping. Open connection with the Mediterranean ceased from the Miocene onward, but narrow marine connections were later re-established from time to time. A brackish Miocene basin was widespread in southeastern Europe. Further transgressions and regressions affected the Caspian depression. One of the greatest regressions was at the beginning of the Pliocene.

At that time, the Caspian Sea occupied only its southern basin and a thick series of sands, silts and clays was deposited, later to become one of the richest oil fields. This regression, named the Balakhan stage, was replaced by the broad Akchagylian transgression. The Caspian basin extended at that time northward to the middle Volga. The Akchagyl Sea was not fresh, but the route of its connection with the ocean is not clear as yet; possibly it was in the north. During the Akchagyl transgression, a tendency for submeridional subsidence is indicated.

The later stages of Caspian development were marked by oscillations in level with ever decreasing areas of transgression. The transgressions of lower Pleistocene (Bakunian), middle Pleistocene (Khazarian) and upper Pleistocene (Khvalynian) are notable. They left many terraces and raised beaches on the Caspian shores, at heights from 300 down to 7 m above present sea level.

The levels of Quaternary terraces are tilted with the continuing orogenic activity of the Caucasus geosyncline. The older terraces of lower Bakunian are the most deformed. The base of the Bakunian is at 200–300 m in the Kura and Terek depressions and rises to 280–320 m above sea level at the southeast end of the Caucasus. The tilting of the younger terraces is less. Maximum deformation is also seen at the southeast termination of the Caucasus.

The regressive phases left submarine terraces and plains on the sea floor. The most clearly expressed level at −700 m probably belongs to the Pliocene. The submarine terrace and the slope break at −300 m are also very marked. The depth of the Caspian shelf outer edge varies from −60 to −120 m. The position of the shelf edge is almost everywhere related to tectonic movements, except off the deltas.

The Caspian Sea is an area of recent orogeny. Structural lines of the mainland continue under the sea floor. Anticlinal folds across it form numerous islands, banks and reefs (Figs. 4 and 5). Many of these anticlinal domes are also oil and gas bearing. The greatest offshore oilfield is the Neftyanye Kamni ("Oil Stones"), represented primarily by a group of small rocks near where passing ships had noted the oil seeps and gas blows.

Geophysical investigations have revealed many oil-bearing structures expressed only very slightly in the bottom relief. The structural lines of the west coast continue not only on the shelf and slopes but also into the bottom beyond the slopes. The latest echo-sounding data show that in the north-west part of the south Caspian, the sea bottom is a

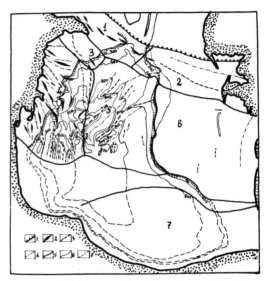

FIG. 4. Sketch map of South Caspian tectonics (after V. F. Soloviev, L. S. Kulakova *et al.*, 1962): (1) southern boundary of epihercynian platform; (2) anticlinal structures fixed by seismic prospecting and by boring; (3) anticlinal lines shown in the relief; (4) synclinal lines; (5) shelf break; (6) isobaths from echo-sounding data; (7) isobaths from nautical charts.

The figures on the sketch-map: (1) region of Apsheron Archipelago anticlinorium; (2) continuation of structures of Balkhan depression into sea floor; (3) continuation of Apsheron Peninsula anticlinal zones south eastward into sea floor; (4) region of structures of Baku archipelago; (5) South-Caspian anticlinal zones, eastern part; (6) shelf—tectonic structures are not expressed in relief; (7) Elburz foredeep.

system of young submeridional ridges 300–400 m high above the surrounding basins (Fig. 4). As in the shallows, many of these structures have oil and gas shows.

Mud Volcanoes

Sedimentary "volcanism" is very widely developed in the Caspian area. Many mud volcanic islands crown the structures on the western and eastern shelves and slopes of the South Caspian. Many submarine explosions are noted here. The sediments contain breccia layers of sedimentary "volcanic material."

Sediments

The present sedimentation in the Caspian Sea depends mainly on two factors: the clastic detritus mostly from the Caucasus and the precipitation of calcium carbonate brought down by the Volga and Ural river waters. The inflow of these two rivers comprises 80% of the total. They drain the region of the chernozem soils; because of this, the carbonates are dominant in their waters. The Caspian Sea receives only 12% of its river water

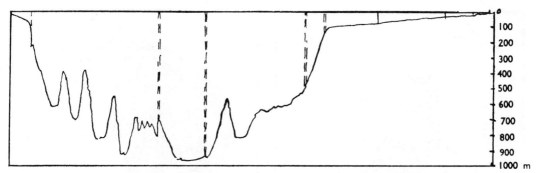

Fig. 5. An east-west profile across the Southern Caspian showing anticlinal ridges of the southwest and the broad shelf of the southeast (Soloviev, Kulakova and Agapova; from Zenkevitch, 1963). (By permission of George Allen & Unwin, London, England.)

from the Caucasus coast, but this includes the most part of the solid inflow. Only one river, the Kura, carries into the sea 36% of all suspended matter. The eolian dust from the east plays a minor role.

Caspian water is marine in origin, but is modified by a great quantity of carbonates and sulfates. It is oversaturated in the $CaCO_3$ which precipitates to the extent of 94 g/m^2 yearly. The $CaCO_3$ accumulates in the shallows and in places of active hydrodynamics in the form of shells, shell sand, oolite and recent submarine "calcrete", and in pelitic form in the muds.

The north Caspian Sea bottom is covered by coarse-grained sediments, mostly sand with a large proportion of shell fragments and unbroken shell. The fields of pure shell occur locally, for example, in the southern part of the northern Caspian. This field continues southward along all the east coast. The shell sediments are composed of Dreissensidae and Cardidae. Most fine-grained sediments occur near the mouth areas of the Terek, Volga and Ural rivers, but also in the central basin of the north Caspian at 8–9 m.

North Caspian sediments contain some quantity of organic carbon, increasing in fine-grained sediments from 0.45% for sand to 1.36% for mud (mean values). This quantity of organic carbon is enough to make a slightly reducing environment; therefore, the fine-grained sediments are of greenish-gray color. The CO_2 content ranges from 2 to 30%.

The distribution of sediments in middle Caspian depends on the bottom relief. Sand with a small admixture of shell and silt—product of river transport—prevails in the shallow depths near the west shore. The sand is well sorted by the north and northeast waves. The sand is replaced by muddy sand, sandy mud and mud at the increasing depth. The $CaCO_3$ in these sediments is not above 12–15%. The $CaCO_3$ content rises quickly with decreasing depth near the east coast to 92% and even more in certain spots.

Outcrops of Quaternary rocks, and among them

of shell-limestones and also oolite sand and recent "calcrete," are noted on the east coast fronting rocky shores. Fine-grained mud accumulates in the bays and is composed of pelitic carbonates. Organic carbon in the middle Caspian sediments range from 0.30% for sand to 2.51% for mud. Its content decreases with increasing of $CaCO_3$ in sediments of the same grain size.

The sediment distribution on the western shallows of the southern Caspian varies very much according to the structural relief. Elevations of the submarine slope are areas of abrasion, the products of which fill up the deeper places. Patches of present-day bottom abrasion (negative sedimentation) often occur here near the eastern coast, and frequently oolite sand and "calcretes" form at these points.

The mineral particles are brought in mainly by the Kura river. It carries out a clayey mud which reaches eastward into the deep basin. The lime content of the sediments in the west is not more than 10–12%, increasing quickly eastward. Sediments in the eastern shallows contain up to 90% $CaCO_3$. There are also shell, oolite sand, and "calcretes" here and carbonaceous pelite in the calm waters.

Mud and clayey mud in the south Caspian basin contain 2.28% (mean) organic carbon. It increases to 3% in the areas of mud volcanoes. The increasing of the mean organic carbon content from 1.22% for 1934 to 1.74% for 1956–1959 has been noted (Pakhomova, 1961).

The manganese content in the Caspian sediments ranges from 0.03% for sand to 0.15% for mud; phosphorus, from 0.03% in sand and shell to 0.08% in the clayey mud. The relative enrichment by manganese and phosphorus is observed near river mouths. Mean manganese content is 0.08–0.09% in the middle and south Caspian at the greater depths, reaching to 0.3%; a maximum occurs near the west coast. The phosphorus content increases on the submarine threshold slopes (more 0.1%).

The Apsheron sill is an erosion area. Quaternary rocks (according to latest data, upper Khvaly-

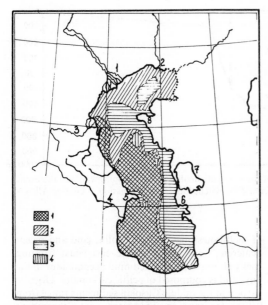

FIG. 6. Recent sediment facies of the Caspian sea: (1) clastic facies; (2) clastic carbonate facies; (3) carbonate facies; (4) diatom-carbonate facies. Geographic names: (1) Volga River; (2) Ural River; (3) Terek River; (4) Kura River; (5) Apsheron Peninsula; (6) Krasnovodsk Peninsula; (7) Karabogazgol; (8) Mangyshlak Peninsula.

nian) lie under a thin cover of recent sediments and, in some places, occur directly at the surface.

Facies

Caspian sediments are generally of clastic, clastic-carbonate and carbonate facies. In places of slow clastic and carbonate sedimentation, the remains of diatom plankton increase relatively; they occur very widely in the Caspian. The quantity of soluble SiO_2 in the richest samples yet found is 12%, and it is possible also to distinguish the carbonate-diatom facies there (Fig. 6).

The main source of the clastic material is in the west, where the rivers have maximum turbidity on account of steep slopes and the continuing Caucasus uplift. Some clastics are carried in by the Volga and Ural rivers. Along the west coast and near the Apsheron Peninsula, the source of clastics are bottom outcrops of Tertiary rocks and Quaternary clays and submarine banks of old Caspian shell limestones. The erosion of mud-volcanic islands and of products of submarine explosions is an important source of sediments in the south Caspian.

All this material is transported by currents and settles in the accumulation areas, i.e., on the slopes and in central parts of the middle and south Caspian basins. Off the east coast the accumulation of clastics is bounded to the narrow nearshore belt

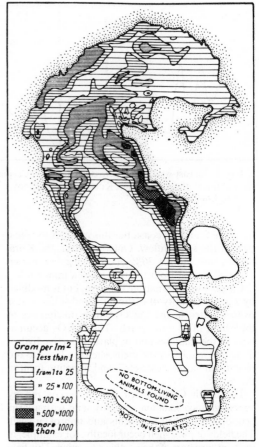

FIG. 7. Distribution of the Caspian benthonic biomass (Birstein *et al.*; in Zenkevitch, 1963). (By permission of George Allen & Unwin, London, England.)

because the abrasion takes place only around the prominent capes owing to the sea-level fall. The eolian transport does not play a large role, and even near the shore line it is only 39 g/m² yearly.

Mineral Distribution

Mechanical sorting and differentiation of clastics also modifies the mineral composition. There is a tendency to enrich the coarse-grained sediments by quartz (among the light minerals) and by amphiboles, kyanite, garnet, zircon (among the heavy ones). Micas have the opposite tendency. Limonite accumulates in the areas of recent submarine abrasion and in the coarse grained sediments; pyrite occurs in the muds. Changes of mineral composition take place following the direction of the current, for instance, the quantity of amphiboles, epidote and others including quartz, rises in the northern Caspian, but diminishes gradually southward along the west coast as far as the Apsheron sill. The concentration of these minerals increases again on the Apsheron sill indicating the erosion of older sediments.

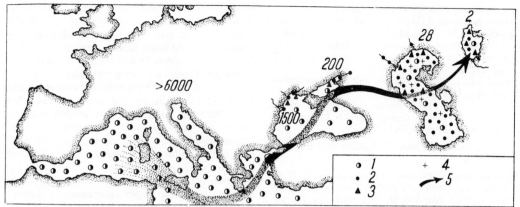

FIG. 8. Qualitative abundance of Mediterranean flora and fauna reaching into the Caspian (and eventually Aral) Sea. Note reduction in species from over 6000 to 2 and modification by other sources. (1) Mediterranean fauna; (2) Caspian fauna; (3) Freshwater fauna; (4) Arctic immigrants; (5) Migration direction (Zenkevitch, 1963). (By permission of George Allen & Unwin, London, England.)

The southern Caspian has its own source of clastic mineral grains. Thus the pyroxenes appear in a considerable measure in the region of Baku Archipelago near the west coast and southward of Krasnovodsk Peninsula in the east. Near the east coast, barite and celestite from Tertiary rocks are noted among the heavy minerals.

Chemical Features

The clastic sediment facies pass into clastic-carbonate and carbonate as one moves away from the source of the clastics. Because of that the chemical composition also changes. The river discharges, especially of the Kura and Volga rivers, are a mixed assemblage corresponding to the average rock composition of the drainage area. The proportion of the chief components continues through the processes of transportation and accumulation, but the sediments are enriched by carbonates, i.e., the ratios of insolubles to solubles decrease.

Iron content rises on the areas of the slow sedimentation, magnesium is augmented in the oolite sands. The quantity of insolubles increases in shell and shell-oolite sand, more in the geosynclinal areas in comparison with the platforms.

Flora and Fauna

The benthonic biomass (Fig. 7) is largely concentrated in the shallows of the north and east, i.e., in the carbonate facies. The composition of the fauna is very varied and reflects the geological history with four main elements, as indicated in Fig. 8 (Zenkevitch, 1963).

Conclusion

In the closed Caspian Basin, we can see all stages of sedimentary differentiation in time and space. Clastic sediments near the west mountain coast are the products of recent denudation of the Caucasus mountain system that was formed in the Tertiary, but where orogenesis still continues.

Clastic-carbonate and carbonate facies originate from the solution products of older rocks forming the Russian Platform. They are deposited on the areas where the clastics become less. Salts, the most soluble components of the terrigenous discharges, precipitate today in the eastern bays of the Caspian, although their migration may have begun as early as the lower Paleozic.

M. V. KLENOVA

References

Anon, 1953, *Bolshaya Sovietskaya Ensiklopediya* (Great Russian Encyclopedia), **20**, 325.

Bruns, Erich, 1958, "Ozeanologie," Vol. I, 345–353, Berlin.

Federov, P. V., 1965, "Quaternary shorelines of Black and Caspian Seas and their possible correlation with Mediterranean terraces," *Rept. VIth Inter. Congr. Quaternary (Warsaw, 1961).* 223–237.

*Klenova, M. V., Soloviev, V. F., Alexina, I. A., Vikrenko, N. M., Kulakova, L. S., Maev, E. G., Richter, B. G., and Skornyakova, N. S., 1962, "Geologicheskoe stroenie podvodnovo sklona Kaspiyskovo morya" (Geologic Structure of the Submarine Slope of the Caspian Sea), *Ed. Akad. Nauk. USSR,* 1–638.

Pakhomova, A. S., 1961, "Organicheskoe veshchestvo v donnikh otlojeniyakh Kaspiyskovo morya" (Organic material in the bottom sediments of the Caspian Sea), *Tr. Gos. Okeanogrc. Inst.,* Part 59, 58–84.

Soloviev, V. F., Kulakova, L. S., Lebedev, L. J., and Maev, E. G., 1962, "Osnovnye cherti reliefai geologicheskoi strukturi dna Srednevo i Youshnovo Kaspiya" (Fundamental Features of Relief and Geologic Structure of the Bottom of the Central and Southern Caspian), in "Strukturno-geomorfologicheskie isledovaniya v Prikaspii" (Structural-geomorphological Investigation in the Pre-Caspian), *Sb. Materialov*

Complexnoy Youshnoy Geol. Expeditii (Material compiled by Southern geol. expedition), Part 7, 446–498.

Strakhov, N. M., *et al.*, 1954, "Formation of sediments in Recent basins: a symposium," Moscow, [lengthy excerpts by G. V. Chilingar in *Intern. Geol. Rev.*, **1**(1), 105–111; **1**(3), 74–81 (1959)].

Zenkevitch, L., 1957, "Caspian and Aral Seas," *Geol. Soc. Am. Mem. 67*, **1**.

Zenkevitch, L., 1963, "Biology of the Seas of the U.S.S.R.," London, George Allen & Unwin; New York, Interscience (Wiley), 955pp.

* Additional bibliographic references may be found in this work.

Cross-references: *Abrasion; Cryptodepressions; Kara-Bogaz Gulf; Quaternary Period; Sediment Transport.* Vol. I: *Black Sea*; Vol. II: *Evaporation.* pr Vol. VI: *Salt Deposits; Soils.*

CATASTROPHISM—*See* pr Vol. VI, ACTUALISM; GEOLOGY, PHILOSOPHY OF; UNIFORMITARIANISM

CATCHMENT AREA—*See* DRAINAGE BASIN

"CATTLE TRACKS"—*See* TERRACETTES, LYNCHETS AND "CATTLE TRACKS"

CAVES—*See* LIMESTONE CAVES; SPELEOLOGY

CHAMPLAIN SEA

The Champlain Sea, a term first used by C. H. Hitchcock (Vermont Geological Survey) in 1861, formed when the shrinking Laurentide glacier withdrew north of the St. Lawrence Lowland and admitted water from the Atlantic Ocean. It covered roughly 20,500 square miles in Ontario and Quebec, between Quebec City and Lake Ontario, including part of the lower Ottawa River valley and the Lake Champlain valley in New York and Vermont.

Extensive but discontinuous shore features, mainly beach ridges, on the south side of the basin, and terraced glacial and proglacial deltas on the north side show that the present altitude of the highest marine submergence is about 650–750 feet in the north and 450–525 feet in the south. It has not yet been possible to trace very far the strandlines of individual water planes except in the Champlain valley.

In the central part of the lowland, marine "clay," locally as thick as 200 feet but generally about 100 feet thick on the north side, wedges out on the south side. It is mainly rock flour and is highly unstable. Earth-flow landslides are common wherever the clay supports escarpments higher than about 50 feet; these have caused much property damage and some loss of life. The clay commonly contains fossil *Yoldia arctica* (formerly *Leda arctica*) and is called "Leda clay." Locally, north of the St. Lawrence River, the clay contains lenses of till and stony marine clay and, in places, has been overridden by a readvancing glacier.

Marine fossils are abundant and reveal the character of the water. Species are numerous and shells are robust in the east near the ocean, but in the west and south where the salinity was low, species are few, and shells are small and thin. Preservation of the fossils depends on the presence of lime in the enclosing sediments so that the fossil record is poor in places, especially near the Precambrian shield. The early, deep phase of this sea was subarctic water containing a littoral mollusk fauna characterized by *Hiatella arctica*. Later, the sea was shallower, and water was a boreal type with relatively low salinity characterized by *Mya arenaria*. The water turned fresh before the basin was drained, and the typical pelecypod is *Lampsilis siliquoidea*.

The Champlain Sea formed after the Laurentide glacier retreated from the Highland Front moraine system in southern Quebec, which was deposited about 12,700 years ago. The maximum submergence during the *Hiatella* phase occurred about 11,400 years ago according to radiocarbon dates on shells. Rapid isostatic uplift caused a relative fall of water level from a present altitude of 565 feet at Montreal to about 160 feet by 10,900 years ago. The shallower water was warmer, and the *Mya arenaria* phase began. Some depression of the crust and local relative rise of sea level followed, probably resulting from the readvance of ice to the St. Narcisse moraine, and a second submergence to about 250 feet near Montreal occurred about 10,300 years ago. By roughly 9300 years ago, uplift west of Quebec City caused a bedrock sill to block the entry of the sea, and the water freshened to form the *Lampsilis* lake when the water level stood at about 185 feet near Montreal. This lake drained as the St. Lawrence River cut a gorge through the bedrock sill. From about 8500 to about 7000 years ago, the rate of eustatic sea level rise equaled and at times exceeded the rate of isostatic uplift, and occasionally brackish water extended up the St. Lawrence River almost to Montreal.

There is no satisfactory recent comprehensive statement on the Champlain Sea; selected references are listed below.

J. A. ELSON

References

Chapman, D. H., 1937, "Late-glacial and postglacial history of the Champlain Valley," *Am. J. Sci., Ser. 5*, **34**, 89–124.

Crawford, C. B., 1961, "Engineering studies of Leda clay," in (Legget, R. F., editor) "Soils in Canada," *Roy. Soc. Canada, Special Publication No. 3*, 200–229.

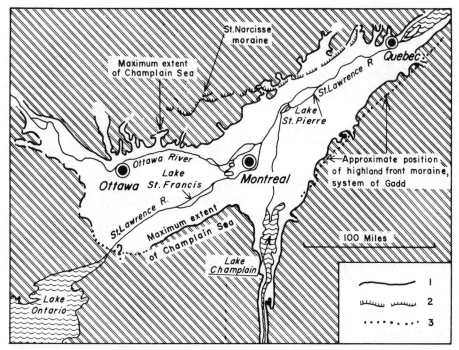

Fig. 1. Location and extent of the late Pleistocene Champlain Sea. (1) Maximum extent of marine submergence, dashed where approximate, dotted where inferred. (2) St. Narcisse Moraine system. (3) Highland Front moraine system of Gadd.

Dawson, J. W., 1893, "The Canadian Ice Age," Montreal, William V. Dawson.

Gadd, N. R., 1960, "Surficial geology of the Bécancour Map-area, Quebec," *Geol. Surv. Canada, Paper 59–8* (Gadd is continuing to write on the Champlain Sea and has several other papers).

Goldring, Winnifred, 1922, "The Champlain Sea; evidence of its decreasing salinity southward as shown by the character of its fauna," *New York State Mus. Bull. No. 232–240,* 153–194.

Johnston, W. A., 1916, "Late Pleistocene oscillations of sea level in the Ottawa Valley," *Geol. Surv. Canada, Mus. Bull. 24.*

Karrow, P. F., 1961, "The Champlain Sea and its sediments," in (Legget, R. F. editor) "Soils in Canada," *Roy. Soc. Canada Special Publication No. 3,* 97–108.

Mason, R. J., 1960, "Early man and the Champlain Sea," *J. Geol.,* **68,** 366.

Terasmae, Jaan, 1959, "Notes on the Champlain Sea episode in the St. Lawrence Lowlands, Quebec," *Science,* **130,** 334–336.

Cross-references: *Beach Ridges; Glacial Deposits; Glacial Geology; Holocene; Postglacial Isostatic Rebound; Quaternary Period.* Vol. V: *Isostasy.*

CHANNEL CHARACTERISTICS—*See*
STREAM CHANNEL CHARACTERISTICS

CHATTER MARKS

These are small closely spaced circuate fractures found on glaciated rock surfaces. They are usually 1–5 cm long, but can range from submicroscopic (*electron microscope*) size (q.v. Vol. IV) to 30–50 cm. The long axes of chatter mark series are parallel to major striations in the bedrock. They were probably described first by T. C. Chamberlin (1888). They are best displayed on hard brittle rocks such as granite, basalt, quartzite, etc., and are believed due to impact and irregular rolling or jerking of boulders carried at the base of the ice. Two distinct types are recognized and have often been found side by side or superimposed:

(a) *Crescentic Fractures,* concave to the downstream side, generally dipping vertical to 70° upstream; a modification is the lunate fracture, produced by a second fracture surface dipping about 20° downstream, meeting the first set at about 90°.

(b) *Crescentic Gouges,* concave upstream, also dipping about 70° upstream and intersected by a second fracture surface dipping about 20° downstream.

At first sight there might appear to be no way of distinguishing ice movement direction from the above, but one should note that the low-angle fracture plane, from which a small crescentic sliver

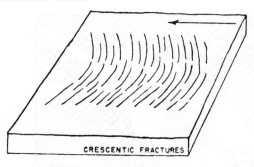

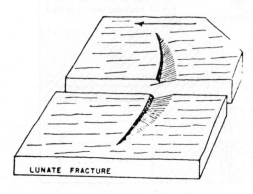

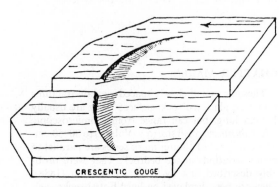

FIG. 1. Three types of chatter marks (Flint, 1957). (By permission John Wiley & Sons, N.Y.)

of rock has been plucked, always dips in a downstream direction.

There are also additional bruises, gouges, impact chatters and so on, mostly characterized by a sudden incidence of the impact, gradually decreasing in size downstream (Gilbert, 1906; Harris, 1943).

RHODES W. FAIRBRIDGE

References

Chamberlin, T. C., 1888, "The rock-scorings of the great ice invasions," *U.S. Geol. Survey, 7th Ann. Rept.*, 1885–86 (1888), 147–248.

Charlesworth, J. K., 1957, "The Quaternary Era," p. 248, London, Edward Arnold, 2 vols.

Flint, R. F., 1957, "Glacial and Pleistocene Geology," New York, John Wiley & Sons, 553pp.

Gilbert, G. K., 1906, "Crescentic gouges on glaciated surfaces," *Bull. Geol. Soc. Am.*, **17**, 303–314.

Harris, S. E., 1943, "Friction cracks and the direction of glacial movement," *J. Geol.*, **51**, 244–258.

Ljungner, C., 1930, "Spaltentektonik und Morphologie der schedischen Skagerrak-Küste," *Bull. Geol. Inst. Univ. Upsala*, **21**, 1–478.

Cross-references: *Striae, Striated Pavements.* Vol. IV: *Electron Microscopy.*

CHEMICAL WEATHERING—*See* WEATHERING; *also* pr Vol. VI

CHENIER—*See* BEACH RIDGES

CHRONOMETRY AND CHRONOLOGY, TIME AND ITS MEASUREMENT—*See* Vol. II

CHUTE OR CUTOFF

A chute is essentially a shortcut across a meander loop. This course can be utilized during flood time. If used frequently, it is kept vegetation-free, and therefore appears as a scar. A series of chutes, cutting adjacent meander loops, provides a shorter, straighter course than does the main channel.

Not all streams have chutes. Where natural levees are large and well-developed, or where the alluvium

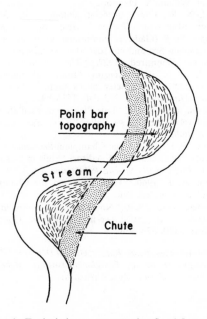

FIG. 1. Typical chutes, representing flood flow channels on a meandering stream; also shown is the point-bar accumulation on the inside curves.

contains considerable binding matter (i.e., clay), chutes may not appear. Where natural levees are relatively low, and have been left standing side by side as a result of migration of the river channel, a chute may develop in the swale between two adjacent but widely spaced levees.

Along some meandering streams, chutes appear only after floods of a certain magnitude have receded, and these floods may develop only once in 5 or 10 years. Hence, on the average, chutes are not maintained as fresh scars.

A chute is a cutoff of one kind, but it must not be confused with the cutoff in which two adjacent parts of the channel intersect each other, leaving the meander loop, which formerly connected them, isolated as an *oxbow lake* (q.v.). A chute operates only during high water; at normal water levels, the flow returns to the longer, more sinuous channel.

W. F. Tanner

References

Leopold, L., Wolman, M. G., and Miller, J. P., 1964, "Fluvial Processes in Geomorphology," San Francisco, Freeman, 522pp.

Thornbury, William D., 1954, "Principles of Geomorphology," New York, John Wiley & Sons, 618pp.

Cross-references: *Alluvium*; *Levee, Natural*; *Oxbow Lake*; *Rivers—Meandering and Braiding*.

CIRQUE

Cirque [French, *Cirque*; German, *Kar*; Norwegian, *Botn*; Welsh, *Cwm*; Scottish, *Corrie*; Spanish, *Hoyo* and *Circo*] as a term in geomorphology was introduced by Charpentier (1823) for basins of semicircular form found in the Pyrenees. They are the most characteristic land form of moderately

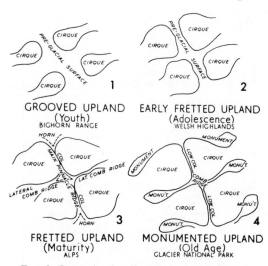

FIG. 2. Stages in the dissection of an upland by cirque growth (redrawn after Hobbs). (By permission of The Macmillan Company, N.Y.)

glaciated mountains and were first recognized as such by A. C. Ramsey (1860). Cirques (see Hobbs, 1911; Cotton, 1942; Charlesworth, 1957), which range in diameter from a few meters to several kilometers, occur (a) at the head of a glacial trough, when they may be called "valley head cirques," and (b) as discrete forms cut into the flanks of glacial troughs or unglaciated mountains. According to Hobbs' (1911) theory of the "cycle of glaciation," progressive expansion of neighboring cirques results in the reduction of the unglaciated slopes between them to sharp, knife-edged comb ridges or *arêtes* which meet in sharp mountain peaks, or *horns* (q.v., Fig. 1). Ultimately, cirque recession reduces the arêtes to low, smooth cols, above which stand a few isolated peaks, or monuments (Fig. 2).

The term "pseudo-cirque" was used by Freeman for certain nonglacial, semicircular valley heads, but this use is not recommended (see *Amphitheater Valley Heads*).

1. Cirque Morphology

Cirques are commonly described as armchair-shaped hollows possessing three distinctive elements: a steep, nearly vertical *headwall*, a concave *floor* meeting the headwall in a sharp break of slope, and a lip or *threshold* at the entrance which may be of bedrock, glacial moraine, or both. The threshold may impound a cirque lake, or tarn (Fig. 3).

In detail, however, cirque morphology varies considerably. While an enclosed depression, and particularly a rock-basin (Fr. *Ombilic*), may be regarded as typical of a well-developed cirque, it is not a diagnostic characteristic, for the floors of many cirques display a continuous fall from the base of their headwalls down to the neighboring valley

Fig. 1. Sharp arêtes about the Dent du Géant in the European Alps (from a photograph in Cotton, 1942). (By permission of Swissair.)

119

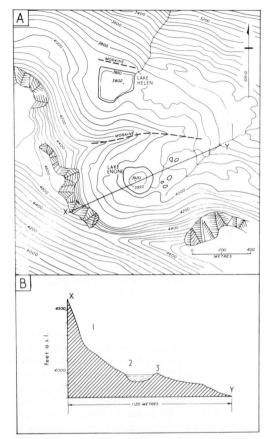

FIG. 4. Nivation cirques and protalus ramparts at 1900 meters above sea level in the Sierra de Peña Labra, northwestern Spain.

(a) Orientation and Preglacial Form of the Higher Relief Features. Because of the importance of wind drift as a localizing factor in snow accumulation, cirques have a strong tendency to form on leeward slopes, particularly where long shadows provide shelter from the afternoon sun. Consequently, the best developed cirques commonly face northeast in the middle latitudes of the northern hemisphere and southeast in the southern hemisphere. However, north-west trending ridges in the southern hemisphere, for example, often possess well-developed cirques on their northeasterly facing leeward slopes. In such cases, it appears that accumulation of wind-drifted snow may be great enough to offset the considerable loss by melting resulting from prolonged exposure to the high summer sun (Fig. 3).

(b) Lithology and Structure. The influence of

FIG. 3. Two cirques on Mt. Olympus, central Tasmania. The profile across the Lake Enone cirque displays (1) a steep headwall, (2) a concave floor (in this case a rock basin modified by talus accumulation at the foot of the headwall), and (3) a threshold of bedrock covered by a thin veneer of glacial drift.

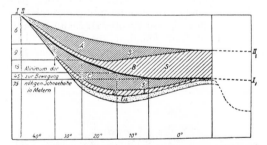

FIG. 5. Schematic diagram showing snow erosion and cirque formation (from Brückner, 1921, after Bowman, 1916). The abscissa indicates the minimum thickness of the snow in meters necessary for movement; the ordinate, the initial slope angle. The thick line is the original slope on which snow accumulated to level II-II₁. This slips down from A-S to form the B-S mass, leading to erosion of the steeper slopes. Such erosion eventually leads to the excavation of the area C-S until a reverse slope has developed up to 5°. Below this, *firn* is found (D-S) and also ice which can excavate further. Motion develops on a 40° slope with 6 meters of snow, 30° with 9 meters, 20° with 15 meters, 10° with 45 meters, 5° with 75 meters, 0° with 80 meters, reverse slope −30° with 90 meters.

floors. The size and shape of moraines are important elements in this diversity. Remarkably large end-moraine ridges of sharp form are found in some small cirques, while neighboring cirques of similar depth and form possess only small, poorly formed moraines or lack them altogether (Fig. 3). In large measure, this is the result of the interplay between variable factors such as the nature of the source of debris supply, the stability of the glacier's snout position, and the steepness of the cirque floor. End moraines are infrequent and of poor form on steep slopes, although lateral moraines may be well developed. It appears that even within quite small areas, every gradation in form may occur from deep rock basin cirques to slightly modified heads of river valleys.

2. Causes of Diversity in Cirques

Differences in the morphology and location of cirques are the result of many factors of which the following are of primary importance.

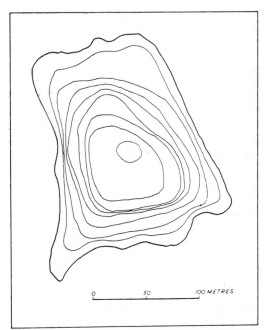

FIG. 6. Bathymetric chart of Lake Tahune, western Tasmania, a rock basin lake in a glacial cirque in dolomite bedrock. Isobath interval is 10 feet. (Bathymetry by J. A. Peterson.)

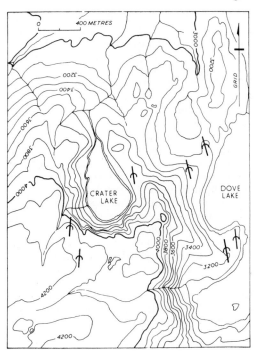

FIG. 8. Overridden cirques in northwestern Tasmania. The cirque containing Crater Lake has been overrun by a small ice sheet which developed on the plateau to the south and west of its headwall. The bedrock is Precambrian quartzite and schist. Arrows indicate direction of movement of the ice sheet as interpreted from ice-mammilated bedrock (based on the *Glacial Map of Tasmania*; cf. Fig. 9).

faults, joints and bedding planes can be traced in the shape of many cirques. Bedding planes may be particularly important in providing a bench upon which a snowdrift can accumulate in the lee of a ridge which acts as a "snow fence." In areas with a climate which is only marginally glacial, the presence of such a bench may dictate whether or not a *cirque glacier* (q.v.) develops. Equally, the height of the "snow fence" ridge above the bedrock bench must reach a critical value. Below that value, cirques and their moraines are replaced by nivation cirques (Russell, 1933), the floors of which are little-modified benches strewn with angular debris, sometimes in ridges (English, *protalus ramparts*; French, *moraines de névé*) which have been emplaced by movement across snow or firn patches (Fig. 4). The extent to which a snowbank may move and

erode the bedrock beneath appears to be primarily a function of the thickness of the snowbank and the steepness of the slope on which it lies (Fig. 5).

Cirques developed in soluble rocks, notably limestones and dolomites, often contain rock basins which are very deep relative to their diameter (Fig. 6).

(c) Regional and Local Climates. The line drawn to join the average altitudes on present-day cirque glaciers where annual accumulation of fresh snow balances annual loss by ablation is called the

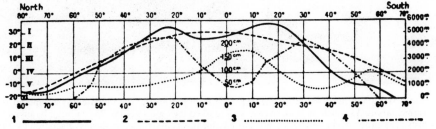

FIG. 7. Mean altitude of the snow line (1), according to latitude compared with temperature (2), precipitation (3), and the aridity index (4) (from Charlesworth, 1957; after de Martonne). (By permission of Societé de Géologie de France.)

average firn line or snow line. By analogy, the plane along which the floors of unoccupied cirques are found to lie is thought to approximate the elevation of the average firn line during the maximum phase of the glaciation which produced the cirques (see *Snow Line*, pr Vol. VI). In general, this plane is found to rise away from the poles, with increase in mean temperatures, reaching its maximum altitude on the equatorward sides of the tropical high-pressure belts at about 20°N and S (Fig. 7). Also, the altitudes of cirque floors are known to increase with distance from the ocean along the path of prevailing winds. Thus, in the middle latitudes of the northern hemisphere, for example, the level of cirque floors rises eastward and southward.

Many cirques are to be found well below the altitude of the regional firn line, however. Their development is a result of some aspects of the local climate which in the past have especially favored the maintenance of ice and firn in an otherwise non-glacial climate. These factors are many and include the extent of shade, the wind regime (especially the eddy effect on lee slopes), and cloudiness which affects both humidity and temperature.

(d) Size and Regimen of the Glaciers which Occupied the Cirques. Large dynamic glaciers tend to produce symmetrical cirques regardless of the bedrock structure. This symmetry is often preserved in areas of strong rocks even where it can be demonstrated that a cirque has been subsequently overrun by a plateau ice sheet made up of coalescing mountain glaciers (Figs. 8 and 9). Niches modified by small glaciers or occupied by glaciers with weak regimens may display marked asymmetry.

(e) Degree of Postglacial Modification. The enclosed basins of cirques, whether or not they contain a tarn, are ephemeral features when considered on the geological time scale.

3. Theories of Cirque Origin

Three theories of cirque development have received strong support in the past half century.

(a) The *bergschrund theory* of W. D. Johnson (1904) envisages diurnal freezing and thawing at the base of the large crevasse, or bergschrund, commonly found in the upper part of a cirque glacier. This results in the sapping of the headwall, the debris produced becoming incorporated into the glacier

FIG. 9. Cradle Mountain, northwestern Tasmania, seen from the north. The mountain is composed of dolerite resting on sedimentary rocks which, in turn, overlie with marked unconformity the Precambrian basement of quartzites and schists. The cirque (right center) cut into this basement was overridden in the last glaciation by an ice sheet which developed on the plateau to the west (right). Cradle Mountain stood above the ice as a nunatak and the rock basin of Dove Lake (foreground) was occupied by over 1200 feet of ice. Cradle Mountain lies immediately south of the area shown on Fig. 8.

and helping to erode the cirque floor by abrasion.

(b) The *meltwater theory* published by Lewis in 1938 (see also Lewis, 1960) stresses the importance of meltwater and rainwater running down the headwall to freeze into the rocks and shatter them, thus undermining the headwall and perpetuating its steepness. An ancillary mechanism may be the existence of pressure release jointing in areas of crystalline rocks, facilitating glacial plucking in the absence of freeze-thaw conditions at the base of the ice.

(c) Finally, recent work has suggested that one component of cirque-glacier movement is *rotational slip* of the glacier upon its bed (Lewis, 1960). This provides a mechanism for the grinding of the rock basin and the perpetuation of the rock threshold.

EDWARD DERBYSHIRE

References

*Charlesworth, J. K., 1957, "The Quaternary Era," London, Edward Arnold, 2 vols.

Charpentier, J., 1823, "Essai sur la constitution géognostique des Pyrénées," Paris.

Clark, Jean M., 1951, "Rotational movement in cirque and valley glaciers," *J. Geol.*, **59**, 546–566.

*Cotton, C. A., 1942, "Climatic Accidents in Landscape Making," Christchurch, Whitcombe & Tombs, 354pp.

*Hobbs, W. H., 1911, "Characteristics of Existing Glaciers," New York, Macmillan, 301pp.

Johnson, W. D., 1904, "Maturity in Alpine glacial erosion," *J. Geol.*, **12**, 569–578.

Lewis, W. V., 1949, "The function of meltwater in cirque formation," *Geograph. Rev.*, **39**, 110–128.

*Lewis, W. V., 1960, "Norwegian Cirque Glaciers," R.G.S. Research Series, No. 4, London, Royal Geographical Society.

Ramsay, A. C., 1860, "Old Glaciers of Switzerland and North Wales," London.

Russell, R. J., 1933, "Alpine land forms of western United States," *Bull. Geol. Soc. Am.*, **44**, 927–950.

*Additional bibliographic references mentioned in the text may be found in this work.

Cross-references: *Amphitheater Valley Head; Bergschrund; Cirque Glacier; Glacial Scour; Horn; Mountain Glacier Landscapes; Moraine; Nivation; Tarn; Valley Glacier.* pr Vol. VI: *Ablation; Snow Line.*

CIRQUE GLACIERS

Cirque glaciers (see Hobbs, 1911; Matthes, 1942) occur in mountainside niches of distinctive shape, called *cirques* (q.v.). Some cirque glaciers are closely adjusted in size to the cirques they occupy, while others become enlarged and overspill the cirque threshold giving rise to a valley glacier. Still others may diminish in size until they occupy only the foot of the cirque backwall, when they are known as "horseshoe" or "cliff" glaciers (Fig. 1).

Formation

Snow accumulation is typically uneven in moun-

FIG. 1. Two "horseshoe" glaciers on Glacier Divide, Sierra Nevada of California. (Photograph: F. E. Matthes).

tain areas where steep slopes favor avalanching and wind drifting of snow, and where deep valley heads, gullies and other niches provide suitable basins of accumulation. When a deep snowdrift fails to melt away during summer, periodic freezing and thawing of the constantly moistened ground around and beneath it leads to the breakup of the rock particles which are then removed by meltwaters. This process is known as *nivation* (Matthes, 1900; q.v.). When a snowbank occupies the characteristically shaped hollow known as a nivation cirque, it may be called a "drift glacier" or "snowbank glacier." Every gradation exists from small snowbank to large cirque glacier (cf. Figs. 1 and 2).

As a snowbank thickens, compaction results in expulsion of air with consequent increases in the grain size and density of the snow (e.g., density of 0.5 compared with 0.1 or less in freshly fallen snow). When the density exceeds 0.6, the mass is referred

FIG. 2. Cirque glaciers filling their basins, Monte Rosa group, European Alps. Well-developed bergschrunds can be seen in the cirque glaciers in the foreground. [Photograph: J. Gaberell, in Cotton (1942). Reproduced by permission.]

to as *névé* (French) or *firn* (German). In maritime areas where high snowfall or marked drifting is combined with mild winter temperatures (e.g., coastal Alaska, western Pyrenees, Cantabrian mountains, southern Chile, New Zealand's South Island and the highlands of southeastern Australia), firn may be produced in a single year, the growth and fusion of grains occurring most readily near freezing point (0°C). In continental regions of low snowfall, the process may take decades. As compaction continues, firn turns to glacier ice (density greater than 0.82). Further compression ("diagenesis") of this white or cloudy ice produces blue glacier ice with densities as high as 0.91 (Seligman 1941).

Cirque Glaciers and Climate

All active cirque glaciers possess two constituent parts—an accumulation zone and an ablation zone.

(1) In the *accumulation zone*, loss of snow by summer melt is less than the winter's accumulation. The line on the glacier surface marking the lower limit of this zone of fresh snow and stratified firn is called the *firn line*, and its mean position over a period of years is the average firn line.

(2) *Ablation* is the generic term for all losses due to melting, evaporation and sublimation. In this zone, annual ablation exceeds accumulation so that no firn is formed.

The relative size of these two zones is indicative of the glacier's regimen. A negative regimen, in which supply is less than ablation over the glacier as a whole, results in a diminution, and perhaps complete elimination, of the accumulation zone (rise of the firn line). An excess of accumulation over ablation gives rise to a positive regimen and a growth of the accumulation zone (lowering of the firn line). Thus changes in the climate of an area control the mass balance of the glacier which, in turn, is reflected in the elevation of the firn line. It follows that changes in the regimen of glaciers provide a useful indication of climatic trends (Ahlmann, 1948, 1953). Cirque glaciers, being relatively small ice masses situated close to the lower limit of perennial snow (regional snow line; Fig. 2) are particularly sensitive to such trends. Some cirque glaciers such as those of the Andes of central Chile are devoid of firn, the principal source of alimentation being the infiltration of meltwaters into the glacier and their subsequent refreezing (Lliboutry, 1956).

Structure

Many cirque glaciers show a marked stratification of alternately dirt-laden and clean ice. This is inherited from sedimentation of snow above the glacier's firn line. The clean ice layers represent successive winter snow accumulation and the dirty layers the debris-stained snow surfaces which develop during each summer melt period. The layering may be preserved in the snouts of small glaciers, although it is destroyed in large glaciers by deforma-

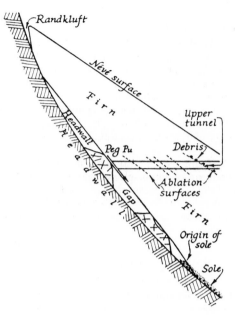

FIG. 3. Ice-rock contact under the névé, showing randkluft, headwall gap and the glacier sole (after McCall; in Lewis, 1960).

tion resulting from prolonged flow. Even in a cirque glacier, however, this stratification may be disturbed locally by overthrust faulting in the brittle frontal ice when the glacier snout is forced to ride over an obstacle such as a rock knob or an end moraine. The lowest layer of ice in the glacier, the *sole*, is heavily charged with rock debris which serves to erode the rock bed. Ultimately this debris may be lodged beneath the snout to form the core of an end moraine. Debris which melts out further up the glacier and washes or slides down its surface may add considerably to the volume of the end moraine.

Cracks ranging in size from a few centimeters to wide *crevasses* (q.v.) are found in most glaciers. In general, they represent lines of failure in brittle ice. They are usually well developed on the convex snouts of cirque glaciers where they assume a radial pattern in harmony with the distribution of tensional stress, thus providing information on the pattern of flow.

A recurrent feature of cirque glaciers is the deep crevasse, or *bergschrund* (German; q.v.), which parallels the cirque headwall and descends from the firn surface down to the rock bed (Fig. 2). Of similar proportions to the bergschrund is the border crack, or *randkluft* (German), between the cirque headwall and the glacier. In some cirque glaciers, the randkluft passes down to a *headwall gap* (McCall, in Lewis, 1960) separating the base of the firn from the rock bed at a point where the headwall slopes down at a steeper angle than the ice flow direction (Fig. 3). Bergschrunds, randklufts and headwall gaps provide an avenue for meltwaters as well as for

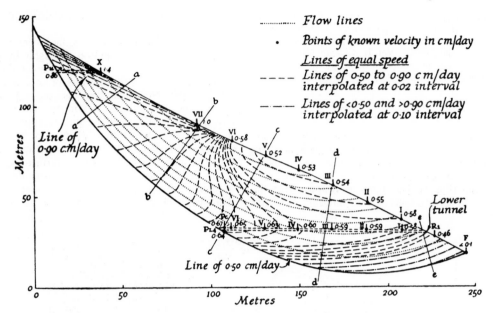

FIG. 4. Velocity distribution in a cirque glacier (Vesl-Skautbre, Norway) shown by lines of equal velocity (after McCall; in Lewis, 1960).

debris derived from sapping of the cirque headwall. With the refreezing of the meltwater at the bottom of the headwall gap, the debris is incorporated into the sole of the glacier. Bergschrunds and randklufts are often hidden beneath the winter snow cover. Many apparently "schrundless" cirque glaciers may possess headwall gaps.

Mode of Flow

Cirque glaciers are mobile masses of ice and firn (see pr vol. VI, *Glacier Geophysics*). Two methods of movement have been recognized, namely

(1) *Rotational slip* (Lewis, 1960) whereby the flow directions are downward near the head of the glacier and upward at the snout, the whole mass rotating on the rock bed rather in the manner of a rotational *landslip*. There is little or no deformation of the glacier mass. In this case, maximum velocity would occur along or close to the base of the rotating mass.

(2) *Extrusion flow* (Matthes, 1942) whereby the ice mass deforms internally by differential creep, maximum velocity occurring toward the base of the glacier but some distance above it. This appears to be only a minor component in cirque glacier flow.

Detailed analysis of the movement of some cirque glaciers in Norway indicates that glacier movement is predominantly of the first type (McCall, in Lewis, 1960). In addition, frictional retardation on the base and retardation by the brittle ice of the glacier's upper surface result in the superimposition of a type of extrusion flow upon the general rotational motion (Fig. 4). Settling and relatively rapid creep of snow and firn in the accumulation zone

results in a concave surface, while the upward flow in the ablation zone tends to produce a snout which is convex in both longitudinal and transverse profiles.

EDWARD DERBYSHIRE

References

Ahlmann, H. W., 1948, "Glaciological Research on the North Atlantic Coasts," R.G.S. Research Series No. 1, London, Royal Geographical Society.

Ahlmann, H. W., 1953, "Glacier variations and climatic fluctuations," Bowman Memorial Lectures, series 3, New York, American Geographical Society.

Cotton, C. A., 1942, "Climatic Accidents in Landscape-making," Christchurch, N.Z., Whitcombe & Tombs, 354pp.

Hobbs, W. H., 1911, "Characteristics of Existing Glaciers," New York, The Macmillan Co., 301pp.

*Lewis, W. V. (editor), 1960, "Norwegian Cirque Glaciers," R.G.S. Research Series, No. 4, London, Royal Geographical Society.

Lliboutry, L., 1956, "Nieves y glaciares de Chile," Santiago de Chile.

Lliboutry, L., 1964, "Traité de Glaciologie," Paris, Masson et cie, 2 vols.

Matthes, F. E., 1900, "Glacial Sculpture of the Bighorn Mountains, Wyoming," *21st Ann. Rpt., U.S.G.S., 1899–1900*, pp. 167–190.

*Matthes, F. E., 1942, "Glaciers," in "Physics of the Earth," Vol. 9 "Hydrology," pp. 149–220, Washington, National Res. Council.

Seligman, G., 1941, "The structure of a temperate glacier," *Geogr. J.*, **97**, 297–317.

*Additional bibliographic references may be found in this work.

Cross-references: *Bergschrund; Cirque; Crevasse; Landslide; Moraine; Mountain Glacier Landscapes; Nivation; Snow: Metamorphism of Deposited Snow; Valley (Mountain) Glaciers.* Vol. II: *Climatic Classification; Climatology.* pr Vol. VI: *Ablation; Glacier Geophysics; Snow, Winter Cover.*

CLAY DUNE

Sand-sized pellets from drying crusts of saline flats with 8% or more of clay, following desiccation and deflation, form stabilized dunes on the flanks and lee margins of intermittent lakes and saline lagoons (Fig. 1). The dunes are known from the hot, arid climatic belts of five continents. None are known from humid or cold arid climates (Price, 1963).

The dune building process is dependent upon a relatively dry climate, and on the highly hygroscopic character of clay when saline. Gain and loss of moisture causes gain and loss of volume and cohesiveness. Nonsaline clay is only weakly hygroscopic. Drying crust is comminuted by the growth of evaporite crystals; sun-crack polygons (Fig. 2) curl and break down when rolled by wind (Coffey, 1909; Roth, 1960); slightly wetted crust forms blisters which collapse on further drying. Large percentages of sand-sized pellets develop in eolian transport of the disintegrating crust (Huffman and Price, 1949); the fines are blown

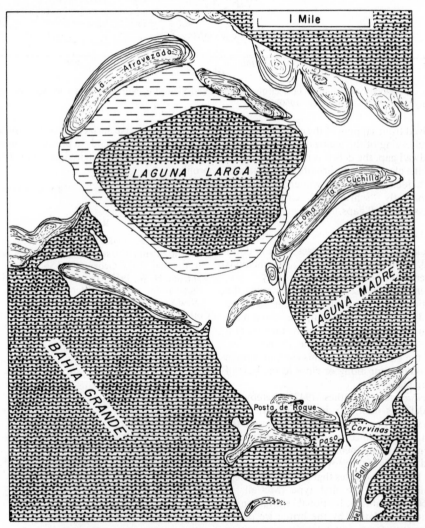

Fig. 1. Map of typical clay foredunes ("Lunettes"). Lee (north to northwest) shores of saline lagoonal and lacustrine flats, semiarid deltaic plain of Rio Grande, near Port Isabel, Texas; 1-foot contours; summits to 30 feet above plain. Volume of lee dunes of Laguna Larga corresponds roughly to one quarter of the volume of basin.

FIG. 2. Sun-cracked, algae-covered clay crust, dune-margined Central Mud Flats. Laguna Madre, Texas. Polygons 1.0 to 1.5 feet wide. (Photo: W. A. Price).

away and the pellets—aggregates of sand and silt with clay—form accumulations which cohere when moistened, later breaking down in the dune to an ashy texture with fines now abundant for the first time. Algal mats (Fig. 3) retard crustal breakdown.

Initial eolian forms in clay are: rippled sheets, low windrows, small barchans and U-dunes, shrub-coppice mounds. Under semiaridity, these

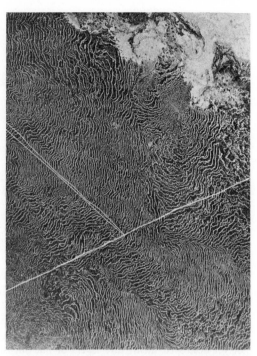

FIG. 4. Desert clay ripples. Salt Lake Desert, Utah. Field of low transverse clay dunes. Scale bar, 1000 feet. Vertical view from 15,600 feet. Thin straight lines are roads. North at top (from Ives, 1946, *Am. J. Sci.*, **244**).

become consolidated and grow into gently sloping foredunes—lunettes (Hills, 1940)—upwards of 100 feet high. In arid regions, known terminal forms are: low shrub-coppice mounds and large fields of low, wavy, transverse *desert ripples* (Ives, 1946), Fig. 4, related to Bagnold's "giant ripples" in sand and gravel (Bagnold, 1942).

In spite of the common gullying of windward faces (Fig. 5), foredunes prograde toward the flat, developing cross-bedding. Prograding during deepening of a deflation basin probably accounts for dune complexes of 260 feet and higher (Boulaine, 1956). Rotation of foredune axes during progradation may mark a growing influence of the dry-period wind resultant over that of the initial shore-line trend (Price, 1958), not necessarily with a shift of wind pattern. Under rapid accumulation, clay dunes temporarily develop sand-dune types (Fig. 6). With less than 8% clay, true sand dunes form (Stephens and Crocker, 1946).

The salt-tolerant vegetation of clay dunes promotes accumulation. Raw pellet sheets deaden plants, but a growth may return after some months or years. Saline dust passing over clay dunes of south Texas has heavily salted the soil for 8 miles inland from the coastal lagoon (Price, 1958) and damaged oak trees for 20 miles.

FIG. 3. Blisters of Algae-covered crust. Central Mud Flats, Laguna Madre, Texas. Drifted sand on northwest sides of blisters. Ruler is 1 by 6.7 inches. (Photo: W. A. Price).

FIG. 5. Badland Gullying, Windward Flank, Lunette. Mud Bridge, Oso Creek, Corpus Christi, 1930. Man stands on sand layer with Archaic artifacts and skeletons 1000+ years old. Vegetation in middle distance is on newest of two progradational ridges. Salt on flat at left, above. (Photo: W. A. Price).

Clay dunes may be bedded, showing old dune-surface crusts where soil-making processes have not yet destroyed them: rare layers of fine shells (Price and Kornicker, 1961), occasional sand layers, middens of aboriginal and younger debris (Huffman and Price, 1949), layers of evaporite crystals, and black clay bands—from an occasional source-flat condition—develop. The soil is saline, ashy and zoneless except in centuries-old relict dunes. The interior of an active dune is loose and ashy. The initial pellet structure is lost in the semi-arid region, but it may persist under the light soil development of the fully arid regions.

Clay dune growth is erratic. On the Texas coast, average net growth in height may approximate 1 foot per century, including the heights of any progadational lenses or ridges. A 30-foot height is reached in one area where dunes have been growing since the end of the last major sea-level rise (Price, 1958).

W. ARMSTRONG PRICE

FIG. 6. Rare clay-pellet slip face. Rapid accumulation in extreme drought. Rio Grande delta, Texas. (Photo: M. C. Johnson, 1952).

References

Bagnold, R. A., 1942, "The Physics of Blown Sand and Desert Dunes," pp. 154–157, London, Methuen and Co., 265pp.

Boulaine, Jean, 1956, "Les lunettes des basses plaines oranaises: formations éoliennes argileuses liées à l'extension de sols salins; le Sebka de Ben Ziane; la dépression de Chantrit," *Actes, Congr. Intern. Quaternaire IV (Rome–Pisa), 1953,* **1,** 143–150.

Coffey, G. N., 1909, "Clay Dunes," *J. Geol.,* **17,** 754.

Hills, E. S., 1940, "The lunette, a new land form of eolian origin," *Australian Geographer,* **3,** 15–21.

Huffman, G. G., and Price, W. A., 1949, "Clay dune formation near Corpus Christi, Texas," *J. Sediment. Petrol.,* **19,** 118–127.

Ives, R. I., 1946, "Desert ripples," *Am. J. Sci.,* **244,** 492–501.

Price, W. A., 1958, "Sedimentology and Quaternary geomorphology of south Texas," *Trans. Gulf Coast Assoc. Geol. Soc.,* **8,** 41–75.

Price, W. A., 1963, "Physicochemical and environmental factors in clay dune genesis," *J. Sediment. Petrol.,* **33,** 766–778.

Price, W. A., and Kornicker, L. S., 1961, "Marine and lagoonal deposits in a clay dune, Gulf Coast, Texas," *J. Sediment. Petrol.,* **31,** 245–255.

Roth, E. S., 1960, "The silt-clay dunes at Clark Dry Lake, California," *The Compass,* **38,** 18–27.

Stephens, C. G., and Crocker, R. L., 1946, "Composition and genesis of lunettes," *Trans. Roy. Soc. S. Australia*, **70**, 302–312.

Cross-references: *Sand Dunes*. Vol. IV: *Clays*. pr Vol. VI: *Cross-bedding*.

CLAYS, STRENGTH OF—*See* pr Vol. VI

CLIFF, MARINE—*See* PLATFORMS—WAVE CUT

CLIMATIC FLUVIAL TERRACES—*See* TERRACES—FLUVIAL

CLIMATIC GEOMORPHOLOGY

As often whimsically noted by the late Professor A. K. Miller, then of the University of Iowa, "the earth has been out of doors a long time." So it has. And thus it is that the inner lithified "bones" of the planet are not everywhere laid bare before us in one vast endogenic landscape. Instead, the consolidated and more-or-less rigidly structured lithosphere is in varying degrees concealed through interaction with atmospherically induced (exogenic) processes. And because of the time factor inherent in geologic evaluations, the most significant atmospheric expressions are generally deemed to be those which endure beyond the transient moods of daily weather and the seasons. It is on this basis that geomorphologists are compelled to consider landscape genesis via climate.

Initially, most climate classifications were attempted by geographers for general descriptive and land-use purposes. For this, they seized upon a number of vegetational and agricultural growing-season limitations in combination with an assortment of related meteorologic subtleties as objects for climatic labels (see *Climatic Classifications*; *Climatology*, Vol. II). This effort culminated in the Köppen System with about 10 major climate types and more than 20 subtypes plus combinations of these. After the turn of the century, a few geomorphologists began to see the genetic importance of climate and the reality of climate changes. Some of these workers (Johnson, 1901; Huntington, 1914) suggested that the lithospheric landscape response to climate was more general and protracted than geographic classifications indicated. Simplified climatic classifications have resulted (Tanner, 1961; see article by him in Vol. II: *Climate and Geomorphology*). However, even the most useful of these attempts to relate landscape phenomena to climatic parameters that are mainly expressed, detected and recorded meteorologically. Even in compound forms such as evaporation/precipitation ratios, atmospheric parameters are rendered geomorphically ambiguous by attendant variables and are commonly inapplicable in the field. Furthermore meteorologic records usually cover too short a range, are areally scattered, and in any case tend to reflect a microclimatic condition. As a consequence, there has grown a recent trend to consider morphogenetic regions delimited in terms of current lithospheric responses independently of weather records (Cailleux and Tricart, 1955; Garner, 1967).

Ground Cover

The only consistent lithospheric response to atmospheric conditions that produces or corresponds to long-term, first-order variations in effective moisture (weathering equilibria; erosional foci, mode, scope and agents; and depositional loci and mode) is *ground cover*. Its geomorphically most critical forms appear as:

(1) Effectively continuous *plant cover* in the intermediate and low latitudes;

(2) *Ice cover* in the higher latitudes and altitudes;

(3) Effectively *exposed land* (discontinuous plant cover) at any latitude.

This is admittedly a simplistic view of the relation between climate and geomorphology, but it appears to be paralleled by similarly simplistic morphogenesis in recognizable categories (Garner, 1959). In most existing morphogenetic systems, lithospheric textural and structural variants are alternatively shrouded beneath a youthful blanket of *sediment* or etched out by *erosion*. The sediment is a coat of regolith amassed during planar or at least generally nonlinear arid or glacial erosion; in the alternative case, the bedrock details are differentially dissected and etched out by linearly localized humid erosion. The third most notable aspect of landscape —the *stripped surface*—occurs sporadically through regional denudation induced by the aforementioned morphogenetic alternation (see *Etchplain*; *Exhumed Landscape*).

Many geomorphically complex landscapes that in times past have led researchers to call for extreme erosional diversity under one meteorologic climate (controlled by imagined tectonics) now appear to comprise assemblages of polyclimatic relics (under relatively stable tectonics). Some landscapes do, in fact, reflect synchronous floral diversity under a single environment, but most express several alternate exposures to two or even all three of the main morphogenetic systems in the same region by reason of repeated climate change. Such polygenetic landscapes are a normal part of the Pleistocene land-form legacy.

It is important to note that the two main nonglacial morphogenetic types are established primarily on the basis of whether surficial agents of erosion (mainly wind and running water) have regional access to land surfaces as in deserts or only local access along humid rivers. The critical importance of these particular relations was experimentally verified by Bennett (1939). Regional access coupled with endorheic runoff causes encroaching aggradation, upland planation, consequent relief reduction and drainage derangement. An allied form of morphogenesis rather similarly planes, aggrades and deranges drainage in areas of continental glaciation. Localized fluvial erosion in increasingly systematic and linear exorheic form differentially accentuates relief under the humid morphogenesis with which both arid and glacial morphogenesis alternate in their respective realms.

Plant cover (like ice) necessarily shifts with the climatic conditions which sponsor it. Even apart from ground fertility variations, phytic-sponsoring conditions are unevenly imposed across the lithosphere by several interacting atmospheric agencies including global wind systems and calms, orographic and adiabatic effects, pressure-cell circulations and temperature inversions (see Vol. II). In response to both geographic and long-term variations in solar radiation (expressed in uneven heating of the atmosphere and oceans), the derivative atmospheric agencies produce belts or zones and patches characterized by particular plant cover continuities. These plant continuities tend to be uniform over broad areas of low relief and limited declivity range. The converse is true of more localized high-relief regions. Where the phytic zones have been geographically fixed for long periods a single type of morphogenesis may prevail. The climax expressions of resulting land forms and deposits are determined by the ground cover type that characterizes the individual systems, whether effectively vegetated or barren. And the areal relation to most categories of geographic-climatic areas is largely incidental.

Climax Equilibrium Land Forms

The pervasiveness, intensity and numbers of Pleistocene climate changes precludes the widespread development of truly climax (dynamic equilibrium) land forms within most existing floral morphogenetic areas. Most such areas (including in North America, glacially eroded Canada, glacially depositional northern United States, the High Plains, and the south central plateaus and mountains) exhibit extensive land forms and deposits developed therein under one or more prior morphogenetic systems. The geomorphically unique relation of special types of uplands (bornhardts, mesas, hogbacks), and some drainage patterns (trellis, dendritic, etc.) and weathering responses to particular country rock lithic expressions is quite apparent. But, geomorphic analogs of particular morphogenetic systems necessarily vary with lithology only to the limits established by ground cover over the time required for related equilibrium to develop. To the extent that there are sequences (cycles) of land-form development, they reflect the dynamic equilibrium tendencies of particulr morphogenetic systems. The obvious imperfections of the sequences reflect the frequent interruptions to these systems plus the fact that each stage is necessarily built on the ruins of a prior stage.

The closest regional approaches to climax land forms are encountered where a single plant cover delimited climate has predominated—not usually to the exclusion of other climates, but rather to the extent that alternative climatic equilibria are not pervasively developed. Relics expressive of these alternative equilibria are thus readily eliminated with each renewal of the dominant morphogenesis. Approaching vegetationless (arid) climax expressions are the closed desert basins of the American southwest and endorheic portions of the Atacama, Kalahari, Sahara and Australia deserts characterized by aggradational plains, bolsons, butte or bornhardt inselbergs and hamada-gibber plain and erg associations. In the waxing humid category are high drainage density, feral (valley ridge) exorheic areas composed of quasi- and actual karst developed on carbonate and noncarbonate terrain under a lateritic-to-bauxitic saprolite or duricrust regolith in subcrestal portions of the southwest Appalachians from northern Georgia through eastern Tennessee into Kentucky; similarly, the humid climax is seen in the southern Nigerian uplands and Mountains of the Moon (East Africa), most of the moderately elevated islands of the East and West Indies and the higher Guayana (Guiana) Plateaus of South America. Yet even many of these regions locally exhibit a thin morphogenetic veneer reflecting some slight recent deviation in climate and vegetation from the developing systemic equilibria.

H. F. GARNER

References

Bennett, H. H., 1939, "Soil Conservation," New York, McGraw-Hill Book Co. (Second ed. 1955).

Cailleux, A., and Tricart, J., 1955, "Introduction à la géomorphologie climatique," *Cours de Géomorphologie*, Paris, C.D.U.

Garner, H. F., 1959, "Stratigraphic-sedimentary significance of contemporary climate and relief in four regions of the Andes Mountains," *Bull. Geol. Soc. Am.* **71,** 1327–1368.

Garner, H. F., 1967, "Geomorphic analogs and climax morphogenesis," *Arkansas Acad. Science Prov.,* **21,** 64–76.

Huntington, Ellsworth, 1914, "The climatic factor as illustrated in North America," *Carnegie Inst., Wash., Publ.,* **192.**

Johnson, W. D., 1901, "The high plains and their utilization," *U.S. Geol. Surv. Ann. Rept.,* **4,** 601–741.

Tanner, W. F., 1961, "An alternate approach to morphogenetic climates," *Southeastern Geol.,* **2,** 251–257.

Cross-references: *Bolson; Bornhardt; Denudation; Drainage Patterns; Duricrust; Endogenic Dynamics; Equilibrium in Geomorphology; Etchplain; Exhumed Landscape; Exogenic Dynamics; Gibber; Hamada; Hogback; Inselberg; Karst; Landscape Types—Genetic;*

Mesa and Butte; *Morphogenetic Classification*; *Morphogenetic Regions*; *Regolith and Saprolite*; *Relict Landforms*; *Weathering*. Vol. II: *Climate and Geomorphology*; *Climatic Classification*; *Climatology*.

CLIMATOGENETIC GEOMORPHOLOGY— *See* GEOMORPHOLOGY—PRINCIPLES; MORPHOGENETIC CLASSIFICATION

COASTAL BENCH, -PLATFORM, -EROSION TERRACE—*See* PLATFORM—WAVE CUT

COASTAL CLASSIFICATION

In the past, there have been attempts by geologists to classify coasts largely according to whether they are submerging, emerging, or stable (e.g., by von Richthofen, 1886; Suess, 1888; Davis, 1898; Gulliver, 1899; Johnson, 1919, 1925). It has become evident, however, that during the

past million years sea level has been repeatedly both lower and higher than at present. This evidence of both emergence and submergence is found along most of the coasts of the world. The rise in sea level since the last glacial episode (Fig. 1) has been so recent that its effect is still apparent in areas where it has not been masked by active marine processes. Accordingly, it seems better to use another method of coastal classification (Shepard, 1937, 1963; see comparative discussions in Guilcher, 1958; King, 1959).

We can use as major divisions Primary and Secondary coasts. Primary coasts are those where the sea has come to rest against a surface that owes its topography to some terrestrial agency. Secondary coasts are those that owe their form to marine processes. Examples of the classification that follows are illustrated by Fig. 2.

Land Erosion Coasts. Under Primary coasts, the most common types are those due to the flood-

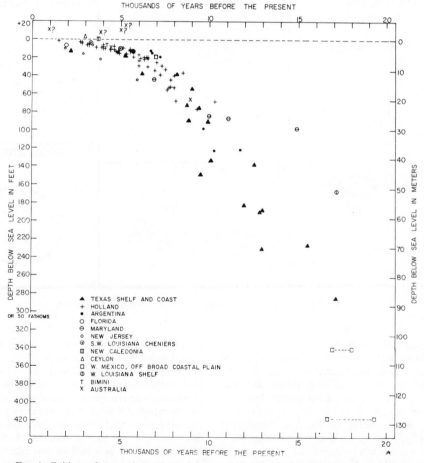

FIG. 1. Evidence from carbon-14 dated organisms indicating the rise in sea level during the past 20,000 years. All data come from relatively stable coasts. Other interpretations of the past 6000 years have been made, but the general picture of postglacial rise seems unmistakable.

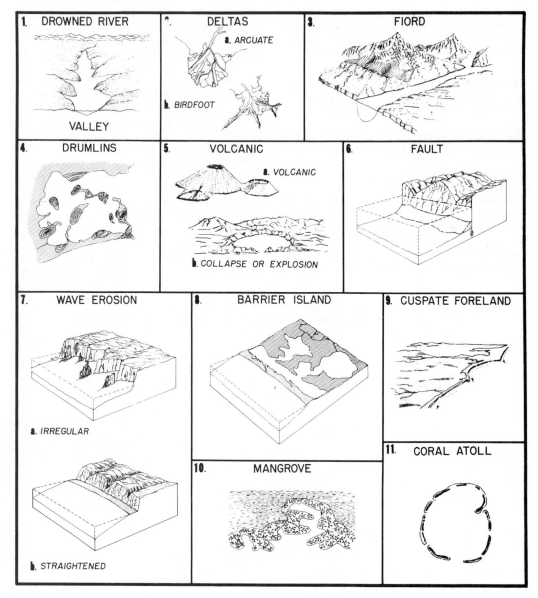

FIG. 2. Thirteen types of coast illustrating the coastline classification.

ing of land-eroded areas by the recent rise in sea level. Thus we have *drowned river valleys*, where the sea has risen along the ordinarily V-shaped valley floors and left the intervening ridges as capes between the embayments. Chesapeake Bay is a well-known example. *Drowned glacial erosion coasts* are found where, during the Ice Age, the glaciers had excavated fiords and, upon melting, these deep U-shaped valleys became filled with seawater. The scenic fiords of Norway illustrate the type. *Drowned Karst topography* is a less-common type found in a few limestone areas where the work of underground water during the periods of low sea level produced caves and sink holes that later have been flooded by the rising ocean.

Subaerial Deposition Coasts. In some places, land depositional processes have been more important than erosion and account for the coastal configuration. Of these, river deposition has been the most important. Thus we have *deltaic coasts* built into the sea at the mouths of rivers. The Mississippi Delta is a well-known example. Delta shorelines may be arcuate (Nile), lobate (Rhone), cuspate (Tiber), or digitate (Lower Mississippi). *Alluvial plain coasts* are relatively straight coasts built out by braided streams coming from a nearby mountain range, as is found along the east side of South Island, New Zealand. *Glacial deposition coasts* include those with islands that are the remains of ice deposits. The drumlins of Boston Harbor represent this type. Among the less common types of subaerial deposition are included *wind deposition coasts*, formed where the winds have built dunes out into the ocean, and *landslide coasts*, where sliding of the hillsides along the shore have produced bulges that extend out into the ocean. Some of these masses are advancing slowly, but at a rate faster than the cutting back of the coast by the waves.

Volcanic Coasts. These are another variety of Primary coasts. They owe their origin to volcanic activity. Three common types are represented by *lava flow coasts*, where the lava has built forward the coast, usually with a bulging shape; *tephra coasts*, where the volcanic activity has been fragmental due to explosive action and the volcanic slopes consist of unconsolidated ash or bombs; and *volcanic collapse* or *explosion coasts*, where the volcano has had one side either collapse or blown out by explosions. Examples of volcanic coasts are found among the true oceanic islands wherever the volcanic activity that formed them has not been subsequently modified to a great extent by erosion or deposition.

Diastrophic Coasts. Some coasts owe their origin to movements of the earth's crust. Suess (1888) named these respectively "Atlantic Type" (faulted) and "Pacific Type" (folded). Among these, fault coasts are fairly common where one side has dropped along a fault scarp, allowing the sea to come to rest along the resulting cliff (see *Atlantic and Pacific Type Coasts*). Fold coasts are less easily recognized, but are due to a warping of the earth's crust leaving the coast as the dip slope resulting from the flexure. Salt dome coasts result from uplift due to intruding bodies of salt. They are relatively rare but are found, for example, in the Persian Gulf.

Wave Erosion Coasts. These are included under Secondary coasts. They owe their form to the result of erosion by wave attack along a coast of other origin. The most common variety is wave straightened coasts, where the waves have removed the projections and cut back the valleys developing a row of cliffs, like those at Dover, England. Coasts made irregular by wave erosion are less common, but are found where the waves have worked along zones of weakness and cut back indentations leaving projecting points of hard rock.

Marine Deposition Coasts. These are another type of Secondary coasts that have been prograded by waves and currents. The extremely common barrier coasts are found where wave deposition has produced islands parallel to the shore, spits connected to the coast at one end, or bars across the mouth of bays that are connected to the land

at both ends. Barriers extend all along the Texas Coast. *Cuspate foreland coasts* are a special type of barrier that has a point projecting toward the open sea, like the well-known Cape Hatteras and Cape Kennedy.

Coasts Built by Organisms. These represent the other main type of Secondary coast. Among them, the coral reef coasts are the most prevalent. These reefs are built up to the surface by corals, algae, and other calcareous organisms and later brought above sea level by the waves. Thus, they are actually a combination of the result of organisms and wave deposition. This type of coast is very common among the islands of the Southwest Pacific. Another type of organic coast that is prevalent in the tropics is the *mangrove coast*, resulting from the growth of mangrove trees out into the water, particularly in bays, and the deposition of mud around the advancing vegetation.

In considering the classification of a coast under the preceding headings, it should be borne in mind that many coasts are a combination of several of the processes which have been considered. Also, many coasts are somewhat on the borderline between a Primary and Secondary classification. In such cases, the seacoast should be referred to by two or more titles.

FRANCIS P. SHEPARD

References

Guilcher, André, 1958, "Coastal and Submarine Morphology," London, Methuen, 274pp. (English translation).
Johnson, D. W., 1919, "Shore Processes and Shoreline Development," New York, John Wiley & Sons, 584pp.
Johnson, D. W., 1925, "The New England Acadian Shoreline," New York, John Wiley & Sons, 608pp.
King, C. M., 1959, "Beaches and Coasts," London, Arnold, 403pp.
Shepard, F. P., 1937, "Revised classification of marine shorelines," *J. Geol.*, **45**, 602–624.
Shepard, F. P., 1963, "Submarine Geology," Second ed., New York, Harper & Row, 557pp.
Valentin, H., 1953, "Die Küste der Erde," *Petermanns Geogr. M. H.*, **246**.

(Additional bibliographic references mentioned in the text may be found in the above works.)

Cross-references: *Atlantic and Pacific Type Coasts*; *Barriers*; *Bars*; *Coral Reefs*; *Cuspate Foreland*; *Deltaic Dynamics*; *Drumlin*; *Mangrove Swamp*; *Prograding Shoreline*; *Retrograding Shoreline*.

COASTAL EROSION AND PROTECTION— *See* **BEACH EROSION AND COASTAL PROTECTION**

COASTAL GEOMORPHOLOGY

The study of the wide range of land forms which develop where the land meets the sea falls within the ambit of coastal geomorphology. The interactions of both subaerial and marine processes on materials of widely differing structure, lithology and resistance to erosion are so variable that the evolution of a coastline in detail is almost infinitely complex. Wave action affects only a narrow littoral zone at any one moment of geological time, but fluctuations in sea level, extending throughout the Pleistocene and Holocene periods, have left evidences of marine processes over a much wider belt. On the one hand, raised beaches occur well inland and, on the other, former land surfaces, with the remains of their terrestrial vegetation, can be observed below present sea level. Coastal geomorphology is concerned, therefore, not merely with a narrow belt developing under present conditions but with the much wider zone over which the sea has migrated in the recent geological past. While involved with such basic geological processes as erosion and sedimentation, the subject makes use of many other disciplines. It is concerned, for example, with studies of the physics of wave motion, hydraulics and sediment transport and calls on such geochemical and paleontological techniques as carbon-14 dating and pollen analysis.

In comparison with the development of scenery inland, coastal change is relatively rapid. A beach may disappear or a port become silted up within a human life span. It has excited thought and comment throughout history. Even in such a relatively tideless sea as the Mediterranean, near which much of western civilization developed, the processes of change were sufficiently remarkable to find a place in ancient Egyptian, Greek and Roman writings. The Nile and Rhone deltas, were, for example, frequently referred to. During the Renaissance period, Leonardo da Vinci's interests included coastal studies. It was, however, the post-Renaissance development of navigation beyond the confines of the Mediterranean which began to stimulate scientific interest in the subject. The growth of interest in marine navigation provided a wealth of information on which investigation could be based, though much of this information tended to be secret. British Admiralty Charts, for example, only became generally available in 1823. The U.S. Coast and Geodetic Survey was established in 1807, but the U.S. Navy Hydrographic Office was not set up until 1830.

The scientific revolution heralded by Newton and the freeing of the earth sciences from the strictly biblical concept of evolution made possible the work of the early geologists including Hutton and Playfair. By this time, maritime influence had passed from the Italian city states—first to Portugal and Spain, then to France, Holland and England.

Much of the early work on waves, tides and coasts thus originated in northwest Europe. The first tide gauge was set up in Amsterdam. The need to protect low-lying coastal land around the shores of the southern North Sea gave special point to these studies. Some of the classic early nineteenth century papers such as those by Brémontier on coastal dunes and those by Airy and Stokes on wave motion and tidal fluctuations are still relevant. Coastal studies developed rapidly in the latter half of the nineteenth century and were carried out on both sides of the Atlantic. Much of this work was originated by coastal engineers or by officers of the various geological surveys. D. W. Johnson (1919, 1925) gathered together the results of this early work and his "Shore Processes and Shoreline Development" is a summary of the subject as it stood in the first decades of the twentieth century. More recently Shepard (1948, 1963), Steers (1946), Guilcher (1954, 1958) and King (1959) have contributed important reviews.

Evolutionary Factors

Present coastlines reflect the sum of all the influences which have operated on them since they were originally established. Most of the world's coasts give clear evidence that the last major relative movements of land and sea have resulted in the drowning of a former land surface, corresponding in time to the melting of the last great ice sheet. Thus Britain was finally separated from the continent of Europe only some 9000 years ago by the cutting of the Straits of Dover aided by the eustatically rising sea level, which reached its maximum about 6000 years ago. The east coast of North America, with its branching, relatively shallow inlets such as Chesapeake Bay and the drowned mouth of the Hudson, reflects the same phenomenon. In this sense, all the world's coasts are relatively new. Indeed, over the last few thousand years, eustatic oscillations have continued over a small amplitude.

Coasts tend to develop toward a smooth uncomplicated outline (corresponding to maturity) at varying rates which are functions of the lithology and structure of their constituent rocks and their exposure to the forces of erosion. However, constant small oscillations lead to frequently revived activity. The most recent eustatic shift of sea level has been a positive one, about 1.2 mm/yr over the first half of the twentieth century, but this is but the last chapter in a much longer evolutionary story. Many of the earth's coastlines (in the broad sense) date originally from the last great geotectonic revolution, the Alpine orogeny, which reached its peak in mid-Tertiary times. Some even antedated this major revolution. Since the Miocene period, there have been many oscillations of sea level. Even on coasts which are obviously recently drowned, the influence of earlier episodes involving emergence can be clearly seen. The Fall Zone of the eastern United States, while meeting the sea in a recently drowned coast, is essentially an emergent area. There is ample evidence that even in recent historic times, changes have continued. Thus in Britain there is evidence of marine transgression in Romano British times and again in the late thirteenth century A.D., but the pattern is complicated by the sinking of eastern England at the present time and is partially masked by upward isostatic readjustment and by sedimentation.

Glacial advance and retreat was accompanied not only by eustatic shifts of sea level but also by displacement of climatic belts with all that this implies in terms of variations in the exposure of coasts to waves, winds and other influences quite different from those which are molding them today. Thus, the western coasts of Hawaii and St. Helena were cliffed during the low sea level stages when they lay in the belt of westerly winds, while today they lie in the trade-wind zones (winds from north-east and south-east, respectively).

Structural Controls

While coasts are subject to continual change, many show (in marked degree) structural control in their origin and development. Indeed, geological structure forms the basis of many systems of classification.

Where structural trends lie at an angle to the coast, the shore tends to be indented. Many ria shore lines (Johnson, 1919) show the relationship between alternating resistant and nonresistant beds set at an angle to the coast. Where structures and shore lines are parallel, straight coasts with few indentations are common. Faulting can have a profound influence. For example, the west coast of the Deccan in India and parts of the coast of the Gulf of California, where cliffs plunge into deeps in excess of 3000 feet, are fault scarps or, more accurately, fault line scarps. Fjords in Norway tend to be dominated by faulting which controls the formation of valleys subsequently deepened by ice.

Minor structures also have considerable influence on the resistance of a coast to erosion. Thus, a cliff cut in a massive quartzite with few faults or joints will offer tremendous resistance to wave attack and to weathering. An equally hard but much jointed and faulted rock will succumb to erosion far more quickly. Beds dipping landward tend to erode more slowly than those dipping seaward. By hydraulic action, the waves tend to exploit any line of weakness. Caves, arches and stacks develop rapidly along joints, faults or shatter zones. A cliff undercut by the waves will tend to collapse along lines of structural weakness.

Oceanographical Factors

Waves and tides are modified on approaching the coast where they become of prime importance in coastal physiography. In shallow water, there is a modification of all the dimensions (except the period) of waves that are generated off shore. Of greatest importance is the increase in wave height and steepness near the break point and the concentration or dissipation of wave energy by refraction, diffraction or reflection. It is these modified ocean waves, which may have traveled as swell far beyond their area of generation, which are most significant in the evolution of coastlines. Waves produced by the local winds tend to have less energy largely because of smaller fetch. The dimensions of waves depend on the velocity duration and fetch of the generating winds. Darbyshire found that waves reach their maximum size with a fetch of somewhat over 100 nautical miles. The exposure of different parts of the coast is, therefore, of great importance. Lewis (1938) demonstrated that beaches and other coastal depositional features tend to align themselves at right angles to the direction of approach of the dominant storm waves. This is because mass movements of water and longshore drift depend on the angle of wave approach as modified by the bottom configuration close to the shore and by the shape of the coast.

Probably the greatest influence of the tides on coastal development is indirect and lies in the variations of sea level which they induce. Wave action operates over a very much wider vertical range and is, therefore, more effective where tidal ranges are highest, as for example, in the Bay of Fundy or the Bristol Channel. Conversely this indirect influence of tides is lowest in restricted waters like the Baltic and the Mediterranean. Tidal currents by themselves are of less significance than waves in molding the coast. This stems partly from the fact that on the open coast tidal currents are strongest some distance away from the shore and partly because they reverse their direction of flow once or twice daily. The ebb largely tends to cancel out what has been achieved on the flood. However, sand banks off the open coast align themselves in the direction of tidal flow and move slowly in the direction of the resultant of the tidal streams. In tropical seas, coral reefs exhibit similar responses. The greatest influence of tidal currents on coastal evolution probably takes place in estuaries. Here, reinforced by the outgoing fresh water they impede, but do not halt, longshore sediment transport and they thus have an important effect on the building of spits, bars and offshore banks.

Wind has significance quite apart from its role in wave generation. It contributes to the movement of material on the one hand by sweeping across beaches and returning sand to the offshore zone, and on the other, by building sand into coastal dunes. Furthermore, the wind can either reduce or substantially increase the vertical range of tidal effect, depending on whether it is blowing on or off the shore. Thus, exceptionally strong winds associated with a deep depression in the North Sea were responsible for the "surge" which overtopped most sea defenses in Eastern England, Holland and Germany in January 1953, with disastrous consequences to lives and property and with considerable long-term effects on the development of the coasts themselves. Similar destructive surges are associated with hurricanes along the eastern coast of the United States. The passage of a deep depression may raise the effective height

of the tide by 3–5 feet, regardless of "*seiche*," "*surge*" and "*tsunami*" (q.v. Vol. I) effects.

Processes

The relatively rapid rate at which coasts change reflects the fact that both subaerial and marine forces are in operation. Erosion by the waves probably plays a smaller part in cliff recession than does normal (chemical) weathering (see *Wave Base*). Coastal processes can be grouped together under three heads: (1) erosion, (2) transport, (3) sedimentation.

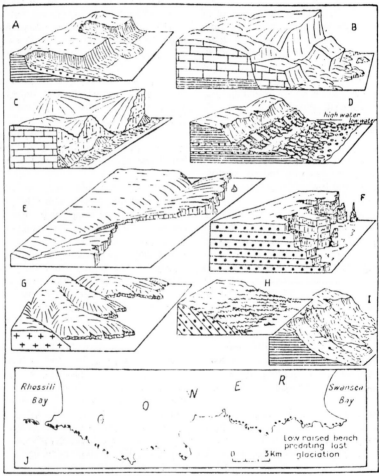

FIG. 1. Cliff types. (A) Clay cliffs with mud flows (after Schou): Rjosnaes, Denmark, type. (B) Cliffs with large landslips: limestones over marls: Seaton type. (C) Chalk cliff with talus and dry hanging valley: Caux type. (D) Cliff in interbedded flagstones and clays, with slabs of flagstones resting on the clay: Alprech, Boulonnais, type. (E) Valley captured by cliff recession and so rejuvenated. (F) Cliff characteristic of horizontal sandstone, limestone or basalt: Frehel or Duncansby type. (G) False cliffs with small modern sea-cliff at base: ancient massif, or Cote d'Azur type. (H) Cliff in sandstones, limestones, or slates with strong seaward dip: Frehel type. (I) Badlands and waste fans developed on clay cliffs. (J) Permanence of Carboniferous Limestone cliffs of the Gower peninsula indicated by the presence of the raised beach (black dots) at their foot (after George, 1932, from Guilcher, 1958, p. 72). (By permission of Methuen & Co., London, England.)

(1) Erosion. Waves erode the coast under storm conditions. When they break against a cliff, the sheer weight of water, the hydraulic compression and release of air in pockets, and the hurling of rock debris against the cliff face all combine to produce mechanical erosion. The rate of erosion reflects both the exposure of a coast to attack and the resistance of its constituent rocks. Currents are much less-effective erosive agents than waves, being normally capable of eroding only loose particles. Tidal currents can, however, be important in the entrances to coastal inlets and estuaries. Limestone coasts are subjected to erosion by chemical processes. Solution takes place even though the sea may be super-saturated with calcium carbonate. Here seepage of fresh land water, diurnal temperature variations and biological activity are each important in different areas. Even non-calcareous rocks may weather rapidly because of the chemical action of salt water. It has been experimentally demonstrated that basalt, obsidian, orthoclase, and hornblende weather 3–14 times faster in salt water than in fresh.

The sea operates in a narrow belt at the base of cliffs where it is a powerful eroding agent (Fig. 1). However, its greatest contribution to coast recession is probably to carry away the products of sub-aerial weathering. The seepage of land water, frost, wind and a whole variety of minor processes operating with the assistance of gravity combine to produce erosion above wave level, and the products of this activity arrive on the beach either in the form of cliff falls or as isolated fragments of rock debris.

(2) Transport. Silt, sand and pebbles are contin-

ually in motion along open coasts. Material is transported along the coast either in solution, suspension or by saltation along the sea floor. Erosion results where this material is not replaced from the up drift direction. Modern techniques of labeling, described by Kidson and Carr (1962), have given much information on the forces involved in transport. Currents by themselves are relatively ineffective, though even large pebbles when made buoyant by wave motion can be transported. Kelp hold-fasts permit quite large boulders to be shifted. In certain regions, the diurnal reversal of tidal streams tends to minimize tidal movement of material. The bulk of movement is brought about by either winds or waves. Wind drifts the smaller fractions of beach material at low tide and builds sand into coastal dunes. Waves have been known to move blocks of great weight under storm conditions, but they achieve a greater part of their work by the process known as beach drifting. The swash of a wave striking the coast obliquely moves material alongshore, and the mass movement of water generated by wave activity contributes to the process. Drift can be in more than one direction (e.g., seasonally) depending on the angle of wave approach. The growth of spits from opposite directions across inlets testifies that on some coasts, drift and "counter drift" are nicely balanced. Estuaries and other inlets restrict the movement of material alongshore but do not halt it. Much material is deposited as spits and bars, but both sand and shingle can cross inlets, very strong tides are encountered, and continue down coast. Promontories and headlands tend to inhibit beach drift and to act as large

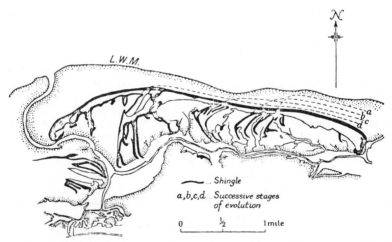

FIG. 2. Scolt Head Island, on the Norfolk coast, England. It possesses many of the features of a complex sand and shingle spit, although it is not joined to the mainland, but has been moving westward close to the shore in the course of its development. Northeasterly waves are mainly responsible for the longshore drift and build the main spit, whereas lesser northwesterly waves help turn the end of the spit and build the laterals (from Lake, P., "Physical Geography," p. 265; for progressively later surveys, see Steers, 1964). (By permission of the University Press, Cambridge.)

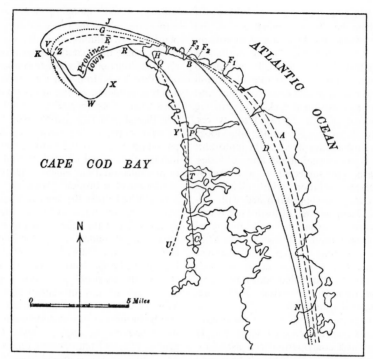

FIG. 3. Reconstruction of the original outline of Cape Cod (indicated by the line NBHQPTC). Progressive stages in the evolution of the present outline are also shown (after Davis, W. M., 1909, "Geographical, Essays," p. 696).

groynes. It has, however, been shown that sand can move past such obstructions in water as deep as 30 feet.

Movement of material normal to the coast tends to be confined to a narrow zone close to the shore. On pebble beaches this zone may be only a few yards wide, but on sand beaches, its width may be measured in miles. Material is combed down in storms and returned to the beach under quiet conditions. A good deal of the finer fractions must be lost from the beach to the sea bed where sand waves and sand streams have been recorded in passage towards the edge of the continental shelf. In certain localities, some of this material may be returned from deep water to the beach, but no experimental evidence has yet confirmed this. There is a good deal of evidence to show that beach pebbles rarely move far over the sea bed in water deeper than about 30 feet. Only in very exceptional storms does any material of this size reach the beach from the sea floor.

(3) Sedimentation. Even where storm waves cause erosion, constructive wave activity, under calm conditions, concentrates the products of erosion to form beaches, spits and bars (see Figs. 2 and 3). Many coasts are formed of recent marine sediments. Wherever quiet ocean conditions exist, even temporarily, material is deposited. Still water, as

for example, during "slack water" observed for about half an hour at high tide, is needed to allow the finest fractions to settle. Thus, salt marshes grow up in the shelter of spits. Halophytic vegetation, notably species such as Rice Grass (*Spartina*) and Common Salt Marsh Grass (*Puccinellia*), assist in the process. In tropical latitudes, various species of mangrove (*Rhizophora*, etc.) take over this role. The size of material in any deposit is an accurate reflection of the relative strength or weakness of the transporting agents at the moment of deposition. The materials forming these depositional features are only in part the products of present coastal erosion. Much is brought down by rivers, and while in many regions of the world the greater part of this fluvial material is building deltas or filling in estuaries, in other areas it contributes to beach circulation. Much beach material is "fossil" in the sense that it is inherited, i.e., the product of past rather than present coastal processes.

Over the greater part of the world, the most recent major movement of sea level has resulted in the drowning of the margins of the land. Around the former glaciated coasts, this rising sea level has swept up, and included in present day beaches, a part of the larger fraction of the deposits left on the sea floor by the Pleistocene ice. This material is now incorporated in the major cobble beaches and shingle bank structures, such as Orfordness on the east coast and Chesil Bank on the south coast of England.

Coastal Classification

Many classifications of coastlines have been made. Classifications can be either morphological or genetic in conception though some systems combine both approaches.

Perhaps the best known of the early classifications was that by Suess (1888) in which coasts are divided into two broad groups, the "Atlantic" and "Pacific" types with the general trend of the geological structures at right angles and parallel to the coast, respectively (see *Atlantic and Pacific Type Coasts*). W. M. Davis (1898) and Gulliver (1899) based their classifications on a broad separation of coasts into those which had been drowned and those which were emergent. Dana (1849), Von Richthofen (1886) and Suess had all recognized emergent and submergent coasts, but their classifications were descriptive rather than genetic in concept. De Martonne's classification (1909) combined the genetic and the morphological approach. Perhaps the best known shore-line classification is that by D. W. Johnson. It is entirely genetic in type, and in addition to shore lines of emergence and submergence, he included neutral shore lines, where vertical movements of sea level had had little influence in their development, and compound shore lines which combined some of the characteristics of his other three types.

Of the more recent classifications, that by Shepard (1948, 1963) recognized two broad groups: (1) Primary or youthful coasts, shaped primarily by nonmarine agencies and including sub-types resulting from erosion with subsequent drowning, from terrestrial deposition, from volcanic activity and from faulting and folding. (2) Secondary or mature coasts shaped primarily by marine agencies. This group includes sub-types arising from marine erosion and marine deposition, respectively. C. A. Cotton (1952) has modified his classification originally put forward in 1918. Basically he regards all coasts as compound in origin but with one evolutionary factor or another having a dominant influence. He separates groups broadly into those of stable regions and those in "mobile" regions. In the latter, coasts are affected by diastrophism as well as by the eustatic changes of base level important in stable regions. Valentin (1952) separates coasts into those which are advancing and those which are retreating. Sub-types in the first group include emerging coasts and those building outwards. In the second class, two types are included—submergent coasts and those which are retreating due solely to erosion.

C. KIDSON

References

Davis, W. M., 1909, "Geographical Essays," New York (Dover Reprint, 1954), 777pp.

*Guilcher, A., 1954, "Morphologie Littorale et Sous-marine," Paris, (Engl. transl. 1958, London, Methuen, 274pp).

*Johnson, D. W., 1919, "Shore Processes and Shore Line Development," New York, John Wiley & Sons, 584pp.

Johnson, D. W., 1925, "The New England-Acadian Shoreline," New York, John Wiley & Sons, 608pp.

Kidson, C., and Carr, A. P., 1962, "Marking beach materials for tracing experiments," *J. Hydraul. Div. Am. Soc. Civ. Engrs.*, **88**, HY4, 43–66.

King, C. A. M., 1959, "Beaches and Coasts," London, Arnold, 403pp.

Lake, P., 1958, "Physical Geography," Fourth edition, Cambridge, The University Press, 483pp.

Lewis, W. V., 1938, "The evolution of shoreline curves," *Proc. Geol. Assoc.*, **49**, 107–27.

*Shepard, F. P., 1948, "Submarine Geology," New York, Harper & Row, (Second ed., 1963, 557pp.).

Steers, J. A., 1946, "Coastline of England and Wales," Cambridge, The University Press (Second ed., 1964).

*Additional bibliographic references may be found in this work.

Cross-references: *Atlantic and Pacific Type Coasts*; *Bars*; *Barriers*; *Beach*; *Beach Ridges*; *Coastal Classification*; *Coastal Plain*; *Coastal Stability*; *Coastlines—Theoretical Shapes*; *Cuspate Foreland*; *Delta*; *Denudation*; *Erosion*; *Estuary*; *Littoral Processes*; *Platforms—Wave Cut*; *Postglacial Isostatic Rebound*; *Prograding Shoreline*; *Retrograding Shoreline*; *Sand Dune*; *Sediment Transport*; *Wave Base*; *Weathering*. Vol. I: *Fetch*; *Seiche*; *Storm Surge*; *Tides*; *Tsunami*; *Wave Theory*.

COASTAL LAGOON DYNAMICS

Coastal lagoons have some of the characteristics of *estuaries* (q.v.) and some of the features of shallow inland *lakes* (q.v.). If the *barrier* (q.v.) enclosing a lagoon is interrupted by one or more permanent tidal entrances, the lagoon is essentially an estuarine system, but if the barrier completely excludes the sea, the lagoon becomes a coastal lake, fresh in regions of high rainfall and brackish or even hypersaline in arid areas (Emery and Stevenson, 1957). Lagoon entrances are generally maintained by the ebb and flow of tidal currents (see *Tidal Inlet*), but where the tide range is small (as on parts of the Australian and South African coasts) it is common for these entrances to be sealed off periodically, particularly during dry phases when river discharge is small and outflow from the lagoon is insufficient to prevent deposition by waves and longshore currents closing the entrance. Such lagoons are estuarine when the entrance is open and lacustrine when it is sealed.

Physiographic Processes in Lagoons

(a) **Changes of Water Level.** In the vicinity of lagoon entrances, the water level rises and falls with the tide—the extent of rise and fall being similar

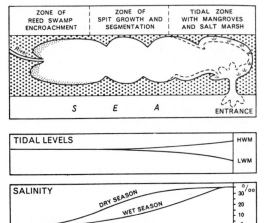

FIG. 1. Diagram of zonation in an estuarine lagoon.

to that on the adjacent seacoast. Tide range usually diminishes into a lagoon away from tidal entrances, and large lagoon systems may have broad zones in which tidal movements are imperceptible (Fig. 1). Lagoons that are sealed off from the sea are usually unaffected by tidal movements, except where the barrier is porous, e.g., calcarenite (as on Rottnest Island, Western Australia). Water levels also rise and fall in relation to rainfall and runoff. River floods may raise a lagoon surface temporarily by as much as 2 meters, the water pouring out to sea through gaps in the barrier, but during dry phases the surface of an estuarine lagoon approximates mean sea level and the surface of an enclosed lagoon may fall below mean sea level as water evaporates. Much depends on the permeability of the enclosing barrier. Water may seep *out* of a lagoon through a narrow shingle barrier during episodes of high lagoon level, and *in* when the lagoon level is low. Transmission of water through sandy barriers is generally limited because the water table within the barrier acts as a buffer to percolation.

Changes of water level also occur when strong winds are blowing across a lagoon, levels falling to windward and rising to leeward, up to 2 meters in a large lagoon system. When the wind drops, normal levels are restored, usually after a sequence of diminishing oscillations (seiches), with complex changes of level around the lagoon shores. Variations in atmospheric pressure are also reflected by elevation or depression of a lagoon surface. Changes related to wind and pressure effects are more marked in completely enclosed lagoons than in those where a raised level can be partly compensated by outflow, or a lowered level by inflow, through a tidal entrance or permeable barrier.

The changes of level which actually occur are the outcome of combinations of these various processes. It is possible for lagoon surfaces to be raised by river flooding or wind action to such an extent that water continues to pour out through the tidal entrance even when the tide outside is rising. Physiographically it is useful to distinguish between the regular (mainly tidal) changes of level which yield a distinct shore zone, with tidal flats, salt marshes and mangrove swamps, and irregular changes which raise or lower the lagoon surface in relation to normal shore line level and where typical lagoon shore features, such as low cliffs, beaches, spits and reedswamp fringes are found.

(b) Wave Action. Waves generated on a lagoon surface are related to the direction, strength and duration of winds blowing over that surface, and to the length of fetch across which the wind is blowing. Ocean waves rarely penetrate a lagoon system beyond the immediate vicinity of a tidal entrance. Lagoon waves are typically short (wave periods up to 5 seconds) and steep, particularly during episodes of strong wind action, when they may develop heights of up to 2 meters; they are capable of eroding sectors of the lagoon shore and transporting eroded sediment for deposition on adjacent sectors as beaches, spits or barriers; they stir up unconsolidated sediment within the lagoon and tend in the course of time to smooth over the contours of the lagoon floor, eroding away shallow areas and filling in deeper sectors. Waves approaching the shore line at an angle of about 45° are more effective in generating longshore drift than waves which arrive at a greater or smaller angle, and waves which arrive in such a way as to fit the outline of the shore do not produce longshore drifting.

There is a tendency within lagoons for shore lines to become oriented at right angles to the resultant direction of onshore winds, taking account of variation in fetch. If the resultant of these wave-generating winds is not the same as the direction of longest fetch, the shore line becomes oriented perpendicular to a line bisecting the angle between the two. Changes in orientation are accomplished either by erosion (retrogradation) or deposition (progradation) of a lagoon shore line, longshore drift moving material from eroding to prograding sectors. Such changes modify the pattern of fetch within a lagoon system until the fetch at any point on the shore coincides with the onshore wind resultant, the lagoon then attaining a configuration which is a direct expression of the local wind regime. If winds from all directions were equivalent in strength and duration, a circular configuration would develop, but usually lagoons become oval in form, elongated in the direction of the prevailing wind.

In long, narrow lagoons, these processes lead to the development of scoured embayments and accreting spits in patterns related to wave conditions. The spits tend to grow and converge in such a way as to divide the lagoon into a series of smaller basins, whose shape reflects the regional wind regime. This process, known as segmentation (Zenkovich, 1967), is illustrated in Fig. 4. As a rule, narrow channels persist between the smaller basins, maintained by current flow (see below), so that a long, narrow lagoon becomes a chain of smaller oval lagoons with connecting straits, as in the example appended to Fig. 4.

(c) Currents. Wave action generates currents flowing in the direction of wave advance in open water. If the waves reach the lagoon shore line at an angle, they develop a long-shore current which contributes to the drifting of sediment along the shore. Currents produced by the ebb and flow of tides have a velocity which is related to tide range and generally diminish away from a lagoon entrance, while river discharge creates current patterns in the vicinity of the point of inflow to the lagoon under normal conditions and over a wider area during episodes of flooding.

Changes of level associated with strong winds and variations in barometric pressure also produce mass movements of water and therefore current flow within a lagoon system, and minor currents develop in relation to variations in temperature and salinity within a lagoon; in a drought, for example, there is a tendency for evaporation losses to be compensated by seawater spreading into the lower layers of a lagoon.

Patterns of current flow are influenced by lagoon configuration. A strong wind blowing along the length of a narrow lagoon sets up a strong current in the center, and weaker reverse currents along the bordering shores. If water is driven through a narrow strait, the current is intensified, and the strong flow may excavate a scour hole in the lagoon floor; in the Gippsland Lakes, a coastal lagoon

FIG. 2. Oblique air photograph of Peel Inlet and Harvey Estuary, Western Australia, showing the open lagoon (foreground) and several landlocked inlets, now salt lakes, notably Lake Clifton and Lake Preston, each over 20 km in length (background). View looking south. Note oblique bars and megaripples, developed under prevailing southwest wind. (Photo: Photogrammetric Section, Dept. of Lands and Surveys, Perth.)

system in southeastern Australia with a mean depth of 5–6 meters, one such scour hole is more than 16 meters deep. More generally, currents mobilize sediment on the lagoon floor, and paths of regular current flow are marked out by relatively coarse bottom sediment (sand or gravel) in contrast with calmer areas where muds (silt, clay and organic matter) are deposited. Occasionally, strong ebb tides, augmented by wind-driven currents or flood-water discharge, sweep a certain amount of sediment out of the lagoon entrance into the sea, but the bulk of the sediment carried into a lagoon is generally retained. Currents have less direct effects on lagoon shore configuration than waves, but are indirectly important in carrying sediment away from wave-eroded sectors and delivering it to shores where waves are building depositional forms. Where currents are constricted by the growth of spits they will tend to maintain a scoured channel, and may either deflect spit growth or be impacted against the farther shore in such a way as to scour out an embayment. Spits often grow symmetrically on open sectors of a lagoon shore but become asymmetrical and trailing in sectors where current effects are strong, notably in the vicinity of a tidal entrance. As a rule, the dominant influence in the development of lagoon outlines is wave action, with currents playing a secondary role.

Factors in Physiographic Evolution

(a) **Initial Configuration.** The initial configuration of a lagoon system is determined by the pre-existing coastal outline and the pattern of the inner margin of the enclosing barrier. Generally speaking, the pre-existing coast has the indented outline of a coast of submergence developed during the Holocene (Recent) marine transgression, which reached its peak about 6000 years ago, with estuarine inlets occupying former valley mouths. In some cases, successive barriers have developed and there is an elongated narrow lagoon between each older barrier beach on the landward side and the inner margin of the enclosing barrier on the seaward side (see Fig. 2).

(b) **Barrier Development.** The enclosing barrier may be transgressive, driven landward in such a way as to reduce the width of the lagoon and eventually extinguish it. Chesil Beach, a shingle barrier on the south coast of England, is being driven landward as the result of occasional storm washover, thus narrowing the enclosed lagoon, The Fleet. Sandy barriers may be locally transgressive where the wind is blowing dune sand over into the lagoon or where storm waves occasionally sweep sand across the inner margin, which develops an irregular outline, punctuated by the noses of spilling dunes and by washover fans. Sectors of the outer barrier north of Cape Hatteras, on the Carolina coast of the United States, appear to be slightly transgressive in this sense, but the broad sandy barriers enclosing

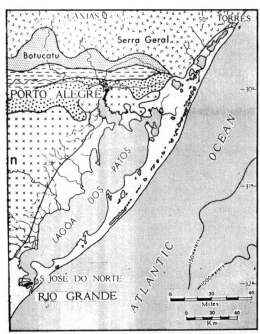

FIG. 3. Map of a large coastal lagoon, Lagoa dos Patos, Rio Grande do Sul Province, Brazil, over 200 km in length. It shows the characteristic scalloped inner shores, while rows of smaller lagoons line the barrier beach zone. The prevailing wind here is from the northeast or east with corresponding dune orientation. The hinterland to the west is Precambrian, overlapped on the north by Permo-Carboniferous, Triassic (Botucatu Sandstone) and the Serra Geral basalt flows (modified from Delaney, 1963).

lagoons on Australia's southeastern coast have a surmounting dune topography well held by a vegetation cover and are relatively stable features, anchored in their present alignments (Bird, 1967).

(c) **Fluvial Contributions.** Inflowing rivers bring sediment to the lagoon system, part of which may be retained in the form of deltas built at the points of entry to the lagoon. In certain lagoons in southeastern Australia, elongated "sedimentary jetties" have been built at river mouths, protruding into sheltered sectors of the lagoon.

(d) **Marine Contributions.** Sediment washed in from the sea through tidal entrances usually takes the form of sandbanks, with intervening channels, constituting a *tidal delta* (q.v.) just inside the entrance. Marine sediment may occasionally be swept over low-lying sections of the enclosing barrier by storm waves.

(e) **Salinity Effects.** Brackish water entering from the sea tends to flocculate and precipitate fine-grained (clay) sediment carried in suspension in fresh water from the rivers. It is often possible to trace the zone within a lagoon where this process is active at a particular time, turbid water giving place to clear blue water. In arid areas, desiccation

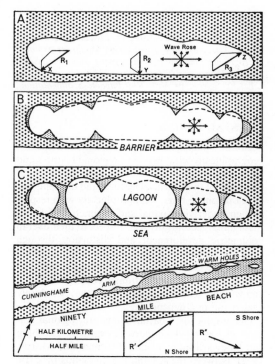

FIG. 4. The process of segmentation in a coastal lagoon (after Zenkovich, 1967). In (A), it is assumed that winds are of equal strength and frequency from all directions, giving a wave rose that reflects within the lagoon. Wave resultants (R_1, R_2, R_3) can be derived from shore-line sectors X, Y, Z. Adjustment of shore lines in relation to these resultants leads to the formation of cuspate spits (B) and eventually to segmentation (C). Under natural conditions, the segmented lagoons are elongated in the direction of the prevailing wind, as in the illustration from Cunninghame Arm, a branch of the Gippsland Lakes, Australia, where the prevailing wind is west-southwest and wave resultants are R' for the north shore and R'' for the south shore. (By permission of Australian National University Press.)

of brackish lagoons yields saline evaporite deposits, or precipitated carbonates, as in the dolomitic deposits of the Coorong lagoon in South Australia, and Aruba in the Caribbean, and as in the gypsum of the Persian Gulf. Salinity is also important as an ecological factor, influencing the nature and distribution of flora and fauna which affect lagoon dynamics.

(f) **Vegetation Effects.** Where vegetation can colonize a lagoon shore and spread forward into the water, it influences the pattern of deposition by trapping sediment and contributing organic material—a process termed swamp encroachment. Where the water is relatively fresh, reedswamp dominated by such plants as *Phragmites* and *Typha* spp. spreads into lagoons, initiating swamp encroachment, especially in areas where the substrate consists of nutrient-rich mud.

Reedswamp gives place to rushswamp (*Juncus* spp.) in more brackish water, but this is less effective in promoting swamp encroachment, and shore vegetation remains restricted unless regular tidal changes of level permit colonization of an intertidal zone by mangroves and salt marsh (*Salicornia* spp., *Spartina* spp., etc.) vegetation. These communities also contribute to accretion of sediments on the lagoon shore. Shore line vegetation reduces the effects of wave and current action, and where there are submerged and floating weeds, such as *Zostera* spp. and *Ruppia* spp., there is considerable "damping down" of wave action, which helps to create a calmer environment in which erosion is impeded and sedimentation promoted.

(g) **Faunal Effects.** These usually take the form of a supply of organic material from shelly and other organisms abundant in the lagoon environment; intact and broken shells can be an important constituent of lagoon beach material.

(h) **Human Interference.** The physiography of lagoons can change markedly where an artificial entrance is cut through the enclosing barrier or a natural entrance is deepened and stabilized for navigation. Increased tidal scour can accentuate lagoon shore erosion, and increased salinity can destroy reedswamp vegetation, initiating erosion on shores previously encroaching. The Gippsland Lakes in Australia (Bird, 1967) and the lagoon at Ringkøbing Fiord in Denmark exemplify this. Alternatively, the building of barrages to seal off tidal entrances can convert an estuarine lagoon into a coastal lake, as in the South Australian lakes at the Murray mouth and in the Etang de Vaccares in the Camargue region of southern France, both of which have developing reedswamp. Within a lagoon system, the dredging and dumping of sediment can modify the physiographic processes at work, as can direct or indirect interference with ecological systems, such as mowing, burning, or stock grazing on reedswamp or salt marshes, and the effects of water pollution. Reduction of vegetation results in increased mobility of lagoon sediment. On the other hand, introduction of exotic vegetation can reduce erosion and initiate new patterns of sedimentation. The introduction of *Spartina* species to Poole Harbour, an estuarine lagoon on the south coast of Britain, led to rapid accretion in the intertidal zone, developing a broad depositional terrace and modifying the configuration of the estuary floor.

Changes in Configuration

It is usually possible to distinguish three zones within a lagoon system (Fig. 1.):

(1) A zone near a tidal entrance, where the tide range is almost as large as on the seacoast and water salinity approximates that of the adjacent sea;

(2) An intermediate transitional zone, where tide

range and water salinity are diminishing away from a tidal entrance;

(3) A zone away from a tidal entrance and close to river mouths, where there is little or no tide range and the lagoon water is normally brackish to fresh.

The extent of each zone will vary with the size and shape of the lagoon system, the number, dimensions, and distribution of tidal entrances and river mouths, tide range and salinity in the adjacent sea, and local climatic conditions, particularly the ratio of precipitation and runoff to evaporation, which influences lagoon salinity. During dry phases brackish water spreads farther into a lagoon and salinity increases, while during wet phases the lagoon is freshened. Contrasts in the salinity regime are likely to be most marked in the intermediate zone.

Where reedswamp or salt marsh vegetation promotes swamp encroachment (zones 1 and 3), the lagoon tends to shrink in area; where the shore line is unvegetated, wave action leads to erosion and deposition in patterns leading toward segmentation into a chain of smaller lagoons (zone 2). Eventually, the lagoon becomes filled with sediment and the rivers wind across a depositional coastal plain to pass directly out to sea through a tidal entrance. Stages in the natural reclamation of lagoons by sedimentation can be recognized in lagoons in various parts of the world. The chief exceptions are where the barrier is transgressive, narrowing and finally extinguishing the lagoon system, or where marine erosion punctures the enclosing barrier and opens up the lagoon as a coastal embayment. Whichever mode is followed, it is clear that lagoon systems are subject to relatively rapid evolution, and in terms of the geological time scale they are but transitory features on the coasts of the earth.

E. C. F. BIRD

References

Bird, E. C. F., 1967, "Coastal lagoons of Southeastern Australia," in (Jennings, J. N., and Mabbutt, J. A., editors), "Landform Studies from Australia and New Guinea," pp. 365–385, Canberra, Austral. Nat. Univ. Press.

Delaney, P. J. V., 1963, "Quaternary geologic history of the Coastal Plain of Rio Grande do Sul, Brazil," *Louisiana State Univ., Coastal Studies Ser.*, **7**, 1–63.

Emery, K. O., and Stevenson, R. E., 1957, "Estuaries and lagoons," *Geol. Soc. Am. Mem. 67*, **1**, 673–750.

Steers, J. A., 1964, "The Coastline of England and Wales," Cambridge, Cambridge University Press, second ed., 750pp.

Teichert, C., 1950, "Late Quaternary sea-level changes at Rottnest Island, Western Australia," *Proc. Roy. Soc. Vic.*, **59**, 63–79.

Zenkovich, V. P., 1967, in (Steers, J. A., and King, C. A. M., editors) "Processes of Coastal Development" (a translation from the Russian by D. G. Fry), Edinburgh, Oliver and Boyd.

Cross-references: *Barriers—Beaches and Islands; Carolina Bays; Coastal Geomorphology; Delta; Drowned Valley, Coast, Reef; Estuary; Eustasy; Karabogaz Gulf; Lagoon; Littoral Processes; Mangrove Swamp; Prograding Shoreline; Retrograding Shoreline; Sediment Transport; Tidal Delta; Tidal Inlet.* Vol. I: *Fetch; Seiche.* pr Vol. VI: *Lagoon Sedimentation; Limnology.*

COASTAL PLAINS

Coastal plains have been studied and defined geographically with respect to regional features and relief; geomorphically with respect to the nature of the origin of their surficial features and their implied development in time; stratigraphically with respect to their underlying spatial and volumetric rock and fossil units; tectonically with respect to their overall volumetric development and distortion through time; temporally with respect to their accretion through the geologic and absolute time scales. The resulting studies and definitions are each gradational and variable within themselves, and they are closely related and interdependent.

Geographically, coastal plains are regional features of low relief bounded seaward by the shore and landward by highlands (Freeman and Morris, 1958). Between the sea and the highlands they rise gently, frequently in a series of terraces or flats separated by scarps or hills to altitudes as high as 100–300 meters. The transition to highlands is abrupt in major interstream areas, but extends landward adjacent to and within major river valleys.

Geomorphically, coastal plains (plus shelf) are the present product of continuing erosional and accretional processes through time. They are bounded landward by highlands and seaward by the continental slope. The shore is ephemeral. There is no difference of structure between the continental shelf and the adjacent continent (Termier, 1963, p. 48). Coastal plains express land forms which are continental and marine in origin formed both at the present time (Von Richthofen, 1886) and in the geologic past (Valentin, 1952) in regions away from glaciated areas. Each terrace, where present, contains land forms which are sequential (constructive). They are continental in origin landward and marine seaward. Relative development of each group is dependent on the rate of sedimentation and subsidence of the coastal plain. The land forms are modified by post-emplacement continental erosion. Coastal plains surficially record only terminal geomorphic surfaces, not the steps necessary to develop those surfaces. They are found in the subsurface.

Stratigraphically, coastal plains are constructed of regional, tabular, wedge-shaped or spindle-shaped sedimentary units containing sequential and frequently fluctuating variations of types of sediments, fossils, and environments which are continental in origin landward and marine seaward (Murray, 1961). The continental sequences are

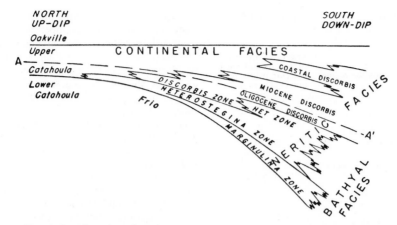

FIG. 1. Interfingering of continental, neritic and bathyal facies in the Tertiary of the mid-Gulf Coast sector (after Lowman, 1949).

deposited on former land surfaces. They contain river, flood plain, lake, swamp, dune and deltaic variations. The marine sequences are deposited on marine scoured surfaces landward and consist of littoral, sublittoral, bar, barrier island, lagoon or bay, tidal marsh or flat, and ultimately alluvial and deltaic facies. The continental and marine sequences are gradational through estuarine and deltaic alluvial facies. Elsewhere, the marine sequence erodes the continental. The variations of the types of sediments may fluctuate through great thicknesses to form cyclic units (Lowman, 1949).

Tectonically, coastal plains grade from nearly stable to sinking lowlands, underlain by thin entrenched continental and essentially tabular marine sequences tilted slightly seaward, 0–500 + meters thick, deposited on "arches" and "shelves," to thick (1000–15,000 meters) lowlands, underlain by relatively unstable basins marginal to the continent, containing regional thick wedge-shaped or spindle-shaped depositional units inclined more steeply seaward with depth. Ultimately, the basins may be destroyed by folding and fracturing to form new mountains, and the coastal plain is obliterated.

Temporally, coastal plains range from regions which began accretion in the Mesozoic Era to areas of essentially Quaternary construction. The older strata outcrop, in general, landward. They are basal stratigraphically and more disturbed tectonically. The younger beds occur surficially and seaward.

Area and Dimensions

Coastal plains occupy more than 5.7 million km² of the earth's land surface, less than one-half of 1% of the total land area, defined as above. Sufficient continental shelf investigation has been carried out in several areas to indicate that structurally they continue to at least the continental slope, but their boundaries within this province are not known with

certainty. An estimate for this additional area raises the total area of coastal plain type to at least 12 million km², less than 1% of the earth's continental regions. It is to be noted that lowlands and shelf areas produced by peneplanation and marine abrasion underlain by Paleozoic or older rocks have been excluded under the above definitions.

Over 95% of the total coastal plain area lies at less than 100 meters altitude. Very rarely does its surface extend higher.

Coastal plains are bounded at depth by "archs," "shelves" and "basins" developed on the surface of older rocks. They include the thickest occurrences of bedded Mesozoic and Cenozoic rocks, which are not folded, or only weakly folded, of the continental regions. Volumetrically, they are the dominant occurrence of these beds, interior plains adjacent to mountain belts being secondary. An approximation of the total volume of post-Paleozoic sediments involved in the coastal plain/shelf structures of the world gives 2.8×10^8 km³ (Fairbridge, 1959).

Location and Origin

Comparison of the geographic characteristics of coastal plains indicates: (a) that most contain at least one major through-flowing stream whose general course is dictated by regional geographic features; (b) that there is a direct relationship between the size of the total drainage basin of that stream or streams and the area and volume of the coastal plain and its landward lowlands and; (c) that the larger coastal plains are bounded by the wider continental shelves. Thus, physically, coastal plains are gradational with the landward drainage basin and the continental shelf.

Comparison of geologic characteristics indicates: (a) that most coastal plains enclose or lie adjacent to one or more large basin or trough-like areas in the subsurface; (b) that they are underlain by beds of

TABLE 1. AREA OF MAJOR AND SOME MINOR COASTAL
PLAINS OF THE WORLD

Geographic Coastal Plain Name	Area (km²; exclusive of continental shelf and landward portions of major drainage basins)
Africa	
Egyptian–North African (Egypt, Libya, Tunisia)	370,000
Niger	90,000
Mauritania, Spanish Sahara	300,000
Mozambique	130,000
Somali	110,000
Asia	
Bengal, Pakistan–India	220,000
Coromandel–Colconda, India	40,000
Irrawaddy, Burma	40,000
Kanto Plain, Japan	5,000
Karachi, Pakistan–India	370,000
Malabar–Konkan, India	25,000
Mekong, Vietnam–Cambodia	100,000
Ob–Khatanga–Lena, USSR	800,000
Persia, Saudi Arabia, Iraq	325,000
Sumatra, Indonesia	160,000
Yellow-Yangtze Plains, China	125,000
Australia	
Nullarbor	120,000
Europe	
Aquitaine, France	25,000
Baltic, Poland	6,000
Flandrian and Netherlands (Belgium, Holland, Germany)	150,000
Po, Italy	25,000
North America	
Arctic, U.S.–Canada	130,000
Atlantic and Gulf Coastal Plain	940,000
Costa de Mosquitas, Nicaragua–Honduras	28,000
Los Angeles, U.S.	21,000
Yucatan–Tabasco–Tampeco, Mexico	125,000
South America	
Amazon, Brazil	245,000
Buenos Aires, Uruguay	270,000
Orinoco–Guianan (Venezuela, Guyana, Surinam, French Guiana)	120,000

Mesozoic (Jurassic and/or Cretaceous) and/or Cenozoic age; and (c) that there is a relationship in area, volume and age between the coastal plain, its gradational lowlands landward and continental shelf seaward, and the age of mountain-building activity of its bounding highlands.

Coastal plains are suppressed generally in areas bounded landward by extensive stable plains or highlands composed of stable ancient (Precambrian) complexes, in areas which lack large drainage basins landward with large through-flowing streams, and in areas with positive (upward) mountain-building

activity or extensive faulting and folding seaward. They are most widely developed in areas bounded landward by extensive folded highlands of Late Paleozoic and/or Mesozoic–Cenozoic age, in areas which possess very large drainage basins landward and large through-flowing streams, and in areas with slight to pronounced downward tectonic movement seaward.

Coastal plains originate from erosion in the landward highlands, transportation of the resulting sediments seaward by rivers, and deposition seaward of the highlands toward the continental margins within continental environments, as well as transportation of sediments introduced into the ocean by rivers, and deposition under marine conditions during fluctuations in sea level. The course of the major through-flowing rivers and drainage basins is guided generally by adjacent regional structural control such as bounding mountain systems (Po Valley) or salients within mountain systems (Indus Valley). These, in effect, dictate the general areas of emergence of the drainage system at the continental margin and, consequently, the location of the widest coastal plain and its gradational lowlands and shelf at the surface and, possibly, the thickest accumulation of sediments in the subsurface. Deposition is sufficient to initiate the subsurface basining through displacement of water by the heavier sediments and consequent depression of the underlying rocks. Deposition, however, cannot account for more than a small amount of the observed depression of many of the basins. The reason for the excess thickness may lie at great depth through phase change in mineralogy, convection currents within the mantle or other causes.

Genesis

Nearly all coastal plains contain Quaternary sediments. Most contain Tertiary terrain and some Jurassic and Cretaceous beds as well. Surficially the older strata often crop out landward adjacent to highland areas within major interstream regions and lie laterally within the major drainage basins leading to the coastal plains. The younger sediments occur seaward along the coastal plain and central within the drainage basins. The older sediments lie basally in the subsurface sequence tilted seaward. The youngest lie surficially and are least disturbed. Coastal plains generally accrete from the continent seaward. They may be subdivided volumetrically in units of geologic time. Such subdivision may be made on the basis of occurrence of fossils or fossil assemblages unique within geologic time, on the basis of time-rock units in which boundaries are chosen at volcanic ash falls or on former land surfaces or other evidences of withdrawal or shoaling of the sea, even though these may not be precisely constant in time. Study of the latter on a worldwide basis is especially fruitful for it indicates actual

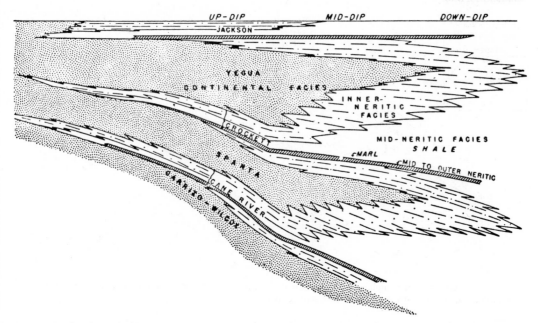

FIG. 2. Cyclic lithology of Eocene (Claibornian) in Louisiana, showing on-lap, off-lap sequences (Lowman, 1949).

fluctuations in the altitude of the surface of the sea when coincidence occurs in many coastal plains.

Volumetric changes between geologic time divisions or within time-rock units underlying coastal plains can serve to indicate mountain building actually obscured by subsequent complication in the highlands, accelerated depression within the associated basins, or accelerated erosion, within drainage basins. Study of the minerals within clastic sediments may indicate the nature of the terrain being eroded and its major tectonic history. The exposure of strained crystals or igneous rock in the highlands is indicated by the appearance of metamorphic and igneous mineral grains in the basins.

Folding and faulting in the highlands is indicated by increased volume of sediments in the basins. Coastal plains containing thick sequences of Cenozoic sediments are often partially bounded by folded Tertiary highlands from which their clastics are derived. Coastal plains containing thick sequences of Mesozoic and early Tertiary sediments are bounded generally by highlands containing Late Paleozoic and Mesozoic complications in structure. The volumetric contrast of Mesozoic and Cenozoic sediments between the Atlantic Coastal Plain, bounded landward by highlands structurally folded during at least the Late Paleozoic, and the Gulf and Mexican Plains with additional complication in sediment source during the Mesozoic and Cenozoic orogeny to the west, as quoted by Murray (1961, p. 283), is noteworthy.

Stratigraphic Features

Divisions. *Rock Divisions.* Coastal plains are constructed of sediments transported from the highlands as discrete particles unchanged in chemical composition, as altered chemical derivatives of their original state, as chemical precipitates deposited from the ocean, or as accumulations of fossils derived from plants and animals living on land or in the sea. Each environment of the coastal plain and shelf is characterized by grades of sediment type and life forms which are controlled by physical, chemical and biotic factors within those and adjacent environments.

Rise and fall in sea level or land surface, a change in the supply of the sediments, or other factors, cause migration of environments and consequent migration in sediment types and life forms. These changes are reflected in beds, rock strata or rock formations as facies or variances of rock types.

Locally and occasionally regionally specific rock types can be mapped as formations which, representing a specific environment which is migrating, are not time constant.

Major fluctuations in sea level cause major shifts in sediment type which may be cyclic and not time constant (cyclothems). These are usefully employed in regional and even international correlations, and seem to represent more natural divisions of stratigraphy (Stephenson, 1928).

Time-related Division. Major physical and chemical factors in environments probably have remained the same over much of geologic time. Biotic factors, and their interaction on the physical and chemical, have not.

Change in life forms with time have been acknowledged since the days of William Smith. Worldwide

147

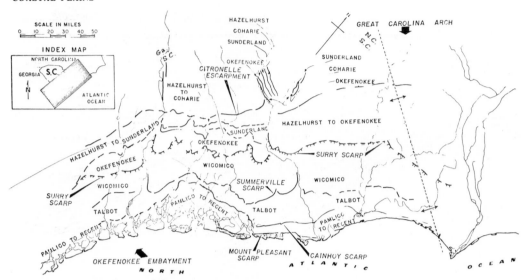

FIG. 3. Terrace sediment complexes in South Carolina as indicated by physiography (aerial photographs and topographic maps), soil maps, and drilled hole samples (Colquhoun).

study of these forms has revealed successions of fossils which have allowed earth history to be divided arbitrarily in time into geologic time units (eras, periods, etc.).

Certain fossils in rapidly evolving lineages occur uniquely within short time periods. Assemblages of fossils can be unique in time. Study of these allows subdivisions of coastal plain sediments into bio-stratigraphic units (zones, assemblage zones, etc.) dependent on both time and environment.

Correlation of rock sections in many areas to a well-known section by means of fossils or unique features (volcanic ash falls) results in further sub-divisions based on rocks and related time, or time-rock divisions (series, stage, etc.).

Shapes. Regional mapping of these divisions reveals characteristic shapes of the resulting units. Formations and beds of relatively constant lithology may be tabular, wedge or spindle-like, thickening and thinning seaward, varying spatially and volu-metrically within the basins and over the arches and shelves, and being limited by transitional facies. Cyclic units are in overall shape similar, but they reveal cyclic seaward and landward changes of area and volume of their contained lithic facies and are more widely occurring. Biostratigraphic units are often similar, but are limited landward, seaward and laterally by other units as dictated by their environments. Time rock units usually reveal one or more cyclic units as dictated by the fossil or time correlations.

History. Subdivision and study of these units spatially at the surface and volumetrically at depth reveals the history of development of coastal plains geometrically, genetically and tectonically. Sub-surface information obtained from drilled holes and geophysical surveys is necessary.

Geomorphic Features

Major Features. Perhaps the most important factors in the evolution of coastal plains and coasts, as they are presently expressed, are tectonic move-ments, present and past climates, and their resulting environment. The thorough understanding of these explains the geomorphic expression of most of the area of all coastal plains.

Terraces. Geomorphic features developed at the surface of coastal plains and coasts are not in harmony with most of their preceding genetic and tectonic history, but with more recent worldwide changes in sea level itself as Suess (1888) recognized. Eustasy can result from deformation of the ocean floor (Darwin), uplift on land because of lightening with erosion (Arambourg, Cailleux), sedimentation in the ocean and tectonic sinking (Suess, Fairbridge) or glacial capture of ocean waters by ice (Agassiz, McLaren, Tylor and others).

Glacio-eustatic changes in sea level have been estimated to occur between maxima of $+100$ (Termier, 1963) and -145 meters (Ewing *et al.*, 1960). Most coastal plain areas and their conti-nental shelves should be affected.

Climatic changes of glacial and interglacial periods and other factors cause major fluctuations in sea level which are expressed as terraces geo-morphically, and terrace formations stratigraphi-cally. The terraces are the terminal surfaces of forma-tions deposited during eustatic fluctuations of sea level. They express sequential and gradational land forms which are continental landward and marine seaward, and erosional, transportational and depositional in origin. Ultimately, through terrestrial and marine sequences, alluvial plains are formed. The nature of these units obliterates much of the preceding geomorphology of the coastal plain surface and buries their associated units. Terraces may be impressed on both stable coasts and faulted coasts.

Cuestas. Many coastal plains include belts of upland areas called cuestas, carved by erosion (as Davis has shown) on units of varying lithologies. Cuestas are best developed in upland areas where tilting may be present. They express scarps inclined steeply landward and slopes dipping gently seaward.

Climatic Control. *Subarctic.* Geomorphic features of subarctic coastal plains within depositional areas are dominated by numerous elevated storm beaches formed during glacial rebound of the land with melting of the ice, and by alluvial (continental) plains deposited because of increased supply of sediments during glacial melting. Glacial advance during the Pleistocene has obliterated or buried many evidences of older interglacial stands of the sea. Elsewhere, glacial erosional, transportational and depositional land forms occur (*rôche moutonnée, drumlins*, etc.).

Minor geomorphic features characteristic of the present environment include:

(a) Pingos, which are circular to oval mounds up to 50 meters high.

(b) Arctic lakes, which are round to oval shallow lakes. They are very similar to the *Carolina Bays* (q.v.) of the southeastern United States and have been noted in central Europe as well. Though relic in these areas, they are possibly of similar origin. (See *Coastal Lagoon Dynamics*.)

Temperate. Temperate coastal plains, e.g., the Atlantic Coastal Plain, are influenced strongly by clastic sedimentation and resultant accentuated depositional continental and shore line geomorphic features. Northern areas are characterized by abundant relict alluvial plains formed from clastic gravels and sands derived from glacial outwash or pluvial conditions. Marine origin land forms are often buried or occur seaward of the present shore. Away from the glacial front, supply of clastic was apparently less and marine origin land form sequences become more apparent. Further away, with warmer temperatures, carbonate deposition becomes more dominant in marine sequences, and solution features are apparent.

Semiarid and Arid. Semiarid and arid coastal plains, e.g., the Morocco or North African Coastal Plains, have undergone great changes during Pleistocene climatic variations. Relict geomorphic land forms characteristic of both wet (pluvial) environments (alluvial plains) and dry (desert) environments (dunes) are present, controlled by these climatic variations and modified by recent processes. Further away from glacial influence, the land forms of drier origin predominate. Drier conditions favor land forms of marine origin along terraces formed during high stands of the sea. Wetter conditions favor land forms of terrestrial origin (see *Sabkha*).

Humid, Tropical and Equatorial. Humid, tropical and equatorial coastal plains, e.g., the Coromandel and Amazon Coastal Plains, respectively, also reflect relict features and land forms characteristic of previous environments. Humid tropic environments are characterized by one wet and one dry season. The climate favors thick red, clayey soils and slower erosion than the equatorial which suffers from deep erosion despite vegetation. The abundant supply of sediments in the latter condition favors the expansion of continental sequences during high stands of the sea. The Amazon Coastal Plain characteristically is underlain by continental facies both at the surface and in the geologic past.

DONALD J. COLQUHOUN

References

Agassiz, L., 1837, "Des glaciers, des moraines et des blocs erratiques," *Act. S. Helv., 22,* **32.**

Arambourg, C., 1952, "Eustatisme et isostasie," *Compt. Rend. Acad. Sci., Paris,* **234,** 226–227.

Authors, various, Bulletin of the American Association of Petroleum Geologists, Yearly Summaries of World Petroleum Exploration.

Cailleux, A., 1952, "Recentes variations du niveau des mer et des terres," *Bull. Géol. France, Ser. 6,* **2,** 135–144.

Darwin, C., 1889, "The Structure and Distribution of Coral Reefs," (Third ed., London, 1896), Smith, Elder and Co.

Ewing, M., *et al.*, 1960, "Revised estimate of ice volume and sea level lowering," *Bull. Geol. Soc. Am.,* **71,** 1861.

Fairbridge, R. W., 1948, "Problems of eustatism in Australia," in "Problèmes des Tarrasses," *6ᵉ Rap. Comm. et Terrasses Plioc. et Pleist. Union Géogr. Int., Louvain,* 47–51.

Fairbridge, R. W., 1959, "Statistics of non-folded basins," *Publ. Bur. Centr. Seismol. Inter.,* Ser. A, **20** (U.G.G.I., Toronto, 1957), 419–440.

Fairbridge, R. W., 1961, "Eustatic Changes in Sealevel," in "Physics and Chemistry of the Earth," Vol. 4, pp. 99–185, London, Pergamon Press.

*Freeman, O. W., and Morris, J. W., 1958, "World Geography," New York, McGraw-Hill Book Co., 623pp.

Lowman, S. W., 1949, "Sedimentary facies in Gulf Coast," *Bull. Am. Assoc. Petrol. Geologists,* **33,** 1939–1997.

*Murray, G. E., 1961, "Geology of the Atlantic and Gulf Coastal Province of North America," New York, Harper and Brothers, 692pp.

Stephenson, L. W., 1928, "Major marine transgressions and regressions and structural features of the Gulf Coastal Plain," *Am. J. Sci., Ser. 5,* **16,** 281–298.

Suess, E., 1888, "Das Antlitz der Erde," Vienna, F. Tempsky (English translation "The Face of the Earth," Oxford, Clarendon Press, 5 vols., 1904–24).

*Termier, H., and Termier, G., 1963, "Erosion and

Sedimentation," London, D. Van Nostrand Co., 433pp.

*Valentin, H., 1952, "Die Küsten der Erde; Beitrage zur allgemeinen und regionalen Küstenmorphologie," *Peterm. Geog. Mitt.*, **246**, 1–118.

von Richthofen, F. F., 1886, "Führer für Forschungsreisende," pp. 294–315, Berlin, Robert Oppenheim.

*Additional bibliographic references may be found in this work.

Cross-references: *Arctic Beaches; Carolina Bays; Coastal Lagoon Dynamics; Coastal Stability; Cuesta; Delta; Drumlin; Eustasy; Lakes; Outwash Plain; Pingo; Plains; Quaternary Period; Roche Moutonnée; Sabkha;* *Sediment Transport; Terraces.* Vol. I: *Continental Shelf; Continental Slope; Mean Sea Level.*

COASTAL PROCESSES—*See* LITTORAL PROCESSES

COASTAL STABILITY

"Coastal" refers to the area adjacent to the shoreline, while "coastal stability" is achieved if the variables defining the shore (tide levels, tectonic activity or crustal quiescence, oceanographic and atmospheric factors) are in a state of dynamic equilibrium such that from year to year there is no permanent change in shore-line configuration. A permanent change in shore-line configuration is an explicit indication of coastal *instability* caused by a shift in one or more of these variables. Changes in coastal configuration due to short- or long-term eustatic changes in sea level are treated elsewhere (see *Eustasy*), as are other exogenic (geomorphological) factors (see *Coastal Geomorphology; Coastal Classification; Littoral Processes;* also *Ocean Currents,* Vol. I). Specifically, coastal stability deals mainly with the effects of endogenic crustal and subcrustal processes affecting the surface of the lithosphere as it relates to shore-line configuration. Thus, this article is largely concerned with both crustal quiescence ("coastal stability") and crustal mobility ("coastal instability").

Historical and Archaeological Evidences of Coastal Instability

Leveling (Geodetic) Surveys. It is possible to test for coastal stability using the results of two or more successive precise leveling surveys separated by a time interval. Although this is theoretically a plausible method of obtaining information concerning contemporary crustal warping, in practice there are a number of inherent problems. Man and nature combine to disturb the essential leveling bench marks. Children, horses, traffic, construction equipment, frost heaving, compaction, consolidation, desiccation, creep, weathering, etc., cause the reliability of any given leveling station to diminish with time. Furthermore, the earlier surveys were performed with less reliable equipment and methods

than are available today. Finally, the differences developed between the original leveling and subsequent relevelings are relative in that one arbitrarily assumes, as a point of departure, the stability of an initial bench mark. Many authorities attempted in the past to circumvent this unrealistic assumption by connecting a leveling net to a tide gauge station and assuming sea level stability. However, sea level itself suffers analytical problems.

Tide Gauges. Tide gauge stations can be influenced by crustal movements that produce anomalous records with respect to those of neighboring tide gauges. Although tide gauge stations suffer from the same disabilities as leveling bench marks, as well as the added hazards inherent to maritime situations, several investigators utilizing tide gauge data from relatively stable stations, and eliminating data from stations in areas which were demonstrably unstable, have derived a figure for the contemporary eustatic rise of sea level for the interval 1890–1955 of the order of 1.0 mm/yr. However, the rate of sea level rise during this interval has not been constant and there is evidence indicating that this rise has diminished within the last decade or two.

Several investigators have assumed that extended departures of tide gauge records from this figure (of more than 1.0 mm/yr) represented a real crustal anomaly (Gutenberg, Valentin, Lisitzin, Pattullo and others—references in Fairbridge 1961). To what extent these anomalies, when consistent over a period of years, can be used as indicators of crustal mobility and coastal instability is still a matter of controversy. There is little doubt that the gauges disclose secular trends, but quantitative data on the respective amounts whereby the tidal gauges reflect changes in atmospheric pressure, water temperature, salinity, wind velocity, longshore currents, the annual water cycle, oceanic circulation, changes in volume due to long-term climatic changes or tectonic effects are difficult to derive, but are being studied today. Yet, after a liberal allowance for the possible non-tectonic effects, an observed rate of sea level rise over the first half of the present century that is substantially greater than about 1.0 mm/yr appears to indicate that such a station is subsiding while a figure substantially less than this suggests that the station is rising. Cailleux (1952) has pointed out that tide gauges on mountainous (orogenic) coasts frequently provide evidence of emergence, while those situated on sedimentary basins most often suggest contemporary subsidence.

Historical Data. The professional literature contains numerous observations of drowned forests and coastal belts as well as of the growth of tidal marshes along many coasts. On the other hand, Finns living along the coast of the Gulf of Bothnia today cultivate fields where they waded in the sea as children; indeed, some 1000 km^2 are being added to their country each century (Charlesworth, 1957). Sweden has also witnessed land uplift and the gradual shoaling of former maritime landings. Fairbridge cites evidence for the submergence and subsequent reemergence of Roman maritime structures along the Mediterranean coast. It is evident that all of these observations cannot be reconciled to a single explanation, e.g., by implementing eustatic changes of sea level, and that, therefore, in many cases some element of coastal instability appears to be involved.

Pre-literate Folklore and Proto-literate Sagas. Ancient literature throughout the world contains a number of references to events which, although recorded in early literate times, fall essentially in the catagory of "folk history" in the sense that they represent the recording of events already old. Examples of "folk catastrophies" are the Noachian deluge and the Atlantis myth which appear to represent the recording of pre-literate folk memory. Similar deluges or inundations appear in many Asiatic and other sagas. It is probable, however, that these tales "remember" for the most part the postglacial marine transgression rather than some manifestation of coastal crustal warping.

Archaeological Evidence. The postglacial eustatic rise of sea level submerged many archaeological sites along coasts formerly occupied by ancient man (Shepard, 1964). However, elevations of a number of essentially contemporaneous coastal sites diverge both positively and negatively from the present sea level datum. The Bolyston Street "fishweir" site in Boston (date: 4600 B.P.) is 25 feet below modern mean high water, while shell middens of similar antiquity along the shore of the Hudson River estuary are located just above mean high water. A number of early Eskimo sites in northern Canada associated with raised marine strandlines are now found up to 30 meters above sea level and up to several kilometers inland from the coast. On the other hand, an Eskimo site on the southwestern tip of Banks Island in the Canadian Archipelago is now awash at high tide. Thus the present level of a number of archaeological sites indicates that these coastal locales have been affected by some combination of both eustatic change in sea level and crustal warping.

Geological Evidence of Coastal Stability

Eustatic Sea Level Curves. At present, most knowledge associated with details of sea level change relates to events of the past 12,000 years. There is general agreement as to the approximate shape of the postglacial eustatic curve, although agreement as to details is lacking. Indeed, controversy still rages among eustatic researchers as to who has

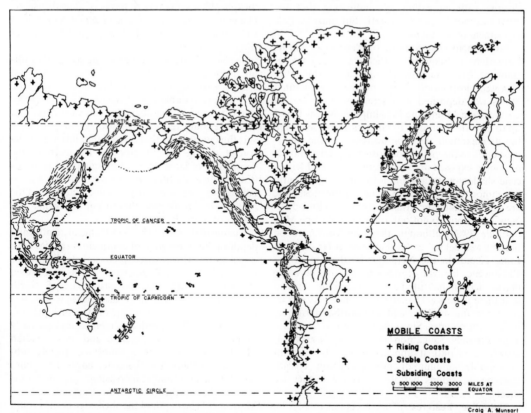

Craig A. Munsart

FIG. 1. World map (Mercator projection), showing coastal areas of relative stability today, with regions of rising and sinking crust.

actually found the stable global tide gauge, i.e., a stable coast. Two schools of thought on the subject have emerged: the North Atlantic-Gulf Coast school led by Jelgersma (1961), Russell (1964) and Shepard (1964) who find that sea level has risen to its present position only during the last few millennia, and the Indo-Pacific school, led by Fairbridge (1961), Gill (1961) and Schofield (1964) who believe that sea level rose to its present level some 5000–6000 years ago and has since fluctuated within 3 meters of its present level, including one or more conspicuous stands at 2–3 meters above present sea level some 2000–6000 years ago. The reason for this lack of agreement is unresolved. Either one or both of the schools include spurious data or the data are incompatible only because one or both eustatic groups of curves include some element of tectonic coastal instability.

As an example of this problem, comparable series of radiocarbon dates obtained from diachronous fresh to brackish water peats found at the base of Holocene tidal marsh, estuarine, and lagoonal sediments have been obtained from several sites along the east coast of the United States by Redfield (1967) and Bloom (1965) and from the coast of the Netherlands by Jelgersma (1961). Plots of the submergence curves obtained from these sites diverge with increasing age indicating that the curves cannot be purely eustatic but must include an element of crustal mobility.

Stratigraphy. The warping of Pleistocene marine formations is frequently indicative of coastal instability. For example, the glacial-marine Presumpscot Formation of the northeastern United States was deposited in a late-Wisconsin sea. In northeastern Maine, the Presumpscot is now found up to elevations of over 100 meters above sea level, but its maximum elevation decreases to the southwest until, in the vicinity of Boston, the formation is no longer exposed above present sea level. Pleistocene shallow-water marine formations, apparently Sangamon (pre-Wisconsin) in age for the most part, are exposed along the Atlantic coast from Florida to New Jersey but do not outcrop north of Cape May (latitude 39°N) although they are known to be present well below sea level at least as far north as Long Island. In the Netherlands, the top of the Pleistocene Eemian formation, a shallow-water marine deposit, has tilted down toward the north so that there is now a 15-meter difference between its surface in the south-central and northeastern portions of the country. Since the formations noted are approximately Sangamon in age (say 100,000 ± 20,000 years old), it appears there has been an appreciable amount of post-Sangamon coastal warping in regions peripheral to the former ice sheets.

Shore-line Features. The acceptance of the hypothesis that shore-line features at approximately the same levels in different parts of the world may be correlated altimetrically, on the assumption that they mark high positions of worldwide sea level in successive interglacial ages, tacitly implies coastal stability. However, a considerable body of evidence has accumulated indicating that these stepped surfaces of marine planation and beach accumulations are not strictly correlatable with respect to age or altitude. Numerous tilted marine terraces are now known as well as examples of converging and even crossing terraces. Even if all the glacial ice in the world were to melt and the land areas of the earth became completely desiccated, it is doubtful that the sea would rise as much as 50 meters above its present level. Yet the early Pleistocene "Calabrian" marine terrace of southern Italy and Sicily occurs well above this level, at 100–200 meters and more (Cotton, 1963). The higher levels are definitely suspect today (Flint, 1966). Indeed, if sea level during the Pleistocene had stood at levels much greater than 30 meters above its present level, one would expect to find extensive evidence of this transgression on low-lying continental areas in the form of marine sediments: such deposits are exceptional.

Warped Pleistocene terraces are in evidence along the coast of California and there are at least several examples of faulted terraces. Thus the terrace dilemma involves Pleistocene terraces at elevations inexplicable exclusively in terms of glacial eustasy; likewise it involves terraces of equivalent age at varying levels and even terraces of different age at similar levels. Since a dynamic view of the Pleistocene coasts recognizes a fluctuating sea level resulting from the summation of glacial eustasy and crustal warping, both operating at varying rates, it is understandable that it would be rather exceptional to find chronologically equivalent and accordant eustatic terraces over widely scattered areas. It is thus postulated that coastal mobility was widespread during the Pleistocene. In addition, the subsidence of large areas of marginal ocean floors (Caribbean, Mediterranean, western Pacific) is believed to have initiated a negative tectono-eustatic movement during the Pleistocene involving 100 meters or more (Fairbridge, 1961).

Continental Shelf. The width, mean depth, and depth of the outer edge of continental shelves have implications with respect to coastal stability. Continental shelves off glaciated coasts are often abnormally wide. Off the east coast of North America in the south, the coastal plain is wide (i.e. the shelf is mostly emerged); off the mid-Atlantic states, the shelf is partially emerged and partially submerged; off New England and the Canadian Maritime provinces, it is almost completely submerged. Furthermore, the outer edge of the continental shelf is found at increasingly greater depths toward the northeast off New England and the Maritimes. The depth of the shelf edge at the Grand Banks at 80 meters is twice that of the shelf break off New England.

Eardley (1964) has noted that there is a progressive deepening of the shelf break toward the poles, suggesting to him a secular slowing in the earth's rotation rate. It is suspected that normally the shelf edge reflects some common equilibrium state relative to sea level. However, since the depth of the shelf break today ranges in various regions from a few meters to at least 400 meters, warping subsequent to formation is implied.

Unstable (Mobile) Coasts

Postglacial Emergence. Regions subjected to glaciation during the last (Wisconsin) ice age include coastal areas that have undergone extensive post-Wisconsin marine submergence accompanied or followed by emergence caused by isostatic rebound. These postglacial emerged coastal areas include the inner fiords of the Atlantic coast of southern and central Norway, the Oslofiord area of Norway, the coasts of Sweden, the Gulf of Bothnia, the north coast of the Gulf of Finland, the borders of the White Sea and Scotland and Northern Ireland. Also emerged in postglacial times are most of the coasts associated with the Canadian Archipelago, the coasts adjacent to Hudson Bay, the Labrador coast, Newfoundland, the St. Lawrence River estuary, New Brunswick, and coastal New England southwest to the vicinity of Boston. Antarctica, Greenland, Spitsbergen and other formerly glaciated areas also exhibit isostatic emerged features.

Deltaic Coasts, Coastal Plains and Depositional Basins. Russell (1964) points out that the deltas of all larger rivers show subsidence and that most continental margins appear to have tilted seaward as indicated by differential tilting of fluvial terraces. For example, the depth to the oxidized contact at the base of recent gravels in coastal Louisiana indicates that at least 33 meters of subsidence has occurred along the central Gulf coast during the Holocene. Accumulating evidence based on the comparison of eustatic curves, leveling surveys, tide gauge data and archaeological information indicates that coastal plains, especially those underlain by only slightly deformed Cenozoic sediments, are slowly subsiding. Examples are the Gulf and Atlantic coastal plains. Sedimentary basins such as that of the North Sea are also subsiding (Jelgersma, 1961).

Mountainous, Orogenic and Faulted Coasts. Mountainous coasts appear for the most part to be uplifted coasts. Russell (1964) mentions a Holocene shell midden in California at an elevation of 200 meters which is associated with one of the numerous raised and broadly warped marine terraces of the west coast of the United States. The mobility of the California coast is witnessed also by the folding and faulting of Pliocene and Pleistocene sediments in the Los Angeles and Ventura basins. Indeed, there is evidence for warping along most of the coasts peripheral to the Pacific Ocean basin as well as those of other Tertiary orogenic belts. Island arc areas possessing strongly negative free-air and Bouguer gravity anomalies such as Timor and Barbados, exhibit raised Pleistocene terraces up to 4000 feet that certainly cannot be explained by glacial eustatic changes in sea level. According to Bonifay (1962), Cotton (1963) and others, the Mediterranean flights of terraces owe at least some of their altitude either to local or to broad regional upwarping. Volcanic islands, including islands having volcanic foundations with calcareous caps, are inherently unstable, as is well illustrated in the Ryukyu Islands (e.g., Okinawa), the Bonins and Palaus. The early Pleistocene terraces of Japan are now mapped to elevations of 500 meters and more (Nakagawa, 1965).

Causes of Coastal Mobility

The instability of glaciated regions may be explained by postglacial isostatic rebound and the collapse of the periglacial "bulge" (Daly: see discussion by Fairbridge and Newman, 1968). The mobility of volcanic, faulted, and, in general, orogenic coasts is obviously related to the causal mechanisms, of volcanism, faulting and orogeny. Other processes involved in coastal mobility are, perhaps, rather more subtle. Figure 1 indicates current knowledge of tectonically stable or mobile coasts.

Continental Flexure Hypothesis. This hypothesis [derived from Jesson, Bourcart (1950) and others] suggests that the margins of continents suffer repeated warping downward toward the ocean basins as noted in the seaward dips of many coastal formations, concurrently with progressive upwarping of the hinterland. The present coastline is often close to the fulcrum. This process is particularly noticeable around the shores of Africa, which broke up with the rupturing of Gondwanaland (see *Continental Flexure*).

The oscillation hypothesis (of R. G. Lewis: discussed by Fairbridge, 1961) has recently been restated by Beloussov (1962) who suggests that oscillatory movements, including reversals of tectonic sign at the earth's surface, occur constantly and are fundamental factors to be considered when dealing with any portion of the earth's surface. A variation on this theme suggests that along continental borders an unstable subcrustal condition exists which leads to alternating subsidence and upwarping. Geodetic releveling in Russia and eastern Europe has disclosed "neotectonic" crustal oscillations of 1–10 mm/yr (wavelength equals a few hundred kilometers; period equals a few hundred years) and is being closely studied (Mescherikov *et al.*; see *Crustal Movements—Contemporary*).

Geodetic Pole Shift Hypothesis. Jardetzky noted that a sudden shift of the axis of rotation would cause a persistent geodetic instability which would adjust to a new equilibrium only with an appreciable time lag. Fairbridge (1961) noted that according to this

153

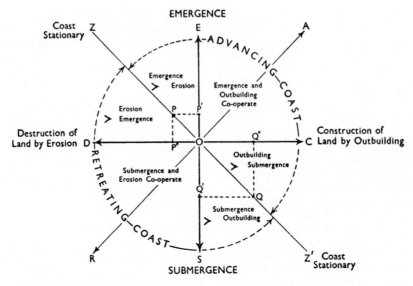

Fig. 2. Graphical representation of H. Valentin's classification of coasts (Holmes, 1965).
(By permission of the Ronald Press Co., N.Y., and T. Nelson & Sons, London)

hypothesis, a sudden polar shift would cause a positive change of sea level along the new equator and negative changes at the new poles.

Variations in the Earth's Rotation Rate. Eardley's study of submerged and emerged shore lines and depths of continental shelves led him to believe that the cause of sea level rise in high latitudes and its apparent fall in low latitudes since the Cretaceous may be due to the slowing of the earth's rotational velocity. This hypothesis is comparable with Jardetzky's (except that the cause is due to a rotational rate change rather than polar shift).

Effects of Ice/Water Loading and Unloading. The loading and subsequent unloading of the lithosphere by ice and water has resulted in a complex and probably rhythmical distortion of the geoid as well as of many coastal areas. The reality of *postglacial isostatic rebound* (q.v.) in Scandinavia and Canada seems assured, but the effects of deglaciation along the edges of formerly glaciated areas are rather more obscure. Daly suggested that glacial loading caused the superelevation of a tract several hundred kilometers wide outside of the glaciated area. He indicated that in this peripheral belt the earth's crust had been slightly bulged upward because of earlier viscous outflow of the subcrust material under the weight of the icecap. The inner portion of the peripheral bulge was initially uplifted when the glacier melted but subsequently subsided.

Evidence now becoming available seems to justify Daly's hypothesis (Fairbridge and Newman, 1968). The excessive subsidence of the east coast of the United States between the Connecticut coast and Cape Hatteras noted from leveling, tide gauge studies, estuaries and embayments, drowned archaeological sites, as well as other evidences of excessive submergence, all support the Daly hypothesis. Furthermore, in northwestern Europe, the shores of Holland, Belgium and northern Germany are subsiding. Differential subsidence has been documented in detail only for the Netherlands (Jelgersma, 1961). A similar pattern of subsidence is noted for eastern England, the coasts of Germany, Poland and the remainder of the southeastern Baltic coast.

Loading and unloading as a result of eustatic changes in sea level probably has had a discernible although unspecified effect on coasts. Higgins (1965), Bloom (1965) and others have suggested that some of the post-Wisconsin coastal submergence may be due to the isostatic depression of the broad continental shelves by the load of water imposed by the postglacial rise of sea level.

Descriptive Geometry of Coastal Change

The classification of coasts is treated elsewhere, but a few words are necessary to clarify certain terminology (see discussions by Valentin, 1952; Vella, 1962; Bloom, 1965; Stephens and Synge, 1966).

The stationary coast is evidently a steady-state situation of equilibrium either (a) between outbuilding (progradation) and submergence (tectonic downwarp and/or eustatic lowering), or (b) between erosion and emergence (likewise either tectonic or eustatic or both). In Fig. 2, based largely on Valentin's system, the stationary state is illustrated by ZOZ', while points P and Q represent equilibrium sites.

The advancing coast O-A is explicable either by emergence E (as at P') or construction of new land C (as at Q") or a combination. The rate is proportional

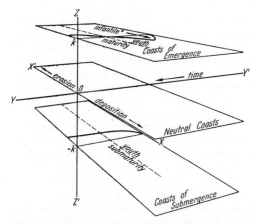

Fig. 3. Johnson's three primary categories of coasts represented within a three-dimensional framework. k and $-k$ are the amounts of (prior) emergence and (prior) submergence (Bloom, 1965).

to the distance from 0. The retreating coast O-R is explicable either by submergence S (as at Q') or destruction by erosion D (as at P'').

Bloom (1965) made a notable contribution by expressing this geometry in cartesian coordinates adding *time* in the Y axis (Figs. 3 and 4). The stationary coast is now expressed as an oblique plane. A hypothetical point A (on Fig. 4) now describes a coast that has advanced through time as a combination of deposition and emergence.

It is only when these relations are clearly established (at least in theory) that the basic problems of local crustal stability and instability can be treated.

WALTER S. NEWMAN

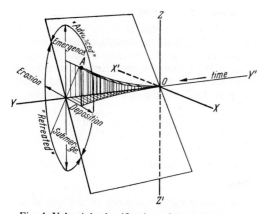

Fig. 4. Valentin's classification of coasts with a time axis added. The oblique line of neither advance nor retreat that forms the primary subdivision of his classification becomes an oblique plane. The present position of hypothetical point A is shown as the result of emergence and deposition through time (Bloom, 1965).

References

*Beloussov, V. V., 1962, "Basic Problems in Geotectonics," New York, McGraw-Hill Book Co., 816pp.

Bloom, A. L., 1965, "The Explanatory description of coasts," *Z. Geomorphol.*, **9**(4), 422–436.

Bonifay, F., 1962, "Quaternaire et préhistoire des régions méditérranéennes françaises," *Quaternaria*, **6,** 343–370.

Bourcart, J., 1950, "La theorie de la flexure continentale," *Congr. Intern. Geogr. Lisbonne*, 1949, **2,** 167–190.

Cailleux, A., 1952, "Recentes variations du niveau des mers et des terres," *Bull. Soc. Géol. France*, Ser, 6, **2,** 135–144.

*Charlesworth, J. K., 1957, "The Quaternary Era," London, E. Arnold, 2 vols.

Churchill, D. M., 1965, "The displacement of deposits formed at sea-level, 6500 years ago in southern Britain," *Quaternaria*, **7,** 239–249.

Cotton, C. A., 1957, "Tectonic features in a coastal setting, etc." *Trans. Roy. Soc. New Zealand*, **84,** 761.

Cotton, C. A., 1963, "The question of high Pleistocene shorelines," *Trans. Roy. Soc. New Zealand*, **2,** 51–62.

Donnelly, T. W., 1965, "Sea-bottom morphology suggestive of post-Pleistocene tectonic activity of the Eastern Greater Antilles," *Bull. Geol. Soc. Am.*, **76**(11), 1291–1294.

Eardley, A. J., 1964, "Polar rise and equatorial fall of sea level," *American Scientist*, **52,** 488–497.

*Fairbridge, R. W., 1961, "Eustatic changes in sea level," in "Physics and Chemistry of the Earth," Vol. 4, pp. 99–185, London, Pergamon Press.

Fairbridge, R. W., and Newman, W. S., 1968, "Postglacial crustal subsidence of the New York area," *Z. Geomorphol. N.F.*, **11**.

Flint, R. F., 1966, "Comparison of interglacial marine stratigraphy in Virginia, Alaska, and Mediterranean areas," *Am. J. Sci.*, **264,** 673–684.

Gill, E. D., 1961, "Changes in the level of the sea relative to the land in Australia during the Quaternary Era," *Z. Geomorphol. Suppl.*, **3,** 73–79.

Hicks, S. D., and Shofnos, W., 1965, "The determination of land emergence from sea level observations in southeast Alaska," *J. Geophys. Res.*, **70**(14), 3315.

Higgins, C. G., 1965, "Causes of relative sea-level changes," *Am. Scientist*, **53,** 464–476.

Holmes, A., 1965, "Principles of Physical Geology," Second ed., New York, Ronald Press Co., 1288pp.

*Jelgersma, S., 1961, "Holocene sea level changes in the Netherlands," *Mededel. Geol. Sticht. Ser. C*, **6**(7).

Kuenen, P. H., 1955, "Sea level and crustal warping," *Geol. Soc. Am. Spec. Papers*, **62** (*Crust of Earth*), 193–204.

Leontyev, O. K., 1963, "Overall features of the geomorphology and evolution of the Azerbaydzhan Coast of the Caspian Sea," *Internt. Geol. Rev.*, **5**(6), 671–691.

Nakagawa, H., 1965, "Pleistocene sea levels along the Pacific coast of Japan," *Sci. Rept. Tohoku Univ.* **37**(1), 31–39.

Putnam, W. C., Axelrod, D. I., Bailey, H. P., and McGill, J. T., 1960, "Natural Coastal Environments of the World," Los Angeles, University of California (ONR contract).

Redfield, A. C., 1967, "Postglacial change in sea level in the western North Atlantic Ocean," *Science*, **157** (3789), 687–692.

Russell, R. J., 1964, "Techniques of eustasy studies," *Z. Geomorphol.*, **8**, 25–42.

Schofield, J. C., 1964, "Postglacial sea levels and isostatic uplift," *New Zealand J. Geol. Geophys.*, 7(2), 359–370.

Shepard, F. P., 1964, "Sea level changes in the past 6000 years; possible archaeological significance," *Science*, **143**, 574–576.

Stephens, N., and Synge, F. M., 1966, "Pleistocene Shorelines," in (Dury, editor) "Essays in Geomorphology," pp. 1–51, Heinemann Educational Books, Ltd.

Valentin, H., 1952, "Die Küsten der Erde," *Peter. Geogr. Mitt.*, 246, 118pp.

Vella, P., 1962, "Terms for real and apparent height changes of sea level and of parts of the lithosphere," *Trans. Roy. Soc. New Zealand Geol.*, 1(6), 101–109.

* Additional bibliographic references may be found in this work.

Cross-references: *Coastal Classification; Coastal Geomorphology; Coastal Plains; Continental Flexure; Crustal Movements—Contemporary; Delta Dynamics; Eustasy; Holocene; Littoral Processes; Postglacial Isostatic Rebound; Prograding Shoreline; Retrograding Shoreline; Terraces—Marine; Warping; Water Loading and Crustal Response.* Vol. I: *Continental Shelf; Ocean Currents.* Vol. II: *Earth's Rotation.*

COASTAL VEGETATION TYPES—*See* pr Vol. VI

COASTLINES: THEORETICAL SHAPES

Introduction

It is a well-known phenomenon that moving water is able to transport sand. The quicker the water runs, the more material it will convey. This means that where the current velocity diminishes, sand must be dropped and when the flow velocity increases, sand must be picked up. In the first case we have deposition, in the latter erosion. It will be obvious that this simple fact determines the configuration of sandy shores. In practice, however, this matter is not so easy to determine because the relation between the flow characteristics, on the one hand, and the character and the quantity of the transported material, on the other, is very complicated. Even for the most simple case of a steady permanent flow over a sand bottom this relation is not known to a satisfactory degree. And the existence of this in nature is very rare! Normally there are tidal streams along a coast. These streams are not steady and permanent. At every instant of time the stream velocities differ from place to place in magnitude and in direction. At a fixed point the stream velocity changes in the course of time as well. In addition, there are winds which cause waves. Normally the velocity and the direction of the winds vary widely, producing waves of different sizes and from different directions.

It happens that in such circumstances large break-

waters must be built. Often they go so far into the sea that they disturb the sand transport considerably. This results in an irrevocable change in the coastline on both sides of the breakwaters. Sometimes these changes are so enormous that for human protection it is desirable to predict them as accurately as possible. In such cases one takes refuge in the model tests. There one tries to imitate on a smaller scale what happens in nature. In many laboratories tests have been made to establish the relation between the wave characteristics and the quantity of transported material. Knowing how difficult it is to establish such a relation in the most simple case of a steady permanent flow, we have to expect much scattering in the results of these tests. In spite of this scatter, however, all tests have a similarity in their results. They show that the intensity of the littoral transport is a maximum when the waves approach the shore obliquely. Some tests show that this maximum is reached when the angle α between the wave front and the shore line is 30°. Other tests show that this happens when this angle is 60°. Whatever the real value may be, it seems to be true that the intensity of the littoral transport has a maximum at a value of α which differs widely from $\alpha = 0°$ and $\alpha = 90°$.

On the supposition that this fact must lead to certain peculiarities in the form of shore lines, the Coastal Research Department of the Rijkswaterstaat in the Netherlands has made a study of this. They have attempted to determine what types of shore lines can mathematically exist assuming that the littoral transport is ruled by the function sin 2α which has its maximum value when $\alpha = 45°$. Note that this study concerns coasts which are exposed only to waves and not to tidal streams. This study and its results are summarized on the following pages.

Mathematical Treatment

Considering a stretch of shore of an infinitely small length, we have the condition that the quantity of deposited (or eroded) material must be equal to the difference between the quantities transported by the sea at the beginning and at the end of that stretch of shore. On the basis of Fig. 1 we write:

$$\frac{\partial q}{\partial \varphi}\, d\varphi\, dt = ar\, d\varphi\, \frac{\partial r}{\partial t}\, dt$$

or

$$\frac{\partial q}{\partial \varphi} = ar\, \frac{\partial r}{\partial t}$$

where

r, φ = the polar coordinates of the considered point of the shore

q = the function that determines the quantity of the littoral transport

t = the time

a = the depth of the water which will be a function of r and φ.

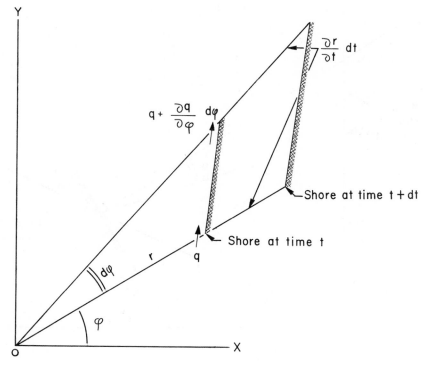

FIG. 1.

Since the magnitude of q depends only on the angle α, this angle is of prime importance. Therefore, we take α as the independent variable instead of φ. This has two consequences. First, the form of the equation of continuity must be reduced to:

$$\frac{\delta q}{\delta \alpha} + ar\left(\frac{\delta r}{\delta \alpha} \cdot \frac{\delta \varphi}{\delta t} - \frac{\delta r}{\delta t} \cdot \frac{\delta \varphi}{\delta \alpha}\right) = 0 \qquad (1)$$

Secondly, we need another equation to relate α and φ. On the basis of Fig. 2 we have:

$$\alpha + \varphi + \psi = \beta \qquad (2)$$

It will be clear that β defines the direction of the wind. But ψ is a new variable also depending on α and t. So we cannot get away from another equation that defines ψ. From the well-known formula

$$\tan \psi = \frac{r}{r'}$$

we derive

$$\tan \psi \cdot \frac{\delta r}{\delta \alpha} = r \cdot \frac{\delta \varphi}{\delta \alpha} \qquad (3)$$

Now the problem is to find functions which satisfy the Eqs. (1), (2) and (3). We shall determine whether the following combination of functions will do.

$$a = cr^n \Phi(\varphi)$$

$$r = R(\alpha)T(t)$$

$$\varphi = \varphi(\alpha)$$

$$q = AQ(\alpha)$$

where Q, φ and R are functions of α only and T is a function only of the time t.

Substituting these functions in the equation of continuity [Eq. (1)] yields:

$$\frac{\dfrac{dQ}{d\alpha}}{R^{n+2}\Phi\dfrac{dQ}{d\alpha}} = \frac{c}{A} \cdot T^{n+1}\frac{dT}{dt}$$

On the left-hand side of this equation, there are expressions of α only; on the right-hand side, only the time t appears. This equation can be satisfied only when both parts are equal to a constant k. This yields the two conditions:

$$dQ = kR^{n+2}\Phi \, d\varphi$$

$$T^{n+1}dT = \frac{kA}{c} \cdot dt$$

The second condition offers no problem while it can be integrated to:

$$T = \sqrt[n+2]{(n+2)\frac{kA}{c}(t - t_0)} \qquad (5)$$

where t_0 is an integration constant. The first condi-

157

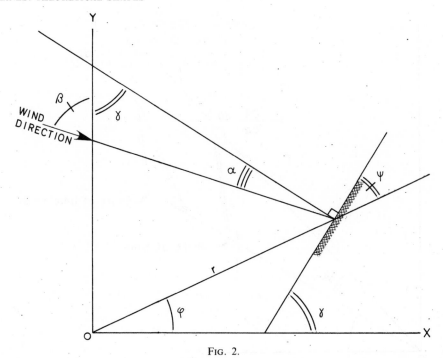

FIG. 2.

tion replaces the original equation of continuity [Eq. (1)]. However, we are not able to solve Eqs. (2), (3) and (4) more easily unless we restrict ourselves further. Therefore, we assume that the bottom of the sea is horizontal. This means that $n = 0$ and that $\Phi = 1$.

Finally, we have obtained the following set of equations which can be solved without difficulty:

$$dQ = kR \, d\varphi \qquad (6)$$

$$\tan \psi \, dR = R \, d\varphi \qquad (7)$$

$$\alpha + \varphi + \psi = \beta \qquad (8)$$

while the function T is:

$$T = \sqrt{\frac{2kA}{c}(t - t_0)}$$

The function Q can have each form. We took for it the function $\sin 2\alpha$. It is useful to realize that the chosen combination of functions shows a certain character. When we divide the radius vector r by T, we obtain a value depending on α only. That means that the shoreline at the time $t = t_1$ and the shoreline at the time $t = t_2$ can be reduced to the very same shape by geometrical multiplying out of the origin. Thus to discuss these shore lines it is sufficient to discuss the curves given by R and φ which satisfy Eqs. (6), (7) and (8). The constant k can have any value. We set it equal to $\frac{1}{2}$ because then the relation of the area between two radius vectors in

the graph of R to the area between the corresponding lines in the prototype is the most simple one.

Results

Before discussing the solutions of these equations obtained by means of a computer, we shall bring to the fore some general remarks on these solutions. First, with respect to the function of $\sin 2\alpha$, it can be proved that when the curve a of Fig. 3 is a solution of the differential equation, the curves b, c and d will also satisfy the equations. Curves a and b and curves c and d are symmetrical with respect to the wind direction. Curves a and c and curves b and d are symmetrical with respect to the polar axis.

The second remarkable thing is that straight lines through the origin satisfy the equations but other straight lines do not.

The third point is that only in the octants 0, 3, 4 and 7 of Fig 4(a) can these lines be asymptotes of the solutions. This means that we can have bays and capes of a shape as shown in Figs. 4(b) and 4(c), but when the angle δ becomes more than 45°, the bays and capes must be shaped as in Figs 4(d) and 4(e), while in the points A the condition of continuity must be satisfied.

The fourth point which requires attention is the fact that when the littoral transport reaches its maximum value the shore line shows a cusp. This will be shown later.

Figure 5 shows the result of a calculation on the computer. The computer was programmed to fol-

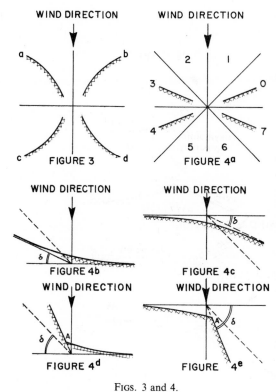

Figs. 3 and 4.

tion, and put a river mouth in point F. Then the condition is that the river brings a quantity of material to the sea equal to twice the quantity of the littoral transport in point F of the original curve.

But there is still a third way to use this curve. The computer has been programmed in such a way that all points of transition were indicated. A point of transition means that in that point the littoral transport along the curve has the same magnitude as the littoral transport that would take place when the shore was situated along the radius vector to that point. In the curve of Fig. 5 there are three such points—C, D and E. At each point, a number is written. This number gives the ratio between the magnitude of the littoral transport at that point and the quantity of material that the sea is able to transport. The magnitude of the littoral transport will be always expressed in this manner. With point C we can construct four other shore lines. This is not possible with points D and E. Finally, Fig. 6 shows all the shore lines which can be constructed from the curve of Fig. 5.

Mathematically, there exists another shape of the shore line for a symmetrical simple delta. It is easy to construct deltas with various river mouths. The only thing that must be done is to link up different curves and put a river mouth in each point of connection. There the river must bring to the sea such a quantity of material that the condition of continuity is satisfied. A mathematical condition in constructing such deltas is that the river arms must be situated along a radius vector. These deltas are still symmetrical ones. It is also very simple to construct nonsymmetrical deltas in the same way. We can thus construct an infinite number of shore lines.

Acknowledgment. It is important to realize that there is a difference in dimensions between reality and the considerations of human beings. In favorable circumstances, there is a good relation between them.

I should like to express my gratitude to Dr. J. C.

low this curve starting from a point A an infinite distance away and stopping at another point B also infinitely distant.

With this one solution of the differential equations, we can construct shore lines of different types. First the curve of Fig. 5 can be interpreted as the shore line of a bay or, by mirroring with respect to the polar axis, as the shore line of a cape. In addition, with this curve we can construct a symmetrical simple delta. Therefore, we take only part A–F, mirror it with respect to the wind direc-

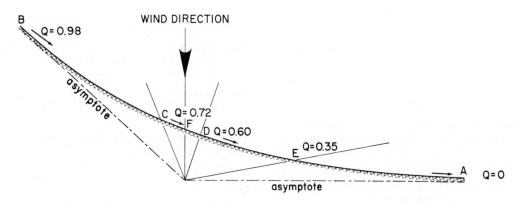

Fig. 5.

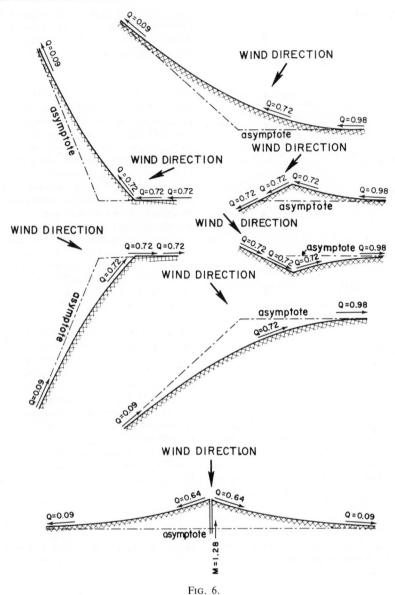

FIG. 6.

Schönfeld; for advice on the mathematical treatment of the problem.

W. GRIJM

References

Bakker, W., and Edelman, T., 1964, "The coastline of river deltas," *Proceedings of the Ninth Conference on Coastal Engineering, Lisbon,* University of California, Council on Wave Research.

Bruun, P., 1953, "Forms of Equilibrium Coastal with a Littoral Drift," University of California, Institute of Engineering Research, No. 347.

Larras, J., 1957, "Plages et Côtes de Sables," *Collection du Laboratorie d'Hydraulique.*

Pelnard, Considerè P., 1956, "Essai de Théorie de l'Evolution de Côtes de Sables et de Inlets, IV.," *Journ. de l'Hydraulique* Question III.

Cross-references: *Cuspate Foreland; Delta; Littoral Processes; Sediment Transport.* Vol. I: *Wave Theory.*

COAST TYPES—*See* ATLANTIC AND PACIFIC TYPE COASTS

COL

A French word for mountain pass, saddle or low point on a ridge, from the Latin *collum* = neck.

In English it has developed two specialized meanings. In meteorology it means a saddle of low pressure between two anticyclones. In geomorphology it has come to mean the meeting point of two opposing cirques or the low place between two *arêtes* (serrate ridges) that may well culminate in *horns* (q.v.). Flint (1957, p. 104) remarks that many Alpine passes have this origin, but "have lost their sharp crests as a result of glacial scour at times when the glaciers expanded and flowed through them, converting them into smoothed U troughs."

RHODES W. FAIRBRIDGE

References

Cotton, C. A., 1942, "Climatic Accidents in Landscape-making," Christchurch, N.Z., Whitcombe and Tombs, 354pp.

Flint, R. F., 1957, "Glacial and Pleistocene Geology," New York, John Wiley & Sons, 553pp.

Cross-references: *Bergschrund*; *Cirque*; *Glacial Valleys*; *Horn*.

COLLUVIUM

Colluvium is a part of the *regolith* (q.v.; also see under "*Head*"), i.e., the superficial mantle of unconsolidated rock debris and soil on the earth's surface. Specifically colluvium is that part which consists of heterogeneous materials of any particle size which accumulates on the lower parts or the base of slopes (Hilgard, 1892; Merrill, 1897). It is transported there by *gravity*, by *soil creep* (q.v.) in humid regions, by *sheet erosion, rainwash* (q.v.) and *mudflows* in semiarid areas, and by *solifluction* (q.v.) in regions subject (now or in the late Pleistocene) to the freeze–thaw processes of *periglacial landscapes* (q.v.). Colluvium may be contrasted with *eluvium*, residual material formed by weathering *in situ*.

Thus colluvium often contains soil, but somewhat transported from its genetic site. At the same time, it is likely to be mixed with boulders still preserved within the eluvium or saprolite (the rock rotted *in situ*), with frost-riven rock fragments from the upper slopes, and the general *mélange* of mixed debris associated with the mud flows and related processes of *mass wasting* (q.v.).

Along the margins of mature stream valleys, colluvium is likely to interfinger with *alluvium* (Lattman, 1960), the stream-transported detritus, and it is not always easy to distinguish between them unless angular debris is included (which most likely indicates colluvium). The lower slopes are often denuded by a mixture of sheet erosion and flowing rills. The latter lead to some water sorting, so although colluvium is characterized by unsorted debris, a small amount of sorting can sometimes be recognized. (cf. "Deluvium:" see under *Loess*.)

In some very early uses (mid-nineteenth century, quoted by A.G.I. Glossary) colluvium was used as a general term for all alluvial and diluvial (Pleistocene) deposits. This is evidently an erroneous extension of its original meaning and has no validity today. Merrill (1897) includes only talus, cliff debris and related soils. The clays so transported by gravity, according to Veatch (1906), are rather distinctive, being "midway between residual and alluvial deposits, and may, by gradual transition, pass into either." He notices how the clay in a weathered granite area is red and yellow near the top of the slope but is white in the colluvial area (leached of its iron during slope wash). In a periglacial region, Dylik (1955) has described rhythmically stratified slope-wash deposits, which indicate strong seasonality.

RHODES W. FAIRBRIDGE

References

Dylik, J., 1955, "Rhythmically stratified periglacial slope deposits," *Biul. Perygl., Lodz*, **2,** 175–185.

Hilgard, E. W., 1892, *U.S. Weather Bureau, Dept. of Agriculture, Bull.* **3**.

Lattman, L. H., 1960, "Cross section of a flood plain in a moist region of moderate relief," *J. Sediment. Petrol.*, **30**(2), 275–282.

Mabbutt, J. A., 1966, "Landforms of the Western Macdonnell Ranges. A Study of Inheritance and Periodicity in the Geomorphology of Arid Central Australia," in (Dury, G. H., editor) "Essays in Geomorphology," pp. 83–119, London, Heinemann Educ. Books, Ltd.

Merrill, G. P., 1897, "A Treatise on Rocks, Rock-weathering and Soils," New York, The Macmillan Co., 411pp.

U.S. Dept. of Agriculture, 1938, "Soils and Men," Washington, D.C., U.S. Government Printing Office.

Veatch, J. O., 1906, "The term 'colluvial' as applied to clay deposits," *Science*, n.s. **24**, 782.

Cross-references: *Alluvium*; *Head, Eluvium*; *Loess*; *Mass Wasting*; *Mudflow*; *Periglacial Landscapes*; *Regolith and Saprolite*; *Sheet Erosion*; *Soil Creep*; *Solifluction*.

CONE—*See* ALLUVIAL FAN, CONE

CONE KARST (PEPINO HILLS)

Also known as "*haystack hills*," or "*tit hills*," the Pepino hills are a characteristic feature of a mature karst landscape in tropical to subtropical latitudes. The names are regional: "Pepino hills" or "haystack hills" are used in Puerto Rico, "tit hills" in the Philippines and elsewhere, "kegelkarst" (conical hill karst) in southern Java. Cone karst is the best general term. An isolated residual hill of a former cone karst is called, in Yugoslavia, a "*hum*" (q.v.), a term sometimes also used internationally.

The distribution of such conical residual hills

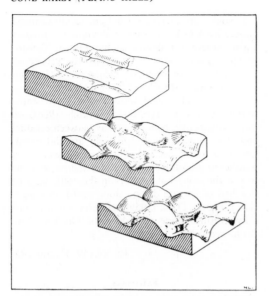

FIG. 1. Evolution of a cone karst from a rectangular drainage (and joint) pattern in flat-lying limestones in southern Java, the Guanag Sevu (Sewoe, in Dutch orthography; from Lehmann).

for limestone solution. Under conditions of alternating tropical rain and high evaporation, the residual limestone areas become intensely hard and "armored" by a thick crust of secondary $CaCO_3$. Thus, as the karst process advances, the hills become progressively harder, while the depressions between them become deeper, and the site for accumulation of rich *terra rossa* and other residual soils.

In Puerto Rico, the Pepino hills are notably asymmetric, much more so than would be explained by the gentle dips. They range from 10–100 meters in height. The east sides are more gentle than the steep westerly sides; Hubbard (1923) suggested that the latter, exposed to the warm afternoon sun, would be less eroded. Thorp (1934) stressed the incidence of the Northeast Trade Wind on the more weathered eastern slope. Meyerhoff (1938) suggested that the much higher *mogotes* (q.v.) of western Cuba, which are essentially symmetrical, are more influenced by convectional rains which lack a systematic orientation.

RHODES W. FAIRBRIDGE

is controlled primarily by the presence of flat-lying or gently dipping limestones, which, if evenly jointed in big rectangles, favor a systematic pattern

References

Doerr, A. H., and Hoy, D. R., 1957, "Karst landscape in Cuba, Puerto Rico, and Jamaica," *Sci. Monthly*, **85** (October).

FIG. 2. Cone karst or "tit hills" on Bohol Island (Visayan), Philippines, latitude 9° 50′ N, longitude 124° 15′ E.

Hubbard, B., 1923, "The geology of the Lares district, Puerto Rico," *N.Y. Acad. Sci., Survey of Puerto Rico and Virgin Islands,* **2**, Pt. 1, 83–93.

Lehmann, H., 1936, "Morphologische Studien auf Java," *Geograph. Abhand.,* **9**, 1–114.

Lehmann, H., 1954, "Der tropische Kegelkarst auf den Grossen Antillen," *Erdkunde,* **8**(2), 130–139.

Meyerhoff, H. A., 1938, "The texutre of karst topography in Cuba and Puerto Rico," *J. Geomorphol.,* **1**, 279–295.

Thorp, J., 1934, "The asymmetry of the Pepino Hills of Puerto Rico in relation to the trade winds," *J. Geol.,* **42**, 537–545.

Wissmann, H., 1954, "Der Karst der humiden-heissen und sommer-heisen Gebiete Ostasiens," *Erdkunde,* **8**(2), 122–130.

Cross-references: *Hum; Karst; Mogote.*

CONGELIFLUCTION—*See* SOLIFLUCTION

CONGELIFRACTION, CONGELITURBATION—*See* FROST ACTION; FROST HEAVING; FROST RIVING; PATTERNED GROUND; PERIGLACIAL LANDSCAPES; SOLIFLUCTION

CONSEQUENT VALLEY, STREAM—*See* DRAINAGE PATTERNS; RIVERS

CONSERVATION—*See* pr Vol. VI

CONTINENT

A hypsographic analysis of elevations over the surface of the earth's solid crust shows a remarkable bimodality (Kossinna, 1921; see also *Hypsographic Curve,* Vol. II), with mean peaks at very contrasting elevations, with respect to mean sea level (MSL). It should be stressed that mean sea level is a datum that varies through time, depending upon the amount of oceanic water in the hydrosphere, and the shape and size of the ocean basins. Apart from oscillations of MSL there has been a secular enlargement of the area of dry land on the Earth (at the expense of continental shelf) that has continued at least since the Cambrian Period.

	Mean Elevation (m)	Area (km²)	Volume (km³)
Continents	+ 875 m	148.1 × 10⁶	130 × 10⁶*
Oceans	−3800 m	361.9 × 10⁶	1370.3 × 10⁶

* Calculated with respect to mean sea level, but assuming a mean crustal thickness of 45 km, the volume of continental crust would be 6700×10^6 km³, thus approximately five times the volume of the ocean.

The mean height of the lithosphere, i.e., the earth's solid surface, is 2430 meters below sea level. The mean depth of the ocean is well below this value, and is approximately − 3800 meters; the mean height of the land (+ 875 meters) is that of the geographical surface of the *continents*, but is in no wise the mean (three-dimensional) level of the continental crust (Figs. 1 and 2) which is close to − 20 km.

The terms continent or continental crust have thus two distinctive meanings in the earth sciences. Geographically, "continent" refers to the surface of large continuous land masses of the earth. Seven such continents are recognized (see *Land Mass Classification*), and distinctive parts bounded by water or high mountains, such as Greenland or the India–Pakistan area, are referred to as *subcontinents*. *Continental islands* (see *Islands*) are those rising from within the same continental shelf as the continents, e.g., the British Isles belong thus to Europe, Newfoundland to North America, Madagascar to Africa, Ceylon to India, Borneo to Southeast Asia, New Guinea to Australasia. Isolated volcanic islands, coral atolls, etc., are non-continental in the structural sense, but are included in statistical figures for the land (continental) areas of the earth.

The geophysical definition of continent or continental crust is three-dimensional. It embraces also the *continental shelf* (Fig. 3), an additional 28.3×10^6 km² of the earth's surface (5.5% of total), together with a less precisely defined fraction of the *continental slope* and *rise* (q.v., in Vol. I). Thus defined, the continental crust has a thickness range of 20–70 km, which strikingly contrasts with oceanic crust of about 5 km. Through and beneath this continental crust there are distinctive paths for seismic wave transmission. Near the surface, at least, it has a distinctive lithologic and geochemical nature, that is close to the mean composition of granodiorite, a silica-alumina-rich rock, which gave rise to the name SIAL given by Suess, in contrast to the basalt-type of ocean crust which is mafic (ferromagnesian) or silica-magnesium-rich, thus SIMA. It is probable that simatic material occurs in some of the lower parts of the continental crust. An important aspect of the continent-ocean contrast is that while each continent contains large sectors of considerable age (radiogenically dated at 1–3 billion years), no part of the ocean is certainly dated as older than Mesozoic (200 million years).

Geophysically all of the continents are tied together: thus Africa to Europe and Asia (Eurasia), Asia to Australia and Asia to North America, thence to South America and finally Antarctica. This is a unique sequence, and there are no cross-connections today, though in the past (before about 200 million years ago) connections existed. These lay between North America and Eurasia ("Laurasia" from Laurentia, the Canadian Shield, and Eurasia) and between the southern or "Gondwanaland" continents: South America, Africa, India, Australasia and Antarctica.

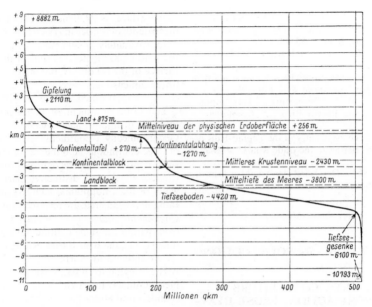

FIG. 1. Hypsographic (or hypsometric) curve of the earth's surface (Kossinna). Note: *Gipfelung* = mean summit height; *Mittelniveau der physischen Erdoberfläche* = average height of earth's (solid and liquid) surface in contact with the atmosphere; *Mittleres Krustenniveau* = mean elevation of crust; *Tiefseeboden* = deep-sea floor; *Tiefseegesenke* = deep-sea depressions (all regions below −5750 meters).

Uniform Components of Each Continent

One of the most remarkable aspects of each and every continent is that it consists of a specific group of geotectonic components (see map: Fairbridge, 1963). These essential components are as follows:

(a) *Shield*: Ancient, crystalline *craton* or nucleus, or series of nuclei, dated variously from about 0.2 back to 3.5×10^9 years. Its tectonic behavior is that of a strong but not completely rigid foundation, capable of broad warping, but largely aseismic and mostly free from modern volcanic activity. The shields largely represent the deeply eroded "roots" of very ancient mountain belts. Today they are

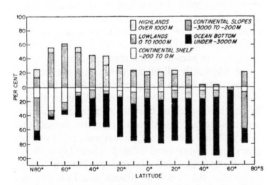

FIG. 2. Variation of elevation with latitude along selected parallels (from data by Kossinna; Howell, 1959). (By permission of McGraw-Hill Book Co., N.Y.)

marked by many of the great mining centers for the metallic ores.

(b) *Platforms*: Broad sedimentary plains overlapping the shield (known from borings to underlie the plains), having the same characteristics as shields, except that there is a veneer of sedimentary cover (often important economically for its artesian water reserves). The thickness of the veneer varies and a transition to component "c" makes its upper limit a matter for arbitrary decision: 300 meters or 1000 feet is a reasonable average.

(c) *Intracratonic and marginal basins*: Broad, often equidimensional downwarps of the shield or craton, filled by shallow-water continental (lacustrine-fluvial) or epicontinental marine sediments. Youthful examples may pass out into parts of the continental shelves and slopes of the modern ocean. Thicknesses are normally up to about 3000 meters (10,000 feet), but exceptionally they exceed 10,000 meters (33,000 feet). They are of enormous economic significance for their resources in water, oil, natural gas, coal, limestone, and evaporites (salt, gypsum, potash).

(d) *Mountain belts*: Long, relatively narrow zones, marked by complex folded ("orogenic") sedimentary structures, often with axial zones exposing granitized roots, metamorphic belts and batholithic intrusions. The younger orogenic belts (*Alpinotype*) are marked by high elevations and jagged mountain scenery; they are frequently

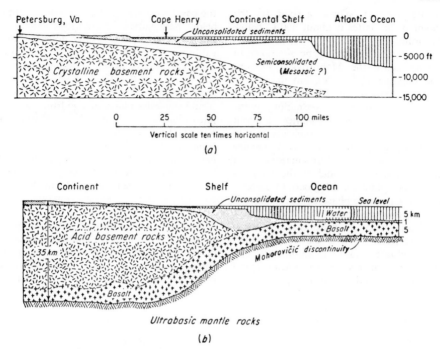

Fig. 3. Generalized section across a stable continental margin (Jacobs, 1959). (By permission of McGraw-Hill Book Co., N.Y.)

paralleled at lower elevations by belts of relatively simple folds (*Juratype*, Appalachian *Valley and Ridge type*). Older orogenic belts may be largely reduced to eroded plains or uplands (e.g., Appalachian *Piedmont*), they may be revived by block faulting and uplift (e.g., French Massif Central, Germany's Black Forest, Scottish Highlands, or Rocky Mts. of Wyoming and Colorado).

(e) *Block-faulted belts*: Long, relatively narrow or "diamond-shaped" segments in zones marked by strong faulting ("taphrogenic" features), in which the principal motions are tensional, strike-slip (torsional) and vertical (both up and down). Either these belts occur in median positions between pairs of orogenic belts (e.g., the so-called *Zwischengebirge* or Intermontane Plateaus and *Senkungsfelder* —the United States Basin-Range Province, Alti Plano of Mexico, of Peru and Bolivia, the Hungarian Plain, the Aegean Sea, Anatolian Plateau, Iran, Tibet and so on), or they occur crossing the great shields (e.g., the great "rift valley" belts— East Africa, South Australia, Siberia; see also *Block Mountains*).

(f) *Volcanic plateaus*: Flattish areas of extensive lava flows, usually of the nonexplosive basaltic type, e.g., Columbia Plateau of the United States Pacific Northwest, the Ethiopian Plateau of Africa or the Deccan "Traps" of India.

(g) *Volcanic belts*: Narrow zones usually marginal to continents or between them in striking "island arcs" or loops, characterized by highly explosive lavas of the andesite-dacite clan, forming the elegant conical-type central volcanics famous from the state of Washington, the Aleutians, central Mexico, Japan, Indonesia and New Zealand.

Differences between continents consist of such matters as the relative sizes, and different ratios of a particular geotectonic component (thus Africa's shield areas are the greatest, while Asia has more fold mountains and volcanic belts). On the surface the climatic belts have profound effects upon weathering history, soils, vegetation and human occupation. The geotectonic structure of the Antarctic continent is thus completely "normal," but its enveloping ice cover (2–3 km thick) makes its appearance unique.

The *character of the continental crust* is still not perfectly understood, but systematic studies in several parts of the world in recent years have shed considerable light on the subject. For example, the United States Geological Survey now maintains a special "Branch of Crustal Studies," and special groups at the Carnegie Institution of Washington, the University of Wisconsin and others are concentrating on this research (see detailed articles in Vol. V). The principal outcome of these recent studies is the recognition of considerable variety in the makeup of the continental crust and upper mantle. The continental crust used to be visualized as an "iceberg" of sial floating on a "sea" of sima (Wegener); this is not really very accurate—for one reason, if the simatic layer were to melt extensively, the sial could not float on it as a solid, for the melting point of the latter is about 400°C below that of the former!

By convention, the "crust" is generally taken to be everything above the Mohorovičić Discontinuity (see *Lithosphere*, Vol. V), but the precise meaning of the "Moho" (or M-discontinuity) is not yet resolved; it is defined in seismology as the sudden transition from wave velocities of about 7 km/sec to about 7.8–8.2 km/sec. Such a transition could be brought about by a geochemical boundary or by a phase change in uniform material to a denser state. A reasonable model for the composition of the Upper Mantle is 20% basalt and 80% peridotite; a low-pressure phase of this mixture is called a "feldspathic peridotite" (by Wyllie, 1963a and b) or basalt-peridotite rock, and the high-pressure phase is referred to as a "garnet peridotite" or eclogite-peridotite rock. The seismic velocity appropriate to the former is close to 7.8 km/sec, and the latter 8.2 km/sec. In the Basin-Range Province,

the basal crust always shows a velocity appreciably below these figures (7.1 km/sec or less) as is appropriate to "basaltic" rocks like dolerite ("diabase"), gabbro and norite. Thus the M-discontinuity is essentially a compositional boundary here. But in the Plains and Rocky Mt. provinces, the basal crustal velocities are appreciably higher, which would suggest a phase change from basalt to eclogite *within* the lower crust; the transformation is not abrupt, however, but occurs through a broad transitional zone. Nevertheless the M-discontinuity *below* the lower crust is still sharp in these provinces which suggests again that it marks a compositional change (from eclogite or an eclogite–basalt mixture to the eclogite–peridotite mixture, mentioned above.)

Heat flow studies may provide a helpful clue as to the composition of the continental crust because of the heating by the radiogenic minerals in sialic (silicic) rocks is *four times* that of simatic (mafic) rocks, i.e., 4 contrasted to 1×10^{-13} cal/cm^3/sec.

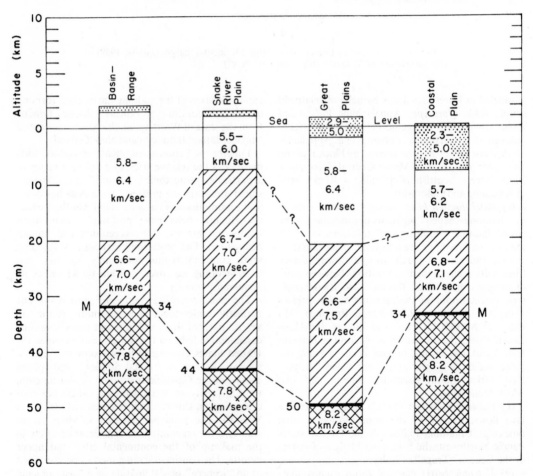

FIG. 4. Generalized crustal models in four provinces of the United States showing approximate distribution of compressional-wave velocity with depth (Pakiser, 1965).

But the calculations are complicated by the differences in thermal conductivity and by the possibility of varied levels of heat flow from the Upper Mantle (generally taken as about 0.6 microcal/cm²/sec).

Studies by heat-flow measurements, seismology (Fig. 4), and gravity surveys combine to suggest the following regional types of crust (Pakiser, 1965):

(a) *Shield and plains-type crust* ("cratogenic" or "cratonic"): Observations of heat flow from one of the most stable shields, that of Western Australia, show a mean rate of 1 mcal/cm²/sec, close to the world average. The crustal thickness for such provinces is 47–50 km (to the M-discontinuity), and this heat flow would seem to be appropriate for a silicic crust of 22–25 km (seismic velocity 5.0–6.4 km/sec) on a mafic layer of 25–28 km (velocity 6.4–7.1 km/sec). As indicated above, the basalt–eclogite phase change is believed to occur *within* the mafic lower crust.

(b) *Mountain-type crust* ("orogenic"): This is illustrated by Pakiser's profiles through the Rocky Mt. front, e.g., Nevada to Kansas. The silicic crust is 33–38 km thick, thus appreciably thicker than under the shield (the lighter "roots" providing isostatic compensation for the 3–5 km elevation of the mountains), but the mafic layer is slightly less thick perhaps, about 20 km. A thick root is also found under the Sierra Nevada. As in the Shield and Plains Province, the basalt–eclogite phase transition zone begins 10–15 km *above* the M-discontinuity (Fig. 5).

(c) *Block-faulted intermontane plateaus and subsidence belts* ("taphrogenic"): These are tectonically active zones of crustal stretching or torsional distortion. In the American West, this province is 2–3 km above sea level, and according to older ideas the crust should be thicker here than under the plains; the opposite is the case. The silicic crust is found to be 20–22 km thick on the average, and the mafic crust 11–12 km thick. The eclogite transition, however, does not begin until about 10 km *below* the M-discontinuity. In certain areas, the mafic crust almost reaches the surface, as in the Snake River Plain of Idaho; the vast basalt flows of the Columbia Plateau show the important role of basalt in this province. An important factor here is that the basalt–eclogite transformation zone extends to great depths, a zone ranging through 40–70 km. One may visualize that under regional tension or torsion, eclogite is transformed to basalt, and the deep block-faulting permits enormous upwelling of basalt. This phenomenon is not just a feature of the American Intermontane Plateau belt but is a worldwide characteristic of the same geotectonic province. The phase change from high- to low-pressure state in the upper mantle would lead to about 3% expansion, and partial melting of basalt would bring about a 10% expansion of the melted part; this would not explain all the uplifts, but in addition there is the possibility that some of the olivine in peridotite or basalt is hydrated to serpentine (Hess, 1955), accompanied by a 25%

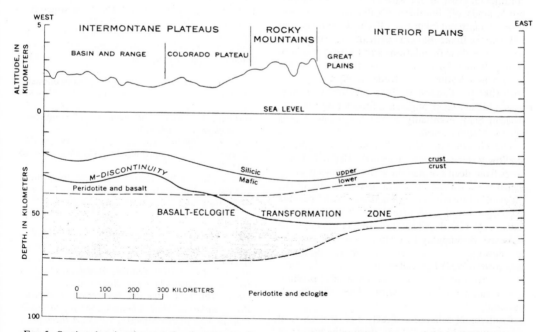

FIG. 5. Section showing the crustal and upper-mantle structure and the inferred basalt-eclogite transformation zone from the Basin and Range Province to the Great Plains. Section extends from central Nevada to southeastern Nebraska.

expansion. Furthermore, a regional lowering of gravity due to a shift in the geoid following polar change would favor such general phase changes and liberation of volatiles to permit serpentinization (see *Plateaus*). Nevertheless, there is a widespread belief that some subcrustal flowage of molten basaltic material would be necessary to maintain the elevation of such plateau regions, possibly at about the "asthenosphere" or "low-velocity layer" at 100 km depth or so. Mass transfer from some oceanic depression seems likely (Pakiser and Zietz, 1965); at 1200°C, basalt would be fluid while the peridotite fraction remained solid. According to Weertman (1963), such flow could be related to convection from the base of the mantle, but this is still very problematic. Local "hot spots" marked by extrusive silicic rocks are also noted in these provinces.

(d) *Quasicratonic, continental-collapse areas or "Senkungsfelder"* ("bathygenetic"): Certain parts of the earth's crust are believed to have been formerly continental and are now undergoing regional collapse. Such vertical lowering of formerly high (continental) crust is proved in regions where non-volcanic atolls are found growing up from platforms that today are 1000–2000 meters below sea level; such regions are sometimes called "microcontinents" or, more romantically, "lost continents." Examples are seen around the western Pacific margin and in Mediterranean-type seas, including the East and West Indies; the Gulf of California has no atolls but has a central zone with no continental crust at all, whereas the block-faulted borderlands off Southern California and downwarped marginal plateaus off the Carolinas and Florida, the Blake–Bahama plateaus appear to have lost part of their foundations and to be slowly subsiding. It may be predicted that the Basin-Range Province is destined to subside slowly to near sea level (like the Pannonian Plain of Hungary), then pass a further stage of general foundering (like the Aegean Sea), eventually to reach oceanic depths like the Mediterranean.

The growth rate of corals and the continuous shallow-water carbonate facies in the Blake–Bahama cores from deep-borings show that the mean subsidence rates of these quasi-cratonic areas are of the order of 0.1 mm/yr, exceptionally for brief periods exceeding 1 mm/yr (Fairbridge, 1965). Such subsidence calls for the silicic roots of a continent to be removed, presumably by melting and mass transfer by flowage processes as yet totally unknown. Beloussov (1962) has called the process "basification," "basaltization" or "oceanization," presuming a mixing of silicic with ultramafic mantle material.

Continental collapse is clearly a phenomenon of "decontinentalization." Thus, during the history of the earth while it is believed that new continental crust developed by accretion along orogenic belts, there is an equally effective process of continental destruction. If, as suggested by certain models (e.g., MacDonald, 1963), the earth is growing progressively hotter, due to radioactive mineral breakdown, such subcrustal melting may be increasing slowly through time.

RHODES W. FAIRBRIDGE

References

Beloussov, V. V., 1962, (Maxwell, J. C., editor) "Basic Problems in Geotectonics," New York, McGraw-Hill Book Co., 816pp. (translated from Russian by P. T. Broneer).

Fairbridge, R. W., 1963, "Map—Geology of the World," in "Great World Atlas," New York, Readers Digest, Pl. 139.

Fairbridge, R. W., 1965, "The Indian Ocean and the status of Gondwanaland," in *Progress in Oceanography*, **3**, 83–136.

Hess, H. H., 1955, "Serpentines, orogeny and epeirogeny," in (Poldevaart, A., editor) "Crust of the earth —A symposium," *Geol. Soc. Am. Spec. Paper* **62**, 391–407.

Howell, B. F., 1959, "Introduction to Geophysics," New York, McGraw-Hill Book Co., 399pp.

Jacobs, J. A., Russell, R. D., and Wilson, J. T., 1959, "Physics and Geology," New York, McGraw-Hill Book Co., 424pp.

Kossinna, E., 1921, "Die Tiefen des Weltmeeres," Berlin, Veroeffentl., *Inst. Meeresforsch. N.F. Ser. A,* No. 9, 70pp.

MacDonald, G. J. F., 1963, "The deep structure of continents," *Rev. Geophys.*, **1**, 587–665.

Pakiser, L. C., 1965, "The basalt–eclogite transformation and crustal structure in the western United States," *U.S. Geol. Surv. Profess. Paper* **525B,** B1–B8.

Pakiser, L. C., and Zietz, I., 1965, "Transcontinental crustal and upper-mantle structure," *Rev. Geophys.*, **3**(4), 505–520.

Weertman, J., 1963, "The thickness of continents," *J. Geophys. Res.,* **68**, 929–932.

Wyllie, P. J., 1963a, "The nature of the Mohorovičić discontinuity, a compromise," *J. Geophys. Res.*, **68**, 4611–4619.

Wyllie, P. J., 1963b, "The Mohorovičić discontinuity and the orogenic cycle," *Trans. Am. Geophys. Union,* **44**(4), 1064–1071.

Cross-references: *Basin-Range Landscape*; *Block Mountains*; *Continents and Oceans—Statistics*; *Hypsographic Curve*; *Island Arcs*; *Islands*; *Land Mass and Major Landform Classification*; *Mountains*; *Piedmont Landforms*; *Plains*; *Plateaus*; *Ridge and Valley Topography*. Vol. I: *Continental Borderland*; *Continental Rise*; *Continental Shelf*; *Continental Slope*; *Submarine Plateau*. Vol. II: *Hydrosphere*. Vol. V: *Asthenosphere*; *Continental Crust*; *Faults and Faulting*; *Geoid*; *Lithosphere*; *Orogenesis*; *Mantle*; *Mohorovičić Discontinuity*; *Shield*; *Zwischengebirge*. Vol. VII: *Gondwanaland*.

CONTINENTAL EROSION

In the classical sense, erosion refers to the disruption and transportation of rock debris from one place to another by a variety of surficial processes. The main agents of erosion are water, ice, wind and mass wastage (see *Erosion*). Some processes operate predominantly within the realm of the continent itself. These tend not to destroy a continent but merely to alter its surficial expression by redistributing its mass. For example, in some cases glacial erosion causes profound topographic changes. The debris eroded by the ice, however, is normally carried to and deposited somewhere else on the continental block. This does little ultimately to destroy the continent since only a small amount of glacially transported material is permanently lost.

The true erosion of continents (i.e., the exchange of detritus from the continents to the ocean basins) is accomplished, in the main, by the inexorable movement of sediment in the major rivers of the world. Therefore, even though other processes are involved, rivers are the primary agents of erosion and denudation of the world's continents.

Rates of Continental Erosion

Measurement and Calculation. Because we can measure the amount of debris being carried by rivers, we can hope to establish how rapidly the continents are being denuded. Measurements are normally made (1) by direct determinations of stream load using samplers devised for that purpose or (2) by observing the volume of reservoir space lost over a period of years by the accumulation of sediment deposited behind the dam.

The magnitude of erosion in a particular drainage basin is estimated by converting, into volumetric terms, the weight measurements of particles carried in the streams. It is usually assumed, but not necessarily true, that on the average 165 pounds (74 kg) of eroded material represents the removal of 1 cubic foot (2700 cm^3) of surface rock (274 kg/m^3). This corresponds to a specific gravity of 2.64. Using this conversion it is possible to calculate the rate of denudation by knowing the weight of annual sediment production per unit area of a drainage basin, i.e., tons of sediment per square mile of drainage basin per year. Denudation is then expressed as a uniform lowering of the surface over the entire basin per unit time, for example, feet per thousand years.

Various equations have been employed to convert rapidly the annual tonnage of stream load into the rate of denudation. Judson and Ritter (1964) used the following equation based on a specific gravity of 2.64, where D is equal to the denudation in inches per thousand years.

$D = 5.2 \times 10^{-3} \times$ sediment yield
(in tons per square mile per year).

Other equations based on the same specific gravity have been employed by Schumm (1963) and Dole

and Stabler (1909) (see references in Judson and Ritter, 1964).

The rate of denudation calculated for a large region should not be taken to imply that every basin within that region is being eroded at the same rate. There may be a wide range of sediment production from one basin to the next. Thus, no single drainage can be expected to mirror the rate of erosion determined for a large region and, conversely, the regional rate cannot be applied to any local area.

Types of Load. The total erosion contains a factor of several different types of transported material: suspended load, traction or bed load and dissolved load.

Suspended Load. Particles suspended in the water constitute the largest fraction of the total load moved by most rivers. Because of this, inaccurate suspended load data may lead to rather extreme errors in the rate of denudation.

Wide variations in suspended sediment loads may occur in successive years. For example, the 8-year record of the Delaware River at Trenton, New Jersey, shows that the maximum annual suspended load recorded in the period of October 1954 through September 1955 was 2,320,000 tons. The minimum annual suspended load at the Trenton station was 431,000 tons, recorded during the preceding 12-month period. Calculation of the rate of denudation by using data collected in only one of the above years would produce greatly erroneous results. It is obvious that the longer the continuous daily samplings, the more valid are the data.

Typical suspended loads carried by streams of the United States are presented in Table 1.

Bed Load. Little data exist concerning that portion of the total load which moves along the stream bottom. Several methods have been devised to sample the bed load but as yet none is completely satisfactory. As a result, the bed load is commonly taken as some percentage of the entire detrital load. It is most probable that in dealing with continental erosion, the bottom load is but a small fraction of the suspended load. Estimates of the bed load at the mouth of the Mississippi River are about 7–10% of the total solid load.

Dissolved Load. All water traversing the continents begins its journey as nearly chemically pure rainwater. Therefore, dissolved solids in streams represent the amount of material which has been eroded from the continental mass during the return of rainwater to its oceanic womb. The weight of these dissolved particles must be included in any denudation rate. Although the suspended load is the dominant factor in denudation, the dissolved load is significant and, under certain climatic and geologic conditions, it may be as important as the detrital load.

Few data concerning concentrations of dissolved solids in streams have been compiled. The available

TABLE 1. SUSPENDED SEDIMENT LOADS BY INDIVIDUAL STREAM BASINS IN THE UNITED STATES (from Judson and Ritter, 1964)

Region and River	Location	Drainage Area (sq miles)	Average Annual Suspended Load (tons × 10³)	Period of Time for Records	Tons/sq mile/yr	Erosion Rate (in./1000 yr)	Source
North Atlantic							
Delaware	Trenton, N. J.	6,780	998	10/49–9/57	147	0.8	a
Schuylkill	Philadelphia, Pa.	1,893	993	11/47–9/57	524	2.7	a
Juniata	Newport, Pa.	3,354	345	1/51–9/57	103	0.5	a
Scantic	Broad Brook, Conn.	98	7.26	11/52–9/57	74	0.4	a
South Fork Shenandoah	Front Royal,Va.	1,638	171	4/52–9/56	104	0·5	a
Rappahannock	Remington, Va.	616	76.8	4/50–9/57	125	0.7	a
Rapidan	Culpepper, Va.	465	74.2	4/50–9/56	160	0.8	a
South Atlantic and eastern Gulf							
Roanoke	Altavista, Va.	1,802	437	10/52–9/56	242	1.3	a
Yadkin	Yadkin College, N. C.	2,280	808	1/51–9/57	354	1.8	a
Tombigbee	Jackson, Ala.	≈19,000	2,290	10/52–9/60	120	0.6	b
Alabama	Claiborne, Ala.	≈22,000	2,130	10/52–9/60	97	0.5	b
Chattahoochee	Columbia, Ala.	≈8,000	1,120	10/52–9/60	139	0.7	b
Western Gulf							
Colorado	San Saba, Tex.	30,600	3,610	10/50–9/57	118	0.6	a
Rio Grande	San Acacia, N. M.	26,770	9,420	10/47–9/56	352	1.8	a
Pecos	Puerto de Luna, N. M.	3,970	2,720	10/48–9/57	685	3.6	a
Rio Hondo	Roswell, N. M.	947	545	10/51–9/57	575	3.0	a
Mississippi							
Mississippi	Baton Rouge, La.	1,243,500	305,000	10/49–9/61	244	1.3	c
Colorado							
Colorado	Grand Canyon, Ariz.	137,800	149,000	10/25–9/57	1,082	5.6	a,d
Pacific slopes in California							
Alameda	Niles, Calif.	633	221	10/56–9/60	349	1.8	e,a
San Joaquin	Vernalis, Calif.	14,010	347	10/56–9/60	25	0.1	e,a
Sacramento	Sacramento, Calif.	≈27,500	2,580	10/56–9/60	94	0.5	e,a
Napa	St. Helena, Calif.	81	63.3	10/57–9/60	781	4.1	e
Eel	Scotia, Calif.	3,113	18,200	10/57–9/60	5,846	30.4	e
Mad	Arcata, Calif.	485	1,800	10/47–9/60	3,711	19.3	e
Trinity	Hoopa, Calif.	2,846	3,250	10/56–9/60	1,141	5.9	e,a
Columbia							
Snake	Central Ferry, Wash.	103,500	13,100	4/50–7/52[g]	127	0.7	f
Columbia	Pasco, Wash.	102,600	10,300	6/50–7/52[g]	100	0.5	f
Green	Palmer, Wash.	230	70.8	10/53–9/57	308	1.6	a

[a] *U.S. Geol. Surv. Water Supply Papers,* Quality of Water.
[b] Unpublished reports. U.S. Army Corps of Engineers; Mobile, Ala.
[c] Unpublished reports. U.S. Army Corps of Engineers; New Orleans, La.
[d] *U.S. Geol. Surv. Profess. Papers.*
[e] Unpublished reports. U.S.G.S.; Branch of Quality of Water; Sacramento, Calif.
[f] Unpublished reports. U.S. Army Corps of Engineers; Walla Walla, Wash.
[g] Incomplete records.

data are presented as the amount (parts per million, i.e., milligrams per liter) of dissolved particles in the water. Conversion of the concentration (ppm) into weight terms is necessary for use in denudation studies.

TABLE 2. ESTIMATES OF ANNUAL CHEMICAL DENUDATION AS GIVEN BY VARIOUS AUTHORS (from Judson and Ritter, 1964).

	Denudation (tons/square miles/yr)		
Drainage Region	Dole and Stabler (1909)	Durum et al. (1959)	Livingstone (1963)
Colorado	51	17	65
Pacific slopes, Calif.	177	81	103
Western Gulf	36	31	118
Mississippi	108	99	110
South Atlantic and eastern Gulf	106	80	175
North Atlantic	130	126	163
Columbia	100	112	163

Examples of several estimates of chemical denudation in the United States are given in Table 2. Note that the range among different estimates is great. This may indicate that many fundamental problems are involved in the collection and interpretation of chemical data. For an excellent discussion of the possible errors in studies of this kind, the reader is referred to Livingstone (1963).

Although the range of chemical erosion as seen in Table 2 may seem large, the effect on the total rate of denudation using the extreme values is not necessarily great. This is especially true where abundant suspended loads are being carried by the streams. In these cases, the dissolved loads constitute only a minor part of the total erosion and the use of erroneous chemical data will cause only small discrepancies in the final denudation rate.

The mean chemical composition of river waters of the world are presented in Table 3. Livingstone (1963) estimates that 3,905,000,000 metric tons of material are being carried annually in solution by rivers flowing into the ocean. For data representing the individual continents and other worldwide data, the reader is referred to Livingstone (1963) or to Durum et al. (1959) and Clarke (1924) (see references in Livingstone, 1963).

Present Rate of Denudation. The rate at which the United States is presently eroding has been estimated in the early part of this century by Dole and Stabler and more recently by Gilluly, Menard, Schumm and by Judson and Ritter (see references in Judson and Ritter, 1964). These studies show that the United States is eroding at a rate of between 1 in./1000 yr and 3 in./1000 yr (2.5–7.5 cm/1000 yr). Taking the average elevation of the United States as 2300 feet (700 meters) and assuming that the rate shown in Table 4 is valid, we can conclude that it would take only 11 to 12 million years to remove a volume of sediment equivalent to the mass of the United States lying above sea level.

Kuenen (1950) estimates that 12 km^3 of undissolved load is carried into the sea each year by streams. If the area of the world's land mass is considered to be 57.5×10^6 square miles (150×10^6 km^2), the world's annual solid load represents 586 tons/sq mile (203 metric tons/km^2) of sediment production on the continents. The dissolved loads suggested by Livingstone are equivalent to 75 tons/sq mile/yr (26 metric tons/km^2) for a total denudation rate of 3.4 in/1000 yr (8.6 cm/1000 yr). This rate once again is only a gross generalization and cannot be considered as representative of one particular continent. Indeed, any similarity between the worldwide denudation and that for a single continent happens merely by chance.

The denudation rates introduced above do not allow for isostatic adjustment of the continental block. Thus, it should be realized that the surface of the continents will not be lowered to sea level in the time suggested by the denudation rates. Iso-

TABLE 3. MEAN COMPOSITION OF RIVER WATERS OF THE WORLD (from Livingstone, 1963)

	HCO_3	SO_4	Cl	NO_3	Ca	Mg	Na	K	Fe	SiO_2	Sum
North America	68	20	8	1	21·	5	9	1.4	0.16	9	142
South America	31	4.8	4.9	0.7	7.2	1.5	4	2	1.4	11.9	69
Europe	95	24	6.9	3.7	31.1	5.6	5.4	1.7	0.8	7.5	182
Asia	79	8.4	8.7	0.7	18.4	5.6	9.3		0.01	11.7	142
Africa	43	13.5	12.1	0.8	12.5	3.8	11	-----	1.3	23.2	121
Australia	31.6	2.6	10	0.05	3.9	2.7	2.9	1.4	0.3	3.9	59
World	58.4	11.2	7.8	1	15	4.1	6.3	2.3	0.67	13.1	120
Anions[a]	0.958	0.233	0.220	0.017	-----						1.428
Cations[a]	-----				0.750	0.342	0.274	0.059	-----		1.425

[a] Millequivalents of strongly ionized components.

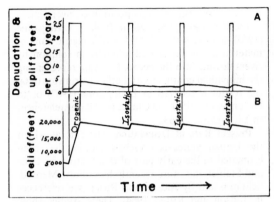

FIG. 1. (A) Hypothetical relation of rates of uplift and denudation to time; (B) hypothetical relation of drainage-basin relief to time as a function of uplift and denudation as shown in A (redrawn from Schumm, 1963).

static compensation will greatly increase the time necessary to accomplish base leveling. Schumm (1963) suggests that a reduction in altitude of 1000 feet requires 5000 feet of denudation, i.e., a five-fold isostatic adjustment (Fig. 1).

On the question of the disparity between present rates of denudation and orogeny, Schumm (1963) tentatively concludes that:

"(1) Rates of denudation for areas of about 1500 square miles average 0.25 feet per 1000 years and reach a maximum of 3 feet per 1000 years. These rates are relatively rapid and are representative of areas for the most part underlain by sedimentary rocks in a semiarid climate. Denudation rates in humid regions are about four times slower.

"(2) Present rates of orogeny exceed rates of denudation significantly. An average maximum rate of orogeny is about 25 feet per 1000 years.

"(3) The rapid rates of orogeny in contrast to denudation and valley cutting make it unlikely that hillslope form can be used to decipher the earth's recent diastrophic history. Rather the form of a hillslope profile in an area of high relief probably reflects the difference in rates of channel incision and hillslope erosion.

"(4) Because denudation has two components, channel and hillslope erosion, which operate at much different rates, a balance between rates of denudation and uplift will not yield time-independent or equilibrium land forms.

"(5) Relatively rapid rates of denudation make peneplanation a very likely event under conditions which were probably common in the geologic past. Planation of 5000 feet of relief may require perhaps 15–110 million years.

"(6) An erosion cycle will be interrupted by periods of rapid isostatic adjustment separated by longer stable periods of denudation.

"(7) The episodic recurrence of isostatic adjustment may partly explain the existence of multiple or warped erosion surfaces, the recurrence of coarse sediments through a thick sedimentary deposit, and isostatic anomalies in old mountain ranges."

Past Rates of Erosion. As seen above, measurements of loads in streams allow us to determine the present rate of erosion. Past continental erosion can also be estimated. This is done by calculating the amount of land-derived sediment which has accumulated in the ocean basins during any specific interval of geologic time. To be valid, this method requires that (1) the volume of debris derived from any particular source area can be accurately determined, (2) the dimensions of the source area are measurable, and (3) the duration of sediment accumulation is known within reasonable limits.

The above conditions are difficult to satisfy. It is impossible, for example, to know if all the dissolved load is returned, by precipitation, to the sedimentary pile, or whether a significant portion of that load is permanently lost. Furthermore, pelagic and volcanic additions make it difficult to ascertain exactly how much of the deposited material was truly the result of continental erosion. Despite these and other problems, some reasonable estimates of past erosion rates have been made (Gilluly, 1955; Menard, 1961; see references in Judson and Ritter, 1964).

These authors agree that for most of the United States, the rate of erosion averaged over the entire

TABLE 4. RATES OF REGIONAL DENUDATION IN THE UNITED STATES (from Judson and Ritter, 1964)

Drainage[a] Region	Drainage Area (square miles × 10³)	Runoff (ft³/sec) (× 10³)	Load (tons/sq mile/yr)			Denudation (in./1000 yr)	Area Sampled (%)	Average Yrs. of Record
			Dissolved	Solid	Total			
Colorado	246	23	65	1190	1255	6.5	56	32
Pacific slopes Calif.	117	80	103	597	700	3.6	44	4
Western Gulf	320	55	118	288	406	2.1	9	9
Mississippi	1,250	620	110	268	378	2.0	99	12
South Atlantic and eastern Gulf	284	325	175	139	314	1.6	19	7
North Atlantic	148	210	163	198	361	1.9	10	5
Columbia	262	345	163	125	288	1.5	39	<2
Totals	2,627	1,658	121	340	461	2.4		

[a] Great Basin, St. Lawrence, Hudson Bay drainage not considered.

Cenozoic is very similar to that of the present. This seems to be contrary to the generally held concept that the present rate of erosion is abnormally high.

Factors Controlling Erosion

The rate of continental erosion is determined by the quantity of rock waste being transported to the continental margins. As mentioned above, this rate is not applicable to any particular drainage basin. The rate of erosion in local areas is controlled by a variety of geologic, topographic and hydrologic factors. Different combinations of these controlling factors may cause divers rates of erosion from region to region.

Drainage Area. Sediment production per unit area is significantly greater in small drainage basins than in relatively larger areas. Schumm notes (1963, p. 3) that "In the smaller basins, steeper slopes allow rapid and generally efficient transport of sediment through and out of the system." Thus, it can be expected that maximum denudation rates will occur in the smallest basins and that the rate in any basin will progressively decrease as the drainage area expands.

Precipitation and Vegetation. Langbein and Schumm (1958) have demonstrated a distinct relationship between the effective mean annual precipitation and the sediment yield from drainage basins within the United States. Maximum sediment production occurs in semiarid regions receiving about 10–14 inches of precipitation. Sediment yield decreases above and below this amount (Fig. 2).

The amount and type of vegetation tends to exert a control over how much sediment will be produced in a particular region. The decreasing sediment yields in basins with greater than 14 inches of annual precipitation (Fig. 2) are attributed to the increase in vegetal density and the change in vegetal type with the increasing precipitation.

Small sediment production where precipitation is less than 10 inches is related to the limited runoff in arid regions. The production of detritus steadily increases to the maximum yield point where precipitation and vegetation are most favorably combined for erosion.

Although the relative concentration of dissolved particles decreases with increasing precipitation and runoff, the total dissolved load tends to increase. At about 25 inches of precipitation, the maximum solution effects are reached and further increases in precipitation will have little effect on the solution activity of groundwater. Dissolved loads and detrital loads are commonly of equal quantities in regions with greater than 25 inches of annual precipitation (for an excellent discussion, see Leopold, Wolman and Miller, 1964).

Elevation and Relief. As one would expect, the production of sediment is regulated, in part, by the elevation and relief of the drainage basin. Corbel (1959) and Schumm (1963) consider lowland regions with gentle slopes to be fundamentally different, with respect to sediment yield, than steeply sloping uplands (Table 5 and Fig. 3). Both authors indicate that low-lying areas are yielding less sediment each year than drainage basins of comparable size and climate which stand at higher elevations. This fact is singularly important because it demonstrates that the rate of denudation is not constant. As any region is denuded, therefore, the decrease in elevation is reflected in a diminishing rate, i.e., each interval of surficial lowering will require a longer time of erosion than the preceding interval.

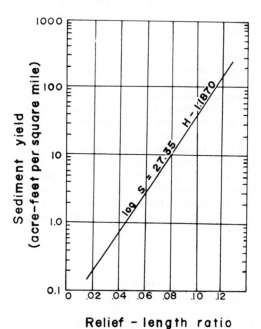

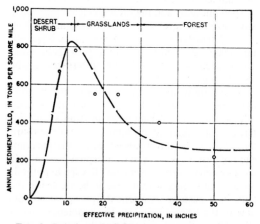

FIG. 2. Relation of effective precipitation and sediment yield (from Langbein and Schumm, 1958).

FIG. 3. Relation of sediment-yield rates to relief-length ratio (redrawn from Schumm, 1963).

TABLE 5. RELATION OF DENUDATION AND ELEVATION AND RELIEF OF DRAINAGE BASINS. NUMBERS REPRESENT DENUDATION IN MM/1000 YR (from Corbel, 1959).

Lowlands	
Climate with cold winter	29
Intermediate maritime climate (Lower Rhine, Seine)	27
Hot dry climate (Mediterranean, New Mexico)	12
Hot moist climate with dry season	32
Equatorial climate (dense rain forest)	22

Mountains	
Semihumid periglacial climate	604
Extreme nival climate (Southeast Alaska)	800
Climate of Mediterranean high mountain chains	449
Hot dry climate (Southeast U.S.A., Tunisia)	177
Hot moist climate (Usumacinta)	92

Rock Type. The lithology underlying any drainage basin exerts a distinct influence on (1) how the region will be eroded and (2) the magnitude of the denudation. In most cases, clastic sedimentary rocks and low rank metamorphic rocks break down readily into debris which can be carried as suspended loads. All other factors being equal, regions underlain by these rock types are usually characterized by large suspended loads and thus by high rates of denudation. Limestone areas and most regions underlain by crystalline rocks are relatively higher in dissolved loads.

Man. The effect of man on erosion is difficult to estimate quantitatively. It is probable, however, that his activities can significantly alter the rate of erosion within any particular drainage basin. Cultivated fields, for example, are known to be more susceptible to the ravages of erosion than are the virgin forests.

Conclusion

Any consideration of continental erosion must invariably lead to larger and more significant geologic questions. Foremost of these is simply why continents continue to exist. If erosion has proceeded at or near the present rate for the last 100 million years, the continents of the world should have been razed ages ago. It is obvious, therefore, that other processes must operate to counterbalance the effects of erosion. These processes are beyond the scope of this discussion. It is well to recognize, however, that continental erosion is only one aspect of a complex and dynamic continuum of crustal change.

DALE F. RITTER

References

Corbel, J., 1959, "Vitesse de l'Erosion," *Z. Geomorphol.,* **1**, 1–28.

* Judson, S., and Ritter, D., 1964, "Rates of regional denudation in the United States," *J. Geophys. Res.,* **69**, No. 16, 3395–3401.

Kuenen, P. H., 1950, "Marine Geology," New York, John Wiley & Sons, 568pp.

Langbein, W., and Schumm, S., 1958, "Yield of sediment in relation to mean annual precipitation," *Trans. Am. Geophys. Union.,* **30**, 1076–1084.

Leopold, L., Wolman, M. G., and Miller, J., 1964, "Fluvial Processes in Geomorphology," San Francisco and London, W. H. Freeman & Co., 522pp.

* Livingstone, D., 1963, "Chemical composition of rivers and lakes," Chapter G in "Data of Geochemistry," Sixth ed., *U.S. Geol. Surv. Profess. Paper* **440-G**.

Schumm, S., 1963, "The disparity between present rates of denudation and orogeny," *U.S. Geol. Surv. Profess. Paper* **454-H**.

* Additional bibliographic references may be found in this work.

Cross-references: *Anthropogenic Influences in Geomorphology*; *Bed Load*; *Denudation*; *Erosion*; *Sediment Transport—Fluvial and Marine*; *Weathering*. pr Vol. VI: *Fluvial Sediment Transport*.

CONTINENTAL FLEXURE

For nearly a century, since the days of Jamieson (see *Warping*) it has been recognized that erosion of the land and the transfer of mass by means of sediment into the adjacent ocean would lead to a continuous isostatic adjustment, the land rising and the ocean crust sinking. Former beaches (strand-lines) are often found in stepped terraces, on steep coasts rising up progressively from the shore, the youngest being lowest and best preserved, the highest and oldest being deeply dissected and sometimes almost effaced.

According to the early students and theorists of eustasy, these higher terraces were merely relics of Pliocene and early Quaternary sea levels, which on theoretical grounds should be higher than the present since they formed before the buildup of land ice in the Antarctic and elsewhere. However, on numbers of coasts these terraces are obviously warped unevenly and may reach heights well above any reasonable level for a eustatic explanation (say, above 200 meters). The Calabrian terrace is warped up to 900 meters in Italy, and in New Guinea and Timor even younger reef-covered terraces can be traced up to over 1000 meters.

According to the "*theory of continental flexure*" developed by Bourcart (1938, 1950), the present coast is close to a fulcrum point and thus all interior terraces are likely to be uplifted and all seaward terraces may be downwarped. Since the phenomenon of eustasy is universally accepted, particularly glacio-eustasy, any continental flexure hypothesis for a given terrace would have to be viewed in the light of a eustatic component appropriate to the date of the terrace (Fig. 1). The problem is that a clear integration is not yet possible, since neither the absolute eustatic component nor the crustal

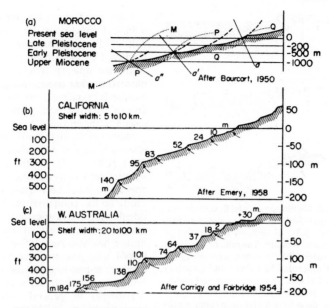

FIG. 1. Continental flexure hypothesis (Fairbridge, 1961). (a) As originally devised by Bourcart (1950) to explain features off the coast of Morocco. Note progressively steeper axis of flexure (*a, a', a''*) from Q (Quaternary), through P (Pliocene) to M (Miocene). A similar profile through a delta area (Rhine) was suggested by Umgrove (1947). (b) Sequence of terraces off the tectonically active coast of southern California, based on surveys by Emery (1958). Terraces slope seaward at 1:30 or more. Terraces around offshore islands and banks average 50% deeper than those adjacent to the mainland. Evidence favors flexure. (c) Sequence of terraces off the tectonically stable coast of Western Australia, based on echo-sounding profiles published by Carrigy and Fairbridge (1954). Terraces are essentially horizontal. Those around offshore islands are the same depth as those around the mainland. Evidence does not favor flexure.

isostatic response rate is properly established. Furthermore, the dating of the terraces is still extremely difficult.

Continental flexuring is best seen around the faulted borders of the rifted Gondwanaland continent, the borders of the Red Sea, eastern Australia, and similar belts (Fig. 2). It was demonstrated by Otto Jessen (1943) on the basis of extensive geomorphic studies around Africa that there seems to be a marginal upwarp for much of that continent, what he called *Randschwellen*. These marginal upwarps cut off the interior basins from the coast except where they were drained by great rivers which have cut deep antecedent gorges, e.g., the Congo, the Zambesi, the Orange and the Niger. The time of the earliest formation of the marginal upwarp (and thus the continental flexure) may generally be traced back to the Cretaceous and the major Gondwana dismemberment. Additional marginal upwarps (partially of younger origin) are seen along the Red Sea (mid- to late Tertiary) and eastern Australia (Pliocene-Quaternary), coastal Brazil (Cretaceous-

Tertiary), the Western Ghats of India (Cretaceous-Tertiary) and so on.

Behind the steep coastal escarpments, the consequent drainage systems are mostly directed inland. Only in a few cases does headward erosion from the coast capture the headwaters of some of the landward-flowing streams. At Mt. Bellenden-Kerr in Queensland, Australia, one can observe the extent of the Great Barrier Reefs, rising from their downfaulted basement on the continental shelf to the east, while to the west the streams head gently away across the westerly tilted plateaus, to flow for thousands of miles to inland regions.

Studies of fluvial terraces on certain major rivers, e.g., the Rhine, show a progressive upwarping of the interior plateau and downwarping near the coast (see, for example, Umbgrove, 1946). Umbgrove called for periodic convection currents within the earth to explain the phenomenon. However, it should be stressed that the Rhine (and the great African rivers, noted above) are by no means typical of all great river systems, and there are in fact

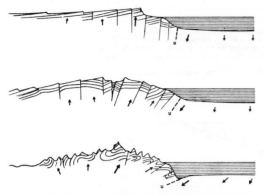

FIG. 2. Three variants of the continental flexure (Jessen, 1943). (a) *Tilted block-faulting*, characteristic of Precambrian crystalline rocks, as seen on the borders of Africa, Brazil, India and Western Australia (see *Atlantic and Pacific Type Coasts*). (b) *Uparching* with rifting, of the type found off California, the Crimea and Caucasus (see descriptions by Beloussov). (c) Fanning and underthrusting (u), characterized by "Pacific-type Coasts," where there is a foredeep trench and deep-focus earthquakes (suggesting the underthrusting of the oceanic crust).

many coastal regions of the world which show no suggestion of continental flexure. There is an attractive logic about the isostatic explanation of continental flexuring. It is, however, largely fallacious, since the area being eroded often extends far beyond the coast region. The heavily loaded delta may be smaller in area by several orders of magnitude.

If we were to carry the continental flexure idea to a logical conclusion, we should expect to find a belt of Precambrian rocks everywhere exposed landward of the present coast, the result of long-continued upwarp (Gigout, 1954). But there are numerous wide coastal plains, often underlain by paralia-geosynclines, which in some cases are known to have been progressively down-warped since Cambrian times.

Studies of the high-level erosion surfaces along the eastern border of Australia and elsewhere have led Geyl (1960, 1961) to the hypothesis that these features are strictly eustatic, but the problem would appear to have been grossly oversimplified. Recently he has compared the high-level valleys with tide-flat meanders (personal communication). An interesting treatment of the lower part of the flexure has also been offered recently by Winslow (1966), who proposed that the unique geomorphic forms of submarine canyons may be recognized in some subaerial valleys. *Underfit valleys* (see *Streams —Underfit*) in general may be considered as formerly marine, in Winslow's view, but apparently in total disregard to the known Quaternary climatic history. Fjords he views as glacially modified submarine canyons, but he ignores the problem of rock hardness.

Conclusions

To sum up, the phenomenon of continental flexuring is clearly a characteristic feature of fairly recently fractured coastlines (*Atlantic Type Coasts*, q.v.), the down faulting of the coastal plain, continental shelf, and oceanic area (continental rise)

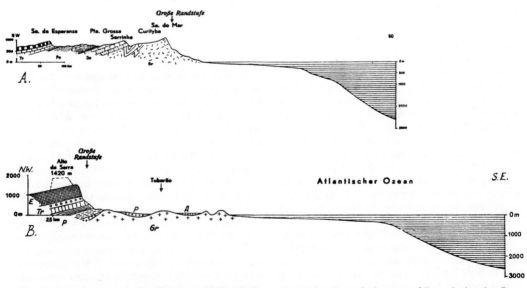

FIG. 3. Coastal upwarp in Brazil (Jessen, 1943). (A) East-west section through the state of Paraná, showing Precambrian basement nearest. (B) East-west section through the state of Santa Caterina, with Precambrian near the coast, followed by Permian, Triassic and Mesozoic dolerite sills (from surveys by R. Maack). *"Grosse Randstufe"* = great coastal escarpment, probably a complex fault-line scarp.

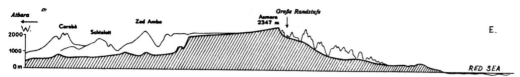

FIG. 4. Coastal upwarp of the Red Sea (Jessen, 1943). East-west section through northern Ethiopia and Eritrea. Note westward tilt of the Tertiary peneplains and lava-capped plateaus), breaking up into a dissected inselberg landscape to the west (from surveys by C. Rathjens). "Grosse Randstufe" = great coastal escarpment.

being matched by fault scarps or fault-line scarps in the coast ranges, while to the interior there are tilted peneplaned surfaces and drainage systems, directed away from the ocean. Continental flexuring is also observed along certain youthful orogenic belts (*Pacific Type Coasts*) which run parallel to the present shore.

RHODES W. FAIRBRIDGE

References

Beloussov, V. V., 1962, "Basic problems in Geotectonics," New York, McGraw-Hill Book Co., 809pp.

Bonifay, E., and Mars, P., 1959, "Le Tyrrhenian dans le cadre de la Chronologie Quaternaire Méditerranéenne," *Bull. Soc. Geol. France, Ser. 7*, **1**(1), 62–78.

Bourcart, J., 1938, "La marge continentale: essai sur les régressions et transgressions marines," *Bull. Soc. Geol. France, Ser. 5*, **8**, 393–474.

Bourcart, J., 1950, "La theorie de la flexure continentale," *Congr. Intern. Géogr., Lisbonne 1949*, **2**, 167–190.

Brouwer, A., 1956, "Pleistocene transgressions in the Rhine delta," *Quaternaria*, **3**, 83–90.

Carrigy, M. A., and Fairbridge, R. W., 1954, "Recent sedimentation, physiography and structure of the continental shelves of Western Australia," *J. Roy. Soc. Australia*, **38**, 65–95.

Cotton, C. A., 1958, "Eustatic river terracing complicated by seaward down-flexure," *Trans. Edinburgh Geol. Soc.*, **17**, 165–178.

Emery, K. O., 1958, "Shallow submerged marine terraces of southern California," *Bull. Geol. Soc. Am.*, **69**, 39–60.'

Fairbridge, R. W., 1961, "Eustatic Changes in Sea Level," in "Physics and Chemistry of the Earth," vol. 4, pp. 99–185, London, Pergamon Press.

Geyl, W. F., 1960, "Geophysical speculations on the origin of stepped erosion surfaces," *J. Geol.*, **68**, 154–176.

Geyl, W. F., 1961, "Morphometric analysis and the world-wide occurrence of stepped erosion surfaces," *J. Geol.*, **69**, 388–416.

Gigout, M., 1954, "Critique de la théorie de la flexure continentale," *Compt. Rend. Congr. Géol. Intern., 19th Alger, 1952*, Sect. 13, No. 14, 45–56.

Jessen, O., 1943, "Die Randschwellen der Kontinente," *Petermanns Geogr. Mitt.*, Erg. No. 241 (ed. 2, 1948).

Kuenen, P. H., 1955, "Sea level and crustal warping," in "Crust of the earth: a symposium," *Geol. Soc. Am.*, Special Paper **62**, 193–204.

Umbgrove, J. H. F., 1946, "Origin of continental shelves," *Bull. Am. Assoc. Petrol. Geologists*, **30**, 249–253.

Umbgrove, J. H. F., 1947, "The Pulse of the Earth," Second ed., The Hague, Nijhoff, 358pp.

Winslow, John H., 1966, "Raised submarine canyons: an exploratory hypothesis," *Ann. Assoc. Am. Geographers*, **56**(4), 634–672.

Cross-references: *Atlantic and Pacific Type Coasts; Coastal Stability; Eustasy; Fjord, Fiord; Inselberg; Quaternary Period; Strandline; Streams—Underfit; Terraces—Fluvial; Terraces—Marine; Warping.* pr Vol. VII: *Gondwanaland.*

CONTINENTALITY—*See* Vol. II

CONTINENTAL SHELF—*See* SUBMARINE GEOMORPHOLOGY; *also* Vol. I

CONTINENTS AND OCEANS—STATISTICS OF AREA, VOLUME AND RELIEF

The following tables are based mainly upon systematic analysis by Kossinna (1921, 1933), who discussed at length their various characteristics. It should be noted that data on the land areas is considered highly accurate, but that modern surveys are rendering some of the oceanic data out of date in some details; a new worldwide bathymetric analysis is urgently needed. Furthermore, the limits, boundaries and names of some of the seas and shelf areas have been changed in recent decades (see *Oceans: Limits*, etc., Vol. I). Some apparent inconsistencies, for example in the areas of continents, rest on the inclusion, or otherwise, of offshore islands; in another instance, the surfaces of lakes, while *within* continents, are not strictly land areas.

Thiel (1962) made various calculations of the amount of ice on land areas. The critical region is Antarctica, where the subglacial continental rock surface was essentially unknown until the time of the Norwegian-British-Swedish Antarctic Expedition (1949–52), and the French Expedition of 1951–52. Thanks to numerous additional seismic

TABLE 1. AREAS OF ELEVATIONS AND DEPRESSIONS OF THE EARTH'S SURFACE
(Kossinna, 1933)

Land Areas			Ocean Areas		
1000 m	10^6 km^2	%	1000 m	10^6 km^2	%
over 5	0.5	0.1	0–0.2	28.3	5.5
4–5	2.2	0.4	0.2–1	15.4	3.0
3–4	5.8	1.1	1–2	15.2	3.0
2–3	11.2	2.2	2–3	24.4	4.8
1–2	22.6	4.5	3–4	70.8	13.9
0.5–1	28.9	5.7	4–5	119.1	23.3
0.2–0.5	39.9	7.8	5–6	83.7	16.4
0–0.2	37.0	7.3	below 6	5.0	1.0
over 0	148.1	29.1	below 0	361.9	70.9

Note the bimodal peaks, at 200–500 m and at −4000 to 5000 m; see *Hypsographic Curve*.

TABLE 2. WORLD DISTRIBUTION OF LAND AND WATER, IN 5° BELTS
[based on the Helmert–Hayford Ellipsoid, from Kossinna (1933)]

Latitude	Northern Hemisphere				Southern Hemisphere			
	Water (1000 km^2)	Land (1000 km^2)	Water (%)	Land (%)	Water (1000 km^2)	Land (1000 km^2)	Water (%)	Land (%)
90–85°	979	—	100.0	—	—	979	—	100.0
85–80°	2,546	384	86.9	13.1	—	2930	—	100.0
80–75°	3,743	1112	77.1	22.9	522	4333	10.7	89.3
75–70°	4,415	2327	65.5	34.5	2,605	4137	38.6	61.4
70–65°	2,457	6118	28.7	71.3	6,818	1756	79.5	20.5
65–60°	3,124	7212	30.2	69.8	10,304	32	99.7	0.3
60–55°	5,400	6615	45.0	55.0	12,007	9	99.9	0.1
55–50°	5,530	8069	40.7	59.3	13,392	207	98.5	1.5
50–45°	6,614	8461	43.8	56.2	14,697	377	97.5	2.5
45–40°	8,413	8018	51.2	48.8	15,837	594	96.4	3.6
40–35°	10,032	7629	56.8	43.2	16,488	1173	93.4	6.6
35–30°	10,809	7945	57.7	42.3	15,787	2968	84.2	15.8
30–25°	11,750	7954	59.6	40.4	15,442	4262	78.4	21.6
25–20°	13,358	7147	65.2	34.8	15,454	5051	75.4	24.6
20–15°	14,986	6166	70.8	29.2	16,152	5000	76.4	23.6
15–10°	16,558	5082	76.5	23.5	17,216	4423	79.6	20.4
10– 5°	16,633	5334	75.7	24.3	16,903	5064	76.9	23.1
5– 0°	17,392	4738	78.6	21.4	16,797	5334	75.9	24.1
90– 0°	154,739	100,311	60.66	39.34	206,421	48,629	80.92	19.08

90° N–90° S — Oceans, 361,160,000 km^2, 70.80 %
Land, 148,940,000 km^2, 29.20 %

TABLE 3. AREAL DISTRIBUTION OF CONTINENTS (Kossinna (1933))

Continent	Area (1000 km^2)	Peninsulas (% of whole)	Islands (% of whole)	All appendages (% of whole)	Nucleus (% of whole)
Europe	10,009	27.1	7.5	34.6	65.4
Asia	44,134	18.0	6.1	24.1	75.9
Eurasia	54,203	19.6	6.4	26.0	74.0
Africa	29,834	—	2.1	2.1	97.9
Australia	8,901	4.7	14.6	19.3	80.7
North America	24,063	8.5	17.0	25.5	74.5
South America	17,788	0.3	0.8	1.1	98.9
Antarctica	14,169	1.3	0.2	1.5	98.5

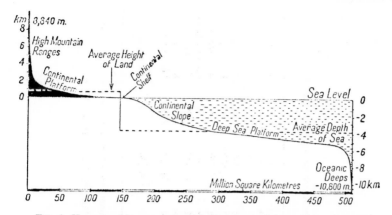

FIG. 1. Hypsographic curve, showing the areas of the earth's solid surface between successive levels from the highest mountain peaks to the deepest oceanic deeps. Note the bimodality (modified after Kossinna, by Holmes, 1965). (By permission of T. Nelson & Sons, London and Ronald Press, N.Y.)

traverses by United States, British, Australian, New Zealand and Soviet expeditions during the I.G.Y. and subsequently, it has been possible to make more precise estimates than heretofore. Using various models, Thiel obtained figures of 24.4×10^6 km^3, based on the anomalous height of Antarctica, of 27.9×10^6 km^3 (based on an allowance for isostatic accommodation to ice loading, 256 m subsidence for every 1000 m of ice), of 27.8×10^6 km^3 (calculating the depression from the anomalously lower continental shelf, giving a mean ice thickness of 2.3 km). From seismic surveys of ice thickness (excluding ice shelves) the best estimate is 26.6×10^6 km^3, equivalent to 24.0×10^6 km^3 of water—the sudden melting of which would raise world sea level by 66.3 m. Some 10% of the earth's land surface is now ice covered, some 14.27×10^6 km^2, with 1.73×10^6 in Greenland (12.1%), 12.09×10^6 in Antarctica (84.7%) and 0.45×10^6 for other glaciers (3.2%). In terms of volume, Greenland has 2.6×10^6 km^3 (9.7%), other glaciers 0.24×10^6 km^3 (0.9%).

TABLE 4. COASTLINES OF CONTINENTS
(Kossinna 1933)

Continent	Area (10^6 km^2)	Coastal Length (km)
Europe	9.22	37,200
Asia	41.48	70,600
Eurasia	50.70	107,800
Africa	29.20	30,500
Australia	7.60	19,500
North America	19.98	75,500
South America	17.63	28,700
Antarctica	14.14	?

TABLE 5. CONTINENTALITY—DISTANCES FROM OCEANS
(Kossinna, 1933)

Continent	Distance from Coast Average (km)	Maximum (km)	Regions Near Ocean (%)	Far from Ocean (%)
Europe	340	1550	62	38
Asia	780	2400	61	39
Africa	670	1800	53	47
Australia	350	920	55	45
North America	470	1650	58	42
South America	550	1600	56	44

TABLE 6. AREAS OF THE CONTINENTS IN ELEVATION STEPS (million km²); ALSO AREA TOTALS, VOLUMES (1000 km³) AND MEAN ALTITUDES (m) from Kossinna (1933)

Continent	below 0	0–200	200–500	500–1000	1000–2000	2000–3000	3000–4000	4000–5000	over 5000	Total Area	Volume	Mean Altitudes	Calculated by
Europe	0.2	5.4	2.1	1.5	0.5	0.2	0.0ᵇ	0.0	—	9.9	3,360	340	Kossinna
Asia	0.5	10.4	9.4	10.5	8.0	2.3	0.9	1.8	0.5	44.3	42,520	960	Kossinna
Africa	0.1 {	2.9	11.6	8.4	5.8	0.8	0.3	0.0	0.0	29.8	22,400	750	Meinardus
Australia	0.1 {	3.5	3.7	1.5	0.2	0.0	0.0	0.0	0.0	8.9	3,040	340	Carius-Murray
North America	0.1 {	7.2	7.4	2.9	4.0	2.2	0.4	0.0	0.0	24.1	17,320	720	Kossinna
South America	—	6.8	5.3	3.4	1.0	0.4	0.5	0.4	0.0	17.8	10,550	590	Kossinna
Antarctica	—	0.9	0.4	0.7	3.1	5.3	3.7	0.0	—	14.1	31,100	2200	Meinardus
Land	0.8	37.0ᵃ	39.9	28.9	22.6	11.2	5.8	2.2	0.5	148.9	130,290	875	Kossinna

ᵃ Since the depressed areas of Africa, Australia and North America are quite small (less than 0·1 million km²), a corresponding amount was subtracted from the 0–200 m group.
ᵇ The figure 0.0 indicates an amount less than tenths of a million km².
NOTE: The mean elevations of continental areas excluding fold belts has not been accurately determined, but is about 400 m; for fold belts the figure is about 1250 m.

TABLE 7. LAND AREAS, SHELF AREAS, CONTINENTAL SLOPES, PLATFORMS AND BLOCKS
(in million km²) [from Kossinna (1933)]

Continent	Land Areas (1)	Shelf Areas (2)	Continental Slopes (3)	Continental Platforms (1 + 2)	Continental Blocks (1 + 2 + 3)
Europe	9.90	3.11	3.13	13.01	16.14
Asia	44.18	9.38	7.01	53.56	60.57
Africa	29.23	1.28	2.25	30.51	32.76
Australia	8.51	2.70	1.64	11.21	12.85
North America	24.06	6.74	6.68	30.80	37.48
South America	17.78	2.43	2.14	20.21	22.35
Antarctica	14.16	0.36	5.41	14.52	19.93

TABLE 8. WORLD OCEAN STATISTICS (INCLUDING MARGINAL SEAS)
(Menard and Smith, 1966; cf. Kossinna, 1933, in parentheses)

Oceans	Areas (10⁶ km²)	Volumes (10⁶ km³)	Mean Depths (m)
Atlantic Ocean*	106.6 (106.5)	350.9 (354.7)	3291 (3332)
Indian Ocean	74.1 (74.9)	284.6 (291.9)	3840 (3897)
Pacific Ocean	181.3 (179.7)	714.4 (723.7)	3940 (4028)
World oceans	362.0 (361.1)	1349.9 (1370.3)	3729 (3795)

NOTE. Compare with Tables 12–16.
* To include Arctic Ocean.

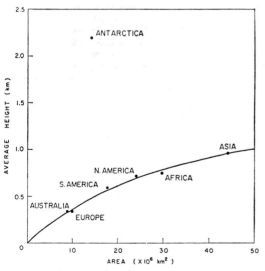

FIG. 2. Average heights of the continents (from Thiel, 1962). The anomalous position of Antarctica is evident; it is due to ice accumulation.

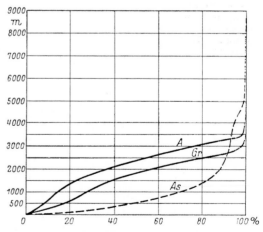

FIG. 3. The hypsographic curves for Antarctica (A) and Greenland (Gr) which are very similar but quite distinct from that of the typical continent Asia (As) (from Kossinna, 1933). (By permission of Gebrüder Borntraeger, Stuttgart.)

TABLE 9. OCEANS: DISTANCES FROM CONTINENTAL COASTS [from Kossinna (1933)]

Oceans	Average Distance from Land (km)	Point of Farthest Distance from Land (km)	Geographical Positions
Atlantic Ocean	606	2050	25°N, 42½°W
Indian Ocean	621	2030	47½°S, 100°E
Pacific Ocean	765	2500	47½°S, 118½°W

TABLE 10. CONTINENTAL SHELF AREAS [from Kossinna (1933)]

Oceans	Including Marginal Seas (10⁶ km²)	(%)	Excluding Marginal Seas (10⁶ km²)	(%)
Atlantic Ocean	14.1	13.3	4.6	5.6
Indian Ocean	3.2	4.2	2.4	3.2
Pacific Ocean	10.2	5.7	2.9	1.7
World	27.5	7.6	9.9	3.1

TABLE 11. AREAS AND DEPTHS OF IMPORTANT CONTINENTAL SHELVES (from Krümmel, Vol. I, p. 113)

Name	Area (1000 km²)	Depth (m)
Northwest European Shelf	1050	Mostly less than 100
Norwegian Shelf	93	200–300
Barents Shelf	830	200–300
North Siberian Shelf	1330	50% less than 50
Iceland–Faeroe Shelf	115	200–300
Newfoundland Shelf	345	150–200
Florida–Texas (Gulf) Shelf	385	Mostly under 50
Campeche (Yucatan) Shelf	170	Mostly under 50
Guiana Shelf	485	Mostly under 50
South Brazilian Shelf	370	Mostly under 50
Patagonian Shelf	960	50–100
Agulhas Shelf	75	Mostly more than 100
Zambezi Shelf	55	Mostly under 50
Bombay Shelf	230	50–100
NW Australian (including Sahul) Shelf	590	50–100
Arafura Shelf	930	50–100
South Australian Shelf	320	50–100
Tasmanian Shelf	160	50–100
Queensland Shelf	190	Mostly under 100
Burma Shelf	290	Mostly under 100
Sunda (Borneo–Java) Shelf	1850	50–100
Tongking–Hongkong Shelf	435	Mostly under 100
Tunghai Shelf	915	Mostly under 100
Okhotsk–Sakhalin Shelf	715	50–100
Bering Shelf	1120	50% less than 50

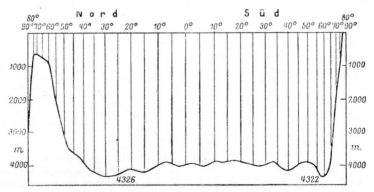

FIG. 4. Mean depths of the world oceans in 5° parallels (Kossinna, 1933). (By permission of Gebrüder Borntraeger, Stuttgart.)

TABLE 12. AREAS, VOLUMES AND MEAN DEPTHS OF OCEANS (EXCLUDING MARGINAL SEAS) [from KOSSINNA (1933)]

Depths (1000 m)	North Atlantic Ocean	South Atlantic Ocean[a]	Atlantic Ocean[b]	North Indian Ocean	South Indian Ocean	Indian Ocean	North Pacific Ocean[c]	South Pacific Ocean[a]	Pacific Ocean	Major Oceans
0.0–0.2	2.6	2.0	4.6	0.8	1.6	2.4	1.1	1.7	2.8	9.8
0.2–1.0	1.8	1.5	3.3	0.4	1.6	2.0	0.8	2.9	3.7	9.0
1–2	1.8	1.2	3.0	0.7	1.6	2.3	0.8	4.7	5.5.	10.8
2–3	3.0	3.2	6.2	1.6	3.9	5.5	1.9	6.2	8.1	19.8
3–4	6.7	9.2	15.9	2.9	15.0	17.9	8.8	22.9	31.7	65.5
4–5	11.5	15.2	26.7	3.8	24.8	28.6	21.2	41.2	62.4	117.7
5–6	8.8	13.1	21.9	0.6	13.9	14.5	33.2	14.4	47.6	84.0
>6	0.6	0.2	0.8	—	0.3	0.3	3.0	0.4	3.4	4.5
Areas, 10⁶ km²	36.8	45.6	82.4	10.8	62.7	73.5	70.8	94.4	165.2	321.1
Volumes, 10⁶ km³	139.6	184.0	323.6	35.6	255.4	291.0	336.7	370.8	707.5	1322.1
Mean Depths, m	3788	4036	3926	3310	4075	3963	4753	3928	4282	4117

Areas, 10^6 km²; Volumes, 10^6 km³.

[a] The Southern or Antarctic Ocean is sometimes distinguished as the region south of latitude 55°S in the southernmost sectors of the Atlantic, Indian and Pacific Oceans.
[b] Including *Gulf of Guinea*: area, 1.533 × 10⁶ km², volume, 4.592 × 10⁶ km³, depth, 2996 m.
[c] Including *Gulf of Alaska*: area, 1.327 × 10⁶ km²; volume, 3.226 × 10⁶ km³; depth, 2431 m.

Note: These figures are not strictly comparable with those of Menard and Smith (1966, see our Table 15), owing to differences in boundary limits, as well as the newer sounding data.

TABLE 13. MARGINAL SEAS (Kossinna, 1933)

Depths (1000 m)	Arctic Sea	Gulf of Mexico and Caribbean[a]	Mediterranean Sea[b]	Asiatic Marginal Seas	Baltic Sea (with Kattegat)[c]	Hudson Bay	Red Sea[d]	Persian Gulf[e]
0.0–0.2	5.55	0.92	0.66	4.14	0.42	1.10	0.18	0.24
0.2–1	2.88	0.44	0.64	1.02	0.00	0.13	0.18	—
1–2	1.48	0.69	0.53	0.78	—	—	0.08	—
2–3	1.59	0.61	0.88	0.73	—	—	0.00	—
3–4	2.59	0.83	0.25	0.64	—	—	—	—
4–5	—	0.72	0.01	0.67	—	—	—	—
>5	—	0.10	—	0.16	—	—	—	—
Areas, 10⁶ km²	14.09	4.31	2.97	8.14	0.42	1.23	0.44	0.24
Volumes, 10⁶ km³	17.0	9.6	4.2	9.9	0.023	0.16	0.21	0.006
Mean Depths, m	1205	2216	1429	1212	55	128	491	25

a Also subdivided *Gulf of Mexico*: area, 1.543 × 10⁶ km²; volume, 2.332 × 10⁶ km³; mean depth, 1,512 m. *Caribbean*: area, 2.754 × 10⁶ km²; volume, 6.860 × 10⁶ km³, mean depth, 2.491 m.

b Including *Black Sea*: area, 0.461 × 10⁶ km²; volume, 0.537 × 10⁶ km³; depth, 1,166 m. Excluding *Black Sea*: area, 2.516 × 10⁶ km²; volume, 3.758 × 10⁶ km³; depth, 1,494 m.

c Excluding *Kattegat*: area, 0.386 × 10⁶ km²; volume, 0.033 × 10⁶ km³; depth, 84 m.

d Newer figures (J. Lyman): area, 0.45 × 10⁶ km²; volume, 0.251 × 10⁶ km³; depth, 558 m.

e New figures (J. Lyman): area, 0.241 × 10⁶ km²; volume, 0.010 × 10⁶ km³; depth, 40 m.

TABLE 14. MINOR SEAS AND GULFS (Kossinna, 1933)

1000 m Depths	North Sea	English Channel	Irish Sea	Gulf of St. Lawrence	Andaman Sea[a]	Bering Sea[b]	Sea of Okhotsk[c]	Japan Sea[d]	East China Sea[e]	Gulf of California	Bass Strait
0.0–0.2	0.52	0.08	0.10	0.18	0.38	1.19	0.57	0.24	1.06	0.06	0.07
0.2–1	0.06	—	0.00	0.06	0.13	0.11	0.50	0.19	0.11	0.05	—
1–2	—	—	—	—	0.13	0.09	0.24	0.26	0.07	0.04	—
2–3	—	—	—	—	0.13	0.11	0.10	0.25	0.01	0.02	—
3–4	—	—	—	—	0.03	0.76	0.12	0.07	—	—	—
>4	—	—	—	—	0.00	0.01	—	—	—	—	—
Areas × 10⁶ km²	0.58	0.08	0.10	0.24	0.08	2.27	1.53	1.01	1.25	0.16	0.07
Volumes × 10⁶ km³	0.054	0.004	0.006	0.030	0.70	3.26	1.28	1.36	0.24	0.13	0.005
Mean depths, m	94	54	60	127	870	1437	838	1350	188	813	70

a Newer figures (J. Lyman): area, 0.602 × 10⁶ km²; volume, 0.660 × 10⁶ km³; depth, 1096 m.
b Newer figures (J. Lyman): area, 2.304 × 10⁶ km²; volume, 3.683 × 10⁶ km³; depth, 1598 m.

TABLE 15. DEPTH ZONES IN THE OCEANS AND MARGINAL SEAS, WITH VOLUMES AND MEAN DEPTHS (Menard and Smith, 1966)
Area in millions of square kilometers

Ocean	Depth Interval in Kilometers												Total Area (Ocean)	Volume, 10^6 km^3	Mean Depth, m
	0–0.2	0.2–1	1–2	2–3	3–4	4–5	5–6	6–7	7–8	8–9	9–10	10–11			
Pacific Ocean	2.712	4.294	5.403	11.397	36.233	58.162	44.691	2.896	0.313	0.105	0.032	0.002	166.241	696.189	4188
Asiatic Mediterranean	4.715	0.841	0.948	1.104	0.608	0.707	0.149	0.007	0.005	0	0	0	9.082	11.366	1252
Bering Sea	1.050	0.135	0.172	0.234	0.670	0	0	0	0	0	0	0	2.261	3.373	1492
Sea of Okhotsk	0.368	0.549	0.311	0.047	0.115	0	0	0	0	0	0	0	1.392	1.354	973
Yellow and East China seas	0.977	0.137	0.072	0.015	0.001	0	0	0	0	0	0	0	1.202	0.327	272
Sea of Japan	0.238	0.154	0.199	0.204	0.218	0	0	0	0	0	0	0	1.013	1.690	1667
Gulf of California	0.071	0.032	0.040	0.010	0	0	0	0	0	0	0	0	0.153	0.111	724
Atlantic Ocean	6.080	4.474	3.718	7.436	16.729	28.090	19.324	0.639	0.058	0.010	0	0	86.557	323.369	3736
American Mediterranean	1.021	0.465	0.589	0.667	0.906	0.586	0.112	0.008	0.002	0	0	0	4.357	9.427	2164
Mediterranean	0.513	0.564	0.437	0.766	0.224	0.006	0	0	0	0	0	0	2.510	3.771	1502
Black Sea	0.177	0.064	0.117	0.149	0	0	0	0	0	0	0	0	0.508	0.605	1191
Baltic Sea	0.381	0.001	0	0	0	0	0	0	0	0	0	0	0.382	0.038	101
Indian Ocean	2.622	1.971	2.628	7.364	18.547	26.906	12.476	0.911	0.001	0	0	0	73.427	284.340	3872
Red Sea	0.188	0.195	0.068	0.003	0	0	0	0	0	0	0	0	0.453	0.244	538
Persian Gulf	0.238	0	0	0	0	0	0	0	0	0	0	0	0.238	0.024	100
Arctic Ocean	3.858	1.569	0.968	1.249	1.573	0.269	0	0	0	0	0	0	9.485	12.615	1330
Arctic Mediterranean	1.913	0.567	0.174	0.118	0	0	0	0	0	0	0	0	2.772	1.087	392
Total each depth	27.123	16.012	15.844	30.762	75.824	114.725	76.753	4.461	0.380	0.115	0.032	0.002	362.033	1349.929	3729

TABLE 16. AREAS, VOLUMES AND MEAN DEPTHS OF SEVEN OCEAN DIVISIONS (INCLUDING MARGINAL SEAS), [from Lyman (1961)]

Ocean	Area (10⁶ km²)	Volume (10⁶ km³)	Mean Depth (m)
Arctic	14.090	17.0	1205
North Atlantic	46.772	153.6	3285
South Atlantic	37.364	152.8	4091
Indian	81.602	349.6	4284
North Pacific	83.462	322.0	3858
South Pacific	65.521	254.9	3891
Antarctic	32.249	120.3	3730
World total	361.06	137.02	3795

Total mass of world oceans: 143×10^{16} metric tons.

TABLE 17. MARGINAL SEAS OF THE EAST INDIES AND SOUTHWEST PACIFIC (included in Pacific by Kossinna; in part as calculated by Schott, 1935; others according to Lyman, 1961)

Sea	Area (10⁶ km²)	Volume (10⁶ km³)	Mean Depth (m)
South China Sea	3.685	3.907	1060
Sulu Sea	0.420	0.478	1139
Celebes (Sulawasi) Sea	0.472	1.553	3291
Makassar Strait	0.194	0.188	967
Molukka Sea	0.307	0.578	1880
Ceram Sea	0.187	0.227	1209
Java Sea	0.433	0.20	46
Bali Sea	0.119	0.49	411
Flores Sea	0.121	0.222	1829
Savu Sea	0.105	0.178	1710
Banda Sea	0.695	2.129	3064
Timor Sea	0.615	0.250	406
Arafura Sea[a]	1.037	0.204	197
Coral Sea[b]	4.791	11.470	2394

[a] Including Gulf of Carpentaria.
[b] I.H.B. Definition (to include New Hebrides).

TABLE 18. TRIBUTARY SEAS OF INDIAN OCEAN, NOT INCLUDING RED SEA AND PERSIAN GULF (see Table 13); from Lyman (1961)

Sea	Area (10⁶ km²)	Volume (10⁶ km³)	Mean Depth (m)
Arabian Sea	3.863	10.561	2734
Bay of Bengal	2.172	5.616	2586
Andaman Sea	0.602	0.660	1096
Great Australian Bight	0.484	0.459	950

TABLE 19. TRIBUTARY SEAS OF THE ARCTIC OCEAN (Lyman, 1961)

Sea	Area (10⁶ km²)	Volume (10⁶ km³)	Mean Depth (m)
Norwegian Sea	1.383	2.408	1742
Greenland Sea	1.205	1.740	1444
Barents Sea	1.405	0.322	229
White Sea	0.090	0.008	89
Kara Sea	0.883	0.104	118
Laptev Sea	0.650	0.338	519
East Siberian Sea	0.901	0.053	58
Chukchi Sea	0.582	0.051	88
Beaufort Sea	0.476	0.478	1004
Baffin Bay	0.689	0.593	861

RHODES W. FAIRBRIDGE

References

Flint, R. F., 1957, "Glacial and Pleistocene Geology," New York, Wiley & Sons, 553pp.

Holmes, A., 1965, "Principles of Physical Geology," Second edition, New York, Ronald Press Co.; London, T. Nelson & Sons, 1288pp.

Kossinna, E., 1921, "Die Tiefen des Weltmeeres," Veröff Inst. Meereskunde, Berlin, N.F., A.9.

Kossinna, E., 1933, "Die Erdoberfläche," in (Gutenberg, B., editor) "Handbuch der Geophysik," Vol. 2, pp. 869–954, Berlin, Borntraeger.

Krümmel, O., 1897, "Handbuch der Ozeanographie," Stuttgart, 2 vols. (Second edition, 1907).

Lyman, J., 1961, "Oceans and Seas," in "Encyclopedia of Science and Technology," New York, McGraw-Hill Book Co.

Menard, H. W. and Smith, S. M., 1966, "Hypsometry of ocean basin provinces," *J. Geophys. Res.*, **71**(18), 4305–4325.

Schott, G., 1935, "Geographie des Indischen und Stillen Ozeans," Hamburg, Boysen, 413pp.

Thiel, E. C., 1962, "The amount of ice on planet earth," in "Antarctic Research," *Geophys. Mono.* 7, Am. Geophys. Union.

Cross-references: *Hypsographic Curve.* Vol. I: *Oceans: Limits, Definitions, Dimensions.*

CONTOUR—*See* pr Vol. VI

CONTOUR DIAGRAM—*See* **INSTRUMENT CONTOUR DIAGRAM**

CORAL REEFS—MORPHOLOGY AND THEORIES

Definition

In the past, there has been some confusion about the definition of "reef," now largely resolved. Traditionally a reef, to a navigator or hydrographer, was any rocky prominence of the sea floor that might endanger shipping. Many fossil reefs at one

FIG. 1. Typical fringing reef around a "continental" island (ancient granite-gneiss), passing into a small barrier ring. Air photograph Lizard Island, Queensland. (Photo: R. W. Fairbridge.)

time must have formed prominences on the sea floor, but in places where the sea was sufficiently deep, waves did not break; consequently, they were not always surrounded by clastic debris as are most modern coral reefs. Accordingly, the term *bioherm* was proposed (Cumings, 1932) for any kind of massive organogenic structure on the sea floor.

A *coral reef* is defined then as a complex organogenic framework of calcium carbonate (primarily of corals) which forms a rocky eminence on the sea floor and customarily grows upward to the tide limit. It thus causes waves to break, and consequently, the internal spaces in this branching framework are packed with fragments of broken reef material, coralline algae, broken up mollusca, echinoid debris and foraminifera. The principal reef builders today are the Madreporarian (or

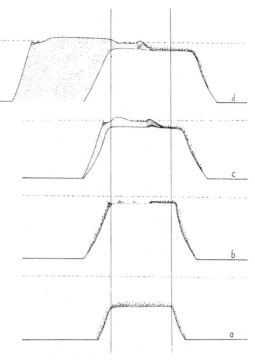

FIG. 3. Upgrowth of a platform reef and formation of an island in the Bay of Batavia (Djakarta, Indonesia). North-south section, schematic (Verwey). Massive coral growth is left white (read from bottom upward), while the accumulating sand and other coral debris is shown dotted. Beachrock is shaded.

Scleractinian) colonial corals of the class Zoantharia, phylum Coelenterata. In the remote geological past, the same ecologic niche was often occupied by other classes or even phyla. Calcareous

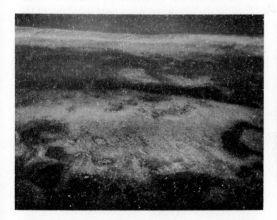

FIG. 2. Patch reefs just inside outer ribbon reefs, Great Barrier Reefs. Note irregular patterns, characteristic of shallow-water growth (and calm seas). (Photo: R. W. Fairbridge.)

FIG. 4. Part of the nearly 1000-km extent of ribbon reefs that form the outer barrier of the Great Barrier Reefs. Note contrast between the very deep water and heavy swell to seaward and mere ripples over the reef (at mid-tide); it is partly dry at low tide. (Photo: R. W. Fairbridge.)

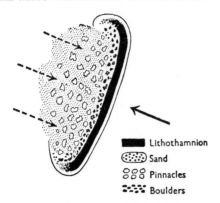

Lithothamnion
Sand
Pinnacles
Boulders

FIG. 5. Single example of a ribbon reef, i.e., part of the outer barrier series (after Yonge). Note building of algal rim (*Lithothamnion*) on the windward exposed face and irregular reef patches and pinnacles on the sand-strewn lee side (dotted arrow suggesting infrequent winds of low energy).

algae often grow over and around the coral colonies, helping to hold them together and sometimes misleading observers into thinking that they are the actual frame builders. Some very fine chalky mud may be chemically precipitated carbonate, formed either at low tide, when isolation and higher temperatures raise the local relative concentration of salts in seawater, or after consolidation, when diagenetic circulation brings additional carbonate solutions to be precipitated and help fill in the pore spaces. Fine particulate carbonate may also be precipitated by microscopic algae or other organic agencies.

Coral reef rock is usually a very porous material with a large variety of clastic components, principally organogenic, with mainly inorganic cementing materials.

Both the outer reef periphery and the lagoon are marked by loose clastic debris that has largely been wave-broken and washed off the reef. This detritus

is known as *bioclastic* or *coral sand*, when fresh, or *calcarenite*, when cemented. A special type of coral sand is found on beaches; after repeated concentration of the interstitial seawater under the hot tropical sun over many low-tide periods, the sand becomes cemented into a *beachrock* (q.v.), *beach sandstone*, or *littoral calcarenite*.

Another special limestone type of reef regions is found in *calcareous dune sands* or cemented as *eolian calcarenite* ("eolianite" of Sayles). Because of the rapid changes of sea level during the Quaternary climatic oscillations, considerable belts of such dune sands accumulated along the beaches of subtropical regions (at various levels) and the calcareous sands became readily cemented by percolating rainwater during "pluvial" phases. Many such eolian calcarenite ridges now form coastal or offshore reefs, the so-called *sandstone reefs* or *coastal limestone reefs*. Since these dunes formed particularly in the mid-latitudes, farther from the equatorial belt than normal coral reefs, they tend to be complementary to the latter (Fairbridge and Teichert, 1953).

Calcareous algae always contribute to coral reefs, but they also form independent *algal reefs* in some areas, particularly in places which are warm but for some reason unfavorable for coral growth. Such spots include Shark Bay (Western Australia) which is mostly too saline for coral growth (Logan, 1961), and parts of the mid-Queensland coast near Cairns where heavy rainfall leads to reduced salinity in the wet season and to excessive turbidity from sediment in suspension.

Reef Types

Darwin's classical divisions include fringing, barrier, and atoll-type reefs, in addition to which there are platform and patch reefs.

(1) Fringing Reefs. These were regarded by Darwin as the basic reef type, forming a shallow veneer or shelf in shallow water at or near the shore of the

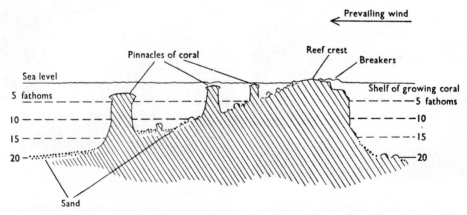

FIG. 6. Section through an outer barrier reef, showing relation of form to prevailing winds (modified after Paradice). Note contrast of Marshall's "rough water reefs" and "calm water type."

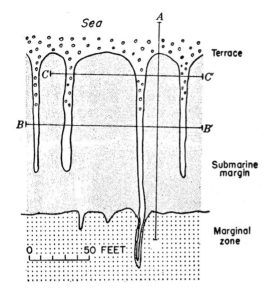

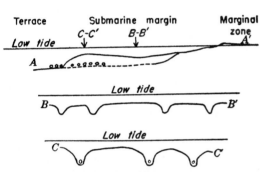

Fig. 7. Margin of reef between Rongelap and Boku-jarito islands, Rongelap Atoll. Elongate spurs growing on a sloping submarine terrace merge into the *Lithotham-nion* ridge at the reef crest (marginal zone). The broad spurs bound straight narrow grooves or channels (Emery, Tracey and Ladd, 1954). The above authors describe the grooves as "erosional reentrants," but this conclusion is not quite accurate, because the spurs are covered by growing reef builders and the grooves are the spaces left between them, admittedly being kept clear by abrasion.

mainland or around offshore islands (Fig. 1). Heavy sedimentation and runoff make tropical mainland coasts less attractive for fringing reefs than the offshore and oceanic islands. The near-shore surface of the reef often becomes veneered by terrigenous sediments (see *Fringing Reef*).

(2) Platform and Patch Reefs. These are gener-ally rounded or ovoid reefs, the large ones (over a mile or so long) being called platforms, the smaller patch reefs (also variously called "shelf," "bank," "table" and "hummock" reefs; Figs. 2 and 3). They are found in water of moderate depth (gener-ally 20–40 meters) on the continental shelves, some-

times dotted in random manner, but more often in recognizable belts, suggesting an evolution from former (drowned) shore lines. Probably they grew around headlands during temporary pauses in the postglacial sea-level rise and then grew on upward as the sea level continued to rise.

Where such reefs are small, they form simple, rounded patches, sometimes only 100 meters or so across. Under the influence of winds, waves, and currents, they gradually build up a downwind sedi-ment train (Hedley and Taylor, 1908; Fairbridge, 1950a), and then as they enlarge, twin spurs or horns develop from the reef, giving successively a horse's hoof and then a horseshoe-shaped struc-ture. The interior hollow becomes gradually filled with smaller reef patches and sediment. Under reversed (monsoon) winds, the lee side often closes around to form an atoll-like reef, but the center is not marked by a deep lagoon, only shallow pools (see *Coral Reefs—Wind and Current Growth Control*). This type of reef is sometimes called a pseudo-atoll, but its origin is distinct from that of atolls and it is best designated as a "platform reef with shallow lagoons or pools." Many examples of a progression from a small reef patch to a big reef platform may be seen in the northern sector of the Great Barrier Reef of Queensland (Australia).

(3) Barrier Reefs. According to Darwin, the effect of crustal (tectonic) subsidence upon a fring-ing reef, if carried out slowly, would be to cause the corals to grow upward, and as the land behind became gradually submerged, a lagoon would form between the land and the up-growing barrier. According to Daly (1915), it was the postglacial rise of sea level that caused the last submergence. In many parts of the world, both factors are con-tributing.

In some places, long *ribbon reefs* are formed; in others, there are discontinuous platform reefs (Fig. 4). The passes or channels between them represent Pleistocene stream valleys that crossed the conti-nental shelf before the postglacial eustatic rise, thus separating the initial fringing reefs. Such passes have strong tidal currents; hence, they are subject to constant sediment scour and are kept open.

Barrier reefs are always strongly asymmetric in plan and section, steep-to on the ocean side, often dropping abruptly away to 1000–5000 meters, grading off gently to the interior with a sediment wedge, dotted by small reef patches, pinnacles and coral heads (Fig. 5). Depths in the lagoon may drop to 50 to 80 meters.

Marshall (1931) has spoken of two distinct reef energy types: these interior facies are his "calm water type"; the exterior facies, his "rough water type" (Fig. 6). The latter is marked by very vigorous surf action which leads to a piling up of the water, permitting calcareous algae to grow to several feet above the normal reef surface. This forms an *Algal Rim* (q.v.), which further helps to protect the inner

189

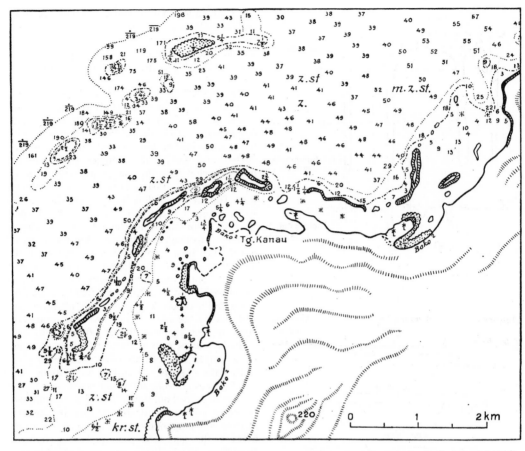

FIG. 8. Multiple barrier reef complex near Celebes (Sulawesi), off the Togian Islands in the Gulf of Tomini (Umbgrove). Note (a) fringing reefs, then (b) a narrow lagoon 5–20 meters deep, (c) an inner barrier (with shelf atolls), then (d) the main lagoon about 40–50 meters, and finally (e) discontinuous outer barrier, partly "drowned"; deep water beyond (a dot over a number is the nautical symbol for ocean depths over a certain figure, the length of the old sounding line).

environment. Under rather rare, calm weather conditions, one can actually walk along the outer rim. The outer face is cut by numerous radial grooves, chutes, or surge channels, down which there is a constant flow of abrading sand, while in between there are spurs or buttresses marked by growing coral and *Lithothamnion* (or other calcareous algae, such as *Porolithon*).

The finest example of a barrier reef in the world is that of Queensland, which stretches 1200 miles from the Gulf of Papua to the Tropic of Capricorn (see *Great Barrier Reefs*). In eastern New Guinea (Papua), there is another fine barrier complex that also rings the Louisiade Group (the Tagula Barrier Reef). Others occur off New Caledonia, Fiji, Borneo and in the Palau Islands. During the postglacial rise of sea level, there were several important secondary oscillations of level, which led to coastal changes. With renewed submergence, new fringing

reefs sometimes became incorporated in the pattern and a double or looped barrier developed.

Along the edge of the Sahul Shelf (Timor Sea), along the edge of the Sunda Shelf (Borneo), and in the Togian Islands (Fig. 8), there are examples of "drowned" barrier reefs. These, for some reason, did not maintain their regular upward growth during the postglacial period and form submarine rims on the outer shelf edges.

Reports of barrier reefs offshore in the mid-latitudes (Morocco, South-West Africa, Western Australia) are incorrect; these are basically "sandstone reefs," though in places they have a veneer of coral.

(4) Atolls. An atoll is a ring-shaped reef, morphologically like a ribbon reef bent into a circle, enclosing a lagoon. Darwin suggested that fringing reefs surrounding volcanic islands, during subsidence, grew up gradually to develop ring-shaped barrier reefs and, as subsidence continued, eventu-

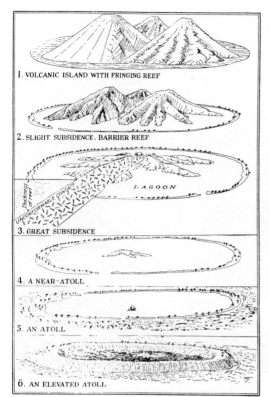

1. VOLCANIC ISLAND WITH FRINGING REEF

2. SLIGHT SUBSIDENCE. BARRIER REEF

LAGOON

3. GREAT SUBSIDENCE

4. A NEAR-ATOLL

5. AN ATOLL

6. AN ELEVATED ATOLL

FIG. 9. Stages in the submergence of a volcanic island to form a barrier and eventually an atoll (also an elevated atoll) as visualized by Darwin (from Lobeck, 1939). Not all atolls are formed in this way (see *Atolls*). (By permission of McGraw-Hill Book Co. N.Y.)

ally became center-island-free ring reefs. (Figs. 9 and 10). This is certainly the origin of some atolls, especially as seen in the Society Islands, but there are several other types of *atoll* (q.v.) (Agassiz, 1903; Fairbridge, 1950a; MacNeil, 1954).

(*a*) *Shelf Atolls.* On the Australian Shelves and likewise off Borneo, there are shelf atolls that do not have volcanic foundations, but appear to have grown up as open platform reefs or from earlier platform reefs. Off northwestern Australia, there are several large atolls rising from depressed outer sectors of the shelf, from 400–500 meters.

(*b*) *Compound Atolls.* In several parts of the world, large continental crustal segments have slowly subsided, so that barrier reefs and platform reefs have grown upward in the same manner as in oceanic atolls, e.g., in the South China Sea, in the Tiger Islands of Indonesia, in the Maldives (Fig. 11), and Laccadives, and in the Australian region—in the Coral Sea Plateau. These reefs often have complex or compound tops. Evidently they grew up during subsidence, but they were exposed during the last glacial low sea level to form a differentially weathered crest (Fig. 11). MacNeil (1954) has demonstrated that this crest would be higher on

the outside and would predispose the old "stump" to the atoll form. Often many little ring reefs (called "*Faros*" in the Maldives) grow upward from the initial annular foundation, the shape of which is only indirectly similar to that of the volcanic seating of oceanic atolls (see below).

On the Western Australian shelf, a group of such compound atolls are found in the Houtman's Abrolhos Islands. Parts of the old stump are exposed, deeply weathered and penetrated by deep holes (former karst pipes). Here there has been no subsidence, so that they are classified as a "compound shelf atoll" group.

(*c*) *Oceanic Atolls.* These are the so-called "mid-Pacific type," rising in the deep ocean basins from isolated volcanic cones (*seamounts* or *guyots*), with up to 2000 meters of accumulated reef growth which may date back as far as the Cretaceous. It is interesting that oceanic atolls often have U-shaped gashes, attributed to landslides down volcanic slopes; in contrast, shelf atolls are more often perfect and smoothly rounded (Fairbridge, 1950b; Figs. 15 and 16).

Reef Islands

Since the days of Captain James Cook, that pioneer explorer of the Pacific, the islands have been known as "high islands" and "low islands" (see *Islands*). The "high" are continental or volcanic rocks, and the "low" are strictly coral islands. The latter are found in five categories (Fairbridge, 1950a, p. 348):

(1) *Simple sand cays* (called "keys" in the Caribbean), which are merely accumulations of loose coral sand and beachrock, generally situated on the lee side of a coral platform where interesecting waves have a minimum of energy, liable to be washed over at high tide.

(2) *Vegetated sand cays*, similar to the type (a) but larger and more mature, covered by a well-established flora, including quite large trees (*Tournefortia, Pandanus, Casuarina*). The sand sometimes blows up into little dunes, and the upper beach offers a site for turtles to lay their eggs. The *beachrock* (q.v.) gives stability to the cay; otherwise it would be washed away during hurricanes (Figs. 17 and 18).

Experiments by the writer have shown that the cement of these modern beachrocks is aragonite; some older beachrocks are exposed in places and the cements have inverted to calcite. A well-known example of a populated cay is Heron Island in the Capricorn Group. The latter is the site of the Research Station of the Great Barrier Reef Committee of Brisbane (Australia).

(3) *Shingle cays* are similar to sand cays in that they are simply accumulations of wave-tossed debris and "*negroheads*" (q.v.) (dead coral heads or "jetsam" thrown onto the reef by storms), but they are normally situated on the windward side of

FIG. 10. Bora-Bora Island in the Society Islands, a partially drowned volcanic island, showing development of extensive barrier reef that represents a potential atoll ring, if further subsidence occurs. Note the drowned embayments of the volcanic stump, proving former deep subaerial erosion to a much lower base level.

platform reefs. The coarse, heavy coral cobbles or shingle is often cemented into a wave-resistant "coral breccia" or "conglomerate." This coral shingle initially forms a discontinuous beach ridge or "rampart." At breakthrough points, storms carry the shingle onto the reef flat to form radial spits. Short ridge sections and long tails are called *hammerhead spits* (Fig. 19).

(4) *Sand cays with shingle ramparts* were called the "Low Wooded Island Reefs" (by Captain Cook). In the protected lee side of the shingle ramparts (which may build up in several zones or generations), there is an opportunity for floating mangrove seedlings to take root (Fig. 20). Mangrove plays an important role in modifying the inner reef environment, for it leads to the accumulation of organic debris, bacterial decay sets in, and the pH may drop to 5. Under these conditions, the coral sands and limestones are rotted, and the interior of the reef flat may become literally dissolved out under contemporary conditions. It becomes the site of a flourishing mangrove swamp.

(5) *Emerged reef islands*. On the better protected or more mature reefs, there are widespread traces of some older reefs that are often found at three distinct levels of mid-Holocene age. Both corals and associated molluscan shells give excellent radio-

carbon dates. In a few islands there is also a nucleus of old reef of Pleistocene age. These emerged reef limestones form the foundations of many atoll islands across the breadth of the Pacific and Indian Oceans. Indeed it would hardly be wrong to say that the Polynesian navigators would have had few places on which to land, were it not for the negative oscillations of sea level since mid-Holocene time, which have resulted in emerged limestone platforms, making the nuclei of all larger islands.

The three principal high levels are (Fairbridge, 1961):

(a) Peron Submergence (3 meters, possibly several oscillations)   6000–3500 B.P.

(b) Abrolhos Submergence (2 meters, also with oscillations)   2700–2100 B.P.

(c) Rottnest Submergence (0.5–1 meter, also with oscillations)   1500–900 B.P.

The submergences alternated with emergences; by diving in the lagoons, it is possible here and there to detect traces of the corresponding shore lines at various depths down to −3 or 4 meters.

In some places, fragments of the old emerged reef terraces are being quarried away by the waves, and remnants lie scattered over the reef flat, forming another type of "negro-head." There has long been an interesting controversy about the origin of these

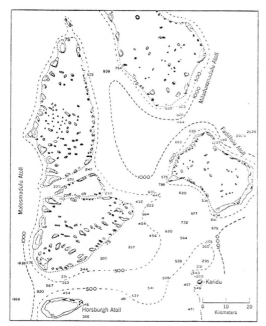

FIG. 11. Part of the group of Maldive (compound) atolls in the Indian Ocean. Note the deep channels dividing Malosmadulu Atoll into separate parts, and the faros. Depths in meters (Kuenen, 1950). (By permission of John Wiley & Sons, N.Y.)

coral blocks. Saville-Kent (1893) claimed that they were "jetsam," thrown up by waves. Agassiz (1898) argued that they were corroded remnants of these former coral limestone platforms. It turns out, after all, that they were both right, each in his own area.

Regional Distribution of Reefs

Reefs may be recognized as falling essentially into four geotectonic settings:

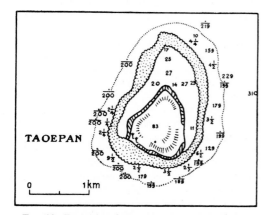

FIG. 12. Transition from volcano to atoll: Taoepan (Taupan) in Indonesia (0° 35'S, 121° 37'E). Note both fringing and barrier rings. Depths in meters. (Dot over 199 or 200 signifies minimum depth.)

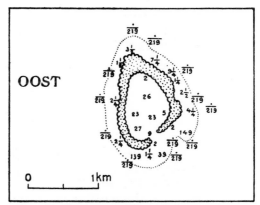

FIG. 13. Simplest possible atoll form, only 1 km across; Oost Atoll, Indonesia.

(a) *Epicontinental reefs*, rather stable foundations, with eustatic features dominant, e.g., Queensland (Great Barrier Reef complex), Florida, Borneo and some other islands in the East Indies.

(b) *Mobile belt reefs*, with rather or highly unstable foundations, eustatic factor often obscured, e.g., gently subsiding zones in the eastern Papua–Tagula–Louisiade Barrier Reef, in New Caledonia and the Banda Sea area of the East Indies (notably in the Tukang Besi Islands, see Kuenen, 1933; Fig. 21); in contrast, there are the strongly positive uplift zones as in Timor, Sumba and along the Finsch Coast of northern New Guinea. Mixed movements are seen in the Mariana and Palau Islands.

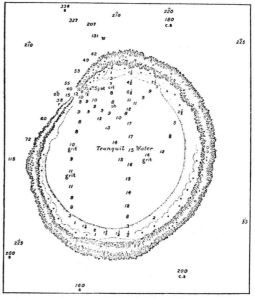

FIG. 14. Perfect atoll ring without islets, Minerva Atoll, north Pacific, 6.6 km across. (Depths in fathoms.)

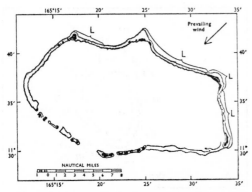

FIG. 15. Bikini Atoll. Outline map, showing arrangement of reefs with islands (shown black), surrounding central lagoon. (L) fully exposed marginal reefs with *Lithothamnion* ridge (modified after Tracey, Ladd and Hoffmeister). Note arcuate margin, suggesting submarine landslides.

(c) *Quasicratonic reefs*, where there is *en bloc* subsidence of appreciable areas of former continental crust, e.g., Coral Sea Plateau, the South China Sea, the Paternoster and Tiger Islands, the Maldive–Laccadives, and the Bahamian block.

(d) *Oceanic volcanic reefs*, where the foundations of atolls lie along the known volcanic trends and by implication are of similar nature (i.e., "mid-Pacific type"); e.g., the Caroline Islands, Marshalls, Gilbert and Ellice Islands, Phoenix and Line Islands, the Cook Islands, and Tuamotus. The true atolls are subsiding examples, but in some other examples, e.g., Christmas Island, Minami Daito, Nauru Island, Ocean Island, etc., subsidence has been followed by uplift, converting them into bird sanctuaries and thus phosphate islands.

A great variety of events lead to a great variety of reef types and islands. By means of a "flow diagram" Guilcher (1958) has illustrated some of the usual combinations (Fig. 22).

Conclusions

(1) Fossil reefs, which are of great economic

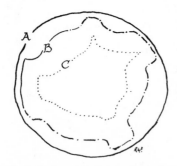

FIG. 16. Evolution of atoll shape from perfect ring to a modified star shape with convex sectors due to progressive submarine landslides (see *Craters*).

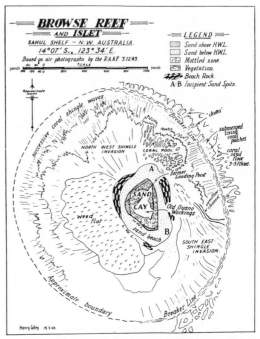

FIG. 17. A simple sand cay on Browse Reef, Sahul Shelf, sufficiently mature to build beachrock and support vegetation. Nesting sea birds have developed a small deposit of guano.

significance (especially for the oil industry) in the Paleozoic and Mesozoic, are epicontinental in nature. They are platform reefs and shelf atolls, but *not* oceanic atolls.

(2) Such epicontinental reefs of today almost exclusively rise from "antecedent platforms" that were only recently established, i.e., during and since the late glacial stage. The antecedent stream and canyon developments of the Sahul and Sunda shelves were probably of about the same age. Although these shelves belong to long-stable continents, the reef platforms of quasi-cratonic belts seem to have suffered recent reactivation. From this may be learned important lessons in the geomorphic history of continents, i.e., marginal belts are upwarped while adjacent sea basins have subsided.

(3) In the history of the earth's crust, it is often claimed that while continents may enlarge, ocean basins remain essentially constant. On the contrary, the oceans are enlarging, in part at the expense of continents. The disposition of shelf and compound atolls over such areas as the South China Sea and Coral Sea Plateau strongly suggests that these are sectors of what Stille calls "quasi-cratonic crust," i.e., new oceans in the process of regeneration; they are currently subsiding *en bloc*, to form new oceanic depressions, on the sites of "lost continents." Fundamental geophysical problems, continental

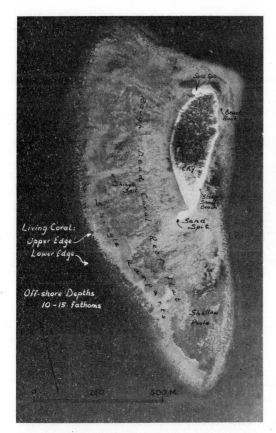

FIG. 18. Sand cay in the Spermonde Archipelago of Celebes (Sulawesi), Barang-Keke (5°05′S, 119°19′E). Note small sandspits at either end of the cay, the curvature of which reverses every six months with the change of the monsoon.

stretching, mantle expansion, convection currents, subcrustal attenuation, etc., are involved.

(4) The dating of eustatic "highs" and "lows" is recorded by former reef terraces. The interrelationships between fluvial events on land and the former reefs through thalassostatic reactions can be helpful

FIG. 19. Three Isles, a small reef platform in the Great Barrier Reefs, supporting shingle cays, partly built up further with sand and mangrove. Hammerhead spits of shingle form radial links from the marginal ramparts toward the land, in places enclosing small "moats."

in contributing to our knowledge of the climatic history of the continents and indeed to fundamental problems of solar control and the principles of paleoclimatology.

(5) The origin of Quaternary coral reefs has generated many, and often contradictory, theories. Modern synthesis shows that most such theories contained well-justified arguments, especially if considered in the light of the particular regional features actually observed by their authors. The theories go wrong when overgeneralization and oversimplification is attempted. In fact, the coral reef question is complex:

(a) Corals of hermatypic character will colonize suitable substrates in any tropical and subtropical seas where the ecologic conditions are appropriate (mean winter temperature generally above 18°C; depth generally less than 20 meters; salinity "normal," 35 ± 2‰; nutrients adequate and ocean currents oriented to bring in fresh juvenile stock).

(b) Fringing reefs will evolve into thick platform, barrier and atoll reefs in regions of subsidence

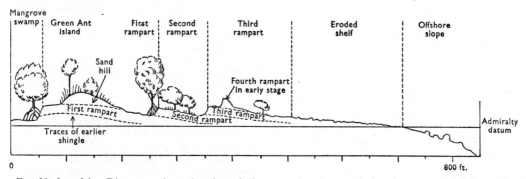

FIG. 20. Low Isles. Diagrammatic section through the rampart system, vertical scale exaggerated 5 times. The fourth rampart has been formed since 1929 (after Fairbridge and Teichert).

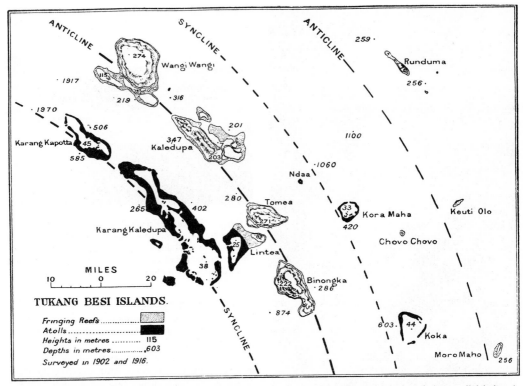

FIG. 21. Tukang Besi Islands—illustrating the formation of atolls and elevated coral reefs in parallel belts. A fringing reef will grow around an island under normal conditions, but (a) if this section of the earth's crust tends to rise (anticline), the former fringing reef will be brought above water, showing flat terraces of coral limestone. Meanwhile a new fringing reef will grow around the elevated island. A repetition of this rising tendency, in fits and starts, will cause a succession of elevated reef terraces, separated by steep step-like escarpments.

In a parallel belt (b) if the earth's crust tends to sink (syncline), the former fringing reef will be carried down, but the corals can generally grow fast enough to keep up with the sinking and there will always be a ring of coral growing up from the position of the former fringing reef. Even when the island itself has completely disappeared, the reef will still be seen, always growing up and up, keeping pace with the sinking substratum, thus forming an atoll (from Molengraaff, 1930).

(tectonic), as seen by Darwin, Dana and Davis. Such reefs are found today both in oceanic regions and in tectonically mobile belts.

(c) Most reefs in the more or less stable regions are relatively thin veneers and rest on antecedent platforms, as urged by Hoffmeister and Ladd.

(d) Practically all Quaternary reefs record evidence of eustatic oscillations as claimed by Daly. The postglacial 100-meter rise of sea level provided a submergence that was indistinguishable in many places from an analogous subsidence of Darwinian type. Daly also recognized the universal (eustatic) small drop of sea level since mid-Holocene time.

(e) Emerged reefs of any type are also found but only in the mobile belts, where tectonic reversal has occurred. It is not true that such reefs developed *during* uplift, as once argued, but rather, they antedated the uplift.

RHODES W. FAIRBRIDGE

References

Agassiz, A., 1898, "A visit to the Great Barrier Reef of Australia in the Steamer *Croydon*," *Bull. Museum Comp. Zool. Harvard Coll.,* **28,** 95–148.

Agassiz, A., 1903, "On the formation of barrier reefs and of the different types of atolls," *Proc. Roy. Soc. London,* **71,** 412–14.

Cumings, E. R., 1932, "Reefs or bioherms?" *Bull. Geol. Soc. Am.,* **43,** 331–351.

Daly, R. A., 1915, "The glacial-control theory of coral reefs," *Proc. Am. Acad. Arts and Sci.,* **51,** 155–251.

Davis, W. M., 1928, "The coral reef problem," *Am. Geog. Soc. N.Y., Spec. Publ.,* **9,** 526pp.

Emery, K. O., Tracey, J. I., Jr., and Ladd, H. S., 1954, "Geology of Bikini and nearby atolls (1)," *U.S. Geol. Surv. Profess. Paper* **260-A.**

Fairbridge, R. W., 1950a, "Recent and Pleistocene coral reefs of Australia," *J. Geol.,* **58,** 330–401.

Fairbridge, R. W., 1950b, "Landslide patterns on oceanic volcanoes and atolls," *Geograph. J.,* **115,** 84–88.

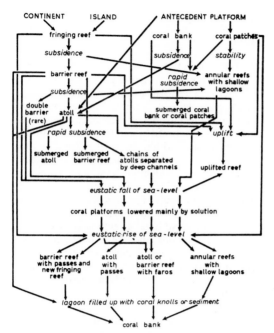

CONTINENT ISLAND ANTECEDENT PLATFORM

FIG. 22. Flow sheet for possible sequences of events in the formation and history of coral reefs (Guilcher, 1958). (By permission of Methuen & Co., London.)

Fairbridge, R. W., 1961, "Eustatic Changes in Sea Level," in "Physics and Chemistry of the Earth," vol. 4, pp. 99–185, London, Pergamon Press.

Fairbridge, R. W., and Fosberg, F. R. (in press), "The reef index, terminology and gazetteer of organic reefs, recent and fossil," *Ann. N.Y. Acad. Sci.*

Fairbridge, R. W., and Teichert, C., 1953, "Soil horizons and marine bands in the coastal limestones of Western Australia," *J. Proc. Roy. Soc. N.S.Wales*, **86**, 68–87.

Guilcher, A., 1958, "Coastal and Submarine Morphology," London, Methuen & Co., 274pp. (translated by Sparks, B. W., and Kneese, R. H. W.).

Hedley, C., and Taylor, T. G., 1908, "Coral reefs of the Great Barrier, Queensland," *Rept. Aust. Assoc. Adv. Sci.*, **2**, 397–413.

Hoffmeister, J. E., and Multer, H. G., 1965, "Fossil mangrove reef of Key Biscayne, Florida," *Bull. Geol. Soc. Am.*, **76**(8), 845–852.

Kuenen, P. H., 1933, "Geology of coral reefs," *Snellius Expedition, Geol. Results*, **5**(2), 125pp.

Kuenen, P. H., 1950, "Marine Geology," New York, John Wiley & Sons, 568pp.

Lobeck, A. K., 1939, "Geomorphology, an Introduction to the Study of Landscapes," New York, McGraw-Hill Book Co., 731pp.

Logan, B., 1961, "*Cryptozoon* and associated stromatolites from the Recent, Shark Bay, Western Australia," *J. Geol.*, **69**, 517–533.

Mabesoone, J. M., 1964, "Origin and age of the sandstone reefs of Pernambuco (northeastern Brazil)," *J. Sediment. Petrol.*, **34**(4), 715–726.

MacNeil, F. S., 1954, "The shape of atolls; an inheritance from subaerial erosion forms," *Am. J. Sci.*, **252**, 402–427.

Marshall, P., 1931, "Coral reefs—rough-water and calm-water types," *Repts. Great Barrier Reef Comm.*, **3**, 64–72.

Milliman, J. D., 1965, "An annotated bibliography of recent papers on corals and coral reefs," *Bull. Atoll Res.*, **111**, 52pp.

Molengraaff, G. A. F., 1930, "The coral reefs in the East Indian Archipelago, their distribution and mode of development," *Proc. Pacific Sci. Congr., Pacific Sci. Assoc., 4th, Java* (*1929*), **2A** and **B**, 55–89, 989–1021.

Saville-Kent, W., 1893, "The Great Barrier Reef of Australia," London, W. H. Allen & Co., 387pp.

Umbgrove, J. H. F., 1947, "Coral reefs of the East Indies," *Bull. Geol. Soc. Am.*, **58**, 729–778.

Yonge, C. M., 1963, "The Biology of Coral Reefs," *Advances in Marine Biology*, **1**, 209–260.

Cross-references: *Algal Reefs; Algal Rim; Atolls; Beachrock; Continent; Coral Reefs—Wind and Current Growth Control; Faro; Fringing Reefs; Great Barrier Reefs; Holocene; Islands; Lagoon—Coral Reef Type; Mangrove Swamp; Negrohead; Quaternary Period.* Vol. I: *Banda Sea; Continental Shelf; Coral Sea; Sahul Shelf; Seamounts (including Guyots); South China Sea; Sunda Shelf; Sulawesi (Celebes) Sea; Timor Sea.* Vol. II: *Paleoclimatology.* Vol. IV: *Geologic Time Scale; Phosphate Deposits (including Guano).*

CORAL REEFS—WIND AND CURRENT GROWTH CONTROL

(1) Basic Concept

The early stages of coral growth and reef building, and also the distribution of reefs, are largely controlled by geomorphological, structural and ecological factors (see *Coral Reefs—Morphology and Theories*). Gradually, however, the winds and currents gain in importance and, particularly in the ultimate stages of reef development, these factors play a dominant role. They influence the rate of reef growth in the various directions and they govern the distribution of coral debris on the reef flat and in the lagoon, if present.

(2) Currents

Where reefs grow up in shallow seas, bottom currents (both geostrophic and tidal) may exert a great influence on reef-form right from the beginning of the reef building, by depositing sediment to the leeward side of the initial coral colonies and by transporting their coral larvae which subsequently initiate reef growth on these leeward sediments. Several investigators hold the opinion that bottom currents loaded with sediment in narrow passes are competent to carve gullies in a shallow sea floor and in this fashion also may affect the shapes of coral reefs at particular sites. This effect of currents has already been recognized by early reef investigators, but it has been stressed especially by Umbgrove in the shelf seas of the East Indies and by Teichert and Fairbridge for the

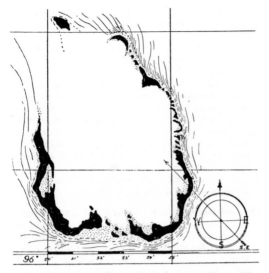

FIG. 1. Map of Cocos Atoll, to show the effects of the prevalent winds upon island—and atoll—formation (from Wood-Jones, 1910).

Sahul Shelf and in the outer barrier reefs of Queensland (see references in Umbgrove, 1947; Fairbridge, 1950).

(3) Wind and Waves

These factors only begin to play a role when the reef upgrowth approaches sea level. The breakers, pounding on the reef, crumble coral colonies and disintegrate them to coral shingle and sand, particularly on the windward side. Once a reef platform has been formed within the tidal range and after coral sand and shingle, produced by wave attack, begins to rise above high tide level, wind and waves become the governing factors in the further development of coral reefs. The effects of this destructive wave action are counterbalanced, however, by the amazingly rapid coral growth, and the process thus is a continuous one. As a result, ridges or "ramparts" of coarse shingle are deposited at some distance in from the reef edge. The finer fragments and the coral sands are carried further on by the waves and only come to rest toward the leeward side of the reef or in the lagoon where the wave energy is greatly diminished. A sand island

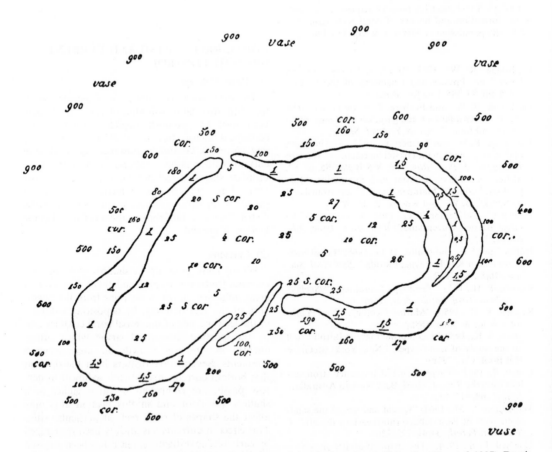

FIG. 2. Discovery Atoll (A. de la Découverte), in the Paracel Archipelago, South China Sea (Krempf, 1927). Depth of lagoon 25 meters, offshore depths 500–900 meters (Cor. = coral bottom; vase = mud).

or "cay" ("key") is thus formed, whose position on the reef is determined by the frequency and force of waves and winds coming from various directions. Part of the coral debris, of course, is carried off into deeper, quiet waters beyond the reach of the waves.

(4) Trade Winds

If winds from one direction are dominant, the sands will be deposited near the leeward edge of the reef and on the leeward submarine slope. Shingle ramparts will be formed along the weatherside. Wood-Jones (1910) clearly stated that the height to which the shingle ramparts can be piled up is limited and depends upon the force of the winds, the waves generated by them, and the tidal range

of the region in question. At the windward side of well-exposed reefs, heights of 20 feet may be reached. The distance of the ramparts in from the reef edge is determined by the mean force of the waves, and after their formation they will gradually be pushed inward by the stronger waves until a certain equilibrium is reached. This equilibrium is disturbed by hurricanes and small sea-level changes. Seaward growth of the island or ramparts, built of sand and shingle, is only possible by the slow process of lateral growth of the reef.

Wood-Jones, in his study of the Cocos–Keeling atolls pointed out the influence of wind and waves on atoll formation. He claimed that the position of these atolls within the south-east Trade Wind belt is the cause of their distinctly horseshoe shaped

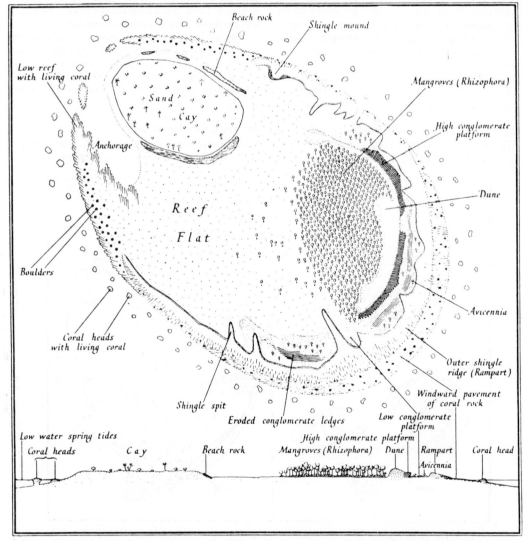

FIG. 3. Sketch plan of a "low wooded island reef" from the Great Barrier Reef, with idealized profile (Steers, 1930). Note orientation due to steady southeast Trade Wind. [By permission of the Trustees of the British Museum (Natural History).]

outline, with the open end pointing to the north-western, leeward side (Fig. 1). He concluded: "The shape of the group, the shape of the atoll and the shape of the individual islands is impressed by the agency of the normal winds and waves." Wood-Jones overemphasized the effects of these factors on larger oceanic atolls, however. These structures rise from great depth and consequently the processes of reef abrasion and deposition of debris have only a limited effect on the ultimate shape of the coral reef (conditioned by a preformed platform, volcanic or coralline: see *Atolls*). His views are fully valid, however, for atolls rising from shallow sea floors ("shelf atolls"). This is confirmed by the studies by Vaughan on the reefs of Florida and by Hedley and Taylor on the Australian Great Barrier Reef (see references in Fairbridge, 1950). There is also no doubt about the effectiveness of winds and waves in "tailing-off" the debris deposits of the individual islands formed on atolls. They will tend to take on a crescent shape with the convex side directed toward the weather side. Coalescing of adjacent debris islands is hampered by the increasing strength of currents as the gaps between them become smaller.

(5) Alternating (Monsoonal) Winds

The studies by Krempf (1927) on coral reefs in the South China Sea are a valuable follow-up of

the above-mentioned observations in the trade wind belts. The equatorial reefs develop under the influence of the alternating winds of the monsoons. In southeast Asia, the winds blow for six months predominantly from the southwest, whereas during the remainder of the year northeasterly winds prevail. Two crescents of debris, opposite to each other, are thus formed under the alternating impact of the two counterposed wind systems (Fig. 2). Ultimately, an annular reef and island may be formed this way. On the strength of these observations, Krempf arrived at the conclusion that all atolls are formed in this fashion. This is undoubtedly correct for shelf atolls rising from shallow marginal seas, like the South China Sea where Krempf carried out his studies. It can hardly be considered a satisfactory explanation for larger oceanic atolls, however. Here, other factors, not related to winds and currents, have to be considered (see *Atolls*).

Debris islands formed on atolls may take on an annular shape due to such monsoonal wind system, and this process may account in part for the existence of ring-shaped reefs and islands or "faros" in complex atolls (as in the Maldive–Laccadive chain).

(6) The Great Barrier Reef

Fairbridge and Teichert (1948), studying the Great Barrier Reef of Australia, were able to con-

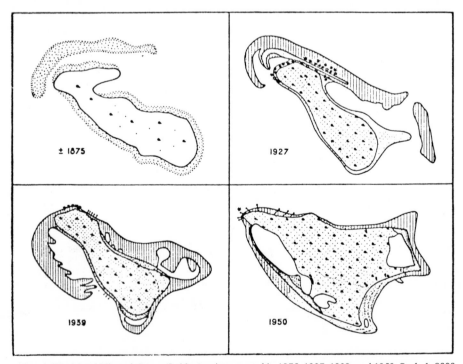

FIG. 4. The island Njamuk Besar (Leiden) as it appeared in 1875, 1927, 1939, and 1950. Scale 1:8000. Key: stippled + trees: old nucleus; stippled: recent accretion (on the 1875 map also shingle ramparts); -.-.-.: lines of growth; hatching: low shingle ramparts (or sparse shingle); dense hatching: high shingle ramparts (Verstappen, 1954).

firm and to elaborate on the influence of winds and waves on the shapes of the coral islands occurring there. Their work on Low Isles is of particular interest as this reef was the site of the British Great Barrier Reef Expedition of 1928–29 and thus, with air photographs at each time, a close comparison of the 1928 and 1945 situations was feasible. Low Isles are located in the Trade Wind belt and southeasterly winds occur 85% of the time. Consequently, the swell usually comes from this side. The effect of the monsoon is felt only during occasional spells of hard northwesterly winds, from December to February. An important factor in this part of the world is the tropical hurricane which may strike the coast with great violence. These gales and the huge waves generated by them may hit Low Isles from any side (Fig. 3).

These conditions have existed in this part of the Australian continental shelf since the postglacial (Flandrian) rise in sea level about 6000 years ago. As a result, the reef platform has a distinct horse-hoof shape, its long axis being in the direction of the dominant influence of the southeast trade winds. The debris deposited on the platform likewise indicates the dominant influence of the southeasterly winds. A small sand cay occurs on the most leeward side of the reef, whereas the shingle ramparts form a perfect crescent with its convex side and highest parts in the southeast. The northwestern "tails" of the ramparts are, however, bent inward, thus witnessing the impact of the occasional high northwesterly winds.

Fairbridge and Teichert observed several, usually more or less parallel, ramparts. The oldest ones are furthest inland since every rampart is gradually pushed landward by the waves after its formation near the reef edge. The occurrence of this elaborate set of ramparts is evidence of the cyclic nature of their formation. It was thought that a rampart is pushed inland by storms and cyclones until a critical equilibrium point is reached when a new system will start to form outside of the first. Outward growth of the living coral fringe would gradually result in the development of a number of ramparts. Fairbridge and Teichert made it clear that a rampart does not necessarily originate simultaneously along its whole extent along the reef edge. The growth may start at exposed parts of the reef and subsequently proceed to its more protected portions.

(7) Southeast Asiatic Monsoonal Area

Umbgrove investigated the wind influence on some coral islands off the north coast of Java, which develop under the influence of monsoonal winds (see references in Umbgrove, 1947). He found that in 1927, shingle ramparts occurred along the northern, northeastern and eastern sides of the reefs, whereas a comparatively large sand cay was located in the southeastern portion of the reef. A shallow moat of varying width separated these two parts of the coral islands. Meteorological data revealed that the product of the mean velocity (V) and the frequency (F) of the winds from the eight

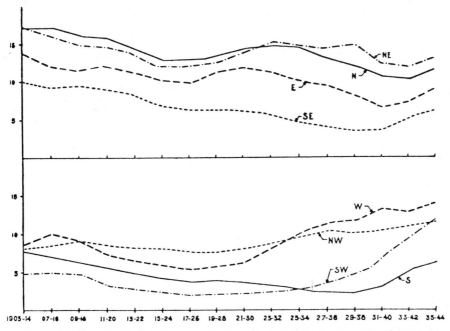

FIG. 5. The 10-year sums (moving averages) of the product of the frequency (F) of the wind in hours per year and the mean wind velocity (V) in meters per second for the eight wind directions since 1905–1914 (Verstappen, 1954).

wind directions was maximal in the north, northeast and east quadrants and showed a minimum for the southwesterly winds. The distribution of coarse shingle and coral sands on the reef platform thus was satisfactorily explained. Umbgrove noticed that the moat on some islands was considerably wider than on others. He initially tried to account for this by attributing a greater age to the latter as a result of which the shingle ramparts there were pushed further landward. It soon became clear to him, however, that the changes in the ramparts were a much more rapid occurrence and had nothing to do with the age of the islands. It thus remained obscure why and when new ramparts were formed. Fairbridge and Teichert faced a rather similar problem on Low Isles, as mentioned above.

(8) Climatic Changes

Verstappen (1954) studied the wind influence on some of the coral islands in Djakarta (Batavia) Bay visited by Umbgrove in 1927 and in 1950. A comparative study of the islands with the aid of maps dating from about 1875, 1927, 1939 and 1950 demonstrated important changes in the position of both shingle ramparts and sand cays. Important growth of shingle ramparts particularly to the western and southwestern sides of the islands occurred since 1927. Figure 4 of the island Njamuk Besar (Leiden) illustrates this. The moving averages of the 10-year sums of the product of wind frequency (F) and velocity (V) were computed from 1905 onward and graphically represented in Fig. 5. It can be seen at a glance that a considerable increase of $F \times V$ of west, southwest and south winds is characteristic during and after the 1920's. The product for the southwest winds during the period 1935–44 was, for instance, about six times larger than in the period 1919–28.

The development of the shingle ramparts is readily explained by these changes in wind intensity from various directions. Even small details, such as the direction of growth of the new shingle rampart in the southwest of the island Njamuk Besar (Fig. 4), from the northwest, via west and southwest to south is also accounted for. The graphs of Fig. 5 show that the northwest winds increased first in strength, and afterward the west, southwest and south winds successively increased likewise.

These changes in wind pattern are associated with the fluctuating intensity of the monsoon, which in its turn depends on changes in the development of the Asiatic anticyclone area during the northern winter. Air pressure and rainfall data for Hong Kong demonstrate this. A well-developed Asiatic high will shift the intertropical zone of convergence to southern Indonesia and cause strong west monsoonal winds on the islands. When, due to lower atmospheric pressure over Asia, the intertropical convergence zone is situated over northern Indonesia for a long time, east winds predominate

in the area. Such climatic variations have complex periods (comparable with sunspots and miscellaneous planetary cycles), and may be accompanied by small changes also in mean sea level, as observed by Fairbridge.

Climatic changes thus govern the ever-changing pattern of distribution of coral debris on reef platforms and determine the time and location of emerging new shingle ridges. It goes without saying that the effects of such comparatively rapid climatic changes on the overall growth of the reefs themselves will be minor since this involves a complex of much slower processes.

H. Th. VERSTAPPEN

References

*Fairbridge, R. W., 1950, "Recent and Pleistocene Coral Reefs of Australia," *J. Geol.*, **58**, 330–401.

Fairbridge, R. W., and Teichert, C., 1948, "The Low Isles of the Great Barrier Reef: A new analysis," *Geograph. J.*, **61**, 67–88.

Krempf, F., 1927, "La forme des récifs coralliens et le régime des vents alternants," *Trav. Serv. Océanographique de l'Indo-chine Mém.*, **2**, 33pp.

Steers, J. A., 1930, "A geographical introduction to the biological reports," *Great Barrier Reef Expedition, 1928–1929*. London; Brit. Mus. N.H., **3**, 1–15.

Umbgrove, J. H. F., 1930, "The influence of the monsoons on the geomorphology of coral islands," *Proc. Pacific Sci. Congr., 4th*, **2A**, 105–113.

Umbgrove, J. H. F., 1947, "Coral reefs of the East Indies," *Bull. Geol. Soc. Am.*, **58**, 729–778.

Verstappen, H. Th., 1954, "The influence of climatic changes on the formation of coral islands." *Am. J. Sci.*, **252**, 428–435.

Wood-Jones, F., 1910, "Coral and Atolls," London, Lovell Reeve, 392pp.

* Additional bibliographic references may be found in this work.

Cross-references: *Atolls*; *Coral Reefs—Morphology and Theories*; *Faro*, Vol. 1: *Ocean Bottom Currents*; *Ocean Waves*; *Wind—Principles*. Vol. II: *Intertropical Convergence Zone*; *Monsoons*; *Siberian High (Asiatic High)*; *Sunspot Cycle*; *Tropical Cyclones*.

CORE STONES—*See* TOR

CORRASION

A process of erosion, corrasion refers to the strictly mechanical wear of bedrock by moving detrital and other materials during (a) their migration downslope under the influence of gravity, and (b) their further transportation by erosional agencies such as running water, moving ice, or wind.

The mechanical wear includes scraping (*abrasion*, q.v.), scratching, striking, grinding, crushing, and in the case of moving ice, gouging. The bedrock may be coherent or incoherent, fresh or weathered.

The earth materials include fragmental rocks, minerals, and organic matter (e.g., tree trunks).

Prior to 1875 corrasion was used almost synonymously with erosion. Its later meaning has been restricted by the definition of attrition, corrosion, and hydraulic action (including plucking or quarrying under ice) as separate agents of erosion.

Corrasion includes (1) the scouring or sand-blasting action of wind-borne particles (Derruau, 1956, p. 178); (2) the scour of bedrock by boulders and debris in moving ice, causing polishing, striations, fluting and grinding (Flint, 1957, p. 76; he terms this abrasion); (3) "when waves, armed with rock fragments, hurl them against the cliffs and, cooperating with currents, drag them to and fro across the rocks of the foreshore" (Holmes, 1965, p. 798).

Vertical corrasion or the downward wearing away of stream beds by the movement of the bed load in running water is the most widespread type of corrasion. Thus "wherever an area of land is above its base level of degradation there corrasion will be manifest by deepening its channel; and wherever dry land has been brought down near to its base level there corrasion is manifest by widening its channel" (Powell, 1876, p. 191).

Lateral corrasion or the back wearing of stream sides or stream banks may lead to the widening of flood plains and hence to "planation," "planes," and "rock plains" particularly in arid and semiarid regions (Gilbert, 1877, p. 126; Johnson, 1931, pp. 174–177, and 1932, pp. 656–665). Such corrasion is effected mostly by the undercutting action of the bed load on the outer sides of stream bends and because the rock here tends to be more weathered and incoherent than that of the stream bed, lateral corrasion may act much more rapidly than vertical corrasion. "Whenever the load reduces the downward corrasion to little or nothing, lateral corrasion becomes relatively and actually of importance" (Gilbert, 1877, p. 126).

Subsurface corrasion or "the forcible incorporation of sedentary weathered rock into the base of a migratory layer (i.e., rock waste in transit)" (Berry and Ruxton, 1961, p. 626), as at the base of a slip, slump, or "soliflual" flow. Where "geliflual" (ice-lubricated) flow is involved, as in periglacial areas, the process has been termed *cryergic corrasion* (Cotton, 1958, p. 421); thus "the bedrock has been shaved by abrasion at the base of the moving ... (geliflual) mass" (Cotton and Te Punga, 1955, p. 1008).

Penck (1953, p. 112) defined *corrasion* as the "freeing of loosened rock fragments from their place of origin ... (by the) force of the material (rock waste) moving over them," and considered that "the mechanical action on a *uniformly inclined substratum* increases with the weight of material moving over it" (Penck, 1953, p. 111). The rock

waste moving solely under the influence of gravity may form "mass streams" and excavate *corrasion valleys* by *linear corrasion*. An example of these are the dells of central Europe termed *corrasion troughs* or *corrasion niches* (Cotton and Te Punga, 1955, p. 1022).

"There can be no absolute distinction between (a) *subsurface corrasion*, and (b) subsurface renewal of the migratory layer by permissive incorporation of sedentary weathered rocks following surface removal of material. If corrasion is defined as a freeing of loosened rock fragments from their place of origin (cf. Penck, 1953, p. 112) then subsurface corrasion can be said to occur under both active mass movement and slow creep. If corrasion is defined as the mechanical wearing of surfaces by rock waste in transit (cf. Malott, 1928, p. 158) then subsurface corrasion will be practically confined to hillslopes" (Berry and Ruxton, 1961, pp. 626–627).

BRYAN P. RUXTON

References

Berry, L., and Ruxton, B. P., 1961, "Mass movement and landform in New Zealand and Hong Kong," *Trans. Roy. Soc. New Zealand*, **88**, Pt. 4, 623–629.

Cotton, C. A., 1958, "Dissection and redissection of the Wellington landscape," *Trans. Roy. Soc. New Zealand*, **85**, Pt. 3, 409–425.

Cotton, C. A., and Te Punga, M. T., 1955, "Solifluxion and periglacially modified landforms at Wellington, New Zealand," *Trans. Roy. Soc. New Zealand*, **82**, Pt. 5, 1001–1031.

Derruau, M., 1956, "Précis de Géomorphologie," Paris, Masson et Cie (Third ed., 1962, 413pp.).

Flint, R. F., 1957, "Glacial and Pleistocene Geology," New York, John Wiley & Sons, 553pp.

Gilbert, G. K., 1877, "Report on the geology of the Henry Mountains, Utah," *U.S. Geol. Surv. Rocky Mtn. Reg.*, 160pp.

Hinman, R., 1888, "The laws of corrasion," *Science*, **12**, 119–120.

Holmes, A., 1965, "Principles of Physical Geology," Second ed., London, Nelson; New York, Ronald Press, 1288pp.

Johnson, D. W., 1931, "Planes of lateral corrasion," *Science*, **73**, 174–177.

Johnson, D. W., 1932, "Rock planes of arid regions," *Geograph. Rev.*, **22**(4), 656–665.

Malott, C. A., 1928, "An analysis of erosion," *Proc. Indiana Acad. Sci.*, **37**, 153–163.

Penck, W., 1953, "Morphological Analysis of Land Forms," London, Macmillan & Co., 429pp. (translated by H. Czech and K. C. Boswell).

Powell, J. W., 1876, "Report on the geology of the eastern portion of the Uinta Mountains and a region of country adjacent thereto," *U.S. Geol. and Geogr. Surv. of the Terr.*, 218pp.

Cross-references: *Abrasion; Corrosion; Dell; Mass Movement; Soil Creep; Solifluction.*

CORROSION, ETCHING

From the Latin verb *corrodere* and the noun *corrosionem*, the classical term corrosion means the act of gnawing away, rusting or fretting. In geological use, it has always referred to chemical erosion in some form, thus analogous to rusting in which a hard native metal, iron, is oxidized to a hydrated iron oxide which is mechanically soft and furthermore may easily be carried away in solution. Corrosion is often simply referred to as "chemical weathering" (Merrill, 1904). The use of the word corrosion in place of *corrasion* (mechanical abrasion) is seen in some books of 50 years ago, but is to be discouraged. To "etch" is to model or eat out by acid action; it is essentially the surface modeling involved in corrosion (as by an artist or printer in acid-etching a metal plate or fine-grained $CaCO_3$ stone, such as the Jurassic Solenhofen Limestone).

The most common landform process involved in corrosion is that of *karst* (q.v.), in which limestone ($CaCO_3$) is attacked by CO_2-enriched groundwater or rain. Numerous related landforms are recognized (*dolina*, q.v.; *hum*, q.v.; *lapiés*, q.v.; *polje*, q.v.; *sinkhole*, q.v.). Because of the liberation of CO_2 by plant roots, microscopic lichens, mosses or algae, and bacteria, soil often has a low pH, and the underlying limestone is etched, bored or deeply corroded. Corrosion by sea spray and wave splash is particularly common in limestones in the intertidal belt and just above (see *Limestone Coastal Weathering*).

Other common soluble minerals give rise to analogous landforms, e.g., ice, in *permafrost* (q.v.) producing *thermokarst* (q.v.), also *cryokarst* and *nivokarst*; evaporites, salt, halite, gypsum, etc., producing *salt karst* (q.v.); certain unstable minerals commonly found in volcanic ash and cinders ("glass", scoria) such as zeolites and some feldspars, producing *volcano-karst* (q.v.). Corrosion also occurs in the feldspars of basalt, producing lapiés under certain conditions, as in Hawaii (Palmer, 1927); it is widely observed in granite surfaces, most commonly resulting in solution pits and pans, gnamma holes, etc. (see *Granite Landforms* and *Solution Pits and Pans*).

Corrosion of minerals (often selectively) takes place also on a large scale during *diagenesis* (see pr Vol. VI) and *metamorphism* (Vol. V).

A geomorphic landform produced by corrosion and mass removal of soluble material (apart from limestone, thus especially salt or ice) often leads to subsidence of the land surface, resulting in lakes or swamps, thus an aspect of *salt karst* (q.v.) or *thermokarst* (q.v.). Examples of the swamps first reported from saline springs in Kentucky were named "corrosion spring swamps" (Shaler, 1890).

Corrosion and Recementation

A curious geomorphologic paradox presents itself in any field examination of corroded lime-stone surfaces. While there is extensive evidence of solution, from deep piping and lapiés to fine etching, the rock itself is frequently extremely hard. It rings to a hammer blow. In thin section under the microscope, it usually discloses a tightly cemented fabric. This hard cementation may be limited to a crust only a few centimeters thick or it may persist to considerable depths; it seems to be a question of (a) the original porosity of the limestone, (b) the length of its exposure, and (c) the effective precipitation/evaporation relationships.

The most complete examples of this phenomenon are to be seen in tropical karst areas, which have both maximum precipitation and fairly high evaporation potential, while the high temperature-humidity favors vigorous vegetation growth with its attendant production of CO_2 and humic acids. In the western Pacific, especially, there are extensive tectonically uplifted *coral reef limestones*, which in many cases may not be over 100,000 years old (see *Coral Reefs* and *Fringing Reef*). Yet they are so deeply corroded and recemented that it is hardly possible to recognize their coral origin; in thin section, in addition to recementation, one may observe wholesale recrystallization, inversion from aragonite and locally dolomite metasomatism.

Widespread examples of corrosion and recementation are to be seen throughout the distribution areas of the Quaternary calcareous *eolianites* (or eolian calcarenites) which characterize the coastal regions of the present semiarid lands or those that were semiarid at some stages during the Pleistocene [western Australia, southern Australia, western India (Kathiawar), southern Arabia, South Africa, Morocco, Egypt, Lebanon, Bahamas, Bermuda, Hawaii and other mid-latitude islands]. In these former dune rocks, the porosity and permeability were as great as, or even higher than, in the tropical coral reefs, so that during the mid-latitude oscillations between pluvial and semiarid climatic conditions there was every opportunity for deep leaching. Today, thick "calcrete" crusts (layered travertine) are found marking the former dune surfaces, which are pock-marked by deep solution pipes, alternately lined by travertine layers and corrosion surfaces; fossil roots (rhizomorphs), likewise paleosols of *terra rossa*, testify to the humid periods, while insect nests and blown sand suggest the alternating dry phases. In the continental coast examples, the calcareous sands are diluted with up to 60% quartz and other insolubles, but the geomorphic effect is minor; the soluble carbonates are mobilized during corrosion and the insolubles either form residual soils or are carried inland by the wind, contributing to the extensive white quartz sand plains, so characteristic, for example, of southwestern Australia; in soil terminology, the process is a special type of *podzolization*.

In the *cool, temperate karst* regions, the frequent presence of a forest cover over the limestones at lower elevations is due to the accumulations of residual soils and the presence of groundwater; however, in higher places there is liable to be a stripping down of the soils to skeletal levels and the karst hydrology so lowers the water table that a heavy vegetation is difficult to maintain. In the formerly glaciated areas, veneers and pockets of glacial drift (till) may support heavy forests. In regions of more or less continuous rainfall (Ireland, north of England), peat soils develop. In spite of the highly acid nature of peat waters (pH 2–5), the soil tends to form a blanket over the rock surface that restricts motion of soil water, so that once it is neutralized at the limestone contact, further corrosion is inhibited. Field experiments by Margaret Sweeting (1966) showed that a rock surface artificially exposed to peat waters suffered very rapid corrosion.

Sweeting's experiments provide a contribution to the experimental answer to the corrosion-recementation paradox. Corrosion can only continue as long as continued access by waters of low pH is possible. *Rainwater* (see pr Vol. VI) usually has a pH of 5–7 and is rapidly neutralized on contact with $CaCO_3$. Groundwaters in karst terrains frequently give readings of pH 8–9 because they are simply flowing in pre-existing channels that can no longer be suffering any solution. The surfaces of such karst stream beds are not corroded—on the contrary, they are frequently coated with layered travertine. An equilibrium situation, geochemical and hydrologic, is thus rapidly established near the surface, below which further corrosion is restricted to interrupted occasions of heavy rain and flooding when the hydrologic intake bypasses the soil areas (where neutralization normally occurs) and pours down through sinkholes to the underground system, where further corrosion will take place.

In northern Yugoslavia (Slovenia), which is probably the area of most vigorous karst development in Europe, the corrosion rates are found to be greatest in the highest mountain areas where the effects of Pleistocene permafrost inhibited much plant cover and facilitated rapid runoff into the underground hydrologic system. Even Pliocene plateaus are now very deeply dissected, with maximum rates of corrosion exceeding $120 \, m^3/km^2$ per year. Average figures in Slovenia are more like 40–$70 \, m^3/km^2$ per year (Gams, 1965).

RHODES W. FAIRBRIDGE

References

Bögli, A., 1951, "Probleme der Karrenbildung," *Geogr. Helvetica*, **6**(3), 191–204.

Gams, I., 1965, "The speleological characteristics of the Slovene Karst," *Naše Jama, Ljubljana*, **7**, 41–50.

Jones, R. J., 1965, "Aspects of the biological weathering of limestone pavement," *Proc. Geol. Assoc.*, **76**, pt. 4, 421–433.

Kaveev, M. S., 1965, "Carbon dioxide generated by the alteration of petroleum deposits and the development of karst features," *Dukl. Akad. Nauk SSSR Earth Sci. Sect.*, **152**(1–6), 191–193 (translated from Russian).

Merrill, G. P., 1904, "A Treatise on Rocks, Rock-weathering and Soils," New York, The Macmillan Co., 411pp.

Ollier, C. D., 1965, "Some features of granite weathering in Australia," *Z. Geomorphol.*, **3**, 285–304.

Palmer, H. S., 1927, "Lapiés in Hawaiian basalts," *Geograph. Rev.*, **17**, 627–631.

Shaler, N. S., 1890, "Tenth Annual Report," p. 266, U.S. Geological Survey, Washington, D.C.

Sweeting, M. M., 1966, "The weathering of limestones. With particular reference to the carboniferous limestones of northern England," in (Dury, editor) "Essays in Geomorphology," pp. 177–210, Heinemann Educa. Books, Ltd.

Williams, J. E., 1949, "Chemical weathering at low temperatures," *Geograph. Rev.*, **39**, 129–135.

Cross-references: *Biological Erosion of Limestone Coasts; Coral Reefs; Dolina; Fringing Reef; Granite Landforms; Hum; Induration; Karst; Lapiés; Limestone Coastal Weathering; Permafrost; Platforms—Wavecut; Polje; Regolith and Saprolite; Salt Karst; Sink, Sinkhole; Solution Pits and Pans; Thermokarst; Volcano-Karst.* Vol. IV: *Dolomite.* Vol. V: *Metamorphism.* pr Vol. VI: *Diagenesis; Evaporites; Groundwater; Hydrology; Leaching; Podzolization; Rainwater; Salts-Cyclic; Soils.*

COULEE, COULEE CLIFF, COULEE LAKE, COULOIR

Widely used in North America for a lava flow, the term comes originally from France, where one may speak of a *coulée de lave*, a *coulée de blocs* (block stream), a *coulée de boue* (mud flow), etc. J. W. Powell (1896) wrote: "The lavas that are poured out form *coulees*, or sheets of rock, when they are cooled, and often one is piled on another" (p. 24). The term *coulee cliff* is sometimes used, thus: "coulees are often formed with very rough edges, which constitute cliffs that may be scores or even hundreds of feet high" (Powell, 1896, p. 51). "Sometimes volcanic lavas are poured across valleys, and the channels of rivers are dammed. These volcanic dams are common, and some rather important lakes are formed in this manner.... Let us call such lakes *coulee lakes*" (Powell, 1896, p. 61).

A second use is also recognized in North America; following Campbell (1915, p. 42), "The term coulee is generally applied throughout the northern tier of States to any steep-sided gulch or water channel and at times even to a stream valley of considerable length." According to Baulig (1956), coulee is sometimes used in the southwest (United States) for dry wash, dry gulch or arroyo (i.e., a deep wadi). In the Pacific northwest, many glacial spillways are today deep channels and are

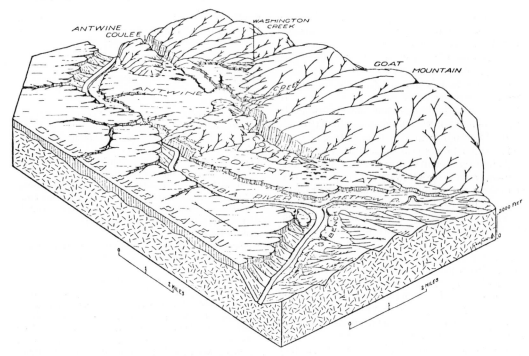

Fig. 1. Block diagram of Alta Coulee (A. C. Waters, 1931).

often called coulees. The temporary diversion of the Columbia River in this way was responsible for the Grand Coulee (Waters, 1931; Flint and Irwin, 1939).

In France and Switzerland, the word *couloir* is often used for gorge, passage or deep gully, and so has also appeared in those parts of North America where French explorers have left their mark. In France, *couloir* may apply to a deep karst gash (*lapiés*). A *couloir calibre* is a strath. A *couloir interdunaire* is an interdune swale (*gassi* in arabic). A *couloir d'avalanche* is an avalanche chute.

The above terms are rarely, if ever, used in the English-speaking world.

RHODES W. FAIRBRIDGE

References

Baulig. H., 1956, "Vocabulaire Franco-Anglo-Allemand de Geómorphologie," Paris (Publ. Fac. Lettres Univ. Strasbourg, No. 130), 230pp.

Campbell, M. R., 1915, "Guidebook of the western United States," Pt. A., *U.S. Geol. Surv., Bull. 611.*

Flint, R. F., and Irwin, W. H., 1939, "Glacial geology of the Grand Coulee Dam, Washington," *Bull. Geol. Soc. Am.,* **50,** 611–680.

Powell, J. W., 1896, "The physiography of the United States," *Natl. Geogr. Soc. Monog. 1.* (Physiographic processes, pp. 1-32; Physiographic features, pp. 33–64).

Waters, A. C., 1931, "Terraces and coulees along the Columbia River near Lake Chelan, Washington," *Bull. Geol. Soc. Am.,* **44,** 783–820.

Cross-references: *Gully Erosion*; *Lapiés*; *Mudflow*.

CRAG AND TAIL

This Scottish expression (properly "craig and tail") has long been used in Britain for a type of "rock drumlin" where a particularly resistant hillock (or crag) formed an obstruction to ice movement and accumulated in its lee a tapered, streamlined tail of ground moraine material. As Cotton (1942) pointed out, these structures differ from *roches moutonnées* by the presence of this tail; the normal *roche moutonnée* has a plucked lee side but no associated till. In some cases the tail may simply be soft bedrock protected behind the resistant crag. A classic example is the volcanic crag of Castle Rock, Edinburgh.

RHODES W. FAIRBRIDGE

References

Charlesworth, J. K., 1957, "The Quaternary Era," London, Arnold Ltd., 2 vols.

Cotton, C. A., 1942, "Climatic Accidents," Christchurch, Whitcombe & Tombs Ltd., 354pp.

Flint, R. F., 1957, "Glacial and Pleistocene Geology," New York, John Wiley & Sons, 553 pp.

Mitchell, G. H., Walton, E. K., and Grant, D., 1960,

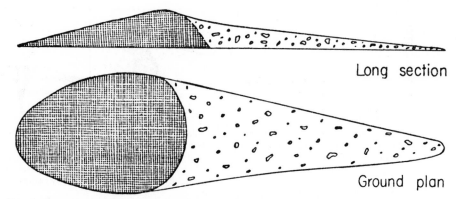

Long section

Ground plan

FIG. 1. One common form of crag and tail. Length ranges from a few meters to 2 km or more (Flint, 1957). (By permission of John Wiley & Sons, N.Y.)

"Edinburgh Geology, An Excursion Guide," Edinburgh, Oliver & Boyd, 222pp.

Sissons, J. B., 1967, "The Evolution of Scotland's Scenery," Edinburgh, Oliver & Boyd, 259pp.

Cross-references: *Drumlin*; *Roche Moutonnée.*

CRATER

Any geological process that involves the effusion of materials from beneath the earth's surface via some sort of vertical pipe or vent usually develops a cone, collar or ring of deposits around the exit. This opening to the vent is the crater. A similar crater is ringed by debris thrown out by the explosive impact of a large meteorite, or by a man-made explosion. Most craters are volcanic, and although more than 95% of the world's volcanic rocks are basaltic, there are numerous categories (to be mentioned below). The complex explosion and collapse structures known as *calderas* (q.v.) often containing secondary craters, are treated separately. Apart from these, among the varied sorts of craters we recognize:

(a) Volcanic cones (cinder, lava; single, linear, nested, etc.), each with distinctive craters,

(b) Meteorite impact craters; also lunar craters (see separate articles, Vol. II),

(c) Craters of mud volcanoes (non-igneous),

(d) Craters of mound springs (hydrologic),

(e) Craters of hot springs and geysers (hydrothermal or pneumatolytic).

(f) Craters of hydrolaccoliths (*pingos*, q.v.), *suffosion* phenomena (tundra craters, etc.). These are dealt with separately in this volume.

Volcanic Craters

A fundamental differentiation is recognized among lavas, based on their geochemistry, which in turn affects their viscosity. The highly fluid magmas (rich in Mg, Fe, Ca) readily lose their volatiles [H_2O (as steam), SO_2, CO_2, etc.], and this reduces the explosive potential; the magma, of high

temperature, flows out gently and steadily as *lava* from stable clusters of vents ("*shield volcanoes*") or from long, irregular vents along fractures ("*fissure volcanoes*") (Figs. 1–2). Such fractures may be associated with a volcano-tectonic horst or sunkland (Fig. 3).

The viscous magmas (rich in SiO_2 and alkalies) are cooler and "stickier." They retain more of their gases. After temperature buildup during quiescence ("dormancy"), there is liable to be fracturing of the older crater-filling, permitting simultaneous gas expansion. Because of the compressibility of gases (cf. Boyles Law), it is accompanied by violent explosions ("Plinian eruptions", as described first by Pliny for Vesuvius), leading to extensive accumulation of ash, cinders or scoria (as well as lavas). The eruptions are characterized by a single vent, the so-called *central volcano* (Figs. 4–10). Entry of water into the vent, as in various eruptions of Krakatoa, enormously adds to the volatile content and explosivity ("phreatic" or "Krakatoan eruptions").

The frequency of such explosions may be very high, with a quick-cooling lava and a high-energy situation, resulting in explosions every few minutes. Alternatively there may be long dormant periods extending over many centuries, climaxed by catastrophic explosions (like the Vesuvian eruption that buried Pompeii, A.D. 79). They lead to complex tectono-volcanic fracture centers or inverted cone-shaped vents that are followed by extensive collapse (see *Calderas*). Depending upon the age and maturity of an eruptive center, the size of the cone tends to decrease with increasing viscosity, but the crater (as evidence of explosivity) increases. On the other hand, the steepest cones tend to be those in the intermediate classes. Also, basalt cinder cones may be very small.

The more fluid magmas commonly belong to the so-called *Atlantic Suite* (alkali-basalts, nepheline rocks); that name suggests also a regional classification for this suite, which is characteristic of non-orogenic regions, mid-oceanic positions (Atlantic,

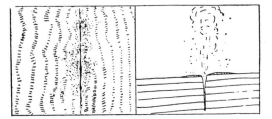

Phase (a) A fissure opens to the accompaniment of earth tremors, and is cleared and widened by explosions. Deposition of a vent-opening breccia.

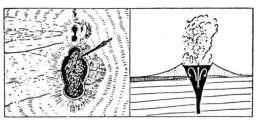

Phase (d) Lava-lakes form in the craters of the cones, in which the lava becomes largely devolatilized through the activity of lava fountains. The crater walls tend to be melted due to exothermic gas reactions; fresh magma is continually brought to the surface by two-phase convection.

Phase (b) Outflow of large quantities of fairly gas-rich, fluid magma, which pours out over the land surface and solidifies to rubbly lava. Formation of a basalt sheet.

Phase (e) The largely devolatilized, but very hot lava breaks through the crater wall, flows out slowly, and solidifies to platy and ropy lava.

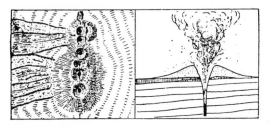

Phase (c) Ejected scoriae and clots of lava build up a row of cones.

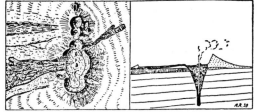

Phase (f) The magma sinks back. The eruption dies away with diminishing vapor emission and fumarole activity.

FIG. 1. Six phases in the evolution of a fissure eruption, based on the eruptions of Threngslaborgir, Iceland, sketched in plan and profile (Rittmann, 1962). (By permission of John Wiley & Sons, N.Y.)

Indian and Pacific, not merely Atlantic), and long-stable continental regions, e.g., African rifts. In contrast, the more viscous magmas belong usually to the *Pacific Suite* ("calcalkaline" basalt, andesite, dacite, rhyolite), or the *Mediterranean Suite* (trachyte, latite, leucitite, leucite-melilitite, -tephrite, -phonolite). Regionally, these Pacific and Mediterranean suites are distributed respectively in the circum-Pacific orogenic belts and in the marginal sea or quasi-cratonic crustal areas (Rittmann, 1962). Thus the types of crater are commonly found in quite characteristic belts, and the crater types may be used further to interpret the types of lava involved.

Eruptive events provide a further classification, into (1) *monogenetic*, which have a single, usually small, eruption, and (2) *polygenetic*, which have a sequence of eruptive events, often with a cyclic variation in lava type. Monogenetic events are usually associated with *fissure volcano* belts, i.e., fracture belts where openings appear once, then freeze over, and reappear at another spot. Polygenetic histories are, in contrast, usually associated with *central volcanoes*. In the former, numerous small craters are preserved, but in the latter the initial crater is buried by later outpourings, or totally obliterated in a caldera-type explosion. In the absence of the latter, a complex series of lavas

FIG. 2. Mount Tarawera, North Island, New Zealand. Craters formed in the 1886 eruption form an almost continuous cleft 3 miles in length along the mountain's summit. They continue in line for a further 6 miles through Lake Rotomahana and the Waimangu Valley. Ash and scoria erupted in 1886 form a mantle on the mountain's flanks. (Photo: S. B. Beatus, New Zealand Geological Survey.)

and ash builds up into a *strato-volcano*, the layering of which may be seen usually in the inner walls of the crater.

Exogenous and Endogenous Craters. Rittmann (1962) refers to the volcanoes that build up from simple surface flows and cinders as *exogenous cones*

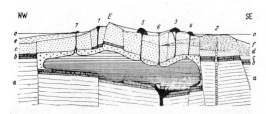

FIG. 3. Section through the volcano-tectonic horst of Ischia, Italy: a = sedimentary basement; b = basalts (including trachybasalts); c = greenish trachytic tuff of Epomeo; d = trachytic volcano of Secca d'Ischia; e = younger tuffs and tuffites; o–o = sea level.

E = Monte Epomeo, the highest uplifted block of the horst. (1) Old vent of Montagna Nuova. (2) Secca d'Ischia. (3) Endogenous dome of Monte Vezzi (alkali trachyte). (4) Endogenous dome of S. Pancrazio (sodalite phonolite). (5) Endogenous volcanic ridge of Monte Trippodi (trachyte). (6) Crater of Molara (latite). (7) Lava flow from endogenous dome in the region of Zara (alkali trachyte).

The differentiation of the magma in the chamber is indicated by the thickness of the shading. The crosses indicate the part of the magma chamber already solidified (Rittmann, 1962). (By permission of John Wiley & Sons, N.Y.)

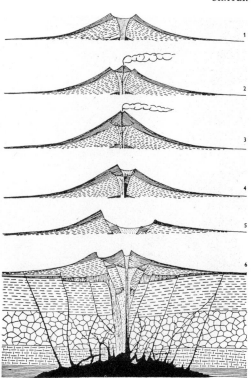

FIG. 4. Evolution of Mt. Vesuvius, an explosive central volcano. (1) After early Plinian eruption, a wide summit crater. (2) New cone builds up inside. (3) In eighth century B.C., gradual buildup. (4) Terminates in explosion, leaving crater plateau. (5) In A.D. 79, explosion destroys Pompeii and Herculanium and broad caldera left; rim still remains as Monte Somma. (6) Regrowth of central cone. Lavas evolved from trachytic tuff and lava to begin with, through phonolite to leucite to tephrite (from Rittmann, 1962). (By permission of John Wiley & Sons, N.Y.)

and those that freeze over readily (the viscous ones) and push up from the inside as *endogenous domes*. The latter tend to be ultimately composite, with the development of coulees (Figs. 11–13). Sometimes the entire neck freezes and is forced up bodily out of the crater as a solid *spine* as in the famous "aiguille" of Mont Pelée in Martinique which in 1902 rose to over 300 meters in this way (see *Volcanic Necks*).

Secondary Craters. Very large strato-volcanoes generally develop secondary outlets over their lower flanks, leading to *parasitic cones*; the latter are usually distinctively asymmetric owing to the slope of the primary cone, and as their life is generally short, they are usually small and uncomplicated (Fig. 14).

After a large strato-volcano has reached mature dimensions, its last major eruptive sequence is marked by the filling of the crater, over which small secondary cones build up, each with its independent

FIG. 5. Vertical air photo of the crater of Mt. Raung in Java, a very large central volcano of the explosive "Pacific Suite" lavas. A new set of cones and nested craters are seen forming within the older explosion crater. In the walls of the latter are alternating layers of ash and lava. The outer slopes of the largely ash cone are deeply dissected by fluvial erosion owing to heavy tropical rainfall. Width of main crater, about 2 km.

crater. The same thing happens in the collapse-crater of a *caldera* (q.v.) type. The sequence of craters may be one in the other, scattered, or over-lapping; these are called *nested craters* (Fig. 15). Smaller and smaller conelets and spatter cones (driblet cones, mamelons, hornitos) follow as the sequence matures (Figs. 16–19). Such spatter cones

are "quiet" eruptions, without great explosions or clouds of ash and largely restricted to lava, scoria and bombs (so-called Strombolian type). This illustrates the "Wolff Rule," which says that (a) successively younger eruptions are smaller than the initial one, in any given sequence, and (b) the younger events reflect progressive solidification of

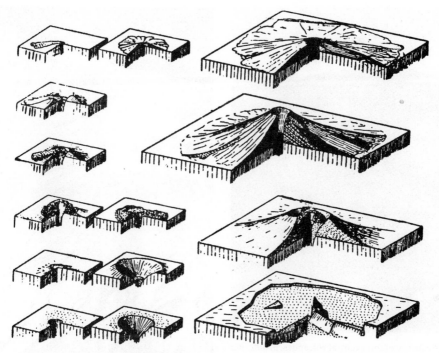

FIG. 6. Schematic block diagrams of simple central volcanoes. The arrangement of the sketches corresponds to that of the systematic classificatory table. The quantity of magma produced increases from left to right, and the viscosity increases from above downward. The largest volcanic structures are not represented (Rittmann, 1962). (By permission of John Wiley & Sons, N.Y.)

the magma. As remarked by Rittmann (1962), one must use this rule with caution because multiple sequences will tend to bury traces of earlier eruptions, and relics of earlier ones may be confused with later events. Such a sequential group might evolve

FIG. 7. Ngauruhoe erupting, 1954 (North Island, New Zealand). Lava flows silhouetted against the snow. Ash blackens the northern slopes (left). (Photo: J. Healy, New Zealand Geological Survey.)

over the period of 50–100 years, for example, and be separated from an earlier one by 500–1000 years. Within each sequence, there is usually a progressive change in the lavas from basic to more acidic, with an attendant trend toward greater explosivity; exceptionally, the sequence begins with acid explosions and passes on to more passive basic flows (as in Iceland).

Where tectonic collapse has occurred, not on a scale sufficient to be called calderas, some authors speak of "craters," but Daly recommends that all such inward-facing subsidences, large and small, should be called *volcanic sinks*. Gravitational sliding, facing outward, also affects many volcanic cones and can be *superficial*, producing U-shaped gashes and radial fissures in the rim of the crater or on the outer slopes (Fairbridge, 1950; Figs. 20–22), or *deep-seated*, producing Van Bemmelen's gravitational slides ("shovel faults" and "sickle faults") which often split the crater in two (Figs. 23 and 24). Cinder cones are of course very easily eroded and, following the overflow of a *crater lake* (q.v.), develop *breached craters* (Figs. 25 and 26). Late-stage cinder eruptions are often followed by lava flows, so that lava-filled breached craters result. The lava often flows down preexisting valleys, blocking drainage and creating lava-dammed lakes. Lyell

FIG. 8. Sequence of three central volcanoes, in differing states of erosion, with graceful Mt. Egmont in the background the most youthful with its unblemished concave slopes. Aerial view from west of New Plymouth looking south across the Taranaki volcanoes (North Island, New Zealand). Note their striking alignment. Kaitake in foreground, Pouakai in the center, and Egmont in the distance. (Photo: S. N. Beatus, New Zealand Geological Survey.)

FIG. 9. Volcanoes of Tongariro National Park (North Island, New Zealand), under snow from the north (July, 1959). Note their striking alignment. In the foreground is the flat-topped North Crater, a part of Tongariro; on its near slopes is a small snow-free valley containing Ketetahi hot springs. Beyond is the cone of Ngauruhoe and in the distance, Ruapehu. A fault cuts across the right-hand slopes below North Crater, and another is seen on its summit. One may observe a geomorphic evolution from Ngauruhoe (extreme youth) to Tongariro (late youth) to Ruapehu (mature) in simple relative terms. (Photo: S. N. Beatus, New Zealand Geological Survey.)

(1850) called these breached cones "craters of denudation."

Finally there is the *erosion crater* or *erosion caldera* (the latter applied simply to larger examples), where a former cone has been extensively degraded. The lower, lava-clad slopes are preserved, as is the neck, and a broad ring (formerly largely represented by a cinder cone) is eroded away. A fine example is the neck (Mt. Warning) and the residual lava slopes of the Lamington Plateau, of Tertiary

FIG. 10. Exogenous and endogenous eruptions: remains of two cinder cones (exogenous), partly overwhelmed by the dome-like eruption, with a central interior pipe but without any crater depression. Outline sketch of the Grand Puy de Sarcouy (trachyte), between the Puys of La Goutte and Little Sarcouy (cinder-cones), in Auvergne, France (Scrope, 1872).

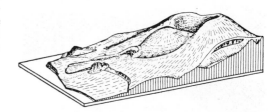

FIG. 11. Monte Rotaro on the island of Ischia, Italy, a complex composite volcanic structure. The main cone, on the right, is a strato-volcano. A large endogenous dome has grown up in a lateral explosion funnel, and later a lava stream has broken out from an eruptive cauldron at its foot. In front of the lava flow lies the small spine of Monte Tabor. The four sites of eruption lie at intervals of about 300 meters along the same fissure (Rittmann, 1962). (By permission of John Wiley & Sons, N.Y.)

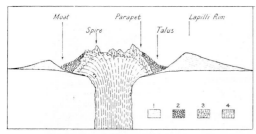

FIG. 12. Internal structure and features of an endogenous filling of a preexisting pyroclastic crater, as seen at the Mono Craters, California. Structure of a typical obsidian dome. Key: (1) ash and lapilli; (2) talus; (3) brown pumiceous obsidian; (4) black obsidian, grading downward into rhyolitic phase (Putnam, 1938).

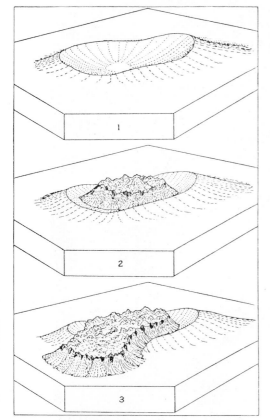

FIG. 13. Morphological development of an obsidian dome and coulee at Mono Craters, California (Putnam, 1938). The coulees represent multiple endogenous filling and breaching of the original crater. They have an extremely rugged and broken up surface because they were more or less solidified on the surface while lava continued to flow up beneath in a viscous, pasty manner.

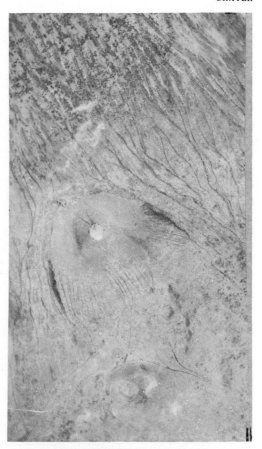

FIG. 14. Parasitic cinder cone craters on the south side of Mauna Loa (Hawaii), showing characteristic asymmetry. Width of photo: 3.5 km.

age, situated on the border between Queensland and New South Wales in eastern Australia (Fig. 27).

To sum up the volcanic craters then, in stages of increasing viscosity, we have:

(1) Long-stable *pit craters* (on Shield volcanos), like the "lava lake" or *"fire pit"* of Halemaumau on Kilauea (on the "Big Island" of Hawaii; see Jagger, 1947); the crater may be circled by successive ring faults associated with collapse of the dome into the magma chamber;

(2) Small craters associated with *spatter cones*, driblet cones, mamelons or "hornitos"; similar lava, but in a fissure volcano sequence, or in nested cones of a mature central volcano;

(3) Craters within small *cinder cones*, with or without minor lava flows. These cones may be variously associated with parasitic vents on a major shield, or strato-volcano, or along fissure systems;

(4) *Ring-wall* or *rampart craters*, cinders or scoria, free from lava; produced by low-energy pyroclastic eruptions;

(5) *Maare* (q.v.) predominantly gas-operated eruptions with pyroclastics and diatremes, leading to deep inverted cone-shaped craters, or *crater rings*, often lake-filled;

213

FIG. 15. Nested craters, the youngest in lava eruption (without steam or ash). Note the high radiation of the hot lavas, about 900–1000°C. In the old crater rim may be seen the interstratified appearance of earlier eruptions. Detailed (bottom) and general (top) oblique air photographs of the Indonesian volcano on Ternate, off Halmahera, with the older cone Tidore in the background, looking north.

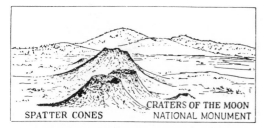

FIG. 16. Spatter cones with steep-sided inner crater walls. At Craters of the Moon National Monument, Idaho (Lobeck, 1939). (By permission of McGraw-Hill Book Co., N.Y.)

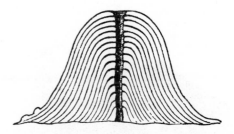

FIG. 18b. Ideal section of Mamelon Central, on the volcano of Bourbon, Réunion Island, Indian Ocean (Scrope, 1872). Height: 50 meters.

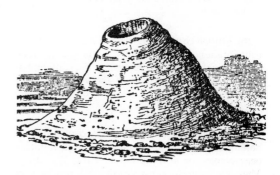

FIG. 19. Mamelon with crater, Réunion Island, Indian Ocean (Bory de St. Vincent).

FIG. 17. Small spatter cone showing small "pancake" layers of lava issuing from a very small orifice, characteristic of highly plastic lava of a fissure eruption or on the crater floor of a mature central volcano (after Dana, *Geology of American Exploring Expedition*).

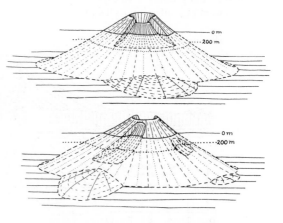

FIG. 18a. The "Mamelon Central," a boss of vitreous lava on the summit of the Volcano of Bourbon (Réunion). A mamelon or dome-like hummock or cupola of spatter cone type. It should not be confused with an endogenous dome, since it possesses a definite miniature crater (after Bory de St. Vincent).

FIG. 20. Block diagrams illustrating slides on Gunung Api (isolated oceanic volcano in the Banda Sea, Indonesia), one of which opened the crater (Kuenen, 1935). Note the 200-meter lower limit of Pleistocene sea level oscillation which favored landsliding due to removal of lateral support.

215

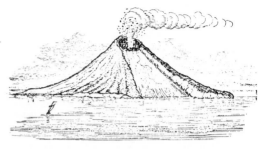

FIG. 21. Gunung Api, Banda Sea, the same island volcano as in Fig. 20. Oblique air photo showing landslide scar, breaching the crater, partially filled by further eruptions. Note stratification of the cone revealed by the landslide gash.

(6) *Erosion craters*, ring-shaped depressions, surrounding a *volcanic neck* (q.v.), much larger than the original crater, representing the differential erosion of the former ring of the volcanic cinder cone.

FIG. 22. Radial fissure with gravitational slide plane. *Top*: A classical sketch of Stromboli (Lipari Islands, Italy) from the north; *bottom*: a sketch plan of the island (Scrope, 1872).

Mud Volcano Craters

Mud volcanoes are not to be confused with boiling solfatara muds (such as seen at Solfatara near Naples, or at Yellowstone Park, Wyoming). They are entirely non-volcanic, the products of "sedimentary volcanism." They are found exclusively in the younger oil-field regions in relatively soft unconsolidated formations, where natural gases (mainly methane and related hydrocarbons) associated with water and mud under compactional tectonic stresses force their way to the surface like diatremes and produce a volcanic-like eruption of mud. The mud is often hot as it comes from depth.

It is usually associated with exothermic reactions (such as the oxidation of pyrite) and with the heat of compression, and so the gas may include a cloud of steam, which helps to give an igneous illusion.

Fine mud volcanoes are known in Trinidad, in the Caucasus, in Burma (Figs. 28 and 29) and Timor. The craters are usually shallow and scattered with secondary bubbling conelets.

Mound Spring Craters

In many artesian basins, water escapes from various springs under appropriate hydraulic head.

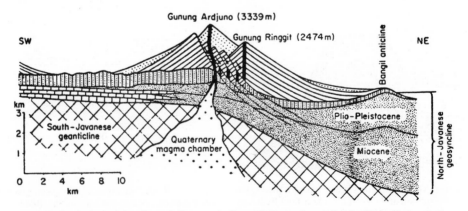

FIG. 23. Geological section through Gunung Ardjuno Welirang, Java (after R. W. van Bemmelen). Note the four "shovel faults" along which Gunung Ringgit has slid towards the north-east, causing several fractures in the vent and pushing up the Bangil Anticline. The old vent resumed its activity and built up Gunung Ardjuno.

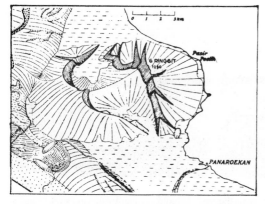

FIG. 24. Major tectonic faults and fissures splitting the old crater of Gunung Ringgit (1230 meters) in East Java (oblique sketch from Van Bemmelen). Note that this is a second and distinct volcano from the Gunung Ringgit of the same name in Fig. 23. Width of cone: 12 km.

Since the underground water has passed through a variety of formations that often contain soluble compounds such as $CaCO_3$, $CaSO_4$, FeS_2, etc., the spring waters may be rich in their ions. Certain combinations have valuable medicinal attributes, formerly much favored as "spas" (see *Medicinal Springs*, pr Vol. VI). The loss of gases, particularly

FIG. 25. Breached crater on the island Nila (6°45'S, 129°32'E, in Indonesia), oblique air view, looking northeast. Foreground is covered with erosional and landslide debris.

FIG. 26. Rows of rather recent cinder cones, with craters breached by basaltic lava streams. The Puys Noir, Solas and La Vache in the Monts Dôme (Auvergne) (Scrope, 1872).

CO_2 and SO_2, on release of pressure at the spring, suddenly lowers the solubility constants for calcite, gypsum, limonite, etc., and these tend to accumulate in a dome around the exit. In semiarid parts of western Queensland, along the western margins of the Great Artesian Basin, there are rows of these "mound springs" which, from the air, appear very much like small volcanoes. Very large discharges such as that of Ras-el-Ain at the head of the Khabour River on the Turkish–Syrian border, which has an annual flow of 1200 million cubic meters, lead to extensive travertine deposits (Burdon, 1963).

Hot-spring and Geyser Craters

Miniature cones, "mamelons" and geyser domes are commonly seen in solfatara and fumarole regions of dying volcanic activity. The waters here are hydrothermal or pneumatolytic, being largely groundwater, with some admixtures of connate and juvenile water in all probability, but owing their heating and mineralization mainly to circulation in a magmatic area. In addition to travertine mounds, silica may play an important role. Hot mud-filled craters are very common.

RHODES W. FAIRBRIDGE

References

Burdon, D. J., and Safadi, C., 1963, "Ras-el-Ain; the great karst spring of Mesopotamia. An hydrogeological study," *J. Hydrol.*, **1**(1), 58–95.

Cotton, C. A., 1944, "Volcanoes as Landscape Forms," Christchurch, New Zealand, Whitcombe and Tombs Ltd., 416pp.

Fairbridge, R. W., 1950, "Landslide patterns on oceanic volcanoes and atolls," *Geograph. J.*, **115**, 84–88.

Gansser, A., 1960, "Ueber Schlammvulkane und Salzdome," *Vierteljahrschr. Naturf. Ges. Zürich*, **105**, 1–46.

Jagger, T. A., 1947, "Origin and development of craters," *Geol. Soc. Am. Mem.*, **21**, 508pp.

Kistler, R. W., 1966, "Structure and metamorphism in the Mono Craters Quadrangle, Sierra Nevada, California," *Bull. U.S. Geol. Surv.*, **1221-E**.

Kuenen, P. H., 1935, "Contributions to the geology of the East Indies from the *Snellius* expedition," *Leidsche Geol. Mededeel.*, **7**, 273–331.

Kugler, H. G., 1933, "Contribution to the knowledge of sedimentary volcanism," *J. Inst. Petrol. Tech.*, **19**, 743–772.

FIG. 27. Mount Warning, the granodioritic plug that represents the eroded stump of a giant volcano, while its lavas, a basalt-rhyolite-basalt alternation, are seen in the Lamington Plateau and McPherson Range in the background. The low-lying country surrounding this center, drained by the Tweed River, is a giant "erosion crater" or "erosion caldera," 30 km in diameter, while the entire cone was over 100 km in diameter. It straddles the Queensland/New South Wales border, in eastern Australia. (Oblique air photos: R. W. Fairbridge.)

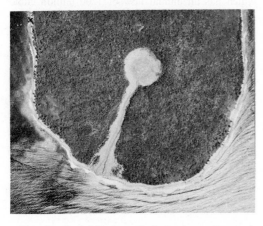

FIG. 28. Foul Island, vertical air photo of a mud-volcano island off the coast of Burma; the name comes from the natural gas seeps. Although shaped like a volcano, it is entirely non-igneous.

FIG. 29. Foul Island, oblique air photo, taken immediately after a mud eruption (1942); note large deltaic fan, which is quickly eroded away by wave action.

Lacroix, A., 1936, "Le volcan actif de l'ile de la Réunion," Paris, Gauthier-Villars, 297pp.

Lobeck, A. K., 1939, "Geomorphology," New York, McGraw-Hill Book Co., 731pp.

Lyell, C., 1850, "On craters of denudation, with observations on the structure and growth of volcanic cones." *Quart. J. Geol. Soc., London*, **6**, 207–234.

Putnam, W. C., 1938, "The Mono Craters, California," *Geograph. Rev.*, **28**, 68–82.

Rittman, A., 1962, "Volcanoes and Their Activity," New York, Interscience Publ., John Wiley & Sons, 305pp. (translated from German, Second ed., by Vincent).

Scrope, G. P., 1872, "Volcanos, the Character of Their Phenomena," London, Longmans, Green, Reader, and Dyer, Second ed., 490pp. (First ed., 1825.)

van Bemmelen, R. W., 1937, "Examples of gravitational tectogenesis from Central Java," *De Ingenieur in Ned.-Indië*, **4**, 55–65.

Williams, H., 1953, "The Ancient Volcanoes of Oregon," Condon Lect., Oregon State System of Higher Education, 55pp.

Cross-references: *Caldera*; *Crater Lakes*; *Maar*; *Suffosion and Tundra Craters*; *Volcanic Landscapes*; *Volcanic Necks and Diatremes*. Vol. II: *Astroblemes and Meteorite Craters*; *Explosion Craters*; *Moon—Lunar Geology*; *Moon—Lunar Impact Craters*; *Moon—Lunar Tectonics*. Vol. V: *Fumerole*. Vol. VI: *Hot Springs*; *Medicinal Springs*; *Sedimentary Volcanism*.

CRATER LAKES

A volcanic crater may be defined as "a vent through which volcanic ejecta has been erupted." Such a feature may become enlarged by explosion but rarely does it exceed 1 mile in diameter. If this becomes filled or partially filled with water, a crater lake is formed. A crater should be distinguished from a *caldera* (q.v.), a much larger feature which results from explosion accompanied by subsidence. Many so-called crater lakes are in fact caldera lakes.

Crater lakes occur in both active and extinct volcanoes. Some are highly acid, such as Laguna de Alegria, in the active volcano Tecapo (El Salvador), which has a pH of 2.7. Others may be alkaline, an extreme example of which is Lago Nejapa (Nicaragua), which has a pH of 9.9. This variation largely depends on the depth of penetration of meteoric water and the composition of gases and connate water which it encounters. Usually there is a near-surface condensation of superheated halogen and sulfur gases, which produces an acid sulfate-chloride lake. If, however, the superheated gases react with the wall rock en route to the surface, they may become more alkaline as well as enriched in Ca, Mg, Fe and Al.

The color of the water may also vary in crater lakes. This may be due to minor mineral deposits such as free sulfur, red or brown iron oxides, black manganese and red and yellow arsenic sulfide, which taken together with the blue of the lakes provide a variety of colors. Microorganisms and algae also play an important role. Bacteria may fix the mineral deposits in solution, and various colored algae, particularly of the blue–green group, are a common feature. Individual types may be quite sensitive to temperature and acidity, and hence closely related lakes may be of different colors. The three lakes of Tiwu Ata Mbupu, Tiwu Nua Muri Koöh Tai and Tiwu Ata Polo, in Flores, Indonesia (shown in Fig. 1) provide an excellent example of this variation. Tiwu Ata Mbupu is the normal blue color, Tiwu Nua Muri Koöh Tai contains a large amount of sulfur which gives the lake a greenish color, and Tiwu Ata Polo is red, perhaps due to the presence of red algae or ferric iron. As temperature and acidity also vary, the colors are probably enhanced by the growth of different species of algae.

At intervals, craters in active volcanoes may produce spectacular steam eruptions. A steam cloud from the lake on Mount Ruapehu, New Zealand, rose to a height of about 3000 feet on July 24, 1966, leaving a strong smell of sulfur in the air. Similar eruptions have occurred at Poás (Costa Rica), and at intervals, as in March 1953, have become so violent that the lake disappeared. Figure 2 illustrates two stages during a steam eruption from this crater during February 1953. Such periodic disturbances are probably due to an increase in temperature with

FIG. 1. Three adjacent crater lakes on Flores, Indonesia; one is blue, one green and one red (see text).

FIG. 2(a). Stages during a steam eruption of Lake Poás (Costa Rica) in February 1953; first stage.

FIG. 2(b). Lake Poás, second stage.

depth in the lakes. Convection would normally restore an even temperature, but if the bottom was above the boiling point, superheating and instability would result, causing sudden vaporization of the water column.

In such active volcanoes, conditions frequently change, and the water may be ejected from the crater by the rise of magma or by explosion from within the vent. This may be disastrous, as it was at Kelut (Keloet) volcano in Java, which became active in 1909 after 18 years of quiescence (Scrivenor, 1929). Water from the crater lake mixed with volcanic ash to form *lahars* (volcanic mudflows). These swept down radial valleys around the mountain and caused the deaths of 5500 persons. A similar eruption took place at Mount Ruapehu, New Zealand, on December 24, 1953, when water from the crater lake broke through an ash barrier, flowed down a river valley carrying large quantities of loose ash and boulders. The force of the lahar swept away a railway bridge in its path, and resulted in the derailment of an express train, killing 151 persons. Old lahars often leave hummocky hills (Fig. 3). The resultant deposits ("diamictite") can be confused with tillite.

Once a volcano becomes extinct, the crater wall frequently collapses into the vent, and a larger crater lake may be formed (Fig. 4). This is usually a stable feature, but the reason water remains in the crater, often surrounded by ash and pumice, may be obscure. However, when similar volcanoes are deeply eroded, numerous dikes and sills may be exposed, and it is probably these which act both as basins to hold in the water and as dams which determine the height of the lake.

FIG. 3. Lahar mounds north of Opunake, North Island, New Zealand. Slopes of Mount Egmont in background. (Photo: S. N. Beatus, New Zealand Geological Survey.)

FIG. 4. Mt. Bagana, Bougainville Island (Soloman Islands), a trio of craters, from the active to the degraded, the crater lake in the foreground showing deeply dissected spillways. The sharp ridge crests and V-shaped valleys are typical of the rapid weathering and erosion of tuffaceous material under heavy precipitation in this equatorial climate.

Finally brief mention must be made of *maars* (q.v.). These are lakes which fill hollows excavated by explosion. The name was coined in the Eifel region of Germany. Maars are probably formed by eruption through water-saturated sediments in regions of shallow water table, the water level being controlled by the water table of the surrounding area. An example of a volcanic maar is Lake Rotomahana, near Rotorua, New Zealand, which was formed by explosive activity during the Tarawera eruption of June 10, 1886.

The principal groups of volcanic and crater lakes in the world (Murray, 1910; Collet, 1925; and others) are:

North America

Oregon, Cascade Range, *Crater Lake*, strictly a caldera depression.

Nicaragua, *Lake Nejapa*, noted for its high alkalinity (see text).

Guatemala, *Lake of Atitlán*, a volcano-tectonic depression, and thus also not a true crater lake.

Costa Rica, *Lake Poás*, a crater lake periodically destroyed by eruptions.

El Salvador, *Laguna de Alegria* in the active volcano Tecapo (see text).

Dominica, *Grande Soufrière*, "Boiling Lake," draining intermittently into the Pointe Mulatre stream.

St. Vincent, *La Soufrière*. The lake is periodically destroyed by eruptions (as in 1902) and then reestablished.

Europe

Germany, Eifel district. *Laacher See*, a maar 2 km across. It has been artificially drained. Smaller ones include *Pulvermaar*, *Weinfelder Maar*, *Gemündener Maar*, *Ulmener Maar*.

France, Auvergne (Massif Central).
Lac Pavin, in a probable explosion crater.
Gour de Tazanat, situated in a cinder cone.

Italy, the *Lago di Bracciano* is 10 km across and situated apparently in a caldera depression.

Asia

India, Deccan plateau. *Lake Lonar*, probably a structural depression within the lava country, and may not be a true crater lake.

Japan, Kusatsu. Three lakes within the crater of Shiranesan—Azuma crater lake in same region.

Java
Gunong Kelut (Kloet, Keloet), famous as the cause of many lahars, now partly controlled by drainage.

221

Tangkuban Prahu, has twin craters each with a crater lake.

Kawah-Idjen, 2120 meters above sea level, fills an explosion crater adjacent to Merapi.

Patuha, 2396 meters above sea level, a crater lake in the cool solfatara stage.

Sumatra, Lake Toba, a very large lake within a caldera of volcano-tectonic type.

Flores, three adjacent crater lakes (noted in text: *Tiwu Ata Mbupu, Tiwu Nua Muri Koöh Tai* and *Tiwu Ata Polo*).

Africa

Tanzania, north of Lake Nyasa (Malawi). Seven crater lakes in a rift zone (Lakes *Kingrie, Ikapa, Kiunguvuvu, Itende, Itamba, Kisiwa* and *Wutiva*).

Australasia

Australia

S.A., Mount Gambier and *Blue Lakes,* C^{14} dated as only 4700 years old.

Queensland, Atherton Plateau, *Lakes Barsine* and *Eacham,* perfect crater lakes on a basalt plateau.

New Zealand, Tarawera Rift. Temporary lakes due either to damming of streams or crater filling—*Lake Rotomahana,* a maar, site of famous sinter terraces destroyed in 1886.

Ruapehu (see text).

J. W. COLE

References

Collet, L. W., 1925, "Les Lacs," Paris, Doint, 320pp.

Cotton, C. A., 1944, "Volcanoes as Landscape Forms," Christchurch, New Zealand, Whitcombe and Tombs, 416pp.

Hutchinson, G. E., 1957, "A Treatise on Limnology," Vol. 1, New York, John Wiley & Sons, 1015pp.

International Volcanological Association, *Catalogues of the active volcanoes of the world.*

Judd, J. W., 1881, "Volcanoes—What They Are and What They Teach," London, Paul & Co., 381pp.

Kerr-Cross, D., 1895, "Crater lakes north of Lake Nyassa," *Geograph. J.,* **5,** 112.

Mitford, C. E. B., 1908, "Notes on the physiography of certain volcanoes in northern Japan," *Geograph. J.,* **31,** 198.

Murray, J., 1910, "Characteristics of lakes in general, and their distribution over the surface of the globe," in *Bathymetrical Survey of the Scottish Freshwater Lochs, Edinburgh, Challenger, Office,* **1,** 514–658.

Rittmann, A., 1962, "Volcanoes and their Activity," New York, Interscience Publishers, John Wiley & Sons, 305pp. (translated by E. A. Vincent).

Sapper, K., 1927, "Vulkankunde," Stuttgart, J. Engelhorns Nachf, 423pp.

Scrivenor, J. B., 1929, "The mudstreams ('Lahars') of Gunong Keloet in Java," *Geol. Mag.,* **66,** 433–434.

Van Bemmelen, R. W., 1949, "The geology of Indonesia," The Hague, Govt. Print. Off., 2 vols.

Cross-references: *Caldera; Crater; Lakes; Lake Atitlán; Lake Toba; Maar; Mudflow; Volcanic Necks.* pr Vol. VI: *Groundwater in Volcanic Terrain; Limnology; pH-Eh Relations.*

CREEP—*See* **MASS MOVEMENT; MASS WASTING; SOIL CREEP**

CREVASSE

Glaciers, ice shelves, snow fields and sea ice are subjected to stresses which are relieved by fissures and cracks called crevasses. Crevasses normally range from a few millimeters to 20 or more meters in width, several meters to several hundred meters in length, and up to 45 meters in depth. In cross section, crevasses are V-shaped and often bridged by snow which makes them difficult to see on the surface. Crevasses are an invaluable aid to glaciologists. Crevasse walls reveal the near-surface stratigraphy and structure of a glacier. Englacial temperatures and meltwater percolation characteristics are readily studied along crevasse walls. Patterns and types of crevasses indicate the mode of flow of a glacier.

Types of Crevasses

Crevasses are generally classified by their orientation with respect to the long axis of the glacier. Several types of crevasses (Fig. 1) are:

(a) *Transverse crevasses:* Transverse crevasses are ordinarily long, initially convex upglacier, and transverse to the long axis of the glacier. They form in areas of extending flow (tensile stress).

(b) *Longitudinal crevasses:* These crevasses are generally straight and parallel to the long axis of the glacier. They develop in areas of compressive flow (compressive stress).

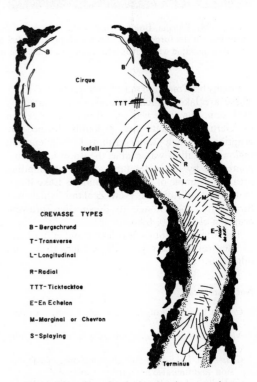

CREVASSE TYPES

B - Bergschrund

T - Transverse

L - Longitudinal

R - Radial

TTT - Ticktacktoe

E - En Echelon

M - Marginal or Chevron

S - Splaying

FIG. 1. Plan view of a glacier showing several types of crevasses.

(c) *Marginal or chevron crevasses:* Marginal crevasses develop at an angle with the valley wall. These crevasses open in areas of stress between the relatively fast-moving ice near the center of the glacier and the slow-moving ice near the valley wall. In areas of compressive flow, the crevasses generally intersect the valley wall at angles less than 45°; and in areas of extending flow, the crevasses generally intersect the valley wall at angles greater than 45° (Nye, 1952).

(d) *En echelon crevasses:* These are a type of marginal crevasse which are short, nearly equal sized and grouped in rows.

(e) *Splaying crevasses:* Splaying crevasses are parallel to the long axis of a glacier on its upglacier end and curve toward the margin on its downglacier end. They form in areas of intense compressive flow.

(f) *Radial crevasses:* Radial crevasses are generally short and appear to radiate from a common point. They are similar to splaying crevasses except that they do not curve.

(g) *Ticktacktoe crevasses:* Uncommon groupings of crevasses which form a ticktacktoe pattern are known as ticktacktoe crevasses. They probably form over a bedrock knob on the valley floor.

(h) *Bergschrund crevasses:* Bergschrunds form when snow or ice pulls away from the valley wall or head wall of a cirque. Usually some snow and ice are left adhering to the rock wall. Bergschrunds may be much deeper than 45 meters.

THEODORE F. FREERS

References

Legally, M., 1929, "Versuch einer Theorie der paltenbuldung in Gletschern," *A. Gletscherk. Glazialgeol.,* **17,** 285–301.

Lliboutry, L., 1965, "Traité de Glaciologie, Tome II, Glaciers, Variations du Climat, Sols gelés," pp. 429–1040, Paris, Masson & Cie.

Meier, M. R., 1960, "Mode of flow of Saskatchewan Glacier, Alberta, Canada," *U.S. Geol. Surv., Profess. Paper* **351,** 70pp.

Nye, J. F., 1952, "The mechanics of glacier flow," *J. Glacio.,* **2,** 82–93.

Cross-references: *Bergschrund; Cirque; Glacial Moulin, Mill or Pothole; Glacial Plucking; Glacial Valley; Moraine; Valley (Mountain) Glacier.* Vol. I: *Sea Ice.* pr Vol. VI: *Glaciology; Ice Shelf.*

CRUSTAL MOVEMENTS— CONTEMPORARY

(I) Definitions

Under contemporary movements of the earth's crust are understood the slow tectonic *warping* (q.v.), uplifts, settlings, displacements and tiltings of the crust which are taking place at the present time and which are studied directly with the help of oceanographic (tide gauge level measuring), geodetic, astronomical, geophysical and other instrumental observations. Usually a period of 50–100 years is embraced by these observations, but in certain cases they extend up to 250 or 300 years (the subsidence of the Netherlands, the uplifts of Scandinavia).

Some investigators broaden the interpretation of "contemporary movements" and include in it those movements which took place in the course of historical time or during the Holocene (the last 10–12,000 years). Their conception is based not upon direct observations, but on indirect deductions. To these indications belong: (a) changes in the landscape determined by comparison of old and new maps (advance of the shore line in the region of an uplift; transgression of the sea onto dry land in a depressed region); (b) archeological evidences (flooding of buildings, encampments of man in regions of depression; emergence of the sea floor and harbors in areas of uplift); (c) geological and geomorphological indications (raising of shore line, terraces, erosion by rivers in regions of uplift; submerged terraces, flooded peat bogs, increased accumulation of rivers in depressed regions). The movements themselves however are inferred; they cannot be observed directly.

The concept of "contemporary movements of the earth's crust" (in both the narrower and wider meanings) must be distinguished from the idea of "*neotectonics*" (q.v.) and "neotectonic movements." Contemporary movements comprise the very last stage of the neotectonic stage of the development of the earth's crust, which by convention is taken to embrace all of the Quaternary and part of the Tertiary period (thus, from the Neogene through Pleistocene; see *Neotectonics*). Synonyms for the contemporary movements of the earth's crust are "slow movements," "secular movements," and "recent tectonic movements."

(II) History of Investigations

Indications of movements of the earth's crust were detected even in antiquity. The flooding of formerly dry land by the sea and the uplift of other parts is mentioned in the works of Aristotle, Strabo, Pliny the Elder and other ancient scholars. Systematic observations about the process of the age-long flooding of dry land in the Netherlands are known since the end of the seventeenth century; the mean rate of the rise of sea level (tectonic plus eustatic factors) in the region of Amsterdam was calculated to be 1.6 mm/yr. The parallel but opposite process, the raising of Fennoscandia, has been studied since 1731, when, following a proposal by Celsius and backed by the Swedish Academy of Sciences, special marks began to be made as scales along the coast for observations of the change in relative level of the Baltic Sea. At the present time, these markings, originally made at sea level, are now raised 1.5–2 meters, which gives an average rate of emergence of about 1 cm/yr. The reason for these changes given by Celsius, and subsequently by E. Suess, was not the raising of the land, but the lowering of the sea level. Lomonosov, Leopold von Buch and Lyell developed opposing views favoring movements of the earth's crust.

After the disastrous earthquake of 1891 in Japan, accompanied by great displacements of the earth's surface, a systematic releveling of survey lines was begun with the purpose of studying these long-term movements of the earth's crust. From that time onward, geodetic methods of studying these movements have gradually received wider and wider attention, and at the present time they are the basic means for revealing secular movements.

(III) Present State of Study

At the present time, the observations of close to 200 stations (using tide gauges or "mareographs") are available. These stations furnish information about secular movements along the coastlines. The distribution of the stations, however, is very uneven.

The assistance of geodetic and geomorphologic data permits the extension of these observations to interior areas. The increase in accuracy and accumulation of leveling data of late has provided a transition from the study of contemporary movements in isolated spots to the preparation of maps of crustal movements over broad areas. Along with the compilation of such maps, geodetic evidences are often controlled and in conjunction with the results of tide gauge observations.

In the past 10–15 years, maps of vertical movements of the crust have been prepared for the western sector of the European part of the U.S.S.R., Finland, Poland and Bulgaria; as a result it is now possible to trace the character of the contemporary movements of the crust in a broad distribution from the Gulf of Bothnia to the Black Sea. The results showed that the uplifts of Fennoscandia do not fade out toward the south, as most geologists supposed, but are continued in a wide belt as far as the region of the Carpathians and the Balkans (Fig. 1). The rate of movement is established at a mean of about 2–4 mm/yr; the maximum rates of uplift are on the order of 1 cm/yr; the possible error of measurement is near ±1 mm/yr.

Maps of contemporary crustal movements in varying degrees of detail have also been drawn for the Netherlands, northern Italy, Hungary, Czechoslovakia, the British Isles and Japan. The first draft of contemporary vertical movements over the United States has also been prepared; according to the character of these movements, the United States is subdivided into two parts—eastern and western. In the eastern, platform and shield part, the rates of maximum movements are expressed at 3–5 mm/yr; in the western, orogenic part, the rates of movement increase to 10–15 mm/yr (preliminary data).

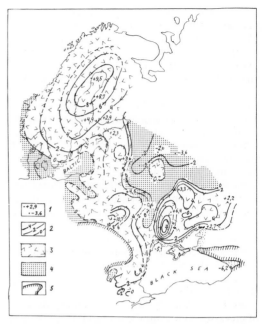

Fig. 1. Contemporary vertical crustal movements of Fennoscandia and the western part of Russian platform. (1) Rates of uplift (+) and depression (−) of the crust in millimeters per year; (2) isolines of rates of movement; (3) regions of uplift; (4) regions of subsidence; (5) contours of the Carpathian Mts. and the Caucasus.

Despite the significant progress in the past 10–15 years, the study of contemporary crustal movements, as a whole, still remains weak. "White patches" on the map remain in broad expanses in each of the continents. Thus, at present, only some more or less valid suppositions and hypotheses may be expressed.

(IV) Basic Traits of Contemporary Crustal Movements

(a) Distribution. At the present time, there is no reason to suppose that the secular movements are peculiar only to isolated, particularly mobile sections of the earth's crust. Contemporary movements appear everywhere; apparently there are no quite stable sections. Uplifts and depressions in the present epoch, as in the geological past, occur conjugately, forming "waves" whose length is greater in platform regions and less in orogenic regions (Fig. 2).

(b) Intensity. The present rates of vertical movements are expressed in terms of millimeters per year. More rarely, there is an intensity on the order of centimeters per year; in certain regions (California), the speeds of deformations of the earth's surface may increase to several tens of centimeters in a single year. A comparison of vertical movements of platform and orogenic regions shows that several phe-

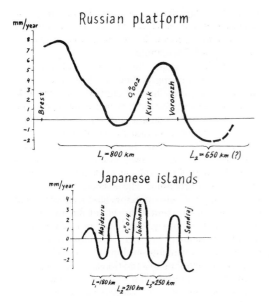

FIG. 2. Graph of rates of contemporary vertical movements for the Russian Platform and the Japanese Islands. L = wavelengths.

nomena are peculiar to the orogenic regions: high differential mode of movements, high rates of gradient change, and the presence of not only vertical but also marked horizontal shifts of the crust (California, New Zealand, Japan).

(c) **Period of Secular Variations.** The rates of secular movements established in the present epoch by geodetic observations must not be extrapolated to long periods of geologic time. For example, if one were to suppose that the uplift of the central Russian uplands continued at its present rate (about 5 mm/yr) even for the duration of the Quaternary period (say 1 million years), then in this flat region there should have been formed mountains 5000 meters high (without allowance for denudation). From this it follows that the secular movements in the course of time must change not only their intensity but also their mathematical sign (direction).

The duration of the period of secular movements evidently goes beyond the limits of the dates of geodetic and tide gauge level measuring observations and, accordingly, cannot be directly defined. Indirect data, such as archeological and geomorphological data, suggest that the period of secular variation is not less, and is probably more, than 500–700 years. It is generally known that the earth's surface experiences oscillations of short period. To these belong: "body tides" in the solid earth set up by *celestial mechanics* (see Vol. II), and variations caused by changes of atmospheric pressure and unequal heating of the earth's surface by the sun. All of these complex variations superimposed upon the secular

movements are set up by external factors. The long-term movements are caused by processes which go on inside the earth's crust and in the upper mantle of the earth. Apparently, these are variations of the shortest period among the geotectonic movements.

(d) **Glacio-isostatic Processes and Contemporary Movements.** Some investigators attach great significance to glacio-isostasy in the distribution of the contemporary uplifts and subsidences of the earth's crust. Certainly the regions of Quaternary glaciation were upwarped after the melting and the relaxation of the earth's crust from the weight of the glacial ice sheets. The extra-glacial regions, also corresponding to the same hypothesis, were either depressed during the melting or else stable. The fact that in extraglacial regions, areas of uplift are now found (e.g., central Russian uplands; also the Donets ridge) runs counter to this hypothesis. The rate of movement in these uplifts is no less than that of the uplift in the glacial regions (Fennoscandia). Special investigations showed that in the first 6000 years or so after melting, the glaciated regions underwent extraordinarily intensive uplifts which undoubtedly had a glacio-isostatic nature. But in the second half of the Holocene (the last 5000 years), the rates of uplift of the formerly glaciated regions have become progressively less. Toward the present epoch, any differences between crustal movements in glaciated and extraglacial regions has been almost completely wiped out. Obviously, the glacio-isostatic factor was very powerful in the glaciated regions, but it was comparatively short-lived. In the contemporary epoch, it has now exhausted itself and has given place to the more stable, although not as intensive, geotectonic processes. The latter now determine the character of crustal movements for both extraglacial and glaciated regions.

(e) **Relationship of Contemporary Movements to Geological Structure and Deep-seated Processes.** The basic proof of the geotectonic nature of contemporary vertical movements of the earth's crust is their congruity with the geologic structures. A comparison of the results of releveling with geotectonic data shows that the distribution of uplifts and subsidences of the earth's surface is inherited from similar structures which raised or depressed crustal masses of varying orders of magnitude and age. For the western half of the Russian platform, an analysis of a statistically valid spread of material showed that there is a direct correspondence between geological structure and contemporary movements in 70% of the area. Some 78% of the areas of anticlinal structures are also involved in contemporary uplifts. Depressions are less satisfactory in relation to contemporary structure: only 57% of the synclinal areas correspond to the present-day depressions. The coefficients of correlation between contemporary movements and geological structure calculated for several areas do not exceed 0.8–0.9. Obviously, since we acknowledge the fluctuating character of the movements, we would not expect a greater correspondence.

The complex correlations of the contemporary movements with the ancient structure may point to areas of revival of tectogenetic processes and are of great interest for our ideas about the causes for crustal movements. In the limits of the Pacific cordillera of the western U.S.A., the maximum present uplift is located not toward the main mountain ranges (Rocky Mts., Coast Ranges), but within the intramontane belt in the Great Basin (Basin and Range region). According to the geophysical data, this specific region stands out because of its peculiar deep-seated structure. Here a thick layer of the lithosphere behaves like a mixture of crust and mantle material. Apparently it corresponds to a zone of extension (dilation) of deep material (Fig. 3). In agreement with this idea is the increased intensity of heat flow, established by geothermic observations in the western parts of the United States. In this way, a comparison of geodetic data on the present crustal movements with varied structural and geophysical data points to the geotectonic nature of the contemporary movements and gives us a key to an understanding of the reasons for tectogenesis.

(f) **Horizontal Movements.** We know less about horizontal movements of the earth's crust than about the vertical movements. In order to test questions about continental drift originally posed by A. Wegener about 50 years ago, a series of major observatories around the world began precise determinations of longitudes according to an agreed program. In 1933, the determinations were repeated. However, some gaps in the observations and a comparatively low level of accuracy did not permit a definite decision to be made as to whether or not "floating continents" really exist. Most recent attempts at discovering horizontal movements of the continents have not given consistent results. If movements of major portions of the earth's crust

are really taking place at the present time, then their velocities should be within the limits of accuracy of the astronomic-geodetic determinations of coordinates of widely distributed points.

On a global scale, the question still awaits a solution, but for separate regions, horizontal deformations of the crust have already been defined with sufficient accuracy. Reliable data have been obtained as the result of systematic and repeated triangulations in California, Nevada and Utah. Observations over a period of years in the region of the San Andreas Fault have shown that crustal blocks on opposite sides of the faults have a tendency to move in opposite directions. The average rate is about 1 cm/yr. Japanese investigators have prepared a map of vectors of horizontal movement for the greater part of their country. The rates are expressed in several centimeters per year. A comparison of the horizontal movements in Japan with the vertical deformations points to a relationship between them. From this it follows that any subdivision of the crustal movements into vertical and horizontal is artificial to some extent. Actually, vertical and horizontal movements represent separate components of complex spatial deformations of blocks of the earth's crust. Accordingly, one must conclude that the rates of contemporary horizontal movements, like the rates of vertical movements, must not be extrapolated into geologically protracted periods of time. Just like the vertical movements, the horizontal component must change not only its intensity in the course of time but possibly also its sign (i.e., direction).

(V) The International Research Project on Recent Crustal Movements

The process of present-day movements of the earth's crust, common to the whole planet, may be understood satisfactorily only by the joint efforts of scholars of various countries. A significant place is assigned to the study of contemporary movements in the Upper Mantle Project, adopted by the International Union of Geodesy and Geophysics. At its thirteenth General Assembly (1963, Berkeley, California), a research project "Recent Crustal Movements" was also adopted, prepared by a special commission of the International Geodetic Association (under the chairmanship of the writer).

The first task of the project is a world map of the earth's crustal movements; to begin with, there is planned the preparation of summary maps of contemporary vertical movements of the earth's crust for the continents of Europe and North America.

The second task of the project envisages the establishment of a series of test areas (polygons) on each continent for the systematic observation of the long-term crustal movements and to feel the "pulse of the earth" (to use Umbgrove's term), with the help of geodetic, geophysical, geomorphological and other methods. It is recommended that the test

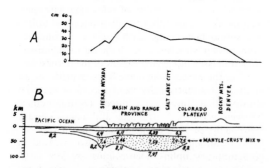

FIG. 3. The relation of contemporary movements to the deep structure of the North American Cordillera. (A) Amplitude of vertical movements in centimeters in the period 1929–63 (according to the data of J. B. Small). (B) Section of the earth's crust (according to the data of K. L. Cook).

areas be placed over active local structures and zones of deep-seated faults which lead into the upper mantle.

The third task of the project is to be devoted to the study of continental drift and envisages an organization of international astronomical observations with the purpose of revealing the long-term changes in position of continents.

The realization of this project will give us valuable data necessary for working out general theories of the structure and development of the planet earth. Also, it will bring us closer to the solution of the problems concerning prognosis of secular deformations of the earth's crust and, most importantly, the prognosis of earthquakes. It will give us data on the general mobility of the earth's crust, important for the construction of geodetic networks and for the planning of major permanent engineering installations (dams, barrages, dikes, canals, electric power stations, harbors, and so on).

YURI A. MESCHERIKOV

References

Cook, K. L., 1962, "The problem of the mantle-crust mix: Lateral inhomogeneity in the uppermost part of the earth's mantle," *Adv. Geophysics*, **9**, 295–360.

Fairbridge, R. W., and Newman, W. S., 1965, "Sea level and the Holocene boundary in the eastern United States," *Rept. VIth Intern. Congr. Quaternary, Warsaw, 1961*, **1**, 397–418.

Gerasimov, I. P., 1962, "The study of recent tectonic movements of the earth's crust in the territory of the U.S.S.R.," *1st International Symposium on Recent Crustal Movements Leipzig, GDR, Berlin, Akad, Verl.*, 324–330.

Gutenberg, B., 1941, "Changes in sea level, postglacial uplift and mobility of the earth's interior," *Bull. Geol. Soc. Am.*, **52**(5), 721–772.

Homorodi, L., 1962, "Untersuchungen der rezenten Erdkrustenbewegungen in Ungarn," *1st International Symposium on Recent Crustal Movements Leipzig, GDR, Berlin, Akad, Verl.*, 92–100.

Kääriäinen, E., 1953, "On the recent uplift of the earth's crust in Finland," *Fennia*, 77(2).

Mescherikov, Y. A., 1959, "Contemporary movements in the earth's crust," *Intern. Geol. Rev.*, **1**(8), 40–52.

Mescherikov, Y. A., 1962, "Secular crustal movements: some results and tasks of researches," *1st International Symposium on Recent Crustal Movements Leipzig, GDR, Berlin, Akad, Verl.*, 304–313.

Mortensen, H., 1959, "Russische Geomorphologische Konferenz, 1958," *Z. Geomorphol.*, **3**, 248–252.

Pécsi, M., 1962, "Ausmass der holozänen Krustenbewegungen in Ungarn," *1st International Symposium on Recent Crustal Movements Leipzig, GDR, Berlin, Akad, Verl.*, 388–395.

"Proceedings of the Second International Symposium on Recent Crustal Movements, Aulanko, Finland, 1965," 1966, *Ann. Acad. Sci. Fennicae*, Helsinki, Ser. A, **3**, Geol.-Geogr., 90.

Small, J. B., 1963, "Interim report on vertical crustal movement in the United States," (Int. Union of Geodesy and Geophysics, Int. Assoc. Geodesy, General Assembly, Berkeley, Calif.)

Sokolovsky, I. L., 1962, "On the inheritance of the contemporary movements of the earth's crust on the territory of the Ukrainian SSR from older movements," *1st International Symposium on Recent Crustal Movements Leipzig, GDR, Berlin, Akad. Verl.*, 362–365.

Wegmann, E., 1955, "Lebendige Tektonik, eine Ubersicht," *Geol. Rundschau*, **43**(1), 4–34.

Whitten, C. A., and Claire, C. N., 1960, "Analysis of geodetic measurements along the San Andreas Fault," *Bull. Seismol. Soc. Am.*, **50**(3).

Cross-references: *Holocene; Morphogenetic Regions; Neotectonics; Postglacial Isostatic Rebound; Quaternary Period; Warping.* Vol. II: *Atmospheric Pressure; Celestial Mechanics; Solar Radiation.*

CRYOLOGY, CRYOSPHERE, CRYERGY

The term *cryology* was proposed by the Polish geologist A. B. Dobrowolski (1923) from the Greek *kryos* (cold), for the scientific study of ice and snow. In industrial engineering it may include the study of *refrigeration.* In geological circles it is rather customary to embrace ice and snow within the broader field of glaciology (Shumskii, 1964; Seligman, 1947). *Cryogenics* is the science of *extreme* cold.

The term *cryosphere* was also proposed by Dobrowolski (1923) for the cold envelope that encircles the earth, in part in contact with the lithosphere (in polar regions), but largely at various elevations in the atmosphere, ice crystals being commonly present in the troposphere from 8–17 km above sea level. The cryosphere averages 10 km in thickness. It is not taken as extending into the stratosphere because of the low moisture content of the latter. In some regions of permafrost, the cryosphere penetrates the lithosphere as deep as 600 meters.

Related terms in geology are *cryopedology, cryoplanation* and *cryoturbation* (of Kirk Bryan, 1946). The *cryostatic hypothesis* (of A. L. Washburn, 1947; see also 1956) involves a type of diapirism, i.e. the upward squeezing of soil and soft sediments between dynamic zones of permafrost development. Another *kryos*-based term is *cryergy*, proposed by Y. Guillien (1949) for a combination of congelifraction, solifluction and cryoturbation; it is rather similar to cryoplanation, but associated more with temperate latitude highlands, for rainwash is added to it. Guillien (1952) also uses *cryonival*, when snow is involved.

RHODES W. FAIRBRIDGE

References

Bryan, K., 1946, "Cryopedology," *Am. J. Sci.*, **244**, 622–642.

Dobrowolski, A. B., 1923, "Historja Naturalna Lodu," Warsaw, 940pp.

Dobrowolski, A. B., 1931, "La Glace au point de vue petrographique," *Bull. Soc. Franc. Mineral. Crist.,* **54,** 5–19.

Guillien, Y., 1949, "Gel et dégel du sol: les méchanismes morphologiques," Paris, *L'Information Géographique,* **13,** 104–116.

Guillien, Y., 1952, "Presentation d'une carte des actions cryonivales et des actions éoliennes en France pendant le temps quaternaires," *Bull. Assoc. Geographe Franc.,* **229/230,** 192–197.

Guillien, Y., Marcelin, P., and Rondeau, A., 1951, "Le modelé cryonival autour de Nimes det d'Avignon," Paris, *Compt. Rend.,* **253,** 1131–1132.

Seligman, G., 1947, "Extrusion flow in glaciers," *J. Glaciol.,* **1,** 12–21.

Shumskii, P. A., 1964, "Principles of Structural Glaciology," New York, Dover, 497pp.

Washburn, A. L., 1956, "Classification of patterned ground," *Bull. Geol. Soc. Am.,* **67,** 622–637.

Cross-references: *Cryopedology, Cryoturbation,* etc.; *Frost Action; Permafrost.* Vol. II: *Troposphere.* pr Vol. VI: *Glaciology.*

CRYOPEDOLOGY, CRYOTURBATION, CRYONIVATION AND CRYOPLANATION

Terms based on the Greek prefix *kryos* (meaning cold or icy) have been introduced in considerable variety to cover various aspects of the glacial and periglacial landscape. *Cryology* (q.v.) of Dobrowolski is the study of ice and snow. *Cryergy* (adjective cryergic, cryergetic) of Guillien (1949) is the general action of ice and freezing phenomena (solifluction, cryoturbation, etc.).

Cryopedology (the study of cold or frozen soils) was proposed by Kirk Bryan (1946, p. 639) as "the science of intensive frost action and permanently frozen ground, including studies of the processes and their occurrence and also the engineering devices which may be invented to avoid or overcome difficulties introduced by them." Many of these studies are undertaken under the heading of *permafrost* (q.v.; Muller, 1947) which has achieved widespread international use in spite of Bryan's opposition (the offending term is a mixture of Latin *permanere* and Anglo-Saxon *frost*); an alternative term *tjaele* (Scandinavian) is sometimes used.

The basic phenomenon involved is the property of ice crystal growth—of growing upward in miniature columns, so-called *needle ice* or *pipkrake* (Swedish) or *Kammeis* (German). The term pipkrake has become quite widely employed in the international literature. Its effect in the soil is to raise little towers or pyramids, crowned by chips of rock, sticks, leaves, etc., usually a matter of 2–10 cm high.

When interstitial (pore) water freezes in the soil, there is little immediate expansion, but since groundwater is liable to continue rising by capillarity from unfrozen levels, it will build up horizons or lenses of "*ground ice.*" As a result of the greater volume of ice with respect to water and the force of crystallization, "*frost heaving*" structures will result (Taber, 1929, 1930). The equivalent terms in Germany, where pioneering studies were made, are *Structurboden* (Beskow, 1930) or *Frostboden.* Since the groundwater supply is irregular, the heaving and thrusting will be both vertical and lateral. Alternate freeze and thaw (diurnal or seasonal) greatly amplify the disturbances. The resultant structures are contorted folds and thrusts known under the general term of *solifluction* (Andersson, 1906). With use, the term has been somewhat broadened (Sharpe, 1938). The adjective form "solifual" is sometimes used (Paterson, 1941).

The term *cryoturbation* has long been used (e.g., Edelman *et al.,* 1936); likewise the synonymous term *congeliturbation* (Latin, *congelare,* to freeze together, plus *turbare,* to stir up), proposed by Bryan (1946) is also used for these frost heaving and related movements. An abbreviated form, *geliturbation,* has gained some popularity. The terms generally used in Europe for the affected soil (*periglacial regolith*) include "*head*" (q.v.) in England and France, and *Erdfliessen* in Germany; in the latter country, *Brodelerde* and *Brodelboden* are used for the extremely contorted layers. Many local terms are used for periglacial regolith in the older literature, e.g., "coombe rock," "clay with flints," "angular drift," "erratic warp," "trail," (in England), and in Europe, the old term "diluvium" is still used sometimes as a comprehensive label for all nonmarine Pleistocene sediments.

Congelifraction (Latin, *congelare,* to freeze, and *fractare,* to break) is used by Bryan for *frost riving* (q.v.), or *cryoclastic processes* (of Baulig), which is dealt with separately in this Encyclopedia, but its products, the "spalling" or fractured rubble, collectively referred to as "congelifracts" by Bryan, are commonly mixed in with the cryoturbation material and regolith generally, so that the two are commonly in close association.

Structures

The contemporary cryopedologic "*soil structures,*" i.e., those produced by cryoturbation, are provided with a legion of names in the various languages. Sharp (1942b) provides a list of some 63 such terms, which basically break down to *stone nets* (*soil polygons*), *stone rings, stone stripes, earth hummocks and terraces* (see below), often treated collectively under the heading *patterned ground* (q.v.).

In contrast to the contemporary structures, seen usually in plan view, the Pleistocene structures resulting from the same cryoturbation processes, but now no longer active, are more often seen in three dimensions or simply in profile. Outcrops are commonly exposed in sand and gravel pits, brick and tile clay pits, road cuts and so on; since they are usually unconsolidated, "classic" exposures often last only a season or two, and it is in actively worked pits that the best examples are found. The characteristic *drag folds, convolutions, involutions, plications, Brodelboden* (German), *frost wedges*, etc., are widely recognized, although the precise mechanisms, a sort of convective rotation or stirring, are not yet universally agreed upon. The interesting experiments of Gripp and Simon (1933, *et seq.*) have been questioned (Sharp 1942a). There is increasing suspicion that many of these features are simply variations of *load casts* and small-scale diapiric structures (Fig. 1), familiar to all sedimentologists and not necessarily related to cryopedology or freeze-and-thaw processes as such (Butrym *et al.,* 1964).

Slope Features

The up-and-down movement of freeze and thaw, from the small scale of pipkrake to general cryotur-

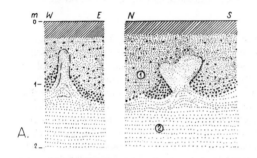

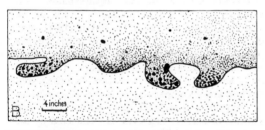

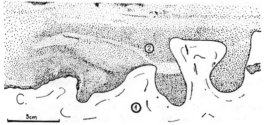

FIG. 1. Diapiric sedimentary structures from three distinct sources (from Butrym *et al.*, 1964). (A) Typical Pleistocene periglacial involutions (or "Brodelboden") from Dobigniewo, Poland (Mojski): (1) coarse sand; (2) medium sand. (B) Typical load-cast deformation, from Tertiary marine turbidites, Ventura Basin, California (Natland and Kuenen). (C) Synthetic load casts produced experimentally in the laboratory: (1) clay; (2) sand (Dzulinski and Walton). Similar experiments by the writer and his students confirm this close analogy.

bation, on a slope will result in *soil creep* (q.v.) which, if sufficiently mobilized in the thaw period, will lead eventually to flowage as *mudslides* (see *Mass Movement*) or *rock streams* (q.v.). Salomon-Calvi (1929) would restrict "solifluction" to such flow over permafrost, but the term is very widely used today; indeed, not merely the process but even the disturbed soil itself is often called "solifluction," in a way analogous to the manner in which a till (or boulder clay) that forms a moraine (a physiographic land form) is simply called "moraine" (i.e., a lithologic label). Such looseness in terminology can hardly contribute to logical thinking. The term *gelifluction* of Baulig is now often used for the type of solifluction involving appreciable displacement by flowage on slopes. The spellings "gelifluxion" and "solifluxion" favored by Baulig (1957) are not generally adopted.

Transported solifluction or gelifluction material at the foot of slopes is often mixed with saprolite and perhaps modern soils. In western Europe, the embracing term *"head"* (q.v.) is most often employed. An even broader term for slope material that does not imply genesis (and is therefore widely used by the U.S. Geological Survey as well as in most European countries) is *colluvium* (q.v.). The mixing of colluvial deposits as one moves down the slope with progressively more and more varied debris (reflecting the underlying bedrock) is equally well seen in solifluction slope material or head (Fig. 2). In nonglacial regions, the mobilizing medium is water; in periglacial areas, it is the alternating play of ice and water; in both, the overall force is gravity.

Cryonivation

Terracing phenomena are intermediate in these slope processes, and *nivation* (q.v.; snow patch erosion) represents a step toward *cirque* glaciation (q.v.). The role of snow has been especially brought out by Guillien (1949, 1951) who proposed the term *cryonivation* (adjective cryonival) for the combined effects of ice and snow. Indeed Guillien recommends *cryonivation* as a general term for all the phenomena embraced in the broad adjectival expression *periglacial* (introduced by Lozinski, 1909) which is used for (1) the former Pleistocene area involved, (2) the former climatic character of that area, and (3) the phenomena characteristic of such regions (past or present). Guillien (1951) discussed the terms periglacial and cryopedology, and each seems to have a useful place.

Soil Layers

In contemporary frozen ground, both the phenomenon and the frozen material (ice and soil) are commonly referred to as "permafrost." The material itself is called *tjaele* or *merzlota* (in Russia) or *pergelisol* (Bryan, 1946). Massive ice lenses are known as *ground ice*. Bryan also suggested several related terms such as *pergelation* and *depergelation* (the freezing and thawing processes). The actual

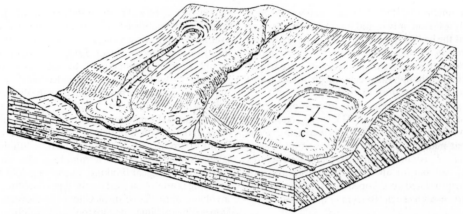

FIG. 2. Block diagram (prepared by Zarubá and Kettner) illustrating typical gravitational displacements of solifluction material, associated also with hill creep of saprolite. Note the mixing in the valley of colluvium with alluvium. (a) Simple alluvial cone from a gully in the deeply weathered saprolitic material; (b) mudstream, initiated at a landslip area and forming a mudflow cone; (c) gravitational slump along a broad slope. (From: Kettner, R., 1960, "Allgemeine Geologie," Vol. 4, Berlin, D.V.W., fig. 137.)

zone of freeze and thaw (annual in high latitudes; diurnal in milder regions) is what Muller (1947) calls the "active layer" and Bryan, the *mollisol*. Lenses of unfrozen ground within the permafrost layer (usually unfrozen because they were impervious and contained no groundwater) are known as *talik* (a Siberian word), and Bryan called them *tabetisol* (Fig. 3).

Cryoplanation

The widespread processes of cryopedologic origin

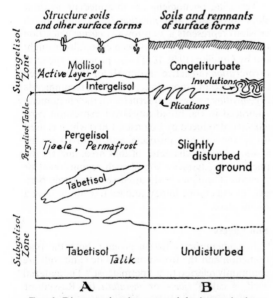

FIG. 3. Diagram showing cryopedologic terminology proposed by Bryan (1946): (A) characteristic parts of the ground in areas of permanently frozen ground; (B) characteristic parts of the ground in periglacial areas.

over the landscape eventually lead to a degrading of the relief. Indeed the gentle, rounded landscapes of southern England, France and parts of the eastern United States, which used to be regarded as typical of temperate humid erosion (the "normal cycle" of W. M. Davis), are now recognized as largely inherited from the Pleistocene times of *periglacial landscapes* (q.v.). Bryan (1946) speaks of the "cycle of cryoplanation." The idea of such degradation is not new, and the term "equiplanation" was proposed for it in Alaska by Cairnes (1912a and b), and *"altiplanation"* (q.v.) by Eakin (1916), and de Terra (1940) pointed out its role in the Tibetan plateau. Bryan (1946, p. 640) defined cryoplanation as "land reduction by the processes of intensive frost action, i.e., congeliturbation including solifluction and accompanying processes of translation of congelifracts, includes the work of rivers and streams in transporting materials delivered by the above processes." The role of vegetation in cryoplanation was brought out by Raup (1951).

RHODES W. FAIRBRIDGE

References

Andersson, J. G., 1906, "Solifluction, a component of subaerial denudation," *J. Geol.*, **14**, 91–112.

Baulig, H., 1957, "Peneplains and pediplains," *Bull. Geol. Soc. Am.*, **68**, 913–930 (translated by C. A. Cotton).

Beskow, G., 1930, "Erdfliessen und Structurböden der Hochgebirge im Licht der Frosthebung," *Geol. Foren. Stockholm Forh.*, **52**, 622–637.

Bryan, K., 1946, "Cryopedology, the study of frozen ground and intensive frost action with suggestions on nomenclature," *Am. J. Sci.*, **244**, 622–642.

Bryan, K., 1949, "The geologic implications of cryopedology," *J. Geol.*, **57**, 101–104.

Butrym, J., Cegla, J., Dzulynski, S., and Nakonieczny, S.,

1964, "New interpretation of periglacial structures," *Akad. Nauk (Krakow), Folia Quaternaria*, 34pp.

Cailleux, A., 1948, "Étude de cryopédologie," *Expéd. polaires franç., Miss. Paul E. Victor*, Paris, C.D.U., 8pp.

Cairnes, D. D., 1912a, "Differential erosion and equiplanation in portions of Yukon and Alaska," *Bull. Geol. Soc. Am.*, **23**, 333–348.

Cairnes, D. D., 1912b, "Some suggested new physiographic terms (equiplanation, deplanation and aplanation)," *Am. J. Sci., Ser. 4*, **34**, 75–87.

De Terra, H., 1940, "Some critical remarks concerning W. Penck's theory of piedmont benchlands in mobile mountain belts," Symposium, Walter Penck's Contrib. to Geomorph., ed. von Engeln, *Ann. Assoc. Am. Geogr.*, **30**, 241–246.

Eakin (Iakim), H. M., 1916, "The Yukon–Koyukuk region, Alaska," *Bull. U.S. Geol. Surv.*, **631**, 67–82.

Edelman, C. H., Florschutz, F., and Jeswiet, J., 1936, "Über spätpleistozäne und frühholozäne kryoturbate Ablagerungen in den östl. Niederlanden," *Verhandel. Geol. Mijbouwk. Ned. Kolonien, Geol. Ser.*, XI, **4**, 301–336.

Gripp, K., and Simon, W. G., 1933, "Experimente zum Brodelbodenproblem," *Centralbl. f. Min.*, Abt. B, 433–440.

Gripp, K., and Simon, W. G., 1934, "Nochmals zum Problem des Brodelbodens," *Centralbl. f. Min.*, Abt. B, 283–286.

Guillien, Y., 1949, "Gel et dégel du sol: les méchanismes morphologiques," *L'Information Géographique (Paris)*, **13**, 104–116.

Guillen, Y., 1951, "Cyropédologie? périglaciaire?," *Ann. Géogr.*, **60**, 52–54.

Guillien, Y., Marcelin, P., and Rondeau, A., 1951, "Le modelé cryonival autour de Nimes et d'Avignon," *Compt. Rend. Acad. Sci. (Paris)*, **253**, 1131–1132.

Hamelin, L. E., and Clibbon, P., 1962, "Vocabulaire périglaciaire bilingue (français et anglais)," *Cahiers de Géographie de Quebec*, No. 12, 201–226.

Hamelin, L. E., and Cook, F. A., 1965, "Illustrated Glossary of Periglacial phenomena. Le périglaciaire par l'image," Geographical Branch-Direction de la Géographie, Ministère des Mines, Ottawa.

Lozinski, W., 1909, "Ueber die mechanische Verwitterung der Sandstein im gemässigten Klima," *Acad. Sci. de Cracovie (Cl. des. Sci., Math. et Nat.) Bull.*, 1–25.

Muller, S. W., 1947, "Permafrost or Permanently Frozen Ground and Related Engineering Problems," Ann Arbor, Edwards Bros. 231pp. (*Strateg. Eng. Study 62*, U.S. Army, 1945).

Paterson, T. T., 1941, "On a world correlation of the Pleistocene," *Trans. Roy. Soc. Edinburgh*, **60**, Pt. 2, 373–435.

Raup, H. M., 1951, "Vegetation and cryoplanation," *Ohio J. Sci.*, **51**, 105–116.

Salomon-Calvi, W., 1929, "Arktische Bodenformen in der Alpen," *Heidelberger Akad. der Wiss. (Math-natur. Kl.)*, 1–31.

Sharp, R. P., 1942a, "Periglacial involutions in northeastern Illinois," *J. Geol.*, **50**, 113–133.

Sharp, R. P., 1942b, "Soil structures in the St. Elias Range, Yukon Territory," *J. Geomorphol.*, **5**, 274–301.

Sharpe, C. F. S., 1938, "Landslides and related phenomena, a study of mass-movements of soil and rock," New York, Columbia University Press, 137pp.

Taber, S., 1929, "Frost heaving," *J. Geol.*, **37**, 428–461.

Taber, S., 1930, "The mechanics of frost heaving," *J. Geol.*, **38**, 303–317.

Cross-references: *Altiplanation; Cirque; Colluvium; Cryology, etc.; Frost Action; Frost Heaving; Frost Riving; Head; Mass Movement; Mass Wasting; Moraine; Nivation; Patterned Ground; Periglacial Landscapes; Permafrost; Regolith and Saprolite; Rock Stream; Slopes; Soil Creep; Solifluction.* Vol. VI: *Pedology.*

CRYPTODEPRESSIONS

A cryptodepression is part of the earth's crust that lies below mean sea level, the floor of which is hidden (hence, the Greek prefix *crypto-*) below the waters of a lake. Since the depths of such water bodies are not obtained by ordinary land survey methods and can only be obtained by soundings from a boat, there are numbers of such depressions with only imperfect data, although most lakes are moderately well known. (*Note*: each of the world's major lakes is treated in detail in separate articles in this volume; see also pr Vol. VI: *Hydrology* and *Limnology*). The presence of deep cryptodepressions of great antiquity in the continental crust is an answer to those geologists and geophysicists who claim that the crust has little strength and will everywhere flow ("like wax"). These narrow depressions, forming clefts 2–3 km deep, have clearly remained gaping open for many millions of years. At the temperatures prevailing in the crystalline rocks of the upper crust flowage is rarely possible. It is primarily in the soft superficial sediments of geosynclines that major flowage occurs. Certain very shallow lakes covering cryptodepressions in the continental interiors like Lake Eyre (South Australia) and the northern Caspian Sea are relatively stable autogeosynclinal depressions.

The causes of such depressions in the continental crust are structural, i.e., they are tectonic depressions, due to block faulting, grabens or general downwarping. Lake Baikal with its floor at −1279 meters not only is the world's deepest continental depression, but also has the greatest volume of any freshwater lake, comparable indeed in volume with that of all the Great Lakes of the United States and Canada put together. It is a graben depression which is believed to go back to the Cretaceous in age—one might say about 100 million years old. The Dead Sea depression is also a graben, the downwarping of which is equally old, but the actual fracturing and lake formation is younger, perhaps 20 million years old. In contrast, the Caspian Sea has a vastly greater area and is actually a landlocked arm of the sea, a geosynclinal depression of Mesozoic age, well over 100 million years old, that became cut off from the ocean in the Quaternary period; it is still an active but slowly subsiding

TABLE 1. MAJOR CRYPTODEPRESSIONS OF THE WORLD (DATA MOSTLY FROM MURRAY, 1910; HUTCHINSON, 1957, AND AVAILABLE MAPS)

	Floor (m)	Depth (m)	Surface (m)
(a) Tectonic Depressions (grabens, downwarps)			
Lake Baikal (U.S.S.R.)	−1279	1741	+462
Caspian Sea (U.S.S.R./Iran)	−972	945	−27
Dead Sea (Jordan/Israel)	−793	394	−399
Sea of Galilee (Lake Tiberius, Israel/Syria)	−260	50	−210
Lake Matano (Celebes or Sulawesi, Indonesia)	−208	457	+249
Lake Asale or Assal, swamp			
(Danakil Depression, Ethiopia)	−119	ca. 3	−116
Lake Enriquillo (Dominican Rep.)	−48	ca. 2	−46
Lake Eyre (South Australia)	−13	1	−12
(b) Glacial Scours			
Great Slave Lake (Canada)	−464	614	+150
Hornindalsvatn (Norway)	−461	514	+53
Salsvatn (near Fosnes, Norway)	−432	448	+16
Lake Mjøsa (Mjösen; Norway)	−325	720	+395
Lake Fagnano, Tierra del Fuego			
(Chile/Argentina)	−309	449	+140
Loch Morar (Scotland)	−310	310	Sea level
Lake Garda (Italy)	−281	342	+61
Lake Manapouri (New Zealand)	−262	444	+182
Lake Como (Italy)	−212	411	+199
Lake Maggiore (Italy)	−176	371	+195
Lake Ontario (U.S./Canada)	−151	226	+75
Lake Chelan (Washington, U.S.)	−129	419	+290
Lake Superior (U.S./Canada)	−124	315	+191
Lake Elena (Chile)	−122	124	ca. 2
Lake Michigan (U.S.)	−88	265	+177
Lake Iseo (Italy)	−65	251	+186
Lake Seneca (New York, U.S.)	−54	190	+136
Lake Huron (U.S./Canada)	−46	223	+177
Lake Cayuga (New York, U.S.)	−17	137	+120
(c) Volcanic, crater lakes (incl. maare, calderas)			
Lake Tazawa (ko) (Japan)	−175	427	+252
Lake Apoyo (Nicaragua)	−110	ca. 200	+90
Lake Toya (ko) (Japan)	−96	96	Sea level
Lake Nicaragua (Nicaragua)	−13	46	+33
(d) Karst (ponors, sink-holes)			
Lake Scutari (or Skader, Yugoslavia/Albania)	−38	44	+6
(e) Deflation Hollows			
Lake (Birket) Qarun (El Faiyum, Egypt)	−48	3	−45
Qattara Depression, swamp (Egypt)	−133	ca. 1	−132
Wadi el Natrun, with 9 salt lakes (Egypt)	−80	ca. 1	−79

Note: The surface levels of most closed lakes are subject to marked variations; those with outlets are fairly constant.

geosyncline, partly block-faulted in the south, in the foredeep of the Elburz Mountains of Iran.

By far the greatest number of lakes in the world, and this holds for cryptodepressions too, are *glacial scour depressions*, due to deep excavation by tongues of ice. Some of these are due to continental ice sheets, others to mountain ice caps and valley glaciers. In cases where a continental ice sheet has withdrawn into mountainous areas such as Scandinavia and Scotland, it is not immediately clear if the major scour was due to the continental ice or to valley glaciation either in the early or late stages of the glacial epoch. Similar deep-scoured depressions (of the order of −1000 meters) were gouged out by the Permo-Carboniferous ice (in Western Australia and South Australia).

Other cryptodepressions are rather special types (what Davis and Cotton call geomorphologic "accidents"): *volcanic depressions* (*crater lakes*, q.v.; *maar*, q.v.; *calderas*, q.v.); *karst depressions* (q.v.; *ponors*, *sinkholes*, q.v.); and *deflation hollows* (wind-scoured depressions).

RHODES W. FAIRBRIDGE

References

Ball, J., 1939, "Contributions to the Geography of Egypt," Cairo, Survey and Mines Dept., 308pp.

Collet, L. W., 1925, "Les Lacs," Paris, Doin, 320pp.

Davis, W. M., 1882, "On the classification of lake basins," *Proc. Boston Soc. Nat. Hist.*, **21**, 315–381.

Gresswell, R. K., and Huxley, A., (editors), 1965, "Standard Encyclopedia of the World's Rivers and Lakes," New York, Putnam's, 384pp.

Guilcher, A., 1965, "Précis d'Hydrologie Marine et Continentale," Paris, Masson & Cie, 389pp.

Hutchinson, G. E., 1957, "A Treatise on Limnology," Vol. 1, New York, John Wiley & Sons, 1015pp.

Murray, J., 1910, "Characteristics of lakes in general, and their distribution over the surface of the globe," *Bathymetrical Survey of the Scottish Freshwater Lochs, Edinburgh, Challenger Office*, **1**, 514–658.

Zumberge, J. H., and Ayers, J. C., 1964, "Hydrology of lakes and swamps," in (Chow, V. T., editor) "Handbook of Applied Hydrology," Vol. 23, pp. 1–33, New York, McGraw-Hill Book Co.

Cross-references: *Caldera; Caspian Sea; Crater Lakes; Dead Sea; Deflation; Finger Lakes; Glacial Lakes; Glacial Scour; Graben; Great Lakes (North America); Karst; Lake Baikal; Lake Eyre; Maar; Quaternary Period; Salton Sea; Sink, Sinkhole, Swallow Hole; Valley (Mountain) Glacier.* pr Vol. VI: *Hydrology; Ice Cap; Ice Sheet; Limnology.*

CRYPTORHEIC DRAINAGE—*See* DRAINAGE PATTERNS

CUESTA

Cuestas are gently sloping plains bounded on one edge by an escarpment. They result when a gently dipping layer of relatively hard sedimentary rock underlain by softer strata is eroded until the latter is exposed producing a feature resembling a plateau or mesa near the scarp edge, and a gentle plain on the dip slope.

The term *cuesta* is a Spanish word meaning hill or slope and, according to Hill (1896), was applied to tilted structural plains in New Mexico and Texas and to other asymmetrical features including tilted fault block mountains. Davis (1899) adopted the term and restricted its usage to the form discussed here.

Cuestas are related to several other land forms, and they form part of a gradational series from hog-

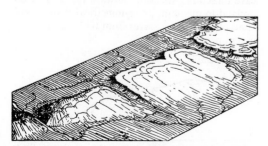

FIG. 1. Progression from hogback on left through homoclinal ridge to cuesta and mesa (after Davis, 1899).

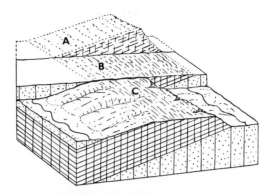

FIG. 2. Development of beveled cuesta (after Cotton, 1948).

backs through homoclinal ridges and cuestas to mesas as illustrated in Fig. 1. Hogbacks are sharp crested, often serrate, and usually have dip slopes exceeding 40–45°. They are relatively stationary as erosion progresses, whereas both homoclinal ridges and cuestas experience migration of crestlines in the direction of dip, a process variously labeled as *homoclinal shifting* (Cotton, 1948) or migration of divides. Homoclinal ridges (Cotton, 1948) are an intermediate form encompassing a range of dip slopes from, say, 40° to perhaps 4 or 5°. Mesas are essentially flat and are scarp-bounded on all sides. Cuestas then loosely embrace those one-scarp plains where the dips lie between, say, 4–5° and $\frac{1}{2}°$.

Cuesta scarps and low-angle thrust fault scarps (Thornbury, 1954) may be confused, but they can be separated by field study of the stratigraphic sequence. Beveled cuestas "are developed in a youthful stage of dissection of a peneplain beneath the surface of which are gently inclined strata" (Cotton, 1948). When uplift occurs, the cuesta is reformed in the lower part of the bed, but the upper part retains the bevel as shown in Fig. 2.

DAVID S. SIMONETT

References

Cotton, C. A., 1948, "Landscape," second ed., pp. 128–135, New York, John Wiley & Sons.

Davis, W. M., 1899, "The drainage of cuestas," *Proc. Geol. Assoc., London*, **16**, 75–93.

Hill, R. T., 1896, "Descriptive topographic terms of Spanish America," *Natl. Geogr. Mag.*, **7**, 291–302.

Thornbury, W. D., 1954, "Principles of Geomorphology," pp. 133–136, 272, New York, John Wiley & Sons.

Tricart, J., 1952, "Cours de Géomorphologie. Part 1: Géomorphologie structurale. No. 2: Les types de bordure de massifs anciens," Second ed., Paris, C.D.U., 118pp.

Cross-references: *Block Mountain (Fault-block Mountain); Escarpment; Hogback and Flatiron; Mesa and Butte.*

CUSPATE FORELAND OR SPIT

The term "cuspate foreland" was probably first devised by Gulliver (1896), though in the same year (1896) W. M. Davis published his classical analysis of Cape Cod. The terms "cuspate bar" (Wooldridge and Morgan, 1937) or "cuspate spit" (Shepard, 1952) refer to the development of *"compound spits"* or bars by progradation of a *barrier bar or island* (q.v.), in a series of *"cusps,"* *hooked spits"* or *"horns"* that curl back into the lagoon or sound. Growth of these cuspate features from intertidal bars into dry land, either by successive storm wave incidence or by successive oscillations of sea level (on a small scale, amounting to the same thing), eventually leads to the development of cuspate forelands. As D. W. Johnson remarked, "they may have a variety of forms, but when most typically developed are more or less triangular in shape with the apex of the triangle pointing out into the water...." (Fig. 1). The successive cusps may be below the water as the foreland grows.

Examples may be seen along the Atlantic coast of North America, at Cape Cod (Mass.), Sandy Hook

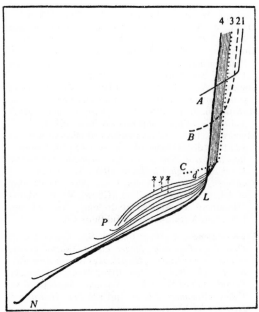

FIG. 2. Evolution of Orford Ness (Steers, 1964). (By permission of Cambridge Univ. Press, London.)

(N.J.), Cape Hatteras (N.C.), Cape Fear (S.C.), and Cape Canaveral (Fla.; recently called "Cape Kennedy"). Examples in Britain include Dungeness (Kent), Orford Ness (Suffolk), Scolt Head Island and so on (Steers, 1964, see Figs. 2 and 3). The historical growth of such headlands in a number of cases can be traced from archeology or in historical documents from Roman times (Lewis and Balchin, 1940; see Fig. 4).

Growth of Cusps

There are some differences of opinion over the nature of the growth of hooked spits or cusps, just as with barrier beach bars and *beach ridges* (q.v.).

Escoffier (1954) suggested that a "traveling cuspate foreland" (also called a "truncated cuspate foreland" by Johnson, 1919) might result from constantly having two opposing wave directions along a shore line with one set of waves clearly predominant over the other (Fig. 5). Migration of the cuspate foreland would be in the predominant wave direction. Alternate outward building of the foreland to maintain its asymmetrical shape would be accomplished by waves from the frequent wave direction.

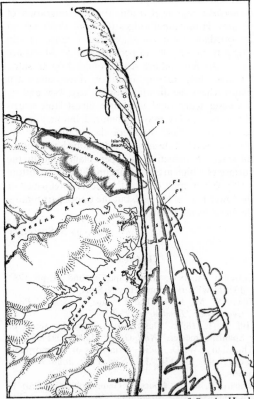

FIG. 1. Stages in the development of Sandy Hook spit, New Jersey (Johnson, 1919). The hinterland consists of Cretaceous sands, locally covered by glacial outwash sands. The loose clastic sediment supply is thus most favorable. (By permission of John Wiley & Sons, N.Y.)

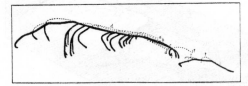

FIG. 3. Evolution of Scolt Head Island (Steers, 1964). (By permission of Cambridge Univ. Press, London.)

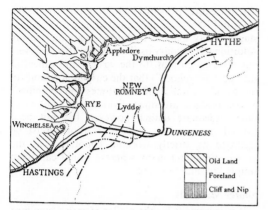

FIG. 4. The evolution of Dungeness (after Gulliver, 1887). Details giving the entire post-Roman evolution have been added by Lewis and Balchin (1940). The great bulk of this foreland has grown during small sea level oscillations (+0.5 to − 2 meters) of the last 2500 years.

It is clearly recognized that the spit grows out across shallow water as a slightly submerged feature but, because of wave refraction, is gradually "shepherded" inward, away from the principal swell. Beaches develop around the inner face of the foreland with the form of a perfect logarithmic curve (Yasso, 1965; see Fig. 6).

Using certain simplifying assumptions as to the relation between rate of erosion and wave direction, Grijm (1964) has shown theoretically that narrow or broad, symmetrical or asymmetrical deltas, or any combination thereof, may form because of waves from a single direction. He suggests that the most important factors in determining equilibrium shape of the cuspate delta are (a) the rate at which sediment is delivered by the stream which exits at the point of the cusp, and (b) the rate at which waves can move sediment in either direction away from the river mouth.

In spit growth, two semi-stable equilibrium conditions are observed : (1) below low-tide limit, a slack-water state at the point of the spit, along the locus of which a submerged bar develops, as a result of longshore drift, sometimes well in advance of the intertidal or supratidal feature; the foot of the bar progrades by gravitational rolling to the point of stability; and (2) between tide limits and up to storm-wave maximum swash, a spit that builds as an extension of the zigzag motion of beach drift, maximum height being likewise controlled by a minimum energy state.

One may readily see that the minimum energy level in the former case lies in progressively deepening water (i.e., the foot of the offshore bar), while in the latter case, it occurs at the upper limit of storm wave activity. The intertidal zone is not a simple transition but rather a zone of maximum energy, whose peak level ranges through the tide cycle (plus storm-wave "setup").

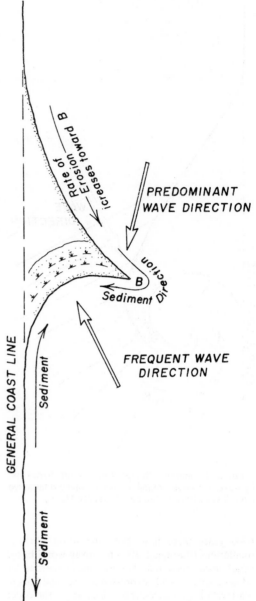

FIG. 5. Traveling cuspate foreland (adapted from Escoffier, 1954).

The development of a new cusp is generated, in the same manner as a new bar and beach ridge combination, under highest tides and maximum wave set up during storm conditions. Such conditions may only be established at cyclic intervals, e.g., during winter storms or during hurricanes that reach exceptionally high latitudes (40–45°), only at peak stages of the 11–22 year sunspot cycles.

In still longer terms, it is the opinion of the writers and some others (though this interpretation is hotly denied by some others) that during the last

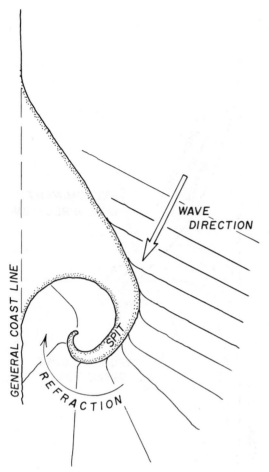

FIG. 6. Formation of a logarithmic spiral-shaped spit by wave refraction around a cuspate foreland (adapted from Yasso, 1964, Columbia University Thesis).

6000 years there have been important climatic oscillations (through 2–3°C on a mean world basis) which have been reflected by glacial melting or advances, eustatically expressed in rises and falls of sea level of ±3 meters, through cycles of the order of 500–1500 years. It is an acknowledged fact that during the first half of the twentieth century, there was (a) a world temperature rise of 1°C, (b) a eustatic rise of over 50 mm, and (c) a widespread melting of glaciers. Earlier correlations have been attempted using archeological and C^{14} dating, but the precision is less satisfactory.

In the known cuspate forelands of the world, it is observed that there are distinctive sets of cusps that suggest periods of strong spit building separated by extended times of reduced activity, if not active erosion. Between the "sheafs" of prograding cusps and each of the preceding generations, there are sometimes traces of bays, lagoons or swamps which contain C^{14}-datable peats or archeological data.

There are three principal high-level stages (*ca.* 5000, 2500 and 1000 years ago), alternating with low-level stages, today marked by buried peats and so on. Additional secondary oscillations are also observed, but it seems curious (to the writers and others of the "eustatic school") that the cuspate forelands of the world, as well as littoral dunes and "families" of beachridges, are often divided into clusters of three. Adequate dating, however, has not been carried out, so that such correlations must be regarded as strictly working hypotheses at the present time, and many workers would call them simply "wishful thinking."

Source Materials

It is important for the reader of early "standard works" on coastal erosion by Gulliver, Davis, Johnson and others, to know that their experience was largely gathered from the shores of New England and they, in turn, were largely impressed by the still earlier observations made in northwestern Europe. What is significant is that both regions were glaciated during the Quaternary and many shores consist of loose accumulations of tills, moraines, outwash gravels and "sandur" (see *Moraine*; *Outwash Plain, Fan, Terrace, Sandur*). These materials are very easily quarried by the waves and provide rich material for spit building. Tropical and subtropical coasts are much less generously endowed, while the coasts of orogenic regions are largely rocky.

Two classic areas of the northeastern United States are Cape Cod and Sandy Hook. At Cape Cod (W. M. Davis, 1896), there is constant erosion of the Pleistocene gravel cliffs to nourish the growth of Cape Cod itself; the Atlantic swells reach the cliffs with their orthogonals almost at right angles and the longshore drift is divided into two almost equal sectors, setting north or south. In the case of Sandy Hook (Gulliver, 1896; Johnson, 1919), the cliffs are of soft Cretaceous sands, but farther south there are extensive Pleistocene sandur plains, so that very liberal sand supply is assured (see Fig. 1). Again, the orthogonals meet the mid-shore (near Atlantic City) at about 90°, so that in the south the sand movement is southward to Cape May, and in the north, northward to Sandy Hook. The cuspate foreland of the latter therefore shows truncation of the earlier shore lines, intersected by progressive encroachment and northward progradation of the compound cusps.

WARREN E. YASSO
RHODES W. FAIRBRIDGE

References

Davis, W. M., 1896, "The outline of Cape Cod," *Proc. Am. Acad. Arts and Sci.*, **31**, 303–332.

Escoffier, F. F., 1954, "Travelling forelands and the shore line processes associated with them," *Bull. Beach Erosion Board*, **8**, No. 4, 11–13.

Fairbridge, R. W., 1961, "Eustatic Changes in Sea-level," in "Physics and Chemistry of the Earth," **4**, 99–185, London, Pergamon Press.

Grijm, J., 1964, "Theoretical forms of shorelines," *Proc. Conf. Coastal Engineering, 9th*, 219–235.

Guilcher, A., and King, C. A. M., 1961, "Spits, tombolos and tidal marshes in Connemara and West Kerry, Ireland," *Proc. Roy. Irish Acad., Sec. B*, **61** (17), 283–338.

Gulliver, F. P., 1887, "Dungeness Foreland," *Geograph. J.*, **9**, 536.

Gulliver, F. P., 1896, "Cuspate Forelands," *Bull. Geol. Soc. Am.*, **7**, 399–432.

Hey, R. W., 1967, "Sections in the beach-plain deposits of Dungeness, Kent," *Geol. Mag.*, **104**, 361–370.

Johnson, D. W., 1919, "Shore Processes and Shoreline Development," New York, John Wiley & Sons, 583pp.

Lewis, W. V., and Balchin, W. G. V., 1940, "Past sea levels at Dungeness," *Geograph. J.*, **96**, 258.

Shepard, F. P., 1952, "Revised nomenclature for depositional coastal features," *Bull. Am. Assoc. Petrol. Geologists*, **36**, 1902–1912.

Steers, J. A., 1964, "The Coastline of England and Wales," (Second edition), Cambridge, The University Press, 750pp.

Wooldridge, S. W., and Morgan, R. S., 1937, "The Physical Basis of Geography: An outline of Geomorphology," London, Longmans, Green & Co., 445pp.

Yasso, W. E., 1965, "Plan geometry of headland-bay beaches," *J. Geol.*, **73** (5), 702–714.

Cross references: *Barriers—Beaches and Islands*; *Bars*; *Beach Ridges*; *Coastal Geomorphology*; *Coastlines— Theoretical Shapes*; *Deltaic Evolution*; *Eustasy*; *Moraine*; *Outwash Plain, Fan, Terrace, Sandur*; *Quaternary Period*; *Sediment Transport*; *Swash. Swash Mark*. Vol. II: *Sunspot Cycles*; *Tropical Cyclones*.

CYCLE ANALYSIS—*See* Vol. II

CYCLES, GEOMORPHIC

One of the most useful concepts for producing some semblance of order in the seemingly unending variety of land forms and processes is the concept of *cycles*. A cycle is usually regarded as constituting the sequence of changes from an initial state via a series of stages to an ultimate state. The ultimate state will be in equilibrium with its environment and will be stable unless some further modification occurs in one or more components essentially involved in creating that equilibrium environment. The initial state is brought about by a change upsetting the balance so that the components are placed in disequilibrium. As soon as this happens, changes will occur which will tend to cause the system to return to a state of equilibrium.

General Systems Theory

Obviously, these cycles obey the laws governing general systems theory (Chorley, 1962). According to systems theory, there are two main kinds of models which we may develop. The first is the *closed system* in which it is assumed that there are clearly defined boundaries across which no import or export of materials or energy may occur (Van Bertalanffy, 1951). Another characteristic is that the system moves in the direction of maximum entropy, i.e., there is a minimum of free energy left in the system.

Thus the concept of the *geographical cycle* of Davis (1899) is now recognized as an example of a closed system (see also *Youth—Maturity—Old Age; Process—Structure—Stage*). Uplift causes the erosion and the erosion continues until the land area has been reduced to a peneplain. When this stage is reached, the system will have minimum free energy (though Davis would not have used such an expression). The entire sequence of events from uplift to the production of the peneplain constitutes one cycle, and it is assumed that this cycle would go relentlessly on its way until the changes were completed. Davis later allowed for modifications of this cycle by other factors, but he did not really change his approach to embrace that of the second type of system, the *open system* (q.v.).

In the case of the open system, an energy supply is essential to its maintenance and preservation. It is maintained by a constant supply and removal of material and energy. The great advantage of this concept is that the system may achieve a "steady state" so that any necessary adjustments of energy within the system may be effected by means of an adjustment of the form or geometry of the system. Clearly, then, most of the cycles considered in geomorphology are better suited for treatment using the "open system" analogy than the closed system models. The first recognition of this fact appears to have been that by Gilbert (1880, p. 117–118) regarding stream action, but this was later disregarded by Davis. On the other hand, Gilbert did not fully develop his ideas, whereas Davis did. Although the application of the cycle concept by Davis was imperfect, at least he did clearly put forward the first working cyclical model.

The adjustment of form in an open system obeys an expansion of the Le Châtelier Principle (originally stated for closed systems): "Any system in . . . equilibrium undergoes, as a result of a variation in one of the factors governing the equilibrium, a compensating change in a direction such that, had this change occurred alone, it would have produced a variation of the factor considered in the opposite direction" (Prigogine and Defay, 1954, p. 262). This works admirably in the case of the concept of a graded stream as stated by Mackin (1948), and Chorley (1962) discusses many other examples.

Another characteristic of the open system is that it behaves "equifinally," i.e., different initial conditions lead to the same end result. This was not anticipated by Davis. Instead he interpreted *all nick points* (q.v.) as being produced by a change in the base level in the middle of the cycle. Production of nick points by climatic or vegetational changes causing an increase in runoff is ignored. Yet they occur and it is only by using the open system concept that we can explain them.

Geographical Cycle

The first cycle which was put forward in a well-developed form was the *geographical cycle* of Davis (1899). The terms *"geomorphic cycle"* or "erosion cycle" are usually employed as synonyms. Developed to cope with the sequences found in humid temperate regions, this cycle should be divided into three parts, namely, *a cycle of river development*, *a cycle of slope development* and a *cycle of landscape development*. In each case, it was assumed that there is an initial condition followed by sequential stages to an ultimate state. The sequence was divided for convenience into youth, maturity and old age. However, a landscape such as the Himalayas might be mature when the rivers were still youthful.

Newly deposited marine sediments uplifted above sea level are immediately subject to weathering and erosion. The land-form assemblages developed as a result of these processes depend upon the climatic regime of the area in question, as well as on the nature and disposition of the sediments; according to the Davisian school, there is yet another factor determining the form of the land surface—*time*. The time factor was formally integrated into geomorphological analysis only late in the last century. Since weathering and deposition, as well as erosion, are involved, "geomorphic cycle" is the preferable term. The gist of the cyclic concept is that commencing with an initial landscape, generally assumed to be one of low relief, the land surface passes through an orderly sequence of forms eventually to return to a surface of low relief, to an assemblage of forms which is, to all intents and purposes, identical with the original; hence, the use of the term cycle. Landscapes in which there are preserved evidences of more than one geomorphic cycle are called *multicyclic* (or *polycyclic*) *landscapes*. In a very real sense the cyclic concept is a product of its age, for it is of course evolutionary in character and was conceived in an age when the scientific climate was dominated by the Darwinian theory.

The Davisian idea was well received; in fact, it was accepted so widely in the English-speaking world that for half a century its validity could hardly be questioned. Davis developed further cycles to deal with land-form development under other climatic conditions, e.g., by glaciation and in arid areas.

These are all developments of the original use of the concept of *cycle of development*, stated by Davis

(1899, p. 187). By this, he meant the interpretation of all facets in the history of development of a landscape. A more general use of the term "cycle" in geomorphology is for the *cycle of denudation* or *cycle of topographical development* (see A.G.I. Glossary, 1960; reference to W. B. Scott, 1907; *Introduction to Geology,* p. 439). This is the alternate upheaval and wearing down of a landscape from base level to base level. It differs from the previous cycles by including the uplifting processes and stages in with the degradational processes and stages. Thus, it does not assume the almost instantaneous uplift postulated by Davis in his geographical cycle.

Other Geomorphic Cycles

The Davisian concept using the closed system models has also been applied to a *cycle of shore line development* especially by Johnson and by Cotton. However, recent work would again indicate that shore lines might best be tackled by considering them as open systems since climate, wave action, ocean currents, height of the sea, and the nature of the material being eroded and providing beach sediments vary so much with time. A *cycle of sedimentation* ("cyclothem") again represents an energy system, extended over its time range of a year or climatic cycle of astronomical length.

The cyclic concept has also been applied to karst regions, though here, a difference of opinion exists as to the stage at which old age is reached. These *karst cycles*, and the associated *cycle of underground drainage* are also closed-system models in their ordinary method of presentation, even though the diversity of theories to explain the development of karst topography suggests that the use of an open system would be desirable.

Open-system models have been developed in a few cases. One is the *hydrologic cycle* (q.v., pr Vol. VI) which is well understood and documented. This is because of its fundamental role in the understanding of meteorology and climatology, and its importance to agriculture and the rest of the activities of man.

It is likely that more open-system cycles will be postulated in the coming years and that these will improve our knowledge of geomorphology and will gradually replace the closed-system cycles used until now.

Discussion of the Geomorphic Cycles

The first elaborate exposition of the geomorphic cycle concerned landscapes developed under humid temperate conditions, generally claimed to be the *"normal"* cycle. However, what is "normal" in New England is highly "abnormal" in Arizona. Davis' presentation of the scheme was both vigorous and vivid, and his colorful analogy of human life and landscapes, both passing through the stages of youth, maturity and old age, caught the imagination of the scientific world. It was generally assumed that uplift of the land was relatively rapid and that under humid temperate conditions, the stream valleys which were initially cut into the mass would be deep and narrow. They separated broad inter-fluves, remnants of the initial surface. As the rivers incised their beds, the amplitude of relief would increase, and this stage of deep narrow valleys, with remnants of the initial surface preserved high in the topography, and increasing relief amplitude, was termed that of *youth*. This stage, however, would terminate when the interfluves were narrowed to knife-edged crests, so that all traces of the initial surface would be eliminated. Thereafter (the *mature* stage) stream dissection and wasting would reduce the interfluves; in the meanwhile, the rivers would closely approach base level so that the rate of inci-sion would decrease, and thus relief amplitude would gradually diminish. Maturity passes im-perceptibly to *old age*, and the downwasting of divides would continue until there was a plain of low relief dominated by broad convex swells—a *peneplain*. If this cycle was interrupted by uplift of the land, causing rivers to be rejuvenated and the landscape to be revived, a similar sequence of developments would probably ensue.

Workers particularly in arid and semiarid lands were able to observe land-form assemblages at variance with those of this Davisian "normal" cycle. In such areas, and especially where resistant rocks occur, the downwasting of interfluves is apparently not important; instead of suffering decline the slopes tend to maintain a constantly steep inclination during recession. The reason for this different behavior of steep slope elements is probably related to the particular system of weathering and erosion in arid lands, where there is a tendency to form crusts, indurated horizons and pans, all of them resistant, at and near the land surfaces. After dissection, they provide hard pro-tective cappings to plateaus thus causing a reduc-tion in the rate of retreat of the upper parts of steep slopes. Moreover the effects of water, the most important agent of weathering and erosion (even in highly arid areas), are most apparent on lower slopes. Thus the morphology of arid-zone escarpments tends to be constant; for a particular lithology and a given set of climatic conditions, slopes are steepened to a maximum compatible with stability. Nevertheless, they retreat, and thus in course of time, the ratio of plateau and plain varies in an orderly manner, so that again the cyclic notion can be applied in the interpretation of the arid and semiarid landscapes.

Although it by no means provides answers to all geomorphological problems, the cyclic concept is surely one of the most fruitful ever formulated in geomorphology. There are of course many dif-ficulties. There is even now little knowledge of many of the physical and chemical details of the processes which Davis invoked to bring about his

sequence of changes, but it can be asserted now that cyclic interpretations of landscape offer a guide to what happened and in what sequence, though not how. The assumption that the initial uplift of the land is rapid was not justified, and the effects of erosion during uplift, remain uncertain. The cyclic concept has also been applied quite uncritically, and erosion surfaces have been "identified" on the basis of dubious evidence, but this is rather the fault of the workers concerned and is not a just criticism to level at either the concept or its author, with such statements as:

"Amongst geographers, William Morris Davis de-layed somewhat our learning about the physical earth by his systems of attractive but unreal cycles of erosion with their stages of youth, maturity, old age and reju-venation" (Sauer, 1952, p. 2.).

Though the sequential development of forms does not take place everywhere as visualized by Davis, the clear identification in many parts of the world of erosional surfaces of low relief, over base-ment structures of great complexity, of widely different age ranges and forming significant el-ements of the present landscape, demonstrates beyond doubt the fundamental truth of the cyclic concept in many areas at least.

Geomorphic Cycle Challenged

The idea of the geomorphic cycle has been seriously challenged. Hack (1960) has elaborated ideas put forward originally by G. K. Gilbert and W. Penck, and in pedology by C. C. Nikiforoff, in relation to land-form evolution in the central Appalachians. In brief, Hack asserts that after a period of adjustment to new environmental condi-tions (tectonic, climatic, vegetational) a condition of dynamic equilibrium is arrived at. Although tectonic activity for instance may continue, weath-ering and erosion adjust to the rate of movement in such a way that as fast as the land mass is raised by earth movements it is removed by denudation. Thus although the land surface is far from static in a geotectonic sense, the land-form processes are in equilibrium with both tectonism and climate and hence remain morphologically constant. Once adjustment to the environment is attained, there is no evolutionary development of land forms in time. Only when the environment changes, as when the rate of tectonic activity alters, or there is climatic change, are there morphological changes as the surface forms are brought into adjustment by the changed processes or the same processes operating at new rates.

This idea has aroused much interest. There are difficulties concerned, for instance, with the controls exerted by base level, and with the degree to which the land forms we see at present are inherited from climatic and tectonic conditions which obtained in the geologic past. At present, the two contrasting hypotheses of cyclic and noncyclic development are being tested in the field in several areas. This is a difficult undertaking, but measurements of rates of erosion on different parts of escarpments and slopes will be useful in this respect. J. H. Bretz, working in the Ozarks, claims categorically that the land forms there are most satisfactorily explained in cyclic terms, but there may well be areas where dynamic equilibrium best explains the geomorphological complex.

S. A. Harris
C. R. Twidale

(*Editor's note*: The following addition is a personal communication from L. Wilson:

A landscape acting as an open system need not achieve a steady state, as suggested by Hack. Such an unchanging topography can only occur where all external and internal conditions are constant. This is rarely the case. Even assuming a constant climate and no tectonic activity there will be an inevitable reduction of relief and, hence, a loss of potential energy within the system. The result is a gradual evolution. perhaps similar to that postulated by Davis. The landscape evolution follows the basic laws of *allometric growth* (in this case the growth is negative). There are thus two forms of dynamic equilibrium in a land-form assemblage. The *steady state* is characterized by unchanging internal and external conditions, a continuous unchanging flow of energy and material through the system, and an unchanging landscape. *Growth* (or evolution) occurs where any internal or external condition changes, either suddenly (e.g., tectonic activity, sudden climatic change) or gradually (loss of relief due to restraint of base level, gradual climatic change). The landscape changes in response to the external or internal variation. These topographic changes may conveniently be described in terms of a cycle. Thus both cyclical change and steady state are equilibrium open system phenomena.)

References

American Geological Institute, 1960, "Glossary of Geology and Related Sciences," Second ed., Washington, D.C., National Academy of Sciences.

Bretz, J. H., 1965, "Geomorphic history of the Ozarks of Missouri," *Missouri Geol. Surv.*, Water Resources, **41**.

Chorley, R. J., 1962, "Geomorphology and general systems theory," *U.S. Geol. Surv. Profess. Paper* **500B**, 10pp.

Davis, W. M., 1899, "The geographical cycle," *Geograph. J.*, **14**, 481–504.

Davis, W. M., 1909, "Geographical Essays," Ch. 12, pp. 249–279, New York, Dover reprint (1954).

Gilbert, G. K., 1880, "Report on the Geology of the Henry Mountains," Second ed., U.S. Government Printing Office, Washington, D.C., 170pp.

Hack, J. T., 1960, "Interpretation of erosional topography in humid and temperate regions," *Am. J. Sci.*, **258A**, 80–97.

Kennedy, W. Q., 1962, "Theoretical factors in geomorphological analysis," *Geol. Mag.*, **99**, 304–312.

Mackin, J. H., 1948, "Concept of the graded river," *Bull. Geol. Soc. Am.*, **59**, 463–512.

Penck, W., 1953, "Morphological Analysis of Landforms," New York, The Macmillan Co., 429pp. (translated by H. Czech and K. C. Boswell).

Prigogine, I., and Defay, R., 1954, "Chemical Thermodynamics," London, Longmans Green & Co., 543pp.

Sauer, C. O., 1952, "Agricultural Origins and Disposals," New York, Amer. Geogr. Soc., 110pp.

Van Bertalanffy, L., 1951, "An outline of general system theory," *J. Brit. Phil. Sci.*, **1**, 134–165.

Cross-references: *Arid Cycle*; *Base Level*; *Climatic Geomorphology*; *Coastal Geomorphology*; *Equilibrium in Geomorphology*; *Erosion*; *General Systems Theory in Geomorphology*; *Interfluve*; *Karst*; *Landscape Types—Genetic*; *Nickpoint*; *Open Systems—Allometric Growth*; *Peneplain*; *Process—Structure—Stage*; *Rejuvenation*; *Rivers*; *Slopes*; *Tectonic Landscapes*; *Weathering—Geomorphological Aspects*; *Youth—Maturity—Old Age*. Vol. II: *Arid Climate*; *Climatology*; *Meteorology*; *Middle-latitude Climates*. Vol. V: *Geotectonics*. pr Vol. VI: *Deposition*; *Hydrologic Cycle*; *Pedology*. pr Vol. VII: *Cyclothem*; *Sedimentary Cycles and Oscillations*.

CYCLES AND PERIODICITIES—*See* Vol. II

CYMATOGENY

Two terms—epeirogeny and orogeny—have long been employed by geologists to satisfy (a) broad, relatively uniform uplift of large areas such as the Canadian Shield, and (b) mountain making in linear belts accompanied by rock deformation that may be intense, e.g., the European Alps.

Cymatogeny (proposed by King, 1959, p. 117) is between these two and refers to the arching—and occasional doming—of belts of country generally scores, but sometimes hundreds, of miles wide, in which the maximum uplift amounts to thousands of feet but in which rock deformation is at a minimum (Fig. 1). Derived from the Greek ($\kappa\nu\,\mu\sigma$ = a wave), the word signifies the heaving of the earth's crust into large undulations, the characteristic expression of which is linear arches and elongated or oval depressions. Some arches are formidable (the Andes), some are inappreciable to the eye (the Congo-Zambesi divide). Some are marked by rift valleys along the crest where the crust has cracked open under tension on the arc-chord relationship of the arch. This is the mechanical explanation for the East African and Brazilian rifts. As the earth's crust is heterogeneous, even the application of simple vertical forces sometimes results secondarily in local compressions and unbalanced forces causing shears and sharply differential local movements (e.g., Jordan rift, Ruwenzori). However, these are minor and the most expressive definition of cymatogeny is perhaps "the undulating -ogeny."

Modern cymatogeny is detected by the differential displacement of Cenozoic cyclic erosional sur-

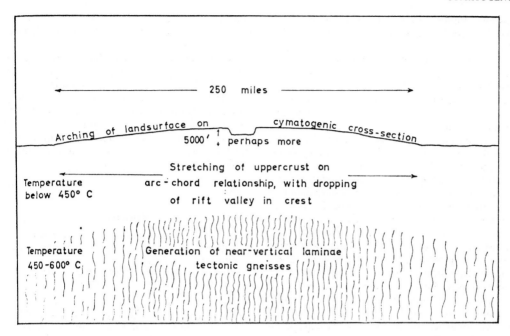

FIG. 1. Crustal section through a typical cymatogen relating major arching and rifting of the surface to formation of tectonic gneisses at intermediate crustal depth. Displacements are in the vertical sense only (from King, 1962).

faces and becomes strikingly evident when these surfaces are mapped. Contours show that since their completion (planation), the surfaces have undergone vertical displacement, much of which dates to around the end of the Pliocene but which locally may be repetitive between the Miocene and Recent.

As examples of cymatogeny: on Ruwenzori, the late Cenozoic surface, generally standing at 5000 feet in this part of Central Africa, is continuously upwarped to 14,000 feet; late Cenozoic landscapes planed at relatively low levels are upwarped to 13,000 feet upon the Andes of Peru and Bolivia; while nearly all the watersheds of southern and central Africa owe their positions to the siting of cymatogenic arches that have in many instances been rejuvenated at intervals since, even, the Mesozoic. Dome and basin cymatogeny is characteristic of parts of the Rocky Mountain belt, e.g., Bighorn Mountains and Wyoming basin.

Modern mountain ranges as a whole are cymatogenic—*not orogenic*. Many, e.g., the Alps, Rockies, Andes, New Zealand and Australian Alps and even the mighty Himalaya, bear traces, ample or meager, of former Cenozoic summit planation. Where intense rock deformations (orogenesis) appear locally, these deformations *antedate* the simple cymatogeny that, followed by erosion and deep valley cutting, has created the modern mountainous aspect. Such relationships of modern cymatogeny following older

belts of orogeny after a time interval, during which the earlier, orogenic mountains were obliterated by erosion, are by no means uncommon. Thus the original Alps in Europe were truly orogenic at the end of the Oligocene. These orogenic mountains were erased and the area planed by the end of the Miocene, when minor cymatogenic uplift occurred, and a further partial planation was developed during the Pliocene before the country was upheaved cymatogenically around the end of the Cenozoic. The modern Alps owe their form to denudation following this later movement, and scarcely at all to the original Oligocene deformations which powerfully folded and thrust the geosynclinal sediments.

The destruction of cymatogenic arches by erosion is usually most actively pursued upon the flanks. Relics of former planation usually survive longest (a) at the crests of the ranges, e.g., *gipfelflur* of the Alps, summit and subsummit peneplains of the Rocky Mountains—Sierra Nevada, *altiplano* of the Andes, Wainihinihi peneplain of the Southern Alps, N.Z., and (b) at the edges of the foothill ranges where the deformed land surface sinks down into adjacent basins and is smothered (usually) beneath cover of younger sediments shed from the incision of mountain valleys and laid in the depressions after the cymatogenic uplifts have begun.

From study of these overlying sediments, dating of phases within the cymatogenic upheaval becomes possible. Within the uplifted area itself, the phases may be recorded in polycyclic topography, valley terraces, etc.

From the mapping of the attitudes of cyclic land surfaces cymatogeny is revealed as widespread in all continents (it may perhaps exist also beneath the sea) and as the most prevalent mode of deformation of the earth's crust in late Cenozoic and Quaternary time.

Cymatogenic deformation of the earth's surface is easily demonstrated, but its explanation involves the much more difficult problem of what happens at depth within the crust to accommodate the displacements. Almost all the visible deformation is in a purely vertical sense and the deeper levels of the crust that are inevitably involved must also have their deformation in a vertical sense. It is suggested that at depths measured in miles where temperatures approximate 400°C, rock movements and mineral transformations create near-vertical tectonic gneisses with characteristic non-igneous suite of minerals (e.g., microcline) (Fig. 1). Belts of such gneisses, devoid of high-temperature minerals, hydrothermal deposits and basic intrusions, occurring in Africa, Brazil and elsewhere, may well represent the roots of former cymatogens now exposed after repeated cycles of cymatogenic uplift and consequent erosion have brought the normally deeper zones to the surface.

At still greater depths, the ultimate "space problem" is presumably solved by horizontal displacements of subcrustal matter on the isostatic principle. The relationship between cymatogeny and isostatic anomalies is often a close one, the contours and isobars often agreeing remarkably well, with the largest negative anomalies sited beneath the axes of maximum uplift, e.g., in Natal, South Africa and in eastern Australia.

L. C. KING

References

King, L. C., 1959, "Denudational and tectonic relief in south-eastern Australia," *Trans. Geol. Soc. South Africa,* **62,** 113–138.

King, L. C., 1962, "The Morphology of the Earth," Edinburgh, Oliver and Boyd, 699pp.

Cross-references: *Dome Mountain; Erosion; Gipfelflur; Planation Surface; Rift Valley.* Vol. IV: *Geological Time Scale.* Vol. V: *Epeirogeny; Gneiss; Isostasy; Orogenesis.* pr Vol. VI: *Contour.*

D

DEAD ICE—*See* DEGLACIATION; STAGNANT
ICE MELTING

DEAD SEA

(I) History of Research

The Dead Sea is first mentioned in the Bible
(Gen. 14: 3) and is called by two names: "Salt
Sea" and "Sea of Death." Strabo (Geography
16.2.42) who calls it by mistake "Lake Sirbonis,"
gives the first good description, stressing the great
depth of water and its high density. He also mentions the asphalt eruptions, hot springs, gas
seepages, and the smell of what is obviously H$_2$S.
Pliny (*Historia Naturalis* V, XV, 70–72), essentially
repeating Strabo's account, calls it *Judaeae lacus*
and *Asphaltites lacus.* Pausanias (Description of
Greece, V, 7, 4–5) first introduced the term "Dead
Sea" into European literature.

The modern study of the Dead Sea started with
the expedition of the U.S. Navy to explore the
Dead Sea (Lynch, 1852) and was continued, among
others, by Lartet (1876) and Blanckenhorn (1912).
The first systematic modern investigation was
carried out by K. O. Emery and D. Neev (unpublished report, 1959) and by Neev (1964).

(II) Location, Geological Setting, Hydrography

The Dead Sea is situated at the deepest part of the
African Rift Valley, between the Judean Desert in
the west and the Mountains of Moab in the east.
The relief from the mountain tops in the east to the
level of the lake is 1300 meters (4300 feet). Politi-
cally, its southwestern part lies within the territory
of Israel, the remainder in Jordan. The climate is
highly arid with a mean annual temperature of
25°C (77°F); mean summer maxima of 40°C (104°F)
and a mean annual rainfall of 50 mm (2 inches).
The size of the drainage area of the Dead Sea is
40,000 km^2 (15,600 square miles). The level of the
lake in 1966 was 399 meters (1,330 feet) below
Mediterranean sea level. Its length from north to
south is 74 km (46 miles), and the average width is
14 km (9 miles). The total surface of the lake as of
1966 was 940 km^2 (363 square miles). The eastern
and western shores are generally steep and formed
by the fault scarps of the Rift Valley. The northern
and southern shores are very shallow, and a salt
marsh (sabkha) extends from the southern shore
for a distance of about 20 km (12.5 miles).

The Dead Sea, which has no exit, is fed mainly
by the waters of the Jordan River, the annual
flow of which, subject to large fluctuations, is about
1.2×10^9 cubic meters (42×10^9 cubic feet). Two

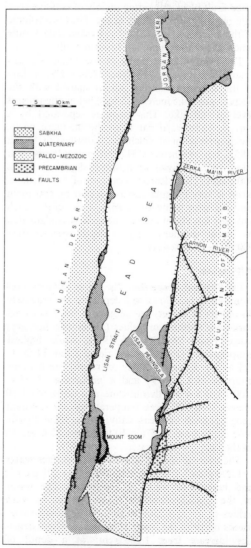

FIG. 1. Geological sketch map of Dead Sea area.
(Note: In legend, for "Paleo-Mezozoic" read Paleozoic
and Mesozoic.)

more perennial rivers discharging from the east are the Arnon, which carries about 30×10^6 cubic meters (1×10^9 cubic feet) per year, and the Zerka Main with an annual discharge of 4×10^6 cubic meters (140×10^6 cubic feet). Additional water is supplied by numerous springs issuing near the lake shores, and by the seasonal, but sometimes large, floods of dry rivers. The total average annual intake of the Dead Sea is estimated at 1.6×10^9 cubic meters (56×10^9 cubic feet).

The Lisan Peninsula, protruding from the eastern shore, divides the lake into two distinctly different basins: a shallow southern one, roughly one quarter of the total lake size, and a deep northern basin. Near the southwest corner of the lake rises Mount Sdom (Sodom or Jebel Usdum), a recently uplifted fault block consisting mainly of massive rock salt, probably late Tertiary in age. The total volume of the Dead Sea is 142 km^3 (34 cubic miles), nine times that of the Great Salt Lake in Utah.

The bottom topography of the Dead Sea has recently been studied by Neev (1964). The bottom of the southern basin is saucer-shaped with the deepest point 4.5 meters (15 feet) below the present level of the lake. This basin is separated by a narrow, submerged bar from the northern basin, the deepest point of which, as established by Lynch (1852), lies 395 meters (1317 feet) below the present lake surface. Down to a water depth of about 300 meters (1000 feet), the bottom of the northern basin is very irregular, and dissected by two main canyons with many tributaries. This relief, which can only have been formed subaerially, is blanketed by recent sediments only at depths greater than 300 meters (1000 feet).

(III) Water

(a) Physical Properties. The water temperatures from the surface down to a depth of approximately 40 meters (130 feet) are subject to large seasonal variations. Minimum values (December–January) range from 19–23°C (66–73°F), while highest temperatures (July–August) range from 34–36°C (93–97°F). Extreme values on record are a minimum of 10°C (50°F) and a maximum of 38°C (100°F). Below the thermocline, at a depth of 40–50 meters (130–170 feet), temperatures are constant geographically and seasonally, and increase slightly with depth from 19°C (66°F) to almost 22°C (72°F) in the deep bottom water.

The average specific gravity of the surface water is 1.206 g/cm^3. It is lowest in summer (1.201 g/cm^3) and highest in winter (1.210 g/cm^3). The water of the shallow southern basin is denser, with values of up to 1.2301 g/cm^3. No seasonal variations occur in the lower water mass, where densities increase from 1.226 g/cm^3 at a depth of 50 meters (170 feet) to 1.234 g/cm^3 from 100 meters (335 feet) down to the greatest depth.

During most of the year the upper water mass has a pronounced density stratification, but in mid-winter it is uniform down to a depth of 40 meters (130 feet). The equalization is probably the result of an overturn of the entire upper water mass in early winter.

The current pattern (Neev, 1964) is largely controlled by the shallow southern basin, although this contains only 0.5% of the total water volume. Lighter, but cooler, water enters the southern basin from the north, flowing along the western lakeshore, while warmer, but denser, water leaves the southern basin northward along the eastern side of the Lisan Strait.

(b) Chemical Properties. The salinity of the Dead Sea water, the highest of any of the major lakes, is 27–29% near the surface, increasing to 32.7% at depth; the average value is 31.55%. Chemical analyses are given in Table 1.

TABLE 1. CHEMICAL COMPOSITION OF DEAD SEA AND RELATED WATERS (mg/l)

	1	2	3	4
Na^+	33,500	34,940	24,813	357.8
K^+	6,300	7,560	15,992	20.0
Ca^{2+}	13,000	15,800	37,240	156.8
Mg^{2+}	34,500	41,960	41,670	80.5
Cl^-	180,800	208,020	247,720	736.4
Br^-	4,100	5,920	2,900	6.89
$SO_4^=$	900	540	107	231.0
HCO_3^-	248	240	127	251.0
Total	273,348	314,980	370,569	1,840.39

1 = Dead Sea surface water.
2 = Dead Sea average.
3 = Average of three salt springs, Mount Sdom.
4 = Jordan River at Jericho.

The water is of the pure halogene type, $SO_4^=$ and HCO_3^- together accounting for only 0.4% of the total anions. Cl^- is the dominant anion, followed by Br^-. The Br^- content of 5920 mg/liter is the highest one known for any surface water, and the Cl^-/Br^- ratio of 35.1 is only one-eighth that of the ocean. The dominant cations are Mg^{2+} and Na^+, followed by Ca^{2+}. The abundance of Ca^{2+}, forming 15.75% of all cations present, is a special feature of the Dead Sea. The Na/K ratio is 4.6, one-sixth that of the ocean. The upper water mass contains 1.6 ml/liter of free oxygen, but none is present at depths exceeding 50 meters (170 feet). The H_2S content varies irregularly from 7–14 ml/liter, and some is found even in the upper water mass in disequilibrium with free oxygen. Dissolved organic C is 6600 mg/m^3 and total N is 7000 mg/m^3, the latter increasing with depth. The oxidation potential (Eh) of the upper water mass is positive: $+50$ to $+100$ mV, but negative at greater depth: -50 to -350 mV. The total amount of major salts in the Dead Sea is given in Table 2.

Table 2. Salt Content of Dead Sea (in 10^6 tons)

$MgCl_2$	23,000
NaCl	12,650
$CaCl_2$	6,119
KCl	2,050
$MgBr_2$	975
$CaSO_4$	105
$Ca(HCO_3)_2$	46
Total	44,945 10^6 tons

Some of the few trace element data known are given in Table 3.

Table 3. Some Trace Elements in Dead Sea (ppm)

Rb	60
Li	~ 15
B	50
Si	40
Al	< 100
Mn	13
I	< 0.1

The scarcity of Li^+ and B^{3+} is explained by the absence of acid volcanics in the drainage area, the small values of Al^{3+} and Si^{4+} by the high salinity. The origin of the Dead Sea Salts was studied by Bentor (1961) who concluded that they are not cyclic. About 1/3 of the salts were brought into the lake by the Jordan River; the remainder were brought by fossil brines left over partly from the Lisan Lake, preceding the present Dead Sea, and partly from older Tertiary and Pleistocene lakes; these highly concentrated brines now issue as springs near the shores of the lake.

(IV) Sediments

The bottom sediments of the northern basin consist of 10–50 cm (4–20 inches) of dark, jelly-like, unconsolidated mud, underlain by rock salt of unknown thickness. The sediments of the shallow southern basin are composed of alternating layers of salt, silty clay and marl. The dominant clay mineral is kaolinite; smaller amounts of illite and montmorillonite are present in all samples, and palygorskite is found in most of them. The marls are finely laminated with aragonite dominant in the lighter, and calcite in the darker, laminae. The Dead Sea water today is slightly undersaturated in respect to NaCl, and halite precipitation takes place at present only very locally. Sediments extracted from the water or caught in traps consist of 50–90% gypsum, 5–20% aragonite, traces of calcite and 5–25% silt and clay. The bottom sediment, in comparison, is much poorer in gypsum, and it is assumed that at least 90% of it is destroyed here, probably by sulfate-reducing bacteria with concomitant development of H_2S.

A peculiar feature of the Dead Sea is the so-called whitening. During these periods, which occur at irregular intervals, averaging 4–5 years but always during the hottest season, the blue color of the lake turns a milky white. The whitening is caused by a sudden precipitation of aragonite and some gypsum from the lake water, strongly oversaturated in respect to $CaCO_3$. As much as 10^{10} tiny crystals of aragonite and 10^8 crystals of gypsum have been found per liter of white surface water.

(V) Life

Notwithstanding its name, the Dead Sea is not entirely devoid of life. Elazari-Volcani (1943a, 1943b, 1944) isolated from the bottom sediments a blue-green alga (*Aphanocapsa* sp.), a flagellate (*Dunaliella viridis*), an amoeba, a ciliate, and bacteria (thiosulfate-oxidizing, cellulose-decomposing, denitrifying, and others).

(VI) Age and History of the Dead Sea

The age of the present Dead Sea has been calculated by Bentor (1961) on geochemical grounds to 12,000 years, an age partly corroborated by preliminary C^{14} determinations. The level of the Dead Sea is subject to considerable changes, which have reached at least 11 meters (37 feet) during the past 150 years. The shallow southern basin was frequently separated from the northern one and occasionally constituted a playa. There is some evidence that during Biblical and Roman times the Dead Sea was confined to the northern basin and that the last flooding of the southern one took place only about 1500 years ago (Neev, 1964). More extensive lakes, ancestral to the Dead Sea, existed in the Jordan/Dead Sea depression during Pleistocene and Tertiary times.

(VII) Economic Geology

Potash has been extracted from the Dead Sea since 1930, and bromine since 1935. Present annual production: 250,000 tons KCl and about 4000 tons Br.

Y. K. Bentor

References

Ben-Arieh, Y., 1964, "A tentative water balance estimate of the Lisan Lake," *Deep-Sea Res.*, **11**, 42–47.

Bentor, Y. K., 1961, "Some geochemical aspects of the Dead Sea and the question of its age," *Geochim. Cosmochim. Acta*, **25**, 239–260.

Blanckenhorn, M., 1912, "Naturwissenschaftliche Studien am Toten Meer und im Jordantal," Berlin.

Bloch, M. R., Litman, H. Z., and Elazari-Volcani, B., 1944, "Occasional whiteness of the Dead Sea," *Nature*, **154**, 402.

Elazari-Volcani, B., 1943a, "Bacteria in the bottom sediments of the Dead Sea," *Nature*, **152**, 274.

Elazari-Volcani, B., 1943b, "A dimastigamoeba in the bed of the Dead Sea," *Nature*, **152**, 301.

Elazari-Volcani, B., 1944, "A ciliate from the Dead Sea," *Nature*, **154**, 335.

Emery, K. O., and Neev, D., 1959, "Preliminary Report on Surveys of the Dead Sea," Unpublished report, Geological Survey Israel, Jerusalem.

Freund, R., 1965, "A model of the structural development of Israel and adjacent areas since Upper Cretaceous times," *Geol. Mag.*, **102**(3), 189–205.

Klein, C., 1961, "On the fluctuations of the level of the Dead Sea since the beginning of the nineteenth century," *Ministry Agri. Hydrol. Serv. Israel, Hydrol. Paper* **7**, 1–73.

Lartet, L., 1876, "Exploration Géologique de la Mer Morte de la Palestine et de l'Idumée," Paris, Bertrand.

Lynch, W. F., 1852, "Official Report of the U.S. Expedition to Explore the Dead Sea and the River Jordan," Baltimore, John Murphy and Co.

Neev, D., and Emery, K. O., 1967, "The Dead Sea, depositional processes and environments of evaporites," *Bull. Geol. Surv. Israel*, **41**.

Neev, D., 1964, "Recent Sedimentary Processes in the Dead Sea," Unpublished Ph.D. Thesis, Hebrew University, Jerusalem.

Quennell, A. M., 1958, "The structural and geomorphic evolution of the Dead Sea rift," *Quart. J. Geol. Soc. London*, **114**, 1–24.

Cross-references: *Block Mountain*; *Cryptodepressions*; *Playa*; *Rift Valley*; *Sabkha*. Vol. IV: *Geological Time Scale*; also Geochemical and Mineral entries.

DEEP LEADS—*See* LAVA-DISPLACED DRAINAGE AND DEEP LEADS

DEFLATION

Deflation is a term of geomorphology used for the removal of solid particles by wind (from Latin: *deflare*, to blow away). Wind erosion may be divided into two types: deflation (actual removal of grains) and *abrasion* (q.v., the polishing and scouring of rock surfaces by wind-carried grains). Deflation can therefore affect only loose or very loosely cemented sediments, not consolidated rock (Walther, 1924). The term was first proposed by Walther in 1891 after observations of the *salt pans* and *vleis* in South Africa, many of which are of this origin.

Deflation is the common and most important form of erosion in flat deserts; in deserts with some relief, rain and running water (however rare) become the major agents. The fine-grained materials, *dust*, are the most easily removed particles and these rise by turbulence into the upper atmosphere, to be transported often several hundred or even a thousand miles from their point of origin. Heavy dust falls thus occur in the Atlantic Ocean, 500 miles off the Saharan coast of Africa. During the late Pleistocene retreat of the ice sheets in Europe, Central Asia and North America, the glacial "flour" was carried by deflation to form the great *loess*

deposits. In Asia alone, the late Pleistocene loess deflation involved over 40×10^{12} cubic meters (Walther, 1924). The distribution of such deposits permits the reconstruction of "paleo-wind" patterns. Reddish loess-like deposits are also on the borders of the Sahara and Arabian deserts, but they seem to differ petrographically from true periglacial loess.

After dust, stronger winds enable sand to be removed by deflation, but only by drifting and saltation (see *Wind Action*). It does not carry so far and accumulates in *sand dunes* (q.v.). This process is one of *winnowing*, whereby the light material is carried away leaving behind progressively coarser material, gravel and boulders. It should be stressed that wind is not the primary agent of erosion, because the clay, sand and boulders were initially weathered out chemically, then were carried out to the foot of the mountains by fluvial erosion, and accumulated in lake basins or alluvial fans (Fitzner, 1939). It is the wind that carries out further transportation.

The residual surface covered with stones is called a *lag-gravel* (Fig. 1), *desert pavement*, *gibber plain* (Australia), or in Africa *hamada* (q.v.) or *reg*. Such stones or pebbles rapidly become coated with a dark reddish coating known as *desert varnish* (q.v.).

Where the underlying formation consists of fine, poorly consolidated materials as in alluvial fans and playa flats, deflation may scoop out hollows of considerable dimensions, up to a mile or so across. These are sometimes called *blow-outs*. Thousands occur in the alluvial high plains from Montana to Texas (Judson, 1950). Big Hollow, in the Laramie Basin of Wyoming, evidently subject to extremely severe wind action in the late glacial period (nearby there are many wind-abraded surfaces), measures 9×3 miles and is 150 feet deep.

There has been much discussion about the origin of some depressions (partly below MSL) in the Western Desert of Egypt, Qattara, Fayum, Wadi Natrun, etc., where a tectonic alternative has sometimes been favored. The most likely explanation is that the lithology in these areas was medium to fine grained and uncemented, probably former deltaic areas of the ancestral Nile, and this predisposed the material to deflation. Large ablation hollows in the Gobi Desert of Mongolia ("P'ang Kiang Hollows"), up to 5 miles across and 400 feet deep, have been described by Berkey and Morris (1927). The *shotts* (chotts) along the southern border of the Atlas Mts. in Algeria and Tunisia are also partly of this origin. This frequent relationship with high mountains provides both the right facies (dry alluvial fans) and also the high velocity winds (see Vol. II, *Katabatic (Gravity) Winds*).

Another ablation form is particularly noticeable in Egypt. This is what Hume (1925) called the "*Sand-cut Hummock*" country especially near the Kharga oasis. In an Upper Cretaceous limestone,

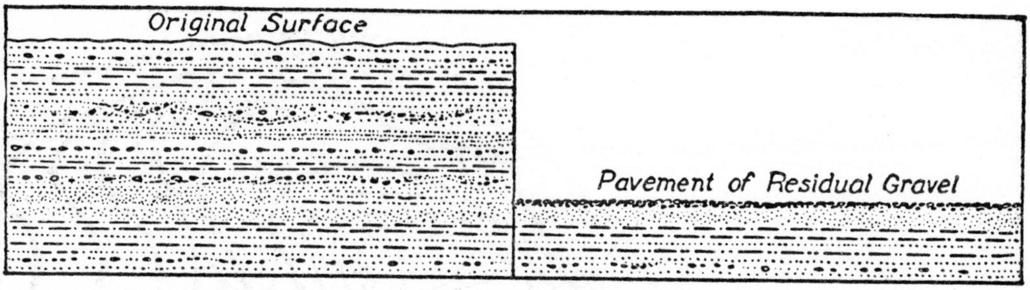

FIG. 1. Diagram illustrating the origin of residual gravels by deflation. The left half of the figure shows a bed of friable sediments containing pebbles. The right half shows the fine material blown away, concentrating the pebbles in a surface "lag" gravel (from Berkey and Morris, 1927).

low round hills are left as residuals, while sand blast has taken out the material between, giving somewhat the impression of a "tit-hill" karst; possibly it developed first as such a karst during an earlier high-rainfall stage and was then modified by deflation. Blackwelder (1931) described small residual mesas about 10 feet high in the Mojave Desert of California isolated by a similar form of deflation. In some cases, pedestal rocks may develop by deflation, but rainwash is the more important agent (see also discussions under *Yardang*, q.v.).

About half a century ago, deflation was considered (by Passarge and others) to be largely responsible for what today are called *pediplains* and *inselberg* landscapes. These are now clearly recognized as the product of running water, although many of the North African and Arabian prototype examples are not being so eroded today, but simply represent relics of Pleistocene rainfall phases.

RHODES W. FAIRBRIDGE

References

Ball, J., 1939, "Contributions to the Geography of Egypt," Cairo, Survey and Mines Dept., 308pp.

Berkey, C. P., and Morris, F. K., 1927, "Geology of Mongolia," New York, American Museum of Natural History, 475pp.

Blackwelder, E., 1931, "The lowering of playas by deflation," *Am. J. Sci.*, **221,** 140–144.

Eardley, A. J., Gvosdetsky, V., and Marsell, R. E., 1957, "Hydrology of Lake Bonneville and sediments and soils of its basin," *Bull. Geol. Soc. Am.*, **68,** 1141–1201.

Fitzner, R., 1939, "Die Entstehung der Dünenlandschaft in der Sahara," *Geogr. Anz. Gotha*, **40,** No. 2, 36–38.

Hume, W. F., 1925, "Geology of Egypt," in "Survey of Egypt," Vol. 1, Cairo, Government Press.

Judson, S., 1950, "Depressions of the northern portion of the southern high plains of eastern New Mexico," *Bull. Geol. Soc. Am.*, **61,** 253–274.

Peel, R. F., 1941, "Denudational landforms in the central Libyan desert," *J. Geomorphol.*, **4,** 3–23.

Tricart, J., 1954, "Influence des solo salés sur la déflation éolienne en basse Mauritanie et dans le delta du Sénégal," *Rév. Géomorphol. Dynamique*, **5,** 124–132.

Walther, J., 1924, "Das Gesetz der Wüstenbildung," Leipzig, Quelle and Meyer, 421pp.

Cross-references: *Abrasion; Alluvial Fan or Cone; Desert Varnish; Gibber; Hamada; Inselberg; Karst; Loess; Mesa and Butte; Pediplanation; Sand Dunes; Wind Action; Yardang.* Vol. II: *Katabatic (Gravity) Winds.* pr Vol. VI: *Ablation.*

DE GEER MORAINES—*See* MORAINE

DEGLACIATION, RECESSION

Just as glaciation normally is taken to mean the covering of the land by an ice sheet or by multiple glaciers, *deglaciation* refers to the uncovering of the landscape, accompanying the melting of those ice sheets. On the grand scale the terms glacierization-deglacierization have some following (Thompson, 1954), but are not widely used. Flint (1957, p. 56) says "by deglaciation is meant the uncovering of any area as a result of glacier shrinkage," but this is not the usual meaning, which involves a large-scale ice retreat, an almost total abandonment of a region by ice sheets.

Recession or *retreat* is used for any negative movement of the ice front or glacier snout. There may be an annual recession (alternating with advance) or a general recession (of centuries or more, alternating with larger or smaller readvances).

It is customary thus to use *deglaciation* for the total ice abandonment of a major region as during the *interglacial* stages of the Quaternary epoch and to speak of a *major recession* for any important step in a deglaciation or for an *interstadial stage*, which would involve perhaps no more than 25% of the total ice volume of a continental ice sheet.

A *recessional moraine* sequence is an end moraine found repeated in succession of temporary stillstands (Salisbury, 1907; Cotton, 1942). Wooldridge and Morgan (1959) prefer the term *stadial moraine*,

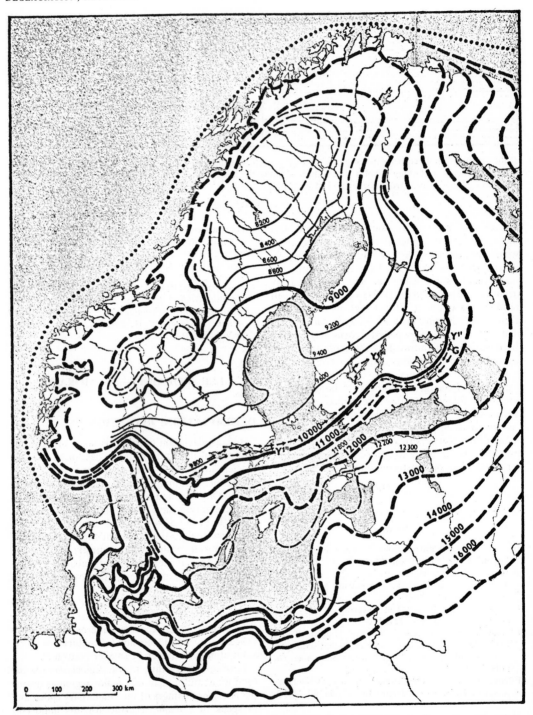

Fig. 1. The deglaciation of Scandinavia over the last 18,000 years, as indicated by groups of recessional moraines dated ("Before Present") by varve counts and C^{14} (E. H. de Geer, 1954).

saying: "In strict usage, 'terminal moraines' are those marking maximum extension of the ice, while 'stadial moraines' mark stages of a retreat, though the former is often used in a general sense covering both cases."

Deglaciation or recession occurs when the glacial

"budget" or "mass economy" becomes strongly negative averaged over periods of the order of centuries or millennia. The ablation loss may be in the form of *melting* (e.g., subglacial streams, etc.), *evaporation* (e.g., from the ice surface and meltwater pools), *sublimation* (transfer directly to water vapor from ice; see Vol. II, *Latent Heat*), *deflation* (mechanical removal of particles by wind), and *calving* [breaking off of large blocks at the distal limit of a glacier to form *icebergs* (q.v., Vol. I), ice islands, etc.]. Heat exchange occurs mainly by condensation and convective turbulence. Continental ice sheets lose relatively little heat by direct melting, and much by evaporation, sublimation and calving, while temperate mountain glaciers lose less than 1% by evaporation and most by melting (Ahlmann, 1948; Troll, 1949; Meier, 1962; Hoinkes, 1964).

Ahlmann believed that the majority of glaciers are more sensitive to ablation than to variations in precipitation. In other words, when thinking of climatic changes that would lead to deglaciation and recessional melting, one should not be so concerned with the sources of moisture (the prime fallacy of the Ewing-Donn Ice Age Theory), but with the variations in solar radiation and the length of the summer melting season. Systematic surveys carried out over many years, especially in mountain (valley) glaciers, have shown a year-to-year sensitivity to local temperature variations. Peak high temperatures are less significant than length of melt season. It is true that a year or cycle of higher temperatures at sea level may well correspond to higher evaporation from the ocean, therefore more cloud, and more precipitation that at higher elevations results in snow, and thus a positive accumulation/ablation economy. This could lead to the anomaly that a cold, high-altitude glacier may advance, at the same time as a low-level glacier in the same region melts. The higher the mean temperatures, however, the greater is the rate of glacier motion and the greater is the net loss, especially by calving.

Studies of climatic variations over the last century show that vigorous reactions in the temperate latitude mountain glaciers are paralleled by the rise and fall of sea level (Fairbridge, 1963), eustasy being the "tide gauge" of the world hydrologic budget, and thus the best overall net world accumulation/recession indicator. During the deglaciation at the close of the Wisconsin Ice Age, it seems likely that it was low-altitude ablation that thinned the distal (equatorward) lobes of the Scandinavian and North American ice sheets, creating stagnant *dead ice* (see *Stagnant Ice Melting*) and waning ice thicknesses, to the point of extinction (Ahlmann, 1938; Mannerfelt, 1945).

RHODES W. FAIRBRIDGE

References

Ahlmann, H. W., 1938, "Uber das Entstehen von Toteis," *Geol. Foren. Stockholm Forh.*, **60**, 327–341.

Ahlmann, H. W., 1948, "Glaciological Research on the North Atlantic Coasts," *Royal Geogr. Soc. Res. Ser.*, **1**, 83pp.

Blake, W., Jr., 1966, "End moraines and deglaciation chronology in northern Canada with special reference to southern Baffin Island," *Canada Geol. Surv. Paper* **66-26**, 31pp.

Cotton, C. A., 1942, "Climatic Accidents in Landscape making," Christchurch, Whitcombe & Tombs, 354pp.

Fairbridge, R. W., 1963, "Mean sea level related to solar radiation during the last 20,000 years," in "Changes of Climate," pp. 229–242, U.N.E.S.C.O., Nat. Res. ser. **20**.

Field, W. O., Jr., 1947, "Glacier recession in Muir Inlet," *Geogr. Rev.*, **37**, 369–399.

Flint, R. F., 1957, "Glacial and Pleistocene Geology," New York, John Wiley & Sons, 553pp.

Flint, R. F., and Demorest, M., 1942, "Glacier thinning during deglaciation; Pt. 1, Glacier regimes and ice movement within glaciers," *Am. J. Sci.*, **240**, 29–66.

Geer, E. H. de, 1954, "Skandinaviens geokronologi," *Geol. Foren. Stockholm Forh.*, **76**.

Hoinkes, H. C., 1964, "Glacial Meteorology," in (Odishaw, H., editor), "Research in Geophysics," Vol. 2, pp. 391–424, Cambridge, Mass., M.I.T. Press.

Lee, H. A., 1962, "Method of deglaciation, age of submergence, and rate of uplift west and east of Hudson Bay, Canada," *Biuletyn Peryglac.*, **11**, 239–245.

Mannerfelt, C. M., 1945, "Några glacialmorphologiska Formelement," *Geogr. Annal.*, **27**, 1–239 (with English summary).

Meier, M. F., 1962, "Proposed definitions for glacier mass budget terms," *J. Glaciol.*, **4**(33), 242–261.

Nelson, J. G., 1963, "The origin and geomorphological significance of the Morley Flats, Alberta," *Bull. Canadian Petrol. Geol.*, **11**(2), 169–177.

Salisbury, R. D., 1907, "Physiography," New York, Henry Holt, 770pp.

Thompson, H., 1954, "Glacierization," *J. Glaciol.*, **2**, 507.

Troll, C., 1949, "Schmelzung und Verdunstung von Eis und Schnee in ihrem Verhältnis zur geographischen Verbreitung der Ablationsformen," *Erdkunde*, **3**, 18–29.

Wooldridge, S. W., and Morgan, R. S., 1959, "An Outline of Geomorphology," Second ed., London, Longmans, Green and Co., 409pp.

Cross-references: *Eustasy*; *Glaciation, Glacierization*; *Moraine*; *Quaternary Period*; *Stagnant Ice Melting*; *Valley (Mountain) Glacier.* Vol. I: *Icebergs.* Vol. II: *Ice Age Theory*; *Latent Heat*; *Little Ice Age.* pr Vol. VI: *Ice Sheet.*

DEGRADATION

This is a rather old-fashioned term referring to the erosion or wearing down of the land surface by any or all epigene agents, already used by Guettard in 1774, and also by Kirwan and Playfair. It is essentially synonymous with *denudation* (q.v.), but W. M. Davis (1902) distinguished it from the latter, saying that degradation implies the later stages of the erosion cycle "in which a graded slope is reduced to fainter and fainter declivity, although maintaining its graded condition all the while." As a general term it has little use, but in this special

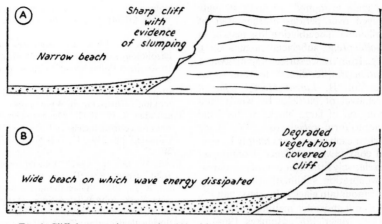

FIG. 1. Cliffs in nonresistant rocks: (A) with active erosion, (B) with no active erosion (from Sparks, 1960). (By permission of John Wiley & Sons, N.Y.)

application is sometimes helpful in dealing with fluvial erosion and valley development.

In coastal erosion, if the rate of marine erosion is less than the general subaerial denudation of a cliff, then the result will be a degraded cliff (Sparks, 1960; see Fig. 1). The late Holocene drop of sea-level (normally about 3 meters) results in many degraded or "fossil" cliffs (*falaises mortes* of the French).

The term degradation is also used in soil science (see *Pedology*, pr Vol. VI) and refers to a heavily leached soil.

RHODES W. FAIRBRIDGE

References

Davis, W. M., 1902, "Base-level, grade and peneplain," *J. Geol.,* **10,** 77–111 (also in "Geographical Essays," New York, Dover, reprint, 1954).

Sparks, B. W., 1960, "Geomorphogy," London, Longmans, Green; New York, John Wiley & Sons, 371pp.

Stamp, L. D., 1961, "A Glossary of Geographical Terms," London, Longmans, Green, 539pp.

Cross-references: *Aggradation; Base Level; Denudation; Equilibrium; Eustasy; Holocene; Rivers.* pr Vol. VI: *Leaching; Pedology.*

DELL

A characteristic but often problematic feature of the periglacial landscape is the dell or dry valley. The typical dell may be described as a small dry valley with no trace of linear, fluvial erosion. It is a special type of *dry valley* (q.v.), well-known examples occurring typically on the Cretaceous chalk landscapes of southern England, France and Germany. Spring sapping is widely favored as an explanation, however, rather than periglacial mechanisms (Sparks and Lewis, 1957; Small, 1964). It may be either (a) a broad depression with a dish-like cross section and long or short extension, or (b) a narrow semi-cylindrical trough of appreciable elongation.

Dells can be found on igneous rocks such as granite, just as well as on sediments including dolomite, limestone, chalk, clay, loess, alluvial loam and gravel sheets. They are best known perhaps from loess profiles and fluvial terrace gravels and loams because these are constantly being exposed in industrial pits and workings. They occur most frequently on slopes, but can also be found on residual river terraces and on plains near relatively deep valleys. They are very widespread in the loess regions of the world. The original word *Delle* is German, meaning, as in English, a "little valley." Other terms used sometimes in German are *Tilke, Muldentälchen, Ursprungmulden, Kerbensprung, Tilkensprung* (Schmitthenner, 1925; Stratil-Sauer, 1931; Kellersohn, 1952; Louis, 1961). In England they are always called "dry valleys," but this expression covers several other concepts. Examples from New Zealand in association with other periglacial features have recently been described by Stevens (1957).

As to origin, it is clear that dells are not rock-morphological features, i.e., peculiar to a certain lithology, but are associated with a specific periglacial climate condition, thus *climatic-morphological phenomena*. In eastern Europe they are classified as "*derasional valleys*," the term "*derasion*" referring to the peculiar erosion and denudation that is achieved without obvious agency of wind or flowing water, but by freeze and thaw activity. Dells are a mixed product of periglacial *nivation* (q.v.), *solifluction* (q.v.) and *pluvionivation*, a mixed season rain and snow condition (Pécsi, 1964). In origin, they are evidently closely related to *nivation hollows.*

Two types of erosional activity can be distinguished in dell evolution: (a) initiation and deepen-

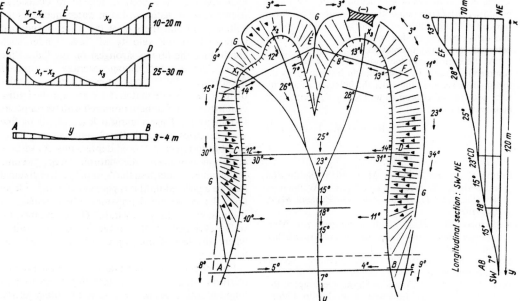

FIG. 1. A twin-headed dell, on dolomitic limestone, near Szar, Hungary (Pécsi, 1964).

ing with accretion in the floors of the dells; (b) overall denudation of the land surface, slope reduction and accretion on the lower slopes and dell floors.

In the low hilly country of the periglacial regions of central Europe (e.g., Thuringia, Bohemia, Moravia, Hungary) the dells make up more than half the relief in the landscape. The number of dells here is a multiple of that of the erosional valleys.

Pécsi (1964, p. 45) described the Hungarian dells (Fig. 1) as follows:

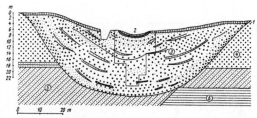

FIG. 2. Section through an early Pleistocene dell, filled with loamy gravel, situated on the Kemeneshát gravel plateau, at Sarvar, Hungary (Pécsi, 1964). Legend: (1) clayey brown forest soil; (2) humic sand filling the youngest derasion valley, underlain by buried brown forest soil; (3) gravel coated by clay crust and bedded in light and dark brick-red clayey sand, the filling material of the ancient dell; it also contains Pannonian clay lumps; (4) gravel of the Kemeneshát, material of the early Pleistocene alluvial fan of the Raba; (5) upper Pliocene cross-bedded sand, with sandy clay in its upper horizon; (6) Pannonian clay, with sandy clay at the top horizon.

"The sizes of the dells chiefly depend on the orographic conditions of the relief, especially, within certain limits, on the relief energy of a relative altitude over 1 km². The gradient curve of the dell which depends partly upon the relative altitude, and partly upon the change in the quality of rocks is the most important feature for us. A common characteristic of the gradient curves is that at the upper wide drainage area of the dell they have a slight angle of dip, but are convex, then at the valley head they become steep, after that at the dell foot they pass into shorter or longer, slightly concave slopes; these patterns of the gradient may repeat themselves over the subsequent sections of the dell. . . . The slope patterns of a considerable number of the dells subjected to agriculture change even at the present time. However, the majority of the valleys were formed during the last glaciation. This is proved by the fact that the slopes of the dells are covered with stratified sediments often bearing the traces of the periglacial freezing effect. The convex slopes of our dells have recently been largely denuded by tillage, whereas the scourways caused by heavy rains are being regularly removed by ploughing and levelling the soil."

Dells are also known which formed prior to the last glaciation, in the early and middle Pleistocene. In the Rába Valley of Hungary, these older dells are so close together that they merge to form "pseudoterraces" on the valley slopes. On the edge of the Kemeneshát Plateau adjacent to this valley, there is large-scale infilling of the older dells due to Riss and Würm solifluction (Fig. 2). Following Pécsi (*op. cit.*, p. 121) once more:

"On the surface of the Kemeneshát, clayey brown forest soils and red clayey soils were formed during the interglacials, just as they are under the current climatic type. These soils offered very favorable conditions for the setting in of processes of gelifluction during the glacial periods. The redeposition of the rock material on slopes caused the filling of most of the former erosional valleys and dells, and the eroded relief became considerably flattened owing to cyroplanation.

"At the beginning of the Holocene, the area became completely covered by forest, but in historic times the forest cover became thin under the influence of agriculture, and the soil erosion as well as the degradation in dells revived again."

RHODES W. FAIRBRIDGE

References

Cotton, C. A., and Te Punga, M. T., 1955, "Solifluxion and periglacially modified landforms at Wellington, New Zealand," *Trans. Roy. Soc. New Zealand*, **82**(5), 1001–1031.

Kellersohn, H., 1952, "Untersuchungen zur Morphologie der Talanfänge im mitteleuropäischen Raum," *Kölner Geogr. Arb.*, 1.

Louis, H., 1961, "Allgemeine Geomorphologie," Second ed., Berlin, W. de Gruyter, 355pp.

Pécsi, M., 1964, "Ten Years of Physico-geographic Research in Hungary," Budapest, Akad. Kiadó, 132pp.

Schmitthenner, H., 1925, "Die Entstehung der Dellen und ihre morphologische Bedeutung," *Z. Geomorphol.*, **1**, 3–28.

Semmel, A., 1961, "Beobachtungen zur Genese von Dellen und Kerbtälchen im Löss," *Rhein-Mainische Forschungen*, **50**, 135–140.

Small, R. J., 1964, "The escarpment dry valleys of the Wiltshire Chalk," *Trans. Inst. British. Geogr.*, **34**, 33–52.

Sparks, B. W., and Lewis, W. V., 1957, "Escarpment dry valleys, near Pegsdon, Hertfordshire," *Proc. Geologists Assoc.* (*London*), **68**, 26–38.

Stevens, G. R., 1957, "Solifluxion phenomena in the Lower Hutt valley," *New Zealand J. Sci. Technol.*, B, **38**, 279–296.

Stratil-Sauer, G., 1931, "Die Tilke," *Z. Geomorphol.*, **6**, 255–286.

Cross-references: *Cryopedology, Cryonivation, Cryoplanation, Cryoturbation; Degradation; Denudation; Dry Valleys; Frost Action; Holocene; Loess; Nivation; Periglacial Landscapes; Solifluction.*

DELTA DYNAMICS

Changes in the configuration and surface morphology of deltas at the present time fall into three categories: (1) those associated with continuing deposition of fluvial sediment, (2) those related to shore processes on the delta margin and (3) those affecting the surface of the delta generally. There is some overlap between these three categories, but it is convenient to consider them separately.

Changes Associated with Fluvial Deposition

The depositional morphology of deltaic plains is often characterized by the development of natural levees bordering river channels. These represent localized vertical accretion, related to occasional flooding, when sediment-laden water inundates the deltaic plain and the size of the water-borne load is related to the velocity of flow. Under such conditions, the flow is strongest on the line of the river channel, diminishing laterally to quieter flood-waters. As the floods subside, large quantities of relatively coarse material are relinquished adjacent to the river channel, compared with fine deposits farther away. Thus a natural levee of silt or fine sand develops alongside the channel, sloping away into bordering clay-floored depressions. As vertical accretion continues, the natural levees become higher and broader, and the floor of the river channel may be aggraded until it is perched at a higher level than the bordering depressions which remain as ill-drained, swampy wetlands. These features are well developed in the lower Mississippi valley, where the levee-flank depressions are known as backswamps.

Fluvial deposition also takes place at the mouths of rivers, where horizontal accretion tends to prolong natural levees seaward as sedimentary jetties. These are well developed in areas of limited wave and current scour, notably in lake or lagoon environments; there are good examples in the coastal lagoons of southeastern Australia (see *Coastal Lagoon Dynamics*). Superabundance of fluvial sediment enables similar protruding jetties and subdelta lobes to develop alongside extending distributaries on the Mississippi delta, where shallow water offshore reduces the effectiveness of wave and current scour. Beyond the river mouth, shoals flanking the deeper outflow channel indicate the probable pattern of future growth of sedimentary jetties as subaerial forms. Once established, they develop as natural levees, built up and broadened by deposition from floodwaters. Crevassing (the

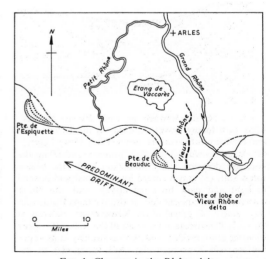

FIG. 1. Changes in the Rhône delta.

local breaching of natural levees during floods) and the initiation of distributary subdeltas are described under *Deltaic Evolution*.

The loading of silt and sand on to prodelta marine clays can lead to the local upwelling of domal structures known as *mudlumps*, a phenomenon that is relatively common off the Mississippi delta (Morgan, 1961).

Changes on the Delta Shoreline

The development of sedimentary lobes and jetties amounts to local progradation of the delta shore line around the mouths of rivers or distributaries. The process is usually modified to some extent by the effects of waves, and associated currents and by tidal action. The delicate, branched forms of the Mississippi subdeltas are possible only in a low wave energy environment. In a moderate wave energy environment, delta shore lines become cuspate in outline, as in the Tiber delta in Italy; in a high wave energy environment, the development of a protruding delta may be completely inhibited, as on the southeastern coast of Australia, where large rivers such as the Shoalhaven have built deltaic plains back of curved, sandy barrier shore lines prograded under the influence of strong ocean swell.

Even in a low wave energy environment, the delicate forms of sedimentary jetties tend to be modified as soon as reduced distributary outflow and diminished sediment yield bring the process of prolongation to an end. The lobate subdelta of the Vieux Rhône has been cut away since this distributary withered in the eighteenth century, and the diminution of the Petit Rhône has been followed by the removal of a similar subdelta lobe (Fig. 1). Erosion, chiefly by waves coming in from the southeast, has been followed by the dispersal of fine sediment and the westward drifting of the coarser sand fraction to be deposited in the sandy forelands of Pointe de Beauduc and Pointe de l'Espiguette, respectively. On the Mississippi delta, the sandy residues sorted from wave-dissected subdelta lobes form low beaches and barrier islands fringing the shore line, the largest being the migrating barrier island (Chandeleur Island) off the submerging and dissected St. Bernard subdelta, east of the modern delta.

In a moderate wave energy environment, sand supplied by the rivers or eroded from the delta shore is built into beaches, spits or barriers enclosing lagoons on the delta margin. This is well exemplified in the Nile delta (see *Deltaic Evolution*, Fig. 1), which has a number of enclosed coastal lagoons. The pattern of growth of some deltas is marked out by successive beach ridges, separated by swamps or plains of silt or clay, indicative of alternating phases of sedimentation on the delta margin. The Tagliamento delta in northern Italy has symmetrical patterns of beach ridges parallel to the delta shore

line, and the Danube delta has a more complicated pattern of intersecting and diverging beach ridges related to the erosion and rearrangement of deposits in successively abandoned subdelta lobes.

A distinction should be made between beach ridges built up on delta shores and later stranded by progradation and the ridges of sand or shell debris that are swept on to deltaic plains during occasional storm surges in a normally low wave energy environment. These are known as cheniers on the Mississippi delta, where they form narrow ridges threading across the deltaic plain. Similar features have been emplaced on deltaic coastal plains in the vicinity of the Orinoco in Venezuela and on the Surinam coast (Price, 1955).

Where there is strong longshore drifting, spits develop on a delta shore and may grow to deflect river mouths or seal off distributary outlets. The southward growth of sand spits under the influence of northwesterly ocean swell has deflected the outflow from the Senegal delta south beyond St. Louis. In Queensland, Australia, the shores of the Burdekin delta show a series of sand spits which have grown northward from distributary mouths in response to the dominant southeasterly waves (Fig. 2). On coasts exposed to strong ocean swell, the outflow from deltaic regions is confined to sectors of diminished wave energy, usually in the shelter of

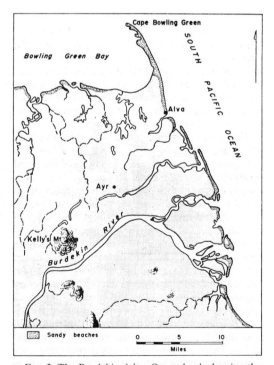

FIG. 2. The Burdekin delta, Queensland, showing the effects of longshore drifting toward the north, with sandy beaches and spits deflecting river outlets and a recurved spit at Cape Bowling Green.

253

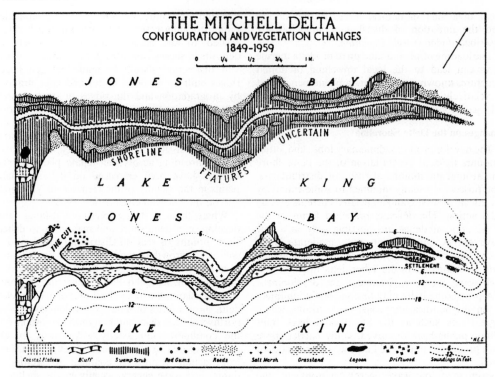

FIG. 3. The Mitchell delta (Gippsland Lakes, Australia) as it was in 1849 (above) and as it was in 1959 (below).

headlands, islands or offshore reefs. This is well illustrated on the New South Wales coast, where the Hunter, Macleay and Clarence rivers have each built extensive deltaic plains fringed on the seaward side by sandy barrier systems, the outflow in each case being located on the north flank of a rocky headland where the energy of the dominant south-easterly swell is reduced by refraction.

On low wave energy coasts, sectors of the delta shore are fringed by swamp vegetation, typically salt marsh, with mangroves in low latitudes, and reedswamp where the sea salinity has been sufficiently diluted by fresh water. The role of vegetation in delta shore dynamics is difficult to assess. In some cases, the vegetation merely occupies shallow water or tidal mud flat habitats made available by sedimentation, but colonization of an area by vegetation can promote sedimentation in patterns that might not otherwise develop, the decaying vegetation adding a quota of organic material to the accreting sediment. Salt marsh and reedswamp communities are probably more effective in promoting sedimentation than mangroves, which tend to spread on to tidal mud flats on low wave energy sectors of tropical deltas. The vegetation factor is evidently critical for sedimentary jetties built into the Gippsland Lakes (Fig. 3), a coastal lagoon system in southeastern Australia, which developed, and continue to grow, in the presence of shore line reedswamp (chiefly

Phragmites communis), but which have become unstable and are eroding away where this reed-swamp has disappeared, mainly as a consequence of increasing salinity following the cutting of an artificial entrance to the lagoons from the sea (see *Coastal Lagoon Dynamics*).

Changes on the Deltaic Plain

The morphology of a deltaic plain changes in response to the incidence of sediment-laden flood-waters which promote vertical accretion, particularly on channel margins; to the effects of the vegetation which colonizes depositional terrain; and to the extent of continuing subsidence, due to compaction of underlying sediment (including peat horizons) or crustal depression, isostatic or perhaps geosynclinal. The effects of subsidence have been accentuated during recent decades by a slight eustatic sea level rise.

The patterns of deposition from floodwaters have already been noted. Salt marshes, mangrove swamps in tidal areas and reedswamp (termed *roseau* on the Mississippi delta) may influence patterns of sedimentation in backswamps and contribute to the accumulation of organic muds and peat. The effects of subsidence are well illustrated on the Mississippi delta by marginal marine submergence and the raising of backswamp water levels in sectors of the delta where the land surface is not being built up more quickly by accretion. The sea gradually fingers into backswamp areas, and eventually the residual levees are drowned or eroded away. Depressions on the deltaic plain become permanent lakes, progressively enlarged and tending toward a rounded outline before they too are invaded by the sea and become marine embayments (Russell, 1936).

The rapidity of change of delta configuration can be seen from successive maps or aerial photographs which show how parts of a delta develop, modify and disappear with the passage of time. Delta dynamics are a response to the interplay of fluvial and marine processes, influenced by climatic and ecological conditions, and usually complicated by continuing subsidence.

E. C. F. BIRD

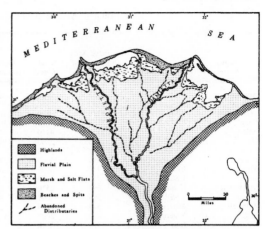

FIG. 1. Subaerial deltaic plain of the Nile River.

References

Bird, E. C. F., 1962, "The River Deltas of the Gippsland Lakes," *Proc. Roy. Soc. Victoria*, **75**, 65–74.
Coleman, J. M., and Gagliano, S. M., 1964, "Cyclical sedimentation in the Mississippi River deltaic plain," *Trans. Gulf Coast Assoc. Geol. Soc.*, **14**, 67–80.
Guilcher, A., 1963, "Estuaries, Deltas, Shelf, Slope," in (Hill, M. N., editor) "The Sea," Vol. 3, pp. 620–654, New York, Interscience Publ.
Morgan, J. P., 1961, "Mudlumps at the mouth of the Mississippi River," *Louisiana Dept. Conserv. Geol. Bull.*, **35**, 1–116.
Price, W. A., 1955, "Environment and formation of a chenier plain," *Quaternaria*, **2**, 75–86.
Russell, R. J., 1936, "Lower Mississippi River Delta," *Louisiana Dept. Conserv. Geol. Bull.*, **8**, 8–199.
Russell, R. J., 1942, "Geomorphology of the Rhône delta," *Ann. Assoc. Am. Geogr.*, **32**, 149–254.
Sykes, G., 1937, "The Colorado Delta," *Carnegie Inst. Wash. and Am. Geogr Soc.*, **19**.
Tjia, H. D., 1963, "Large deltas in Kalimantan," *Institute Technology Bandung*, No. 53, 73–90.
Van Straaten, L. M. J. U., 1960, "Some recent advances in the study of deltaic sedimentation," *Liverpool Manchester Geol. J.*, **2**, 411–22.

Cross-references: *Aggradation; Barriers—Beaches and Islands; Beach Ridge; Coastal Lagoon Dynamics; Cuspate Foreland or Spit; Deltaic Evolution; Levee—Natural; Mangrove Swamp; Sediment Transport.* Vol. 1: *Ocean Currents; Ocean Waves.*

DELTAIC EVOLUTION

Deltas are the product of rapid deposition of stream-borne sediments into relatively still-standing bodies of water. Their presence represents the continuing ability of a river to supply and deposit sand, silt and other detrital materials more rapidly than they can be removed by currents. Nearly 2500 years ago, Herodotus noted that the alluvial land enclosed between the diverging distributary branches of the Nile and the sea is deltoid in shape and used the Greek letter Δ (delta) to identify this land (Fig. 1). Since that time, the term delta has been modified in various ways, but it is generally applied to the subaerial plain formed by a river at its mouth without reference to its precise shape. Recent studies of modern deltas have shown that the subaqueous portions of a delta are characterized by a high rate of sedimentation, building up to create new land. In this manner, the shore line of the delta plain tends to move seaward or prograde with time. Therefore, geologists have had to direct their attention to the whole three-dimensional complex of deltaic deposits in order to understand the evolution of a deltaic sequence.

Present-day deltas display an enormous variety in size, shape, structure, composition and genesis (van Straaten, 1960). These differences exist because the same kind of event takes place under a wide range of settings (Table 1). Some of the major factors that influence the character of a delta include: (1) geologic setting and sediment sources in the drainage basin, (2) climatic conditions in both drainage and depositional basin, (3) tectonic stability of the basin, (4) river gradient and river regime, (5) depositional and erosional processes and their intensities within the delta proper, and (6) tidal range, eustasy and offshore hydrologic conditions. The numerous combinations between these factors and the element of time result in a dynamically changing complex of environments within delta regions. This is expected since deltas result from the interaction of forces of construction and forces of destruction. The relations between the effects of these mechanisms of supply and removal depend on the interaction and intensities of physical, biological and chemical processes operative within a delta.

A major phenomenon in deltaic evolution is the shifting of river courses into successive distributaries (Russell, 1936; Guilcher, 1963). As a delta progrades farther and farther into the sea, the

TABLE 1. MAJOR RIVER SYSTEMS OF THE WORLD[a]

River System	Country	Drainage Area (thousands of square miles)	Length (miles)	Delta Area (square miles)	Average Discharge (thousands of cfs[b])	Tidal Range at Mouth (ft)	Climate in Delta Area[c]
Amazon	Brazil	2231	4000	estuary	3500	18.7	Tropical rainforest (Am)
Congo	Belgian Congo	1550	2900	800	1400	5.6	Tropical savanna (Aw)
Mississippi	USA	1240	3890	10,100	611	1.5	Humid subtropical (Caf)
Lena	USSR	1169	3000	10,000	547	1.0	Tundra (ET)
Nile	Egypt	1150	4160	7,810	100	1.5	Subtropical desert (BWh)
Ob	USSR	1125	2800	1,100	441	2.3	Subarctic (Dcf)
Yenisey	USSR	1042	2360	950	614	1.3	Tundra (ET)
Paraná	Argentina	890	2000	1,320	526	3.3	Humid subtropical (Caf)
Yangtze	China	750	3000	estuary	770	13.8	Humid subtropical (Caf)
Amur	USSR	712	1770	estuary	338	7.5	Subarctic (Dcw)
Mackenzie	Canada	697	2520	2,520	280	1.3	Tundra (ET)
Volga	USSR	563	2300	4,280	—	0.0	Middle latitude desert (BWk)
Zambezi	Mozambique	513	2200	2,760	250	13.1	Tropical savanna (Aw)
Niger	Nigeria	430	2600	11,130	215	7.2	Tropical rainforest (Am)
Shatt-al-Arab	Iraq	430	1700	—	51	9.2	Subtropical steppe (BSh)
Ganges	E. Pakistan	430	1540	} 23,000 {	660	18.5	Tropical rainforest (Am)
Brahmaputra	E. Pakistan	361	1800		700	18.5	Tropical rainforest (Am)
Nelson	Canada	414	1660	—	80	17.1	Subarctic (Dcf)
Murray-Darling	Australia	414	2300	—	13	9.3	Mediterranean (Csb)
Indus	W. Pakistan	372	1980	3,300	196	13.8	Subtropical desert (BWh)
Yukon	Alaska	360	2300	2,240	180	4.0	Subarctic (Dcf)
Tocantins	Brazil	350	1000	—	360	14.1	Tropical rainforest (Am)
Mekong	Vietnam	350	2600	5,200	390	11.5	Tropical savanna (Aw)
Danube	Romania	347	1760	1,660	300	0.3	Humid continental (Da)
Orinoco	Venezuela	325	2200	9,480	600	7.2	Tropical rainforest (Am)
Hwang Ho	China	294	2700	950	700	11.1	Middle latitude steppe (BSk)
São Francisco	Brazil	260	1600	—	100	8.2	Tropical savanna (Aw)
Kolyma	USSR	249	—	1,430	—	0.2	Tundra (ET)
Dnieper (Dnepr)	USSR	194	1400	247	59	0.3	Middle latitude steppe (BSk)
Irrawaddy	Burma	166	1250	7,700	479	18.0	Tropical rainforest (Am)
Don	USSR	160	1220	250	—	0.0	Middle latitude steppe (BSk)
Dvina	USSR	139	1100	475	124	9.8	Subarctic (Dcf)
Indigirka	USSR	139	1113	3,540	64	0.4	Tundra (ET)
Amu Darya	USSR	115	1500	1,360	—	0.0	Middle latitude desert (BWk)
Godovari	India	115	900	—	127	5.9	Tropical savanna (Aw)
Magdalena	Colombia	93	950	950	265	2.0	Tropical steppe (BSh)
Fraser	Canada	92	700	—	113	10.2	Marine west coast (Cbf)
Rhine	Netherlands	56	800	—	78	18.0	Marine west coast (Cbf)
Rhône	France	37	500	650	59	0.7	Mediterranean subtropical (Csa)

[a] Compiled from various sources.
[b] Cubic feet per second.
[c] Simplified Köppen climatic classification.

gradient and carrying capacity of the river gradually decrease, and much shorter routes to the sea can be found in adjacent areas. Generally, the actual point of diversion occurs far inland from the delta, and its position is either accidental or develops because some favored crevasse continued to develop. From that point, the topography of the basin determines the new river course. The creation of a new course causes a shift in the site of active deltaic sedimentation. The abandoned or inactive delta is quickly attacked by the sea since it is no longer fed with sediment by the river; the balance between sea and river forces then favors erosion.

The new delta, however, progrades seaward rapidly, going through several stages of development until it also is abandoned and another site of active sedimentation is formed. The Mississippi River deltaic plain illustrates this point: seven deltaic lobes have been constructed in the past 5000 years (Fig. 2). The oldest delta lobe, the Sale-Cypremort, has undergone inundation and modi-

fication for the past 4000 years, and only a few remnants of the subaerial delta remain on the surface today. Each of the successive deltas has been modified to varying stages, depending on its age (Russell, 1936). The modern delta, the Balize or birdfoot, is the present locus of active deposition and has built its delta into relatively deep water. Other large river systems, such as the Nile, Ganges-Brahmaputra, Orinoco, and Niger, however, have not constructed and abandoned such well-defined delta lobes. Rather, certain distributaries have been built out, only to be abandoned in favor of another distributary located within the delta. For instance, the waters of the Nile reach the sea through two main distributaries, the Rosetta and the Damietta, yet several abandoned courses can be mapped (Fig. 1). It is apparent that these courses served as major distributaries sometime in the past.

The Mississippi delta has long served as a laboratory for detailed study of deltaic sedimentation. Its geologic history, morphology, sedimentary

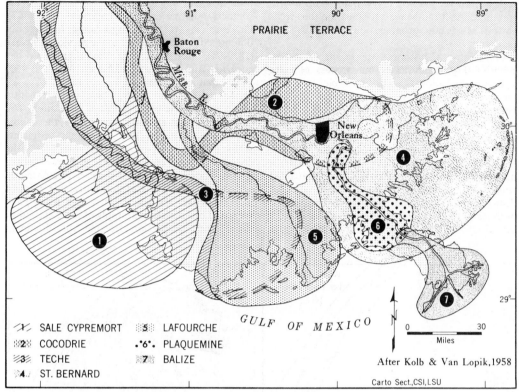

FIG. 2. Recent delta lobes of the Mississippi River.
(Interpretation is discussed also in article *Platforms—Wave-cut*.)

framework, and evolution have been well documented (Russell, 1936; Fisk, 1944; Scruton, 1960).
The large size of the major lobes of this delta and
their age cause difficulty in deciphering the details
of deltaic progradation. However, within the modern delta of the Mississippi River, there exists a
series of "*crevasses*" or subdeltas that form the bulk
of the "dry land" present in the area (Fig. 3). These
crevasses have formed in shallow bays between or
adjacent to the major distributaries. Four of the
crevasses shown in Fig. 3 have formed in historic
times, and much of their history can be traced by
historic maps. Initially, each crevasse system forms
as a break in the natural levee during flood stage
and gradually increases in size through successive
floods. During this time, a system of radial bifurcating channels is established. As the channels build
seaward, the slope or gradient of the distributary
becomes progressively flatter; water velocity, turbulence and sediment-carrying ability become accordingly less. Active deposition then ceases and
the process of abandonment begins. As a result of
regional subsidence and localized compaction, the
abandoned crevasse is inundated and eventually re-
verts back into a bay environment. The active life
of historically documented crevasse systems is
usually about 100 years. Thus, a crevasse is a

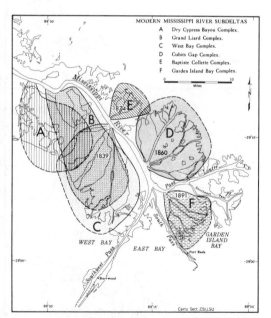

FIG. 3. Subdeltas or crevasses of the modern birdfoot
delta of the Mississippi River. Dates indicate year of
crevasse breakthrough (after Coleman and Gagliano,
1964).

257

scaled-down version of a major delta, both in size and time, and it can be used to illustrate the mechanisms of deltaic progradation (Coleman and Gagliano, 1964).

Comparison of historic maps of the West Bay subdelta (Fig. 4) illustrates the process of delta evolution. A shallow brackish water bay existed in the area as shown on several maps prior to 1839. Historical documents showed that in 1839, a break in the Mississippi River levee occurred. Figure 4(A) is a map of the West Bay area in 1845. The crevasse is shown only as an opening in the levee, and the bay had not begun to fill. By 1875 [Fig. 4(B)], a major portion of the former bay had been filled with deltaic sediments. A well-defined system of distributaries existed and had extended seaward a distance of 10 miles. During the succeeding 47-year period (1875–1922), the crevasse increased only a

little in area, principally near the mouths of the southerly discharging distributaries [Fig. 4(C)]. However, the rate of progradation had greatly diminished when compared to the previous 39 years (1839–75). Since 1922, very little progradation has occurred, and comparison of Figs. 4(C) and 4(D) shows that large areas of former marsh have reverted to bays and lakes. These maps illustrate nearly a complete cycle of deltaic deposition. The shallow bay that existed in the area in the middle 1800's was virtually filled by deltaic sediments within a 40–50 year period. By the latter 1800's, the channels of this crevasse were practically abandoned. They had extended themselves sufficiently seaward so that they had no appreciable gradient advantage over the major Mississippi River Pass. Deprived of a continuing supply of sediment, subsidence and compaction became the dominant

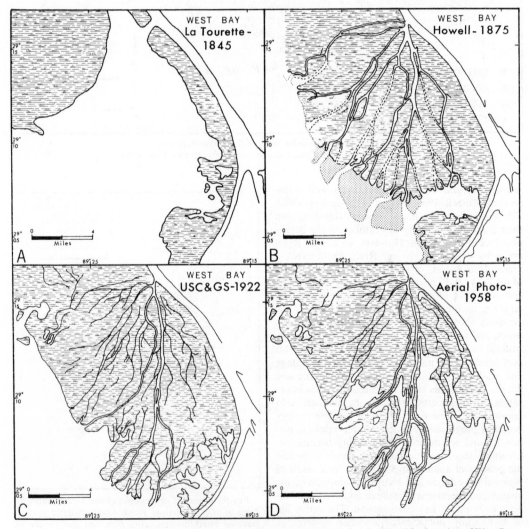

FIG. 4. Historic maps of the West Bay subdelta, Lower Mississippi River Delta. See Fig. 3 for location of West Bay.

operative processes, and the area began to be inundated by marine waters. Much of the remaining marshlands will be inundated in the near future, thus completing an entire cycle in the history of this part of the Mississippi River delta.

The map study serves only to show the plan view of the fill of West Bay, but it gives very little information on the three-dimensional picture of the deltaic deposits. Figure 5 shows the plan view of environmental relationships of an idealized crevasse system. The crevasse, as depicted, has been active for some time, filling a shallow bay between two major passes of a river. The breakthrough initiated at point A, and with time, channels became established, bifurcated and reunited to form an anastomosing distributary pattern. Later in its history, some distributaries became favored, while others were abandoned and became inactive. A locus of active deposition occurs outward from the prograding distributary mouths and is referred to as the delta-front complex of environments. This front advances into the bay, resulting in the deposition of a sheet of relatively coarse detritus which thickens locally in the vicinity of the channels. Seaward of the delta front is an area of fine clay accumulation or the prodelta environment. Other parts of the system, which have been partially

abandoned, are being inundated by marine waters.

The relationships between depositional facies can be more easily understood when viewed in cross section (Fig. 6). Note that section A–A' is approximately parallel to the trend of the distributaries while section B–B' is transverse. The basal facies consist of bay or marsh sediments and represent deposits that accumulated prior to crevassing or delta progradation. Once a crevasse begins to build seaward actively, the prodelta clays are the first river-borne sediments deposited on top of the marine clays. This is the first event in a deltaic constructional phase of vertically coarsening sediments that will accumulate as the delta front builds out into the bay. There is an upward passage from the pro-delta clays to delta front silts and sands deposited at the river mouth. Finally, subaerial deltaic plain deposits will extend over portions of the delta front deposits. These facies (prodelta, delta front, and subaerial delta) form the detrital lens of a delta mass (Fig. 6) and have a distinctive geometric form related to a radial bifurcating system of channels originating from a point source. Grain-size distribution within the lens grades from fine to coarse both upward in the section and horizontally from the distal ends of the system toward the point source of sediment supply. Once the crevasse system has been

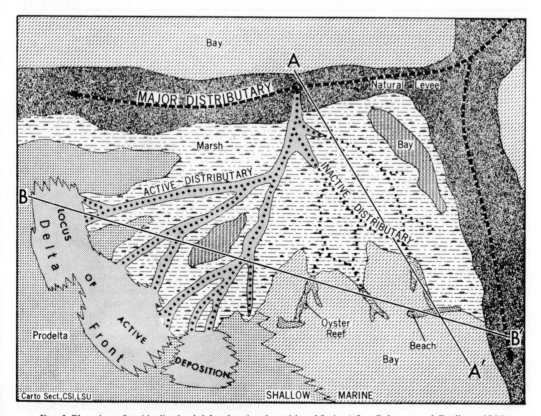

Fig. 5. Plan view of an idealized subdelta showing depositional facies (after Coleman and Gagliano, 1964).

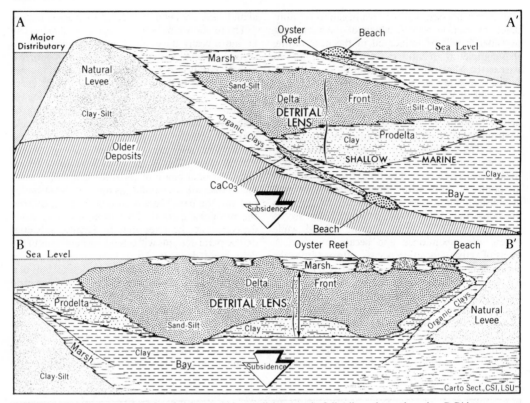

FIG. 6. Cross section of subdelta. Section A-A' is parallel to trend of distributaries and section B-B' is transverse. Location of sections is shown in Fig. 5 (after Coleman and Gagliano, 1964).

abandoned, subsidence, compaction, and coastal retreat become the dominant processes. During this time, organic-rich marsh and bay deposits tend to accumulate over the detrital lens of the delta. These sediments will continue to accumulate until introduction of new detritus by another advancing delta, and the cycle is repeated once again.

Thus, the crevasses of the Lower Mississippi River undergo a definite evolutionary cycle with time. The initiation, growth and abandonment of a delta lobe results in the preservation of two major components—detrital deposits and bounding deposits. The detrital lens is characterized by a high percentage of coarse clastics, abrupt facies changes, and rapid accumulation and burial rates. The bounding sediments are richer in organic constituents and chemical precipitates, have slower depositional rates, and tend to be tabular accumulations with considerable lateral continuity.

The process of deltaic evolution described is based primarily on data gathered from the Mississippi River delta. However, the process and the resulting vertical sequence of lithofacies are similar in all known modern deltas that have been studied in some detail. Variations in this sequence appear to be mainly in the size, shape and thickness of the units. These variations result from similar processes operating under differing geologic and climatic settings.

JAMES M. COLEMAN

References

Coleman, J. M., and Gagliano, S. M., 1964, "Cyclic sedimentation in the Mississippi River Deltaic Plain," *Trans. Gulf Coast Assoc. Geol. Soc.*, **14**, 67–80.

Fisk, H. N., 1944, "Geological Investigation of the Alluvial Valley of the Lower Mississippi River," Miss. River Comm., Vicksburg, Miss.

*Guilcher, A., 1963, "Estuaries, Deltas, Shelf, Slope," in (Hill, M. N., editor) "The Sea," Vol. 3, Ch. 24, 620–654, New York, Interscience Publ.

Russell, R. J., 1936, "Lower Mississippi River Delta," *Bull. Louisiana Geol. Surv.*, **8**, 8–199.

*Scruton, P. C., 1960, "Delta Building and the Deltaic Sequence," in "Recent Sediments, Northwest Gulf of Mexico," 82–102, Amer. Assoc. Petrol. Geol., Tulsa, Okla.

Shirley, M. L. (editor), 1966, "Deltas in their Geologic Framework," Houston Geol. Soc., 251pp.

Van Straaten, L. M. J. U., 1960, "Some recent advances in the study of deltaic sedimentation," *Liverpool Manchester Geol. J.*, **2**, 411–442.

* Additional bibliographic references may be found in this work.

Cross-references: *Braided Streams*; *Delta Dynamics*; *Eustasy*; *Levee*; *Rivers*. Vol. II: *Climatic Classification*.

DENDROCLIMATOLOGY—See Vol. II, TREE-RING ANALYSIS (DENDROCLIMATOLOGY)

DENUDATION

From the Latin *denudare* to uncover, the term denudation is one of the oldest technical terms in geology, referring to a consequence of the stripping of loose, weathered material from the landscape by various processes of *erosion* (q.v.) and *mass-wasting* (q.v.). It is the complement to *deposition*, the phenomenon of sedimentation, the two together representing the fundamental exogenic phases of the *geological cycle*.

A number of different interpretations and restrictions to this definition have been proposed by various writers from time to time, but the basic concept persists, i.e., as erosion involves the wearing down of the land surface, so denudation involves the exposing of deeper rock structures. Erosion has been compared with the carpenter's plane that strips away layer upon layer in the finest shavings, while denudation is the disclosure of what is often called a new *erosion surface*. It is evident that erosion and denudation are semantically very close, the first is the process and the second the consequence; as Jukes–Browne (1884) stressed, denudation refers to the uncovering of a particular stratum. One may say that a karst is an eroded landscape, but not necessarily a denuded one.

Davis (1909, p. 408) suggested that denudation belonged particularly to the youth and mature stages of a landscape cycle. One may visualize, for example, a landscape such as that of the southwestern United States that evolved through much of the Tertiary in a warm-humid climate, developing a thick chemically weathered soil cover. Toward the beginning of the Pleistocene (or late Pliocene, Blancan times), the world climate underwent a fundamental change; the former subtropical vegetation of the American southwest was severely curtailed by long and repeated droughts and by brief, seasonal thunderstorms resulting in rapid gullying and short transport. Thus a vast erosion cycle began that stripped the weathered regolith from the mountain slopes, dumping the detrital material into the existing river valleys (like the Rio Grande, Gila, etc.) and *leaving the landscape denuded*. Climatic oscillations and tectonic activity during the Quaternary have revived this denudation cycle in the upper slopes, correspondingly leading to deposition cycles in the lower valleys. Under dominantly arid conditions the sediments do not reach the sea; under brief "pluvial" (rainy) conditions there is a scouring of the valleys with progressive seaward transports, season by season, eventually carrying the silts into the ocean.

Analogous situations have now been worked out in many of the great African river systems (Fairbridge, 1964b): the Nile, Congo, Niger, Senegal, etc., and also in Australia and South America (Garner, 1959; Bigarella and de Andrade, 1965). During the glacial periods the reduced solar radiation and cooler ocean water resulted in reduced evaporation in the subtropical latitudes (the belts of maximum evaporation), so that very restricted monsoonal rains reached the savanna interiors and even the equatorial rains were greatly curtailed. The loss of vegetative cover in the regions of seasonal rains thus led to vast *denudation* where the slopes were adequate and to siltation in the middle courses of the great rivers, essentially a filling in and a drying up of the great tropical rivers (other than those fed by snow mountains).

According to Büdel, many of the world's uplands today disclose extensive tracts of these old denudation surfaces, as relict or "fossil" landscapes. (They are not strictly "fossilized"; the term *relict landforms*, q.v., according to Cotton, is more appropriate.) The important feature of such denudation surfaces is that they correspond to the lower limit of the earlier chemical weathering (cf. *Etchplains*) and not to any fluvial base levels, as Davisian geomorphologists would presume.

The processes leading to erosion and denudation are thus twofold: (1) There is *weathering*, the deep chemical breakdown of the bedrock that leads to regolith (and saprolite), in which the significant agents are the biochemical soil acids (H_2CO_3 and "humic acids") that depend on a constantly warm-wet organic humus favorable to rich plant growth and strong bacterial activity (Clarke, 1910, and others). (2) There is *transport*, the removal of the soluble and insoluble debris, which is absolutely essential for denudation to proceed. Without transport of insoluble debris, we can have a land surface that is deeply weathered and chemically eroded, but *not* denuded.

During the Pleistocene cold phases *three unusually effective transport agencies* were active over the earth's surface: (a) *Continental and mountain (valley) glaciers* mechanically scoured off the regolith and even gouged into massive bedrock. The regolith, often reddish-yellow, may still be preserved today along deeply weathered joint and fault planes, and in some deep valleys in regions where the ice scoured all surface debris down to polished bedrock. (b) *Periglacial frost riving (gelifraction)* and *solifluction* tended to clean off the highland slopes [leaving *tors* (q.v.) and craggy escarpments] and to round off the upland slopes; the gentle rounded "whaleback" contours of the English Chalk downs and the mild relief of the "fair land" of northern France and also Bavaria, the undulating landscapes of southern Pennsylvania, southern Ohio and Kentucky—all these were taken by Davis to be typical of the "*normal*" cycle of humid erosion, falsely, alas, for they are the direct outcome of now-arrested periglacial processes (Troll, 1948). (c) *Arid erosion agencies* became more effective over vast regions of the globe due to the extended droughts and loss of vegetation, the brief but violent action of running water from monsoonal-type precipitation and occasional summer thunderstorms (in latitudes 5–25°), and equatorward displacement of westerlies (latitudes 30–40°). A criticism of the effectiveness of summer rainfall in Arizona by R. J. Russell (1936) is parochial and ill-founded. Violent summer "freshets" had the effect of stripping uplands and spreading sand and silt over the piedmont areas and along valley floors. Here they would rapidly dry out and, lacking retentive grasses or scrub, they would be picked up by the wind to build vast dune fields. At the foot of high mountains, a combination of agencies aided this process: *Cirque* (*corrie*) *glaciers* (q.v.) and *solifluction* (q.v.) in the high slopes started the mass transport, and brief but heavy rains and thaw floods carried the debris from the lower slopes and valleys to spread it out in the piedmont plains, as in the Rocky Mountain foothills (leading, for example, to the Nebraska sand hills and extensive loess) or in the southern Atlas Mountains (contributing to the vast sands of the Sahara Desert). Wind is not a strong agency of mechanical weathering (*abrasion*), but it is an excellent mechanism for transportation.

Traces of the glacial stage sand dunes are found disappearing below sea level in West Africa and Northern Australia, and this evidence, coupled with C^{14} dating of the last glacial silts, proves that the great deserts built up during the glacial periods, not during hot interglacial times as heretofore assumed. It is true that "pluvial" conditions (with westerlies) were pushed equatorward of the continental ice fronts, but these were limited to about latitude 30°, and from 30° to 5° vast dunes developed. The traces of these dunes can be clearly seen (now overgrown with vegetation) in the present jungles of the Congo and in northern Australia. The old concept that mid-latitude "cold" pluvials corresponded to equatorial "hot" pluvials is contrary to all the principles of meteorology (Fairbridge, 1964b). On the other hand, the lowering of the glacial age snow lines in the tropics in some high areas did lead to increased rainfall on the middle slopes while the rest of the low-latitude, low-altitude lands were suffering extreme aridity (Van Zinderen Bakker, 1966).

Catastrophism

As outlined above, denudation is seen over the long term of geologic time as an actualistic, uniformitarian phenomenon, but over the geologically short term of the Plio-Pleistocene (say, the last 5 million years), it is seen as a catastrophic episode. It would take at least 50 million years of warm-wet climate to rebuild the saprolite weathering "mantle" to reestablish the preglacial "normality." Curiously enough, pre-Lyell geologists (e.g., Farey, 1811) in England referred to the "Great Denudation," impressed by the evidence of an essentially single-cycle uncovering of the bedrock. It took a French soil scientist Henri Erhart (1956) to recognize that this was only one phase of a regular cyclic repetition of saprolite (regolith) building, alternating all through geologic history with periods of lowered sea level, marked by aridity, mechanical erosion and wholesale denudation—his theory of *Biorhexistasy* (q.v., Vol. VI). We still appear to be living in a time of highly accelerated denudation, and judging from the rates of accumulation of deep-sea sediments, the mean Quaternary rates are at least an order of magnitude greater than the rates for the mid-Tertiary, due to larger land area exposed, relatively low eustatic levels and accelerated runoff (for a contrary opinion, see *Continental Erosion*).

Degradation versus Denudation

Degradation is another ancient term of geology referring to the downwasting of land surfaces. Lyell (1833) replaced "degradation" by "denudation" as a general term for all weathering and erosion, but this was criticized by Jukes–Browne and others. Davis (1909) contrasted the two, reserving denudation for the major landscape stripping and retaining degradation for "those leisurely processes, characteristic of the later stages of the cycle, in which a graded slope is reduced to ... fainter declivity ..." or, as Cotton says, when the transport energy exceeds the waste supply. Geologists do not generally accept this distinction.

Marine Denudation

Davisian–Johnsonian geomorphology was largely oriented to the concept that in combination with sub-aerial forces, the mechanical effects of wave action would eventually produce a marine abrasion surface that would span the continent. Unfortunately this was another of those idealistic dreams that disregarded the facts of isostasy, geotectonic cyclicity and paleoclimatic history, and in general assumed a high-speed effectiveness of erosion, evidence for which is totally lacking.

The idea of marine denudation largely goes back to de la Beche and especially to Ramsay (1846), followed by Lyell, all being very impressed by the dynamism of wave action around the coasts of Britain. Von Richthofen (1886) developed a concept of wide platforms of marine abrasion. Lyell's influence spread extensively in North America to Gulliver, Fenneman, Davis, Barrell and Johnson. It is now recognized that although marine abrasion is impressive in areas of low cliffs in unconsolidated debris, (e.g., glacial accumulations around Cape Cod and Long Island, in eastern England and in Denmark), these are highly "accidental" examples

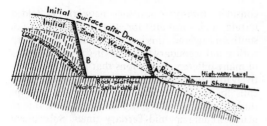

FIG. 1. Diagrammatic profile through an evolving cliff line in maturely weathered rock. Weathered rock (saprolite) is quickly removed by wave action, forming a "normal" profile at A. Seawater saturation prevents further rotting of the landward rocks and only the subaerial part becomes weathered, so that a horizontal wave-cut rock platform develops to point B, progressively advancing to the left. Initially quarried away to high-water level, this platform becomes eventually cut down to low-tide level which is the ultimate lower limit of subaerial weathering (Bartrum, 1926).

and represent vastly less than 1% of the world's coastlines. The usual picture is either of sandy coasts or hard rock cliffed shores that resist marine erosion more or less indefinitely; for example, the igneous plug of Rockall in the North Atlantic has been subjected to the violence of westerly storms for 60×10^6 years (from recent isotopic dating) and shows no sign of marine erosion at all, although its less resistant "country rock" has long since been planed down. In this way, a wide *wave-cut platform* is produced (for other examples, see profiles of Hawaii and other mature islands, e.g., Lord Howe Island by Standard, 1963; see our Fig. 1), but it must be remembered that numerous eustatic oscillations assist the long term process, as brought out by Penck, Daly and Davis (1928).

It is true that if deep chemical weathering has rotted a rock down to water level, then marine erosion can remove the insoluble debris (Bartrum, 1926), but this represents a minuscule role in the denudation of continents (Fig. 2). In the case of sandy shores, it is now recognized that the beach

quickly adjusts to a steady-state equilibrium, patterned to every dynamic modification of wave action and sea level, even down to the diurnal tidal cycle (Schwartz, 1965). The sand beach thus protects the shore from further erosion unless grossly disturbed by human agency. Hutton, Maw, Whitaker, Green, Jukes-Browne and others (see Fairbridge, 1952) repeatedly commented on the effectiveness of subaerial chemical weathering processes which are inhibited at sea level; the low pH of "fresh" groundwater meets the high pH of seawater between mean sea level and mean low tide level. Mellard Reade (1877) wrote: "The chemical agency decomposes the matrix . . . the ocean acts merely as a mechanical distributor of matter." In America, J. D. Dana recognized this clearly, but his words were lost in the subsequent flood of publications from the supporters of the mechanical theory.

Within the ranks of the marine denudation theorists, there were essentially two schools: the *Ramsay-Richthofen School*, which believed that marine abrasion would work progressively into the continent until the energy of waves was so reduced that the result would be an eventual standstill at the inner limit of a wide abrasion surface; it may be commented that there are shelves over 500 km wide off southeast Asia and northern Australia, but one can hardly say that wave action there is brought to a standstill. The second category was the *Barrell–Johnson School*, which postulated that as the debris from wave attack was carried off into the ocean, sea level would slowly rise permitting further attack into the interior, so that eventually the entire continent would become reduced to a submarine peneplain; another fine idea, alas, but such an eventuality never once appears to have taken place in the 4.5 billion-year history of this planet. It is significant that sub-bottom seismic reflection profiling across continental shelves (see Vol. I, "Encyclopedia of Oceanography") shows that most shelves are accumulating sediment and lack any evidence of being drowned wave-cut platforms. The theory of marine denudation of the continents must therefore be rejected in its entirety.

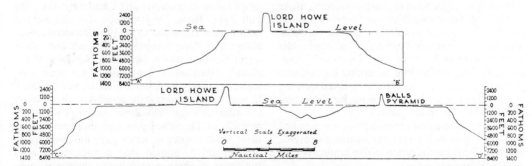

FIG. 2. Profiles of Lord Howe Island and Ball's Pyramid, southwest Pacific. Above: east-west. Below: north-south profile. Note extensive wave-cut platform, leaving only the more resistant volcanic necks as topographic residuals. They are probably of Pliocene age (Standard, 1963).

An interesting reaction to the philosophy of catastrophism in eighteenth century geology was the almost universal importance attributed to denudation by some nineteenth century geologists. Indeed, the fact that all valleys were not products of tectonic catastrophism had to be argued up till the 1870's. But extremists then began to doubt that earth movements had anything to do with shaping the surface of the land. Eventually it was largely the work of Russell and Gilbert in the American west that brought in a "modern" balanced judgment (Gregory, 1926).

Stage in Denudation

Davis offered the concept of youth-maturity-old age in any cycle, but this assumed a simple one-step uplift followed by progressive degradation. This structural setting, however, is but one of an infinity of potentials. It is much more usual in the tectonic history of a region to observe the slow, discontinuous uplift of a domal area or orogenic belt, accompanied by slow, discontinuous downwarp of an adjacent trough or basin, following isostatic principles. Further, this geotectonic "ground swell" is modulated by utterly independent oscillations of paleoclimatic nature.

Geotectonically positive structures tend to go through cycles of uplift and quiescence, although the positive trend may be repeated again and again over periods of 10^8 or 10^9 years. Crickmay (1959) has suggested that within any one diastrophic-denudation cycle, one may distinguish a positive *anagenetic stage*, marked by stripping, dissection, terraces and Penckian "Treppen" (steps). This eventually passes over into a decadent *catagenetic stage*, continuing over a very extended time, the end-point of which will be the nearest approach to a *peneplain* (q.v.), although in semiarid landscapes, headward erosion is more important than the rounding effects of periglacial weathering and the result will more closely approach the *pediplain* (q.v.). However well these catagenetic stages seem to advance in various regions, there is often evidence of a polycyclic or multicyclic history (anagenetic revival).

In analyses of the relief of eastern Australia, there has been an interesting discussion between Cotton (1949), who argued essentially for the tectonic warping and multiple faulting of a single late Tertiary monocyclic surface (a "Davisian" view), and L. C. King (1959), who, accepting the evidence of much faulting, stressed also the repeated warping of polycyclic erosion surfaces during his "*cymatogeny*" (q.v.; a "Penckian" view).

The term *denudation chronology* is now applied to the dating of such stages, the sequence of events which leads to the evolution of the landscape (see further discussion, below).

The question of monocyclic or polycyclic denudation stages comes sharply into focus when one considers *transverse drainage* networks in folded terrain. A classical area for study was the Weald of southern England; this is a broad anticlinal upwarp with minor secondary anticlines in Cretaceous rocks of many different formations that respond distinctively to erosional energy. The one-cycle explanation calls for the development of consequent streams during and after emergence above sea level due to gentle folding in mid-Tertiary times. Subsequent streams developed in the synclines (e.g., the Thames) and in the axial regions of the anticlines. Following the breaching of the central axis, progressive but gradual lowering of base level permitted the major transverse streams to maintain themselves, but minor ones suffered capture and the former valleys through the ridges are now left as *wind gaps* (q.v.). The two-cycle (or polycyclic) hypothesis requires the reduction of almost the entire area to a peneplain by late Pliocene times; a transgressive Pliocene sea left traces here and there (sinkholes with marine fossils: the Lenham beds). Following further upwarping, new drainage systems developed over the Pliocene marine surface and thus became *superimposed* (superposed) on the older structures. Key points for the second group of theories are the pockets of Pliocene shells and structural truncation (about 600 feet) of the gently tilted Cretaceous formations (the famous Chalk).

The origin of transverse valleys in fold belts always seems to lead to the same debate. In the Appalachians, Johnson (1931) postulated that peneplanation occurred prior to the Cretaceous and that a broad consequent drainage system developed over a veneer of transgressive Cretaceous sediments and, with subsequent slow upwarp, the great rivers became superimposed (with water gaps), while subsequent, structurally modified, streams developed on the underlying folded terrain and, by progressive capture, led to the formation of wind gaps. Thompson (1949) postulated a progressive loss of drainage from the west-flowing streams in favor of the shorter, more energetic eastward drainage. A weak point in the Appalachian peneplain picture is the absence of any Cretaceous remnants in the interior, though clearly the summit accordance drops below the transgressive Cretaceous along the Fall Zone. Hack (1965) argued that the summit accordances attributed to the pre-Cretaceous peneplain ("Fall Zone Peneplain" of Sharp) and subsequent (lower) erosion surfaces ("Schooley Peneplain," "Harrisburg Peneplain," etc.) were consequences of lithologic similarities. In New England, Flint (1963) also reached the conclusion that summit accordances in the "Fall Zone" surface were simply artifacts of like lithologies and uniform wearing rates. With respect to water gaps and wind gaps, Strahler (1945) argued that a coincidence with transverse faulting would help explain a non-superimposed origin, but reached the conclusion that there were no gross structural controls; small kinks and brachyanticlines do in fact occur in a number of these gaps (Epstein, 1967). Clearly the whole question is still subject to much further research and debate. Other fold belts are the focus of similar discussions: the Alps, the Juras, the Rockies, the Himalayas, the Coast Ranges of Brazil, the Great Dividing Range of Australia, and most recently the Zagros Mountains of Iran (Oberlander, 1965).

Some of the points of the argument are relatively minor; for example, the present Appalachian streams can be superimposed from either a marine Cretaceous veneer (evidence for which is lacking) or from a mature erosion surface, so that superposition would be true for either. The critical point, it seems to the writer, is whether the highest elevation surfaces ("Fall Zone," with or without "Schooley"), where steeply dipping folded rocks are truncated by gently undulating "planes," are relics of a formerly continuous erosion surface at or close to sea level, or whether they are random coincidental relics of regional denudation (Hack, 1965).

The key to this point is our knowledge of the *weathering resistance* of various lithologies, an area where much research is still needed. Geologists who have worked in subtropical shield regions are often astonished by the evident longevity of ancient soil surfaces. If those paleosols are situated on surfaces of relatively little relief, and particularly if they are supported by silica or ferruginous hardpans ("silcrete" or "ferricrete"), they become semipermanent features of the landscape. In North Africa, the French speak of the *cuirasse de fer* (steel breastplate). One example, in Queensland (Australia), is penetrated by a dolerite dike that was recently dated as early Miocene or late Oligocene. In the African and South American shields, King has identified quite well-preserved erosion surfaces dating back to the late Paleozoic. In northwestern Australia, a pre-Proterozoic (Nullagine) erosion surface extends over a broad area, although undoubtedly it was partly covered and then stripped bare again. These ancient surfaces could not stand up unscathed to glacial weathering, but in regions beyond the zone of intense Pleistocene periglacial activity, we may expect to find silica and iron-reinforced paleosol remnants on denudation surfaces of great antiquity where the present denudation rate is effectively nil.

The high ridges of the Appalachians consist largely of sandstones and conglomerates such as the Silurian Shawangunk and Tuscarora formations that today are mostly converted by diagenesis to sedimentary quartzites. Along the gently undulating ridge tops, where the actual sedimentary layers are sharply truncated, the formations have often been converted to silcretes, i.e., massively recemented. The downward erosion rate on such surfaces is essentially nil over periods of the order of 10^7 years. Headward erosion on the adjacent slopes (largely in less-resistant formations) will naturally continue,

but with progressive, aperiodically accelerated upwarping since the late Tertiary, the Appalachians are gradually becoming mountains of greater relative relief. This apparently anomalous picture is repeated in all the world's fold belts; periods of quiescence and general denudation to a given base level are found to alternate with periods of renewed uplift with concomitant stages of increasing relief, Crickmay's anagenetic stages. Schumm (1963) speaks of "*epicycles*" of uplift.

There is a certain impression among some geomorphologists that the cycle concepts are incompatible with the steady-state concepts. This, it seems to the writer, is unfortunate, because both approaches serve useful purposes. The latter most effectively treats short-term dynamics and the former long-term dynamics.

During Crickmay's anagenesis general denudation is highly active, but only during catagenesis does it approach the cycle end-point of peneplanation. That cycle may be replaced by the next anagenetic stage before total peneplanation is achieved; this may leave only partial erosion surfaces with monadnocks [panplanation and/or, alternatively, the anastomosis of pediments (Cotton, 1939)]. Confusion has been caused by geomorphologists using the term "peneplain" for features such as the Harrisburg erosion surface in the Appalachians, which is about 1000 feet lower than the principal ridges. Some authorities urge that this "surface" is only an artifact of an equilibrium erosion budget in a uniform lithology. This is a deduction based on faulty field work and ignorance of the variability in lithologic resistance within any given formation. A "limestone" or a "shale" does not have constant erosion responses through hundreds of feet of section. Each formation is merely a convenient field designation for a mappable sequence of beds, whose microfacies often show an extensive range of components arranged differently from one individual layer or bed to the next and cemented under varying degrees of diagenesis.

In the definition of denudation, its role as a product of exogenic processes was stressed, but in the above discussion it is clear that endogenic processes (orogenesis, epeirogenesis, isostasy) play a fundamental role in creating structural cycles or epicycles that are in turn modulated by paleoclimatic cycles and epicycles. In geomorphologic analysis, therefore, one should consider the possible combinations of processes. Kennedy (1962) recognizes that nine such cases are possible, with three direct consequences. Where uplift exceeds erosion there will be:

(1) *Increased relief,* where erosion is greater than denudation;

(2) *Stable relief,* where erosion and denudation are equal;

(3) *Decreased relief,* where erosion is less than denudation. Where uplift is equaled by erosion [cases (4), (5) and (6)] the effects and their causes will

be the same as above, though in different degrees. Where uplift is less than erosion there will be:

(7) *Increased relief*, where denudation is greater than erosion;

(8) *Stable relief*, the factors again being equal;

(9) *Decreased relief*, where denudation is less than erosion.

All nine cases are then subject to the modulation of climatic change. As established by Langbein and Schumm (1958) where precipitation exceeds about 12 inches (30 cm), desert shrubs and cacti give way to grasslands (see reproduction of their standard curve in *Continental Erosion*). Below this critical level, an increase in precipitation means more runoff and thus more erosion. Thus, in regions with precipitation over 30 cm, Kennedy's nine cases now have 18 combinations, and under 30 cm 18 more, so that 36 combinations are theoretically possible.

What often leads to confusion in geomorphic analysis is a failure to recognize that integrated study is *always* essential. One must study the tectonic history, the lithology, the pedology and the geomorphology simultaneously. Climatic changes have epicycles of as little as 11 years (the *Sunspot Cycle*, see Vol. II) and major cycles of the order of 90,000 years. The isostatic and tectonic epicycles may be of the order of 10^6 years. Therefore, stream terraces are the most likely to reflect paleoclimatic events, while peneplains usually reflect tectonic events. In fact, the regional unconformity of the stratigrapher is the partly covered peneplain of the geomorphologist.

Pediment systems are more difficult to resolve, because pediments evolve quickly under semiarid climates, but they may also be generated by uplift. There is little doubt today that the climatic factor has been more important in shaping the pediments of the Rocky Mountain front than the tectonic factor, whereas a few years ago the opposite view was more favored.

Some important deductions regarding denudation in general can be drawn up, following Kennedy (1962) and others:

(a) The time sequence concept of geomorphic evolution is still valid.

(b) New topography may not be adjusted to base level (though a local equilibrium may well be established).

(c) A peneplain could develop during uplift if denudation exceeds erosion.

(d) Major relief mainly reflects tectonic history (while Davis said it reflected *stage* in erosion, i.e., youth–maturity–old age).

(e) Minor relief, terraces, pediments, microrelief forms, recent continental sediments and most soils reflect climatic changes.

(f) Ancient erosion surfaces may carry duricrust caps or traces of paleosols that date from paleoclimatic events through every stage of the Quaternary, back into the Tertiary and even the Mesozoic Era.

(g) Marine denudation is effective in producing broad wave-cut platforms around islands and in materials easily transported mechanically, but not on continental coasts where sediment from rivers protects the shore and shelf.

(h) Continental denudation is effective only where relief is sufficient to permit transport of debris. Vast areas of the continents are at present in a sluggish, catagenic state of geomorphic development.

Denudation Chronology

A part of the general field of historical geology, denudation chronology is more often studied by geomorphologists than by stratigraphers (King, 1966). This is a pity because there is no real distinction between the two areas, except that denudation chronology treats the evolution of the earth's surface over the last few million years and conservative stratigraphy deals with the earlier parts of the story, which have largely lost their geomorphic features, and the records are only preserved in the sediments of the period. Nevertheless, there are many geologists who describe themselves as "Holocene stratigraphers" or "Quaternary stratigraphers," because they study the sedimentary formations of the time and their fossils, leaving the strictly erosional features to geomorphologists. To complete the story, it is essential for the erosional remnants to be correlated with the sedimentary deposits that were transported from them. "Denudation chronology is largely concerned with the vestiges of past fluviatile processes" (Kimball, 1948), and for this reason stream dynamics becomes a key discipline in preparing for its study. However, coastal terraces are also important.

As pointed out in the above discussion on "stage in denudation," pure morphology (e.g., increased or decreased relief) gives ambiguous results, unless integrated into tectonic, stratigraphic, pedologic and paleoclimatic studies. Thus, the denudation chronologist must depend in large measure on studies of the associated deposits. Chorley (1965), and others, stress the importance of statistical processing. However, one must be careful to establish that the statistics are worth processing. The first requirement is usually a good topographic map, then slope surveys, and eventually a geomorphic map; but there's the rub, for very few countries have yet developed a detailed geomorphic mapping program (see *Geomorphic Maps*).

Denudation chronology was pioneered by Baulig in the Massif Central of France and has been extended to many parts of the world with various degrees of success. A full recognition of its complexities is essential. We have noted above 36 theoretical combinations of relief-control factors, without going beyond tectonics, erosion rate, denudation rate and climatic (precipitation) trend. Baulig was one of the first to recognize also the role of eustasy, but he erred in underestimating tectonic motion and climate.

Because of the interfingering of erosion surfaces with marine formations around the Massif Central and elsewhere along the Atlantic coasts of France and Britain, it has been possible to achieve considerable progress there. Around much of the Atlantic coasts from southern England to Portugal, the marine Pliocene is found resting on an erosion surface of 600–700 feet (*ca.* 200 meters). In the positive tectonic areas, e.g., Pyrenees, Alpine foothills, Massif Central, Welsh highlands, etc., this surface has been traced in the field, mile by mile, up to much higher elevations. Tide gauges show the coasts of the Pyrenees and Alpes Maritimes to be rising today at rates of up to 1 mm/yr. Geodetic surveys over the Alps show active uparching over the present century at comparable rates. While the matter is still controversial, an appreciable part of the "Gipfelflur" of the Alps may consist of relics of this Pliocene surface, now warped to heights of over 4000 meters and more (say, in the course of 4 million years, a mean rate of 1 mm/yr).

Analogous arguments have been marshaled in studies of the Rockies and Sierra Nevada. What causes confusion in areas like the Rocky Mountain front is that we are so far from the sea that we do not have any reliable datum or fixed base level; both anastomosed pediments and pediplains may slope upward at fairly steep gradients. How do we know that the so-called peneplains are not mature upland pediment surfaces?

In southern England, distances from the sea are minute in comparison and furthermore many of the lower erosion surfaces (below 700 feet) are associated with marine cobbles, beach deposits and even fossiliferous formations (Sparks, 1949, and others; (see Figs. 3–4)). Waters *et al.* (1964) have tentatively established the following surfaces in southwestern England:

> Eocene: 1900–1500 ft
> Oligocene: 1350–1050 ft
> Mio-Pliocene: 950–750 ft

with seventeen late Pliocene to Quaternary surfaces below 700 feet.

In the eastern United States, numbers of terraces have been known for a long time and it was tempting to correlate these on an altimetric basis with suspected eustatic terraces in other parts of the world. Unfortunately these U.S. terraces were largely preserved in uncemented, porous quartz sands and silts in a high-rainfall area; as a result, carbonate fossils would tend to become leached out. However, careful mapping by a number of geologists (Colquhoun, Oaks, Coch and others) has demonstrated that the "erosional" terraces are largely littoral and lagoonal accumulations, and although the work is incomplete, it may be possible to follow them to marine members with fossil control, providing the following tentative chronology:

> ? Miocene ("Hazelhurst"): 270–250 ft
> ? Early Pliocene ("Coharie"): 220–200 ft
> ? Late Pliocene ("Sunderland"): 180–170 ft
> Early Pleistocene ("Okefenokee"): 140–125 ft
> Early Pleistocene ("Wicomico"): 108–95 ft
> Middle Pleistocene ("Penholoway"): 70–60 ft
> Middle Pleistocene ("Talbot"): 50–40 ft
> Late Pleistocene ("Pamlico"): 25–20 ft
> Late Pleistocene ("Princess Anne"): 20–15 ft
> Late Pleistocene ("Silver Bluff"): 5–10 ft

From the above examples it is clear that systematic geomorphic mapping, core drilling and normal stratigraphic procedures can be coordinated in order to establish a denudational chronology for a given region. The rates of differential uplift, offset against eustatic components, thus provide an essential basis for understanding the denudational processes.

Rates of Denudation

The *rates of continental denudation* can be calculated by two procedures: (a) measuring the mean dissolved, suspension and bed load transports of the world's rivers, and (b) calculating the volume of deep-sea sediments, submarine cones, abyssal plains, and so on.

The classical review of North American and world river loads, a *United States Geological Survey Water Supply Paper* by Dole and Stabler (1909), furnished basic statistics and estimates that have not yet been properly verified on a world basis, though for certain areas excellent data are now available (Livingstone, 1963a; Corbel, 1964). For the United States, for various basins, using the fluvial discharge method, Judson and Ritter (1964) calculated denudation rates of 1.2–16 cm/1000 yr, the average rate suggesting that the United States could be totally eroded to sea level in 12×10^6 years (see detailed figures in *Continental Erosion*).

On the other hand, it should be remembered that large areas of the world are arheic or endorheic (as shown by de Martonne) and these largely arid or subpolar (tundra) regions are essentially static with a denudation rate of zero. At the other end of the scale, a mature tropical volcanic island like Hawaii appears to be denuded at about 13 cm/1000 yr, as indicated by a combined soil weathering and marine accumulation study (Moberly, 1963). For parts of an orogenic belt like New Zealand, geomorphic studies (Suggate, 1965) indicate rates of denudation exceeding 100 cm/1000 yr (1 mm/yr). For the Alps a combined calculation based on discharge plus marine accumulation gave an average of 10 cm/1000 yr since the Oligocene (Menard *et al.*, 1965).

The writer attempted a similar type of calculation for determining the mean denudation rate of the Himalayas, working out the volume of the Ganges sedimentary cone on the floor of the Bay of Bengal

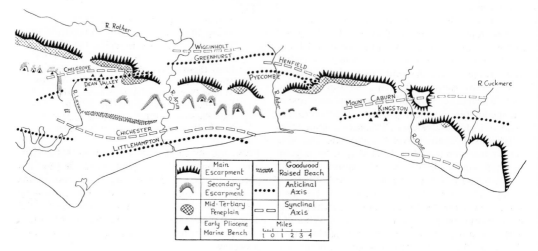

FIG. 3. Denudation chronology of the South Downs of England (Sparks, 1949). Note that this is geomorphic mapping on a reconnaissance scale, designed to extract the key features only in geomorphic history. For detailed statistics, see Fig. 4.

(by far the world's largest), the catchment area and the period of uplift. The result, admittedly very rough, came out as 60 cm/1000 yr (*Encyclopedia of Oceanography*, p. 871).

Reviewing the methods generally, one may say that for temperate-humid regions of moderate relief a rate of 1 cm/1000 yr is about average, but different climatic belts and certain rock types can throw off this figure completely. Thus certain quartzitic ridges in arid central Australia appear to be relics of a pre-Mesozoic peneplain giving them an age of over 2×10^8 years. Other examples were noted above to indicate the existence of broad regions of essentially zero denudation over periods of 10^7 years. Cotton (1963) quotes evidence to show that even in the high relief areas of southeastern

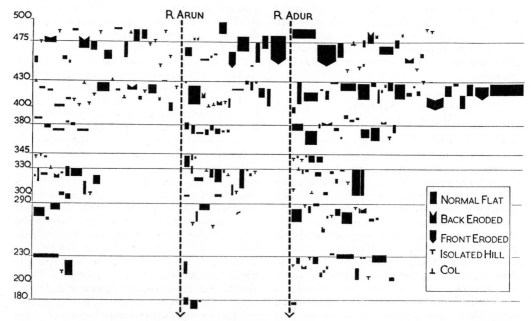

FIG. 4. Graphic statistical analysis of part of a denudation chronologic survey of the South Downs of England (see also Fig. 3; Sparks, 1949). Height ranges of platform fragments.

Australia much of the landscape "has been practically immune from erosion for some 250 million years."

A calculation of the mean world rate of denudation today gives some 12 km³ of sediment supplied to the ocean annually (Kuenen, 1950), in round figures some 8 cm/1000 yr off the entire land surface, which is close to Judson and Ritter's average for the United States. There is a certain fallacy in measuring modern stream loads, because cultivation in places has greatly raised the erosion rates though the principal land forms and slopes are precultivation in origin (Mortensen, 1963). We have the impression, therefore, that the present figures are too high in comparison to other geological times.

Consideration of deep-sea sediments provides some insight into long-term world denudation rates, but we should take great care, since gross problems about the history of the oceans are still not solved. Measurements of mid-ocean sedimentary thickness disclose about 200 meters on the average for the last 1×10^8 years, a mean accumulation rate of 0.2 cm/1000 yr spread over nearly two-thirds of the earth's surface, which would leave a world average for land denudation of 0.4 cm/1000 yr. This omits, of course, shelf and geosyncline deposits, which are more important in rate, if not in volume. Kay (1955) calculated mean rates for the filling of ancient geosynclines at 7–80 cm/1000 yr (compacted sediment). Our own calculation for the modern Ganges cone accumulation was 10 cm/1000 yr (less compacted).

The area of modern oceanic closed basins and marginal seas ("geosynclines") is about 40×10^6 km²; the world's land area covers nearly 150×10^6 km², so this sediment catchment area constitutes 27% of it, and if one takes 1 cm/1000 yr as an average accumulation rate for these small basins (cf. Menard, 1967), it would appear that the mean continental denudation rates of today (*ca.* 10 cm/1000 yr) are an order of magnitude too high, in comparison with the mean rate of the last 20 million years or so. The mean rates for the general course of geological time may be even less.

Why should the present denudation rate be one or two orders of magnitude above that for the geological past? There seems to be a number of good reasons, admittedly hard to evaluate numerically:

(a) Man-induced soil erosion, following vast deforestation and massive ploughing, obviously raises the currently observed sediment transport rates measured in rivers of heavily populated regions.

(b) Rates calculated from studies of humid, mid-latitude North American and western European rivers are quite out of line with the whole world figure. Very large areas, from the Arctic tundras and lake regions to the great deserts, are endorheic or arheic and have no runoff. Also, many low-lying equatorial jungle areas have very poor drainage,

much precipitation returning to the atmosphere by evaporation.

(c) The Quaternary period has been marked by extensive orogeny, block faulting and epeirogenic warping, so that present relief is maximal. (This is a key factor in the maintenance of an ice age potential, Ramsay's "Relief Theory.")

(d) Eustatic oscillations during the Quaternary have been repeatedly lowering base levels and accelerating fluvial transport to the ocean.

(e) Quaternary cold climatic oscillations have involved enormous extensions of semiarid zones. [The present world land area is about 150×10^6 km², oceans being 360×10^6 km². In millions of square kilometers, for the glacial maxima, the ice-covered areas were 35–40, the continentality increase (exposed shelves) was 25 and the area affected by increased aridity was 70–80.] The Langbein–Schumm curve illustrates the increased erosion engendered by decreasing rainfall in formerly humid regions.

(f) The "normal" climate of the geological past, excluding ice ages (Quaternary, Permo-Carboniferous, etc.), has been humid-semitropical, as required by meteorological principles and as proved by oxygen isotope studies, paleontological studies and sedimentological studies. Equatorial rivers in low relief areas today have little transporting power and the drainage network is extraordinarily sparse, vast regions being undrained swamp.

(g) As demonstrated by Erhart's "Theory of Biorhexistasy" (1956; see also pr Vol. VI), the more "static" phases of geologic history were marked by a dominance of chemical sediments (carbonate, silica), the sources of which are normally furnished by leaching in equatorial soils.

(h) The relative area of continental land exposed has increased through time, as shown by Egyed on the basis of paleogeographic maps drawn up independently by Strakhov and by the Termiers. A combined curve (Fairbridge, 1964a) shows a one-third mean increase in exposed land area since the Cambrian.

(i) Ronov's calculation of ancient mean sedimentation rates (from Carboniferous to Jurassic) was 0.73–3.43 km³/yr, compared to Kuenen's contemporary rate of 12 km³/yr (see Livingstone, 1963b).

The general conclusion is therefore that denudation is a highly variable quantity, both in time and space, the present mean rates being well above the average.

RHODES W. FAIRBRIDGE

References

Bartrum, J. A., 1926, "Abnormal shore platforms," *J. Geol.*, **34,** 793–806.

Baulig, H., 1928, "Le Plateau Central de la France," Paris, Colin, 590pp.

Bigarella, J. J., and de Andrade, G. O., 1965, "Contribution to the study of the Brazilian Quaternary," *Geol. Soc. Am. Spec. Paper* **84,** 433–451.

Chorley, R. J., 1965, "The Application of Quantitative Methods to Geomorphology," in (Chorley, R. J., and Haggett, P., editors), "Frontiers in Geographical Teaching," pp. 147–163, London, Methuen.

Clarke, F. W., 1910, "A preliminary study of chemical denudation," *Smithsonian Inst. Misc. Collections*, **56**(5), 1–19.

Corbel, J., 1964, "L'érosion terrestre, étude quantitative," *Ann. Géogr.*, **398**, 385–412.

Cotton, C. A., 1939, "Lateral planation in New Zealand," *New Zealand J. Sci. Technol.*, 227B–232B.

Cotton, C. A., 1949, "A review of tectonic relief in Australia," *J. Geol.*, **57**(3), 280–296.

Cotton, C. A., 1963, "The rate of down-wasting of land surfaces," *Tuatara*, **11**, 26–27.

Crickmay, C. H., 1959, "A Preliminary Inquiry into the Formulation and Applicability of the Geological Principle of Uniformity," Calgary (priv. print. E. de Mille Books), 53pp.

Davis, W. M., 1909, "Geographical Essays," New York, Dover Reprint (1954), 777pp.

Davis, W. M., 1928, "The coral reef problem," *Am. Geogr. Soc. Spec. Publ.*, **9**.

Dole, R. B., and Stabler, H., 1909, "Denudation," *U.S. Geol. Surv., Water Supply Paper* **234**, 78–93.

Epstein, J. B., 1967, "Structural control of wind gaps and water gaps and of stream capture in the Stroudsburg Area, Pennsylvania and New Jersey," *U.S. Geol. Surv. Profess. Paper* **550-B** (Research 1966) B80-B86.

Erhart, H., 1956, "La genèse des sols...Esquisse d'une theorie géologique et géochimique," in "Biostasie et rhexistasie," Paris, Masson.

Fairbridge, R. W., 1952, "Marine erosion," *Proc. 7th Pacific Sci. Congr., New Zealand, 1949*, **3**, 347–359.

Fairbridge, R. W., 1964a, "The Importance of Limestone and its Ca/Mg Content to Palaeoclimatology," in (Nairn, A. E. M., editor) "Problems in Palaeoclimatology," pp. 431–477, London, John Wiley & Sons—Interscience.

Fairbridge, R. W., 1964b, "African Ice-age Aridity," in (Nairn, A. E. M., editor) "Problems in Palaeoclimatology," pp. 357–363, London, John Wiley & Sons —Interscience.

Farey, J., 1811, "An account of the great Derbyshire denudation," *Phil. Trans. Roy. Soc., London*, 242–256; also *Phil. Mag.*, **39**, 1812, 93–106.

Flint, R. F., 1963, "Altitude, lithology and the Fall Zone in Connecticut," *J. Geol.*, **71**, 683–697.

Garner, H. F., 1959, "Stratigraphic–sedimentary significance of contemporary climate and relief in four regions of the Andes Mountains," *Bull. Geol. Soc. Am.*, **70**, 1327–1368.

Gass, I. G., 1967, "Geochronology of the Tristan da Cunha Group of islands," *Geol. Mag.*, **104**(2), 160–170.

Gregory, J. W., 1926, "The relative influence of denudation and earth-movements in moulding the surface of the Earth," *Scientia*, 217–230.

Hack, J. T., 1965, "Geomorphology of the Shenandoah Valley, Virginia and West Virginia, and origin of the residual ore deposits," *U.S. Geol. Surv. Profess. Paper* **484**, 84pp.

Johnson, D. W., 1931, "Stream Sculpture on the Atlantic Slope, a Study in the Evolution of Appalachian Rivers," New York, Columbia University Press, 142pp.

Judson, S., and Ritter, D. F., 1964, "Rates of regional denudation in the United States," *J. Geophy. Res.*, **69**(16), 3395–3401.

Jukes-Browne, A. J., 1884, "The Students' Handbook of Physical Geology," London, 514pp.

Kay, M., 1955, "Sediments and subsidence through time," *Geol. Soc. Am., Spec. Paper* **62** ("Crust of the Earth"), 665–684.

Kennedy, W. Q., 1962, "Some theoretical factors in geomorphological analysis," *Geol. Mag.*, **99**(4), 304–312.

Kimball, D., 1948, "Denudation chronology: the dynamics of river action," *Univ. of London, Inst. Archaeol., Occ. Pap. 8.*

King, C. A. M., 1966, "Techniques in Geomorphology," London, Edward Arnold, 342pp.

King, L. C., 1959, "Denudational and tectonic relief in south-eastern Australia," *Trans. Geol. Soc. S. Africa*, **62**, 113–138.

Kuenen, P. H., 1950, "Marine Geology," New York, John Wiley & Sons, 568pp.

Langbein, W., and Schumm, S., 1958, "Yield of sediment in relation to mean annual precipitation," *Trans. Am. Geophys. Union*, **30**, 1076–1084.

Livingstone, D., 1963a, "Chemical composition of rivers and lakes," in "Data of Geochemistry," Sixth ed., Ch. G., *U.S. Geol. Surv. Profess. Paper* **440-G.**

Livingstone, D. A., 1963b, "The sodium cycle and the age of the ocean," *Geochim. Cosmochim. Acta*, **27**(10), 1055–1069.

Lyell, C., 1833, "Principles of Geology," Second ed., Vol. I, London, Murray.

Menard, H. W., 1967, "Transitional types of crust under small ocean basins," *J. Geophys. Res.*, **72**, 3061–3074.

Menard, H. W., *et al.*, 1965, "The Rhone deep-sea fan," in (Whittard, W. F., and Bradshaw, R., editors), "Submarine geology and geophysics," *Colston Symp.* **17**, 271–285.

Moberly, R., Jr., 1963, "Rate of denudation in Hawaii," *J. Geol.*, **71**(3), 371–375.

Mortensen, H., 1963, "Abtragung und Formung," *Neue Beiträge zur internationalen Hangforschung*, (Nach. der Akad. der Wissens. in Göttingen, II Math.-Phys. Klasse), 17–27.

Oberlander, T., 1965, "The Zagros Streams: a new interpretation of transverse drainage in an orogenic zone," *Syracuse Geogr. Ser. No. 1*, Syracuse University Press, 168pp.

Penck, W., 1953, "Morphological Analysis of Land Forms," London, Macmillan & Co., 429pp. (translation by H. Czech and K. C. Boswell of 1924 German edition).

Ramsay, A. C., 1846, "On the denudation of South Wales and the adjacent counties of England." *Mem. Geol. Surv. Gr. Brit.*, **1**, 297–335.

Reade, T. M., 1877, "President's address, 1876," *Proc. Liverpool Geol. Soc.*, **3**(3), 211–235.

Russell, R. J., 1936, "The desert-rainfall factor in denudation," *Rept. Intern. Geol. Congr. XVI, Washington, 1933*, 753–763.

Schumm, S. A., 1963, "The disparity between present rates of denudation and orogeny," *U.S. Geol. Surv. Profess. Paper* **454H**, 1–13.

Schwartz. M., 1965, "Laboratory study of sea-level rise as a cause of shore erosion," *J. Geol.*, **73**(3), 528–534.

Sharp, H. S., 1929, "The Fall Zone peneplain," *Science*, **69**, 544–545.

Sparks, B. W., 1949, "The denudation chronology of the dip-slope of the South Downs," *Proc. Geologists. Assoc., Engl.,* **60,** 165–215.

Sparks, B. W., 1960, "Geomorphology," London, Longmans, Green; New York, John Wiley & Sons, 371pp.

Standard, J. C., 1963, "Geology of Lord Howe Island," *J. Proc. Roy. Soc. N.S. Wales,* **96,** 107–121.

Strahler, A. N., 1945, "Hypothesis of stream development in the folded Appalachians of Pennsylvania," *Bull. Geol. Soc. Am.,* **56,** 45–88.

Suggate, R. P., 1965, "The tempo of events in New Zealand geological history," *New Zealand J. Geol. Geophys.,* **8**(6), 1139–1148.

Thompson, H. D., 1949, "Drainage evolution in the Appalachians of Pennsylvania," *Ann. N.Y. Acad. Sci.,* **52,** art. 2, 31–62.

Troll, C., 1948, "Der subnivale oder periglaziale Zyklus der Denudation," *Erdkunde,* **2,** 1–21.

van Zinderen Bakker, E. M., 1966, "The Pluvial Theory —an evaluation in the light of new evidence especially for Africa," *The Paleobotanist,* **15**(1–2), 128–134.

von Richthofen, F., 1886, "Führer für Forschungsreisende," Hanover.

Waters, R. S., *et al.,* 1964, "Denudation chronology of parts of S.W. England," *Field Studies,* **2**(1), 115–132.

Whitaker, W., 1867, "On subaerial denudation and on cliffs and escarpments of the chalk and the Lower Tertiary beds," *Geol. Mag.,* **4,** 447–483.

Cross-references: *Abrasion; Arid Cycle; Base Level; Continental Erosion; Cycles, Geomorphic; Cymatogeny; Duricrust; Equilibrium; Erosion; Etchplain; Eustasy; Geomorphic Maps; Holocene; Karst; Landscape Analysis; Mass Wasting; Monadnock; Pediplanation; Peneplain; Piedmont Landforms; Quaternary Period; Regolith and Saprolite; Relict Landforms; Slopes; Solifluction; Terraces; Tor; Tropical Weathering and Relief; Valley (Mountain) Glaciers; Weathering; Wind Gap; Youth—Maturity—Old Age.* Vol. 1: *Continental Shelf; Submarine Cones or Fans.* Vol. II: *Arid Climates; Paleoclimatology—Astronomic Cycles; Sunspot Cycles; Vegetation Classification and Description.* Vol. IV: *Carbon-14 Dating.* Vol. V: *Epeirogeny; Geosynclines; Isostasy; Orogenesis.* pr Vol. VI: *Biorhexistasy; Fluvial Sediment Transport; Glaciers; Paleosol; Pedology; Runoff; Silcrete; Uniformitarianism.*

DERASION—*See* DELL

DESERTS AND DESERT LANDFORMS
Deserts

Definition and Distribution. A desert (from Latin, *desertis,* barren or deserted) is a deserted region capable of supporting only a few forms of life. On this basis the glacial expanses of Antarctica and Greenland as well as areas of soil infertility represent true deserts, but most commonly the term is used to denote regions which are barren because they are dry. Deserts of aridity are characterized by an excess of evaporation over precipitation, by specialized plants of low stature and

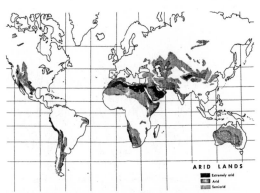

FIG. 1. Sketch map of the world distribution of arid lands, slightly modified after Meigs, 1956.

open spacing, by thin, rocky, and often saline soils, and by distinctive landforms developed under the influence of the arid regimen. They occupy 11,500,000 square miles of the continental masses, approximately 20% of the surface area and occur on all continents with the exception of Europe. Two great belts of deserts (Fig. 1) encircle the earth between 15 and 50° north and south of the equator; the dominant area of aridity is in the Eastern Hemisphere where deserts cover much of the Middle East, North Africa, and Central Asia.

Types and Causes of Deserts. There are two general types of deserts, the low latitude which are hot and dry, and the cold and dry mid-latitude deserts. Low latitude zones of aridity occupy the central and western portions of continents in a broad belt between 15 and 35° north and south latitude. These are in the latitude of the subtropical high pressure air masses and the trade winds, and they are referred to as either trade wind or tropical deserts. The trade winds are evaporating winds and are not favorable to precipitation inasmuch as they become warmer as they move from higher to lower latitudes, and the subtropical highs are regions of descending dry air which have lost most of their moisture. In addition to being dry, the descending air currents tend to dissipate cloud cover and allow more sunlight to heat the land. Included in the low latitude group are the fog or west coast deserts which occur where cold oceanic currents parallel the western margins of continents. Moist air is condensed to form persistent fogs over the cool water. Rain in the adjacent land area is rare. The deserts of North Africa, Australia, India, and Arabia are typical tropical deserts, and the Atacama of Chile and Peru and the Namib of West Africa are characteristic fog deserts.

Mid-latitude deserts occur 30 to 50° north and south of the equator in the interior of continents far from the ocean, as the Great Basin of western United States and the Gobi and Taklamakan of Asia. Other mid-latitude deserts are related to the

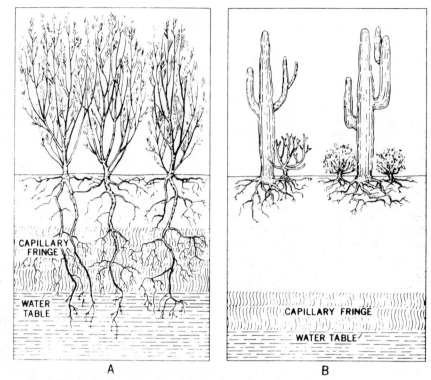

A   B

Fig. 2. Distinction between phreatophytes (A) and xerophytes (B) shown by their occurrence in relation to the water table (Robinson, T. W., 1958, "Phreatophytes," *U.S. Geol. Surv. Water Supply Paper*, **1423**).

presence of a mountain barrier between moist marine air and the interior portions of a continent. After precipitation on the seaward side of the barrier, there is little moisture left in the atmosphere and humidity is further reduced by warming of the atmosphere during its descent on the lee side of the mountains. Arid regions behind mountain barriers are rain shadow or orographic deserts exemplified by the Mojave of California and portions of the Gobi.

Characteristics of Deserts. Despite the different modes of origin and the wide latitude range in which they exist, there are certain characteristics common to all deserts.

Desert rainfall is meager, irregular, and unreliable. Annual precipitation is 10 inches or less, and in the Atacama mean annual rainfall may be under 0.5 inch. Irregularity of rainfall is typical, often occurring as storms which provide more moisture than has fallen in 5 or even 10 years. Desert rainfall is considered by some writers to be torrential, but it is probable that the sparseness of vegetation, the abundance of loose debris, and rapid runoff lead to this impression. Records for heavy precipitation for 1-hour or 24-hour periods are for humid regions rather than deserts.

Evaporation rates are great, often 15 to 20 times

the annual precipitation. Cloud cover is low, normally clear skies prevail over 70% of the time, and in the summer months may exceed 90%. Low relative humidity is characteristic of most deserts; 15–30% is normal and readings as low as 5% were recorded in parts of the Egyptian Sahara. However, in some of the coastal fog deserts, relative humidity may be high, 60–100%, for example, in the coastal Namib of Southwest Africa.

It is impossible to characterize desert temperatures. The mid-latitude deserts have a wide annual temperature range and much lower winter temperatures than tropical deserts. As an example of the latter, at Urga in the Mongolian deserts the mean temperature is below freezing 6 months of the year. Tropical deserts are typified by large diurnal temperature variations and by very high daytime temperatures during the summer. Summer temperatures of 90–105°F are common. A maximum of 136.4°F was recorded at Azizia in Tripoli and 134°F at Greenland Ranch in Death Valley, California. Fog deserts are cool and exhibit a much smaller annual temperature range than other deserts.

Desert soils are lacking in humus and are gray or red in color. Much of the soil is rocky, consisting of coarse alluvium. These soils (lithosols) are

Fig. 3. Desert dry washes. Note braiding of ephemeral channels. Drainage pattern formed by intermittent streams on surface of an alluvial fan. After heavy rains the channels may be filled with muddy and turbulent water—in the "flash flood" of the desert. (Vertical aerial photograph; width of photo = 4000 feet.)

immature and without soil profiles. Other desert soils are intrazonal with weakly developed profiles and either contain appreciable amounts of calcium carbonate (the pedocal soils) or have relatively high concentrations of other soluble salts (the halomorphic soils).

Drainage channels in arid regions are occupied by short and discontinuous intermittent streams that contain water only during and shortly after rain. Rainfall is insufficient to maintain perennial streams except in a few instances, as the Nile River of Africa, the Indus, and the Colorado River of the United States, but these originate in more humid regions and are able to persist across the desert. Drainage channels are towards the lowermost portion of the enclosed basins or bolsons in which they occur, and the drainage pattern formed is centripetal. Interior or enclosed basins without exit to the sea are typical of all desert regions.

Desert plants are widely spaced, scrubby, and often possess thorns or spines. They have adapted to the meagerness of available moisture as well as the rocky or saline soils. Some have done so by developing long tap roots which penetrate to or near the water table. This group, the phreatophytes, include such well-known plants as the date

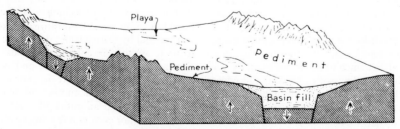

Fig. 4. Typical desert landforms in a basin-range area, where block faulted depressions are largely filled with continental debris (Leet, L. D. and Judson, S., 1958, "Physical Geology," Second ed., Englewood Cliffs, N.J., Prentice-Hall).

FIG. 5. Alluvial fan in Death Valley, California. Symmetrical fan-shaped deposit of detritus formed by intermittent streams issuing from desert mountains. Note dry drainage channels, small alluvial cones and vegetation alignment along shallow washes. (Vertical aerial photograph; width of photo = 5 miles.)

palm, tamarisk or salt cedar, and mesquite. They commonly grow in and along dry stream channels, near springs, or on the margins of saline lakes. The halophytes or salt-loving plants such as salt grass, inkweed, and a wide variety of saltbushes (*Atriplex*, sp.) have great tolerance to saline water and grow in areas of highly saline soils and near the edges of saline dry lakes. Still others are drought resistant. The xerophytes, the most abundant type of desert vegetation, exemplified in the American deserts by creosote bush and burrobush, have managed to persist by several methods: by means of leaflessness during the dry season or by avoiding transpiration

losses with small and waxy leaves; by developing shallow and widely branching root systems which quickly acquire as much moisture as possible during storms; and by storing water during the wet season so as to survive the long dry periods that ensue. The last named are succulents, and include cacti which accumulate moisture in pulpy stems. The annuals represent still another adaptation. These plants go through an entire life cycle during the rainy season, or even in a few weeks after an especially heavy rain.

Desert Weathering and Erosion. Rock breakdown is accomplished by mechanical (disintegration) and

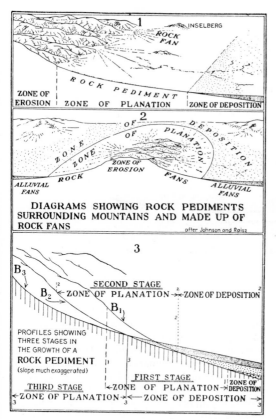

DIAGRAMS SHOWING ROCK PEDIMENTS
SURROUNDING MOUNTAINS AND MADE UP OF
ROCK FANS

after Johnson and Raisz

FIG. 6. Zones of stream action in arid regions (Lobeck, A. K., 1939, "Geomorphology," First ed., New York, McGraw-Hill Book Co.). (By permission.)

chemical (decomposition) processes. At higher elevations in deserts and especially in cold deserts, the expansive forces of ice are effective in fragmenting rocks. The wide diurnal temperature variation typical of hot deserts sets up expansive and contractive forces in rocks which may assist in mechanical breakdown. Although this is disputed, temperature change coupled with the effects of moisture is apparently responsible for some of the coarse rock debris in desert areas. For chemical weathering to be effective, moisture is necessary, and because of skimpy rainfall in arid regions, decomposition has been considered of little importance. Yet there is moisture in the atmosphere, even in the driest of deserts, and when one considers that the atmosphere is in contact with rock surfaces to a much greater depth, due to the low water table, than in humid regions, it must be acknowledged that chemical weathering plays an important and often underrated role in rock weathering in arid regions.

Ice thrust and frost wedging produce angular slabs of rocks, whereas the effects of temperature change coupled with chemical processes cause granular disintegration, especially in coarse crystalline rocks. Angular fragments of crystal grain size (grus) are common to all deserts.

Gravity, running water and wind are the geologic agents of erosion which mold desert landscapes. Such movement of rock debris induced by gravity as talus creep, rock creep, and debris slides all transport rock fragments to lower elevations. Running water is the most effective force in modifying desert surfaces. Because of the sparse vegetation and the abundance of loose rock debris, after rains vast amounts of sediment are carried

FIG. 7. Dry lake or playa: Hard, vegetation-free surface of silt and clay deposited in a temporary (ephemeral) lake. Only on rare occasions are playas flooded and then the lake is seldom more than a few feet in depth.

A. CLAY PAN OR DRY TYPE PLAYA

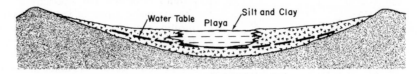

B. SALT PAN OR MOIST TYPE PLAYA

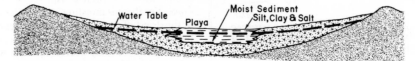

FIG. 8. Types of playas. (*Note*: Moist sediment is usually only within the top 3 feet, and rarely exceeds 10 feet.)

toward the central portion of desert basins. Most effective are intermittent streams which transport rock fragments of all sizes from upland areas onto piedmont slopes bordering the mountains. Since this happens only after heavy precipitation, the process is known as streamflood. Rainsplash, sheet-flood, and rill wash are related mechanisms of rock breakdown and transport. Fine-grained sediment is moved by the impact of raindrops striking unprotected surfaces. It has been shown by careful measurements that during a heavy rainstorm as much as 100 tons of sediment an acre may be dislodged by rainsplash. In sheetflood erosion, runoff may cover the entire surface of piedmont slopes in a film a few inches or less in depth which acts as a powerful erosive agent. As sheetflood continues downslope, a myriad of minute drainage channels or rills develop which are effective in transporting fine sediment. Occasionally in steep canyons a large mass of loose rock material is thoroughly saturated with water during a storm, thereby forming a thick slurry which moves out onto lower slopes as a mudflow.

Scanty vegetation cover permits the wind to pick up fine sediment and move it to a new site within a desert basin, or for the finest sediment, outside the basin. Also, wind-transported sand particles are polished and abraded as they strike one another during transport, and in some instances larger rocks are polished and fluted by wind-driven sand. The importance of wind as an erosive and depositional agent has been ranked highly in the deserts of Africa and the Middle East, but in the arid lands of North America it plays a role very subordinate to the effects of running water.

Desert Surfaces and Landforms

Desert landscape is diverse, consisting of a variety of mountains, plateaus and plains. Desert mountains vary from isolated prominences to major ranges and are often barren and usually angular and bold in outline. They are characterized by an abundance of rock outcrops and the general absence of round smooth slopes associated with mountains of more humid regions. Where mountains give way to plains, the change in slope is abrupt and sharp rather than gradual as in more moist areas. Plains are extensive, comprising one-half or as much as three-fourths of the surface area. Land surfaces in plains also differ greatly. A nearly flat solid rock surface is a hammada; a gravel surface is a reg; and there are still other surfaces which are covered with sand. If the sand accumulations are extensive and if they approximate a "sand sea," they are termed erg.

It might be assumed that landforms of arid and humid regions would be nearly alike, for the same processes act in both environments. Yet the desert landscape of steep, angular mountains, wide alluvium-filled valleys, innumerable dry drainage channels, and broad sloping surfaces leading to mountain fronts, is in strong contrast to the rounded outlines of humid regions and the perennial streams which drain them. It is the impact of aridity on geologic processes rather than the action of different processes which produces the strikingly different landforms of deserts.

Desert basins are not filled with water because of low precipitation and high evaporation rates. This condition imposed by the arid climate has a profound effect on landscape development. Drainage is by ephemeral streams which empty into internal basins, and the products of weathering and erosion accumulate within the basin. In humid regions, basins are filled to overflowing, and drainage is by permanent streams which transport large amounts

FIG. 9. Desert flat or llano: Gently inclined alluvial plain of a wide desert basin. Typical desert vegetation is in the foreground.

of sediment out of the region and to the sea. In deserts, the base level of erosion—the lowest elevation to which a stream can erode—is the surface of the interior basin to which a stream drains, and because of sedimentation this level is a slowly but continuously rising level. In humid regions, base level of erosion is sea level, and streams can reduce upland areas almost to sea level.

Aridity is also responsible for the slowness of weathering, the sparse and widely spaced vegetation, and the thin and discontinuous soils, all factors in landform development. Sparseness of vegetation permits heavy runoff and rapid sediment transport. Also the absence of soils or the very thin soils of upland regions makes soil creep ineffective. The lack of such downslope movement accounts for both the steep and angular nature of desert mountains as well as the abrupt change in slope between mountains and plains.

Desert mountains are cut by steep-walled gorges and often by precipitous valleys which contain runoff water only during storms. Due to the sharp break in slope at the mountain front, sediment-laden streams quickly deposit most of their load to form fan-shaped deposits of boulders, gravel, sand and minor amounts of silt and clay. Such crudely stratified and poorly sorted deposits are alluvial fans. They have an average slope of 3.5°, but range from as little as $\frac{1}{2}°$ at the base or toe to as much as 7° at the apex or top of the fan. Alluvial cones consist of coarser detritus and have slopes as great as 15°. They are deposits of streams which do not head as far back in the mountains and which have steeper gradients than those which form alluvial fans. With each succeeding storm, alluvial fans increase in size and eventually coalesce with adjoining fans to form a continuous alluvial blanket or bajada along the base of the mountain. As the mountain front re-

treats under the influence of lateral stream planation and by the effects of sheetflood and sheet wash, a gently inclined bare rock surface develops. The erosional surface, a pediment, extends basinward from the base of the mountain until it disappears beneath the sediments of fans and bajadas. Pediment surfaces may be thinly veneered with gravel or be buried beneath several feet of coarse alluvium. (For a detailed discussion of these features see *Pediments*.)

Residual knobs of bedrock may rise above the pediment surface or protrude through the alluvium of bajadas and alluvial fans. Originally, inselberg (literally, "island mountain") was applied to a residual mass on an extensive pediment surface and bornhardt to any remnant of a former prominence reduced to small dimensions by desert erosion. Now, inselberg is generally used to describe residual bedrock masses whether related to pediments, bajadas, alluvial fans or the desert flat.

On the surface of fans and bajadas is an intricately branching system of dry drainage channels or dry washes. They may be a few feet in width and depth to a hundred or more feet. Some are steep-walled, such as the arroyos of western United States, and others are shallow undulations that form a distinctly braided pattern. The sand and gravel bottomed dry wash of the North American deserts is equivalent to the wadi of the African deserts, the quebrada of the Atacama, the chapp of the Gobi, and the laagte of the Kalahari.

On rare occasions, runoff may extend across the pediment-fan surface and reach the lowermost portion of the basin. The transported load is fine-grained, largely silt, clay, and dissolved salts. A temporary or playa lake is formed which may persist for a few weeks or, rarely, for several months. Once the lake waters evaporate a nearly level sur-

277

FIG. 10. Desert dome: Smooth rounded outline of Cima Dome of Mojave Desert. This land form is a result of prolonged backweathering in homogeneous rocks and represents the old-age stage in the semiarid erosion cycle.

face of clay or salt remains. The playa or dry lake surface is nearly flat, vegetation-free, and in the case of clay-surfaced playas is mud-cracked. There are two general playa types: the clay pan or clay flat playas which are in valleys where the water table is a considerable distance beneath the surface, and salt pan or saline playas, where the water table is within 10 feet of the surface and is usually within a foot or two. In some instances a small portion of a playa contains water throughout the year or is kept moist; these are salinas.

In narrow basins alluvial fans and bajadas may extend to the playa margin, but in broad valleys there is a surface of low relief and gentle inclination between the playa and the alluvial deposits of the mountain front. The desert flat or llano, as these surfaces are called, consist of much finer sediment than the adjoining fans and can also be differen-

FIG. 11. Badlands: Rugged terrain formed by intricate dissection of soft sediment by the combined action of rill wash, stream flood and wind-driven rain. Death Valley, California badlands.

tiated from fans by their gentler slopes which range from 1–0.1°.

If uplifted surfaces in the desert are broad and low and the initial relief is slight, a surface with extremely uniform and smooth slopes, a desert dome, results from the combined effects of prolonged weathering and stream flood action. Domes develop in areas of homogeneous rocks, commonly granitic, and if the bedrock surface is elongate in plane view rather than roughly circular, the landform is a desert arch. Desert domes and arches are landscape features of the old age stage of the desert cycle of erosion.

As the name implies, badlands consist of rugged and intricately eroded terrain. Where soft, unconsolidated rocks (such as lake beds, soft volcanics, shales and poorly cemented sandstones) are exposed, they are susceptible to rapid erosion. Rainsplash, wind-driven rain, and sheetwash rapidly carve the rocks into a series of sharp-edged ridges and narrow steep-walled gullies.

Wind modifies desert landscape by piling sand-size material into a wide variety of forms. Dunes develop on the desert flat, around the margins of dry lakes, and may be banked against the lower slopes of desert prominences. Sand dunes, although spectacular features of arid regions, are not as common or widespread as generally believed. In the American deserts they occupy less than 1% of the surface area, in the Sahara, less than 20%, and even in the most sandy of all deserts, the Arabian, only about 30%. (For a detailed description of dune origin and types, see *Sand Dunes*.)

Desert pavement is a surface feature that may develop on the desert flat, on fans and bajadas, and especially on Pleistocene lake or river terraces. Most pavements occur on nearly level or very gently sloping surfaces and consist of rounded or sub-

FIG. 12. Desert pavement near Yuma, Arizona. Pebble mosaic is formed by removal of fine sediments by rainsplash and rill wash coupled with deflation by wind. Extensive gravel and pebble surfaces are called reg.

angular pebbles from about $\frac{1}{2}$ to 3 inches in length. A pebble armor or serir is formed when the fragments are tightly interlocking. Desert pavements are developed by the removal of fine sediment with the resulting concentration of pebbles. Wind is a factor in removing sand, silt, and clay, but rainsplash and rill wash are also important in effectively concentrating pebble-sized fragments.

RICHARD STONE

References

Clements, T., *et al.*, 1957, "A Study of Desert Surface Conditions," *U.S. Army Tech. Report, EP-53*, Office of Quartermaster General, 111pp.

Gautier, E. F., 1935, "Sahara, the Great Desert," New York, Columbia University Press, 264pp.

Jaeger, E. C., 1957, "The North American Deserts," Stanford, Stanford University Press, 308pp.

Meigs, P., 1956, in (White, G. F., editor), "The Future of Arid Lands," *Am. Assoc. Adv. Sci.*, **43**, end papers.

Thompson, D. G., 1929, "The Mojave Desert Region, California," *U.S. Geol. Survey Water-Supply Paper*, **578**, 759pp.

Thornbury, W. D., 1954, "Principles of Geomorphology," New York, John Wiley & Sons, Inc., 618pp.

Cross-references: *Alluvial Fan or Cone*; *Alluvium*; *Badlands*; *Bajada*; *Base Level*; *Bolson*; *Bornhardt*; *Drainage Patterns*; *Erosion*; *Frost Riving*; *Gully Erosion*; *Hamada*; *Inselberg*; *Mudflow*; *Pediment*; *Playa*; *Sand Dunes*; *Sediment Transport*; *Sheet Erosion*, *Sheetwash*, etc.; *Talus Fan or Cone*; *Ventifact*; *Weathering*; *Wind Action*. Vol. I: *Ocean Currents*. Vol. II: *Air Mass*; *Arid Climate*; *Evaporation*; *Evapotranspiration*; *Fog, Smog, Mist*; *Insolation*; *Orographic Precipitation*; *Precipitation (Rainfall)*; *Relative Humidity*; *Temperature*; *Trade Winds*. pr Vol. VI: *Groundwater*; *Soils*; *Soil Profile*.

DESERT VARNISH (PATINA)

Almost all pebbles or rocks on a desert surface, particularly those long subject to *abrasion* and *defla-*tion (q.v.), e.g., the *hamada* or *reg* deserts of the Sahara, or *gibber plains* of Australia, have over them a thin film, varnish, lacquer or patina (in German: *Wüstenlack*). It consists usually of iron and manganese oxides, with some silica, sometimes largely silica. The coating is thus generally dark red to black, giving a characteristic appearance to the stony deserts. Postglacial or periglacial cold deserts in North America, Central Europe and Central Asia, are marked by similar pebbles and rocks, but generally have a softer hue, pale yellow or tan-colored, because of the lower iron and manganese availability in cooler latitudes.

The patination process is believed to be linked to dew and to capillarity. Constantly repeated droplets evaporate with the soil salts therein; the soft halides are rapidly removed by wind action leaving the durable iron and manganese oxides and silica. Gentle polishing by wind abrasion gives the final gloss. Hume (1925) mentions that many travelers have been convinced that these blackened rocks were somehow related to fires.

A similar varnish or patina marks the high-water mark of the Nile floods at the various cataracts. Indeed, old and higher Nile levels dating back 15,000 years or more are still perfectly traced by these marker horizons. At the Second Cataract, some Mesolithic petroglyphs were found covered up to half their height by an oscillation of the Nile level sometime after they were inscribed (Fairbridge, 1963). Evidently this patination is a very helpful tool in desert geochronology. It is apparent that the varnish forms very quickly, in a few weeks in the case of the Nile, but is extremely durable since some of them in exposed positions are over 10,000 years old.

A detailed chemical study of desert varnish has been summarized as follows by Celeste Engel and R. P. Sharp (1958):

"Wet chemical analyses of varnishes, the underlying weathered rinds, and fresh rocks from southern California deserts show that principal varnish elements are

O, H, Si, Al, Fe, and Mn. Manganese and Fe give varnish its distinctive characteristics, and Mn is enriched 66 to 292 fold from rock to varnish. Rocks relatively high in Mn and Fe bear the best varnishes.

Quantitative spectrographic analyses of 22 varnishes show that Ti, Ba, and Sr are the most abundant trace elements, followed by Cu, Ni, Zr, Pb, V, Co, La, Y, B, Cr, Sc, and Yb. Cadmium, W, Ag, Nb, Sn, Ga, Mo, Be, and Zn were recorded in some varnishes. Spectrographic analyses of rocks, soils, and airborne material indicate that variations in trace-element content are related to the local geochemical environment.

Chemical and field data suggest that: (1) varnish on stones seated in soil or colluvium is derived largely from that material, (2) varnish on large bedrock exposures comes from weathered parts of the rock, and (3) airborne material is probably a minor contributor.

Desert varnish is primarily a weathering product involving solution, transportation, and deposition of the specified elements. Sources are largely local, and movement can occur by mechanical transport in solution or possibly by ionic diffusion through films of moisture. Dew may be an important source of this moisture. Rate of varnish formation varies widely with local conditions, but at one locality in the Mojave Desert a good varnish has formed in 25 years."

Hunt (1962) has pointed out that desert varnish was forming in the American Southwest probably during the last pluvial stage (? early Holocene). Older gravels are varnished, but younger ones are not. The Indian cliff dwellings at Mesa Verde were built over varnished surfaces, but the process does not appear to have been active during the last 2000 years. Blackwelder (1948) noted the same thing in Egypt. While high evaporation is clearly necessary for the varnish to develop, in the case of varnished cliffs it is also necessary to have sufficient precipitation to furnish groundwater seeps.

RHODES W. FAIRBRIDGE

References

Blackwelder, E., 1948, "Historical significance of desert lacquer," *Bull. Geol. Soc. Am.,* **59,** 1367 (abs.).

Engel, C. G., and Sharp, R. P., 1958, "Chemical data on desert varnish," *Bull. Geol. Soc. Am.,* **69,** 487–518.

Fairbridge, R. W., 1963, "Nile sedimentation above Wadi Halfa during the last 20,000 years," *Kush* (Khartoum), **11,** 96–107.

Hume, W. F., 1925, "Geology of Egypt," Vol. 1, Cairo, Government Press.

Hunt, C. B., 1954, "Desert varnish," *Science,* **120,** 183–184.

Hunt, C. B., 1962, "Stratigraphy of desert varnish," *U.S. Geol. Surv. Profess. Paper* **424-B,** 194–195.

Knaust, W., 1930, "Ueber Sole von Eisenhydroxyd und Manganhydroxyd in ihrer Beziehung zur Bildung der sogenannten Schutzrinden und des Laterits," *Chemie der Erde,* **4,** 529–548.

Scheffer, F., Meyer, B., and Kalk, E., 1963, "Biologische Uraschen der Wüstenlackbildung," *Zeit. Geomorph.,* N.F. **7,** 112–119.

White, C. H., 1924, "Desert varnish," *Am. J. Sci.,* Ser. 5, **207,** 413–420.

Cross-references: *Abrasion*; *Deflation*; *Gibber*; *Hamada.* Vol. II: *Capillarity*; *Dew, Dew Point.* Vol. IV: *Spectrophotometry.*

DESSICATION CRACKS—*See* MUDCRACKS

DIATREMES—*See* VOLCANIC NECKS AND DIATREMES

DILUVIAL THEORY—*See* pr Vol. VI

DISCHARGE—*See* SEDIMENT TRANSPORT; also pr Vol. VI, FLUVIAL SEDIMENT TRANSPORT

DISSECTION—*See* DRAINAGE PATTERNS

DISTRIBUTARIES—*See* DELTAIC EVOLUTION

DIVIDE—*See* WATERSHED

DOLINA

Dolina, a Slav word meaning simply a valley, has been incorporated into the terminology of limestone erosion in karst landscapes. It was introduced in works on the Carinthian karst in the last century and popularized by Cvijić (1918), and its French and German form *doline* is often seen in English works, although without real justification. Dolina is applied to any basin or closed depression in a karst-affected limestone, of larger dimensions than a *swallow-hole, sink* or *sinkhole* (q.v.), often enlarged by the collapse of caverns. The shape may vary from round to oval to elongate. Its floor is generally flat, often partly filled with *alluvium* (q.v.) or residual *terra rossa* type soils. In extreme cases,

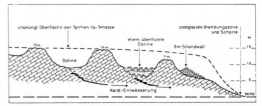

FIG. 1. Dolinas related to sea level in the "coastal karst" near Santander, Spain (H. Mensching, 1965: *Erdkunde,* **19,** 24–31). The Upper Cretaceous limestones have been truncated by a Tyrrhenian (Pleistocene interglacial) sea, which rose eustatically to about 15 meters above the present mean sea level. Dolinas developed during subsequent exposure above MSL and seaward dolina floors were partly sedimented during a late Tyrrhenian 8 meter sea stand. Since the base level dropped appreciably during low sea level stands, a deep karst hydrologic (cryptorheic) drainage developed.

dolinas may be funnel-shaped depressions up to 3000 meters across and 200 meters in depth. Coalescent dolinas are called "*uvalas*" (q.v.).

In Slovenia, "classical" karst country in Yugoslavia, the term *draga* is used locally in the ordinary sense of dolina, while the term *vrtača* is applied to a large dolina containing water (Gams, 1961). Dolinas, in general, are favored by relatively high relief and high precipitation. In New Guinea, for example, Jennings and Bik (1962) reported that at 3000-meter elevation there are three common karst types: (1) dolina karst (simple), (2) pyramid-and-dolina karst, and (3) arête-and-dolina karst. The dolinas here are clearly solution forms and not due to collapse. This is the mature tropical form as established by Grund (1914).

RHODES W. FAIRBRIDGE

References

Cvijić, J., 1918, "Hydrographie souterraine et évolution morphologique du Karst," *Rec. Trav. Inst. Géogr. Alpine* (Grenoble), **6,** No. 4, 56pp.

Cvijić, J., 1960, "La geographie des terrains calcaires," *Acad. Serbe Sci. Arts (Belgrade) Monogr.,* **391.**

Gams, I., 1961, "H geomorfologiji Belle Krajine," *Geogr. Sbornik,* **6,** 191–240.

Grund, A., 1914, "Der geographische Zyklus im Karst," *Z. Ges. Erdk.,* 621–640.

Jennings, J. N., 1967, "Some Karst Areas of Australia," in (Jennings, J. N., and Mabbutt, J. A., editors), "Landform Studies from Australia and New Guinea," Australian Nat. Univ. Press, 256–292.

Jennings, J. N., and Bik, M. J., 1962, "Karst morphology in Australian New Guinea," *Nature,* **194,** 1036–1038.

Von Engeln, O. D., 1942, "Geomorphology," New York, The Macmillan Co., 655pp.

Wray, D. A., 1922, "The Karstlands of western Yugoslavia," *Geol. Mag.,* **59,** 392–409.

Cross-references: *Alluvium; Blind Valley; Karst; Sink, Sinkhole; Uvala.* pr Vol. VI: *Terra Rossa.*

DOME MOUNTAIN

The term "dome" has been used in a simple topographic (relief) sense for rounded mountain tops ("bald tops") for centuries. The word is used in French, e.g., Puy de Dôme (Auvergne), and is derived from Italian *Duomo* (house of God and thus to the church dome), which goes back again to *domus* (Latin, house).

In geomorphology, there are two distinctive types of *dome mountain,* one igneous, the other tectonic, thus:

(1) Intrusive Dome Mountains

Three varieties are known, the mountains best known and simplest in form being the stripped *laccolithic domes* or "laccolith mountains" (Geikie, 1914) (or laccolites), such as widely developed in

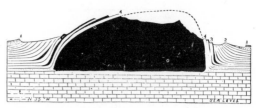

FIG. 1. Section of Hillers laccolite, Mount Henry Region, Utah, showing simple structure (Lobeck, 1939). (By permission of McGraw-Hill Book Co., N.Y.)

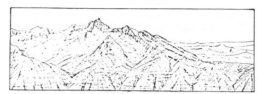

FIG. 2. West Elk Mountains, Colorado, showing upturned strata on flank of laccolite (U.S. Geological Survey).

the Henry Mountains of Utah and described in a classic monograph by G. K. Gilbert (1877). Many others are known in the Colorado Plateau and Rocky Mountain region (Wyoming, South Dakota, Colorado, New Mexico and Arizona). Every stage is known, from the igneous domes more or less covered with their original sedimentary envelope as in Navajo Mountain (Arizona) or Hillers Dome, Utah (Fig. 1), down to maturely dissected examples, e.g., the Abajo Mountains of Utah (Fig. 5a), and the El Late Mountains of Colorado (Fig. 5b). The Devil's Tower of Wyoming is sometimes claimed to be an eroded laccolithic dome (Lobeck, 1939; following Darton, 1907), and there are certainly laccoliths in the area, but its striking vertical "organ-pipe" jointing is characteristic of lava that has cooled in a crater (joints vertical, normal to the crater floor); thus Von Engeln (1942; following Johnson, 1907) classifies it as a volcanic plug.

The second type is the *complex laccolith* (or lopolithic) intrusion with broad sill-type interfingering tongues of igneous material penetrating the surrounding sediments, e.g., in the La Plata Mountains, Colorado (Fig. 6).

The third type is the stripped *pluton,* the dome-shaped plutonic igneous intrusion found in smaller

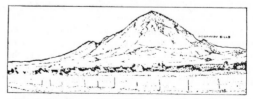

FIG. 3. Bear Butte, Black Hills, South Dakota; a small laccolite showing upturned beds (Lobeck, 1939; from U.S. Geological Survey).

A TYPICAL LAVA DOME
HUALALAI, HAWAII

FIG. 4. A dome mountain of volcanic origin, characteristic of the non-orogenic basalts ("Atlantic Suite"). Example from Hawaii (from Lobeck, 1939). (By permission of McGraw-Hill Book Co., N.Y.)

batholiths. The surfaces often show a striking system of joints parallel to the original surface, hence the name *exfoliation domes*. There is a classic example at Stone Mountain, Georgia, which probably represents a piedmont zone monadnock, i.e., isolated by peneplanation or pediplanation (Fenneman, 1938, see his Fig. 35, p. 133). Vast numbers of examples are to be seen in Africa, Brazil and Australia (see *Bornhardt* and *Inselberg*).

(2) Tectonic Dome Mountains

In this type, the dome is tectonically uplifted or arched up over a broad radius, leading to quaquaversal dips (radiating omnidirectionally). Fine examples in North America are the Adirondack Dome of New York State, the Ozark Dome of Missouri and the Black Hills Dome of South Dakota (Newton and Jenny, 1880). In each, a core of Precambrian basement is exposed, overlapping which is a ring-shaped belt of Paleozoic and younger platform-type sediments. Interesting drainage patterns develop, primarily consequent streams in a radial pattern, modified by subsequents in an annular pattern (Fig. 7). Notably annular is the

FIG. 5a. Abajo mountains. A maturely dissected laccolithic dome in the Colorado Plateau, eastern Utah. This small dome has a diameter of about 6 miles, and the highest summits rise 3000–4000 feet above the surrounding plateau. The sharply upturned Dakota sandstone beds are shown at *c, c* in the middle of the view at the base of Abajo Peak. Elsewhere the Cretaceous shales *d, d, d* dip away more gently from the mountains (Holmes, U.S. Geological Survey).

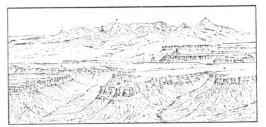

FIG. 5b. El Late Mountains. A maturely dissected laccolithic dome in the Colorado Plateau, southwestern Colorado. The plateau consists of horizontal rocks which are turned up at the base of the mountains. The higher peaks rise somewhat more than 3000 feet above the plateau surface. The central core of the mountain mass consists of several varieties of igneous rocks, and there are also layers of fine-grained igneous rocks interbedded between the upturned sandstones and shales. These form minor hogbacks and ridges (Holmes, U.S. Geological Survey).

Red Valley almost surrounding the Black Hills. A younger dome, exclusively in sediments, is the Zuni Uplift in New Mexico, or Middle Dome, Harlowtown, Montana (see air photo in Hinds, 1943, p. 216). The Lake District of England is another tectonic dome, from which the younger cover has been largely stripped, leaving a superimposed drainage on the early Paleozoic core. The Wealden Dome in southern England is exclusively in Mesozoic rocks (and marginal Tertiaries); curiously enough, its basement is a syncline in Paleozoic rocks. It is extended across the channel in the Boulonnais of France. Another fine example of a youthful dome (in late Tertiary sediments) is Signal Hill in the Los Angeles Basin.

Other Dome Structures

Besides these dome mountains of the different types, there are certain domal structures, not normally classified as mountains, which may under certain conditions assume considerable relief.

(a) *Salt domes*, diapiric or piercement structures that are the product of "halokinesis," the tectonic property of rock salt (halite) to flow under very mild temperature and pressure. On the Gulf coast,

FIG. 6. Section of La Plata Mountains, Colorado; a laccolite with many sills (Lobeck, 1939). (By permission of McGraw-Hill Book Co., N.Y.)

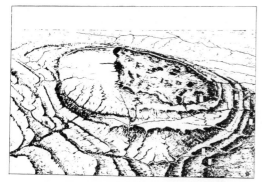

FIG. 7. Dome mountain of the Black Hills, South Dakota, dissected by fluvial erosion (radial and annular). From the middle to the outside the formations are (1) Crystalline core (Precambrian granite and gneiss). (2) Carboniferous (Mississippian) sediments. (3) Triassic. (4) Upper Cretaceous (Dakota Sandstone). (5, 6) Towyer formations (redrawn from a sketch by Henry Newton).

the salt domes either are buried or produce only a very gentle doming of the coastal plain (see air photo in Lobeck, 1939, p. 508), but in the foothills of Iran, under arid conditions, the salt is not easily dissipated, and some veritable salt mountains occur (Gansser, 1960). Jebel Usdum (Sodom) at the south end of the Dead Sea is a salt mountain, the "pillar of salt" of the biblical tale of Lot's wife.

(b) *Volcanic domes* of basaltic character, due to high-temperature, low-viscosity lavas, which do not form the familiar conical volcanoes but broad dome volcanoes, the largest and best-known example being that of Mauna Loa and Mauna Kea on the "Big Island" of Hawaii. Such lava domal mountains are normally classified as "volcanic mountains."

A special type of small, steep-sided, volcanic dome mountain is the endogenous dome (Rittmann, 1962), or "Staukuppe" of Cloos, characteristically represented by the famous Puy de Dôme, in the Auvergne of the French "Midi." This sort of dome is produced by volcanic lava and gas pressure arching up the crater filling with the lava flowing out laterally. A related dome mountain is produced by the lava intruding its own tuffs ("Quellkuppe" of Cloos) as in the Roche de la Tuilière in the Auvergne. The nature of the intrusion is well displayed by the columnar joint patterns. Familiar lava domes are also seen in the Mono Craters of eastern California. These are rhyolitic lava extrusions of very viscous type.

RHODES W. FAIRBRIDGE

References

Fenneman, N. M., 1931, "Physiography of the Western United States," New York, McGraw-Hill Book Co., 534pp.

Fenneman, N. M., 1938, "Physiography of the Eastern United States," New York, McGraw-Hill Book Co., 714pp.

Gansser, A., 1960, "Ueber Schlammvulkane und Salzdome," *Vierteljahrschr. Naturfossch. Ges. Zuerich,* **105**, 1–46.

Geikie, J., 1914, "Mountains, Their Origin, Growth and Decay," Princeton, N.J., D. Van Nostrand Co., 311pp.

Gilbert, G. K., 1877, "Report on the geology of the Henry Mountains, Utah," *U.S. Geol. Surv. Rocky Mtn. Reg.,* 160pp.

Hinds, N. E., 1943, "Geomorphology, the Evolution of Landscape," Englewood Cliffs, N.J., Prentice-Hall, 894pp.

Holmes, W. H., 1878, "Report on the geology of the Sierra Abajo and west San Miguel Mountains," *U.S. Geogr. Surv. Territ. (Hayden), Ann. Rept.,* **10**, 187–195.

Lobeck, A. K., 1939, "Geomorphology, an Introduction to the Study of Landscapes," New York, McGraw-Hill Book Co., 731pp.

MacCarthy, G. R., 1925, "Some facts and theories concerning laccoliths," *J. Geol.,* **33**, 1–18.

Miller, W. J., 1911, "Exfoliation domes in Warren Co., N.Y.," *New York St. Mus. Bull.,* **149**, 187–194.

Newton, H., and Jenney, W. P., 1880, "Report on the geology and resources of the Black Hills of Dakota," Washington, D.C., U.S. Government Printing Office, 566pp.

Rittmann, A., 1962, "Volcanoes and their Activity," New York, Interscience (Wiley), transl. E. A. Vincent, 305pp.

Stearns, H. T., and Clark, W. O., 1930, "Geology and water resources of the Kau district, Hawaii, including parts of Kilauea and Mauna Loa volcanoes," *U.S. Geol. Surv., Water Supply Paper* **616**, 194pp.

Thornbury, W. D., 1965, "Regional Geomorphology of the United States," New York, John Wiley & Sons, 609pp.

Von Engeln, O. D., 1942, "Geomorphology," New York, The Macmillan Co., 655pp.

Witkind, I. J., 1964, "Geology of the Abajo Mountains area, San Juan County, Utah," *U.S. Geol. Surv., Profess. Paper* **453**, 110pp.

Cross-references: *Bornhardt; Crater; Drainage Patterns; Inselberg; Monadnock; Mountain Types; Pediplanation; Peneplain; Piedmont Landform; Structural Control in Geomorphology.*

DRAINAGE BASIN

A drainage basin, alternately described as a *catchment area*, is in geomorphology and hydrology a region drained by a particular stream or by a river system. The amount of water reaching the stream (or artificial reservoir) is dependent upon the size of the basin, the total precipitation, and the losses due to evaporation and to absorption by soils and vegetation. "Drainage basin" reflects the geomorphologists' study of terrain. "Catchment area" is used more by hydrologists with water supply in mind; it also refers to an area of snow accumulation.

The drainage system may be analyzed with respect to *time*: perennial (permanent flow), seasonal, intermittent, periodical, episodical, and ephemeral (the last four being essentially synonyms). The drainage also has a *pattern*: dendritic, trellis, crow-foot, rectangular, pinnate, radial and annular. The *direction* may be basically centrifugal (as on an island) or centripetal (as in lake basins, inside a glacial lobe, or inside an inactive volcanic crater). The drainage *density* will also provide the texture of the system; this aspect is susceptible to advanced statistical analysis (Melton, 1958).

Drainage basins themselves may be classified on a broad scale (de Martonne, 1950); the terms employ the Greek root *rhein*, to flow.

(a) Exorheic or exoreic ("exoréique" or "exoré-isme" in French), where the basin debouches directly or eventually into the ocean; exorheism is essentially "normal."

(b) Endorheic, where the drainage is internal and has no outlet to the sea, debouching either into lakes or dissipating into desert sands; on a small scale, glacial moraine country (kettle holes) and karst country (swallow holes) are sometimes marked by endorheism.

(c) Arheic, where there are no obvious drainage basins at all, as in some sandy deserts where the rainfall is negligible and the intensity of dune activity totally obscures periodic or former rainfall and drainage patterns; also in muskeg and tundra regions.

Sometimes, it is appropriate to add a fourth type:

(d) Cryptorheic, where the drainage basin is hidden, i.e., underground, in a karst sink-hole and river system. The streams may eventually join deep vadose waters, as in artesian basins, or may rejoin the surface drainage. The dry landscape ("causses" in France) is pock-marked by small endorheic centers (swallow holes, poljes, dolinas).

A stream or river system that is initiated in one region, as in a high rainfall area like Ethiopia or central Africa, and flows through a dry area for much of its course, like the Nile, is known as *allogenous*, allogenic or allochthonous. Many examples are known of basins which were formerly endorheic at certain stages and have become exorheic through change of climate, overflow, capture or tectonic activity. Formerly exorheic systems may equally well become blocked by tectonics, change of climate, siltation, overwhelming by sand dunes, etc.

RHODES W. FAIRBRIDGE

References

Boulton, A. G., 1965, "Morphometric analysis of river basin characteristics," *Water Resources Board (U.K.)*, Reading, 10pp.
Jutson, J. T., 1934, "The physiography (geomorphology) of Western Australia," *Bull. Geol. Surv. W. Australia* **95**, 2d ed., 366pp.
Martonne, E. de, 1950–55, "Traité de Géographie Physique," Paris, A. Colin 3 vols.
Melton, M. A., 1958, "Correlation structure of morphometric properties of drainage systems and their controlling agents," *J. Geol.*, **66**, 442–460.
Milton, L., 1965, "Quantitative expression of drainage net patterns," *Australian J. Sci.*, **27**(8), 238–240.
Schenck, H., Jr., 1963, "Simulation of the evolution of drainage-basin networks with a digital computer," *J. Geophys. Res.* **68**(20), 5739–5745.

Cross-references: *Dolina*; *Drainage Patterns*; *Ephemeral Streams*; *Karst*; *Kettle*; *Polje*; *Quantitative Geomorphology*; *Sink, Sinkhole*, etc.; *Texture-Topographic*; *Watershed*.

DRAINAGE, GENESIS—*See* DRAINAGE PATTERNS; RIVERS

DRAINAGE PATTERNS

Drainage patterns or arrangements refer to spatial relationships among streams or rivers, which may be influenced in their erosion by inequalities of slope, rock resistance, structure and geologic history of a region. The degree of erosion is referred to as *dissection* or *relief*. *Topography* originally meant the position of all geographic features in an area, including relief. It has subsequently come to mean only the relief and general surface configuration, such as shown on a contoured map (Stamp, 1961). By *dissected topography*, we mean topography characterized by a definite pattern of incised hills or mountains separated by lower-lying areas, i.e., cut up by erosion into a network of valleys and interfluves.

As soon as a new *initial surface* rises or otherwise becomes exposed above sea level or after glacial retreat, surface wash from rains will start to produce valleys cutting into the new landscape (see *Cycles, Geomorphic*). These streams (consequents) will flow in the direction of maximum slope and will produce the first ridges and valleys. Since water erosion occurs in all but continental glacial areas and desert dune country, it has been found to be most convenient if we describe the *dissection* of the landscape, the pattern of ridges and valleys in terms of the drainage pattern, the main kinds of which are summarized in Table 1.

At first the pattern produced by the stream will depend on the slope of the initial surface. Since this will probably be uneven, the drainage pattern will often be chaotic. This initial pattern is called a *deranged drainage pattern*, and good examples may be found in the areas covered by the Wisconsin ice sheets and also in desert areas. A common characteristic of these regions is that there are numerous local inland drainage basins with streams flowing into the center (*centripetal drainage*). This pattern may persist for long periods of time in those desert areas where wind action is dominant over water erosion.

TABLE 1. TYPES OF DRAINAGE PATTERN (STUART A. HARRIS, PARTLY AFTER THORNBURY, 1954)

Note: The classes are not mutually exclusive. Thus a deranged drainage pattern may include many examples of centripetal drainage.

Drainage Type	Form	Cause	Examples
Deranged	Drainage not coordinated—numerous local drainage basins and lakes.	Blocking of older drainage by till, moraines, etc. Insufficient time for coordination since the present drainage system came into existence.	Canadian Shield, and Siberian tundra landscapes.
Centripetal	Drainage converging on the centers of inland drainage basins ("arheic drainage," i.e., no systematic stream systems).	Constructional land forms containing small basins. Insufficient time or rainfall or surface runoff to produce coordination of drainage; as in deserts, volcanic craters, calderas, meteor craters, kettle-holes, cryptovolcanic depressions.	Arid areas, e.g. parts of California or New Mexico, or in karst or deranged areas of drainage.
Karst	Numerous sinkholes, few surface streams ("cryptorheic drainage," i.e., underground).	Solution of the underlying limestone causing the drainage to move underground. (See also under "Centripetal")	Dinaric belt, Yugoslavia; Mammoth Cave area, Kentucky. Karst regions, in general.
Dendritic	Random pattern of branching; integrated streams.	No structural control, e.g., where sediments are flat lying, or possess homogeneous lithology, e.g., loess, tuff.	Very widespread in Great Plains of North America; concentrated examples in *Badlands* (q.v.), e.g., South Dakota.
Parallel	Regularly spaced in parallel or subparallel streams.	Pronounced slope or structural controls (hard and soft rocks, faults and monoclinal or isoclinal folds).	Rare, Mesa Verde National Park, Colorado; other regions of plateaus with monoclinal warps.
Trellis	One dominant direction with a subsidiary direction of drainage at right angles to it linking up the main streams.	Tilted or folded alternating hard and soft sedimentary rocks.	Folded Appalachians, Ridge and Valley Province; Jura Mountains of France and Switzerland.
Annular	Circular drainage patterns linked by one radial stream.	Dome in alternating hard and soft sedimentary rocks.	Black Hills of South Dakota.
Rectangular	Drainage in two directions at right angles, both equally developed.	Joint or fault control in otherwise homogeneous strata.	Adirondack Mountains, N.Y.
Angulate (Rhombohedral)	Drainage equally developed in two directions meeting at acute and obtuse angles.		Fjords of Norway and Scotland; rejuvenated shield areas.
Barbed	The stream bends abruptly back to flow in the reverse direction, with "boat hook" bends.	River capture, glacial diversion or tectonic diversion.	Maumee River, Fort Wayne, Indiana; eastern Australia; New Zealand.
Radial	Streams radiating out from a common center.	Volcanic cones; domes in relatively homogeneous strata.	Mt. Rainier, etc.; Lake District of England. Some salt domes, e.g., Avery Dome, La.
Complex	Drainage obviously structurally controlled but not falling into one of the other groups.	Very complicated geological structure or geomorphological history.	Laurentian Mountains, Quebec.

Adjustment to Structure

In humid regions, the streams rapidly cut into the hills, thus linking up the formerly isolated drainage basins. As they do so, they cut downward and tend to erode the softer rocks more readily, should a lithologic alternation be present. This gives rise to a whole range of drainage patterns which are dependent on the geological structure of the region and on the resistance to erosion of the strata (see Table 1). Idealized examples of some of these will be found in Fig. 1, while numerous excellent examples will be found in Lobeck (1939), the "Relief Form Atlas" of the French Institut Géographique National (1956) and the "Atlas of Landforms" (Scovel, *et al.* 1966).

These patterns form the main evidence for the geological structure and nature of the underlying strata in areas where vegetation and soils mask the actual rocks (see *Structural Control*). They are therefore of fundamental importance in geological photo-interpretation. They will show up best in late youth and early maturity of the cycle of river erosion of W. M. Davis. After early maturity, local relief is decreased as are the areas of the *interfluves* (q.v.). In old age, the valleys become plains and the interfluves are reduced to isolated hills and thus the pattern is essentially destroyed.

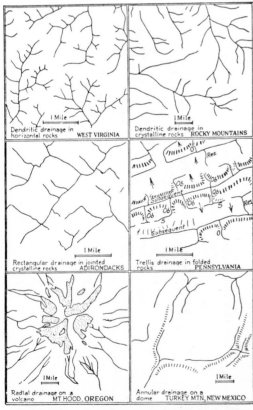

FIG. 1. Types of stream patterns (from Lobeck, 1939). (By permission of McGraw-Hill Book Co. N.Y.)

Should there be a change in the base level, the streams either will be rejuvenated or will normally actively aggrade the lower parts of their valleys. In the case of *rejuvenation* the streams will cut down and back from the base level into the previous flood plain, reducing it to a series of paired terraces along the valley sides, while a new flood plain will gradually be formed adjusted to the new base level. Valleys showing such features are referred to as polycyclic or *multicyclic valleys* (Cotton, 1948). Most streams have multicyclic valleys due to changes in sea level and diastrophic movements (see *Landscape Types, Genetic*). Recent work seems to invalidate the idea that a rise in base level causes alluviation upstream from the new level (Garner, personal communication).

Landscapes which show the effects of only one cycle of erosion are called monocyclic landscapes by Horberg (1952), as opposed to multicyclic landscapes formed by more than one cycle of erosion. Monocyclic landscapes are rarely found except in very recently formed land surfaces.

Lack of Adjustment to Structure

Notable cases of dissected topography occur where the drainage is not fully adjusted to the geological structure and topography. One of the most striking examples is that of the Brahmaputra drainage from the Tibetan plateau flowing south and carving its way through the highest mountain range in the world to reach the Indian Ocean. In any other direction, it would merely have to flow down a gentle gradient to the sea. This is regarded as indicating that the streams were there before the mountains began to be uplifted, i.e., it is a case of *antecedence* (see *Rivers*). The uplift of the mountains was sufficiently slow for the main streams to

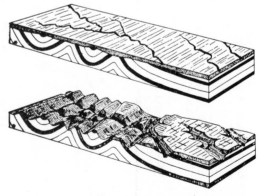

FIG. 2. Superposition from either an unconformably overlying horizontal formation or from a discordant abrasion plain (peneplain, pediplain, etc.) will initially establish a primary dendritic pattern. However, with deeper dissection of the underlying structure the dendritic pattern will become "overprinted" by the structural control of the newly exposed features (diagram by R. Kettner).

be able to cut down their beds and more or less keep pace with the uplift. Since the streams cut through the high mountains, the uplift in the middle of their courses was much greater than at their sources. This theory is borne out by the presently available data on the river terraces (see Sparks, 1960). Another example is the Rhine rift valley where block faulting has occurred since the Rhine started flowing northward.

Sometimes a stream may flow across a level plain toward a ridge made up of resistant rock, and flow in a gorge through it to the continuation of the plain on the other side. Examples of this are common in areas without recent tectonic activity, e.g., in some of the more stable parts of Wyoming (Atwood and Atwood, 1938), and they cannot possibly be the result of subsequent localized earth movements. However, there is good reason to believe that the streams flowed over vast alluvial fans which had buried most of the ridges in Miocene times. Uplift of the region caused downcutting and entrenchment of the rivers so that they cut down into whatever rocks happened to underlie their course. In this way, they were *superimposed* (or "superposed") on the harder buried ridges. Since then, the softer alluvial material has been removed, but the resistant ridges have remained (Fig. 2).

Superimposition is much more common than antecedence, since the latter is confined to the belt of late Tertiary mountains around the Pacific Ocean (e.g., the Columbia River through the Cascade Mountains) and the Alpine–Himalayan mountain ranges. Proof as to which is the cause of lack of adjustment to structure can only be achieved by detailed geomorphological studies. Occasionally it may be found that a given stream may be consequent upon one phase of warping but antecedent in relation to later movements. Cotton (1917) calls these *anteconsequent* streams, and examples have been described from the eastern side of the Adriatic Sea (Davis, 1901) and from New Zealand (Cotton, 1948).

An extreme case of antecedent drainage is a gorge cutting through a youthfully folded anticline. A very gentle case of antecedence still preserves the pattern of the preexisting drainage and receives an "overprint" corresponding to the new slopes. This has been termed *palimpsest drainage* by Howard (1962); incidentally, a palimpsest is a partially erased manuscript, used for subsequent writing, and the term has also been employed by Tyrrell in metamorphic petrology. Howard (1962) gives the example of a gently rising anticline in Taiwan that betrayed its presence on air photos particularly by the preferred orientation of the paddy fields around the dome, which later proved to have an elevation of only 25 meters, but seismic work and drilling showed subsurface dips up to 60° and a fold amplitude of the order of 1200 meters.

Similar gentle upwarps leading to palimpsest patterns may be recognized where there are very sensitive ecologic guides to precise elevation, as in the swamps and bayous of Louisiana. Salt domes have been characteristically discovered in this way, since they are often still rising gently, and one may well walk or fly over them without perceiving any relief, yet in flat swampy country, the slight modification of the drainage pattern is quickly brought out by vegetation changes and adaptations.

Types of Drainage Pattern

Zernitz (1932) summarized seven major types of drainage plan: dendritic, trellis, rectangular, radial, annular, parallel and irregular. The classification is a strictly non-genetic, geometric system of description, and although she states that certain genetic stream types characterize these drainage patterns, one must beware of assuming that a spatial arrangement of streams implies origin.

Dendritic Drainage. The term, first used by I. C. Russell (1898), was later defined by Cleland (1916) as a nonsystematic or treelike (branching) pattern of valleys extending in many directions in a region of horizontally bedded rocks. This interpretation has subsequently been modified, and in its present usage, no specific country rock is named. The pattern is typically developed on rocks of uniform resistance, such as horizontal sedimentary units and massive igneous and complex metamorphics, providing that there is no dominant slope or structural control.

Modified dendritic drainage may be described as pinnate, subparallel or anastomatic. The pinnate pattern is feather-like, with tributaries parallel and joining the master stream at acute angles. In the subparallel dendritic type, the acute angles formed at the junction of the master stream and tributaries are so small as to make the major and subsidiary streams nearly parallel. The anastomatic pattern, characteristic of flood plains and deltas, consists of braided streams separated by channel bars; oxbow lakes, bayous and chutes are common features (see *Chute*; *Oxbow Lake*; *Rivers—Meandering and Braiding*).

Trellis Drainage. In 1895, Bailey Willis named and described the trellis drainage pattern. In the ridge and valley province of the Appalachians, an area of folded and tilted strata where formations outcrop in parallel belts, he noted that secondary tributaries are commonly elongated, parallel to the master stream, and join the primary tributaries at right angles; the primary tributaries are, in turn, orthogonal to the major streams. Willis named such an arrangement the trellis pattern because of its resemblance to a garden trellis.

Trellis drainage may be developed in glaciated areas, in the presence of linear glacial features, as well as in regions where parallel belts of rocks of varying resistance outcrop. In other examples, primary sedimentary structures such as cross-

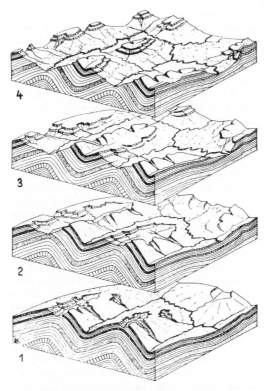

FIG. 3. Initiation of a trellis pattern on newly established fold structures without previous drainage. Evolution is from bottom to top diagram (1–4). Such a case could only evolve from submarine folding accompanied by rapid emergence, e.g., in very young orogenic belts (diagram by R. Kettner).

bedding and paleocurrent effects may be the control (Warner, 1965). Wind blowing steadily from the same quarter may also exercise this sort of influence (Stokes, 1964).

Rectangular Drainage. Characterized by orthogonal bends in both the tributaries and the master streams, this configuration is generally attributed to the presence of right-angle faults or joints. The presence of secondary tributaries is not required; the properties of secondary subsidiary streams, if present, distinguish the trellis from the rectangular pattern. Drainage with acute or obtuse angles, of similar origin, is called *angulate* or *rhombohedral*. Drainage with acute angles, consistently with "boat-hook bends," is known as *barbed drainage* and is due to large-scale river capture.

Radial Drainage. Radial drainage may be developed on a structural or geomorphic quaquaversal basement, such as a volcano, pluton, laccolithic dome, salt dome, or circular monadnock. In the radial outward pattern, drainage lines radiate out from a common center, while in the centripetal or radial inward type, streams flow into a common center from circular basin walls. The *centripetal pattern* is noted in craters, calderas, structural basins and breached domes (relief inversion).

Annular Drainage. On maturely dissected domes and basins, as a result of the capture of radial streams, a ring-like or annular pattern will develop. As breaching proceeds, the initial radial streams completely disappear, slope control influence ceases, and concentric arrangements of streams (the annular pattern) on the least resistant formations will develop if other factors are negligible. Examples of this type of drainage can be found in the Henry Mountains and in the Black Hills.

Parallel Drainage. The parallel pattern, as the name implies, consists of parallel master and tributary streams. Pronounced regional slope, parallel faults, and parallel topographic features such as drumlins and lateral moraines are conducive to the formation of this drainage type.

Irregular Drainage. In regions which have been recently glaciated, one often finds local modifications of streams and discordance with courses on higher land. Abandoned valleys may form if the stream flow has been blocked by a moraine. Prominent swamps and lakes, pitted outwash, moraines and drumlins all contribute to what Zernitz (1932) has termed an irregular drainage pattern. Since this type of drainage is largely produced by blocking or displacement of an earlier system, the term *deranged* drainage is often preferred. Mature or rejuvenated shields may also develop an irregular pattern with traces of tectonic "grain" and are then termed *complex drainage* areas.

Genetic Aspects

Although such a classification of drainage patterns cannot be genetic, genetic terms such as *consequent, subsequent, obsequent, resequent* and *insequent* (see also *Rivers*) are often applied to the individual streams composing the patterns. In many discussions of drainage arrangements, however, the genetic series of terms is often used in a descriptive sense, not necessarily implying the method by which the stream acquired its course.

Melton (1959) believes that there is universal superposition of drainage in flatland areas; i.e.,

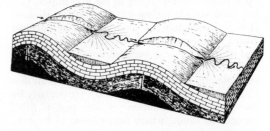

FIG. 4. Initiation of antecedent dissection of rising folds to be followed by evolution of subsequent (plus obsequent and resequent) drainage system (diagram by R. Kettner).

streams developed on a sedimentary cover cut down and are imposed upon a foreign structure, thereby masking their origin. Since the genetic terms (consequent, subsequent, etc.) refer only to the surficial relations between streams and rocks, if superposition is the rule rather than the exception, then genetic terms should not be included in the classification of drainage patterns; they should be used only when one is intentionally formulating a hypothesis or origin for a specific location.

In the case of superposition onto a folded "basement," the ridge and valley evolution of the latter will introduce a subsequent style drainage with *trellis patterns*. In the folded Appalachians, the *master stream patterns* are generally believed to be inherited from a consequent system and so display *dendritic forms*. Polycyclic histories thus lead to compound patterns being established (Fig. 2). Such eventualities are often commonly observed. In the case of the flat-lying Appalachian Plateau, a fracture net becomes dominant (Lattman and Nickelsen, 1958).

Reasoning *a priori*, there is also to be considered the situation created when folded structures are freshly formed or forming. The new folds must evolve either below sea level or above it. If below sea level, then emergence will be marked by the initiation of a drainage system: crests of anticlines attacked first and short consequent streams are followed soon by subsequents and a trellis pattern evolves (Fig. 3), but it will lack the master system of dendritic type. Stream capture may be expected to develop a through-running drainage, but it is hardly likely to develop the random distribution of a true superposed system. The remote chances of such an emergence of folds from beneath the sea and institution of a trellis pattern, that is today still unmodified, would be limited to the youngest folded regions in coastal ranges. For most continental stream analysis problems, this concept becomes a rather theoretical "textbook" case; one might look for them only in parts of New Zealand or Japan.

Consider the second possibility: folds being initiated subaerially. A preexisting stream system must exist, e.g., consequent streams crossing a coastal plain or debouching into an interior basin, in which a thick sequence of sediments has accumulated. Folding initiates antecedent valleys, the latter forming gorges through the rising folds, while alluvial fans tend to fill the troughs. The preexisting drainage was consequent and dendritic in pattern. The master streams now become antecedent (Fig. 4) and the tributaries will follow the rule for subsequents. Again the pattern is a trellis. How will one distinguish this *antecedent-subsequent* compound pattern from the *superposed-subsequent* dendritic-trellis? If in the latter case there are still outliers of the original uncomformable flat-lying formations or traces of the discordant plain (paleosols of the former peneplain or pediplain), the problem can be resolved; if they are all lost to erosion, their former existence may be deduced from paleogeographic data, such as the character of marginal unconformities, or from paleoecologic arguments and sedimentological interpretation.

In conclusion, it must be stressed that the simple drainage pattern terminology offers an inductive geometric description, and even compound patterns

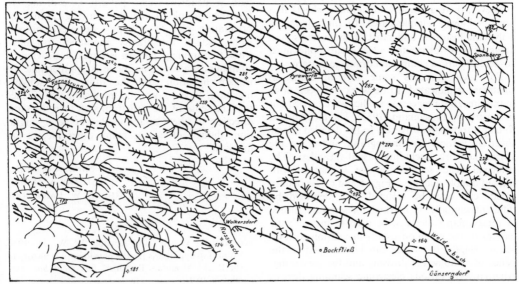

FIG. 5. Drainage network north of Bisamberg in the Austrian Alps, showing strong trellis overprint on an ancient dendritic pattern (Engelmann, 1933).

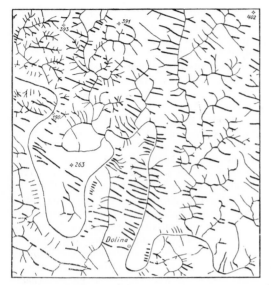

FIG. 6. Drainage network near Dolina, western Ukraine, showing "parallel" pattern overprint (due to structures of Precambrian basement) on an old-age meandering dendritic pattern of the Dniester River, established on nearly flat-lying Cenozoic and Mesozoic rocks, thus superposed (Engelmann, 1933).

such as "dendritic-trellis" are recognized, but should not be taken to infer genetic histories that require complex interdisciplinary investigation.

Technical Procedures

Consideration of Fig. 1 or selected topographic map sheets of ideal areas gives the impression that simple visual scanning by the "trained eye" should be adequate to evaluate the average stream pattern. However, there are many topographic sheets that are not "ideal" simple cases. In the regions of polycyclic histories, and most of the world's land areas show evidence for such events, one must suspect *ab initio* a compound drainage pattern.

For such purposes some sort of statistical treatment is indicated. Little work has been done in this area, but pioneering studies were carried out in Austria by Engelmann (1933). The technique is to take a transparent overlay to the detailed survey sheet or vertical air photograph and trace the stream network, excluding casual meanders. The principal trend, selected by eye, is marked with lines of double thickness (Figs. 5 and 6); secondary trends can later be selected and identified by different symbols or marked on separate sheets. A rotary map scaler can be used to measure the lengths of the common trends in relation to total stream length; the scaler can be strapped to the pencil to combine the drawing and the measuring. Alternatively, various electronic scanning devices can be developed; the I.B.M. electrographic pencil would facilitate electromagnetic scanning.

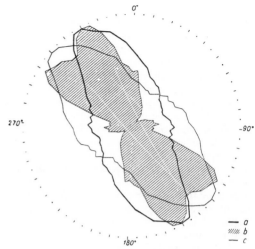

FIG. 7. The direction distribution of (*a*) gravity isogams; (*b*) the drainage pattern; (*c*) isohypses of 50 meters, in the Esztergom Basin, Hungary (Egyed, 1957).

An interesting development demonstrated by Egyed (1957) with an example from the Esztergom Basin of Hungary utilizes not only the drainage pattern but also the topography and the gravity field (assumed to reflect underlying tectonic structure). Since the time of the pioneering work of Pávai-Vajna on the Recent revival of deep-seated structural lines across the Hungarian Plain, it is recognized that the superficial drainage pattern, while giving the impression of being a simple dendritic system of consequent origin, is in fact subject to subtle movements of the underlying folds. Thus a compound antecedent-subsequent system with a dendritic-trellis pattern is evolving. In Egyed's example, it may be seen (Fig. 7) that the orientation plot of isohypses deviates markedly from that of the gravity anomalies (isogams), while the drainage pattern is bimodal, proving its compound nature. One mode is approaching the isogam lineation and the other the isohypse lineation. Egyed notes the interesting coincidence that the sense of the structural shift is in the same direction as the Cretaceous-Recent polar migration, though of course many other factors are involved.

SANDRA FELDMAN
STUART A. HARRIS
RHODES W. FAIRBRIDGE

References

Atwood, W. W., Sr., and Atwood, W. W., Jr., 1938, "Working hypothesis for the physiographic history of the Rocky Mountain Regions," *Bull. Geol. Soc. Am.*, **49**, 957–980.

Baulig, H., 1938, "Questions de Terminologie," *J. Geomorphol.*, **1**, 224–229.

Brigham, A. P., 1892, "Rivers and the evolution of geographic forms," *Bull. Amer. Geograph. Soc.*, **24**, 23–43.

Campbell, M. R., 1929, "The river system: a study in the use of geographic terms," *J. Geogr.*, **28**, 123–128.

Cleland, H. F., 1916, "Geology, Physical and Historical," New York, American Book Co., 718pp.

Cole, W. S., 1937, "Development and structural control of erosion surfaces," *J. Geol.*, **45**, 141–157.

Cotton, C. A., 1917, "Block Mountains in New Zealand," *Am. J. Sci.*, **44**, 249–293.

Cotton, C. A., 1948, "Landscape," Wellington, New Zealand, Whitcombe & Tombs, 509pp.

Davis, W. M., 1890, "Rivers of northern New Jersey with notes on the classification of rivers in general," *Nat. Geogr. Mag.*, **2**, 99.

Davis, W. M., 1901, "An Excursion to the Grand Canyon of Colorado," *Bull. Museum Comp. Zool. Harvard Coll.*, **38**, 121–126.

Egyed, L., 1957, "The role of tectonics and morphology in the development of the drainage-pattern," *Gerlands Beitr. Geophys.*, **66**, 271–273.

Engelmann, R., 1933, "Talnetzstudien," *Jahrb. Geol. Bundesanstalt*, **83**, 189–198.

Garner, H. F., 1966, "Derangement of the Rio Caroni, Venezuela," *Rev. Géomorph. Dyn.*, No. 2, 54–83.

Glock, W. S., 1931, "The development of drainage systems: a synoptic view," *Geograph. Rev.*, **21**, 474–482.

Horberg, L., 1952, "Interrelations of geomorphology, glacial geology and Pleistocene geology," *J. Geol.*, **60**, 187–190.

Howard, A. D., 1962, "Palimpsest drainage and Chungchou photogeologic anomaly," *Bull. Am. Assoc. Petrol. Geologists.*, **46**, 2255–2258.

Institut Géographique National, 1956, "Relief Form Atlas," Paris, 179pp.

Johnson, D. W., 1932, "Streams and their significance," *J. Geol.*, **40**, 481–497.

Johnson, D. W., 1933, "Development of drainage systems and the dynamic cycle," *Geograph. Rev.*, **23**, 114–121.

Kettner, R., 1958, "Allgemeine Geologie," Berlin, Verlag Wiss., 4 vols.

Lattman, L. H., and Nickelsen, R. P., 1958, "Photogeologic fracture-trace mapping in the Appalachian Plateau," *Bull. Am. Assoc. Petrol. Geologists*, **42**, 2238–2245.

Lobeck, A. K., 1939, "Geomorphology, An Introduction to the Study of Landscapes," New York, McGraw-Hill Book Co., 731pp.

Melton, F. A., 1959, "Aerial photographs and structural geomorphology," *J. Geol.*, **67**, 351–370.

Meyerhoff, H. A., and Olmsted, E. W., 1936, "The origins of Appalachian drainage," *Am. J. Sci.*, 5th ser., **32**, 21–42.

Nemenyi, P. F., 1952, "Annotated and illustrated bibliographic material in the morphology of rivers," *Bull. Geol. Soc. Am.*, **63**, 595–644.

Pinchemel, P., 1957, "Densités de drainage et densités de vallées," *Rev. Géomorph. Dyn.*, Paris, **8**, 153.

Russell, I. C., 1898, "Rivers of North America," New York, Putnam, 327pp.

Scovel, J. L., McCormack, J. C., O'Brien, E. J., and Chapman, R. B., 1966, "Atlas of Landforms," New York, John Wiley & Sons, 163pp.

Sparks, B. W., 1960, "Geomorphology," London, Longmans, Green and Co., 371pp.

Stamp, L. D., 1961, "Glossary of Geographical Terms," London, Longmans, Green and Co., 539pp.

Stokes, W. L., 1964, "Incised, wind-aligned stream patterns of the Colorado Plateau," *Am. J. Sci.*, **262**(6), 808–816.

Thornbury, W. D., 1954, "Principles of Geomorphology," New York, John Wiley & Sons, 618pp.

Warner, M. M., 1965, "Cementation as a clue to structure, drainage patterns, permeability, and other factors," *J. Sediment. Petrol.*, **35**(4), 797–804.

Wentworth, C. K., 1928, "Principles of stream erosion in Hawaii," *J. Geol.*, **36**, 385–410.

Willis, B., 1895, "The northern Appalachians," *Nat. Geogr. Soc. Mon.* 1.

Zernitz, E. R., 1932, "Drainage patterns and their significance," *J. Geol.*, **40**, 498–521.

Cross-references: *Base Level; Chute or Cutoff; Cycles, Geomorphic; Drainage Basin; Eustasy; Interfluve; Landscape Types, Genetic; Oxbow Lake; Rivers; Stream Capture, Piracy; Structural Control in Geomorphology.* Vol. I: *Mean Sea Level Changes.* Vol. V: *Taphrogeny.* pr Vol. VI: *Photo Interpretation.*

DREIKANTER—*See* VENTIFACT; WIND ACTION

DRIFT, GLACIAL; DRIFT THEORY

Drift is a term of multiple uses, in mining, electronics, oceanography (wind drift, drift ice), meteorology (snow drift), geotectonics (continental drift) and so on, but in general geology it has long been a useful term applied to all kinds of material related to the Quaternary glaciation, especially till or boulder clay of ground moraines (lodgement till) and terminal moraines, etc., and meltwater products such as outwash plains (sandur), eskers, kames and other fluvioglacial products; it is not generally taken to include glacial loess or other eolian features.

In Britain, many geological survey maps are printed in two editions, "Drift" or "Solid", the former including all superficial Quaternary materials, including terrace deposits, paleosols, solifluction products, "*head*" (q.v.); the "Solid" map presents the underlying geology (Tertiary and older) with all structural detail, such as may have been obtained from excavations, mines, boring, etc.

The term "drift" applied to glacial materials goes back over a century, to the time when it was believed that the Biblical Flood (of Noah) had carried floating ice across the landscape, leaving in its wake melted-out debris of "drifted" ice floes and icebergs. Sir Charles Lyell (1830) notably espoused the "*Drift Theory*" to explain the distribution of erratic blocks. Murchison (1836) recommended that "Drift" should be used in preference to "Diluvium" in order to avoid the Biblical connotation of the latter, and still believed in water-borne transport. An alternative river flood theory was developed in Germany. Wrede, a Berlin physicist, suggested that the "foundling blocks" of the North German Plain were brought by ice floes from the Silesian mountains. Von Buch in 1810 found that the erratics actually matched those of Scandinavia and also assumed gigantic floods as the means of transport. Bernardi in 1832 was the first in Germany to postulate the former extension of arctic continental glaciers as a source (Von Zittel, 1901).

Ground moraine was first recognized in North Germany in 1847 by Martin, and this initiated the true glacial concept.

"*Stratified drift*" refers to fluvioglacial or glacio-lacustrine sediments. Flint (1957) mentions the terms *modified drift* or *washed drift* as a lag deposit of till boulders, partly washed clean of its fine-grained fractions. *Angular drift*, in contrast to glacial drift (till), is a layer of angular rock fragments due to intensive periglacial frost action.

Average thicknesses of drift over the mid-continent of North America are variable: 30 meters overall, 15 meters over uplands, 62 meters in buried valleys, to a maximum of 260 meters (Flint). In the mountainous areas local accumulations exceed 400 meters.

The petrology and fabric are treated under "Till" (see pr Vol. VI).

RHODES W. FAIRBRIDGE

References

Charlesworth, J. K., 1957, "The Quaternary Era," London, Edward Arnold, 2 vols.

Flint, R. F., 1957, "Glacial and Pleistocene Geology," New York, John Wiley & Sons, 553pp.

Lyell, C., 1830–33, "The Principles of Geology," London, 3 vols.

Murchison, R. I., 1836, "On the gravel and alluvia of South Wales and Siluria, as distinguished from a northern drift . . .," *Proc. Geol. Soc. London*, **2**, 230–336.

Von Zittel, K. A., 1901, "History of Geology and Palaeontology," London, W. Scott, 562pp. (translated by M. M. Ogilvie-Gordon).

Cross-references: *Eolian Transport*; *Erratic Block*; *Esker*; *Frost Action*; *Glacial Deposits*; *Head, Eluvium*; *Kame*; *Loess*; *Moraine*; *Outwash Plain*; *Quaternary Period*; *Solifluction*. pr Vol. VI: *Diluvial Theory*; *Paleosols*; *Till and Tillite*.

DRIFTLESS AREA

A unique feature of the continental glaciated surface of North America is the so-called *Driftless Areas*, of southern Wisconsin, northwestern Illinois and adjacent Iowa (described by Whitney, 1862, but first explained by Irving, 1878). N. H. Winchell (1873, p. 61) wrote "the rocks stand out prominently in bluffs and terraces caused by their various capacities to withstand the elements, covered with very little besides the decomposed debris of their own beds" (i.e., a periglacial texture). The area is locally cloaked by loess. This relief, free from the usual cover of drift, is a result of the lobate character of the successive ice advances and the fact that each glacial phase was marked by different areas of maximum advance. In the continental basement, there is an ancient Precambrian ridge that runs from the center of the Canadian Shield southwestward across Lake Superior to the southern Rocky Mts.; in Wisconsin and northwestern Illinois, it still forms a slight topographic rise. The most extensive Nebraskan and Kansan ice lobes reached out to the west of it across the lowlands of Iowa, while the biggest lobes of Illinoian and Wisconsin age moved out to the east of this "high" in the *Great Lakes Lobe*. In the Wisconsin phase, the *Iowan Lobe* was considerably smaller.

As pointed out by Thwaites (1935), the Driftless Area is surrounded thus by tills of different ages, but was never "an island in the ice." Nevertheless, it was intensively affected by periglacial phenomena and offers unique opportunities for geomorphic comparison with the adjacent drift-covered areas.

Black (1960) has pointed out that the area may well have been glaciated in parts during pre-classical Wisconsin times, because underlying the loess in places there is a paleosol C^{14} dated at 24,600 B.P., under which may be Altonian till. Locally the bedrock is stripped of saprolite, contorted and covered by erratics weighing several tons. It also lacks any older loess.

Rather similar areas subjected to rigorous periglacial action are encountered in the areas of central Europe between the Scandinavian Ice on the one hand and the mountain ice caps of the Alps, Bohemia and the Carpathians on the other.

RHODES W. FAIRBRIDGE

References

Black, R. F., 1960, " 'Driftless Area' of Wisconsin was glaciated," *Bull. Geol. Soc. Am.*, **71**(12), Pt. 2, 1827 (abstract).

Flint, R. F., 1957, "Glacial and Pleistocene Geology," New York, John Wiley & Sons, 553pp.

Irving, R. D., 1878, "Origin of the Driftless Area of the northwest," *Am. J. Sci.*, **115**, 313–314.

Thwaites, F. T., 1935, "Outline of Glacial Geology," Ann Arbor, Edwards Bros., 115pp.

Whitney, J. D., 1862, "Report of the Geological Survey of the State of Wisconsin," Vol. 1, Albany, N.Y., 455pp.

Winchell, H. V., 1873, "The Geological and Natural History Survey of Minnesota," Saint Paul.

Cross-references: *Drift*; *Glacial Geology*; *Lobes, Lobation*; *Loess*; *Periglacial Landscape*.

DROUGHT—*See Vol. II*

DROWNED VALLEY, COAST, REEF

Any physiographic land form which displays a subaerially molded terrain and which plunges below sea level without gross interruption of the original relief is described as a submerged or "drowned" feature. Evidently the land has sunk or the sea has risen. Specifically one speaks of a *drowned valley* or *drowned coast* (French, *ennoyé*; German, *ertrunken, untertaucht*). *Rias* are non-glacial drowned valleys of high relief. *Fjords* are drowned glaciated troughs of similar relief. *Fjärds* are drowned glacial channels of low relief. F. von Richthofen (1886) classified all such coasts as *Coasts of Ingression* (German, *Eingriff*), or *Embayed Coasts*.

The thalwegs of the former rivers form submarine channels which beyond the continental shelf may or may not pass into submarine canyons. Large systems of such submarine fluvial networks are traced on the great continental shelves off southeast Asia (*Sunda Shelf*, q.v., Vol. I), and off northern Australia (*Sahul Shelf*, q.v., Vol. I).

Drowned reefs (see *Coral Reefs*) are commonly found in tropical and subtropical seas. Since hermatypic corals do not generally build vigorous colonies of reef potential at depths much greater than 30 m, the surfaces of such drowned reefs are generally marked by dead coral and by small, scattered corals and algae which are adapted to the cooler, darker and less turbulent water. It is concluded that the reef builders were killed by rapid tectonic subsidence or some factor that inhibited or slowed growth during the postglacial eustatic rise (such as cold upwelling, volcanic ash showers, poisoning by overturn of H_2S-rich waters, etc.). In most cases studied, the result was inconclusive (Fairbridge and Stewart, 1960).

The principal cause of drowning of coastal features may be set down to specific factors according to regional geotectonic factors, with a moderate degree of assurance:

(a) Eustatic Rise of Sea Level. Comprehensive C^{14} dating of late and postglacial shore lines from different parts of the world has proved that in the period 15,000–6000 B.P. there was a rise of sea level of approximately 100 m; the maximum glacial lowering may have been somewhat more. The rise was oscillatory with brief negative interludes following the Bölling, Alleröd and Yoldia stages (Fairbridge, 1961). The relatively stable coasts of the world (those of the low latitudes, removed from active geosynclines, large deltas and tectonic belts) show a "standard pattern" of drowned features, characteristic for various lithologic coast types and corresponding relief.

(b) Postglacial Isostatic Crustal Warping. In high latitudes toward the interiors of former continental ice sheets (e.g., Gulf of Bothnia, Baltic, Hudson Bay), this has led to emerged coasts. In places peripheral to the former ice sheets (e.g., coastal

Norway, Scotland, Iceland, Greenland, northeastern North America, Alaska, British Columbia, Chile, South Island of New Zealand), there is extensive drowning. This drowning is partly attributable to postglacial eustatic rise which outstripped isostatic crustal uplift, and partially to peripheral downwarping or collapse of the "peripheral bulge" recognized by Daly (1934). Some dated measurements of these movements in New England have been given by Bloom and Stuiver (1963).

(c) Tectonic Lowering of the Crust. This is observed, in various parts of the world, to take place at varying rates. In Japan and certain other active tectonized areas, secular crustal movements of the order of 10 mm/yr have been measured over the last century of observations. Deltaic centers (Mississippi, Rhine) are commonly subsiding at about 1 mm/yr; parageosynclinal areas (shelf basins, etc.) generally subside axially at about 0.1–0.01 mm/yr. It is evident, therefore, that in the highly tectonic areas the eustatic factor is less important than the tectonic, but in parageosynclinal areas the reverse is the case.

RHODES W. FAIRBRIDGE

References

Bloom, A. L., and Stuiver, M., 1963, "Submergence of the Connecticut coast," *Science,* **139,** 332–334.

Daly, R. A., 1934, "The Changing World of the Ice Age," New Haven, Yale University Press, 271pp.

Fairbridge, R. W., 1961, "Eustatic Changes in Sea Level," in "Physics and Chemistry of the Earth," Vol. 4, pp. 99–185, London, Pergamon Press.

Fairbridge, R. W., and Stewart, H. B., Jr., 1960, "Alexa Bank, a drowned atoll on the Melanesian Border Plateau," *Deep-Sea Res.,* **7,** 100–116.

Thornbury, W. D., 1954, "Principles of Geomorphology," New York, J. Wiley & Sons, 618pp.

Von Richthofen, F., 1886, "Führer für Forschungsreisende," Hanover, Jänecke, 734pp.

Cross-references: *Coastal Stability; Continental Flexure; Coral Reefs; Eustasy; Fjärd; Fjord; Postglacial Isostatic Rebound; Ria; Thalweg; Warping.* Vol. 1: *Sahul Shelf; Sunda Shelf.*

DRUMLIN

A drumlin is a smooth, stream-lined, dome-shaped hill formed beneath flowing glacial ice. Drumlins have the shape of an inverted spoon elongated in the direction of ice movement with the long gentle slope pointing in the direction toward which the ice moved. The crest of these features varies in height from 20–200 feet above the general land surface; lengths up to several miles are common. Drumlins are built of fine-grained till and in some places have a rock core. They have been attributed by some workers to the overriding of a previous

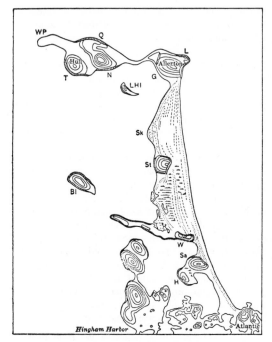

FIG. 1. Drumlins in the Nantasket Beach complex tombolo, near Boston, Mass. (Johnson, 1925). (By permission of John Wiley & Sons, Inc., New York.)

FIG. 2. Map showing part of a drumlin tract in County Down (from Holmes, 1965, after Charlesworth). (By permission of T. Nelson & Sons, London.)

moraine. Drumlins rarely form singly, but occur in irregular groups or in swarms along a belt. Examples of drumlin groups may be seen in New England (see Fig. 1), New York, and Wisconsin in the United States, and in the British Isles, Germany, and Switzerland (see *Glacial Deposits*).

Drumlin fields are often arranged linearly or in echelon, reflecting the general ice motion, creating series of "whalebacks," or what is called a "basket of eggs" terrain in County Down, Ireland (Fig. 2). Because the drumlins block the general drainage lines, there are frequently swamps or sometimes small lakes and ponds between them.

Postglacial drowning has led to some interesting coastal features in such areas as Boston Bay (Massachusetts) and Strangford Lough (Northern Ireland). Johnson (1925) has illustrated the progressive wave erosion and building of *tombolos* (q.v.) from drowned drumlins in New England. In Northern Ireland the postglacial "*Littorina*" (mid-Holocene) raised beach is often found forming a notch on the exposed side of a drowned drumlin. Also in Northern Ireland are examples of an extensive drumlin field very largely "drowned" by peat and other swamp deposits (Charlesworth, 1957, p. 392).

Kendall (1924) remarked that "a drumlin is a *roche moutonnée* expressed in boulder clay." There is every transition from a normal drumlin to a "*rock drumlin*," one with a rock core and a veneer of till,

FIG. 3. Air photo of a group of partially "drowned" drumlins at Islandmore, Strangford Lough, Northern Ireland (see Stephens and Synge, 1966). Note the raised beach and subdued cliff on the right hand side, indicating the effect of wave action during the mid-Holocene "Littorina" period, about 5000 B.P. (Photo: Aerofilms and Aero Pictorial Ltd., London).

to "*crag-and-tail*" (q.v.), a *roche moutonnée* (q.v.) with a "tail" of till. A "*drumlinoid*" (Tyrrell, 1906; Dean, 1953) is a spindle-shaped hill of till or a series of "streaks" of till not developed into the typical drumlin shape.

VINCENT C. SHEPPS
RHODES W. FAIRBRIDGE

References

Charlesworth, J. K., 1957, "The Quaternary Era," London, Edward Arnold, 2 vols.

Dean, W. G., 1953, "The drumlinoid landforms of the Barren Grounds, N.W.T.," *Canadian Geogr.,* **3,** 19–30.

Embleton, C. and King, C. A. M., 1968, "Glacial and Periglacial Geomorphology," London, E. Arnold Ltd., 608pp.

Fairchild, H. L., 1907, "Drumlins of central western New York," *Bull. N.Y. State Museum,* **111,** 391–447.

Gravenor, C. P., 1953, "The origin of drumlins," *Am. J. Sci.,* **25,** 674–681.

Holmes, A., 1965, "Principles of Physical Geology," Second ed., New York, Ronald Press Co.; London, T. Nelson & Sons, 1288pp.

Johnson, D. W., 1925, "The New England-Acadian shoreline," New York, John Wiley & Sons, 608pp.

Kendall, P. F. and Wroot, H. E., 1924, "Geology of Yorkshire," Leeds, 995pp.

Slater, G., 1929, "The structure of the drumlins exposed on the south shore of Lake Ontario," *Bull. N.Y. State Museum,* **281,** 3–19.

Stephens, N., and Synge, F. M., 1966, "Pleistocene Shorelines," in (Dury, G. H., editor), "Essays in Geomorphology," pp. 1–51, New York, American Elsevier Publ. Co.

Tyrrell, J. B., 1906, "Report on the Dubawni, Ferguson and Kazan Rivers," *Ann. Rept. Can. Geol. Surv., 9.*

Wright, H. E., Jr., 1957, "Stone orientation in Wadena Drumlin Field, Minnesota," *Geografiska Annaler,* 1, **39,** 19–31.

Cross-references: *Crag and Tail*; *Glacial Deposits*; *Holocene*; *Moraine*; *Roche Moutonnée*; *Tombolo.* pr Vol. VI: *Till and Tillite.*

DRY VALLEY

Dry valleys are valleys which appear to have been cut originally by streams, but which are now streamless for part or all of the time.

Field Characteristics

(a) On the soft chalk limestone of southern England and corresponding parts of France, whole integrated networks of dry valleys occur. After very heavy rain, some of these carry surface streams, and many such streams rise in springs controlled by local aquifers. Valleys of this type were formerly ascribed to dissection of the chalk, with accompanying lowering of the water table—a view consistent with Davis's two-cycle hypothesis of the origin of the southern English landscape. It is now clear, however, that the main cause of lowering of the water table and of reduction of streamflow is

the climatic shift with drop of mean rainfall responsible for producing *underfit streams*. The total disappearance of the diminished surface flow left after climatic change results from the permeability of the chalk in general.

(b) On more cohesive and generally more resistant limestones, such as the Carboniferous limestone of northern England, underground (karst) drainage is strongly guided by joints and bedding planes. When streams go underground, they vanish at well-marked sinks, such as are not common on the chalk. If a sink operates for a long time, its lip can be greatly lowered; in this way, the valley upstream of the sink continues to be incised, whereas its much shallower extension downstream of the sink is left streamless. Deepening of the reach of a dry valley is unlikely to be pronounced, unless collapse dolinas form in the floor.

(c) Dry valley heads in areas of channeled surface drainage are to be expected, between the divide and the points where runoff is enough to sustain channeled flow. However, many such heads are likely to be longer than they would otherwise be, because of the climatic shift already mentioned: in some valley heads, this is known to have increased the distance from divide to head of channel.

(d) Dry gaps at sites of capture and dry channels which formerly discharged glacial meltwater or spillwater represent special cases; their nature is usually evident from their field relationships.

GEORGE H. DURY

References

Daniels, R. B., Rubin, M., and Simonson, G. H., 1963, "Alluvial chronology of the Thompson Creek Watershed, Harrison County, Iowa," *Am. J. Sci.,* **261,** 473–487.

Davis, W. M., 1895, "The development of certain English rivers," *Geograph. J.,* **5,** 127–146.

Dury, G. H., 1964–65, "General Theory of meandering valleys," *U.S. Geol. Surv. Profess. Paper* **452.**

Fagg, C. C., and Hutchings, G. E., 1929 in (Ogilvie, O.G., editor) "Great Britain," pp. 23–25, Cambridge, The University Press.

Thornbury, W. D., 1954, "Principles of Geomorphology," pp. 324–328, New York, John Wiley & Sons.

Warwick, G. T., 1964. "Dry valleys of the southern Pennines, England," *Erdkunde,* **18**(2), 116–123.

Cross-references: *Blind Valleys*; *Climatic Geomorphology*; *Dell*; *Dolina*; *Humid Cycle*; *Karst*; *Streams—Underfit*; *Wind Gap.* Vol. II: *Climate and Geomorphology.*

DUST—*See* Vol. II, **COSMIC DUST; INTERSTELLAR GAS AND DUST**

DUNES—*See* **CLAY DUNES; SAND DUNES**

DURICRUST

This is the generic term for any indurated surface formed above (case hardening) or within a soil. It may consist of limonite (ironstone), bauxite, silica or limestone. Widespread local names for duricrusts are *hardpan* and *billy* (English-Australian), *bové* or *boval* (West African). French writers refer to it generically as *carapace* or *cuirasse*, i.e., armor plate. The three characteristic chemical types of duricrust are called "*ferricrete*" (iron-rich), "*silcrete*" (silica-rich), and "*calcrete*" (lime-rich), following the terminology of Lamplugh (1902).

In general, duricrusts begin to form during warm wet climatic phases but during successive drier phases are then stripped of any protective layer and become rock-like *paleosols*.

Most widespread are the lateritic duricrusts of Africa and Australia, in which bauxite and limonite are represented in varying proportions, so much so that in some places (e.g., Weipa on Cape York Peninsula, Queensland, and Elcho Island in the Northern Territory) there are enormous economic deposits of bauxite, and in other places, especially in West Africa (e.g., Conakry) and Western Australia, there are rich deposits of limonite.

In these duricrusts, which may occur on almost any type of parent rock, the sesquioxides (Fe_2O_3 and Al_2O_3) are the cementing agent. They are at first transported in solution by groundwater and behave like colloidal pigments, coating cavities and particles in the soil with successive films which harden and form lamellar structures (D'Hoore, 1954). Only in clays which can adsorb large amounts of fluid is the hardening retarded or even prevented; in coarse, non-adsorbing soils even a small amount of Fe_2O_3 can produce cementation. Thick cemented layers presuppose a fairly mature but not necessarily flat surface and ample vertical oscillations of the water table, as occur in times of climatic variation and, seasonally, in the widespread tropical savannas (Koeppen's *Aw* climate, see Fig. 1). In each wet season some Fe_2O_3 is dissolved and made mobile; in the dry season, it moves upward by capillarity and is deposited again. Generally, forests tend to impede lateritic cementation, and conversely, cementation, by reducing the depth of soil available, tends to hamper forest growth. According to Aubréville (1949), the spread of the lateritic duricrust has led to the widespread death of trees in North Africa by isolating their roots from the water table in times of drought; this, in turn, has led to the spread of seasonal savanna grasses and to erosion which eventually exposes the duricrust (*Boval*). Human action may also favor the process by burning the forest, causing its replacement by seasonal grasses, greater movement of the water table, and soil erosion.

Old duricrusts may persist a long time as capping ("primary or high-level laterites") while geomorphological processes dissect the exposed surface. Thus they preserve the earlier surfaces of erosion. Material from the high-level laterites is likely to be moved downhill where it may accumulate on lower-level surfaces; there, it is likely to be affected by groundwater again and become cemented once more ("secondary or low-level laterite"). The primary laterite then behaves as a parent rock, and a very gravelly (pisolitic) soil, poor in plant nutrients, may develop on or from it, to evolve further to a gravelly-sandy texture. In the primary laterite itself, intermittent erosion produces overhanging ledges (*breakaways* in Western Australia), but increasingly wet climate causes the formation of caves and col-

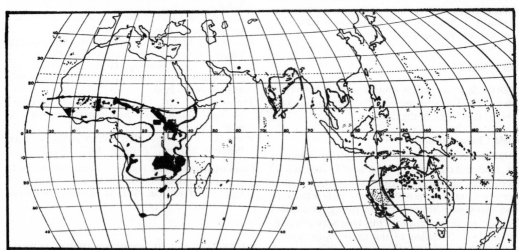

Fig. 1. The major occurrences of lateritic duricrust ("ferricrete") are shown in black. The finely dotted area in Western Australia has a massive siliceous duricrust. Data from Prescott and Pendleton, and Teakle. The winding line shows the boundary of Koeppen's Aw climate; the curved arrows show the most frequent paths of tropical cyclones in Western Australia.

lapse basins because of the work of groundwater on the underlying rock, and the gradual disintegration of the duricrust by chemical and mechanical action is aided by increasingly effective vegetational successions (D'Hoore, 1954). The very widespread fragmentary lateritic duricrust of southwestern Australia (see Fig. 1) was referred to as "laterite" by most of the early writers (Simpson, 1912; Walther, 1915), but is in fact what is left of an eroded earlier laterite initially formed under a more tropical humid climate than the present one, with higher water table, probably dating from the Pliocene (Prescott and Pendleton, 1952; Stephens, 1961). In spite of its hardness, this cemented lateritic duricrust of the Australian southwest supports one of the great forest areas (*Eucalyptus* spp.) of the world.

Perhaps the most widespread siliceous duricrust (150,000–200,000 square miles) is the *hardpan* of the red and brown soils of the Mulga (*Acacia aneura* and allied species) semi-desert of Western Australia (see Fig. 1). The hardpan occurs some 50 cm below the surface and continues downwards for 10 meters or more. It contains some ferruginous matter and is brown to red in color, laminated, and extremely hard. The parent material, often granite-gneiss, is rich in silica rendered mobile by the high summer temperatures, and the duricrust itself is siliceous (Teakle, 1936). It was suggested (Teakle, 1950) that the duricrust is the *billy* or silicified residual layer of a truncated lateritic profile. It is suggested here that this unique occurrence of a massive laminated duricrust under an arid climate is due to the waterlogging caused about once a year by *tropical cyclones* (q.v. Vol. II; see Fig. 1).

The common travertinized crust of calcium carbonate (Hispano-American *caliche*) formed on calcareous materials in semiarid and arid regions (e.g., Texas, Arizona, New Mexico, Morocco) must also be considered a duricrust, a "calcrete," and is also the result of climatic fluctuation. Similar material is known in India as *kankar*. The term *caliche* is also used for the crust or concretionary beds of sodium nitrate and other salts of Peru and northern Chile (Atacama) which were for many years the main world source of nitrate fertilizers.

J. GENTILLI

References

Aubréville, A., 1949, "Climats, Forêts et Désertification de l'Afrique Tropicale," Paris, Soc. d'Édit. Géogr., Maritimes et Coloniales, 351pp.

Browne, W. R., 1964, "Grey Billy and the age of tor topography in Monaro, N.S.W.," *Proc. Linnean Soc. N.S. Wales*, **89**(3), 322–325.

D'Hoore, J., 1954, "L'accumulation des sesquioxydes libres dans les sols tropicaux," *Publ. I.N.E.A.C.*, *Ser. Sci.*, **62**.

Fermor, L. L., 1911, "What is laterite?," *Geol. Mag.*, **5**, 454–462, 507–516, 559–566.

Lamplugh, G. W., 1902, "Calcrete," *Geol. Mag.*, **9**, 575 (letter).

Mabbutt, J. A., 1965, "The weathered land surface in central Australia," *Z. Geomorphol.*, **9**, 82–114.

Moseley, F., 1965, "Plateau calcrete, calcreted gravels, cemented dunes and related deposits . . . of Libya," *Z. Geomorphol.*, **9**, 166–185.

Prescott, J. A., and Pendleton, R. L., 1952, "Laterite and lateritic soils," *Cwlth Bur. Soil Sci., Tech. Commun.*, **47**.

Prider, R. T., 1966, "The lateritized surface of Western Australia," *Australian J. Sci.*, **28**(12), 443–451.

Ruhe, R. V., 1956, "Landscape evolution in the High Ituric Belgian Congo," *Publ. I.N.E.A.C. Ser. Sci.*, **66**.

Simpson, E. S., 1912, "Notes on laterite in Western Australia," *Geol. Mag.*, **6**, 399–406.

Stephens, C. G., 1961, "The soil landscapes of Australia," *C.S.I.R.O. Austr., Soil Publ.*, **18**.

Teakle, L. J. H., 1936, "The red and brown hardpan soils of the *Acacia* semi-desert scrub of Western Australia," *J. Dep. Agr. W. Australia*, **13**, 480–499.

Teakle, L. J. H., 1950, "Red and brown hard-pan soils of Western Australia," *J. Australian Inst. Agr. Sci.*, **16**, 15–17.

Walther, J., 1915, "Laterit in West-Australien," *Z. Deut. Geol. Ges.*, **57**, 113–132.

Cross-references: *Gibber*; *Hamada*; *Induration*. Vol. II: *Arid Climate*; *Capillarity*; *Climatic Classification*; *Equatorial and Tropical Climates*; *Tropical Cyclones*. Vol. IV: *Bauxite*; *Limonite*. pr Vol. VI: *Caliche*; *Groundwater*; *Paleosols*.

DYNAMIC GEOMORPHOLOGY

Dynamic geomorphology is a method of geomorphic analysis involving treatment of land forms and processes in terms of: (1) basic principles of physics and general systems theory and (2) the formulation of empirical equations and mathematical models. Dynamic geomorphology is distinct from several other methods of analysis, e.g., *geomorphic maps* (q.v.), *paleogeomorphology* (q.v.), cyclic (Davisian) geomorphology (see *Cycles, Geomorphic*), denudation chronology (see *Denudation*), *morphoclimatic* (genetic) *geomorphology* (q.v.) and *structural control in geomorphology* (q.v.). Dynamic geomorphology involves the use of *quantitative geomorphology* (q.v.) but is a considerably more fundamental method of approach.

Dynamic geomorphology *per se* was first discussed by Strahler (1952). However many of the concepts involved in this method of analysis (e.g., equilibrium, mathematical models, fluid dynamics) date back to earlier workers such as Gilbert. A few ideas are traceable to Italian and French hydrologists as far back as the seventeenth century. The concepts of dynamic geomorphology were offered by Strahler as a much needed supplement to the explanatory–descriptive methods of study used by W. M. Davis and his followers. Some geomorphologists have virtually abandoned the Davisian approach in favor of the dynamic method, but more recently attempts have been made to reconcile the two in order to preserve the virtues of each (see discussion in Howard, 1965).

As stated above, dynamic geomorphology is a method of analysis; specifically it is grounded in basic principles of mechanics and fluvial dynamics and enables processes "to be treated as manifestations of various types of shear stresses, both gravitational and molecular, acting upon any type of earth material to produce the varieties of strain or failure which we recognize as the processes of weathering, erosion, transportation, and deposition" (Strahler, 1952).

Types of Stress

The following is a brief discussion of geomorphic stresses, strains and materials (for a more complete discussion, with references, see Strahler, 1952). Tables 1–3 summarize the organization of a dynamic treatment of geomorphology. The first subdivision is made according to the nature of the stresses involved—gravitational or molecular.

(A) **Gravitational Stresses.** Gravitational stresses act upon all earth materials. Where there is a sloping surface, components of gravitational stress tend to produce downslope movement of material. Downslope movements include both *mass movements* (e.g., creep, *landslides* (q.v.), *mudflows* (q.v.)) and the movement of the erosional-transportational media: water, ice and air. These media can be considered *fluids* since their motion can be analyzed in terms of fluid dynamics.

The energy involved in downslope movement of material has two forms and three sources. The forms are *potential energy*, which results from the position or elevation of the fluid or material, and *kinetic energy* (heat, motion) which results from the transformation of potential energy during erosion and transportation. The main source of energy is the gravitational field of the earth. Without gravitational forces, there would be no transformation of potential energy to kinetic energy. The original potential energy of position or elevation results from forces working against gravity. These are diastrophism, in the case of the material, and thermal energy (solar heating) in the case of the fluids. Of interest is the fact that only a small part of the transformed energy is actually used in erosion and transportation; most energy is dissipated by friction, turbulence, etc.

The work of wind is due to pressure gradient stresses resulting from solar heating. Differential heating results in differences in air mass densities which tend to be equalized by air flow from regions of higher pressure to regions of lower pressure (with modifications of flow by the Coriolis effect).

Ocean and shore currents may also be geostrophic (like the wind), or they may be wave induced, in which case the generation of waves may be traced back to gravitational stresses through the winds which produced them. Thirdly, they may be tide induced, in which case gravity flow responding to differences in water level occurs.

(B) **Molecular Stresses.** These may act in any direction with respect to gravity; in a homogeneous or isotropic soil or rock material, the stresses may be distributed at random in all possible directions through a given point. The characteristic movement resulting from molecular stresses is a dilation or change of volume. If molecular stresses occur on a slope, a component of the gravitation stress adds its vector to the otherwise random stress distributions, and creep occurs.

(C) **Chemical Processes.** Chemical processes (changes of state, solution) are not of themselves stress producing, although they are of great importance in geomorphology. Chemical processes such as hydrolysis and oxidation which produce expansive stresses by increasing volume and developing adsorptive properties have been placed under molecular stresses.

Types of Material

Three fundamental types of material can be recognized at the earth's surface: (1) rigid or elastic solids (2) plastic solids and (3) fluids.

An *elastic* (rigid) solid is a mass (e.g., rock, soil) which yields by elastic strain. Ideally this strain follows Hooke's law according to which strain is proportional to stress. Stresses beyond a certain critical point cause failure by rupture and may take the form of *shearing* or *tension* fractures.

A *plastic* solid is a material that deforms by distributed intermolecular or intergranular shear. If the shear stresses exceed a limit set by the internal cohesion or friction of the mass, the material undergoes flowage in the manner of a fluid.

A *fluid* is a substance that offers little resistance to deformation (i.e., has low viscosity). Fluids include both gases and liquids.

Types of Strain

The type of failure, or strain, that may be predicted as a result of the application of gravitational or molecular stresses on elastic, plastic or fluid earth materials determines the resultant geomorphic process and form.

Rock or soil behaving as an elastic solid fails by one of two possible ways: (1) by shearing and differential movement of one mass over another (e.g., *landslides*, q.v.) and (2) by tension and fracture (e.g., *frost shattering*; see *Frost Riving, Shattering*).

In fluids, and in plastic solids stressed beyond the yield limits (e.g., *Reynolds, Froude numbers*, q.v., Vol. II), flowage occurs in two forms: laminar and turbulent flow, both of which are important in geomorphic processes. In *laminar flow* (q.v., Vol. II), parallel layers of fluid are in motion without crosscurrents; as a result, movement of particles by suspension is virtually impossible (although viscous

TABLE 1. DYNAMIC BASIS OF GEOMORPHOLOGY: GRAVITATIONAL STRESSES (STRAHLER, 1952)

	MATERIAL INVOLVED IN MOTION	PROPERTIES OF MATERIAL	TYPE OF FAILURE (STRAIN)	GEOMORPHIC PROCESSES AND FORMS
1.	Crystalline rocks, arenaceous rocks, limestones; dry soils	Rigid, elastic solid or "elastic continuum" Obeys Hooke's Law: Strain ∝ stress	Sudden rupture along shear surfaces or tension fractures.	Landslides: Slump, slide (compressional stress); rock-fall (tensional stress).
2.	Glacial Ice, near surface.	Plastic solid in region of elastic behavior.	Sudden rupture along shear surfaces or tension fractures.	Crevassing, overthrusting, calving of glaciers.
3.	Argillaceous rocks and soils	Plastic solid in region of slow creep.	Continuous, slow laminar flow (distributed shear)	Large-scale creep phenomena. Superficial deformation of clays.
4.	Unconsolidated rock, soil + water	Plastic solid in region of flowage. Obeys Bingham's law: Rate of shear proportional to stress, above a yield limit.	Plastic flow (shear between grains) when stress exceeds yield limit. Movement ceases below yield value. Flow laminar or turbulent.	Solifluction, earth flow, mudflow, highly turbid streams, turbidity currents.
5.	Glacial ice under heavy load.	Plastic solid with high yield value. Non-linear increase of shear rate with increase of stress.	Laminar plastic flow above yield limit. Below yield limit, returns to brittle elastic solid.	Continental and alpine glaciers. Erosion forms due to ice abrasion. Depositional forms moulded by ice flow.
6.	Water film on sloping surface.	Newtonian fluid. No yield value. Linear increase of shear rate with stress. Subject to capillary influences.	Laminar flow, ceasing when water thins below capillary control limit.	Sheet runoff on slopes and rock surfaces. Slope reduction by removal of ions, colloids, clays. Fluting, grooving of limestone.
7.	Water in permeable rock, soil. (No surface slope)	Newtonian fluid, subject to capillary influences.	a). Silts: Laminar flow following Darcy's Law. b). Sands: Mixed laminar and turbulent flow. c). Gravels: Turbulent flow.	Infiltration of precipitation, carrying down of ions, colloids, clays, silts (illuviation). General slope reduction. Karstic forms in highly soluble rocks.
8.	Water layer on sloping surface	Newtonian fluid.	Sheet runoff in turbulent or mixed turbulent-laminar flow.	Slope erosion, transportation. Slope forms of fluvial drainage basins.
9.	Water in sloping linear channel	Newtonian fluid.	Stream flow, turbulent except in bed layer.	Stream erosion, transportation, deposition. Drainage systems. All fluvial landforms.

Indirect Responses to Gravitational Stresses

	MATERIAL INVOLVED IN MOTION	PROPERTIES OF MATERIAL	TYPE OF FAILURE (STRAIN)	GEOMORPHIC PROCESSES AND FORMS
10.	Standing water bodies. Oceans, lakes.	Newtonian fluid.	Turbulent flow as a). Pulsating or oscillating currents caused by waves. b). Tide-induced currents.	Shoreline processes of erosion, transportation, deposition. Shoreline landforms: cliffs, benches, beaches, bars, spits.
11.	Air	A gas: compressible fluid of extremely low viscosity.	Turbulent flow induced by pressure gradients. (gravitational stress on air masses)	Wind erosion, transportation, deposition. Deflational and abrasional forms. Dunes, loess.

Note: Items 10 and 11 are properly "Pressure-gradient Stresses" (Strahler, personal communication).

plastic solids such as glacier ice may carry "suspended" matter). In thin films of water (e.g., sheet flow), laminar flow may remove ions, colloids or clays from a rock or soil surface. In deeper water, laminar flow cannot result in erosion or transportation of coarse particles, but it does permit the settling of suspended sediment. In high-viscosity fluids such as ice, laminar flow may operate exclusively. Air, by contrast, has such low viscosity that for all practical purposes any air currents which are transporting material can be considered to be in turbulent flow.

Turbulent flow sets in when flow velocity exceeds a critical velocity determined by factors of depth,

viscosity and roughness of the bounding surface. Turbulent flow is characterized by components of velocity in many directions within the moving fluid. Vertical components of flow can sustain solid particles; thus the transportation of rock materials in suspension is possible by flowing air and water at the velocities normally prevailing in streams, wave-induced currents and winds.

In plastic earth material, the definition of "flow" is broadened to include shear more or less uniformly distributed throughout the mass and occurring by the rotation or slippage of grains with respect to one another (Strahler, 1952, p. 928). Examples include *earth-flows* and *mudflows*.

TABLE 2. DYNAMIC BASIS OF GEOMORPHOLOGY: MOLECULAR STRESSES (STRAHLER, 1952)

	MATERIALS INVOLVED	PROPERTIES OF MATERIAL	STRESS AND CAUSE	KIND OF FAILURE	WEATHERING PROCESS AND FORM
1.	Rock: strong, hard crystalline, glassy or crystal aggregate.	a). Elastic solid, non-homo-geneous.	Shear stress due to non-uniform expansion-contraction in cyclic temperature changes.	Rupture by shear or tension fractures between grains, along cleavages, joints, bedding planes.	Granular or blocky disintegration of rocks, esp. coarse-grained crystalline rocks.
		b). Elastic solid, homogeneous	Shear stress set up by thermal gradient from surface heating.	Rupture between layers paralleling rock surface.	Exfoliation of rock by fire, lightning; solar or atmospheric heating-cooling.
2.	a). Permeable rock + water b). Clay soils	a). Elastic solid. b). Plastic solid.	a). Shear stress set up by interstitial ice crystal growth. b). Stress from growth of ice lenses, wedges.	a). Rupture between grains, cleavage pieces, joint blocks, beds. b). Plastic deformation of clays adjacent to ice.	a). Frost disintegration of rocks. Felsenmeer. b). Heaving of clay soils, frost mounds, polygons.
3.	Permeable rock or soil + water and salts	Elastic solid or elastic continuum	Shear stress set up by interstitial growth of salt crystals.	Rupture between grains, cleavage pieces, joint blocks or beds.	Effloresence, granular disintegration in dry climates. Caliche heaving.
4.	Rock or soil + colloids and water	Elastic or plastic solid	Shear stress set up by dilitation accompanying water adsorption and drying.	a). Rupture between grains. b). Plastic deformation of clays during swelling.	Exfoliation of basaltic, granitic rock upon alteration of silicates. Slaking of shales, argillaceous ss.
5.	Rock or soil + capillary water	Elastic or plastic solid	Shear stress set up by dilitation accompanying changes in capillary film tension.	Rupture between grains or masses of soil.	Disintegration of granular permeable rocks. Heaving or subsidence of clays, silts.
6.	Rock or soil + plant roots	Elastic or plastic solid	Shear stress set up by swelling of rootlets under osmotic pressure.	Rupture between grains, cleavage pieces, joint blocks or beds.	Disintegration of rock by prying of roots. Deforma-tion of soils.
7.	Strong, hard monolithic bedrock	Elastic solid	Shear stresses of tectonic origin stored as elastic strain at depth.	Rupture of rock on planes paralleling surfaces after release of confining pressure.	Exfoliation of domes, slabs, shells. Quarry rupture, rock-burst.

Gravitational Stress Phenomena

Table 1 outlines the various gravitational stress phenomena, listed in a general way according to the property of the material involved. Beginning with rock, soil or ice behaving as elastic solids, the table proceeds through the plastic earth materials to the fluids, taken in order from higher to lower viscosity, with laminar flow ahead of turbulent flow. Most of the processes covered by this table involve the downslope movement of material due to stress resulting from gravitational force. The sine of the slope angle determines the magnitude of the gravitational stress and, hence, the intensity of erosional and transportation activities. In areas of very low surface slopes, subsurface flow may be quantitatively important. Table 1 is discussed further in Strahler (1952), and in Leopold *et al.* (1964).

As an example of how this analysis is applied, consider the case of a glacier. Deeply buried ice can be considered as a plastic solid with a high yield value (i.e., it will not flow except under high stress). Once stress begins strain does not vary simply with stress. The type of failure, as in most highly viscous plastic solids, is laminar plastic flow (shear distributed throughout the ice). Surficial ice, or ice at a glacial snout, is also a plastic solid, but one in which the yield value is not approached. Thus behavior is that of an elastic solid, and strain is proportional to stress. Failure occurs by rupture or tension (e.g. *crevasses*, q.v., calving) or by shear along distinct surfaces (thrusting at the snout).

Molecular Stress and Surficial Creep Phenomena

Table 2 outlines the molecular stress phenomena, more conventionally termed the "weathering processes." Molecular stress is principally set up by physical-chemical changes or changes of temperature. The stress acts in directions which are independent of gravity and, in homogeneous material, may be distributed randomly. Because the source of energy is solar in most of the phenomena listed, the processes are limited to surface or near-surface locations. Strahler (1952, pp. 932–933) gives examples and references for each process in Table 2.

Not listed in the table, but clearly a result of simultaneous action of both gravitational and molecular stresses, is slow surficial *soil creep* (q.v.) or creep of weathered rock or weak bedrock down a slope.

TABLE 3. DYNAMIC BASIS OF GEOMORPHOLOGY: CHEMICAL PROCESSES (STRAHLER, 1952)

	MATERIALS	PROCESS	FORMS PRODUCED
1.	Soil, rock + acids, water	Reaction between acid ions and mineral surfaces. Removal of products in solution.	Lowering of rock and soil surfaces. Pitting, cavitation of rocks, esp. carbonates. Cavern and karst forms (see Table A, no. 7). Weakening of bonds between mineral grains.
2.	Soil, rock + water	Simple solution (ionization) of susceptible minerals.	Cavitation of soluble salt formations. Slow attrition of exposed mineral surfaces.

Chemical Processes

Chemical processes (Table 3) are set apart because they do not directly produce shear stresses, yet are of great importance in land-form development. Distinction is made between: (1) chemical reactions in which acidic ions react with mineral surfaces, and (2) simple solution or ionization of unusually soluble minerals. Both permit removal of ions in groundwater and hence are a form of mass reduction. Both weaken rock and reduce its resistance to gravitational and molecular shear stresses. In extreme cases (e.g., *karst topography*, q.v.), chemical processes are responsible for much or all topography in a given area.

General Systems Theory

"Geomorphology will achieve its fullest development only when the forms and processes are related in terms of dynamic systems and the transformations of mass and energy are considered as functions of time. Many of the geomorphic processes operate in clearly defined systems that can be isolated for analysis" (Strahler, 1952, pp. 934–935). Geomorphic systems are *open systems* (q.v.) which tend to achieve a dynamic equilibrium which is dependent upon continuous transport of materials and energy into and out of the system. Over a short time period, the system may exhibit unchanging geometry (time-independent steady state), but over a long period of time, geomorphic systems generally exhibit a slowly growing state (time-dependent growth state). This is because the supply of material and energy changes with time; hence, the form of the system adjusts to the changing supply. For example, in a simple drainage basin relief decreases with time. This results in decreasing amounts of energy and material passing through the system; hence, the slopes of the system undergo a gradual loss of average inclination (see also *General Systems Theory in Geomorphology*).

Mathematical Models

There are two general types of mathematical procedures open to the geomorphologist who is attempting to quantify statements of process and form. One method is by statistical analysis of experimental and field data in order to derive empirical equations that best state observed relationships between two or more quantities. Such techniques are mentioned in the article on *Quantitative Geomorphology* (q.v.) and are summarized by Chorley (1966).

As a second general procedure, the geomorphologist may formulate simple mathematical models in order to state some point of important general theory which is otherwise definable only qualitatively. Unfortunately, there are few established mathematical models for geomorphic forms. Many models have been formulated (e.g., Scheidegger, 1961), but most are extremely theoretical and so far have demonstrated little relationship to physical reality. This reflects a lack of quantitative data upon which mathematical models must be based. It should be emphasized that generalizations about geomorphic forms and processes are of little use without quantitative statements; conversely, quantitative statements are of little use unless they are interpreted in regard to actual land forms and field relationships.

LEE WILSON

References

Chorley, R. J., 1966, "The Application of Statistical Methods to Geomorphology," in (Dury, editor) "Essays in Geomorphology," pp. 275–387, New York, American Elsevier.

Howard, A. D., 1965, "Geomorphological systems—equilibrium and dynamics," *Am. J. Sci.*, **263**, 302–312.

Leopold, L., Wolman, M. G., and Miller, J., 1964, "Fluvial Processes in Geomorphology," San Francisco., W. H. Freeman, 522pp.

Scheidegger, A. E., 1961, "Theoretical Geomorphology," Berlin, Springer-Verlag, 327pp.

Strahler, A. N., 1952, "Dynamic basis of Geomorphology," *Bull. Geol. Soc. Am.*, **63**, 923–938.

Cross-references: *Cycles, Geomorphic*; *Denudation*; *Equilibrium*; *Frost Riving, Shattering*; *Geomorphic Maps*; *General Systems Theory in Geomorphology*; *Landslides*; *Mass Movement*; *Mudflow*; *Open Systems—Allometric Growth*; *Paleogeomorphology*; *Quantitative Geomorphology*; *Sediment Transport*; *Soil Creep*; *Structural Control in Geomorphology*; *Weathering*. Vol. II: *Coriolis Force*; *Fluid Mechanics*; *Geostrophic Wind*; *Gravity and Geopotential*; *Laminar Flow*; *Pressure Gradient*; *Reynolds, Froude and other Dimensionless Numbers*; *Viscosity*. Vol. V: *Diastrophism*. pr Vol. VI: *Deposition*; *Fluvial Sediment Transport*; *Groundwater*; *Ice—Structure and Properties*.

E

EARTH—GEOLOGY OF THE PLANET—*See* Vol. II

EARTH—ORIGIN AND EVOLUTION—*See* Vol. II, **PLANET EARTH—ORIGIN AND EVOLUTION**

EARTH MOTIONS—*See* Vol. II

EARTH PILLARS OR PYRAMIDS

These are geomorphic weathering phenomena, characteristic of erosion of poorly cemented, unsorted sediments or alternate layers of very contrasting resistance. One of the earliest discussions was by Lyell. He stressed that here one could observe a rare case of the denuding action of rain as distinct from running water, i.e., sheet wash as

In the Italian Alps (Tyrol), the French Alps, and the Pyrenees, a particular lithology predicates the development of earth pyramids; it is a valley-fill of morainic origin (as noted by Lyell), a sandy till or kame-terrace deposit, but not strictly a boulder clay as stated by Mill.

In the Badlands of South Dakota and in Bryce Canyon (Utah), the pyramids are controlled by alternate hard and soft bands in horizontal formations; they are sometimes called "hoodoos" in the West. In Colorado, north of the Arkansas River, a soft shale formation is studded with calcareous concretions, and the resultant conical pyramids have a fancied resemblance to old Indian camps and are known as "tepees" or "tepee buttes" (Gilbert and Gulliver, 1895).

A third lithologic type favorable to earth-pyramid formation is a soft tuff with volcanic bombs or a tuffaceous agglomerate, as in Yellowstone (Wyoming) or at Crater Lake (Oregon). Others are illustrated by Holmes (1965).

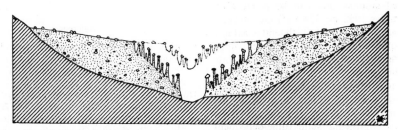

FIG. 1. Sketch indicating the origin of earth pillars or pyramids in the Tirol (after Lyell, redrawn by R. Kettner). According to Becker (1963) those in the Finster Valley have developed since A.D. 1400, when the road was built.

opposed to fluvial action. Following H. R. Mill (in Stamp, 1961):

"A mass of softer material capped by a harder rock which shields the underlying portions from the effects of denudation, though all the surrounding material may have gone. If rain is the chief agent of removal the block acts as an umbrella, and the pillar widens out toward the base all round. If a stream does most of the work it will eat more and more into the pillar, which will therefore narrow down towards the base. They are commonest in boulder clay. In the French Alps these pillars are called demoiselles, cheminées de fées (fairy chimneys), penitents."

Miniature examples are often seen in sand and gravel pits after rainstorms; they have, of course, a very brief existence.

RHODES W. FAIRBRIDGE

References

Becker, H., 1963, "Uber die Entstehung von Erdpyramiden," *Neue Beiträge zur internationalen Hangforschung* (Nach. Akad. Wissen. Göttingen, II Math.-Phys. Klasse), 185–194.

Gilbert, G. K., and Gulliver, F. P., 1895, "Tepee buttes," *Bull. Geol. Soc. Am.,* **6,** 333–342.

FIG. 2. Earth pillars or pyramids at Bolzano (Bozen), Tyrol. This is the classic locality for this phenomenon described by Lyell (from Von Engeln, 1942).

Holmes, A., 1965, "Principles of Physical Geology," second ed., London, T. Nelson & Sons; New York, Ronald Press, 1288pp.

Hsu, T. L., 1964, "Hoodoo rocks at Yehliu, northern coast of Taiwan," *Bull. Geol. Surv. Taiwan*, **15**, 37–43.

Kettner, R., 1959, "Allgemeine Geologie," Berlin, Verlag Wissen., 4 vols.

Lyell, C., 1867, "Principles of Geology," Tenth ed., Vol. 1, London, J. Murray.

Stamp, L. D., 1961, "A Glossary of Geographical Terms," London, Longmans, 539pp.

Von Engeln, O. D., 1942, "Geomorphology," New York, Macmillan, 655pp.

Von Klebelsberg, R., 1927, "Die Südtiroler Erdpyramiden," in "Geologischer Charakterbilder," Vol. 35, Berlin.

Cross-references: *Badlands*; *Denudation*; *Erosion*; *Sheet Erosion*, *Sheetwash*, etc.

EARTH'S DIMENSIONS—*See* pr Vol. V

EARTH'S FEATURES, STATISTICS—*See* **CONTINENTS AND OCEANS**

EARTH'S ROTATION—*See* Vol. II

EAST AFRICAN LAKES

General Description

The lakes of East Africa provide the greatest expanse of inland water in the tropics and include both the second largest lake, Victoria, and the second deepest lake, Tanganyika, in the world. With the exception of Lake Victoria, which occupies the central basin, all the large lakes lie within the two Great Rift Valleys (Fig. 1). The Western Rift stretches from the Zambesi northwards for about 1500 miles to the Uganda–Sudan border and includes Lakes Nyasa*, Tanganyika, Kivu, Edward and Albert. The Eastern Rift from Northern Tanganyika almost to Addis Ababa (about 900 miles) contains a number of small lakes in its southern section in Kenya, one large lake, Rudolph, and a chain of small lakes in Ethiopia. There are also many very small lakes in the craters of extinct volcanoes both inside and just outside the rift valleys. In certain regions, especially in the highlands of southwest Uganda and the neighboring northeast Ruanda, lava flows during the Late Pleistocene have dammed river valleys and formed branching fjord-like lakes such as Lakes Kivu, Bunyoni and

* Lake Nyasa, like several others, forms an international boundary; on the west side (Malawi) it is now known as Lake Malawi.

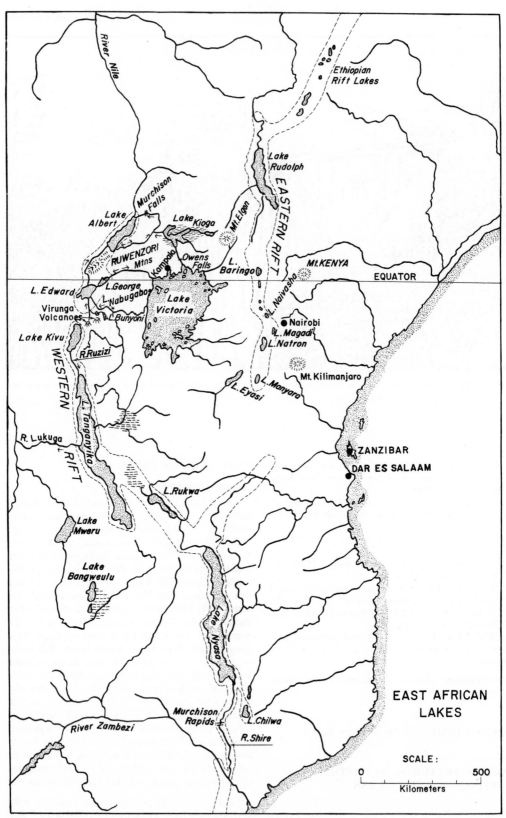

FIG. 1. Lakes of East Africa, showing lake due to reversal of drainage (Lake Kioga), lake in depression due to upwarping of margins of a region (Lake Victoria) and lakes in grabens.

Buleru. In the central basin, the gradients are relatively slight and much water is held up in shallow swamps blocked with vegetation; in Uganda alone, there are more than 2500 square miles of permanent swamp. Lake Victoria and Lakes Edward and Albert in the northern section of the Western Rift drain into the Nile; Lake Tanganyika has a small outlet to the Congo, and Lake Nyasa flows via the Zambesi into the Indian Ocean. All the lakes in the Eastern Rift are in closed basins, though Lake Rudolph has until recently drained to the northwest into the Nile.

The contemporary lake levels are determined by a balance between gain and loss to which the outflow, if present, makes an insignificant contribution and loss by evaporation is by far the most important item on the debit side. The gain from rain falling directly onto the surface is an important component, and in very large lakes, such as Victoria, it is thought that the seasonal and cyclical changes of level, while caused mainly by fluctuations in rainfall, may be significantly affected by alterations in the rate of evaporation through changes in the amount of cloud cover (Table 1).

TABLE 1. APPROXIMATE ANNUAL INCOME AND LOSS BUDGETS AS MMS OF WATER OVER AREA OF LAKE*

	Victoria	Tanganyika	Nyasa
Rainfall on lake surface	1260	900	1000
Inflows	330	530	490
Total income	1590	1430	1490
Loss by evaporation	1310	1350	1300

Additional loss to balance accounted for by outflows and perhaps seepages.

* From Gillman, 1933, *Tanganyika Geol. Surv. Dept. Bull.*, 5.

In general, the waters are relatively saline and alkaline due to the leaching of soda-bearing volcanic rocks extruded in association with the rifting movements. In many crater lakes and in closed drainage basins, especially in the Eastern Rift, the salinity is extremely high, and saline springs and deposits are common.

Exploration

The ancient legend of the sources of the Nile from great lakes fed from the mountains of the moon was known to Herodotus in the fifth century B.C. and was illustrated in Ptolemy's map in the second century A.D., but owing to the impenetrable desert and the swamps of the Upper Nile, the near-truth of this legend was only confirmed in the mid-nineteenth century by Burton and Speke who reached Lakes Tanganyika and Victoria from the East African coast and by Baker who, arriving from the north, completed the link with the Nile and discovered Lake Albert (Moorehead, 1960). The first truly scientific expedition was conducted by the geologist J. W. Gregory in 1893; he explained the nature of the Rift Valleys and laid the foundations for our present knowledge of the geological history of East Africa.

Starting with J. E. S. Moore's expedition to Lake Tanganyika in 1899, there have been many scientific expeditions concerned primarily with the lakes, mostly from Britain and Belgium. Much of the research is conducted nowadays under the auspices of the East African Inland Fisheries Research Organization; the Joint Fisheries Research Organization of Northern Rhodesia and Nyasaland*; the Fisheries, Water Development, and Geological Departments of the East African Governments; the University of East Africa, and (until 1960) l'Institut pour la Recherche Scientifique en Afrique Centrale (Section Hydrobiologie) in the Congo.

Origin of the Lakes and Their Faunas

All these lakes owe their existence directly or indirectly to the earth movements which have formed the Rift Valleys. The evidence suggests that during the Miocene, before the major rifting had begun, the highlands of East Africa provided a north-south watershed along the longitude of western Kenya from which rivers flowed westward to the Atlantic and eastward to the Indian Ocean. From paleontological and contemporary biological evidence, we are led to the conclusion that this ridge formed a barrier between two different aquatic faunas. The rivers to the east were short and steep and supported a rather poor fauna, whereas those to the west, flowing with a gentler slope across the whole continent and expanding in places into lakes, had a rich fauna whose relatively unchanged descendants are now to be found in the Nile, Niger, Congo and Lake Chad. This so-called nilotic fauna includes such genera of fish as *Lates* (Nile perch), *Hydrocyon* (Tiger fish) and *Polypterus* (Bichir).

The Rift Valleys therefore cut across the Miocene river system and, by providing basins for large lakes, offered a whole range of new habitats to which the fauna has become adapted. Moreover during subsequent history drastic changes due to earth movements, volcanic action and alternations of wet and dry periods have caused great changes in water levels, salinity, and interconnections between the lakes and with outside water systems.

The evidence for great fluctuations in the lake levels, associated with alternations of pluvial and dry periods during the Pleistocene, derives mainly from raised beaches and fluvial deposits. A causal connection has been suggested between these cycles and the glacial-interglacial cycles in the northern hemisphere, but opinions differ as to the nature of this connection and to the relative timing of the

* Now separated as the Fisheries Depts. of Zambia and Malawi.

305

events, which cannot be resolved without more direct C^{14} dating in Africa.

The evolutionary response to these changes from the aquatic fauna has been impressive and has been much favored by the varying degrees to which each lake has been isolated. Those groups of animals such as fish, mollusks and crustacea, which are incapable of dispersion except in water, have evolved rapidly into a large number of endemic species and even genera. The fauna of each lake has in fact diverged from the original miocene "nilotic" fauna in proportion to the extent and duration of its isolation (Table 2). For example Lake Albert is connected to the Nile and has a typical nilotic fauna, whereas Lake Rudolph, though now a closed basin, has probably been connected with the Nile via the Sobat River within the last few thousand years. Its nilotic fauna has consequently diverged more than that of Lake Albert.

TABLE 2. ENDEMIC FISH IN THE EAST AFRICAN LAKES (BASED ON RECORDS UP TO 1955)

Lake	Total Species	Endemic Genera	Endemic Species	Endemic Species (% of total)
Albert	44	0	3	7
Rudolph	36	0	12	32
Edward	49	1	24	49
Victoria	114	4	87	76
Nyasa	223	20	192	86
Tanganyika	162	42	136	84

Lake Tanganyika, which occupies the deepest section of the Western Rift and whose maximum depth is over 1400 meters, has not only remained a large and deep lake since its origin in the Pliocene but has been a closed basin for most of this time. Its fauna as a result includes a great number of endemic species and genera of fish, mollusks and crustacea, and like Lake Baikal in Siberia, it is an outstanding example of the effects of isolation on the course of evolution.

Lake Nyasa has existed as a large lake for a much shorter time, but it has been effectively isolated from the main nilotic fauna. The fish, which are primarily related to those of the Zambezi, from which they are now cut off by the Murchison Rapids, have evolved at a great rate (Table 2).

Lake Victoria has been formed in a large shallow depression between the highlands bounding the two Rift Valleys and has received only a small proportion of the nilotic fauna. The relatively recent outflow via the Victoria Nile which has drowned an old river valley to form the shallow swampy Lake Kioga now connects with Lake Albert and the Nile, but the Murchison Falls are a barrier to the aquatic fauna, and Lake Victoria has produced a large number of endemic species of fish especially among the cichlidae.

Lake Edward in the Western Rift is also connected by the Semliki River with Lake Albert and thus with the Nile, and as the fossil beds at Ishango show, the fauna of this lake was predominantly nilotic as late as mesolithic times and was at that time being caught by the local fishermen. The disappearance of several of the nilotic species, such as the nile perch, was contemporary with and probably caused by violent volcanic activity in this region some six to eight thousand years ago. Recolonization from Lake Albert has been prevented by the Semliki rapids, and the fauna, though abundant, is now relatively poor in species. The small number of endemic species suggests that isolation was recent and that the origin of the Semliki rapids may have been contemporary with the mesolithic volcanics.

Another interesting situation is presented by Lake Kivu, which is clearly formed by the upper branches of a river which previously flowed to the north into Lake Edward but in the Late Pleistocene was blocked and drowned by lava flows from the Virunga volcanoes. The valley filled to produce a very deep lake and eventually overflowed to the south over the falls at Bukavu into the Ruzizi river and Lake Tanganyika. This history is well supported by the present fish fauna which is clearly recently derived from that of a river, has close affinities with the fauna of Lake Edward, and is quite different from that of Lake Tanganyika from which it is isolated by the falls.

At the present time, apart from Lake Rudolph, which was previously connected with the Nile, there are no large lakes in the Eastern Rift, though abundant lacustrine deposits show that there were large sheets of water during much of the Pleistocene, which, with the contemporary low rainfall in the Eastern Rift, have mostly been reduced to a series of extremely saline and alkaline remnants such as Nakura, Magadi and Manyara. Two exceptions to this are Lake Baringo which drains the Elgeyo and Mau Escarpments and Lake Naivasha which is fed from the Mau and Aberdare mountains where the rainfall is high. These lakes are both 60–70 square miles in area and, in spite of having no surface outlet, are fresh and for this reason are suspected of having subterranean outlets. There is no fossil evidence for a nilotic fauna in the previous lakes in the Eastern Rift, except for Rudolph. The contemporary indigenous fish, of which there are very few species, were presumably derived from the eastward flowing Miocene rivers. There are, however, some remarkable examples of evolution in a very restricted area in adaptation to extreme conditions close to the limits which can be tolerated by living organisms. There are three species of *Tilapia*, each endemic to Lakes Magadi, Natron and Manyara, in water as saline as seawater and composed mainly of sodium carbonate and bicarbonate and therefore extremely alkaline (pH over 11) and, in the case of

Lake Magadi, issuing from hot springs at over 40°C.

The above is a brief and simplified summary of the main course of evolution of some of the lakes and their fauna. Much remains to be discovered especially in the fields of geology and paleontology, and many of the known facts are as yet difficult to fit into a coherent story, but we have here a good example of the evolutionary divergence of animals which can be clearly related to geological and climatic events in the past.

Hydrology and Productivity

The chemical and physical processes in the water of these lakes which determine their productivity are influenced by factors which vary considerably from one lake to another (Table 3). There are

water from the inland hills. Acid sphagnum swamps have developed here, and the aquatic fauna and flora are poorly developed. The complete absence of decapod crustacea and the extreme scarcity of mollusks, both of which are common in the main lake, suggests that the ionic balance of these animals (particularly of calcium) cannot be maintained, and this has been confirmed experimentally for the planorbid mollusks.

Most of the lakes however have an inorganic composition favorable to high productivity which then depends primarily on the degree to which there is circulation of plant nutrients between surface and bottom waters. The tropical temperature region with its small diurnal and seasonal fluctuations and the high density-temperature coefficient of water at tropical temperatures, favors prolonged

TABLE 3.

	Lake	Latitude	Altitude (m)	Area (km²)	Max. Depth (m)	Bottom Temperature (°C)	Permanent Deoxygenation (m)	Conductivity at Surface (K_{20})	pH at Surface	Alkalinity at Surface (meq/liter)	Outflow
Western Rift	Nyasa	9° 30' S–14° 27' S	477	26,000	760	22.4	300–760	210	8.5	2.5	Shire–Zambezi
	Tanganyika	3° 20' S–8° 45' S	773	34,000	1430	23.1	200–1430	610	7.6	6.7	Lukuga–Congo
	Kivu	1° 34' S–2° 30' S	1463	2,300	480	24.4*	65–480	1,400	9.5	16.0	Ruzizi–LakeTanganyika
	Edward	0° 0'–0° 45' S	920	2,250	110	24.8	50–110	920	9.0	9.8	Semliki–Lake Albert
	Albert	1° 9' N–2° 17' N	619	5,600	42	27.0	—	730	9.0	7.3	Nile
Eastern Rift	Magadi	1° 45' S–1° 58' S	570	115			—	160,000	11	1180	None
	Naivasha	0° 38' S–0° 50' S	1880	180	20	20	—	330	8.5	3.3	None at surface. Subterranean?
	Baringo	0° 33' N–0° 43' N	950	170	8	23	—	416	8.8	5.0	None at surface. Subterranean?
	Rudolph	2° 26' N–5° 0' N	375	930	70	27	—	3,000	9.5	24	None
Between Rifts	Victoria	0° 20' N–3° 0' S	1240	75,000	81	26	—	95	8.0	1.0	Victoria Nile
	Nabugabo	0° 20' S–0° 23' S	1240	15	5		—	28	7.5	0.25	Lake Victoria
	Bunyoni	1° 13' S–1° 25' S	1973	35·	45	19	15–45	270	8.0	2.0	Lake Mutanda–Lake Edward

Note: All data, except latitude, altitude and bottom temperature of the five permanently stratified lakes, are subject to much variation and the figures are only approximations.
The electrical conductivity (K_{20}) of a 100 ppm NaCl solution is about 100.
Alkalinity, from acid titration, given as the sum of HCO_3^- and CO_3^{--} ions.
*The bottom temperature of Lake Kivu is much higher than expected at that altitude, but is due to seepage from below of warm water much more saline than that at the surface.

examples of extremes of salinity and alkalinity, in some cases approaching saturation (e.g., Lake Magadi, Nakuru, Elmenteita and others), where nothing other than a rich culture of blue-green algae and a few specially adapted insect larvae are to be found. At the other extreme is Lake Nabugabo, a small swampy lake on the west shore of Lake Victoria, which is fed with extremely low-salinity

stratification which is in fact permanent in some of the large lakes, e.g., Lake Tanganyika, Nyasa and Edward. Organic decomposition, accelerated by a high temperature, deoxygenates the lower stagnant water, and in Lake Tanganyika, 1200 of the 1400 meters are permanently free of oxygen and charged with H_2S. Lake Kivu is peculiar in having a lower stagnant layer (65–480 meters) with a much higher salinity than the surface water due to seepage of very saline water from below.

In the absence of a large winter temperature drop, which in temperate climates initiates the annual overturn, the main factor in mixing the water in tropical lakes is wind, and deep stirring due to seasonal heavy winds is common. In large stratified lakes, such as Tanganyika, this involves only the upper portion of the stagnant underlying layer, but in Lake Victoria, where there is slight stratification in the calm season, complete circulation follows in the season of high winds.

Stratification and mixing depend much on the shape of the basin (e.g., depth/surface area ratio) and on its orientation, as well as on the morphological and climatic features of the surroundings, all of which determine the degree to which a lake is exposed to wind action. Very shallow and exposed lakes are permanently stirred. Such is Lake George in western Uganda whose fishery is consequently one of the most productive (per unit surface area) in the world, though it is thought that this is assisted by fertilization from the excreta of a dense population of Hippopotamus.

Apart from seasonal mixing, which normally proceeds relatively slowly, there are reports from most of the stratified lakes of rare catastrophic stirring due to sudden and abnormally violent storms. These can bring deoxygenated water so rapidly to the surface that vast numbers of fish are killed within a few hours.

Economic Importance

(1) **Fisheries.** Before the 1920's fish caught by traditional methods were the main diet of the people living near the lake shores. With the introduction of the gill net, improvements in methods of drying and salting, increased transport facilities for fresh, frozen and dried fish, and alterations in feeding habits, the inland fisheries are becoming a natural resource of major importance in East Africa, and there are great potentialities for expanding the fisheries of the Great Lakes which are as yet generally underfished. With more knowledge of the biology of the fauna and of the factors controlling the productivity of tropical lakes, and with improved techniques, the inland fisheries might well become the main source of animal protein for the interior of East and Central Africa.

(2) **Hydroelectric Power.** The earth movements associated with the later stages of rifting have left a number of faults and abrupt changes of level on the course of most of the major rivers. There are thus large potential sources of hydroelectric power. In East Africa, the Owen Falls dam on the outlet of the Nile from Lake Victoria is supplying the entire present needs of Uganda and part of those of Kenya. Further development of hydroelectric schemes will be limited only by the demand.

(3) **Water Transport.** Travel by canoe along the shores of Lake Victoria was formally a safer and more convenient means of transport for men and goods than the swamp and river crossings, dense forests, and other hazards of a longer land route. Most of the early missionaries to Uganda arrived by canoe. Communications by water have in fact played an important role in the early history of the countries bordering the Great Lakes. After the introduction of roads and railways, their importance declined though steamboat traffic on Lakes Victoria, Tanganyika and Nyasa is an essential part of the present transport system.

(4) **Salt Deposits.** Edible salt has always been a valuable commodity in the interior of Africa and has had to be carried vast distances from the few sources of supply. The saline lakes and springs in East Africa which are associated with the volcanic activity are mostly extremely alkaline due to sodium carbonates, but a few have a sufficiently high proportion of sodium chloride to be edible. One of the best known is the Crater Lake Katwe at the north end of Lake Edward where there is a very ancient industry which has always supplied salt many hundred of miles into the Congo. The saline springs at Kibero on the east shore of Lake Albert are another source with a long history.

The Lake Magadi Soda Co. has been engaged for many years in producing and exporting soda for making glass.

L. C. BEADLE

References

Annual Reports of East African Freshwater Fisheries Research Organization and Joint Fisheries Research Organization of Northern Rhodesia and Nyasaland.

Beadle, L. C., 1962, "The Evolution of species in the Lakes of East Africa," *Uganda J.* **26**, 44–54.

Hurst, H. E., 1952, "The Nile," Constable, London.

Livingstone, D. A., 1965, "Sedimentation and the history of water level change in Lake Tanganyika," *Limnol. Oceanog.*, **10**(4), 607–610.

Van Meel, L., 1954, "Le Phytoplankton," *Explor. Hydrobiol. Lac Tanganyika (1946–47)*, **4**(1). Inst. Roy. Sci. Nat. Belg. Bruxelles.

Moorehead, Alan, 1960, "The White Nile," Hamish Hamilton, London.

Mueller, G., 1963, "Dissolved gases in East African Lakes," *Nature*, **198**, 569–570.

Nilsson, E., 1963, "Pluvial lakes and glaciers in East Africa," *Stockholm Contr. Geol.*, **11**(2), 21–57.

Talling, J. F., and Talling, I. B., 1965, "The chemical composition of African lake waters," *Int. Rev. Hydrobiol.*, **50**.

Scaetta, H., 1937, "Variations du climat Pleistocene en Afrique Centrale," *Ann. Géogr.*, **46**(250), 164–171.

Willis, B., 1936, "The East African plateaus and rift valleys," *Carneg. Inst. Wash., Publ.*, **470**.

Cross-references: *Crater Lake; Holocene; Lake Baikal; Lake Chad; Lava-displaced Drainage; Rift Valley.* Vol. II: *Evaporation; Rainfall Distribution.*

EMERGED SHORELINES—*See* **EUSTASY;
TERRACES-MARINE**

ENDOGENIC DYNAMICS

Processes originating within the earth were
designated by Penck (1894) as endogenic (from
the Greek *endon*, within). The opposite concept is
exogenic. The most familiar endogenic processes
involve *vulcanism, metamorphism, earthquakes,
crustal warping, folding* and *faulting*. Webster's
dictionary finds a distinction between endogenic
and endogenetic, but this is illusory; the second
form is more commonly used in Britain. In geomorphology, one may distinguish structural land
forms (endogenic) from denudational land forms
(exogenic). Grabau (1904) used the terms
somewhat
differently in stratigraphy, whereby a chemical
precipitation was endogenic while a clastic sediment
was exogenic; this use has not been widely adopted.

The earth's principal endogenic energy sources
are (a) *thermal*, primarily due to radioactive decay,
and locally to chemical exothermic reactions, and
(b) *gravitational*, due to the balance between the
earth's own mass and its angular momentum.

The geothermal energy source leads to the concept of heat flow, precisely measurable in deep
bores and mines and, with modern equipment,
through the ocean floor. The theory of convection
currents in the outer core or at certain levels of
the mantle has been strongly advocated and
equally strongly opposed by different experts.
Worldwide heat-flow studies suggest that the
flow is rather constant, except where fracture
zones (probably marking belts of pressure release)
permit a steep rise of geoisotherms, up to one order
of magnitude. Such fracture zones appear to be
related to crustal weakness established by mass
transfer (exogenically stimulated), isostatic reactions and forces related to the earth's rotation.

It seems likely therefore that geothermal forces
should be regarded only as potentials, not activated
unless localized and triggered by the earth's
gravitational and rotational dynamics in combination with the mass transfer effects of the exogenic dynamics. A minor example of an endogenic
phenomenon, completely independent of geothermal forces is that of salt diapirism; here the
buried salt layer is differentially loaded, and having
a lower specific gravity than that of the sedimentary
load, it rises in a dome or anticline until equilibrium
is reestablished.

The Mid-Ocean Ridge, for a major example,
often quoted as a product of a rising convection
"cell," is in fact 40,000 miles long and emerges
into continental margins in the Gulf of Aden,
Gulf of California, etc., at which points the convective cells should be descending. Thus a key
feature of the convectional hypothesis seems to
contradict itself. Fundamental movements of large

parts of the earth's crust can better be related geometrically to rotational dynamics.

RHODES W. FAIRBRIDGE

References

Challinor, J., 1964, "A Dictionary of Geology," Se-
cond ed., Cardiff, University of Wales Press, 289pp.
Grabau, A. W., 1904, "On the classification of sedimen-
tary rocks," *Am. Geologist*, **33**, 228–247.
Keindl, J., 1942, "Die Geomorphologie als Weg zur
Erkenntnis der endogene Krafte," *Petermanns Geogr.
Mitt.*, **88**(4), 141–142.
Penck, A., 1894, "Morphologie der Erdoberfläche,"
Stuttgart, Engelhorn, 2 vols.
Thornbury, W. D., 1954, "Principles of Geomorphol-
ogy," New York, John Wiley & Sons, 618pp.

Cross-references: *Exogenic Dynamics; Warping.* Vol. I:
Mid-Oceanic Ridge. Vol. II: *Angular Momentum;
Earth's Rotation.* Vol. V: *Earthquakes; Faulting;
Folding; Heat Flow; Metamorphism; Volcanoes and
Volcanology.*

ENDRUMPF—*See* PRIMÄRRUMPF

ENERGY—*See* EQUILIBRIUM. In Vol. II, SOLAR ENERGY. In pr Vol. VI, COAL: GEOLOGY, GENERAL: GEOTHERMAL ENERGY: OIL SHALES: PETROLEUM: TIDAL POWER: WATER POWER

EOLIAN PROCESSES—*See* ARID CYCLE: SAND DUNES: WIND ACTION

EOLIAN TRANSPORT

Hurricanes, choking dust and scouring sand-
storm; vast loess blankets and towering dunes;
some thick festoon-bedded sandstones in the stratigraphic record—all attest to the work of the wind.
Solar radiant energy drives the atmospheric heat
engine which starts the work. The kinetic energy of
the wind drives sand grains in bouncing paths along
the ground. Turbulence tends to dissipate this
kinetic energy, but also creates upward and downward eddy movements. These keep silt and clay
particles suspended as long as upward current
velocities exceed particle settling velocities, unless
grains are impacted on vegetation or other obstacles.
Both sand and dust settle down when (or where) the
velocity, and hence transporting power, of the wind
diminishes below the rate of energy transfer needed
to keep these particles in motion (Bagnold, 1941).

(1) *Wind erosion* is ineffective over smooth dust
surfaces where the fine particles do not protrude
above the *laminar boundary layer* (q.v. Vol. II)—a
viscous film of slowly moving air that hugs the surface. Particle removal is also retarded by surface
attraction, and sometimes by moisture, salt crust or

309

humus. Yet sand-size aggregates (see *Clay Dunes*) and, more especially, the 0.1–1.0 mm grains of quartz and other minerals can roll and be caught up in the turbulent eddies. Most sand is too heavy to remain suspended; grains fall and dislodge other grains (and dust) as each grain impacts upon the surface at a glancing angle in the driving wind. The horizontal component of the sandblast may scour coarse clods, or even hard stones (see *Ventifacts*), bedrock or vegetation.

(2) *Sand transport* by wind, like that of water, is governed by the fluid's power, or rate of energy expenditure, per unit area. Bagnold (1941) expressed the quantity of transported sand (q) as a product of wind velocity v times stress of wind on the sand (or drag of sand on the wind). In turn, this drag is the product of air density ρ times V_*^2. Here V_* (called friction velocity) is 5.75 × the slope of the graph of wind velocity (v) with respect to the logarithm of height (Fig. 1). V_* increases, essentially, in proportion to v. Substitution in the preceding formula ($q = $ constant $\cdot v \cdot \rho V_*^2$) suggests an approximate expression of quantity of transported sand in proportion to the *cube* of wind velocity. More precisely, transport starts only after a certain threshold velocity V_t (or threshold friction velocity V_{*t}) is passed. Then q increases in proportion to the cube of the wind velocity *above* the threshold velocity, V_t, at which the sand begins to move (Fig. 2).

$$q = a(v - V_t)^3 \qquad (1)$$

Normal sands keep moving when average wind velocity at a height k' near 1 cm above the sand surface exceeds V_t (about 4 m/sec, or 9–10 mph). Further increase in v at height z (effective height in centimeters of the anemometer measuring v) does

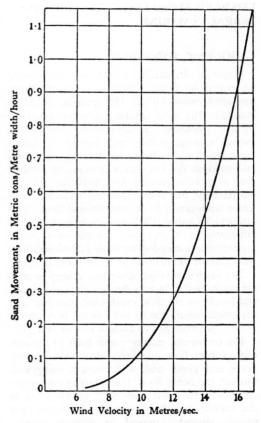

FIG. 2. Flow of average dune sand as a function of wind velocity measured at a standard height of 1 meter: $q = 5.2 \times 10^{-4}(v - v_t)^3$ (from Bagnold 1941, Fig. 22, p. 70). (Courtesy Methuen & Co. Ltd.)

not lead to appreciable increase in the velocity at 1 cm; the added power of the wind is spent instead on the spectacular increase in the sand flow rate, q, as $(v - V_t)^3$ increases.

Now consider a series of weather records, with P readings per day and with N observations in velocity class v_i per year. Then cubed velocity terms $(v_i - V_t)^3$ for each velocity class can be added to predict the liters of sand S that *could* be driven past a meter's width of bare desert or dune in a given compass direction: $S = \dfrac{3.25}{\log_{10} z} \dfrac{N}{P}(v - V_t)^3$. Analyses of effective wind by compass direction have corresponded well with apparent dune movement in Arabia, Denmark, Great Britain, Michigan and elsewhere. Actual amounts of sand moved may be well below this theoretical capacity as a result of moisture or obstacles. Dune-building vegetation especially increases the surface roughness so that velocities at the effective sand blowing height of 1 cm rarely exceed the threshold velocity required for transport (Olson, 1958 a, b).

(3) *Sand deposits* may be initiated simply by the decrease in wind power after a storm over a bare

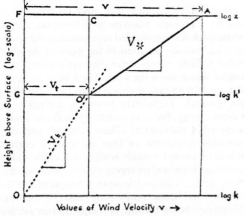

FIG. 1. Relations between wind velocity v (in meters per second), log height z (in centimeters), wind gradient $V_*(= 5.75 \times$ slope of $v/\log z$), and threshold velocity V_t. Profiles of velocity of winds weaker than this threshold converge at point O, which is determined by V_t' and k' (approximately 1 cm for normal sands, from Bagnold 1941, Fig. 21, p. 68). Note: On the figure, V_* should read $0.174V_*$. (Courtesy Methuen & Co. Ltd.)

area. The dune itself may become a "sink" for further sand accumulation and may proceed to grow, move, devour smaller dunes, or sometimes reproduce new ones. When dune-building vegetation can invade bare areas, it traps sand and starts getting buried. However, it keeps growing up and recreates surface roughness, which helps to trap more sand [Fig. 3(a)].

(4) *Nutrient additions to ecosystems:* In some of the most arid dunes, winds bring in organic matter for animals to live on. There is usually a stabilization, biological development and soil formation on the older dunes of a series in all but the most arid regions. Dunes of different ages often show a dramatic *succession* of transitions from the bare physical system of sand and air ($\pm$ water) to a complex eco-

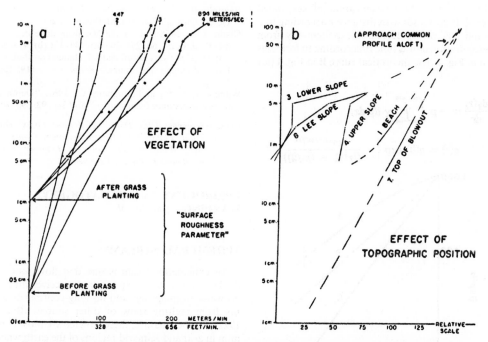

FIG. 3. Modification of wind velocity profiles by vegetation and dune topography. (a) Change in surface roughness height *k* before and after planting of marram grass on upper windward slope of dune at Gary, Indiana. (b) Shift in profile as wind moved from beach (1), over a low foredune to protected lower windward slope (3), upper windward slope (4), rear crest of blowout dune (7), and protected lee slope (8), measured by Landsberg, Riley and Rossby (from Olson, 1958a, Fig. 2, p. 256). (Courtesy University of Chicago Press.)

Interception of sand supply near its source may stabilize the more leeward dunes thus shielded from a former source. Or if sand is still being removed (even slowly) from an area where replenishment ceases to occur, blowout activity may be initiated in the normal course of dune development without disturbance. Where there is deterioration due to the vegetation's own senescence, or to drought, fire, grazing, traffic, wave cliffing or other disturbance, blowout action can be accelerated dramatically. Blowout dunes alter geomorphic patterns (see *Sand Dunes*) and topography modifies the wind [Fig. 3(b)]. Further sand transport and physical development of one dune system often depend on neighboring dune systems and on several controlling factors of the surrounding landscape.

logical system (ecosystem) with plants, animals, microbes and soil. Eolian transport of dust and of mineral nutrients through rain may be important in transforming such ecosystems from very poor biological communities to communities which are richer in species and nutritional conditions (Olson, 1958 b–d).

(5) *Dust and loess* transport and deposition can be interpreted by the theory of atmospheric diffusion. Random eddy movements tend to disperse and dilute particles in a cloud that spreads from a point source, or from a line or area source like a Pleistocene outwash plain or a playa dust bed. A model by Waggoner and Bingham (1961) assumes normal distribution of particle density around cloud centers, and deposition rate *p*, proportional

to the amount left in the cloud volume moving along the ground surface. This implies a decrease in the logarithm of loess blanket thickness b with the logarithm of distance r from source, which is linear with a slope $-m/2$. Their model fits data of the midwestern United States better than previous models:

$$b = kd = \frac{k3pq(r)}{(2\pi)^{1/2}\sigma} = \frac{k3pq(r)}{\pi^{1/2}Cr^{m/2}} \qquad (2)$$

In Eq. (2), q is the concentration of suspended material. It decreases with distance r according to a function $q(r)$ which decreases exponentially from a concentration $q(0)$ at time 0, according to formulas given in Fig. 4. The theoretical curve B in Fig. 4 (for

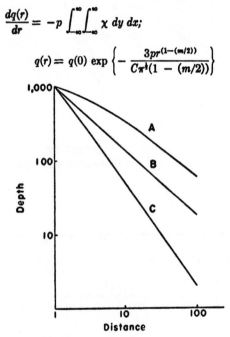

$$\frac{dq(r)}{dr} = -p \int_{-\infty}^{\infty} \int_{-\infty}^{\infty} \chi \, dy \, dx;$$

$$q(r) = q(0) \exp\left\{-\frac{3pr^{(1-(m/2))}}{C\pi^{1}(1-(m/2))}\right\}$$

FIG. 4. Relation of predicted loess depth (centimeters) and distance from source (kilometers). An idealized linear source with negligible depletion (B), is compared with an area source 10 km wide (A), and with depth accounting for depletion due to deposition at a rate of $p = 0.05$ (C). Turbulence parameter m taken as 1.75 (from Waggoner and Bingham 1961, Fig. 3, p. 398). (Courtesy Williams & Wilkins Co.)

a line source of sediment like a narrow floodplain) would be modified in the direction of curve A as the source area broadened (e.g., a Pleistocene outwash plain or desert playa). It would be modified in the direction of curve C as deposition or depletion rate increased. These deviations would tend to cancel each other out so the simple line B describes the depth-distance relations as well as can be expected for field data.

Similar theoretical treatment should apply to the eolian transport of other small particles (pollen, spores, seeds, minute animals) which are geologically important in biogeography, as well as to the spread of air contamination and plant diseases (which stimulated earlier developments of turbulent dispersal theory).

JERRY S. OLSON

References

Bagnold, R. A., 1941, "The Physics of Blown Sand and Desert Dunes," London, Methuen, 265pp.

Olson, J. S., 1958 a–d, "Lake Michigan dune development," *J. Geol.*, **66**, 254–263 (a); 345–351 (b); 473–483 (c); "Rates of succession and soil changes on southern Lake Michigan and dunes," *Botan. Gaz.*, **119**, 125–170 (d).

Waggoner, P. E., and Bingham, C., 1961, "Depth of loess and distance from source," *Soil Sci.*, **92**, 396–401.

Cross-references: *Clay Dunes; Deflation; Loess; Outwash Plain; Playa; Sand Dunes; Sediment Transport; Ventifact; Wind Action.* Vol. II: *Laminar Flow, Laminar Boundary Layer; Turbulence.*

EPEIROGENY—*See* CYMATOGENY; WARPING; *also* Vol. V

EPHEMERAL STREAMS

An ephemeral stream is one that flows only in direct response to precipitation. It receives little or no water from springs and no long-continued supply from melting snow or other sources (Bryan, 1922). By their nature, these streams are most common in arid and semiarid regions of the earth where precipitation is scant and a moisture deficiency exists most of the time. A distinction should be made between the terms stream and channel. The stream is the flowing water, which is ephemeral or transitory. The channel is the geomorphic feature that conveys ephemeral flow. Channels may change with time in shape and longitudinal profile by processes of degradation and aggradation, but they are not ephemeral.

Many names have been applied to ephemeral stream channels; they are all generally synonymous, and none is preferred more than another except as regional use dictates. In the United States, the names most commonly used are arroyo, gully, wash, and coulee. In North Africa and Arabia, the name *wadi* is common; in South Africa, *donga*; in India, *nullah*.

Even in the less arid regions of mediterranean climates, periodic streams are often distinguished with special names, such as *fiumare* in Italy and Sicily (Walther, 1924; Pardé, 1933).

Characteristics of Flow and Sediment Transport

The dry channel of an ephemeral stream, which

FIG. 1. A general view of Oraibi Wash, an ephemeral stream channel in northeastern Arizona. Note how deeply the channel has been entrenched in the valley alluvium.

often carries flow for only a few days each year, can be transformed dramatically into a raging torrent of muddy water and debris in a few minutes as a result of a high-intensity thunderstorm. Almost as quickly, the flow recedes and the channel is dry once again. This is in sharp contrast to a typical perennial stream, which generally does not experience such tremendous variations in flow.

Observations of flood flows in many of the ephemeral streams in western United States show that many flows are completely absorbed by the dry channels in a short distance downstream because of the short duration and small areal extent of summer thunderstorms that produce runoff. Therefore, in basins having ephemeral flow, discharge or water yield may decrease downstream despite the increase in drainage area. In fact, some headwater tributaries that experience only ephemeral flow seldom contribute any runoff or sediment to master streams because of these losses by absorption.

The characteristics of sediment transport in ephemeral streams distinguish them from perennial streams. Principally because of flow absorption, ephemeral streams are characterized by an increas-

ing concentration of suspended sediment in a downstream direction. Other channel parameters may adjust themselves to this change in sediment concentration (Leopold and Miller, 1956). However, in many ephemeral stream channels, the orderly increase in channel width and depth in a downstream direction that characterizes perennial stream channels is often lacking.

Aggradation of Ephemeral Stream Channels

Aggradation is common in the valleys of western United States because of the flow absorption in the channels of ephemeral streams and deposition of the sediment load. Aggradation generally occurs in two topographic situations: (1) near the mouth of tributaries that are graded to a broad flood plain rather than debouching into a larger channel, and (2) in tributary channels that drain areas of high sediment yield where the flow has been insufficient to transport sediment through the drainage network. Most of these deposits are unstable and short-lived, but some have become stabilized by vegetation and continue to trap sediment. Flood plain aggradation of as much as 3 feet in 30 years has been documented by measurements of buried fence posts in the Cheyenne River basin, Wyoming (Hadley and Schumm, 1961).

A minor feature of some ephemeral streams is the formation of *clay balls*, averaging 5 cm in diameter but reaching up to 40 cm. Some are structureless, but most show concentric banding of sand and clay (Nordin and Curtis, 1962).

Degradation of Ephemeral Stream Channels

Studies in western United States show that many ephemeral stream channels exhibit a marked convexity or local steepening of gradient at the downstream edge of an aggrading reach. This increased gradient causes an increase in flow velocity which may initiate local channel erosion (Schumm and Hadley, 1957). In most cases, trenching apparently begins on the steepened reach and then erodes principally headward with only minor downstream development. Eroding reaches often are separated by undissected or aggrading reaches to form a discontinuous gully system. Integration of the disconnected, eroding reaches into a continuous channel may occur during a single, large flood or may be accomplished by slow, headward cutting over a period of years. Evidence of channel aggradation and subsequent degradation of about 8 feet in 60 years is shown by exposure of previously buried trees in a channel in western Nebraska (Schumm and Hadley, 1957). Many such occurrences are known and suggest that aggradation and degradation of ephemeral stream channels in historical time take place at rates more rapid than generally recognized.

Channel Characteristics

The character of alluvium in which the channel of an ephemeral stream is cut helps to determine the channel shape. According to Schumm (1961), a channel whose perimeter is composed primarily of highly cohesive silt and clay will have a low width-depth ratio, whereas a channel composed of material coarser than silt will have a relatively high width-depth ratio. In addition, riparian vegetation influences the channel shape. Fine-grained deposits in the channel will retain moisture more effectively than coarse sand and permit vegetation to become established. This vegetation can induce aggradation by increasing channel roughness and reducing velocity of flow (Hadley, 1961).

RICHARD F. HADLEY

References

Bryan, Kirk, 1922, "Erosion and sedimentation in the Papago Country," *Bull. U.S. Geol. Surv.* **730-B,** 88.

Hadley, R. F., 1961, "Influence of riparian vegetation on channel shape," *U.S. Geol. Surv. Profess. Paper* **424-C,** 30.

Hadley, R. F., and Schumm, S. A., 1961, "Sediment sources and drainage basin characteristics in upper Cheyenne River basin," *U.S. Geol. Surv. Water-Supply Paper* **1531-B,** 182–191.

Keppel, R. V., and Renard, K. G., 1962, "Transmission losses in ephemeral stream beds," *J. Am. Soc. Civil Engin., Hydraul. Div.,* **88,** 59–68.

Leopold, L. B., and Miller, J. P., 1956, "Ephemeral streams—Hydraulic factors and their relation to the drainage net," *U.S. Geol. Surv. Profess. Paper* **282-A,** 37pp.

*Leopold, L. B., Wolman, M. G., and Miller, J. P., 1964, "Fluvial Processes in Geomorphology," Chs. 7 and 11, San Francisco, W. H. Freeman & Co., 522pp.

Nordin, C. F., Jr., and Curtis, W. F., 1962, "Formation and deposition of clay balls, Rio Puerco, New Mexico," *U.S. Geol. Surv. Prof. Paper* **450-B,** 37–40.

Pardé, M., 1933, "Fleuves et rivières," Paris, Coll. A. Colin, 224pp.

Schumm, S. A., 1961, "Effect of sediment characteristics on erosion and deposition in ephemeral-stream channels," *U.S. Geol. Surv. Profess. Paper* **352-C,** 63–64.

Schumm, S. A., and Hadley, R. F., 1957, "Arroyos and the semiarid cycle of erosion," *Am. J. Sci.,* **255,** 161–174.

Walther, J., 1924, "Das Gesetz der Wüstenbildung in Gegenwart und Vorzeit," Leipzig, Verlag Quelle & Meyer, 421pp.

* Additional bibliographic references may be found in this work.

Cross-references: *Aggradation*; *Alluvium*; *Coulee, Coulee Cliff*, etc.; *Degradation*; *Gully Erosion*; *Sediment Transport*. Vol. II: *Climatic Change in American Prehistory*; *Precipitation*. pr Vol. VI: *Armored Mud Ball*.

EPHEMERIS—*See* Vol. II

EPIGENE

Epigene was defined by Archibald Geikie (1882) as "the changes produced on the superficial parts of the earth, chiefly by the circulation of air and water set in motion by the sun's heat." At the present-day, it has several uses:

(1) In geomorphology, it is used to indicate exogenous factors (meteorological/gravitative) affecting landscape evolution, such as weathering, mass movements, fluvial and eolian erosion, glaciation, subsurface water action, waves, currents and tides.

(2) To indicate the opposite of Lyell's term "hypogene" (any phenomenon due to internal heat and ascending magmatic causes).

(3) In mineral genesis (see Vol. IV, *Economic Geology*), the term "supergene" is often used in preference for near-surface phenomena.

Lawson (1915) describing "epigene profiles of the desert" remarks that "For mountains of approximately homogeneous rock the epigene profile ... comprises three elements: (1) the rock slopes, having an angle of less than 35°; (2) the alluvial fan slope rarely exceeding 5°; and (3) the flat of the playa." The slope angle of such desert epigene profiles was not, in Lawson's opinion, a function of the stage or degree of degradation, as it seems to be in humid regions where chemical weathering is paramount.

Some writers prefer *exogenous*, *exogenetic*, or *exogenic* to epigene, in a geomorphic context (see *Exogenic Dynamics*), and leave epigene and *epigenetic processes* more for geochemical application (Perelman, 1967). Just as Lawson used epigene versus hypogene, Penck (1953), for example, would use exogenous versus endogenous. Von Richthofen (1886), and likewise De Martonne (1951), wrote of *epigenic valleys* (superimposed stream channels). De Martonne also extended it to *epigenic coasts* ("*contraposed coast*" of Clapp, 1913, e.g., as in Maine, a discordant structure, with submergence followed by emergence—note: the endogenic control!).

RAYMUNDO J. CHICO

References

Clapp, H., 1913, "Contraposed shorelines," *J. Geol.*, **21**, 537–540.
De Martonne, E., 1951, "Traité de Géographie Physique," Vol. 2, Paris, A. Colin.
Geikie, A., 1882, "Textbook of Geology," London, Macmillan & Co., 971pp.
Lawson, A. C., 1915, "The epigene profiles of the desert," *Univ. Calif. Bull. Dept. Geol. Sci.*, **9**, 23–48.
Penck, W., 1953, "Morphological Analysis of Land Forms," London, Macmillan & Co., 429pp. (translation of 1924 German edition by H. Czech and K. C. Boswell).
Perelman, A. I., 1967, "Geochemistry of Epigenesis," New York, Plenum Publ. Corp., 300pp. (translated from Russian by N. N. Kohanowski).
Von Richthofen, F., 1886, "Führer für Forschungsreisende," Hanover, Jänecke, 734pp.

Cross-references: *Endogenic Dynamics*; *Eolian Transport*; *Exogenic Dynamics*; *Geomorphology*; *Glaciation*; *Mass Movement*; *Rivers*; *Weathering*. Vol. I: *Ocean Currents*; *Ocean Waves*; *Tides*. Vol. IV: *Economic Geology*; *Hypogene*; *Supergene*.

EQUILIBRIUM IN GEOMORPHOLOGY

By the term equilibrium is meant the idea that material, process and geometry form a self-correcting balance. Equilibrium is properly one of the basic tenets of geology, along with uniformitarianism. Reluctance to adopt and apply equilibrium concepts over the past six or eight decades —even though they were readily available—has hindered the development of geological thought.

The equilibrium, or steady-state, postulate is fundamental to every branch of geological work: tectonics, sedimentology, geomorphology, geophysics, paleontology, hydrology, geochemistry. It can and should be applied in any situation where a process—of any kind—is operative.

The best-known clash between equilibrium and non-equilibrium thought involves *river-erosion studies*. According to the Davis school of geomorphology, water flowing across a land mass produces a geometry which evolves with time, *even though* all other controlling factors (such as materials present and processes operating) remain constant; i.e., in a sense, shape changes in response to the passage of time. Or, worded differently, a statement of materials and processes is not sufficient to specify the form which is present; one must also know how long (relatively) a given process has operated on given materials. The Davis scheme therefore includes sequential stages: *youth*, referring to early (or juvenile) geometry; *maturity*, referring to a more advanced geometry; and *old age*, referring to very late geometry. For regions cut by running water, youth is taken to be characterized by slightly dissected uplands, maturity by an "all in slope" aspect, and old age by widespread lowlands. An equilibrium approach would require that form *not* be related to time. [See, however, editorial note under: "Cycles, Geomorphic].

Mackin (1948) applied equilibrium thinking to rivers, as follows:

"A *graded stream* is one in which, over a period of years, slope is delicately adjusted to provide, with available discharge and with prevailing channel characteristics, just the velocity required for transportation of the load supplied from the drainage basin. The graded stream is a system in equilibrium; its diagnostic characteristic is that any change in any of the controlling factors will cause a displacement of the equilibrium in a direction that will tend to absorb the effect of the change."

In the statement, the geometry ("slope") is controlled by materials ("load supplied" and "discharge") and by process ("transportation"). The only time provision is that short-term effects be discounted. As long as the same discharge brings the same load from upstream, and the same process operates, the same geometry will be maintained. The passage of time, in itself, makes no changes, but changes of the physical parameters, such as headward erosion in a stream, are to be expected.

In a similar fashion, concerning coastal studies, we can state that: The equilibrium beach has curvature and sand prism characteristics adjusted to each other so delicately that the potential littoral motion provides precisely the energy needed to transport the detritus supplied at the upcurrent end. The time element in this balance is long-term rather than instantaneous, and the period may be diurnal or seasonal.

In this statement, the geometry ("curvature") is controlled by materials ("detritus") and process ("transportation").

Similar statements can be contrived for each erosional or depositional agency or feature: sand dune, river delta, glacial tongue, barrier island, etc. Rather than accumulate an assortment of specially tailored definitions, we would do better to develop a generalization, somewhat as follows:

According to the concept of dynamic equilibrium, every geometric element is the product of adjustment between materials and process. When topography is in equilibrium, and materials and process remain the same, all elements of the topography are being modified (i.e., lowered or elevated or shifted) at the same rate. Differences in geometry are to be explained in terms of local variation of materials and processes, rather than as steps in an evolutionary sequence. The equilibrium is dynamic, in that the form may be shifting its position in space (either up or down, or laterally), and in that disturbances dictate changes in process which tend to reestablish or maintain the pre-disturbance geometry.

A kite, apparently stationary while it flies in a strong, steady breeze, illustrates the principle of dynamic equilibrium. There is motion (the air is moving), and the kite may even shift position slightly from time to time. But the geometry of the system is firmly fixed, despite the motion, until there is a change in materials or processes. A bank account which always maintains the same average balance, despite deposits and withdrawals, also illustrates the principle.

The generalized statement of dynamic equilibrium, given above, was restricted to operation of the sediment transport system, and hence to geomorphology. The same principle can be further generalized, however, and applied to other aspects of geology. During the long, slow uplift of a mountain range, a shifting equilibrium of some kind may be maintained. *Isostasy* (q.v., Vol. V) is an equilibrium concept. By substituting "organisms" for "materials," and "demography" for "geometry," we can apply the equilibrium concept to biology and hence to paleontology.

The equilibrium concept does not refer to static conditions. It is only the geometry which appears to be static, and even that can change, as the equilibrium shifts in response to alterations in materials and processes. Consequently, a history might include respresentations of sub-equilibrium as well as equilibrium states, and there might be more than one operative equilibrium condition. It seems likely that Davis' "youth" was a term for what, in the equilibrium scheme would be considered as sub-equilibrium, and that "maturity" and "old age" refer to two different equilibrium states. The Davis sequence, from beginning to end, could be shown as

$$E_s \rightarrow E_1 \rightarrow E_2$$

where the subscript "s" indicates incomplete development of equilibrium (i.e., immaturity or sub-maturity), and the second arrow is intended to mean that the processes which operate in lowlands may be quite different from those which operate in uplands.

Such a scheme does not constitute a theory in itself; it represents an approach, by use of which pertinent observations can be made and integrated into an appropriate theory.

The short-term changes which must be excluded from any equilibrium formulation depend in part on the effective frequencies of the pertinent processes. A sand dune, for example, must have an equilibrium form on a time scale in which either daily or seasonal fluctuations, or both are averaged out. The same may be true of a beach. A river, however, is modified most by floods which occur at 1–10 year intervals, and a glacier may respond to minor fluctuations having periods of the order of 100 years. Other systems may have even longer periods, such as the 10^4 or 10^5 years required for isostatic balance to be achieved. The equilibrium threshold—that value below which minor fluctuations tend to mask long-term trends—may be estimated in terms of relative amounts of "work" done. The latter can be approximated by plotting frequency versus rate. From such a plot, a maximum can be derived to indicate the level at which the largest portion of work is being done.

A useful classification of certain landform elements can be based on the equilibrium concept. For instance, shore lines can be classified as non-equilibrium (i.e., zero-energy coasts); sub-equilibrium; shifting equilibrium: prograding; shifting equilibrium: retrograding; and stable equilibrium. Likewise, river-cut regions might be classified as sub-equilibrium; stable equilibrium: high energy (i.e., high relief); stable equilibrium: low energy (low relief); and shifting equilibrium.

W. F. TANNER

References

Bryan, Kirk., 1940, "The retreat of slopes," *Ann. Assoc. Am. Geog.,* **30**, 254–268.

Davis, W. M., 1954, "Geographical Essays," New York, Dover Publications, 777pp.

Glock, W. S., 1932, "Available relief as a factor of control in the profile of a land form," *J. Geol.,* **40**, 74–83.

Hack, John T., 1960, "Interpretation of erosional topography in humid temperate regions." *Am. J. Sci.;* **258-A** (Bradley Volume), 80–97.

Mackin, J. H., 1948, "Concept of the graded river," *Bull. Geol. Soc. Am.,* **59**, 463–512.

Tanner, W. F., 1958, "The equilibrium beach," *Trans. Am. Geophys. Union,* **39**, 889–891.

Tanner, W. F., 1960, "Florida coastal classification," *Trans., Gulf Coast Assoc. Geol. Soc.,* **10**, 259–266.

Tanner, W. F., 1962, "Geomorphology and the sediment transport system," *Southeastern Geol.,* **4**, 113–126.

Wolman, M. Gordon, and Miller, John P., 1960, "Magnitude and frequency of forces in geomorphic processes," *J. Geol.,* **68**, 54–74.

EROSION

Erosion (Latin, *erodere*, to gnaw away) is a term for the way in which geologic agencies of movement secure and remove rock debris and associated organic matter. Strictly speaking, erosion is the acquisition of material by geologic agencies, but many geologists loosely include processes both of acquisition and *transportation. Weathering* (q.v.) causes the breakdown of rock material, but is not a necessary prerequisite to erosion. Erosion is the wearing away or denudation of land masses, in a broad sense. High mountains and entire continents are reduced in elevation through the removal of earth materials oceanward or to intermediate base levels in endorheic drainage areas or lake basins.

Figure 1 indicates the place of erosion in the vast "*Geocycle*" of breakdown of rocks and their reformation. Well-known examples of erosion are wind erosion as observed in dust storms and sand storms; stream erosion; soil erosion by water and wind; marine erosion including attack of land by waves; mass-wasting movement of materials under the force of gravity as in landslides and slower creep. To these examples should be added the less easily observed phenomena of submarine erosion, among which submarine canyons are striking examples.

Geologists who live under a humid-temperate climate observe that streams are continually dissecting the land. It may be assumed that if we could watch a land mass from the moment it was lifted up out of the sea by diastrophism, we would see that rivers excavate valleys and gradually degrade uplands to plains lying near sea level. The dissection of a young volcanic island illustrates this concept. W. M. Davis (1850–1934) conceived of stages of

this process of denudation which he termed (1) youth, (2) maturity and (3) old age. Figure 2 illustrates these stages by a series of diagrams. In the initial stage of erosion of a newly exposed land surface, segments of steep-walled valleys form where original slopes were most marked. With time, these segments of valleys are integrated into canyon-like drainage patterns, between which the upland remains nearly level, and possibly even poorly drained.

Waterfalls and rapids may occur in the river courses wherever exceptionally hard rock layers are crossed by the streams. In the stage of maturity, tributaries of the streams cut back into the flat uplands until all divides are sharp and ridge-like. More of the landscape is sloping than at any other stage. In old age, the land surface has been reduced almost to a plain and is called a "*peneplain*" (q.v.), alternatively "peneplane." The process is "*peneplanation.*" At this stage, valleys are broad, streams meander, and only a few hills called "monadnocks" have survived erosion.

The concepts of youth, maturity and old age have been useful in describing the nature and genesis of landscapes. One may wonder why the continents have not all been worn down to peneplains, reduced almost to sea level. In complex land areas there has been uplift of land—both orogenic, or mountain-making, and epeirogenic, or plateau-making—to counteract the destructive work of erosion. Vulcanism has produced lava flows and cinder cones. Warping and folding of sedimentary rock strata of different degrees of hardness permit erosion to etch out the soft layers, leaving the more resistant ones standing out as cuestas and as anticlinal and synclinal ridges and valleys. The stages of erosion from youth to old age, therefore, may not be as simple and uninterrupted as illustrated in Fig. 2.

In contrast to the gradual softening of slopes, visualized by Davis (1930), hill slopes erode in many landscapes in such a way that the entire slope gradually moves back into the upland. This is basically the concept of W. Penck (1953). Figure 3 illustrates two landscapes in which slopes are retreating steadily at the expense of the flat upland. This "Penckian erosion" is distinct from erosion by streams. It is a kind of sheet, rill and gully erosion which attacks the upland fairly uniformly along the

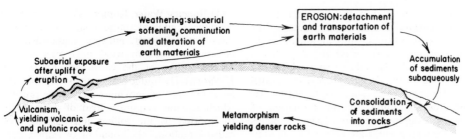

Fig. 1. Simplified diagram showing relationships between some geologic processes in the "geocycle."

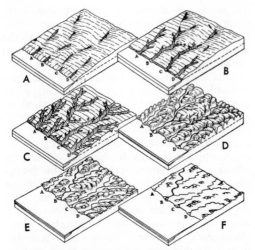

FIG. 2. Ideal fluvial cycle, after Davis (1930), under a humid-temperate climate and homogeneous rock. The stages shown may be labeled as follows: (A) initial stage; (B) early youth; (C) later youth; (D) early maturity; (E) later maturity; (F) old age (peneplain with monadnocks). (Modified after Longwell, Knopf and Flint, 1941)

entire slope and delivers debris to the streams. The movement of talus (a), and of soil or pedisediment (b) is considered to be in equilibrium with the wasting at the free face (B). L. C. King suggests that a complete hillslope consists of four elements: a waxing or increasing slope (A), a free face or escarpment (B), a debris slope (C), and a waning or decreasing foot (pediment) slope (D).

the merging of growing pediments. It seems likely that pediment formation is characteristic of erosion cycles in arid and semiarid lands, while the degradation of land through the stages of youth, maturity and old age occurs in humid-temperate regions. Figure 4 contrasts this process of parallel retreat of slopes (left) with the process of declining slope (right) described by Davis.

The karst cycle of erosion occurs in regions of limestone bedrock in which surface valleys are replaced to a considerable extent by sinkholes, caverns and underground channels. With later collapse of caverns and with further solution of limestone material in the hills and ridges, a karst landscape in old age is reduced to a lower level, and is drained again by surface streams (See *Karst*).

Although it seems unlikely that marine erosion could ever erode away a continent and permit the sea to cover it, nevertheless action of waves and currents is vastly destructive of land. Erosion by waves creates cliffs on headlands as it cuts them back. Currents build spits, bars, tombolos and beaches. The result of prolonged marine erosion on shore lines both of submergence and emergence may be ultimately to erase promontories, bars, lagoons and tidal marshes, yielding a fairly even, abrupt shore.

Agents of Erosion

Six agents of erosion are listed in Table 1, along with processes by which they acquire loosened material and transport it. Of these, running water accomplishes the most work.

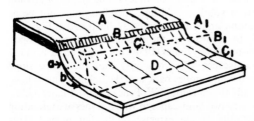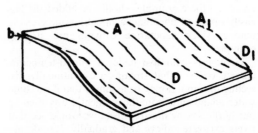

FIG. 3. Elements of a hillslope (after L. C. King). The block diagram on the left shows: (A) waxing slope; (B) free face; (C) debris slope; (D) waning slope or pediment; (A$_1$) former extension of the waxing slope; (B$_1$) a previous position of the free face; (C$_1$) a previous position of the debris slope; (a) talus; (b) soil. The block diagram to the right illustrates a hillslope with only two elements present.

Many hillsides have only the first and last of these four elements. The essential process is the parallel retreat of hillslopes into the upland, with the flow of sediment coming off the slope like a sheet, and moving slowly to the streams, which then carry away the material. The process of parallel retreat of slopes has been called "pediment formation" in order to emphasize the formation of extensive gently sloping foot slopes. Extensive plains in arid and semiarid areas are referred to as *pediplains*. They are considered to be produced by

(1) Running Water. Running water in the form of permanent and intermittent streams, along with sheet flow of water, gullying, mass-wasting and possibly deflation by wind, have excavated most of the valleys of the earth (see *Rivers; Valley Evolution*). Hydraulic action, the sweeping away of loose material by moving water, is the process by which streams acquire a load of debris. This is transported by the rolling and pushing process called "traction," the bounding or leaping process known as "saltation," the carrying process called

FIG. 4. Constructed slope profiles that characterize the widening of valleys and changes in slopes; left, "Penckian" parallel retreat of slopes and pedimentation; right, "Davisian" cycle from youth to old age (modified after C. D. Holmes, 1955).

"suspension" for particles and "solution" for ions, and the minor process of "flotation." Approximately one-third of all the rainfall on the earth is carried to the sea by streams and continues to produce the features of erosion and deposition characteristic of valleys and of some underground stream channels.

of the dissolved load of groundwater enters into streams and is carried to the oceans, which have become salty by a vast and prolonged distillation process (see pr Vol. VI: *Groundwater*; *Hydrology*; *Pedology*).

(3) Waves and Currents. Waves and currents of lakes and oceans erode shores by hydraulic action, abrade and corrode rock materials, and carry away sediment by the same processes enumerated for running water (see *Beach Erosion* and *Littoral Processes—Intro.*). Just as a stream during a single flood may do more erosive work than for months and years at low-water, so wind-induced storm waves and tsunamis induced by earthquakes, volcanic eruptions or landslides accomplish the major part of marine erosion.

Shore currents and small waves and breakers abrade rock debris nearly continuously. Tidal cur-

TABLE 1. AGENTS AND PROCESSES OF EROSION

Agents Involved	Processes by Which Loosened Material is Acquired	Processes of Transport of Material
Running water (streams, both surface and underground; sheet flow of water.)	Hydraulic action	Traction, saltation, suspension, solution, flotation
Groundwater (not including underground streams)	Leaching, corrosion	Solution
Waves, currents, tides	Hydraulic action	Traction, saltation, suspension, solution, flotation
Wind	Abrasion, deflation	Traction, saltation, suspension
Glaciers	Scouring, plucking, sapping	Traction, suspension
Gravity	Mass-wasting (flowage, landslide, subsidence)	Traction, suspension

(2) Groundwater. Groundwater is nearly all supplied by precipitation. Probably the volume of fresh groundwater is more than ten times the average annual precipitation on land. Of the precipitation as water and snow a certain proportion soaks into the ground and comes out later in seeps and springs to contribute to lakes and streams. Because underground streams are not considered here, groundwater can be said to move slowly, to erode only by corrosion or solution, and to transport its load of mineral matter by solution. Groundwater with a high content of mineral matter, such as calcium bicarbonate, is commonly referred to as "hard" water, and is usually softened for domestic use. The growth of sinks in karst landscapes and the deposit of stalactites and stalagmites in caves attest to the corrosive action of groundwater. Some

rents are of little significance as agents of erosion, even in the Bay of Fundy, where they act chiefly as agents of deposition. Marine erosion is formidable but not as extensive as stream erosion. It seems unlikely that marine erosion could ever erode away an entire continent, because of the muting of the waves over shallow water, and because of up-building of the land mass by diastrophism and vulcanism.

(4) Wind. Wind carries rock and organic debris by traction, saltation and suspension. Meteorologists report that each raindrop forms around a nucleus which may be a clay particle or salt crystal blown from great distances. It is quite possible that each square mile of land contains particles of matter from every other square mile of land of the earth's surface, because of wind erosion and deposition over thousands of years. Wind work has deflated large and small desert basins by lifting out tons of fine material and carrying it completely out of the basins. Vast extents of desert pavement, sand dunes, and deposits of loess and volcanic ash testify to the work of wind.

Violent wind storms accomplish a major part of wind erosion. Students of deserts emphasize, however, the primary importance of running water in shaping land forms developed on bedrock in arid regions. Wind erosion does account for polishing, pitting, faceting and grooving of rock surfaces (see *Deserts*; *Sand Dunes*; *Eolian Transport*).

(5) Glaciers. Continental and mountain glaciers of the Pleistocene, more than 10,000 years ago, were widespread to the extent of at least 6 million square miles more than today. At present, the continental glaciers of Greenland (about 800,000 square miles) and Antarctica (5 million square miles) and the mountain glaciers continue to erode land surfaces. Some spectacular features of the Alps, Rocky Mountains, Andes and Himalaya mountains were produced by glacial erosion. Glacial horns, cirques, serrate ridges, striated roches moutonnées, glacially plucked or quarried cliffs, U-shaped valleys or glacial troughs and fiords, and hanging valleys are examples of such features. Despite the brittleness of ice in hand specimen, plasticity of ice under pressure in mountain glaciers permits them to flow slowly down their valleys. Continental glaciers expand like huge blobs of honey or tar oozing under their own weight. The currents of ice in glaciers acquire a load of rock material by scouring and plucking, and by means of these rock tools abrade and gouge bare rock surfaces over which they pass. Debris suffers attrition as it is transported by traction and suspension in the glacial ice. Large areas of Canada are occupied by ice-scoured plains on granitic bedrock. The basins of the Great Lakes of North America are thought to have been largely excavated by glacial erosion (see *Great Lakes*).

(6) Gravity. The movement of rock and organic materials under the force of gravity, as in landslides, avalanches, solifluction, mudflows, and creep is called *mass-wasting* (q.v.). By the process of creep, large blocks of rock may move down-slope from the base of a rock cliff over a period of centuries. In landslides, enormous volumes of rock debris may slide down thousands of feet into a valley, and even splash part way up the opposite slope, all in a matter of minutes. Solifluction, or the flow of loose soil-like material, is most active in regions of permafrost. Thawed, wet rock waste flows slowly downslope. Patterned ground of cold regions and gilgai topography on black clay soils of warm regions are produced by local cyclical movement of material during mass-wasting.

Some of the agricultural and industrial activities of man have so exposed the soil and geologic materials that erosion has been accelerated. During a single storm, the direct impact of raindrops on unconsolidated rock materials moves tons of debris a few inches up into the air and downslope. Sheet erosion and gully extension can rapidly strip a hillside of soil.

Although erosion has impoverished some areas of the earth by removing fertile soil and making topography less favorable for cultivation, erosion does supply fertile soil to other areas, such as the Nile Valley, and uncovers fertile geologic materials in other areas. Many coal beds and other valuable geologic deposits are accessible to men because erosion has uncovered them.

FRANCIS D. HOLE

References

Davis, W. M., 1930, "Rock floors in arid and in humid climates," *J. Geol.*, **38**, 1–27 and 136–158.

Engeln, O. D. von, 1942, "Geomorphology," New York, The Macmillan Co., 655pp.

Holmes, C. D., 1955, "Geomorphic development in humid and arid regions," *Am. J. Sci.*, **253**, 377–390.

King, L. C., 1953, "Canons of landscape evolution," *Bull. Geol. Soc. Am.*, **64**, 721–752.

Longwell, C. R., Knopf, A., and Flint, R. F., 1941, "Outlines of Physical Geology," Second ed., New York, John Wiley & Sons, 381pp.

Penck, Walther, 1953, "Morphological Analysis of Land Forms, A Contribution to Physical Geology," translated by Czech and Boswell, London, The Macmillan Co., 429pp.

Cross-references: *Abrasion*; *Anthropogenic Influences in Geomorphology*; *Avalanche*; *Base Level*; *Beach Erosion*; *Cirque*; *Corrosion*; *Degradation*; *Denudation*; *Deserts and Desert Landforms*; *Drainage Patterns*; *Eolian Transport*; *Glacial Geology*; *Glacial Scour*; *Great Lakes (North America)*; *Gully Erosion*; *Karst*; *Landslide*; *Littoral Processes*; *Mass Movement*; *Mass Wasting*; *Monadnock*; *Patterned Ground*; *Pediment*; *Pediplanation*; *Peneplain*; *Permafrost*; *Quaternary Period*; *Rivers*; *Roche Moutonée*; *Sand Dune*; *Sediment Transport*; *Sheet Erosion*; *Sink, Sinkhole*; *Slopes*; *Soil Creep*; *Solifluction*; *Valley Evolution*; *Valley (Mountain) Glacier*; *Weathering*; *Youth-Maturity-Old Age*. Vol. 1: *Ocean Currents*; *Ocean Waves*; *Submarine Canyons*; *Tides*; *Tsunami*. Vol. II: *Arid Climate*; *Middle Latitude Climate*. Vol. V: *Diastrophism*; *Folding*; *Gravity*; *Orogenesis*; *Volcanoes and Volcanology*. pr Vol. VI: *Glaciers*; *Groundwater*; *Hydrology*; *Pedology*.

EROSION SURFACE—See PLANATION SURFACE: *also* **BIOLOGICAL EROSION OF LIMESTONE COASTS: LIMESTONE COASTAL WEATHERING**

ERRATIC BLOCK

Erratic blocks, or simply erratics, were first so designated by de la Beche in 1819 (see 1830) to describe anomalous rocks and boulders that did

FIG. 1. Giant erratic of Precambrian limestone, known as the "White Horse" in the Permian tillites of Irwin Basin, Western Australia. (Photo: Rhodes W. Fairbridge.)

not belong to the immediate countryside and had evidently been transported there by some natural means (in view of their almost random distribution and, in some cases, giant size, 10–100 tons).

The term *exotic block* implies also transportation from some distant source, but by convention, this expression is reserved for tectonic transportation, by nappes, gravitational slide tectonics, etc., while "erratics" are taken to be exclusively glacial. In the early part of the last century, it was assumed that ice rafting would account for the erratics (Lyell's *Drift Theory*, q.v.), for today ice-rafted boulders are commonly observed being moved by icebergs, ice islands, ice floes both in polar oceans and, during the thaw, down rivers in subpolar

latitudes (theories of de Saussure and Von Buch). The erratics of northwestern Europe were thus, at first, often attributed to the universal flood and were called "drift erratics." Their true nature was proposed by Playfair (1802) and conclusively demonstrated by Agassiz (1840). Only later in the century, however, was it universally agreed that they had been distributed by glacial ice.

Some rock types are easily identified and can be positively traced to unique source areas. In this way, transport distances of 500–1200 km are established. Such examples are referred to as "*indicator boulders*" (q.v.).

The surface of the erratic is usually marked by intensive striation in multiple directions since blocks near the base of the ice are constantly turned over and over, as well as subjected to abrasion.

RHODES W. FAIRBRIDGE

References

Agassiz., L. J., 1840, "Études sur les glaciers Neuchâtel (translated in part in, "A Source Book in Geology," p.332, New York, McGraw-Hill Book Co., 1939).

Charlesworth, J. K., 1957, "The Quaternary Era," London, Arnold Ltd., 2 vols.

De la Beche, H. T., 1830, "Sketch of a Classification of the European Rocks," in "Geological Notes," p.XXXV, London.

Flint, R. F., 1957, "Glacial and Pleistocene Geology," New York, John Wiley & Sons, 553pp.

North, F. J., 1943, "Centenary of the Glacial Theory," *Proc. Geol. Assoc.*, **54**, 1–28.

FIG. 2. Ice-rafted erratic of Precambrian granite in Permian sandstones, St. George Range, Kimberley Div., Western Australia, at latitude 18°S. (Photo: Rhodes W. Fairbridge)

Playfair, J., 1802, "Illustrations of the Huttonian Theory of the Earth," Edinburgh (University of Illinois Press, 1956 reprint, 528pp.)

Von Zittel, K. A., 1901, "History of geology and Palaeontology, London, W. Scott, 562pp. (translated by M. M. Ogilvie-Gordon).

Cross-references: *Abrasion*; *Drift, Glacial*: *Drift Theory*; *Indicator Boulder*; *Perched Block*; *Striae*.

ESCARPMENT, SCARP

An escarpment or "scarp" is defined as a cliff or steep rock face of great length. Two general types are recognized—structural and erosional escarpments.

Structural Escarpments

Fault escarpments are a direct product of fault displacement, and *fault-line escarpments* are formed by differential rate of weathering of harder and softer rocks on either side of the fault trace. An example is the Balcones escarpment of Texas (Fenneman, 1931, p. 51, and Fig. 4A 10). The abbreviated form "scarp" is sometimes reserved for the structural features, e.g., fault scarp or fault-line scarp (Stamp, 1961).

Erosional Escarpments

Erosional escarpments may be formed along sea or lake shores because of wave erosion (sea cliffs) or laterally along streams by back-wasting of valley walls. Wherever tributaries are lacking, escarpments may closely parallel streams. Where lateral tributaries are involved, mass-wasting of valley sides of the tributaries as well as those of the major stream may produce escarpments that do not retain a parallel relationship but may indeed be asymmetrical in places, insofar as the trunk or main stream is concerned. A series of tributaries on one side of a trunk stream (Fenneman, 1931, Fig. 3B) or a series of parallel streams flowing into the sea provide a concomitant series of valley sides which may be back-wasted to the point where all of them meet and are destroyed more or less completely. The divides provide the loci of buttes, and in the head area, spurs and reentrants form arcuate or sinuous escarpments parallel with the trunk stream or strandline (Fenneman, 1931, Fig. 3A). Escarpments of this type occur abundantly in the Colorado Plateau area (Fenneman, 1931, p. 275–276). The Pine Ridge Escarpment in Nebraska and South Dakota (Fenneman, 1931, p. 6, Fig. 2 and p. 8, Fig. 3) is an example of an escarpment paralleling a river valley.

The Boston Mountain and Eureka Springs escarpments, Arkansas (Fenneman, 1938, p. 655–656; Fig. 187, p. 658 and p. 653–654) are examples of an irregular or sinuous escarpment formed as in Fig. 1.

The term *"scarped plain"* has been applied to those parts of the Great Plains (in Kansas), which are divided by long, sinuous escarpments (Moore, 1918). In *cuestas* (q.v.) and related homoclinal ridges, a *"scarp slope"* is distinguished from a "dip slope." A cuesta is a special form of escarpment, transitional to "hogback." *Waterfalls* (q.v.) often coincide with escarpments or with reentrants therefrom. In glaciated mountain country, hanging valleys terminate in escarpments with waterfalls.

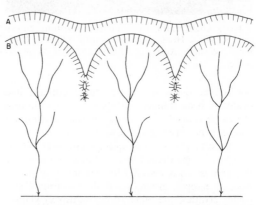

FIG. 1. Erosional escarpments formed by lateral erosion of valley walls producing escarpments A (mature) and B (submature) parallel with trunk stream or strandline. Escarpments formed in this manner tend to be sinuous and of very great length. The Eureka Springs Escarpment of northern Arkansas (Fenneman, 1938, pp. 653–654) is of this type.

Sea cliffs, ancient or modern, are not usually classified with erosional escarpments related to fluvial processes and the geomorphic characteristics of each are markedly different. Notably the sea cliffs terminate *downward* along a fixed plane (mean sea level), while subaerial escarpments—at least in flat-lying rocks—terminate *upward* in a more or less even surface (Whitaker, 1867). This criterion may be useful in the recognition of "fossil" cliffs. Stream beds tend to terminate at present-day cliff-lines, whereas they often originate along scarplines. Traces of former clifflines are thus often associated with polycyclic drainage systems.

JAMES H. QUINN

References

Fenneman, N. M., 1931, "Physiography of Western United States," New York, McGraw-Hill Book Co., 534pp.

Fenneman, N. M., 1938, "Physiography of Eastern United States," New York, McGraw-Hill Book Co., 714pp.

Moore, R. C., 1918, State Geological Survey of Kansas, *Bull. 4.*

Stamp, L. D., (editor), 1961, "A Glossary of Geographical Terms," London, Longmans, Green & Co., 539pp.

Whitaker, W., 1867, "Subaerial denudation," *Geol. Mag.*, **4**, 447–483.

Cross-references: *Cuesta; Fault Scarp; Hanging Valley; Hogback; Mass Wasting; Mesa and Butte; Strandline; Waterfalls; Weathering.*

ESKER

An esker is a sinuous low ridge composed of sand and gravel which formed by deposition from meltwaters running through a channelway beneath glacial ice. Eskers vary in height from several feet to over 100 feet and vary in length from hundreds of feet up to many miles (see Fig. 1). The course of many eskers is similar to that of a stream, being at times straight and at times curving; tributaries are not uncommon. Materials composing these features are water-laid sands and gravels with cross lamination persistently in one direction indicating the downstream flow. One theory holds that eskers form in tunnels beneath the glacier; a second attributes them to seasonal deposition both in a tunnel and as an associated delta. Because eskers rise above the general land surface and contain moderately well-sorted materials, they are frequently used as a source of construction materials. Large areas of eskers are to be found in Canada and in the Fennoscandian countries (see *Glacial Deposits* and *Kame*).

The term "esker" is of Irish (Gaelic) origin and sometimes, in the older literature, spelled "eskir," "eskar," "escar," "eiscir." Page (1865) defines it thus: "The name given in Ireland to the elongated and often flat-topped mounds of postglacial gravel which occur abundantly in the great river-valleys of that country." Cotton (1942), however, says: "Most of the 'eskers' of Ireland are not true eskers in the technical sense;" and Wooldridge and Morgan (1937) say that eskers are "comparable but not identical with Swedish *osar*." The implied distinction (corresponding to different "theories," mentioned above) is not really justified, since there seems to be every transition from the ice tunnel to the lake delta (see detailed discussion and references in Flint, 1957).

Lewis (1949) has reviewed the problem of esker formation as follows:

"The best formed are flat topped and steep sided, and they may exhibit contortion, faulting and other disturbances which can well be attributed to the presence of ice during their formation. The nature of the bedding clearly indicates that the materials were laid down in water and their association with glacial deposits suggests that they were formed by melt water streams emerging from glaciers or ice sheets. They cross the country, continuing uphill and downhill over the minor features of the landscape. This latter characteristic favors Hummel's (1874) explanation which regards them to be the casts of sub-glacial streams. This raised the question as to why sediments should be deposited in such places where one would have expected the streams to have flowed swiftly under hydrostatic pressure and so to have been fully capable of clearing out their channels. Also the frequently claimed perfection in the form of the cross section hardly suggested that they had been formed under moving ice. Furthermore the Moray Firth and other eskers subdivide and rejoin just like the distributary pattern of a glacial stream well laden with glacial outwash. This led me to follow Wright (1937) in favoring Shaler's suggestion (1884) that eskers originate when outwash streams end in standing water, as did the great

FIG. 1. An esker. A winding ridge of stratified or crudely stratified sand and gravel. These are commonly found associated with kames and are thought to have formed in the tunnel in or beneath the ice of a glacier. Because of their winding nature and their association with kames, they have at times been called "serpent kames."

eskers of Sweden in the waters of an expanded Baltic in Yoldia and earlier times. Where no such semipermanent bodies existed the eskers were supposed to have been deposited in lakes formed by the ice blocking the normal drainage channels. It is easy to understand why an esker formed in such a manner would remain in an excellent state of preservation after the lake waters had disappeared."

"Flint (1928), in an admirable summary of the different views on esker formation favors their sub-glacial origin. Even when referring to those formed where lakes lapped against the retreating ice front he follows de Geer in suggesting that the narrow parts of eskers were formed in the sub-glacial tunnels leading to the lakes."

"Thus recent authorities on the subject of eskers vary in their emphasis, if not in their actual interpretation, from Wright, who advocates the theory of their origin in lakes, to Flint who considers that this only accounts for what is really a variant of an esker rather than the true form. Whilst Flint is probably very much nearer the truth than Wright, rival theories continue to claim supporters because no one yet seems to have described an esker in process of formation."

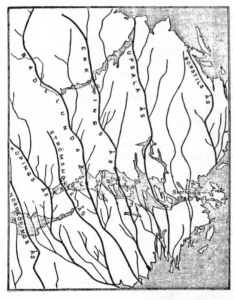

FIG. 2. Early sketch map of the eskers (osar) in east-central Sweden, after A. Erdmann, dating from 1868. Width of map: 200 km. (A modern detailed color-printed map was issued by the Geological Survey of Sweden in 1947.)

Lewis (*op. cit.*) went on to describe his experience of discovering a freshly forming esker in the Rondane district of eastern Norway (Mannerfelt, 1945; Strøm, 1945) that had undoubtedly formed under stagnant, melting ice. According to Mannerfelt, some of the eskers formed here during the Scandinavian deglaciation were even due to extra-glacial streams plunging down the steep valley sides and entering tunnels melted under the glacier. Ice collapse in tunnels under stagnant ice can cause

some channels to clog with sediment and then branch into new ones. Some of the higher eskers are pitted with kettle holes from the melting of dead ice blocks.

The freshly formed esker described by Lewis was at the end of Böverbreen where the contemporary valley glacier terminates on a gentle slope covered with solifluction debris. The flat-topped esker emerging from the glacier front is in striking contrast to the latter. Trenching showed the horizontal top-set deposits over steeply dipping foresets (up to 35°). Blocks of ice on the top marked the sites of kettles in all stages of development. The new esker exposed was only 120 feet in length, but with a high ablation rate that season it may have taken only six weeks to emerge. The deposits had evidently accumulated in standing water, but not that of a lake—rather a ponding of meltwater under the ice.

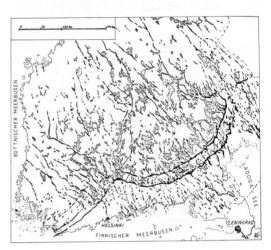

FIG. 3. Map of southern Finland (after Sauramo), showing both radial and ice-margin eskers (in solid black), in relation to the postglacial lakes (horizontal shading). The two principal ice-margin belts correspond to the Salpausselkä pauses which mark the beginning of the Holocene epoch about 10,500 years B.P.

As the ice retreated, this ponded water was seen escaping from either side of the emerging esker. Some lateral collapse and slumping in the esker deposits accompanies the release of the ice walls.

A detailed study of the stratigraphy of eskers in the Stockholm area by Eriksson (1960) has revealed many important details. The eskers (*ose*, pl. *osar*; or *ås, åsar* in Swedish) here run from NNW to SSE. As the partly stagnant ice melted out there was a progressive shift of ice movement from NNW to N to NNE to NE (youngest) with accompanying striations. In the north there is a transition from till to fluvioglacial material. The meltwater was clearly coming down in part from the continental ice surface so that eskers are not limited to valleys but may be found passing over hills and steep

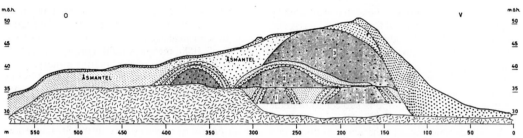

Fig. 4. Composition of a multiple esker ridge near Stockholm (Eriksson, 1960). Three years' accumulation is represented (1, 2, 3). The cores (vertical lines) are coarse gravels and boulders (summers), covered by finer debris (winters). The whole feature is blanketed by secondary slump ("Asmantel") and soil material.

slopes. Some eskers show traces of shore lines corresponding to the high eustatic stands of the mid-Holocene (Littorina beaches), now isostatically uplifted to as much as 50 meters above mean sea level. The pebbles of the higher shore lines are marked by manganese/iron crusts (curiously comparable to *Desert Varnish*, q.v.).

The mean grain size of esker sediments increases progressively as one goes upstream. The granulometric study of esker sediments by the "point inventory method" of Hörner (1947) can be used for pebbles over 40 mm. Below this, U.S. standard sieves are satisfactory. Sorting varies greatly, from very good to very poor. Wave-washed material from the old beaches is restratified.

Near their southern (coastal) ends the eskers are multiple and complex (Fig. 4). Each esker has a core of coarse gravel and boulders (a "summer bed" in the sense of von Post) with a cover of finer materials ("winter bed"), which strongly suggests rapid accumulation for any one sector, spanning only 2–3 years. Eriksson's study proves clearly that in the Stockholm area the lower (earlier) eskers were subglacial, while the uppermost (younger) parts were ice marginal (de Geer's theory, first stated in 1897; see de Geer, 1940). The age of these eskers is about 970 B.P., the annual recession rate of the ice margin at that time being 250–300 m/yr.

Analysis of the provenance of esker pebbles and boulders is sometimes possible by petrographic study, especially if long transport has not been involved. Thus, in southern Finland, the material is found to have come distances of 5–100 km (Matisto, 1961). This study shows that, as in parts of Sweden too, the early ice movements during glacial maxima reflected the general ice sheet dynamics, while in the later thinning stages, the local basement topography notably modified the ice flow directions.

VINCENT C. SHEPPS
RHODES W. FAIRBRIDGE

References

Cotton, C. A., 1942, "Geomorphology: An Introduction

to the Study of Landforms," Christchurch, Whitcombe & Tombs, 505pp.

De Geer, G. J., 1940, "Geochronologia Suecica Priniciples," Stockholm, Almqvist, 2 vols.

Embleton, C. and King, C. A. M., 1968, "Glacial and Periglacial Geomorphology," London, E. Arnold Ltd., 608pp.

Eriksson, K. G., 1960, "Studier över Stockholmsasen vid Halmsjön," *Geol. Foren. Stockholm Forh.*, **82**, 43–125.

Flint, R. F., 1928, "Eskers and crevasse fillings," *Am. J. Sci.*, Ser. 5, **15**, 410–416.

Flint, R. F., 1957, "Glacial and Pleistocene Geology," New York, John Wiley & Sons, 553pp.

Hörner, N. G., 1947, "Granulometrical aspects of some Late-Glacial deposits of central Sweden," Bruxelles, *Sess. extraord. Soc. Belges. Géol. Sept. 1946.*

*Lewis, W. V., 1949, "An esker in process of formation: Böverbreen, Jotunheimen, 1947," *J. Glaciol.*, **1**(6), 314–319.

Mannerfelt, C. M., 1945, "Några glacialmorphologiska Formelement," *Geogr. Annal.*, **27**, 1–239 (with English summary).

Matisto, A., 1961, "On the relation between the stones of the eskers and the local bedrock in the area northwest of Tampere, southwestern Finland," *Bull. Comm. Geol. Finlande*, **193**, 53pp.

Page, D., 1865, "Handbook of Geology," Edinburgh, W. Blackwood & Sons.

Strøm, K. M., 1945, "Geomorphology of the Rondane area," *Norsk Geol. Tidsskr.*, **25**, 360–375.

Wooldridge, S. W., and Morgan, R. S., 1937, "Outlines of Geomorphology," London, Longmans, Green and Co., 445pp.

* Additional bibliographic references may be found in this work.

Cross-references: *Desert Varnish*; *Fluvioglacial Processes*; *Glacial Deposits*; *Glacial Geology*; *Glacial Lakes*; *Holocene*; *Kame*; *Kettle*; *Solifluction*; *Stagnant Ice Melting*. pr Vol. VI: *Foreset Beds*; *Ice Sheet*.

ESTUARY

The term estuary comes from the Latin *aestus*, the tide, and *aesto*, boil, from the boiling effect of the rising tide at river mouths where the river and ocean waters meet. The estuary is usually defined as that part of the lower river course that is affected by the mixing of salt water and fresh. The tidal rise and fall may extend considerably farther upstream; the Oxford English Dictionary gives this tidal limit definition as "rare in modern usage." The upper limit of watermixing varies with the state of the tide, the freshwater discharge and the season of the year, so that the brackish biotope is subject to extreme variations.

A river debouching into the sea may do so in a number of ways or associations, including:

(a) *Direct*, as with a "youthful" type stream on a steep coast, there being no delta and no salt-water encroachment;

(b) *Delta-building*, where the sediment discharge exceeds the net wave energy available for sediment dispersal (see *Delta Dynamics*);

(c) *Lagoonal*, the river emptying (often with a delta) into an embayment or lagoon that is almost cut off from the ocean by barrier islands and bars (see *Lagoon*);

(d) *Estuarine*, where the river bed is "over-deepened," i.e., it lies well below mean sea level and, at least from time to time, there is encroachment of seawater upstream.

Classification of Estuaries

Basically there are two fundamentally different types of estuary unrelated to dimensions or genesis, i.e., applicable to estuaries of all sizes and histories:

(a) *Funnel-shaped estuaries*, completely open to the ocean;

(b) *Barred estuaries*, in some way partially cut off from the ocean, by rock promontories, rock thresholds, sand bars or spits, barrier islands, mudbanks or deltaic accumulation; there is often a transition into a *coastal lagoon* (q.v.).

The first category is hydrologically more related to the ocean, with strong tidal effects, oceanic waves and swell, relatively high salinity and relatively great depths; sediment tends to be moved *inward* under wave action. Examples range from the Bay of Fundy to some "*firths*" of Scotland and the Wash of England. Many rias and fjords are of this open type. Hard-rock coasts do not readily furnish the sand and shingle necessary to form bay mouth bars.

The second category is hydrologically directed more toward the river, with strong mixing, but with reduced tidal effects; oceanic wave action is often negligible, and sediment tends to move *downstream* from the river. Periodically, in semiarid regions the sand bar may be totally closed and the estuary converted temporarily into a barred basin, marked by stagnation, low oxygen, H_2S production at the bottom and the formation of pyrite concretions in the sediments (Baas Becking and Moore, 1959).

A subdivision of estuaries was suggested by Dionne (1963; with additional proposals by Brochu) on the basis of studies of the St. Lawrence estuary in Canada—probably the world's largest:

(a) *Marine or lower estuary* in the St. Lawrence; this involves 257 km up to the mouth of the Saguenay. Brochu suggested that in the major estuaries a width of 1000 meters would correspond rather generally to the limit of the "marine estuary."

(b) *Middle estuary* in the St. Lawrence, 195 km from the Saguenay up to the eastern tip of Ile d'Orleans (Montreal). This stretch is affected by strong mixing of salt and fresh water.

(c) *Fluvial or upper estuary* in the St. Lawrence, 134 km from Ile d'Orleans to the outlet of Lake St. Peter, the limit of tidal movement; this stretch is essentially fresh, i.e., fluvial, but subject to tidal blocking. (According to the dictionary definition, noted in the introduction, some authorities would not classify this "fluvial" sector as estuarine at all, although the tidal influence clearly differentiates it from a strictly fluvial regime.)

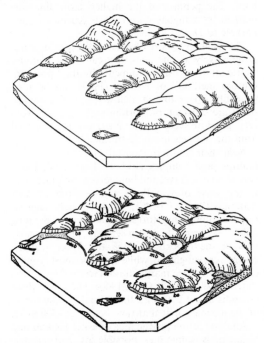

Fig. 1. Two stages in the evolution of an estuarine situation (Johnson, 1919). Above: a drowned coast showing initial cliffing of headlands. Below: a more evolved coast (?softer materials) showing the development of beaches, bars, spits and so on.

Morphogenesis of Estuaries

The reason for the "overdeepening" of river mouths that transforms them into estuaries usually depends on several factors, which vary in relative importance according to *coastal stability*, *tectonics*, *latitude* (*climatic regime*), *Quaternary history*, *tidal characteristics* and so on. Almost always, the most important single factor is the postglacial rise of sealevel of somewhat over 100 meters (see *Eustasy*;

Terraces—Thalassostatic). Traces of the course of the ice-age river are usually to be found across the continental shelf, sometimes part of an extensive "drowned" drainage network, as on the *Sunda Shelf* (q.v., Vol. I) and *Sahul Shelf* (q.v., Vol. I). The seaward end of such drowned channels often passes on the continental slope into a *submarine canyon* (q.v., Vol. I).

Regardless of whether the overdeepening of the river mouth is primarily due to eustatic rise of sea level or tectonic subsidence, it is said to be a *drowned valley* (q.v.). If the drowning affects a normal dendritic river pattern that has incised a mature upwarped hinterland, the result is a deep, steep-sided estuary, known as a *ria* (q.v.).

Where a similar drowned landscape has previously been glaciated into deep ice-scoured troughs, the estuary is even deeper and even steeper sided, and constitutes a *fjord* (q.v.), a Norwegian name. In regions where the postglacial isostatic upwarp has been less important than the eustatic rise, as in southwestern Sweden, the drowning is more complete and includes the development of skerries and coastwise channels, as well as the estuaries; in this case they are called *fjärds* (q.v.) a special technical use of the Swedish name for fjord.

A drowned coast analogous to that of fjärds, with coastwise channels as well as radial estuaries, but in an unglaciated region, is the "dalmatian type," from the type area in Dalmatia, Yugoslavia (Baulig, 1930).

Transitional types of estuary are known between the strictly glacial fjord and fjärd, and the structurally controlled. Many of the major estuaries in England (Humber, Wash, Mersey, Dee) were partly modeled by continental ice, but lack the steep sides and deep scouring of the classic fjords (Gregory, 1913; Gresswell, 1964).

Examples are known of late Pleistocene and early Holocene estuaries which have now become isolated during the postglacial upwarping. These are particularly well known in the St. Lawrence and Ottawa River valleys (Terasmae, 1965). In southern Sweden they have also been examined in some detail; Bergdahl (1963) has recently published a series of studies on the Närke plain where estuarine clays from the Baltic progressively overlap closely spaced ridges of retreatal moraines, each winter season being marked by another ridge, at 170–280 meter intervals. Estuarine clays in the "firths" of Scotland, known as the "carse clays," have also been subjected to recent surveys. Postglacial estuarine clays began to form in the Midland Valley as the ice withdrew and were then overlain by coastal peats between 9500 B.P. and 8000 B.P. during isostatic uplift; eustatic rise then outstripped the latter and deposition of estuarine carse clays took place. About 5500 B.P. the eustatic rise had reached its maximum, but gentle isostatic uplift continued, and the peat formation began again (Sissons and Smith, 1965).

Apart from the structural aspects of estuary morphogenesis (the degree of tectonic warping) and its interaction with eustasy, there are dynamic aspects that control sedimentation and may eventually modify the form of the estuary quite fundamentally. In this way the progressive building of *bay-mouth bars* by longshore drift may progressively isolate the lower estuary until it is largely converted into a lagoon. Progressive and vigorous longshore drift has achieved the almost complete siltation of many estuaries in Britain since Roman times (e.g., Romney Marsh and Dungeness, see Ward, 1922; Steers, 1964). Drift is not always in one direction, especially in the mid-latitude belts of variable winds, so that usually there are two advancing spits that eventually merge or overlap (Kidson, 1963).

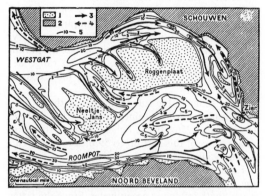

Fig. 2. Part of the Scheldt estuary in the Netherlands (Van Veen, 1950; from Guilcher, 1958). Explanation: (1) sandbanks and mudflats; (2) land (protected by dikes); (3) scour channels formed by the incoming (flood) tide; (4) scour channels formed by the outgoing (ebb) tide; (5) bathymetric contours in meters below mean low spring tide. Note the −55 meter deep scour on the extreme right (Zieriksee Light).

Another dynamic process, but restricted to the warm tropics, is the growth of coral reefs which may eventually convert an open estuary into an effectively barred one. In areas of high precipitation, the freshwater and muddy suspension prevents final closing of the barrier, but it frequently becomes so narrow that the passage may be a serious navigational hazard.

A quite exceptional type of estuary is that known as a *scherm* or *sherm*, commonly seen only along the coasts of the Red Sea in Saudi Arabia and the Sudan. Some writers have proposed a tectonic origin for them (Schmidt, 1923; Rathjens and Von Wissmann, 1933). It seems rather to the present writer that they are former stream channels that dissected the coastline under heavier rainfall conditions at some stage of lower sea level, but with the postglacial eustatic rise there was drowning accompanied by upgrowth of fringing coral reefs, narrowing the mouths of the estuaries and sometimes closing them completely;

reduced stream discharge under present-day arid conditions renders such estuaries largely inactive. Somewhat analogous cases are known in the semi-arid part of northwestern Australia.

Bathymetry and Currents

The bedrock floor near the mouth of estuaries may generally be encountered at about 30 meters depth, as shown by considerable numbers of engineering bores and sub-bottom echo sounding. Rarely, where there is vigorous deltaic subsidence or continental flexure tectonics, the late Pleistocene floor may exceed 100 meters in depth; in this case it is generally buried by a thick accumulation of gravels, sands and silts.

Strong tidal scour is a feature of estuaries, especially where the regional tidal range is great. Where the mouth of the estuary is a wide bay and the feature is funnel shaped, the amplitude of the tide tends to increase toward the head of the estuary, as in the *Bay of Fundy* (see Vol. I). Where the mouth of the estuary is constricted, the tidal range decreases as one goes upstream, as in most coastal *lagoons*.

Tidal scour in the soft sediments of the estuary floor leads to a highly uneven submarine thalweg (Robinson, 1956). In the Scheldt estuary there are tidal scours of this sort up to 59 meters deep (Van Veen, 1950).

From the hydrologic point of view the estuary is the most important site of mixing of fresh river waters with inflowing ocean water. Since the latter is salty and dense, it tends to force itself under the outflowing stream as a "salt-water wedge," and turbulence only gradually brings about mixing. Details of this hydrology and the associated current may be found in pr Vol. VI, "*Estuarine Hydrology*."

Sedimentation

Sediment is carried downstream as a bed load of gravel, sand or silt, but on reaching the low-gradient/low-velocity reaches of an estuary, it tends to be deposited as sandbanks and bars. Clays brought down in colloidal form are flocculated on reaching the salt water which acts as an electrolyte. Clays are thus mixed with the silts and sands in mudbanks. In the back bays, the clayey muds become dominant and salt marsh vegetation becomes important at high-tide level; peat deposits are often formed, some Holocene estuarine peats exceeding 5–10 meters in thickness.

According to studies by Francis-Boeuf (1947) the electrolytic flocculation of the clays in the estuaries of western France is effective in coagulating clay particles but does not bring about instant deposition. Further investigations by Berthois (1954) and others suggest that rising salinity does help, and rising temperatures also play a role, especially at low tide in the summer (see *Estuarine Sedimentation*, pr Vol. VI). When the large clay floccules come to rest,

especially when exposed intertidally, they become extraordinarily sticky (as every investigator observes to his dismay!), so that with the rising tide the particles do not readily become dislodged. This intertidal sedimentation (less effective below low-tide level) results in the enlargement of tide flats but permits the maintenance of tide channels in which 2–3 knot currents are often observed. Historical records show that some channels remain in perfect equilibrium for several centuries at least. As the channel banks become oversteepened, there is minor scouring, and *slumping* occurs from time to time during the ebb tide period.

Short-term changes in estuarine sedimentation have been closely studied by the Hydraulics Research Station in Britain. Undisturbed cores collected from the bed load and suspended load in the Lune estuary show that at flood tide silt is brought in to be deposited on the mud flats, and remains there, while a fine sand (0.1–0.2 mm) is carried away with the ebb tide (Kestner, 1961).

The shaping of estuarine and lagoonal mud-flat channel meanders has long attracted attention. Here in the mud flats is an ideal homogeneous medium that often demonstrates with remarkable elegance the operation of "random walk" within a given physical framework, having achieved something close to a steady-state equilibrium (Langbein, 1963). Both ebb and flow tides exert an erosional potential while deposition takes place at slack tide, high and low. As remarked above, the meanders have remarkable stability in terms of historical time. From studies in Chesapeake Bay it has been suggested (by Ahnert, 1960) that they may be inherited from fluvial forms dating from the time of the last major transgression; on the other hand, progressive coastal subsidence along much of the sea-board of eastern North America prompts the opinion that the meanders are in adjustment, i.e., in dynamic equilibrium with the various estuarine parameters which change very slowly along with the subsidence, apart from adjustments to minor oscillations of sea level itself. Engineering scale models for estuary modification operations attempt, in particular, to establish the time factor in equilibrium establishment (see, for example, studies of the Seine estuary: Banal, 1961). The concept, sometimes expressed, that a steady state implies a geographical stability is misleading. While the meanders may remain year after year, certain parameters (oscillation of sea level, crustal subsidence, etc.) are constantly active. Kestner (1962) attempted to establish whether an "ultimate balance" would be achieved in the Wash after dike construction and reclamation. While the net picture there since A.D. 1650 is accretion, any long-term future projection would seem hazardous.

The current patterns in the estuary control essentially the distribution of sediment. The back bays and lagoons are sites of relatively still water and permit muds to settle out aided by salt marsh vegetation. Intertidally there is an extensive development of mud flats (*slikke* in the Netherlands and the international literature). In the main channel the floor never dries out, and in any case fairly strong scouring of the sides is commonly observed. According to observations and experiments by Glangeaud (1938a and b), in a straight reach the maximum current velocity is near the surface in mid-channel, so that there are two maxima of turbulence on either side at distances from the shore approximately one-third of the channel width, and midway from the surface to the bottom. Accordingly, there is a descending current in midstream which brings coarser sediments to rest as a medial bank. Eventually channel division occurs and the process repeats in the anabranches. Characteristic channels are developed independently with the rising and falling tide. They are designated respectively as *flood channels* and *ebb channels* (Robinson, 1960).

Ripples form in the channel floor sands. Giant ripples, "megaripples" or "subaqueous dunes" tend to develop where the bottom is sandy and tidal current velocities are high, e.g., in the deltaic estuaries of the Rhine and Scheldt in the Netherlands (Van Straaten, 1950).

There has been some confusion in the past over the net motion of sediment deposited in estuaries. It was first shown by Van Straaten and others working on the Wadden (or Watten) coast of the Netherlands, North Germany (see Gripp, 1956) and Denmark (see Hansen, 1951) that the net sediment transport in these relatively open estuaries was from the sea toward the land. Other open estuaries, like the Thames and the Wash, in eastern England, show the same thing (Evans, 1965). Previously the opposite had generally been assumed (e.g., Ward, 1922, p. 16), although Murray (1861) and Sollas (1883) had questioned it long ago. Close studies, however, supported by radioactive tracer experiments, have proved conclusively that under heavy wave action, offshore sediments are stirred up and carried inshore. There is, of course, downstream transport, but much of this material is trapped in flood plains before reaching the estuary.

In contrast, the closely barred estuaries have little chance of being supplied from the ocean and the net sediment transport is clearly downstream and thus fluvial.

RHODES W. FAIRBRIDGE

References

Ahnert, F., 1960, "Estuarine meanders in the Chesapeake Bay area," *Geogr. Rev.*, **50**(3), 390–401.

Baas Becking, L. G. M., and Moore, D., 1959, "The relation between iron and organic matter in sediments," *J. Sediment. Petrol.*, **29**, 454–458.

Banal, M., 1961, "Essai d'analyse des phénomènes intervenant dans la formation d'un estuaire," *Proc.*

7th Conference Coastal Engin., Council Wave Res., The Engineering Foundation, 2 vols., 1001pp.

Baulig, H., 1930, "Le littoral Dalmate," *Ann. Géogr. (Paris)*, No. 219, 305–310.

Bergdahl, A., 1963, "Glaciofluvial estuaries on the Närke Plain. III. The ice margin in the area of Norrbyas," *Lund Studies in Geography, A. (Physical Geogr.)*, **26**, 8pp.

Berthois, L., and Barbier, M., 1954, "Recherches sur la sédimentation en Loire," *Bull. C.O.E.C.*, **6**, 387–397.

Berthois, L., and Berthois, C., 1955, "Étude de la sédimentation dans l'estuaire de la Rance," *Bull. Lab. Marit. Dinard*, **40**, 4–15; **41**, 3–18.

Dionne, J.-C., 1963, "Towards a more adequate definition of the St. Lawrence estuary," *Z. Geomorphol.*, **7**(1), 36–44.

Evans, G., 1965, "Intertidal flat sediments and their environments of deposition in the Wash," *Quart. J. Geol. Soc. London*, **121**(2), 209–241.

Francis-Boeuf, 1947, "Recherches sur le milieu fluviomarin et les dépôts d'estuaire," Thesis, Paris, *Ann. Inst. Océanogr.* (Paris), N.S. 23, 3, 149–344.

Glangeaud, L., 1938a, "Transport et sédimentation dans l'estuaire et à l'embouchure de la Gironde," *Bull. Soc. Géol. France*, **8**(5), 599–631.

Glangeaud, L., 1938b, "Études quantitatives et expérimentales sur l'érosion et le transport par les eaux courantes," *Rev. Géog. Phys. Géol. Dyn.*, **2**, 323–370.

Glangeaud, L., 1941, "Évolution morphologique et dynamique des estuaires," *Bull. Assoc. Géogr. France*, **140**, 95–103.

Gregory, J. W., 1913, "The Nature and Origin of Fjords," London, John Murray, 542pp.

Gresswell, R. K., 1964, "The origin of the Mersey and Dee estuaries," *Geol. J.*, **4**(1), 77–86.

Gripp, K., 1956, "Das Watt: Begriff, Begrenzung und fossile Vorkommen," *Senkenbergiana Lethaea*, **37**, 149–181.

Guilcher, A., 1958, "Coastal and Submarine Morphology," London, Methuen, 274pp. (translated by B. W. Sparks and R. H. W. Kneese).

Hansen, K., 1951, "Preliminary report on the sediments of the Danish Wadden Sea," *Medd. Dansk Geol. Foren.*, **12**(1).

Hoyle, J. W., and King, G. T., 1959, "Estuaries and beaches," *J. Inst. Munic. Enginrs.*, 65–79.

Johnson, D. W., 1919, "Shore Processes and Shoreline Development," New York, John Wiley & Sons, 584pp.

Kestner, F. J. T., 1961, "Short-term changes in the distribution of fine sediments in estuaries," *Proc. Inst. Civil Engrs.* (London), **19**, 185–208.

Kestner, F. J. T., 1962, "The old coastline of the Wash," *Geogr. J.*, **128**(4), 457–478.

Kidson, C., 1963, "The growth of sand and shingle spits across estuaries," *Z. Geomorphol.*, **7**(1), 1–22.

Langbein, W. B., 1963, "The hydraulic geometry of a shallow estuary," *Bull. Intern. Assoc. Sci. Hydrol.* **8**(3), 84–94.

Murray, J., 1861, "On the North Sea, with remarks on some of its firths and estuaries," *Min. Proc. Inst. Civ. Engin.*, **20**, 314–374.

Rathjens, C., and von Wissmann, H., 1933, "Morphologische Probleme im Graben des Roten Meeres," *Pet. Mitteil.*, **79**, 183–187.

Robinson, A. H. W., 1956, "The submarine morphology of certain port approach channel systems," *J. Inst. Navigation*, **9**, 20–46.

Robinson, A. H. W., 1960, "Ebb-flood channel systems in sandy bays and estuaries," *Geography,* **45**(3), 183–199.

Schmidt, W., 1923, "Die Scherms an der Rotmeerküste von el-Hedschas," *Pet. Mitteil.,* **69,** 118–121.

Sissons, J. B., and Smith, D. E., 1965, "Peat bogs in a post-glacial sea and a buried raised beach in the western part of the Carse of Stirling," *Scottish J. Geol.,* **1**(3), 247–255.

Sollas, W. J., 1883, "On the estuaries of the Severn and its tributaries; an inquiry into the nature and origin of their tidal sediment and alluvial flats," *Quart. J. Geol. Soc. London,* **39,** 611–626.

Steers, J. A., 1964, "The Coastline of England and Wales," second ed., Cambridge, The University Press, 750pp.

Terasmae, J., 1965, "Surficial geology of the Cornwall and St. Lawrence Seaway Project areas, Ontario," *Bull. Geol. Surv. Canada,* **121.**

Ting, S., 1937, "The coastal configuration of Western Scotland," *Geogr. Ann.,* **19,** 62–83.

Van Straaten, L. M. J. U., 1950, "Giant ripples in tidal channels," *Tijd. Kon. Nederl. Aard. Genoot.* (*Wadden-symposium*), 76–81.

Van Straaten, L. M. J. U., 1954, "Composition and structure of recent marine sediments in the Netherlands," *Leidse Geol. Mededel.,* **19,** 1–110.

Van Veen, J., 1950, "Eb-en vloedschaar systemen in de Nederlandse getijwateren," *Tijd. Kon. Nederl. Aard. Genoot.* (*Waddensymposium*), 42–65.

Ward, E. M., 1922, "English Coastal Evolution," London, Methuen, 262pp.

Cross-references: *Barriers* ; *Bars* ; *Coastal Lagoon Dynamics* ; *Delta Dynamics* ; *Deltaic Evolution* ; *Drowned Valley* ; *Eustasy* ; *Fjärd* ; *Fjord* ; *Holocene* ; *Lagoon* ; *Postglacial Isostatic Rebound* ; *Quaternary Period* ; *Ria* ; *Terraces—Thalassostatic.* Vol. I: *Bay of Fundy* ; *Ocean Currents* ; *Ocean Waves* ; *Sahul Shelf* ; *Subaqueous Sand Dune* ; *Submarine Canyons* ; *Sunda Shelf.* pr Vol. VI: *Estuarine Hydrology* ; *Estuarine Sedimentation* ; *Tidal Flat Geology* ; *Wadden Sea.*

ETCHED PEBBLES; CRACKED AND CRUSTED COBBLES

Pebbles, cobbles and boulders of varying composition that are found scattered on or near the land surface in semiarid or desert regions are liable to be affected by a number of curious weathering phenomena, whose properties may be useful as environmental indicators and thus helpful in paleoclimatic reconstruction.

Three distinct processes are involved:

(a) *Solution phenomena,* chemical pitting, facetting, with miniature rims, rills, *lapiés* (q.v.), etc. The appearance and process depend on the rock type, usually limestone, quartzite, granite or basalt.

(b) *Encrusting phenomena,* chemically precipitated crust, rind or patina (see *Desert Varnish*). The coating is often formed on the opposite side of the pebble to the solution features. Transitions in scale occur to a condition where the whole soil surface is encrusted (see *Duricrust* and *Induration*).

(c) *Cracking and wedging phenomena,* chemical weathering combined with insolation results in cracks both radial and circumferential, followed sometimes by crystal growth within the fractures that leads to fretting and wedging. (The role of *salt weathering or fretting* is treated separately.) Extensively indurated surfaces (duricrusts) often contain a breccia of cracked and fractured pebbles or a dismembered hard pan.

Examples

Solution weathering or faceting of pebbles and boulders has been described by Udden (1914) from the fluvial terraces of the Rio Grande, and Bryan (1929) has studied them ranging from Montana to New Mexico. They are also very commonly observed in North Africa and Australia, evidently correlating closely with mediterranean to semiarid climates where precipitation (rain) is brief and evaporation is dominant. Hume (1925) pointed out that when rain falls in the desert, the air temperature may be 10°C cooler than the rocks, and indeed the rainwater may even be 20–30°C cooler (sometimes with hail). The pH of the rainwater is generally 5.5–6.5, being saturated with CO_2, and thus readily dissolves limestone and feldspathic rocks. The water is rapidly warmed, and precipitation of a travertine ("calcrete" or "caliche") crust takes place on the lower side of the pebble; this protected side remains saturated for many hours and slowly dries out so that much of the $CaCO_3$ dissolved from the upper surface is reprecipitated on the lower surface, though some of it is carried downward into the soil profile. In high latitudes and certain mountain areas, the presence of lichens contributes to the etching of pebbles (see *Solution Pits and Pans*).

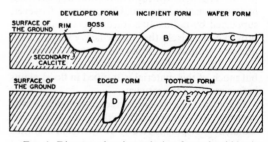

FIG. 1. Diagram showing solution-faceted pebbles in relation to the ground surface. Note the reduction of the upper part and calcite precipitation on the buried part of each pebble (Bryan, 1929).

Since crystalline rocks such as granite and basalt are rich in feldspars, the selective weathering of the latter permits a loosening of the less soluble components, which are then dispersed mechanically, leaving corroded surfaces of the parent rock. Wentworth (1925) has described the reduction of originally spheroidal boulders of basalt from Hawaii to hemispherical remnants in this manner.

Silica is essentially insoluble within the usual soil pH range (5–9), but in certain swamps and playa regions these limits are exceeded. Rotting vegetation depresses the pH, while rising concentrations of alkalies raise it. Hayes (1897) has described solution of quartz pebbles in a manner quite comparable to that of limestone pebbles.

Blackwelder (1927, 1933) has stressed the importance of insolation cracking, from temperature contrasts under day and night conditions in the desert and during brief rainstorms. He noted also the thermal effects of scrub fires. Examination of many of these fracture surfaces discloses that chemical rotting of feldspars (especially in granites) contributes notably to the thermal expansion and contraction. Furthermore, the mechanical force of crystal growth within the cracks is observed to be a third factor of great importance; the role of salts (sulfates and chlorides) in crumbling the ancient Egyptian monuments that have fallen and lain on the Nile alluvium has been studied by Blanck and Passarge (1926) and abundantly confirmed by Reiche (1950), Knetsch (1960) and Winkler (1965). Salt "fretting" (see *Salt Weathering or Fretting*) is now recognized as a major factor in desert and coastal weathering, especially in coarse-grained crystalline rocks like granites, a characteristic erosion form being *alveolar weathering* or *tafoni* (q.v.).

The disruptive effect of $CaCO_3$ (calcite) growth as soil travertine (calcrete or caliche) has been observed in sandstone gravels and boulders in Utah and Colorado by Young (1964). Examples are further modified by induration due to *desert varnish* (q.v.) of iron and manganese oxides (Fig. 2). Similar pebble

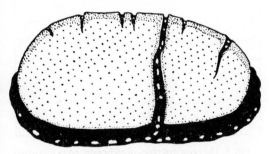

FIG. 2. Section of cobble encrusted with calcrete or caliche (black). Caliche also fills fractures. The dark rind, which is thicker on upper surface, is due to limonite-stained caliche and to iron and manganese oxides of desert varnish. Width of section is about 10 cm (Young, 1964).

splitting under the force of crystallization has been noted in the broad sheets of Pleistocene piedmont gravels ("Tehuelches") of the Argentine, but in this case sulfates in the groundwater solutions are dominant so that the cement is gypsum (Cortelezzi and Kilmurray, 1965).

Finally a type of boulder fracturing has been encountered in central Australia by Ollier (1965) which he describes as "*dirt cracking.*" The boulders are quartzites, and following the initiation of insolation cracks, particles of desert dust (largely silica) sink into the cracks, acting as progressive wedges, a purely mechanical process, in contrast to the mixed mechanical and chemical processes noted above.

RHODES W. FAIRBRIDGE

References

Blackwelder, E., 1927, "Fire as an agent in rock weathering," *J. Geol.*, **35**, 134–140.

Blackwelder, E., 1933, "The insolation hypothesis of rock weathering," *Am. J. Sci.*, **26**, 97–113.

Blanck, E., and Passarge, S., 1926, "Die chemische Verwitterung in der aegyptischen Wüste," *Hamburgische Universität, Abh. aus Gebiet Auslandskunde*, **17**, *Reihe C. Naturwissenschaften*, **6**.

Bryan, K., 1929, "Solution-faceted limestone pebbles," *Am. J. Sci.*, **18**, 193–208.

Cortelezzi, C. R., and Kilmurray, J. O., 1965, "Surface properties and epigenetic fractures of gravels from Patagonia, Argentina," *J. Sediment. Petrol.*, **35** (4), 976–980.

Hayes, C. W., 1897, "Solution of silica under atmospheric conditions," *Bull. Geol. Soc. Am.*, **8**, 213–220.

Hume, W. F., 1925, "Geology of Egypt," *Cairo, Egypt Surv. Dept. (Ministry of Finance)*, **1**, 14.

Knetsch, G., 1960, "Arid weathering with special reference to both natural and artificial walls in Egypt," *Z. Geomorphol. Suppl.*, **1**, 190–205.

Ollier, C. D., 1965, "Dirt cracking—a type of insolation weathering," *Australian J. Sci.*, **27** (8), 236–237.

Reiche, P., 1950, "A Survey of Weathering Processes and Products," Revised ed., Albuquerque, University of New Mexico Press, 95pp.

Udden, J. A., 1914, "The flattening of limestone gravel boulders by solution," *Bull. Geol. Soc. Am.*, **25**, 66–68.

Wentworth, C. K., 1925, "Chink-faceting: a new process of pebble shaping," *J. Geol.*, **33**, 260–267.

Winkler, E. M., 1965, "Weathering rates as exemplified by Cleopatra's Needle in New York City," *J. Geol. Educ.*, **13** (2), 50–52.

Young, R. G., 1964, "Fracturing of sandstone cobbles in caliche cemented terrace gravels," *J. Sediment. Petrol.*, **34** (4), 887–889.

Cross-references: *Deflation; Desert Varnish; Duricrust; Granite Landforms; Induration; Lapiés; Playa; Salt Weathering; Solution Pits and Pans; Tafoni.* Vol. II: *Evaporation; Insolation; Precipitation.* pr Vol. VI: *Caliche; pH-Eh Relations.*

ETCHPLAIN

An etchplain is a form of planation surface associated with crystalline shields and other ancient massifs which do not display tectonic relief, and developed under tropical conditions promoting rapid chemical decomposition of susceptible rocks. The concept was introduced by Wayland (1933) to account for well-developed surfaces of erosion in Uganda which he thought were *etched* into a summit peneplain of Cretaceous age in the following manner: "absence of any marked relief, a flat gradient and a seasonal climate lead to vertical rather than horizontal movements of groundwaters and the consequent rotting of all but chemically resistant rocks... to a depth of tens of feet. This zone of rotted rock, or saprolite, is largely removed by denudation if and when land elevation supervenes and the process may be repeated again and again as the country rises" (Wayland, 1933, note 376). The lower plains of Uganda were thus described as "*etched plains* and as such are indicative not of tectonic stability and quiescence but of instability and upward movement ... relatively rapid vertical movements punctuating the slow discontinuous rise" (Wayland, 1933, note 377). According to the original theory, etchplains are produced from pre-existing plains, not from a diversified topography, and alternating phases of *deep weathering* and *stripping* of the regolith materials, in response to irregular uplift of the crust, are the main processes responsible. Little departure from the plain form is envisaged, and the general flatness of the terrain may become accentuated by the formation and exposure of laterite sheets over wide areas.

Essential to this concept is the acceptance of the importance of interstream degradation by slope processes and the comparative feebleness of stream erosion in the areas concerned. According to many writers, this circumstance results from the combination of intense rainfall leading to rapid run-off on slopes and the speed and thoroughness of weathering depriving streams of adequate abrasive load in (seasonally) humid tropical environments. These concepts have been developed by Büdel (1957) whose hypothesis of "double surfaces of leveling" (*Doppelten Einebnungsflächen*) can be viewed as an elaboration of the etchplain concept. This hypothesis states that surface erosion is restricted over wide areas to the modification of a weathered surface, while at varying depths beneath this the bedrock surface (basal surface of weathering or weathering front) is molded by chemical weathering processes. Surface erosion affects the unaltered rock only if accelerated erosion from climatic changes or crustal disturbance causes the stripping of the regolith and the exposure of the basal surface of weathering. Mabbutt (1961a, b, 1965) and Wright (1963) have successfully applied these ideas in Australia where desiccation of climate has led to widespread stripping of deeply weathered rock. Mabbutt saw the etchplain as a stripped land surface of widely exposed rock, its level controlled by the depth of former weathering profiles and its form "should reproduce the form of the prior weathering front" (1965, p.99).

Mabbutt thus distinguishes between a "weathered land surface" and a "stripped land surface" or *etchplain*. However *etching* is the process of differential groundwater weathering which is accompanied or followed by wash processes and creep, leading to the stripping of the surficial materials. The concept of the etchplain must logically include both weathered and stripped surfaces. Thus, Thomas (1965) suggested a classification of etchplains, realizing that "a wide variety of intermediate categories of etchplain may be recognized between the etchplain *sensu stricto* and the stripped plain... The progress of weathering has not always or everywhere kept pace with increased rates of surface erosion ..., and varying proportions of the undulating basal surface of weathering have in many areas become exposed as outcrops displaying a generally domical form .... It is logical to regard the wide range of surfaces produced in this way as varieties of etchplain" (Thomas, 1965, p.130). The suggested categories are shown in Fig. 1.

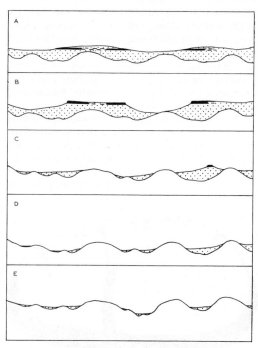

Fig. 1. The principal types of etchplain: (A) Lateritized etchplain (undissected). (B) Dissected etchplain. (C) Partially stripped etchplain. (D) Dominantly stripped etchplain. (E) Incised etchplain. Key: laterite deposits, black; other zones of weathering profile, stippled; unaltered bedrock, unshaded.

Understanding of these landscapes is far from complete; some of the difficulties inherent in the concept have been discussed by Thomas, and alternative explanations of such terrains by Trendall (1962) and De Swardt (1964). Many authors still regard these land surfaces as *pediplains*. Pediment formation within the weathered materials results from the stripping process, and pediments may be formed around residual hills (see Büdel, 1957). Nevertheless the term has gained wide currency, and the concept of the etchplain may prove important to the understanding of many surviving or former land surfaces in higher latitudes that experienced warmer climates during the Tertiary (Bakker and Levelt, 1964). Wright (1963) also applied the term to land surfaces developed from weathered sedimentary rocks so that the term is not applicable solely to the landscapes of the crystalline rocks.

MICHAEL F. THOMAS

References

Bakker, J. P., and Levelt, Th. W. M., 1964, "An enquiry into the probability of a polyclimatic development of peneplains and pediments (etchplains) in Europe during the Senonian and Tertiary period," *Publ. Serv. Luxembourg,* **14**, 27–75.

Büdel, J., 1957, "Die 'Doppelten Einebnungsflächen' in den feuchten Tropen," *Z. Geomorphol.,* **1**, 201–228.

Mabbutt, J. A., 1961a, " 'Basal surface' or 'weathering front'," *Proc. Geol. Assoc.,* **72**(3), 357–358.

Mabbutt, J. A., 1961b, "A stripped landsurface in Western Australia," *Trans. Inst. British Geogr.,* **29**, 101–114.

Mabbutt, J. A., 1965, "The weathered landsurface of Central Australia," *Z. Geomorphol.,* **9**, 82–114.

Swardt, A. M. J. de, 1964, "Lateritisation and landscape development in parts of equatorial Africa," *Z. Geomorphol.,* **8**, 313–333.

Thomas, M. F., 1965, "An approach to some problems of landform analysis in tropical environments," in (Whittow, J. B., and Wood, A. D., editors) "Essays in Geography," pp. 118–144, Reading, Austin Miller.

Trendall, A. F., 1962, "The formation of 'apparent peneplains' by a process of combined lateritisation and surface wash," *Z. Geomorphol.* **6**, 183–197.

Wayland, E. J., 1933, "Peneplains and some other erosional platforms," *Annual Report and Bulletin, Protectorate of Uganda, Geological Survey Dept., Notes* **1**, 74, 376–377.

Wright, R. L., 1963, "Deep weathering and erosion surfaces in the Daly River Basin, Northern Territory," *J. Geol. Soc. Australia,* **10**, 151–163.

Cross-references: *Denudation; Geomorphology; Pediplanation; Regolith and Saprolite; Slopes; Weathering.* pr Vol. VI: *Groundwater.*

EUSTASY

1. Origins of Sea-level Changes

Just as the land was once thought to have been unchanging, so sea level was long considered to have been constant. The medieval idea of a static world has given place to more and more dynamic concepts. In the case of sea level, the static concept lasted well into the twentieth century (Fairbridge, 1961a). A concomitant of a mobile land is a changing sea level relative to that land. The gradual erosional transfer of mountain ranges into the sea

in a major sedimentary cycle will change the level of the sea ("Sedimento-Eustasy"), as also will the sinking of the ocean floor to form a geosyncline, or the uplift of the land in a major orogenic cycle ("Tectono-Eustasy"). The flexing of the extensive deep ocean floors, as is suggested by Darwin to explain the history of coral islands (and applying equally to guyots), will change relative sea level too, but in the case of such broad changes, geodetically controlled changes in the earth's shape (i.e., the geoid) may occur, following polar shifts and changes in angular velocity.

But there is still another major source of sea-level change. Charles Darwin's diary reflects the general concern occasioned by the discovery of the Quaternary Ice Ages, and in the century that followed, the Glacial Control Theory of coral reefs emerged (Daly, 1934). Radiocarbon dating has now proved the contemporaneity of climatic change and glaciations in northern and southern hemispheres, and the coinciding of periods of low sea level with periods of glacial advance, glacial retreat being conversely linked with high sea level ("Glacio-Eustasy").

Additional oceanographic factors affect sea level. Temperature is the most fundamental parameter in gauging climate, and the lowering of temperature in a glacial period had two further effects on sea level:

(1) Cooling caused "steric" contraction of the molecules of the water mass, thus lowering sea level by a few meters.

(2) The shift of atmospheric circulation patterns also greatly modified oceanic currents. Since the accumulation of thousands of meters of ice over the polar and contiguous land masses caused the removal of vast quantities of water from the oceanic reservoirs (up to 80×10^6 km^3), there was a lowering of ocean level by two hundred meters or so with respect to the Pliocene sea level.

This considerable lowering of sea level changed the relationships of land and sea in many areas, cutting off seaways, uniting island clusters into a common land mass, and linking former islands to continents (Fairbridge, 1961b). The continental shelf was exposed, increasing the size of the continents by about 8%, and the area of shallow seas was very greatly reduced. The surface area relative to the volume of ocean water was altered, and the salinity increased slightly (from about 35–36°/$_{oo}$). The "continentality" of the climate of the land masses was thus appreciably increased.

2. Dynamic Concept of Sea-level Changes

Ideas of eustatic change of sea level were at first somewhat unrefined. To begin with, there was a rather simple concept of a retreat of the sea during a glacial period to a low stillstand, at which the sea remained until, with the coming of an interglacial period, the melting ice caused sea level to rise to a fixed interglacial high eustatic level or stillstand. There is now a much more dynamic concept of sea level. It is constantly changing. Superimposed upon the major oscillations of glacial periods are the smaller oscillations of the interstadials, and upon these again are smaller oscillations down to the order of seasonal cycles. Fairbridge (1961a) has given a lead in the recognition of the complexity of sea-level changes. It may be anticipated that more and more long-term cycles and aperiodic disturbances in the level of the sea will be recognized (Rossiter, 1962).

Since so many more oscillations of sea level have been recognized for a given length of time (e.g., over the past 20,000 years), it holds that at times the rate of change has been far more rapid than originally believed. Rates of sea level change will be high when several major cycles are in the same phase. The average rate of change during the present century has been given as of the order of 1 mm/yr, but during rapid deglaciation, the rate must have reached at least 50 mm/yr for several centuries at a time. Minor climatic events led to temporary reversals. Such oscillations leave behind terraces or beach lines (with shells datable by C^{14}) as testimony of the changes.

Changes of ocean level due to glacial control are worldwide and thus are extremely valuable for intercontinental correlation. They are so relatively rapid that they may obscure the effects of tectonic movement. As the oceans cover more than 70% of the earth's surface, a local tectonic movement does not affect sea level very much, but it may considerably alter mutual relations in that particular locality (e.g., Tokyo Bay or Hawke's Bay after recent earthquakes).

By reason of the physical problems of accessibility, the submerged shorelines are very poorly known compared with the emerged ones (see *Submerged Shorelines*). The modern development of oceanography is greatly assisting the study of submarine shorelines, and investigations by aqualung ("Scuba") divers are helping the study of the shallow water areas. Nevertheless, the imbalance between knowledge of former shorelines now under the sea and former shorelines now on land is a serious defect in this field of scientific investigation.

The adjective "eustatic" was introduced by Suess in 1888 (English transl., 1906, p. 680), and the substantives "eustasy" and "eustatism" are used variously. The extensions of it, such as glacio-eustasy, sedimento-eustasy, and tectono-eustasy, were popularized by Baulig (1935).

3. The Mediterranean "Standard"

A series of former marine shorelines established in the Mediterranean by Depéret (summarized in 1918) has become classic, and is widely quoted:

Name of Stage and Shoreline	Height (m)	Author	Type Locality
1. Sicilian	90–100	Doderlein	Gulf of Palermo, north Sicily
2. Milazzian	55–60	Depéret	Cape Milazzo, north Sicily (170 km from Palermo)
3. Tyrrhenian	28–30	Issel	Oran coast, Algeria, north Africa
4. Monastirian	18–20	Depéret	Monastir, Tunisia, north Africa
5. Unnamed ("Grimaldian" of Breuil; "Late Monastirian" of Zeuner)	6–8	Depéret	French coast, north Africa

For further discussion, see Zeuner (1959) and papers by Gignoux, Gigout, Blanc, Pfannenstiel and others (see bibliography in Zeuner). It should be noted that:

(a) Depéret meant by these terms not just shorelines, but also stages corresponding to sedimentary cycles (1918, p. 482). As stage names they are valuable, but the absolute elevations need extensive research.

(b) The type localities are all removed from one another, and so extrapolations are involved. The effects of tectonic movements on altitudes are thus difficult to assess. The type Milazzian and Monastirian localities are almost certainly disturbed.

(c) The associated faunas were described as being of cold-water type in the Sicilian, intermediate but warmer than now in the Milazzian, and warm in the Tyrrhenian and Monastirian. As the shorelines represent the high limits of sea level for those respective periods, a comparatively warm fauna would be expected in all periods. The terms "Tyrrhenian I, II, III" are now often applied to the paleontology of the last three stages.

(d) The 6–8 meter and lower levels seem to have been regarded as of little importance yet they are more widespread and better preserved than the higher (and older) ones.

The Mediterranean "standard" thus requires reassessment and absolute dating; accordingly, research workers could well report accurate observations in their areas of study without endeavoring to fit their findings into the classic series.

4. Evidences of Former Shorelines

These may be erosional and/or depositional. Most important are the littoral terraces, ancient shore benches or platforms of rocky coasts. There have been differences of opinion as to whether the sea at its present level can cut single or a multiple series of closely related terraces in a homogeneous rock; there is also confusion as to what is the base level for a contemporary rock platform and what is the level of the outer edge of the shore platform. Evidently, shoreline processes of the present time are not well understood (see *Platform* and *Wave Base*).

Depositional evidence of former shorelines is provided by stranded dune lines, belts of beach sands, shingles or boulders, and by emerged shell beds (coquinas, commonly called "raised beaches"). Advances in the knowledge of the granulometric characteristics of littoral sediments have greatly assisted the recognition of former dune and beach deposits (e.g., by *electron microscopy*, q.v., Vol. IV). Comparatively new studies of coastal ecology have assisted the recognition of various types of shelly sediments—beds laid down below low water level, shelly beach deposits, and shelly storm beach accumulations. Geochemists have made a contribution by isotopic studies, distinguishing between shells grown in fresh water, shells grown in estuarine water, and shells grown in fully marine conditions. Knowledge of the geochemical cycles and characteristics of calcium, strontium, magnesium and other elements has been greatly increased.

Although there is still much discussion about the times and heights of Quaternary sea levels, it is possible to measure and date the Holocene and Last Glacial levels with some accuracy. Also there appears to be unanimity that during the Last Interglacial (Riss-Würm or Sangamon) there were sea levels of the order of 7.5 meters (25 feet) and 3.5 meters (12 feet) higher than the present. By reason of lack of knowledge of present shoreline processes there is difference of opinion about lower levels of Holocene age. By reason of erosion and uncertainty about tectonic effects, many have doubts about the higher levels of the early Pleistocene. However, the Sangamon 7.5 meter level can often be used as a datum; it is certainly well marked and worldwide. That there have been higher and lower levels of the sea is beyond doubt, but the precise measure of those changes has yet to be established; the 7.5 meter level is generally accepted because the evidence for it is the most obvious.

5. Determination of Mean Sea Level

At the present time it is a simple task to determine accurately, with tide gauges, mean sea level over a few years, but it is difficult to establish it from terrace features because of the various geomorphic, exposure, tidal, meteorologic and other conditions. Although it is a good thing to compare the height of a given feature at the present time (say, the inner edge of a shore platform) with the height of the same feature in an emerged shoreline in the same general area, this does not necessarily provide a measurement of universal applica-

tion. In addition to possible tectonic movements, there is the possibility, for instance, of a gross change in geomorphic conditions. An open embayment may have the same tidal range as the rest of the local coast, but the sea, on retreating to a glacial low level, may leave a dune of calcareous sand across the mouth of the bay that hardens into a lithified bay bar with but a small opening that greatly diminishes the tidal range. The difference in height between the inner edge of the shore platform formed under open bay conditions and the inner edge of the shore platform formed under closed bay conditions is not a completely accurate measure of the change in mean sea level between the two periods.

It is evident therefore that in the study of eustasy it is necessary to consider processes rather than discrete events, and to study process in relation to time. Time and space are the basic parameters in earth sciences. Careful consideration of time brings processes into true perspective. In an area of small tectonic activity, for instance, the tectonic factor can be neglected as insignificant when emerged beds a few thousand years old are studied, but the older the formation the more likely it is that there is a significant tectonic correction factor. Similarly, a recently emerged feature can be expected to be fairly free of erosion, whereas an early Pleistocene structure can be expected to have suffered dissection. To refer to successive Quaternary cycles as a flight of terraces of similar geomorphic sharpness is to lack perspective with relation to time.

6. Interdisciplinary Role

The study of eustatic changes of sea level is of interest to many sciences. The incision of deep valleys during retreat of the sea and the emplacement of widespread formations of marine and fluvial sediments during transgressions is of interest (along with many other factors) to stratigraphers (see *Terraces—Thalassostatic*). Such features as the evolution of the coastline under changing conditions and the extension or reduction of stream systems through change of sea level are of interest to geomorphologists. The climatologists and glaciologists are concerned with the relationships of water levels and volumes to worldwide paleoclimatic events. The emergence of the continental shelves to provide new environments with the establishment of land bridges are of interest to botanists, zoologists and archeological anthropologists.

There are also important economic implications, such as the accumulation of black sand, and the formation of diamond-bearing beaches. Estuaries scoured out during low sea levels may make fine harbors and anchorages. Conversely, valleys and estuaries infilled with soft sediments during transgressions create problems for engineers seeking foundations for bridge and harbor installations.

Changing sea levels have left vast quantities of fairly well-sorted siliceous and calcareous sands available as constructional raw materials.

EDMUND D. GILL

References

Baulig, H., 1935, "The Changing Sea Level," *Inst. Brit. Geographers, Publ. 3*

Daly, R. A., 1934, "The Changing World of the Ice Age," New Haven, Yale University Press, 271pp.

Depéret, C., 1918, "Essai de coordination chronologique des temps quaternaires," *C. R. Acad. Sci. Paris.* **166,** 480–486; "Essai de coordination générale des temps quaternaires," *Ibid.,* **166,** 636–641, 884–889; **167**: 418–422, 979–984; **168**: 868–873.

Fairbridge, R. W., 1961a, "Eustatic Changes in Sea Level," in "Physics and Chemistry of the Earth," Vol. 4, pp. 99–185, Pergamon Press.

Fairbridge, R. W., 1961b, "Convergence of evidence on climatic change and Ice Ages," *Ann. N.Y. Acad. Sci.,* **95**(1), 542–579.

Rossiter, J. R., 1962, "Long-term Variations in Sea Level," in (Hill, M. N. editor) "The Sea," Vol. 1, pp. 590–610, New York and London, John Wiley & Sons, Inc.

Suess, E., 1904–24, "Face of the Earth," Oxford, Clarendon, 5 Vols.

Valentin, H., 1952, "Die Küsten der Erde," *Petermanns Geogr. Mitt., Erg. 246.*

Zeuner, F. E., 1959, "The Pleistocene Period," Second ed., London, Hutchinson, 447pp.

Cross-references: *Estuary*; *Glacial Geology*; *Holocene*; *Littoral Processes*; *Platform*; *Quaternary Period*; *Raised Beach*; *Strandline*; *Submerged Shorelines*; *Terraces—Marine*; *Terraces—Thalassostatic*; *Wave Base.* Vol. I: *Mean Sea Level Changes—Eustatic and Long-Term*; *Scuba as a Scientific Tool.* Vol. II: *Continentality.* Vol. IV: *Electron Microscopy.* Vol. V: *Epeirogeny*; *Geoid.*

EVORSION—*See* GLACIAL MOULIN; POTHOLE

EXFOLIATION

Exfoliation, from Latin *ex* (out) and *folia* (leaf), is the peeling off of curved surfaces from rocks, also known as "sheeting" (on a large scale). On a small scale, it is referred to as "*spheroidal weathering*" (q.v.) and mostly affects granite and other coarse-grained rocks. It was believed to be entirely due to differential heating and expansion but is now ascribed to (a) the original concentric cooling of the mass of magma, with the resulting predisposition to concentric dome-like differentiation in texture; (b) the relief of internal pressure by the removal of load by erosion; (c) the expansion of the moist joint surfaces due to the hydration of feldspars to form kaolin, and other chemical changes; and (d) the expansion and contraction of the. rock's surface due to diurnal differential heating.

Some authors, e.g., Farmin (1937), recommend that the term "exfoliation" should be restricted to sheeting and spalling of a primarily mechanical sort along curvilinear fractures (pressure release, and so on, along primary joints), and to keep "spheroidal weathering" restricted to primarily chemical flaking, e.g., "onion-skin peeling," although this process is predisposed by joints, bedding planes and flow lines.

As early as 1895, Merrill, discussing the disintegration of granitic rocks in the District of Columbia, mentioned that hydration was to be held chiefly responsible for this process. The decay of granite could be viewed as a higher oxidation and separation of protoxides in the form of hydrous sesqui-oxides and as a general hydration of alkaline silicates accompanied by the formation of alkaline carbonates, which are water-soluble and easily removed. Rocks found at depths of over 100 feet below the surface were found to be in varying conditions, some of them readily disintegrating after a short exposure to the elements. This fact could perhaps be explained by the penetration of moisture to the rock *in situ*, causing hydration and swelling of the rock but without the actual falling apart of the materials because of the pressure exerted by the surrounding rocks (Merrill, 1895).

Merrill did not specifically mention exfoliation in that paper, but the subject of exfoliation was discussed only a year later by Branner in a very comprehensive study of rock decomposition in Brazil. Branner noticed that decomposition proceeds along joints and other planes of weakness, and as it penetrates to greater depths, undecayed masses are left behind in the shape of boulders. The decomposition of granite and gneiss gives rise to special topographic forms which are quite characteristic. As a whole, structure has more to do with the weathering of granite than has variation of temperature. On closer examination, it is also found that coarse crystalline rocks are more readily attacked than fine-grained crystalline rocks (Branner, 1896). In the same year, Dana (1896) stated that the force of expansion due to hydration is the chief cause of exfoliation.

Barton (1916), working on the granite monuments of Egypt, also noticed that fine-grained granite is less affected by weathering agents than coarse granite. In the latter, distant joints give rise to huge piles of boulders under concentric exfoliation, whereas closer joints produce smaller angular and subangular blocks. At Aswan, inscriptions on the southward side of granite surfaces do not show incipient exfoliation or flaking. Farther north, where humidity in the air is greater, the rate of disintegration is higher, and some weathering could be noticed on a sheltered statue. On the other hand, sarcophagi kept in a deep dry underground chamber were still intact. At Gizeh the granite blocks of the temple of the second pyramid show a dis-

FIG. 1. Massive sheeting in Gawlor Range porphyry, near Yardea, northern Eyre Peninsula, South Australia. Note general absence of chemical weathering. (Photo: C. R. Twidale).

tinctly stronger disintegration below what appears to be an old soil level. Barton also noticed that the orientation of the disintegration varies according to certain trends within the rock, possibly the lineation or grain, or a faint schistosity. Most likely, an alternation of wet and dry conditions is conducive to the most rapid weathering (Barton, 1916).

Blackwelder (1925) first subjected the temperature explanation of exfoliation to close scrutiny. In his paper he gave a list of factors which have been quoted as causes of exfoliation, and he discussed each one at length. Changes in temperature due to sudden heating by fire or lightning should be ruled out as major factors because of their limited occurrence, as contrasted with the general occurrence of exfoliation. Hourly, daily and seasonal temperature changes, hitherto almost universally accepted as the cause of exfoliation, should be considered very cautiously in the absence of any reliable evidence. Blackwelder also listed the expansion of freezing water, of crystallizing salts,

FIG. 2. Massive sheeting in granite, Ucontitchie Hill, Eyre Peninsula, South Australia. In this case chemical weathering has played a dominant role. (Photo: C. R. Twidale).

FIG. 3. Blocky disintegration due to insolation weathering, in quartzite, at Mt Conner, Northern Territory, Australia. (Photo: C. R. Twidale).

and of plant rootlets as factors which may be at work on a very small scale; the expansion of freezing water is of great importance in contributing to rock splitting and felsenmeer formation, but this is a phenomenon quite distinct from exfoliation. In addition, there were chemical changes such as the absorption of water by colloids, the hydration and oxidation of silicates, and other forms of mineral decay. Hydration was considered to be extremely important (Blackwelder, 1925).

In another paper, Blackwelder (1933) presents experimental evidence against the temperature theory of spalling and exfoliation, stating that in most rocks no spalling occurs below 250–300°C.

In 1937, Farmin formulated the theory of the hypogenic origin of exfoliation, discussing two factors: the concentric rock structure around nuclei of crystallization when the rock was first solidified and the expansion of the rock after unloading due to the progress of weathering on the overlying surface (Farmin, 1937).

Barton (1938) expressed the opinion that "exfoliation in Egypt cannot be even partly hypogene...; disintegration and exfoliation are directly or indirectly the effect of moisture; and ... much of the extensive known disintegration and exfoliation of granite in the most temperate regions of the world is not a result of unloading of the rock but an effect of moisture...."

There is no exfoliation on the upper surface of any boulder rounded enough in shape to shed moisture and to prevent the percolation of rainwater. Granitic rocks still buried in the ground show copious signs of exfoliation on their upper surface, which is subject to very active percolation. Exfoliation would occur radially around the center of

FIG. 4. Large-scale sheeting on granite domes in Rocky Mountain National Park, Estes Park, Colorado. (Photo: R. W. Fairbridge.)

the upper surface of the boulder if the rain falls vertically. When the rain falls at an angle smaller than the vertical, the distribution of exfoliation around the point of greatest rainfall impact might be expected along component lines dictated by the angle of rainfall impact, the slope of the rock surface, and gravity.

The presence of latent "hypogenic joints" shown by Farmin (1937) to occur in rocks of this type can only favor the development of exfoliation and spalling along the lines suggested, and there is no difficulty in accepting this theory of hypogenic origin. The development of gneissic features and the uneven distribution of minerals other than quartz in the rock are other contributing factors.

J. GENTILLI

References

Barton, D. C., 1916, "Notes on the disintegration of granite in Egypt," *J. Geol.*, **24**, 382–393.

Barton, D. C., 1938, "Discussion: the disintegration and exfoliation of granite in Egypt," *J. Geol.*, **46**, 109–111.

Blackwelder, E., 1925, "Exfoliation as a phase of rock weathering," *J. Geol.*, **33**, 793–806.

Blackwelder, E., 1933, "The insolation hypothesis of rock weathering," *Am. J. Sci.*, **26**, 97–113.

Branner, J. C., 1896, "Decomposition of rocks in Brazil," *Bull. Geol. Soc. Am.*, **7**, 255–314.

Dana, J. D., 1894, "Manual of Geology," Fourth ed., New York, American Book Co., 1088pp.

Farmin, R., 1937, "Hypogene exfoliation in rock masses," *J. Geol.*, **45**, 625–635.

Gentilli, J., 1950, "Rainfall as a factor in the weathering of granite," *Compt. Rend. Congr. Int. Géographie* (*Lisbon, 1949*), **2**, 263–269.

Harland, W. B., 1957, "Exfoliation joints and ice action," *J. Glaciol.*, **3**(21), 8–10.

Helal, A. H., 1964, "Die Bedeutung eines ägyptischen Felsbildes bei Mekka für die Frage nach dem Alter von Blockmeerbildungen und Desquamationen in Saudi-Arabien," *Z. Geomorphol.*, **8**, 366–369.

Merrill, G. P., 1895, "Disintegration of the granitic rocks of the District of Columbia," *Bull. Geol. Soc. Am.*, **6**, 321–332.

Cross-references: *Felsenmeer*; *Frost Action*; *Frost Riving*; *Spheroidal Weathering*; *Weathering*. Vol. IV: *Hypogene*.

EXHUMED LANDSCAPE

Something "exhumed" means that it is dug up again, after burial. It is commonly applied to geomorphic features, particularly ancient relief features, that were buried by such materials as glacial drift, alluvial deposits or transgressive marine sediments (Fig. 1). Then at some subsequent date, the former landscape is re-eroded and exhumed. The term *"resurrected relief"* is also applied equally well to this feature (Thornbury, 1954). Johnson (1925) recognized a "resurrected peneplane shoreline."

A term of similar root often used in structural geology is "posthumous," referring to structural revival at various stages after the initial diastrophism. The identification of ancient relief surfaces eventually becomes a matter for stratigraphic subsurface research (Martin, 1960). Indeed, Kay (1945), and later Thornbury (1954) and Zekkel (1958), have suggested that a new science of Paleogeomorphology should be established to comprehend its significance.

In the Nullagine area of northwestern Australia, there is a broad plain, an erosional surface cleanly transecting a variety of middle and early Precambrian rocks. Driving across it one might well call it a "peneplain" in the Davisian sense, but suddenly, rising above this surface is a steep escarpment formed by near-horizontal late Precambrian sediments. Evidently this surface was reduced to a peneplain (or pediplain) in pre-Proterozoic times. For nearly one billion years it was covered over by the transgressive Proterozoic, and only in late geological history is it being stripped bare once more, an exhumed land surface. In North America, notably in Wisconsin, one may observe a peneplaned Precambrian surface dipping gently under an onlap of Cambrian and Ordovician sediments, but here the old relief is somewhat modified by Pleistocene ice scour and other features. Such examples may be multiplied from all parts of the world. Exhumed land surfaces need not be ancient plains. Pre-Pleistocene surfaces containing *buried valleys* (q.v.) and a complex relief are being widely exhumed today. Varied examples of exhumation are mentioned by Thornbury (1954, p. 194) from the Colorado Front Range, from New Mexico, etc.

Perhaps the classic example of the exhumed landscape is the Precambrian inlier of Charnwood Forest, England, which is surrounded by continental Triassic. On the old granite surfaces are signs of the desert wind action, the scouring and polishing of Triassic times (Watts, 1947). Many of the Cretaceous chalk dipslopes, that face in toward the Tertiary London Basin today, are regarded as exhumed subEocene surfaces (Wooldridge and Linton, 1955).

Secondary modification of two ancient exhumed surfaces over the Massif Central of France by numbers of marine and fluvial terraces or partial peneplains has been worked out in detail by Baulig (1928), and critically discussed by Sparks (1960). The post-Hercynian erosion surface was largely buried by Triassic and Jurassic transgressions, the tropical soils of the former being reflected in the lithology of the transgressive sediments. A new erosion surface developed after mid-Tertiary uplift. Faulting followed, and in the troughs ("limagnes"), late Tertiary deposits rest on the early Tertiary erosion surface. Then in Quaternary times, the well-known glacio-eustatic (and tectono-eustatic) phenomena led to widespread emergence and terracing. Baulig believed it was all glacio-eustatic,

FIG. 1. Section of an exhumed erosion surface (from Sparks, 1960). (By permission of John Wiley & Sons, N.Y.)

but there was an important regional tectonic warping, as well as worldwide tectonic effects, each playing its respective role (see *Morvan*).

Thornbury (1954, p. 26) stresses that "little of the earth's topography is older than Tertiary ..." and that so-called Precambrian topographic features are most likely exhumed. This is true enough, but it is equally important to indicate that much of the modern shield topography shows traces of inherited features of very great antiquity (see Fig. 5.6 in Thornbury, 1954).

either superficially or completely lithified and massively cemented to become a quartzite, it is totally resistant to normal subaerial chemical weathering. Thus quartzite ridges stand up above the old pediplains of Africa, South America and Australia to bear witness to ancient erosion surfaces, while the surrounding rocks, mica-schists, granites, etc., may be rotted to saprolite (regolith) to depths of 200–300 meters. In the case of mechanical weathering, quartzites are liable to suffer somewhat from insolation-exfoliation, but this is neg-

FIG. 2. Approximate exhumation of an unconformity by a series of erosion terraces (from Sparks, 1960). (By permission of John Wiley & Sons, N.Y.)

An ancient peneplain of a geomorphologist is simply an unconformity (or disconformity) of a stratigrapher. The "Schooley Peneplain" of the Appalachians is warped and dips unmistakably under the mid-Tertiary transgressive onlap of the Atlantic Coastal Plain. To the stratigrapher, it is the trace of an old erosion surface, but whether it be classified as a peneplain, pediplain, gipfelflur or "summit accordance" is almost a matter of semantics. It is probable that the Schooley surface is not exhumed over the Appalachians, since the Cretaceous-Eocene did not appear to transgress the whole mountain belt; it did overlap the margins, however, and these areas are therefore exhumed.

It should be stressed that lithology is a matter of great significance in these ancient or exhumed surfaces (Sparks, 1960). A "hardpan," "duricrust," calcrete, ferricrete or silcrete crust (paleosol features) often marks the old surface (Debenham, 1952). For example, once a sandstone has been

ligible compared with the chemically aided reaction on granite; quartzite joint planes may also suffer somewhat from fluvial and glacial attack. However, the general record of quartzites shows that once such a rock type is established on or below a broad cratonic erosion surface, it may be regarded almost as a permanent feature.

In the case of the Silurian (Tuscarora), Lower Carboniferous (Pocono) and Upper Carboniferous (Pottsville) quartzitic "ridge makers" in the Appalachians, one may ask if they were not perhaps denuded to a fundamental erosion plane while still in the state of poorly cemented sandstones and then, under SiO_2-saturated groundwater conditions, converted to "silcrete," i.e. cemented quartzites. Progressive, interrupted upwarp of the Appalachians since that time (Mesozoic) has led to differential erosion, leaving behind partial peneplains, etchplains, straths, terraces, etc. The quartzitic ridges, even where overwhelmed by Pleistocene icesheets,

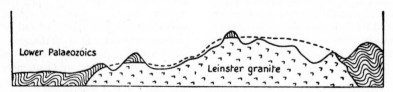

Lower Palaeozoics

Leinster granite

FIG. 3. Section across the Wicklow Mountains (after Charlesworth; from Sparks, 1960). (By permission of John Wiley & Sons, N.Y.)

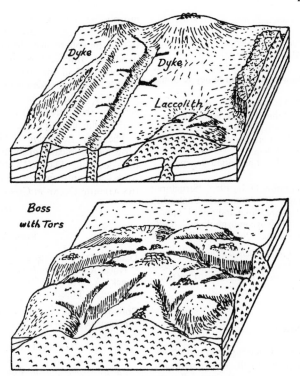

FIG. 4. Block diagrams of exhumed igneous surfaces. Above, a laccolith with two examples of differential weathering of harder and softer dikes (dykes). Below, a granitic boss, with tors, in part a structural and in part an erosional surface, buried and exhumed (from Sparks, 1960). (By permission of John Wiley & Sons, N.Y.)

show little subsequent modification, except at specific sites of concentrated mechanical abrasion (*water gaps, wind gaps,* q.v.).

The exhumed surface in some cases may be tilted and then affected by a second or more truncations, as may be seen on the Appalachian margins and many other places; the term *morvan* (q.v.) is sometimes applied to these.

Exhumed Structure

It is not always necessary for the exhumed surface to be a former erosion surface, but it may be established by any differential erosion of a former structural discontinuity. Sparks (1960) mentions the Leinster granite of the Wicklow Mountains in southeastern Ireland as an example where a batholithic surface has been stripped of its Lower Paleozoic sedimentary cover and somewhat modified subsequently (Fig. 3). The domed shape of many of the Henry Mountains in Utah, from the classic descriptions of Gilbert (1877), evidently reflects the exhumation of the laccolithic structural form (Fig. 4). The granite bosses of Devon and Cornwall in England probably represent a combination of structural form, exhumation, sedimentary burial and re-exhumation.

RHODES W. FAIRBRIDGE

References

Ambrose, J. W., 1964, "Exhumed paleoplains of the Precambrian Shield of North America," *Am. J. Sci.,* **262,** 817–857.

Baulig, H., 1928, "Le Plateau Central de la France," Paris, Colin, 590pp.

Birot, P., 1949, "Essais sur quelques problèmes de morphologie generale," Lisbon, *Inst. Alta Cult., Centro Est. Geogr.,* 17–33.

Cotton, C. A., 1916, "Block mountains and a "fossil" denudation plain in northern Nelson," *Trans. N.Z. Inst.,* **48,** 59–75 (reprinted in *N.Z. Geomorph.,* 1955, 114–138).

Cotton, C. A., 1952, "The erosional grading of convex and concave slopes," *Geogr. J.,* **118**(2), 197–204.

Davies, G. L., 1960, "The age and origin of the Leinster Mountain Chain: a study of the evolution of southeastern Ireland from the Upper Paleozoic to the Later Tertiary," *Proc. Roy. Irish Acad.,* **61B,** 79–107.

Debenham, F., 1952, "The Kalahari today," *Geograph. J.,* **118,** 12–23.

Gilbert, G. K., 1877, "Report on the Geology of the Henry Mountains," *U.S. Geogr. Geol. Surv.,* Washington (also second ed. 1880).

Harrington, H. J., 1963, "Recent explanations of Victoria Land north of Terra Nova Bay," *Geogr. J.,* **129,** 36–52.

Johnson, D., 1925, "The New England-Acadian Shoreline," New York, John Wiley & Sons, 608pp.

Kay, G. M., 1945, "Palaeogeographic and palinspastic

maps," *Bull. Am. Assoc. Petrol. Geologists,* **29,** 426–450.

Martin, R., 1960, "Principles of paleogeomorphology," *Trans. Can. Mining Met. Bull.,* **63,** 351–360.

Sparks, B. W., 1960, "Geomorphology," London, Longmans, Green; New York, John Wiley & Sons, 371pp.

Thornbury, W. D., 1954, "Principles of Geomorphology," New York, John Wiley & Sons, 618pp.

Watts, W. W., 1947, "Geology of the Ancient Rocks of Charnwood Forest, Leicestershire," Leicester Literary and Philo. Soc., 160pp.

Wilson, A. W. G., 1903, "The Laurentian peneplain," *J. Geol.,* **11,** 615–669.

Wooldridge, S. W., and Linton, D. L., 1955, "Structure, Surface and Drainage in South-east England," second ed., London, George Philip and Son, 176pp.

Zekkel, J. D., 1958, "Paleogeomorphology," *Bull. All-Russian Geographical Soc.,* 366–368 (in Russian).

Cross-references: *Buried Valley; Denudation; Duricrust; Etchplain; Gipfelflur; Morvan; Paleogeomorphology; Peneplain; Quaternary Period; Water Gap; Wind Gap.* pr Vol. VI: *Paleopedology.*

EXOGENIC DYNAMICS

All externally generated geodynamic processes are classified (after Penck, 1894) as *exogenic* (in Britain usually written *exogenetic*). Thus, all processes connected with *weathering* and *denudation* (q.v.) in geology are related to exogenic dynamics. The earth's principal exogenic energy source is the *sun,* the radiations from which lead to atmospheric heating and circulation. The geostrophic wind systems in turn are coupled to the oceanic current circulation. Together they account for most of the thermal budget of the earth's surface. A very minor source of heat is *endogenic* (q.v.), from terrestrial heatflow; in atmospheric calculations it is generally disregarded.

Also coupled to atmospheric-oceanic circulation is the earth's *hydrologic cycle* (q.v. pr Vol. VI) which leads to the production of cloud, precipitation, rock weathering to soil, erosion and mass transport of eroded rock material and soil from one part of the globe to another, thus, to sedimentation. An important equilibrioturbal agency thus exists, which is believed to play a major role in periodic shifts in the earth's axis of rotation (with respect to the crust, but not with respect to the orbital plane).

A second major exogenic energy source is gravitational, related to the *celestial mechanics* of the sun, earth, moon and other planetary bodies. The most obvious effect is the production of oceanic tides and related currents; atmospheric tides are also important and solid earth tides are gaining recognition. The latter may well play a part in "triggering" endogenic motions such as earthquakes, volcanism and tectonic action.

In the geological disciplines, much of geo-morphology (as concerns surface modeling), climatology, pedology, stratigraphy and the evolution of the biosphere are closely related to exogenic dynamics. Interactions with endogenic dynamics are observed in the structural deformation of the earth's crust and such events as ice ages, which are primarily exogenic, but probably basically triggered by the building of high mountains and shifts of the polar axis to coincide with them.

The term *exogenous* is not very different from exogenic. It means growing or derived from the outside; thus Dana (1890) spoke of the North American continent beginning to grow out toward the Atlantic Ocean in Cretaceous times.

RHODES W. FAIRBRIDGE

References

Dana, J. D., 1890, "Areas of continental progress in North America," *Bull. Geol. Soc. Am.,* **1,** 36–48.

Penck, A., 1894, "Morphologie der Erdoberfläche" Stuttgart, Engelhorn, 2 vols.

Cross-references: *Climatic Geomorphology; Denudation; Endogenic Dynamics; Geomorphology; Sediment Transport; Weathering.* Vol. I: *Dynamics of Ocean Currents; Tides.* Vol. II: *Atmospheric Circulation; Atmospheric Tides; Celestial Mechanics; Climatology; Earth—Geology of the Planet; Energy Budget of the Earth's Surface; Geostrophic Wind; Ice Age Theory; Solar Radiation.* pr Vol. VI: *Hydrologic Cycle; Pedology.* pr Vol. VII: *Stratigraphy.*

EXOTIC BLOCK—*See* PERCHED BLOCK, BOULDER

EXPLOSION CRATERS—*See* Vol. II

EXUDATION (Exsudation)*

Exudation is a geomorphic weathering process involving the splitting off, granulation or distintegration of small rock fragments from the parent mass by the force of crystallization of intergranular (interstitial) salts or ice. In semiarid lands the irregular rainfall soaks into the rock, causing some solution; subsequently, capillary action takes place, bringing the solutions to the surface, where evaporation and crystallization occur. The actual salts are generally concentrated 1–2 mm below the surface so that a powerful spalling force is generated.

The salts involved may be marine salts (typically NaCl) introduced by the cyclic, atmospheric salt nuclei in rain, or they may be produced by solution within the rock itself. If $CaCO_3$ solutions are involved, the geomorphic product will not be erosion

---

* The spelling "exsudation" is used by many geomorphologists but both the Oxford English Dictionary and Webster's International Dictionary give it as an obsolete variant of "exudation."

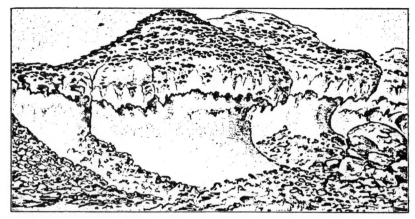

Fig. 1. Pedestal rocks in the Eastern Desert of Egypt, 30 feet high with caps of ferruginous crusts, protecting chalky marls, undercut by exudation (drawn by G. Schweinfurth: in Walther, 1924).

but the development of a travertinous crust ("calcrete"); Fe_2O_3 and MnO_2 will produce iron crust ("ferricrete") and manganese crusts, respectively; SiO_2 will produce a siliceous crust ("silicrete") on the rock surface. Such rock crusts due to exudation are small-scale analogs of a similar capillary process in forming soil crusts (see *Duricrust*).

Exudation granulation takes place typically on the *sides* of granite tors and inselbergs in semiarid climates, where large caverns may develop. Pedestal or "mushroom" rocks in the desert typically show exudation around the sides and a protective capping of ferruginous duricrust (see Fig. 1). Bryan (1922) referred to these undercuts as "niches." Exudation is probably the chief mechanism of tafoni, alveolar or honeycomb weathering in coastal localities, especially in Mediterranean lands. It may even occur in polar latitudes, where the crystallization is with ice (Thornbury, 1954; Calkin and Cailleux, 1962). The crumbling action occurs also on the floors of salt lake basins, where there is a rock floor (Jutson, 1934), and deflation carries away the particles. Indeed the arid-zone lake floors may be appreciably lowered by this mechanism. Some rock holes, "gnamma-holes," "solution pans," etc., typical of granite weathering should probably be ascribed to this process (see *Exfoliation*; *Granite Landforms*; *Spheroidal Weathering*).

In some cases, particularly in caves, under "breakways" and at the edges of salt lakes, the capillary salts will accumulate as white crusts of *efflorescence deposits*. The appearance of these deposits, accompanied by a crumbling of the rock, at the level of Nile flooding near the bases of Pharonic monuments in Egypt is responsible for serious damage (Knetch, 1960).

The term "exudation basin" is also used in glaciology (according to A.G.I. Glossary) for a "spoon-shaped depression found at the heads of outlet glaciers of the Greenland ice cap."

RHODES W. FAIRBRIDGE

References

Blackwelder, E., 1929, "Cavernous rock surfaces of the desert," *Am. J. Sci.*, Ser. 5, **17.**

Bryan, K., 1922, "Erosion and sedimentation in the Papago Country, Arizona," *Bull. U.S. Geol. Surv.*, **730(B).**

Calkin, P., and Cailleux, A., 1962, "A quantitative study of cavernous weathering (taffonis) and its application to glacial chronology in Victoria Valley, Antarctica," *Z. Geomorphol.*, **6,** 317–324.

Jutson, J. T., 1917, "The influence of salts in rock-weathering in sub-arid Western Australia," *Proc. Roy. Soc. Victoria*, **30** (2), 165–172.

Jutson, J. T., 1934, "The physiography (geomorphology) of Western Australia," *Bull. Geol. Surv. W. Australia*, **95,** 366pp.

Knetch, G., 1960, "Ueber aride Verwitterung unter besonderer Berücksichtigung natürlicher und künstlicher Wände in Aegypten," *Z. Geomorphol.*, suppl., **1,** 190–205.

Panzer, W., 1954, "Verwitterungs- und Abtragungsformen im Granit von Hongkong," *Abhandl. Akad. Raumforschung* . . . (Bremen), **28** (H. Mortensen Vol. —Ergebnisse und Probleme moderner geographischer Forschung), 41–60.

Thornbury, W. D., 1954, "Principles of Geomorphology," New York, John Wiley & Sons, 618pp.

Walther, J., 1924, "Das Gesetz der Wüstenbildung," Fourth ed., Leipzig, Quelle & Meyer, 421pp.

Cross-references: *Desert Varnish*; *Duricrust*; *Exfoliation*; *Granite Landforms*; *Induration*; *Spheroidal Weathering*; *Tafoni*. Vol. II: *Salt Nuclei*.

F

FACETED SPUR—*See* **FAULT SCARP**

FALL LINE, ZONE

Fall Line is a term applied to the sharp junction between the Appalachian Piedmont Province and the Atlantic Coastal Plain of eastern North America, being marked by waterfalls or rapids on each of the principal rivers—the Delaware, Potomac, James, Roanoke, Savannah and so on. This characteristic was appreciated by the pioneer colonists and modest water-power installations were constructed at such points. Since navigation was also interrupted here, it was a geographical consequence that principal cities grew up about these centers: from north to south—Trenton (N.J.), Philadelphia, Baltimore, Washington, Richmond (Va.), Raleigh (N.C.), Columbia (S.C.), Augusta (Ga.), Macon (Ga.) and Columbus (Ga.).

The term "fall line" or "fall zone" (Lobeck, 1939) is thus of some antiquity in American usage and has been adopted in geomorphology as a general term to identify the boundary between a more resistant crystalline upland or plateau province and a coastal plain of weak rocks (Davis, 1904, pp. 157–158). Lord Avebury (1902, p. 455) gives an example from England, where the peaty Fenlands are bordered by a line of important towns: Cambridge, Peterborough, Lincoln, and others. More characteristic, however, are the immensely long examples along the inner margins of the coastal plains of Africa, India, Western Australia and Brazil. These "Gondwanaland" countries all have Precambrian shields in the interior, cut off along faults or monoclines from narrow coastal plains.

Not everywhere do the falls or rapids occur exactly at the junctions of the adjacent provinces, because headward migration of the *nickpoint* (q.v.) may take place, although this is a slow process in crystalline rocks stripped of their saprolite mantle.

In the case of the eastern American Fall Line, it has been suggested that the contact is the trace of an ancient peneplain, a mid-Mesozoic (pre-Cretaceous) erosion surface that plunges beneath the coastal plain deposits. The transgression of the latter began in early Cretaceous time and buried a truncated land surface of rocks varying from Paleozoic (locally Precambrian) to Triassic. This erosion surface, the *Fall Zone Peneplain* of Henry Sharp (1929), is real (but imperfectly planed) as a buried feature, but whether or not there are traces of it in the mid-Appalachian summit accordances is a matter of considerable contention. Renner (1927) suggested that the Fall Line represented the intersection of two peneplains (with a younger Tertiary Harrisburg Peneplain). Where the line comes out near the coast in the vicinity of New York City and Long Island Sound, it is clear that the summit accordances of the crystalline hinterland come down gradually to the sea, and in adjacent parts of New Jersey and Long Island, there is a classical transgressive overlap of the Cretaceous formations. However, the correlation of those summits with this particular erosional phase is not so clear and has been questioned specifically by Flint (1963).

The progressive uparching of the Appalachian massif and downwarping of the coastal plain has been in progress since the Cretaceous; over a 500-km-wide belt there has been differential uplift and subsidence of about 1 km spread over about 10^8 years, or some 0.01 mm/yr. During this very gentle secular process, there has evidently been periods of acceleration and deceleration, for distinctive intermediate planation surfaces are identifiable (see *Morvan*). Calculations of erosion rates are notoriously difficult, and some attempt has been made by Hack (1965), but the conclusions are far from settled. One thing, however, seems rather certain: that the mean fulcrum of the differential warping has remained fairly constant, i.e., near the Fall Line, although the actual locus has shifted to-and-fro with eustatic oscillations and the coastline of today is farther seaward than the average of Tertiary time (a non-glacial era).

RHODES W. FAIRBRIDGE

References

Avebury, Lord (J. Lubbock), 1902, "The Scenery of England," London, Macmillan, 534pp.
Davis, W. M., 1904, "Elements of Physical Geography," Boston, Ginn, 401pp.
Flint, R. F., 1963, "Altitude, lithology and the Fall Zone in Connecticut," *J. Geol.*, **71**, 683–697.
Hack, J. T., 1965, "Geomorphology of the Shenandoah

Valley, Virginia and West Virginia . . .," *U.S. Geol. Surv. Profess. Paper* **484**, 84pp..

Lobeck, A. K., 1939, "Geomorphology, An Introduction to the Study of Landscapes," New York, McGraw-Hill Book Co., 731pp.

Renner, G. T., 1927, "The physiographic interpretation of the Fall Line," *Geograph. Rev.,* **17**, 276–286.

Sharp, H. S., 1929, "The Fall Zone peneplane," *Science,* **69**, 544–545.

Thornbury, W. D., 1965, "Regional Geomorphology of the United States," New York, John Wiley & Sons, 609pp.

Cross-references: *Coastal Plain; Morvan; Nickpoint; Piedmont Landforms; Warping; Waterfalls.*

FAN—*See* ALLUVIAL FAN, CONE; ALLUVIUM; ROCK FAN

FARO

A faro is a special type of annular reef, a small shelf atoll, formed on the rim or interior bank of a major compound or composite atoll or barrier reef; thus, an atoll of second order, a miniature atoll, but not to be confused with a *microatoll* (q.v.), which is usually less than 10 meters across.

The term "faro" comes from the Maldive Islands of the Indian Ocean, where these phenomena are best known (Gardiner, 1903, p. 155; Agassiz, 1903, p. xii). The Maldivian term *velu* is applied here to the lagoons of the faros. Faros are also found on the edges of the big compound atolls of the Flores Sea (Paternoster Islands, Tijger Islands: see Kuenen, 1933).

It is evident that faros are developed basically in a two-cycle evolution: (a) the development of the initial major atoll platform (which probably involved a negative eustatic sea-level oscillation, with subaerial erosion into a saucer-shaped platform (see MacNeil's explanation under *Atoll*); (b) followed by a phase of submergence and stability with the colonization and growth of fringing reefs around the rim projections, and then upward growth in miniature atoll form, probably during the post-glacial eustatic rise.

The question may be asked, why did not all big atolls pass through this evolutionary sequence during late Quaternary time, since evidently the eustatic controls were worldwide? Two additional factors in the Maldives and East Indian examples require consideration: (1) these, and all other known cases, are strictly equatorial and may have been marked by glacial phase growth, while in the marginal seas reef growth was inhibited by the lower temperatures; and (2) these reefs are not of the mid-oceanic type, but are situated exclusively on non-volcanic foundations, in quasi-cratonic crustal regions that suffered extensive Quaternary subsidence, i.e., tectonic lowering over and above

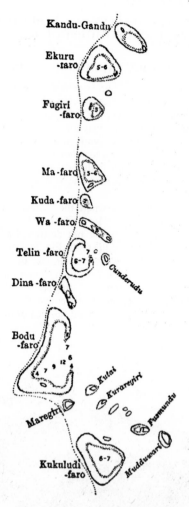

FIG. 1. A line of typical faros on the western rim of North Mahlos in the Maldive Islands (Gardiner, 1903, Fig. 32). Length of southermost faro: 1000 meters.

glacio-eustatic effects. Faros thus present a complex, but still unsolved, problem of marine geology and geophysics.

RHODES W. FAIRBRIDGE

References

Agassiz, A., 1903, "The coral reefs of the Maldives," *Mem. Museum Comp. Zoology, Harvard Coll.,* **29**, 168pp.

Gardiner, J. S., 1903, "Coral reefs of the Indian Ocean," in "The Fauna and Geography of the Maldive and Laccadive Archipelagoes," Vol. 1, Cambridge, Cambridge University Press.

Kuenen, P. H., 1933, "Geology of coral reefs," *Snellius Exped.,* **5**, Part 2, 125pp.

Cross-references: *Atoll; Eustasy; Fringing Reef; Lagoon; Microatoll; Quaternary Period.*

FAULT-LINE VALLEY—*See* STRUCTURAL CONTROL IN GEOMORPHOLOGY

FAULT SCARP, FAULT-LINE SCARP

"Scarp" is an abbreviation for "escarpment" meaning an abrupt rise in relief, a cliff or cuesta. The abbreviated form has been used at least from the days of Hutton and Playfair. Although the terms are, strictly speaking, synonymous, scarp is more commonly limited nowadays in North America to cliffs associated with faulting; in Britain, no distinction is made between the two words (Stamp, 1961).

A *fault scarp* is one where the footwall surface is exposed; in other words, the feature must be very fresh, so that erosion has not destroyed all traces of the actual plane of the fault (Fig. 1). The latter is marked by *slickensides,* or striations, and polished surfaces (from "slick," meaning smooth), intersected by minute steps (1–3 mm high) which drop away in the direction of movement (Fig. 2). The slickensides may be preserved in silica or in calcite.

FIG. 2. Slickensides displayed on a calcite-filled fault zone in the Devonian Onondaga Limestone near Catskill, New York State.

The direction of the slickenside striations shows the *last* motion on the fault, but since multiple movements are often involved, overlapping generations of striations of various directions are often seen. Fault scarps may thus only be seen properly in regions of recent earthquakes and active faulting,

FIG. 1. A small fault scarp, 5 meters high, photographed just after the fault occurred (on the White Creek Fault in the Murchison Earthquake of 1929 in New Zealand). (Photo: M. Ongley, New Zealand Geological Survey)

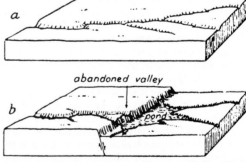

FIG. 3A. Ponded drainage in Parowan Valley, Utah, where a stream apparently flowing directly across a small rift valley was long able to maintain its antecedent course despite continued relative uplift of one of the bounding blocks; it has recently been partially obstructed by further uplift (Johnson, 1930).

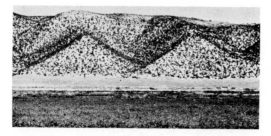

FIG. 3B. Triangular fault facets, truncating spurs and structure (note gentle dip to right). Location: southwestern Utah, Red Hills near Parowan Gap. (Photo: R. L. Threet.) (Courtesy American Library Color Slide Co.)

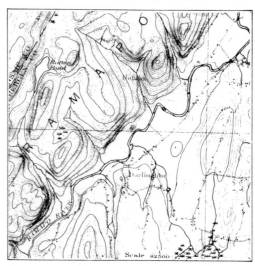

FIG. 5. Topographic map of a section of the fault-line scarp along the western side of the Triassic Lowland of New Jersey. The Ramapo Fault was active during the Triassic, but not since. Its topographic prominence is due to resistant Precambrian crystalline rocks (to the northwest) and the relative weakness of the Triassic sandstones and shales (to the southeast).

FIG. 4. Faceted spurs along the Awatere transcurrent fault in New Zealand, last active in 1848. It separates graywacke mountains on the right from soft Cretaceous beds on the left. (Photo: S. N. Beatus, New Zealand Geological Survey)

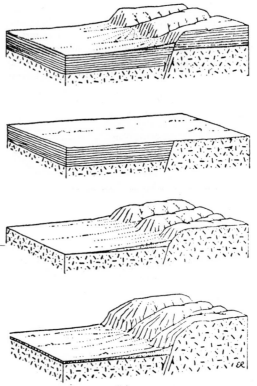

FIG. 6. Four sketches showing progressive evolution of a fault scarp (top) to a featureless plain, and then to renewed relief. The fourth (lowest) diagram shows how renewed faulting has given a scarp of double slope, the base of the scarp being steeper, the upper part more gently inclined. In this case, it is evident that the upper portion is a fault-line scarp due to erosion, while the lower part is a fault scarp due directly to movement along the fracture plane. An excellent example of such a composite scarp is found in the Hurricane Ledge south of the Virgin River in Arizona (Johnson, 1930).

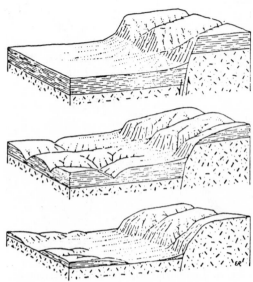

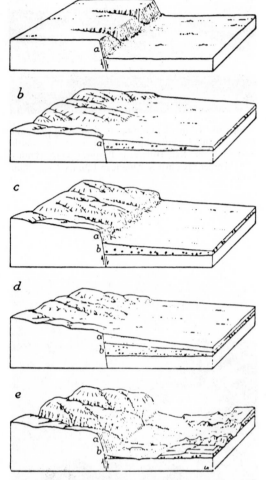

FIG. 7. A similar topographic form to Fig. 6, but the history is just the reverse. Here the upper part of the scarp is a true fault scarp, as can be seen from the first and second diagrams, while the base is a fault-line erosion scarp, caused by later removal of weaker beds, some remnants of which remain in places (Johnson, 1930).

ideally in semiarid country where they are well preserved, e.g., in Nevada. In more humid country, e.g., Oregon and California, the drainage patterns show striking effects (Fig. 3). Fresh scarps are also frequently observed in Japan, New Zealand and Turkey. They usually range from 1–10 meters in height, as representative of the last movement, but the total displacement of the fault may be far greater, traces of the earlier motions being largely

FIG. 9. A true fault scarp (a) is buried (b), again exposed, not by erosion, but by a renewal of the faulting (c). Further accumulation of alluvium again buries the scarp (d). Renewed uplift (e) resurrects the upper portion of the scarp "a," while stripping away of the alluvium gives a fault-line erosion scarp at the base "b" (Johnson, 1930).

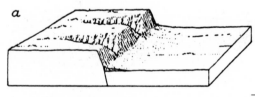

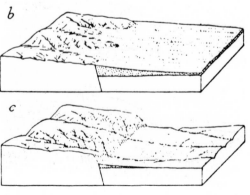

FIG. 8. Both fault scarps and fault-line erosion scarps may be more or less completely buried by accumulating alluvial or other debris. Alluvium washed from the uplifted block shown in the first diagram ultimately spreads across the fault plane into the valleys of that same block as shown in the second diagram; the remnants of the scarp still rising above the alluvial accumulation will appear irregular or ragged, with embayments of the sloping piedmont plain between projecting spurs of the upland. In the third sketch, renewed erosion strips away the alluvium, and we have a resurrected fault scarp, or a resurrected fault-line erosion scarp, as the case may be. A key to the history will sometimes be found in terraces or benches of alluvium high up on the valley walls, as shown in the third diagram (Johnson, 1930).

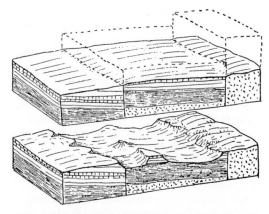

FIG. 10. Obsequent fault-line scarp (on the left) and a rejuvenated fault-line scarp (on the right), producing a physiographic graben, at Séverac-le-Chateau in France (de Martonne, 1951, p. 778). The top diagram depicts the peneplanation stage prior to rejuvenation.

obscured by erosion (Blackwelder, 1928; Reiche, 1938).

In the case of transcurrent or tear faults (with strike-slip motion) which intersect hill or mountain country, the fault scarps are in the form of facets terminating ridges ("faceted spurs," Fig. 4) and may be matched by corresponding facets on the laterally displaced side, a "shutter effect." Streams are thus

displaced, so that often segments of their courses follow the fault trace (Cotton, 1957). Numerous examples can be seen in California (e.g., associated with the San Andreas fault system) and in New Zealand (the Great Alpine fault system). It should be added that not all faceted spurs are caused by fault scarps; they are also associated with marine abrasion, with glacial valleys and with actively rejuvenated river valleys.

A *fault-line scarp* (of W. M. Davis) is a cliff that is subparallel to the fault trace, but is so modified by erosion that it does not reflect the fault plane in any way (Fig. 5). Weathering may simply degrade the initial slope of the fault plane, burying the base of the footwall in a *bajada* (q.v.) type apron of alluvial fans, or the scarp may recede (possibly some hundreds of meters) so that the actual fault trace lies buried beneath the alluvial fans at some unspecified distance. Only renewed action of the fault movement sometimes discloses the precise line, so that frequently, as in the *Basin-Range Province* (pr Vol. VIII), the geological maps mark the fault with a broken line although the surveyor has not the slightest doubt that the fault trace lies in that approximate position.

W. M. Davis (1913) has treated the terminology of fault-line scarps, proposing two useful categories in stratified rocks:

(a) *Resequent*, in which the entire land surface has been degraded, disclosing a more resistant

FIG. 11. A fault-line valley, produced by constant revival of movement along the great Alpine transcurrent fault of New Zealand's South Island, where it is followed by the Jackson River, and separates schists (on the right) from graywacke and granite (on the left). (Photo: S. N. Beatus, New Zealand Geological Survey).

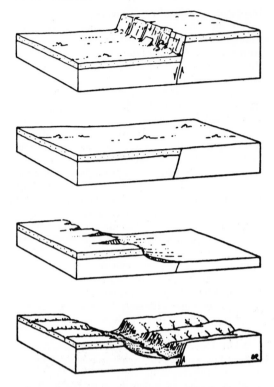

FIG. 12. A fault-line valley produced by fault revival after peneplanation and obsequent scarp development (Johnson, 1930)

formation in the hanging wall, so that a cliff actually approximates the fault trace on the upthrown side;

(b) *Obsequent*, in which the land surface has been further degraded, but the hard formation of the hanging wall has been entirely removed and is exposed on the footwall side. A relief inversion is

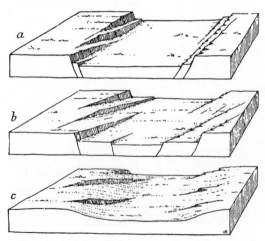

FIG. 13. Echelon fault steps produced by a small dextral strike-slip (right lateral) component in the basement, leading to tilted steps (Johnson, 1930)

thus established and the footwall now occupies the upland position. The same sort of inversion sometimes occurs in *horsts* (q.v.) and *grabens* (q.v.).

A *fault-line valley* frequently results from either normal or strike-slip faulting, usually subject to a long history of rejuvenation (Fig. 11) either because of simple differential erosion along the fault line (the faulting leads to extreme brecciation and permits easy erosion), or because the revival of faulting brings a formerly upthrown block once more to prominence (Fig. 12).

We have considered only normal and strike-slip faults. Two other movements of the adjacent blocks are possible:

(a) *Rotation* along the strike, usually leading to oblique shears, is a common situation where there is strike-slip motion in the basement, but in soft superficial cover sediments the result is a series of *echelon blocks*, or *step blocks* (Fig. 13). Numbers of these structures pass longitudinally into monoclines, with associated hogbacks in the geomorphology.

(b) The remaining type of block movement is the *over-thrust block* (Fig. 14), where the footwall is frequently covered by gravity slips or normal faults, which may well obscure its real character. Since a low-angle fault intersects the earth's surface at a very acute angle, the trace of that fault across the landscape is frequently meandering and forms deep reentrants in streams; it may even be exposed

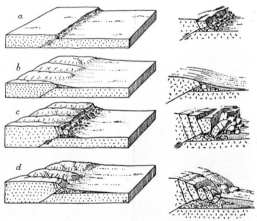

FIG. 14. A thrust block in the first diagram is softened by erosion; the base of the scarps may be sharpened and steepened by renewed movement along the thrust plane. Scarps with multiple slopes, gravel benches, rock terraces and rejuvenated valleys may thus in time be observed along the bounding walls. As the mass advances, its forward edge may be unsupported, with conditions favorable for the development of landslides, shown in the enlargement. In time, weathering and deposition of alluvium will obliterate the slide topography, and the form shown in the second diagram will be indistinguishable from a weathered normal fault scarp. Renewed movement will recreate conditions favorable for slipping (Johnson, 1930).

in "tectonic windows" if the fault plane is un-dulating (as it often is, due to a second generation of folding).

RHODES W. FAIRBRIDGE

References

Blackwelder, E., 1928, "The recognition of fault scarps," *J. Geol.*, **36,** 289–311.

Cotton, C. A., 1957, "Geomorphic evidence and major structures associated with transcurrent faults in New Zealand," *Rev. Géomorph. Dyn., Paris*, **8,** 155.

Davis, W. M., 1913, "Nomenclature of surface forms on faulted structures," *Bull. Geol. Soc. Am.*, **24,** 187–216.

Johnson, D. W., 1930, "Geomorphologic aspects of rift valleys," *Intern. Geol. Congr. 15th, South Africa*, 1929, *Compt. Rend.*, **2,** 354–373.

Kennedy, W. Q., 1946, "The Great Glen Fault," *Quart. J. Geol. Soc., London*, **102,** 41.

Martonne, E. de, 1951, "Traité de Géographie Physique," Vol. 2, Paris, A. Colin, 1057pp.

Reiche, P., 1938, "Recent fault scarps, Organ Mountain district, New Mexico," *Am. J. Sci.*, **36,** 440–444.

Stamp, L. D. (editor), 1961, "A Glossary of Geographical Terms," London, Longmans, Green & Co., 539pp.

Wooldridge, S. W., and Morgan, R. S., 1937, "The Physical Basis of Geography: An Outline of Geomorphology," London, Longmans, Green & Co., 445pp.

Cross-references: *Bajada*; *Basin-Range Landscape*; *Block Diagram*; *Cuesta*; *Drainage Patterns*; *Escarpment*; *Exhumed Landscape*; *Graben*; *Horst*; *Inversion of Topography* (*Relief*); *Piedmont*. Vol. V: *Slickenside*. pr Vol. VIII: *Basin-Range Province*.

FELSENMEER (BLOCK FIELD)

The German terms *Felsenmeer* or *Blockmeer* (plural—*e*), or the English "*block field*," are applied in geomorphology to a chaotic assemblage of fractured rocks in any flat lowland area in the polar regions or any high plateau or summit in temperate latitudes, where well-jointed massive rock types outcrop. Under *frost riving* (q.v.) intense shattering occurs and the landscape becomes a sea of jagged boulders and rock fragments. *Exfoliation* (q.v.) or *spheroidal weathering* (q.v.) may convert larger boulders into subrounded forms. On slopes marginal to *felsenmeere*, there may be *stone rivers*, *rock streams* or *rock glaciers*, where *frost heaving* (q.v.) in combination with gravity sets the boulders in sluggish motion.

Characteristic examples of *felsenmeere* are seen in the Colorado Rockies, at the summits of Pikes Peak, Mt. Evans, etc., as well as in the Appalachians (Smith, 1953).

RHODES W. FAIRBRIDGE

References

Aubert de la Rüe, 1932, "Étude géologique et géographique de l'Archipel de Kerguelen," *Rev. Geogr. Phys.*, **5,** 1–231.

Bryan, Kirk, 1928, "Glacial climate in non-glaciated regions," *Am. J. Sci.*, **216,** 162–164.

Charlesworth, J. K., 1957, "The Quarternary Era," 2 vols. London, Ed. Arnold.

Drygalski, E. von, 1892, "Grönlands Gletscher und Inlandeis," *Z. Geogr. Erdk.* (*Berlin*), **27,** 1–62.

Potter, N., Jr. and Moss, J. H., 1968, "Origin of the Blue Rocks block field and adjacent deposits, Berks County, Pennsylvania," *Bull. Geol. Soc. Am.*, **79,** 255–262.

Schott, C., 1933, "Die Blockmeere in den deutschen Mittelgebirgen," *Forsch. Deutsch. Landeskunde*, **29**(1).

Sharpe, C. F. S., 1938, "Landslides and Related Phenomena," New York, Columbia University Press, 137pp.

Smith, H. T. U., 1953, "The Hickory Run boulder field, Carbon County, Pennsylvania," *Am. J. Sci.*, **251,** 625–642.

Von Engeln, O. D., 1942, "Geomorphology," New York, The Macmillan Co., 655pp.

Cross-references: *Exfoliation*; *Frost Heaving*; *Frost Riving*; *Mountain Glacier Landscapes*; *Periglacial Landscapes*; *Spheroidal Weathering*.

FERRICRETE, FERRALITE—*See* INDURATION

FINGER LAKES

Geography

A group of semiparallel and en echelon lakes in central New York are referred to as the "Finger Lakes." The name originated in the Indian legend of the Great Spirit placing his hand on the earth causing the finger-like indentations. Most academicians now recognize eleven lakes in this grouping although there are other nearby lakes. Indian names have been given to most of the Finger Lakes, which are, from east to west: Otisco, Skaneateles, Owasco, Cayuga, Seneca, Keuka, Canandaigua, Honeoye, Canadice, Hemlock and Conesus (Fig. 1). The seven eastern lakes are tributary to the Seneca River, the western four flow to the Genesee River, and all drain north to Lake Ontario. Other bonds that unite this group of lakes include similarities in elongation ratio (about 10), geomorphic setting and geologic origin. When all such factors are considered, this arrangement of lakes is not duplicated elsewhere on earth.

A wide range in physical characteristics of the Finger Lakes is evident in Table 1. For example, differences occur of 700 feet (213 meters) in surface elevation, 600 feet (183 meters) in depth, 1200 feet (366 meters) in bottom elevation, and 58° in directional trend. Great volume disparity also exists since either Seneca or Cayuga (546 and 333 billion cubic feet, respectively; Birge and Juday, 1914), the largest lakes by far, contain more water than the other nine lakes combined. The Finger Lake Region

TABLE 1. FINGER LAKE PHYSICAL PROPERTIES

Lake	Surface Eleva-tion (ft)	Greatest Depth (ft)	Mean Depth (ft)	Bottom Eleva-tion (ft)	Water Area (square miles)	Basin Area (square miles)	Length (miles)	Trend
Otisco	788	66	33	722	4	3.5	6	N 38 W
Skaneateles	863	297	143	576	14	81	15	N 35 W
Owasco	711	177	96	534	10	213	11	N 19 W
Cayuga	381	435	179	− 54	66	879	38	N 21 W
Seneca	445	633	290	− 188	67	504	35	N 7 W
Keuka	709	186	—	523	17	248	20	N 20 E
Canandaigua	687	274	128	413	17	175	16	N 18 E
Honeoye	803	30	—	773	2	42	4	N
Canadice	1096	91	54	1005	1	12	3	N 2 E
Hemlock	905	96	—	899	3	40	7	N 6 W
Conesus	818	66	—	752	5	67	8	N 5 E

is 80 miles (129 km) long in an east-west direction and 50 miles (80 km) at the widest part in a north-south direction. Precipitation increases from about 30 inches in the western part of the area to 39 inches in the east (76–100 cm).

Geology

The Finger Lakes are incised into sedimentary rocks of predominant marine origin that range in age from Upper Silurian at the northern tip of Cayuga Lake to Upper Devonian in the southern part of the region. The rocks are mostly fine-grained clastics but include Onondaga limestone in the north and a belt of Tully limestone that extends eastward from Canandaigua Lake. Structurally, the Finger Lakes are part of a homocline that dips about 40 ft/mile (8 m/km) in a S 25° W direction. Slight flexures occur that gently plunge somewhat south-west, but locally doming is more important (Wedel, 1932; Sutton, 1959). Watkins Glen and Ithaca contain salt extraction industries, where, for example, in Cayuga Lake, Silurian salt beds are reached by a mine and a salt well 1800 feet (550 meters) below lake level. Other structures include thrust faults with about 100-foot (30-meter) displacements (see, e.g. Cole, 1959, p. 12), some small gravity faults, and three joint sets. Apparently the north-trending joints are extension fractures since this is the only set that contains the more than 70 serpentinized mica peridotite dikes that range up to 12 feet (3.6 meters) in thickness.

Geomorphology

The Finger Lakes largely occur in the glaciated Appalachian Plateau and are bounded on the north by the Lake Erie–Ontario Lowland and on the south by tributary drainages of the Susquehanna River. The serrate and somewhat poorly developed easterly trending Allegheny escarpment is notched by the lakes on the north, with a large embayment occurring in the Seneca-Cayuga district. The elevation

range is 381 feet (116 meters) at Cayuga Lake to about 2300 feet (700 meters) in the western part of the region. The highest elevations in the east are about 1900 feet (580 meters), with several hills in the southern part of the area rising to elevations greater than 2000 feet (610 meters). Some of the higher hills, such as Connecticut Hill (von Engeln, p. 34, 1961) may be structurally controlled by synclines.

All Finger Lakes occur in trough-like valleys with impoundment of waters between Valley Heads end moraine on the south and massive morainic deposits on the north. Fenneman (p. 314, 1938) provides the following valley-side description:

"They are wonderfully smoothed, increasing in steepness toward the lakes with a gently convex curvature. Except for a few postglacial ravines, the contour lines are almost as straight as the lakes. For many miles together the absence of tributaries is almost complete. Not only were the lateral ravines of preglacial time filled, but the divides between them were smoothed off. Nothing but a glacier could have made the sides of these lake basins so simple."

Thus, upper slopes are more gentle with grades of about 5% that increase downward to grades of more than 20% and containing occasional vertical bedrock cliffs.

The bottoms of two lakes, Seneca and Cayuga, are below sea level, and the greatest water depths usually occur about two-thirds the linear distance from the northern outlets. Soundings by engineering classes at Cornell University in the late 1800's and more recently by the U.S. Army Corps of Engineers (1961) indicate irregular lake floors for the larger lakes. In Seneca and Cayuga lakes water depth differences of 200–300 feet (61–92 meters) occur in horizontal distances of less than 1000 feet (305 meters). In many cases, the underwater valley sides of the lakes are as steep or steeper than land slopes with depths greater than 200 feet (61 meters) occurring near shore. Extensive deltas have been formed

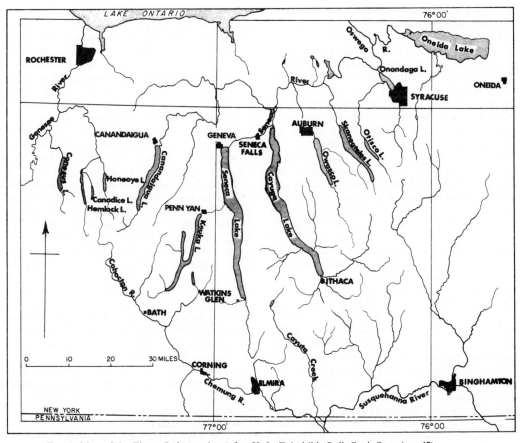

FIG. 1. Map of the Finger Lakes region (after H. L. Fairchild, *Bull. Geol. Soc. Am.*, **45**).

by streams flowing into the south end of the lake basins. These deposits are at least 435 feet (133 meters) thick at Ithaca and may be more than 1000 feet (305 meters) thick at Watkins Glen.

Glaciation

(A) Origin of Valleys. The Finger Lakes were covered by ice more than 3000 feet (915 meters) thick during both Illinoian and Wisconsinan glaciations, and terminal moraines occur about 60 miles (97 km) south of the area. Illinoian deposits have not yet been identified in the region, and the number of separate ice advances during Wisconsinan time is debatable (Moss and Ritter, 1962). The influence and amount of glacial sculpture in the region has been a recurring controversy. About 100 years ago in a visit to the new Cornell institution at Ithaca (1868), Louis Agassiz spoke of the glacial heritage of the region. Among the first to record the amount of ice erosion were Lincoln and Tarr. Thus, Lincoln (1892, p. 300) states ". . . the lakes are deeply gouged by ice . . .", and (1894, p. 113) "the trough of Seneca Lake . . . is . . . irreconcilable with the hypothesis of pure river erosion, with or without crust bending." That he attributed valley initiation to fluvial causes, however, is evident (1892, p. 299) ". . . the preglacial river which has been developed into Seneca Lake must have occupied a level many hundreds of feet above the present bed of the lake." As to the status of glacial erosion, Tarr seems to have wavered and changed his mind several times. In 1894 he argued for glacial erosion, but by 1904 he had changed his mind and stated (1904, p. 290–291) "The glacial erosion theory is opposed by various facts; the rejuvenation theory must at present be considered a possible explanation . . . . The current theory for the origin of these valleys by glacial erosion . . . cannot be considered established." Tarr discussed seven different lines of evidence that were opposed to the glacial erosion theory. However, by 1906 Tarr stated, "I am now convinced that the interpretation that this discordance is opposed in the glacial-erosion theory was incorrect, and that these two valleys are really confirmatory of the glacial-erosion theory", and ". . . rejuvenation seems utterly impossible." Thus, although Tarr (1909) finally concluded the significance of glacial erosion,

353

H. L. Fairchild never wavered, and disavowed glaciation from any importance in the sculpturing of Finger Lake valleys in all his writings. In 1905 (p. 65) he wrote, "It is plainly evident that the ice did not produce the valleys; it did not even enlarge them . . .", and in 1934b (p. 1086) he reaffirmed this belief, "On the high lands and the valley walls the abrasive action of the ice sheet was a smoothing effect. Valley deepening is ruled out". Other geologists, notably Carney (1909), Dryer (1904) and Holmes (1937), argue for Finger Lake origin as valley initiation by streams with overdeepening by glacial ice. Flint (1957, p. 83) has summarized this position: The Finger Lakes, "were first cut by preglacial streams flowing north. They were widened, greatly deepened, and straightened by subglacial erosion when the Laurentide Ice Sheet repeatedly filled and overran them from the north." All advocates of the general theory, however, would not agree with the flow direction of preglacial streams. For example, Monnett (1924) summarizes earlier views on drainage direction and concludes that at least Skaneateles and Otisco Lakes formerly drained south. Von Engeln (1961, p. 39–40) divided the region into two sets of lakes, believing that the five eastern lakes occupy valleys where rivers flowed north while the six western lakes represent ancestral valleys that drained south. Fairchild (1925) traces the evolution of drainage in the area, believing that in preglacial times all of the Finger Lake region drained north into an ancestral Ontarian River that flowed west into Mississippi River drainage. Thus, although there was disagreement about the amount of glacial erosion and preglacial drainage direction, all workers prior to 1965 believed the Finger Lakes to be occupants of ancestral fluvial valleys.

In a 1965 article, Clayton compared the Finger Lakes with certain Scottish lakes and claimed, ". . . the whole of the relief near the Finger Lakes is the work of ice, and is quite independent of the form of the preglacial landscape" (p. 50), and that the valleys ". . . were initiated as the southward-moving ice overrode the escarpment, forming . . . 'intrusive troughs' " (p. 51). The numerous "through valleys"* were also ". . . cut into the plateau independently of . . . preexisting water partings . . ." (p. 53). Thus, Clayton developed a theory that the major valleys of the Finger Lakes were not fluvial in origin, but instead gouged out by ice. He attributed the small size of the easternmost and westernmost lakes to their greater distance from the main thrust of the ice sheet that radiated outward from the Lake Ontario region. Coates (1966a) believes a multicyclic theory is necessary to explain all features of the Finger Lakes Region (p. 472), which require a ". . . combination of a long period of

---

* A term first used by W. M. Davis to describe oppositely flowing streams that occupy and head into the same valley.

preglacial erosion followed by a series of unusual glacial, interglacial, and proglacial stream diversion channels that were repeatedly exploited by later ice movements." In a 1966 article, Clayton modified his earlier opinion by stating, "In my view the ice locally initiated valley development. Far more commonly it occupied, enlarged and joined up existing fluvial valleys . . ." (p. 477). Thus, in the geological literature of the Finger Lakes there is a full range for their excavation entirely by fluvial processes or largely by glacial processes, or some combination of the two. Arguments that have been advanced as indicative of negligible glacial erosion in Finger Lake valleys include: (1) convexity of valley-side slopes, (2) preglacial remnants of transverse tributary valleys, (3) bedrock islands such as Frontenac Island near the north end of Cayuga Lake, and (4) preglacial rock-weathered clays preserved under till in several quarries on the valley walls. Regardless of the final disposition of the debate, deposits such as the varves in Sixmile Creek and deltaic beds at the Fernback locality that are both older than 34,000 years and lie in exposed positions indicate that at least the latest Wisconsinan glaciation, and probably earlier Wisconsinan glaciations as well, were incapable of destroying and moving some nonlithified sediments. Thus, older glaciations must be called upon to have created the glacial deepening of the valleys, amounting to more than 1000 feet (305 meters) in the larger basins of the region.

(B) Former Lakes. The present Finger Lakes represent only one lake phase in the total lacustrine history of the region. A series of proglacial lakes were formed both during the advance and the retreat of the ice sheets and the most prominent levels have been given names and elevations. The history of the Cayuga basin is best known and can serve as an example. Fairchild (1934a, p. 272) provides the following names and elevations of former lakes: Ithaca—1000 feet (305 meters), Newberry—945 feet (288 meters), Hall—825 feet (252 meters), Vanuxem I down—825 feet (252 meters), Cayuga I—325 feet (100 meters), Vanuxem II up—785 feet (239 meters), Warren—795 feet (242 meters), Dana—615 feet (188 meters), Cayuga II—321 feet (98 meters), Iroquois—362 feet (110 meters), and Cayuga III—381 feet (116 meters). The lake history has been interpreted from a variety of evidence that includes overflow channel characteristics, lake clays and sands on hillslopes, well-defined deltas, etc. For example, a series of more than six excellent hanging deltas occur at the Coy Glen locality southwest of Ithaca (Chisnell, 1951). Although the duration of a particular lake level is unknown, Schmidt (1947, pp. 77–78) was able to calculate, on the basis of varves in Sixmile Creek southeast of Ithaca, that it took 600–700 years to deposit the varve sequences.

As proglacial lake waters receded to successive lower levels, tributary streams extended downward to meet the lower elevations. The new valleys that were incised were not always in juxtaposition with preglacial or interglacial valleys, since many had been covered by drift, thereby causing a new post-glacial valley or "glen" in bedrock with cascades, falls, chutes and rapids. The two most famous glens are at Watkins Glen near Seneca Lake and Enfield Glen southwest of Ithaca. In some cases, streams in the glens alternate between flowing in the older valleys and in the postglacial gorges. The highest waterfall in the United States east of the Rocky Mountains is the 215-foot (65-meter) Taughannock Falls on the west side of Cayuga Lake. Interglacial time was longer than postglacial time since the older valleys are deeper and broader (Muller, 1957, p. 1771). Recent study of deltaic beds on the west side of Cayuga Lake (Bloom, 1967) indicates that interglacial time for the region was more than 54,000 years ago and that temperatures were warmer, producing fauna similar to the middle Don beds at Toronto.

The weight of the ice and of deeper lake waters caused isostatic elevation changes in the Finger Lakes Region. Fairchild concluded (1934a, p. 244) that land has risen 2.2 ft/mile (0.4 m/km) in a N 20° E direction. Chisnell (1951) measured strand-line differences in the Coy Glen vicinity of 1.34 ft/mile (0.2 m/km) for the higher lake levels and 0.74 ft/mile (0.1 m/km) in lower lake sequences along northwest traverses. Krall (1966) working in the eastern Finger Lakes measured uplift toward the north of 2 ft/mile (0.4 m/km).

(C) Deposits. Surficial glacial deposits show a wide range in form, thickness and composition. The most prominent deposits are the Valley Heads end moraine at the southern boundary of the area and the thick drift deposits that dam the Finger Lakes on the north. Much of the glacial drift is considered Valley Heads whose outwash deposits are more than 12,000 B.P. and probably correlative with the Port Huron Substage (Lake Escarpment; Muller, 1965, p. 108). The hills and divides between the Finger Lakes are mantled with a variety of ground moraine and a conglomeration of arcuate, poorly defined and discontinuous patches of reces-sional morainic drift. In some areas, till thickness is thin and underlying bedrock joint patterns are visible on aerial photographs. Carney (1909) in mapping the Moravia 1:62,500 quadrangle east of Cayuga Lake found that average till thickness was about 25 feet (8 meters) above 1300 feet (396 meters), and Coates (1966b) calculated average till thickness on hills south of the Valley Heads moraine to be about 60 feet (18 meters). Thickness of stratified drift is much greater and is at least 435 feet (133 meters) at Ithaca, more than 200 feet (61 meters) at Geneva, 646 feet (197 meters) in Honeoye Lake, and more than 1000 feet (305 meters) thick near Watkins Glen.

The composition of Valley Heads drift (Holmes, 1952) is mostly local with materials traveling less than 50 miles (80 km). For example, more than 95% of the materials were derived from outcrops south of Lake Ontario. The lithology is largely shale, silt-stone and sandstone, with less than 15% of the pebbles, as limestones and crystallines, coming from outside the region.

Limnology

Cayuga Lake has received more limnological study than all other Finger Lakes combined (see Henson, Bradshaw and Chandler, 1961). The most complete studies of the entire region were done by Birge and Juday (1914, 1921), and more recently additional data has been collected by Larkin, of the N.Y. State Department of Health (1956). Berg (1963) summarizes much of the information, and Table 2 presents chemical data for eight of the lakes. It is noteworthy that Seneca and Cayuga contain sig-nificantly more Na + K and Cl than other lakes, which can largely be attributed to greater depres-sion of the water table and depth of valley incision. Canadice, probably representative of the four western lakes, has exceptionally low values for most chemical components measured. This is a reflection of the remoteness of the effluent groundwaters, both

TABLE 2. CHEMICAL CHARACTERISTICS OF SELECTED FINGER LAKES[a]

Lake	pH	ppm							
		Alkalinity	Ca	Mg	Na + K	HCO₃	SO₄	Cl	NO₃
Canadice	7.0	27.9	12	2.8	3.2	34	17	2.3	0.4
Canandaigua	8.1	103.3	35	9.7	7.5	126	28	5.1	1.7
Cayuga	7.4	105.7	47	9.6	61.0	129	55	88.0	2.8
Conesus	7.7	108.2	40	11.0	9.4	132	31	13.0	0.9
Otisco	7.3	110.6	40	8.5	2.3	135	19	5.7	1.1
Owasco	7.5	99.2	36	7.4	4.3	121	20	4.8	3.4
Seneca	7.1	104.9	40	10.0	85.6	128	39	125.0	1.6
Skaneateles	7.5	93.4	36	6.2	2.9	114	16	3.6	2.0

[a] Berg, 1963, p. 201.

in vertical and horizontal distances, from any limestone or salt beds.

Studies of the larger lakes such as Cayuga and Seneca indicate there are two limnology seasons: (1) the summer season from late May to November with stratified waters and (2) the winter circulation season. The lowest recorded temperature (average of waters to 133-meter depth) was 1.3°C on April 3, 1940, and the highest was 9.9°C on August 27, 1952. These large lakes rarely freeze except near the shore, and for only 9 years in the 1796–1914 period were the lakes entirely frozen. It should be noted that several of the winters in which Cayuga was frozen over were during or immediately after the explosive volcanic eruptions of Krakatoa in 1883 and Katmai in 1912. Thus it takes exceptionally cold and calm weather or other conditions to freeze these homothermous lakes. Waters in Cayuga Lake are replaced about every 9 years.

In a study of lakes Canandaigua, Cayuga, Keuka, Owasco and Seneca (Larkin, 1956), the following data were obtained: summer temperatures 24–27°C. pH 8.1–8.4, dissolved oxygen (ppm) 8.0–13.4, B.O.D. (ppm) 1.8 average, and coliforms M.P.N. per 100 ml generally less than 3.6 but greater than 2000 in some areas. There are more than 200 industrial and municipal sources of pollution in these five lakes.

DONALD R. COATES

References

Berg, C. O., 1963, in (Frey, D. G., editor) "Limnology in North America," pp. 191–237, Madison, Wisc., The University of Wisconsin Press.

Birge, E. A. and Juday, C., 1914, "A limnological study of the Finger Lakes of New York," *U.S. Bur. Fish. Bull.*, **32**, 525–614.

Birge, E. A., and Juday, C., 1921, "Further limnological observations on the Finger Lakes of New York," *U.S. Bur. Fish. Bull.*, **37**, 210–252.

Bloom, A. L., 1967, " 'Fernbank': a rediscovered Pleistocene Interglacial deposit near Ithaca, N.Y.," *Geol. Soc. Am. Northeastern Section Meeting*, Program, p. 15.

Carney, F., 1909, "The Pleistocene geology of the Moravia quadrangle," *Denison Univ. Sci. Lab. Bull.*, **14**, 335–442.

Chisnell, T. C., 1951, "Recognition and Interpretation of Proglacial Strand Lines in the Cayuga Basin," Ph.D. thesis, Cornell University.

Clayton, K. M., 1965, "Glacial erosion in the Finger Lakes Region (New York State, U.S.A.)," *Z. Geomorphol.*, **9**, 50–62.

Clayton, K. M., 1966, "Reply to Professor Coates," *Z. Geomorphol.*, **10**, 475–477.

Coates, D. R., 1966a, "Discussion of K. M. Clayton 'Glacial erosion in the Finger Lakes Region (New York State, U.S.A.)'," *Z. Geomorphol.*, **10**, 469–474.

Coates, D. R., 1966b, "Glaciated Appalachian Plateau: till shadows on hills," *Science*, **152**, 1617–1619.

Cole, W. S. (editor), 1959, "Geology of the Cayuga Lake basin," Guidebook for 31st Ann. Mtg. N.Y. State Geol. Assoc., 36pp.

Dryer, C. R., 1904, "Finger Lake Region of western New York," *Bull. Geol. Soc. Am.*, **15**, 448–460.

Fairchild, H. L., 1905, "Ice erosion theory a fallacy," *Bull. Geol. Soc. Am.*, **16**, 13–74.

Fairchild, H. L., 1925, "The Susquehanna River in New York and evolution of western New York Drainage," *N.Y. State Mus. Bull.*, **256**, 99pp.

Fairchild, H. L., 1934a, "Cayuga Valley lake history," *Bull. Geol. Soc. Am.*, **45**, 233–280.

Fairchild, H. L., 1934b, "Seneca Valley physiographic and glacial history," *Bull. Geol. Soc. Am.*, **45**, 1073–1109.

Fenneman, N. M., 1938, "Physiography of Eastern United States," New York, McGraw-Hill Book Co., 714pp.

Flint, R. F., 1957, "Glacial and Pleistocene Geology," New York, John Wiley & Sons, 553pp.

Henson, E. B., Bradshaw, A. S., and Chandler, D. C., 1961, "The physical limnology of Cayuga Lake, New York," *Cornell Univ. Agr. Expt. Sta. Mem.*, **378**, 63pp.

Holmes, C. D., 1937, "Glacial erosion in a dissected plateau," *Am. J. Sci.*, **33**(5), 217–232.

Holmes, C. D., 1952, "Drift dispersion in west-central New York," *Bull. Geol. Soc. Am.*, **63**, 993–1010.

Krall, D. B., 1966, "Fluvioglacial Drainage between Skaneateles and Syracuse, New York," M. A. thesis, Syracuse University, 156pp.

Larkin, W. H. (editor), 1956. "Finger Lakes drainage basin," *New York State Department of Health Oswego River Drainage Basin Survey Series Report no. 1*, 361pp.

Lincoln, D. F., 1892, "Glaciation in the Finger Lake region of New York," *Am. J. Sci.*, **44**(3), 290–301.

Lincoln, D. F., 1894, "The amount of glacial erosion in the Finger Lake region of New York," *Am. J. Sci.*, **47**(3), 105–113.

Monnett, V. E., 1924, "The Finger Lakes of central New York," *Am. J. Sci.*, **8**(5), 33–53.

Moss, J. H., and Ritter, D. F., 1962, "New evidence regarding the Binghamton substage in the region between the Finger Lakes and Catskills, New York," *Am. J. Sci.*, **260**, 81–106.

Muller, E. H., 1957, "Filled bedrock gorges in the drainage basin of Cayuga Lake, New York," *Bull. Geol. Soc. Am.* (abstract), **68**, 1771.

Muller, E. H., 1965, "Quaternary Geology of New York," in (Wright, H. E., and Frey, D. G., editors), "The Quaternary of the United States," *VII Congress of the International Assoc. for Quaternary Research*, 99–112.

Schmidt, V. E., 1947, "Varves in the Finger Lakes Region of New York," Ph.D. thesis, Cornell University.

Sutton, R. G., 1959, "Structural geology of the Dryden and Harford quadrangles New York," *N.Y. State Mus. and Sci. Service*, 15pp.

Tarr, R. S., 1894, "Lake Cayuga, a rock basin," *Bull. Geol. Soc. Am.*, **5**, 339–356.

Tarr, R. S., 1904, "Hanging valleys in the Finger Lake region of central New York," *Am. Geologist*, **33**, 270–291.

Tarr, R. S., 1906, "Glacial erosion in the Finger Lake region of central New York," *J. Geol.*, **14**, 18–21.

Tarr, R. S., 1909, in (Williams, H. S., Tarr, R. S., and Kindle, E. M.), "Watkins Glen-Catatonk Folio, New York," *U.S. Geol. Surv. Geol. Atlas*, **169**, 33pp.

U.S. Army Corps of Engineers, 1961, "U.S. Lake Survey of New York State Barge Canal System," Cayuga and Seneca Lakes, Chart 187.

von Engeln, O. D., 1961, "The Finger Lakes Region: Its Origin and Nature," Ithaca, N.Y., Cornell University Press, 156pp.

Cross-references: *Cryptodepressions; Fluvioglacial Processes; Glacial Lakes; Glacial Spillways and Proglacial Lakes; Glacial Valley; Lakes; Moraine; Postglacial Isostatic Rebound; Proglacial Deposits.* Vol. II: *Krakatoa Winds.* pr Vol. VI: *Glacier Geophysics; Limnology; Varves.*

FIRN—*See* SNOW: METAMORPHISM OF DEPOSITED SNOW

FJÄRD

A rocky, irregular inlet of low relief, glacially scoured and deeply drowned, characteristic of the west coast of Sweden and some of the skerry areas of Norway. There are lateral channels as well as radial. It is distinguished from a fjord in that it is irregular in shape and lacks the high relief and U-shaped cross sections of the fiord coasts. For these reasons it might be confused with *rias* (q.v.), but of course the latter are not glaciated and often show overlapping spurs.

The term fjärd (plural *fjärdar* in Swedish) is often anglicized, as by J. W. Gregory (1913) into fiard (plural fiards). It would be wise to retain the Swedish accent and pronunciation ("fee-air-d") to avoid confusion in speech with fjord. Many of the Scottish *firths* are better characterized as fjärds than fiords, as are many of the drowned rocky estuaries of Connecticut and Maine.

RHODES W. FAIRBRIDGE

References

Gregory, J. W., 1913, "The Nature and Origin of Fiords," London, J. Murray, 542pp.

Stamp, L. D., (editor), 1961, "A Glossary of Geographical Terms," London, Longmans, Green & Co., 539pp.

Cross-references: *Fjord; Ria.*

FJELL (FJELD, FJÄLL)

Fjell, or fjäll, are respectively Norwegian and Swedish words for mountain areas above the tree line. Fjeld is the old Norwegian spelling. Edgar Kant (in Stamp, 1961) stresses that it is not just simply any

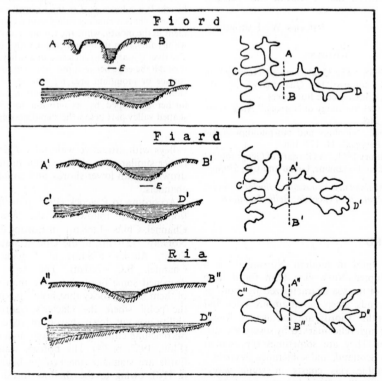

FIG. 1. Comparative diagrams of fiord, fjärd, and ria. A–B, Cross sections; C–D, longitudinal sections; E, the level of maximum depth in the fiord, and fjärd (from Gregory, 1913). (By permission of John Murray, Publishers, London.)

such mountain area, but flat undissected highland terrain. It thus has a special place in geomorphic literature. "Fjeld" (old Norwegian spelling) and the English equivalent "fell" are sometimes used.

After studying the Norwegian fjells, Rudberg (1962) indicated that the tree line was not a critical part of the definition, since it is more variable in the maritime climate of Norway. Both in Norway and in the adjacent parts of Sweden the fjells correlate with the low-angle thrust sheets of the Caledonian orogenic belt, so that a measure of structural control is present. The critical feature is that they are high level remnants of preglacial erosion surfaces, probably former peneplains. In Norway, they are often bare rock and considerably dissected by U-shaped glacial valleys, a feature less evident in Sweden where many fjells are till covered. Nunataks are claimed by some botanists to have existed, even at the height of the Quaternary glaciation, and would thus have provided botanical "refuges", but few geologists now accept this interpretation.

It should be remembered that parts of the Scandinavian Shield represent an exhumed Cambrian surface. In a few places, old stream channels in this "peneplain" are found with remnants of older Paleozoic marine sedimentary fills. Most of it is a classical "*stripped peneplain*," secondarily dissected by fluvial action during the Tertiary uplift and by Pleistocene ice.

RHODES W. FAIRBRIDGE

References

Anderson, B., 1965, "The Quaternary of Norway," in (Rankama, K., editor), "The Quaternary," pp. 91–138, New York, Interscience Publishers.

Holtedahl, O., 1960, "Geology of Norway," *Norg. Geol. Undersokelse*, **208**.

Rudberg, S., 1962, "Geology and morphology of the 'fjells'," *Biul. Peryglac.*, **11**, 173–186.

Stamp, L. D. (editor), 1961, "A Glossary of Geographical Terms," London, Longmans, Green and Co., 539pp.

Cross-references: *Exhumed Landscape*; *Glacial Refuges*; *Monadnock*; *Nunatak*; *Peneplain*; *Relict Landforms*.

FJORD, FIORD

A fiord (or fjord in modern Norwegian) is a universally adopted Norwegian term for a deep and long arm of the sea characterized by more or less straight trends, steep mountainous sides and very great depths. Fjords are exclusively found along coasts of high relief marked by severe Pleistocene glaciation. They are sometimes represented by *sea lochs* in Scotland, and sometimes by *firths*.

Fjords resemble rias coasts in some ways; both are "drowned" valleys, but the latter have normal tributaries, while fjords often have truncated spurs, rock floors, and hanging tributary

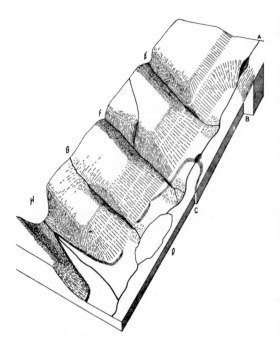

FIG. 1. Schematic representation of some forms effected by ice erosion. *A* is the valley floor above a high step or valley end, *B* where the river is about to cut a canyon of adjustment. *C* is a lower step with a canyon of adjustment. The river from *F* is cutting a canyon through the valley bench. *D* is a lower part of the valley floor, with a lake. *E* is a U-shaped hanging valley with a canyon of adjustment in the mouth, while the tributary valley *F* is nearly wholly fluvial in its form, being a valley of adjustment. The river *G* is about to cut a scar or a valley of adjustment through the edge between the valley side and the upland surface or mountain area (cp. the scar in the side of valley *F*). In the valley *H* a canyon in a step has been further developed by ice erosion forming a funnel-shaped valley part below the step (Gjessing, 1966).

valleys with attractive waterfalls. *Fjärds* (q.v.) are rather similar, also glaciated but more extensively drowned, with lower shores, and containing lateral channels.

According to Peacock (1935, p. 669) the deepest fjords are as follows: in the World (Messier Channel, Chile—1288 m); in Europe (Sogne Fjord, Norway—1210 m); in the United States (Chatham Strait, Alaska—878 m); in Canada (Finlayson Channel, B.C.—780 m). The scour has over-deepened some fjords by more than 900 m, most of them having rocky thresholds, possibly marking the point where the glacier's rigorous scouring ability was cut down sharply by reduced gradient, on reaching either the piedmont area or the ocean (Flint, 1957, p. 94). The bottom waters of many fjords are stagnant, marked by black muds rich in H_2S, owing to the shallow thresholds (Strøm, 1939).

RHODES W. FAIRBRIDGE

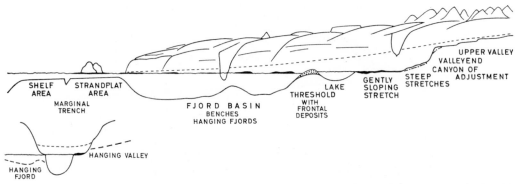

FIG. 2. Some form elements of Norwegian fjords and fjord valleys, longitudinal profile and cross profile through the fjord. The strandflat, the fjord-side benches, and the gently sloping valley stretch at the head of the fjord are found near the same level which is nearly in accordance with the present sea level. The canyons of adjustment in the steep stretches and in the valley end are indicated by dash-dotted lines. A possible preglacial valley floor is indicated by a dashed line (Gjessing, 1966).

References

Boyd, L. A., 1935, "The fjord coast of East Greenland," *Am. Geog. Soc. Spec. Publ. 18.*

Charlesworth, J. K., 1957, "The Quaternary Era," London, Arnold Ltd., 2 vols.

Flint, R. F., 1957, "Glacial and Pleistocene Geology," New York, John Wiley & Sons, 553pp.

Gjessing, J., 1966, "Some effects of ice erosion on the development of Norwegian Valleys and Fjords," *Norsk Geogr. Tidsskr.*, **20**, 273–299.

Gregory, J. W., 1913, "The Nature and Origin of Fjords," London, J. Murray, 542pp.

Holtedahl, H., 1967, "Notes on the formation of fjords and fjord-valleys," *Geogr. Ann.*, **49A**, 188–203.

Peacock, M. A. 1935, "Fiord-land of British Columbia," *Bull. Geol. Soc. Am.*, **46**, 633–696.

Skerman, T. M., 1964, "Studies of a southern fiord," New Zealand, *Oceanogr. Inst. Mem.*, **17**, 102pp.

Strøm, K. M., 1939, "Land-locked waters and the deposition of black muds," in "Recent Marine Sediments" (A. A. P. G., Tulsa, Okla.), pp. 356–372.

Upham W., 1898, "Fjords and submerged valleys of Europe," *Am. Geologist*, **22**, 101–108.

Cross-references: *Estuary*; *Fjärd*; *Glacial Scour*; *Glacial Valley*; *Ria.*

FLATIRON—*See* **HOGBACK AND FLATIRON**

FLOOD PLAIN

Geomorphologically, a flood plain is among the most dynamic of topographic surfaces. This dynamic quality is due to its interrelatedness to the dynamics of a whole system of processes that constitute a stream system and the adjustments such a system makes to the variable flows and loads derived from its drainage basin. Thus, the flood plain can be properly thought of as both a product and a functional part of the whole stream environment, and it plays a necessary role in maintaining the overall adjustment that a stream system makes to the variable quantities of water, solubles, and solid particles imposed on it. The complexity of the process relationships between flood plain and stream system has only recently been appreciated and still remains sketchily understood. Current knowledge of the nature of flood plain development and modification is based on very limited observations; hence, any generalized model such as proposed in the following statement is a tentative conclusion from a very limited body of data.

Definition

To define a flood plain depends somewhat on the goals in mind. As a topographic category, it is quite flat and lies adjacent to a stream; geomorphologically, it is a land form composed primarily of unconsolidated depositional material derived from sediments being transported by the related stream; hydrologically, it is perhaps best-defined as a land form subject to periodic flooding by the parent stream. A combination of these perhaps comprises the essential criteria for defining the flood plain.

Nevertheless, to define the extent of a flood plain at a place poses additional problems. In keeping with the term itself, the criterion of being flooded is essential, but how frequently must there be flooding to qualify? Wolman and Leopold suggest that the active flood plain is that area subject to inundation by the annual flood (highest discharge in each year), or in terms of probabilities, it is that land subject to inundation with a recurrence interval of between one and two years. Using this definition for many streams, especially large rivers, only a portion of the topographic flood plain would be included. If the frequency requirement for flooding is reduced to something like a recurrence interval of one in ten years, however, then in most cases the topographic and hydrologic flood plain are more nearly similar in extent.

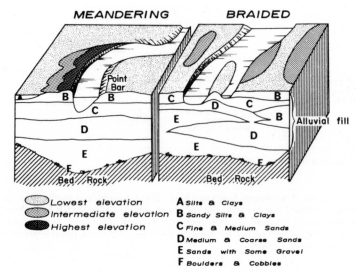

Fig. 1. Schematic characteristics of flood plains and alluvial fills.

The uniform frequency of flooding suggests an interrelationship between the height of a flood plain and the stream that built it. In essence, the depth of a stream channel is the height of its flood plain, and this dimension is adjusted to a frequency function of the parameter of discharge in particular. Thus, the flood plain is seen as an integral part of the stream system and the adjustment mechanism needed to meet the requirements of discharge and load imposed by the basin it serves.

Surface Configuration

The relative flatness of flood plains compared to other land forms is deceiving of the widely varying subtlety of microrelief that can be found on them. Generally, the zone within one or two stream widths from the parent stream will have the most irregular surface configuration. Lenticular, bar-like forms, intervening swales and shallow hollows, all of various sizes, are characteristically found in this zone, imparting to the surface a microrelief of a few feet for smaller streams to 10 or more feet along some large rivers. The formation of these rather complex surface forms in this zone can be broadly grouped under two distinguishable stream environments: (a) *bar building* in the stream channel, and (b) *overbank deposition* and erosion during flood flows (Fig. 1). Though the relative significance of each will vary between streams and from site to site along individual streams, basically a flood plain is built by bar development and this original surface configuration is then modified by flood activity, modifications which are sometimes substantial by even one flood in the zone near the stream.

Where the flood plain extends more than one or two stream widths from the stream channel, surface configuration of such more remote areas is normally

less irregular, though local relief may remain as great. Extensive flatness of surface normally prevails, though isolated swells or low knolls might not be uncommon, especially on flood plains of larger rivers. In most cases, the relief, however, is provided by rather widely spaced channels of tributary streams or vestigal channel-like forms. The greater flatness may well stem from the gradual modification of the original surface by repeated flooding, but in general, the available evidence suggests that changes to this zone by any one flood are minor; deposition tends to be quite thin (fractions of an inch), patchy and of relatively fine texture, and erosional activity is even less in evidence. The role of vegetation in flood-flow deposition and the resultant surface configuration may also be important (see below).

Surface Materials

Variations in texture of surface materials can be crudely generalized by stating that texture decreases with increasing distance from the stream. Or, perhaps a better statement of the trend is that coarser-textured materials are most extensive nearer the stream than farther away, since it is also true that occurrences of finer-textured materials are not uncommon even near the stream bank, nor are coarser-textured materials necessarily absent from the more remote areas. The proportionate extent of each depends on local conditions of flooding and character of the sediment load.

Subsurface Structure

Many stream valleys contain fills of unconsolidated sediments that are much thicker than the depth of the present river channel. Such alluvial fills in bedrock valleys generally show a rough stratification of textures with the coarsest materials at the base, often including boulders and coarse gravel, and progressing to finest textures at the surface where silts, clays and sands usually predominate. Available data indicate that fills may be stratified in more or less horizontal layers of similar textural composition, or may be a series of overlapping and interfingered lenses of similar textural characteristics, or may show only poor sorting of materials. No single explanations can account for such diversity, but there is a general suggestive relationship between meandering and braided channel patterns and stratified and lenticular structures of alluvial fills (see below).

Flood Plain Development

The processes that are involved in flood plain development are those of the parent stream channel and those that occur during flood flow. Since the flood plain is composed of unconsolidated material, it is normally rather easily eroded, and the stream can adjust its depth, width, length (by meandering) and, to some extent, slope to satisfy the demands of discharge and load. Thus, the adjustments of the stream are made by eroding and depositing (Fig. 2). One of the most common forms of the eroding and depositing activity is that found in the meandering channel. In such a channel, the cross section is asymmetrical, or triangular, with undercutting and caving along the concave bank where the channel is deepest. This material moves downstream and across the channel to the shallower convex side where deposition (point bar building) prevails. Available evidence suggests that any widening that takes place by erosion is more or less equaled by deposition, or bar building, on the opposite side of the channel. Hence, by bank erosion and point bar building, the stream moves across its flood plain, tearing it down and rebuilding it. As a result, the surface layer of a flood plain to the depth of the channel is redeposited horizontally, not vertically. The coarsest textures tend to concentrate toward the base of the bar, and finer sediments are found toward the top along the outer edge of the channel. Each of these horizontally accreted bar masses can generally be identified in alluvial fills as one or, more often, several horizontal deposits of relatively similar textures (the coarser basal deposits and the finer top deposits serve to illustrate the possible divisions).

The rate of channel movement across a flood plain is related to bank stability which, in turn, is a function of the texture of the alluvium. As an example, sandy alluvium is easily eroded and generally has more unstable banks than silty and clayey alluvium. Along the lower Missouri River, with a flood plain composed largely of sandy alluvium, the river reworked approximately one-third of its flood plain in about half a century, or averaged in excess of 125 ft/yr. For rivers with mostly clay and silt bank material, rates of movement are more likely to be a small fraction of this figure.

Much the same process of building and reworking the flood plain is found with the multi-limbed or braided channel. However, in this case bar building and bank cutting are not restricted to particular sides of a channel. In fact, bar building takes place within the channel, creating islands and splitting the stream into several channels. With time, some of the channels will be abandoned and the islands will become a part of the flood plain. In the structure of the alluvial fill, this process of bar building results in lenticular bodies of material rather than horizontal strata.

By the bar-building process, or lateral accretion, the basic elevation of the flood plain above the channel is built. Sediment from overflow seems to be a very minor source for adding to the height of the flood plain, probably rarely accounting for more than 10 % of its height, but it can be significant in creating the micro-landform character of the flood plain surface. Additions to the flood plain from this source are, in contrast to channel deposits, added on top rather than side by side, and hence are often referred to as vertical accretion. Flood deposits are thickest and most noticeable near the stream bank, especially along concave banks. Sediment is most accessible to the overflow here, because the greatest concentration and coarseness of sediment, associated with highest stream velocities, are displaced toward this side of the stream channel. When the flood water activity moves from the channel onto the flood plain, the flow is in the form of a shallow but wide stream, and resistance to flow increases. Bar deposition is the immediate result, coming mostly from the coarser fraction of the load and producing elongated bars with intervening depressions whose axes normally strike toward a right angle to the bank line. These forms and pattern are further complicated when the bank zone is covered with closely spaced trees, but in either case, the net result of near-bank deposition is to produce an irregular surface of coarser-textured materials previously described as typical of the flood plain within one or two stream widths of the parent stream. Where the channel has stable banks and its lateral movement is relatively slow, the repeated additions of these deposits are probably responsible for the development of natural levees. However, for many rivers, such deposits are soon destroyed as the channel migrates laterally and no noticeable natural levee exists.

CUT

FILL

FIG. 2. Progressive erosion and deposition in a cross section of a channel.

Beyond this most active zone of flood deposition, vertical accretion is for the most part quite thin from any one flood (fraction of an inch) and patchy. Inundation of these areas is normally by backwater, i.e., water that has creeped up the gradient of the flood plain rather than actively flowing with the gradient. Such flooding has low energy and can carry only particles of fine silt and clay textures. Thus, unless it remains on the flood plain for some time, much of its load will stay in suspension and return to the main stream as the flood recedes. Where backwater becomes entrapped in low places, the suspended material is deposited as a thin veneer over the surface, and it is perhaps from many repetitions of this process that the smoother surfaces of the more remote zone of the flood plain are in part developed. Another source of deposition in the more remote zone comes from tributary flooding, and in many cases, this source is far more important for modifying the surface than floods from the parent stream. The finer texture of surface soil plus more remote location mean that this zone has relatively poor surface and subsurface drainage, and is often referred to as the backswamp. Where natural levees have developed, it also has slightly lower elevations and becomes an ideal entrapping basin for flood waters that reach it.

Theoretically, vegetation should play a significant role in the development of flood plain land forms since it would stabilize banks and should act to dissipate the energy of flood waters moving across the flood plain. The actual role played by vegetation in large measure remains to be investigated. However, it has been observed that tree growth along the banks of streams does encourage concentration of overbank deposition, and there seems to be some evidence that tree cover on the flood plain may have significance to the development of the flatter surfaces away from the stream. Additional evidence, however, is needed.

THEODORE H. SCHMUDDE

References

Schmudde, T. H., 1963, "Some aspects of land forms of the lower Missouri River floodplain," *Ann. Assoc. Am. Geogr.* **53**, (1), 60–73.

Schumm, S. A., 1960, "The effect of sediment type on the shape and stratification of some modern fluvial deposits," *Am. J. Sci.*, **258**, 177–184.

Schumm, S. A., 1963, "Channel widening and flood plain construction along Cimarron River in southwestern Kansas," *U.S. Geol. Surv. Profess. Paper* **352-D**.

Speight, J. G., 1965, "Meander spectra of the Angabunga River," *J. Hydrol.* **3**, (1), 1–15.

Sundborg, Å., 1956, "The River Klarälven, a study of fluvial process," *Geograf. Ann.*, **38**, 127–316.

Wolman, M. G., and Leopold, L. B., 1957, "River flood plains: some observations on their formation," *U.S. Geol. Surv. Profess. Paper* **282-C**.

Cross-references: *Alluvium; Bars; Deltaic Evolution; Drainage Basin; Grade, Graded Stream; Levee (Natural); Rivers (General); Rivers—Meandering and Braiding; Slipoff Slope; Terraces—Fluvial; Yazoo River.*

FLOW—*See* STREAM FLOW

FLUID MECHANICS—*See* Vol. I, II and pr Vol. VI

FLUVIAL CYCLE—*See* CYCLES, GEOMORPHIC

FLUVIAL SEDIMENT TRANSPORT—*See* SEDIMENT TRANSPORT—FLUVIAL AND MARINE; also pr Vol. VI

FLUVIAL TERRACES—*See* TERRACES—FLUVIAL

FLUVIOGLACIAL PROCESSES

Introduction

Fluvioglacial (or glaciofluviatile) facies are generally distributed downstream from glaciers. On the plains, they form broad, flat surfaces of accumulation with a gentle slope, which originate at the end moraines. In mountain regions, they are of comparable appearance, but the lateral extent of the deposits is limited by the breadth of the valleys. Generally, these facies are called fluvioglacial or proglacial. The two terms are often used interchangeably in the study of glacial geomorphology. They designate the accumulations of fluviatile nature, usually interpreted as having been deposited at the time of the glacial retreat by the sudden liberation of a great volume of water, due to climatic warming and the consequent melting of the ice.

Detailed sedimentological studies of the deposits accumulated downstream from a number of glacial systems often reveal, however, the existence of at least two successive series, deposited under different conditions. Regional climatic, or rather paleoclimatic, characteristics influence the regional facies of the sequences. Depending upon the climate, the fluvioglacial processes were sometimes purely erosional and lacked accumulative material, whereas at other times they led to the formation of a succession of lenses bounded by the limits of the valley or developed the heterogeneous characteristics of a *mudflow* (q.v.).

To avoid any confusion, we shall limit the terms "proglacial" and "fluvioglacial" to their etymological meaning. The first is more general and applies to all the deposits, land forms and processes observed "in front or at the foot of the glacier." The second is more precisely limited to the actions essentially governed by the water of glacial thawing.

Three typical examples are here described. They are from different mountain areas of Europe which had quite different ice age climates. They illustrate the nature of the mechanisms formerly active in many proglacial regions and establish the connection between these mechanisms and the former regional climatic conditions.

(I) The Vosges of Lorraine (Eastern France)

Downstream from Remiremont, the valley of the Moselle is transversely crossed by a broad terminal moraine at the foot of which are seen two clearly distinct *terraces* (q.v.) which begin at the contact of the moraine. The upper terrace grew from the coalescing of two *alluvial fans* (q.v.), the apex of each being situated on each end of the *moraine* (q.v.), at the respective contacts with the two sides of the valley. At first the upper terrace has a concave longitudinal profile, but going downstream it becomes more gentle and the accumulation becomes thinner (Fig. 1).

The lower terrace evolved from the development of braided channels with broad meanders, due to the dissection of the fan terraces. These channels developed a valley-in-valley structure, somewhat terraced, which shows there was fluviatile erosion both laterally and vertically. This double action is due to the anastomosis and lateral displacement of the channels (see *Braided Streams*). The upper terrace, on the contrary, is characterized by a complete absence of any superficial microrelief.

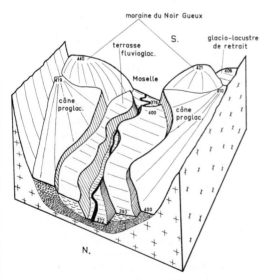

FIG. 1. The coalescent proglacial cones and the fluvioglacial terrace at the foot of the morainic arc of the Noir Gueux (Dept. Vosges, France).

The different aspect of the two terraces is accentuated by studying their respective deposits. Those of the upper terrace are of the order of 30–40 meters thick. The lower terrace is thinner, only 6–7 meters. Sedimentological study furnishes some good criteria for distinguishing between the two formations. In the fan terraces, the beds are even and extensive, very heterogeneous, but in a regular sequence. This bedding reveals their mode of origin. The beds are in a regular and distinct sequence, without cut and fill or disturbing the underlying beds upon which they are successively overlapping. The lower terrace, on the other hand, shows an accumulation of lenticular cut and fill with fine cross-bedding. The distribution of the debris is quite different, governed by a broadly winding stream with anastomosis, braiding and an unstable bed, and frequently modified by the action of lateral erosion. Each major lens reflects a change in the stream energy. While the desposition of the upper formation was abrupt, that of the lower terrace was gradual, with complex structures and small-scale details.

The succession of the two terrace formations is clearly the consequence of climatic modifications which affected the glacier, as disclosed by a close study of the abandoned land forms upstream from the moraine. The position of the two coalescent fans, the summits of which are situated at the moraine-slope contact, shows that they are the proglacial prolongment of two kame channels.

It was only during the glacial maximum that they were deposited. In fact, after retreat began, the channels at the moraine-slope contact were no longer reached by the subglacial (kame) streams, being no longer held in place due to the melting of the ice and its recession from the end moraine. At this time, the drainage shifted to cut a gap in the center of the valley through the morainic arc at the opening of which the lower terrace originates. This latter is thus a retreat feature, occurring at the time of melting.

In conclusion, therefore, the lower terrace is an important erosion feature, cut into the upper formation. This erosional character weakens the hypothesis often accepted of a formation, deposited suddenly at the moment of retreat under the action of abundant meltwaters which were supposed to have created a "sluicing effect." Moreover, the formation which corresponds to the upper terrace is caused by the coalescing of two fans derived from the proglacial prolongation of the subglacial marginal channels. The phase of accumulation must have been thus contemporaneous with the maximum extension of the ice. In the body of this fluvioglacial accumulation, the depositing of long, even layers suggests a formation of a seasonal nature, occurring during summer periods and caused by a succession of appreciable, but brief, concentrations of water at the surface of the glacier. A considerable volume of snow can well be expected under maritime winds in a massif such as the Vosges of Lorraine; this would be suddenly liberated in summer, with abundant quantities of meltwater, which, due to the configuration of the relief, would have been concentrated on both sides of the glacier, at the foot of each slope. Very heavily loaded because of their strong flow over the lateral moraines and the periglacial sediments of the valley slopes, these waters ran along the surface of the glacier to the terminal moraine which would have been cut through at both ends of its arc, as is shown by the position of the summits of the proglacial fans. The accumulation of the alluvial fans ceased only at the beginning of the glacial retreat, giving way to a stage of lateral and vertical erosion which eventually fashioned the lower terrace.

With regard to the course of the last cold epoch, these two geomorphic features belong, respectively, to the maximum of extension of the ice and to the retreat stage. Nourished particularly by the seasonal thaw of the snows, the fan terraces of proglacial accumulations are associated more with the periglacial than with the fluvioglacial domain. In fact, the melting water of the glacier scarcely plays any role in their deposition. Moreover, by their abundance and extent, the contemporaneous cryoturbations of the alluvium show that it was formed under a periglacial climate. The lower terrace, contemporaneous with the retreat, is clearly a result of climatic change, a warming trend.

(II) Southern Slope of the Spanish Pyrenees

At the center of the Pyrenees chain, the southern slope joins the Aragon basin of northern Spain. Small, high-altitude glacial phenomena have been observed. The *cirque glaciers* (q.v.) never attained any great extent. The glacial climate, especially in summer, was too dry, because it came under the continental influence, and too warm, because of its relative proximity to the Mediterranean zone. As in the Vosges, the sections reveal two stages characterized by distinct alluvial facies.

At the base, the debris is well sorted and associated with small gravel lenses. Both very fine elements

and large pebbles are absent. This is followed above by an abrupt change to an unbedded deposit of bouldery gravel of very varied dimensions, with blocks sometimes exceeding several tons, which float in a fine matrix with smaller pebbles. It is deposited without any sorting or imbrication, in an irregular formation (Fig. 2).

The succession of these two alluvial units explains the evolution of fluvial processes during the cold stage. The relatively fine-grained lenses, at the base of the sequence, characterize a stream with a gentle but regular flow, which could carry only pebbles of rather limited size, but whose regular flow washed away the fine components. This shows up from dimensional analysis, and clearly the stream carried out a very uniform, though relatively weak, winnowing of its own alluvium (Fig. 2, lower part).

The irregular and non-bedded formation above gives evidence of a powerful flow and strong discharge of the stream. Quite irregular in size, the variable rounding of the pebbles also illustrates this fact.

The lower formation belongs to a *periglacial fluviatile* phase. Upstream, the hydrological glacial balance was in no way deficient, and the ice, retaining a major part of the water, regularized the flow of the streams. The voluminous debris above is contemporaneous with the melting of the ice and is thus *fluvioglacial*. The abundant meltwaters carried the morainic debris into the valley as *mudflows*, devoid of fine bedding or of any other delicate sedimentary feature. This irregular fluviatile activity is characteristic of the particular regime of the glaciers of the southern Pyrenees. With their limited volume, the cirque glaciers could not survive warming climatic trends, which were probably as sudden during the Quaternary cold epochs as they are now. The melting and disappearance of the ice was very rapid, and the mass of water liberated was appreciable, causing rather excessive loading and alluviation. Moreover, the morainic arcs are deeply dissected by the sluicing effect which has spread them out downstream.

(III) Northern Piedmont of the Austrian Alps

The example is taken from the Salzach basin, to the north of Salzburg. The regional aspect of periglacial and fluvioglacial fluviatile phases can easily be reconstructed there, notably by the variation of the respective lithologic facies.

To the north of the Alpine piedmont, near the Austro-German border and close to the river Inn, the proglacial alluvial fans show deposition in long, nearly flat lenses, but the nature of the alluvium varies from the base to the top of the formations. Quartz and quartzite are dominant in the pebbles at first, then decrease by degrees toward the top, the alluvium becoming calcareous. These relationships were worked out in the proglacial alluvium of Würm age, far downstream from the frontal moraines.

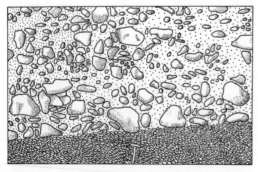

FIG. 2. Succession of alluvial nappes in the proglacial basin of Aragon, Spain (sketch from a photo).

The moraines, consisting essentially of limestone boulders, were derived from the Northern Limestone Alps during the last glaciation.

The quartz pebbles in the lower alluvial sequences were furnished by lateral supply from the interfluve plateaus. These thick formations belong to the Early Quaternary and correspond to the proglacial accumulations of the Mindel and Günz. Much altered, the soft constituents of these formations have largely disappeared. The limestone has dissolved out and most of the crystalline boulders are deeply weathered. More resistant, the quartz pebbles have escaped alteration. With the disappearance of the other elements, quartz gravels thus represent the principal remnants of the Early Quaternary.

In the proglacial alluvium of Würm age, the increasing ratio toward the top of limestone pebbles is connected with the succession of periglacial and later fluvioglacial stages. Before the melting of the glaciers, the drainage network, being in a periglacial environment, was extensively filled by the lateral mass transport (*solifluction*, q.v.). This mass transport affected especially the quartz pebbles of the older terraces. When the ice retreated, these pebbles were first mixed with the morainal material, then, by degrees, they were replaced by fluvioglacial deposits with mainly limestone pebbles. The source of periglacial debris rich in quartz was exhausted. This variation in the nature of the components illustrates once again the succession of two distinct fluviatile stages, caused by the passage of a cold climatic period. The periglacial is below, and the fluvioglacial above.

Conclusion

During the cold stages of the *Quaternary* (q.v.), which brought about the appearance of the glacial conditions in many parts of the world, fluviatile processes underwent an evolution governed both by climatic conditions and by the magnitude of the glaciers. The sedimentological facies are the reflection of these regional climatic characteristics.

At first, a periglacial regime was instituted which, in the case of the somewhat maritime Vosges, was favored by heavy snow and high meltwater runoff. Thick alluvial fans accumulated at the outer foot of the frontal moraines.

In the Austrian Alps and the Aragon Pyrenees, the more marked continentality of the climate limited the flow of the streams. Lateral mass transport by solifluction has encumbered the Austrian valleys, causing them to be silted up. In the southern Pyrenees, the weak flow of the rivers has led to an excellent sorting of the alluvium.

Then, with the warming of the climate and the retreat of the ice, fluvioglacial mechanisms took over. At this time a slow progressive period of downcutting of the drainage system was begun in the Vosges. In the valleys, the channels were braided and the alluvium was deposited in thin-bedded lenses. With its considerable volume, the Vosges ice mass long resisted melting, and the fluvioglacial discharge was never very great.

In the southern Pyrenees, the small size of the glaciers and the probably sudden temperature increases led to an accelerated melting rate. Downstream, rather coarse, unsorted bouldery formations were deposited. They reflect a powerful sluicing which spread out, downstream, a large portion of the morainic material.

In the Austrian Alps, a certain progression of the melting appears to be confirmed by a regular increase in the limestone components of the alluvium. The latter reveals a distinct siltation phase, but not a sudden one. The accumulation resulted from the piling up of small lenses.

These three examples demonstrate the variability of the landforms and facies of proglacial alluvium. To understand each of them, one must examine the regional climatic characteristics as well as the flow regime and size of the glaciers situated upstream. It appears, however, that one conclusion can be drawn: In each cycle a periglacial period preceded the fluvioglacial stage. The sluicing effect during deglaciation and the resulting fluvioglacial accumulation are just some of the many regional facies observed. Otherwise, the fluvioglacial processes are predominantly erosive.

G. SERET

References

Embleton, C. and King, C. A. M., 1968, "Glacial and Periglacial Geomorphology," London, E. Arnold Ltd., 608pp.

Flint, R. F., 1957, "Glacial and Pleistocene Geology," New York, John Wiley & Sons, 553pp.

Gherardelli, L., 1931, "Il dominio glaciale nella valle d'Aosta e sua influenza sul regime dei deflussi," *Min. Lavori Publici, ufficio idro del Po-Parma*, No. 10, 15.

Sekyra, J., 1961, "Traces of the continental glacier on the territory of northern Bohemia," in "Studies on geology of the Sudetic Mountains," *Zeszyty Nauk. Uniw. Wrocławskiego*, **B**, 71–79.

Seret, G., 1965, "La succession des épisodes fluviatiles périglaciaires et fluvioglaciaires à l'aval des glaciers," *Z. Geomorphol.*, **9**, 305–320.

Tricart, J., and Cailleux, A., 1962, "Le modelé glaciaire et nival," p. 378, Paris, Sedes.

Troll, C., 1957, "Tiefenerosion, Seitenerosion und Akkumulation der Flusse im fluvioglazialen und periglazialen Bereich," *Peterm. Mitt.*, **262** (Machatschek-Festschrift), 213–226.

Wegmann, E., 1935, "Gletschermurgang im Suess-Land (Nordostgrönland)," *Mitt. Naturforsch. Ges. Schaffhausen*, **12**, 35–58.

Cross-references: *Alluvial Fan, Cone*; *Alluvium*; *Braided Streams*; *Cirque Glacier*; *Cryopedology, Cryonivation, etc.*; *Kame*; *Moraine*; *Mudflow*; *Quaternary Period*; *Slopes*; *Solifluction*; *Stream Flow*; *Terraces*; *Trumpet Valley*. Vol. II: *Continentality*; *Paleoclimatology*. Vol. VI: *Crossbedding*; *Glacier Geophysics*; *Glaciers*; *Sedimentology*.

FLYSCH—*See* pr Vol. VI

FORMKREIS—*See* **MORPHOGENETIC REGION**

FRINGING REEF

The basic form of coral reef, as first recognized by Charles Darwin (1842), is the fringing reef. This reef type is initiated by the growth of scattered coral colonies, close inshore, generally from a foundation of non-coral rocks exposed at a headland. The fringing reef flat may be anything from 50 meters across to 1000–1500 meters. The sandy beaches or mangrove-choked muddy bays between headlands are usually devoid of fringing reefs, since the hermatypic (reef-building) corals are inhibited by the excessive amounts of mud (leading to turbid water and limited light penetration), by abrasiveness of loose sand, and by the fresh water from rivers or creeks that may debouch into the bays. In unfavorable areas for corals, the ecologic niche is sometimes filled by *algal reefs* (q.v.).

Fringing reefs therefore tend to form a semicircular fan around headlands along a tropical mainland coast (Fig. 1). However, along limestone coasts, as for example in the island arcs when older reef limestones are uplifted, coastal erosion is by solution and there is a dearth of sand and mud, so that fringing reefs may be almost continuous. Freshwater streams may maintain either a narrow passage (Figs. 2, 3, 4 and 5) or, if small, may be

FIG. 2. Fringing reef of Pameumpeuk on the south coast of Java near the mouth of the Tji-Laut-Eureun.

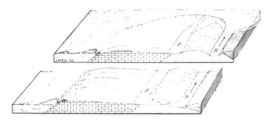

FIG 3. Diagrammatic sketch of the reef in Fig. 2. Z = "moat" carrying seawater from behind the reef over a low waterfall (foreground) into the river (R). Terrace to the rear of moat is an eroded limestone (from Umbgrove, 1947).

sufficiently diluted and dispersed that they follow a superficial channel across the fringing reef. The fresher inshore water may maintain a narrow "boat channel" or canoe (prahu, prau) passage parallel to the beach, up to a few meters deep and 10–100 meters wide, like a miniature barrier lagoon. Usually the waves that are breaking along the outer edge of the reef carry across the reef flat in subdued ripples to maintain a steady lateral current in the boat channel to return to the open ocean at one of the creek openings.

FIG. 1. Small fringing reef on the south coast of Timor, in an active orogenic belt. Reefs are partly inhibited by sand and mud, and limited on this coast to headlands. Note discoloration of water from a stream debouching to the west.

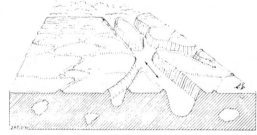

FIG. 4. Algal-rimmed pools near the reef margin (as in Figs. 2 and 3).

FIG. 5. Algae-encrusted buttresses of growing coral and algae separated by chutes, channels or grooves. On the reef margin at Pameumpeuk (Figs. 2, 3 and 4), facing the heavy swell of the Indian Ocean. (Photo: J. H. F. Umbgrove).

FIG. 7. Healthy coral "heads" growing to 30–50 cm above extreme low water spring tide level at Palm Island near Townsville, Queensland. (Photo: W. Saville-Kent, 1893).

The reef flat of the fringing reef may be littered with coral sand and storm-tossed shingle or blocks of reef limestone carried in from the outer margin. Often successive "waves" of shingle may be identified, corresponding presumably to occasional hurricanes of the past. The latter only strike once in 50 or 100 years, so that successive generations of shingle tend to become almost obliterated before the next "wave" arrives. Along mainland shores with easily eroded country rock, there may be mudbanks of terrigenous clays washed onto the reef flat. Where there is plentiful sediment of this sort, colonization by mangrove (usually *Rhizophora*) often takes place (Fig. 6). Mangrove roots and decaying vegetation lead to acidification of the muds, so that broad circular solution depressions develop and fill with mud, thus providing a natural hazard to men wading across reef flats or especially for amphibious vehicles.

Inner parts of broad fringing reef flats often show the truncated surfaces of deep reef corals that formerly grew much higher (Figs. 7 and 8). These are traces of mid-Holocene or even Pleistocene reefs that have now been planed down to the present level. They are comparable to "platforms of marine abrasion," except that the erosive process is largely solution, partly biological, partly physicochemical (see *Limestone Coastal Weathering*). On air photos, the contrast between the older, truncated zone and the newly grown outer belt is often very striking. Sometimes there has been cliff retreat and the abrasion platform is partly cut into the country rock.

Irregular pools on the reef flats are found which vary from 50 cm to about 3–5 meters in depth. Some are due to mangrove solution; others are inherited karst solution pipes; or again they may be irregular pools which were haphazardly missed

FIG. 6. Fringing reef of Yule Pt., North of Cairns, Queensland. Sand and mud accumulate on the inner parts of the reef and support mangrove swamps. (Photo: R. W. Fairbridge).

FIG. 8. Inshore parts of reef at low tide on Thursday Island, Torres Strait, Queensland. Old coral platform heavily corroded, but locally (foreground) plastered over by living coral, next to a channel where there is sufficient swash to keep it alive. (Photo: W. Saville-Kent, 1893).

FIG. 9. Air photomosaic of elevated fringing reefs and marine terraces (cut in late Tertiary volcanic rocks—tuffs, agglomerates, etc.) on Atauro Island (just north of Timor), an active orogenic belt. Note deep dissection of stream valleys. Length of coast, 20 km; north to the top left. (Photos taken at 9.40 a.m. in November, southern summer, so strong shadows from the east.)

in the general colonization. The pools often carry the only coral colonies now living on the reef, except those along the seaward margin.

Elevated Fringing Reefs

In some of the tectonic belts, particularly in the island arc regions, fringing reefs are frequently uplifted (Figs. 9, 10 and 11). While subsidence is sometimes followed by uplift to give uplifted barriers or even atolls, it is much more usual to observe belts of parallel stepped terraces that may, in certain areas (e.g., the Finsch coast of New Guinea, or in Timor), rise to over 1000 meters above sea level. The growth of fringing reefs (under steady conditions) has evidently been interrupted by rapid uplift of the order of 10–50 meters, followed by growth of another fringing belt, and so on. The rates involved would be of the order of 1–10 cm/yr for uplift, alternating with stillstands of the order of a few centuries during which a massive fringe 5–10 meters wide will grow up.

The elevated coral benches under topical climatic conditions rapidly develop karst weathering features, known in Indonesia and the Malay-speaking islands as "*Karang*" (which literally means "coral"). Deep *lapiés* (q.v.) sometimes produce a fearsome microrelief of giant spikes 2–5 meters high, alternating with precipitous sinkholes. Karst caves, of course, are very common. Since the initial rock is highly porous, some of this cryptorheic drainage may be related to primary passages and caverns.

RHODES W. FAIRBRIDGE

References

Cloud, P. E., Jr., 1952, "Facies relationships of organic reefs," *Bull. Am. Assoc. Petrol. Geologists*, **36**, 2125–2149.

Crossland, C., 1907, "Reports on the marine biology of the Sudanese Red Sea. IV. The recent history of the coral reefs of the mid-west shores of the Red Sea," *J. Linnean Soc. London*, **31**, 14–30.

Darwin, C., 1842, "The Structure and Distribution of Coral Reefs," London and New York (third ed., 1889, appendix by Bonney).

Davis, W. M., 1928, "The coral reef problem," *Am. Geogr. Soc. Spec. Publ.*, **9**, 526pp.

Fairbridge, R. W., 1950, "Recent and Pleistocene coral reefs of Australia," *J. Geol.*, **58**, 330–401.

Guppy, H. B., 1885, "Observations on the recent calcareous formations of the Solomon Group made during 1882–1884," *Trans. Roy. Soc. Edinburgh*, **32**, 545–581.

Guppy, H. B., 1886, "Notes on the characters and mode of formation of the coral reefs of the Solomon Islands, being the results of observations made in 1882–1884, during the surveying cruise of H.M.S. *Lark*," *Proc. Roy. Soc. Edinburgh*, **13**, 857–904.

Guppy, H. B., 1887, "The Solomon Islands; Their Geology, General Features, and Suitability for Colonization," London, Swan, Sonnenschein, Lowrey & Co., 152pp.

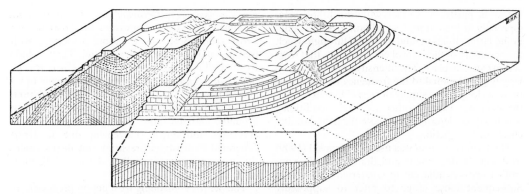

FIG. 10. Block diagram of Kisar, Indonesia (Kuenen, 1933) showing the island with elevated fringing reef terraces. Present condition after considerable erosion, especially of the soft, folded Tertiary volcanic rocks (tuffs, agglomerates) and sediments in the core.

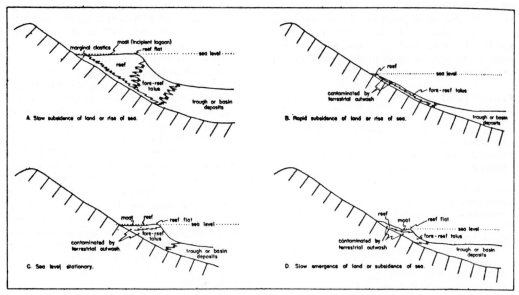

FIG. 11. Conjectural relationships of fringing reefs under conditions of subsidence, stability or emergence of land relative to sea (Cloud, 1952).

Kuenen, P. H., 1933, "Geology of coral reefs," *Snellius Expedition Geol. Results*, **5**(2), 125pp.

Mayor, A. G., 1924a, "Structure and ecology of Samoan reefs," *Carnegie Inst. Wash. Publ.*, **340**; *Pap. Dept. Marine Biol.*, **19**, 1–25.

Mayor, A. G., 1924b, "Causes which produce stable conditions in the depth of the floors of Pacific fringing reef-flats," *ibid.*, 27–36.

Saville-Kent, W., 1893, "The Great Barrier Reef of Australia," London, W. H. Allen & Co., 387pp.

Umbgrove, J. H. F., 1947, "Coral Reefs of the East Indies," *Bull. Geol. Soc. Am.*, **58**, 729–778.

Cross-references: *Algal Reef*; *Algal Rim*; *Coral Reefs*; *Holocene*; *Karst*; *Lagoon*; *Lapiés*; *Limestone Coastal Weathering*; *Mangrove Swamp*; *Sink Hole*.

FROST ACTION

Frost action involves the weathering processes caused by repeated cycles of freezing and thawing (the "multigelation" of some European writers). Frost action is thus differentiated from glacial action, which involves the processes related to moving ice. Frost action is limited to climates in which the temperature both drops below, and rises above, 32°F (0°C) and can be described as occurring near the boundary of the *cryosphere*. The cryosphere is the cold envelope that encircles the earth (Dobrowolski, 1923, from the Greek *kryos*, meaning cold; see articles on *Cryopedology*, etc.). The cryosphere is largely at various elevations in the atmosphere, but it is partly in contact with the lithosphere, especially at high altitudes and latitudes. It is only in the latter situation, and at points through which the boundary of the cryosphere fluctuates, that frost action can take place. The intensity of frost action is largely proportional to the frequency of freeze and thaw, as long as the supply of freezable water meets the demand. Certain other localized conditions, which will be described, facilitate the denudational effects of frost action.

The term *periglacial* was used by Lozinski (1909) to designate the climate and the climatically controlled features adjacent to Quaternary ice sheets. Subsequent loose usage to refer to supposedly similar climates and features, whether or not they are related to glaciers, has introduced ambiguity. Furthermore, the periglacial environment includes features unrelated to frost action (outwash plains or sandur, for example). A broader term *cryonival* (for any frost and snow condition or environment), proposed by Guillien (1949), is sometimes useful. Another term initiated by Guillien is *cryergy*, which refers to the action of frost or cold (adjective *cryergenic*).

TABLE 1. FROST ACTION PROCESSES AND LAND FORMS

Frost Action Processes
  Frost cracking; frost heaving; Clay deflocculation
  Gelifluction and solifluction; Cryostatic movement
  Frost-churned ground
  Other frost action processes

Frozen Ground
  Permafrost phenomena
  Hydrolaccoliths, pingos

Patterned Ground
  Sorted and nonsorted circles (stone, soil, peat circles, rings)
  Sorted and nonsorted nets
  Sorted and nonsorted steps
  Sorted and nonsorted stripes
  Sorted and nonsorted polygons

Slope Features (erosional)
  Asymmetric valleys; Dry valleys; Nivation hollows; Dell

Slope Accumulations
  Grèzes litées (bedded scree)
  Protalus ramparts
  Rock glaciers
  Block fields

Frost Action Processes

Frost action phenomena result from the modification of the properties of water when it passes from the liquid to the solid state, and vice versa. Specifically, water expands about 10% upon freezing (ice being characterized by a high expansion coefficient, as seen in the growth of ice needles or *pipkrake*;

see *Cryopedology, Cryoplanation, Cryoturbation*). Confined ice exerts a pressure of 2,000 lbs./in.^{2} Frost action processes are those associated with freezing and thawing of the ground. They include frost wedging and cracking (see *Frost Riving, Shattering, Splitting, Wedging*), *frost heaving* (q.v.) and thrusting, frost creep, clay deflocculation, gelifluction (solifluction associated with frozen ground), and the more problematic processes of cryostatic movement (movement due to frost-generated hydrostatic pressure) and displacement due to saturation-controlled density differences (diapiric folding).

The factors controlling frost action processes are complexly interrelated. Basic factors are climate (temperature, precipitation, wind), topography (altitude, slope, exposure) and material (structure, texture, color). Dependent factors include moisture (varying with climate, topography, material), vegetation (varying with climate, topography, material), insolation (exposure and relief), insulation (varying especially with vegetation and snow cover), and diffusivity (expressed as the ratio of thermal conductivity to heat capacity and unit weight of the material, and varying with the nature of the material and its moisture content). Clearly the multiplicity and the interrelation of these variables indicate that great care must be taken before drawing detailed conclusions from frost action effects.

Recent experimental studies (Wiman, 1963) have shed some light on frost action processes, emphasizing particularly that frost action requires *both* freeze-thaw cycles *and* the presence of water. It was recognized that there are (a) *Icelandic* type freeze-thaw cycles (diurnal cycles, with relatively small temperature range), which seem to be quantitatively more important than (b) *Siberian* type cycles (fewer cycles, with greater temperature range).

Frost Cracking

Frost cracking, also termed frost splitting and *frost riving* (q.v.), occurs when moisture soaks down into joint and cleavage crevices of hard rocks during the thaw season. The water freezes when the temperature is sufficiently lowered; ice expansion causes the rocks to split. Bryan (1946) has designated this process *congelifraction*; the French, and others, have abbreviated this simply to *gelifraction*. Two cases are possible: Water may seep into joints separating large particles and result in block fields, *felsenmeer*, and, on slopes, *rock streams* or *rock glaciers*. This process is designated *macrogelifraction*. In contrast, *microgelifraction* occurs when water freezes in the pores of the rock; the result is general crushing ("fretting") and production of sand or silt (analogous to *Salt Weathering*, q.v.).

Frost Heaving

Frost heaving results from freezing of groundwater; ice crystals develop, tend to grow unidirectionally, and force individual soil particles upward. In porous material, freezing of water seems to be an osmotic phenomenon. Unless the material is completely homogeneous, freezing is always irregular. Ice concentrates in soil phases with most accessible water, mainly where silt and sand are more abundant (see *Periglacial Landscapes*). The irregular freeze and thaw of the groundwater results in differential heaving; hence, surficial patterns result. Particles in the soil may even migrate, without slope, simply due to freeze and thaw (*geliturbation*). On slopes, the gravity component results in *solifluction features*, *rock streams* and *stone stripes*.

Clay Deflocculation

Clay deflocculation results from ionic migration under the influence of differential freezing. Pure water freezes first so that ions concentrate in the places which freeze last. The result is disequilibrium and soil disaggregation. Addition of meltwater results in the formation of a mud.

Frost-affected clay soils are thus nearly always without cohesion. As a result, these soils offer a very low resistance to erosion. In the presence of permafrost, such soils can become liquid, leading to *mudflows* and *solifluction*.

Gelifluction and Solifluction

The term *solifluction* was first used by J. G. Andersson, in 1906, to describe naturally occurring downslope movement of water-saturated soil material; it is used only in relation to frost action. The term *gelifluction* is preferred by Baulig and others, to avoid confusion with other types of soil creep.

Solifluction results in terracette features or in larger terraces (Fig. 1); however, the phenomenon may occur with little surface indication. Many types of solifluction have been described; the rate of movement varies with type. Maximum rates seem to be approximately 15 cm/yr (Rapp, 1960). Landslide or mudflow features resulting from frost action may give rise to sporadic and localized movements which are far faster, such features are not always considered to be solifluction.

The cause of solifluction is not well understood. Frost-heaved soils (with ice crystals) will, upon

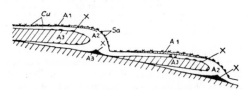

FIG. 1. Composition of terracettes (*Fliesserdterrassen*) from the Troger Alm above the Glockner-Haus, Hohe Tauern, Austria, at 2300 meters (Troll, 1944). *Soil horizons:* A_1 = 5 cm humus, A_2 = gray sand, A_3 = rust-brown stony saprolite; X = dark brown peaty soil. *Vegetation:* Cu = *Carex curvula*, Sa = *Salicetum*.

melting, settle with a resultant downslope displacement. Spring thaw in areas of permafrost may result in saturated soil and subsequent flowage; some movement may take place while the soil material is in the frozen state. In any case, solifluction is one of the most potent agents of mass movement known, more effective than those generally occurring in temperate regions. When occurring over large areas, solifluction may produce characteristic smooth slopes.

Cryostatic Movement

Progressive freezing from the surface downward to the permafrost table may set up large hydrostatic pressures in pockets of unfrozen material confined between these surfaces. Such pressures are termed *cryostatic* (Washburn, 1950). Cryostatic pressures result in differential heaving known as cryostatic movement.

Other Frost Action Processes

The above summary covers briefly the most important frost action processes. Subsequent parts of this article will deal with geomorphic phenomena resulting from such processes. The following material will involve, in part, additional frost action processes considered unimportant for inclusion in the previous discussion.

Frozen Ground

Frozen ground occurs, at least seasonally, throughout the cryosphere. The quasi-equilibrium range of *permafrost* (permanently frozen subsoil) or *tjaele* (Scandinavian; *merzlota*, Russian) is essentially limited to the polar and subpolar zones and to certain middle-latitude highlands. The southern limit of permafrost in the northern hemisphere is highly variable in latitude and is bounded by mean annual temperatures; the latter are reported to vary from 0°C (Terzaghi, 1952) to $-8\frac{1}{2}$°C (Büdel, 1953). Differences may not be constant; Brown (1963) gives -1 to -4°C for locations in Canada.

Permafrost is distinguished from *seasonal frost*, i.e., frozen ground which thaws annually. In regions where permafrost exists, a surficial layer generally thaws each summer and is called the "active layer" (see *Cryopedology*). Black (1954) estimated that about 2,950,000 square miles of land in the northern hemisphere are underlain with almost continuous permafrost (Fig. 2). South of the continuous zone in the northern hemisphere, permafrost is divided into large discontinuous bodies in an additional area of about 2,860,000 square miles. Further south, permafrost becomes more and more sporadic until it disappears, except for isolated bodies in high mountains such as the Alps, Himalayas and Andes. Antarctica (5,100,000 square miles) is wholly in the continuous zone of permafrost but the land is largely glacial-ice covered. Altogether about 24% of the total land area of the earth is in areas where

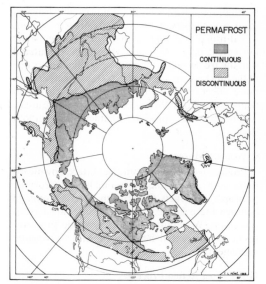

FIG. 2. Distribution of permafrost in the northern hemisphere. (Courtesy of Troy L. Péwé.)

permafrost is known. The maximum known thickness of permafrost is reported to be at Nordvik in Siberia (Black, 1954) where it is about 2000 feet. In North America, the general range of thickness in the continuous zone is 800–1200 feet. Permafrost is generally composed of ice veins, ice-filled pores, and non-ice material (which dominates).

Ice wedges (Black, 1952) are a particularly striking and common form of clear ice in perennially frozen regolith in the continuous zone of permafrost [Figs. 3 (a), 3(b), 3(c)]. The wedges range from short vertical dikelets less than 1 mm in width to massive wedges more than 10 meters in width and 10 meters in height. Individual wedges commonly join in polygonal networks whose surface configurations range from the extremes of low-centered to high-centered types, with relief of a few inches to several feet. Sizes of individual polygons can be correlated with the ages of the ice wedges, the types of material in which they are found, and the ranges of ground temperature. Their origin is attributed to the accumulation of ice in periodic contraction cracks resulting from temperature changes. Taber (1943) proposed that the wedges of ice segregated from water drawn up from below while the permafrost was forming. In northern Alaska, ice wedges are growing today at the rate of perhaps 0.5–1.5 mm/yr (Black, 1954).

Numerous studies of active ice wedges have resulted in the following information: Structures in active ice wedges are generally smaller and more complex than those in glacial ice; all wedges have myriad layers of air bubbles and inclusions of organic material and soil which commonly produce marked foliation subparallel to the sides; grain size ranges from 0.1–100 mm; shapes are equi--

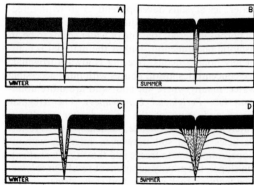

FIG. 3a. Four sketches illustrating the development of an ice wedge. Black: top zone of soil which thaws in summer and freezes in winter. White: permanently frozen subsoil.

(A) First winter. Soil frozen throughout. Intense cold causes contraction, and a crack ("frost crack") opens.

(B) Following summer. Meltwater fills the crack and soon freezes in the level of the permanently frozen subsoil. The topsoil is thawed, and mud and vegetation close the opening more or less. Some mud enters the crack.

(C) Second winter. Owing to intense cold, a crack opens within the ice wedge. In the following summer, this secondary crack is filled as described under (B).

(D) This process is repeated annually, and the freezing pressure of the ice presses the adjoining strata aside. The ice wedge has become thick, and the bedding in the permanently frozen subsoil is disturbed (Zeuner, 1959). (By permission of Hutchinson & Co., London.)

dimensional to irregular; individual grains respond to stress by strain, fracture, granulation, reorientation and recrystallization.

Permafrost results when the heat balance (net) of the surface of the earth over a period of several

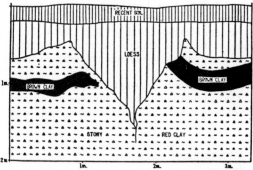

FIG. 3b. A fossil frost crack, or ice wedge. Loess covers Permian clay. An ice wedge occupied and widened a frost crack, cutting through both loess and Permian sediments. When the climate improved and the permanently frozen subsoil disappeared, the ice wedge melted away, and material from above (in this case, loess) replaced the ice. The lateral distortions caused by freezing pressure are striking. From the Mittelsteine, Sudetan Mountains (Zeuner, 1959). (By permission of Hutchinson & Co., London.)

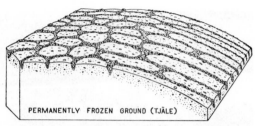

FIG. 4a. Sorted *stone circles* on the flat surface merge into *stone stripes* on the slope (Sharpe, 1938).

like or striped, and (2) the presence or absence of obvious sorting between stones and fines. As pointed out by Black (1952), some patterned ground forms are gradational in pattern and/or sorting. For example, some sorted circles grade into sorted polygons and unsorted circles.

Sorted circles [Fig. 4(a)] are patterned ground whose mesh is dominantly circular and has a sorted appearance commonly due to a border of stones surrounding finer material. Such features are also called *stone circles*. *Debris islands* are sorted circles occurring amid blocks or boulders. The size of these features is about 1–3 meters in diameter; the border of the circle may comprise everything from pebbles to boulders while the central areas generally, but not

FIG. 3c. Foliated ground-ice mass (ice wedge) in organic rich silt exposed near Livengood, Alaska. (Photo: T. L. Péwé)

years produces a temperature continuously below freezing. Some of the primary factors in the heat exchange are: (1) climatic, (2) chemical and physical characteristics of the ground, and (3) the changing interface between the ground and the atmosphere (particularly vegetation and snow cover).

The direct effects of permafrost are limited; locally important effects include those on the local hydrologic regime. Indirect effects are many. Soil structures and microrelief features are more widespread and better developed in areas of permafrost (Denny, 1952). The active layer is commonly supersaturated with ice so that mass movements, frost heaving, etc., are commonplace. *Patterned ground* (q.v.), *solifluction* (q.v.) and other microfeatures result.

Patterned Ground

Cold-climate patterned ground comprises more or less symmetrical forms such as circles, polygons, nets and stripes that are characteristically developed in regolith subject to intense frost action. However, some closely similar forms of patterned ground occur in warm climates as well. Important experiments by Dzulynski (1963) and Butrym *et al.* (1964) suggest a simple diapiric cause.

The standard classification of patterned ground is that of Washburn (1956). Two common characteristics of patterned ground which can be used in classification are: (1) the pattern—whether dominantly circular, polygonal, intermediate (nets), step-

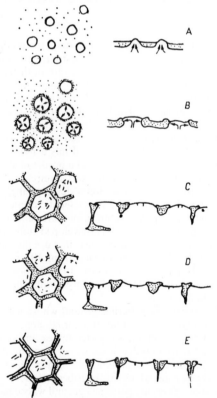

FIG. 4b. Successive stages of development of experimental sorted circles and polygons in plane view, left, and in cross section, right (Dzulynski, 1963).

FIG. 4c. Large scale polynomial ground, Donnelly Dome area, Alaska. (Air photo: T. L. Péwé).

always, contain abundant fine-grained material. In any one area, the size of bordering stones commonly increases as the depth and the breadth of the stone borders increase and the size of stones increases with the overall size of a form. Debris islands consist of more or less isolated patches of fine-grained material surrounded by boulders or blocks.

Nonsorted circles are patterned ground whose mesh is dominantly circular and has a nonsorted appearance due to the absence of a border of stones such as that characterizing sorted circles. Like sorted circles, nonsorted circles develop singly or in groups. Vegetation is a characteristic element in outlining the pattern. Dimensions are similar to those of sorted circles. Well-developed nonsorted circles tend to have central areas that are distinctly domed, the local relief varying from 10 cm to 1 meter (Hopkins and Sigafoos, 1951). Nonsorted circles consist of silt with few large fragments. Ice lens content is high.

Sorted nets are patterned ground whose mesh is intermediate between that of a sorted circle and a sorted polygon and has a sorted appearance commonly due to a border of stones surrounding finer material. Except for pattern, sorted nets resemble sorted polygons, which are described below.

Nonsorted nets are patterned ground whose mesh is intermediate between that of a nonsorted circle and a nonsorted polygon and has a nonsorted appearance due to the absence of a border of stones

such as that characterizing a sorted net. Except for pattern, nonsorted nets resemble nonsorted polygons, although some nonsorted polygons (including many ice-wedge polygons) have a mesh larger than that of any nonsorted net. *Earth hummocks* are a particular type of nonsorted net with a mesh characterized by a three-dimensional knoblike shape and a cover or vegetation (Sharp, 1942). A synonymous term is *thufur*. Earth hummocks form in groups, are 25–50 cm high, 1-2 meters in diameter, and tend to be elongate along hillslopes.

Sorted polygons are patterned ground whose mesh is dominantly polygonal and has a sorted appearance commonly due to a border of stones surrounding finer material. More or less synonymous terms include stone polygons, stone rings, stone nets, and others.

In contrast to circles, sorted polygons (Fig. 4) apparently never develop singly. As with sorted circles, vegetation, if present, does not in most places emphasize the pattern as strongly as it does in nonsorted forms of patterned ground. Sorted polygons range in size from a few centimeters in diameter to large forms 10 meters across, with the size tending to increase with increasing severity of climate and availability of water. Size range and sorting of stones and fine-grained material in sorted polygons are similar to sorted circles. Especially in large polygons, tabular stones of the borders tend to be on edge and oriented parallel to the border. The stony borders of many sorted forms, including nets, narrow downward. Other types show increased width of borders with depth, suggesting that further classification is possible. As with circles, polygons occur on mantle derived from subjacent bedrock or on transported mantle.

Nonsorted polygons are patterned ground whose mesh is dominantly polygonal and has a nonsorted appearance due to the absence of a border of stones such as that characterizing sorted polygons. Synonymous terms include fissure polygons, contractional polygons, and others.

Ice-wedge polygons are nonsorted polygons characterized by bordering ice wedges. In general, nonsorted polygons never develop singly; the borders are commonly marked by obvious fissures in the ground. Diameters range from a few centimeters to many meters. Ice-wedge polygons are large, with typical ranges of 10–40 meters.

Sorted steps are patterned ground with a steplike form and a sorted appearance due to a downslope border of stones embanking an area of finer material upslope. Sorted steps generally form in groups, are 1–3 meters wide, parallel to the contour, and up to 8 meters long in a downslope direction; the stone borders are more pronounced at the downslope end where they form distinct embankments (Fig. 5). Sorted steps are characteristic of moderate slopes

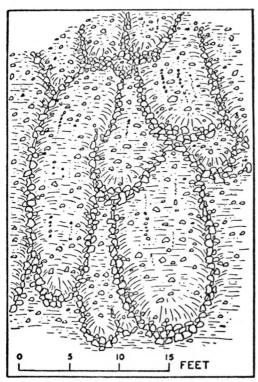

FIG. 5. Sketch of sorted steps in till. View looking up 10° slope (from Sharp, 1942).

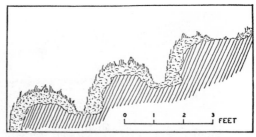

FIG. 6. Diagrammatic longitudinal section of earth hummocks and nonsorted step. (Nonsorted step upper right.) Lined material is earthly debris; other is largely vegetation mat (from Sharp, 1942).

and seem to consist of treads of gravelly sand, silt, and clay, with borders containing boulders up to 30 cm across. Tabular stones in the borders are commonly on edge.

Nonsorted steps are patterned ground with a steplike form and a nonsorted appearance resulting from a downslope border of vegetation embanking an area of relatively bare ground upslope. Nonsorted steps (Fig. 6), like sorted steps, form in groups and have lower borders which tend to be convex downslope. Vegetation is a characteristic element in outlining the pattern. Stone borders, such as those which characterize sorted steps, are absent. Rather, nonsorted steps consist of an earthen core with a 10-cm hull of humus, moss and plant roots.

Sorted stripes are patterned ground with a striped pattern and a sorted appearance due to parallel lines of stones and intervening strips of dominantly finer material oriented down the steepest available slope (Fig. 7). Synonymous terms include soil stripes, striped ground, rock stripes and others. Sorted stripes never form singly; they are essentially parallel and may be sinuous. The width of individual stony stripes ranges from a few centimeters to 2 meters or more, and the intervening stripes of finer material may be two to four times wider (Sharp, 1942). The stones of sorted stripes range from pebbles to boulders; tabular fragments may be on edge and oriented parallel to the stripes. The depth of sorting tends to vary with the size of the forms, as in sorted polygons and circles, extending to a depth of nearly 1 meter in the forms observed by Sharp (1942). The stony stripes commonly narrow downward in vertical section, but this may not be universal. Sorted polygons may merge into sorted stripes through a transition gradient of approximately 3–7°, and sorted steps may occur as transition forms. Some sorted stripes, however, occur without associated sorted polygons. Maximum slopes on which sorted stripes have been reported range from 15–30° (Sharp, 1942; see also Fig. 8 and Caine, 1963).

Nonsorted stripes are patterned ground with a striped pattern and a nonsorted appearance due to

FIG. 7. Stone stripes (sorted) in the Rocky Mountain National Park, Colorado, at about 3500 meters (altitude). (Photo: R. W. Fairbridge)

parallel lines of vegetation-covered ground and intervening strips of relatively bare ground oriented down the steepest available slope. A synonymous term is solifluction stripes. Nonsorted stripes resemble sorted stripes, but vegetation is a characteristic element in outlining the pattern. The absence of lines of stones is the essential feature of nonsorted stripes.

Washburn (1956) presented nineteen hypotheses to explain the origin of patterned ground; it is not necessary to go into these hypotheses in detail in this paper. Hypotheses include those based on expansion due to freezing; weathering; contraction due to drying, cooling and thawing; convection; moisture-pressure phenomena; differential thawing; solifluction, and others. Specifically, the more accepted theories include the following: (1) These features are due to alternate thrust and contraction of fine-grained material during the oft-repeated freezing and thawing process termed multigelation (Washburn, 1950). (2) They are brought about by differential heaving due to inequalities in snow cover and vegetation. (3) Cryostatic movement, described earlier, can cause important heaving (Müller, 1945). (4) Contraction due to desiccation is considered a primary cause of nonsorted polygons, and perhaps of other features. (5) The contraction of frozen ground at very low temperatures is

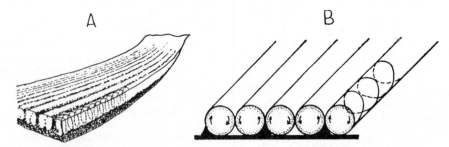

FIG. 8. Possible origin of sorted stripes (from Butrym *et al.*, 1964). Boulders moving downslope are rotated by differential frost action to produce net spiral motion. Motion produces alternating concentrations of coarse and fine particles.

(A) Schematic presentation of the origin of sorted stripes (after Gripp; Steche, 1933, Fig. 5).

(B) Schematic presentation of the origin of longitudinal parallel mud ridges by moving suspension (based on experiments of Dzulynski and Walton, 1963).

considered to be important, particularly in the formation of ice-wedge polygons. (6) A very hypothetical process involves the existence of soil density differences due to differential saturation. Thawing of ice lenses may produce local supersaturation, lowering of intergranular pressure and induction of seepage pressure. These pressures may result in material being squeezed into unfilled pore spaces; fine-grained material would tend to concentrate this way and to induce further differential saturation. (7) The activity of rills is believed to account for some but not all sorted stripes. (8) Finally, solifluction is considered very important in the formation of patterned ground on slopes.

Washburn concluded that (1) the origin of most forms of patterned ground is uncertain and often very speculative; (2) patterned ground is *polygenetic*; (3) some forms may be combination products in a continuous system having different processes as end members; (4) climatic and terrain interpretation of patterned ground, both active and "fossil" (i.e., inherited), is limited by lack of reliable data about the formative processes.

Recent work suggests that a probable mechanism for the bringing of stones to the surface is the fact that ground freezing occurs first immediately beneath buried stones; ice crystals in the freezing ground impart an upward force to the stone, tending to raise it to the ground surface. Subsequent sorting may reflect diapiric action. Saturated fines may punch through coarser surface material, producing a fine-grained central mound surrounded by stones. This process may be localized by ice wedges.

Asymmetric valleys

Asymmetric valleys (q.v.) are valleys having one side steeper than the other. They may be due (locally) to differential thawing and associated consequences affecting one side more than the other. Very probably, asymmetric valleys have multiple origins and cannot be always ascribed to frost action processes. However, it is observed that they are most common in modern or formerly periglacial regions and are not reported from equatorial or subtropical regions. Relative *insolation* (q.v., Vol. II) appears to be critical. In the northern hemisphere, the west- and south-facing slopes are most likely to be affected by diurnal cryergenetic erosion.

Dry Valleys

Dry valleys (q.v.) are flat-floored valleys now devoid of streams. It has been argued that many dry valleys developed when the water table was held up by frozen ground and when surface streams and gelifluction were active, and that they are now dry because thawing of frozen ground lowered the water table and permitted runoff to infiltrate to depth (Dury, personal communication). Dry valleys are thus disequilibrium features. Although similarly

shaped stream-occupied valleys occur in the polar zone, they are not confined to it. The frozen ground explanation for dry valleys cannot be accepted unless solution, beheading and former greater precipitation and other changes of regimes can be eliminated as causes. Dry valleys may provide evidence of former frozen ground in places, but they hardly constitute evidence of permafrost, and in many places they are probably unrelated to frost action.

Nivation Hollows

Nivation hollows are bowl-shaped depressions caused by frost action and mass-wasting beneath lingering or perennial snowdrifts; they are closely related to the orographic snowline. These hollows are quasi-equilibrium forms; "fossil" forms are easily confused with earth-flow scars, but where correctly identified, they are acceptable evidence of former greater frost action (due to either greater snowfall or lower temperatures).

Grèzes Litées

Grèzes litées (Guillien, 1951) are bedded slope deposits of pebble-size rock chips. They have been interpreted as due to frost wedging, gelifluction, sheetflow and rillwork in association with perennial snowdrifts on vegetation-free slopes. Differential creep alone has also been suggested (Baulig, cited by Malaurie and Guillien, 1953). Their origin does not seem to be firmly established, and their quasi-equilibrium range is not accurately known.

Protalus Ramparts

Protalus ramparts (Fig. 9) are ridges formed of blocks, frost wedged from slopes above, that accumulate by sliding over snowdrifts. They occur most commonly in cirques. Like nivation hollows they are closely related to the orographic snowline; however, they are more closely identified with

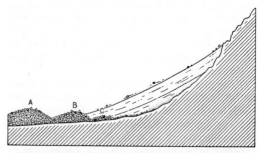

Fig. 9. Origin of winter talus ridges, nivation ridges or protalus ramparts. The snow bank or neve prevents the formation of a normal talus at the foot of the cliff; instead a ridge of rock waste is built parallel to the cliff but separated from it by the snow-filled depression. With larger or smaller snow banks, ridges would form at different distances from the cliff as A, B, C, above (modified after Howe, U.S. Geol. Survey; from Sharpe, 1938).

highlands than are nivation hollows. "Fossil" forms are easily confused with cirque moraines and are not necessarily reliable climatic indicators.

Rock Glaciers

Rock glaciers (see *Rock Streams, Rock Rivers, Rock Glaciers*) are tonguelike deposits of angular boulders, resembling a small glacier, generally occurring at high altitudes in rugged terrain. Analogous terms are *rock streams* and *rock rivers*. The classic study of rock glaciers is that of Wahrhaftig and Cox (1959) from which the following information was taken. Rock glaciers in the central Alaska Range are of three types: lobate (length less than width), tongue shaped (length greater than width), and spatulate (tongue shaped but with an enlargement at the front). Lobate rock glaciers line cliffs and cirque walls, and probably represent an initial stage; the other two move down valley axes and represent more mature stages.

The rock glaciers studied by Wahrhaftig and Cox are composed of coarse blocky debris that is cemented by ice a few feet below the surface. The top quarter of the thickness is coarse rubble, below which is coarse rubble mixed with silt, sand and fine gravel. Fronts of active (moving) rock glaciers are bare of vegetation, are generally at the angle of repose, and make a sharp angle with the upper surface. Fronts of inactive rock glaciers are covered with lichens or other vegetation, have gentle slopes, and are rounded at the top. Active rock glaciers average 150 feet in thickness; inactive rock glaciers average 70 feet in thickness. The upper surfaces of many rock glaciers are marked by sets of parallel rounded ridges and V-shaped furrows, and by conical pits, crevasses and lobes.

Actual rates of movement have been measured: One rock glacier showed an advance of its front of 1.6 ft/yr (over 9 years), while its upper surface advanced 2.4 ft/yr. Motion is not confined to thin surface layers but is distributed throughout the interiors of the rock glaciers, which in Alaska are probably frozen. Viscosity is slightly higher than that of ice glaciers (a factor of 10); maximum average shear stresses range from 1–2 bars (values which are quite large relative to those for solifluction and creep features).

Rock glaciers occur on blocky fracturing rocks which form talus that has large interconnected voids in which ice can accumulate. They are rare on platy or schistose rocks whose talus moves rapidly by solifluction. Rock glaciers are much less responsive to microclimate than ice glaciers due to the insulating effect of the debris cover.

Wahrhaftig and Cox concluded that rock glaciers move as a result of the flow of interstitial ice and that they require for their formation the following: steep cliffs, a near-glacial climate cold enough for the ground to be perennially frozen, and bedrock that is broken by frost action into coarse blocky debris

with large interconnected voids. The longitudinal furrows are thought to result from the accumulation of ice-rich bands in the swales between talus cones at the head of the rock glaciers and the subsequent melting of this ice as the rock glacier moves downvalley. The transverse ridges are thought to result from shearing within the rock glacier that would occur where the thickness increases or the velocity decreases downstream. Measurements indicated an average rate of erosion of 1–3 feet of bedrock per year for active rock glaciers.

Block Fields

Block fields (*felsenmeere*) are considerable areas, usually fairly level or of only gentle slope, covered with moderate-sized or large blocks of rock (Sharpe, 1938). *Block streams* are extensive accumulations of similar blocks confined to valleys or forming narrow linear deposits extending down the steepest available slope.

Solifluction and Gelifluction Deposits

Gelifluction deposits are deposits made by solifluction associated with frozen ground. They may have the form of sheets, benches, lobes, debris streams and stripes, and may occur on slopes as low as 2°. The material is typically angular and tends to be nonsorted but may show a crude structure parallel to the slope. Gelifluction deposits are easily confused with other types of mass-wasting deposits.

Frost-churned Ground

Frost-churned ground is regolith whose components have been stirred by frost action (Fig. 10). It is commonly recognized by distortion and mixing of preexisting regular features (such as bedding and soil horizons) or by scattering of surface stones (such as ventifacts) throughout the regolith. Involutions, which are interpenetrating tongues of frost-churned regolith, constitute a special variety usually associated with permafrost, but not neces-

Fig. 10. Frost contortions, Siberia. (Photo: S. A. Strelkov)

sarily so (Wright, 1961). Theoretically, frost-churned ground is due to frost heaving and thrusting and/or other processes involved in the development of cold-climate patterned ground. Similar features can be produced by mass-wasting and (except for involutions) by growth and decay of tree roots and by solution. "Fossil" frost-churned ground, if correctly identified, is indicative of former greater frost action; it has a wide climatic spectrum except for involutions, the "fossil" forms of which may be indicative of permafrost.

Pingos

Pingos are dome-shaped hills occurring in regions of permafrost; their growth results from the up-lifting of a layer of frozen ground by the pressure of water freezing in the substratum to form large ice lenses (see *Pingos*). They may rise tens of meters or more above the surrounding terrain. Usually circular or oval at the base, they often measure several hundred meters in circumference. The dominant characteristic is the internal massive lens of clear ice. The overlying layer of material, varying from 1–10 meters or more in thickness, is frequently ruptured at the top; the resultant crater may contain a lake. The term *hydrolaccolith* is a genetic term, commonly applied to pingos.

Pingos occur dominantly in the zones of discontinuous or thin-continuous permafrost. Open-system pingos occur where circulating groundwater

TABLE 2. RANGE OF FROST ACTION EFFECTS: UNDER PRESENT CLIMATIC CONDITIONS. i.e., QUASI-EQUILIBRIUM
Predominant ranges are suggested by (1) and lesser ranges in decreasing order by (2) and (3)

Feature	Lowlands			Highlands			
	Polar	Subpolar	Middle-latitude	Polar	Subpolar	Middle-latitude	Low-latitude
Permafrost	1	2		1	2	3	
Nivation hollows	1	2		2	1	2	3
Protalus ramparts				2	1	1	3
Rock glaciers				2	1	1	
Block fields and block streams	2	2		1	1	2	3
Gelifluction deposits	1	2		1	1	2	3
Frost cracks	1	2	3	2	2	3	
Ice-wedge polygons	1	2		2	3		
Large sorted forms of patterned ground	1	3		2	2	3	
Pingos	1	2					
Frost-churned ground (excluding involutions)	1	2		1	2	3	(?)
Frost-churned ground (involutions only)	1	2		2	3		

Note: Ranking is tentative and highly subjective. A generally increasing persistence of snow cover at high altitudes and decreasing number of freeze-thaw cycles at high latitudes are taken into consideration in the suggested ranking. Due to extreme continentality, certain mid-latitude regions demonstrate seasonal frost churning (adapted, by kind permission, from unpublished notes of A. L. Washburn).

can develop sufficient hydrostatic pressure to push up the impervious frozen surface layer. Valley bottoms of alluvial material are particularly favorable (but not exclusive) locations for this type of pingo. Closed-system pingos are generally found in the center of broad shallow lakes or lake basins: they occur where permafrost advances into the lake basin, producing an excess of hydrostatic pressure which in turn injects excess pore water into the ice lens. The frozen surface layer then yields to this pressure by updoming. "Fossil" forms would be proof of former permafrost, but they have rarely been reported and are difficult to identify with certainty.

Conclusion

It is clear that many features are products of frost action, but few are diagnostic of a given process or situation. This is particularly true of "fossil" (inherited) forms and their attendant difficulties of precise and unequivocal identification. Table 2 is an attempt to determine the quasi-equilibrium range of frost action effects. Most frost action phenomena occur frequently in polar lowlands, less frequently in subpolar lowlands, and virtually never in middle-latitude lowlands. Highland phenomena are more widespread, occurring especially in subpolar latitudes, and extending well into middle, and in some cases equatorial, latitudes.

Despite increased interest and investigation into frost action processes and effects in recent years, many subjects of interest to students of cold climates remain enigmatic and present tantalizing problems for future study.

LEE WILSON

References

Andersson, J. G., 1906, "Solifluction, a component of subaerial denudation," *J. Geology*, **14**, 91–112.

Black, Robert F., 1952, "Growth of ice-wedge polygons in permafrost near Barrow, Alaska (Abstract)," *Bull. Geol. Soc. Am.*, **63**, 1235–1236.

Black, Robert F., 1954, "Permafrost—A review," *Bull. Geol. Soc. Am.*, **65**, 839–856.

Brown, R. J. E., 1963, "The relation between mean annual air and ground temperatures in the permafrost region of Canada," *Natl. Acad. Sci.—Natl. Res. Council, Intern. Conf. Permafrost, Purdue Univ.*, 26pp.

Bryan, Kirk, 1946, "Cryopedology—the study of frozen ground and intensive frost-action with suggestions on nomenclature," *Am. J. Sci.*, **244**, 622–642.

Büdel, Julius, 1953, "Die periglazial-morphologische Wirkungen des Eiszeitklimas auf der ganzen Erde," *Erdkunde*, **7**, 249–266.

Butrym, J., Cegla, J., Dzulynski, S., and Nakonieczny, S., 1964, "New interpretation of periglacial structures," *Folia Quaternaria, Krakow*, No. 17, 34pp.

Caine, T. N., 1963, "The origin of sorted stripes in the Lake District, northern England," *Geografiska Annaler*, **45**(2–3), 172–179.

Corte, A. E., 1953, "Contribución a la morfología periglacial de la alta cordillera con especial mención del aspecto criopedológico," *Univ. Nac. Cuyo (Mendoza, Argentina), Dept. Inv. Cient. Anales,* **1**, No. 2, 1–54.

Denny, C. S., 1952, "Late Quaternary geology and frost phenomena along Alaska Highway, northern British Columbia and southeastern Yukon," *Bull. Geol. Soc. Am.*, **63**, p. 883–922.

Dobrowolski, A. B., 1923, "Historja naturalna lodu," Warsaw, 940pp.

Dzulynski, S., 1963, "Polygonal structures in experiments and their bearing upon some periglacial phenomena," *Bull. Acad. Polonaise Sci.*, **11**(3), 145–150.

Embleton, C. and King, C. A. M., 1968, "Glacial and Periglacial Geomorphology," London, E. Arnold Ltd., 608pp.

Guilcher, André, 1950, "Nivation, cryoplanation et solifluction Quaternaires," *Rev. Géomorphologie Dynamique*, **1**, No. 2, 53–78.

Guillien, Y., 1949, "Gel et degel du sol: les mechanismes morphologiques," *L'information Geogr.*, Paris, **13**, 104–116.

Guillien, Yves, 1951, "Les grèzes litées de Charente," *Rev. Géogr. Pyrenées Sud-Ouest*, **22**, 154–162.

Hopkins, D. M., and Sigafoos, R. S., 1951, "Frost action and vegetation patterns on Seward Peninsula, Alaska," *U.S. Geol. Surv. Bull.*, **974-C**, 51–100.

Jahn, Alfred, 1960, "Some remarks on evolution of slopes on Spitsbergen," *Z. Geomorphol. Suppl.*, **1**, 49–58.

Lozinski, W., 1909, "Über die mechanische Verwitterung der Sandsteine im gemässigten Klima," *Acad. Sci. Cracovie, Bull. Intern., Cl. Sci. Math. et Nat.*, No. 1, 1–25.

Malaurie, Jean, and Guillien, Yves, 1953, "Le modelé cryo-nival versants meubles de Skansen (Disko, Groenland). Interpretation générale des grèzes litées," *Soc. Géol. France Bull.*, Ser. 6, **3**, 703–721.

Müller, Siemon W., 1945, "Permafrost or permanently frozen ground and related engineering problems," *U. S. Geol. Surv. Spec. Rept.*, Strategic Engineering Study 62, Second ed., 231pp. (1947, reprinted by J. D. Edwards Bros.)

Péwé, T. L., 1963, "Ice wedges in Alaska—Classification, distribution, and climatic significance," *Natl. Acad. Sci.—Natl. Res. Council, Intern. Conf. Permafrost, Purdue Univ.*, 16pp.

Rapp, Anders, 1960, "Recent development of mountain slopes in Kärkevagge and surroundings," *Geografiska Annaler*, **42**, 185.

Richmond, G. M., 1949, "Stone nets, stone stripes, and soil stripes in the Wind River Mountains, Wyoming," *J. Geol.*, **57**, 143–153.

Sharp, R. P., 1942, "Soil structures in the St. Elias Range, Yukon Territory," *J. Geomorphol.*, **5**, 273–301.

Sharpe, C. F. S., 1938, "Landslides and Related Phenomena," New York, Columbia University Press, 137pp.

Taber, Stephen, 1943, "Perennially frozen ground in Alaska: Its origin and history," *Bull. Geol. Soc. Am.*, **54**, 1433–1548.

Terzaghi, Karl, 1952, "Permafrost," *Boston Soc. Civil Eng. J.*, **39**, 1–50.

Troll, Carl, 1944, "Strukturböden, Solifluktion, und Frostklimate der Erde," *Geol. Rundschau*, **34**, 545–694.

Troll, Carl, 1958, "Structure soils, solifluction and frost

climates of the earth," *U.S. Army Corps of Engineers, Snow Ice and Permafrost Research Establishment, Translation* 43, 121pp.

Wahrhaftig, Clyde, and Cox, Allan, 1959, "Rock glaciers in the Alaska Range," *Bull. Geol. Soc. Am.*, **70**, 383–436.

Washburn, A. L., 1950, "Patterned ground," *Rev. Can. Géographie*, **4**, No. 3–4, 5–59.

Washburn, A. L., 1956, "Classification of patterned ground and review of suggested origins," *Bull. Geol. Soc. Am.*, **67**, 823–866.

Wiman, S., 1963, "A preliminary study of experimental frost weathering. A laboratory study," *Geografiska Annaler*, **45**(2–3), 113–121.

Wolfe, P. E., 1953, "Periglacial frost-thaw basins in New Jersey," *J. Geol.*, **61**, 133–141.

Wright, H. E., 1961, "Late Pleistocene climate of Europe: A review," *Bull. Geol. Soc. Am.*, **72**, 933–984.

Zeuner, F. E., 1959, "The Pleistocene Period," London, Hutchinson Sci. and Techn., 447pp.

Cross-references: *Asymmetric Valleys; Cryopedology, Cryoplanation, Cryoturbation; Dell; Dry Valleys; Felsenmeer; Frost Heaving; Frost Riving; Landslide; Mass-wasting; Mudflow; Nivation; Patterned Ground; Periglacial Landscapes; Permafrost; Pingos; Quaternary Period; Regolith and Saprolite; Rock Stream; Salt Weathering or Fretting; Sheet Erosion; Slopes; Solifluction; Suffosion; Talus; Terracettes, etc.; Thermokarst. Vol. II: Insolation. pr Vol. VI: Groundwater.*

FROST HEAVING

Ice crystals developing from ground water tend to grow unidirectionally and force individual soil particles or pebbles upwards. Under certain conditions they may form miniature analogs of earth pillars. Such "needle ice" is sometimes called *pipkrake* (Troll, 1944). Frost heaving was intensively studied by Taber (1930) in connection with the breaking-up of highways and other cemented pavements; he concluded that they should be kept as free as possible from intergranular moisture. This process, combined with the force of gravity, applied on a slope, is fundamental in such phenomena as *soil creep, rock streams, rock glaciers, patterned ground* (q.v.) and a variety of *solifluction* features (q.v.).

RHODES W. FAIRBRIDGE

References

Steeger, A., 1944, "Diluviale Bodenfrosterscheinungen am Niedershein," *Geol. Rundschau,* **34,** 342–434.

Taber, S., 1929, "Frost heaving," *J. Geol.,* **37,** 428–461.

Taber, S., 1930, "The mechanics of frost heaving," *J. Geol.,* **38,** 303–317.

Troll, C., 1944, "Strukturböden, Solifluktion und Frostklimate der Erde," *Geol. Rundschau,* **34,** 545–694.

Cross-references: *Patterned Ground; Rock Stream; Soil Creep; Solifluction.*

FROST POLYGONS—*See* PATTERNED GROUND

FROST RIVING, SHATTERING, SPLITTING, WEDGING

In the same manner as *frost heaving* (q.v.) but with respect to hard rocks, moisture which soaks down into joint and cleavage crevices during the thaw season, freezes, expands and causes the rocks to split. The role of freezing in mechanical weathering either in subpolar latitudes or at high altitudes has long been recognized. The term *congelifraction* was proposed by Kirk Bryan (1946) to cover this aspect of what he called *cryopedology*. The expressions frost riving, frost shattering, frost splitting and frost wedging are used somewhat indiscriminately. The end product is the *felsenmeer,* block field, and on slopes, the *rock stream* or *rock glacier*.

RHODES W. FAIRBRIDGE

Reference

Bryan, K., 1946, "Cryopedology—The study of frozen ground and intensive frost-action with suggestions of nomenclature," *Am. J. Sci.,* **244,** 622–642.

Potter, N., Jr. and Moss, J. H., 1968, "Origin of the Blue Rocks block field and adjacent deposits, Berks County, Pennsylvania," *Bull. Geol. Soc. Am.,* **79,** 255–262.

Cross-references: *Cryopedology; Felsenmeer; Frost Heaving; Rock Stream, Rock River, Rock Glacier.*

FROZEN GROUND—*See* PERMAFROST

G

GENERAL SYSTEMS THEORY IN GEOMORPHOLOGY

A promising new methodologic and conceptual framework is afforded by "general systems theory," which in its present state is less a theory than a collection of complementary concepts useful in treating complex macroscopic phenomena as an organic whole. The present article introduces some of these concepts useful in the study of geomorphic forms and processes. For a general view of systems concepts and applications, the reader is referred to "General Systems," the yearbook of the Society for General Systems Research. Additional references and a systems treatment of the landscape as a whole may be found in Howard (1965).

The System

A *system* consists of elements (objects), their instantaneous state and their interrelationships, and it may change through time. In general, those subjects of investigation which show interdependence of elements and a unity in change lend themselves to the systems methodology. Such systems are generally composed of contiguous elements located within a finite area or volume. Representative defined systems in geomorphology might include: a drainage network, the energy relationships of a drainage basin, a weathering profile, or sediment sources and transport within a drainage basin.

The state of a system and its change through time are measured by system parameters, or variables, which characterize its instantaneous composition and organization and its dynamics (flow of energy and mass). The characterizing parameters are selected for their utility in defining the state to the accuracy desired, their ease of measurement, and relevance to the dynamics of the system. Parameters in geomorphology might include chemical composition and concentrations, gradients or slopes, velocities, physical measurements, dimensionless ratios, etc.

Those factors not in the defined system but which control the dynamics of the system are the *external* variables. Geomorphic systems are essentially passive; i.e., they change only through change of the surroundings. This can be true only if all sources of mass and energy ultimately derive from, and are lost to, the surroundings. A complication to the passive concept arises where the system partially controls its environment (the *feedback principle*), e.g., the control of microclimate by topographic form and the corresponding effects of microclimate variations on landscape forms. When empirical relationships between internal and external parameters rather than causal explanations are desired, this "feedback" can be ignored and the factors may be considered to be independent. Alternatively, the system may be expanded to include the interrelated factors, e.g., including the zone of microclimate as part of the landform or including vegetation and soil as a unit.

A change of one external variable usually causes greater or lesser readjustment of all system parameters. Thus, geomorphic systems should respond as an organic whole to changes of environment. For example, stream discharge, sediment load, slope, channel width, depth, etc., are clearly interrelated. The above stream parameters are similarly interrelated with drainage area, discharge, drainage basin shape and relief, and stream order within the same drainage complex.

Although systems may be dominated in their response by one type of external variable, most geomorphic systems exhibit *multivariate control* by such agencies as climate, geology, tectonics, flora and fauna, and human modifications.

All natural macroscopic systems must be considered to be completely determined in their state and responses through the action of external factors upon the system. Nevertheless, the analysis of system responses need not be causal. Where the external and internal variables only roughly define the state of the system and environment (as slope, width, depth, velocity, discharge and sediment load characterize the fluvial system) and are related by statistical methods, empirical probabilistic or thermodynamic relationships may be found which predict without explaining. For example, see Langbein's paper on the geometry of river channels (1964) and Scheidegger's application of statistical mechanical methods to geomorphic analysis (1964).

Equilibrium and Dynamics

The concept of *equilibrium* is quite basic to system theory and is considered here to imply a complete adjustment of the internal variables to external conditions (see *Equilibrium*; also *Open Systems—Allometric Growth*, this volume). Equilibria in geomorphology may arise in several types of system-environment relationships. The degree of approach of system variables to equilibrium may be measured by two methods: (a) if all external variables remain constant through time, then the parameters of a system in equilibrium should also remain constant (however, the sensitivity of specific internal variables to changes of the external variables is indeterminate by this method); (b) if the value of an external variable changes through time or space while all other external variables remain constant, have little effect upon the system, or can be corrected for, then a correlation of low variance between the value of the external variable and that of the system property indicates a close approach to equilibrium, and, additionally, a high correlation coefficient indicates a high sensitivity of the system property to changes of the external variable. Each combination of external variables defines a unique system equilibrium state.

Crucial to the study of equilibrium and dynamics of a system is the concept of the resistance to change (*inertia*) of a system variable. Following a change of an external variable, the system will tend to adjust to the new regime. In the case of a system which is manifesting no secondary responses (see below) and is changing from one equilibrium state to another, the internal parameters in many natural systems tend to approach the new equilibrium at a rate proportional to their distance from the equilibrium value. Such an exponential approach implies a time constant characteristic of the system and of the type of change of external variable. Although a system may never achieve exact equilibrium, it will within a finite time reach any desired approximation to equilibrium.

The rate of change of an external variable compared to the capacity for adjustment of the system determines the behavior of the system. When an external variable remains constant through time or changes very slowly in value, the system (or subsystem) remains in constant equilibrium. For example, when lithology and structure are of constant composition or only slowly varying in the vertical direction, a complete adjustment between landforms and geology is to be expected, but when vertical erosion exposes new parent rock and structure, landforms must adjust, and transitional (nonequilibrium) landforms should be expected.

Some external factors act upon the topography with great effect, but over such a geologically short time period that no equilibrium state is to be expected. Volcanic eruptions, earthquakes, glaciations, major floods, and forest fires might fall in this category depending upon their frequency. Each action of such a variable must be individually considered as an "event" in its action upon the system. These intensive agents act upon the system to produce forms in disequilibrium with the "normal" operation of the system. When such intensive variables cease to operate, the system tends to revert to its "normal" state and economy (a type of succession) and the forms produced through the action of the intensive variable become less prominent with time.

Because of *inertia in natural systems*, external factors which fluctuate rapidly (in comparison to the adjustive capacity of corresponding system parameters) influence the parameters only as their average; the rapid fluctuations are "filtered out" in system response. For example, weather acts in this manner upon many geomorphic features. The external variable to which the system parameter is most sensitive would be a climatic factor measured by weather averages for periods of the same order of magnitude as the response-time constant of the system parameter. If these climatic averages in turn maintain a consistent value over a period of time, the system parameter will attain equilibrium (of a special sort).

Secondary responses to changes of external variables arise in systems composed of interrelated subsystems. In such cases, the rate and path of adjustment may not be a simple asymptotic function but may have secondary responses which can enter into or dominate the adjustment. System variables and subsystems showing pronounced primary adjustments are, in general, closely related to the mass and energy flow between the system and the surroundings, whereas secondary effects often result from adjustment of the larger structural features and subsystems.

In certain cases the response of a system to a change of external variables may involve a *threshold*, or discontinuity, which separates two rather different system economies. *Landslides* and *gullying* are two striking large-scale examples of this. On a smaller scale, many sediment transport phenomena require a minimum shear stress for sediment transport, and many chemical transformations have such thresholds. Changes of external factors which require system parameters to cross a threshold may allow metastable nonequilibrium states to continue because of the great change required to initiate an equilibrium regime.

In natural systems, several external variables may be simultaneously changing. Thus a system may be continuously adjusted to one external variable while not in equilibrium with others. Reference to equilibrium in natural systems must therefore be directed to specific external variables. Even if it is demonstrated that a system or system parameter is not in equilibrium with an external parameter, the existence of a theoretical equilibrium state retains its significance as it defines the direction of system response.

The extent to which the past action of an external variable influences a present system parameter is a positive function of its relative intensity of action upon the system and of the length of time over which it acts (for recurring events, this represents their frequency and magnitude). However, the influence of past values of the external variables decreases with time at a rate that is a function of the ability of system variables to adjust to changes in external conditions. A variable which acts with low frequency but high intensity may have an equal or greater effect than those acting less strongly but more constantly, e.g., the importance in erosion and sediment transport of the infrequent thunderstorm.

The decreasing influence with time of past actions of the environment upon the system means conversely that the more remote the past is, the less may be inferred about past conditions of the system and the external variables. Consequently, the present state of a system may have been reached through any of an infinity of past states, with a wider range of past states theoretically possible as the time considered is more remote. Similarly, for a system variable in equilibrium with an external factor, the constancy through time of the external factor becomes less certain in the more distant past.

Different geomorphic system parameters and subsystems have unequal response times to changes in the same external factors; therefore, some elements of the system will carry a longer-term historical record than others. Streams are usually sensitive to small or rapid fluctuations in the environment and therefore carry a more complete record in flood plains and terraces of the recent past than do slopes and divides.

As secondary geomorphic responses, the coarser features of geomorphic systems may be completely in equilibrium with, say, geologic controls and long-term climatic averages, while the primary land form responses, such as stream cross-sectional parameters, vary with short-term climatic fluctuations. On the other hand, the nice adjustment (quasi-equilibrium) of subsystem (e.g., stream) parameters to small-scale variations of climate does not imply that other features or the system as a whole is at equilibrium.

Conclusion

In conclusion, it should be emphasized that the systems concept is a model which is dependent upon the purpose at hand and the scale of the investigation. Schumm and Lichty (1965) discuss the effects of size and time period considered (scale) upon the definition of the system, the internal and external variables to be measured and related, independent

and dependent relationships, and cause and effect. In parenthesis, it should be noted that the present author has defined equilibrium in a more liberal manner than have Schumm and Lichty; therefore, some of our conclusions are at variance.

ALAN D. HOWARD

References

*Howard, Alan D., 1965, "Geomorphological systems— equilibrium and dynamics," *Am. J. Sci.*, **263**, 302–312.

Langbein, W. B., 1964, "Geometry of river channels," *J. Hydraulics Div., Am. Soc. Civil Engrs.*, **90**, 301–312, discussion (1965), **91**, 297–313.

Scheidegger, A. E., 1964, "Some implications of statistical mechanics in geomorphology," *Bull. Intern. Assoc. Sci. Hydrology*, **9**, 12–16.

*Schumm, S. A., and Lichty, R. W., 1965, "Time, space, and causality in geomorphology," *Am. J. Sci.*, **263**, 110–119.

* Additional bibliographic references may be found in this work.

Cross-references: *Drainage Basin; Equilibrium; Open Systems-Allometric Growth; Quantitative Geomorphology; Rivers; Sediment Transport; Slopes; Stream Channel Characteristics; Stream Orders.*

GENETIC CLASSIFICATION—*See* **CORAL REEFS: LANDSCAPE ANALYSIS: LANDSCAPE TYPES—GENETIC; MOUNTAINS; RIVERS**

GEODESY—*See* pr Vol. V

GEODETIC SURVEYING—*See* pr Vol. VI, **SURVEYING**

GEOGRAPHIC CYCLE—*See* **CYCLES, GEOMORPHIC**

GEOGRAPHIC NOMENCLATURE—*See* pr Vol. VI

GEOGRAPHICAL REGIONS—*See* **REGIONS, NATURAL AND GEOGRAPHICAL**

GEOGRAPHY: CONCEPT, GROWTH, AND STATUS

1. Concept

Geography deals principally with the surface of the earth and in particular with the importance and the locations of the phenomena on it. Although the discipline is the oldest one with continuity of name within man's organized knowledge, it is paradoxically just in the present age finding its central intellectual problem. This long delay has been caused largely by the lag in the development of human geography. Now, geographers recognize three levels of approach to their subject and, in so doing, successfully transcend several age-old dilemmas that have marked their subject.

(a) **Descriptive Geography.** The first of these geographic levels consists of the description of characteristics of selected places. In descriptive geography, places are selected and described in the manner that best suggests the uniqueness of the places. The descriptions are largely verbal, and the terms used are borrowed in the sense that they come from other disciplines or general language. It is, of course, impossible fully to describe the unique, for the very terms of any communication are general; but skillful writers indicate the character and appeal, and they convey the feeling of uniqueness, of given places by describing the particular way in which many things are combined there. No matter how sophisticated, incisive, or inventive these presentations may be, the level of geography involved is the simple descriptive one in which location or place is assumed as naïvely given. Much of travel literature, "local color" in novels, and adventure narrative also is of this type. So too may be the work of anthropologists, economists, historians, climatologists, soil scientists, geologists and others who, while they may sometimes write about places and may rise to highly sophisticated levels of analysis or synthesis, do so principally in the terms of their own disciplines. Generally the structures and processes investigated and adduced are non-spatial. This applies even to ecologists (and certain geographers) who examine and purport to explain the total interrelatedness of phenomena at a place and who, no matter how far they may rise above mere description in other terms, remain essentially at the descriptive level in geography.

(b) **Classificatory Geography.** It is true, for example, that every square inch on the earth's surface differs in some way from every other square inch. No two places, however small, are exactly alike. To know about the locations of phenomena in such minute detail is virtually impossible. Moreover, such unorganized detail would have limited use; and, as in science generally, a method of grouping "similar" elements, in this case places, is essential for many purposes. The classification of the earth's surface lies at the heart of *regional geography*. The number and characteristics of the geographical classes (i.e., regions) so defined, obviously and of necessity depend upon the nature and the purpose of the classificatory scheme employed and thus may be expected to differ from purpose to purpose. In this respect, the essence of regional classification is like the problem of classification in all academic disciplines. There is, however, one factor always present in regional classifications, and that is location. It is this factor and the concepts related to it, such as concentrated, dispersed, clustered, evenly distributed, contiguous, etc., that are essentially geographic. It can be shown that the terminology and methods developed in science generally for classification are relatable precisely by vocabulary equivalences to those developed independently in geography through the years when that factor that is peculiarly geographical, namely location on the earth's surface, is added.

The exercise of regionalizing is not too unlike the operations performed in set theory in mathematics. Translated into the terms of real space upon the earth's surface, unions, intersects, and sub-sets are valid ideas expressing "uniform" geographical regions. A geographer may well regard the earth's surface as the "set of all sets." So too, the Venn diagrams, used to portray graphically the relations among nonspatial sets, have their counterpart in geography in maps showing the extents and boundaries of various so-called homogeneous regions. In Venn diagrams only topological properties are utilized, whereas on geographical maps all geometrical properties are utilized, and scale, direction, size, and shape have precise meaning in terms of the kind of map projection utilized.

(c) **Theoretical-predictive Geography.** As intriguing as the ideas associated with the geographical classification of the earth's surface may be, it is in the now emerging level of theoretical–predictive geography that the greatest research activity is evident. The emergence of geography at this level as a science of spatial relations has been dependent upon two things. For one, geographers have emphasized that common characteristics relating to spatial structure (form) and spatial process (movement) are found for a wide variety of phenomena, drawn from both the physical and nonphysical world. That is to say, morphological laws or spatial patterns repeat themselves, regardless of the nonspatial dissimilarities present among the phenomena. The development of human geography in theoretical terms was required before this grand advance could be made. William Bunge (1962) has emphasized the simultaneous necessity and efficiency for such an organization of the discipline.

In the second place, as Bunge also notes, recent gains in the development of geography as a science at the theoretical-predictive level have been accomplished largely as a result of the simultaneous increase in both the sophistication and the naïveté with which geographers view the phenomena of the real world. This seeming paradox is explainable, for example, with reference to mathematics. More than ever before, geographers are using the tools of calculus, probability, topology, symbolic logic, the various algebras, geometries, and so on. But at the same time, the concepts of topology and the various geometries are being taken more literally than ever before. The study of actual earth-related surfaces, paths, and movements has now been extended far beyond its original application which included such things as landforms, contour mapping, drainage patterns, etc., in physical geography alone.

The modern geographer conceives of surfaces based also on social, economic, and cultural phenomena portraying not only conventional densities but other things such as potentials, probabilities, costs, times, and so on. Always, however, these conceptual surfaces are regarded as capable of overlying the surface of the real earth, and the geometric and topological characteristics of these surfaces thus describe aspects of the geography of the real world.

New research includes the investigation of the abstract properties of "surfaces" and movements on them. Special attention is being paid to the dynamics of the relationship of structure and process in this connection. Surfaces studied include physical landforms, atmospheric pressure distributions, minimum flight time surfaces, and potential of population surfaces, among others. The geography of surfaces represents a high level of abstraction in geography.

Bunge, and Warntz as well (1964), have noted that any geographic explanation or prediction of the location of phenomena on the earth's surface, human, physical, whatever, involves reference to movements such as circulation, diffusion, interaction, orbits, and flows. This is what we think distinguishes purely geographic processes from other kinds of processes. These movements, whether of rivers on the earth's mantle or the migration of people to urban areas produce change in the spatial arrangement of features, that is, changes in the geometry. Geometry is general enough to embrace all the other subconcepts of spatial structures such as pattern, morphology, the metric of distance, distribution, local relief, shoestring shaped, oriented, connected, and so on. Geometry and movement, viewed in this way are linked duals; one interacts with the other. Rain falling on a mountain erodes that surface. One can understand this erosion by viewing the mountain as a fixed form and by understanding the gradient and the movement down it of the soil particles. That is true, but ultimately a continued movement of soil particles changes the geometry of the mountain. There is the interaction between the geometry and the movement. Similarly, by transforming an atmospheric pressure distribution, one can find the path of an airplane across, say, the North Atlantic Ocean, which minimizes its time en route between two airports for that particular pressure distribution. This path, of course, except very rarely, is not the least distance path or geodesic great circle arc on the earth's spherical surface.

In addition, migration from one area with its income distributions—potentials, densities, and per capitas—to another can be understood in the short run in terms of those differences, but ultimately that migration must change the nature of the income distributions themselves. These are co-equal approaches, together constituting spatial relations. It can be suggested that over and over again the earth and the phenomena in and on it tend to arrange themselves so that spatially interacting objects are as near each other as possible. This minimizing tendency seems to pervade geography. This spatial *lex parsimoniae* emerges as a strong candidate for geography's central theoretical problem.

2. Growth

As a growing, changing body of thought, geography has arrived at its present condition en route to unification and generalization only through a long, tortuous career marked by numerous episodes involving the spawning of new scientific disciplines. Physics, biology, chemistry, economics, and so on, have their roots in geography. These disciplines owe their emergence to the concern for and the development of the understandings of the nonspatial, in the sense of nongeographic, processes attendant. Specializations in these processes and the systems underlying them have proceeded apace. Through the centuries, geographers have continued to describe, classify, and predict locations while surrendering the nonspatial sciences to others. It is the geographer's continuing concern for the eternal question, *Where?*, and their appreciation of its significance that have set geographers apart from their fellowmen. People in every age and every society have felt the importance of this question.

In ancient Greece, physical geography advanced from the descriptive to the theoretical-predictive level concerning the figure, magnitude, and motions of the earth and specially with regard to celestial appearances as they vary across the earth's surface. Here, too, the essentials of cartography and map projections were laid down as well. These developments culminated in the presentations of Claudius Ptolemy in the second century A.D. These compilations set standards that were observed through the following period of the Roman Empire. The descriptions in human geography as found in Herodotus and Strabo also were preserved, and the rudiments of physical environmental determinism were recognized. However, once the Roman Empire lost its stabilizing and civilizing influences, geography, like science in general, was forced to endure a long sterile period in Europe. But the thread of development was not lost completely, for the Arab world continued, preserved, cultivated and, on a number of points, improved Greek geography. This basis was recovered during the European Renaissance, and scientific progress resumed both in theory and in empirical support through the assembling of vast quantities of data through the age of geographical discovery and exploration.

A call for order between general theoretical geography and special descriptive geography and a system for achieving this order was issued in 1650 by Bernhard Varenius. His *Geographia Generalis* marked a critical point in the development of geographical thought. In 1669, Isaac Newton assumed the Lucasian Chair in Mathematics and Natural Philosophy at Cambridge University in England. He was required to lecture and advise on mathematics, astronomy, and geography. Newton organized the geography course for the "young gentlemen of Cambridge University" around the Varenius opus and personally revised it several times. For a century this revised work remained the standard for British universities, and it also shaped the course of academic geography in the early American colleges by its widespread use there.

3. Status

In the United States and elsewhere, geography at present occupies a rather low but rapidly improving status. This latter development, of course, is coming about largely as a result of the intellectual vigor the subject is now demonstrating.

Warntz (1964) has shown that in American colonial colleges, physical geography, following Newton's lead, was regarded as part of universal knowledge and a manifestation of natural law and had a high intellectual standing. It lost this early in the nineteenth century when it became burdened with practical minutiae—human as well as physical—in the new nation obsessed with the details of its territorial expanse. The subject, previously taught only at the college level, was now relegated to the rote learning of the elementary and secondary schools.

From the mid-nineteenth century when geography's reintroduction to the college curriculum was led by the appointment in 1854 of the Swiss scholar, Arnold Henry Guyot, to the faculty of Princeton University (then the College of New Jersey) as Professor of Geography, geography's status grew rapidly under a teleological organization which regarded the earth as the divinely created home; this was then modified by the Darwinian influence. That which was new and which revitalized the subject after its long dormancy, was the view of theoretical-predictive geography as pertaining to all nature *and* human societies. Physical geography again was to receive attention, but more importantly, human phenomena were at last to be included within a systematic analysis; and although the causes were regarded as originating within the physical world and as controlling human activity, this philosophy of *environmental determinism* regained for geography a high status for the time being.

After World War I, the successful destruction of environmental determinism as an organizing principle in geography came about largely as a result of the inadequacies of the concepts involved to explain spatial patterns of human phenomena in terms of the rising importance of the impacts of man on man as these modified and, in some cases, replaced the controls of the physical environment. But, no other powerful ideas emerged immediately to reorganize and unify the subject in the void left by the rightful rejection of physical environmental determinism with its inconsistencies, contradictions, vagueness and, above all else, its growing lack of pertinence. Instead, in the inter-war period the subject of geography rapidly became characterized principally by the plethora of studies of limited scope emphasizing descriptive detail of separate small areas, and the wide variety of methods used, and limited concepts employed, virtually precluded significant intellectual advances. Post World War II advances in the subject, however, have brought it to the present state described above in Section 1 and have developed within the profession a peak of enthusiasm that occurs at most perhaps only once in a century.

4. Present International Aspects

The status and importance of geography is currently increasing on a global basis. Very old geographical societies in numerous countries have recently extended and intensified their activities. Included are such institutions as the American Geographical Society of New York, U.S.A.; The Berlin Geographical Society, Germany; The Austrian Geographical Society; The Brazilian Geographical Society; The Geographical Society of Paris, France; The Royal Geographical Society, England; The Geographical Society of the U.S.S.R.; The Mexican Society of Geography and Statistics, and The Italian Geographical Society. These and other societies and associations of geographers publish journals of international scope, with regard to content and contributors, and reach international audiences.

Particularly important in the development of international cooperation and understanding in geography is the International Geographical Union with its more than four thousand members. Organized in Brussels in 1922, it made formal the arrangements by which geographers of the world could continue to meet periodically at international congresses to promote the study of geographical problems, initiate and coordinate researches requiring international cooperation, and provide for scientific discussions and their publication. Large-scale international geographical meetings (see Table 1) had been held ten times prior to 1922, beginning with the one in Antwerp in 1871 arranged largely through private initiative. Since formal organization, ten more congresses have been held with another scheduled for New Delhi, India in 1968.

387

TABLE 1. INTERNATIONAL GEOGRAPHICAL CONGRESSES

No.	Date	Place	No.	Date	Place
I	1871	Antwerp	XI	1924	Cairo
II	1875	Paris	XII	1928	Cambridge, Eng.
III	1881	Venice	XIII	1931	Paris
IV	1889	Paris	XIV	1934	Warsaw
V	1891	Bern	XV	1938	Amsterdam
VI	1895	London	XVI	1949	Lisbon
VII	1899	Berlin	XVII	1952	Washington
VIII	1904	Washington	XVIII	1956	Rio de Janeiro
IX	1908	Geneva	XIX	1960	Stockholm
X	1912	Rome	XX	1964	London
			XXI	1968	New Delhi

The scientific work of the Union is carried out principally through commissions appointed for the study of special matters during the interval between congresses. At the congresses, selected papers drawn from among those contributed by the Union's members are presented in commission and other section meetings. At present there are 18 commissions and 9 sections, with the most recently formed of these being the Commission on Quantitative Methods. In so doing, the International Geographical Union has lent its prestige to, and has encouraged even more, the rapidly accelerating growth in theoretical-predictive geography.

WILLIAM WARNTZ

References

*Bunge, William, 1962, "Theoretical Geography," The Royal University of Lund, Lund, Sweden, 210pp.

Hartshorne, Richard, 1959, "Perspective on the Nature of Geography," Chicago, Rand-McNally and Co., 201pp.

Meynen, Emil, 1960, "Orbis Geographicus," Wiesbaden, Germany, Franz Steiner Verlag GMBH.

*van Paassen, Christiaan, 1957, "The Classical Tradition of Geography," Groningen, the Netherlands, J. B. Wolters.

Warntz, William, 1964, "Geography Now and Then," American Geographical Society, New York, 162pp.

Warntz, William, 1964, "Geography, Geometry, and Graphics," Princeton University, Department of Graphics and Engineering Drawing, Princeton, N.J.

* Additional bibliographic references may be found in this work.

Cross-references: *Geomorphic Maps; International Organizations for Geomorphology; Regions, Natural and Geographical. Vol. VI: Cartography; Earth Science; Earth Science Information and Sources.*

GEOLOGIC CENTERS AND SOURCES—*See* pr Vol. VI, **EARTH SCIENCE INFORMATION AND SOURCES**

GEOLOGIC MAPS—*See* pr Vol. VI

GEOLOGIC MAP SOURCES—*See* pr Vol. VI

GEOLOGIC METHODOLOGY—*See* pr Vol. VI

GEOLOGIC SURVEYS—*See* pr Vol. VI

GEOLOGIC TIME SCALE—*See* pr Vol. IV, pr Vol. VII

GEOLOGY—ENERGY—*See* pr Vol. VI

GEOLOGY, HISTORY OF—*See* pr Vol. VI

GEOLOGY, PHILOSOPHY OF—*See* pr Vol. VI

GEOLOGY—SCOPE AND CLASSIFICATION —*See* pr Vol. VI

GEOLOGY: TERMINOLOGY, DICTIONARIES, BIBLIOGRAPHY—*See* pr Vol. VI

GEOMORPHIC CYCLE—*See* **CYCLES, GEOMORPHIC**

GEOMORPHIC MAPS

Historical Background

Geomorphology is the science which is concerned with the study of landforms at the surface of the earth. Its purpose is to describe and explain these landforms. Until the late 1940's the description of a landform or group of landforms, and the explanation of their origin and age, were done almost exclusively through written reports. Because of the lack of a precisely defined terminology, it was extremely difficult, if not impossible, to make any intelligent comparison between work being done in various parts of the world.

The "physiographic maps" which sometimes accompanied these reports were of little use since they did not result from a systematic field survey but were constructed to illustrate the author's conclusions.

It is somewhat surprising that the idea of constructing a mapping system that would make accurate comparisons possible did not come about sooner. The first such map was published by S. Passarge in 1914. In spite of all its merits, this map remained the only example of its type until after World War II when requests from planners, agronomists, engineers and others demanded something more precise and useful than learned discussions in scientific reports.

Purpose of Geomorphological Maps

The purpose of geomorphological maps is the accurate graphic representation of the landforms of an area and the indication of the wide range of influences, both past and present, that have made it what it is. Such maps covering areas of differing geological structure under differing climatic conditions make comparisons possible; they show the sequence of events and the rules which governed the development of the relief. Furthermore, maps of different areas will permit the forms of the same age (Holocene, for instance) to be compared from both a qualitative and a quantitative point of view. Thus the exact recognition of the role played by climatic conditions in the formation of the relief of the earth's surface will be possible. The climatic relief types as well as the morphoclimatic zones and regions will be more precisely defined. Geomorphological mapping is, beyond doubt, a major step forward in the development of geomorphology.

TABLE 1. COLORS USED IN THE DETAILED GEOMORPHOLOGICAL MAP (EDITOR: KLIMASZEWSKI, 1963)

Forms	Agent		Process	Age	Color
(A) Tectonic	Endogenic forces	Endogenic forces and gravity	Constructive	Tertiary	Indigo/grey
				Pleistocene	Indigo/orange/green
				Holocene	Indigo/vermilion/blue
(B) Volcanic	Endogenic forces		Destructive	Pleistocene	Indigo
				Holocene	
	Exogenic forces (gravity)		Constructive	Pleistocene	Madder lake, deep
				Holocene	Madder lake, pale
(A) Denudative	Gravity and water	Flowing water and gravity	Destructive	Paleogene	Delft blue
				Neogene	Neutral tint
				Pleistocene	Orange
				Holocene	Vermilion
			Constructive	Pleistocene	Sap-, May-, emerald green
				Holocene	Ultramarine
(B) Fluvial	Stream water		Destructive	Tertiary	Grey
				Pleistocene	Orange
				Holocene	Vermilion
			Constructive	Neogene	Olive green
				Pleistocene	Sap-, May-, emerald green
				Holocene	Light blue
(C) Fluvial-denudative	Stream water and gravity		Destructive	Tertiary	Neutral tint
				Pleistocene	Orange
				Holocene	Vermilion
(D) Fluvio-glacial	Proglacial streams		Destructive	Pleistocene	Orange/violet bluish
				Holocene	Vermilion/violet bluish
			Constructive	Pleistocene	Sap-, May-, emerald green/brown
				Holocene	Light blue/brown
	Subglacial streams		Destructive	Pleistocene	Orange/violet bluish
				Holocene	Vermilion/violet bluish
			Constructive	Pleistocene	May-, emerald green/brown
				Holocene	Prussian green/brown
(E) Karstic	Surface and underground water		Destructive/ solution	Tertiary	Carmine
				Pleistocene	(differentiated thickness of
				Holocene	lines)
	Stream water predominates		Destructive	Tertiary	
				Pleistocene	
				Holocene	
			Constructive	Pleistocene	Emerald green/carmine
				Holocene	Light blue/carmine
	Underground water		Constructive	Pleistocene	Vegetable green
				Holocene	Cobalt blue
(F) Suffosional	Underground water		Destructive	Holocene	Vermilion

TABLE 1 (CONTINUED)

Forms	Agent		Process	Age	Color
(G) Glacial	Glaciers	Frost, snow and ice	Destructive	Pleistocene	Violet bluish, deep
				Holocene	Light violet bluish
				Riss	Burnt sienna
					Indian red
			Constructive	Würm	Burnt umber
					Sepia
					Raw umber
					Van Dyke brown
				Holocene	Burnt light ocher
(H) Nival	Snow		Destructive	Pleistocene/Würm	Violet reddish, deep
			Constructive	Holocene	Light violet reddish
(I) Cryogenetic	Frost		Destructive	Pleistocene/Würm	Violet reddish, deep/emerald green
			Constructive	Holocene	Light violet/reddish light blue
(J) Thermokarstic	Sun and ice		Destructive	Pleistocene	Violet reddish, deep
				Holocene	Light violet reddish
(K) Eolian	Wind	Wind	Destructive	Pleistocene	Crimson, deep
				Holocene	Light crimson
			Constructive	Pleistocene	Chrome yellow, pale
				Holocene	Chrome yellow, deep
(L) Limnic	Lake water	Waves	Destructive	Pleistocene	Rose, deep
				Holocene	Light rose
			Constructive	Pleistocene	Paris blue, deep
				Holocene	Paris blue, pale
(M) Marine	Seawater		Destructive	Pleistocene	Rose, deep
				Holocene	Light rose
			Constructive	Pleistocene	Paris blue, deep
				Holocene	Paris blue, pale
(N) Organogenetic	Plants and animals	Organisms	Destructive Constructive	Holocene	Sepia
(O) Man-made	Man		Destructive Constructive	Holocene	Black

Development of Legend Systems

In the 1950's geomorphological mapping systems were devised in various European countries, notably Poland, France and Russia (see Klimaszewski, Tricart and Baszenina). Not surprisingly these systems differ widely from one another, making comparisons between mapped regions rather difficult. One of the purposes of the International Geographical Union's Subcommission on Geomorphological Mapping which was set up at the 1960 Stockholm meeting was to standardize legends. This has not been possible so far mainly because of the amount and type of information that must be shown on such maps. Legends differ according to which aspect an author wishes to emphasize on his maps. The amount and scope of information these maps attempt to portray is illustrated by the Polish legend reproduced in Tables 1 and 2 (Klimaszewski, 1963).

The Polish legend, although very extensive, cannot be considered exhaustive. Detailed studies are constantly adding to the list, with the result that legends based on symbols tend to become cumbersome and very complicated. If an attempt is made to show variations of a given landform type, the number of symbols needed becomes quite impossible. To get around this problem attempts have been made by F. Gullentops and D. St-Onge to map slope categories rather than landform types. This way, symbols (i.e., hachures in this case) can be used to portray slope categories, thus drastically cutting down on the number of symbols needed (Fig. 1).

Various Types of Legends

A geomorphological map must give information about the appearance (*morphology*), the dimensions and slope values (*morphometry*), the origin (*morphogeny*) and the age (*morphochronology*) of each form.

TABLE 2. SYMBOLS FOR THE DETAILED GEOMORPHOLOGICAL MAP
(EDITOR: M. KLIMASZEWSKI, 1963; MINOR CORRECTIONS: R.W.F.)

	Symbol			Symbol
Landforms Due to Endogenic Forces		dolomite		∣ ∣ ∣ ∣ ∣
(A) *Tectonic Forms*		marl		∣−∣−∣−∣
(1) Slopes of fault scarps		lava		⋋⋌⋋⋌⋋
(a) heavily modified		Remnants of a late mature relief not rejuvenated:		
(b) slightly changed with a gradient of 2–4°		(2) Remnants of an erosion surface		≡≡≡≡
9–19°		(a) flat (with gradients up to 4°)		
19–45°		(b) inclined (with gradients of 4–9°)		
45–64°		initiated during the Paleogene		
more than 64°		Miocene		
(2) Slopes of monoclinal scarps (see §A1)		Pliocene I		
(3) Slopes of thrust scarps (see §A1)		Pliocene II		
(4) Flanks (slopes) of tectonic folds		Pliocene III		
(5) Open earthquake rifts		(3) Remnants of pediments formed by erosion and denudation		
(6) Small tectonic scarps		with gradients of . . .		
(7) Local subsidence		(4) Remnants of pediments formed by slope wash		
(B) *Forms due to Vulcanicity*		with gradients of . . .		
(1) Slopes of volcanic cones with gradients of		(5) Remnants of surfaces of planation		
2–4°		(a) flat		
4–9°		(b) inclined		
9–19°		exhumed during the . . .		
19–45°		(6) Fragments of structural surfaces		
(2) Remnants of volcano slopes (see §B1)		uncovered during the . . .		
(3) Rim of crater		(7) Remnants of the planed surfaces exhumed from beneath a sheet of insoluble residue		
(a) fresh		(a) flat		
(b) modified		(b) inclined		
(4) Inner slope of crater (see §B1)		during the . . .		
(5) Rim of caldera		(8) Breaks of slope separating different surfaces of planation or different pediments		
(a) fresh		(9) Ridges at the intersection of valley sides:		
(b) heavily modified		(a) sharp and rocky (crests)		
(6) Inner slopes of caldera		(b) narrow and rocky		
(7) Parasitic cones		(c) narrow and rounded		
(8) Lava tongues (confined to valleys)		(d) broad and rounded		
(9) Lava flows		(10) Resistant ridges		
(10) Lava fields		(a) sharp and rocky		
(11) Lava bridges or tunnels, spatter cones, driblet cones, lava cascades and tumuli, spines		(b) narrow and rocky		
Landforms due to Exogenic Forces		(c) narrow and rounded		
(A) *Forms Due to Denudation*		(d) broad and rounded		
(I) Destructional Forms Due to Denudation		consisting of sandstone		
(1) Remnants of a structural surface		quartzite		
(a) flat (with gradients up to 4°)		limestone		
(b) inclined (with gradients of 4–9°)		volcanic rocks		
consisting of sandstone	∣·∣·∣·∣·∣	other crystalline rocks		
quartzite	∣•∣∘∣•∣∘∣			
limestone	∣ ∣ ∣ ∣ ∣			

TABLE 2 (CONTINUED)

	Symbol
(11) Monoclinal ridges	
(a) sharp and rocky	
(b) narrow and rocky	
(c) narrow and rounded	
(d) broad and rounded	
consisting of quartzite	
sandstone	
limestone	
dolomite	
lava	
(12) Double ridges	
(13) Summits	
(a) sharp and rocky (arête, horns)	
(b) cone	
(c) mound	
(d) dome	
(14) Passes, cols	
(15) Slopes of structural escarpments	
(a) steep slope on outcrop of resistant rocks with gradients of . . .	
(b) gentle slope (glacis) on outcrop of less resistant rocks with gradients of . . .	
(16) Slopes of fault-line scarps	
(a) obsequent, with gradients of . . .	
(b) resequent, with gradients of . . .	
(17) True monadnocks (erosion remnants of former surfaces)	
Slopes of true monadnocks with gradients of . . .	
consisting of . . .	
(18) Necks	
Slopes of necks with gradients of . . .	
(19) Residual ridges and outliers	
Slopes of outliers with gradients of . . .	
(20) Monadnocks (residual peaks)	
Slopes of monadnocks with gradients of . . .	
(21) Inselbergs	
Slopes of inselbergs with gradients of . . .	
(22) Small residual forms	
(a) cornices (overhangs)	
(b) rock walls	
(c) buttresses and recesses	
(d) pulpit rocks	
(e) mushroom rocks	
(f) needle rocks	
(g) castellated rocks	
(h) natural arches-bridges	
(i) earth pyramids, pillars	
(j) balanced or rocking stones	

	Symbol
(k) erratic boulders	
(l) rock block fields (felsenmeer)	
(23) Structural-erosional breaks of slope	
convex in profile	
concave in profile	
(24) Scarps or escarpments due to resistant outcrops of quartzite	
sandstone	
limestone	
dolomite	
(25) Flat surface of structural rock terraces	
(26) Cornices de résistance (overhangs)	
(27) Structure-controlled troughs on slopes	
(28) Valleys formed by corrasion	
(29) Valleys formed by solifluction— dells/coombs	
(a) long	
(b) short on the slopes	
(c) with a flowing bottom	
(30) Ablation troughs	
(31) Rock faces	
(32) Chutes	
(33) Scar of a rock-fall	
(a) fresh	
(b) old	
(34) Scar or step of a rockslide	
(a) fresh	
(b) old	
(35) Scar or step of a landslide, -slip	
(a) fresh	
(b) old	
(36) Scar or edge of a rock slump	
(a) fresh	
(b) old	
(37) Scar or edge of a land slump	
(a) fresh	
(b) old	
(38) Fissures above the scars of landslides, -slips	
(39) Small landslides, -slips and slumps	
(II) Constructional Forms Due to Denudation	
(II₁) Forms produced by gravity	
(1) Scree or talus heaps	
(2) Talus slopes	
(3) Talus cones	
(4) Landslide, -slip tongues	
(5) Solifluction tongues	
(6) Slopes with terracettes	
(7) Boulder tongues	

TABLE 2 (CONTINUED)

	Symbol
(8) Mudflow tongues	
(9) Rock streams or rock glaciers	
(10) Laves torrentieles (Muren) pebbly mudflows	
(11) Colluvial fans	
(12) Creep-built (colluvial) plain	
(13) Solifluction-built plains	
(a) free solifluction	
(b) constricted solifluction	
(II₂) Forms of proluvial origin	
(1) Proluvial fans	
(2) Plains due to proluvial accumulation (playa, sabkha)	

(B) *Fluvial Forms*

(I) Destructional Forms Due to River Erosion

	Symbol
(1) River bed of permanent streams	
(a) cut in rock	
(b) cut in alluvium	
less than 1 m in depth	
more than 1 m in depth	
(2) Channels of temporary streams	
(a) cut in rock	
(b) cut in alluvium and colluvium	
less than 1 m in depth	
more than 1 m in depth	
(3) Channel and river banks	
(a) undermined	
(b) fixed	
(c) growing by upbuilding	
(4) Abandoned loops (cutoffs, oxbows, mort lakes)	
(a) fresh and deep, with water	
(b) old, shallow, dry	
(5) Steps in river bed	
(a) low (rapids)	
(b) high (waterfalls)	
(6) Rocky ledges in river bed	
(7) Potholes, evorsion channels, plunge pools	
(8) Hanging valley steps	
(9) Recession terrace scarps	
(10) Gorges less than 3 m in depth	
3– 6 m in depth	
6–12 m in depth	
more than 12 m in depth	
(11) Undermined slopes, river-cliff	
less than 3 m in height	
3– 6 m in height	
6–12 m in height	
more than 12 m in height	

	Symbol
(12) Edges and slopes of river terraces and alluvial fans	
(a) well preserved	
(b) badly preserved	
less than 3 m in height	
3– 6 m in height	
6–12 m in height	
more than 12 m in height	
(13) Cut plains	
(14) Suballuvial fan plain (alluvial piedmont slope or glacis) with a veneer of . . .	

(II) Constructional Forms Due to Fluvial Accumulation

	Symbol
(1) River-built plain	
consisting of gravel	
sand	
mud	
dating from the . . .	
(2) Alluvial terrace plains	
consisting of fluvial gravel	
sand	
mud	
dating from the . . .	
(3) Rock terrace plain	
overlain by fluvial gravel	
sand	
mud	
dating from the . . . (time)	
(4) Alluvial fan (-cone) plain	
consisting of fluvial gravel	
sand	
mud	
with gradients less than 1°	
1–3°	
3–6°	
more than 6°	
dating from the . . . (time)	
(5) Piedmont fans	
dating from the . . . (time)	
(6) Delta plains	
formed by gravel	
sand	
mud	
clay	
(7) Delta levees	
(8) Intervening depressions	
(9) Fluvial gravelbanks	

TABLE 2 (CONTINUED)

	Symbol		Symbol
(10) Fluvial sandbanks		(d) Tilke	
(11) Riverine mud banks		(e) badlands or scablands	
(12) Natural embankments (levees)		(18) Steep slopes of asymmetrical valleys	
(13) Interfluvial aggradational spurs		(19) Barrancos (ravines)	

(C) *Fluvial-denudational Forms*

(I) Destructional Forms Due to River Erosion and Denudation

    (1) Valley sides cut during the . . .

        (a) very gently inclined (2–4°) mantled with waste or solifluction deposits, now slightly denuded

        (b) gently inclined (4–9°) mantled with waste or solifluction deposits, now slightly denuded.

        (c) Steep (9–10°) mantled with waste undergoing degradation or solifluction, now markedly denuded

        (d) very steep, partly rocky (19–45°), now intensively denuded

        (e) precipitous, rocky (45–64°), now intensively denuded

        (f) Rocky faces (65°), now intensively destroyed by rock falls

    (2) Sides of structural gaps cut in

        quartzite

        sandstone

        limestone

        dolomite

        extrusive rocks

    (3) Sides of antecedent gaps

    (4) Sides of epigenetic gaps

    (5) Sides of gaps formed by headward erosion

    (6) Sides of overflow gaps

    (7) Sides of dry cols (wind gaps)

    (8) Sides of inherited gaps

    (9) Cutoff, severed spurs

    (10) Pseudo-cutoff hills

    (11) Epigenetic hills

    (12) Valley spurs

    (13) Funnel-shaped valley head

    (14) Kettle-shaped valley head

    (15) Break of slopes separating various generations of valleys of differing age

    (16) Small valleys produced in cooperation with solifluction

        (a) trough-like valleys on steep slopes

        (b) dells or coombes resulting from the transformation of erosional valleys

        (c) Incipient troughs

    (17) Small valleys produced by periodic water acting in cooperation with denudation

        (a) fresh loess canyons, gorges

        (b) ravines

        (c) old canyons

(D) *Fluvioglacial Forms*

(I) Destructional Forms Due to Proglacial Water Erosion

    (1) Valley, channel sides cut by proglacial water during the former glaciations Würm

        with gradients of . . .

    (2) Sides of glacier margin valley trains (Urstromtal) cut by proglacial and extraglacial water during the former glaciations Würm

        with gradients of . . .

    (3) Sides of inherited gaps

        dating from the former glaciations Würm

        with gradients of . . .

    (4) Trompetentäler (trumpet valleys)

    (5) Edges and slopes of outwash (sandur) terraces and fluvioglacial fans

    (6) Cut sandur terrace plains

    (7) Old and dry spillways

    (8) Erosional residuals of the ground moraine

(II) Constructional Forms Due to Proglacial Water Deposition

    (1) Outwash (sandur) plains

        consisting of gravel

        sand

    (2) Glaciofluvial (fluvioglacial) fan plains

        consisting of gravel

        sand

    (3) Glacio-lacustrine plains

        consisting of clay

        silt

    (4) Kame terrace plains

        consisting of gravel

        sand

        silt

    (5) Fluvioglacial kame ridges and hills

        consisting of gravel

        sand

        less than   5 m in height

            5–10 m in height

            10–30 m in height

            more than 30 m in height

    (6) Glacio-lacustrine kame ridges and hills

        consisting of sand

        silt

TABLE 2 (CONTINUED)

	Symbol
less than 5 m in height	
5–10 m in height	
10–30 m in height	
more than 30 m in height	
(7) Supraglacial esker ridges and hillocks	
formed by (a) deposition	
(b) squeezing	
less than 5 m in height	
5–10 m in height	
10–30 m in height	

(III) Destructional Forms Due to Erosion of Subglacial Water

	Symbol
(1) Subglacial channel sides belonging to former glaciations	
Würm	
with gradients less than 9°	
10–19°	
more than 20°	
(2) Potholes (marmites)	
(3) Flat subglacial channel floors	
(4) Sides of lake cirques	
with gradients less than 9°	
10–19°	
more than 20°	

(IV) Constructional Forms Due to Subglacial Water Deposition

	Symbol
(1) Subaquatic esker ridges	
up to 5 m in height	
5–10 m in height	
10–30 m in height	
(2) Esker ridges and hillocks formed in tunnels . . . in height	

(E) Karst Forms

(I) Forms Due to Solution

	Symbol
(I₁) Forms developing in limestone	
dolomite	
gypsum	
rock salt	
(1) Swallow, sinkholes (dolinas)	
formed through solution	
less than 5 m in depth	o
5–10 m in depth	O
more than 10 m in depth	O 15
(a) rocky and steep sides	
(b) smooth sides with soil cover	
(c) flat-floored	⊙
(2) Sinkholes resulting from the collapse of cavern roof (see §1a)	◎
(3) Uvalas	

	Symbol
(4) Large karst depressions (cock-pits)	
(a) due to solution	
(b) due to cavern collapse	
(5) Sinkhole, fields	
(6) Lapiés, karrenfields	
(7) Groups of jamas	
(8) Chasms (with depth in meters)	65
(9) Chimney-like shafts (with depth in meters)	Tert. Pleist. Holocen inact. act / 50
(10) Funnel-shaped shafts (with depth in meters)	50
(11) Natural bridges and cave arches	
(12) Ponors	
(a) pit ponors	
(b) arch ponors	
(13) Cavern entrances at valley floor level	
(14) Hanging cavern entrances	

(I₂) Karst forms reproduced in insoluble rock-cover

	Symbol
(1) Swallow, sinkholes due to solution	
(2) Swallow, sinkholes due to collapse	
(3) Small karst depressions	

(II) Forms Due to Solution and Water Erosion

	Symbol
(1) Slopes of karst gorges	
with gradients of . . .	
dating from . . .	
(2) Sides of blind karst valleys	
(3) Steep terminal walls of blind valleys	
(4) Corrosion notches (niches)	
(5) Flat floors of central poljes covered	
with gravel	
sand	
silt	
with rocky bottom	
(6) Flat floors of marginal poljes	
(7) Sides of poljes	
(8) Surfaces due to karst planation (see destructional surfaces)	
(9) Hanging karst valley steps	
(10) Karst gateways	
(11) Karst spurs	
(12) Segments of karst gorges formed by collapse of cavern roof	
(13) Mogotes (haystacks), hums	

(III) Karst Forms Due to Deposition of Calcium Carbonate

	Symbol
(1) Travertine bars	
less than 5 m in height	
5–10 m in height	
more than 10 m in height	
(2) Travertine terraces	

TABLE 2 (CONTINUED)

	Symbol		Symbol
(IV) Forms Due to Deposition of Mineral Salts by Heated Underground Water		(8) Walls of trough heads	
(1) Cones, funnels		(9) Flattened trough shoulders (benches, shelves)	
(2) Rims		(10) Steps on the floor of troughs	
(F) *Suffosional (Piping) Forms*		(11) Hanging tributary valley steps	
(I) Forms Due to Corrasion of Underground Water		(12) Cirque terraces	
(1) Suffosional (subcutaneous) dimpling		(13) Fragments of planated surfaces due to glacial erosion	
(2) Suffosional pits		(14) Fjeld plain (i.e., above tree line) due to alteration of old surfaces of planation	
less than 2 m deep		(III) Constructional Forms Due to Continental Ice Deposition	
more than 2 m deep		(1) Flat ground moraine	
(3) Suffosional blind valleys		local relief up to 2 m	
(4) Suffosional shafts		with gradients ranging up to 2°	
(5) Suffosional cavern entrances		dating from the Riss I	
(G) *Glacial Forms*		Riss II	
(I) Destructional Forms Due to Glacial Erosion		Brandenburg Stage	
(1) Rôches moutonnées		Frankfurt Stage	
less than 5 m in height		Pomeranian Stage	
5–10 m in height		Later Substages	
10–30 m in height		(2) Undulating ground moraine, local relief from 2–5 m	
more than 30 m in height			
with gradients of slope . . .		with gradients ranging up to 5° dating from the . . . (see §1)	
with a thin morainic veneer		(3) Depressions due to irregular glacial deposition dating from the . . . (see §1)	
(2) Grooves separating rôches moutonnés		(4) End, terminal, frontal morainic hills and ridges dating from the . . . (see §1)	
(3) Smoothed surfaces			
(4) Sides of glacial rock basins and channels		formed by	
with gradients less than 30°		(a) deposition	
more than 30°		thrust	
(5) Glacial riegels (stairway barriers)		(b) less than 5 m in height	
(6) Plains due to scouring with a thin morainic veneer		5–10 m in height	
(7) Terminal basins		more than 10 m in height	
(II) Forms Due to Modification of Proglacial Features by Mountain Glaciers		(c) fresh	
(1) Corries, cirques due to alteration of former river valley heads (spring amphitheaters)		altered	
		(5) Depressions separating end morainic ridges	
(2) Corries, cirques due to alteration of landslip scars		(6) Ablation morainic hummocks and ridges	
(3) Valley corries, cirques due to alteration of portions of unrejuvenated proglacial valleys		less than 10 m high	
		more than 10 m high	
(4) Sides of corries, cirques with gradients of less than 15°		(7) Drumlin ridges	
15–30°		less than 10 m high	
more than 30°		more than 10 m high	
(5) Sides of glacial troughs with gradients of less than 15°		(8) Grooves separating drumlins	
15–30°		(IV) Constructional Forms Due to Valley Glacier Deposition	
more than 30°		(1) Irregular surface of the ablation moraines	
(6) Sides of glacial troughs covered with a lateral moraine		(2) Lateral morainic ridges	
(7) Break of the slope of glacial trough (margin of glacial scour)		(a) less than 5 m high	
		5–10 m high	

TABLE 2 (CONTINUED)

	Symbol		Symbol
10–30 m high		less than 2 m deep	
more than 30 m high		2– 5 m deep	
(b) fresh		5–10 m deep	
altered		more than 10 m deep	
(3) Lateral morainic ridges		(2) Large basins	
(4) Lateral morainic ridges due to ablation (lateral pseudo-moraine)		(3) Channels due to melting out of buried ice masses	
(5) Transverse ablation morainic ridges		(4) Groups of kettles	
(6) Medial morainic ridges		(II) Forms Due to Melting Out of Hydrolaccoliths	
(a) up to 5 m high		(1) Ablation troughs surrounded by a mound (post-pingo)	
5–10 m high		(2) Shallow ablation pits	
10–30 m high		(K) *Eolian (Aeolian) Forms*	
(b) fresh		(I) Destructional Forms Due to Wind Erosion	
altered		(1) Wind-excavated depressions (blow-outs)	
(7) Ridges of block moraines ("bear-den moraines")		(a) stabilized	
(a) less than 5 m high		(b) scoured by wind	
5–10 m high		(2) Wind-excavated troughs and basins	
10–30 m high		with gradients of . . .	
more than 30 m high		(3) Floors of wind-excavated troughs and basins	
(b) fresh		(4) Eolian corrasion grooves (fields)	
altered		(5) Corrasional residuals	
(H) *Nivation Forms*		(6) Yardang fields	
(I) Destructional Forms Due to Nivation		(7) Wind-excavated grooves (fields)	
(1) Nivation cirques and niches		(8) Deflation residuals	
(2) Nivation hollows and nivation troughs		(9) Slopes of deflation crests	
(3) Nivation terraces		(10) Mushroom rocks	
(4) Nivation pavement		(11) Wind-polished surfaces	
(5) Avalanche scars		(12) Ventifact fields	
(6) Avalanche tracks		(13) Plains with desert pavement	
(II) Constructional Forms Due to Nivation		(a) stony	
(1) Fans and avalanche heaps		(b) pisolitic iron	
(2) Protalus ramparts, nivation ridges, winter talus ridges		(14) Hollows left by uprooted trees	
(3) Protalus steps		(15) Swales/Couloirs Gassi	
(I) *Forms Due to Frost Action*		(II) Constructional Forms Due to Eolian Deposition	
(I) Cryogenetic Forms		(1) Barchans	
(1) Patterned ground		less than 5 m high	
(2) Polygonal ground		5–10 m high	
(3) Soil stripes		10–30 m high	
(4) Pingo		more than 30 m high	
(5) Thufur (tussock) fields		(2) Evolving barchans	
(6) Planed surfaces due to cryoplanation		up to 5 m high	
(7) Terraces due to cryoplanation		5–10 m high	
(a) fresh		10–30 m high	
altered		(3) Longitudinal (seif) dunes	
(J) *Thermokarst*		(a) less than 5 m high	
(I) Forms Due to Melting Out of Buried Ice Blocks		5–10 m high	
(1) Kettles			

TABLE 2 (CONTINUED)

	Symbol
10–30 m high	
more than 30 m high	
(b) active	
stabilized	
(4) Transverse dunes	
(a) less than 5 m high	
5–10 m high	
10–30 m high	
more than 30 m high	
(b) active	
stabilized	
(5) Parabolic dunes	
(a) less than 5 m high	
5–10 m high	
10–30 m high	
more than 30 m high	
(b) active	
stabilized	
(6) Dune fields (irregular dunes)	
(7) Dune nets (crest lines marked)	
(8) Conical dunes	
(9) Sandy plains due to eolian accumulation	
(10) Sand heaps	
(11) Sand strips	
(12) Sand and silt mounds around vegetation	
(13) Loess plains due to eolian accumulation	

(L) *Forms of Limnic (Lacustrine) Origin*

(I) Destructional Forms Due to Abrasion by Lake Water

	Symbol
(1) Active cliff	
(2) Abandoned cliff	
(3) Wave-cut platform	
(4) Wave-cut terrace plain	
(5) Wave-cut notches (abandoned)	

(II) Constructional Forms Due to Lake Water Deposition

	Symbol
(1) Beach	
formed by gravel (shingle)	
sand	
silt	
(2) Bar	
formed by gravel (shingle)	
sand	
silt	

(M) *Forms of Marine Origin*

(I) Destructional Forms Due to Marine Abrasion

	Symbol
(1) Young active cliff	
permanently undercut	
periodically undercut	
consisting of sandstone	
quartzite	
limestone	
dolomite	
marl	
lava	
unconsolidated rock	
(2) Ancient abandoned cliff	
(3) Wave-cut platform	
(4) Wave-cut terrace plain	
(5) Stacks	
(6) Headlands (spurs)	
(7) Sea arches	
(8) Sea caves	
(9) Submarine outer edge of wave-cut platform	
(10) Priele (tidal channels)	
(11) Wave-cut notches, nips	

(II) Constructional Forms Due to Marine Deposition

	Symbol
(1) Beach	
consisting of gravel (shingle)	
sand	
silt	
(2) Bay mouth bar	
consisting of gravel (shingle)	
sand	
silt	
(3) Spit	
consisting of gravel (shingle)	
sand	
silt	
(4) Bay bar	
consisting of gravel (shingle)	
sand	
silt	
(5) Tombolo	
consisting of gravel (shingle)	
sand	
silt	
(6) Coastal terrace plain	
consisting of gravel (shingle)	
sand	
silt	
(7) Beach ridge	
(a) consisting of gravel (shingle)	
sand	

TABLE 2 (CONTINUED)

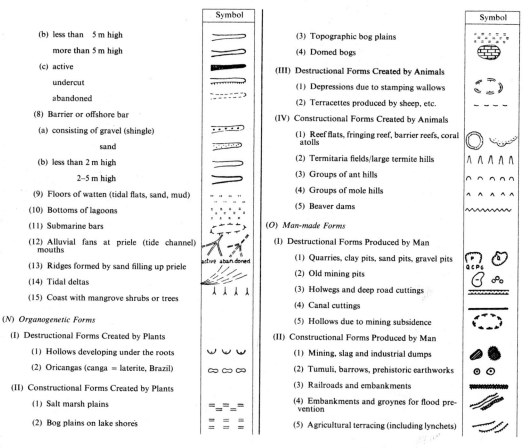

	Symbol			Symbol
(b) less than 5 m high		(3) Topographic bog plains		
more than 5 m high		(4) Domed bogs		
(c) active		(III) Destructional Forms Created by Animals		
undercut		(1) Depressions due to stamping wallows		
abandoned		(2) Terracettes produced by sheep, etc.		
(8) Barrier or offshore bar		(IV) Constructional Forms Created by Animals		
(a) consisting of gravel (shingle)		(1) Reef flats, fringing reef, barrier reefs, coral atolls		
sand		(2) Termitaria fields/large termite hills		
(b) less than 2 m high		(3) Groups of ant hills		
2–5 m high		(4) Groups of mole hills		
(9) Floors of watten (tidal flats, sand, mud)		(5) Beaver dams		
(10) Bottoms of lagoons		(O) *Man-made Forms*		
(11) Submarine bars		(I) Destructional Forms Produced by Man		
(12) Alluvial fans at priele (tide channel) mouths		(1) Quarries, clay pits, sand pits, gravel pits		
(13) Ridges formed by sand filling up priele		(2) Old mining pits		
(14) Tidal deltas		(3) Holwegs and deep road cuttings		
(15) Coast with mangrove shrubs or trees		(4) Canal cuttings		
		(5) Hollows due to mining subsidence		
(N) *Organogenetic Forms*		(II) Constructional Forms Produced by Man		
(I) Destructional Forms Created by Plants		(1) Mining, slag and industrial dumps		
(1) Hollows developing under the roots		(2) Tumuli, barrows, prehistoric earthworks		
(2) Oricangas (canga = laterite, Brazil)		(3) Railroads and embankments		
(II) Constructional Forms Created by Plants		(4) Embankments and groynes for flood prevention		
(1) Salt marsh plains		(5) Agricultural terracing (including lynchets)		
(2) Bog plains on lake shores				

The adequate representation of these aspects on a single map is an extremely complicated problem; it is even more difficult when lithology has to be added to the four previous elements. Of the various legends prepared for detailed geomorphological mapping (at scales between 1:10,000 and 1:50,000), very few meet all the foregoing requirements.

In this paper, the treatment of geomorphological legends is far from complete. Only those are considered that are sufficiently extensive in their application to be of more than local interest, namely, the legends of the U.S.S.R., Czechoslovakia, Poland, France, Belgium and Canada (St-Onge, 1964).

Russian Legend. The Russian legend for geomorphological mapping at scales from 1:25,000 to 1:50,000 is by far the most elaborate (Baszenina *et al.*, 1960). It includes more than 500 items divided into two major groups: families of forms and single forms.

The families of forms are represented by a wide variety of shades, often difficult to distinguish from one another. The pattern in which the color is printed indicates the age of these forms. For instance, greyish blue (2.5 PB 7/4, Munsell) printed

with white dots every 5 mm indicates a marine terrace of Holocene age. The same color printed with a pattern of vertical and oblique lines indicates a marine terrace of Upper Pleistocene, and so on. The legend provides 36 such patterns, which makes it possible to indicate the age of forms from the Mesozoic to the Holocene period.

Single forms—volcanic cones, glacial striae, nunataks, eskers, and so on—are shown by symbols whose colors indicate the origin. For example, red is for volcanic forms and blue for fluvial forms. The symbols are overprinted on the colors that indicate the family of forms. The only indication of the difference between active and fossil forms is conveyed by the appearance of the symbol—a solid line for an active form and a broken line for a fossil form. The symbols in grey indicate lithology. This legend can thus represent a terrace of fluvial origin of Upper Pleistocene age (a pattern of triangles printed in green with yellow binding lines), composed of silt (slanted grey lines) on which there is patterned ground (polygonal drawing in violet).

The foregoing might give the impression that the use of this legend would result in a medley of colors.

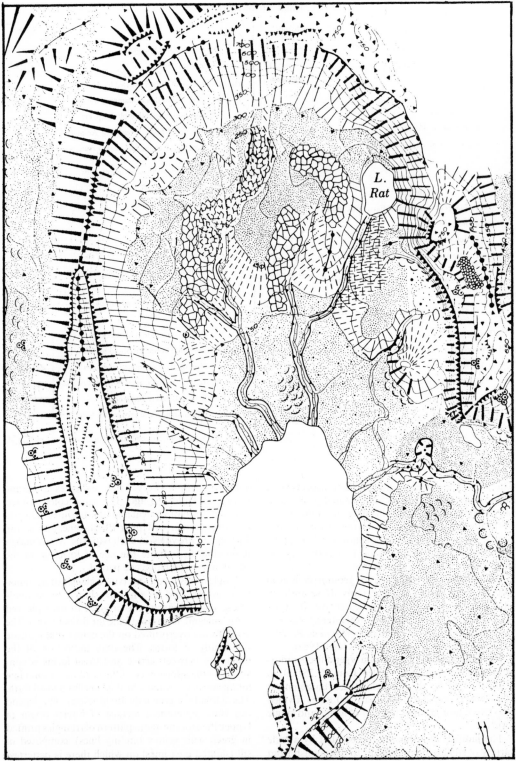

Fɪɢ. 1. Example of fragment of a geomorphic map of Ellef Ringnes Island, near Isachsen, in the Canadian Arctic (Northwest Territories) originally on 1:30,000 scale; width of map area—5 km (St-Onge, 1964). It should be stressed that this sort of geomorphic maps stresses slope categories rather than landform types (see Tables 1 and 2).

This, however, is not so. The Russian maps are very attractive, but the complexity of the legend makes them difficult to read. Their greatest drawback is the absence of any morphometric (slope) data. Contours can give only a rough approximation of slope values and of the dimension of certain forms such as the edges of river terraces. The Russian maps concentrate on the origin and age of landforms but neglect the descriptive aspect of the relief. As a result, these maps are extremely interesting for specialists in geomorphology but are of less value for practical purposes.

Czechoslovakian Legend. Late in 1963, the Geographical Institute of the Czechoslovak Academy of Sciences, Prague Branch, published a geomorphological map legend for scales of 1:25,000 and 1:50,000.

The legend is based on a genetic classification, landforms being grouped under four main headings: structural, erosion-denudation, accumulation and anthropogenic. Colors indicate origin: volcanic forms in violet, karst in red and all accumulation forms in shades of blue. Age is shown by a pattern overprinted on these colors. A terrace of Upper Pleistocene VII would be shown, for instance, by dark-blue dots on a light-blue background. Individual forms are shown either by lined patterns or by symbols. Slope values are not given.

It is difficult to evaluate this map and its legend at the time of writing before a sample is made available. The lack of morphometric indications, however, is a serious shortcoming.

Polish Legend. Since 1950, the geomorphological survey of Poland has been one of the major undertakings of Polish geographers. The Poles were among the first to realize the great potential of geomorphological mapping in the field of applied geography. Since 1952 there has been very close liaison between the regional planners and the Geomorphological Section in the Division of Geography, Polish Academy of Sciences. The Polish maps produced in Cracow at 1:50,000 are probably the most attractive and the easiest to read of any existing set of maps. A judicious use of color suggests relief in a remarkable way.

The Polish legend makes it possible to distinguish three periods ("Neogene," Pleistocene and Holocene), three slope values (less than 4°, from 4–20°, and more than 20°) shown by shades of color, and at least three orders of magnitude for terrace scarps. Fossil slopes of "Neogene" age (a term for late Tertiary) are indicated in grey, while ridges, summits and similar features are indicated in black. Erosion-denudation forms of the Pleistocene are shown in orange, and those of construction-sedimentation in green; for the Holocene, the red indicates erosion, and blue is used for sedimentation. Maps constructed with this legend are attractive, clear and very easy to read. Their principal shortcoming is the absence of lithological information:

The nature of unconsolidated deposits, whether recent or old, is not given.

French Legend. In December 1962, an international symposium was held in Strasbourg to compare various detailed geomorphological map legends. Tricart presented a legend consisting of 265 symbols and six pages of explanatory text along with five sample maps: two at 1:50,000 and three at 1:25,000.

In this legend, lithology is shown by colors (orange for crystalline rocks, light blue for limestone, etc.). Solid colors indicate fresh rock, and lined patterns weathered rock. Landforms are denoted by symbols that are overprinted on the lithological colors, grouped according to process and drawn in such a way as to convey the visual impression of the form. The colors of the symbols indicate the age of the forms, which can be grouped into eight classes extending from the "Neocene" to the present.

Despite certain shortcomings, which will be explained later, the symbols used by Tricart are particularly good, and maps constructed with this legend might be expected to be clear and easy to read. Clarity and legibility, however, are lacking, particularly in areas that depict unweathered rock. Even when printed in contrasting colors, the symbols do not stand out from the solid lithological color. Another limitation is that slope values are not given except for terrace edges and cornices. In short, Tricart's legend emphasizes lithology, genesis and age.

Belgian Legend. The legend suggested by Professor F. Gullentops of the University of Louvain illustrates the interest of the Belgian geomorphologists in the study of slope development (Gullentops, 1964). The succinct legend makes it possible to give quantitative values for all landforms, including hydrographical forms.

Slopes are indicated by hachures, the density of which corresponds to the value. The slope classes are based on a geometric scale. For example, lines 6 mm apart indicate a slope of 0.5–1°, lines 4 mm apart a slope of 1–2°, and so on. Breaks in slopes are indicated by a line with arrowheads whose frequency shows the number of degrees missing between the two slope segments. There is a similar system for ridges, gullys, banks and structural forms.

Landforms of sedimentary origin are denoted by dots of different sizes or by small symbols such as crosses for clay and very fine dots for silt. Where slopes are associated with these sedimentary landscapes, the dots or symbols are aligned along the slopes; the spacing between the alignments is related to the slope value as shown by the hachures already mentioned. A form is represented by symbols only where the scale of the map does not permit the breaking of the form into its slope elements. To avoid all possible confusion, the author insists that in such cases the landform be described with great care. The color of a sign (element of a form) or of the symbol (a small form) indicates its origin, e.g., carmine red denotes fluvial erosion and bright green indicates sedimentation. Shades of the same color make it possible to date the forms, the brighter shades indicating active forms and the paler shades older ones.

The obvious advantage of this legend is that interpretation never obscures the description. The disadvantages are of a technical nature: These maps are difficult to draw and extremely complicated to print. With a legend made up of linear and dotted symbols, it is impossible to use patterns to obtain shades of color. Each shade must be in a different ink; this multiplies the number of printing plates. The printing cost, therefore, is comparatively high.

Canadian Legend. In Canada, St-Onge has constructed a geomorphological map at a scale of 1:30,000 for the Isachsen area, Ellef Ringnes Island (Fig. 1). The map was part of a doctoral dissertation written under the supervision of Professor Gullentops. While similar to the Belgian, the Canadian legend is simpler yet contains more symbols. Slopes are represented by lines whose thickness indicates slope values. The unconsolidated material is shown on subhorizontal surfaces but not on slopes. Symbols are used to show different types of patterned ground, small nivation forms and other features. The color of the signs and symbols indicates origin. As the relief, save for the highest summits, is Pleistocene, the problems of chronology are not considered. The lithology of the area appears on a small inset map at a scale of 1:4,000,000. The advantages and disadvantages of Gullentop's maps are found in this one also.

Geomorphological Maps and Applied Geomorphology

Because of the amount and nature of information they contain, geomorphological maps are extremely useful to planners and economists. A geneticochronological classification makes it possible to separate active from inactive forms; it also makes it possible to forecast the effects of any man-made modification on the relief. When morphometric information is added, it is possible to distinguish forms which are favorable from those which are not favorable to a given type of economic activity.

In agriculture, it is not only necessary to know the general character of the relief and the value of surface materials but also the present morphogenetic processes which are actively modifying the landscape. In any land reclamation program, before a sound decision can be made on what should be done, it is essential to know not only what is there now but also the effects on landscape evolution that will be triggered by a given type of economic activity in the area. Thus, although surface materials and soils in an area may be favorable to agricultural development, the wanton destruction of the forest or natural

grass cover may initiate catastrophic gullying which would turn the area into a man-made desert. The geomorphological map which describes the land forms and indicates the processes responsible for their development makes it possible to forecast man's effect on the landscape with a reasonable degree of certainty.

The planning of towns, settlements and industrial complexes, and the projecting of urban, rural and industrial buildings and communication lines (roads and railways), require the knowledge of both the main relief features (including slopes) and the distribution of unsuitable forms such as scarps, walls, steep slopes, gorges, canyons, karst sinkholes, inundated terraces, active alluvial fans, landslides, hollows and so on.

An accurate description of relief and of morphogenetic processes actively modifying valley walls and river basins is essential in the planning of dams and canals as these are the elements that will determine the long-range success of such constructions.

The knowledge of the relief and forms both favorable and unfavorable to various types of economy, as well as the knowledge of the distribution of the landforms, facilitates a better planning and the more rational use of the particular areas. The knowledge of both the rules of development of young forms and the conditions of their development makes it possible to deal with unfavorable processes and forms (e.g., ravines, landslides, sinkholes, etc.) in order to control and to transform nature.

In some respects, however, the geomorphological map's content is too complicated to be easily understood by a non-geomorphologist. For this reason, special maps may be constructed from the detailed geomorphological map which forms a basis for all studies and special works just as the geological map forms a basis for every special study in geology. There may be maps showing the distribution of certain forms unsuitable for a particular type of economic activity (e.g., landslides, ravines, talus cones, active alluvial fans, sinkholes), as well as improvement maps and qualification maps.

Since all forms occurring in an area and registered on a geomorphological map have been assessed in terms of their value and their use to a particular type of economic activity, the construction of an improvement or qualification map becomes a simple matter. On these maps, individual forms or form complexes are shown as either favorable or unfavorable to a particular type of economic activity. Depending on the economic activity being considered, several qualification or improvement maps can be extracted from a single geomorphological map.

The use made of the geomorphological map by planning and economic institutions indicates not merely its scientific and theoretical value but also its practical one. Because of this, every geomorphologist who is examining and mapping a particular area has to take notice of every form, process and phenomenon both from a theoretical and scientific point of view (age, origin) and from a practical one (its economic evaluation, its use for economic purposes).

DENIS A. ST-ONGE

References

Baszenina, N. V., *et al.*, 1960, "Legend for the Geomorphological Map of the Soviet Union," Moscow University, Dept. of Geography.

Botch, S. G., 1955, "Sur la question du contenu de la carte géomorphologique d'ensemble," *Bull. Comm. Et Quat.*, No. 20, 5–15 (Trad CEDP, No. 1.337).

Fourneau, R., 1964, "Essai de cartographie géomorphologique," *Rev. Belge Géogr.*, **87**(3).

Gellert, J. F., and Scholz, E., 1964, "Katalog des Inhaltes von geomorphologischen Detailkarten aus verschiedenen europäischen Ländern," *Potsdam Inst. Geogr.*, 119pp.

Geze, B., Penelon, P., Joly, F., and Tricart, J., 1965, "La cartographie du Quaternaire," *Bull. Assoc. France Etude Quaternaire*, **2**(1), 1–16.

Gullentops, F., 1964, "Trois exemples de cartes géomorphologiques détaillées," *Acta Geographica Lovaniensia*, **3**, 425–488.

Hammond, E. H., 1964, "Analysis of properties in land form geography: an application to broad-scale land form mapping," *Ann. Assoc. Am. Geogr.*, **54**, 11–19, and map 4.

Institut Géographique National, 1952, "Relief Form Atlas," Paris.

Klimaszewski, M., 1963, "Problems of geomorphological mapping," *Polish Academy of Science, Inst. Geogr., Geogr. Studies*, No. 46.

Miller, A. Austin, 1948, "The dissection and analysis of maps," *Trans. Papers Inst. British Geographers* (*Publ.* 14), 1–13.

Nakano, T., 1961, "Landform classification—its principle and its application," *J. Geogr., Tokyo*, **70**(2), 53–64.

Pécsi, M., 1963, "Legende der detaillierten geomorphologischen Karten Ungarns," *Budapest, Geogr. Inst. Akad. Wiss.*

Seret, G., 1963, "Enchantillon de la carte géomorphologique de Han-sur-Lesse," *Rev. Géomorph. Dynam.*, **14**, 121–128.

St-Onge, D., 1964, "Geomorphological map legends, their problems and their value in optimum land utilization," *Geographical Bulletin*, No. 22, 5–12.

Tricart, J., 1965, "Principes et Méthodes de la Géomorphologie," Paris, Masson et Cie, 496pp.

Tricart, J., Hirsch, A. R., and le Bourdiec, F., 1965, "Présentation d'un extrait de carte géomorphologique détaillé," *Z. Geomorphol.*, **9**, 133–155.

Tricart, J., and Michel, M., 1965, "Monographie et carte géomorphologique de la région de Lagunillas (Andes vénézueliennes)," *Rev. Géomorph. Dyn.*, **15**, 1–33.

Cross-references: *Anthropogenic Influences in Geomorphology; Land Mass and Major Landform Classification; Morphogenetic Regions; Quantitative Geomorphology; Slopes.*

GEOMORPHOLOGY

Geomorphology—the word means "form and development of the earth"—has often been used as a synonym for Physiography, which is the description of landscape. This is a restricted and incorrect usage.

In the early days of landscape study, during the nineteenth century, *two* methods of research were employed: the first was primarily descriptive and the second, largely experimental. The descriptive "physiographic" method was used chiefly in Britain and America and was much handled by geographers; the second method was used chiefly in France under the title of *"Géologie Dynamique"* and at no time commanded as numerous or as influential a following among students as did Physiography.

A semblance of dynamism was, however, given to Physiography by W. M. Davis's introduction of the "cycle of erosion" concept, and the subject became almost a popular science early in the present century. However, it remained basically descriptive and lacked roots in the geologic past. It finally became a geographer's rather than a geologist's topic of inquiry and was limited in scope almost solely to the description and elucidation of erosional landforms.

Modern approaches to study of the earth's surface have been much more broadly based. First, there was a revival of interest in the agents of denudation—wind, stream flow, sheet flow, glacier flow, etc.—with emphasis upon the physical laws governing their operation. Then the materials upon which these agents act came to be more closely and exactly studied in terms of their physical properties and relations to engineering usage. Use of mathematical formulas that would have horrified the older physiographers is now a common approach in advanced courses. Statistical methods have been tentatively applied, though without marked progress so far.

Nowadays, too, erosion is seen as only one side of a dual problem in geomorphology. The land waste supplied and transported under denudation must be laid down somewhere, and studies of sedimentary sequences, both continental and coastal, are now increasingly undertaken in conjunction with denudational studies. Often such sequences provide a time scale not derivable from the erosional landforms alone.

The physiography of the ocean basins, with study of the erosional and depositional agencies active therein, has currently become an integral part of geomorphology that has been vigorously pursued.

All major episodes of erosion and deposition require the intermittent creation of new crustal states by tectonic activity within, and perhaps also below, the earth's crust. Modern geomorphologists find, indeed, that a large part of their field of study covers crustal behavior as interpreted from rock structures and from gravity and seismic data. Seemingly, much crustal deformation derives from the sub-crust or mantle, above whose activity the crust, lying as a blanket, reacts in major diastrophisms almost as a passive member.

The student of Geomorphology, defined as the form and development of the earth, finds indeed that, from an initial review of the surface features of the earth, his studies are required largely to furnish a working model for the outer part, at least, of that earth.

LESTER KING

References

Christian, C. S., Jennings, J. N., and Twidale, C. R., 1957, "Geomorphology," UNESCO (Paris) "Guide Book . . . Arid Zone Development," pp. 51–65.

Davis, W. M., 1909, "Geographical Essays," New York (Dover reprint, 1954), 777pp.

King, L. C., 1962, "The Morphology of the Earth; a Study and Synthesis of World Scenery," New York, Hafner Publ. Co., 699pp.

King, L. C., 1963, "South African Scenery," Third ed., Edinburgh, Oliver & Boyd, 308pp.

Lobeck, A. K., 1939, "Geomorphology," New York, McGraw-Hill Book Co., 731pp.

Stamp, L. D. (editor), 1961, "A Glossary of Geographical Terms," London, Longmans, Green and Co., 539pp.

Thornbury, W. D., 1954, "Principles of Geomorphology," New York, John Wiley & Sons, Inc., 618pp.

Cross-references: *Denudation*; *Erosion*; *Quantitative Geomorphology*; *Sheet Erosion*; *Stream Flow*; *Submarine Geomorphology*; *Wind Action.* Vol. I: *Ocean Bottom Features.* pr Vol. VI: *Glaciers.*

GEOMORPHOLOGY—EXPANDED THEORY

The science of geomorphology commenced as pure taxonomy and was found to provide abstract definitions which are almost universally applicable to landforms. To this day, much of geomorphology remains descriptive. In classical geomorphology, modulations of the earth's surface are divided into orders; the most common of these are in brief:

1st-ORDER: continental platforms and oceanic basins.

2nd-ORDER: provincial features including continental shelves, coastal plains, oldlands, mountain ranges.

3rd-ORDER: massive structures such as single mountains, domes, basins.

In all cases, the classical scheme developed from topographic observations. In reality, all geomorphic description has a basis in physical processes operating on the substance of the lithosphere, these processes being driven by exogenetic (outside) and endogenetic (from within) energies. Recently, careful quantitative observations and mathematical descriptions have expanded "topographic geomorphology" into the science of quantitative geomorphology.

The development of space hardware over the past few years and the necessity of deploying these costly equipments as effectively as possible led to the expansion of descriptive methods used in geomorphology. Space mission planning forced the expansion of geomorphological description into a method of describing any part of any celestial body and concurrently indicating how to search this body in order to optimize information gain. This is because all of the early mathematical mission planning was concerned with maximizing information returns from space missions per monetary unit spent on these missions. An outgrowth of this expansion of geomorphology has been the development of the first approach to planetology as a systematically descriptive science. As in quantitative geomorphology of terrestrial features, the systematic description of planetary features has made quantitative planetology a more manageable and comprehensible science. The manner in which the theories of geomorphology were expanded on is easily outlined in a few paragraphs. The expansion is based on the following considerations:

(1) *Geomorphic description has been expanded to describe objects geometrically, instead of just their upper surfaces.* The orders used in classical geomorphology have a deeper significance than mere descriptions of the extent of topographic modulations. This is because the shapes of things are not accidental. Their shapes are imposed by the sum total of external, internal and stored energies. Often their shapes are mainly expressions of still smaller structures of which the larger shapes are comprised. Ultimately, all material structures, and hierarchies of material structures, are dominated by configurations of nuclear fragments, determined by various fields, as functions of time. These ultimate structures are described by quantum mechanics.

(2) *Twelve orders have been designated as boundary conditions on hierarchies of organized matter in various states. Middle orders contain the most information.* The orders are most distinct for the highest and lowest ones, and therefore are better defined representations of boundary conditions at these extremes. The order system is somewhat blurred into maxima in a continuum in middle orders of all geospheres. It is interesting to note that the information content within geospheres varies, the lowest information being within the highest and lowest orders. This is intuitively obvious because it takes relatively few bits to describe, for example: (zero-ORDER) layers, (1st-ORDER) prolateness or oblateness, (11th-ORDER) nuclear fragments, (10th-ORDER) members of the periodic table, as compared with the number of bits that would be needed to describe a (5th-ORDER) weathered boulder.

The expansion of geomorphological description into 12 ORDERS per geosphere necessitated a one-digit shift in the classical numbering system. This was done because the simplest departure from sphericity is prolateness or oblateness rather than the harmonically more complex surface modulations due to continental platforms and depressed oceanic basins. The changes have been tabulated below:

Expanded Theory of Morphological Description	Classical Geomorphological Description
(A) DESIGNATE TYPE OF BODY Terrestrial-type planet (the earth)	—
(B) DESIGNATE GEOSPHERE Lithosphere	—
(C) zero-ORDER LAYER Continental sial	—
(D) 1st-ORDER features oblateness from circumplanetary rotational bulge, moving prolateness, the antipodal, hemispheric, lunar and solar tidal bulges	—
(E) 2nd-ORDER continental platforms and oceanic depressions	**1st-ORDER** continental platforms and oceanic depressions
(F) 3rd-ORDER provincial structures associated with geosynclinal/geanticlinal structures as developed in regions of no sial, thin sial, and thick sial; including submarine trenches, island arcs, continental shelves, coastal plains, oldlands, mountain ranges, etc.	**2nd-ORDER** provincial structures modulating continental areas above the surface of the oceans, including mountains, etc.

TABLE 1. GEOMORPHIC FEATURES OF THE EARTH'S ATMOSPHERE

ZERO ORDER ↑	1st ORDER	2nd ORDER	3rd ORDER	4th ORDER	5th ORDER
HETEROSPHERE THERMOSPHERE ↓ *homopause* MESOSPHERE ↑ (noctilucent clouds) HOMOSPHERE STRATOSPHERE (ozone) TROPOSPHERE ↓	(1) Subsolar-spot and thermal-equator (2) Light and dark hemispheres (3) Ecliptic cold poles (4) Thermal bulges (*Note*: It is a thread in equatorial troposphere, and global in the mesosphere) (5) Summer (hot) and winter (cold) hemispheres (based on double and triple point substances) (6) Rotational bulges (7) Solar and lunar tidal antipodal bulges	(1) Intertropical convergence zone (2) Tropical jets due to interhemispheric momentum exchange (3) Secondary convection Hadley, Ferrel, polar (4) Troughs and ridges greater than secondary convection cell (5) Coupling of oceanic and continental extent (monsoons, highs, lows)	(1) Ridges and fronts (2) Jet streams of secondary convection cells (3) Waves of secondary convection cells (4) Hurricanes (vortices that cross several secondary convection cells) (5) Coupling to 3rd-order features in other zones, of province size	(1) Cyclones and anticyclones (2) Structure of major hurricanes (3) Coupling to 4th-order features in other zones: (a) land/sea winds (b) valley winds (c) reef and crater mixing layers (d) cloud caps	(1) Single cloud convection (2) Third stage vortices from cyclones, anticyclones and hurricanes (3) Coupling between atmospheric layers (4) Coupling to 5th-order lithospheric and other zones

6th ORDER	7th ORDER	8th ORDER	9th ORDER	10th ORDER	11th ORDER
(1) Vortex and other structures of single clouds (2) 6th-order vortices in convection-cyclone/anticyclone line of descent (3) Coupling between atmospheric layers (Helmholtz shear) (4) Couple to ground and water thermal spirals, lee waves dune: hot/cold loops	(1) Minor single cloud vortices (2) Last vortices in convection/cyclone descent (3) Last vortices in interlayer coupling (4) Last vortices from couple to ground	(1) Viscosity, end of vortex regimes from all lines of descent. Viscosity regime vortices transfer kinetic energy to thermal energy which is radiated away	Molecules	(1) Elements	Fundamental particles such as electrons, protons, etc.

TABLE 2. GEOMORPHIC FEATURES OF THE EARTH'S ATMOSPHERE—THE IONOSPHERE

ZERO-ORDER LAYERS	1st ORDER	2nd ORDER	3rd ORDER	4th ORDER	5th ORDER
	Exogenetic	*Exogenetic*	*Exogenetic*	*Exogenetic*	*Exogenetic*
F_2 LAYER (photons)	(1) Winter anomaly (F LAYERS)	(1) Sub solar "eye"	(1) Two auroral zones about each pole (F LAYER)	(1) Auroral streamers	(1) Auroral filaments
F_1 LAYER (photons)	(2) Tides: solar, lunar, etc.	(2) Mid-latitude and polar motor currents (E LAYER)	(2) Absorption zones	(2) Spread F anomaly	(2) Spread F-structure
E LAYER (20–200 Å X RAYS)	(3) Solar thermal bulges	(3) High-latitude and mid-latitude dynamo currents (F LAYER)	(3) F_2 motor pools above intake to E LAYER dynamo pools		(3) Meteor trails
E SPORADIC (METEORITES, ION DRIFT)	(4) Diurnal F_1/F_2 DAY-TIME split	(4) Polar dynamo pools (E LAYER)			(4) Continuum of meteor debris
	(5) Equatorial electrojets eastward				
	(6) Polar electrojets westward				
	Endogenetic	*Endogenetic*			
	(1) Rotational oblateness	(1) African, North American and Scandinavian magnetic anomalies in F_1 and F_2 layers			
D LAYER < 20 Å X RAY + 1 Mcv PROTONS LYMAN α					
The zero-order layers of the ionosphere are all formed by exogenetic forces	First-order ionospheric layers in atmospheres of a slowly rotating planet are likely to be zero-order features in atmospheres of rapidly rotating planets				

6th ORDER	7th ORDER	8th ORDER	9th ORDER	10th ORDER	11th ORDER
			Simple molecules Simple ions Simple radicals	The elements	Fundamental particles such as electrons and protons

TABLE 3. GEOMORPHIC FEATURES OF THE EARTH'S HYDROSPHERE

ZERO-ORDER LAYERS	1st ORDER	2nd ORDER	3rd ORDER	4th ORDER	5th ORDER
Endogenetic					*Endogenetic*
Warm surface waters (thermocline)	Oblate rotational bulge (waves)	Waves and vortices	Waves and Gyre vortices:	Waves and vortices	Waves and vortices
			Subtropical gyre currents of the northern and southern hemispheres		
Abyssal waters			Subpolar gyres of northern and southern hemispheres (due to Coriolis deflection of convection currents)		
Exogenetic					*Exogenetic*
Vortex:	Wave:	Waves and current vortices:			
Probable global circulation with cold waters descending at the cold Antarctic seas. The Arctic regions would be the hot pole.	Prolate tidal bulges, solar, lunar, jupiter, etc.	Equatorial current and counter-currents West Wind drifts of northern and southern hemispheres Easterlies, polar currents	Waves and vortices	Waves and vortices	Waves and vortices
	Vortex:				
	Hemispheric circulations from polar cold poles to equatorial warmth by body creep of abyssal waters				

TABLE 3 (CONTINUED)

6th ORDER	7th ORDER	8th ORDER	9th ORDER	10th ORDER	11th ORDER
Endogenetic					*Endogenetic*
Waves and vortices	End of wave and vortex regime of endogenetic origin	Large complex molecules which will go into solution; if they won't go into solution, they are of lithospheric nature	Simple molecules mostly H_2O with minor NaCl and other salts	Elements	Fundamental particles such as electrons, protons, etc.
Exogenetic					*Exogenetic*
Waves and vortices	Smallest vortices and waves. Smaller structures don't exist because of viscosity. End of wave and vortex regime of exogenetic origin.				

TABLE 4. CLASSIFICATION OF VOLUMES WITHIN THE EARTH'S LITHOSPHERE

ZERO-ORDER	1st ORDER	2nd ORDER	3rd ORDER	4th ORDER	5th ORDER
	Endogenetic				
The solid volume of the lithosphere	Circumplanetary sial bulges	Continental sial masses	Provinces with characteristic shapes and compositions Batholiths of the largest size Lopoliths of the largest sizes	Smaller batholiths Chonoliths Laccoliths Asthenoliths Harpoliths	Stocks Pipes Agmatite (migmatite) series from size of large houses to size of pebbles Orbicules
	Exogenetic		Impact features	Impact features	Impact features

6th ORDER	7th ORDER	8th ORDER	9th ORDER	10th ORDER	11th ORDER
Agmatites Crystals	Perthite Microperthite Voids	Microcrystals Microvoids Defect structures	Molecules	Elements	Fundamental particles such as protons, electrons, etc.
Exogenetic					

TABLE 5. CLASSIFICATION OF INCREMENTS DETACHED FROM THE UPPER SURFACE OF THE EARTH'S LITHOSPHERE

ZERO ORDER	1st ORDER	2nd ORDER	3rd ORDER	4th ORDER	5th ORDER
	Endogenetic		*Endogenetic*	*Endogenetic*	*Endogenetic*
	Breakup start at rotational bulge		Décollement of an entire mountain range such as the Juras, or parts of the Himalayas	Décollement—such as Jura Mountains due to gravitational sliding Ice islands of the Arctic Ocean	The sequences of boulders. pebbles and granules from volcanoes
	Exogenetic			*Exogenetic*	*Exogenetic*
	Breakup start at tidal bulge when body is within Roche limit (really an endospheric response)			Fractions of crust blasted loose by impact	Mass waste sequence from boulders through pebbles

6th ORDER	7th ORDER	8th ORDER	9th ORDER	10th ORDER	11th ORDER
Endogenetic	*Endogenetic*	*Endogenetic*	*Endogenetic*	*Endogenetic*	*Endogenetic*
Fine volcanic ejecta, but coarser than fine ash	Micro jet	Colloidal ejecta	Molecular exhalations of the earth (such as water)	Elements	Emitted atomic fragments
Exogenetic	*Exogenetic*	*Exogenetic*	*Exogenetic*	*Exogenetic*	*Exogenetic*
Sedimentary regime (sand)	Micro (pelitic) sediments	Colloidal sediments	Detachment of molecules from solid surfaces	Elements detached from surfaces	Atomic fragments detached or altered by cosmic rays

TABLE 6. INCREMENTS OF THE TOPOGRAPHIC CLASSIFICATION OF THE EARTH'S LITHOSPHERE

ZERO ORDER (Entire Lithosphere)	1st ORDER	2nd ORDER	3rd ORDER	4th ORDER	5th ORDER
	Endogenetic	*Endogenetic*	*Endogenetic*	*Endogenetic*	*Endogenetic*
The existence of a lithosphere composed mainly of O, Si, Al, Fe, Na, Ca, K; often of ice; often of frozen gases: H, He, O, N, CO_2, NH_4, etc. Any solid crust.	Rotation bulge Global rifts	Continental domains Oceanic domains Great basins and domes (Great Lakes)	Trenches Island arcs Andesite line Continental shelves Coastal plains Oldlands Mountains Massifs Granite strips (Kheis, Grenville) Lava plains	Volcanoes	Lava spines (Pelée) lava flows, and caves Hot spring terraces
	Exogenetic	*Exogenetic*	*Exogenetic*	*Exogenetic*	*Exogenetic*
	Tidal bulge Precipitation rings (Mercury)	Impact features Post fracture structure (planetoids)	Impact features	Mountains Impact features	Weathered forms of boulder to pebble size Impact features

6th ORDER	7th ORDER	8th ORDER	9th ORDER	10th ORDER	11th ORDER
Endogenetic		*Endogenetic*	*Endogenetic*	*Endogenetic*	*Endogenetic*
Small nodules and concretions the size of sediments		Colloids	Simple molecules	Elements	Fundamental particles such as protons, electrons, etc.
Exogenetic	*Exogenetic*	*Exogenetic*			
Texture of weathered forms the size of sediments Impact features	Microtextural features of surfaces Impact effects	Impacts			

TABLE 7. GEOMORPHIC FEATURES OF THE EARTH'S ENDOSPHERE

ZERO ORDER LAYERS	1st ORDER	2nd ORDER	3rd ORDER	4th ORDER	5th ORDER
Endogenetic					*Endogenetic*
Outer mantle Inner mantle Liquid-like outer core Solid-like central body (all seem to be due to gravitational differentiation)	Oblate rotational bulges	Major convection cells in mantle and core? Active regions extent of ocean basins and continents	Features indicated by gravitational anomalies and seismic events; but of unknown nature	Features indicated by gravitational anomalies and occasionally seismic events; but of unknown nature	Unknown
Exogenetic					*Exogenetic*
	Prolate tidal bulges due to Sun, Moon, Jupiter, etc. Possible asymmetry due to slowing down of earth's rotation				

6th ORDER	7th ORDER	8th ORDER	9th ORDER	10th ORDER	11th ORDER
Endogenetic					*Endogenetic*
Unknown	Unknown	Complex silicates in upper mantle; probably absent under higher pressures	Simple molecules and radicals; in the mantles the SiO_4 structures would be abundant	The elements	Fundamental particles such as electrons, protons, etc.
Exogenetic					*Exogenetic*

(3) *Ideally the twelve ORDERS represent sequences of material structures organized in lines of descent as matter and energy move from sources to sinks.* Ultimately all objects of all orders must fall into either simple or complex lines of descent. At this time, only a few simple lines of descent have been described, and a minority of those described are understood quantitatively. Objects within orders really represent relatively stable time-domain configurations in source-sink cascades. The temporal duration of objects varies; generally, but not universally, the highest- and lowest-order configurations are the most stable in planetary environments. For example—11th-ORDER: nuclear fragments; 10th-ORDER: elements; 1st-ORDER: rotational bulges; and 2nd-ORDER: continental platforms tend to endure longer than middle orders.

The temporal duration of objects within orders as compared with the time rates at which unmanned or manned perform observations determines modes of description. 11th-ORDER: nuclear configurations are described *statistically*. 4th-ORDER: meteorological features of the earth's troposphere are described on quasi-real-time *synoptic graphs*. 3rd-ORDER: provincial features of the earth's lithosphere such as plains, hills and mountain ranges are described by *mapping*.

The concept of geomorphic orders containing structures acting as lines of descent as energy moves from source to sink is most easily perceived in the earth's troposphere. Much of the energy entering the atmosphere in the equatorial regions as optical-band photons departs from the atmosphere in the polar regions through the following cascade: optical photons establish 1st-ORDER hemispheric convection; 2nd-ORDER: tropical-Ferrel, temperate-Hadley, and frigid-polar vortices form from 1st-order kinetic energy; 3rd-ORDER: waves between the cells form 4th-ORDER: highs—anticyclones and lows—cyclones, and so down to viscosity with radiation of infrared photons back to interplanetary space. This process is nicely paraphrased by Rayleigh's verse:

> "Big Swirls have lesser Whirls
> That feed on their velocity
> And these Whirls have smaller Swirls
> And so down to viscosity."

(4) *Geospheres tend to differentiate into relatively permanent layers, designated as zero-ORDER features.* Essentially geospheres represent states of matter. As far as current knowledge extends, the so-called states of matter are: *plasma, gas, liquid, solid* (the lithosphere and realm of classical geomorphology), *stressed solids* (of planetary *interiors*), *thermonuclear plasmas* (of stellar interiors), and *ultra dense plasma* (as probably found in white dwarf stars). Geospheres of the planet earth and their zero-ORDER subdivisions are tabulated below:

Gravisphere
Perturbation zone (about sun where smaller planets cannot exist)
Satellite zone
Roche's limit

Electrosphere
Boundary with solar corona and tail
Electron belts
Proton belts

Atmosphere (Ionosphere is Subcase)
Thermosphere
Mesosphere
Stratosphere
Troposphere

Hydrosphere
Surface waters
Abyssal waters

Lithosphere
Regolithic (soils, rocks, detached masses)
Granitic layer (SIAL)
Basaltic layer (SIMA)
Peridotite and ecologite layers?

Endosphere
Mantle (from Mohorovičić surface to Wiechert-Gutenberg surface)
Mantle (from Wiechert-Gutenberg to Jeffries surface)
Liquid-like core (within Jeffries surface)

Tables 1–7 indicate in outline currently acceptable subdivisions of the planet earth into geospheres, division of the geospheres into zero-ORDER layers, and further subdivision of these into orders. In some cases, it has been indicated that the objects belong to one or another line of descent such as vortex or wave. In other cases, it has been indicated that the formation of objects has been dominated by exogenetic, endogenetic or stored energies acting on a lower-order continuum.

ROBERT DUNCAN ENZMANN

References

Annals of the N.Y. Academy of Sciences, 1966, Vol. 140, Article 1, pp. 1–683, "Planetology and Space Mission Planning."

Enzmann, R. D., and Miller, R., 1966, "Space mission planning in planetary environments," in (Enzmann, R. D., editor), "Planetology and space mission planning," *Ann. N.Y. Acad. Sci.*, **140**, 592–627.

Fairbridge, R. W., 1966, "Endospheres and interzonal coupling," in (Enzmann, R. D., editor), "Planetology and space mission planning," *Ann. N.Y. Acad. Sci.*, **140**, 133–148.

Fairbridge, R. W., 1967, "Geological and cosmic cycles," in (Fischer, R., editor), "Interdisplinary perspectives of time," *Ann. N.Y. Acad. Sci.*, **138**, 433–439.

Wolfe, C. W., 1966, "Energy, time, and physical morphology," in (Enzmann, R. D., editor), "Planetology and space mission planning," *Ann. N.Y. Acad. Sci.*, **140**, 16–34.

Cross-references: *Landscape, Geographical*; *Morphotectonics*; *Quantitative Geomorphology*. Vol. II: *Atmosphere*; *Ionosphere*; *Mesosphere*; *Stratosphere*. Vol. V: *Lithosphere*. pr Vol. VI: *Hydrosphere*.

GEOMORPHOLOGY, HISTORY OF

The Greeks, Romans and Arabs recognized many physical processes of landscape-formation, but their ideas had no real effect on later geomorphological thought. In contrast, the Renaissance stimulated landscape studies and during it geomorphic processes were mentioned by several authors. For example, in Italy, Leonardo da Vinci (1452–1519), in Germany, Agricola (Georg Bauer, 1494–1555) and in France, Bernard Palissy (1510-90) all believed in the erosive power of rivers. These early writings on stream erosion appeared at the same time as many translations of the Bible which, with the help of the printing press, soon caused the ideas of the Creation and of earth history in Genesis to dominate European geological thought. A biblical or Mosaic chronology was gradually evolved, and in 1654 Archbishop Ussher and others concluded that "Heaven and Earth, centre and circumference, were made in the same instance of time, and clouds full of water, and man were created on the 26th October 4004 B.C. at 9 o'clock in the morning." This catastrophic attitude henceforth strongly influenced the main trend of geomorphological thought.

During the eighteenth century, a few writers such as Giovanni Targioni-Tozetti (1712–84) and Jean Étienne Guettard (1715–86) expressed a belief in river-erosion, but geomorphology was swamped by *geognosy* or the teachings of Abraham Gottlob Werner (1749–1817), who postulated a universal ocean in which the precipitation of sediments formed in succession first the primitive rocks, then the transitional (secondary) and derivative (tertiary), and finally the volcanic rocks. The Wernerians, or Neptunists as they were called later, could not explain how the universal ocean had disappeared, but it was assumed to have gone suddenly. In such a scheme, the landscape was presumably formed partly by submarine deposition and erosion, and largely by a sudden rush of retreating oceanic water.

Birth of Geomorphology

When Neptunism was at its height, direct field observations by naturalists led to the birth of modern geomorphology. Some credit for this must go to the detailed researches into water flow and river work by Italian and French hydraulic engineers, including L. G. Du Buat, whose "*Principes d'Hydraulique*" (1779) was based on experiments carried out for the government. In France, a few geologists believed in river erosion, notably Jean Baptiste de Lamarck (1744–1829) whose "*Hydrogéologie*" (1802) stated definitely that mountains had been carved out of plains by running water and that Mosaic chronology was not applicable to geology. But Lamarck and the hydraulic engineers alike were virtually ignored as geological ideas on the Continent were strongly dominated by Baron Georges L. C. Cuvier who, from the existence of unconformities, broken strata and accumulations of fossil-shells, postulated great catastrophes, the last of which was the biblical flood. According to Cuvier and his numerous followers, when the deluge ceased, the ocean subsided and its rushing waters carved out the present landscape.

In Switzerland, Horace Bénédict de Saussure (1740–99) broke partly from this catastrophic dominance. He considered that the small valleys were cut by torrents whereas large valleys were carved out by the rushing waters when the universal ocean disappeared into subterranean cavities. De Saussure also studied glaciers and had a considerable influence on Hutton and Playfair.

James Hutton (1726–97) was the first great fluvialist and the real founder of modern geomorphology. In Scotland, he led the Vulcanists or Plutonists who believed that granite and volcanic rocks were formed by "the heat of fusion and erected by an expansive force acting below." These were distinct from the Wernerian Neptunists who considered such rocks were precipitated chemically in a universal ocean. The violent controversy between Vulcanists and Neptunists, and Hutton's obscure prose, caused his excellent geomorphological ideas to be neglected. In his "Theory of the Earth" (Edinburgh, 1788; second ed., 1795), he maintained that the present is the key to the past, that the earth's surface is an ever-changing succession of forms, the study of which must be based only on observable data, powers and processes. The key to landscape development was largely stream erosion and the laying down in the oceans of river-borne deposits which were later elevated as land masses. "Our land has two extremities; the tops of the mountains, and the sea-shores: where there is a seashore and a higher ground, there is that which is required for the system of the world." The succession of erosion, deposition and land-mass elevation made it "vain to look for anything higher in the origin of the earth. The result, therefore, of our present enquiry, is that we find no vestige of a beginning,—no prospect of an end."

On Hutton's death, his friend John Playfair expanded his views in lucid, flowing prose in "Illustrations of the Huttonian Theory of the Earth" (1802). Playfair stressed that moving water (rivers, waves and glaciers) was the great agent of landscape formation; that rivers cut their own valleys and that in river systems trunks and tributaries were perfectly adjusted (Playfair's law of accordant junctions). He grasped clearly the idea of stream super-imposition, of debris transport by glaciers and observed, for example, that streams impel rock-fragments "by a force proportional to the square of the velocity with which the water rushes against them, and proportional also to the quantity of gravel and stones which it has already put in motion."

The Heyday of Diluvialism

There was no great immediate support for Play-fair's Huttonian ideas partly because of the counter-attractions of stratigraphy after William Smith had published his map of the strata of England and Wales in 1815 and largely because of the hold of the Church on learning. Clerical geologists such as William Buckland and Adam Sedgwick en-deavored scientifically to reconcile geology and the Bible. By evidence from underfit rivers and from erratics and "drift" deposits (especially gravels now known to be fluvioglacial), they provided scientific proof of a "universal deluge at no very remote period of time." The Noachian Flood (officially dated at 2348 B.C.) was held responsible for most landscape features, particularly valleys. Such diluvi-alism also dominated geomorphological thought in the New World.

The Upsurge of Uniformitarianism

Diluvialism was largely discredited by Charles Lyell (1797–1875) whose geomorphological views were propounded at length in his famous "Prin-ciples of Geology. Being an Inquiry into how Far the Former Changes of the Earth's Surface are Referable to causes now in Operation" (2 vols. 1830–1832, twelfth ed. 1875). This great work in-cluded a strong attack on catastrophism and on diluvialism and gave scientific details of erosional and denudation processes. For example, quantita-tive measurements were given for the sediment content of the Ganges and for the retreat of chalk cliffs in England. The emphasis throughout was on the gradualness of landscape change and on the value of modern scientific findings as the key to the past. By 1845, uniformitarianism began to dominate geomorphological (geological) thought in Britain and in the United States, which Lyell visited occasionally. Unfortunately, about this time Lyell's views on landscape-formation swerved increasingly away from the fluvialism of Hutton and Playfair. Although remaining truly uniformitarian in method, he gradually placed increasing importance on marine action. Large valleys were imputed to dissection by ocean currents and waves on an emerging land mass; striations on rock surfaces and most drift deposits were attributed to sea-borne icebergs. Lyell was helped in these views by leading mathematicians such as William Hopkins of Cambridge, who formulated his "sixth-power law of traction," whereby, for example, if the velocity of a current was doubled, the size of boulder it could move was increased by 2^6 or 64 times. Inevitably, Lyell's overemphasis on dissection by marine action and on iceberg transport was challenged by the Huttonians and by a new school of glaciologists.

Rise of Glaciology

Studies of mountain glaciers and of continental ice-sheets originated in Europe and especially in Switzerland where Alpine glaciers were studied, for example, by Johann J. Scheuchzer (1672–1733), De Saussure, F. G. Hugi, the Charpentier brothers and Jean Louis Rodolphe Agassiz (1807–73). However, it was Agassiz, a noted paleontologist, who popu-larized the idea of an ice age with ice sheets, and whose "Étude sur les Glaciers" (1840) preceded a rather superior work by Charpentier by one year. Agassiz visited Britain and converted Buckland and Lyell, at least temporarily, to the reality of trans-portation and deposition by land ice. Later he went to the United States and finally settled there. Yet the idea of continental ice sheets did not greatly displace the iceberg theory in Britain till after 1860, when A. C. Ramsay suggested that extensive glaciation had occurred more than once. In Ger-many the iceberg theory declined rapidly after 1875 when Otto Troll described the movement of glacier ice and of erratics southward from the Scandinavian plateau on to the North German Plain (Von Zittel, p. 232). The idea of glacier erosion was accepted even more slowly although Ramsay suggested in 1862 that some Swiss lakes were due to glacial gouging-out (overdeepening) of the valley-floors.

The Arrival of Marine Planation

When Lyell's marine dissection theory was universally popular, Ramsay suggested in his account of the denudation of South Wales (*Mem. Geol. Surv.*, **1**, 1846) that the accordant or gently-sloping lines of summit levels in southwestern Britain were due to marine planation (*shaving off* by the sea) on a stationary or slowly subsiding land mass, later elevated above sea level. This idea of planation followed later by emergence has never lost its popularity. Joseph Beete Jukes in 1862 dis-cussed how the main rivers of southern Ireland probably originated upon an emerged marine plain and so were independent of the present relief which was formed by subaerial denudation *after* the plain had emerged. Similar explanations of river direc-tion and of denudation chronology soon became commonplace in Europe, and massive use was made of *platforms of abrasion*, or marine planation on a subsiding land mass, by Baron Ferdinand von Richthofen in his volumes on China (1882).

The Recovery of Fluvialism

The relative neglect by Lyell of Hutton and fluvialism was gradually remedied after 1840 by the work of naturalists, field geologists and civil engineers. Of the hydraulic studies, two are outstanding from a geomorphological viewpoint: Alexandre Surell's "Études sur les Torrents des Haute–Alpes" (1841) which demonstrated how torrents grade their beds; and A. A. Humphrey's and H. L. Abbot's "Report on the Physics and Hydraulics of the Mississippi" (1861) which gave full details of the river's load and provided quantitative data for numerous geologists, including Archibald Geikie who showed clearly from such measurements that marine erosion was insignificant compared with subaerial denudation (*Geol. Mag.,* 1868).

Of studies made by naturalists and field geologists, at least three exerted a strong influence: in Britain, Colonel George Greenwood's "Rain and Rivers, or Hutton and Playfair against Allcomers" (1857) which was purely fluvialistic; in continental Europe, Ludwig Rütimeyer's "Ueber Thal-und See-bildung" (1869) which demonstrated the antiquity of rivers and how different parts of a river course might show distinct types of erosional features, such as lakes and waterfalls; and in North America, James Dwight Dana's long-lived "Manual of Geology" (1863) which showed acute appreciation of the nature of torrents and of river work.

Dana also illustrates the influence of geological exploration on the recovery of fluvialism to its rightful status. Geological work by T. Oldham, W. T. Blanford and others in the humid tropics, gave a new dimension to rainfall and surface-wash, while geological surveys in the American semi-arid West threw a new light on river incision. The American surveyors revealed the Grand Canyon and made notable contributions to geomorphology. John Wesley Powell, especially in his "Exploration of the Colorado River of the West" (1875) emphasized the principle of base level, which formed the basis of the modern concept of peneplanation. He also described the nature of landforms in arid climates, and presented a genetic classification of rivers or river valleys (antecedent, consequent, superimposed). Grove Karl Gilbert in his "Report on the Geology of the Henry Mountains" (1877) provided an influential American thesis on the mechanics of fluvial processes and on the formation of sediments. His other great works included the "History of Lake Bonneville" (1890) in which the geomorphic utility of former shore lines and terraces was clearly demonstrated. Clarence E. Dutton is best remembered for his contributions to isostatic compensation on the removal by erosion of vast amounts of strata and his descriptions of individual landforms such as cliffs or scarps which he considered retreated parallel to themselves in arid climates.

This nineteenth-century work ensured that the power of river erosion could no longer be doubted nor could the difference between landscapes in humid and arid regions.

The Davisian Cyclical Synthesis

Before 1900, quantitative studies had been made on most aspects of subaerial denudation, and several texts rich in statistical and experimental information had appeared, among them "Les Formes du Terrain" (1888) by G. de la Nöe and Emm. de Margerie. Undoubtedly the most comprehensive, however, was Albrecht Penck's "Morphologie der Erdoberfläche" (2 vols., 1894) which contained a genetic discussion of surface features, contrasting strikingly with F. von Richthofen's "Führer fur Forschungsreisende" (1886) which was primarily concerned with classification. Penck's work was limited, however, as was V. V. Dokuchayev's "Modes of Formation of the Stream Valleys of European Russia" (1878), by his individual treatment of landform origins and by his failure to link together landforms as temporal sequences or areal associations in a systematic manner. This was the achievement of the Harvard professor William Morris Davis.

Between 1884 and 1889, Davis evolved a theoretical model involving the progressive, sequential and irreversible development of humid erosional landforms under the influence of base level, in which forms could be described and explained with reference to a time sequence of *stages* (youth, maturity and old age) occurring during a long period of stability following a rapid initial uplift of the land mass. Each stage was held to exhibit characteristic form elements comprising a characteristic assemblage appropriate to each geological *structure* and each type of geomorphic *process*. Davis' earlier work (collected in "Geographical Essays," 1909) had great influence in Europe (e.g., E. de Martonne's "Traité de Géographie Physique," 1909 *et seq.*), and his suggestions for an arid cycle (1909, pp. 296–322), shore-line cycle (1909, pp. 700–707) and upland glacial cycle (1909, pp. 658–666) were widely developed (e.g., D. W. Johnson's "Shore Processes and Shoreline Development," New York, 1919). To these were added a karst cycle (Cvijic, *Rev. Trav. Inst. Géog. Alpine*, 6(4), 1918) and a periglacial cycle (Peltier, *Ann. Assoc. Am. Geog.*, 1950).

During the remainder of his long life (1850–1934), Davis propounded, explained and defended his cyclic concept, particularly in his "Die Erklärende Beschreibung der Landformen" (1912), although in his last years he introduced certain modifications to his original ideas on peneplanation (*Bull. Geol. Soc. Am.*, 1922), on slope development and the relation between humid and arid landforms (*J. Geol.*, 1930). Davis exercised a predominant influence over geomorphology for almost half a century and despite objections which have arisen to some of his ideas, "geomorphology will probably retain his stamp longer than that of any other single person" (W. D. Thornbury, "Principles of Geomorphology," p. 11, 1954).

Denudation Chronology

The idea that sequences of erosional and depositional phases of landform development could be established had previously been exploited in Europe by A. C. Ramsay (*Quart. J. Geol. Soc.*, 1872, 1874 and 1876) and in the Appalachians by McGee (*Am. J. Sci.*, 1888). This essentially geological aim of elucidating the latest parts of earth history became fused with the cyclical approach, and it was symptomatic that Davis' first complete cyclic statement was made in his denudation chronology of the rivers of Pennsylvania (*Nat. Geog. Mag.*, **I**, 1889 and 1909). In his "Complications of the Geographical Cycle" (*Rept. 8th Intern. Geog. Cong.*, 1905 and 1909) Davis confirmed that different erosional cycles could be referred to base levels occupied at successive time periods, and much of geomorphology in France, the United States and Britain before the Second World War became concerned with such work, culminating in Baulig's "Le Plateau Central de la France" (1928), Johnson's "Stream Sculpture on the Atlantic Slope" (1931) and Wooldridge and Linton's "Structure, Surface and Drainage in South-East England" (1939). Such historical studies of specific areas were partly promoted by the regional preoccupation of geography in western Europe, particularly in France after 1902, under the influence of Vidal de la Blache, and in the United States (N. M. Fenneman, "Physiography of the Western and Eastern United States," 1931 and 1938). European denudation chronologists drew inspiration from the synchronous eustatic swings of sea level proposed as the dominating diastrophic control over earth history by Eduard Suess ("Das Antlitz der Erde," Vol. 2, 1888) which they believed to provide the key for the universal correlation of erosion surfaces by elevation, whereas American workers preferred to view stepped erosion surfaces as evidence of intermittent land uplift of a post-orogenic character.

The Revolt against Davisian Dominance

By the middle of the 1930's severe objections were being raised to the cyclical concept and to the stylized manner in which denudation chronology was being conducted. Many of the nineteenth-century features of Davis' theory, particularly its evolutionary, qualitative, dialectical and semantic ones, as well as its dominantly theoretical basis, began to weigh more heavily against it, especially in the United States where the trend towards the human ecology view of geography was forcing geomorphology into the field of geology. Fenneman's essay on noncyclic erosion (*Science*, 1936) pointed to some of these basic theoretical difficulties.

The increasingly uncritical use of supposed erosion surfaces, "straths," breaks of slope, and other purely geometrical features of polycyclic landforms also came under attack (e.g., J. L. Rich, *Bull. Geol. Soc. Am.*, 1938), and the general decline of interest in traditional denudation chronology was hastened by a weakening belief in the simple eustatic notion. Only in Britain, due to the dominant influence of S. W. Wooldridge, and to a less extent in France (sometimes in the form of the recognition of "exhumed" erosion surfaces, e.g., A. Cholley *et al.*, "Carte Morphologique du Bassin de Paris," 1956) do studies of denudation chronology form a large part of the contemporary geomorphological effort, although there is some evidence of its revival in the Soviet Union.

These weaknesses of Davisian geomorphology have prompted recent developments in three main directions, all overlapping to a certain extent. They may be loosely designated as tectonic, climatic, and quantitative geomorphology.

The Tectonic Influence on Landforms

Geological interest in central and eastern Europe had long been centered on problems of Alpine tectonics, and it was natural that geomorphologists there should be especially concerned with the possible influences of endogenetic processes on the geometry of landforms. German work, especially, during the inter-war period was characterized by the assumption that accordances (e.g., associated with the *gipfelflur, primärrumpf*, etc.) could be formed unrelated to the influence of "grand" base level and that the relationship between such surfaces (e.g., *piedmont-treppen*), as well as the geometry of the slopes joining them, could be used to interpret the character of crustal movements. Such work as that by Albrecht Penck (*Sitzungsber. Preuss. Akad.*, **18**, 1919) and by his son Walther ("Die Morphologische Analyse," 1924; English translation, 1953) led many continental geomorphologists to believe that crustal movements often were continuous, of varying intensity and relatively long-lived, rather than discontinuous, simple and short-lived as required by the Davisian scheme. It was inevitable that these conclusions should be refuted by Davis (*J. Geol.*, 1923; *Bull. Geol. Soc. Am.*, 1932) and that this disagreement should dominate methodological thought in geomorphology in the decade or so prior to 1940 (e.g., *Ann. Assoc. Am. Geog.*, 1940). While the form of this conflict tended to obscure the many theoretical affinities between the two approaches, it had the effect both of challenging the complacency of Davisian geomorphologists and of centering a general interest on problems of erosional slope development which has persisted to the present in a somewhat different form (e.g., Strahler, *Am. J. Sci.*, 1950). Work in Russia too, ever since the time of Lomonosov (1763), has been concerned with the influence of both endogenetic and exogenetic processes on landforms, and research into the character of crustal movements has formed an important part of Russian geomorphology especially since about 1890, being exemplified today by that of Yu. A. Mescherikov and I. P. Gerasimov (*see* Chorley, *Bull. Geol. Soc. Am.*, 1963; Schumm, *U.S. Geol. Surv. Profess. Paper* **454-H**, 1963).

The Growth of Climatic Geomorphology

The influence of climate on morphogenetic processes and the associated landform assemblages had been emphasized by work in the western United States (Powell, Gilbert and Dutton), in Asia (von Richthofen) and in Africa, where the findings of J. Walther ("Das Gesetz der Wüstenbildung," 1900) and S. Passarge ("Die Kalahari," 1904) were used by Davis in the conception of his arid cycle. Generally, however, the early German workers overstressed the erosive action of wind, and underestimated the action of running water. Davis (1909, pp. 312–3), for example, disagreed with Passarge's contention that the vast desert plains studded with inselbergs were too flat to be the work of running water. In fact, the dominant twentieth-century trend in desert research has been the concentration on the action of running water (e.g., Bryan's Papago Country monograph; *U.S. Geol. Survey Bull.*, **730-B**, 1922), especially with respect to the formation of pediments (Lawson, *Univ. Calif. Publ. Geol. Sci.*, 1915; Blackwelder, *J. Geol.*, 1931; Bryan, *Rept. 16th Intern. Geol. Congr.*, 1935) and the possible effect of past pluvial periods in present deserts (e.g., J. Büdel). Throughout the twentieth century, the arid climatic landscape has continued to attract much attention as for example in E.-F. Gautier's "Le Sahara" (1923); H. Mortensen's study of the north Chilean desert (*Abhandl. Akad. Wiss. Göttingen, Math. Phys. Kl.*, 1927); and the recent valuable research emanating from the Instituts de Recherches Sahariènnes (Algiers) and Scientifique Chérifien (Rabat). However, since the end of the 1920's, interest has been turning more and more to other climatic landform assemblages.

At the beginning of the century, Vladimir Köppen (1900, with many subsequent revisions) suggested his important classification of the world into climatic zones and regions, and about the same time, the soil-type groupings of the great Russian pedologists was stemming from the stimulus of Vasilü Dokuchayev's monumental "The Russian Chernozem" (1883). Such a proliferation of zonal and regional classifications was unfavorable to Davis's concept of a master "normal" cycle with glacial and arid "accidents." Climatic geomorphology grew from such general summaries as E. de Martonne's "Le Climat Facteur du Relief" (*Scientia*, 1913) into the detailed analysis and comparison of many zones presented at the 1926 Düsseldorf Symposium (F. Thorbecke, editor, "Morphologie der Klimazonen"; *Düsseldorfer*

Geogr. Vorträge und Erörterungen, Part III, Breslau, 1927). Thereafter such studies were extended (e.g., Karl Sapper's "Geomorphologie der feuchten Tropen," 1935), global morphoclimatic schemes were proposed, and the effects of paleoclimatic changes estimated. Some of the more outstanding general works are J. Büdel's "Das System der klimatischen Morphologie" (*Deut. Geographentag*, Munich, 1950); L. Peltier's summary of nine morphogenetic regions (glacial, periglacial, boreal, maritime, selva, moderate or the "normal" of Davis, savanna, semiarid, and arid—*Ann. Assoc. Am. Geog.*, 1950); J. Tricart and A. Cailleux's "Introduction à la Géomorphologie Climatique" (1955); and P. Birot's "Le Cycle d'Érosion sous les Different Climats" (1960). Their general contention is that the "normal cycle" is so oversimplified a concept and, for existing conditions, either unreal or so areally abnormal that present landforms "must be interpreted as a product of complex evolution, as a mixture of newly developing agents and of survivals in course of removal at varying rates" (Tricart and Cailleux, 1955, p. 171).

An interesting variant of climatic geomorphology has been presented by recent treatments of the tropical tablelands of the old "Gondwanaland." A year after E. de Martonne's "Problèmes Morphologiques du Brésil Tropical Atlantique" (*Ann. Géog.*, 1940), L. C. King of South Africa began a series of publications, culminating in his "Morphology of the Earth" (1960). Following the suggestion by Wood (*Proc. Geologists Assoc. Engl.*, 1942), King proposes the widespread formation of "pediplains" by the parallel retreat of bounding slopes under the action of subhumid processes, which he believes to have been once more extensive than at present. While accepting Davis' idea of cyclic development, he postulates a revision by including in the mature stage the parallel retreat of slopes and the extension of pediments into pediplains. New uplift causes erosional scarps to work back across wide areas, and landforms can be broadly regarded as a series of such erosional levels separated by intervening scarps.

The Explosion of Quantitative Geomorphology

The employment of deductions based on measurements are not new in geomorphology (A. Geikie, *Geol. Mag.*, 1868; A. P. Pavlov, "Du Relief des Plaines et de Ses Variations sous l'Influence des Eaux Souterraines et Superficielles," 1898; Gilbert, *U.S. Geol. Surv. Profess. Paper*, **86**, 1914), but since the 1930's the increasing opportunity for such work in terms of facility of measurement, availability of data, and the imaginative and technical advances in treatment, has given post-war studies much of their distinctive flavor. Such studies draw some of their inspiration from the attack on practical problems such as, for example, "conservation" and hydrological investigations (T. V. Zvonkova, "The Study of Relief for Practical Purposes," Moscow, *Geografgiz*, 1959).

Among the aspects elaborated in detail are the evaluation of the processes of weathering (Reiche, *Univ. New Mex. Publ. Geol.*, **1**, 1945; Keller, "The Principles of Chemical Weathering," 1957); of fluvial action (e.g., F. Hjulstrom, *Bull. Geol. Inst. Univ. Upsala*; A. Sundborg, *Geograph. Ann.*, 1956), and of marine agencies (e.g., Krumbein, *U.S. Beach Erosion Board, Tech. Memo.*, No. 3, 1944; V. P. Zenkovich, "Coasts of the Black Sea and Sea of Azov," Moscow, *Geografgiz*, 1958; C. A. M. King, "Beaches and Coasts," 1959). More "academic" studies have been directed towards processes operating in the "periglacial" environment named by W. von Lozinski (*Bull. Acad. Sci. Cracow*) in 1909 (e.g., Högbom, *Bull. Geol. Inst. Upsala*, 1914 and 1926; A. Jahn, "Quantitative Analysis of Some Periglacial Processes in Spitsbergen," 1961), and in the physics of glacier movement (*J. Glaciol.*), although, with the exception of some work on cirque glaciers, little basic contribution has been made towards explaining upland glacial features since Matthes' classic work on the Yosemite Valley (*U.S. Geol. Sur. Profess. Paper* **160**, 1930). Bagnold ("Physics of Blown Sand and Desert Dunes," 1941) has led modern research into aeolian action as Sokolov did earlier ("Dunes, Their Formation, Development, and Internal Structure, 1884). Corbel's karst studies continue the traditions of subterranean research established by Grund (*Penck's Abhandl.*, 1903) and E.-A. Martel ("Nouveau Traité des Eaux Souterrains," 1921) and of climatic influences by Cvijic (*C.R. Acad. Sci.*, 1925). In very recent years, also, interesting studies of processes have begun to contrast rates of operation in different environments (Langbein and Schumm, *Trans. Am. Geophys. Union*, 1958; M. F. Fournier, "Climat et Érosion," 1960) and the relative effects of different magnitudes and frequencies of operation (Wolman and Miller, *J. Geol.*, 1960).

Studies of topographic form were encouraged by the twentieth-century extension of mapping in different structural and climatic environments. The United States map coverage reached 31 and 41% in 1904 and 1919, respectively, and important extensions of Russian mapping took place in the 1930's. A further stimulus came from the development of aerial photography, with its aid to precise mapping, during and after the World War II. Analysis of topographic maps has broadly taken the form of "morphometry" and "morphological mapping." The study of the geometry of landscape (morphometry) has progressed both by the extension of techniques first used to identify erosion surfaces (e.g., the "hypsometric integral" of Strahler, *Bull. Geol. Soc. Am.*, 1952) and, more important, by new techniques based on hydrology (Horton, *Bull. Geol. Soc. Am.*, 1945). The broad categorizing of

landform types and assemblages, or morphological mapping, often with a bias toward denudation chronology or climatic geomorphology, has been carried on by Dylik and the Polish Academy of Sciences, the British Geomorphological Research Group, and by Gerasimov in the Soviet Union.

Among the most stimulating trends of recent work has been a revival of research into the relationships between geomorphic processes and the associated equilibrium landforms which formed the focus of interest for G. K. Gilbert (1877, Ch. 5). The important work of Horton (1945), which examined the relationships between drainage basin forms and hydrological processes, was extended by Strahler and his students at Columbia University (e.g., Schumm, *Bull. Geol. Soc. Am.*, 1956; Melton, "An Analysis of the Relations among Elements of Climate, Surface Properties and Geomorphology," 1957; Chorley, *J. Geol.*, 1957). Such studies have been based on field surveys (H. N. Fisk, "Geological Investigation of the Alluvial Valley of the Lower Mississippi River," 1944; Strahler, 1950); on map analysis; on experimental scale models (e.g., Friedkin's work on meandering at U.S. Waterways Experiment Station, 1945); in a minor way on mathematical models (e.g., Bakker's development of erosional slopes, *Proc. Koninkl. Ned. Akad. Wetenschap.*, 1946 *et seq.*); and on theoretical considerations (e.g., Mackin's work on "grade," *Bull. Geol. Soc. Am.*, 1948). Some of the most successful research has been in the field of "hydraulic geometry" by L. B. Leopold and his associates (e.g., *U.S. Geol. Surv. Profess. Papers*, **252**, 1953 and **282-B**, 1957), whose work finds some measure of counterpart in that of N. I. Makkaveyev ("The Bed of a River and the Erosion of its Basin," *Akad. Nauk. SSSR*, 1955).

To sum up, geomorphology since 1945 has been generally progressing towards a more secure scientific footing through its concern with measurement, the statistical analysis of data (e.g., Strahler, *J. Geol.*, 1954; Melton, 1957), its association with kindred sciences and with practical problems, and its attempt to break out of the narrow scholasticism which characterized much of its prewar development. It is, perhaps, symptomatic that recent methodological writings (e.g., *U.S. Geol. Surv. Profess. Papers*, **500-A** and **500-B**, 1962) have been concerned that geomorphology should both draw on and contribute to the wealth of scientific experience which is the most distinctive intellectual achievement of our age.

R. P. Beckinsale
R. J. Chorley

References

Baulig, H., 1957, "La Géomorphologie en France jusqu'en 1940," in "La Géographie Française au Milieu du XXe Siecle," pp. 27–35, Paris.

Bryan, K., 1941, "Physiography 1888–1938," in 50th annual volume, *Geol. Soc. Am.*, 1–15.

Chorley, R. J., 1963, "Diastrophic background to twentieth century geomorphological thought," *Bull. Geol. Soc. Am.*, **74**, 953–970.

*Chorley, R. J., Dunn, A. J., and Beckinsale, R. P., 1964, "The History of the Study of Landforms," Vol. 1, London, Methuen, 678pp. (deals with up to 1893).

Dylik, J., 1953, "Charactères du developpement de la géomorphologie Moderne," *Bull. Soc. Sci. Lettres Lodz*, **4** (3), 1–40.

Markov, K. K., 1948, "Basic Problems of Geomorphology," pp. 7–46, Moscow.

Nikolayev, N. I., 1958, "The history of the development of the basic ideas in geomorphology," *Ocherki Istorii Geologicheskikh Znzniy Akad. Nauk SSSR*, **6**, Moscow.

von Zittel, F. A., 1901, "History of Geology and Palaeontology," London, Walter Scott, 562pp.

* Additional bibliographic references mentioned in the text may be found in this work.

Cross-references: *Base Level*; *Denudation*; *Eustasy*; *Fluvial Processes*; *Fluvioglacial Processes*; *Geomorphology—Statistical Analysis*; *Gipfelflur*; *Glacial Scour*; *Inselberg*; *Pediment*; *Peneplain*; *Quantitative Geomorphology*; *Rivers*; *Slopes*; *Youth-Maturity-Old Age*. Vol. VI: *Actualism*; *Diluvial Theory*; *Uniformitarianism*.

GEOMORPHOLOGY — PRINCIPLES

The earth may be regarded as consisting of seven great spheres:

(1) The *interior of the earth* consists of igneous material, the primary source of magma. Being subjected to high pressure and high temperature, it is largely solid though its molecules are mobile.

(2) It is enveloped by the earth's crust or *lithosphere* with a thickness of merely 30–50 km beneath the continents, 5 km below the oceans, and 10–12 km in intermediate marginal belts.

(3) On top of this the continents have an additional *soil layer* or *pedosphere* with a depth generally of only 1–2 meters. Hydrologists speak also of the "solusphere," the depth limited by the penetration of meteoric waters with their dissolving potential (Rainwater and White, 1957).

(4) The *surface* of the solid crust forms as it were a two-dimensional "sphere" of its own, displaying a varied relief of deep sea, continents, lowlands, uplands and Alpine mountain ranges.

(5) Almost two thirds of this surface (71%) are covered by the oceanic *hydrosphere.*

(6) In the polar regions and high mountain ranges a small part is covered by the *cryosphere* in the form of ice caps and glaciers.

(7) Only about one quarter (26%) of the lithosphere is in direct contact with the *atmosphere.*

Geomorphology is concerned with the investigation of the fourth of these spheres, viz. the relief of the solid earth's surface. The *subaerial relief* of the continents is particularly varied and complicated. It is joined by the *subglacial relief* exposed by melting glaciers. The *submarine relief* of the sea floors is described elsewhere (Vol. I).

The earth's surface receives the sunlight and partly transforms it into heat, some of which is reflected into the atmosphere. This provides the principal impulse of meteorological processes in the troposphere. These react upon the earth's surface through rainfall, streams and rivers, wind and glaciers. Thus meteorologic processes have a major control over weathering, soil formation and above all, relief development. On this surface alone is the life of plants, animals and mankind possible. The earth's surface therefore is the great site of energy transformation on the earth. After solar energy comes gravitational energy that leads to *mass wasting* (q.v.), *transportation* (see *Sediment Transport*), etc. (Strahler, 1952). Finally the gross relief is controlled by endogenic (geotectonic) energy.

Atmosphere, hydrosphere and cryosphere represent the *easily mobile external envelope* of the earth. The molecules of air, water and ice are always seen to be in motion. But this motion is *essentially contemporary* in nature. It leaves no permanent traces in the form of *old or fossil structures*. The same applies to the magmatic interior of the earth. Therefore, spheres (1), (5), (6) and (7) properly form subjects of research in various branches of *geophysics* (see Vols. I, II, V).

It is different with the *earth's solid crust*. This contains traces of former events that may go back billions of years. Geology retraces the *history of earth* by investigating both new and old rocks. The development of the relief of the earth's surface is somewhat more recent, but still goes back 10–100 million years (Fig. 1). Present-day processes, conditioned by the climate of the postglacial or Holocene epoch and covering no more than 10,000 years, are responsible for only 5% of the existing relief in the mid-latitudes, while 95% belongs to earlier generations. Thus geomorphology is also a *historical science*; most of the detailed evolution of the present-day geomorphology developed during the Quaternary Period. Besides the climatic changes during this time in many mobile belts and many scattered regions, an immense geotectonic revival of relief has occurred (Termier and Termier, 1961).

Historical Survey

Geomorphology as a science is younger than geology. For a long time the geological structure of the earth's crust was thought to be mainly responsible for the relief forms. The folded structures found by the geologist were considered to be the cause of mountain ranges and valleys. Before the beginning of the nineteenth century Playfair (see *Playfair's Law*) recognized the erosional character of rivers in cutting valleys, but nevertheless L. Rütimeyer (1869) had to argue that valleys, the

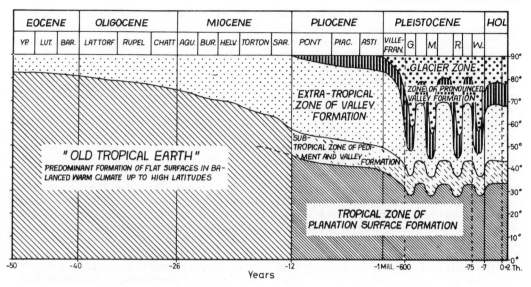

EOCENE			OLIGOCENE			MIOCENE					PLIOCENE			PLEISTOCENE					HOL
YP.	LUT.	BAR.	LATTORF	RUPEL	CHATT	AQU.	BUR.	HELV.	TORTON	SAR.	PONT	PIAC.	ASTI	VILLE-FRAN.	G.	M.	R.	W.	

FIG. 1. Climato-morphological zones of the northern hemisphere within a meridional section from the Equator to the North Pole, through Central Europe since the early Tertiary.

chief element in relief formation, were not caused by *endogenic* (geological) activities but were produced by rivers flowing within these valleys. In other words, they are *exogenically* dependent upon the energy of the sun. O. Powell (1875), F. v. Richthofen (1886) and E. de Martonne (1909) developed the modern concept of river erosion and valley formation. A. Penck (1909) described the main features of subglacial relief and was the first to divide the earth's surface into three climatic-controlled zones of relief formation, the "nival" (associated with glaciers), the humid (associated with rivers), and the arid zone (associated with wind action). This system was taken over by W. M. Davis (1899, 1912) who developed from it the first genetic theory of geomorphology, though still without direct relationship to geological or climatic history. Notwithstanding the early work of Passarge (1912) this last step has been introduced consistently into geomorphology only within the last fifteen years.

The first result of this integration has been the identification of those processes which occur in the Holocene or recent epoch under our very eyes. They are mainly the concern of the physically oriented branch of geomorphology, i.e., *dynamic geomorphology*. We have to distinguish clearly between these processes and the relief forms they produce. Both of them vary over the earth's surface depending on the exogenic influences of climate. Within major climatic zones there are some characteristic complexes or relief expressions, and the investigation of these is the business of *climatic geomorphology*. The earth's crust presents differential resistance to the exogenic agents through

its structure, and the influence of this on relief formation is the concern of *structural geomorphology*. The most important modern development however is the recognition that existing relief is not everywhere merely a synthesis of present climatic conditions and present structural features but contains also older relief generations originating in earlier periods of climatic and tectonic history. The investigation of these varied generations in the evolution of the relief is the task of *climato-genetic geomorphology*; the latter is closely interrelated with Quaternary stratigraphy and chronology.

Modern Methodology

Dynamic Geomorphology. On the continents, fluviatile relief types are dominant. They are formed by the combination of the following processes:

Weathering. This is the mainly inorganic disintegration of the upper zone of the earth's crust through temperature variations, ground-water penetration and ice action. The associated mechanical and chemical processes can affect the rocks to a considerable depth. In polar regions, this is achieved mechanically by permafrost down to a maximal depth of 1000 meters. In the tropics a maximal depth of 600 meters is reached by predominantly chemical weathering. In mid-latitudes significant weathering generally penetrates only a few meters downward except for chemical solution in limestone regions (karst phenomena). Obviously, the depth of weathering depends very much on climate; at the same time, the depth zones of weathering differ significantly in accordance with the nature of the parent rock.

417

Soil Formation. The uppermost layer of the weathering zone, in general only 1–2 meters deep, undergoes a much more intensive physical and chemical transformation through the participation of the biosphere, in the form of plant roots, burrowing animals and above all soil bacteria. Soil composition and soil horizons change quite systematically with climatic zones and are much less influenced by the local parent rock.

Denudation. Almost all surfaces of the earth's relief have a soil cover, from the peneplains of the lowlands to the steep slopes and flanks of high mountain ranges. Its loose top layer is being constantly worn away by rainwater, meltwater or wind. The resulting detrital material is transported by the rivers and finally reaches the ocean. Everywhere the soil cover is removed from above, while at its base, weathering penetrates the solid rock at the same rate if an equilibrium condition exists. Thus the whole land surface is progressively worn down; this process is called *denudation.* Other things being equal, it is more active on steep slopes than on gentle ones. Above all, it differs with climate. The severest denudation occurs in those areas where disequilibrium caused by drastic climatic change leads to accelerated erosion. Regions of maximal and frequent disequilibrium are those adjacent to the tropics and polar regions.

River Erosion. The general wearing down of land by denudation is intensified by the incisional work of rivers. Rivers dissect the land in linear fashion. This form of degradation is called fluvial or fluviatile erosion. Nearly always it works in advance of denudation, creating new and often steeper valley slopes, thus engendering intensified denudation. The speed of fluvial erosion and its relation to denudation vary with climate. The strongest erosion, and through it the *most active valley formation,* is found where a high discharge is supplied with abundant abrasive detritus, as in the non-glaciated parts of sub-polar regions. Here erosion works ahead of denudation to a greater degree than anywhere else. On the other hand, an equilibrium between denudation and river erosion is observed in the marginal tropics with seasonal rain, because both processes work downward with equal speed. Consequently, it is only in this climatic region that widespread erosion surfaces (Rumpfflächen, degradation surfaces or pediplains) with isolated inselbergs can develop. Therefore this is the zone of planation surface formation (see below).

River Deposition. This refers to deposition in valleys, interior basins and lowlands: gravel fans, gravel sheets, terraces, clay plains, lacustrine and marine deltas, etc.

Some 80% of the surface of the continents is dominated by these processes. The remaining 20% is accounted for by the following processes:

Substantial Mass Movements. This includes *screes, talus* (q.v.), *mudstreams* (frana), *landslides* (q.v.), etc. [Note: *frana* is an Italian expression for major mass displacements—Kayser, 1963.]

Glacial Degradation and Deposition. See articles on *Glacial Deposits, Moraine, Till,* etc.

Marine Abrasion and Coastal Deposition. These processes are differentiated climatically into non-tropical coasts without coral reefs and tropical coasts with coral reefs. In addition, there is the sedimentation on the bottoms of lakes and on the ocean floor.

Wind Erosion (Deflation) and Deposition (Sand Dunes). These processes occur especially in desert regions and on alluvial coasts.

Karst Erosion. This takes place in limestone areas. There are very great differences between non-tropical and tropical karst, even under comparable rock conditions (Lehmann, 1960).

Each of these activities represents really a complex of different but interdependent physical processes. They can rarely be separated so as to enable their individual identification in laboratory experiments.

For that reason such experiments in dynamic geomorphology often lead to artificial results not found in the field. Moreover, in nature there are always several of these processes working in combination. Thus soil formation, denudation and erosion together form a process complex of higher order. Above all, these process complexes are not the same everywhere but differ in various climatic zones (see below).

Structural Geomorphology. The earth's surface presents differential resistance to the exogenic dynamic processes working on it since structural features differ from one place to another. In this, the following variables have to be distinguished.

Petro-variance. The resistance of rocks to denudation varies according to their morphological (not physical) hardness (i.e., response rate to ambient chemical and physical agents).

Epeiro-variance. The speed of epeirogenetic uplift or subsidence of any part of the earth's crust determines the major morphological category of the latter, such as high mountains, uplands, lowlands or zone of subsidence. It is also responsible for the topographical layout of these features (e.g., Appalachian Mts., Alps, Harz Mts., Rhine rift valley).

Base Level. The height above general base level has a great bearing on the size and gradient of a river and the width of its valley. In proximity to the divides, only small headwater streams occur. Large rivers in wide valleys are generally found approaching the principal base level (largely as a product of the water-gathering capacity of the system).

Total Relief Influence. This may be (a) *denudative,* i.e., any slope steeper than the one below influences the denudation processes acting on the latter; (b) *abrasive*—glacier-covered high mountains may sup-

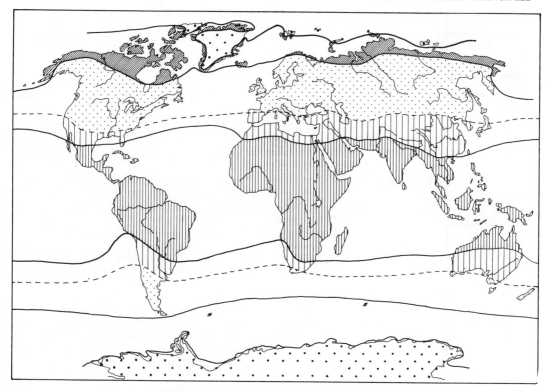

ZONE OF GLACIATED AREAS
ZONE OF PRONOUNCED VALLEY FORMATION
EXTRA-TROPICAL ZONE OF VALLEY FORMATION
SUBTROPICAL ZONE OF PEDIMENT AND VALLEY FORMATION
TROPICAL ZONE OF PLANATION SURFACE FORMATION

FIG. 2. Climato-morphological zones of the earth.

ply major rivers with heavy gravel loads. But downstream in terms of valley widths and gradients, they achieve effects quite disproportionate in comparison with the autochthonous streams. Related to this is (c) distant climatic influence. Extensive mountain ranges with high rainfall may send allochthonous (allogenic) rivers even across major climatic boundaries into distant deserts (e.g., the Nile).

Human Influence. This term covers all forms of human interference with the course of morphological processes such as river regulation, cutting down of forests leading to soil erosion, etc. (See *Anthropogenic Influences*).

Climatic Geomorphology. *Climatic variance*, which controls all dynamic processes, takes precedence over all structural components. Every climatic zone has its own specific complex of dynamic processes in terms of present-day activity. This means also that the significance of the structural features of the earth's crust changes in relation to current dynamic processes. In different climates, for example, the morphological hardness of rocks differs. Thus limestone is a morphologically soft

rock within the permafrost area of polar regions. In other regions, however, it offers extreme resistance to surface degradation, because karst development takes the rain water into subterranean channels along joints, thus preventing surface run-off. On the other hand, granite in the tropics under conditions of deep chemical weathering, is a soft rock similar to sand, but it is extremely hard in most nontropical areas. Similarly the influences of epeiro-variance, base-level distance, total relief and the human factor vary with different climates. The reason is that everywhere climate determines the mode of exogenic processes which *actively* shape relief. In contrast non-climatic structural factors only represent varying *passive* phenomena. Moreover in their haphazard distribution over the earth they carry merely local significance. Climatic variance, on the other hand, changes systematically with the great climatic zones over the entire earth.

In accordance with the climatic mode of interactions, i.e., the total complex of current exogenic processes, and also according to the typical relief forms actually produced in every climatic zone by

419

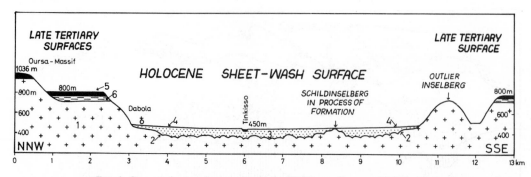

FIG. 3. Current sheetwash planation in the Tinkisso valley near Dabola (Guinea).

1. Dolerite-Diabase bedrock.
2. Lower limit of weathered zone.
3. Layer of red, kaolin-rich loam, 10-30 meters thick.
4. Sheet wash surface.

5. Lateritic hardpan, 2–4 meters thick.
6. Basal bauxitic hardpan, 10–15 meters thick (5 and 6 on uplifted earlier planation surfaces).

these processes, the land surface of the earth can be divided into the following climato-morphological zones (Fig. 2):

(I) Zone of glaciated areas, i.e., polar regions and high mountain ranges.

(II) Zone of pronounced valley formation, i.e., parts of subpolar regions at present ice-free, mostly with permafrost.

(III) Extratropical (i.e., temperate) zone of valley formation. This includes most of the mid-latitudinal regions. To-day, it is characterized by very moderately active processes and usually strongly marked fossil features of cold glacial periods (Fig. 1).

(IV) Subtropical zone of pediment and valley formation, i.e., transition zone between III and V, internally highly differentiated.

(V) Tropical zone of planation surface formation, i.e., the humid, particularly the seasonally humid tropical regions.

Outside the glacier-covered areas, zones (II) and (V) represent extreme cases of pronounced but, at the same time, greatly differentiated denudation processes. In both cases they are aided by deep weathering, mechanical (permafrost) in zone (II), chemical in zone (V), each of which may penetrate to depths of 600 meters or even 1000 meters beneath the surface.

In the zone of pronounced valley formation much coarse detritus (tools of abrasion) comes into the rivers during the summer melting period, owing to a high runoff coefficient. The origin of this detritus lies in slope denudation brought about by the combined effect of drainage work, solifluction and the loosening of the subsurface by the freezing and melting of ground ice (so-called "Eis-Rinde"). As this also takes place beneath the rivers, the latter, instead of having to cut slowly into the exposed solid bedrock in the river bed, merely transport away the material already loosened by the melting process together with the other load brought down from the slopes. This is the principal reason why

pronounced valley deepening over the entire width of river bottoms occurs simultaneously with retention of a smooth gradient, in a dominant way in this zone.

Wherever areas within the tropical zone of planation surface formation show only a small degree of epeiro-variance (Fig. 3), chemical weathering penetrates deeply and gives rise to dense red loams rich in kaolin; this process facilitates the formation of extensive degradation surfaces at river levels owing to the effect of the two planation surfaces (i.e., the upper, exposed, *sheet-wash surface* and the subterranean *lower limit of weathering*). Subsequently uplifted surfaces of that kind may, apart from dissection at their lower margin, remain largely undissected for a long time and even retain the ability to expand further at their upper margin at the expense of areas of higher slopes. In their cross sections the valleys of tropical high mountain ranges frequently show very steep slopes without a proper valley bottom and irregular longitudinal profiles with knick points and waterfalls, especially in tributaries where they join the main river.

Climato-genetic Geomorphology. This research method adds *time* as a factor to what has been described so far. It represents therefore a synthesis in four dimensions.

Complete adaptation of the entire relief to the characteristic complex of exogenic processes in any morphological zone takes some ten million years or so according to empirical data, gathered from all these zones. Within a period of such length, however, climatic changes may occur so that a new complex of morphogenic processes becomes established leading to a different relief peculiar to itself. Nevertheless, relics of the former relief persist for a long time. In the mid-latitudes several such changes have taken place during the last 10–12 million years (Fig. 1). Consequently we observe many ancient relief features owing their existence to earlier process complexes under differ-

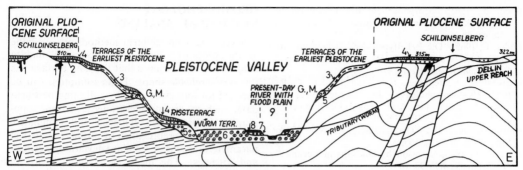

FIG. 4. Relief generations of the mid-latitudes, illustrated by an upland valley in Central Europe.

Generation I: Original Pliocene surface, truncating varying rock conditions faults and (present-day) water divides.
    1 = Karst fissures filled up with red and brown Pliocene loams.
Generation II: Terraces of the earliest Pleistocene.
Generation III: Pleistocene valley.
    2 = Cryoturbation mantle on planation surfaces.
    3 = Solifluction mantle on slopes.
    4 = Loess cover overlying 2 and 3.

    5 = Gravel of Early and Middle Pleistocene terraces G = Günz, M = Mindel, R = Riss.
    6 = Gravel of the older Würm terrace.
Generation IV: Late glacial and prehistoric Holocene.
    7 = Younger Würm terrace (late-glacial period).
Generation V: Post-Palaeolithic (cultivation).
    8 = Valley loams on 7.
    9 = Present-day river with flood plain.

ent climates, in addition to the modern features resulting from the morphogenic processes of today. Due to several changes of climate over the last ten million years, a corresponding number of *landform generations* may therefore be distinguished in the present total relief. To effect their identification as precisely as possible is the aim of climatogenetic geomorphology. Like stratigraphic geology and all the other historical natural sciences, geomorphology uses first and foremost the logical method of historical circumstantial evidence.

So far this task of modern geomorphology has been tackled only in a few representative examples. Nevertheless, these already demonstrate that everywhere from the poles to the equator, we are faced with several earlier climato-genetic relief generations besides the present one. For that reason, too, we know now that the present-day processes cannot run their course independently but have their development circumscribed, often narrowly, by the relics of earlier relief generations.

A particularly large number of relief generations can be differentiated in the present polar regions and *mid-latitudes*, because there the climate has changed frequently and vigorously within the more recent geological past (Fig. 1). Figure 4 illustrates this with an example of a typical valley in one of the moderately high plateau uplands in Central Europe. Here we find the following relief generations:

(1) the generation of the dominant Miocene or Pliocene surfaces.

(2) the remains of valley bottoms (terraces) of shallow valleys of the earliest Pleistocene,

(3) the narrower, deeply incised valley of the Pleistocene cold (glacial) periods with terraces, fossil permafrost soil and loess cover,

(4) the later glacial and prehistoric Holocene relief elements,

(5) the features of human influence dating from the historic Holocene.

Subtropical regions show a similar complexity of climatic relief generations. This is in contrast to the tropics, in the present-day zone of planation surface formation. While in the mid-latitudes, present-day processes have been at work for only about 10,000 years and therefore have formed a mere 5% of the present total relief, sheet-wash processes have dominated the picture in the tropics with little variation for several millions of years, i.e., from the late Tertiary (Pliocene) through the whole Quaternary period to the present time. Thus a much greater part of the present relief in these areas owes its origin to processes still active today. The relics of earlier relief generations are less important. Where they exist (Fig. 3), they often call for a special analysis in order to establish whether they are climato-genetic relief generations or epeirogenetic relief generations, i.e., whether the "fossilization" of the earlier relief elements has been caused by a different tectonic behavior of the respective block in former times or by a different climate.

To sum up: the weaker the present-day processes are, and the shorter the period of their operation in an area, the more evident are the older relief generations there and the greater is the part played by climato-genetic factors in their formation as compared with that of tectono-genetic factors.

J. BÜDEL

References

Birot, P., 1949, "Essai sur Quelques Problèmes de Morphologie Générale," Lisbon, Instituto para Alta Cultura, Centro de Estudos Geográficos, 176pp.

Büdel, J., 1961, "Morphogenese des Festlandes in Abhängigkeit von den Klimazonen," *Naturwissenschaften*, **48**.

Büdel, J., 1965, "Die Relieftypen der Flächenspülzone Süd-Indiens am Ostabfall Dekans gegen Madras," *Colloquium Geographicum*, **8**.

Christian, C. S., Jennings, J. N., and Twidale, C. R., 1957, "Geomorphology," in "Guide Book to Research Data for Arid Zone Development," pp. 51–65, Paris, UNESCO.

Cotton, C. A., 1952, "Geomorphology," New York, John Wiley & Sons, 505pp.

Kayser, B., 1963, "Erosion by landslips in Lucanie," *Mediterranée*, **4**(1), 93–100.

King, L., 1962, "The Morphology of the Earth," Edinburgh and London, Oliver and Boyd, 699pp.

Lehmann, H., 1960, "La Terminologie Classique du Karst pour l'aspect critique de la morphologie climatique moderne," *Rév. Géogr. Lyon*, **35**.

Lobeck, A. K., 1939, "Geomorphology," New York and London, McGraw-Hill Book Co., 731pp.

Louis, H., 1961, "Allgemeine Geomorphologie," Berlin, Walter de Gruyter & Co., 355pp.

Miller, J. P., 1959, "Geomorphology in North America," *Pol. Geog. Rev.*, **31**, 567–585.

Passarge, S., 1912, "Physiologische Morphologie," Hamburg, Friedericksen, 205pp.

Rainwater, F. H., and White, W. F., 1957, "Solusphere, its significance and study," *Bull. Geol. Soc. Am.*, **68**, 1783–1784.

Sparks, B. W., 1960, "Geomorphology," New York, John Wiley & Sons, 371pp.

Strahler, A. N., 1952, "Dynamic basis of geomorphology," *Bull. Geol. Soc. Am.*, **63**, 923–938.

Termier, H., and Termier, G., 1961, "L'Évolution de la Lithosphere," Vol. III, "Glyptogénèse," Paris, Masson & Cie, 471pp.

Thornbury, W. D., 1954, "Principles of Geomorphology," New York, John Wiley & Sons, 618pp.

von Engeln, O. D., 1942, "Geomorphology, Systematic and Regional," New York, The Macmillan Co., 655pp.

Wooldridge, S. W., and Morgan, R. S., 1959, "An Outline of Geomorphology," London, Longmans, Green and Co. Ltd., 409pp.

(Additional bibliographic references mentioned in text may be found in above works.)

Cross-references: *Anthropogenic Influences in Geomorphology; Base Level; Climatic Geomorphology; Continent; Coral Reefs; Cryology, Cryosphere; Cryergy; Deflation; Denudation; Dynamic Geomorphology; Endogenic Dynamics; Equilibrium in Geomorphology; Erosion; Exogenic Dynamics; Glacial Deposits; Holocene; Karst; Landslides; Mass Wasting; Moraine; Organisms as Geomorphic Agents; Playfair's Law; Quaternary Period; Relict Landforms; Sand Dunes; Sediment Transport; Structural Control in Geomorphology; Submarine Geomorphology; Talus; Weathering; Youth-Maturity-Old Age. Vol. I: Ocean Bottom Features. Vol. II: Atmosphere; Climate and Geomorphology; Climatic Classifications; Climatic Variations; Climatic Zonation Theory; Meteorology; Solar Energy. Vol. V: Gravitation; Lithosphere; Magma.* pr *Vol. VI: Glaciers; Groundwater; Icecap; Meteoric Water; Soil Genesis; Till and Tillite.*

GEOMORPHOLOGY—STATISTICAL ANALYSIS

Several basically different methods are available to the geomorphologist who wishes to analyze landforms. One assumes that the land surface has the *most probable* shape. This assumption can be checked for any given area by collecting pertinent data, such as ground elevations (i.e., from topographic maps). When classified and cumulated, these data can be represented by ordinary statistical parameters (i.e., mean, standard deviation, skewness and kurtosis). The mean elevation is really an index of position, rather than of geometry, and therefore can be set aside momentarily. (A plot of classified elevation figures can be used for simple analysis.)

Of the three remaining parameters, the two most interesting ones are *skewness* (the degree to which measurements tend to fall above, or below, the mean elevation) and *kurtosis* (the degree to which measurements tend to fall into a few clusters, regardless of their symmetry about the mean). Skewness, then, is a measure of departure from a "most probable" shape, in the direction of an

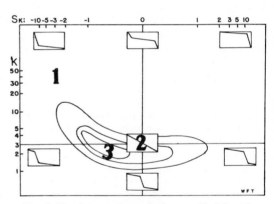

FIG. 1. The skewness-kurtosis diagram. Each inset is a probability plot, based on cumulated elevation figures from a specific area. On each inset, the probability scale occurs on the horizontal ordinate, and the elevation scale on the vertical ordinate; these scales are not detailed. The central inset (behind the large number "2") represents any region in which the distribution of hillside elevations follows the gaussian (i.e., normal) law, or can be transformed to follow the gaussian. The upper right inset is mostly uplands, with some steeper slopes. The upper left inset is mainly low lands, with some steeper slopes. The other insets show various combinations of uplands, slopes and lowlands. In the Davis scheme, the upper right inset would be labeled "youth," the central inset "maturity" and the left inset "old age." These insets are shown here against a background chart where elevation skewness has been plotted against elevation kurtosis (Sk versus K). Use of these two parameters permits comparison of any one region with any other, or with the idealized insets. Most regions apparently fit in the crescent-shaped part of the chart which has been isoplethed near the large number "3."

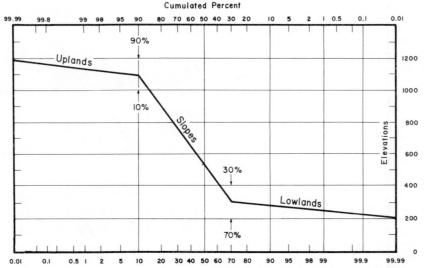

FIG. 2. Hypothetical example showing probability plot of elevations, in one area. (The plot shows 10% of the area in uplands, 60% in slopes, and 30% in lowlands.) Data which were cumulated were obtained (hypothetically) by reading elevations at the corners of an arbitrary grid (spacing = 0.5 mile or 1 mile) (or 1 or 2 km).

asymmetrical shape (largely above, or largely below, the mean elevation). Kurtosis is a measure of the presence, or absence, of important horizontal areas (plains and benches) and vertical areas (cliffs). These two parameters can be plotted against each other.

The "most probable shape" is assumed to be that represented by the central inset in Fig. 1: a gaussian, or normal, distribution of elevations. Six less probable shapes are indicated by the other insets. The contoured strip includes most water-cut regions which have been studied.

Such a chart can be interpreted in terms of the classical cycle concept of W. M. Davis; the upper right inset would represent his stage of youth; the middle inset, maturity; and the upper left inset, old age. Most regions do not fall in the Davis class of old age, however. Alternate interpretations can be made on the basis of major differences in lithology or structure, or on the assumption that a single equilibrium ("most probable") shape does not necessarily cover the entire study region.

A "most probable" profile can also be developed from an entropy concept. Entropy refers to the distribution of energy; hence, it can be treated in terms of the probabilities of various states in the system. The most probable condition of a river develops when the energy in the system is as uniformly distributed as existing constraints will allow. Therefore, a "random walk" model can be devised, and tested, which should produce the most probable profile. Random walk models match field observations rather closely.

The geometry of the drainage basin can be represented in other ways. The hypsometric integral

(the ratio of land-mass volume to volume of body with base equal to basin area and height equal to maximum relief) can be replaced, for practically all purposes, by the mean height. The *drainage density* is the number of streams per unit area or the sum of stream lengths per unit area; the inverse measure (D^{-1}) is the average distance between streams. The "order" of the basin is obtained by counting stream orders, as follows: all unbranched "finger-tip" wet-weather rills are assigned as first order; any stream into which the only tributary is a first-order stream is of second order; two second-order streams combine to form a third-order stream, etc.; and the order of the highest stream is also the order of the basin. Identification of first-order streams should be done on air photos or in the field, rather than on ordinary topographic maps, unless the latter are of exceptionally high quality.

Discharge of water, through the main channel, can also be used in an interpretation of geometry of the drainage basin.

Orientation problems require a special statistical technique; for a discussion of this, see *Crossbedding* (pr Vol. VI). For treatment of statistical methods in other areas, see pr Vol. VI, *Statistical Analysis*.

W. F. TANNER

References

Horton, Robert E., 1945, "Erosional development of streams and their drainage basins; hydrophysical approach to quantitative morphology," *Bull. Geol. Soc. Am.*, **56**, 275–370 (reprinted 1962).

Leopold, Luna B., and Langbein, Walter B., 1962, "The concept of entropy in landscape evolution," *U.S. Geol. Surv., Profess. Paper* **500-A,** 20pp.

Morisawa, Marie, 1959, "Relation of quantitative geomorphology to stream flow in representative watersheds of the Appalachian Plateau province," Columbia Univ., Dept. of Geology, Technical Report No. 20, 94pp.

Scheidegger, A. E., 1961, "Theoretical Geomorphology," New York, Prentice-Hall, 333pp.

Schumm, S. A., and Hadley, R. F., 1961, "Progress in the application of landform analysis in studies of semiarid erosion," *U.S. Geol. Surv. Circ.,* **437,** 14pp.

Strahler, A. N., 1958, "Dimensional analysis applied to fluvially eroded landforms," *Bull. Geol. Soc. Am.,* **69,** 279–305.

Tanner, William F., 1960, "Numerical comparison of geomorphic samples," *Science,* **131,** 1525–1526.

Cross-references: *Drainage Basin; Equilibrium; Geomorphology, History of; Hypsometric Analysis; Quantitative Geomorphology; Stream Orders; Youth—Maturity—Old Age.* Vol. VI: *Crossbedding; Statistical Analysis.*

Fig. 1. Gibber on pedimented surface in the northwest of New South Wales.

GEOMORPHOLOGY—STEADY STATE PROCESSES—*See* EQUILIBRIUM IN GEOMORPHOLOGY

GIBBER

Gibber is the term applied in Australia to arid or semiarid country which is abundantly littered with loose rock fragments or with pebbles. The litter itself is called *gibber* or *gibber gravel.* Gibbers constitute a subclass of stony desert, which also includes expanses of bouldery *duricrust* (q.v.) in which particles range above 3 feet (1 meter) in width.

Classification and Field Characteristics

No complete classification is yet available, but two types of gibber are widely represented in the great total extent of gibber country:

(a) Quartz gibber, which results from the breakdown of conglomerate containing quartz pebbles, and which mantles pediments cut below the level of the conglomerate beds.

(b) Silcrete gibber, which results from the breakdown of silcretic duricrust, and which mantles pediments cut below the level of residuals representative of a formerly extensive duricrusted surface.

(c) Gibber of some other provenance may occur, but has been little studied; it seems likely to be restricted in account, by reason of the widespread silcretic duricrusting of the Australian inland.

(d) Quartz gibber varies in component size with the dimensions of quartz pebbles in the parent conglomerate; so far as is known, it is rarely more than one pebble deep, and seems rarely to provide a complete surface cover.

(e) Silcrete gibber (Fig. 1) varies in spacing from a complete cover to a cover with gaps amounting to 50% or more of the total area; downslope, it degenerates into sparsely arrayed small fragments. Contrary to some reports, it can be much more than one particle deep, for many gibbers incorporate a noticeable proportion of fine-grained material in which some particles are buried; these fines (see *Parna*) have probably been blown in. Heaving of the fines on account of wetting and drying can produce distinctive patterns among the surface stones (cf. periglacial *"patterned ground"*, q.v.).

Current research indicates that silcrete gibbers, derived from the edges of residual hills or scarps with silcrete cappings, diminish in size downslope in an orderly fashion. Processes of diminution involve the debate about mechanical as opposed to chemical weathering: since this material is chemically rather inert, it would seem unlikely to respond to soil solution. Whatever the cause of diminution, however, reduction seems unlikely to bring the fragments below the sand grade.

GEORGE H. DURY

References

Jessup, R. W., 1960, "An introduction to the soils of the south-eastern portion of the arid zone," *J. Soil. Sci.,* **11,** 92–105.

Mabbutt, J. A., 1965, "Stone distribution in a stony tableland soil," *Australian J. Soil Res.,* **3,** 131–142.

Ollier, C. D., 1961, "Lag deposits at Coober Pedy, South Australia," *Australian J. Sci.,* **24,** 84–85.

Ollier, C. D., 1963, "Insolation weathering: examples from Central Australia," *Am. J. Sci.,* **261,** 376–381.

Cross-reference: *Duricrust; Hamada; Parna; Patterned Ground; Weathering.* Vol. VI: *Silcrete.*

GILGAI

Gilgai is an Australian aboriginal name which has now come into international use for certain types of microrelief in areas with alternate wet and dry seasons. The microrelief consists of undulations which, in cross section, can be divided into two or three distinct parts (Fig. 1). The *channel* consists of a depression which may lie up to eight feet (250 cm) below the general ground level. The general level of the microrelief is called the *shelf*, while any upraised portions are called *puffs* (see Langford-Smith, in Stamp, 1961). The latter are not always present, and this has sometimes resulted in misnaming of the parts.

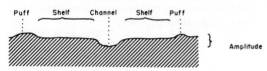

FIG. 1. Cross section of gilgai microrelief showing the names given to the constituent parts.

Looked at from above, the microrelief takes the form of one of several patterns (Fig. 2). First there are the channels in the form of circular depressions in otherwise level areas of shelf. These are called *round gilgai*. Width of the channel varies from 15–150 feet (5–50 meters) with a spacing of 50–300 feet (15–100 meters). These occur where the slope is less than 30 seconds. A variant is the *mushroom gilgai* with an upraised circular puff on an otherwise level shelf.

The second type of gilgai is the *lattice gilgai*. Here there are two distinct forms. In type A the channel is continuous and the shelf is discontinuous but arranged in rows parallel to the direction of greatest slope. Each shelf may be 15 feet long and 6 feet wide (4½ × 2 meters). In type B, the channels are discontinuous but occur in rows parallel to the direction of slope. The individual channels are 4–8 feet (120–240 cm) in diameter. This form is sometimes called the network type (Hallsworth *et al.*, 1955). These occur where the slope is slightly greater than in the case of the round gilgai.

The *wavy gilgai* are restricted to land sloping at between 15 minutes and 3°. The puffs and shelves (or shelves and channels) are continuous but are arranged in regular lines more or less at right angles to the contours. They form parallel waves differing in height by up to nine inches and extending for long distances.

The *depression gilgai* are found in inland drainage basins with very gentle slopes. These take four different forms depending on the slope of the basins (Fig. 3). All four forms consist of combinations

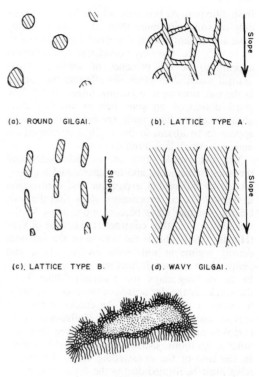

(a). ROUND GILGAI.

(b). LATTICE TYPE A.

(c). LATTICE TYPE B.

(d). WAVY GILGAI.

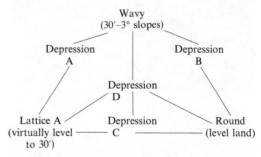

(e) DEPRESSION
TYPE D.

FIG. 2. Main types of gilgai modified from Hallsworth *et. al.* (1955) and Harris (1959). In cases (a)–(d), the channel is cross-hatched, while in case (e), it is shown in black.

of two or more of the previously mentioned groups.

Several modifications of these basic types have been described, e.g., the tank gilgai which are a giant form, and stony gilgai formed on stony parent material.

Gilgai are found in all areas of Vertisols (the black swelling clay soils) throughout the tropics and sub-tropical zones and may also occur on Chernozems, Sierozems, Meadow Soils and on

Wavy
(30'–3° slopes)

Depression
A

Depression
B

Depression
D

Lattice A
(virtually level
to 30')

Depression
C

Round
(level land)

FIG. 3. Relationship between wavy, round and lattice A gilgai and the various depression gilgai (after Harris, 1959, p. 30).

fresh alluvium. At first they were believed to occur only on soils with more than 30% clay, but they have subsequently been described from soils with up to 96% silt. The only non-climatic requirement appears to be the presence of sufficient finer-grained material to block the effective pore space in the soil, causing it to become impermeable. The gilgai developed on soils rich in swelling clays always seem to have puffs present, whereas puffs appear to be absent in those gilgai developed on materials which lack swelling clays.

The soil profile often shows slickensides and thrusting movements, and the microrelief is clearly related to differential expansion and contraction in the soil. Recent experiments show that the soils lacking swelling clays become more dense in the wet season; i.e., they contract at this time of year (Harris, 1964). This is the reverse of the seasonal density regime in soils with swelling clays, and clearly there are two distinct mechanisms involved. In the swelling clays, the materials falling down the cracks in the dry season cause excess material to occur at the bottom of the cracks in the wet season, and this is believed by Hallsworth *et al.* (1955) to cause the microrelief. However, there are other suggestions, usually not thoroughly tested. In the case of the nonswelling clays, the micro-relief must be formed during the drying-out phase at the onset of the dry season (see Harris, 1964).

Fig. 4. Gilgai country near Gregory Downs, Queensland, Australia. (Oblique air photo: F. W. Whitehouse)

The importance of gilgai lies in the fact that they cover large areas of otherwise fertile soils in semiarid regions where the slope is sufficiently gentle to make irrigation possible. The microrelief makes it possible to grow crops on only a limited percentage of the land, while it also wastes irrigation water in filling up the channels. It is usually associated with a soil structure which makes crop growth difficult. If the microrelief is leveled out by machinery, it is formed again at the same sites in as little as three years. The thrusting movements within the soil cause fence posts to tilt at sharp angles within a year or so of being erected on the land. Thus, these otherwise potentially fertile soils must be left under pasture.

In French literature the term *mottureaux* is favored as the equivalent of gilgai (Verger, 1964), and in German the corresponding term seems to be *Musterböden* (Bremer, 1965).

STUART A. HARRIS

References

Bremer, H., 1965, "Musterböden in tropisch-subtropischen Gebieten und Frostmusterböden," *Zeit. f. Geomorph.*, **9**, 222–236.

*Hallsworth, E. G., Robertson, G. K., and Gibbons, F. R., 1955, "Studies in pedogenesis in New South Wales. VII. The 'gilgai' soils," *J. Soil Sci.*, **6**, 1–34.

Harris, S. A., 1958, "The gilgaied and bad-structured soils of Central Iraq," *J. Soil Sci.*, **9**, 169–185.

*Harris, S. A., 1959, "The classification of gilgaied soils; some evidence from Northern Iraq," *J. Soil Sci.*, **10**, 27–33.

Harris, S. A., 1964, "Seasonal density changes in the alluvial soils of Northern Iraq," *Trans. Intern. Congr. Soil Sci. 8th, Bucarest*, Commission I, 41.

Stamp, L. D., 1961, "A Glossary of Geographical Terms," London, Longmans, 539pp.

Verger, F., 1964, "Mottureaux et Gilgais," *Ann. Geogr.*, **398**, 413–430.

* Additional bibliographic references may be found in this work.

Cross-references: *Alluvium; Drainage Basin; Patterned Ground; Slopes.* pr Vol. VI: *Soils.*

GIPFELFLUR

The expression Gipfelflur (German peak, plus floor or level) was first used in the Alps (see analysis by Albrecht Penck, 1919) to embrace the idea of an accordance of summit levels, often observed in mountain terrains. In English, it is sometimes rendered as "peak-plain," "summit-plain," or "accordance of summit levels," but normally the German term is used (Stamp, 1961).

Penck pointed out that the glacial modeling of a mountain range such as the Alps was not adequate to destroy traces of the gipfelflur, which evidently represented relics of a preexisting (Pliocene) erosion system. He believed that the development of equally spaced valleys would lead to an

Fig. 1. Gipfelflur in the eastern Alps of Austria, from the Hohe Tauern (elevation 3500–3800 meters).

accordance of summit heights between them. Uniform lithology and structure over a broad area would certainly favor such a process, but these are not to be found in the Alps. Richter suggested that accordance of snow levels and timberlines might bring the necessary uniformity, but great variations of these occur, especially seen in the light of Pleistocene oscillations (Baulig, 1952).

Walter Penck (1955) has discussed the question further. The gipfelflur is essentially independent of the ancient folded structures of the mountain and even of the lithology (weathering resistance). However, it is claimed that it is not the warped heritage of an originally nearly flat peneplain, but "shows a notable connection with the distribution of slope form" (Penck, 1955, p. 231), and "one can only fitly speak of a gipfelflur when the mountain masses have been broken up into peaks and sharp edges, and when slopes of maximum gradient meet in such edges" (Penck, 1955, p. 264).

On the other hand the Alpine valley systems are certainly polyphasic, and the summit levels suggest rather "the remnants of a number of local and sometimes imperfect planations, and not one broad surface still in process of being lowered.... The crests... are the intersections of slopes now fossilised..." (Sparks, 1960, p. 339). There is no doubt that the summit accordance of the gipfelflur is *composite*, as shown already by Daly (1905). In other words, a gipfelflur does not prove a former peneplain, but it does reflect an integration of former base levels, which is today broadly upwarped.

In the case of the Alps, that upwarping evidently occurred largely during late Pliocene and Pleistocene times: a maximum uplift of about 5000 meters in perhaps 5×10^6 years, or of the order of 1 mm/yr. A similar accordance of peaks in the Himalayas and a similar record of uplift would give an uplift rate of double this figure. Geodetic leveling, repeated every few decades, shows that vertical (and horizontal) motions are still in progress today.

Accordance of summit levels as seen in the maturely denuded Appalachians is a milder equivalent of the Alpine gipfelflur. Davis (1899; see reprint 1909, p. 353) firmly attached to them the peneplain correlation, but here too the rigid concept of peneplain may be replaced by the concept of slope erosion converging to a common base level. The topographic distinction in a mature humid landscape is probably rather slight.

Rhodes W. Fairbridge

References

Baulig, H., 1952, "Surfaces d'aplanissement," *Ann. Géogr.*, **61**, 161–183, 245–262.

Daly, R. A., 1905, "The accordance of summit levels among the Alpine mountains: The fact and its significance," *J. Geol.*, **13**, 105–125.

Davis, W. M., 1909, "Geographical Essays," New York, Ginn (also Dover reprint, 1954).

Penck, A., 1919, "Die Gipfelflur der Alpen," *Sitzber. Preuss. Akad. Wiss.* (*Berlin*), **17,** 256.

Penck, W., 1955, "Morphological Analysis of Land Forms," London, Macmillan (translated from German by H. Czech and K. C. Boswell), 429pp.

Sparks, B. W., 1960, "Geomorphology," London, Longmans, Green & Co., 371pp.

Stamp, L. D., 1961, "A Glossary of Geographical Terms," London, Longmans, Green & Co., 539pp.

Thompson, W. R., 1962, "Cascade alp slopes and gipfelfluren as clima-geomorphic phenomena," *Erdkunde*, **16**(2), 81–94 (with German abs.).

Cross-references: *Base Level*; *Crustal Movements— Contemporary*; *Peneplain*; *Slopes*; *Treppen Concept (Penck)*; *Warping*; *Weathering*.

Appendix

Dr. Therese Pippan of Salzburg has been kind enough to prepare the following notes on some characteristics of the Gipfelflur in the Eastern Alps and the views of some authors who have done research in this area, with the corresponding references.

The Alpine Gipfelflur generally is a slightly rolling arched surface, sloping down from the center of the mountains toward the margins. For the most part, the summits rise above rather broad old surfaces which provide the local base level. Many German and Austrian authors presume the initial form of the Gipfelflur to have been of flat relief which, according to Winkler v. Hermaden (1957), is of late Miocene age. A. Penck (1919) and Heim (1927) held the view that the Gipfelflur is the effect of an upper denudation level resulting from the balance of strong uplift and denudation. The ridges and summits cannot reach above this upper denudation level. According to Krebs (1928), the height of the base level and the intensity of dissection by rivers are important for the development of the Gipfelflur. According to Leyden (1921), Krebs (1928), Machatschek (1959) and Aigner (1925), the Gipfelflur, however, does show some available relief. According to Machatschek (1959), these regional differences of its level, insofar as they cannot be explained by petrographic and orographic factors, are due to a different degree of uplift of the mountains caused by warping on a large scale; this is a very important fact. Sölch (1922), von Klebelsberg (1935) and Leutelt (1929) associate the Gipfelflur with the terraced structure of the Alps. According to Richter (1928), Gipfelfluren of different ages are arranged in a stair-like manner, forming the *Gipfelflurtreppe* whose steps correspond to the several storeys (terrace levels) of the mountains which developed by intermittent uplift (Fig. 1). Machatschek (1959) has pointed out quite correctly that the Gipfelflur cannot be independent of lithological control. With soft beds, it will be located at a lower level provided that the same conditions prevail for the rest.

References

Aigner, A., 1925–1926, "Die geomorphologischen Probleme am Ostrand der Alpen," *Z. Geomorphol.* **1**, 29–44.

Heim, A., 1927, "Die Gipfelflur der Alpen," *Neujahrsblatt der Naturforschenden Gesellschaft, Zürich.*

Klebelsberg, R. von, 1935, "Geologie von Tirol," Berlin, Borntraeger, 872pp.

Krebs, N., 1928, "Die Ostalpen und das heutige Osterreich," Stuttgart, J. Engelhorns, 2 vols.

Leutelt, R., 1929, "Die Gipfelflur der Alpen," *Geol. Rundschau*, **20**, 330–337.

Leyden, F., 1921, "Die Gipfelflur der westlichen Hochalpen," *Pet. Mitt. Gotha.*

Machatschek, F., 1959, "Geomorphologie" (7th ed.), Stuttgart, Teubner, 219pp.

Richter, M., 1928, "Zum Problem der alpinen Gipfelflur," *Z. Geomorphol.*, **4**, 149–160.

Sölch, J., 1922, "Grundragen der Landformung in den nordöstlichen Alpen," *Geograf. Ann.*, **4**, 147–193.

Winkler von Hermaden, A., 1957, "Geologisches Kräftespiel und Landformung," Wien.

GLACIAL BREACHING

Glacial breaches, eroded in preglacial divides by ice, cause the postglacial pattern of drainage to differ from the preglacial pattern and to contain apparent anomalies which cannot be explained by stream capture. Modern ideas on glacial breaching date back to the nineteenth century and were systematized in the early 1900's (see references in Linton, 1949, to Suess, A. Penck, Davis, and others). Interest in breaching was revived by Linton (1949 and later papers), who, followed by

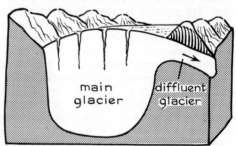

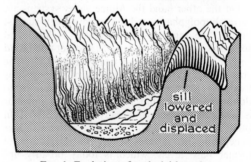

FIG. 1. Evolution of a glacial breach.

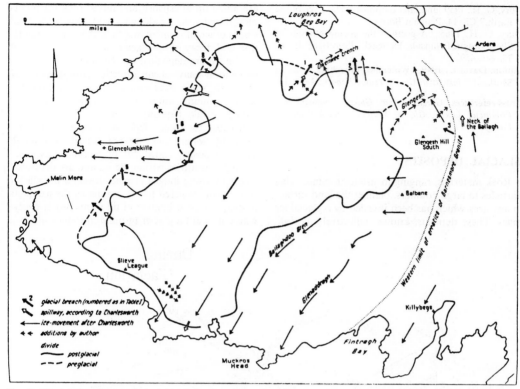

FIG. 2. Glacial directions and glacial breaches in relation to main watershed at Slieve League, Ireland (Dury, 1965).

Dury (1955, 1965, and references therein), took up the study of British cases.

Classification and Field Characteristics

(a) Breaches made by *diffluent ice* (Fig. 1) occur where distributaries branch off from trunk glaciers, passing through lateral cols and lowering and displacing the sills of these. Displacement of a sill is usually minor and normally in the opposite direction to ice movement. The course of this movement is commonly indicated by rock knobs, scoured on the up-ice side and plucked on the down-ice side. The postglacial divide within the sill lies off the line of crests on either side; it is frequently indeterminate, consisting of alluvial fans or patches of swamp.

(b) Breaches made by *transfluent ice* occur where a preglacial divide is either overridden completely by ice, or where powerful ice streams cross it. The ice may come from a continental cap (as on the margins of Greenland), a local cap (e.g., in Scotland, northwest Ireland), or from an accumulation in a valley basin with constricted outlet (e.g., North Wales). If the divide is completely overridden, breaching is effected by basal ice.

Breaches by transfluent ice also frequently contain, or are associated with, rock knobs which indicate the direction of ice movement into and through them. Some contain lakes, particularly where the walls of the gap are cut in strong rock and where the floor is weakened, e.g., by diking, faulting, or shattering; lines of structural weakness are precisely those likely to have been severely eroded by preglacial streams and to have been marked by deep cols in the high ground. Even so, some gaps have proved unable to accommodate the discharge of ice wholly, or even mainly, by excavation of their floors, and scour of the sides has in places amounted to the shearing-off of whole mountainsides.

Many of the breaches made by transfluent ice involve considerable rearrangement of the drainage pattern, with postglacial divides ill-marked at the heads of diverted streams and bearing very little relationship to the main array of relief. The radial drainage of the Snowdon area of North Wales, and the partly radial drainage of the Slieve League Peninsula of Northwest Ireland (Fig. 2), have replaced preglacial centripetal drainage on account of multiple glacial piercings of their mountainous rims.

G. H. DURY

References

Dury, G. H., 1955, "Diversion of drainage by ice," *Science News*, **38**, 48–71.

Dury, G. H., 1959 (and later editions), "The Face of the Earth," Ch. 14, Penguin Books.

Dury, G. H., 1965, "Aspects of the geomorphology of Slieve League Peninsula, Donegal," *Proc. Geol. Assoc.*, **75**, 445–459.

Linton, David L., 1949, "Watershed breaching by ice in Scotland," *Inst. Brit. Geog., Trans. Papers*, **15**, 1–16.

Cross-references: *Glacial Scour*; *Glacial Spillways and Proglacial Lakes*; *Glacial Valley*; *Stream Capture, Piracy*.

GLACIAL DEPOSITS

Rock materials, ranging in size from minute clay particles to large boulders, blanket the land surface in any area which has been invaded by a glacial ice mass. These deposits, known collectively as *drift*, are made up of crushed and mixed rock fragments picked up by the ice along its path. During the final stages of ice movement and especially upon stagnation and decay of the glacier, the sediments carried by the ice are deposited on the land surface. Final deposition may occur directly from the ice or indirectly when sediments are picked up from the ice by running water and are deposited later as stream or lake deposits.

Because the direct deposits of ice are not acted upon by water, they are not sorted or layered. These deposits, called *till* or *moraine* (q.v.), are carried beneath or within the ice and are deposited either by being lodged in place beneath the glacier or by being lowered to the ground as the ice melts or evaporates. A blanket of till forms nearly everywhere beneath a glacier (ground moraine) and as a

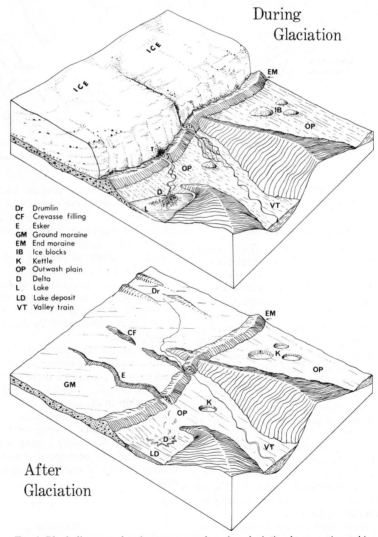

Dr Drumlin
CF Crevasse filling
E   Esker
GM Ground moraine
EM End moraine
IB Ice blocks
K   Kettle
OP Outwash plain
D   Delta
L   Lake
LD Lake deposit
VT Valley train

Fɪɢ. 1. Block diagrams showing an area undergoing glaciation by a continental ice sheet and the resulting topography and deposits after the ice has melted away.

thickened rim around the glacier's margin (end moraine). The thickness of this till blanket decreases progressively as one moves farther back from the edge of the ice. Till is deposited both when the glacier is actively moving and after it has stopped and has stagnated. Unusual till formations created while the ice is moving are elliptical, streamlined hills known as *drumlins* (q.v.).

Glacial sediments not laid down directly from the ice are deposited indirectly from meltwaters. Such sediments are known as *fluvioglacial deposits*. Meltwater streams flow over, under, and adjacent to the ice mass following a course which will eventually lead them away from the glacier. The channels of these streams are filled by deposition of some of the sediments which are being carried. Water activity is concentrated in front of the ice sheet, and deposition in this area builds a broad fill of sediments known as an *outwash plain*. Valleys leading away from the front of a glacier likewise receive a fill of sediments which may extend for miles down the valley; this type of outwash fill is called a *valley train*. Streams moving away from the ice may carry glacial sediments for hundreds of miles before depositing them, the finest-size material being carried the farthest.

Fluvioglacial deposits formed by streams flowing adjacent to or on the glacier are called *ice-contact deposits*. These deposits show characteristics typical of stream deposits, but because ice melting may change the course and character of the stream, sediment size and direction of deposition may shift frequently. Collapse of supporting walls of ice may cause distortion of previously formed bedding. Clay and silt pockets are included in the sediments when ponding or sluggishness occurs in stream movement.

Ice-contact deposits are classified on the basis of their topographic expression. Since the deposits were formed in stream channels artificially elevated above the land surface by the confining ice, they rise above the general land surface after the ice melts, forming mounds or ridges measuring tens of feet up to 100 or more feet in height. A single mound is known as a *kame* (q.v.); the terms *kame group*, *kame field*, or *kame complex* refer to coalescing swarms of kames. Undrained depressions known as *kettles* are abundant between kames in some areas and, where well developed, form an irregular surface topography called *kame and kettle topography*.

Kames in the form of a ridge testify to stream flow within a channel restricted on both sides by ice walls. Where these walls are straight, as in a crevasse, a straight ridge called a *crevasse filling* forms. Winding ridges of gravel are called *eskers* (q.v.). These may trend across the countryside for miles and may be continuous or in detached segments.

The deposits left behind by a glacier are the record of the glacier's invasion. Areas invaded by ice on more than one occasion may contain sequences of deposits of differing character which may be deciphered to allow the glacial history of a region to be reconstructed. The study of multiple drift layers has revealed a complex history of repeated glaciations in Canada and northern United States, in Europe north of central Germany and in the Alps, in northern and in high parts of eastern Russia, in the high mountains of western China and Mongolia, in the Andes Mountains of South America and in New Zealand.

VINCENT C. SHEPPS

References

Flint, R. F., 1928, "Eskers and crevasse fillings," *Am. J. Sci., Ser. 5*, **15**, 410–416.

Flint, R. F., 1957, "Glacial and Pleistocene Geology," New York, John Wiley & Sons, 533pp.

Gravenor, C. P. 1953, "The origin of drumlins," *Am. J. Sci.*, **25**, 674–681.

Holmes, C. D., 1952, "Kames," *Am. J. Sci.*, **245**, 240–249.

Thornbury, W. D., 1957, "Principles of Geomorphology," New York, John Wiley & Sons, 618pp.

Cross-references: *Crevasse*; *Delta*; *Drift, Glacial*; *Drumlin*; *Erratic Block*; *Esker*; *Fluvioglacial Processes*; *Kame*; *Kettle*; *Lakes*; *Moraine*; *Outwash Plain*; *Terraces, Fluvial*. Vol. VI: *Ice Sheet*; *Till, Tillite*.

GLACIAL GEOLOGY: INTRODUCTION

Glacial Geology is that branch of geology (study of the earth) which deals with erosion and deposition by glaciers. Inasmuch as glaciers are very slowly creeping streams of massive ice (see *Glaciology*, pr Vol. VI) these records are all made at the earth's surface. Most of the effects change the landscape: (1) by the sandpapering (*abrasion*, q.v.) and *plucking action* of the moving ice which reshapes the land (rock and soil) over which it passes and (2) by the *transportation* and *deposition* of the eroded materials which tend to fill old valleys, or coat hills and plains, or are dumped as hummocks and ridges. Much of the deposition is from the moving ice itself, further quantities by meltwater, and some of it is carried by wind systems associated with the presence of the ice.

Most of the principles of glacial geology have been worked out from studies of the earth's surface records of the last "ice age," which is called the Pleistocene Epoch of the Quaternary Period. Four times and more during this two to three million year epoch, glaciers the world over expanded and retracted from less than 10% of the land which they now cover until they covered about 30% of all land areas of the globe (Figs. 1 and 2). The redistributed debris is still largely preserved over the surface to-

KEY

Existing Glaciers

Areas covered by ice during the Ice Age

FIG. 1. Map of North America indicating the contrast between existing glaciers (mainly in Greenland, Canadian Arctic and Alaska), and the area glaciated during the Pleistocene.

day. Thus *Pleistocene geology* and *glacial geology* are concerned with many of the same things, the emphasis in the first case being sequential or historical (when did it happen?), and in the second, the nature and dynamics of the event (what happened and why?). Much of the Quaternary record of changing climate is worked out from non-glacial or near-glacial ("periglacial") deposits like frost-patterned soils, buried layers of fossil plants, fossil shells, pollen and spores, although these are not always critical to glacial geology as such.

There is a third question: *How* did it happen? Perhaps the best way to learn how a glacier does

things is to observe one in action. For this reason, another overlapping subject is *glaciology* (see pr Vol. VI). This deals with living glaciers only. It approaches them from the climatic and energy (physical) point of view. Glaciology also embraces the study of sea ice (see Vol. I, "Oceanography") and other kinds of ice not directly critical to a glacial geologist. The land actually covered by a glacier today is said to be "glacierized," and a region affected in the past is said to be "glaciated."

Not all of the evidence of glacial geology is now found on the earth's outer surface. Ancient glacial deposits, now often lithified into rock (*tillite*), may

FIG. 2. A typical continental ice sheet near the coast of northwest Greenland, south of Petermann Glacier Outlet. Glaciers form tongues that debouch from the inland ice sheet into the floe ice of Bessels Fjord. Note the *faceted spurs* along the fjord walls and the ogives (crescents) and intersecting crevasses in the glacier.

be buried as layers within the earth's crust. Most ancient deposits of the common small mountain glaciers must now be lost forever because mountains themselves are vigorously eroded. Nevertheless, several earlier general "ice ages" of widespread continental ice sheets are now preserved, being tilted or raised and eroded in places. The earliest generally recognized ice age was about one billion years ago (Middle Precambrian or lower Huronian time). Then, about the turn of the Late Precambrian/Cambrian there was the so-called Eocambrian ice age. In parts of South America and Africa, extensive Silurian and Devonian continental ice was present. One ice age at least (in Permo-Carboniferous time) was more extensive than the last ice age for it affected

over 50% of the land area of 260 million years ago. Curiously enough, it was largely limited to what is now the southern hemisphere. This, too, is glacial geology for it is a record of glaciers. It should be made clear, however, that glacial epochs have been relatively rare during the geological past, and most of geologic time was marked by mild climates (see *Glaciation* in this volume and *Paleoclimatology*, in Vol. II, and items treated under *Stratigraphy* in pr Vol. VII). The term "glacial geology" as commonly used applies mainly to Quaternary studies, the more complete record of which permits the application of *dynamic geomorphology* (q.v.).

The principal fields of study in glacial geology are mainly treated independently in this Encyclopedia,

433

Fig. 3. *Cirques* and *glacial troughs* in the process of formation by *mountain glaciers* on the north slopes of Chugach Range in Alaska. Between the valleys, the steep avalanche-infested slopes meet back to back, forming jagged ridges called *arêtes*. The high triangular peaks are *horns* on the crest of this *serrate topography*.

but it is desirable to draw these scattered threads together in some degree of integration. We may summarize them briefly as follows:

Glacial Erosion

Small Features. The efficiency of glaciers as instruments of erosion has long been recognized. Wherever glaciers slide at the base, they begin immediately to modify the area that they occupy. Glacial erosion is achieved by *abrasion* (q.v.), erosion caused by the raising (accumulation) of soil and rock debris which becomes lodged in the base of the glacier and is dragged along beneath it. In addition, glaciers modify the landscape by lifting out and carrying away blocks of bedrock which have been loosened by expansion after former deep confinement aided by freezing of basal water in joint fractures. This latter erosive process is known as *glacial quarrying* or *plucking*.

As a solid glacier creeps forward over the landscape, the mutual abrasion between bedrock and the debris in the base of the ice imparts a smooth *polish* to much of the rock surface over which the ice slips. This polish may be very glossy just after glaciation or where protected by cover, if it is produced by very finely powdered rock debris called *rock flour*.

The abrasive sliding of larger rock particles under a moving glacier also produces numerous straight,

subparallel scratches, or *striations*, on both the bedrock pavement and on the abrading fragments carried by the ice. Each mark is engraved by a single sharp grain or corner of quartz or other tough mineral. More persistent or extensive local abrasion wears irregularities and softer areas into *grooves*, 1 cm to 1 meter wide, in the bedrock paralleling the direction of glacier flow, and containing numerous striations themselves, they are the work of hundreds of etching tools. Many of the fragments embedded in the base of the glacier display, in addition to striations, one or more flattened or smoothed faces called *facets*. Boulders shaped in this manner are known as *faceted boulders* and sometimes occur within glacial soils. They may form a residual on one formerly eroded soil horizon called a *boulder pavement*. Where the pressure of the glacier ice is great or the abrading fragments are large, half-moon shaped markings are sometimes produced on the bedrock. These markings are variously called *crescentic gouges, crescentic fractures, lunate fractures* and *chatter marks* (Flint, 1957), depending upon their size, shape and orientation with respect to the direction of ice movement (see *Chatter Marks*).

Large Features. On a larger scale, glacial erosion produces a variety of streamlined forms. Most common among these are rounded, asymmetric bed-

F IG. 4. Ancient *cirques* and *glacial troughs* on the east side of the Presidential Range in the White Mountains, New Hampshire. On the left is Tuckermans Ravine; on the right, Huntingtons Ravine. Above is Mt. Washington which has been rounded by the last continental glacier. In a Pleistocene glaciation before the very last one, mountain glaciers like those of Fig. 1 began to cut back into this upland surface. Much of this rolling Presidential Upland remains, however, as this is *biscuit-board topography*, as described by Hobbs, 1911.

rock knobs called *roches moutonnées* (q.v.). These small glaciated knobs generally display a gently sloping, striated and polished upstream (stoss) slope and an oversteepened lee slope which has been quarried by the overriding ice. Sometimes knobs of resistant bedrock with smoothed and sharply pointed stoss slopes have elongate ridges of glacial debris (till) or more easily erodible bedrock, or both, trailing from their lee sides. They may be from a centimeter to a kilometer long. This combination is known as *crag and tail* (q.v.), an old Scottish term.

Rock drumlins are related to crag-and-tail forms but they are generally more elliptical in shape (like the inverted bowl of a spoon), up to 5 km long, and they consist almost entirely of bedrock with only a thin veneer of glacial soil.

Continental glaciers, by definition, override the hills and low mountains in the glacierized area. They round the hills, especially the low ones, leaving a subdued topography. Low cliffs predominate on the downglacier or lee direction. As with precursor rivers, they erode most deeply in fractured, weak, soft, or already rotted bedrock. The result differs from rivers, however, in producing rather smooth, broad *glacial basins* like the Great Lakes, depres-

sions scooped 10–1000 meters deep and extending below sea level. Many glacial lake basins are very irregular in map outline, but elongation may be either along bedrock structures or in the direction of ice motion. Where the ice sheet passed over an escarpment, it left extra-deep *finger lakes,* canoe shaped and located in the former river valleys where solid ice streamed ten or a hundred times as fast (see *Finger Lakes*).

The ability of glaciers to modify profoundly the landscape is nowhere more strikingly visible than in areas of mountain glaciation. Highland areas which have been subjected to the rigors of glaciation display unique topographic features such as the spectacular glacial *cirque* (q.v.). This is a steep-walled, amphitheater-shaped hollow at the head of a glaciated valley. The floor of a cirque is basin shaped and rises at the downvalley margin to a bedrock lip called the *threshold*. During the period of maximum glaciation, a cirque is nearly filled with ice which spills over the threshold as a glacier down the valley (Figs. 3 and 4). Many cirques today are occupied by small remnants of formerly more extensive glaciers or renewed small glaciers known as *cirque glaciers* (q.v.). In the absence of glacier ice, cirque basins are

FIG. 5. Idealized sketch of a mountain glacier leaving successive moraine loops and lateral moraines as it melts back. In the Sierra Nevada where the glaciers carried relatively little rock debris, many of the moraines are of the sharp-crested, clean-cut type here portrayed (Matthes, 1930).

often occupied by small lakes called *tarns* (q.v.) and tend to fill rapidly with *talus* (q.v.) from the surrounding cliffs. Below the cirque threshold, there is generally an abrupt drop to the floor of the *glacial trough* or U-shaped *glacial valley* (q.v.). Typically glaciated valleys are rather straighter than the preglacial stream valleys which the glacier occupied. Projecting spurs of the original stream valleys have been planed away by the abrasive action of the ice to produce truncated spurs (Lobeck, 1939). The floor of the glacial trough is generally very unevenly eroded and is commonly marked by a series of *glacial steps*. The relatively flat areas (treads) between successive steps have sometimes been scoured by the glacier to form *rock basins*. Where a series of such lakes is strung out down a glacial valley, they are known as *paternoster lakes*. Tributary valleys joining a major glacial trough, unlike stream valleys, are quite commonly discordant, i.e., the floors of the tributary valleys "hang" above the floor of the main valley; the bigger the stream of ice, the greater is its flow and the deeper its abrasion. Such discordant tributary valleys are appropriately named *hanging valleys* (q.v.) and may be the sites of spectacular waterfalls.

Peculiar to coastal regions which have been strongly glaciated are deep glacial troughs which reach the coast below present sea level. These are called *fjords* (*fiords,* q.v.) and are characterized by the steepness of their walls and the great depth of their floors. The seaward entrance of fjords is generally restricted by a shallow bedrock threshold, like that of a glacial cirque. All true fjords are in mountainous areas. Those fjords of southeast Alaska, Chile, Norway and New Zealand were produced by greatly enlarged mountain glaciers. On the other hand, those in Antarctica, Greenland, Baffin Island and some in British Columbia, were *outlet glaciers*

or *ice tongue glaciers* from a continental ice sheet streaming through very high mountains. The fjords in Antarctica are still glacierized today.

Many of the features which typify glaciated mountain regions are those produced by *frost action* (q.v.) and rockfall in the high summit areas. Incomplete or initial erosion in cirques may leave gently rolling portions of the proglacial upland surface called *biscuit-board topography* (Hobbs, 1911). These are covered with patterned soils due to *permafrost* (q.v.). As cirques develop and grow from opposite sides of a divide at the expense of the area of uplands, all that is left is a pinnacled ridge called an *arête*. The principal erosion above the glaciers on oversteepened slopes results from the loosening of blocks and snow masses by temperature changes or by expansion and contraction by freezing and thawing, plus the general instability due to gravity. The rockfalls, *snow avalanches* (q.v.) and debris avalanches wear the exposed slope back in craggy notched cliffs. Where headward cirque erosion continues actively, two cirques may join from *headwalls* from opposing sides of a divide to produce a sharp-edged gap known as a *col* (Flint, 1957). The peaks all become sharp pointed *horns* (q.v.), pyramidal in shape, and very steep-sided; they have formed where three or more cirques have carved into a local high portion of the summit region. This is the more common *serrated topography* (Lobeck, 1939).

Glacial Deposits

Nonlayered and Unsorted Deposits. The material carried by and deposited from glaciers and the streams associated with them has been called *glacial drift* [the term "drift" refers to the old idea of drifting ice floes, long since abandoned (see *Drift, Glacial*)]. Deposits of glacial drift were early recognized to be of two distinct varieties: *unstratified drift*, deposited directly by the ice, and *stratified drift*, deposited by the waters associated with the ice (see below). Although called unstratified at most places, there are several distinct layers of drift due to repeated advances of a glacier front. Between these two end members there is a complete gradation of deposits and indeed most unstratified "hardpan" contains small pockets and lenses of stratified sand. Unstratified drift, or *till*, consists largely of a uniform mixture of sand with liberal mixtures of fines (silts and clay, 5–50%) and modest quantities (commonly under 10%) of coarse stones and boulders. The term "*boulder clay*" is often used in Britain for till in which a stiff, clayey matrix (10–30% clay) is predominant.

Most till contains boulders and stones which differ in character from the bedrock upon which the till has been deposited; these "different" fragments are called *erratics* or *erratic blocks* (q.v.). They may even rest all alone on an open glaciated ledge and in precarious "perched" positions (see *Perched Block, Boulder*). If the place of origin of an erratic is known,

Fig. 6. *Kame* hummocks and *esker* ridges (as points and islands) in Pine River Pond at East Wakefield, New Hampshire. *Continental glaciers* scooped *glacial basins* in these weak rock zones in old valleys and the *ice contact* deposits of decaying ice further blocked this area to form a lake.

the erratics are called *indicator boulders*. Groups of erratics having a fanlike distribution from their source are called *boulder trains*.

Ninety per cent of the particles in till may originate no more than 1–10 km from known source areas. This means that for all the scratching and thorough mixing, much of the till has traveled only a few kilometers. There are famous exceptions in the coarse sizes; larger and larger erratics, a few pebbles and, in some places, most of the boulders may be indicators from 100–1000 km away. As a glacier advances into the zone of wastage beyond the zone of active erosion, it may become heavily burdened with debris which is deposited ever more rapidly; the outer 300 km of travel by continental ice in North America or Europe left an average till sheet 10–20 meters thick, whereas ice source areas in the Canadian or Finnish "barrens" have glacial drift that is usually less than 3–5 meters thick.

The resultant accumulations of drift directly from the glacier ice often have distinct constructional topographic forms and are collectively referred to as

moraine (from the French). Two classes of moraine can be distinguished: *ground moraine* and *end moraine*. *Ground moraine* is deposited as a thin sheet of drift over the landscape; it lacks a conspicuous or systematic ridgelike form and is generally of low relief (Flint, 1957). It may consist largely of basal till (sometimes called *lodgment till*), which is deposited from the base of the glacier. Recent studies and theory show that much of this is due to the melting of basal ice as it flows, for the pebbles are oriented with their long axes parallel to the glacier motion (*till fabric*). Some upper material may be *ablation till*, which is let down from within or upon the terminal area of a glacier during the final stages of downwasting. *Till plains* are formed as the result of regional deposition by continental glaciers of ground moraine on a flat bedrock surface or a complete filling and masking of deep underlying rock valleys by repeated glacial advance.

Ridgelike accumulations of drift which form along the margins of a standing body of glacier ice are called *end moraines* (Flint, 1957). The larger ones

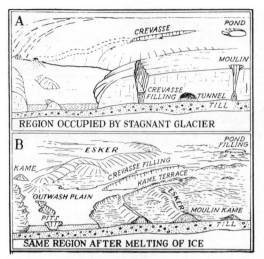

FIG. 7. Sketches showing the evolution of crevasse fillings, eskers, kames, etc. (Lobeck, 1939). (By permission of McGraw-Hill Book Co., N.Y.)

are really better described as belts of hummocks, 1–100 meters high. The material comprising end moraines may be deposited by lodgment, but more is observed as the pushing up of former soil, and the majority is dumped ablation till; these same moraines have been called *push moraines* or *dump moraines* (Flint, 1957). End moraines are referred to as *terminal moraines* where they have formed around a glacier at the position of its farthest stillstand. *Recessional moraines* mark the positions of halting periods during the shrinkage of a glacier, and many of these involve a limited readvance. End moraines of valley glaciers commonly develop as prominent ridges which can be traced continuously around the snout of the glacier like a railroad embankment and along the valley sides as *lateral moraines* (Fig. 5).

Not far up-ice from some well-developed moraine systems there are tens or hundreds of elliptical hills mostly 100–5000 meters long and 5–200 meters high, all aligned with long axes parallel to an ice motion. These are *drumlins* (from the Gaelic). Almost always, they consist of a covering of till like the inverted bowl of a giant spoon resting on an inner core which may be older compact till sand and gravel, with or without bedrock knobs. This evidence convinces most geologists that they formed subglacially by erosion of earlier deposits, becoming a streamlined hill over which accumulates a smear of 1 or 2 meters of till under the same ice. Air photos of mountain glaciers that have recently retreated and of some continental till plains reveal much longer, shallow scallops engraved in the till by overriding ice; these *grooved tills* may be $\frac{1}{2}$–10 km long but only 10 cm to 5 meters deep.

Layered and Sorted Deposits. At the margin of every glacier, most or all of the runoff for the whole year occurs during the few months of summer. This intense flood of meltwater occurs down the ice surface of the outer 1–50 km of the glacier and through a honeycomb of ice tubes in the basal ice. It thus charges these subglacial streams with all sizes of debris from the ice. Rock flour makes the water opaque and white to gray, the so-called *glacier milk*. As with any fluvial process, these sediments are progressively or repeatedly sorted and deposited in layers in a variety of forms as stratified drift. That which is left within the tubes and holes of the glacier or in ice-walled trenches represents about one-third of the total glacial debris and remains as *ice contact deposits* when the ice melts away. The greater portion is carried beyond the glacier margins to become *proglacial deposits*. These are generally *glaciofluvial* or *fluvioglacial deposits*, being left as a gently sloping plain or down a valley, or they may become *glaciolacustrine deposits* and *glaciomarine deposits* if they settle in standing water.

Ice contact deposits outline the holes and tunnels in the last wasting of the basal ice; they are much more abundant in valley areas than in open country. Each sorted layer tends to reflect a contrasting energy situation; they may be composed entirely of large rounded boulders (rare), well-packed cobbles, uniform sands or, rarely, silt grains, and any combination of these. They are not separated on the basis of content, however, as much as shape. The typical landform is the *esker* [from the Irish; *ose* or *osar* (pl.) of Scandinavia] which is a long, crooked ridge or discontinuous chain of ridges end on end (Fig. 6), sometimes running out to sea where it was drowned by postglacial rise of sea level. The *crevasse filling* (Fig. 7) is a straighter variety occurring as subparallel ridges side by side (*en echelon*): the *kame* (from the Celtic) is a mound shape, or a group called a *kame field*, while a *kame terrace* forms as a shelf between decaying ice and the valley wall. All of these deposits here and there may contain a few enormous boulders or masses of till or deformed beds indicating former ice contact, and most contain round enclosed pits called *kettle holes* (see *Kettle*) where residual ice masses melted away. Where kames can be identified as making up the belt along an old ice edge, we have a feature called a *kame moraine* (Thornbury, 1961). In all cases, they represent thin wasting last ice.

By far the largest resources of washed bedload materials (gravel and sand) are the *outwash plains* ("sandur" of Iceland and Scandinavia). Bedding is closely related to the surface. Some are in the form of broad *outwash fans* (Fig. 8) with concave slopes as low as 1 m/km at the distal edge, but 30 m/km in a bouldery apex. If glacial streams are confined to a valley, as is so common below mountain glaciers, the outwash deposit is known as a *valley train*. Some of these outwash fans were spread right up over the wasting ice only to be let down centuries later as an undulating gravel deposit with accordant flat-topped residuals; this is called *collapsed outwash*.

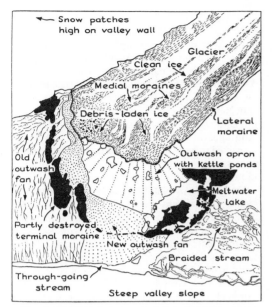

FIG. 8. Outwash fans, terminal moraines and modern glacier snout (sketched from an air photo of an example from Alaska; from Gilluly *et al* 1968). (By permission of Freeman & Co., San Francisco.)

There may be many large kettle holes where ice masses melted out in an otherwise uniformly sloping plain; this is *pitted outwash*. At the downstream end, the glacier reaching a lake or the ocean produces the more steeply inclined prograding beds of an outwash delta (see *Deltaic Evolution*). Some of these deltaic deposits are still almost perfectly preserved and may be closely studied as they are opened up for sand and gravel sources.

Some of the suspended silt load gets left in bars in the multitude of outwash channels (see *Braided Streams*). Strong winds coupled with dry spells or winter low water will pick up tons of this dust, sifting it down over the leeward countryside as a *loess* blanket (q.v.). This eolian silt deposit may be 10 cm to 20 meters thick. It covers extensively the outer glacial areas and periglacial areas in North America, Europe and Asia. In some mountain valleys (notably in central Europe), it appears in a series of layers, one for each glaciation or stadial, separated by paleosols. These are particularly useful in dating Pleistocene events; this is known as *loess stratigraphy* (see *Quaternary Period*).

Most of the clay and much silt from the dirty basal ice, being easily carried by meltwaters, eventually reaches a lake or an arm of the sea. In deep fresh water, at least, these clays and silts settle out in cyclical thin laminae called *varves* (from the Swedish). Light-colored, thick silt layers, representing spring flood or a storm, grade upward to a dark, waxy clay later, representing quiet deposition under winter ice. These "varve couplets" may range from 1–100 mm in thickness. Shallow glacial lakes may be

stirred up by waves, and salt ions will aggregate clays to settle as fast as silts, so that minor laminations, in addition to the annual varves, may result. Contemporaneous shores may make little cliffs with lines of wave-washed boulders, but most shores are sandy with shingle beaches, and shore drift forms the usual spits and bars. *Glacial lakes* (q.v.) become lower or disappear in time as the glacier evacuates a region or because new lower outlets are uncovered by the ice. These glacial *strandlines* (q.v.) are particularly instructive as their present inclination (commonly a 1 or 2 m/km) tells of the rebound and tilting since ice unloaded the area.

RICHARD P. GOLDTHWAIT
GEOFFREY W. SMITH

References

Charlesworth, J. K., 1957, "The Quaternary Era with Special Reference to Its Glaciation," Vol. I, London, Arnold, 592pp.

Flint, R. F., 1957, "Glacial and Pleistocene Geology," New York, John Wiley & Sons, 553pp.

Gilluly, J., Waters, A. C., and Woodford, A. O., 1968, "Principles of Geology," Third ed., San Francisco, W. H. Freeman & Co., 687pp.

Gravenor, C. P., 1953, "The origin of drumlins," *Am. J. Sci.*, **251**, 674–681.

Hobbs, W. H., 1911, "Characteristics of Existing Glaciers," New York, Macmillan, 301pp.

Holmes, A., 1965, "Principles of Physical Geology," New York, Ronald Press, 1288pp.

Holmes, C. D., 1947, "Kames," *Am. J. Sci.*, **245**, 240–249.

Lobeck, A. K., 1939, "Geomorphology," New York, McGraw-Hill Book Co., 731pp.

Matthes, F. E., 1930, "Geologic history of the Yosemite Valley," *U.S. Geol. Surv. Profess. Paper* **160**, 137pp.

Thornbury, W. D., 1961, "Principles of Geomorphology," New York, John Wiley & Sons, 618pp.

Woldstedt, P., 1954–65, "Das Eiszeitalter," Stuttgart, Enke Verlag, 3 vols.

Cross-references: *Abrasion; Bergschrund; Braided Streams; Chatter Marks; Cirque; Cirque Glacier; Col; Crag and Tail; Crevasse; Deltaic Evolution; Drift, Glacial; Drumlin; Dynamic Geomorphology; Erratic Block; Esker; Finger Lakes; Fjord, Fiord; Frost Action; Glacial Deposits; Glacial Lakes; Glacial Plucking; Glacial Scour; Glacial Stairway; Glacial Valley; Glaciation, Glacierization; Great Lakes—North America; Hanging Valley; Horn, Matterhorn; Kame; Kettle; Lobes, Lobation; Loess; Moraine; Outwash Plain, Fan, Terrace, Sandur; Perched Block, Boulder; Periglacial Eolian Effects; Permafrost; Proglacial Deposits; Quaternary Period; Roche Moutonée; Sediment Transport; Snow Avalanche; Stagnant Ice Melting; Strandline; Striae, Striated Pavement; Talus, Scree, Cliff Debris; Tarn; Valley (Mountain) Glacier; Waterfalls.* Vol. I: *Sea Ice; Sea Ice Transportation.* Vol. II: *Ice Age Theory; Paleoclimatology; Sea Ice; Climatic Changes.* pr Vol. VI: *Ablation, Glacial Milk; Glaciology; Gumbotil; Ice Sheet; Parna; Till and Tillite; Varves and Varved Clays and Silts.* pr Vol. VII: *Pleistocene Epoch; Varve Chronology.*

GLACIAL GEOLOGY: PERIGLACIAL AND GLOBAL EFFECTS

As explained in the article *Glacial Geology: Introduction*, the study of this subject may be directed both to Quaternary glacial events and to earlier glaciations (Permo-Carboniferous and others), but in practice so much is preserved of the last events of this sort, and so little of the earlier ones, that it is especially the Quaternary glaciations that furnish the best information about the principles involved.

The chronology of the *Quaternary* (q.v., including *Pleistocene*) is treated separately, and so too is the chronology of the last 10,000 years—the *Holocene* (q.v.)—which, although generally regarded as an *interglacial* stage, covers events in some regions of the globe which are still glacierized (see also *Glaciation, Glacierization*; *Deglaciation*).

The events of glacial geology in regions that were glacierized during the coldest stages were often worldwide in cause and effect. From the dynamic viewpoint, complex "feedback" mechanisms were involved, effected through the atmosphere, the oceans, by crustal (tectonic) reactions, and so on. Any analysis should adopt an *open system* (q.v.) approach.

In this entry, we shall simply review some of the extraglacial processes and phenomena, in an attempt to tie together some of the loose ends and guide the reader into special areas.

Periglacial Regions

In the periglacial regions, i.e., unglaciated areas marginal to glaciers, landforms are greatly affected by the cold and the neighboring ice front, and there is a whole suite of characteristic geomorphologic features (see *Periglacial Landscapes*). They even occur on high mountains in the tropics. Such features depend in part on the intensity of the freeze-thaw phenomena. In regions of deep, almost continuous cold with brief summer melting of the superficial soil, the ground water beneath the surface is involved in a massive *permafrost* (q.v.) which may descend many hundred meters in depth. In less extreme areas, there is much more in the way of diurnal freeze and thaw, and paradoxically there is much more disturbance to the soils and the general landscape. *Ground ice* tends to form anywhere in the high latitudes where groundwater comes up near the surface into the permafrost zone. After a climate change it takes a long time for this ground ice to dissipate, and as it is gradually dissolved away into the groundwater it leads to caves, tunnels and collapse structures, in a manner somewhat analogous to the formation of limestone solution caves; they are therefore known as *thermokarst* (q.v.).

Where the groundwater rises up in springs, the water freezes and *hydrolaccoliths* develop. Near the surface this growth forces up the soil into an eruptive "tumor" like a miniature volcano up to 100 meters or so in height, a feature known widely in northern Siberia, Canada and Greenland as a *pingo* (q.v.). When the pingo eventually melts away after a climate change, a small round pond or lake remains. Along the peripheral belts of the last glaciation in the eastern United States (especially Long Island and New Jersey) or in western Europe (southern England, France, Belgium, etc.) there are tens of thousands of little swampy depressions or ponds suspected to be of this origin; radiocarbon dates and pollen studies of the peaty deposits in some of them show their age to be late glacial.

Undulating or hilly landscapes in the periglacial regions underwent profound changes. Diurnal freeze-thaw processes led to a gradual dismemberment of the rock (see *Frost Action*; *Frost Riving* or *Gelifraction*); any porous soils would become especially friable. Frost effects on soils constitute a speciality themselves (see *Cryopedology*, from the Greek word *kryos* for cold). A whole series of such words are now in the literature: *cryergy* covers the general regime of ice and snow; *cryoturbation*, the contortion and disturbance to soil profiles. At the thaw stage, clays become highly mobile [in some cases converted to *quickclays* (see pr Vol. VI) and *soil creep* (q.v.), *landslides* (q.v.) and *mass wasting* (q.v.)] and in general become widespread. The flowage of soil and rocks under these conditions is known as *solifluction* (q.v.); some writers prefer *gelifluction* or *congelifluction* for the same thing. Pseudomorphs of *ice wedges* or *frost wedges* are often preserved.

High-altitude solifluction often leads to terrace effects that are sometimes classified as *altiplanation* (q.v.). Areas of frost-riven boulders partly moved by gravity constitute a *felsenmeer* (q.v.) or *block field*. Moving bodies of such blocks found on mountainsides are known as *rock streams* (q.v.) or *rock glaciers*.

It used to be thought that the violent contortions found today in former periglacial sands and clays were something peculiar to permafrost and freeze-thaw phenomena, but it is now becoming recognized that much of this disturbed structure is simply diapiric and has developed in the same manner as *load casts* (see pr Vol. VI). In places, these highly mobile clays burst out on the surface in little eruptions, 1–5 meters in height, called *frost boils* and *tundra craters*, a process collectively known as *suffosion* (q.v.).

Periglacial soil movements result in a great many microrelief forms, so-called *patterned ground* (q.v.). The diapiric motion, combined with frost wedging, in flat country leads to *stone nets, stone rings, stone polygons, soils rings*; hillslopes apparently lead to a spiral motion with linear development, resulting in *stone stripes* (see *Frost Action*).

An area within a glaciated region which was never glaciated or where the traces of till have been removed or obscured is called a *driftless area* (q.v.). Such areas are marked by extreme solifluction and frost effects. Some of these areas, generally regions of broad uplift or mountains, have enabled various biotas to eke out an existence during the glacial maxima; they are called *glacial refuges* (q.v.). A theory employing this concept, once greatly favored for explaining the rapid repopulation of a deglaciated landscape, was called the *Nunatak theory*, after an eskimo name for the hills that project above the ice.

In spite of the generally low relief of the great land areas affected by continental ice in North America and northern Europe, the ice sheets did not advance smoothly over them, but tended to pick out existing valleys and hollows, selectively scouring out everdeeper troughs and depressions so that glacial gouges as much as 500–1000 meters deep were created. In the more mountainous areas, such as western Scandinavia, Scotland, Greenland, Alaska, Chile, New Zealand and the borders of Antarctica, deep scours 3 or 4 times such depths led to great U-shaped valleys; in many cases they were subsequently drowned by the rising sea level to become *fjords* (q.v.). Mountain or *"valley" glaciers* (q.v.) developed peculiarly undulating or wave-like longitudinal profiles, the so-called *glacial stairways* (q.v.). In marginal areas where only the mountain tops are sufficiently cold, erosion may be simply by snow accumulation (*nivation*, q.v.), or on a larger scale by *cirque glaciers* (q.v.), the resultant amphitheaters or *cirques* (q.v.) being characteristic of low-latitude, high-altitude glaciation.

Large-scale lowering of the landscape was not achieved by continental ice, but a general scrapingoff of the pre-Quaternary *regolith* (q.v.—residual soil) took place so that much of the northern glaciated areas are now bare of soil. The deeper gouges are filled with morainic debris or with *glacial lakes* (q.v.). In contrast the mountain glacier regions suffered fairly extensive dissection, great valleys like that of Yosemite being lowered by 1000 meters and more. Nevertheless, the accordance of summits of the mountain peaks in Alpine-type areas suggests that the *Gipfelflur* (q.v.) represents a preglacial surface.

Large-scale shearing and thrusting may occur around the front of a continental ice sheet, miniature Alpine-type structures being found, both in the rocky basement (if it contains easily disturbed and faulted sediments) and in *push moraines*, the morainic debris of earlier ice-front deposition, (see *Ice Thrusting*).

During glacial advances, the valley glaciers, ice tongues or ice lobes (of continental ice) tend to cut off existing drainage lines and form *ice-dammed lakes* (see *Glacial Spillways and Proglacial Lakes*), which sometimes overflow in *glacial spillways* with possibly quite catastrophic effects. During ice retreat stages, *periglacial* or *proglacial lakes* develop

thanks to large volumes of meltwater and the hollows in front of the ice due to depression of the earth's crust under ice loading. During deglaciation there is *isostatic rebound* of the crust (see discussion below) and the lakes become emptied (or partially so) through still greater glacial spillways or overflow channels. Modern rivers flowing in these valleys are often much too small for the size of the valley so they are called *underfit streams* (q.v., Streams—Underfit); not all misfit streams are of this sort, the anomalous dimensions being explained by any significant change in the energy of the system, such as might equally well be engendered by postglacial climatic changes. Glacial overflow channels, however, are distinguished by their great size, nonmeandering courses and infilling of immense boulders. *Outwash plains* ("*Sandur*") that have been scoured through and dissected by catastrophic glacial lake floodings, such as occurred on the Snake River in Washington, are named *scablands* (q.v.) from their obviously injured appearance.

In the outer peripheries of the glaciated regions the most extreme cold epochs of the Pleistocene were marked by excessive aridity, and the outwash silts and sands were further distributed by wind (see *Deflation*). The big ice sheets would tend to build up anticyclonic (high-pressure) centers, which resulted in cold, dry winds radiating from the ice surfaces. Amplified by katabatic effects, these winds must have attained very high velocities. Sand dunes of this periglacial type are thus quite extensive. The dune orientations prove the anticyclonic interpretation. Winnowing of the glacial outwash afforded immense volumes of fine dust which today are represented as *loess* deposits (q.v.) that have a curious unstratified lithology of fine sand, silt and clay-size particles; most of the loess accumulated on steppes and prairie landscapes, as is shown by the nature of the soils and the snail species found in them.

Quaternary Stratigraphy

With a growing understanding of the paleoclimatic meaning of various periglacial formations, it is now possible to unravel thick sedimentary profiles of glacial-interglacial stages, aided by the paleontological studies of fossil soil (*paleosol*) mollusca, vertebrate bones, spores and pollen (*palynology*), and associations with human artifacts (*archeological pre-history*). Dates for the last 50,000 years are reliably established now by *radiocarbon*, and C^{14} has also confirmed the usefulness of dating by the method of *varve counting* (seasonal layers in periglacial lakes, see pr Vol. VII). At least ten major glacial-interglacial cycles are now known in loess profiles, which probably take back the history over one million years.

As a result of this stratigraphy with its absolute dating for the last glacial epoch and the postglacial or *Holocene epoch* (q.v.), it is now possible to determine rates and periodicities, so that dynamic processes can be appraised more in terms of classical physics, using real figures for distance-mass-time. For absolute chronology prior to the mid-Wisconsin, new techniques are being developed, the most satisfactory so far being restricted to volcanic ash layers and other igneous intercalations (using K/Ar) and to marine shells (using traces of uranium), but by dint of stratigraphic-geomorphic correlations with dated marine members a reasonable age structure for the entire *Quaternary* (q.v.) is being established. A particularly important avenue for correlating marine and continental glacial stratigraphy is provided by fluvial terraces (see *Terraces, Fluvial— Environmental Controls*) and their relations with sea level oscillations (see *Terraces—Thalassostatic*).

Quaternary Climates

The paleoclimatic meanings of the various geomorphic phenomena and lithologies, summarized above, are gradually becoming well established. Supported by evidence from paleontology (e.g., paleobotanic markers) and certain isotopic indicators (e.g., $0^{16}/0^{18}$), average *paleotemperatures* can now be mapped. The absolute dating has now made a correlation with the Milankovich hypothesis of astronomic control of climates almost a certainty (Broecker, 1965). A cause and effect relationship can now be postulated on a precise time scale showing radiation-climatic effects (see Bacsák's table, in Fairbridge, 1961a; for revised correlation, see *Quaternary*).

A further important step provides for a broad estimation of precipitation characteristics, leading to the revolutionary deduction that the low effective solar radiation levels of the glacial periods should have resulted in greatly reduced evaporation from the tropical oceans, which in turn would lead to greatly reduced equatorial rainfall. While it was formerly believed that a glacial stage in high latitudes equaled a pluvial stage in low latitudes, this is not correct. It is now proved (by systematic studies in Africa, South America and Australia, supported by C^{14} dating) that glacial maxima were matched by widespread development of deserts in the tropics. Indeed, during the cold-dry maxima, the great rivers of central Africa, the Nile, Congo, Niger and Senegal, almost dried up, and the now-vegetated "fossil" dunes can be traced respectively from the Sahara and from the Kalahari into the Congo. It is now said that "there is scarcely a jungle tree in the Congo basin that does not have its roots in desert sand."

Since the advance of continental ice caused a displacement of the westerly wind belts into the latitudes of the "Mediterranean" climates, in these regions there were at times anomalously heavy rains, particularly near the beginning and end of a glacial stage, so that here it is perhaps proper to equate glacial roughly with pluvial stages. Enormous *pluvial lakes* (q.v.) developed. The dating of such lakes and, likewise, *cave deposits* by means of travertines (by C^{14}) and associated human artifacts as well as mollusk and mammal paleontology has provided a good measure of mid-latitude hydrology; early and late glacial pluviosity seems to be generally separated by mid-glacial aridity.

As for the gross causes of ice age climate changes in general, there is a concensus that such stages in earth history were relatively unusual. While four or five such ice ages are fairly well documented now, they were separated by long, mild eras of 200 million years or so duration when apparently there were no great continental ice sheets on earth at all. On the other hand, ice ages, when they occurred, were not brief but lasted about 10–50 million years, though certainly with glacial-interglacial oscillations (see Vol. II, *Ice Age Theory*). What made the ice ages unique was that paleogeographic processes such as polar wandering, continental shifting, and the building of great orogenic belts, resulted from time to time in the appearance of large mountainous areas in polar latitudes. The progressive buildup of snow and ice on these land areas resulted in a critical drop of sea level (*eustasy*, q.v.), thus increasing the *continentality index* (q.v. Vol. II) for the whole earth. Numerous meteorologic feedback mechanisms became operative: semi-dry areas became deserts; growth of ice caps set up anticyclonic systems that tended to maintain cold-dry conditions.

Although planetary motions (*precession*; *astronomic cycles*, etc., q.v. Vol. II) permitted glacial-interglacial oscillations, the enormous cold reserve of ice masses as large as Antarctica and their high albedo (amplified in high latitudes) would call for such a vast heat supply to bring about melting (the *latent heat* phenomenon, see Vol. II) that the Antarctic ice would not achieve more than 10–20% of melting during the 50,000–100,000 year periods of warm interglacials. The lower-latitude continental ice masses of North America and Europe did achieve eventual melting, but only subject to a considerable delay, the *retardation* phenomenon of Croll (see Vol. II); in the last deglaciation this delay was of the order of 10,000 years, so that atmospheric warm-up, beginning to be felt about 16,000 years ago, was followed by the glacio-eustatic rise of sea level to its present mean only about 6000 years ago. The present writer can perceive no support for the interesting Ewing–Donn hypotheses which propose to control earth climates by means of a freezing and unfreezing of the Arctic Ocean, which is largely isolated from the world ocean; the incoming heat budget of the earth is in fact channeled through the tropical and temperate regions, and thus the absolute land area in middle and low latitudes (leading to high continentality extremes) is a critical parameter. Another important factor was the essential isolation of the equatorial oceanic regions into discrete parcels by the uplifts of the Panama Isthmus, the Suez-Syrian arc and the East Indian Archipelago (Fairbridge, 1961a), whereas prior to the late Tertiary, warm equatorial currents circulated the entire globe and, in the early Tertiary, even bottom temperatures in the Pacific were 8–12°C above the present.

Crustal and Eustatic Processes

With any ice advance over the continental land areas there is a depression of the crust that amounts to about one-third of the ice thickness (the ratio of ice density to upper mantle density being roughly 1:3). Broad deformation of the crust by any process is known as *warping* (q.v.). Ice sheets tend to build up to an elevation of about 3 km or 10,000 feet, a height corresponding to the mean maximum of the moisture-bearing winds; ice flow and ablation also tend to keep the ice field from building any higher (see pr Vol. VI, *Ice Sheet*; *Antarctica—Glaciology*, etc.).

Following, or together with, a deglaciation there is *postglacial isostatic crustal rebound* (q.v., see also *Water Loading and Crustal Response*). Ideally this would be to its original elevation, but it is doubtful if total recovery can be achieved. Former *strandlines* (q.v.) can be mapped across the country; these up-lifted beach deposits are dated by C^{14}, varve counting and palynological sampling, and provide chronological markers (*isochrons*), while the difference between these and present altitude contours permits the plotting of *isobases* (q.v.), the lines of equal up-lift or depression. Beyond the outermost margin of the ice sheets there was a tendency for a peripheral bulge to develop, a low upwarp, which was apparently a modest elastic response to the principal down-warp beneath the ice sheet itself. During deglaciation it seems likely that this marginal bulge would subside and possibly migrate back as a wave with the receding ice (Fairbridge and Newman, 1968). In the meantime, rising sea level drowned ice-scoured valleys, creating *fjords* (q.v.) and deep estuaries.

The rate of crustal rebound was very rapid at first, more than half being achieved within the first 800 years or so, but the subsequent adjustment is very slow and may occupy tens of thousands of years. It is possible that this difference in isostatic recovery rates reflects different crustal and mantle levels of low strength, e.g., at 40–50, 100–200 and 350–400 km, where adjustments by sluggish plastic flow and mineral phase changes may take place. The very broad shallow depressions of Africa (e.g., Chad and Congo basins) probably reflect Paleozoic ice centers that have never completely recovered.

The removal of water from the ocean by the ice sheets during glacial buildup resulted in a worldwide drop of sea level, the phenomenon of glacio-eustasy. Approximately 360×10^9 cubic meters (tons) of water correspond to a sea level change of about 1 mm. At the glacial maxima there was about 80×10^6 km^3 of ice covering the globe which would mean an approximate 200-meter drop of sea level from a non-glacial (e.g., mid-Tertiary) period. With each glacial-interglacial oscillation, the ice of

Antarctica would remain largely unmelted (retardation, mentioned above), so that sea level oscillations of the order of 100 meters could be expected.

Changes in the loading of the earth's crust by the advance of seawater across continental shelves on the one hand, and by the eccentric loading of the Greenland ice and the North American and European ice on the other, must have set up a great variety of planetary wobbles (*nutations,* see Vol. II) in earth rotation as well as local variations of the crust. Continued subsidence of certain ocean basins was accelerated during the Quaternary, especially in the western Pacific and in the Mediterranean, so that an additional lowering of sea level must have taken place (tectono-eustatic lowering of sea level), believed to have amounted to about another 100 meters (due to about 35×10^6 km^3 of crustal down-warping, causing a eustatic drop averaging 2 mm/century). At the same time, heavy sedimentation at the great deltas (such as the Mississippi) must have raised sea level a little (about 0.03 mm/century, according to Fairbridge, 1961b).

RHODES W. FAIRBRIDGE

References

Broecker, W. S., 1965, "Isotope Geochemistry and the Pleistocene Climatic Record," in "The Quaternary of the United States," pp. 737–753, Princeton, N.J., Princeton University Press.

Charlesworth, J. K., 1957, "The Quaternary Era," London, Edward Arnold, 2 vols.

Daly, R. A., 1934, "The Changing World of the Ice Age," New Haven, Conn., Yale University Press, 271pp.

Embleton, C., and King, C. A. M., 1968, "Glacial and Periglacial Geomorphology," London, E. Arnold Ltd., 608pp.

Fairbridge, R. W., 1961a, "Convergence of evidence on climatic change and ice ages," *Ann. N.Y. Acad. Sci.*, **95**(1), 542–579.

Fairbridge, R. W., 1961b, "Eustatic Changes in Sea Level," in "Physics and Chemistry of the Earth," Vol. 4, pp. 99–185, London, Pergamon Press.

Fairbridge, R. W., and Newman, W. S., 1968, "Postglacial crustal subsidence in the New York area," *Z. Geomorphol.*, N.F. **12.**

Flint, R. F., 1957, "Glacial and Pleistocene Geology," New York, John Wiley & Sons, 553pp.

Schwarzbach, M., 1963, "Climates of the Past," London and Princeton, D. Van Nostrand Company, (translated from Germ. 1961 ed. by R. O. Muir).

Woldstedt, P., 1954, 1958, 1965, "Das Eiszeitalter," Second ed., Stuttgart, Enke Verlag, 3 vols.

Zeuner, F. E., 1959, "The Pleistocene Period: Its Climate, Chronology and Faunal Successions," London, Hutchinson Sci. & Co. (Second revised ed. of 1945 work), 447pp.

Cross-references: *Altiplanation; Cirque; Cryergy; Deglaciation; Driftless Area; Eustasy; Frost Action; Gipfelflur; Glacial Lakes; Glaciation; Holocene; Loess; Outwash Plain; Periglacial Landscape; Pluvial Lakes; Quaternary Period; Solifluction; Strandline; Suffosion;*

Terraces, Fluvial; Thermokarst; Warping; Water Loading and Crustal Response. Vol. II: Glacial Meteorology; Ice Age Meteorology; Ice Age Theory. pr Vol. VI: Antarctica—Glaciology and Glacial Geology; Glacier Geophysics; Glaciers; Glaciology. pr Vol. VII: Periglacial Stratigraphy; Quaternary of Central Europe; Quaternary of North America.

GLACIAL ICE THICKNESS—See pr Vol. V, ANTARCTICA, GLACIAL AND SUB-GLACIAL TOPOGRAPHY AND CRUSTAL STRUCTURE

GLACIAL LAKES

Glacial lakes are all those lakes which owe their origin in some way to the presence, or former presence, of glaciers, both continental ice sheets and valley (mountain) glaciers or ice caps. Glacial lakes are not to be confused with *pluvial lakes* (q.v.) which waxed and waned during the Quaternary epoch, often in latitudes quite remote from glaciers, but related to the glacial advance and retreat by the shift of rain-bearing wind belts and so on. Some transitional cases are known, e.g., Glacial Lakes Bonneville and Lahontan, where glacial meltwaters were involved as well as shift of the zonal winds.

Six principal genetic types of glacial lake may be distinguished:

(a) Ice-scoured Basin or Trough. This represents the overdeepened valley floor, as often observed in extreme form in *fjords* (q.v.; see also discussion under *Glacial Scour*). Ice-scoured depressions may range in dimensions from thousands of square kilometers, down to the little undulations which occur in great profusion as *roche moutonnée* (Rundhöcker) landscapes, characteristic of the crystalline shield country. Selective erosion of softer horizons is the dominant factor.

(b) Subglacially Scoured Trough. This is another

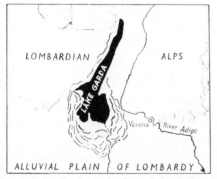

FIG. 1. Lake Garda at the foot of the Italian Alps, with its bordering lateral and terminal moraines. The lake owes 490 feet of its depth to the thickness of the morainic barrier. Below that level (down to a maximum depth of 1,135 feet, the lake occupies an ice-excavated rock basin (from Holmes, 1965). (By permission of T. Nelson & Sons, London and Ronald Press, N.Y.)

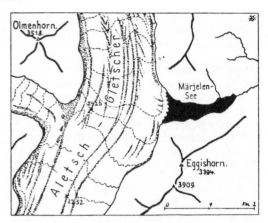

FIG. 2. Lake Märjelen (Märjelen-See), an ice-dammed lake in the Bernese Alps, Switzerland, blocked by the Aletsch Glacier (from Kettner).

type of over-deepening of the valley floor, scoured in bedrock, but eroded by the abrasion (corrasion) of a subglacial stream possessing high energy and a high bedload of glacial boulders.

(c) Moraine-dammed Basin. This type of basin is a product of glacial retreat, either in a mountain valley or across a continental surface with various scoured grooves and preexisting valleys (Fig. 1); the periodic stillstands of the receding ice cause morainic walls to be left extending from side to side of the valleys and thus form ideal dams (impervious because of the high clay size content of the till). Some less perfect, partly permeable membranes of streamwashed tills with a high proportion of gravel may still form dams. Morainic dams do not last indefinitely, however, and such lake basins are now often drained. During glacial retreats, such lakes would be normally frozen over in the winter and in summer fed by meltwater leading to varved sedimentation.

(d) Ice-dammed Basin (q.v. *Glacial Spillways*). In this case, the existing (tributary) valley is dammed by an ice barrier in the main trough, causing a block in the drainage (usually at an altitude below the snow line, thus including both local rainwater precipitation and meltwater). Such lakes are ephemeral, of course, but frequently leave striking terraces, etc. Two types of such lake exist: (1) long narrow ones, in mountainous areas (Fig. 2); (2) broad, extensive ones, more or less parallel to the ice front, in undulating "plains" country.

(e) Isostatically Warped Basins. These originated as ice or moraine-dammed lakes in the peripheral troughs left by continental ice retreat. Isostatic recovery is partly hindered by water loading, and the lake basins persist as autogenetic features.

(f) Kettle Lakes (see *Kettle*). Stagnant ice deposits a ground moraine or "lodgement till" over the entire glaciated surface in irregular heaps. Depressions ("kettles") mainly represent the sites of residual ice blocks that melted out last, and today are occupied

FIG. 3. Cirque lake in Australia (36° S latitude). Lake Cootapatamba (Australian aboriginal name for "the frozen waters where the eagle swoops to drink") with the slopes of the summit of Mt. Kosciusko (7316-foot elevation) rising on the right of the lake. In winter the Cootapatamba Valley and "saddle" are entirely blanketed in snow. Foreground is strewn with erratic blocks. (Photo: New South Wales government).

by small lakes, ponds or partly filled swampy depressions. These small-scale features occur in great number in some areas, e.g., in the "Kettle Moraine" of Wisconsin. They should not be confused with certain depressions in the *periglacial landscape* (q.v.) such as

(*i*) *Pitted outwash* (sometimes loosely called "kettles") attributed also to stagnant ice-block melting, but beyond the ice margin (Thwaites, 1926).

(*ii*) *Fossil pingo depressions*, small ponds or swamps which are the sites of hydrolaccoliths— *pingos* (q.v.). Both these features leave areas dotted with small lakes or ponds but are not strictly glacial, but periglacial.

(*iii*) *Permafrost depressions and thermokarst collapse basins*—features produced by freeze and thaw phenomena, and by solution of deep ground ice (not glacier ice). (See *Patterned Ground*; *Permafrost*; *Thermokarst*).

Since deglaciation from the last (Wisconsin) ice maximum began about 17,000 years ago, many lakes have had time since then to form, fill with sediment, overflow and cut through their various barriers, morainic or (less readily) country rock.

Continental Glacial Lakes

By far the greatest number of glacial lakes are to be found in the hard (Precambrian) bedrock of the Canadian Shield and the Scandinavian Shield. In an area the size of an average midwestern (U.S.) state, 100,000 square miles, there are often over 10,000 lakes—thus at least one lake for every 10 square miles (see maps of Minnesota, northern Ontario, Quebec, Finland).

The bulk of these glacial lakes are ice-scoured basins and troughs, characteristic of the roche moutonnée landscapes, though many are additionally dammed by morainic plugs. Many of the depressions are now, after 10,000 years or so of evolution, filled with sediment or muskeg swamps. Such country is known in Canada as "Barren Grounds" on account of its bare rocks and endless swamps (tundra; termed "Arctic Prairies" by Stefansson). Since in Shield areas, the ice movement tended to scour out long troughs differentially in the softer formations, strongly jointed zones and fault gouge, the resultant patterns of lakes tend to pick out the "grain" of the crystalline country rock and its tectonic framework. In coastal regions, the "grain" is similarly etched out by the pattern of fjords.

445

FIG. 4. Club Lake, Mt. Kosciusko, southeastern Australia. Cirque lake with breached moraine. (Photo courtesy of New South Wales government).

In the Great Lakes of North America and likewise in the Baltic Sea of Northern Europe (which was also lacustrine at various stages in the retreat of the last Quaternary ice sheet: Wisconsin = Weichsel = Würm glacial stage) there were further complications. The preglacial condition in both regions (Pliocene time) was probably merely a major river system: in the one flowing easterly into the proto-St. Lawrence; in the other flowing west into the Kattegat. Fairly extensive ice and subglacio-fluvial scouring occurred (e.g., Straits of Mackinac, and the Sounds of Denmark), but the most important feature in the initiation and maintenance of these large water bodies was the morainic damming to the south. Once established in the peripheral downwarp left by the retreating ice front, an appreciable degree of isostatic recovery caused some of the early lakes to be drained (thus, Chicago, Maumee, Whittlesey, Warren on the one hand; the Baltic Ice Lake on the other). Some of these early lake shores are now 300–600 feet above the present beach levels.

Once established, however, the load of water tends to hold a large lake basin autogenetically in place; as postulated by Gilbert for Lake Bonneville (see below) and confirmed by Crittenden (1963), the load of water for a big water body of this sort is enough to depress the earth's crust several hundred feet. The outlet area, being at the periphery, will tend to rise if the lake level recedes, so that an equilibrium is established. Fundamental changes in the lake regime call for climatic changes or long-term tectonic activity. A ring of Paleozoic basins ("parageosynclines") surrounds both the Canadian and the Scandinavian shields, and it is a well-known property of old structural features to be revived from time to time; there is some evidence of minor rejuvenation in these belts, no doubt "triggered" by the violent loading and off-loading events of the Quaternary.

A rather special category of such continental proglacial lakes are the peripheral "finger lakes," named after the celebrated Finger Lakes of central New York State. When the continental ice extended across the present Lake Ontario and its adjacent lowlands, it came to a final halt, overlapping the edge of the Appalachian Plateau in northern Pennsylvania. Ice and subglacio-fluvial scour gouged fingerlike troughs radial to the ice front, and during retreat, extensive ice-dammed lakes evolved here. At first, they overflowed southward into the Allegheny and Susquehanna; then they merged to form Lake Newberry also to drain into the Susquehanna; later, as Lake Hall, outflow to the west became possible to Lake Warren; then as Lake Vanuxem, outflow oc-

FIG. 5. Cradle Mt. and Barn Bluff (5114-foot elevation), western Tasmania (latitude 42° S), showing glacial cirque lakes in rock-cut amphitheaters. High plateau was smoothed by an earlier phase of continental glaciation, while the cirques represent a milder stage with isolated glacial activity.

curred to the east through the Mohawk to the Hudson. After a brief lake-free state, isostatic rebound to the north caused the "fingers" to tilt southward and the present form was adopted; upwarping in the north of New York State is still in progress (1–3 mm/yr, with respect to the coast at New York City).

A characteristic feature of the retreat stages of continental ice across deeply scoured terrain, such as Scandinavia, eastern Canada and New England, is the development of relatively small and narrow proglacial and moraine-dammed lakes that normally freeze over in winter and thus develop varved sediments. In Sweden, Baron de Geer showed that it was possible to measure profiles of such sediments (facilitated by the numerous brick pits in that country) which gave a systematic thickness pattern that varied annually according to the melt rate and thus the climate. Counting of these varves permitted a dating of the postglacial lakes back to over 10,000 years; these dates, although questioned at the time, have now been confirmed by C^{14} dating, and the Swedish Geological Survey maintains a unit constantly engaged on lake clay boring and dating work. Palynological (pollen) analysis and diatom stratigraphy now provide additional controls. In North America, the varve-dating methods were introduced by the Swedes Antevs and Caldenius. Interesting profiles were measured in the Hudson Valley, Connecticut Valley and elsewhere, but the valleys were scattered and the records did not overlap conveniently as they did in Sweden, so that the results were in part misleading. In the Cochrane district of Ontario, the varve correlations by Antevs have recently been confirmed by recounts and C^{14} dating (Hughes, 1965), though the dates estimated by Antevs were in error.

Mountain Glacial Lakes

Mountain (or Valley) or "Alpine-type" glaciers may be discrete (as cirque or corrie glaciers), extended (as piedmont glaciers), or coalescing (as icecaps). Numbers of varieties are known (see *Valley Glaciers*), but their potential for creating lake basins is mainly due to ice scour, as with continental icesheets; however, the preexisting mountain and valley topography greatly favors deep scouring of narrow U-shaped valleys with overdeepened sections, so that in proportion to the volume of ice, the scouring capacity of mountain ice is remarkable. Moraine-dammed lakes are relatively unimportant

447

FIG. 6. Cirque lake with hanging valley. Lake Quill and the Sutherland Falls, South Island, New Zealand. (Photo: White's Aviation Ltd., Auckland, New Zealand).

in the strictly mountain areas, but they assume a greater role in the piedmont areas. In dimensions, the smallest category is the cirque lake and the largest is the moraine-dammed.

(a) **Cirque or Corrie Lakes** (*tarns* in England; *cwms* in Wales; *corries* in Scotland). These are products of the rotary, landslide type of motion in *cirque glaciers* (q.v.) that results in plucking along the *bergschrund* (q.v.) and scouring at the foot, rising to a rock threshold (Fig. 3). An excavated rock basin is thus the normal product of cirque erosion, though the lake may be further dammed by morainic material around the rock lip (Fig. 4). A common feature of such lakes is a more or less circular plan, and since they occupy a rock amphitheater, they are fed by sheet-wash or multiple small torrents, rather than by a distinct drainage channel (Figs. 5, 6).

(b) **Rock-scoured Basin Lakes.** In general, these are represented by a host of mountain lakes. Differential scouring of hard and soft rock types and brecciated fault zones generally prescribe their location. A number of well-known examples in Glacier National Park (Montana) and adjacent

Waterton Park (Alberta) include McDermott, Red Eagle, Ellen Wilson and the upper two Medicine Lakes (Campbell, 1914).

(c) **Paternoster Lakes.** This name is taken from the term for rosary prayer-beads. These lakes are characteristic of *glacial stairways* (q.v.) which represent a stage further than glacial cirques, where a mountain (valley) glacier extends for some distance down a valley, alternating the points of maximum scouring between harder rock bars or thresholds. The result is a string of lakes in the "treads" of the stairway, alternating with rapids or waterfalls over the "risers." Again, moraines often add to the rock barriers above each "riser." A particularly well-studied series is the Yosemite-Merced sequence in the Sierra Nevada of California; a formerly extensive Yosemite Lake is now filled with sediments (Matthes, 1930).

(d) **Piedmont Lakes.** This name is derived from the French term, pertaining to the foot of the mountains. These lakes are particularly well-developed around the foot of the Alps, being usually the result of a deep scouring of the lower part of the mountain

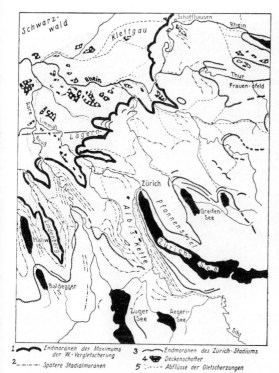

FIG. 7. Sketch map of the Zürich area, Switzerland, showing the terminal moraines of the last (Würm) glaciation, and the present moraine-dammed lakes (in black). Legend : 1. Terminal moraine of Würm maximum. 2. Younger retreat stage moraines. 3. Terminal moraine of the Zürich stadial. 4. Early Pleistocene plateau gravels (residuals of early glacial outwards). 5. Traces of former glacier tongues. Lake Constance is on the Rhine (Rhein) in the top right-hand corner. Width of map area = 50 km. (after Heim, 1919).

valley, and are dammed by rings of end moraines over the plain. Classic examples are Lake Garda in Italy (Fig. 1), Lake Zürich in Switzerland (Fig. 7) and Chiemsee in Bavaria. Both Lake Constance (on the Rhine) and the Lake of Geneva (or Léman, on the Rhone) are less perfect examples being linked up with major river systems. In Britain, most of the radially fanned troughs of the Lake District (Cumberland) are of this type. In North America, a very beautiful example is Jackson Lake, at Jackson Hole, at the foot of the Tetons in Wyoming (Fryxell, 1938).

(e) Kettle Lakes and Stagnant Ice Depressions (see *Kettle*). Melting of stagnant ice blocks is relatively unusual in mountain glacier areas, but numbers of centers played a double role at different periods of their existence. In Scotland, Ireland, the English Lake District, Wales and elsewhere, there were local mountain glacier centers probably both before and after the general advance of the Scandinavian continental ice sheets. In North America, the same was true of the Adirondacks, Catskills and New England centers. Thus there are extensive

sheets of ground moraine ("lodgment tills") or terminal moraines of the last retreat; sometimes the materials are composite. The lodgment till is generally only 2–3 meters thick, but at lake dams it may be 20 meters or more. In the Adirondacks, well-known morainic dammed examples include Lakes Placid, Saranac, Raquette, George and Schroon; only a few show traces of glacial scour (Ogilvie, 1902).

(f) Moraine-dammed and Fluvial-wash-dammed Lakes. These are characteristic of mountains which experienced long histories of retreat and readvance, thus creating extended valleys with numerous barriers. They are numerous in the Northern Rockies, which are at relatively low latitudes, yet in their mid-continent position they are susceptible to marked changes in climatic regime even during an interglacial epoch. In Glacier National Park (Montana), fluvial-wash dams maintain Kintla, McDonald and the lower two Medicine Lakes, while moraines dam Bowman and Quartz Lakes (Campbell, 1914).

Minor Features of Glacial Lakes

The ephemeral nature of the ice-dammed or proglacial lake is apparent. The enormous volumes of meltwater available to fill these and the newly exposed moraine-dammed depressions also need little

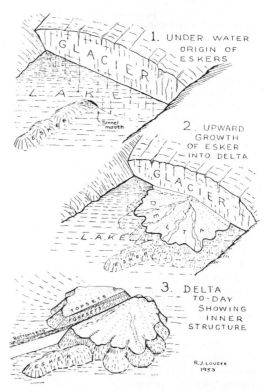

FIG. 8. Esker and delta growth at a submerged ice front debouching into a proglacial lake (Lougee, 1956).

FIG. 9. Proglacial lake terraces. The "Parallel Roads" of Glen Roy, Scotland, being old shore lines (terraces) of a former ice-dammed glacial lake. They are not quite horizontal today because of postglacial crustal tilting. (H.M. Geological Survey; Crown copyright: by permission).

emphasis. Most of the former continental ice-sheet lakes are now dried out, filled or reduced to the status of swamps, after periods of evolution ranging from about 6000–17,000 years. Interesting features of such lake sedimentation can therefore be studied today in three dimensions. Numerous pits and excavations disclose their nature and geometry since the lake deposits are much in demand economically—the clays for brick and tile manufacture, and the sands and gravels for highway and building construction. In regions where the glaciated area includes extensive limestones, as in the Northern Alps, the lakes may contain deposits of a marl, useful for agricultural lime.

Lougee (1956) has illustrated his ideas about the origin of *eskers* (q.v.) from a subglacio-fluvial ice tunnel issuing onto the floor of a proglacial lake (Fig. 8). These deposits eventually build up with a transition to proglacial deltas, and eventually, when the ice recedes, the delta is left standing as an isolated flat-topped hill in the middle of the valley; an excellent example of the latter, in part exposed by sand quarries, may be observed a few miles west of Stroudsburg, Pennsylvania.

Terraces, in part wave-cut and in part "raised beaches" of old glacial lake levels, are known partic-

ularly from the North American Great Lakes (see Table 1), and emerged coastal plains ("lake plains") in steps with intervening beach lines, sometimes with multiple beach ridges, are found in profusion (Leverett and Taylor, 1915; Hough, 1958). Most of the raised beaches around the borders of the Baltic, in contrast, are marine, except for the early "Ice-Lake" stage. On a smaller scale, the famous "Parallel Roads of Glen Roy" in Scotland (Fig. 9) have attracted attention since early in the last century (Jamieson, 1863), and many smaller proglacial lakes in Britain have been largely traced by these terraces (see *Glacial Spillways and Proglacial Lakes*).

Some glacial lakes developed in proglacial positions or in intra-morainic deposits near the late Wisconsin seacoast. Their deposits are now in the process of being discovered here and there on the continental shelves. Lougee postulated such lakes in the present Long Island Sound, Block Island Sound, etc., and they have now been located by sub-bottom oceanographic seismic surveys and confirmed by coring.

Around the borders of Antarctica today a number of ice-scoured basins were at first drowned by the Holocene eustatic rise of sea level and then emerged due to isostatic rebound, since even in Antarctica

TABLE 1. GLACIAL LAKES OF NORTH AMERICA[a]

	Maximum Elevation (ft)	Mean Age (yr Before Present)
Agassiz (greater Lake Winnipeg, much of Manitoba, western Ontario, North Dakota and Minnesota)	Successively: 1230, 1440, 1070, 910	12,000–9,200
Albany (middle New York State)	340	13,400
Algonquin (greater Lake Michigan and Huron)	607	11,000–12,000
Amsterdam (Mohawk Valley)	700–420	13,600 (?)
Arikaree (North and South Dakota)		
Arkona (a low-level stage in Erie basin and south of Lake Huron)	710–695	13,500
Barlow (see Ojibway)		
Bascom (New York, Vermont, New Hampshire)	1120, 1110	Mid-Wisconsin
Calumet (Lake Michigan)	620	12,500
Calvin (Iowa River and Cedar River valleys)	680	
Chicago (southern Lake Michigan)	640–605	14,500–13,500
Chippewa (Lake Michigan, discharge to Lake Stanley)	230	9,600
Coeur d'Alene (Idaho)	2660–2400	(Early Pinedale, Bull Lake)
Columbia (Washington)	2350–1950	(Bull Lake)
Dakota (in James River Valley)	1300	
Dana (see Lundy)	590 (?)	12,700
Dawson (see Lundy)	370 (?)	12,500
Duluth (western Lake Superior)	1085	10,000 (?)
Early Lake Erie		12,000
Glenwood (Lake Michigan)	640	13,500
Grassmere	640	12,200
Hackensack (New Jersey)		Mid-Wisconsin
Hall (greater Finger Lakes, outflow west to Lake Warren)	1000–900	12,800 (?)
Herkimer (Mohawk Valley)	1440–1220	14,200
Houghton (Lake Superior)		9,600
Iroquois (greater Lake Ontario)	335	12,500–10,500
Jean Nicolet (Green Bay)	800	
Keweenaw (Lake Superior)	(unknown)	11,800
Lundy, or Dana and Dawson in New York (southern Lake Huron and Erie)	620	12,500
Madawaska (St. John R., N.B.)	525	?12,000–10,000
Maumee (Lake Erie)	800–760	14,000
McConnell (northern Alberta)	900	
Memphremagog (Vermont, Province of Quebec)	1284	12,800
Mignon (Lake Superior)		
Minnesota (Driftless area of Minnesota)	1150	
Missoula (Washington, Idaho, Montana)	4400–4200	(Bull Lake)
Newberry (united Finger Lakes, outflow to Susquehanna)	1000	14,000 (?)
Nipissing Great Lakes (post-glacial higher Great Lakes, draining through Ottawa Valley; later Port Huron)	605	6,000–5,000
Ojibway-Barlow (north central Ontario)	800–1020	9,000
Ontario (Early)		10,000
Ontonagon (northern Michigan)		10,200
Passaic (eastern New Jersey)	331, 387, 158	Early or pre-Wisconsin
Peace (Alberta)	1800–1500-1200	?Early Wisconsin
Rycroft (to Peace River, Alberta)	2800	12,000
Saginaw (southwest of Lake Huron)	695	13,000–12,800
St. Louis (valley of St. Louis River)	1700	
Saskatchewan (mid-course of Saskatchewan River)		

TABLE 1. GLACIAL LAKES OF NORTH AMERICA—continued

	Maximum Elevation (ft)	Mean Age (yr Before Present)
Schoharie (middle New York State)	1200–860	14,000 (?) or mid-Wisconsin
Souris (western Manitoba and North Dakota, draining to ? James River)	1600–1100	
Stanley (Lake Huron, draining to Ottawa Valley)	190	9,600
Toleston (Lake Michigan)	605	12,000
Tyrrell (west of Lake Athabasca)	1840–1600-1300–1100	Late Wisconsin
Vanuxem (greater Finger Lakes, outflow east to the Mohawk)	900	13,500
Vermont (Coveville and Fort Ann phases, to Lake Champlain)	729 and 749 (in North) 230 and 160 (in South)	ca. 12,000
Warren (southern Lake Huron, Erie and Finger Lakes)	680–670	12,600–12,300
Wayne (low level stage at Erie basin)	653–658	12,700
Whittlesey (greater Lake Erie, southern end of Lake Huron)	738	13,000–12,800
Wisconsin (Wisconsin)	1000	
Wollaston (discharged west to Athabasca)	1500–1300	
Modern Great Lakes		
Superior (outflow at Sault Ste. Marie rapids)	602	2,800
Michigan (continuous at Mackinac Straits with Lake Huron)	581	2,800
Huron (outflow at St. Clair River)	581	2,800
Erie (Niagara Falls)	572	12,400
Ontario (Thousand Islands, St. Lawrence)	246	10,500

[a] This Table was prepared with the kind assistance of A. Dreimanis, J. A. Elson, R. G. LaFleur, and the following members of the Pleistocene Geology Section of the Geol. Surv. of Canada: B. C. Craig, R. J. Fulton, N. R. Gadd, E. P. Henderson, C. F. M. Lewis, B. C. McDonald, V. K. Prest, A. M. Stalker, J. Terasmae.

there was about a 10% ice melting during the Holocene. As a result, there are a number of basins that are salt lakes today, e.g., Bunger's Oasis and Lake Vanda; the former melts entirely in summer, but the latter only at the margins, though its bottom temperature exceeds 70°F, possibly a geothermal effect. The actual salts today are likely to be modified by the selectivity of cyclic salt additions, solution from adjacent sediments, and so on (Nichols, 1962).

RHODES W. FAIRBRIDGE

References

Bakker, J. P., 1965, "A forgotten factor in the interpretation of glacial stairways," *Z. Geomorphol.*, **9**, 18–34.

Bell, G. L., 1963, "The Red River Valley of North Dakota," Bismarck, North Dakota, Conrad Publishing Co., 31pp.

Campbell, M. H., 1914, "Glacier National Park; a popular guide to its geology and scenery," *U.S. Geol. Surv. Bull.*, **600**.

Charlesworth, J. K., 1963, "The bathymetry and origin of the larger lakes of Ireland," *Proc. Roy. Irish Acad.*, **63B**(3), 61–69.

Clark, R. H., 1965, "The oases in the ice," in (Hatherton, T., editor), "Antarctica," pp. 321–330, London, Methuen.

Clayton, L., et al., 1965, "Intersecting minor lineations on Lake Agassiz Plain," *J. Geol.*, **73**(4), 652–656.

Coleman, A. P., 1909, "Lake Ojibway, last of the great glacial lakes," *Ontario Bur. Mines*, **18**(1), 284–293.

Crittenden, M. D., 1963, "New data on the isostatic deformation of Lake Bonneville," *U.S. Geol. Surv. Profess. Paper* **454-E**, 1–31.

Drehwald, H. R., 1955, "Zur Entstehung der Spillways in Nordengland und Südschottland," *Kölner Geogr. Arbeit.*, **8**.

Embleton, C., and King, C. A. M., 1968, "Glacial and Periglacial Geomorphology," London, E. Arnold 608pp.

Fairchild, H. L., 1909, "Glacial waters in central New York state," *N.Y. State Museum Bull.*, **127**, 66pp.

Fryxell, F., 1938, "The Tetons," Berkeley, University of California Press, 77pp.

Gilbert, G. K., 1897, "Old tracks of Erian drainage in western New York," *Bull. Geol. Soc. Am.*, **8**, 285–286.

Heim, A., 1919, "Geologie der Schweiz," Leipzig, Tauchnitz, **1**, 704pp.

Holmes, A., 1965, "Principles of Physical Geology," Second ed., London, T. Nelson & Sons; New York, Ronald Press Co., 1288pp.

Hough, J. L., 1958, "Geology of the Great Lakes," Urbana, University of Illinois Press, 313pp.

Hughes, O. L., 1965, "Surficial geology of part of the Cochrane district, Ontario, Canada," *Geol. Soc. Am., Spec. Paper*, **84**, 535–565.

Jamieson, T. F., 1863, "On the parallel roads of Glen Roy, and their place in the history of the glacial period," *Quart. J. Geol. Soc. London*, **19**, 235–259.

Lemke, T. W., 1965, "Quaternary Geology of Northern Great Plains," in (Wright, H. E., Jr., and Frey, D. G., editors) "The Quaternary of the United States," pp. 15–27, Princeton, N.J., Princeton University Press.

Leverett, F., and Taylor, F. B., 1915, "The Pleistocene of Indiana and Michigan and the history of the Great Lakes," *U.S. Geol. Surv. Mon.*, **53**, 529pp.

Lougee, R. J., 1956, "Pleistocene terraces," *Int. Geogr. Union (Rio de Janeiro), 8th Rept. Comm. Erosion Surfaces*, Pt. 4, N. America, 49–54 (also Rept. of Secretary, 5–10).

Mannerfelt, C. M., 1945, "Nagra glacialmorphologiska Formelement," *Geogr. Annal.*, **17**, 1–239.

Matthes, F. E., 1930, "Geologic history of Yosemite Valley," *U.S. Geol. Surv. Profess. Paper* **160**.

Muller, E. H., 1965, "Quaternary Geology of New York," in (Wright, H. E., Jr., and Frey, D. G., editors) "The Quaternary of the United States," pp. 99–112, Princeton, N.J., Princeton University Press.

Nicholls, R. L., 1962, "Geology of Lake Vanda, Wright Valley, South Victoria Land, Antarctica," in "Antarctic research," *Am. Geophys. Union, Geophys. Mono.*, **7**, 47–52.

Ogilvie, I. H., 1902, "Glacial phenomena in the Adirondacks," *J. Geol.*, **10**, 397–412.

Peterson, J. A., 1964, "Fieldwork in the upper George River basin, Labrador-Ungava," *McGill Sub-Arctic Res. Paper*, **18**, 69–92.

Richmond, G. M., *et al.*, 1965, "The Cordilleran Ice Sheet of the Northern Rocky Mountains, and Related Quaternary History of the Columbia Plateau," in (Wright, H. E., Jr., and Frey, D. G., editors) "The Quaternary of the United States," pp. 231–242, Princeton, N.J., Princeton University Press.

Salisbury, R. D., *et al.*, 1902, "The glacial geology of New Jersey," *New Jersey Geol. Surv., Final Rept.*, **5**, 802pp.

Shepard, F. P., 1937, "Origin of the Great Lake basins," *J. Geol.*, **45**, 76–88.

Spencer, J. W., 1891, "Origin of the basins of the Great Lakes of America," *Am. Geol.*, **7**, 86–97.

Spencer, J. W., 1907, "The falls of the Niagara; their evolution and varying relations to the Great Lakes," *Can. Geol. Surv.*, 490pp.

Stanley, G. M., 1938, "The submerged valley through Mackinac Straits," *J. Geol.*, **46**, 966–974.

Theakstone, W. H., 1965, "Contorted glacial lake sediments, and ice blocks in outwash deposits at Osterdalsisn, Norway," *Geogr. Ann.*, **47A**(1), 39–44.

Thornbury, W. D., 1954, "Principles of Geomorphology," New York, John Wiley & Sons, 618pp.

Thwaites, F. T., 1926, "The origin and significance of pitted outwash," *J. Geol.*, **34**, 308–319.

Troll, K., 1925, "Die Rückzugstadien der Würmeiszeit im nördlichen Vorland der Alpen," *Mitt. Geogr. Geos. München*, **18**.

Wayne, W. J., and Zumberge, J. H., 1965, "Pleistocene Geology of Indiana and Michigan," in (Wright, H. E., Jr., and Frey, D. G., editors) "The Quaternary of the United States," pp. 63–84, Princeton, N.J., Princeton University Press.

Weis, P. L., and Richmond, G. M., 1965, "Maximum extent of Late Pleistocene Cordilleran glaciation in northeastern Washington and northern Idaho," *U.S. Geol. Surv. Profess. Paper*, **525-C**, C128–C132.

Wilson, M. E., 1918, "Timiskaming County, Quebec," *Geol. Surv. Canada Mem.* **103**, 197pp.

Woldstedt, P., 1954–65, "Das Eiszeitalter," Second ed., Stuttgart, Enke Verlag, 3 vols.

Zoltai, S. C., 1965, "Glacial features of the Quetico-Nipigon area, Ontario," *Can. J. Earth Sci.*, **2**(4), 247–269.

Cross-references: *Bergschrund; Cirque Glacier; Esker; Finger Lakes; Fjord; Glacial Lakes* (specific examples); *Glacial Scour; Glacial Spillways and Proglacial Lakes; Glacial Stairway; Glacial Valley; Great Lakes (North America); Holocene; Kettle; Moraine; Patterned Ground; Periglacial Landscape; Permafrost; Pingos; Pluvial Lakes; Postglacial Isostatic Rebound; Quaternary; Roche Moutonnée; Stagnant Ice Melting; Thermokarst; Valley (Mountain) Glaciers; Water Loading.* pr Vol. VII: *Palynology; Varve Chronology.*

GLACIAL LAKE AGASSIZ

This glacial lake, named by Warren Upham in 1879, formed between the retreating Laurentide glacier and the height of land between Hudson Bay and Gulf of Mexico drainage, and covered about 200,000 square miles in Manitoba, eastern Saskatchewan, western Ontario, eastern North Dakota, and northwestern Minnesota. Not all this area was flooded at once. Lake Agassiz discharged alternately southward through the Minnesota River and eastward through the Lake Nipigon basin.

Varved and massive clays occur in several basins including the Red River valley, the Lake of the Woods region, the Dryden-Lac Seul area of western Ontario, the Sandy Lake-Lake Winnipeg area of northeast Manitoba and northwest Ontario, and the Grass River region of northern Manitoba.

At least one disconformity exists in the clay sequence. In the Red River basin clay is overlain by silty clay and the two units are separated either by sand containing peat, wood, or fossil mollusks, or by a desiccation surface discovered in the course of engineering studies. In Ontario, a band of red clay about 60 cm thick in the east and only 10 cm thick at the Lake of the Woods occurs in a varve sequence. Locally clay is overlain by till.

Strandlines representing at least 35 lake levels are mostly sandy or gravelly beach ridges, but locally wave cut scarps and terraces are prominent. Several can be traced for hundreds of miles. The most persistent is the Campbell strandline which

1	Gross River	6	Trout Lake	11	Red River
2	Nelson River	7	Lake Seul	12	Minnesota River
3	Lake Winnepeg	8	Rainy Lake	13	Sheyenne River
4	Lake Manitoba	9	Lake Nipigon	14	Assiniboine River
5	Sandy Lake	10	Lake of the Woods	15	Saskatchewan River

FIG. 1. Sketch map showing approximate limits of glacial Lake Agassiz (heavy line). Limit is definite in south and west, approximate in north and east. Lake Agassiz has not as yet been distinguished from older lakes in the Saskatchewan River valley or younger lakes north of Lake Nipigon. The northern and eastern boundaries were at times formed by ice, and those shown are not synchronous with the southern and western shores, and probably not with each other. Positions of principal outlets are shown by arrows, as well as in valley No. 12. The hachured lines are end moraines; lines hachured on both sides are interlobate moraines. The data from western Ontario are compiled from recent works of Prest and Zoltai.

follows the Manitoba escarpment from northern Saskatchewan 700 miles south to the southern outlet at Lake Traverse, Minn., and more than 250 miles northeastward into Ontario, perhaps as far as Trout Lake. In Ontario, it is discontinuous and must be interpolated between former islands. The Campbell strandline formed when Lake Agassiz discharged southward through the Minnesota River, and the lake level was stable because a bed-rock sill retarded erosion of that outlet. Higher beaches are numerous in the southern part of the basin and represent phases during the initial downcutting of the southern outlet. Lower beaches abound farther north; these formed when the lake discharged east into the Lake Nipigon basin. The strandlines were warped by differential crustal uplift. The Campbell water plane rises from an altitude of about 980 feet at Lake Traverse in Minnesota to about 1500 feet at Trout Lake in

Ontario, in a distance of about 400 miles; its average slope is about 1.2 ft/mile to the southwest.

Deltas, with areas ranging from scores to hundreds of square miles, were deposited along the western margin of the lake where rivers from the plains to the west debouched: the Sheyenne, Pembina, and Assiniboine rivers deposited the largest. Smaller deltas and alluvial fans are abundant. In several of the western tributary valleys, terraces and alluvial fills show that the lake level subsided and rose again, as do the discontinuities in the sediments within the lake basin. The fluctuations occurred when eastern outlets were opened and closed by retreat and readvance of glaciers north of Lake Superior.

Radiocarbon dates show that the highest level of the lake in the southern part of the basin occurred more than 11,700 years ago. One or more low levels of the lake occurred between 11,000 and 10,000 years ago. A high level of the lake with southward discharge terminated around 9200 years ago; south of Winnipeg, Lake Agassiz was drained by 6700 years ago.

The early high phase of Lake Agassiz had a sparse fauna, but during an early low level, an abundant molluscan fauna spread through the basin and fossils are common in valley fills related to later high-water phases. The influx of vegetation into the area and the spreading of plants such as white spruce from east to west and grasses from west to east across the basin apparently depended on the draining and reflooding of the southern part of the basin. The lake influenced the movements of early man (paleo-Indian cultures), and artifacts typical of the period from 5000–9000 B.C. are found around its margins.

J. A. ELSON

References

Antevs, Ernst, 1931, "Late-glacial correlations and ice recession in Manitoba," *Geol. Surv. Can. Mem.*, **168**.

Elson, J. A., 1957, "Lake Agassiz and the Mankato-Valders problem," *Science*, **126**, 999–1002.

Elson, J. A., 1961, "Soils of the Lake Agassiz Region," in (Legget, R. F., editor) "Soils in Canada," *Roy. Soc. Can. Spec. Publ.*, **3**, 51–79.

Johnston, W. A., 1916, "The genesis of Lake Agassiz; a confirmation," *J. Geol.* **24**, 625–638.

Johnston, W. A., 1946, "Glacial Lake Agassiz, with special reference to the mode of deformation of the beaches," *Geol. Surv. Can. Bull.*, **7**.

Leverett, Frank, 1932, "Quaternary geology of Minnesota and parts of adjacent states," *U.S. Geol. Surv., Profess. Paper*, **161**.

Löve, Doris, 1959, "The postglacial development of the flora of Manitoba: a discussion," *Can. J. Botany*, **37**, 547–585.

Mozley, Alan, 1934, "Post-glacial fossil mollusca in western Canada," *Geol. Mag.*, **71**, 370–382.

Prest, V. K., 1963, "Red Lake–Lansdowne House area,

northwestern Ontario, Surficial geology," *Geol. Surv. Can. Paper*, **63–6,** 23pp.

Upham, Warren, 1895, "The Glacial Lake Agassiz," *U.S. Geol. Surv. Monograph*, **25,** 658pp.

Zoltai, S. C., 1961, "Glacial history of part of north-western Ontario," *Proc. Geol. Assoc. Can.*, **13,** 61–83.

Zoltai, S. C., 1965, "Glacial features of the Quetico-Nipigon Area," *Canadian J. Earth Sci.* **2,** 247–269.

Cross-references: *Beach Ridge*; *Delta*; *Glacial Geology*; *Lobe, Lobation*; *Quaternary*; *Strandline*; *Warping*.

GLACIAL LAKE ALBANY

In the Hudson-Champlain Lowland of eastern New York, recession of late Wisconsin ice was accompanied by a sequence of glacial lakes. Near-continuous deposits of gravel, fine sand, and clay occur throughout the lowland, recording first

the presence of Lake Hackensack south of the Hudson Highlands, and then Lakes Albany and Vermont north from the Hudson Highlands into southern Quebec. As the wasting ice finally cleared the eastern St. Lawrence Lowland, marine waters of the Champlain Sea flooded southward into the Champlain Lowland about 11,000 years ago.

The details of early deglaciation of eastern New York are incompletely known, but the character of Lake Albany and its relation to its successor, Lake Vermont, have been determined with some certainty. As the stagnating Hudson ice block thinned by downwasting, it also backwasted northward, forming a barrier to the expanding Lake Albany on the south. Positions of sequential ice margins are now recorded by kame deltas, formed where rivers flowing out of the ice emptied directly into the lake, and by kame terraces, deposits formed between the edge of the ice block and the valley

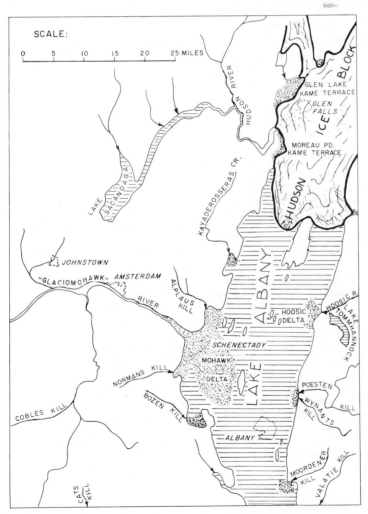

FIG. 1. Map of Glacial Lake Albany and related drainage at the time of deposition of the Mohawk Delta.

walls. These glaciofluvial terraces are typically found for several miles north from the lake and range topographically up to 100 feet or more above the lake level.

In addition to the gravel and sand deposits laid by rivers in contact with the ice, the open waters of Lake Albany also received fine rhythmically banded sediments, largely alternations of silt and clay. This material was apparently washed directly out of the melting ice block and spread as cloud-like blankets over the lake bottom. Curiously, the sedimentary structures found in these beds, such as graded bedding and sole-markings, duplicate those also found in deep marine sediments and in ancient rocks of deep marine origin. It is demonstrable that a turbidity current mode of transport is responsible for many of the rhythmic beds.

As the backwasting ice block cleared side valleys of the Hudson Lowland, rivers such as the Mohawk and Hoosic, fed and enlarged by drainage from melting ice and waning upland lakes, emptied into Lake Albany. The city of Schenectady is built on the broad delta of the glacial Mohawk River.

Along the eastern shore of Lake Albany a beach developed for a distance of nearly 50 miles. Particularly well-formed beach ridges occur where stormy lake waters reworked the edges of earlier kame terraces and deltas. The beach trends north-south and is deflected upward about $2\frac{1}{2}$ ft/mile by postglacial crustal uplift. The fact that the ice-contact, beach, and delta deposits of Lake Albany are now found to lie progressively higher toward the north was first appreciated by Peet (1904) and Woodworth (1905), who early called attention to the rebounded condition of the earth's crust in New York State.

At full extent, Lake Albany stood 350 feet above present sea level at the latitude of Troy, N.Y. and inundated much of the Hudson Lowland. Draining of the lake southward was encouraged by crustal uplift as the ice withdrew. Falling lake levels are recorded throughout the Lowland by minor beaches and by river terraces cut into earlier deltas, particularly that of the Hoosic River.

Successor to Lake Albany was Lake Vermont, defended in similar fashion on the north by ice in the Champlain Lowland. Some of the late falling Albany levels appear to coincide with the Quaker Springs and Coveville phases of Lake Vermont, suggesting a more or less continuous withdrawal of ice from eastern New York once deglaciation began. Local, minor readvance of the Hudson ice lobe to near Glens Falls is probable, but the theme of lake development suggests a general ice recession.

The deposits of Lake Albany have long been of economic value. Brickmaking through use of the clays was a thriving industry, as was the production of molding sands. Ice-contact, and delta gravel and sand deposits remain a major source of aggregate for concrete and foundation purposes.

ROBERT G. LaFLEUR

References

Chadwick, G. H., 1928, "Ice evacuation stages at Glens Falls, N.Y.," *Bull. Geol. Soc. Am.,* **39,** 901–922.

Chapman, D. H., 1937, "Late-glacial and post-glacial history of the Champlain Valley," *Am. J. Sci.,* **34,** No. 200, 89–124.

*Flint, R. F., 1953, "Probable Wisconsin substages and Late-Wisconsin events in northeastern United States and southeastern Canada," *Bull. Geol. Soc. Am.,* **64,** 897–920.

LaFleur, R. G., 1965, "Glacial Lake Sequences in the Eastern Mohawk-Northern Hudson Region," Guidebook, N.Y. State Geol. Assn., 22pp.

LaFleur, R. G., 1965, "Glacial geology of the Troy, N.Y. quadrangle," *N.Y. State Museum and Science Service Map and Chart Series No. 7,* 22pp.

* Additional bibliographic references mentioned in text may be found in this work.

Cross-references: *Champlain Sea; Delta; Fluvioglacial Processes; Glacial Lakes; Glacial Spillways and Proglacial Lakes; Postglacial Isostatic Rebound; Water Loading and Crustal Response.*

GLACIAL METEOROLOGY—*See* Vol. II

GLACIAL MOULIN, MILL OR POTHOLE

From the French *moulin,* mill, the glacial moulin or pothole formed in the bedrock under glacial ice is a term that dates back in the literature to Jean de Charpentier (1841), that admirable early explorer of the Alps. Brögger and Reusch (1874) recognized traces of moulins in the deglaciated region near Oslo in Norway, describing them as giant's kettles, since in places they scour to astonishing depths. Warren Upham (1900) reintroduced the term "moulin or glacial mill," distinguishing between the "giant kettle" (the pothole) and the moulin (the waterfall). G. K. Gilbert (1906) was careful to label the pothole itself as "moulin work."

The moulin hypothesis, as first conceived, was based on the observation of summer meltwaters pouring into gaping crevasses in glaciers, and so-armed with boulders, pebbles and sand that a deep pothole would be scoured out (analogous to those of mountain torrents or waterfalls). Series of moulins would be generated by the gradual movement of the glacier. Higgins, 1957, notes an amusing discussion in the Victorian era over the delicacy of using the term "pothole"; the Spanish term *remolino* was urged as a solution to the difficulty. The French term *marmites de géant* and the German *Riesentöpfe* are sometimes employed, though the modern German term is *Gletschermühle.* Ängeby, 1951, proposed the term *evorsion* for the mechanics

Fig. 1. (A, left) Glacial moulin, waterfall from surface melt-water disappearing into crevasse. (Photo: W. Flaig.) (B, right) The eventual pothole, now inactive, looking down into 9-meter-deep example in the "Glacier Garden," Lucerne, Switzerland. Note circumferential scour marks produced by the spiral motion of the "mill."

of pothole erosion under vortices or eddies in torrents and waterfalls.

The difference between the glacial moulin and the ordinary fluvial pothole is mainly one of size and the fact that the latter is always part of a sequence connected by stream-bed abrasion, while the glacial ones are scattered over the glaciated rock floor without particular regard to any thalweg.

The traditional moulin explanation has been criticized on various grounds, including the fact that size is not always diagnostic, that large boulders ("grinders") are found in both fluvial and glacial potholes, that flared edges which are supposed to be unique to stream potholes were later found in the glacial ones, and so on. It has been claimed, therefore, that the so-called glacial moulins were more easily explained by fluvial erosion, or at least by subglacial streams, that it would be hard to imagine crevasses remaining long enough in one place to permit the moulin to develop to giant size (thus disregarding a stagnant ice melting stage), and that an oblique eddy motion produced by a fluvial torrent is hard to visualize in a crevasse waterfall. Experiments by H. S. Alexander (1932) sought to prove the validity of these objections. Points favoring the fluvial hypothesis have been summarized by Higgins (1957).

The question does not rest at that point, however, and numbers of experienced authors have protested in favor of the glacial origin. The most telling argument is the demonstration that moulins may occur on hilltops or slopes in no way suitable for fluvial transport. In New York City, for example, in the hard Manhatten Schist of Inwood Park, there is a fine moulin in the middle of a steep glaciated slope, which must have been inspected by thousands of students; a fluvial origin is utterly out of the question in such a case. On the other hand,

there are other potholes in glaciated terrain that do have fluvial appearances; indeed, subglacial streams would be expected to develop their own potholes, as well as enlarging existing moulins.

A third theory has called on erosion of subglacial potholes by plastic ice scour. Gjessing (1967) suggests that the scour, particularly on the lee side of rock barriers, might be accomplished by a viscous mixture of water, ice and rock fragments.

RHODES W. FAIRBRIDGE

References

Alexander, H. S., 1932, "Pothole erosion," *J. Geol.,* **40,** 305–337.

Ängeby, O., 1951, "Pothole erosion in recent waterfalls," *Lund Studies in Geogr. Ser. A.,* No. 2, 1–34.

Ängeby, O., 1952, "Recent, subglacial and lateroglacial pothole-erosion (evorsion)," *Lund Studies in Geogr. Ser. A.,* No. 3, 14–24.

Brögger, W. C., and Reusch, H. H., 1874, "Giant's kettles at Christiana," *Quart. J. Geol. Soc.,* **30,** 758–71.

Charpentier, J. de, 1841, "Essai sur les glaciers et sur le terrain erratique du bassin du Rhône," Lausanne, Marc Ducloux, 363pp.

Dahl, R., 1965, "Plastically sculptured detail forms on rock surfaces in northern Nordland, Norway," *Geogr. Ann.,* **47A**(2), 83–140.

Dewart, G., 1966, "Moulins on Kaskawulsh Glacier, Yukon Territory," *J. Glaciol.,* **6**(44), 320–321.

Embleton, C., and King, C. A. M., 1968, "Glacial and Periglacial Geomorphology," London, E. Arnold, 608pp.

Faegri, K., 1952, "On the origin of pot-holes," *J. Glaciol.,* **2**(11), 24–25.

Gilbert, G. K., 1906, "Moulin work under glaciers," *Bull. Geol. Soc. Am.,* **17,** 317–320.

Gjessing, J., 1965, "On 'plastic scouring' and 'subglacial erosion'," *Norsk Geogr. Tidsskr.,* **20**(1–2), 1–37.

Gjessing, J., 1967, "Potholes in connection with plastic scouring forms," *Geogr. Ann.,* **49A**, 178–187.

Higgins, C. G., 1957, "Origin of potholes in glaciated regions," *J. Glaciol.,* **3,** 11–12.

Hollingworth, S. E., 1951, "Pot-holes and glacier mills, some comments on Dr. Streiff-Becker's article," *J. Glaciol.,* **1**(9), 490.

Streiff-Becker, R., 1951, "Pot-holes and glacier mills," *J. Glaciol.,* **1**(9), 488–490.

Upham, W., 1900, "Giant's kettles eroded by moulin torrents," *Bull. Geol. Soc. Am.,* **12,** 25–44.

Cross-references: *Abrasion; Crevasse; Glacial Scour; Kettle; Potholes; Thalweg.* pr Vol. VI: *Glaciology.*

GLACIAL OUTWASH, SANDUR, ETC.—*See* OUTWASH PLAIN, FAN, TERRACE, SANDUR

GLACIAL PLUCKING (QUARRYING)

In glacial erosion, in addition to *abrasion* (q.v.) which leaves striations, gouge marks, etc., a peculiar pulling away process is called glacial plucking or quarrying, because it involves the dislodging and removal of large fragments and boulders. It is a characteristic process of lee sides of *roches moutonnées* (q.v.), of the downstream side of "glacial stairs," and of the inner and deeper parts of the bergschrund crevasses of cirque glaciers. It is probable that very often meltwater running into the joint planes causes frost splitting (Carol, 1947), but also the mechanical process of ice freezing onto projecting rocks has the ultimate effect, as the glacier moves on, of pulling the rocks away from their foundations. The pressure changes as the glacier moves over may also lead to stress release effects (Lewis, 1954). Comparisons of the amount of erosion on the stoss and lee sides of glaciated hills (Flint, 1957, p. 78) show that by and large the lee side (i.e., plucked side) is more eroded than the stoss (abraded) side.

RHODES W. FAIRBRIDGE

References

Carol, H., 1947, "The formation of *roches moutonnées*," *J. Glaciol.*, **1**, 58–59.

Flint, R. F., 1957, "Glacial and Pleistocene Geology," New York, John Wiley & Sons, 553pp.

Lewis, W. V., 1954, "Pressure release and glacial erosion," *J. Glaciol.*, **2**, No. 16, 417–422.

Cross-references: *Abrasion*; *Bergschrund*; *Cirque Glacier*; *Frost Action*; *Glacial Stairway*; *Roche Moutonnée*.

GLACIAL PLUCKING, SAPPING—*See* BERG-SCHRUND; CIRQUE

GLACIAL REFUGES (NUNATAK THEORY)

It has long been thought by some botanists that during the glacial periods, particularly the last, there were certain mountains that projected above the continental ice sheets, i.e., *nunataks*, or other ice-free areas, where isolated colonies of hardy vegetation could survive the rigorous conditions for a few thousand years, and then serve as centers for the rapid reoccupation of the later deglaciated landscape. The animals were much more mobile in general than the plants, so that with them the same problem was hardly of any importance.

The term given for such an ice-free area within or close to a continental ice sheet is a *glacial refuge*; the latin form *refugium* (pl. *refugia*) is also often used. From the climatic point of view it is true that certain arctic regions receive extraordinarily little snow; they could remain cold deserts even when adjoining areas were glacierized. The fact that the precise location of such ice-free areas is difficult to prove geologically, however, is not a good argument against their existence (Faegri, 1963). Also it is possible that the refuges were merely south-facing (well insolated) cliffs in otherwise snow- and ice-covered regions, and not necessarily projecting peaks. Another point made by Faegri (personal

communication) is that the refuge may have been a moving one, migrating progressively as the ice age meteorological conditions shifted.

As long ago as 1860, Charles Darwin discussed the migration of vegetation belts during the last glaciation (Firbas, 1964). For a long time, a considerable controversy persisted between mono-glacialists and polyglacialists, eventually to be conclusively won by the latter, for the role of long interglacial (even subtropical) intervals between successive ice advances has now been thoroughly established. Thus, repeated migrations, to and fro, would be involved.

Pollen analytic work has shown that several ice-free areas of Europe, e.g., the seaboard strip from southern Ireland to Portugal, and interior basins, such as the Bohemian depression and the Hungarian plain, were tundras during glacial stages. Forests in the glacial maxima were limited to the Mediterranean shores of southern Europe and North Africa. In North America, the Gulf of Mexico probably played the same role. But these were peripheral areas, not "islands" in the ice-covered areas. It has been argued that the *Driftless Area* (q.v.) was such a refuge, but possibly not continuously (Cushing, 1965, p. 405).

The idea, once promulgated so widely, that large nunataks and mountain areas projected above the ice sheets, thereby offering refuge sites, is really unnecessary and no longer greatly favored. It was thought that the absence of glacial striations on high mountains indicated that they projected above the ice, but increased understanding of periglacial phenomena (often still active there, and certainly active in early postglacial times) has led to the conclusion that these highland areas have been weathered severely since the deglaciation, thus destroying many traces of ice movement (Goldthwait, 1940; Flint, 1957).

In North America this so-called *Nunatak Theory* was especially championed by Fernald (1925). Prominent nunataks quoted were the Torngat and Kaumajet Mts. of Labrador, Long Range in western Newfoundland, Shickshock Mts. of Gaspé, the Keeweenaw Peninsula of Lake Superior, the Adirondacks, Catskills and high points of New England. On the one hand, closer local studies have often revealed glacial traces, and on the other hand, botanical research has shown the relative speed of recolonization and adaptability of some of the "relict" species (Wynne-Edwards, 1937).

RHODES W. FAIRBRIDGE

References

Charlesworth, J. K., 1957, "The Quaternary Era," London, E. Arnold, 2 vols.

Cushing, E. J., 1965, "Problems in the Quaternary Phytogeography of the Great Lakes Region," in "The Quaternary of the United States," pp. 403–416, Princeton, N.J., Princeton University Press.

Dahl, E., 1955, "Biogeographic and geologic indications of unglaciated areas in Scandinavia during the glacial ages," *Bull. Geol. Soc. Am.* **66,** 1499–1519.

Davis, M. B., 1965, "Phytogeography and Palynology of Northeastern United States," in "The Quaternary of the United States," 377–401, Princeton, N.J., Princeton University Press.

Faegri, K., 1963, "Problems of Immigration and Dispersal of the Scandinavian Flora," in (Love, A., and Love, D., editors), "North Atlantic Biota and their History," Oxford, London, Pergamon Press.

Fernald, M. L., 1925, "Persistence of plants in unglaciated areas of boreal North America," *Am. Acad. Arts and Sci., Mem.,* **15,** 237–342.

Firbas, F., 1964, "Die glazialen Refugien der europäischen Gehölze (ohne Osteuropa)," *Rept. VI Int. Congr. Quat.* (INQUA, Warsaw, 1961), **2,** 375–382.

Flint, R. F., 1957, "Glacial and Pleistocene Geology," New York, John Wiley & Sons, 553pp.

Goldthwait, R. P., 1940, "Geology of the Presidential Range," *New Hampshire Acad. Sci., Bull.,* **1,** 1–41.

Hultén, E., 1937, "Outline of the History of the Arctic and Boreal Biota during the Quaternary period," Stockholm, Bokf. Ak. Thule, 168pp.

Løken, O. H., 1966, "Baffin Island refugia older than 54,000 years," *Science,* **153**(3742), 1378–1380.

Nordhagen, R., 1933, "De senkvartoere klimavekslinger og deres betydning for kulturforskningen," *Inst. Sammenl. Kulturforsk., (Oslo),* A.2.

Raup, H. M., 1941, "Botanical problems in Boreal America," *Botan. Rev.,* **7,** 147–248.

Woldstedt, P., 1954–65, "Das Eiszeitalter," second ed., Stuttgart, Enke Verlag, 3 vols.

Wynne-Edwards, V. C., 1937, "Isolated arctic-alpine floras in eastern North America: A discussion of their glacial and recent history," *Trans. Roy. Soc. Can., Ser. 3,* **31,** 33–58.

Cross-references: *Driftless Area; Nunatak; Tundra Landscape.* pr Vol. VI: *Ice Sheet.* pr Vol. VII: *Palynology.*

GLACIAL SCOUR, EROSION

The motion of glacier ice, thanks to its "arming" by moraine boulders, has long been known to carry out large-scale erosion of the preexisting landscape.

This process is often known as *glacial scour.* Considerable controversy has ranged about the question of "how much." Were certain valleys preexisting and merely enlarged by the ice movement? Or were they primarily glaciated valleys, and just modified somewhat by postglacial river activity?

In mountain areas it is often possible to demonstrate that the floor of any particular valley is filled to bedrock by glacial debris. The major *fjords* (q.v.) of Norway, Alaska, Chile and New Zealand, some with depths to over 1000 meters, are features limited to glaciated regions, and not easily confused with *rias* (q.v.). In places they are partly barred by morainic dams, but in others there is a rising rock floor to a shallow threshold.

In continental ice areas some buried valleys may not have been spillways, but ice scoured and filled by drift. In shield areas where local tectonic disturbances are least probable, deep scour sometimes is found to descend far below the level of any pre- or proglacial drainage system, e.g., in the bed of Lake Superior. Examples of extremely deep scour have been traced for the great Permo-Carboniferous ice sheets of Australia. In regions of Precambrian stabilization (subsequently undeformed), softer formations, e.g., belts of mica-schists within a region of granite gneiss, have been scoured to a depth of 1000 meters over distances of 30–50 km and widths of 3–10 km. Several such basins later became filled by Permian coal swamps, but deep drilling shows the bedrock floor to be covered by tillite (Fairbridge, 1952).

Estimates of the volume of glacial erosion are difficult to make. In most mountain glacial regions, the traces of preglacial erosion surfaces (e.g., the Gipfelflur of the Alps) are easily identified. The total post-Pliocene erosion (glacial and interglacial) can thus be determined quite readily; the ratio of one to the other is less simply established. For continental glaciation, the traces of preglacial erosion surfaces (summit accordances) also seem to be present; indeed they are only superficially furrowed. However, they lack almost all trace of

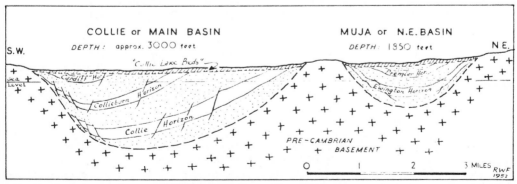

FIG. 1. Example of a Permo-Carboniferous glacial scour in unwarped Precambrian granite greiss, filled with Permian coal measures and Tertiary lake sediments (Fairbridge, 1952).

Tertiary soil or regolith. In marginal areas, e.g., in central New York state and parts of New Jersey, some of that regolith remains in protected depressions. It appears likely that much of the continental ice motion was rather sluggish and that its erosive activity was limited to a skimming off of the soil and regolith-covered surface. The latter may well have been 100 meters or more in thickness, to judge from warm humid landscapes of today; throughout Mesozoic and Tertiary time the bulk of North America lay in a subtropical climatic belt. Deep scouring would be engendered by preexisting relief that led to blockage over domes (e.g., Adirondacks) and accelerated scour in the depressions, especially where favored by deep weathering on softer rocks. Some quantitative figures for continental ice erosion could be gained through a study of the mean dimensions of the various till sequences. Fluvial erosion has obviously removed much fine-grained material, but few boulders could have reached the ocean from the southern ice fronts of the European and North American ice sheets. Since the Mississippi was the principal ice front drainage channel for the latter, estimates of total fluvioglacial transport can be obtained from thickness measurements of the turbidite sequences in the Gulf of Mexico. A careful survey of this sort should prove rather interesting.

RHODES W. FAIRBRIDGE

References

Charlesworth, J. K., 1957, "The Quaternary Era," p. 314, London, Edward Arnold, 2 vols.

Dahl, R., 1965, "Plastically sculptured detail forms on rock surfaces in northern Nordland, Norway," *Geogr. Ann.*, **47**A(2), 83–140.

Fairbridge, R. W., 1952, "Permian of South-western Australia," *Congr. Geol. Intern. Compt. Rend., 19, Algiers,* **1952,** Gondwana Symposium, 136–146.

Flint, R. F., 1957, "Glacial and Pleistocene Geology," New York, John Wiley & Sons, 553pp.

Gjessing, J., 1965, "On 'plastic scouring' and 'subglacial erosion'," *Norsk Geogr. Tidsskrift*, **20**(1–2), 1–37.

Cross-references: *Buried Valley; Fluvioglacial Processes; Fjord; Gipfelflur; Glacial Spillways and Proglacial Lakes; Great Lakes (North America); Regolith and Saprolite; Ria.*

GLACIAL SPILLWAYS AND PROGLACIAL LAKES

In ice-free valleys tributary to glaciers, meltwaters from the ice and snow are impounded to form ice-dammed lakes. These are relatively rare at the present time. The Märjelen See (see Holmes, 1965, photographs on p. 669), marginal to the Aletsch Glacier, in the Swiss Alps, is perhaps the best-known example; it is now 78.5 meters deep and in 1878 attained a length of 1600 meters. Graenalon, in Iceland, is today some 200 meters deep and 188 km^2 in area. Similar lakes are known from Norway, the Himalayan region, the Rocky and Andes mountains, the Caucasus, Baffin Island, Iceland, and especially Alaska. These features are best termed *"proglacial lakes"*, though the term "extra-morainic lakes" has also been used, as well as "ice-dammed marginal" and "hyperglacial lakes."

During the Pleistocene, ice masses spread equatorward, and to lower elevations, far below modern limits. Glaciers extended down main valleys, or across or against the regional slope of land, and lakes were similarly dammed back by the ice margin, filling ice-free valleys or depressions between the ice margin and other obstructions such as earlier morainic ridges. The level of some such ice-dammed marginal lakes (proglacial or hyperglacial lakes) was stable sufficiently long for beaches and associated features to be developed. These include both aggradational and erosional forms, including lake terraces, beaches, spits, hooks, and bars on the one hand, and cliffs, stacks, and benches eroded by the lake waters, on the other. The classic examples of beaches associated with proglacial lakes are found in the Lochaber district of the Scottish Grampians, where in Glen Roy, for instance, there are the famous "parallel roads," at average elevations of 1151, 1075 and 848 feet, representing successive stands of a lake occupying the valley, and of the ice point, as worked out by Jamieson in 1863 (see Fig. 1).

Of the debris carried into such lakes from the glaciers and from the land, the coarser was deposited as deltas, either isolated or confluent, near the lake edge. Near the ice margin, confluent deltas, with steep frontal slopes, and lobate in plan, were reasonably common, especially in Scandinavia, but where major rivers debouched into such lakes, large isolated deltas were built. The town of Pickering, in north Yorkshire (England), for example, is situated on a delta built in Pleistocene times by a great stream of meltwaters from the Esk and Tees valleys southward into a lake occupying the present Vale of Pickering (Fig. 2). The distal parts of such deltas and beaches pass into silts and clays, the finer debris which gradually settled on the floors of the proglacial lakes; many modern proglacial lakes are milky with such silt and clay particles in suspension. Such fine lacustrine deposits (see *Varve*, Vol. VI) form exceedingly fine lamellae and extend over large areas of the former lake beds; in some cases they completely filled the lake basin.

These ice-dammed lakes were fed by meltwaters both from glaciers and from the adjacent land. They would rise in level until the lowest col was attained, when the waters overflowed either to adjacent proglacial lakes, or to areas free of ice.

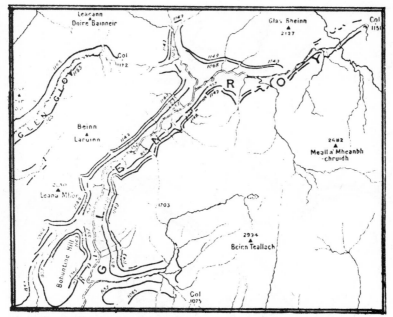

Fig. 1. The parallel roads of Glen Roy (after Geological Survey map).

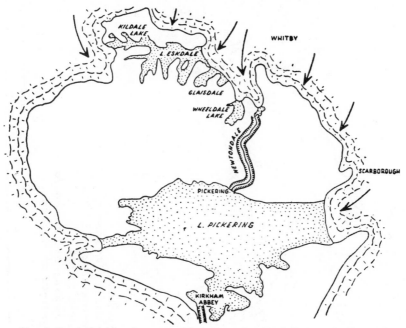

Fig. 2. Proglacial lakes in eastern Yorkshire (after Kendall, from Sparks, 1960).
Width of map area—70 km. (By permission of John Wiley & Sons, N.Y.)

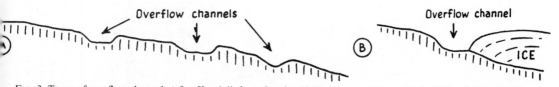

Fig. 3. Types of overflow channels (after Kendall, from Sparks, 1960). (By permission of John Wiley & Sons, N.Y.)

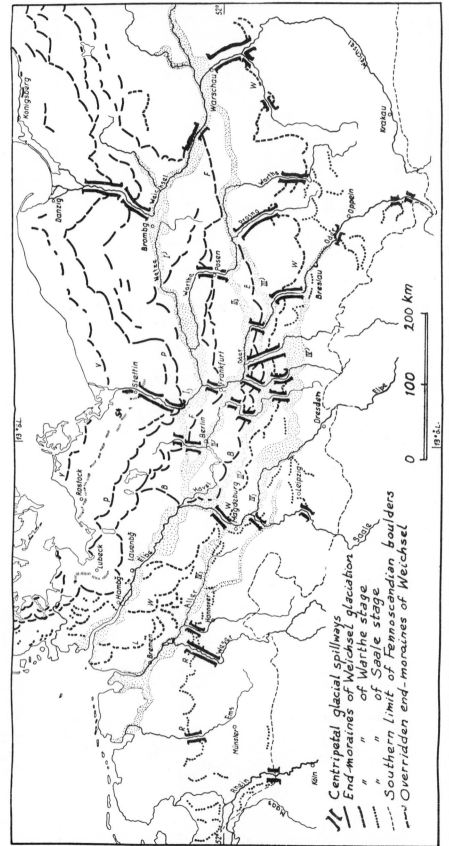

FIG. 4. End moraines, old glacial drainage channels (*Urstromtäler*: indicated by fine dots) and centripetal spillways in North Germany and Poland (after Woldstedt). R = Rehburg Stage, L = Lamstedt Stage, W = Warthe Stage of Saale or Riss Glaciation (*ca.*100,000 B.P.), B = Brandenburg Stage (*ca.*70,000 B.P.), F = Frankfurt or Poznan Stage (*ca.*15,000 B.P.), P = Pomeranian Stage (*ca.*13,500 B.P.), V = Velgast or Belt Stage (*ca.*12,000 B.P.) of the Weichsel or Würm Glaciation. IV = Breslau-Magdeburg-Bremen Channel, III = Glogau-Baruther Channel, II = Warsaw-Berlin Channel, I = Thorn-Eberswalder Channel.

The shorter channels are straight or nearly so, but the larger overflows may display a sinuous form in plan. Such drainage channels, which are called *overflow channels, sluiceways* or *spillways* (in German: *Rinnentäler*), are anomalous with respect to normal regional drainage patterns. They differ morphologically from the usual river-eroded valley, for they are characteristically flat-floored and steep-sided, with sharp edges at both top and bottom (Fig. 3). Many display a humped or undulating longitudinal profile, commonly complicated by the presence of marsh-filled depressions. Tributary valleys are rare or absent, but if present they display normal valley morphology. Most of these channels are now dry, having been abandoned once the ice withdrew and the lakes they drained disappeared; in some, however, the glacial modifications of drainage persist, and they remain as parts of the present valley network, anomalous in position, form and size, for many are occupied by grossly underfit streams (see *Stream–Underfit*).

Where the overflow took place very close to the ice front, the spillway may be distinctly arcuate in plan, where the eroding waters flowed around a lobe of ice, or may be represented by a notch on the hillside—merely half a channel, the other half, since disappeared, having been excavated in the ice itself (in the manner of a kame channel).

Where the ice front abutted against a maturely dissected upland, many valleys came to be occupied by lakes, and spillways developed between these. Such a series of channels related to a given position of the ice front, and correlating with respect to the elevation of their inflows and outflows, with adjacent lakes and overflows, is described as an *aligned sequence*. On the other hand, a single spur may be breached by several spillways draining lakes of different levels and related to several positions of the ice-front; such channels, are said to be in *parallel sequence*.

Such systems of overflow channels merely drain from one proglacial lake to another and are referred to as *indirect* overflow channels, in contrast with the *direct* overflows which carry meltwaters to ice-free areas. Newton Dale (England), already referred to, is an example of a direct overflow channel.

One of the best preserved spillways has been traced through central Sweden from Stockholm to Lake Mälaren to Lake Vänern, the Göta River and Göteborg. The deep gorge connecting the two lakes is known as the Svea Älv (River) and has been the subject of much study (see Fredén, 1967). At a time when isostatic land uplift closed the Baltic, forming a vast glacial lake, the *Ancylus Lake*, it was inevitable that a tremendous spillway would have to exist. It was eventually discovered in the Svea Älv which forms a deep canyon in hard crystalline rocks; at its maximum this spillway discharged at 20,000 m³/sec, according to von Post, lasting approximately from 9000–8000 B.P.

Many systems of proglacial lakes and spillways have been described from Europe and North America. In Europe where the basic ideas were first worked out, the most complex and extensive system is that of the North German *Urstromtäler* (Polish; *pradoliny*) which extend over the North European plain from the North Sea to the U.S.S.R. and which are today of great economic significance because those that floored valleys provide easy routeways, especially for canals, right across the continent (Fig. 4). It is generally agreed that these marshy flat-floored trenches were eroded by meltwaters from the Baltic ice sheet and from the uplands to the south flowing westward around the southern margin of the ice sheet and thence into the "Channel River" (*Kanal-Urström*, named by Penck in 1936, see Fig. 5) that flowed through the Straits of Dover and into the Atlantic. As the ice front receded, so the channels were cut at successively lower levels, thus forming an overall pattern of incomplete concentric arcs. Each aligned sequence of channels skirts moraines, and each possesses deposits brought in by streams entering from north and south. Divergent views of cause have been propounded, but this general thesis is generally accepted; alternative views, including preglacial, interglacial, subglacial, and tectonic origins have each been invoked, but each has been vigorously argued and ultimately rejected. The abandoned channels furnished sand for extensive dunes that built up across eastern Europe, and the fine-grained (silt-size) material was the source of much of the loess (Fig. 6).

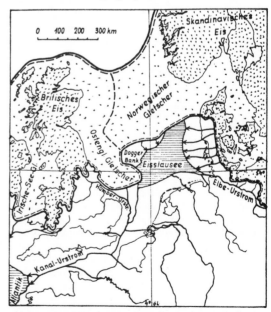

FIG. 5. The Elbe-North Sea-Channel River, during the maximum of the last glaciation (after Valentin, 1957). *Elbe-Urstrom* = Elbe drainage channel. *Eisstausee* = Ice-dammed lake. *Kanal-Urstrom* = Channel river.

FIG. 6. Distribution of loess and *Urstromtäler* in Europe (loess after Grahmann, 1932; in Flint, 1957). (By permission of John Wiley & Sons, N.Y.)

It is, however, in North America that the most extensive and complicated system of glacial lakes and spillways has been worked out. In late glacial times, enormous volumes of water were impounded around the margin of the Laurentian ice sheet in a series of peripheral basins caused by the crustal loading of this same ice sheet (Fig. 7). These lakes, the precursors of the North American Great Lakes, extended in area as the ice margin receded northward, and though they continued to overflow southward into the Mississippi and Hudson valleys until relatively recently, the exposure of lower ground, like the Ottawa and St. Lawrence valleys, eventually caused the abandonment of the southerly over-

flow channels and led the present flow of the Great Lakes to the St. Lawrence Valley. In detail, the evolution of the Great Lakes drainage is bewilderingly complex, but it has been largely worked out by C^{14} dating in conjunction with skilled stratigraphy and geomorphology (Hough, 1958).

To the northwest of Lake Superior, in the vicinity of the present Lake Winnipegosis, there was in glacial times a lake larger in area than the present Great Lakes combined. This was *Lake Agassiz* (q.v.), which at its maximum was 600–700 miles long, 200–250 miles wide, 650 feet deep, involving at one stage or another an area of some 200,000 square miles. Several strandlines and out-

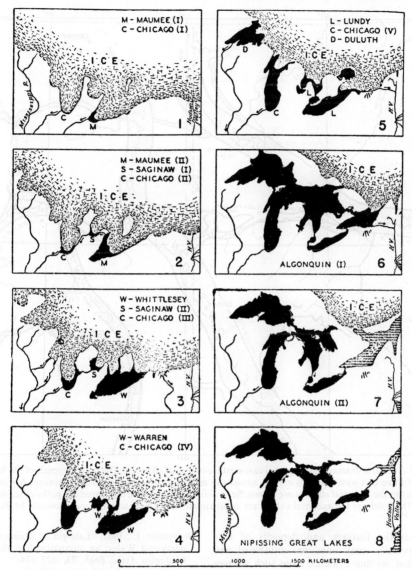

FIG. 7. Eight stages in the history of the Great Lakes, in chronological order, 1 to 8 (Daly, 1934). (By permission of Yale University Press.) [For details and dates see article *Great Lakes (North America)*.]

lets of this vast water body have been identified, and the tracing of its complex history continues. Everything connected with Lake Agassiz was on a grand scale: one of its outlets, or spillways, breached the continental divide into the Minnesota valley near Fort Snelling and is a huge valley up to 4 miles wide and 300 feet deep; its effects can be traced hundreds of miles downstream. The preglacial valleys of the upper Missouri and Yellowstone drained to the north-east, but after ice blockage and the evolution of ice marginal channels in North Dakota, a southeasterly pattern evolved (Howard, 1958; see Fig. 8).

Some of the systems of proglacial lakes and spillways are well evidenced, and their interpretation, though difficult to work out in detail, in broad outline cannot be disputed. The origin of other channels, sometimes interpreted as overflows, has, however, been seriously questioned. The evidence for the former presence of lakes in some areas is scanty or absent, and it is possible that the lakes proposed largely on the basis of channels of abnormal situation and morphology never existed and that the channels in question originated in some way other than erosion by overflow waters from proglacial lakes. Alternatively, it may be

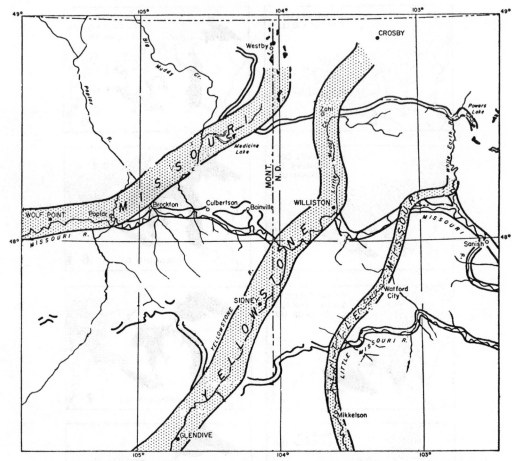

FIG. 8. Ancestral drainage and regional east-west ice-marginal channels. The present trench of the Missouri is one of three east-west channels cutting across the ancestral paths of the master drainage. A number of tributaries to the ancestral streams are shown. Several of these may have influenced the paths of ice-marginal waters. The widths of the ancestral valleys are approximate valley floor widths (from Howard, 1958).

argued that the features and deposits of lake basins, especially small ones, are unlithified and easily eroded, so that evidence from such sources is likely to be at best fragmentary, particularly in areas long and intensively occupied by man. On the other hand, the morphology of some of the channels presents difficulties in terms of simple overflow. Many exhibit humped profiles, some distinct hollows, and others have no intake but commence abruptly on the sides of hills. It appears reasonable in such cases to suggest that the channels were excavated by meltwaters flowing in crevices and caverns in and beneath the ice, and thus that they did not connect or drain proglacial lakes.

C. R. Twidale

References

Charlesworth, J. K., 1957, "The Quaternary Era," London, Edward Arnold, 2 vols., 1700pp.

Daly, R. A., 1934, "The Changing World of the Ice Age," New Haven, Yale University Press, 271pp.

Derbyshire, E., 1962, "Late-glacial drainage in part of north-east Wales: an alternative hypothesis," *Proc. Geologists Assoc. Engl.,* **73,** 327–334.

Flint, R. F., 1957, "Glacial and Pleistocene Geology," New York, John Wiley & Sons, 553pp.

Fredén, C., 1967, "A historical review of the Ancylus Lake and the Svea River," *Förh. Geol. Fören. Stockholm,* **89,** 239–267.

Holmes, A., 1965, "Principles of Physical Geology," Second ed., London, T. Nelson & Sons; New York, Ronald Press, 1288pp.

Hough, J. L., 1958, "Geology of the Great Lakes," Urbana, University of Illinois Press, 313pp.

Howard, A. D., 1958, "Drainage evolution in northeastern Montana and northwestern North Dakota," *Bull. Geol. Soc. Am.,* **69,** 575–588.

Jamieson, T. F., 1863, "On the parallel roads of Glen Roy, and their place in the history of the glacial period," *Quart. J. Geol. Soc., London,* **19,** 235–259.

Kendall, P. F., 1902, "A system of glacier-lakes in the Cleveland Hills," *Quart. J. Geol. Soc., London,* **58,** 471–571.

Sissons, J. B., 1958, "Sub-glacial stream erosion in

southern Northumberland," *Scot. Geogr. Mag.,* **74,** 163–174.

Sparks, B. W., 1960, "Geomorphology," London, Longmans Green; New York, John Wiley & Sons, 371pp.

Thorarinsson, S., 1939, "The ice dammed lakes of Iceland with particular reference to their values as indicators of glacier oscillations," *Geogr. Ann., Stockholm,* **21,** 216–242.

Twidale, C. R., 1956, "Longitudinal profiles of some glacial overflow channels," *Geogr. J.,* **122**(1), 88–92.

Valentin, H., 1957, "Glazialmorphologische Untersuchungen in Ostengland," Berlin, Univ. Geog. Inst., Abh. **4,** 86pp.

Woldstedt, P., 1950, "Norddeutschland und angrenzende Gebiete im Eiszeitalter," Stuttgart, Geogr. Handbücher.

Woldstedt, P., 1954/65, "Das Eiszeitalter," Second ed., Stuttgart, Enke Verlag, 3 vols.

Cross-references: *Buried Valleys; Eskers; Glacial Lakes; Glacial Lake Agassiz; Great Lakes* (*N. America*); *Kame; Loess; Postglacial Isostatic Rebound; Streams —Underfit.* pr Vol. VI: *Varves.*

GLACIAL STAIRWAY

The longitudinal profile of a former mountain (or valley) glacier is rarely graded to a more or less smooth exponential curve as is the "ideal" fluvial profile. Instead it is subdivided into numbers of giant steps often with overdeepened hollows between. This profile is known as a *glacial stairway.* Continuing the analogy, the flattish sectors are known as *treads,* and the steep parts are known as *risers;* the rock bar at the crest of the rise is sometimes called the *threshold* or *riegel* (an Alpine term). Riegel is any natural rock dam (Stamp, 1961). Where the overdeepened treads are undrained, there are rock-cut depressions or partly morainedammed pools, and these occur in series. They are known as *paternoster lakes,* an allusion to a string of prayer beads.

The wavelike scour and flattening profile of some alpine-type glaciated valleys has long attracted attention, but the precise cause has been a subject of considerable discussion. Overdeepened scours (of over 1000 meters) have been noted even in the low-relief, continental glaciated landscapes of the Permo-Carboniferous (in Australia) and those of the Quaternary glaciation on the Canadian Shield (see *Glacial Scour*). It has sometimes been suggested that the outstanding glacial stairs of the Yosemite Valley are due to the well-recognized youthful uplift of the Sierra Nevada during the late Quaternary. This valley rises a total of 7600 feet in 21 miles, but differential uplift was not the preferred explanation of Matthes (1930) whose "professional paper" on the Yosemite Valley is one of the classics of geology. Yosemite was the inspiration for numbers of hypotheses to explain the stairways, and the principal ones may be summarized here:

(1). "Frost-sapping" was proposed by Willard D. Johnson (1904, though later abandoned according to Matthes, 1930, p. 94). This concept involved freeze-and-thaw action in the valley walls and floor at such points as crevasses which permitted sharp temperature contrasts, a sort of modified *Bergschrund* (q.v.) hypothesis, a theory that also had to be revised considerably to explain the excavation of *cirques* (q.v.).

(2) An ice-fall hypothesis was advocated by the Australian geologist E. C. Andrews (1910), who pointed out that the erosive energy of the glacier in its steep ice-fall sectors would be much greater than in the gentle grades, and thus the steeper sectors would become progressively enlarged and, incidentally, would migrate gradually headward (as would Johnson's ice-sapping fronts).

(3) A slightly different version of this glacial energy concept invokes the presence of wider and narrower sectors along the valley. At the wider points, erosive energy would decrease, while in

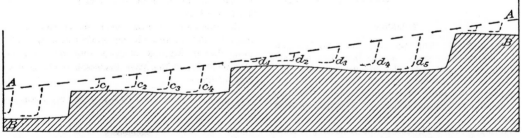

FIG. 1. Longitudinal section of a canyon illustrating the process whereby, according to Willard D. Johnson, a glacial stairway would be produced by the recession of successive nickpoints. AA represents the profile of the preglacial canyon floor; BB that of the glacial stairway. A nickpoint or cliff such as c_1 would be cut back by intense frost action at the foot of crevasses in the glacier, thus receding in the course of time to the successive positions marked c_2, c_3, etc., and leaving a flat or slightly basined tread. Meanwhile another cliff, d_1, situated at a higher level, would recede headward to the successive positions marked d_2, d_3, etc. The steps of a glacial stairway, according to this conception, would be essentially migrant features that would shift their positions rather rapidly while the glacial processes were active, regardless of the structure of the rock (Matthes, 1930). Compare with Fig. 2.

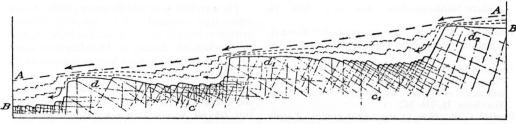

Fig. 2. Longitudinal section of a canyon illustrating the mode of development of a glacial stairway by selective quarrying. AA represents the profile of the preglacial canyon floor; BB that of the glacial stairway. Bodies of closely jointed rock, such as c and c_1, are readily quarried out by the glacier, but bodies of sparsely jointed, unquarriable rock, such as d and d_1, are very difficult to erode. Competent rock like this is reducible only by abrasion, and remains standing as obstructions with flattened and smoothed tops and steep, more or less hackled fronts. The broken lines indicate successive stages in the development of the steps and treads. The arrows indicate the direction of ice movement (Matthes, 1930).

constricted passages, the glacier would thicken and erosive energy would be enhanced, causing deep scouring. Unfortunately, not all rises coincide with constrictions.

(4) A rock-competence hypothesis was urged by Matthes (1930), who pointed out that close jointing marks inner "treads" in the crystalline rocks of Yosemite valley (i.e., incompetent), while the "risers" and threshold of the treads are marked by extremely massive and scarcely jointed rocks. Thus there would be a selective quarrying by the moving ice over rocks of differential competence or strength. In fluvial terminology, therefore, a semipermanent rockbar is found to coincide with the risers rather than a random distribution of headward-migrating nick points. At Yosemite, the lowering of the canyon floor in this way has been on the order of 1000 meters since the first glaciation, and 500 meters since the last interglacial.

While there is little doubt that the conclusion reached by Matthes is correct, an important aspect has been noted by Bakker (1965), which was previously ignored. That is the question of pre-Quaternary or interglacial chemical weathering. This "predestination" by rock rotting (saprolite) underlines all glacial scouring.

RHODES W. FAIRBRIDGE

References

Andrews, E. C., 1910, "An excursion to the Yosemite (California), or studies in the formation of alpine cirques, 'steps,' and valley 'treads',' *J. Proc. Roy. Soc. N.S. Wales,* **44,** 262–315.

Bakker, J. P., 1965, "A forgotten factor in the interpretation of glacial stairways," *Z. Geomorphol.,* **9,** 18–34.

Johnson, W. D., 1904, "The profile of maturity of alpine glacial erosion," *J. Geol.,* **12,** 569–578.

Matthes, R. C., 1930, "Geologic history of the Yosemite Valley," *U.S. Geol. Surv. Profess. Paper* **160,** 137pp.

Stamp, L. D. (editor), 1961, "A Glossary of Geographical Terms," London, Longmans, Green and Co., 539pp.

Thornbury, W. D., 1954, "Principles of Geomorphology," New York, John Wiley & Sons, 618pp.

Cross-references: *Bergschrund; Crevasse; Cirque; Frost Action; Glacial Scour; Nickpoint; Quaternary Period; Regolith and Saprolite; Valley (Mountain) Glacier; Weathering.* pr vol. VI: *Glacier Geophysics.*

GLACIAL VALLEY

A valley that is primarily U-shaped is not to be found in regions that have not been glaciated. Valleys today that are partly occupied by retreating mountain glaciers also show the distinctive U-shaped profile in the sector recently abandoned by the ice. The U-shaped valley or trough is therefore taken to be a characteristic feature of mountain glaciation. Its walls are frequently marked by striated pavements, while the floors are generally veneered by till of the ground moraine or by successive abandoned end moraines. The tributary streams to the glacial valley are today often hanging and decorated by high waterfalls, e.g., Lauterbrunnental, Switzerland.

Since the floor of a glaciated valley is often undulating (due to morainic dams) or with a step-like rock floor (see *Glacial Stairway*), it is sometimes marked by a succession of lakes, strung out like a row of beads, and hence rather fancifully named *paternoster lakes,* after the beads of a rosary (Cotton, 1942).

The question of how much the erosion of a glacial valley represents the modification of previous fluvial drainage features and *vice versa* is controversial; it has been discussed in the article *Glacial Scour.*

RHODES W. FAIRBRIDGE

References

Cotton, C. A., 1942, "Climatic Accidents," Christchurch, N.Z., Whitcombe & Tombs, 354pp.

Davis, W. M., 1900, "Glacial erosion in France, Switzerland, and Norway," *Proc. Boston Soc. Nat. Hist.,* **29,** 273–322 (also in "Geographical Essays," 1909, New York, Dover reprint, 1954).

Davis, W. M., 1906, "The sculpture of mountains by

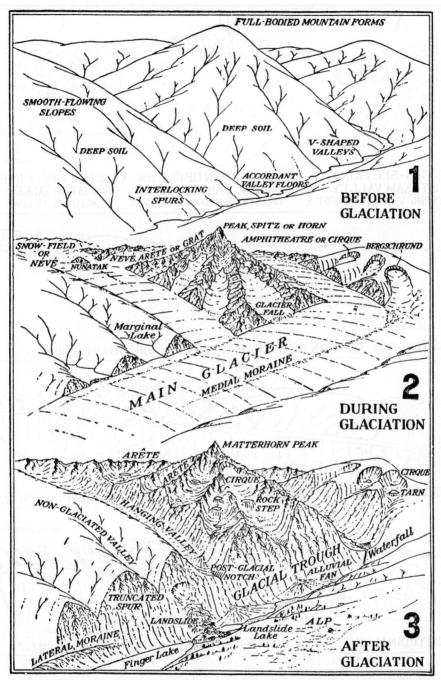

FIG. 1. A mountain region before, during, and after glaciation, illustrating the history of a glacial valley (after W. M. Davis, from Lobeck, 1939). (By permission of McGraw-Hill Book Co., N.Y.)

glaciers," *Scot. Geogr. Mag.,* **22,** 76–89 (also in "Geographical Essays," 1909, New York, Dover reprint, 1954).

Embleton, C. and King, C. A. M., 1968, "Glacial and Periglacial Geomorphology," London, E. Arnold Ltd., 608pp.

Lobeck, A. K., 1939, "Geomorphology," New York, McGraw-Hill Book Co., 731pp.

Cross-references: *Corrasion; Fjord; Glacial Scour; Glacial Stairway; Glaciation; Hanging Valley; Moraine; Mountain Glacier Landscapes; Striae.*

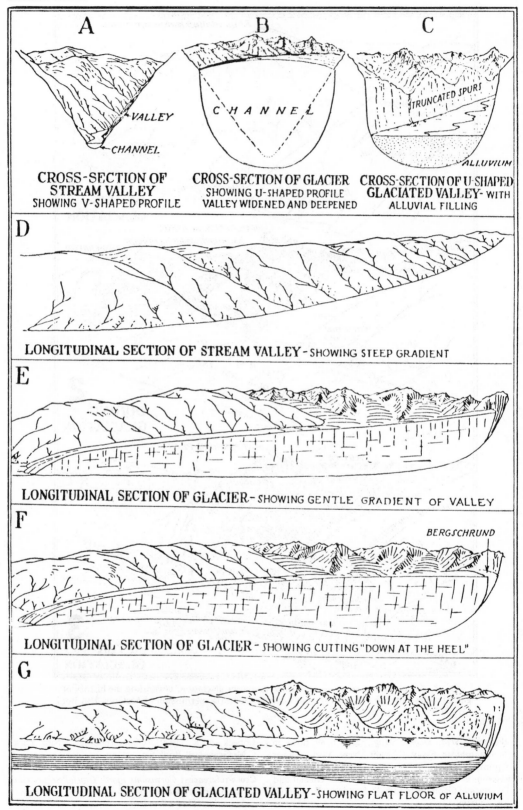

A

VALLEY

CHANNEL

CROSS-SECTION OF
STREAM VALLEY
SHOWING V-SHAPED PROFILE

B

CHANNEL

CROSS-SECTION OF GLACIER
SHOWING U-SHAPED PROFILE
VALLEY WIDENED AND DEEPENED

C

TRUNCATED SPURS

ALLUVIUM

CROSS-SECTION OF U-SHAPED
GLACIATED VALLEY- WITH
ALLUVIAL FILLING

D

LONGITUDINAL SECTION OF STREAM VALLEY-SHOWING STEEP GRADIENT

E

LONGITUDINAL SECTION OF GLACIER- SHOWING GENTLE GRADIENT OF VALLEY

F

BERGSCHRUND

LONGITUDINAL SECTION OF GLACIER - SHOWING CUTTING "DOWN AT THE HEEL"

G

LONGITUDINAL SECTION OF GLACIATED VALLEY-SHOWING FLAT FLOOR OF ALLUVIUM

FIG. 2. The development of glacial troughs (Lobeck, 1939). (By permission of McGraw-Hill Book Co., N.Y.)

GLACIATION, GLACIERIZATION

In general terms, glaciation refers to the processes related to the formation of glaciers, the erosion, shaping and modeling of the landscape by moving ice and its partial mantling by glacial deposits. Normally, nothing about scale is implied. As Flint (1957) has pointed out, a few minor striations may be the only known trace of a continent-wide glaciation.

In 1922 Wright and Priestley (who had been on the famous Scott Antarctic Expedition) sought to distinguish between the *process* of ice action (regardless of scale), and the ice age *phenomenon* of vast continental areas of ice coverage, thus: (a) *Glaciation*, "the erosive action exercised by land ice upon the land over which it flows" (p. 134). (b) *Glacierization*, "the inundation of land by ice." One may say of a contemporary ice-covered landscape that it is being "glacierized," but after it has been laid bare once more one says it has been "glaciated." This distinction is sometimes recognized, particularly in Britain and in some European countries, but a broader usage of "glaciation" is so widespread that the exclusive, limited definition is likely to cause confusion. Implications of time and scale normally emerge from the context. Thus one speaks of *mountain* (or valley or Alpine-type) *glaciation,* versus *continental glaciation.* The distinction is made between an individual *glacier,* an *icecap* (as in Spitzbergen today, or the Alps during the Quaternary glacial stages), and an *ice sheet* (as in Greenland or Antarctica today or over North America or northern Europe during the Quaternary glacial stages; see for example, Demorest, 1943).

Using ice temperature as a criterion for classification, Ahlmann distinguished three types:

(a) *Temperate glaciers:* at 0°C, or close to the

FIG. 1. High alpine-type glaciation in mid-latitudes. Southeast face, Mount Cook, South Island, New Zealand, Mount Tasman right background. Caroline Glacier bottom foreground. Anzac Peaks mid-right. Complexly folded Mesozoic greywackes. Note the relatively large rocky areas where seasonal melting occurs and the restricted, narrow and steep sectors of glacier ice with many precipitous ice falls. Frost riving, bergschrund plucking and mass-wasting compete with ice transport as erosion agents. (Photo: S. N. Beatus, New Zealand Geological Survey).

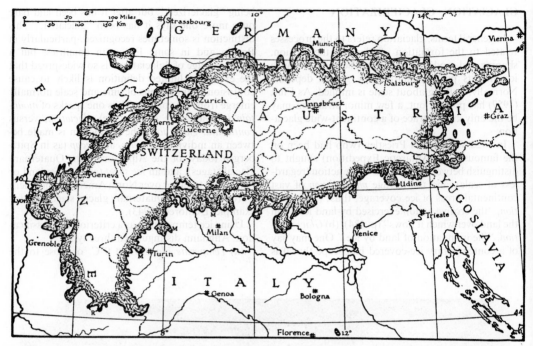

FIG. 2. Map of the best-known Pleistocene icecap, the Alps of Switzerland, France, Italy, Austria and southern Germany (from E. Antevs, 1929). Outer border: maximum ice extent during Riss and Mindel stages; inner border: maximum ice extent during Würm (last) glaciation.

appropriate temperature for melting, corresponding to the local pressure.

(b) *High-polar glaciers:* always below the melting point temperature, at least in their accumulation areas.

(c) *Subpolar glaciers:* in the accumulation areas, the temperature from the surface to a dozen meters or more is below the freezing point, but in summer superficial melting occurs.

The statistics of former glacierization (Flint, 1957) are largely derived from identification of areas once covered with ice (evidence of tillites, etc.) and from thickness estimates. The latter present problems; ice loading may sometimes be gauged from consolidation tests of overridden clays and silts (Harrison, 1958), while in mountain areas the maximum heights of glacial deposits and striated surfaces may be surveyed. Certain peaks ("nunataks") may have projected above the ice, but many difficulties arise. Ice striations once present may be lost because of postglacial frost weathering of surfaces. Also, what of the areas with no such height gauges?

Periods of Glaciation

In stratigraphy the term "glaciation" is usually taken to be an event on the grand scale, i.e., associated with an *ice age* (see Vol. II, *Ice Age Theory*). During earth history there have been definite periods in which glacierization was widespread. There were

several distinct stages of the Precambrian to earliest Cambrian, the Siluro-Devonian (of South America and Africa only), the Permo-Carboniferous (of all the southern hemisphere, but not the northern), the Quaternary (Pleistocene, plus Holocene). Very many reports of suspected glaciation at other times are now found to be incorrect (Salomon-Calvi, 1931, 1933; Schwarzbach, 1963), having been engendered in part by overanxiety to support the Lyellian doctrine of Uniformitarianism, by a desire to negate the theory of Continental Displacement, or simply by careless observation of the criteria for past glaciation. It seems very likely that periods of ancient glaciation lasted for epochs of 10 million to 50 million years; there is no evidence whatever for assuming that the Quaternary ice age is over just because we are in a warm phase, inasmuch as it may be merely an interglacial oscillation.

The continuity of the present ice age is suggested by the continued ice coverage (glacierization) of Antarctica, 13×10^6 km^2. and Greenland and smaller icecaps, 2×10^6 km^2. During the Quaternary ice age, there has been a repeated advance and retreat of continental ice sheets over North America and northern Europe, to achieve a maximum extent of 45×10^6 km^2, corresponding to a world ice volume estimated about 80×10^6 km^3 compared to a present volume of about 30×10^6 km^3. (The calculations are difficult because the topography of the ice floor is still not well established.) The latest

FIG. 3. Valley glaciers, showing development of ablation moraines, additionally fed by extensive talus cones. Tasman Glacier, New Zealand. (Photo: S. N. Beatus, New Zealand Geological Survey).

Soviet figures (Voronov, 1965) suggest that at the glacial maximum Antarctica carried 12×10^6 km³ more ice than today (= 30-meters sea level drop), plus 42×10^6 km³ for the rest of the world (= 105 meters), thus a total glacial advance of 54×10^6 km³ (= 135 meters.) Such *glacial stages* (lasting 20 thousand to 50 thousand years) were separated by *interglacial stages* (of equal or greater length). Minor advances and retreats are termed *stades* or *stadials* and *interstades* or *interstadials* (Lüttig, 1965), respectively representing "kryomers" (cold) and "thermomers" (warm oscillations).

Criteria for Glaciation

Unequivocal proofs of the presence of former glaciers are far from easily established, since numerous pseudo-glacial indications are now known. The best criteria for former glaciations on a large scale are:

(a) *Striated pavements,* where the striations, furrows and gouges may be followed some distance, preferably in parallel or subparallel patterns, and following recognized *regional* trends.

(b) *Till, tillite or boulder clay* in extensive accumulations, in geotectonic settings inappropriate for mudslides.

(c) *Faceted pebbles and boulders* in great numbers, upon which the striations are largely parallel and the facets pronounced; the striae of "pseudo-glacial" boulders are generally irregular and short while facets are unusual.

(d) *Topographic modification,* such as disruption of drainage, scouring of deep troughs, closed basins and so on.

(e) *Erratic boulders* ("*perched blocks*") in anomalous topographic positions requiring glacial transport.

Other *compatible evidence* can be used, e.g., stunt-

ing of marine faunas, widespread traces of eustatic regressions (e.g., a replacement in the stratigraphic record of shallow marine facies by continental formations), mid-latitude appearance periglacial phenomena (solifluction, cryoturbation, frost riving, thermokarst).

It is the *convergence of multiple evidence* that convinces geologists rather than any isolated criterion, together with the *repetition of the evidence over broad geographic regions* and the *absence of contra-indications* (rich and varied faunas, coral reefs, carbonate rocks in general, lateritic soils and so on). The first thorough examination of the many false claims for "glacial" events was made by Salomon-Calvi (1931) and also developed in his book "*Die permokarbonischen Eiszeiten*" (1933). Schwarzbach (1963) has prepared a good summary of these indications (see Table 1).

It is often considered to be a wise policy nowadays to label an unusual mixture of pebbles and boulders in a fine-grained matrix as "*pebbly mudstone*" or "*diamictite*," which may be a mudslide deposit or indeed any sort of "accidental" mixture such as is caused by a gravitational flow, but can easily be taken for a glacial till, i.e., it is a *pseudotillite*. *Striations* may be made during landslides and mudslides or by the movements of gypsum or salt "glaciers." The latter are not formed by gravitational movements at all but by diapirism. These features may be called *pseudo-glacial striations*. Crowell (1964) calls randomly transported boulders of unspecified origin "dispersed megaclasts". Till, mudflow and turbidite have been compared by Heezen and Hollister (1964). Stunted fossils may be due to growth limitations instituted by the cold, but they may also be stunted by hypersalinity and other causes.

FIG. 4. The site of a glaciated valley in relatively soft rocks, now being extensively dissected by postglacial consequent streams. Glacial benches, Rakaia Valley, South Island, New Zealand. (Photo: S. N. Beatus, New Zealand Geological Survey).

TABLE 1. CHARACTERISTICS OF MORAINES AND PSEUDOMORAINES (SLIGHTLY MODIFIED AFTER SCHWARZBACH, 1963)

	Moraines (Till and Tillite)	Glacio-marine Deposits, in part tillite	Pseudomoraines in Part				
			Slumped Masses		Fanglomerate	Volcanic Breccias	Tectonic Breccias
			Subaerial	Subaqueous			
Cause	Glaciers	Icebergs	Gravity, often + earthquakes (landslides): thixotropic and periglacial processes	Gravity usually + earthquakes	Flowing water in arid regions	Volcanic processes (fissure filling, pyroclastics)	Tectonic processes (may combine with subaerial or subaqueous slumps)
Bedding	Absent (but boulders mostly oriented)	Present (at least in lenses)	Absent	Absent or present	Often indistinct	Absent or present	Absent
Sorting	Absent	Absent	Absent	Absent or present	Often indistinct	Absent or present	Absent
Shape of blocks	Rounded and faceted boulders often present	As for moraines	Mostly angular: rounded boulders possible[a]	Mostly angular (possibly rounded boulders[a])	Often poorly rounded	Angular	Angular
Striated blocks	Normally present	Present	Rare (short, curved striae)	Rare	Absent	Possible	Rare (irregular)
Striated pavements	Occasionally present: best criterion for glaciation	Possible in a few cases	Rare	Rare	Absent	Possible, with pyroclastics: slickensides	Slickensides possible
Contortion of the bedrock	Not uncommon	Possible in a few cases	Rare	Occasionally present	Absent	Absent	Possible
Type of blocks	Polymict	Polymict	Often monomict	Monomict or polymict	Usually polymict	Always include blocks of volcanic rocks	Usually few types
Source of blocks	Often distant (100–1000 km)	Mostly distant	Local	Local or fairly distant	Mostly fairly local	Sometimes from great depth	Mostly local
Initial dip	Almost horizontal, or conforms to relief	Horizontal	Shallow dip	Shallow dip	Almost horizontal	Vertical, inclined or horizontal	Steep or shallow
Peculiarities	Often extensive distribution, matrix clay or silt (unweathered), usually more abundant than blocks	Associated marine fossils: matrix usually clay (poorly weathered)	Notably in clays rich in montmorillonite or salts	Often with slumped balls and limnic or marine fossils	Little matrix (washed out, or in pockets)	Often with weathered ash (bentonite, etc.)	Often in narrow zone, a structural boundary

a Already faceted boulders may be caught up in slumped mass.

Theory of Glaciation

The concept that there might once have been very much more extensive glacierization than today did not emerge in geologic literature until the nineteenth century. As Flint (1957) has pointed out, Swiss peasants, who lived near glaciers that periodically advanced or retreated, must have appreciated the local meaning of glacierization and deglacierization; indeed some of the Swiss glaciers were twice as long in Roman times as today, having readvanced extensively since mid-Holocene (Neolithic) days.

The very idea of *climatic oscillation* was very late in gaining acceptance. In 1686, Robert Hooke in England recognized that the rich fauna of giant ammonites, turtles, etc., in Jurassic rocks reflected a much warmer environment than today and suggested that variation in the tilt of the earth's axis was responsible for global climatic change, an example of astounding prescience, which was only confirmed in the mid-twentieth century. The possible climatic role of celestial mechanics was discussed in 1830 by Sir John Herschel and in 1842 by J. F. Adhémar in Paris, but it received little attention (see references in Schwarzbach, 1963). Buffon in France (1778), so wise in his understanding of many paleontological facts, believed evidences of climate change to be simply products of secular cooling of a once molten earth, failing to recognize a once cooler environment.

In Switzerland, erratic blocks scattered over the lush lower pastures had been recognized in the eighteenth century (de Saussure, Kuhn, Hugi) as evidence of former glaciers, but the cause-and-effect relationship was not wildly remote. Even so their transportation was attributed by de Saussure and others to catastrophic floods. Hutton, on reading de Saussure's work, argued that they were glacier transported. On the other hand, in Scotland, totally devoid of glaciers today, the mental jump was considerably greater and thus it was a revolutionary event when Playfair in 1802 first identified erratic blocks there. In 1821, a Swiss engineer, Ignatz Venetz, demonstrated the former vast extent of the Alpine glaciers, and in 1824, Esmark argued the same case for Norway. A professor of forestry, R. Bernhardi (1832), recognized the erratics of north Germany as products of glacier transport. This was a particularly significant step, because by no stretch of the imagination could one argue that erratics far out on the North German Plain could be the debris of extended Alpine valley glaciers. Jean de Charpentier (1834), on the basis of extensive field work, confirmed the idea that much of northern Europe, as well as the Alps, had once been ice covered. His major work *Essai sur les Glaciers* unfortunately did not appear until 1841, thus after the work of Agassiz and others (see below).

In opposition to this grand glaciation concept,

FIG. 5. Former glaciated valley, now extensively modified and silted up. Eglinton Valley, a U-shaped glaciated valley, South Island, New Zealand. (Photo: White's Aviation Ltd., Auckland, New Zealand).

FIG. 6. Former glaciated U-shaped valley, now a fjord, drowned by postglacial rise of sea level. Milford Sound, South Island, New Zealand. (Photo: V. C. Browne, Christchurch, New Zealand).

the Rev. Dean Buckland at Oxford, a very remarkable general geologist and stratigrapher, was anxious to maintain some compatibility with his theological concepts and proposed that the Quaternary "drift" was evidence of the biblical or Noachian flood; this became the celebrated *Drift Theory*, the idea that erratic blocks were dropped by drifting ice floes at the time of the flood. For deposits of the Pleistocene, Buckland and Mantell (1822) proposed "diluvium," in contrast to alluvium, which designates the present (Holocene) fluvial deposits. The name *diluvium* has persisted especially in central Europe as a general name for the Pleistocene (though latterly with no genetic connotation). Both "drift" in English-speaking countries and "diluvium" in central Europe are thus often retained as anachronisms, to remind us of the widespread correlation in the early nineteenth century between the Noachian flood and what we now know as evidence for glaciation.

In 1830, there appeared the first volume of Sir Charles Lyell's "*Principles of Geology*" which was destined to establish earth study as a fundamental science. Lyell correctly regarded climate change as closely related to physical change of land and ocean relationships, but he too was early misled by the Drift Theory, being particularly impressed by the importance of Arctic ice floes, at that time much in the news because of pioneer polar exploration.

In 1837, the celebrated plant geographer, K. F. Schimper, first used the term "ice age" (*Eiszeit* in German). It was in the same year that the youthful Swiss zoologist Louis Agassiz (destined to become Harvard's "most famous professor") pictured to the Swiss National History Society the former extension of vast ice sheets of northern Europe and Asia, *before* the significant rise of the Alpine chain. This remarkable contribution *Études sur les Glaciers* appeared in 1840, but it was not until 1847 that he revised his opinion and recognized the Alpine glaciers as distinct from the continental ice sheets originating in Scandinavia.

Buckland visited Agassiz in Switzerland in 1838 and there became convinced. Together they studied and verified the evidence for glaciation also in Britain, but the glacial theory at that time gained

476

FIG. 7. Stages in the evolution of a glaciated mountain landscape according to W. M. Davis (redrawn by R. Kettner). (See p. 469 for details.)

little acceptance and was largely ridiculed. Even Lyell, though accepting the mountain glaciation of Scotland, found the idea of iceberg transport for the English "drift" more acceptable for many years. The Drift Theory was only finally crushed by the work of T. F. Jamieson (1865) and Archibald Geikie (1863). In North Germany, the geologists were not finally convinced until the Swede Otto Torell demonstrated the association of striations with erratics of Scandinavian origin.

In North America there was early but isolated recognition of the meaning of glacial striae and the probability of ice transport. According to Flint (1965), one of the first to see the light was Peter Dobson in 1826 (in Connecticut). The paleontologist Conrad had heard of the work of Agassiz and, in 1839, had attributed to glaciation the striated rock surfaces of western New York state, to be followed in 1841 by Hitchcock with similar views of New Hampshire. In 1846, L. Agassiz was appointed to Harvard, and J. D. Dana at Yale soon accepted the new concept, but there was widespread opposition to the idea of continental glaciation, as in Europe, that lasted throughout the nineteenth century.

As for pre-Quaternary glaciations, in 1855 Ramsay attributed (wrongly) the Permian boulder beds of northern England to ice action, but in 1856 the first of the genuinely glacial Permian moraines of "Gondwanaland" was discovered in India by Blanford. Discoveries of ancient tillites later followed in Australia, South Africa and Brazil. A fantastic planetary paradox was presented when it was realized that they were all essentially contemporaneous, that they spanned the equator and encompassed approximately one-half of the entire globe. This is surely one of the most important geological discoveries of all time since it opened a "Pandora's Box" of brilliant hypotheses, including continental spreading, polar migration and climatic change that even now rank among the greatest problems of the earth sciences.

Some Consequences of Glacierization

Maclaren (1841) first pointed out the effect of glaciation on sea level, and in North America the subject was discussed in detail by Whittlesey (1868) and later workers. It was only in 1886 that Suess applied the term *eustasy* to it. It was decades later that Daly brought out the effects of glacio-eustasy on *coral reef* (q.v.) development.

The theoretical consequences of the temporary loading of the earth's crust by ice sheets, causing depression and subsequent isostatic recovery, were developed by Jamieson (1865) and later applied to the coast of Maine by N. S. Shaler (1874). The time lag in crustal recovery (due to subcrustal viscosity, etc.) was recognized by McGee (1881). On pluvial Lake Bonneville, water loading was studied by Gilbert (1890) who determined that its subsequent disappearance has led to upwarping of the lacustrine terraces. The Great Lakes region, the Canadian shield and the Scandinavian shield have since been systematically mapped, and recovery rates have been determined precisely. The "Gondwanaland" Permo-Carboniferous deformation left basins that have not yet totally recovered, because ice loading was replaced by till, and then by lakes and by continental deposits.

The Pluvial Theory and Tropical Desiccation

Extensive fluvial gravel deposits and boulder trains that seem to correspond in time to the ice age exist in regions far removed from glaciation (e.g., north Africa). The term *pluvial periods* was coined by Alfred Tylor (1868) for the successive episodes of extensive terrace gravel building. Hull (1885),

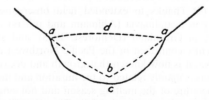

FIG. 8. Transverse profile section of a glaciated valley (*aca*). *aba*, valley before glaciation; *ada*, original surface of ice. Note the shoulders at *a, a* (from Lahee, 1961).

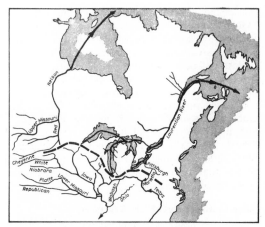

FIG. 9. Modification of preglacial drainage of North America. Note how the upper Missouri and Red River formerly flowed into the Nelson and how the ancient Teays formerly took much of the Appalachian drainage. The modern Great Lakes represent excavation and broadening of the former Laurentian drainage (modified after Horberg, Flint and others; from Termier, 1963). (By permission of D. Van Nostrand Co., Princeton, N.J.)

Blanckenhorn and others later extended the term to the subtropics. The false concept arose that glaciation was caused by a worldwide increase in precipitation, and this still clouds certain theories of climate change and glaciation (cf. the Ewing-Donn hypothesis; see Schwarzbach, 1963; Fairbridge, 1964a and b). In 1863 Escher von der Linth and E. Desor had proposed a diluvial "Sahara Sea" as the cause of the Pleistocene continental ice of the northern hemisphere. An unfortunate confusion of cause and effect was established that is still repeated by some observers. Furthermore, it was widely presumed that fluvial gravels reflected evidence of great rainfall. Increased precipitation at high altitudes was supposed to lead to snow accumulation and thus to the growth of glaciers. This assumption was wrong in most (but not all) areas on two separate counts: (1) The heavy alluviation of rivers is generally thought to be due to an increase of load, so-called overloading, or a decrease in discharge during glacial periods. Alluviation can be a mixed consequence of decreasing vegetative cover, periglacial slope movements (solifluction), high subglacier gravel discharge and possibly *reduced* rainfall. (2) Thanks to extended field observations, partly in Scandinavia (Ahlmann and others) and partly in Greenland (Demorest, 1943), and subsequently confirmed in the Pacific Northwest and Alaska, it is now known that growth and decay of glaciers is mainly related to the duration and mean temperature of the melting season and not simply to the quantity of snow that falls. The snowfall may be actually greater in a mild season, and anomalous ice advances may coincide with warmer periods. The

long-term picture calls for a general drop in temperature during glacial advances and a rise during deglaciation.

In 1875, James Croll published his epoch-making "Climate and Time in Their Geological Relations," which developed Adhémar's concept of glaciation due to the earth's orbital and tilt relationships; later it was developed still further by Milankovitch and by Bacsák, and its geological correlations were explored by Soergel and by Zeuner (1959). Croll pointed out that if climate change was due to small variations in the earth's effective insolation, then at times of deglaciation an important delay should be experienced, a *retardation factor* that would require the mean air temperature to rise well in advance of total glacial melting (latent heat, ice volume/surface area ratio, etc.). The writer has demonstrated that in fact there was a retardation of over 10,000 years involved in the Würm/Wisconsin deglaciation (Fairbridge, 1961). The time when the effective solar radiation (insolation) curve passed the present mean level going from the low peak to the postglacial high peak was 16,000 years B.P.; however, the postglacial curve of mean sea level rise just reached the present level at 6000 B.P.; since that time there have been only minor oscillations. These dates were first established with the aid of de Geer's varve counting method and were later confirmed by C^{14} methods. An extension of absolute dating back to several hundred thousand years, together with a minor recalculation of one of the astronomic parameters used by Milankovitch, has recently permitted Broecker (1966) to achieve a brilliant correlation between glaciation events and astronomic control for a sufficient number of cyclic oscillations to be statistically valid beyond any reasonable doubt.

Consideration of the meteorological conditions attendant upon glaciation (see *Ice Age Meteorology*, Vol. II) discloses that reduced solar radiation during glacierization leads to reduced evaporation from the ocean (Flohn, 1963) by a factor of at least 20 %, not even allowing for reduced oceanic surfaces; although in certain areas increased wind velocities may have raised evaporation rates, the latter cannot have been significant in the shrunken trade wind belts. Because of westerlies displaced 1000 km or more toward the equator, higher rainfalls occurred in certain regions that led to great pluvial lakes, as already envisioned by Jamieson in 1863, extended by Whitney (1865) to the Basin-Range Province, and strikingly demonstrated by Russell (1889) at Lake Lahontan and by Gilbert (1890) at Lake Bonneville, where glacial debris interfingers with high lake terrace deposits. Meinzer (1922) showed that the wettest areas of this province today were driest during glaciation and vice versa; he also made a pioneer attempt at determining a numerical mean temperature difference.

In the immediate periphery of the ice front, anti-

FIG. 10. A glacially modified valley, Glenariff, County Antrim, in Northern Ireland. Partly ice scoured, and serving as a late-glacial spillway, it was then flooded by the postglacial eustatic transgression (note "relict cliffs," lower right) and later isostatically uplifted; the slopes were modified by periglacial talus (from the basalt capping) and solifluction. (Photo: Aerofilms, London).

cyclonic and katabatic winds led to extreme desiccation and traces of sand-abraded rock surfaces are matched by extended dune fields, as in Nebraska and across the North German Plains. The *loess*, the fine dust from this wind erosion, was found right across North America and from western Europe to China. It was after travels in China that both Von Richthofen (1877) and Pumpelly (1879) eventually traced the loess to its origin in glacial outwash material. Some loess has clearly been recycled by streams, and until quite recently certain geologists still tried to claim its fluvial origin.

In subtropical to tropical regions the pluvial theorists (e.g., Blanckenhorn, Nilsson and others) claimed that "glaciation" equals "pluviation," thus correlating formerly much more extensive Quaternary lakes in central Africa (Lake Chad, Lake Victoria, etc.) with glacial ice maxima. This concept is absolutely opposed to meteorological principles, since cooler ocean waters must lead to reduced evaporation. Furthermore, eustatic lowering of sea level led to a total oceanic area reduction by about 10%, while extensive ice floe coverage further reduced its potential evaporating surface area. In addition, there was the extended cooling influence of iceberg melting, traced by their dumped erratics to latitudes 30–40° in both northern and southern hemispheres.

The idea that much of tropical Africa became a desert during periods of mid-latitude glaciation is partly due to the author (Fairbridge 1962, 1964b), but clues to such conclusions were obtained in discussions and from readings in the French literature of archeology from West Africa and the Congo (Balout, Tricart, Michel, Vogt, de Plooey and others). Confirmation also came from Brazil (Bigarella, 1965) and from personal observations in Australia. In both West Africa and northwestern Australia, the desert dunes could be observed disappearing below sea level and extending over the continental shelf, clear evidence that the desertic phases were to be correlated with glaciation events. This conclusion could be drawn also from the evidence of fluvial arkoses (arid indicators) found

FIG. 11. Glacial striations on a roche moutonnée, the ultimate criterion of glaciation. Riverside Park, New York City. (Photo: R. W. Fairbridge).

down to 100 meters below sea level in bores near the coast (e.g. Brazil), even before the availability of C^{14} dates. It is now recognized that the great rivers of Africa, the Congo, Nile, Niger, Senegal, etc., largely dried up during glacial epochs. The great pluvial stages of the tropics were interglacial in their timing.

Dating of Glaciations

Relating nonmarine formations to the geologic time scale has always been difficult, because of the absence of marine fossils, the standard yardstick. In the Quaternary, this difficulty has been aggravated by the rapid alternations of glacial and interglacial conditions and the relatively short overall extent of the period. The latter is now believed to be about 2.0×10^6 years, judging from fossil data and the appearance of glacial debris in deep-sea cores in the Southern Ocean, cross-checked by absolute dating of contemporary igneous events and the sequence of paleomagnetic reversals. Although with each magnetic reversal there appears to have been a subtle change in genetic mutations, resulting in the appearance of new species, these faunal modifications were relatively minor and too few in overall number to stimulate a gross evolutionary development such as would permit easy paleontologic zonation. In contrast, the fossil changes from horizon to horizon often reflect rather the climatic and general environmental changes, and consequent migrations led to diachronism more readily than to direct evolution. A certain rather arbitrary decision is usually made by stratigraphers for deciding such transitional boundaries. A particularly characteristic site and horizon is selected, usually one that has a historical priority, and then formally adopted by international agreement.

The lower boundary of the Pleistocene was thus settled by agreement at the International Geological Congress in London (1948) as the base of the marine Calabrian and its equivalent, the continental Villafranchian facies in Italy (marked paleontologically by certain mammals, such as early elephants and primitive man). The upper boundary is still under discussion by the International Union for Quaternary Research (INQUA), but it is customarily taken to be the middle Swedish and Salpausselkä moraines that mark the last ice advance in northern Scandinavia, dated by varves and confirmed by C^{14} at between 10,500 and 10,300 years B.P. A well-marked boundary about this age is found in most deep-sea cores. Subdivisions within the Pleistocene are based upon Alpine moraine groups (e.g., Günz, Mindel, Riss, Würm of Penck and Brückner, 1909) or on continental till equivalents (e.g. in North America: Nebraskan, Kansan, Illinoian, Wisconsin) and interglacial stages. Unfortunately, a completely satisfactory correlation is not yet possible.

Several different methods of dating are thus employed, often an integrated approximation being the best available. The dating of certain progressive geomorphic evolutionary sequences has appealed to some workers. Thus Flint (1965) quotes the fascinating early attempt to extrapolate the wearing back of Niagara Falls and its gorge by William Maclay, a Senator from Pennsylvania, based on measurements by Andrew Ellicott, an American surveyor in 1789; his friend calculated that the falls would have taken 55,440 years to erode the gorge, thus giving "the age of the world, or at least . . . the period when the water began to cut the ledge of rock . . .". Other attempts have been made, but all were futile because of unknown variables such as climate and runoff (Johnston, 1928). A dating procedure based on an assumption of soil weathering, combined with a coincidence of numbers led to the classical failure of Sayles (1931) who correlated the fossil dunes of Bermuda and their interdune soils with the four glacial periods and their interglacials. From evidence of similar eolianites in south-western Australia, Fairbridge and Teichert (1953, p. 84) wrote: "it is utterly wrong to correlate each soil with an interglacial stage . . . and any empirical formula deducing an absolute duration of

FIG. 12. Glacial grooving on the same pavement shown in Fig. 11. Older Paleozoic metamorphics, Riverside Park, New York City. (Photo: R. W. Fairbridge).

time from a certain thickness of soil accumulation is equally fallacious."

Such extrapolations, applied periodically to the cutting of waterfalls, the erosion of cliffs, the building of spits and forelands, the excavation of valleys, the growth of dunes, the weathering of soils and so on, are all doomed to failure due to gross errors; ignorance of the episodic nature of many dynamic geologic processes, ranging from the occasional flood to the occasional hurricane, has been compounded with a slavish adherence to the outdated concept that Lyellian "Uniformitarianism" automatically implied gradualness in all geologic mechanisms, disregarding such things as the well-known critical numbers in fluid mechanics, the cyclic oscillations of climate and the recognized motions of the solar system. It is interesting that calculations based on long-term extrapolations caused Wright to cast doubt on Croll's astronomically based dating (which admittedly contained some minor errors), to which Flint (1965) added: "Some geologists today would express similar doubts about the more elaborate astronomical theory put forth by Milankovitch."

The effective methods for dating glaciations are the tried and true stratigraphic methods. The difficulties lie in the fact that a complete succession is found only in certain parts of deep-sea basins, while on land the locus of major sedimentation has shifted to and fro across the continents, alternating with episodes of erosion causing evidence of the preceding stage to be effaced. The recognition of four principal glaciations in the Alps (Penck and Brückner, 1909) and their apparent match with epochs of continental ice, both in northern Europe and in North America, easily led to a "numbers game," wherein an approximately similar repetition of events was allowed to be taken as a persuasive basis for correlation. However, it has emerged that each glacial stage had several advances separated by interstadial retreats; these interstadials are all too easily confused with the major interglacial oscillations. Milankovitch showed 17 major oscillations for the last 600,000 years, the coldest part of the Pleistocene, and Sprigg (1952) observed precisely 17 major raised beach ridges on the south coast of Australia; the question must be asked—is this significant or mere coincidence? How can one check for gaps? An open-ended extrapolation is simply not scientifically acceptable. It is partly to Milankovitch, to Soergel (1925) and Zeuner (1959) that credit must go for recognizing that a multiplicity of subdivisions *should* exist, but the final correlation must await further painstaking work, in stratigraphy, paleontology, absolute dating and paleomagnetic reversal studies.

RHODES W. FAIRBRIDGE

References

Agassiz, L., 1840, "Études sur les Glaciers," Neuchatel, privately published, 346pp. Facsimile reprint.

Ahlmann, H. W., 1953, "Glacier variations and climatic variations," *Am. Geogr. Soc., Bowman Mem. Lect., Ser. 3.*

Antevs, E., 1929, "Maps of the Pleistocene glaciations," *Bull. Geol. Soc. Am.,* **40,** 631–720.

Bigarella, J. J., and de Andrade, G. O., 1965, "Contributions to the study of the Brazilian Quaternary," *Geol. Soc. Am., Spec. Paper* **84.**

Broecker, W. S., 1966, "Absolute dating and the astronomical theory of glaciation," *Science,* **151**(3708), 299–304.

Buckland, W., 1823, "Reliquiae Diluvianae; or Observations... Attesting the Action of an Universal Deluge," London, J. Murray, 303pp.

Buckland, W. and Mantell, G. A., 1822, "The fossils of the South Downs . . . ," London.

Charlesworth, J. K., 1957, "The Quaternary Era," London, E. Arnold, 2 vols.

Chamberlin, T. C., 1877, "Geology of eastern Wisconsin," in "Geol. of Wisconsin, survey of 1873–1877," *Madison, Wisc., Comm., of Publ. Prtg.,* **2,** 97–246.

Chamberlin, T. C., 1888, "The rock-scorings of the great ice invasions," *U.S. Geol. Surv. Ann. Rept.,* **7,** 147–248.

Chamberlin, T. C., 1895, "The classification of American glacial deposits," *J. Geol.,* **3,** 270–277.

Croll, J., 1875, "Climate and Time in Their Geological Relations: A Theory of Secular Changes of the Earth's Climate," London, E. Stanford, 577pp.

Crowell, J. C., 1964, "Climatic Significance of Sedimentary Deposits Containing Dispersed Megaclasts," in (Nairn, editor) "Problems in Palaeoclimatology," 86–99, New York, Interscience Publ.

Demorest, M., 1943, "Ice sheets," *Bull. Geol. Soc. Am.,* **54,** 363–400.

Embleton, C. and King, C. A. M., 1968, "Glacial and Periglacial Geomorphology," London, E. Arnold Ltd., 608pp.

Fairbridge, R. W., 1961, "Convergence of evidence on climatic change and ice ages," *Ann. N.Y., Acad. Sci.,* **95**(1), 542–579.

Fairbridge, R. W., 1962, "New radiocarbon dates of Nile sediments," *Nature,* **195,** 108-110.

Fairbridge, R. W., 1964a, "The Importance of Limestone and Its Ca/Mg Content to Palaeoclimatology," in (Nairn, editor) "Problems in Palaeoclimatology," pp. 431–477, New York, Interscience Publ.

Fairbridge, R. W., 1964b, "African Ice Age Aridity," *ibid.,* pp. 356–360.

Fairbridge, R. W., and Teichert, C., 1953, "Soil horizons and marine bands in the coastal limestone of W.A.," *J. Roy. Soc. N.S.W.,* **86,** 68–87.

*Flint, R. F., 1957, "Glacial and Pleistocene Geology," New York, John Wiley & Sons, 553pp.

Flint, R. F., 1965, "Introduction: Historical Perspectives," in (Wright and Frey, editors) "The Quaternary of the United States," pp. 3–11, Princeton, N.J., Princeton University Press.

Flohn, H., 1963, "Zur meteorologischen Interpretation der pleistozänen Klimaschwankungen," *Eiszeitalter Gegenwart,* **14,** 153–160.

Geikie, J., 1874, "The Great Ice Age and Its Relation to the Antiquity of Man," London, W. Isbister, 575pp.

Gilbert, G. K., 1890, "Lake Bonneville," *U.S. Geol. Surv. Monograph* **1,** 438pp.

Harrison, W., 1958, "Marginal zones of vanished glaciers reconstructed from the preconsolidation-pressure values of overridden silts," *J. Geol.,* **66**(1), 72–95.

Heezen, B. C., and Hollister, C. D., 1964, "Deep-sea current evidence from abyssal sediments," *Marine Geol.*, **1**, 141–174.

Hull, E., 1885, "Mount Seir, Sinai, and Western Palestine," London, R. Bentley, 227pp.

Jamieson, T. F., 1865, "On the history of the last geological changes in Scotland," *Quart. J. Geol. Soc. London*, **21**, 161–203.

Johnston, W. A., 1928, "The age of the upper great gorge of Niagara River," *Trans. Roy. Soc. Can., Sect. IV*, **22**, 13–29.

Lahee, F. H., 1961, "Field Geology," New York, Mc-Graw-Hill Book Company, 926pp.

Lüttig, G., 1965, "Interglacial and interstadial periods," *J. Geol.*, **73**, 579–591.

Lyell, C., 1830–33, "Principles of Geology," London, 3 vols.

Maclaren, C., 1841, "The glacial theory of Professor Agassiz of Neuchatel," Edinburgh, The Scotsman Off., 62pp.

Matthes, F. E., 1930, "Geologic history of the Yosemite Valley," *U.S. Geol. Surv. Profess. Paper* **160**, 137pp.

McGee, W J, 1881, "On local subsidence produced by an ice-sheet," *Am. J. Sci.* **22**, 368–369.

Meinzer, O. E., 1922, "Map of Pleistocene lakes of the Basin-Range province and its significance," *Bull. Geol. Soc. Am.*, **33**, 541–552.

Newberry, J. S., 1874, "Geology of Ohio—surface geology," *Ohio Geol. Surv. Rept.*, **2**, 1–80.

Penck, A., and Brückner, E., 1901–09, "Die Alpen im Eiszeitalter," Leipzig, 3 vols.

Pumpelly, R., 1879, "The relation of secular rock-disintegration to loess, glacial drift and rock basins," *Am. J. Sci.* **17**, 133–144.

Richthofen, F. von, 1877, "China," Vol. 1, p. 758, Berlin, D. Reimer.

Salomon-Calvi, W., 1931, "Epeirophorese. III. Die vordiluvialen Eiszeiten. A. Die Eiszeiten des Tertiärs und Nesozoikums," *Sitzber. Heidelberg. Akad. Wiss., Math. Naturw, Kl. Abhandl.* No. **8**.

Salomon-Calvi, W., 1933, "Epeirophorese. III. Die vordiluvialen Eiszeiten. B. Die Eiszeiten des Karbons und Perms," *ibid.*, No. 1.

Sayles, R. W., 1931, "Bermuda during the Ice Age," *Proc. Am. Acad. Arts Sci.*, **66**, 381–468.

*Schwarzbach, M., 1963, "Climates of the Past," London, D. Van Nostrand Co., 328pp. (translated by R. O. Muir).

Shaler, N. S., 1874, "Preliminary report on the recent changes of level on the coast of Maine," *Boston Soc. Nat. Hist. Mem.* **2**, 320–340.

Soergel, W., 1925, "Die Gliederung und absolute Zeitrechnung des Eiszeitalters," *Fortschr. Geol. Pal.*, **4**, 13.

Sprigg, R. C., 1952, "The geology of the South East Province, South Australia, with special reference to Quaternary coast-line migrations and modern beach developments," *Geol. Surv. South Australia, Bull.* **29**.

Termier, H., and Termier, G., 1963, "Erosion and Sedimentation," London and Princeton, D. van Nostrand Co., 433pp. (translated by D. W. and E. E. Humphries).

Tylor, A., 1868, "On the Amiens gravel," *Quart. J. Geol. Soc. London*, **24**, 103–125.

Voronov, P. S., 1965, "Attempt at a reconstruction of the Antarctic ice cap of the epoch of the earth's maximum glaciation," *Soviet Antarctic Exped.*, **3**, 88–93.

Whitney, J. D., 1865, "Geological Survey of California," *Geology*, **1**, 498pp.

Woldstedt, P., 1954–65, "Das Eiszeitalter," Second ed., Stuttgart, Enke Verlag, 3 vols.

Wright, G. F., 1889, "The Ice Age in North America," New York, Appleton-Century-Crofton, 622pp.

Wright, C. S. and Priestley, R. F., 1922, "British (Terra Nova) Antarctic Expedition, 1910–13. Chapt. 7, Glaciology," London, Harrison, 581pp.

*Zeuner, F. E., 1959, "The Pleistocene Period; Its Climate, Chronology and Faunal Successions," London, Hutchinson & Co., 447pp. (Second revised ed. of 1945 work).

Zittel, K. A. von, 1901, "History of Geology and Paleontology," London, W. Scott, 562pp. (translated by M. M. Ogilvie-Gordon).

* Additional bibliographic references may be found in this work.

Cross-references: *Bergschrund; Coral Reef; Cryopedology, Cryonivation, etc.; Erratic Block; Eustasy; Frost Action; Frost Riving; Glacial Geology; Glacial Lakes; Great Lakes; Holocene; Loess; Moraine; Nunatak; Perched Block; Pluvial Lakes; Postglacial Isostatic Rebound; Quaternary Period; Roche Moutonnée; Solifluction; Striae; Terraces, Fluvial—Environmental Controls; Thermokarst.* Vol. II: *Ice Age Meteorology; Ice Age Theory.* pr Vol. VI: *Diluvial Theory; Glaciology; Icecap; Ice Sheet; Uniformitarianism.* pr Vol. VII: *Gondwanaland; Paleontology; Varve Chronology.*

GLACIER GEOPHYSICS—*See* pr Vol. VI

GLACIERS, INTRODUCTION—*See* pr Vol. VI

GLACIO-EUSTASY—*See* **EUSTASY**

GLACIOLOGICAL ISOTOPE STUDIES—*See* pr Vol. VI

GLACIOLOGY—*See* pr Vol. VI

GLACIOLOGY AND GLACIAL GEOLOGY OF ANTARCTICA—*See* pr Vol. VI, **ANTARCTICA, GLACIOLOGY AND GLACIAL GEOLOGY**

GLYPTOGENESIS

This word is derived from the Greek *glyptos*, detailed sculpture or carving, and *genesis*, origin. The term was first proposed by the French geologist Emile Haug in 1904. It has hardly been used by other writers except Grabau (1924) and, more recently, Henri and Geneviève Termier as Volume 3 ("Glyptogénèse") in their *L'Évolution de la Lithosphère* (1961) which essentially represents a mid-century revision of Haug's celebrated *Traité*. [The term *glyptolith* has nothing to do with this topic. It is a now obsolete word used by J. B. Woodworth (1894) for a ventifact.]

The advantage claimed for the term is that it embraces only that aspect of geomorphology that deals with the results of earth sculpturing, the consequences of erosion engendered by the atmosphere and hydrosphere together with related processes of orogenesis and petrogenesis, and their consequences in the form of sedimentation at the present time. Ancient glyptogenesis is treated under *paleogeography* (pr Vol. VII). Modern glyptogenesis is conceived as evolutionary geomorphology, especially the historical geomorphology of the Quaternary period, i.e., the last few million years.

English-speaking geomorphologists generally treat this field as regional geomorphology and morphotectonics. It embraces also morphogenetic and morphoclimatic landscape types. The term as such is not really needed.

RHODES W. FAIRBRIDGE

References

Grabau, A. W., 1924, "Principles of Stratigraphy," 2nd edition, New York, A. G. Seiler, 1185pp. (also in Dover reprint, 2 vols.).

Haug, E., 1903–04, "Le cycle des phénomènes géologiques," *La Science au XXe siecle*, **1**, 343–349; **2**, 17–19.

Termier, H. and G., 1961, "L'Évolution de la Lithosphere: III Glyptogénèse," Paris, Masson & Cie, 471pp.

Cross-references: *Landscape Types, Genetic; Morphogenetic Classification; Morphogenetic Regions; Morphotectonics; Quaternary Period.* pr Vol. VII: *Paleogeography.*

GONDWANA LANDSCAPE

Most of the world's scenery was carved in late Tertiary or Quaternary time from a widespread landscape of low relief that had been developed throughout the early Tertiary. In all continents a similar smooth summit planation is often evident upon high country, mountains as well as plateaus. Indeed it might almost be thought to have been ubiquitous but for the fact that upon some major divides still higher series of once-planed remnants record traces of a yet older planation which in many places appears to have been equally smoothly planed during its heyday (Fig. 1). In the continents of the southern hemisphere (the erstwhile Gondwanaland) this ancestral landscape has been called

the Gondwana cyclic landsurface, and its age has been determined as late Mesozoic (locally Jurassic or Cretaceous).

Remnants of ancient erosion surfaces dating back to the Mesozoic have indeed been identified in many lands and occur in every continent with the possible exception of Antarctica which is currently buried in large measure beneath a carapace of ice so that evidence is now lacking (King, 1962).

Typical areas from which these superelevated remnants of former cyclic erosion have been described are: the highlands of Basutoland, Nyasaland and Windhoek in Southern Africa (Dixey, 1938), Nilgiri and Cardamom Hills of India, and the Brazilian Highlands (King, 1962). Sometimes ancient duricrusts still mantle the surface, forming a regolith of remarkable antiquity.

Elsewhere the old land surface may be found warped down in basin-form to pass as an unconformity beneath continental sediments of late Mesozoic age which have preserved it from later denudation, and which serve to date the cyclic cutting of the surface as pre-late Mesozoic. In this buried form it may survive over large areas, e.g., within the Kalahari and Congo depressions, and beneath continental Cretaceous rock series of North Africa, or upon the interfluves capped with Cretaceous sands between the northward flowing affluents of the lower Amazon in Brazil.

At coastlines the same ancient cyclic landsurface may be monoclinally warped down to pass beneath marine sequences of Jurassic or Cretaceous rocks: as on both east and west coasts of Africa, Western Australia, eastern Brazil, and Trichinopoly in India. Because the surface bears the earliest marine sediments at these, and other modern coasts, it plainly antedates the formation of those coasts and the outlines of the present continents, which were created by its monoclinal down-warping. Thus it is related not to the modern continents but to the earlier supercontinent of Gondwanaland, and is known as the *Gondwana* cyclic landsurface.

All the evidence points to these relicts of an ancient erosion cycle as belonging to a landscape familiar to the dinosaurs, and to a global geography that would now be unrecognizable (see *Gondwanaland*, in pr vol. VII).

Where it stands now upon the highest divides, this ancient Gondwana landsurface has, according to all the evidence available, been exposed continu-

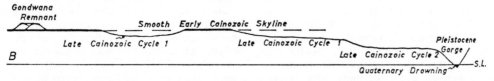

FIG. 1. The pattern of world cyclic landscapes (denudational) expressed in diagrammatic profile (L. C. King). (By permission of Oliver & Boyd Ltd., Edinburgh.)

ously to the elements ever since the date of its formation during the Mesozoic. In detail its surface will
usually be found to have been etched into minor
later relief under Tertiary and later weathering and
erosion, but it has never departed in great measure
from the originally planed form which may still be
clearly recognizable upon the very highest parts.

Doubt has been expressed whether any land
surface could survive the action of weathering and
erosion continuously over so long a period without
burial and exhumation. Despite any preconceived
ideas regarding the efficacy of weathering and erosion, the answer must be arrived at that apparently
such surfaces do, in favorable watershed regions,
survive almost indefinitely. While it is universally
acknowledged that the creation of new base levels
by uplift causes rejuvenation of river systems with
excision of valleys and destruction of earlier landscapes, such processes operate principally in the
lower and middle reaches of the rivers. Near the
headwaters very little of this action may take place.
Unless it does, there is little to alter the ancient
landscape. Provided that it be initially flat, it may
survive almost indefinitely.

Such conditions obtain where previous terrains
of very low relief are arched to form new divides,
as has happened not unusually in relation to the
early Tertiary smooth planation, and which indubitably happened also to the older, Mesozoic
smooth planation, sometimes along the same
tectonic axes.

In general the landscape was planed in the
Jurassic period and may still bear relicts of Jurassic
continental formations but in many places the cycle
continued into the Cretaceous with little change,
and the final date of the planation, as defined by
superincumbent formations which have buried it
locally, is then Cretaceous. Over southern Africa
for example, the Jurassic surface came to be incised
by Cretaceous valleys of a distinct (post-Gondwana)
cycle in which deposits containing dinosaur bones
are known; but farther north over the Congo and
northern Africa, there is no such change and the
Jurassic state of planation continued into the
Cretaceous without dissection.

The Gondwana landscape was broken up by the
fragmentation of Gondwanaland, when new coasts
were roughed out by monoclinal warping which
created the outlines of the modern southern continents. The surface is thus important in relation to
the hypothesis of continental drift. The opening
along the east coast of Africa, for instance, began
in the middle Jurassic in Somalia, East Africa and
Madagascar and was completed to the Southern
Cape by the earliest Cretaceous as defined by the
earliest marine sediments in these localities. The
opening of the Atlantic basin on the western side
was somewhat later, beginning with lagoonal
Aptian followed by marine Albian deposits of the
early mid-Cretaceous in West Africa, Angola and

Brazil. With the generation of these new coastlines
a fresh base level was created enabling the earlier
Gondwana landscape, which had stood possibly as
high as 2000 feet above the sea in southern Africa
(the central region of Gondwanaland), to be dissected by Cretaceous valleys assignable to the post-
Gondwana (Cretaceous) cycle of landscape development. Such valleys, with occasional local valley-
floor planations, are now found about 1000 feet
below the Gondwana summit bevel in high Basutoland, South West Africa, Rhodesia and Nyasaland.

LESTER KING

References

Dixey, F., 1938, "Some observations on the physio-
graphical development of Central and Southern
Africa," *Trans. Geol. Soc. S. Afr.*, **41**, 113–170.
King, L. C., 1967, "The Morphology of the Earth,"
Second ed., Edinburgh, Oliver and Boyd, 726pp.

Cross-references: *Base Level*; *Cycles—Geomorphic*;
Denudation; *Duricrust*; *Quaternary Period*; *Relict
Landforms*; *Warping*. Vol. V: *Continental Drift*. Vol.
VII: *Gondwanaland*.

GRABEN

Definition

A graben is a fault block, generally elongate,
that has been lowered relative to the blocks on
either side without major disturbance or pronounced tilting. The bordering faults, or fault zones,
are usually of near-parallel strike and are steeply
dipping, along which the vertical displacement has
been approximately equal. Grabens vary greatly
in size, but the dominance of a long fault trough is
a characteristic feature.

General Features

The movements of the blocks that define a graben
are relative. All blocks involved may have moved
with respect to their original position, but the
middle block must have subsided more than the
outer two. Thus, a true graben in its initial surface
form is characteristically a linear structural depression (Fig. 1A). The flanking highland areas are
commonly *horsts* (q.v.). Under conditions of
prolonged denudation, the distribution of variably
resistant strata in the fault blocks may be such that
the initial graben relief may become reversed, i.e.,
the graben becomes an upland (Fig. 1B).

The border faults of grabens are usually either
vertical or high-angle gravity (normal) faults that
dip toward each other. Valleys that occupy the
sites of such grabens have been termed *rift troughs*,
rift valleys, *rift-block valleys*, or *taphrogeosynclines*. Half-grabens are downdropped blocks that
have been displaced principally along one border
fault. Rarely, one or both faults may dip in a

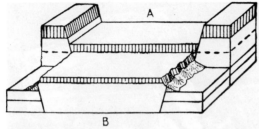

FIG. 1. Block diagram of a graben in its initial surface form (A), and the reversal of relief that may follow extensive erosion (B). Border faults are high-angle gravity faults (from Fig. 226 in Lahee, F. H., 1952, "Field Geology," p. 249, McGraw-Hill Book Co., 883pp.) (By permission.)

direction opposite to that shown in Fig. 1; these are thrust (reverse) faults. A graben that is bounded by thrust faults, or ramps, is a ramp trough or ramp valley.

Origin

The origin of the majority of grabens is believed due to lateral tension, i.e., rift troughs with normal faulting. Common examples are those formed on domes or anticlines (crestal grabens). Similarly, grabens are associated with block faulting in areas of regional upwarp and stretching. Examples: Basin and Range province (of Nevada-Utah-Arizona) and Triassic Newark series basins of the eastern United States, East African rift system, Rhine shield of Germany. The Upper Rhine rift valley is the type example of a large complex graben. The origin of grabens through compressional stresses has been proposed by various ramp trough interpretations (particularly in East Africa), but very generally rejected. Certain grabens are undoubtedly related to lateral displacement along intersecting wrench (transcurrent) faults. Many of the larger graben-like depressions, such as the Red Sea and Dead Sea rifts, show evidence of having a composite origin. The association of volcanism with grabens is well known and may be fundamentally related to their origin.

DAVID L. GILES

References

DeSitter, L. U., 1956, "Structural Geology," New York, McGraw-Hill Book Co., 552pp.
Hills, E. S., 1963, "Elements of Structural Geology," New York, John Wiley & Sons, 483pp.
Kay, M., 1951, "North American geosynclines," *Geol. Soc. Am. Mem.*, **48**, 143pp.
Lensen, G. J., 1958, "A method for graben and horst formation," *J. Geol.*, **66**, 579–587.
Weeks, L. G., 1958, "Factors in sedimentary basin development that control oil occurrence," *Bull. Am. Assoc. Petrol. Geologists*, **37**, 2071–2124.

Cross-references: *Basin and Range Landscape*; *Horst*; *Inversion (of Topography, Relief)*. Vol. V: *Taphrogeny*. Vol. VIII: *Basin and Range Province*.

GRADATION

The concept of gradation in geomorphology is an important one in slope reduction, involving the modification of the landscape to lower gradients ultimately to nearly uniform gentle slopes. A two-fold process is involved:

(a) *Degradation*, the erosional reduction of formerly higher relief, so that a degraded surface exposes the country rock (cf. *Pediments*);

(b) *Aggradation*, the filling-in of depressions, basins and valleys, filling by implication (in part) with the detritus freed during degradation of adjacent uplands. These accumulations, alluvium, etc., equally assist in the lowering of the general land-surface gradient.

After the development of an equilibrium, a steady-state graded profile, and a change of regime (climate and stream change, lowering or raising of base level, etc.), a new grade will be approached; this is called *regradation*.

In the *humid cycle*, mature gradation is synonymous with the mature landscape. However, even in a most youthful stage some gradation is immediately involved (Miller, 1958).

Mean sea level represents the ideal boundary between degradation and aggradation on an initial landscape. Every place above the zone of permanent saturation by alkaline seawater (in porous rocks) is susceptible to potential rotting (weathering) by groundwater, generally acidified by the presence of CO_2 in solution. The zone of "saprolite" is thus most liable to ready erosion and transport. Below mean sea level, stream and ocean current transport velocities progressively drop; this is the zone of shelf aggradation. Maximum energy (wave) is developed in the intertidal zone. (A bathyal belt of high energy is involved in turbidity flows, but this does not concern the present discussion.)

In certain basins where limestone formations reach below mean sea level it is not unusual for deep karst solution to develop, resulting, in shelf areas, in offshore springs.

A second belt of maximal energy development (fluvial) may be traced about the hill or mountain slopes, a zone ultimately definable in terms of a mathematic integration of slope gradient, precipitation efficiency, and rock strength (or inversely, the degree of rotting or loss of cohesion).

Thus two distinctive graded profiles may be recognized (subaerial and shelf), as a minimum (Fig. 1), but since long valley thalwegs frequently have nickpoints, and varying geological structures present rock basins and barriers leading to successive base-level controls, numerous graded sectors

FIG. 1. Two zones of gradation illustrated by vertical air photomosaic of a fairly youthful island (southwest coast of Atauro, Indonesia; 8° 15′ S, 125° 35′ E.) Scale: width of figure 4 km (north to the left).

Note: (a) Intertidal zone, repeated in several terraces due to tectonic uplift, a characteristic planar surface. (b) Fluvial channels with maximum downcutting in their mid-courses, minimal on the ridges and minimal again near sea level.

could be identified over a landscape of continental dimensions. An interesting and useful series of maps could be prepared, subdividing continents into gradational units, but as far as the writer is aware, this cartography has never been attempted.

Exceptions to the gradation concept are found in the eolian, glacial and volcanic landforms (the "climatic accidents" of W. M. Davis). Gradation is characteristic, therefore, of humid to semiarid cycles, dominated by fluvial erosion and by the marine cycle, but it is not universal.

RHODES W. FAIRBRIDGE

References

Cotton, C. A., 1942, "Geomorphology: An Introduction to the Study of Landforms," Christchurch, Whitcombe & Tombs, Ltd., 505pp.

Davis, W. M., 1909, "Geographical Essays," New York (Dover reprint, 1954), 777pp.

Hack, J. T., 1957, "Studies of longitudinal stream profiles in Virginia and Maryland," *U.S. Geol. Surv. Profess. Paper* **294B**, 97pp.

Holmes, C. D., 1952, "Stream competence and the graded stream profile," *Am. J. Sci.*, **250**, 899–906.

Leopold, L. B., and Miller, J. P., 1956, "Ephemeral streams—hydraulic factors and their relation to the drainage net," *U.S. Geol. Surv. Profess. Paper* **282A**, 37pp.

Leopold, L. B., Wolman, M. G., and Miller, J. P., 1964, "Fluvial Processes in Geomorphology," San Francisco, W. H. Freeman & Co., 522pp.

Mackin, J. H., 1948, "Concept of the graded river," *Bull. Geol. Soc. Am.*, **59**, 463–512.

Miller, J. P., 1958, "High mountain streams: effects of geology on channel characteristics and bed materials," *New Mexico Bureau Mines Mineral Resources*, 53pp.

Cross-references: *Aggradation; Base Level; Cycles, Geomorphic; Degradation; Equilibrium in Geomorphology; Glacial Valleys; Grade; Pediment; Playfair's Law; Regolith and Saprolite; Slopes; Thalweg.* Vol. I: *Mean Sea Level.*

GRADE, GRADED STREAMS

A stream is said to be at *grade* when it is neither eroding nor depositing material at any point along its course. In this condition, the *thalweg* (q.v.) or longitudinal profile consists of a continuous concave curve or curves just steep enough to transport all the load from one end to the other. The steepest slopes are near the headwaters and the most gentle slopes close to the *base level* (q.v.). The curves vary from stream to stream but always show the same general form in well-established streams. A smooth concave profile, flattening downstream, is usually taken therefore to be typical of a *graded stream*.

In fairly homogeneous rocks, this grading, called *stream gradation*, is achieved when approximately 25% of the mass of the basin has been eroded (Schumm, 1956), and thereafter the form of the valley will remain graded as erosion proceeds to completion. The time taken to achieve this "steady state" obviously varies with climate, but it is interesting to note that all of the 25 larger rivers studied by Büdel (1963) in permafrost areas with "pronounced valley formation" were graded, even

FIG. 1. Idealized thalweg of a graded river, perfectly graded to base level (from Cotton, 1952). Note that this ignores stream bed topography, bedrock lithology and base-level history; in short, it is purely a geomorphological abstraction. (By permission of John Wiley & Sons, N.Y.)

though they were also usually *misfit streams* (q.v.). Most of the valleys had been ice covered in the Wisconsin period, and the streams must have cut down or *degraded* their channels at a rate of up to 1 m/1000 yr in some cases. Elsewhere material transported by the stream was deposited so as to fill in overdeepened hollows by *aggradation*.

After the general concept of grade became established (see the discussion in Davis, 1902), attempts were made to fit mathematical formulas to the curves of the thalweg in an attempt to relate form to process (Jones, 1924). However, there were too many modifying influences. It now seems that volume, speed of flow, slope, size and weight of the load form a balance. Each section of channel tends to alter its slope and shape so that the load entering equals the load being passed on. Any increase in load will produce an increase in load throughout the stream.

In view of the many variable factors, the question arises as to whether there really is such a thing as grade (see Mackin, 1937, 1948; Kesseli, 1941; Howard, 1965). Runoff varies from hour to hour and day to day, and each change is reflected in a change in the cross section of the channel and in the channel course. Then again, material eroded in the region of the headwaters means a lower gradient to the existing thalweg, while deposition

of the transported sediment in a delta will increase the length of the stream and so cause regrading of the channel. Changes in climate over long periods of time are well-established facts, and these would be reflected in the shape of the channel. Then again, not all rivers flow in basins with homogeneous rocks.

Careful checking shows that the very rapid volume changes cause great variation in the shape of the channel from day to day. However, the flood plain will be in equilibrum with the homogeneous rocks in several tens to several hundreds of years, depending on the amount and frequency of runoff (Leopold and Maddock, 1953; Daniels, 1960). For this reason, the level of the flood plain adjacent to the stream course is measured in determining the thalweg of a stream. This will be in equilibrium with the climate of the last decades or centuries, provided no change in this or the other factors has occurred. However, lack of grade or adjustment of grade, including a *nickpoint* (q.v.), does not necessarily mean a climatic change; it may only mean modification of the vegetation cover by man within this period.

Lithological variations can cause problems with the achievement of grade by a stream. Least effective are probably nearly vertical, alternating hard and soft strata. Here the hard bands form local base levels with steeper gradients which act as local

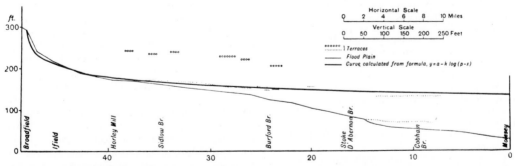

FIG. 2. Typical thalweg of a relatively short stream (River Mole) Surrey, England, showing an ideal profile calculated according to the formula $y = a - k \log(p - x)$, a simple logarithmic curve, where k is proportional to the greatest curvature of the profile. Evidently the terraces show former approximations to such curves, but repeated rapid lowering of base level has segmented the thalweg into rejuvenated sectors (after Green, in Bull *et al.*, 1943; see discussion by Wooldridge and Morgan, 1959).

base levels, while the softer strata tend to have more gentle gradients. Nearly horizontal strata produce the large water falls such as the Niagara Falls between Lakes Erie and Ontario, the Victoria Falls of the Zambesi, and the Kaieteur Falls in British Guiana. In these cases, stream gradation may be held up for many thousands of years even in the humid tropics (see Holmes, 1965). On any given strata, a stream will have a characteristic gradient for a given climate and erosive power, which can help the photointerpreter in recognizing different rocks and structures.

The graded profile often consists of multiple concave curves. Causes of these include the great increase in volume of water at confluences of streams. Baulig (1950) cited the example of the confluences of the fast-flowing, heavily loaded Isère and the slower flowing Rhône in France. Below it, the Rhône has a steeper gradient. Slow flowing tributaries have the reverse effect, e.g., below its confluence with the Saône, the Rhône has a more gentle gradient. These breaks in the profile are quite different from either *nickpoints* (or *knickpoints*).

Another obvious cause of multiple curves is the "thalassostatic" fluctuation in sea level which is the base level of stream action. Lowering of sea level causes downcutting of the river beginning at the sea and working upstream, producing the breaks in grade called knickpoints.

Thus it will be seen that the concept of grade is very important in geomorphology. It gives us a means of recognizing strata and structures on air photographs, while measurements of the graded thalweg can tell us much about the possible history of the area and the sediment loads of the streams. It must also be explained in all its manifestations by any theory purporting to explain the evolution of the landforms of river erosion.

STUART A. HARRIS

References

Baulig, H., 1950, "Essais de Géomorphologie," Paris.
Büdel, J., 1963, "Klimatische Geomorphologie," *Geographische Rundschau*, **15**.
Cotton, C. A., 1952, "Geomorphology," Sixth ed., New York, John Wiley & Sons, 505pp.
Daniels, R. B., 1960, "Entrenchment of the Willow Drainage Ditch, Harrison County, Iowa," *Am. J. Sci.*, **258**, 161–176.
Davis, W. M., 1902, "Base-level, grade, and peneplain," *J. Geol.*, **10**, 77–111.
Holmes, A., 1965, "Principles of Physical Geology," London, Nelson & Sons; New York, Ronald Press, 1288pp.
Howard, A. D., 1965, "Geomorphological systems—equilibrium and dynamics," *Am. J. Sci.*, **263**, 302–312.
Jones, O. T., 1924, "Longitudinal profiles in the River Towy," *Quart. J. Geol. Soc.*, **80**, 568.
Kesseli, J. E., 1941, "Rock streams in the Sierra Nevada," *Geog. Rev.*, **31**, 203–227.
Leopold, L. B., and Maddock, T., Jr., 1953, "The hydraulic geometry of stream channels and some physiographic implications," *U.S. Geol. Surv. Profess. Paper* **252**, 57pp.
Mackin, J. H., 1937, "Erosional history of the Big Horn Basin, Wyoming," *Bull. Geol. Soc. Am.*, **48**, 813–894.
Mackin, J. H., 1948, "Concept of the graded river," *Bull. Geol. Soc. Am.*, **59**, 463–512.
Schumm, S. A., 1956, "Evolution of drainage systems and slopes in badlands at Perth Amboy, New Jersey," *Bull. Geol. Soc. Am.*, **67**, 597–646.
Wooldridge, S. W. and Morgan, R. S., 1959, "An Outline of Geomorphology," Second ed., London, Longmans, Green & Co., 409pp.

Cross-references: *Aggradation*; *Base Level*; *Climatic Geomorphology*; *Floodplain*; *Misfit Streams*; *Nickpoint*; *Rivers*; *Stream Channel Characteristics*; *Terraces—Thalassostatic*; *Thalweg*.

GRANITE LANDFORMS

Granite and granitoid rocks are one of the most common constituents of the earth's crust. On the continents they form extensive outcrops, covering large areas of the shield-lands and occurring in abundance in the orogenic areas. Some granite outcrops have no peculiar surface expression: the landforms evolved are no different from those developed on many other rocks under similar conditions. But many occurrences of granite and granitic rocks are typified by the development of landforms which, though not exclusive to this lithology, are nevertheless best, and most commonly, formed upon it.

One of the most characteristic granite landforms is the *tor*. Tors are isolated masses of rock consisting of either a single or of numerous joint blocks displaying varying degrees of angularity or roundness. Some tors are comprised of great masses of joint blocks, only slightly rounded, piled one upon the other in their original situations and forming castellated piles or *castle koppies*; others consist of but a single boulder or a cluster of individual boulders in close proximity, the single boulders varying in diameter between 1 and 50 feet. The Devil's Marbles, in central Australia, are amongst the largest tors known, and attain a maximum diameter of about 40 feet. At the other end of the scale, there are tors at Palmer, South Australia, as small as 18 inches maximum diameter.

Tors are widely known. The southwest peninsula of England is the classic area for castellated tors, which have been extensively studied, but similar forms, and especially the great piles of rounded joint blocks, occur in many parts of the world. In southern California, for instance, such fields of tor boulders are very well developed and form the backdrop for many a chase and gun battle in western films.

Many tors originate from differential subsurface weathering. Water penetrates along joint planes

Fig. 1. Tor exfoliated and split by weathering along joint plane, near Palmer, South Australia. (Courtesy C. R. Twidale).

and the rock adjacent to the planes is weathered, leaving a roughly spherical mass of fresh granite, a *corestone*, or "boulder of disintegration," in the center of each joint block. With the subsequent lowering of the ground surface the weathered marginal areas of each block are eroded; the corestones are exposed and are called tors. The castellated tors are due to the occurrence of a jointed mass of bedrock resistant to weathering (Fig. 1). This so-called two-stage development of tors, described in general terms above, certainly applies in many instances. In the southwestern peninsula of England, for instance, the sub-surface rotting of the less-resistant granite occurred principally in the Tertiary. The removal of the weathered rock or "gruss" followed in the Pleistocene when mass movement of debris was facilitated by periglacial conditions. Clearly, the shape and size of tors is closely related to the geometry of the joint system. Where joints are widely spaced and tight, castellated tors occur. Where there are massive monolithic blocks subdivided into arched sheets, domed *inselbergs* or *bornhardts* are formed. Where the joint blocks are elongated or tabular, the tors weathered from them are likewise elongated or tabular, the latter being typical of granites of gneissic tendency. Where joint blocks are closely spaced, tors are very small. And where the rock is so readily attacked by weathering agencies that it is uniformly altered, corestones (and hence tors) are not formed.

The contrast between granite that is widely jointed and that which is closely jointed and generally shattered is easily seen in many localities. An early granite that has been subjected to tectonism may be uniformly shattered and have no tors

Fig. 2. Tor, split by weathering and tree growth along joint plane, near Palmer, South Australia. (Photo: C. R. Twidale).

FIG. 3. Deep gnamma or weather pit at Pildappa Hill, Eyre Peninsula, South Australia. (Photo: C. R. Twidale.) Compare with "kamenica" from Yugoslavia: Gavrilović, D., 1968, *Zeit. Geomorph.*, **12**, 43.

developed upon it, and may be in a region of all-slopes indistinguishable from other deeply dissected areas in similarly unresistant bedrock. A later granite may have been emplaced after the main tectonic movements had ceased, and may be subdivided into quite massive joint blocks and gives rise to distinctive landforms. Tors will be strewn over the plateau surface and the valley side slopes of the streams that have penetrated into the resistant mass.

It is generally assumed that the weathering of joint blocks to produce corestones is accomplished primarily by water. Granite exposed to water dis-

integrates. Often, mineral changes involving hydration and hydrolysis are effected. Biotite, for instance, which is the first of the granite minerals to undergo alteration, is converted to hydrobiotite, vermiculite and chloritic minerals. The orthoclase feldspars suffer kaolinization. The few detailed analyses that have been made to compare fresh and weathered granite reveal that the differences are small, but it is assumed that the resultant volume changes are sufficient to cause the disintegration of the rock. In some regions, however, the detached and discolored peripheral areas are not altered at all, but merely disintegrated and iron-stained, lead-

FIG. 4. Shallow gnamma with flat floor or pan in Kulgera Hills, N.T., Australia, comparable with coastal spray pools in limestone. (Photo: C. R. Twidale.)

Fɪɢ. 5. Arm-chair-shaped gnammas, Pildappa Hill, South Australia. (Photo: C. R. Twidale).

ing to a suggestion that at least some of the weathering observed in certain areas is secondary, taking advantage of preexisting fissures or structural weakness in the marginal areas. Some of the weathering is guided by flow structures in the bedrock.

Once exposed, tors suffer further weathering: their surfaces crumble particle by particle; half-lenses are split off; and joint planes that play no part in the delineation of joint blocks are exploited by weathering agencies causing the tors to split into two parts along remarkably straight planes.

Where there are a large number of massive joint blocks, and where the joints are tight, gigantic monolithic masses resist weathering and erosion and form domed inselbergs or bornhardts. They originate in essentially the same manner as do tors but are, of course, on an altogether larger scale. Their outlines in plan are determined by prominent joints which parallel major regional tectonic trends or *lineaments*. The inselbergs in plan comprise a variable number of closely juxtaposed or attached blocks of rhomboidal or rectangular shape. In cross section, the outlines of the inselbergs are dominated by massive rock sheets (commonly many feet thick) or remnants of such sheets; the domes are made up of numerous massive shells concentrically arranged one upon the other. Elsewhere massive lenses of rock occur. Such shells and lenses control slope form in many areas. Many workers consider these shells and lenses the result of offloading—the release of pressure consequent upon erosion; thus, they believe that the form of the hills determines the structure. Others hold the view that structure determines morphology and that the arched shells are the result of lateral pressures. There is some field evidence in support of this last view.

Upon exposure to the atmosphere, the shells of the inselbergs break down into rectangular or subrectangular joint blocks which are in turn weathered, especially at the edges and corners, to become subrounded. Morphologically, these weathered blocks are indistinguishable from tors that have evolved in two stages (differential subsurface weathering and development of corestones first, followed by the exposure of the corestones by erosion). Tors can thus develop in two ways, one subsurface in part and the other wholly subaerial.

Several distinctive forms are developed in association with inselbergs and tors. On the flattish upper surfaces of inselbergs, hollows of several types have developed. They are known collectively as *gnammas* or weather pits though several local names are extant. Weather pits have been described from many areas—the humid and arid tropics, the temperate regions and even arctic lands. Although in Britain and on the continent of Europe, they were believed to have originated in connection with Druidical (or similar) ceremonial, they are of geologic origin. At least three major forms are known. One of the most common, developed in the laminated upper zone of the granite bedrock, is the flat-floored, relatively shallow *pan*. Its sides tend to be steep and even overhanging, especially on the shady aspects and on the upslope sides. Less common is the hemispherical *pit*, which is found in essentially homogeneous rock. Some attain great depths relative to their diameter in plan: for example, one on northwestern Eyre Peninsula is at least 9 feet deep but has a maximum diameter in plan of only 6 feet. One reported from Bahia in Brazil is some 10 × 18 feet across and 27 feet deep. Some of these pits develop into flask-shaped hollows, with narrow entrances. A third type, characteristic of steeper inclines is an *armchair-shaped hollow* that is distinctly asymmetrical in shape.

The steeper slopes of many domed inselbergs are grooved and fluted. The slopes are furrowed by distinct depressions known as *Granitrillen* or *Granitkarren*. They are due to a combination of weathering and erosion by running water.

The edges of many sheets and the sides and bases of many blocks and tors are pierced by inverted hollows or caverns widely known as *tafoni* (q.v.). Their origin and development are not clearly understood, but many are initiated at or near present and former soil levels.

Thus, forms typical of granite bedrock owe their morphology in part to the distinctive and pronounced joint patterns of the rock and in part to the susceptibility of granite to disintegration under the influence of moisture. The strong control exerted by these structural and mineralogical factors is indicated by the distribution of the various characteristic granite landforms; they are known from every type of climatic region.

C. R. TWIDALE

References

Jutson, J. T., 1934, "The physiography (geomorphology) of Western Australia," *Bull. Geol. Surv. W. Australia*, **95**, 366pp.

King, L. C., 1958, "The problem of tors," *Geogr. J.*, **124**, 289–291 (letter).

Klaer, W., 1956, "Verwitterungsformen im Granit auf Korsika," *Pet. Geogr. Mitt.*, **261**, 146pp.

Linton, D. L., 1955, "The problem of tors," *Geogr. J.*, **121**, 420–487.

Ollier, C. D., 1965, "Some features of granite weathering in Australia," *Z. Geomorphol.*, **3**, 285–304.

Panzer, W., 1954, "Verwitterungs- und Abtragungsformen im Granit von Hongkong," *Abh. Akad. Raumforschung* (*Bremen*), **28**, (H. Mortensen Vol.: "Ergebnisse und Probleme moderner geographischer Forschung"), 41–60.

Twidale, C. R., 1964, "Contribution to the general theory of domed inselbergs. Conclusions derived from observations in South Australia," *Trans. Papers Inst. Brit. Geogr.*, **34**, 91–113.

Wilhelmy, H., 1958, "Klimamorphologie der Massengesteine," Braunschweig, G. Westermann, 238pp.

Cross-references: *Bornhardt; Inselberg; Periglacial Landscape; Solution Pits and Pans; Structural Control in Geomorphology; Tafoni; Tor; Weathering.*

GREAT BARRIER REEFS

The Great Barrier Reefs (Fig. 1), the only barrier reef system off the coasts of Australia and the greatest in the world, runs from near the mouth of the Fly River in the Gulf of Papua to near Sandy Cape—approximately from latitude 9–24°S, a distance of about 1200 miles.

The term *Great Barrier Reef* (singular) is frequently used but is not a good one, for it is not a continuous barrier, but a linear series of a multitude of reefs of varying sizes separated by passages, constituting the "outer barrier" together with a vast number of reefs between the "barrier" and the mainline coast. Indeed, Captain Cook referred to the maze of reefs in the northern part as "The Labyrinth." The plural form, Great Barrier Reefs was used by Beete Jukes (1847) and by Steers (1929, 1937) who pointed out that the plural is used on Admiralty charts; "Reefs" is also used in the Australia Pilot.

The passages between the reefs are mostly narrow (usually about half a mile wide) and shallow, but include a few such as Trinity Opening and Magnetic Passage which are navigable by ocean-going ships. Its distance from the coast varies from about eight miles at Cape Melville (14° 10′S) to over 150 miles at the Swain Reefs in the south.

Within this tremendous length of 1200 miles, two main types of reef have been recognized—"ribbon reefs" and "platform reefs."

The ribbon reefs, "linear reefs" (Jukes, 1847, Fig. 2), extend from the Murray Islands (latitude 9° 58′S) to Trinity Opening (16° 20′S) opposite Cairns. Very variable in length, 2–15 miles, less so in width, 1000–1500 feet, with inwardly curved extremities, they form a festoon along the precipitous edge of the continental shelf, the 100-fathom line. In contrast to the very steep oceanward slope, the sea bed slopes gently to the west to a depth of only 20–30 fathoms. Exceptionally, as described by Haddon, Sollas and Cole (1894), the ribbon reefs have unvegetated sand cays such as Anchor Cay (9° 22′S), but these are few and are known only north of about 14°S. Figures 1(A) and (B) show the form of typical ribbon reefs. Yonge Reef, about 14° 48′S is an example which has been described in detail by Stephenson, Tandy and Spender (1931).

South of about latitude 16°S, the character of the outer reefs changes to that of irregularly shaped *barrier, patch or platform reefs* (Fairbridge, 1950, p. 341). Not only do these lack the linear character of the ribbon reefs, but they are, in most cases, set back several miles from the 100-fathom contour; sand cays are very rare and known only in the Swain Reefs in the extreme southeast.

The term *patch* or *platform reef* applies only to the broad, flat, tabular form of the reef; it has no genetic significance and in particular does not necessarily imply that the reef has grown up from an antecedent platform. "Patch" implies a smaller reef than "platform." Patch and platform reefs, mostly awash at low tide, are very common in the "lagoon," the area between the reef and the mainland coast where they generally arise from the shallower parts of the continental shelf.

Atoll Reefs (Fairbridge, 1950, p. 341), "*bank atolls*" (Davis, 1928), "*lagoon atolls*" (Davis, 1928),

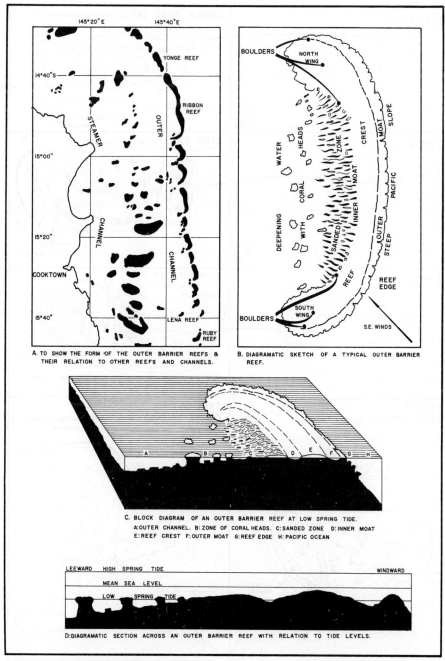

FIG. 1. Diagrams of a typical outer-barrier reef, based on observations of Yonge Reef, Ribbon Reef and others (after Fairbridge, 1950).

"pseudo-atolls" (Molengraaff, 1930) are morphologically similar to the atolls of deep oceans, but are of quite different origin, rising as they do from the continental shelf. They have the general form of a ribbon-shaped reef but enclose a lagoon. A few occur on the "outer barrier" itself, in the 10-mile-long east-west portion north of Cape Melville as described by Jukes (1847). Others occur interspersed among the platform reefs of the "lagoon."

Fairbridge (1950, p. 343) writes that "there appears to be a transition between simple reef patches, horseshoe reefs, complete atolls and ovoid platform reefs with the appearance of filled-in lagoons in the center."

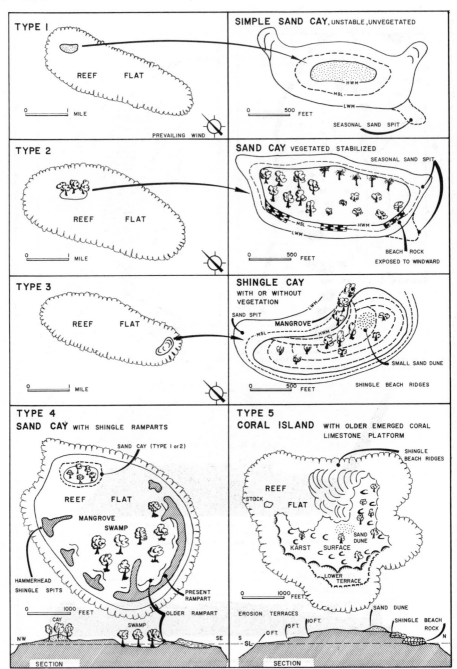

FIG. 2. Coral Island types (after Fairbridge, 1950).

Reefs with Islands

A fundamental division is into "continental islands" and "coral islands." The former will be dealt with on page 496.

The "coral" islands have been classified in various ways. Spender (1930) suggested five divisions: (1) islandless reefs with scattered debris only;

(2) reefs with a sand cay but no shingle ramparts (peripheral beach ridges of coral shingle); (3) reefs with sand cay and ramparts but with no vegetation on the latter; (4) reefs with sand cay and ramparts, with vegetation on the latter; and (5) reefs with all the features of class (4), together with a mangrove swamp on the reef flat. Spender called his class (5)

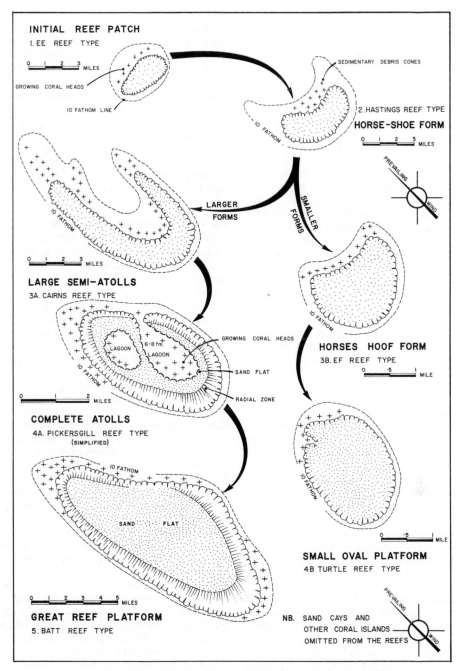

FIG. 3. Evolution of shelf atolls and platforms (after Fairbridge, 1950).

"*island reefs*," Steers (1929, 1937) called them "*low wooded islands*." Fairbridge (1950, p. 347) noted objections to this and other classifications and proposed a division into five types (see Fig. 2):

(1) *Sand cay, unvegetated*, commonly unstable and migrating seasonally. Numerous and found in all areas on all except fringing reefs. Examples:

Sudbury, Undine, Mackay, Pickersgill and Chapman reefs, all within the "lagoon." Steers (1937, 1938) mentions at least eighteen on the outer barrier north of 16° 13′S.

(2) *Sand cay, vegetated*, moderately stabilized, generally with beach rock. Widely distributed but generally missing from the outer, more exposed

reefs. Examples: many of the Capricorn Group (23° 20′S) (as Heron, North-West and Masthead Islands) and Arlington and Michaelmas Reefs and Green and Pelican Islands in the more northerly part.

(3) *Shingle cay, with or without vegetation*, moderately stabilized, widely distributed, generally found on smaller, more exposed reefs. Examples: Steers described a number in the Capricorn and Bunker Groups, including Lady Musgrave and One Tree Islands.

(4) *Sand cay with shingle ramparts (beach ridges)*, unvegetated to completely vegetated including mangrove swamp. Stabilized. Restricted to smaller reef platforms in protected areas of the northern part of the "lagoon." Includes the *"low wooded islands"* of Steers, and Spender's classes (3) and (5). Examples vary from the simplest variety without vegetation on the ramparts as Bee Reef and one of the Turtle Group to the much more complex with mangrove swamps as Low Isles, Pipon, Night, Beewick and Hope Islands and many others. Grades from examples with small areas of older, emerged reef-core material in the ramparts into type (5).

(5) *Island with exposed platform or older, emerged coral-reef material*, with or without a fringe of recent sand or shingle beach ridges or ramparts. Platform vegetated and stable. Rare, but Fairbridge cites Raine Island (12°S) as an example.

Most authors agree that sand cays on reefs are the products of present-day wind and wave action (Gardiner, 1903). There are two important stabilizing factors—vegetation and *beach rock*, although neither nor both give complete protection against erosion. Spells of heavy westerly winds and also hurricanes tend to cause rapid erosion.

Beach rock which grades into *coral conglomerate* consists of coral and shell fragments with a calcareous cement. Whereas the interior of pieces and slabs is soft and easily broken the rock has a hard outer skin which seems to owe its hardness in part at least to the growth of coralline algae.

There is much difference of opinion regarding the mode of formation of beach rock.

Continental or High Islands. These are islands with a core of mainland rock (Steers, 1929) and have also been referred to as "Hilly Timbered Islands" (Hedley and Taylor, 1908). They vary greatly in size and height, in size up to Hinchinbrook Island which is 20 miles long and 5–9 miles broad and in height to Mount Bowen on Hinchinbrook, 3650 feet high. The nature of the continental rock core varies greatly though islands with a predominance of igneous material are in the majority. However, ancient metamorphic rocks occur on some islands and relatively young, unaltered sandstones on others. Many have been described by Jones and Jones (1956). The majority lie close to the mainland, though the Percy Islands (21° 45′S) are some fifty miles from the coast.

Fringing Reefs

These reefs, which, as the name implies, fringe the shore line without enclosing a significant lagoon, grow along much of the mainland coast from Cape York to Cairns. Although in places, as between Cape Flattery and Cape Melville, they may reach nearly a mile in width, along much of the coast growth is restricted, and in places even inhibited, by the abundance of sediment in the water and by low salinity resulting from dilution of the seawater by fresh acidic water discharged by the coastal streams. Growth is considerably restricted around nearshore continental islands, but much more vigorous reefs are found around those further offshore.

The Living Architecture of the Reefs

Dorothea Sandars (1961, p. 109) writes "Representatives of almost every phylum in the animal kingdom may be found in its 80,000 square miles; furthermore most of the species occur in rich profusion. It is the most extensive area of the world with such a dense population of living organisms." These organisms fall into three groups.

(1) Those which contribute to the building up of the reef. The most important of these are, of course, the corals, forming as they do the great physical bulk of the reef. However, the residual skeletal structures of all forms of reef life are reduced to fragments and eventually to sand, and fill in the spaces within and between living and dead coral masses. The most important contribution to this aspect of reef building is made by the hundreds of millions of skeletons of certain tiny single-celled organisms—the foraminifera. But, while such are important in bulk, the coralline algae—seaweed which secrete an external calcareous coating or skeleton—form a most important binding and reinforcing agent especially on the outer margins of the reef and the reef crest. They render the reef resistant to the eroding action of the waves and, in fact, are vital for its continued existence in the zone of wave action.

(2) Those to which the coral is an essential part of their environment, such as the small crab *Hapalocarcinus marsupialis* which forms a gall on the coral within which the female is imprisoned, whereas the smaller male passes in and out through a small opening; and the tube-dwelling worms *Spirobranchus*, large numbers of which live in smoothly lined tubes or burrows in the coral. Many in this group aid the breaking-down process of the waves which is going on simultaneously with the building-up process of the growing coral.

The maximum expression of the breaking-down process is seen in the so-called *"negro-heads"*—large masses of dead coral, coral conglomerate, reef limestone or beach rock resting on the surface of the reef, usually near the outer, windward margin. These coral blocks have been interpreted as masses

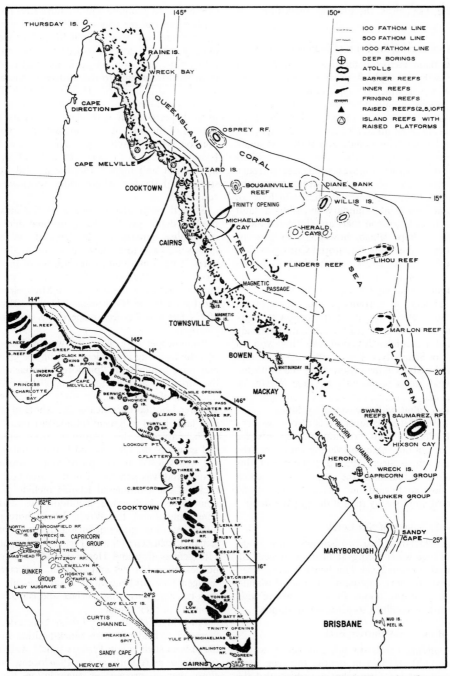

FIG. 4. Map of Queensland showing the Great Barrier Reefs and distribution of reef types (modified from Fairbridge, 1950).

torn off the reef and thrown up ("jetsam") on to the surface by hurricanes (Saville-Kent, 1893, and most observers), but Agassiz (1898), Jukes (1847), Dana (1849, 1872) and Semper (1881) favored the idea that they are solution relics of emerged coral platforms. The former explanation is most generally applicable as they do not commonly occur in areas where there are no hurricanes (Umbgrove, 1931, 1947).

(3) Organisms living on or about the reef, but to which the reef is not essential—Porifera, Echinoderms, Mollusca, Crustacea and many others and,

of course, fish, birds, the dugong, turtles and sea snakes.

Factors Influencing the Form of Individual Reefs

Three main factors determine whether or not coral growth is possible; flourishing coral is restricted to waters in which (1) the average temperature for the coldest month does not drop below 18°C, (2) the variations from normal salinity in either direction are small, and (3) the amount of suspended sediment, which reduces light penetration, is small.

Beyond these factors, the form of the reefs is affected by structural features, winds and currents. The northern part of the reef is situated near the outer edge of the continental shelf which is an important structural boundary (possibly a fault scarp). Thus, the ribbon reefs are elongated along this line, a shape which, however, may also be influenced by the South Equatorial Current which, diverted from its westerly course by the land masses of the East Indies and Australia, flows strongly south-southeast along the edge of the Barrier.

The influence of currents is also very clear in Torres Strait where the tidal currents flow strongly east and west and many of the reefs are strikingly elongated in a similar direction. The "low-wooded islands" of Steers (type 4 of Fairbridge) are found only north of 16°S in the region where the southeast trade wind blows persistently for nine months of the year and is interrupted only by a short season of summer calms with occasional cyclones.

The form of the Platform Reefs also show very well the effects of wind direction and currents (see Fig. 4) for not only is the prevailing wind from the southeast, but, as Steers (1937, p. 5) points out, this wind often outbalances the ebb current which should flow southward but instead merely flows northward more slowly than it does at the flood.

Effects of Changes of Sea Level

Steers (1937) described two benches, a lower one, awash at high water springs indicating a recent fall of sea level of about 5 feet. This bench is widespread and found on many continental and coral islands. A higher platform, about 15–17 feet above low-water mark, is confined to continental islands.

Origin of the Great Barrier Reef

Reef-building corals do not flourish in waters exceeding 120–180 feet in depth; the reef, then, must grow upward from what may be called the "platform," solid rock or otherwise, wide and platform-like or narrow and ridge-like.

The questions then are two: How thick is the reef material and what is the origin and nature of the "platform"?

The first of these questions has been at least partially answered by the sinking of three bores in the reef area. Two of these were put down by the Great Barrier Reef Committee, a Queensland

Committee to promote and organize Reef research, and the third in the course of oil exploration. That on Michaelmas Cay (16° 36′S) penetrated reef material to 476 feet, then quartz sand, in parts glauconitic, and containing foraminifera and littoral shell fragments to the bottom of the bore at 600 feet; the bore on Heron Island (23° 26′S) revealed coralline material to 506 feet, then foraminiferal quartz sand with shell fragments to the bottom of the bore at 732 feet; the oil exploration bore on Wreck Island, seven miles north of Heron Island, penetrated to 1898 feet with reef material to 398 feet and marine Pleistocene and Tertiary strata to 1795 feet where older rocks were encountered.

Even if coral growth began at the maximum possible depth, say 150 feet, additional thicknesses of coralline material of 326, 356 and 248 feet, respectively, have to be accounted for in the three bores. Thus a minimum submergence of the "platform" of 250–350 feet is indicated. In addition, the quartz sand below the coral in the Michaelmas Cay and Heron Island bores suggest further subsidence of 124 feet and 226 feet, respectively, at those two locations.

If the deeper part of the reef were of Pleistocene age, the lowering of sea level during the glaciation may have brought the "platform" sufficiently near the surface to account for a part of the additional thickness of coral. But the study of the fossils in all three bore cores indicates the whole of the reef is of late-glacial to Recent (Holocene) age.

The nature of the "platform" from which the reef grew up, the Queensland Continental Shelf, is not well known. It is exposed in the continental islands and was penetrated in the three bores. The rocks of the continental islands include granites, ignimbrites, high-grade metamorphics and flat-lying sandstones; the Wreck Island bore passed out of coralline material into a thickness of 1395 feet of Pleistocene (?) and Tertiary sediments; the Michaelmas Cay and Heron Island bores proved not less than 124 feet and 226 feet, respectively, of terrigenous sands beneath the coral. The "platform" then has a very irregular surface and is made up of a variety of rock types.

Fairbridge (1950, pp. 378–9) concluded that "tectonic subsidence with block-faulting initiated the present shelf in late Tertiary times" with further subsidence as recently as late Pleistocene, but that since then a process of aggradation has been dominant.

Research Facilities

The Great Barrier Reef Committee (affiliated with the University of Queensland) maintains a research station at Heron Island (laboratories, boats and living facilities) for scientists wishing to work on problems appertaining to the reef. It is also used for teaching purposes by several of the Australian universities.

O. A. JONES

References

*Fairbridge, Rhodes W., 1950, "Recent and Pleistocene Coral Reefs of Australia," *J. Geol.*, **58**, 330–40, numerous figs. and plates.

Jones, Owen A, and Jones, J. B., 1956, "Notes on the geology of some North Queensland Islands," *Reports of the Great Barrier Reef Committee*, **6**, Pt. 3.

Sandars, Dorothea, 1961, "The Great Barrier Reef of Australia," "Handbook 35th Congress A.N.Z.A.A.S," pp. 109–116, Govt. Printer, Brisbane (a popular account with emphasis on zoology).

"Scientific Reports of the Great Barrier Reef Expedition 1928–29," 1930–1958, Vols. 1–6, London, The British Museum (Natural History).

Steers, J. A., 1929, "The Queensland Coast and the Great Barrier Reef," *Geogr. J.*, **74**, 232–257, 341–370.

Steers, J. A., 1937, "The Coral Islands and associated features of the Great Barrier Reefs," *Geogr. J.*, **89**, 1–28, 119–146.

* Additional bibliographic references may be found in this work. Many individual papers are also contained in *Reports of the Great Barrier Reef Committee*, 1925–1956, **1–6**.

Cross-references: *Algal Reef*; *Atoll*; *Beach Ridge*; *Beachrock*; *Coral Reef*; *Fringing Reef*; *Holocene*; *Lagoon Dynamics*; *Mangrove Swamp*; *Negrohead*; *Organisms as Geomorphic Agents*. Vol. I: *Continental Shelf*; *Ocean Currents*. Vol. II: *Trade Winds*; *Tropical Cyclones*; *Winds*. Vol. VI: *Lagoon Sedimentation*.

GREAT LAKES (NORTH AMERICA)

Geography

The Great Lakes of North America, the five large lakes of the St. Lawrence River system, lie between 76°10′ and 92°10′W and 41°22′ and 49°00′N. The boundary between Canada and the United States runs through four of them—Superior, Huron, Erie and Ontario; one lake, Michigan, lies wholly within the United States.

Lake Superior, farthest northwest, has the largest area ($82,477 \text{ km}^2$) of all freshwater lakes in the world (Lake Baikal has a larger volume). Its wide crescent form, convex to the north, has an east-west long dimension of 564 km and a breadth of 258 km. The surface is 184 meters above mean sea level, and the point of maximum depth, 407 meters, is 223 meters below sea level. The volume of the lake is $12,240 \text{ km}^3$.

Lake Michigan, with an area of $58,061 \text{ km}^2$, is 494 km long in a north-south direction, and its width, including Green Bay, is 190 km. The surface is 177 meters above mean sea level, and the point of maximum depth, 282 meters, is 105 meters below sea level. The volume of the lake is 4880 km^3.

Lake Huron, which includes Georgian Bay, has an area of $59,642 \text{ km}^2$. Its long dimension, in a northwest-southeast direction, is 332 km, and its width is 163 km. The surface, like that of Lake Michigan, is 177 meters above mean sea level. The point of maximum depth, 229 meters, is 52 meters below sea level. The volume of the lake is 3540 km^3.

Lake Erie, with an area of $25,739 \text{ km}^2$, is 388 km long in an east-west direction and is 92 km wide. The surface is 174 meters above mean sea level, and its deepest point, 64 meters, is 110 meters above sea level. The lake is generally shallow, with an average depth of only 17.7 meters. The volume of the lake, 456 km^3, is about 1/30 that of Lake Superior.

Lake Ontario, with an area of $19,492 \text{ km}^2$, is 310 km long (east-west) and 85 km wide. The surface is 75 meters above mean sea level, and its deepest point, 237 meters, is 162 meters below sea level. The volume of the lake is 1680 km^3.

Hydrology

Lake Superior discharges $2106 \text{ m}^3/\text{sec}$ through the St. Mary's River, a 101-km-long channel, with a drop of 6.7 meters to Lake Huron. Lake Michigan is connected with Lake Huron by the 6-km-wide Straits of Mackinac, and discharges about $1430 \text{ m}^3/\text{sec}$ into Lake Huron. Lake Huron discharges $5075 \text{ m}^3/\text{sec}$ through the St. Clair River, Lake St. Clair and the Detroit River, a 124-km-long waterway with a drop of 3 meters, to Lake Erie. Lake Erie discharges $5610 \text{ m}^3/\text{sec}$ into Lake Ontario, through the Niagara River. This river descends 18 meters in its upper course, drops 51 meters over Niagara Falls, then descends 30 meters further in the Niagara Gorge, and flows across a lake plain to enter Lake Ontario. Lake Ontario discharges $6700 \text{ m}^3/\text{sec}$ into the St. Lawrence River. That river flows 435 km to reach sea level at Quebec, and from there it is 1300 km to the open Atlantic Ocean.

The source of water of the Great Lakes is precipitation, and the annual precipitation in the region ranges from 74 cm in the north to 86 cm in the south.

The total surface area of the five lakes, $245,400 \text{ km}^2$, is about one-third of their total watershed (including lake) surface area of $749,100 \text{ km}^2$ (Table 1). Approximately one-third of the precipitation therefore falls directly on the lakes.

Before control measures were installed, the monthly mean surface altitudes of the lakes ranged, in an irregular manner over a period of years, from 1.2 meters in Lake Superior to nearly 2 meters in Lake Ontario. Changes in lake levels are correlated with variations in precipitation when such variations are weighted to allow for a lag in delivery of surface runoff and groundwater seepage to the tributary streams. Annually, the levels of the lakes range from lows in winter to highs in summer. It is estimated that 60% of the precipitation on the region is lost by evaporation, transpiration and all other causes.

Channel improvements, control works, and diver-

TABLE 1. PHYSICAL CHARACTERISTICS OF THE GREAT LAKES

Lake	Surface Altitude (m above MSL)	Maximum Depth (m)	Length (km)	Maximum Breadth (km)	Surface Area of Lake (km²)	Area of Drainage Basin Including Lake (km²)	Volume of Lake (km³)	Discharge (m³/sec)
Superior	184	407	564	258	82,470	210,100	12,240	2106
Michigan	177	282	494	190	58,060	176,000	4,880	1430
Huron	177	229	332	163	59,640	188,400	3,540	5075
Erie	174	64	388	92	25,740	84,300	450	5610
Ontario	75	237	310	85	19,490	90,300	1,680	6700
Totals	—	—	—	—	245,400	749,100	22,790	—

sions have modified the discharges and lake levels, as follows.

Diversion of 170 m³/sec from Long Lake into Lake Superior (used for power development) has a tendency to raise the level of Superior and that of the lower lakes as well. Its effect on Michigan and Huron would be to raise them 14 cm. Diversion of 100 m³/sec from Lake Michigan (for disposal of wastes and navigation) to the Illinois River tends to lower the level of Lakes Michigan and Huron by 8 cm. Channel deepening in the St. Clair and Detroit Rivers has increased their discharge, and this tends to lower the level of Lakes Huron and Michigan about 16 cm. The net effect of these is a lowering of 10 cm. Use of Lake Erie water to operate the Welland Canal (which provides for navigation to Lake Ontario) and from the upper Niagara River to operate the New York State Barge Canal (which connects with the Mohawk and Hudson Rivers), tends to lower Lake Erie.

Spillway gates at the St. Mary's locks are operated to increase discharge from Lake Superior at times of high water, and decrease it at times of low water, to limit the variation of lake level to a 0.6-meter range. Control works at the head of the St. Lawrence River are operated to maintain an adequate flow through the St. Lawrence Seaway system of channels and locks, and this tends to increase the fluctuations of the level of Lake Ontario.

Lake Waters

The Great Lakes are "fresh" at all depths. Total dissolved solids in parts per million in the outflowing streams, as reported by Clarke (1924) for each of the lakes, were as follows; Superior, 60; Michigan, 118; Huron, 108; Erie, 133; Ontario, 134. More recent studies have shown no increase in Superior, but appreciable changes in the lower lakes. By 1952, Lake Michigan had an average of 170 ppm, and amounts of 150–370 ppm were common in Lake Erie.

Dissolved oxygen is present at all depths and all seasons, except for recent occurrences of severe oxygen depletion near the bottom in western Lake Erie in the summertime. The lake waters are alkaline,

with the pH generally ranging from 7.8–8.4. Calcium, magnesium, bicarbonate, carbonate and sulfate are the most abundant ions.

The surface waters generally have a temperature range from 0°C in the winter to more than 20°C in the summer (Lake Superior is somewhat cooler). Below a depth of about 20 meters, all of the lakes have a temperature close to 4°C throughout the year. They exhibit an annual cycle of isothermal water, with mixing or overturn in the spring, a strongly developed thermocline and stratification in the summer, isothermal water (with overturn) in the fall, and at least occasionally a reverse temperature gradient with stratification in the winter.

Ice forms in the lakes during the winter but, except in protected embayments, there has not been a complete cover of ice in historic time. In the open lakes there is generally a narrow belt of fast ice alongshore, and more or less extensive floes which are moved about by the winds. Navigation of the lakes generally is closed from mid-December to mid-April, but navigation is maintained throughout the winter on Lake Michigan by ice-breaking railway car ferries.

Waves in the lakes, during storms, commonly reach a height in excess of 3 meters, and wave heights as great as 7.5 meters have been reported. True astronomic tides are negligible, the largest tidal effect ever reported being a range of less than 4.5 cm. Seiches, however, are common and produce changes of level commonly of 30 cm and up to 2.5 meters (in Lake Erie). "Stokes edgewaves," produced by a moving atmospheric pressure-jump line, occur occasionally and produce solitary waves up to 3 meters in height.

Currents generally are set up by wind stress, and are affected by Coriolis force and the basin configurations. There is, therefore, no constant pattern of surface circulation.

During summer stratification, surface water is drifted by winds to cause a tilting of the thermocline and, in extreme cases, to cause an upwelling of cold bottom water to the surface along the windward shore.

The lakes affect the local climates of the region,

principally by damping the ranges of temperature over the adjacent lands. As a consequence of prevailing onshore winds, areas such as Western Michigan, southern Ontario and northwestern New York are important fruit growers. A striking meteorological effect is the common occurrence of heavy snowfall in the upper peninsula of Michigan, in southwestern Michigan, and in the Buffalo, New York, area east of Lake Erie.

Biology

Because of their geologic youth, the Great Lakes are, biologically, still in a formative stage. Only a relatively few species of fish and invertebrate animals have so far been able to invade the lakes and become established there. Lakes Superior, Michigan, Huron and, to a somewhat lesser degree, Lake Ontario are oligotrophic; i.e., essential plant nutrients are present in relatively dilute quantities and the overall production of living organic material is comparatively small. These lakes are cold and deep, and

a plentiful supply of dissolved oxygen is present throughout their waters at all seasons of the year. Lake Erie, on the other hand, is shallower and warmer, and through the influx of large amounts of pollution the quantities of nutrient chemical substances in this lake have attained much higher levels than in the other lakes. At least a part of Lake Erie is of a eutrophic, or highly productive, character.

The flora and fauna of the lakes, with the partial exception of Erie, are not unlike those of other large, cold, deep North American lakes. The phytoplankton, that community of single-celled algae which constitutes the base of the food chain, consists almost entirely of the silica-shelled diatoms. The zooplankton, consisting largely of microcrustacean forms, is supported directly or indirectly by the primary food supply furnished by the phytoplankton. Another ecologically important group, the bottom-dwelling or benthic organisms, consists principally of small crustaceans, oligochaete worms, fingernail clams and the larvae of certain flying

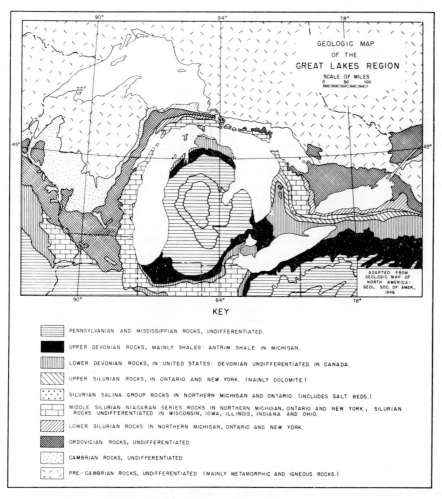

KEY

	PENNSYLVANIAN AND MISSISSIPPIAN ROCKS, UNDIFFERENTIATED.
	UPPER DEVONIAN ROCKS, MAINLY SHALES: ANTRIM SHALE IN MICHIGAN.
	LOWER DEVONIAN ROCKS, IN UNITED STATES: DEVONIAN UNDIFFERENTIATED IN CANADA.
	UPPER SILURIAN ROCKS, IN ONTARIO AND NEW YORK. (MAINLY DOLOMITE.)
	SILURIAN SALINA GROUP ROCKS IN NORTHERN MICHIGAN AND ONTARIO. (INCLUDES SALT BEDS.)
	MIDDLE SILURIAN NIAGARAN SERIES ROCKS IN NORTHERN MICHIGAN, ONTARIO AND NEW YORK; SILURIAN ROCKS UNDIFFERENTIATED IN WISCONSIN, IOWA, ILLINOIS, INDIANA AND OHIO.
	LOWER SILURIAN ROCKS IN NORTHERN MICHIGAN, ONTARIO AND NEW YORK.
	ORDOVICIAN ROCKS, UNDIFFERENTIATED.
	CAMBRIAN ROCKS, UNDIFFERENTIATED.
	PRE-CAMBRIAN ROCKS, UNDIFFERENTIATED. (MAINLY METAMORPHIC AND IGNEOUS ROCKS.)

FIG. 1. Geologic map of the Great Lakes region.

midges. They are also dependent upon the production of phytoplankton in the upper lighted waters. Dead and dying remains of both plant and animal plankton settle slowly to the bottom, where they become the food supply of the bottom dwellers.

The same sorts of communities occur in Lake Erie, but over much of the lake there is a dominance of different organisms. For instance, green and blue-green algae as well as diatoms are common in the phytoplankton, and the amphipods, so common in the bottom of the other lakes, are restricted to a few localities in Lake Erie.

The animal forms found in both the zooplankton and the benthos constitute an important food source for the fish. The lakes were naturally populated by lake trout and a number of species of whitefish, as well as yellow perch, burbot and, particularly in Lake Erie, walleye, sheepshead, and blue pike. In recent years, serious disruptions of the ecology of the lakes have been brought about by two invaders from the Atlantic Ocean. The trout, whitefish, and burbot stocks were, by the early 1950's, virtually destroyed by the sea lamprey, a parasitic eel-like native of salt water which entered the lakes by way of the St. Lawrence River and the Welland Canal. With the predator species eliminated by the lamprey, a second marine invader, the small herring-like alewife, was able to enter and spread throughout the lakes in astronomical numbers.

Successful control measures against the lamprey have been brought about through cooperative efforts of the United States and Canada, in which selective poisoning of the larvae is carried out in lamprey spawning streams. As a result, lake trout are being restocked successfully in Lakes Superior and Michigan, and recently the Pacific coho salmon has also been established in these two lakes. Successful maintenance of the trout and salmon stocks will do much to control the alewife upon which these larger fish feed, and prospects are presently favorable for a return to ecological balance in the Great Lakes.

Origin of the Lake Basins

The basins of the Great Lakes (Fig. 1) four of which extend well below sea level, were formed by a combination of stream erosion during Mesozoic to Pleistocene time and glacial ice scour in the Pleistocene. The Lake Superior basin is largely in a synclinal structure in Precambrian rocks of the Canadian Shield which was filled by late Precambrian sediments and covered by Paleozoic marine rocks, and reexcavated by erosion. The four lower lake basins lie in belts of the softer Paleozoic rocks, mainly shales of either Ordovician or late Devonian-early Mississippian age. The Pleistocene ice sheets moved into the region and, being guided by the basin topography, further deepened the lowlands. Each advance of the ice encountered a successively more pronounced basin topography, and the last major advance was one with a pronounced lobate character which left end moraines that are distinctly concentric around the basin margins.

Geologic History of the Lakes

It is likely that a number of lake stages existed at various times during the retreats and advances of the earlier phases of Pleistocene glaciation, but all evidence of them was obliterated by the last ice advance that filled the basins.

The first known lakes date from only about 15,000 years ago, when the margin of the Wisconsin age ice retreated north of the southern watershed boundaries and allowed water to pond. First existing as narrow ice-margin lakes, the early stages drained over low spots on the divides and to southward-flowing rivers. Then, through a series of events involving retreats and readvances of the ice front, diversion of discharge through new outlets uncovered by retreat, blocking of outlets by readvance,

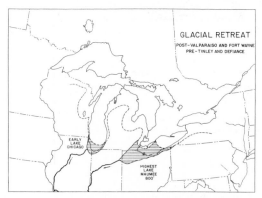

Fig. 2. Late glacial lake stages, earliest Lake Chicago and Lake Maumee, somewhat pre-14,000 years B.P. (altitude in feet).

Fig. 3. Late glacial lake stages, dating from approximately 13,500 years B.P. (early Lake Arkona or Bölling interstadial).

FIG. 4. Late glacial lake stages, dating from approximately 13,000 years B.P. (Lake Arkona-Bölling interstadial).

FIG. 6. Late glacial lake stages, dating from approximately 12,200 years B.P. (late Port Huron-Velgast stadial).

downcutting of outlets by discharging waters, and uplift of the land to the north as the weight of glacial ice decreased, a complicated series of lake stages occurred.

In the Lake Erie basin there were three Maumee stages, at 244, 232 and 238 meters above mean sea level, respectively (Fig. 2); the first and third discharged down the Wabash River of Indiana, to the Ohio and Mississippi Rivers, but the second, at 232 meters, discharged down the Grand Valley of Michigan to the Lake Michigan basin. Meanwhile, in the Michigan basin (Fig. 2) there was an Early Lake Chicago (inferred, altitude unknown but probably a little higher than 195 meters above mean sea level) discharging down the Illinois River, then a slight ice advance that refilled the basin, then the initiation of the Glenwood stage at 195 meters above mean sea level. While the Glenwood persisted, there were three Arkona stages (Fig. 3) in the Erie basin, at 217, 213.5 and 212 meters above mean sea level, which extended into the Southern Huron basin and Saginaw Bay and discharged down the Grand Valley to the Michigan basin. In the Ontario basin there was an ice margin lake, Vanuxem I, which extended

into the Finger Lakes basins and which drained eastward to the Mohawk and Hudson Rivers.

A more extensive retreat of the ice front then occurred, in the Cary-Port Huron (Mankato) Interval (Fig. 4), during which lake levels in the Michigan, Huron and Erie basins dropped below present lake levels because of discharge eastward through the Ontario basin. The Port Huron (Mankato) ice then closed the dischargeway to the east, filled the Huron basin, and rode up the "thumb" of Michigan to impound Lake Whittlesey in the Erie basin at an altitude of 225 meters above mean sea level (Fig. 5). This lake discharged through the Ubly channel, in the "thumb," to a Lake Saginaw and from there down the Grand Valley and to the reestablished Glenwood stage (Glenwood II) in the Michigan basin. Both Glenwood stages discharged through the Chicago outlet to the Illinois and Mississippi Rivers.

Glacial ice front retreats and readvances, through the later Port Huron age events (including the Bay City and Tawas advances) caused a series of lake stages (Fig. 6) in the Huron and Erie basins which included three Lake Warren stages at 210, 208 and

FIG. 5. Late glacial lake stages, dating from approximately 12,500 years B.P. (Port Huron-Velgast stadial).

FIG. 7. Late glacial lake stages, dating from approximately 12,100 years B.P. (post-Port Huron).

FIG. 8. Late glacial lake stages, dating from approximately 12,000 years B.P. (altitude in feet).

FIG. 10. Late glacial lake stages, dating from the maximum of the brief Valders readvance stage, approximately 11,400 years B.P. (altitude in feet).

206 meters above mean sea level, all of which discharged down the Grand Valley, and a Wayne stage at about 210 meters; this probably occurred between the second and third Warren stages, and its direction of discharge is unknown. In the Ontario basin, glacial ice formed a dam for the lakes to the west, but ice-margin lakes were present, including a second Vanuxem stage.

During further retreat in late Port Huron time, and while glacial ice still existed in the Ontario basin, the Grassmere stage at 195 meters (Fig. 7), the Lundy stage at 189 meters, and the Early Algonquin stage at 185 meters above mean sea level occurred in the Huron and Erie basins. In the Michigan basin, the Glenwood II stage at 195 meters was followed by the Calumet at 189 meters and the Toleston at 185 meters above mean sea level, all of which discharged through the Chicago outlet and down the Illinois River. The relationships between these lakes of the Michigan and the Huron-Erie basins are not known, but it seems likely that the sill of the Chicago outlet, alternately stable and cut down by the outflowing stream, was the determinant of the lake levels in both the Michigan and Huron-Erie basins,

with the discharge of the latter being into the Michigan basin by passing around the northern end of the southern peninsula of Michigan.

In the eastern part of the Ontario basin, the second Vanuxem lake was followed by Lake Dana with eastward discharge through the Marcellus-Cedarvale channel to the Mohawk Valley. Retreat of the ice margin then opened the Rome outlet to the Mohawk Valley, and Lake Iroquois came into existence at about 100 meters above mean sea level. At this time, the Erie basin discharged to Lake Iroquois and Early Lake Erie existed at a level below that of the present Lake Erie, and Lake Algonquin discharged at both the Chicago and Port Huron outlets (Fig. 8). Further retreat of the ice margin in the east then opened a dischargeway around Covey Hill, northeast of Lake Ontario, giving rise to a brief Frontenac stage in the Ontario basin. A large freshwater lake then existed in the upper St. Lawrence Valley and lower Ottawa Valley, and extended into the Champlain Valley to discharge southward down the Hudson River.

The Two Creeks Interval then occurred (Fig. 9), with retreat of the ice margin northward far enough

FIG. 9. Late glacial lake stages, dating from approximately 11,800 years B.P. (Two Creeks or Alleröd interstadial).

FIG. 11. Late glacial lake stages, dating from the post-Valders (early Holocene) retreat, approximately 11,000–10,800 years B.P.

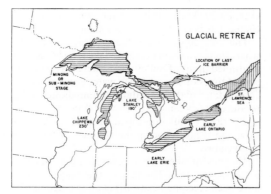

FIG. 12. Final late glacial lake stages, dating from approximately 10,700 years B.P.

to allow the opening of the St. Lawrence Valley and the drainage of all of the Great Lakes eastward. Lake Keweenaw existed in the Superior basin. In the Michigan basin, the Two Creeks forest bed (11,800 radiocarbon years B.P.) extended down at least as low as present lake level. The low stage of the Michigan and Huron basins, the Kirkfield (at about 170 meters above mean sea level), discharged down the Trent Valley to Early Lake Ontario in the Ontario basin. Seawater flooded up the St. Lawrence Valley and the lower Ottawa Valley to form the "Champlain Sea."

The Valders ice advance then occurred (Fig. 10). Its maximum extent in the east was marked by the Ste. Narcisse-St. Faustin moraines which lie on the north sides of the St. Lawrence Valley and the Ontario basin. Farther west, the Valders ice advance closed the Kirkfield outlet and caused the Huron basin waters to rise and discharge southward through the Port Huron outlet to the Erie basin. The Valders ice crossed the Straits of Mackinac area to close the connection between the Huron and Michigan basins, causing lake level to rise in the Michigan basin and discharge southward through

FIG. 13. Postglacial Great Lakes, at approximately 4500 years B.P.

the Chicago outlet. In the Michigan basin, the Valders ice overrode the Two Creeks forest bed, and extended southward to the latitude of Milwaukee and Muskegon (43°N).

The reestablished southward-discharging lakes in the Michigan and Huron basins, at the Algonquin stage altitude (185 meters above mean sea level), existed during the Valders maximum as separate bodies of water.

When the waning Valders ice margin retreated north of the Straits of Mackinac, Lake Algonquin became a single body of water, connected through the Straits, but it continued to discharge at both the Chicago and Port Huron outlets. Soon, however, retreat of the ice margin from the old Kirkfield outlet east of Georgian Bay allowed discharge at that point and drained the Huron and Michigan basins down once again below present lake level. This occurred about 11,000 years B.P., while ice still occupied the eastern part of the Superior basin (Fig. 11).

In the Superior basin, several stages of Lake Duluth existed during the waning of the Valders ice, and they discharged through the St. Croix River, in northwestern Wisconsin, to the upper Mississippi.

Following the main Algonquin stage, and during retreat of the ice margin northward, there were several successively lower stages, the last being the Stanley (Fig. 12) at only about 58 meters above mean sea level in the Huron basin and discharging northeastward at North Bay, Ontario, to the Mattawa and Ottawa Rivers and thence to the St. Lawrence. Lake Chippewa, in the Michigan basin, was held at a higher level (70 meters above mean sea level) by the sill of a channel through the Straits of Mackinac (Fig. 13).

By this time, discharge of the Superior basin was to the Huron basin, resulting in several low stages in Superior, the lowest of which was the Houghton, at about 104 meters above mean sea level, which discharged over a sill at Sault Ste. Marie.

These various low stages, with the three upper Great Lakes discharging through the North Bay outlet and down the Mattawa Valley of Ontario, occurred because the land had been depressed by the load of glacial ice and retreat of the ice margin exposed the low outlet. As the ice mass diminished, the land rose. Some uplift occurred during the glacial ice retreats associated with earlier lake stages, but the greater part of the observed uplift occurred after the ice margin retreated north of North Bay. Rise of the North Bay outlet caused lake level in the Huron, Michigan and Superior basins to rise until their waters reached the altitude of the old southern dischargeways (Fig. 13). Then, lake surface was stabilized at the Nipissing Stage, at or close to the old Algonquin level (185 meters above mean sea level) about 4500 years B.P. This lake, discharging at the North Bay, Chicago and Port Huron outlets, extended into the Lake Superior basin. The southern

505

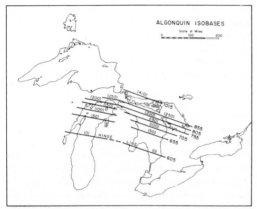

ALGONQUIN ISOBASES

FIG. 14. Isobases, showing lines of equal uplift of the Algonquin beach, with present altitudes above mean sea level in feet given by figures at ends of lines, and amount of uplift above original altitudes in feet by figures in parentheses. South of the zero (605-foot) line, the beach is horizontal.

parts of the Huron and Michigan basins were south of the area of uplift (Fig. 14), but farther north the land continued to rise.

When the North Bay outlet was raised above the Nipissing level, the entire discharge of the upper three Great Lakes went southward. Because the Chicago outlet was on bedrock, it could not be cut down, but the Port Huron outlet, bottomed on till of the Port Huron moraine, was cut down. During the downcutting, a stable Algoma lake stage occurred, at 182 meters above mean sea level, at about 3200 radiocarbon years B.P. Then the water surface in the Huron and Erie basins was lowered to the level of Lakes Huron and Michigan, 177 meters above mean sea level.

Continued (though diminishing) uplift in the north raised the outlet of the Superior basin above the water surface in the lakes to the south, and Lake Superior became a higher-level lake about 2200 years B.P., and slowly rose to its present altitude of 184 meters above mean sea level. This caused a rise of the lake on its southern shores, while the northeastern shores rose out of the lake.

In the east, meanwhile, uplift had raised the St. Lawrence Valley above sea level, and the marine water of the Champlain Sea had drained out. Continued uplift raised the outlet of the Ontario basin, and lake level there is still rising.

The outlet of Lake Erie has risen slightly, to bring the lake surface to its present altitude of 174 meters above mean sea level, and to rise on its southern shores.

Most of the earlier lake stages existed for a few hundred years, at the most, because of the relatively rapid changes in positions of ice margin and, later, because of the relatively rapid rate of uplift. The present pattern of the lakes was established, how-

ever, by 2000 years B.P. and the rate of geological change has been very slow since then.

The lake shores are being eroded, particularly where there is a slight net rise of lake level because of continued uplift of outlets, and where waves occurring at times of seasonal high water impinge on unconsolidated material. Sedimentation, though it has produced a few hundred meters of deposits in some of the deep basins in postglacial time, is generally slow and is not reducing the volumes of the lakes appreciably.

The present lake outlets are not being cut down at a measurable rate. The falls of the Niagara River have been receding headward at an average rate of nearly 2 meters in historical time, but this will not cause the drainage of Lake Erie, for about 25,000 years.

Though the physical regimen of the lakes is essentially stable, changes in the quality of the water in some of the lakes (notably in western Lake Erie and southern Lake Michigan) have been accelerated in recent years and control of pollution has become a matter of serious concern.

JACK L. HOUGH

References

Canadian Hydrographic Service (Annual), Great Lakes Pilot, Ottawa.

Clarke, F. W., 1924, "The composition of the river and lake waters of the United States," *U.S. Geol. Surv. Profess. Paper* **135**, 199pp.

Corps of Engineers, U.S. Army (Annual), Great Lakes Pilot, U.S. Lake Survey, Detroit.

Farrand, W. R., 1962, "Postglacial uplift in North America," *Am. J. Sci.*, **260**, 181–199.

Hough, J. L., 1958, "Geology of the Great Lakes," University of Illinois Press, 313pp.

Hough, J. L., 1963, "The prehistoric Great Lakes of North America," *Am. Scientist*, **51**, 84–109.

Hough, J. L., 1966, "Correlation of glacial lake stages in the Huron-Erie and Michigan basins," *J. Geol.*, **74**, 62–77.

Leverett, F., and Taylor, F. B., 1915, "The Pleistocene of Indiana and Michigan and the History of the Great Lakes," *U.S. Geol. Surv. Mono.*, **53**.

Pincus, H. J. (editor), 1962, "Great Lakes Basin," *Am. Assoc. Adv. Science*, Publ. No. 71, 320pp.

Wold, R. J., and Ostenso, N. A., 1966, "Aeromagnetic, gravity, and sub-bottom profiling studies in western Lake Superior," *A.G.U. Geophys. Mon.* No. 10, 66–94.

Cross-references: *Champlain Sea; Deglaciation; Finger Lakes; Glacial Geology; Glacial Lake Agassiz; Glacial Lake Albany; Glacial Lakes; Glacial Scour; Glacial Spillways and Proglacial Lakes; Lake Baikal; Lakes; Postglacial Isostatic Rebound; Strandline.* Vol. I: *Coriolis Force; Seiche.*

GREAT SALT LAKE

Great Salt Lake, in northwestern Utah, U.S.A., ranks thirty-third in area, first in shallowness, and from first to second in salinity among the world's lakes.

(1) Geographic Setting

Great Salt Lake is an irregular, ameoboid-shaped remnant of Lake Bonneville, a large Pleistocene lake. Great Salt Lake is in the northeastern part of the Basin and Range Province of the Great Basin area which occupies a large part of the western United States and is characterized by internal drainage (Fig. 1). The lake is oriented northwesterly, and historically has fluctuated in area within latitudes 40°20′ and 41°40′N and longitudes 111°52′–113°6′E (Fig. 2). The exceedingly low profile of the lake basin allows the lake to range widely in size and area in response to cyclic climatic changes which characterize this semiarid region.

Great Salt Lake has an average elevation of 4200 feet (1280 meters) above mean sea level. It occupies a depression formed by the same faults that flank the east-lying Wasatch Mountains and other north-south oriented fault-block mountains which form islands or nearshore uplands in the vicinity of the lake. Eight islands or inselbergs lie within this depression. Although all of the islands appear to be remnants of fault-block mountains, no bounding faults are known to have been active in either historic or late prehistoric times. The fluctuating lake divests itself of all of its islands when it shrinks to an elevation of 4191 feet (1278 meters), and encompasses all of them when it rises 19 feet (5.79 meters) to 4210 feet (1283 meters). The watershed of Great Salt Lake is approximately 23,000 square miles (59,570 km²) and has a relief of 8285 feet (2526

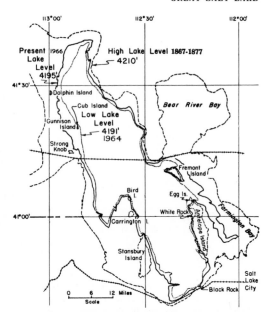

FIG. 2. Great Salt Lake showing the location of islands and the Lake levels. High levels, 1867–77; low level, 1964.

meters; Fig. 3); the highest point is Hayden Peak in the Uinta Mountains which stands at 12,485 feet (3805 meters); the relief of the islands in the lake ranges from 35–2445 feet (10.7–745 meters) above mean lake level.

(2) Salient Physical Features

Since the days of scanty recollections in journals of early explorers and trappers and from the dates of earliest records in 1850 through 1966, the lake has ranged in length from 70–81 miles (113–130 km), in width from 24–47 miles (39–76 km) and in area from 915–2185 square miles (2370–5659 km²). The highest historic lake stage was attained in June 1873 when the surface was 4211.65 feet (1283.65 meters) above mean sea level, some 46.85 feet (14.28 meters) above the lowest known point of its bottom [4164.8 feet (1269.4 meters)]. The lowest lake stage was in November 1963 when it was at 4191.35 feet (1277.52 meters), and its deepest water was 26.55 feet (8.09 meters). The 20.3-foot (6.18 meter) range of the lake level represents a volume change of 6.3 cubic miles (26.3 km³) from a low volume of 2.6 cubic miles to a high of 8.9 cubic miles (10.8–37.1 km³; see Table 1 and Fig. 4).

(3) Hydrology and Climatology

(a) Temperature. The semiarid continental climate of the Salt Lake Basin is marked by large variations in mean temperature due to topographic differences. Mean average annual temperatures (Peck and Richardson, 1966) range from 53.2°F at Antelope Island in Great Salt Lake to 44.9°F at Snowville, Utah, about twenty miles north of the

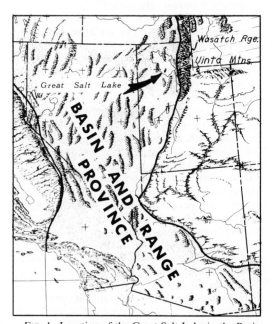

FIG. 1. Location of the Great Salt Lake in the Basin and Range Province.

TABLE 1. RELATIONSHIP OF AREA AND VOLUME CHANGES TO CHANGES OF LAKE LEVEL

Lake Level (ft above sea level)	Area (sq miles)	Area (acres)[a]	Volume (acre-ft)[b]	Volume Change (acre-ft)
4167	0	0	0	
4170	180	115,300	288,320	288,320
4175	423	270,550	1,253,000	964,680
4180	626	400,970	2,931,810	1,678,810
4185	770	492,700	5,166,050	2,234,240
4190	884	565,600	7,811,890	2,645,840
4195	1096	701,300	10,979,190	3,167,300
4200	1680	1,075,380	15,420,920	4,441,730
4205	2016	1,290,100	21,334,620	5,913,700
4210	2133	1,358,200	27,955,400	6,620,780

[a] 640 acres/square mile.
[b] 3,379,200 acre-ft/cubic mile.

lake. Temperatures around the southern and western shores range between 51 and 52°F, and slightly colder temperatures of 49–50°F characterize the stations to the north. The highest temperature recorded in the vicinity of the lake was 111°F at Antelope Island in July 1959, and the lowest was −32°F near the north shore at Corrine, Utah in December 1924. Thus the annual range of extreme temperatures in the lake area has been 143°F. At Antelope Island, for a period from 1951–60, temperatures of 90°F or higher were recorded for an annual average of 72 days.

(b) **Precipitation.** The heaviest precipitation is in

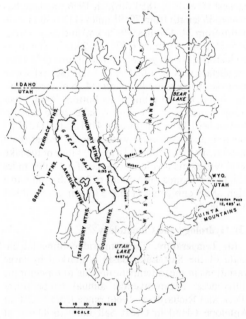

FIG. 3. Great Salt Lake watershed.

the spring, with a secondary maximum in the fall; both are related to upper air low-pressure systems and eastward-moving storm fronts. Late summer precipitation is more irregular due to thunderstorms resulting from topographic and convective lifting of moist unstable air from the Gulf of Mexico. The driest period of the year is in late June and early July. The average annual precipitation ranges from 5–15 inches over the lake to approximately 60 inches in the Wasatch Mountains.

(c) **Humidity.** The sunrise and sunset humidities respectively average 81–73% in December to 49–18% during July. Extremes in relative humidity range from 100% during winter fogs to as low as 4% on some hot summer afternoons.

(d) **Winds.** The winds are extremely variable because of topography. The southeast shore area has a prevalence of southerly winds, whereas north and northwesterly winds predominate in the northern shores. The highest winds seldom exceed 50 miles/hr (80 km/hr) for short periods during severe weather.

(e) **Snow.** Snowfall ranges from 7.5 inches (19 cm) on the western shores to 63.6 inches (164 cm) near the eastern shore. Snowfall averages 453 inches (1151 cm) at Alta, Utah which is one of the higher areas of the watershed. A high water content in a relatively low-level (altitude) snow pack is conducive to a rapid rise in an increment of lake level, provided that the snow pack is maintained into late spring by a period of cold weather. The sudden onset of warm weather causes rapid production of meltwater in excess of the groundwater intake capacity. Such a condition of high runoff occurring below water storage facilities results in greater than average flow to the lake.

(f) **Evaporation.** Evaporation studies to date have not determined an average evaporation factor for the lake. Early studies indicated a value of 37.2 inches (94.5 cm), whereas later studies indicate a value of

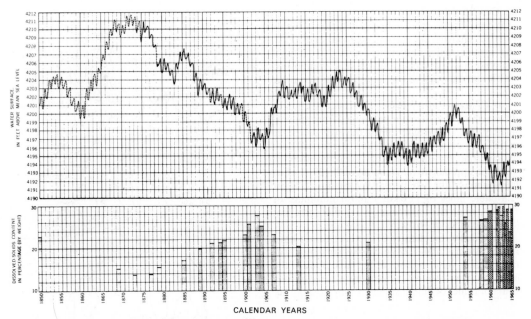

FIG. 4. Hydrograph showing yearly maximum and minimum elevations of lake surface, and histograms of dissolved-solids concentration of brine. The cross-hatched bars represent the northern part and stippled bars the southern part of the lake. Histograms represent single analyses, except for the years 1889, 1892, 1900, 1904, 1959, 1960, 1964 and 1965, which represent the average of several analyses (from Water Resources Division, U.S. Geological Survey, Salt Lake City, Utah).

near 40 in./yr (101.6 cm/yr). The evaporation rate from the lake surface is related to the salinity of the surface water. If the lake surface is near 4196 feet (1280 meters) above mean sea level, it is nearly saturated with dissolved solids and the evaporation rate is only about 70% of fresh water. Also, during periods of calm, lighter fresh waters from rivers will float for several to as many as 10 miles (16 km) over the lake brines, resulting in greater evaporation. Evaporation pan observations on the south shore have shown that the lake can gain water while fresh water is losing water by evaporation. Generally it can be concluded that evaporation from Great Salt Lake is erratic and occurs in intense spurts which are localized in time and space. The presence of nearby topography, the mountainous terrain and desert areas, more significantly affects evaporation from the lake than is indicated in evaporation from pans.

(g) **Sources of Water to the Lake.** The direct precipitation into the lake ranges from 4.5–6 inches (11.4–15.2 cm) on the western shores and 14–18 inches (35.6–45.7 cm) on the eastern shores. The annual runoff and river discharge range from 0.8–1.3 million acre-feet during low water stages to 1.9–3.5 million acre-feet during the high stages. This surface water represents an approximate stage gain of 19.7 inches (50 cm) during low stage and a 23.7-inch (60.2-cm) gain during a high stage. If average evaporations of 37.2 inches (94.5 cm) for a low stage and

45.5 inches (115.6 cm) for a high stage are assumed, then the groundwater increment would be 8.2 inches (20.8 cm) and 9.8 inches (24.9 cm), respectively, for low and high stages or 22% of the inflow budget (see Fig. 5).

(h) **Seasonal and Cyclic Variations in Lake Level.** The stage of the lake is dependent upon inflow versus evaporation. Though uncommon, the seasonal fluctuation of level during a static stage is between 0.6 and 2 feet (18 and 61 cm). The high level generally occurs in June and the low level in November. Historically, the lake, except for short intervals of 3–4 years (see Fig. 4), has been either increasing or decreasing in size. Its greatest gain was during a series of wet years from 1862–70 when the lake rose 11 feet (3.4 meters). The net annual increase or decrease in a lake stage has ranged from a few inches to 3 feet (centimeters to 1 meter).

Great Salt Lake rapidly adjusts to annual variations in precipitation and evaporation but responds relatively slowly to climatic changes. Since the date of the earliest records (1850), the lake has experienced three major periods of both high and low stages. Each high stage is from 4–7 feet (1.3–2.3 meters) lower than the previous high, and each low stage is 2 feet (61 cm) lower than the previous low (see Fig. 4); it is not clear whether the gradual stage reduction is the result of a broad climatic change or of cultural development or a combination of both.

(4) Geochemistry

The geochemistry of Great Salt Lake is highly variable, changes are diurnal, seasonal and cyclic, and occur areally and with depth. No suite of samples has yet been gathered and composited which can be regarded as a representative brine sample.

(a) **Character of the Brine.** The concentration of dissolved solids in the brine has ranged from approximately 13 % (by weight) during the high lake stage in 1873 to about 28.5 % in 1963. Historical data indicate that the dissolved solids concentration of the brine approaches a maximum of 28–29 % when the volume of the lake is near 9.7 million acre-feet (2.8 cubic miles or 11.6 km^3) and a minimum of 13–14 % when the volume is 30.0 million acre-feet (8.8 cubic miles or 36.5 km^3).

Historically, the density of the lake brines have ranged from 1.104–1.223 g/cc. Recent investigations of deep water stations of the main body of the lake (south part) show that as many as three or four strata of brines of differing density may exist during

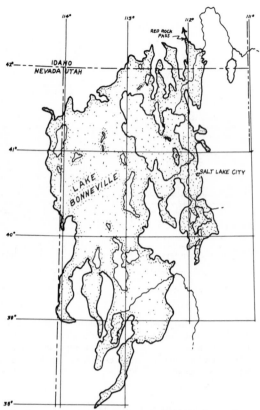

FIG. 6. Map of Lake Bonneville.

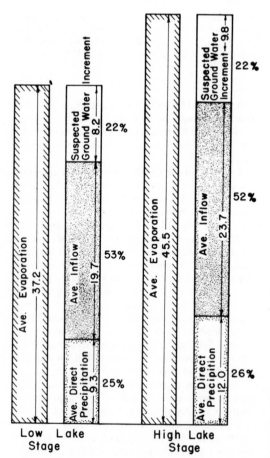

FIG. 5. Graphs showing relationships of recharge waters to evaporation for high and low lake stages (Cohenour, 1966).

periods of calm weather and that turbulent mixing during foul weather may reduce the strata to two layers.

The temperatures of the near surface brines, though variable, are generally slightly less than the monthly mean air temperatures. Temperatures of the bottom brines of deeper waters may range from equivalent to the surface brine (at 3 feet) to as much as 15°F warmer; summer temperatures near the bottom may be as much as 20°F cooler than the near surface brine. Temperature changes cause variations in the solubility of sodium sulfate (Glauber's salt— $Na_2SO_4 \cdot 10H_2O$), resulting in winter precipitation of Glauber's salt which is deposited as a thin crystal mush on the deep lake bed and as beach bars. The temperature of the brine annually fluctuates almost 70°F.

(b) **Chemical Characteristics.** The dissolved solids concentration of the Great Salt Lake brine changes with lake stage and volume; however, historically the percentage composition of the dissolved solids remains constant. Sodium and chloride are dominant constituents, with significant amounts of sulfate, magnesium and potassium; bicarbonate, calcium and other ions are minor constituents (Table 2; data from Richardson, Clarke, Hahl and Mitchell, in Handy and Hahl, 1966).

TABLE 2. PERCENTAGE COMPOSITION (BY WEIGHT) OF DISSOLVED SOLIDS IN SELECTED SAMPLES OF GREAT SALT LAKE BRINE

Constituent	1850[a]	1869[b]	August 1892[a]	October 1913[b]	March 1930[c]	April 1960[c]	November 1961[c]	July 1964[d]	July 1965[d]
Silica, SiO_2	—	—	—	—	—	0.002	0.003	0.002	0.002
Iron, Fe	—	—	—	—	—	0.00002	0.00004	—	—
Calcium, Ca	—	0.17	1.05	0.16	0.17	0.12	0.10	0.10	0.12
Magnesium, Mg	0.27	2.52	1.23	2.76	2.75	2.91	3.49	3.32	3.31
Sodium, Na	38.29	33.15	33.22	33.17	32.90	32.71	31.55	32.25	32.58
Potassium, K	—	1.60	1.71	1.66	1.61	1.71	1.95	2.12	2.06
Lithium, Li	—	—	—	—	—	—	—	0.02	0.02
Bicarbonate as carbonate, CO_3	—	—	—	0.09	0.05	0.06	0.07	0.08	0.09
Sulfate, SO_4	5.57	6.57	6.57	6.68	5.47	6.60	8.21	7.29	7.67
Chloride, Cl	55.87	55.99	56.22	55.48	57.05	55.88	54.63	54.81	54.14
Boron, B	—	—	—	—	—	0.01	—	0.01	0.01
Totals	100.00	100.00	100.00	100.00	100.00	100.00	100.00	100.00	100.00
Dissolved solids, in percentage (by weight) of the brine	22.28	14.994	22.83	20.349	21.0	24.7	26.9	22.1	22.2

[a] Computed from data reported by Richardson (1906, p. 34).
[b] Reported by Clarke (1924).
[c] From Hahl and Mitchell (1963, p. 38); sample collected about 6 miles west of Promontory Point south of the causeway.
[d] Sample collected 1 mile south of the causeway in 25 ft of water at 5-ft depth.

(c) Chemical Characteristics of Recharge Waters. The streams contributing the greater portion of the 2 million plus acre-feet of water to the lake annually are calcium bicarbonate type and generally contain about 1300 ppm total dissolved solids. The contribution of solids in the streams amounts to between 2 and 4 million tons annually, and the groundwater increment delivers upward from 1.3 million tons of solids to the lake.

(d) The Effect of the Causeway. In 1957, a rock-fill railroad causeway was completed across the lake from Promontory Point to Lakeside on the west shore. The fill replaced a 12.6-mile (20.2-km) wooden trestle which had allowed free exchange of water between the northern third and the southern two-thirds of the lake. The combined effect of the permeability of the rock fill and two 15-foot (4.6-meter) culverts does not provide sufficient exchange between the two bodies of water. Thus, in effect, there are two lakes. The southern body receives about 95% of the surface inflow and thus the recharge-deficient northern arm is more affected by evaporation (Adams, 1964). The northern arm of the lake may stand as much as 0.75 inch (1.8 cm) lower than the southern portion. The density of the northern arm is about 2% more than the near surface brines of the south arm. The density of the northern body ranges from 1.215–1.223 g/cc and no apparent density stratification has been observed. The differences in head and in density result in counterflow of brines measured in culverts during calm weather. The upper 3–4 feet (91–122 cm) of southern brine flows north while as much as 5 feet (152 cm) of the northern brines immediately beneath flow southward as a density of current. Tables 3 and 4 show the ranges of concentration and the differences between the northern and southern arms of the lake for 1963–65 (from Handy and Hahl, 1966).

The result of the severance, though quantitatively partially determined, indicates that the northern arm is saturated with respect to sodium chloride in periods of low lake stage and possibly in high stages and that halite will be precipitated on the bottom. The bittern-enriched brines flowing southward through culverts and permeating the rock fill will increase the bittern content of the south lake brine. It is not known whether a pronounced density stratification existed in the lake prior to the completion of the fill. However, the present bottom waters, those within a few feet of the bottom, in the deeper portions of the south arm of the lake are slightly murky and brownish in color, and have a hydrogen sulfide odor. The hydrogen sulfide con-

TABLE 3. RANGES OF CONCENTRATIONS OF SOME DISSOLVED CONSTITUENTS IN THE BULK OF THE NORTHERN PART OF GREAT SALT LAKE, 1963–64

Constituent or Property[a]	Minimum	Maximum
Silica (SiO_2)	1.1	4.2
Calcium (Ca^{++})	164	312
Magnesium (Mg^{++})	11,200	13,500
Sodium (Na^+)	76,000	85,600
Potassium (K^+)	6,780	7,740
Lithium (Li^+)	42	66
Bicarbonate (HCO^-)	477	523
Carbonate ($CO_3^=$)	0	0
Sulfate ($SO_4^=$)	20,000	27,400
Chloride (Cl^-)	141,000	155,000
Fluoride (F^-)	4.8	6.0
Boron (B)	29	52
Dissolved solids[b]	277,000	296,000
Density, g/cc	1.214	1.223
pH	7.4	7.7

[a] Concentrations in ppm, unless stated otherwise.
[b] Residue on evaporation at 180°C.

TABLE 4. RANGES OF CONCENTRATIONS OF SOME DISSOLVED CONSTITUENTS
IN THE SOUTHERN PART OF GREAT SALT LAKE, 1963–65

Constituent or Property[a]	An Inflow Area[b]	Remainder of Southern Part of Lake	
		Minimum	Maximum
Silica (SiO_2)	11	2.0	5.1
Calcium (Ca^{++})	62	126	342
Magnesium (Mg^{++})	805	7,100	11,300
Sodium (Na^+)	7,330	65,100	86,100
Potassium (K^+)	616	4,170	6,700
Lithium (Li^+)	0.0	34	58
Bicarbonate (HCO_3^-)	303	369	473
Carbonate ($CO_3^=$)	14	0	0
Sulfate ($SO_4^=$)	1,430	11,400	24,800
Chloride (Cl^-)	12,900	113,000	149,000
Fluoride (F^-)	0.6	3.8	5.8
Boron (B)	0.0	19	46
Dissolved solids[c]	25,200	212,000	286,000
Density, g/cc	1.011	1.153	1.218
pH	8.3	7.5	7.8

[a] Concentrations in ppm, unless stated otherwise.
[b] Between Promontory Point and Fremont Island, October 1965.
[c] Residue on evaporation at 180°C.

tent has not been quantitatively determined. In the late 1940's during a period of late summer calm, the writer observed bubbles, presumed to be hydrogen sulfide, rising to the surface of deep waters of the southern part of the lake. It was not determined whether or not the brines in close proximity to the bottom were of greater density than the near surface brine. The anaerobic conditions conducive to the formation of hydrogen sulfide do suggest the possibility that a denser brine could have been present.

The color of the brine in the northern part of the lake is reddish brown in contrast to the green of the southern part. The reddish coloration is apparently due to an algae which thrives in the saturated brine in numbers which limit visibility to about 2 feet. The green brines of the south part, although

clouded in places by brine shrimp, detrital material or seed crystals of Glauber's salt (winter only) are clearer, and bottom features which are 10–15 feet (3–4.6 meters) below the surface are clearly visible.

(5) Inventory of Salts

Very approximate calculations of various salts in Great Salt Lake indicate greatly different bulk amounts for the high and low lake stages (see Tables 5 and 6). Some investigators theorize that the difference in tonnages arises because of evaporites deposited on and in the relicted sediments. However, except in midsummer the relicted lands are devoid of evaporites. This suggests that possibly the more dense brines of the low lake stages encroach into the sub-lakeshore areas, thus accounting for some of

TABLE 5. HIGH LEVEL BRINE ESTIMATED SALTS INVENTORY

June 1873—Elevation 4211.65 ft—Salinity 14.2%; Density 1.104 g/cc—Area 1,400,000+ acres; Storage 30,000,000 acre-ft; Lake water weighs 68.89 lb/ft³ and contains 9.78 lb of salt

Assumed Chemical Combinations	% of Total Dissolved Solids (approx.)	Salt Content of Brine			
		(lb/ft³)	(lb/acre-ft)	(tons/acre-ft)	(thousand tons in lake)
Sodium chloride, NaCl	77	7.53	328,007	164.0	4,920,000
Sodium sulfate, Na_2SO_4	9	0.88	38,333	19.1	573,000
Magnesium chloride, $MgCl_2$	5	0.49	21,344	10.7	321,000
Magnesium sulfate, $MgSO_4$	4	0.39	16,988	8.5	255,000
Potassium chloride, KCl	4	0.39	16,988	8.5	255,000
Others	1	0.10	4,356	2.2	66,000
Totals	100	9.78	426,016	213.0	6,390,000

TABLE 6. LOW LEVEL BRINE ESTIMATED SALTS INVENTORY

November 8, 1961—Elevation 4191.6 ft—Salinity 28.5%; Density 1.221 g/cc—Area 585,567 acres; Storage 8,733,000 acre-ft; Lake water weighs 76.19 lb/ft³ and contains 21.71 lb of salt

Assumed Chemical Combinations	% of Total Dissolved Solids (approx.)	Salt Content of Brine			
		(lb/ft³)	(lb/acre-ft)	(tons/acre-ft)	(thousand tons in lake)
Sodium chloride, NaCl	77	16.72	728,323	364.1	3,180,000
Sodium sulfate, Na₂SO₄	9	1.95	84,942	42.6	372,000
Magnesium chloride, MgCl₂	5	1.08	47,045	23.5	205,000
Magnesium sulfate, MgSO₄	4	0.87	37,897	18.9	165,000
Potassium chloride, KCl	4	0.87	37,897	18.9	165,000
Others	1	0.22	9,583	4.8	42,000
Totals	100	21.71	945,688	472.8	4,129,000

the deficiency in the inventory. At high lake stages, the hydrostatic head provided by a higher groundwater flow reverses the brine encroachment and returns it to the lake, thus providing a higher inventory.

(6) Hydrography

(a) **Waves.** Severe storms sometimes with squall line winds gusting to 60 mph (96 km/hr) and sustained for several hours in excess of 40 mph (64 km/hr) can cause a calm lake to yield 10-foot (3-meter) waves. The brine weight of 76 lb/ft³ (1217 kg/m³) operating in conjunction with wave action is a forceful agent of erosion.

(b) **Currents.** The distribution of currents in the lake has never been adequately determined; however, the morphology of the headlands, spits and bars indicates a dominant counterclockwise circulation. Longshore currents are effective in distributing materials along the beach. Currents slightly in excess of 1 mph (1.6 km/hr) have been observed along the west shores of the lake.

(c) **Seiches.** Sustained winds from south or north cause the lake to oscillate; the resulting wind tides may be in excess of 2 feet (61 cm). Prior to the severance of the lake by the railroad causeway, the period of oscillation was 9 hours; it is presently 6 hours for the south arm of the lake.

(7) Biology

The life in the waters of Great Salt Lake is represented by only a few species. The biota presents a unique opportunity for ecological study, yet no complete study on a seasonal basis has been made. The known organisms include eleven species of bacteria, four algae, two arthropods and several protozoa. Flowers and Evans (1966) report on the biota as follows:

(a) **Algae of the Lake.** "The only plants growing and reproducing in the main body of Great Salt Lake include two species of Cyanophyta, *Coccochloris*

elabans Drout and Daily,* *Entrophysalis rivularis* (Kutz.) Drouet†(?), and two undescribed species of *Chlamydomonas* of the Chlorophyta. *Coccochloris elabans* is by far the most abundant alga and consists of single small oval or short oblong cells, great numbers of which are rather closely disposed in gelatinous colonies. Young colonies consist of minute bluish-green granules of firm texture, and as they increase in size the color changes to brown and finally pink or yellowish, while the gelatinous matrix becomes soft and flaccid. When the lake level is high and the salt concentration is less than 20% the spherical colonies enlarge to about 1 cm in diameter, become hollow and eventually break open, forming more or less expanded undulate gelatinous laminae 6–12 cm long. Great masses of the alga frequently become locally aggregated and on bright days appear at a distance as brown areas in the surrounding blue water. Storm waves frequently deposit large masses of the alga on some of the eastern beaches, sometimes 10–25 cm deep.

"*Entrophysalis rivularis* rivularis consists of aggregates of single subspherical cells, each with a rather thick, firm gelatinous sheath and disposed in short irregular filaments which sometimes become compacted side by side in mats. The mass as a whole forms bluish-green, yellowish or dark-brown mats less than 1 mm thick on rocks and wood in shallow water.

"*Chlamydomonas* are free-swimming biflagellate green algae, and the two forms, one ovoid and the other oblong, occur widely distributed in all parts of the lake. They seem to adjust readily to gradual changes in salt concentrations, although they reach

---

* Formerly known variously as *Polycystis packardii* Farlow, *Microcystis packardii* (Farl.) Setchell and *Aphanothece utahensis* Tilden.

† Formerly referred tentatively to *Pleurocapsa entophysaloides* Setch. and Gard. by Dr. Francis Drouet. This name has since gone into synonomy. See comments in Eardley, 1938, p. 1333.

their maximum development when the water contains 13–15% salt.

"In Bear River Bay and East Bay of Great Salt Lake the water is very shallow and the salt content is greatly reduced by the inflow of fresh water from Bear River and Jordan River, respectively. In these places *Cladophora fracta* (Dill.) Kutz. often becomes so abundant as to appear like a green meadow at a distance. It becomes adapted to a gradual increase in salt content up to as much as 3–4%, whence it ceases to grow but apparently is not all killed. *Rhizoclonium hieroglyphicum* (Ag) Kutz. and *R. crispum* Kutz. are less tolerant of salt but will persist where the water contains as much as 0.8% salt. Strong winds from the west often blow the brine from the main body of the lake into these bays, killing great quantities of algae."

(b) Bacteria. "Frederick (1924) reported eleven species of bacteria inhabiting the waters of the lake. These organisms cause decay in dead algae, animals and organic wastes entering the lake by way of rivers and wind, and at times during the summer months foul odors pollute the air in the vicinity of the lake.

"The bacteria are as follows: *Micrococcus subflavis* Bumm.; nonmotile spheres. *Bacillus cohaerens* Gottheil; motile rods, single or in pairs. *Bacillus freudenreichii* (*Urobacillus freudenreichii* Miguel); motile rods, single or in chains. *Bacillus mycoides* Flugge (*B. ramosus* Eisenb., *B. radicosus* Zimm.); rods in chains with spores. *Achromobacter solitarium* (*Bacillus solitarius*); slender motile rods, nonmotile in cultures. *Achromobacter album* (*Bacillus albus*); nonmotile rods. *Achromobacter hartlebii* (*Bacillus hartlebii*); motile single rods. *Flavobacterium arborescens* (*Bacillus arborescens*); nonmotile rods in pairs or chains. *Bacterioides rigidus* (*Bacterium rigidum* Destoso); motile slender rods, single or in pairs. *Serratia salinaria* (*Pseudomonas salinaria*); single motile rods, nonmotile in Great Salt Lake. *Cellulomonas subcreta* (*Pseudomonas subcreta*); single motile rods, nonmotile in Great Salt Lake."

(c) Fauna of the Lake. "According to published reports, animals belonging to only two phyla, Arthropoda and Protozoa, have been found in the waters of Great Salt Lake. The arthropods may be found there in vast numbers in spring, summer and fall, but only rarely during the winter months. Most conspicuous is the brine shrimp, *Artemia salina*. Eggs of two types are formed: thin-walled summer eggs which hatch internally (viviparous) and thick-walled winter eggs which seem to require desiccation prior to hatching. It has been observed that males are scarce and that parthenogenetic development is common. Winter eggs numbered in the billions collect in windrows along the leeward beaches and hatch in the spring into nauplii. About three weeks later, having passed through twelve or more instars, adults appear. It is said that hatching and development is affected by concentration of salts,

by specific ions, by temperature, and by light. Winter eggs more than 25 years old have maintained their viability. Development is better in diluted lake water than in concentrated brine, indicating that the brine shrimp is not fully adapted." Lowering water temperatures in the fall probably kills most or all of the adults. The average size for mature *Artemia* is 10–12 mm. Color ranges from light reddish brown to a light blue green. "Observers have noted a tremendous decline in brine shrimp during 1961; this may be the result of low level of the lake (new all-time record) and accumulation of industrial and organic wastes.

"Larvae and pupae of the brine flies [*Ephydra cinerea* (*gracilis*)] are abundant in summer. They are found in open waters; *E. hians* are found near shore. The female adults lay eggs on the surface of the water, the eggs hatching into long cylindrical larvae which respire through "tracheal gills" found in long, forked anal tubes. The pupal coat consists of the last larval skin. Pupation occurs in the water, the larvae shrinking, leaving a gas-filled space. Coming to the surface, the adult can fly away.

"Several species of protozoa have been found in Great Salt Lake, some of them not identified. Thus far, none has been thoroughly investigated and much work is required to work out details of morphology, taxonomy and physiology. The ciliates comprise *Uroleptus packii, Chilophrya utahensis* and species of *Podophrya* (a Suctorian), *Euplotes, Cyclidium, Pseudocohnilembus* and *Cothurnia*. Other undetermined species have been seen. With the exception of *Podophrya*, which feeds upon *Euplotes* and *Pseudocohnilembus*, all are bacterial feeders. It has been shown that all will grow at optimum rates in salt concentrations of 2 or 3% and up to 18 or 20%. Little if any growth occurs at saturation (27.7%). Cysts of *Pseudocohnilembus* will survive complete desiccation in the brine, however. Two amoebae have been seen in large numbers and several species of Flagellates, including *Tetramitus, oikomonas* and at least two others have been seen in large numbers in cultures taken from the lake and the briny and brackish water ponds nearby. Additional studies should result in finding many more forms of protozoa, and if reports from casual observers are correct, it is likely that larvae of several insects may be found and identified."

(d) Lakeside Vegetation. Flowers states that the margins of the lake and the islands support halophilic plants such as *Salicornia*, salt grass (*Distichlis stricta*), ink weed (*Sualda sp.*), and shadscale (*Atriplex confertifolia*).

(e) Birds. There are five major species of colonial-nesting birds breeding in Great Salt Lake and in marshes around the lake. These are (1) great blue herons (*Ardea herodius treganzai*), (2) double crested cormorants (*Phalacrocorax auritus auritus*), (3) white pelicans (*Pelcanus erythrorhynchos*), (4) Caspian terns (*Hydropronge caspia*), and California gulls (*Larus californicus*). For additional information on birds, see Behle (1958).

(8) Lake Sediments

There are three principal types of bottom sediments: "clay," oolitic sands and algal reefs; in recent years sodium chloride has been subaqueously precipitated.

(a) **Clay.** The "clays" of Great Salt Lake are of three general lithologic types (Schreiber, 1958); they total approximately 1450 square miles of the lake bottom below the 4200-foot contour. Type I consists chiefly of very calcareous silts and clays with oolites and abundant fecal pellets from the brine shrimp *Artemia salina*; it averages 50% sand, 34% silt and 16% clay. Type II consists primarily of a calcareous, clayey silt; it averages 5% sand, 70% silt and 25% clay. Type III lithology is a calcareous, very silty sand; it averages 53% sand, 35% silt and 12% clay. Most of the clay sediments are dark gray to black when first recovered, but they oxidize to lighter shades of gray and olive. Organic matter ranges from 0.45–4.50% by weight. One of the outstanding characteristics of the lake sediments is their high carbonate content. The carbonate of the "clays" ranges from 10–75%. Laminations are commonly present that closely resemble glacial varves. Though generally indistinct, the laminae range from 1–3 mm in thickness (composite of one light and one dark band) and average 12 per inch of sediment.

(b) **Oolites.** The oolitic sands comprise the next most abundant bottom and nearshore sediment. Except in areas where algal bioherms are developed, oolitic sands are dominant on and along shore lines which abut the main body of the lake. They cover approximately 125 square miles of the lake bottom and relicted lands. There is little or no development of oolites in the back bay area, the area between Antelope-Fremont Islands trend and the east shore. Oolite sands are largest and best developed along windward shores where waves from the open lake impinge on headlands. Here the oolites average 0.8–1.0 mm in diameter; elsewhere oolites are between 0.14 and 0.63 mm in diameter (Eardley, 1938). The nuclei of the oolites are mineral grains and the rodlike bodies or fragments of fecal pellets of the brine shrimp, *Artemia salina*. Quartz grains are the most common of the mineral particles, with orthoclase and calcite in significant amounts; some heavy minerals are also present. Microscopically, the cross section most of the oolites display has well-developed concentric bands, and many of these have strongly developed secondary radial structure. The banding is most notable in oolites where an abundance of clay particles occurs at the interfaces of the concentric layers. Aragonite comprises the dominant mineral of the oolites, with the balance of 3–7.5% being dolomite. The origin and growth of the oolites is closely related to the chemistry of the lake brine and the physical conditions of the near-

shore areas. Oolite growth seems to be related to the late summer period of greatest evaporation. The winnowing and tumbling of the oolites allow for concentric growth. It is also suggested that the relatively insignificant maximum size of the oolites is directly related to the density of the lake brines. Allowing that exceptional shore line conditions of vigorous wave action can produce large oolites, for the most part the size ranges of the oolites are related to the sink-float cutoff properties of the brine. In other words, larger oolites would form on the shore lines of a receding lake, whereas smaller maxima would prevail when the lake rises and becomes less dense.

(c) **Algal Reefs.** The algal reefs or bioherms similar to the oolite development are confined to the more shallow saline portion of the lake. Bioherms range from a few inches to as much as 15 feet in thickness. Areally the reefs comprise an excess of 100 square miles of the lake and relicted area below the 4200-foot contour. Biohermal structures are the result of secretions of calcium and magnesium carbonate in a ratio of 11:1 by the algae *Coccochloris elabans*. The bioherms develop in the shallow water as rounded pillowlike masses which gradually coalesce into broad "trough and mound" areas. The mounds may range up to 30 feet in diameter with irregular secondary mounds which average 18 inches in relief. The surface texture of the reefs is rough and hackly; internally the individual "heads" or mounds show crude banding.

(d) **Evaporites.** Evaporites deposited in Great Salt Lake consist of sodium chloride and hydrous sodium sulfate. Until 1957 there was practically no subaqueous precipitation of sodium chloride to the lake bottom. Sodium chloride that was precipitated was the direct result of wind which produced seiches (wind tides), thus filling shallow depressions of relicted bottom areas with lake brines. Insignificant amounts of salt form on rocks, beaches and pilings that front areas of deep water where wave action is severe. These crustations of salt are temporary, and they are dissolved and returned to the lake by action of rain and snow meltwater.

Mirabilite, the hydrous sodium sulfate being less soluble in cold water than in warm, accumulates as temporary crystal mesh deposits in the deeper bottom areas during winter months. These deposits are local in extent and are redissolved as the lake warms. Also, during the winter months, mirabilite crystals coat objects along the shore, and seed crystals grow in the lake brines where they remain semisuspended and subsequently are swept ashore to form rather extensive snow-white bars several feet deep, often scores of feet in width. These bars form almost continuously along the shores subjected to the most violent and prevalent wave action. Under favorable conditions, oolite sands are washed over the mirabilite and may be preserved as shallow shore line deposits of recrystallized mirabilite cementing a mixture of oolites and clay. Beds of sodium sulfate are responsible for much of the foundation support of the rock fill which replaces the trestle of the Lucin Cutoff of the Southern Pacific Railroad. The salt extends from the eastern shore area to beyond mid-lake, a distance of 9.5 miles (15.2 km). It lies between 15 and 30 feet (4.6–9.1 meters) below the lake bottom and ranges from a featheredge of crystal mush at the midlake locale to as much as 70 feet (21.3 meters) in thickness near the eastern shore. There is some question as to the origin of this salt layer. However, Eardley (1962) postulates that it was precipitated because of thermal variations of the lake brine, and that the precipitates were rapidly buried by protective coverings of clay (the thin clay interbeds). Not to be ruled invalid is the possibility of vertical and lateral migration of dense brines enriched in sodium sulfate ions into a thermal environment conducive to sodium sulfate precipitation, the dense brine being derived from redissolving of mirabilite deposited in deeper portions of the lake. Also, the role of bacteria operating in conjunction with thermal gradients might be a factor in the distribution of these mirabilite deposits.

(e) **Cores of Earlier Sediments.** Eardley (1966) states: "Cores were obtained from the mid-lake sediments to a depth of 44 feet (13.4 meters) in 1952, and were described by Joseph Schreiber (1957). The cores were tentatively correlated with the shore line chronology by Eardley (1957). It was concluded that the brine-deposited sediments give way to fresh water sediments at a depth below the bottom of the lake of about 17 feet (5.2 meters), and at a C^{14} age of 12,500 years ago. The freshwater sediments continue to a depth of 30 feet (9.1 meters) with an age of about 25,000 years, whereupon brine deposits are again encountered. They continue to the maximum depth cored, 44 feet (13.4 meters).

"A continuous core was taken to a depth of 650 feet (198.2 meters) on the shore of Great Salt Lake, 1 mile (1.6 km) north-northeast of the Saltair resort, about halfway between the Oquirrh Mountains and Antelope Island, Utah. Its contents and properties were examined and analyzed to determine the Pleistocene record of lakes and climatic changes (Eardley and Gvosdetsky, 1960). Of significance in the interpretation were Ca and Mg carbonates, clay minerals, sand fractions, volcanic ashes, soils, radioactivity, laminations, oolites and fecal pellets, ostracodes, mollusks, and C^{14} dates. By integrating the several climatic indicators and other data the following conclusions were reached.

"The core probably penetrated sediments deposited during the Wisconsin, Sangamon, Illinoian, Yarmouth, Kansan, and part of the Aftonian ages of the Pleistocene. The several times of soil formation represent hiatuses in the sedimentary record, but they were probably short."

(9) Geology of the Lake Basin

(a) **Stratigraphy and structure.** Great Salt Lake lies principally on both younger and older Precambrian metamorphic terranes which in turn are surrounded by Paleozoic miogeosynclinal sedimentary rocks. Nearly 70,000 feet (21,336 meters) of sedimentary rocks, principally limestone and quartzite with dolomite and shale, comprise the sediments which range from Precambrian to Recent. Geomorphic features shaped by wind, glacial ice, rivers and lake currents are prominently displayed in and around adjacent mountains, canyons and foothills. The tributary rivers and streams pass from mountain youth into maturity and finally meander to embayments of Great Salt Lake with characteristics of old age streams.

The older structures are typically early Laramide and consist mainly of north-south trending folds, some of which are recumbent. Impressed upon the Laramide structure is a younger set of early Tertiary compressive features which include concentrically distributed arcs of recumbent and chevron folds and thrust faults along with radial strike-slip faults. The focal point of the energy which caused late structures is a few miles northwest of Antelope Island in Great Salt Lake. The very latest structures are the great normal faults of the Basin and Range continental tensional episode of the later Tertiary.

(b) **History and Origin.** Great Salt Lake is the fortuitous result of structural events which began in late Cretaceous or early Tertiary times. The latent beginning is marked by concentric and radial structures, possibly the result of a collision with an extraterrestrial object. The theory of continental drifting suggests continental motion during this episode, and it is postulated that a greater westward movement of the injured deeper crustal elements removed the rebound support and allowed the cratered area to further sag. Subsequent continental movement provided subcrustal stretching and crustal rupture which is represented by the Basin and Range faults. Miocene and Pliocene sediment began filling the intermontane valleys which periodically were further displaced by recurrent normal faulting. This phase of faulting cut deeply into the subcrust and tapped basaltic magma which further assisted in valley filling and isolating Great Basin ranges into regional internal drainage units. This, the late Pliocene-Pleistocene episode, provided basins for the great ice age lakes, Lake Bonneville and Lake Lahonton, of western North America.

Great Salt Lake is a remnant of *Lake Bonneville*, a large Pleistocene lake which inundated nearly 20,000 square miles (51,800 km^2), situated mainly in western Utah but extending into southern Idaho and eastern Nevada (Gilbert, 1890). This lake (Fig. 6) extended 285 miles (456 km) from latitudes 38°–42°20′N and was 140 miles (224 km) wide from longitude 111°40′–114°15′E. Its deepest point, more than a thousand feet (305 meters), coincides with the deepest section of Great Salt Lake. The lake filled several times during the ice age, and during the mid-

Wisconsin glacial stage it overflowed its confining rim at 5135 feet (1565 meters) and flowed northward into the Snake-Columbia river system through its breach at Red Rock pass. Its flow caused much downcutting, and the lake's surface subsequently stabilized at the Provo level at 4800 feet (1463 meters) above sea level when the water budget became slightly unbalanced in favor of evaporation. During the giant evacuation or destruction of the lake from its Bonneville extent to the Provo configuration, the resulting catastrophic flood into the Columbia River drainage aided in forming the Grande Coulee of that system. It has been estimated that the maximum discharge during the Bonneville Flood was about 15 million ft^3/sec (425,000 m^3/sec), which is nearly four times the average discharge of the Amazon River.

Lake Bonneville gradually receded from its Provo stage and the salts became concentrated in a large saline remnant, Great Salt Lake. The latest work on this subject was done by Morrison and others (see papers and references in Stokes, 1966). The salt in the lake itself is not of sufficient quantity to account for the amount added by inflowing streams, suggesting that much of the salt is in the deeper subbottom strata and, further, that some of it has been removed by atmospheric processes.

ROBERT E. COHENOUR

References

Adams, T. C., 1964, "Salt migration to the northwest body of Great Salt Lake, Utah," *Science*, **143**, 1027–1029.

Behle, W., 1958, "The Bird Life of Great Salt Lake," pp. 1–203, Salt Lake City, University of Utah Press.

Cohenour, R. E., 1966, "Great Salt Lake, Utah, and its environment," *Second Symposium on Salt: Northern Ohio Geol. Soc.*, **1**, 201–214.

Eardley, A. J., 1938, "Sediments of Great Salt Lake, Utah," *Bull. Am. Assoc. Petrol. Geologists*, **22**, 1305–1411.

Eardley, A. J., 1962, "Glauber's salt bed west of Promontory Point, Great Salt Lake," *Utah Geol. Mineral. Surv., Spec. Studies*, **1**, 1–12.

Eardley, A. J., 1966, "Sediment of Great Salt Lake," in "The Great Salt Lake," *Utah Geol. Soc. Guidebook*, **20**, 105–120.

Eardley, A. J., and Gvosdetsky, Vasyl, 1960, "Analysis of Pleistocene core from Great Salt Lake, Utah," *Bull. Geol. Soc. Am.*, **71**, 1323–1344.

Flowers, S., and Evans, F. R., 1966, "The Flora and Fauna of the Great Salt Lake Region, Utah," in (Boyko, Hugo, editor) "Salinity and Aridity," pp. 367–393, The Hague, Dr. W. Junk.

Gilbert, G. K., 1890, "Lake Bonneville," *U.S. Geol. Surv. Monograph*, **1**, 1–438.

Handy, A. H., and Hahl, D. C., 1966, "Great Salt Lake: Chemistry of the water," in "The Great Salt Lake," *Utah Geol. Soc. Guidebook*, **20**, 135–151.

Peck, E. L., and Richardson, E. A., 1966, "Hydrology and climatology of Great Salt Lake," in "The Great Salt Lake," *Utah Geol. Soc. Guidebook*, **20**, 121–134.

Schreiber, Joseph F., 1958, "Sedimentary Record in Great Salt Lake, Utah," pp. 1–99, unpublished Ph.D. thesis, University of Utah.

Stokes, Wm. Lee, (editor), 1966, "The Great Salt Lake," 10 papers, *Utah Geol. Soc. Guidebook*, **20**, 1–173.

Woolley, R. R., and Marsell, R. E., 1946, "Great Salt Lake, a selected bibliography with annotations," *Am. Geophys. Union Trans.*, **27**, 103–107.

Cross-references: *Algal Reefs*; *Aral Sea*; *Basin and Range Landscape*; *Holocene*; *Pluvial Lakes*; *Quaternary Period*; *Salton Sea*; *Scabland*; *Water Loading and Crustal Response*. Vol. I: *Seiche*. Vol. II: *Climatic Change in American Prehistory*; *Climatic Variation (Historical Record)*. pr Vol. VIII: *Basin-Range Province*.

GREYWETHER, GRAYWETHER, GREY BILLY—*See* INDURATION

GRÈZES LITÉES (BEDDED SCREE)—*See* FROST ACTION

GROUND WATER—*See* pr Vol. VI

GULLY EROSION

Erosion (q.v.) is the wearing away of the land surface mainly by detachment and transport of mineral grains through the action of geologic agents; these may be mechanical or chemical. *Normal* or *geologic erosion* is the wearing away of the land under natural environmental conditions. "*Accelerated erosion*," as used here, is a term applied to that erosion brought about by man or by climatic changes, and occurs at a rate greater than normal for the site, being usually enhanced by a reduction in the vegetation cover. Accelerated erosion may be divided into two classes: *sheet erosion* and *channel erosion*. Gully erosion is possibly the most destructive and certainly the most spectacular form of the latter.

Gully erosion, caused by a thinning of the vegetation cover, is typified by the nineteenth century epicycle of valley trenching (or arroyo cutting) in the alluvial valleys in the southwestern United States. The presently observed gullies are cut into deposits laid down in the last few thousand years. This deposit was not a product of continuous aggradation as evidenced by numerous filled channels and terraces of different ages. Cycles of erosion are widespread, having been reported throughout the Mediterranean region, in Europe, Asia and Africa. The geomorphic problem is the separation of the effects of climatic change from those of man's activities which cause or promote accelerated erosion.

In the southwestern United States, man's misuse

FIG. 1. Gullying in the unconsolidated sediments of alluvial fans (bajadas) situated in front of the Willunga Scarp, South Australia. (Photo: C. R. Twidale).

of land culminated in the period 1880–1900, at which time the number of livestock using western ranges was at an all-time high. The rapid erosion of alluvial valleys at that time led many observers to conclude that the erosion epicycle was the result of overgrazing, uncomplicated by climatic variation. This interpretation does not, however, explain pre-settlement eras of similar gully erosion.

Climate Change

A more likely explanation is that climatic change was responsible for the deterioration of the plant cover and the initiation of gully erosion. Tentative evidence in some places points to degradation with increasing aridity and aggradation with increasing humidity, while elsewhere the opposite appears to be the case. Analysis of rainfall records extending back to 1848 at Santa Fe, New Mexico shows that despite the absence of significant secular changes in monthly or annual totals, unusually heavy summer rainfalls characterized the decades of greatest erosional activity. More intense rains occur in the early

and late portions of the record; i.e., there was a decreasing number of low-intensity rains which succor vegetation but an increase in heavy rains acting upon a weakened vegetation cover and thus promoting erosion. This would indicate that gully erosion is related to intense and local summer thunderstorms and not to the low-intensity widespread precipitation of winter.

Observations of loess-covered valleys and hill slopes in the north-facing foothills of Uzbekistan, Central Asia, show that there was no epicycle of gully erosion in the last century. This is attributed to the nearly complete lack of summer thunderstorm rainfall in the steppe area of Central Asia. The Piedmont of South Carolina is characterized by extensive gullying. Many of these were prepared for accelerated erosion by poor agricultural practices. The area is in a region of heavy summer rains associated with channel cutting and clearing and winter drizzles causing caving of gully walls. That gullies tend to be a product of reduced vegetation cover due to cultivation or grazing is indicated by the widespread occurrence of gullies in the wheat and sheep belts of Western Australia, New South Wales, Victoria and in the downlands of Queensland, Australia (see figure in *Plains*).

New gully systems or *discontinuous gullies* in the semiarid southwestern United States are characterized by a vertical headcut, a channel immediately below the headcut which is often more deep than wide, a downstream decrease in channel depth, and a fan at the intersection of the gully floor with the more steeply sloping plane of the original valley floor. The discontinuous gully is a semicyclic phenomenon in which alluviation on the valley floor develops locally on a gradient too steep to be stable and subsequently erodes. The fan forming at the mouth of a discontinuous gully has a local slope steeper than the average for the valley; thus the fan may form the locus of a new gully. The flat gradient of a new gully floor is only a temporary feature, for as the system of discontinuous gullies finally coalesces and a single uninterrupted channel is formed, the end result is a gully whose bed has a gradient practically identical to the gradient of the original valley floor.

Considerations of sediment transport indicate that as widening progresses and flow depth decreases, an increase in the slope would be necessary to maintain sufficient shear to transport the sediment load. Thus the low gradient of the bed should characterize the early and narrow stage of the discontinuous gully, and slope would be expected to increase as the channel widens. One characteristic of such gullies is the depth to which they have cut. In each of several successive post-Pleistocene periods of valley trenching, the gully in an individual valley was cut to practically the same depth, this depth generally being limited by bedrock or hard beds relatively resistant to erosion.

Gully Growth

Sapping at the base is one of the more effective processes in headward extension. Many gullies, particularly in relatively uniform material, advance headward, maintaining vertical cliffs at the gully headwall. In others, slumping at the base leaves a jumble of blocks at the vertical face. Sapping is intensified by the emergence of moisture moving under gravity to the base of the vertical wall.

In the gullies of the Piedmont of South Carolina, a stratum of relatively friable material occurs near the base of the headcut, but the top stratum is tough and resistant. This leads to *undercutting* by the emergence of groundwater, and large blocks of the upper material cave in, leading to rapid headward extension. Undercutting of the vertical headcuts by plunge-pool action is aided by slumping of the moistened headwall after the storm flow ends.

Piping (q.v.) is an important element in the headward extension of many vertical cuts. These pipes may extend for hundreds of feet in ungullied alluvium. Gullies on nearly flat slopes in the middle west of the United States and in Canada are apparently the result of piping since water moving through the fine- to mixed-grained material carries fine particles and dissolved materials away from their place of deposition and leaves voids. The voids concentrate the flowing water, accelerate soil removal and result eventually in the formation of collapsed holes from which full-fledged gullies develop.

Recent Quantitative Measurements

Quantitative measures of gullying processes near Santa Fe, New Mexico tentatively indicate that the

Fig. 2. Headcut of Coyote C. Arroyo near Santa Fe, New Mexico. The gully floor is presently aggrading at the rate of 0.05 ft/yr while the headcut continues to advance 2.6 ft/yr in the upstream direction and 0.3 ft/yr in the lateral direction. Most of the material for alluviation is derived from the adjacent slopes.

recent epicycle of erosion may be at an end and the valleys are beginning to fill. The 6-year period of 1958–64 shows stream channels to be aggrading at the rate of 0.05 ft/yr. The material for this alluviation appears to be derived from sheet wash rather than gully erosion because even the smallest headwater rills are alluviating. Measurements indicate that sheet erosion presently accounts for 97.8% of the total sediment production; gully erosion by headcutting, for 1.4%; mass-movement along the gully walls, for 0.7% (see Fig. 2). These data conform closely to those reported for the southeast United States which indicate that sheet erosion is responsible for 66–100% of the total sediment production.

WILLIAM W. EMMETT

References

Bryan, K., 1940, "Gully gravure, a method of slope retreat," *J. Geomorphol.,* **3,** 89–106.

Ireland, H. A., Sharpe, C. F. S., and Eargle, D. H., 1939, "Principles of Gully Erosion in the Piedmont of South Carolina," *U.S. Dept. Agr. Tech. Bull.,* **633,** 143pp.

*Leopold, L. B., Emmett, W. W., and Myrick, R. M., 1966, "Channel and hillslope processes in a semi-arid area, New Mexico," *U.S. Geol. Surv. Profess. Paper,* **352G.**

Leopold, L. B., Wolman, M. G., and Miller, J. P., 1964, "Fluvial Processes in Geomorphology," San Francisco, W. H. Freeman and Co., 522pp.

*Peterson, H. V., 1950, "The Problem of Gullying in Western Valleys," in (Trask, P. D., editor) "Applied Sedimentation," Ch. 23, pp. 407–434, New York, John Wiley & Sons.

Schumm, S. A., and Hadley, R. F., 1957, "Arroyos and the semi-arid cycle of erosion," *Am. J. Sci.,* **255,** 161–174.

* Additional bibliographic references may be found in this work.

Cross-references: *Aggradation; Alluvial Fan; Alluvium; Anthropogenic Influences in Geomorphology; Bajada; Climatic Geomorphology; Degradation; Erosion; Grade, Graded Stream; Loess; Mass Movement; Piedmont Landforms; Piping; Plains; Quantitative Geomorphology; Sediment Transport; Sheet Erosion, Sheetwash, etc.; Slopes.*

GUMBOTIL—*See pr* Vol. VI

H

HALDENHANG OR WASH SLOPE

Haldenhang is a German geomorphic expression introduced by W. Penck (1924, see translation 1953) for a "basal slope—the less steep slope found at the foot of a rock wall, usually beneath an accumulation of *talus* (q.v.). . . . It is the top part of the *Fuss-hang* or foot-slope, which includes all the slopes of diminishing gradient" (p. 419). The steep upper slope of uniform gradient was termed the *Steilwand* (rock wall); the latter is Meyerhoff's (1940) *gravity slope* (the "constant slope" of King and Fair, 1944), while the haldenhang is Meyer-hoff's *wash slope* (King and Fair's "waning slope"). There is usually a sharp angular difference between the two slopes, a "knickpunkt." The haldenhang is normally steeper in arid regions than in humid regions because there is less running water available to shift rock debris over it. Penck claimed that once the characteristic slope angles were established for any climatic/lithologic setting, a parallel slope retreat would follow; this was quite in contrast to the Davisian concept of gradual degradation, i.e., down-wasting. A mature development leads to an accumulation phase, with a "waxing slope," in all, the "Slope Cycle" (Wood, 1942).

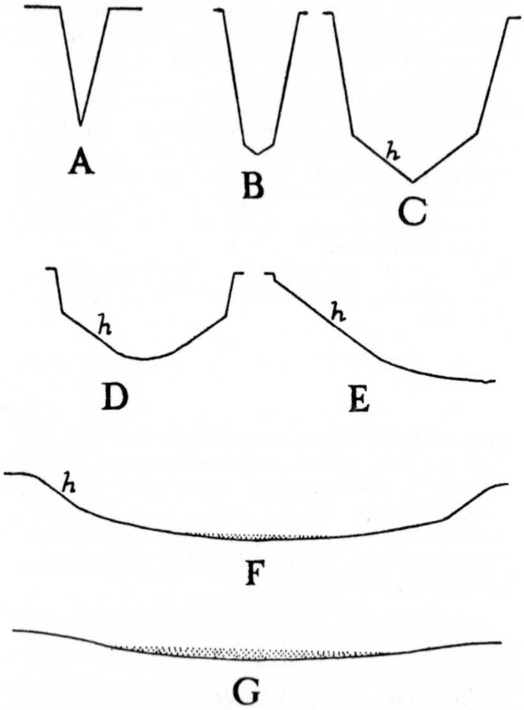

RHODES W. FAIRBRIDGE

References

Birot, P., 1949, "Essais sur quelques problèmes de morphologie générale," pp. 17–33, Lisbon.
Cotton, C. A., 1952, "The erosional grading of convex and concave slopes," *Geogr. J.*, 118(2), 197–204.
Holmes, C. D., 1955, "Geomorphic development in humid and arid regions: A synthesis," *Am. J. Sci.*, **253**, 377–390.
King, L. C., and Fair, T. J. D., 1944, "Hillslopes and dongas," *Trans. Proc. Geol. Soc. S. Africa*, **47**, 1–4.
Meyerhoff, H. A., 1940, "Migration of erosional surfaces," *Ann. Assoc. Am. Geogr.*, **30**, 247–254.
Penck, W., 1953, "Morphological Analysis of Land Forms," London, Macmillan (translated by H. Czech and K. C. Boswell), 429pp.
Wood, A., 1942, "The development of hillside slopes," *Proc. Geol. Assoc.*, London, **53**, 128–140.

Cross-references: *Bajada*; *Degradation*; *Nickpoint*; *Pediment*; *Slope Analysis*; *Talus*.

FIG. 1. The slope cycle, seen in lateral profiles (modified after A. Wood, 1942). (A) Free slope only, cut in flat, recently upraised land surface. (B and C) The constant or gravity slope (Steilwand) forms. (D and E) Waning or wash (Haldenhang) slope develops. (F) Waxing slope forms, waning slope rises up side of constant slope, alluvial filling represented by dots. (G) Constant slope has been consumed, alluvial fill deepens, slopes gradually flatten and approach a peneplain.

HAMADA, REG, SERIR, GIBBER, SAÏ

In hot desert regions a number of deflational relief or textural landforms are developed that have received specific names, mainly of Arabic origin, stemming from the Sahara or Arabia.

Hamada or *hammada* is a desert high plain or plateau where deflation has removed the fine-grained surface materials and left behind a surface of sand-scoured bedrock with or without a veneer of pebbles or boulders (Gautier, 1935). The word *hamada* in Arabic means strictly a rocky plane surface, and the term *rock plain* is sometimes given as the English equivalent.

The terms *Reg* (in the western Sahara), or *Serir* (in the eastern Sahara) or *Gibber Plain* (Australia), or *Saï* (Tarim Desert, central Asia), apply to a sandy plain or broad depression largely covered by lag gravels or angular boulders, from which the finer soil and sediment has been stripped by eolian ablation. As noted by Termier (1963), the regs of the Sahara tend to be followed by the caravan routes rather than the rocky hamadas (which also often have steep escarpments). The pebble surfaces may be so closely packed that a smooth surface results; in other places larger and less closely packed boulders make the surface very rough. The regs can be (a) *Allochthonous*, where the valley-fill in closed basins is provided by large wadis (*oueds*, in French orthography), as seen in the western Sahara, and somewhat analogous to bolsones of the American southwest and adjacent Mexico; or (b) *Autochthonous*, where there is a residual soil or *eluvium*, due to weathering of the underlying rocks *in situ*, as extensively seen in the central Sahara and Libyan Desert (Lelubre, 1952).

The reg boulders, or "gibbers" of Australia (Hills, 1940, see his Fig. 131), are frequently faceted by wind action (ventifacts, dreikanter, etc.). Their surfaces are often stained reddish black by "*desert varnish*" or "patina" (q.v.). In many cases these boulders are simply the product of soil-stripping from a silicified and/or ferruginous hardpan (a modified soil "B" horizon), the so-called ferruginous *duricrust* or "cuirasse de fer" of the French African geologists. Over widespread areas of northeastern Australia there are plains of siliceous duricrust or silcrete; locally it breaks up into boulders known as "billy" (from "billy goats"). The desiccation and cementation of this crust has been accompanied by shrinkage, jointing and cracking, so that it is today a brecciated surface, locally recemented into a *boulder pavement* or the smoother *desert pavement*. In parts of the American southwest, in Morocco and parts of western Australia the duricrust is calcareous, a "calcrete" or "caliche" (the Spanish word).

RHODES W. FAIRBRIDGE

References

Capot-Rey, R., Cornet, A., and Blaudin de Thé, B., 1963, "Glossaire des principaux termes géographiques et hydrogéologiques sahariens," *Alger, Inst. Rech. Sahariennes*, 82pp.

Gautier, E. F., 1935, "Sahara, the Great Desert," New York, Columbia University Press (translated by D. F. Mayhew), 264pp.

Hills, E. S., 1940, "The Physiography of Victoria," Melbourne, Whitcombe and Tombs, 292pp.

Johnson, D. W., 1932, "Rock planes in arid regions," *Geogr. Rev.*, **22**, 656–665.

Lelubre, M., 1952, "Conditions structurales et formes de relief dans le Sahara," *Univ. d'Alger, Trav. Inst. Rech. Sahariennes*, **8**, 189–238.

Termier, H., and Termier, G., 1963, "Erosion and Sedimentation," London and Princeton, D. van Nostrand Co., 433pp. (translated by D. W. and E. E. Humphries).

Cross-references: *Ablation*; *Arid Cycle*; *Bolson*; *Desert Varnish*; *Duricrust*; *Sabkha*; *Ventifact*; Vol. VI: *Caliche*.

HANGING VALLEY

A characteristic feature of glaciated mountain topography, a hanging valley is a tributary to a main valley which has been deeply scoured by

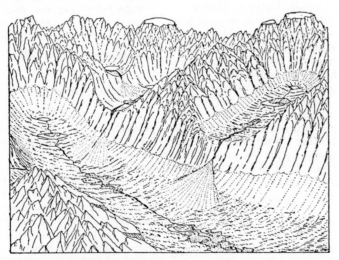

FIG. 1. A wall-sided, cirque-headed trough, bordered by hanging valleys (after Davis).

FIG. 2. Hanging valleys due to rapid marine erosion of white chalk cliffs. The Seven Sisters, Sussex, England.

glacial ice, leaving the tributary valley "hanging" above the main valley. The situation of such phenomena is sometimes below the perennial snow line appropriate to the last glaciation, so that the tributary valley was not glaciated, while the main trunk was scoured out by a glacier that was being fed much farther up in the mountains. The classic example is in the Lauterbrunnental, Switzerland; another is in the Yosemite Valley, California.

The tributary valley itself may or may not have been glaciated. If glaciated (as indicated in Fig. 1), it might appear to break *Playfair's Law* (q.v.) but in fact the ice streams of very contrasting volume did meet at grade at the surface, though not at the floor.

Interesting examples of hanging valleys may also be seen entering fjords, notably in Norway and New Zealand. Hanging valleys also occur sometimes along non-glaciated coasts where the rate of cliff retreat is higher than the adjustment potential of the smaller streams, e.g., in the chalk cliffs in the south of England. They are also to be seen along youthful fault scarps.

RHODES W. FAIRBRIDGE

References

Cotton, C. A., 1942, "Climatic Accidents," Christchurch (N.Z.), Whitcombe & Tombs, 354pp.
Davis, W. M., 1900, "Glacial erosion in France, Switzerland, and Norway," *Proc. Boston Soc. Nat. Hist.*, **29,** 273–322 (also in "Geographical Essays," 1909, New York, Dover reprint, 1954).
Garwood, E. J., 1902, "On the origin of some hanging valleys in the Alps and Himalayas," *Quart. J. Geol. Soc. London*, **58,** 703–716.
Johnson, D. W., 1911, "Hanging valleys of the Yosemite," *Geogr. Soc. Bull.*, **43,** 1–25.
Matthes, F. E., 1930, "Geologic history of Yosemite Valley," *U.S. Geol. Surv. Profess. Paper*, **160.**
Thornbury, W. D., 1954, "Principles of Geomorphology," New York, John Wiley & Sons, 618pp.

Cross-references: *Glacial Valley*; *Playfair's Law*.

HEAD, ELUVIUM

The term "head" has many different uses in physical geography, hydrology and geology, including a coastal headland or cape, the source of a stream, the hydrostatic head in ground-water or artesian basins, a tidal condition such as a bore. The term "head" when applied to superficial deposits on the land surface is derived from the English quarrymen's old term for *overburden* (see de la Beche, 1839). In geomorphology, it is used in Britain (including official use by the Geological Survey), and rather generally in France, too, for superficial deposits or youthful "mantle" other than soil (Dines *et al.*, 1940; Tricart, 1963). These

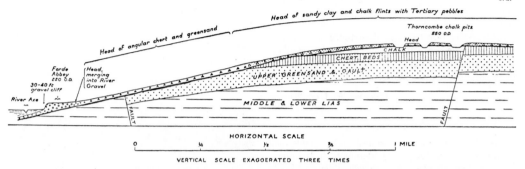

FIG. 1. Types and distribution of head on the slopes of the Axe Valley, England (Dines *et al.*, 1940). Note progressive change in character of head over different substrata; the insoluble nature of the flint nodules in the chalk and the underlying stratified chert shows that the head is in part saprolitic.

deposits are often described as "rubble drift" in earlier works. The older term "mantle" or "mantle rock" is not widely used today because of its possible confusion with the earth's mantle (i.e., between crust and core).

The term *eluvium* is sometimes given as equivalent to head. In the United States, the equivalent of "head" would be included within the broad category of *regolith* (q.v.; rarely "rhegolith"), defined as the superficial blanket of soft, unconsolidated material that mantles the earth's surface. It specifically includes soil, weathered residual *in situ* rock (saprolite, see below), transported or loose boulders, as well as transported material of glacial, eolian, alluvial and colluvial origin. In short, it includes everything but solid rock that may be conveniently "lumped" together. Naturally, if one particular facies, e.g., an eolian sand, is sufficiently distinctive, it is appropriately mapped as a separate formation and the same is true for head. Soil scientists sometimes use "regosol" for soils developed without distinctive horizons over deep unconsolidated "rock," e.g., a mature alluvial formation.

The term *saprolite* (also saprolith) is sometimes used synonymously with regolith, but incorrectly according to the original definition. Saprolite applies strictly to rotted or weathered rock *in situ* that has not been transported at all. It is often loosely embraced by the expression "residual deposits." Soil scientists often classify it as the "lower B" or "C" horizon. This rotted rock may extend under tropical or subtropical weathering conditions for tens or even hundreds of meters; it is evident that a thick saprolite originally extended over much of the Canadian Shield or the Rocky Mountains, as well as Scandinavia and northern Europe, but was very largely stripped off by the continental ice sheets of the Quaternary glaciations. In the Rockies it was largely the reduced vegetation cover in the late Pliocene and early Pleistocene that facilitated this wholesale stripping by both wind and water erosion.

According to Webster's *Dictionary*, saprolite is a synonym of *eluvium*, a term originally proposed by Trautschold (1879) for a soil formed *in situ*, but he also included deposits transported by wind (loess), thus more than strictly residual deposits. Apart from this ambiguity, Stamp (1961) pointed out that in speech the difference between "alluvium" and "eluvium" is so slight that in his opinion the latter would best be dropped. ("*Illuvium*" is material in soils carried from upper horizons to lower parts of the profile, to be redeposited either from suspension or solution, often in the "B" horizon, sometimes causing the formation of "hardpan" on soil concretions.)

Seen in the broader context of superficial deposits, it is apparent that the "head" of Britain and France is not synonymous with either saprolite or regolith. The rubble drift and other materials involved are now recognized as largely *solifluction* debris (Dines, Hollingworth *et al.*, 1940), the product of multiple freeze-thaw cycles. These often contain angular rock fragments, as well as insoluble residuals, e.g., flints (Fig. 1), which have led to hill creep under gravity, sheet erosion and effects of *mass wasting* (q.v.) under periglacial conditions (Bryan, 1946). It is important to recognize that it is only during fairly recent decades that subarctic periglacial phenomena have been correctly identified in western Europe and in the periglacial parts of the United States (largely an outcome of work by European geologists in Poland, Iceland, Spitsbergen, and Scandinavia, and by North American geologists in Canada, Alaska and Greenland).

In the typical head profile, on the granites of Devonshire (Linton, 1955), at the base, one may recognize undisturbed saprolite (sometimes in Britain called by the old Celtic term "growan," in French *grouan*, in German *grus*, in Portuguese *saibro*). Next comes disturbed saprolite (hill or slope wash, etc.), overlain by clear solifluction debris with further hill-wash, finally capped by scattered boulders of the local granite ("clitter," also known as "clatter" on Dartmoor, "glyder," "glydr" in Wales, "éboulis" in France: general terms for scree or *talus*, q.v.).

Linton has pointed out that there is a crude *reversed* grain-size gradation in such profiles, grading from finest below to coarsest at the surface. The boulders are often marked by *frost riving* (q.v.).

RHODES W. FAIRBRIDGE

References

Breuil, H., 1934, "De l'importance de la solifluction, dans l'étude des Terrains Quaternaires de la France et des pays voisins," *Rév. Géogr. Phys. Paris*, **7**, 269–331.

Bryan, K., 1946, "Cryopedology—the study of frozen ground," *Am. J. Sci.*, **244**, 622–642.

De La Beche, Sir H. T., 1839, "Report on the Geology of Cornwall, Devon, and West Somerset," London, Longmans, 648pp.

Dines, H. G., Hollingworth, S. E., Edwards, W., Buchan, S., and Welch, F. B. A., 1940, "The mapping of head deposits," *Geol. Mag.*, **77**(3), 198–226.

Linton, D. L., 1955, "The problem of tors," *Geograph. J.*, **121**, 470.

Prestwich, J., 1892, "The raised beaches, and 'Head' or rubble-drift, of the South of England," *Quart. J. Geol. Soc. London*, **48**, 263–343.

Stamp, L. D. (editor), 1961, "A Glossary of Geographical Terms," London, Longmans, 539pp.

Trautschold, H., 1879, "Ueber Eluvium," *Z. Deut. Geol. Ges.*, **31**, 578–583.

Tricart, J., 1963, "Géomorphologie des Régions Froides," Paris, Presses Univ. Fr., 289pp.

Cross-references: *Cryopedology*; *Frost Riving*; *Loess*; *Mass Wasting*; *Patterned Ground*; *Periglacial Landscape*; *Quaternary*; *Regolith and Saprolite*; *Solifluction*; *Talus*; *Tor*; *Tropical Weathering and Relief*; Vol. VI: *Soils*.

HEADWARD EROSION—*See* STREAM CAPTURE

HILL WASH—*See* SHEET EROSION, SHEETWASH, RAINWASH, SHEETFLOOD

HOGBACK AND FLATIRON

Hogback is a term in geomorphology applied to a long narrow ridge or series of hills, structurally controlled by the presence of homoclinal sedimentary strata that dip steeply. With steep dips (over 50°), a nearly symmetric hogback develops. With gentler dips, the ridge often displays a *dipslope* corresponding to the dip of the sediments (20–50°) and an escarpment, *scarp slope* or *face slope* which cuts across them more or less at right angles, often disclosing the principal joint surfaces

FIG. 1. (A, above): Hogbacks in Jurassic rocks looking north from Van Bibber Creek, Colorado. (B, below): Similar rocks at Bear Creek, near Morrison, Colorado. The ridge formers are limestones and the gentler slopes are due to red shales. (Field sketches: Powell, 1875)

(see Thornbury, 1954, Fig. 10-7). Escarpment ridges of 40° down to 5° are sometimes called *homoclinal ridges* (Cotton, 1952). Hogbacks develop best in sediments that are in hard and soft layers of marked contrast. They are also favored by the sheetwash and pediment erosion of semiarid climates. Because of their steep dips, hogbacks remain more or less fixed in the landscape, and do not retreat as will a *cuesta* (q.v.).

Where stratified rocks are preserved on the slopes of uplifted domes or nomoclines, fluvial dissection and differential erosion tends to preserve triangular faces (dipslopes) on the spurs, that are commonly known as *flatirons* (Lobeck, 1939, p. 511). Also recognized by Lobeck (ibid, p. 535) are *buried hogbacks*, where such features have been drowned by alluvial fans at the front of a mountain range; they may later be exhumed in part. Further, there

FIG. 2. Oblique air photo of hogbacks in late Precambrian to Ordovician sediments of the Macdonnell Ranges, central Australia (see description by Mabbutt, 1966). This "ridge-and-vale" tract has traces of a pre-Cretaceous "summit-plane" at about 2600 feet.

are *limestone hogbacks*, as found in the karst regions of Istria (Yugoslavia), where the limestone has been stripped from the central uplift and radial streams disappear underground when they reach the peripheral belt of limestone hogbacks. Lastly there are *igneous hogbacks*, as, for example, around the laccolithic domes of the Henry Mountains, Utah. A hogback may also be controlled by a near-vertical resistant dike (Cotton, 1944).

RHODES W. FAIRBRIDGE

References

Cotton, C. A., 1944, "Volcanoes as Landscape Forms," Christchurch, Whitcombe & Tombs, Ltd., 416pp.

Cotton, C. A., 1952, "Geomorphology," sixth ed., New York, John Wiley & Sons, 505pp.

Gilbert, G. K., 1877, "Report on the geology of the Henry Mountains, Utah," *U.S. Geol. Surv. Rocky Mtn. Reg.,* 160pp.

Lobeck, A. K., 1939, "Geomorphology, an Introduction to the Study of Landscapes," New York, McGraw-Hill Book Co., 731pp.

Mabbutt, J. A., 1966, "Landforms of the Western Macdonnell Ranges," in (Dury, G. H., editor), "Essays in Geomorphology," pp. 83–119, New York, American Elsevier Publishing Co.

Powell, J. W., 1875, "Exploration of the Colorado River of the West and Its Tributaries," Washington, 291pp.

Thornbury, W. D., 1954, "Principles of Geomorphology," New York, John Wiley & Sons, 618pp.

Cross-references: *Cuesta; Escarpment, Scarp; Mesa.*

HOLOCENE, POSTGLACIAL OR RECENT EPOCH

The youngest epoch of the hierarchy of stratigraphic terminology is the *Holocene* (referring to the fossil organisms—"entirely modern"); alternative terms are "postglacial" and "Recent." During the Cenozoic era there were six earlier epochs, each characterized by progressively less modern types of organisms according to the biostratigraphic plan of classification initiated by Sir Charles Lyell (1833, pp. 52–53).

During the general retreat of the continental glaciers of the Wisconsin (Weichsel or Würm) stage, the last important glacial pause and (brief) readvance was the *Valders* (*Salpausselkä* I or late *Gothiglacial*). This post-Valders hesitant retreat began about 10,500 years ago. The same glaciation in Siberia is called the *Sartanian*. Since then much warmer and distinctive conditions have evolved.

The "Holocene" fills the need for a term to cover the period of the last ten millenia of geological time and in the present century it has become widely adopted, though various other terms are still applied to it—e.g., "Postglacial," "Recent." Both are out of keeping with the rest of Cenozoic stage terminology

and are quite vaguely descriptive and relative terms. "Postglacial," proposed by Forbes (1846), and more precisely defined by Munthe (1892), is widely and appropriately used in northern Europe to cover the last 10,000 years or so, but in northern Canada and Alaska the postglacial stage began only about 6000 years ago; in Greenland it has not even started yet. Besides, in equatorial regions, for example, it is equally necessary to identify post-Pleistocene formations, but it is hardly appropriate to speak of "postglacial" in this sense in an area that has not been glaciated since the Permian. Equally objectionable is "Recent," which is a relative term; if employed as a chronological term it destroys the use of the word in the general language. Antevs (1953) called it the "Neothermal," but that is little better. Clearly a formal name is preferable.

Since 1903 the U.S. Geological Survey employed the term "Recent" (of Lyell) but in 1967 officially adopted "Holocene." Today the International Union for Quaternary Research (INQUA) prefers "Holocene," and it has a special commission for the study of the Holocene (present chairman: B. P. Hageman, of the Netherlands). The name *Holocene* itself was first proposed at the International Geological Congress (1885) by the Portuguese Committee.

LeConte (1877, p. 114) wanted to make the "Recent" the last of several epochs in the Quaternary and to elevate the Quaternary to an era, in view of its domination by man, rather optimistically proposing for it the name *Psychozoic Era*, the age of reason, but the term has not had much support from cynical geologists. Nevertheless Holocene geologists clearly recognize the overwhelming importance of man as a geological agent corresponding to this particular period, and we speak of "anthropogenic sediments" (e.g., modern river loams) and "anthropogenic geomorphology." During man's long Pleistocene evolution, he did not emerge from the primitive *Stone Age* (Paleolithic), but with the inception of the Holocene he began an "explosive" stage of development which quickly brought him through the Mesolithic and Neolithic into the Age of Metals and the Machine.

The Holocene or Recent *Epoch* is a chronostratigraphic division, the equivalent of a *series*, the actual lithostratigraphic sequence of rocks, following the *Pleistocene Epoch.* It is the second of two epochs that make up the *Quaternary Period* (and its rock sequence, the *system*). In central Europe, the old-fashioned terms *Alluvium* and *Diluvium* are still used occasionally for the Holocene and Pleistocene; the expression "Alluvium" was first applied simply to all youthful "cover sediments," etc., especially those of fluvial origin. "Diluvium" was originally introduced by Mantell and by Buckland as the time corresponding to the Biblical deluge of Noah; the "deluge sediments" are in fact glacially transported boulders which were misinterpreted at first as "*drift*" (q.v.),

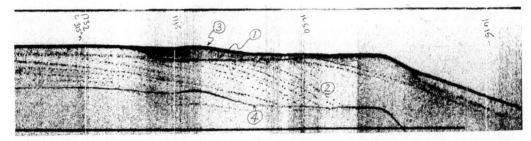

FIG. 1. Subbottom ("sparker") profile of the continental shelf, south of Long Island, New York (profile courtesy of Lamont Geological Observatory). It shows the unconformity (1) at 145 meters, due to the truncation of foreset Tertiary formations (2), over which there is a thin veneer of horizontal Holocene. Please ignore the second echo trace (at 4). (The foreset bedding has been very slightly retouched for clarity.)

carried by ice floes on a great transgressive sea that drowned the continents.

Some American geologists (though not the U.S. Geological Survey) followed the recommendation of Kay and Leighton (1933) in extending the range of the term Pleistocene right up to the present, on the basis of an argument that the Pleistocene was the period of the ice age and there is no evidence that the latter is really over (Flint, 1957). This is true, of course, but it ignores the important stratigraphic fact that following the last glacial period (Wisconsin stage) in most parts of the world there was an important change of facies and often an unconformity (Figs. 1–2). This feature is worldwide in deep-sea deposits (Broecker, Ewing and Heezen, 1960), accompanied by change in the coiling direction of key foraminifera (Ericson and Wollin, 1956). Continental shelves are universally marked by transgressive facies (Curray, 1960). Furthermore, the Holocene is marked by important land faunal breaks, from the major mammals (extinction of mastodon, etc.) down to the snails. These breaks are as important, if not more so, than those that separate the Pliocene and Pleistocene. Both for convenience, and by convention, this new stratigraphic event calls for a new epoch term. Thus, following the general consensus, the last 10,000 years or so are called the "Holocene" (T. Nilsson, 1965). [Some authors, e.g., Neustadt

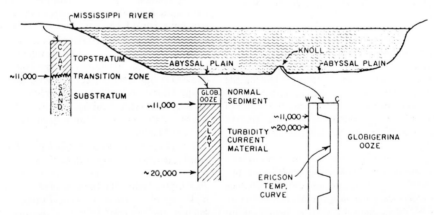

FIG. 2. Schematic diagram showing the Pleistocene/Holocene unconformity in the Mississippi delta region (left) and in the abyssal plain of the Gulf of Mexico (middle). Turbidity current material was provided in abundance by the proglacial and periglacial streams of the late Pleistocene, but became greatly reduced in the Holocene due to the growth of vegetation on the land surface (reducing runoff and bed load) and to the thalassostatic blocking due to rise of sea level. It should be noted that there is no unconformity in the pelagic Globigerina ooze sediments found on knolls and ridges isolated from the continental rise, unless there is local slumping. There is, however, almost always a paleontological change, and the temperature curves of Ericson (based on coiling directions) and of Emiliani (based on oxygen isotopes) both show an abrupt swing from cold to warm (from Broecker, Ewing and Heezen, 1960).

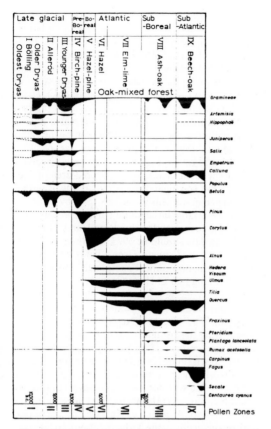

FIG. 3. Generalized pollen diagram, showing the development of the flora in Denmark (simplified after Iversen, 1960, *Dan. Geol. Und.* IV, 4, 3). Note the progressive changes in almost all the profiles from about the zone III/IV boundary, usually taken as the beginning of the Holocene. The date is given as 8300 B.C. (10,250 B.P.).

and Gudelis (1965) would begin it earlier, in the Alleröd, *ca.* 12,000 B.P.; others later, e.g., Morrison (1961) *ca.* 3000–5000 B.P.].

The Holocene is a time of enormous significance to geomorphologists because during its 10,000-year duration many modern soils and landscapes evolved. This is not to deny that many land forms and paleosols are inherited from the Pleistocene or even from far back in the Tertiary (see *Relict Landforms*), but the "finishing touches" have often been added during this epoch. Considering any geomorphic process as an equilibrium phenomenon, it is evident that since far-reaching climatic changes occurred during the Holocene, each such change introduced a modification of the equilibrium parameters. The timing of such changes is very helpful because it provides a measure of duration to be applied to any phase of such equilibrium conditions. While the sequential nature of the Davisian cyclic interpretation has in the past been unquestionably overstated, land forms nevertheless do possess many sequentially inherited

features, and the timing of the changes can lead to a quantitative understanding of successive phases.

In regions of periglacial nature during the major continental glaciations, where there are complex sequences of interglacial formations as well as the Holocene, the problem often arises as to how one

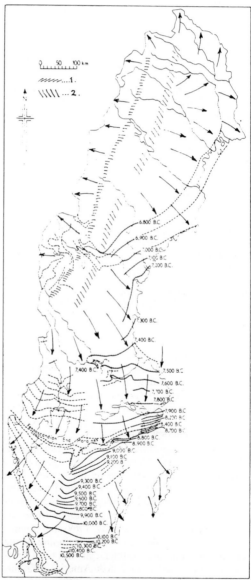

FIG. 4. Geochronology of the late Pleistocene/early Holocene moraine belts of Sweden (modified after Lundqvist, 1965). Arrows indicate the principal ice movement directions. Fine shading (1) indicates the line of the younger ice divide and open shading (2) the main ice divide. In Sweden the Holocene is generally taken to be the period since the formation of the Fennoscandian (or Central Swedish) end moraines, *ca.* 10,500 B.P.

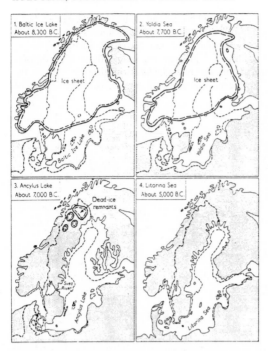

FIG. 5. Four stages in the evolution of the Holocene Baltic (Lundqvist, 1965), reflecting the deglaciation of Fennoscandia, its isostatic rebound and the glacio-eustatic rise of sea level. (1) Baltic Ice Lake = Pollen Zone III/IV Pleistocene/Holocene boundary. (2) Yoldia Sea = IV/V, end of Preboreal. (3) Ancylus Lake = V, early Boreal. (4) Litorina Sea = VIIa, early Atlantic.

distinguishes the latter from the former. While the climatic conditions of the warm stages have been closely comparable, there is often an excellent criterion for distinguishing the pre-Wisconsin deposits; they are disturbed by solifluction, ice wedging and so on, while the Holocene deposits are undisturbed.

Pleistocene/Holocene Boundary

International agreement has not yet been reached as to the precise lower boundary of the Holocene—different national groups mostly favor some time about 10,500–10,000 B.P. (B.P. = Before Present; by convention of the Radiocarbon Absolute Dating conferences, this means before AD. 1950). In northern Europe and Britain (de Jong, 1967), the boundary is commonly taken to be the beginning of the retreat from the late Gothiglacial moraines (Salpausselkä) or Valders of North America (Wright, 1964), marked by a disappearance of the vegetation characteristics of the tundra and taiga, *Dryas* (mountain avens), *Salix* (osier), and *Betula nana* (silver birch) that belonged to the last tundra stage (Valders, i.e., pollen zone III). The earliest Holocene pollen is that of the "*Preboreal*" substage, pollen zone IV (of the Firbas scale, 1949), marked by widespread expansion of *Betula pubescens* (birch)

and *Pinus silvestris* (pine) forests, i.e., deciduous and coniferous trees characteristic of subarctic forests of northern Scandinavia and Canada (Fig. 3). This continental cool episode was soon followed by still fairly cold winters but warmer summers and moderate precipitation, the "Boreal" substage (V), together with *Corylus* (hazel), *Quercus* (oak), *Ulmus* (elm), *Tilia* (lime), *Fraxinus* (ash) and *Acer* (maple).

The continental ice sheet of Scandinavia had already withdrawn from most of Sweden by the end of the late Gothiglacial retreat stage, at 6839 B.C. according to de Geer (1940). In northern Sweden at this moment the remnant ice-covered area divided in two, the so-called Bipartition at the Ragunda moraine (Fig. 4). This event was used by Baron de Geer for marking the beginning of his "postglacial"; according to a revision by Borell and Offerberg (1955), the date should be 6923 B.C. (thus 8873 B.P.), the "zero varve" in de Geer's varve chronology, which is thus now almost completely substantiated by C^{14} dating (see E. H. de Geer, 1957).

In pollen zone V, a fresh-water lake formed from the accumulation of meltwater in the Baltic, the "Ancylus Sea," the "pre-Neolithic" lake, that was breached by the rising of sea level about 7000 B.P. (Fig. 5). As early as 1872, Reade proposed that the Recent epoch should be taken as beginning with the rise of world sea level from the melting ice of the last glaciation. He was not aware, however, of the fact that there were several glacial readvances during the general retreat. As mentioned above, the last important readvance was the Valders, about 10,500 B.P. Sea level was then about -35 or -40 meters (Fig. 8). Following this event, sea level rose at a mean rate of about 2 cm/yr for the next 1000 years or so. There were probably peak rates of eustatic rise at about 5 cm/yr for some centuries (Fairbridge, 1961b; Cullen, 1967), alternating with stillstands or reversals for a few years. The vast scale of the melting may be judged by the fact that 5 cm/yr corresponds to 18×10^{12} metric tons of meltwater annually being returned to the ocean. Marine deposits of this early Holocene time were marked by the "Flandrian" transgressive facies (so-named by Dubois, 1924) in

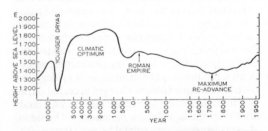

FIG. 6. Snow line in Norway during the last 12,000 years (after O. Liestöl, from Schwarzbach, 1963). Note logarithmic scale, using A.D./B.C. dates. The Holocene begins with the Younger Dryas (Valders in North America). (By permission of D. Van Nostrand Co., Princeton, N.J.)

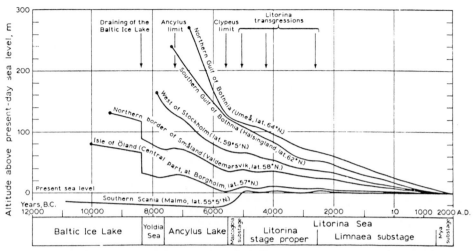

FIG. 7. Curves of the shore-line displacement in different parts of Sweden from the time of deglaciation up to the present. The black dot at the beginning of each graph marks the highest coastline. [Redrawn after Magnusson, Lundqvist, and Granlund (1957) and corrected according to Lundqvist (1965), and radiocarbon datings.]

the North Sea, the *Ostendian I*, and the Baltic region was flooded by the *Yoldia Submergence*. In eastern North America, the transgressive *Champlain Sea* came in somewhat earlier (because of delayed isostatic response) but reached its warmest temperatures in its *Mya arenaria* phase, about 10,300 B.P. (Terasmae, 1960).

In the deep ocean, worldwide changes of facies are always noted at about 10,000–11,000 B.P., and the appearance of the foraminifera *Globigerina*

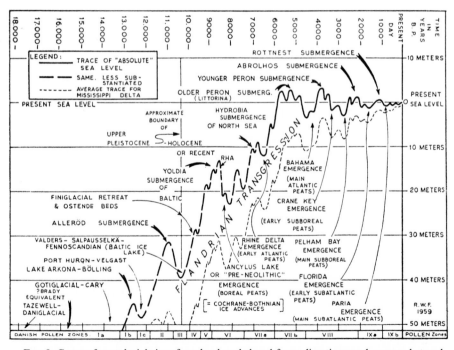

FIG. 8. Curve of postglacial rise of sea level as deduced from climatic record, emerged strand-lines and radiocarbon dating (Fairbridge, 1961b). It should be noted that this curve is controversial (see Jelgersma, 1966), since many of the world's radiocarbon dated littoral facies are in subsiding deltaic regions (see broken line for equivalent curve in the Mississippi delta).

menardii menardii as a new and unique form. Other species reacted to the major environmental temperature changes by migrations, switch in coiling directions and other characteristics (Ericson and Wollin, 1956). Tropical surface water temperatures at the time are shown by means of oxygen isotope analyses, which indicate a rise from the last glacial stage of about 5°C (Emiliani, 1955). On land in the latitude of central Europe, plant fossils show that the mean air temperatures had risen about 8–10°C from the last glacial level, but in tropical regions the temperature change was only about 2°C.

In the tropical world, the worldwide warming trend which began the great continental ice retreat in the late Wisconsin was accompanied by increased precipitation, as shown in Africa by the levels of the Nile floods (Fairbridge, 1962), and violent changes in rainfall conditions occurred at about this critical 10,000–11,000 B.P. transition stage. In the periglacial "pluvial" lake basins of the Rocky Mountains and Great Basin (e.g., Lakes Bonneville and Lahontan), similar remarkable oscillations of precipitation followed the cold arid time of the glacial maximum (Broecker and Kaufman, 1965).

On a worldwide basis, therefore, it seems that the beginning of the Holocene is one of the clearest and most striking of stratigraphic boundaries. Geomorphically it is expressed by very remarkable changes over broad climate regions:

(a) In subequatorial latitudes (5–15°N-S), there were widespread late Pleistocene dunes, but with the return of the monsoon rains in the earliest Holocene they began to become "fixed," or "anchored dunes," vegetated and locally cemented.

(b) The great rivers of "dry" Africa—the Nile, the Senegal and the Niger—were marked by intense late Pleistocene alluvial siltation (they had all dried up). This arid condition gave way to heavy rains, vigorous flooding and channel cutting. Oscillating cut-and-fill cycles of a few centuries or so resulted in complex terracing of almost all river valleys, in every latitude.

(c) Tropical and monsoon-fed lakes in Africa (from Lake Victoria to Lake Chad), in central Mexico and so on, expanded greatly after the Wisconsin desiccation.

(d) In the mid-latitudes, the Wisconsin "pluvial" lakes, like Bonneville and Lahontan in North America, having oscillated remarkably about the turn of the Holocene, began to dry up again as the westerly wind systems shifted north.

(e) Loess development in the arid periglacial areas gave way to warm humid forest development and strong river cutting (locally much amplified by glacial overflow channels). The Mississippi briefly carried five to ten times its present load. Most streams dating from this period (and earlier interglacials) are today regarded as "underfit," i.e., the valleys were adjusted to much higher runoff than now.

(f) Periglacial lakes developed on a vast scale, such as the Baltic "Ice Lake" and, in North America, Lakes Agassiz, Barlow, Ojibway and the ancestors of the Great Lakes (Superior, etc.).

(g) In the glacially loaded and depressed coastal areas, marine invasions occurred, e.g., the Champlain Sea in North America, the Yoldia Sea in Scandinavia. In non-glaciated areas vast numbers of river mouths became *estuaries* (q.v.) or *rias* (q.v.).

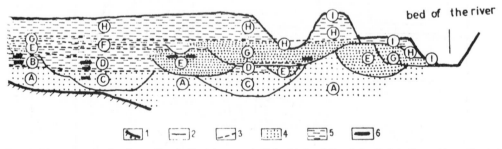

FIG. 9. Diagrammatic sketch profile of alluvial cut-and-fill in the foothills of the Polish Carpathians (Starkel, 1966).
Key:
1. Older substratum
2. Erosion surfaces
3. Accumulation contact planes of strata
4. Deposits of river-bed facies
5. Deposits of terrace (flood) facies
6. Peat

A to I: alluvial beds of different ages
C: Alleröd (11,800–10,900 B.P.)
D: Younger Dryas, pre-Boreal and Boreal periods (10,900–8200 B.P.)
E: Atlantic periods (8200–5300 B.P.)
F: Sub-Boreal period (5300–2300 B.P.)
G: Older sub-Atlantic period (2300–1300 B.P.)
H and I: Younger sub-Atlantic period (1300–0 B.P.)

Note how the present time (I), relatively cool and wet, is marked by incision (with slopes well vegetated), while in the early Medieval time with warmer and drier conditions there was more erosion of the upland slopes, but flooding and sedimentation in the valleys (H). The older sub-Atlantic or Roman time (G) was also mainly cool and wet, and marked by incision. Earlier stages are marked by similar cut-and-fill.

530

Holocene Climatic History

Since its inception about 10,500 years ago, the Holocene has gone through an oscillating sequence of climatic changes. The standard *Blytt-Sernander classification*, developed first in Scandinavia (Sernander, 1908), was worked out on the basis of paleobotanic indicators, primarily from pollen analysis, and named descriptively (with pollen zones, in Roman letters; see Hansen, 1965; Lundqvist, 1965; see Table 1). The eustatic record, combined with palynological and other data, suggests about 18 climatic cycles (Fairbridge, 1961a); there is some trace of a 550-year cycle which may have an astronomic basis (Bennema, 1954; Stacey, 1963). In tropical regions, the effect of such changes is less marked by temperature effects than by precipitation, but at high latitudes the opposite is true.

As a broad generalization, it may be said that the Holocene is marked by *three temperature substages* (Antevs, 1948, 1953; Flint and Deevey, 1951):

(1) Early stage, cooler than today, but much warmer than the late Pleistocene; Antevs called it his "anathermal" stage;

(2) A *"climatic optimum"* (q.v., Vol. II), "altithermal," "xerothermic" or "hypsithermal," in mid-latitudes up to 2.5°C above the present on the average (Fig. 6);

(3) Late stage, "medithermal," cooling, locally and briefly marked by *little ice ages* (q.v., Vol. II). (The last term—an informal one by Matthes, like "climatic optimum," should be used with great care; different authors have employed these terms in a great variety of ways.)

It should be noted that just as there is a 12-month meteorological cycle, there are also 2- and 5-year cycles, longer cycles that correspond to the sunspot 11-22 year periods, astronomic cycles of 550-1100-1650 years, and so on (see articles in Vol. II). One of the most naive assumptions of early twentieth century meteorology and geomorphology (the Davis-Johnson school) has been that climate patterns and mean sea level were essentially fixed standards. Nothing could be further from the truth. Extremely complex cycles of solar activity and celestial mechanics are constantly at play, sometimes out of phase, sometimes in phase, and rarely with several multiple cycles in phase, but never constant or static.

Thus, although some three major thermal trends are noted above for the Holocene, in detail there are many finer divisions. These are clearly recognized in pollen stratigraphy. An attempt has been made by the writer to distinguish them also in eustasy and in semiarid fluvial regimes, but not without adverse criticism, and evidently much remains to be done.

Geomorphic Events of the Holocene

(a) **Preboreal and Boreal Stages (10,300–8,200 B.P.).** In formerly glaciated areas this time was marked by the spread of vegetation, the stabilization of slopes and the fixing of dunes. In the continental climate areas, dunes were still active, but westerly winds represented a shift from the more northerly winds which formerly came from the ice fronts. Precipitation was still relatively low, so that lakes were poorly developed and rivers were mainly braided. Permafrost was disappearing slowly. In northern Scandinavia, Canada and mountain ice centers, long series of recession moraines reflected short stillstands in the glacial retreat. These stillstands are reflected by kinks in the isostatic uplift curves (Fig. 7). In the Alps, the substages *Gschnitz, Daun* and *Egesen* seem to represent brief but distinctively colder oscillations. Analogous recession moraine sequences are seen in the Rocky Mountain valleys and other areas of valley glaciation.

In the tropics and equatorial belt, the early Holocene is marked very generally by increased precipitation with filling of lakes to high levels. Rivers that had become clogged with silt during the Wisconsin began to receive more runoff in the last few thousand years of the Pleistocene and in the early Holocene. Oscillations of climate led to repeated cut-and-fill, successively lowering the thalweg until the rock floors were reached. The rainy period is most strikingly displayed in the Sahara, where late Paleolithic, Mesolithic and Neolithic man left pictographs and other records of former fauna and flora of a well-watered period, the latest Wisconsin/early Holocene. As the epoch progressed, the vegetation that had spread out over the formerly arid regions (central Sahara, Kalahari, central Australia, parts of India and Brazil) began to recede once more. These regions have now reverted to desert or very dry savanna.

Equatorial regions that were partially covered by dunes in the Wisconsin now, in the early Holocene, became once more cloaked with jungle. Slopes that bore pediments in the cold, arid time now became vegetated by heavy forest. Piedmont and colluvial deposits that contained feldspars and other easily weathered minerals now became permanently saturated and tropical saprolitic weathering began. As a result, kaolinitic clays replaced arkoses, and landslides began where stable slopes existed before (Bigarella and de Andrade, 1965).

(b) **Atlantic Stage (8,200–5,300 B.P.).** This is the time of the so-called *climatic optimum* or "hypsithermal" of northern Europe; it should just be remembered that one man's meat is another man's poison, and that "optimum" may be "pessimum" in the tropics. In high latitudes, the ice retreat enabled peat bogs and lakes to form; marls and gyttja accumulated. In the peat sequences of Scandinavia, dry stages are represented by oxidation zones ("*recurrence horizons*"), followed by warm, damp stages: notably 6200–5700 (VII) and 4900–4300 B.P. (VI). In limestone terrain, travertine and tufa spring deposits accumulated. Podzols and brown-earth soils began to develop.

TABLE 1. COMPARATIVE TABLE OF LATE QUATERNARY POLLEN ZONES (PARTLY AFTER LUNDQVIST, 1965)[a]

	Years B.P.	Denmark	Germany	Southern Sweden	Central Sweden	Northern Sweden	Recurrence Horizons	Letter Code (Nilsson, 1961)	North America
Subatlantic	1,000			I			I	SA-2	C₃
		IX	XI		I	II	II	SA-1	
	2,000			II			—		
	—		—				III	SB-2	—
	3,000		X	III	II	III	IV	SB-1	C₂
Subboreal	4,000	VIII					V	AT-2	—
			IX						
	5,000			IV	III		VI		—
	—	—	—	—		—	VII	AT-1	
Atlantic	6,000				IV	IV			C₁
			VIII	V					
	7,000	VII			V	V		BO-2	—
	8,000			VI					—
Boreal		—	VII	VII	VI	VI		BO-1	B
	9,000			VIII	VII				
Preboreal		V	VI				VII		—
	10,000	IV	V	IX				PB	—
	—	III	IV	X					
Younger Dryas	11,000	II	III	XI				DR-3	A
Alleröd	12,000	I						AL	L
			II						
	—							DR-2	T₃
Older Dryas	13,000		I	XII					
Bölling								BO	T₂
	14,000							DR-1	T₁

[a] When pollen zones are used in general correlation it is rather customary to adopt the Danish standard.

In mid-latitude mountain areas most of the glaciers disappeared completely or retreated to restricted cirques. The tree line rose to 300–500 meters above present limits (and 1000 meters or more above late Pleistocene limits), so that high-altitude peat swamps began to form, and chemical rotting helped high-level soil formation (Fig. 6). Landslides and mudflows resulted in such mountain areas, where only rockslides occurred before under more arid and colder conditions (Starkel, 1966).

In coastal regions, the postglacial eustatic rise of sea level reached its present height during this

TABLE 2. CHRONOLOGY OF LATE GLACIAL AND HOLOCENE TIME
(N.B. the older dates may need to be raised somewhat to allow for Suess effect, etc.)

Years Before Present	Danish Pollen Zone T. Nilsson Code	Blytt-Sernander Classification Key Dates	North Europe Archeol. Cultures	Mid-latitude Mean (Century) Tempera-ture Depar-tures (°C)	Marine/or Glacial Equivalents	Eustatic Phases
0–1000	IXb (Beech and Heath) SA$_2$	**Late Subatlantic** −600 B.P. (present climate) −1000 B.P.	Historic Viking	−1° +0.5°	Medieval Cold Phase Dunkerquian III	Paria Emergence
1000–2300	IXa SA$_1$	**Early Subatlantic** −1600 B.P. −2000 B.P. −2300 B.P.	Roman Iron Age	+1° −0.5° +1°	Dunkerquian II (*Mya* in Baltic) Roman Cold Phase Dunkerquian I (*Limnaea* in Baltic)	Rottnest Submergence Florida Emergence Abrolhos Submergence
2300–3700	VIIIb (Oak and Ash) SB$_2$	**Late Subboreal** −3000 B.P.	Bronze Age	−1°		Pelham/Crane Key Emergence
3700–5300	SB$_1$	**Early Subboreal** −4100 B.P. −4300 B.P.	Neolithic	+2° −0.5°	Calaisian II (Late Littorina III in Baltic)	Younger Peron Sub-mergence Bahama Emergence
5300–6600	VIIb (Oak-Elm and mixed forest) AT$_2$	**Main Atlantic** −5500 B.P. −6500 B.P.	Mesolithic (Ertebölle)	+2.5° +1°	Calaisian I (Middle Littorina II in Baltic)	Older Peron Submergence Rhine Delta Emergence
6600–7500	VIIa	**Early Atlantic** −7000 B.P.	(Maglemose)	+2°	Ostendian II (Early Littorina I in Baltic)	Hydrobia Submergence
7500–8700	VI (Hazel-Oak) BO$_2$	**Late Boreal** −7500 B.P. −7800 B.P.	(Maglemose)	+0.5° +1°	Ostendian I	Clypeus Emergence (Baltic) Mastogloia Submergence (Baltic)
8700–9800	V (Hazel-Pine) BO$_1$	**Early Boreal** −8800 B.P. (de Geer Zero Varve 6923 B.C.) −9000 B.P.	(Klosterlund)	−0.5°	Bothnian Glacial (N. Am. Cochrane)	Ancylus Emergence (Baltic Lake)
9800–10,300	IV (Birch-Pine) PB	**Preboreal**		+1°	Finiglacial	Yoldia Submergence (with Rha Sea)
10,300–10,900	III DR$_3$	**Younger Dryas** (Arctic tundra climate)		−3°	Fennoscandian (Valders)	Salpausselkä Emergence (Baltic Ice Lake)
10,900–11,800	II AL	**Alleröd** (Subarctic climate)	Late Paleolithic	−2°	Alleröd (Two Creeks)	Alleröd Submergence (−30 M)
11,800–ca. 15,000	I DR$_2$ DR$_1$	**Older Dryas Bölling** (Arctic tundra climate)		−7°	Gotiglacial	Bölling Submergence (−45M)

Atlantic stage. In the Baltic, it is known as the *Littorina (Litorina) Sea* (Fig. 8), and in Flanders its formations are called *Calaisian*. Several distinct peaks are reflected by the Baltic raised beaches (Fromm, 1963; Lundqvist, 1965; Tynni, 1966). Estuaries were drowned and low-level valley peats began to form along many of the lower flood plains. On prograding coasts, the innermost beach ridges and littoral dunes developed in the period 6000–4600 B.P. Unless there has also been postglacial isostatic or tectonic uplift, there are no radiocarbon-dated shore-line deposits at the surface prior to this; the earlier shore features are situated out across the continental shelf. Only in the formerly glaciated areas can one find a complete profile of pre-6000 B.P. dated emerged strandlines, e.g., in Scandinavia and Canada. In subsiding, deltaic areas, on the other hand, a more complete marine sequence can be found; thus in the Netherlands and North Germany, some six transgressive cycles are preserved (Kliewe, 1959; Lüttig, 1967). The rising sea level also brought more maritime climatic conditions to many areas that were previously continental. Anomalously, this had the effect in places of producing lower summer temperatures, though milder annual means (McCulloch and Hopkins, 1966). On the other hand, in the more interior and drier situations of the middle latitudes, "hot" steppeland conditions developed.

In the subequatorial dry tropics and equatorial belt, the "climatic optimum" is marked by the effects of the strengthened monsoons so that lateritic soil cycles were reinstituted, and with general extension of vegetation, many formerly braided streams became more or less stabilized and meandering between vegetated banks. Traces of these old braided patterns are often seen (especially from the air) beneath a cloak of contemporary jungle. In the more arid tropical and subtropical areas, the Atlantic Stage saw the beginnings of the desert encroachment that has gradually increased and persisted till today. One observes the "apparent" anomaly that while the mid-latitudes were emerging to the full flower of an interglacial climate with its associated geomorphic features in the Atlantic Stage, the semi-arid tropics had passed through that well-watered warm stage several thousand years earlier and now showed signs of expanding deserts. The anomaly seems to be explicable in terms of the Milankovitch solar radiation curve, which passed its high peak (for 65°N latitude) at 10,000 B.P.; it would operate under the principle of *retardation* (see *Climatic Retardation* Vol. II), and the delayed ice melting and sea level rise would explain why high-latitude situations were slower to warm up after the glaciation than the lower latitudes (Fairbridge, 1962).

(c) **Subboreal Stage (5,300–2,300 B.P.).** This stage marks the beginning of a climatic "deterioration" in many high- and middle-latitude situations. From the pollen record, Godwin (1960) calls it the "Ulmus (elm) decline." Some writers speak of a

"little ice age" (q.v., Vol. II) being initiated, for certainly in many mountain situations a renewed building and advance of glaciers can be established. At lower elevations in the continental interiors there were colder winters, but still hot summers; nevertheless, there was a rather general reduction of chemical weathering in the brown soil areas and an increase in steppe conditions. In Scandinavian peat swamps, a "recurrence horizon" (dry pause) was followed by moist conditions at 3200 and 2600 B.P. (IV and III). There were oscillations and drops in lake levels, and many stream profiles show the effects of a drop in discharge. Land clearing and deforestation by Neolithic and then Bronze Age man produced increased anthropogenic colluviation and alluviation in many parts of Europe.

In the tropics at this time, one observes an oscillating but secular drop in precipitation, suggesting a weakening of the monsoons. Along the Nile valley there was the great flowering of the ancient Egyptian culture (Early and Middle Kingdom), in part stimulated, we surmise, by the need to develop irrigation systems to utilize to the utmost the Nile floods which were less than in the preceding stage. Winter rains along the North African coast favored cultivation development. In the central African lakes, oscillations were growing progressively smaller, and the last (and lowest) high stand of Lake Victoria is radiocarbon dated at about 3500 B.P.

(d) **Subatlantic Stage (2300–0 B.P.).** The last of the paleobotanically established Holocene stages is, of course, also the historical period, and far more is known about its variations, especially for Europe, than for any previous time. One must seek to establish a *mean* climatic picture for the time, as well as the major modulations. In the high and mid-latitudes the mean pattern is usually cooler and wetter (but drier in continental climates); in detail, the following principal modulations can be distinguished: *early Roman times*—cooler and wetter (Fig. 9): *late Roman times* (and Carolingian epoch)—warmer, drier, with rising sea level (last transgressive marine phase named *Dunkerquian*); *Norman times*—still warm, but with marked oscillations; *Medieval times* (A.D. 1170–1530, according to Lamb)—mild and wetter; A.D. 1530–1720—mainly continental, with Schove's "Little Ice Age I," milder at end; A.D. 1720–1890—continental, with Schove's "Little Ice Age II and III"; A.D. 1890–present—progressively milder glacier retreat, with rising sea level. One of the best-documented hydrologic records has been for the level of the Caspian Sea (Rikhter, 1961), which reflects precipitation over a broad area of northeastern European Russia. High peaks occurred around 700 B.C. and A.D. 200, 600, 1000, 1400 and 1750; the water level has been falling progressively during the present century rise in world temperature and glacial retreat and is thus evidently a measure of cold (and lower evaporation), which is confirmed by long-term climatic data (see *Karabogaz Gulf*).

Significant processes of climatic origin in geomorphology have become increasingly hard to distinguish from those generated by man since about the Bronze Age. Removal of forests and ploughing introduce a soil condition comparable to an advanced arid phase, but if the precipitation is not reduced at the same time, the increase in stream discharge, in colluviation, and in both stream cutting and alluviation must lead to a highly complex picture. Great care must be exercised by geomorphologists today who would establish a quantitative, dynamic base for their work, following Lyellian principles. In the face of anthropogenic disturbances to the equilibrium that are superimposed upon the secular climatic trends, the extraction of significant figures from this new quantitative approach is becoming increasingly difficult.

Trends that are essentially independent of man are nevertheless easy to establish in the Subatlantic Period. In the high mountain regions, the advance of valley glaciers was very marked in early Roman times and again since late Medieval times; the present century has usually been characterized by tremendous recessions and concurrent rise of sea level. In the Mediterranean and semi-arid regions, the late Roman warm trend was marked by an advance of the desert sands in North Africa (ruining Rome's wheat "granary"); alluviation occurred in many rivers there, also in Italy, Greece and Spain, covering up Roman settlements beneath 3–5 meters of silt (Vita-Finzi, 1964). Some authorities would quote overgrazing and deforestation as factors in this loading of the streams, but it was universal within this climatic belt and coincides with comparable trends in other belts. For example, in Scandinavia there was an important warm, wet phase from A.D. 400–1200 bounded by "recurrence horizons" (I and II). Then the Viking settlements of Iceland, Greenland and Newfoundland occurred at the warmest stage about A.D. 900–1000. In tropical regions like Yucatan and Guatemala, on the other hand, the Mayan settlements of the coast were largely abandoned at this time in the face of encroachment of the jungle (presumably with undesirable aspects of extreme humidity, as malaria), and civilization turned to higher, more salubrious mountain areas.

In the highly vegetated monsoon lands, there is little evidence of minor climatic fluctuations in their geomorphology. This is because none of the variations reach critical proportions. In the marginal semiarid lands, however, where the rainfall fluctuates from, say, 15–45 cm, remarkable geomorphic responses are forthcoming. It is thus in the drier country of eastern Europe, central Asia and the American southwest that a much more emphatic story of recent geomorphic history can be established.

RHODES W. FAIRBRIDGE

References

Andersen, B., 1965, "The Quaternary of Norway," in (Rankama, K., editor), "The Quaternary," pp. 91–138, New York, Interscience Publishers.

Antevs, E., 1948, "The Great Basin, with emphasis on glacial and postglacial times. III. Climate changes and pre-white man," Univ. Utah. Bull., 38, 168–191.

Antevs, E., 1953, "Geochronology of the deglacial and neothermal ages," J. Geol., 61, 195–230.

Bennema, J., 1954, "Holocene movements of land and sea-level in the coastal area of the Netherlands," Geol. Mijnbouw, 16(2), 254–262.

Bigarella, J. J., and de Andrade, G. O., 1965, "Contributions to the study of the Brazilian Quaternary," Geol. Soc. Am. Spec. Papers, 84, 433–451.

Borell, R., and Offerberg, J., 1955, "Geokronologiska undersökningar inom Indalsälvens...," Sveriges Geol. Undersok. Arsbok, Ser. Ca, Avhand. Uppsat., 31.

Broecker, W. S., Ewing, M., and Heezen, B. C., 1960, "Evidence for an abrupt change in climate close to 11,000 years ago," Am. J. Sci., 258, 429–448.

Broecker, W., and Kaufman, A., 1965, "Radiocarbon; chronology of Lake Lahontan and Lake Bonneville II. Great Basin," Bull. Geol. Soc. Am., 76, 537–566.

Cooper, W. S., 1958, "Terminology of post-Valders time," Bull. Geol. Soc. Am., 69, 941–945.

Cullen, D. J., 1967, "Submarine evidence from New Zealand of a rapid rise in sea level about 11,000 years B.P.," Palaeogeogr., Palaeochim., Palaeoecol., 3, 289–298.

Curray, J. R., 1960, "Sediments and history of Holocene transgression, Continental Shelf, northwest Gulf of Mexico," in "Recent sediments, Northwest Gulf of Mexico, 1951–1958," Am. Assoc. Petrol. Geologists, 221–381.

de Geer, E. H., 1957, "Old and new datings of Swedish ice lakes and the thermals of Bölling and Alleröd," Geol. Foren. Stockholm Forh., 79, 93–100.

de Geer, G., 1940, "Geochronologia Suecica: principles," Kungl. Svensk. Vetensk. Akad., Handl., Ser. 3, 18(6).

de Jong, J. D., 1967, "The Quaternary of the Netherlands," in (Rankama, K., editor), "The Quaternary," Vol. 2, pp. 301-426, New York, Interscience Publishers.

Dubois, G., 1924, "Recherches sur les terrains quaternaires du nord de la France," Mem. Soc. Géol. Nord., 8, No. 1.

Emiliani, C., 1955, "Pleistocene temperatures," J. Geol., 63, 538–578.

Ericson, D. B., and Wollin, G., 1956, "Micropaleontological and isotopic determinations of Pleistocene climate," Micropaleont., 2, 257–270.

Fairbridge, R. W., 1961a, "Convergence of evidence on climatic change and ice ages," Ann. N.Y. Acad. Sci., 95(1), 542–579.

Fairbridge, R. W., 1961b, "Eustatic changes in sea level," in, "Physics and Chemistry of the Earth," Vol. 4, pp. 99–185, London, Pergamon Press.

Fairbridge, R. W., 1962, "New radiocarbon dates of Nile sediments," Nature, 195, 108–110.

Firbas, F., 1949–52, "Spät- und nacheiszeitliche Waldgeschichte Mitteleuropes nördlich der Alpen," Jena, G. Fischer, 2 vols.

Flint, R. F., 1957, "Glacial and Pleistocene Geology," New York, John Wiley & Sons, 553pp.

Flint, R. F., and Deevey, E. S., Jr, 1951, "Radiocarbon dating of late-Pleistocene events," *Am. J. Sci.*, **249,** 257–300.

Forbes, E., 1846, "On the connection between the distribution of the existing fauna and flora of the British Isles, and the geological changes which affected their area, especially during the epoch of the Northern Drift," *Geol. Surv. Gt. Brit. Mem.* **1,** 336–342.

Fromm, E., 1963, "Absolute chronology of the late Quaternary Baltic," *Baltica,* **1,** 46–55.

Gams, H., 1963, "Waldgrenzeverschiebung und Palynologie," *Grana Palynologica,* **4**(2), 292.

Godwin, H., 1960, "Radiocarbon dating and Quaternary history in Britain," *Proc. Roy. Soc. London, Ser. B.,* **153,** 287–320.

Hansen, S., 1965, "The Quaternary of Denmark," in (Rankama, K., editor), "The Quaternary," pp. 1–90, New York, Interscience Publishers.

Jäger, K. D., 1962, "Über Alter und Ursachen der Auelehmablagerung thüringischer Flüsse," *Praehistor. Zeit.,* **40,** 1.

Jelgersma, S., 1966, "Sea-level changes during the last 10,000 years," *Roy. Met. Soc. Symp. on World Climate 8000–0 B.C.,* 54–71.

Kay, G. F., and Leighton, M. M., 1933, "Eldoran epoch of the Pleistocene period," *Bull. Geol. Soc. Am.,* **44,** 669–674.

Kliewe, H., 1959, "Ergebnisse geomorphologischer Untersuchungen im Odermündungsraum," *Geogr. Berichte,* **10/11,** 10–26.

LeConte, J., 1877, "On critical periods in the history of the Earth and their relation to evolution; and on the Quaternary as such a period," *Am. J. Sci.,***14**(3), 99–114.

Leverett, F., and Taylor, F. B., 1915, "The Pleistocene of Indiana and Michigan and the history of the Great Lakes," *U.S. Geol. Surv. Mon.,* **53,** 529pp.

Lundqvist, J., 1965, "The Quaternary of Sweden," in (Rankama, K., editor), "The Quaternary," pp. 139–272, New York, Interscience Publishers.

Lüttig, G., 1965, "Interglacial and interstadial periods," *J. Geol.,* **73**(4), 579–591.

Lüttig, G., 1967, "Ostsee-küstenlinien, Nordsee-ingressiva und Geochronologie des Holozäns.," *Geol. Foren. Stockholm Forh.,* **88,** 520–532.

Lyell, C., 1830–33, "Principles of Geology," London, J. Murray, 3 vols.

McCulloch, D., and Hopkins, D., 1966, "Evidence for an early Recent warm interval in northwestern Alaska," *Bull. Geol. Soc. Am.,* **77**(10), 1089–1107.

Morrison, R. B., 1961, "A suggested Pleistocene-Recent (Holocene) boundary for the Great Basin Region, Nevada–Utah," *U.S. Geol. Surv. Profess. Paper* **424,** D-115-116.

Morrison, R. B., Gilluly, J., Richmond, G. M., and Hunt, C. B., 1957, "In behalf of the Recent," *Am. J. Sci.,* **255,** 385–393.

Müller, W., 1962, "Der Ablauf der holozänen Meerestransgression an der südlichen Nordseeküste und Folgerungen in bezug auf eine geochronologische Holozängliederung," *Eiszeitalter Gegenwart,* **13,** 197–226.

Munthe, H., 1892, "Studier öfver Baltiska hafvets quartära historia," *K. Svenska Vet. Akad. Handl.,* **18**(1), 1–120.

Neustadt, M. J., 1959, "Geschichte der Vegetation der UdSSR im Holozän," *Grana Palynologica,* **2,** 69–76.

Neustadt, M. I., and Gudelis, V., 1965, "Holocene problems," *Rept. VIth Intern. Congr. Quat. (Warsaw)* 1961, 467–477.

Nilsson, T., 1961, "Ein neues Standardpollendiagramm aus Bjärsjöholmssjön in Schonen," *Lunds Univ. Arsskr. Avd.* 2, **56**(18).

Nilsson, T., 1965, "The Pleistocene-Holocene boundary and the subdivision of the Late Quaternary in Southern Sweden," *Rept. VIth Inter. Congr. Quat. (Warsaw)* 1961, 479–494.

Reade, T. M., 1872, "The post-glacial geology and physiography of west Lancashire and the Mersey estuary," *Geol. Mag.,* **9,** 111–119.

Rikhter, V. G., 1961, "The bottom sediments of the Kara-Bogas-Gol Bay as indicator of the Caspian Sea level fluctuations," *Bull. M.O-A Isp. Prirody. Otd. Geol.,* **31,** 115–126.

Schwarzbach, M., 1963, "Climates of the Past," Princeton, N.J., D. Van Nostrand Co., 328pp. (transl. by R. O. Muir).

Sears, P. B., 1942, "Xerothermic theory," *Botan. Rev.,* **8,** 708–736.

Sernander, R., 1908, "On the evidences of Postglacial changes of climate furnished by the peat mosses of Northern Europe," *Geol. Foren. Stockholm Forh.,* **30,** 465–473.

Stacey, C. M., 1963, "Cyclical measures—some tidal aspects concerning equinoctal years," *Ann. N.Y. Acad. Sci.,* **105,** Art 8.

Starkel, L., 1966, "Post-glacial climate and the moulding of European relief," *Roy. Met. Soc.: Symp. on World Climate 8000 to 0 B.C.,* 15–33.

Terasmae, J., 1960, "Contributions to Canadian palynology," *Can. Geol. Surv. Bull.,* **56.**

Tynni, R., 1966, "Über spät- und postglaziale Uferverschiebung in der Gegend von Askola, Südfinnland," *Bull. Comm. Geol. Finlande,* **223,** 97pp.

U.S. Geological Survey, 1903, "Nomenclature and classification for the geologic atlas of the United States," *24th Ann. Rept.,* 21–27.

Vita-Finzi, C., 1964, "Synchronous stream deposition throughout the Mediterranean area in historical times," *Nature,* **202,** 1324.

Williams, M. A. J., 1966, "Age of alluvial clays in the western Gezira, Republic of the Sudan," *Nature,* **211,** 270–271.

Wright, H. E., Jr., 1964, "The classification of the Wisconsin glacial state," *J. Geol.,* **72**(5), 628–637.

Cross-references: *Anthropogenic Influences in Geomorphology; Caspian Sea; Champlain Sea; Drift; Eustasy; Glacial Lakes; Glacial Spillways and Proglacial Lakes; Karabogaz Gulf; Periglacial Eolian Effects; Pluvial Lakes; Quaternary Period; Relict Landforms; Rias; Streams—Underfit; Terraces, Fluvial—Environmental Controls.* Vol. II: *Climatic Change; Climatic Optimum; Climatic Retardation; Ice Age Theory; Little Ice Age; Time and Astronomic Cycles.* Vol. VI: *Soils.* pr Vol. VII: *Palynology; Varve Chronology; Volcanic Ash Chronology.*

HOMOCLINAL RIDGES, VALLEYS—*See* STRUCTURAL CONTROL IN GEOMORPHOLOGY

HOODOO ROCKS—*See* EARTH PILLARS OR PYRAMIDS

HORN, MATTERHORN

A pyramidal peak, characteristic of mountain glaciation (Alpine-type), which is produced by the encroaching of three or more cirques or cirque glaciers, which sculpture the preexisting surface to a stage where three serrated ridges (*arêtes*, French; *Grat*, German) converge upwards into a pyramid.

The classic example is the Matterhorn in Switzerland, and Lobeck (1939) has referred to others as "Matterhorn peaks," but since rather numerous mountains of the same type are also known as *horns* it seems more appropriate to retain the simpler term (e.g., Von Engeln, 1942).

RHODES W. FAIRBRIDGE

References

Cotton, C. A., 1942, "Climatic Accidents in Landscape-making," Christchurch, N.Z., Whitcombe and Tombs, 354pp.
Lobeck, A. K., 1939, "Geomorphology," New York, McGraw-Hill Book Co., 731pp.
Von Engeln, O. D., 1942, "Geomorphology," New York, The Macmillan Co., 655pp.

Cross-references: *Arête; Cirque; Cirque Glacier.*

HORST

Definition

A horst is a fault block, generally elongate, that has been raised relative to the blocks on either side without major tilting or folding. The bordering faults, or fault zones, are usually of near-parallel strike and are steeply dipping, along which the vertical displacement has been approximately equal. Although horsts vary greatly in size, the dominance of a linear upland bounded by faults is a characteristic feature. The derivation of "horst" is from the German term (Stamp, 1961).

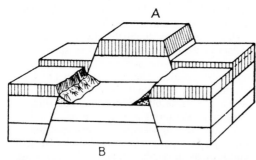

FIG. 1. Block diagram of a horst in its initial surface form (A), and the reversal of relief that may follow extensive erosion (B). Border faults are high-angle gravity faults (modified from Fig. 230 in Lahee, F. H., 1961, "Field Geology," Sixth ed., p. 264, McGraw-Hill Book Co., 883pp.). (By permission.)

General Features

The movements of the blocks that define a horst are relative. All blocks involved may have moved with respect to their original position, but the middle block must have risen more than the outer two. Thus, a true horst in its initial surface form is an elongate structural uplift (Fig. 1A). The flanking lowland areas are quite commonly grabens (*q.v.*). Under conditions of prolonged denudation, the distribution of variably resistant strata in the fault blocks may be such that the initial horst relief may become reversed, i.e., the horst becomes a lowland (Fig. 1B).

The border faults of horsts are usually either vertical or high-angle gravity (normal) faults that dip away from each other. Rarely, one or both faults may dip in a direction opposite to that shown in Fig. 1. Horsts that are bordered by parallel-dipping gravity faults are not primary, but are erosional features; they reflect a series of parallel faults thrown in the same direction (step faulting). The upland areas that occupy horsts have been termed fault ridges, block mountains, rift-block mountains, or *fault-block* mountains. Half-horsts are upthrown blocks that have been displaced principally along one border fault. Horst blocks that have been tilted are frequently termed *tilt blocks*.

Origin

The origin of the majority of horsts is believed due to lateral tension or stretching induced by vertical movements. Examples are common in areas of regional upwarp associated with block faulting, such as the Basin and Range province of the western United States. A classic example of the latter is the Ruby–East Humboldt Range, Nevada. Horsts are sometimes associated with salt tectonics (halokinesis). Many massif structures such as the Harz Mountains and the Black Forest of Central Europe are complex horsts. Many horsts are associated with terrains better noted for large grabens, e.g., Rhine shield, Germany; East Africa. The origin of horsts through compression has also been proposed from studies of lateral displacement along intersecting wrench (transcurrent) faults, or from excessive compression during folding. Examples of the latter are the horst-like structures of the Alps.

DAVID L. GILES

References

Billings, M. P., 1954, "Structural Geology," Englewood Cliffs, N.J., Prentice-Hall, 514pp.
Hills, E. S., 1963, "Elements of Structural Geology," New York, John Wiley & Sons, 483pp.
Illies, H., 1962, "Oberrheinisches Grundgebirge und Rheingraben," *Geol. Rundsch.*, **52**, 317–331.
Lensen, G. J., 1958, "A method for graben and horst formation," *J. Geol.*, **66**, 579–587.

Sharp, R. P., 1939, "Basin-Range structure of the Ruby-East Humboldt Range, northeastern Nevada," *Bull. Geol. Soc. Am.*, **50**, 881–920.

Stamp, L. D. (editor), 1961, "A Glossary of Geographical Terms," London, Longmans, 539pp.

Cross-references: *Basin and Range Landscape*; *Block Mountain*; *Graben*; *Inversion of Topography*. Vol. V: *Taphrogeny*. pr Vol. VIII: *Basin and Range Province*.

HORTON'S LAWS—*See* QUANTITATIVE GEOMORPHOLOGY

HOT SPRINGS—*See* pr Vol. VI

HUM

Hum is a term from Yugoslavia used to identify a conical residual limestone hill in a mature, deeply eroded karst landscape (Cvijić, 1918). According to the Commission on Karst Phenomena of the International Geographical Union, the term is equivalent to *Karstinselberge* (in German). Numerous hums may form a series of components in a *cone karst* (q.v.), kegelkarst or tit-hill landscape, best known in America from their occurrence in Puerto Rico as *Pepino Hills* or haystack hills. Very large hums formed in Cuba, Tonkin and southern China are generally known under the Cuban Spanish name of *mogote* (q.v.); these are especially products of subtropical or equatorial rainfall, while the smaller hums are found in drier mediterranean latitudes.

RHODES W. FAIRBRIDGE

References

Cvijić, J., 1918, "Hydrographie souterraine et évolution morphologique du karst," *Rec. Trav. Inst. Géogr. Alpine (Grenoble)*, **6**, No. 4, 56pp.

Cvijić, J., 1960, "La geographie des terrains calcaires," *Monogr. Acad. Serbe Sci. Arts (Belgrade)*, **391**.

Thornbury, W. D., 1954, "Principles of Geomorphology," New York, John Wiley & Sons, 618pp.

Cross-references: *Cone Karst*; *Karst*; *Mogote*.

HUMID CYCLE

Concept of Cycle

The idea of geomorphic cycles is well entrenched today. The humid cycle ranges from the life of a river to the history of a region. It came to us mainly from William Morris Davis.

As early as 1889, Davis recognized in the normal history of rivers, a system of natural features that depicted an early stage, an intermediate stage, and an advanced stage. This conclusion was stimulated by the diverse nature of the rivers and valleys of Pennsylvania. He stated that the length of time needed for a river to reduce an elevated land mass to its base level should be called a cycle, disregarding the true meaning of cycle. He implied the existence of a series of events that recurred regularly, and thus stressed the idea of repetition in nature. With further usage, not only rivers but whole landscapes passed through cycles of development, with distinct stages—youth, maturity, and old age.

It is not clear exactly how Davis came to think in terms of cycle. Fenneman believed that Davis thought out the cycle of erosion after Powell (1875) introduced the idea of a common base level of erosion for the streams that had carved the great canyons of the Colorado River. In another account, Roderick Peattie stated that in an autobiographical article, Davis mentioned that he had obtained the idea from a work on Wisconsin by T. C. Chamberlin in which valleys were described as young or as old.

The expression "great geological cycle" had been used already by Playfair (1802) in his "Illustrations" of Hutton (see Chorley, *et al.*, 1964).

Development of Cycle Idea

Through his teaching and voluminous writings, Davis soon made popular the notion of cycle. The idea gained favor in many forms. In 1889, Davis elaborated upon the idea, naming it the Geographical Cycle, although five years before Lawson had suggested Geomorphic Cycle. Since Davis related cycles of river and landscape development to the moist temperate region of northeastern North America, it was referred to as the Normal Cycle, the Fluvial Cycle, or the Erosion Cycle in a temperate humid region. From such usage, it was a short step to Humid Cycle.

Further diversification led to the Fluvial Geomorphic Cycle on ancient erosion surfaces, on domes, on folded and on faulted structures, as well as leading to the Desert Geomorphic Cycle, the Glacial Geomorphic Cycle, the Shore-line Cycle, and the Karst Cycle. Davis' enthusiastic followers may be held accountable for some of this proliferation, rather than Davis himself.

There can be no doubt that Davis intended his readers to assume that the series of stages in the development of a stream system or of a large region were to be repeated. They were supposed to lead to the attainment of ultimate base level—the level of the sea. He wrote often about the "interruptions" of the cycle, the forms produced in the "previous" cycle, and the appearance or disappearance of landscape features in the "new" cycle. He wrote cautiously about movements of land mass with respect to base level and made clear that he understood the difficulties inherent in the ideal geographic cycle, due to interruptions of the ideal cycle by uplift, and to the required repeated uplifts and stillstands of large land masses. But his students did not write as cautiously nor did they warn their readers that this scheme involving repetition of erosion, uplift, and erosion was so theoretical as to be applicable perhaps only in special instances.

Summary of the Humid Cycle

If it be assumed that a region, once uplifted and followed by a long period of stability, may be eroded by running water, then that region will be so dissected by the processes of erosion that it will undergo changes in height and in appearance from the earliest of erosional forms through later stages to a final stage. If stability be maintained and without change in climate or regime of stream, the last stage of erosion—the almost-a-plain or featureless surface—would be reached when the land mass was eroded nearly to sea level. Inherent in this idea is the insistence that the changes in rivers and of landforms with time should be progressive. The rivers should advance from young streams to mature streams to old streams. Simultaneously, the developmental stages of land reduction should also go forward from youth through maturity into old age.

The Peneplain—Corollary to the Humid Cycle

The formation of the near featureless plain, at any place the world over and ocurring apparently during any stage of geologic time, has been championed as the expectable result of the humid cycle carried to completion. The name given to this ideal plain, produced by subaerial erosion of the land mass reduced almost to base level in a humid temperate region across rocks of varying resistance, is *peneplain*. Davis wrote much about the peneplain; for him and for many others, this was the ultimate in the long series of stages of land reduction, i.e., the end result of the cycle of erosion. For Davis this was always in reference to erosion of a region in humid temperate climate. The two concepts, the humid cycle and peneplanation, went hand in hand. Yet some of his followers either misunderstood him or, in their enthusiasm to find and name another peneplain, disregarded his requirements for peneplain.

Difficulties with the Concept of Peneplanation

Geologists and geographers were and still are hard put to find a peneplain as "defined" by Davis anywhere on the face of the earth. Presumably if the theory of peneplanation be valid, examples of peneplains should exist today. There are, however, many examples of widespread erosion surfaces now uplifted, warped, folded, and dissected or buried. Most of these surfaces are but scattered remnants and doubt exists concerning their former extent and surface relief prior to uplift and dissection, or burial.

The appearance of "peneplains" seems unlikely in regions of repeated crustal disturbances, in polar regions long under the influence of solifluction, or in regions of desert climates. Humid climates cover only a fraction of the earth's surface, and one should expect other forms of erosion to have developed elsewhere.

Skepticism Regarding Concept of Peneplanation

There can be no doubt about erosion in a region of humid climate, but geologists influenced by the quantitative approach to landform studies are beginning to question the existence of Davis' progressive stages of erosion over the great length of time required for a humid cycle.

This skepticism and concern over the concept of peneplanation is not entirely a recent development. Fenneman, two years after Davis' death, wrote that Davis' cycle of erosion was really a philosophical concept and not a physical process. He also called attention to the difficulty of having a period of peneplanation followed by a series of incomplete peneplanations interrupted by a decelerating succession of diastrophic events. One might point out a weakness of certain geomorphological arguments, that the events must be assumed to have occurred in a diminishing order of intensity. In any event, as John P. Miller pointed out in 1959, by the beginning of World War II "interest in peneplains and other aspects of the Davis cycle had dwindled" to such an extent that any publication on the subject was rare.

Penck's Approach to Geomorphology

Probably the most significant objections to the Davis concept of the humid cycle and to its end-phase, the peneplain, are those of Walther Penck. In effect, Penck's main purpose in studying land forms, in his "Die Morphologische Analyse" (published posthumously in 1924, translated in English only in 1953), was to learn about the structural history of a region. His argument was as follows: the opposing actions of erosion and uplift determine the landforms. In the interrelationship of these actions, the landforms are measurable, the forces of degradation are measurable (or certainly should be known), but the tectonic forces within the earth are not known. Therefore, we should study landforms and the erosional processes that produced them in order to determine the internal actions that have occurred. Hence, when used properly, geomorphology is a useful tool in the hands of the structural geologist. Erosional processes had to be studied qualitatively and quantitatively. Since uplift and erosion are dissimilar processes occurring at varying rates, a calculus for their study is necessary. His now celebrated sixth chapter on the "Development of Slopes" was a serious attempt to establish this calculus. Unhappily, he did not live long enough to apply it.

Further, Penck would not follow Davis in using

deduction as a means of investigation, nor could he agree with the interpretations on which Davis' assumptions were based. Penck was convinced that before Davis assumed that certain erosional processes occurred he should have proved their existence and their ability to produce the slopes he described. And before Davis assumed that degradation operated on a stable land mass, he should have proved that the diastrophic forces had in fact elevated the land mass and then ceased to elevate it.

Results of Penck's Approach to Geomorphology

Needless to say, such a doctrine had a considerable impact on the Davis school of geomorphology. Davis himself objected strenuously, but its effect was slow to materialize since Penck's German was difficult to read or translate. Attempts by several interested groups of American geomorphologists to translate Penck were made, and translations of chapters were mimeographed and circulated. But it was not until 1953, 29 years after Penck's book was published, that a complete translation appeared. On the other hand, American geomorphologists had begun to criticize Penck and then the whole German school of geomorphology, led by Penck's father who still lived. In addition, and more importantly, during the thirties Americans also had begun to reconsider Davis' assumptions concerning the humid cycle of erosion and the concept of peneplanation.

In 1939, Oscar von Engeln of Cornell University, first by correspondence and then later by a meeting, organized a symposium on Penck's contribution to geomorphology, the results of which were published in the *Annals of the Association of American Geographers* in 1940. As a result, it was clear that the American geomorphologists were divided over the significance of Penck's doctrines, with the faithful still adhering to the Davis ideal while others were clearly having second thoughts. Perhaps the most important paper at that meeting was "The Retreat of Slopes" by Kirk Bryan. The significance of Penck's radical approach to geomorphology has become much more evident in later years, for it became a continually irritating thorn in the sides of the more complacent geomorphologists and produced far ranging effects, particularly a closer examination of the assumptions made by Davis and his many followers.

Davis was a great teacher in his day, and many still regard his erosion cycle scheme, along with his "oversteepened slope," "overloaded stream," and other concepts, as quite useful, indeed very successful pedagogic devices. Certainly in elementary geology and geography, students are thankful for labels which are easy to remember, such as young, mature, old, and the general notion of a humid cycle. Geologists familiar with active tectonic regions have become particularly outspoken in their condemnation of widespread peneplanation

and the cyclical development of landforms. Miller wrote in 1959 that knowledge of erosional processes and their products today is so slight as to endanger any conclusions of a geomorphological analysis based upon untested assumptions.

Recent Developments

Even today, the theory of the humid cycle has not been replaced by any other concept. However, attempts to construct worthwhile substitutes are now in progress. For years, Arthur N. Strahler of Columbia University has labored to bring out the dynamic basis of geomorphology wherein all geomorphic processes should be treated as either gravitational shear stresses or as molecular shear stresses. He has introduced, a new approach to the analysis of stream drainage systems, the hypsometric (area-altitude) analysis of erosional topography. Lester C. King's "Canons of Landscape Evolution" in 1953, from a more regional, world viewpoint has treated the transgressions of Davis and his followers in a critical manner.

In a paper on geomorphic development in humid and arid regions, Chauncey D. Holmes (1955) claimed that arid climate landscapes are best explained by the Penckian geomorphic concepts and that humid climate landscapes vary only from arid climate landscapes by some small factors. Charles S. Denny in 1956 came to the conclusion that in north-central Pennsylvania, the classic area of Davis' peneplains, the topography today seems to be controlled almost wholly by anticlinal and synclinal structures in resistant ridge-forming beds; restored contour maps of the hilltops thus controlled indicated to him that the upland slopes parallel the dip of the structure. The major streams cross the ridges and valleys of the restored surface in such a way as to prompt disbelief in the existence of any uplifted and eroded peneplain.

In 1959, John Miller summarized the status of geomorphology in North America with penetrating reflections on the decline of Davis' cyclical concept, as well as the general trend of recent developments in other aspects of geomorphological research. Publications refuting the teachings of Davis appear in growing numbers and suggest alternative explanations for uplifted erosion surfaces, as, for example, Jane Forsyth's work on the upland flats in eastern Ohio.

Trends in Elementary Textbooks

Many of the recently published elementary texts in geology avoid the humid cycle and peneplanation entirely or else come out emphatically against cyclic erosion and peneplains. Works such as those by Gilluly, Waters and Woodford, by Leet and Judson, by Longwell and Flint, and by Bates and Sweet, all take a stand expressing doubt concerning the validity of the humid cycle and peneplanation, or else avoid usage of terms such as old streams, old age, and peneplains. On the other hand, other elementary textbooks such as those by Brown, Monnett and Stovall, by Emmons, Allison, Stauffer and Thiel, and by Zumberge still follow Davis; one by Spencer offers both sides of the argument.

Modern Trends

John T. Hack in 1960 wrote a carefully documented synthesis on the interpretations of erosional topography in humid temperate regions in which he returned to the approach to the study of landforms offered by G. K. Gilbert as long ago as 1877. The principle of dynamic equilibrium provided by Hack may replace Davis' cyclical concept. Hack assumes that all the variable parts of any one stream system are related to each other in such a way that they are all being eroded at the same rate, and that both the slopes and the processes producing them are in a "steady state of balance" with freedom from any progressive stages of development related to time. Any variations in slopes may be interpreted by their positions in respect to each other and by the types of bedrock available. The effects of opposing forces, uplift and erosion, with energy continually entering and leaving a system cancel each other, so that as soon as a force changes, or different bedrock is encountered, all landforms adjust rapidly, taking new attitudes in order to maintain equilibrium. As long as forces change slowly enough, equilibrium is continual and the landforms remain in a steady state of balance despite the evolving topography.

Luna B. Leopold and Thomas Maddock, Jr., in 1953, on the basis of data on hydraulic characteristics of streams all over United States, were able to describe the hydraulic geometry of stream channels and draw physiographic implications about the immediate appearance of a temporary near-equilibrium among the many stream variables studied whenever one of the variables changed. This near-equilibrium is demonstrated for many streams, tributary as well as main stream, under differing climatic conditions. One of the variables in near-equilibrium is sediment load and is related directly to supply from adjacent slopes. An additional implication, hinted at by Leopold and Maddock, that may be extended here, is that the adjacent slopes also are in near-equilibrium, and therefore, there is no need to wait for long periods of time, as Davis required, for the slopes to progress from youth through maturity into old age in order to obtain equilibrium. If the many stream variables quickly reach near-equilibrium, including the adjacent slopes, upon alteration of any one of them, then immediate establishment of near-equilibrium of all erosional processes within any stream drainage system may be independent of time, and consideration of the cyclical development of landscapes is unnecessary. The original physiographic implica-

tions of the Leopold and Maddock thesis were supported further in Leopold, Wolman and Miller's book in 1964 on fluvial processes in geomorphology.

Notwithstanding the current trends in geomorphology, the humid cycle as originally conceived by Davis is still supported by some geologists and geographers. For some, the humid cycle is as produced by fluvial erosion at the center of a horizontally uplifted plateau. Erosion continues at the same pace as it did prior to uplift, while all about the plateau is change and dissection. But for most, the humid cycle of Davis has outlived its usefulness. For its time, it served its purpose well, but with the modern trend toward quantitative geomorphology, the concept of the humid cycle seems destined to fade away and provide in the future only historic interest.

While the Davisian humid cycle may thus be laid to rest, there is such a thing as humid morphogenesis, i.e., erosion and deposition as it occurs in vegetated, humid lands. It carries no connotation of graded streams or base leveling, but is clearly climate dependent. The rate of *denudation* (q.v.) for any given vegetation/lithology/relief condition is related to the degree of morphogenetic equilibrium achieved since the inception of the humid condition. On a small scale, the landforms are likely to achieve local equilibrium, while larger forms are dominated by inheritance (see *Geomorphology—Principles*).

SIDNEY E. WHITE

References

*Bryan, Kirk, 1940, "The retreat of slopes," *Ann. Assoc. Am. Geogr.*, **30**, 254–268.

Chorley, R. J., Dunn, A. J., and Beckinsale, R. P., 1964, "The History of the Study of Landforms," Vol. 1, London, Methuen & Co., 678pp.

*Hack, John T., 1960, "Interpretation of erosional topography in humid temperate regions," *Am. J. Sci.*, **258-A**, 80–97.

Holmes, C. D., 1955, "Geomorphic development in humid and arid regions: a synthesis," *Am. J. Sci.*, **253**, 377–390.

King, Lester C., 1953, "Canons of landscape evolution," *Bull. Geol. Soc. Am.*, **64**, 721–752.

Leopold, Luna B., and Maddock, Thomas, Jr., 1953, "The hydraulic geometry of stream channels and some physiographic implications," *U.S. Geol. Surv. Profess. Paper*, **252**, 57pp.

*Leopold, Luna B., Wolman, M. Gordon, and Miller, John P., 1964, "Fluvial Processes in Geomorphology," San Francisco, W. H. Freeman and Co., 522pp.

*Miller, John P., 1959, "Geomorphology in North America," *Polish Geogr. Rev.* **31**, nr. 3–4, 567–587.

Penck, Walther, 1953, "Morphological Analysis of Land Forms," London, Macmillan and Co. 429pp. (translated by Hella Czech and Katharine C. Boswell).

* Additional bibliographic references may be found in this work.

HYDRAULICS—*See* Vol. I, II, pr Vol. VI, **FLUID MECHANICS;** *also* pr Vol. VI, **HYDRAULIC MODELS**

HYDROCLIMATE—*See* Vol. II

HYDROGEOLOGY, HYDROLOGY—*See* pr Vol. VI

HYDROLOGIC CYCLE—*See* pr Vol. VI

HYDROSPHERE (GROUND WATER, SEA WATER)—*See* Vol. II and pr Vol. VI

HYPOGENE—*See* Vol. IV

HYPSOGRAPHIC CURVE

Definition

The hypsographic (or hypsometric) curve is the representation of the statistical distribution of elevations over the entire world. In the areas which are covered with water (lakes, seas, oceans), the relief is mostly below sea level and the figures are consequently negative (generally): they are bathymetric values, determined nowadays by acoustic sounding. The curve was first prepared in the last century but the modern curve is based on the statistics of Kossinna (1921, 1933).

Let us call dS the total of the areas whose elevation (positive or negative) is included between the values z and $z + dz$, and let us call S the total area of the world. The hypsographic curve represents dS/S as function of z (Fig. 1, devised by Wegener, 1924).

Instead of such a "curve of frequencies," we may consider the "curve of cumulative frequencies," i.e., the representation of the integral of dS/S (Fig. 2).

We may also use a schematic table, such as Table 1.

TABLE 1

z between	dS/S (%)
Zero and $+1000$ m	21.3
$+1000$ and $+2000$ m	4.7
$+2000$ and $+3000$ m	2.0
$+3000$ and higher	1.2
Zero and -200 m	5.5
-200 and -1000 m	2.9
-1000 and -2000 m	3.5
-2000 and -3000 m	7.1
-3000 and -4000 m	15.5
-4000 and -5000 m	22.0
-5000 and -6000 m	13.2
-6000 and deeper	1.1

Peculiarities

The peculiarities of this curve are:

(1) The existence of two maxima of frequencies, i.e., bimodal; they appear in Fig. 1 and are located at the elevations $+100$ and -4700 meters. In the same Figure, the broken line represents a gaussian (stochastic) distribution.

(2) The existence of two zones of elevations in which the cumulative frequency changes quickly with an increasing magnitude (this peculiarity is not independent from the first one).

(3) The existence of an intermediate zone (continental slope) where the integral curve (Fig. 2) is characterized by a sharp curvature (beginning at the shelf edge).

(4) The hypsographic curve is such that the so-called mean "eustatic level" of the oceans, controlled by isostatic equilibrium, does not depend on the volume of continental ice.

Explanations

The existence of two frequency maxima reveals two plainly different parts of the earth's crust (independent of the presence of water in the oceans). Such a duality, confirmed by the seismologic and

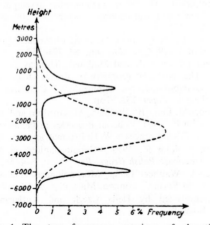

FIG. 1. The two frequency maxima of elevation (after Wegener).

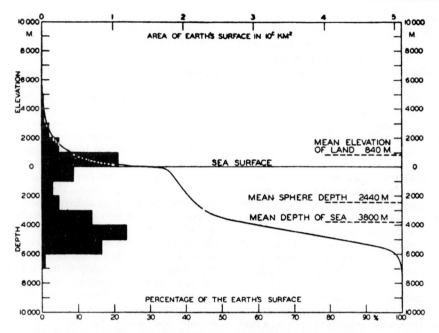

F<small>IG</small>. 2. Hypsographic curve showing the area of the earth's solid surface above any given level of elevation or depth. At the left in the figure is the frequency distribution of elevations and depths for 1000-meter intervals (from Sverdrup, Johnson, Fleming, 1942). (By permission of Prentice-Hall, Inc., Englewood Cliffs, N.J.)

gravimetric studies, conforms to the isostatic hypothesis of Airy, as modified by Gutenberg; it played an important part in the Wegener theory of continental drift, which has both numerous supporters and numerous opponents. Wegener pointed out that if there was a uniform crust as argued by some of his critics, the hypsographic frequency curve would have to be controlled by the gaussian law of errors. Goguel (1950), for example, urged an originally random distribution of the earth's crust, modified only by erosion/sedimentation and isostasy.

The rapid variation of frequency in the two domains (modes) of elevation correlates with the existence of two frequency maxima. But the fact that one of these domains includes the zero level must be explained: We are in the presence, on the one hand, of epeirogenic processes (the theories of which have yet to be proved) and, on the other hand, of the processes of erosion and sedimentation. The principal consequence of these opposed actions is that the continental areas only gently emerge from oceans; they are smoothed down to near the zero level in proportion to the degree of their epeirogenic uplift.

This is the reason why the first frequency maximum is of low altitude (+ 100 meters).

The intermediate zone (with steep curve) corresponds to the transition between the continental and oceanic domains; here, the following

peculiarity must be noted: The sudden change of frequency near the zero level does not stop at that zero level itself, but at about the isobath of 200 meters; at that negative level, the transition or intermediate zone begins. The continental shelf statistically extends to that level and must be considered as an integral part of the continental domain. The continental slope, with its steep declivity constitutes the intermediate zone.

If an isostatic readjustment takes place, following a major variation of the volume of the continental ice, we must presume that the vertical motion of the oceanic floor (subsidence after a melting of the ice, uplift after a glacial accumulation) will be limited to the deepest zones, whereas the intermediate zone constitutes a more or less plastic junction between oceans and continents.

Lastly, the form of the hypsographic curve is such that the so-called eustatic level of the oceans, controlled by isostatic equilibrium, does not depend on the volume of the continental ice. That statement has the following implication: Let us imagine a general melting of the continental ice (Greenland, Antarctica and so on), in a short time (on the geological scale). The volume of the oceans increases, and a transgression takes place; but such a displacement of mass from the continental ice to the ocean, disturbs the isostatic equilibrium. The mass displacement is consequently followed by a compensating displacement of mass beneath the earth's crust, somewhere in the mantle; this is an isostatic readjustment. For the oceans the effects of this will be a subsidence; for the continental zones initially with ice caps, this means uplift; for the continental areas without initial ice, there will be only a moderate uplift.

The variation of the mean elevation of the continents (considered before the melting and after the readjustment, assuming in both cases a perfect isostatic equilibrium) is proportional to the value of the expression $a - (1 + \varepsilon)/\delta$, in which a is the total continental area (the unit being the area of the whole earth), $1 + \varepsilon$ is the density of the oceans, and δ is the density of the mantle (Airy's model). With the values $1 + \varepsilon = 1.05$ and $\delta = 3.27$, the expression $a - (1 + \varepsilon)/\delta$ is zero for $a = 0.32$.

The value 1.05 takes into account the mean depth of the oceans; the value of δ is not quite certain. The value of a represents approximately the true continental area, including the continental shelf. Consequently, although the mean elevation of the continents may show small variations, corresponding to temporary disturbances in the equilibrium, the readjustments tend to bring it back to a constant value, independent of the volume of the continental ice (after allowing time for adjustment). We would get a different result with another hypsographic curve; if a was greater, then a glaciation would cause an increase of the mean elevation and melting would cause a decrease; if a was smaller, then those consequences would be reversed. One does not know if this peculiarity is fortuitous or not.

J. LAGRULA

References

Francis-Boeuf, C., 1942, "Les Océans," Paris, Presses Universitaires de France.

Goguel, J., 1950, "Sur l'interprétation de la courbe hypsographique," *Acad. Sci. Paris*, *C.R.*, **230**, 219–221.

Lagrula, J., 1950, "Sur la courbe hypsographique," *Acad. Sci., Paris, C.R.*, **230**, 1413–1415.

Lagrula, J., 1959, "Nouvelles études gravimétriques," *Bull. Serv. Carte Géol. Algerie*, No. 25.

Kossinna, E., 1921, "Die Tiefen des Weltmeeres," *Veroeffentl. Inst. Meereskunde, Berlin*, **9**.

Kossinna, E., 1933, "Die Erdoberfläche," in (B. Gutenberg ed.) "Handbuch der Geophysik," Vol. 2, pp. 869–954, Berlin, Borntraeger.

Krümmel, O., 1897, "Handbuch der Ozeanographie," Stuttgart, Engelhorn's Nacht., 2 vols.

Sverdrup, H. U., Johnson, M. W. and Fleming, R. H., 1942, "The Oceans," Englewood Cliffs, N.J., Prentice-Hall, 1087pp.

Wegener, A., 1924, "The origin of continents and oceans," London, Methuen, 212pp. (translated by J. G. A. Skerl).

Cross-references: *Continents and Oceans; Eustasy; Hyp-* sometric Analysis; Postglacial Isostatic Rebound; Quantitative Geomorphology; Warping. Vol. I: Mean Sea Level Changes. Vol. V: Isostasy.

HYPSOMETRIC ANALYSIS (of Land Forms)

*A hypsometric (or hypsographic) curve is one which is plotted to indicate the proportions of a given area of the earth's surface at various elevations or depths above or below a certain datum. The best known example is for the entire earth's surface (see *Hypsographic Curve*). The most significant fact emerging from this curve (developed by de Lapparent, 1883; Murray, 1888; Penck, 1894: see Clarke, 1966) was the discovery that the earth's surface is divided into two statistically distinct "levels" or steps, the continental platforms (about 100 meters above sea level) and the deep-sea floor (about 4700 meters below sea level). If the earth's crust consisted of randomly distributed materials one would expect a simple gaussian curve (with a peak of about -2450 meters), so that the discovery of two levels suggested to O. Fischer, Suess, Gilbert, Wegener and others that there was continental crust (SIAL) and oceanic crust (SIMA) of different densities, approximately 2.7 and 3.2. Interesting differences also exist between the various continents.

The simplest approach to a quantitative analysis of landforms is an *altimetric frequency curve* (q.v.). Baulig (1935) recommended the use of large-scale topographic maps overlain with a grid of small squares, counting and plotting the highest elevation within each square. One obtains a histogram or a curve that is ideally gaussian, but negative oscillations mark topographic benches or plateaus. A less satisfactory variation of this procedure (used by Thompson, 1936) is to count

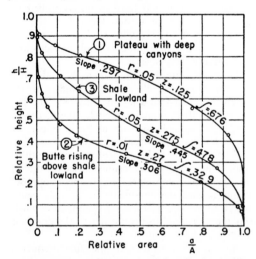

FIG. 1. Hypsometric curves of three basins in Mesa Verde Region, New Mexico. From Chimney Rock Quadrangle, New Mexico, U.S. Geological Survey, 1:62,500 (from Strahler, 1952).

the highest closed contours, thus indicating summits; it can be made more accurate by using a planimeter to determine the area covered by the closed contour summits (Thompson, 1941).

A more thorough treatment involves the *hypsometric curve*, which calls for a determination of the total area between every pair of contours for a given map area. This is considerably more time-consuming than Baulig's method and does not usually extract much more information. A newly developed random sampling technique (Haan and Johnson, 1966) has, however, greatly reduced the time factor, and certain advantages emerge.

The simple hypsometric curve is an *ogive* or *cumulative frequency curve*. Heights and areas may be expressed in absolute or relative values. As pointed out by Clarke (1966, p. 270), a curve of this sort lacks any slope indication, so that it is not particularly useful as a rule in helping to delineate old erosion surfaces, which consist of benches and slopes; for this purpose the spot height/summit/grid method of morphometry is probably best. On the other hand, the hypsometric curve is recommended for establishing average heights with the degree of dissection; it is thus useful in regional geophysics and studies of neotectonics, because the hypsometric curve of a given mountain system or massif may be utilized to help judge if it is in isostatic equilibrium, and to compare the roles of fluvial erosion and eustasy in its denudational history. The curve is thus helpful in appraising the contemporary tectonic status (stable or unstable, rising or sinking), but does not always bring out details of the denudational chronology (de Martonne, 1941a, 1941b; Birot, 1955; Baulig, 1957).

For the study of individual drainage basins, Strahler (1952) has recommended a *percentage hypsometric method*. A hypsometric integral is worked out which shows the ratio of the area below the hypsometric curve to the total area of the grid square. Contrasting erosion forms are clearly recognizable (see Fig. 1).

Yet another technique is the compilation of *relative relief maps*. The difference in elevation between highest and lowest contour within each grid square is measured and plotted. Lines of equal relief, isopleths, provide a somewhat better idea of relief than an ordinary contour map, since they are a measure of general steepness, though not of local steepness. An example is given for the state of Ohio by G. H. Smith (1935; see also in Thornbury, 1954, Fig. 21.5).

RHODES W. FAIRBRIDGE

References

Baulig, H., 1935, "The Changing Sea Level," London, George Philips and Sons, Ltd.

Baulig, H., 1957, "Les méthodes de la géomorphologie, d'après M. Pierry Birot," *Ann. Géogr.*, **66**, 97–124, 211–236.

Birot, P., 1955, "Les Méthodes de la Morphologie," Paris, P.U.F.

Clarke, J. I., 1966, "Morphometry from Maps," in (Dury, editor), "Essays in Geomorphology," pp.235–274, Heinemann Educ. Books, Ltd.

de Martonne, E., 1941a, "Hypsométrie et morphologie," *Ann. Géogr.*, **50**, 241–254.

de Martonne, E., 1941b, "Morphométrie et morphologie comparées du Massif Central et du Massif Bohémien," *Bull. Assoc. Géogr. Français*, **140**(1), 113–114.

Haan, C. T., and Johnson, H. P., 1966, "Rapid determination of hypsometric curves," *Bull. Geol. Soc. Am.*, **77**(1), 123–125.

Smith, G. H., 1935, "The relative relief of Ohio," *Geograph. Rev.*, **25**, 272–284.

Strahler, A. N., 1952, "Hypsometric (area–altitude) analysis of erosional topography," *Bull. Geol. Soc. Am.*, **63**, 1117–1142.

Thompson, H. D., 1936, "Hudson gorge in the Highlands," *Bull. Geol. Soc. Am.*, **47**, 1831–1848.

Thompson, H. D., 1941, "Topographic analysis of the Monterey, Staunton, and Harrisonburg quadrangles," *J. Geol.*, **49**, 521–549.

Thornbury, W. D., 1954, "Principles of Geomorphology," New York, John Wiley & Sons, 618pp.

Cross-references: *Altimetric Frequency Curve*; *Continents and Oceans*; *Hypsographic Curve*; *Quantitative Geomorphology*; *Slopes*.

I

ICE-THRUSTING

Along the margins of ice-covered lakes and seas and the shores of the Arctic Ocean the effects of floating ice pressure (under wind stress) may be observed, leading to the building of large *pressure-ridges* in the beach gravels and other littoral deposits. Even massive rock outcrops are dislodged. The terms *ice-shore ridges* and *ice ramparts* are also used sometimes (in German: *Stauwälle*).

FIG. 1. An ice-pushed ridge on the margin of a lake at Resolute Bay, Cornwallis Island, N.W.T., Canada. (Photo: Robert L. Nichols)

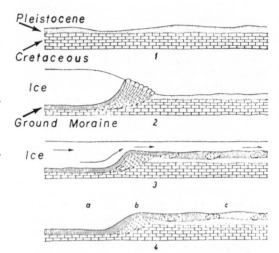

FIG. 2. Stages in the evolution of ice thrusting producing sheared blocks of a Cretaceous chalk in North Germany (Gripp, 1947). Some of these blocks are over 1000 meters long.

Continental ice advancing over relatively soft or plastic deposits commonly leads to pressure ridges on a much larger scale. Deformation was avoided over broad areas of the plainlands by the existence of deep permafrost, permitting the ice snout to slide forward with minimal disturbance. However, around obstructions and along the ice margins, either maximal or during small readvances of the last retreat phase, some remarkable *glacial tectonics* are observed.

Soft unconsolidated strata may be "cemented" at the time of glacial tectonic stress, so that brecciation, shearing and massive displacement may occur. The temporary "cement" consists of ground ice, which later melts away. Distinctive belts of "pseudotectonics" remain (Rutten, 1960, 1965). In the late glacial stages, ice margins may be water-logged by proglacial lakes so that plastic deformation results (Mackay and Mathews, 1964).

Slater (1929) recognized two types of ice-thrust structures:

(a) *Frictional drag*, which deforms the pre-existing strata. A classic example is to be seen in the present sea cliffs at Cromer, Norfolk (England), which Slater mapped in detail. Large blocks of Cretaceous Chalk (up to 540 meters long) have

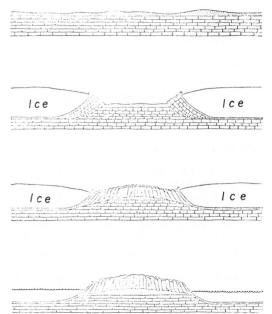

FIG. 3. Growth of a thrust-moraine "gable nunatak" (Gripp, 1947). The islands Jasmund and Möen in the Baltic stood out as nunataks and ice thrusting pushed the blocks of Cretaceous chalk into vertical stacks, like a gabled roof, partly burying some earlier till.

been sheared off and transported southward over-riding glacial gravels and till. Similar and even larger transported blocks of Chalk are found in North Germany. Magnificent pseudo-Alpine tectonics are seen in the easily deformable Pleistocene sediments of Møens Klint (Denmark) and Rügen (Germany). Some rather similar, but less well-exposed examples were described by Slater from southern Alberta.

(b) *Glacial pseudomorph structures* were recognized by Slater in some of the glacial formations. The latter are *contemporary* "englacial" till materials, which were distributed through the ice during its deformation. Then when they melted out, the same deformed shapes were preserved as pseudomorphs. The characteristic structures are imbrications, such as seen in the glacial snouts. Belts of anticlinal ridges or *push moraines* (*Stauchmoränen* in German) are commonly preserved today marking the lobate retreat limits of the last

Scandinavian ice in North Germany and Holland (Carlé, 1938). In New England and Long Island all formations back to the Cretaceous may be seen in the upthrusts (Shaler, 1894). Such ridges have been called *pseudomoraines* (Woodworth and Wigglesworth, 1934, p. 67). They would only be preserved under a stagnant, wasting regime during glacial retreat, probably under the protective cover of a thick *ablation moraine* (q.v.).

A third type of structure, is *diapiric* in character, the static load of the stagnant ice causes plastic clays to rise up wherever possible, e.g., in the axial zone of an esker (as in Denmark). Examples of broad flexures in clay formations have been described on Long Island by Fuller (1914). Such diapiric motion is only possible if the permafrost has not reached too deeply, as in peripheral regions. Clastic dikes may be formed (Lupher, 1944). Ice-thrust phenomena on a small scale are widely observed in periglacial lake and fluvioglacial deposits. Where alternating sands, silts and clays provide cover contrasts, these structures can be very striking. Faulting is frequently involved, suggesting complete permafrost, since these sands have no cementing materials.

RHODES W. FAIRBRIDGE

References

Andersen, S. A., 1931, "Om Aase og Terrasser inden for Susaa's Vandomraade og deres Vidnesbyrd om Isafsmeltningens Forløb," *Danmarks Geol. Undersoegelse, II,* **54,** 201pp. (English summary, 169–201).

Carlé, W., 1938, "Das innere Gefüge der Stauch-Endmoränen und seine Bedeutung für die Gefüge des Altmoränengebietes," *Geol. Rundschau, 29,* 27–51.

Challinor, J., 1947, "A remarkable example of superficial folding due to glacial drag, near Aberystwyth," *Geol. Mag., 84,* 270–272.

Dhonau, T. J. and Dhonau, N. B., 1963, "Glacial structures on the north Norfolk coast," *Proc. Geol. Assoc. London,* **74**(4), 433–439.

Fuller, M. L., 1914, "The geology of Long Island, New York," *U.S. Geol. Survey Profess. Paper* **82,** 231pp.

Gripp, K., 1947, "Jasmund und Möen, eine glacial-morphologische untersuchung," *Erdkunde,* **1,** 175–182.

Kupsch, W. O., 1962, "Ice-thrust ridges in western Canada," *J. Geol.,* **70,** 582–594.

Lupher, R. L., 1944, "Clastic dikes of the Columbia

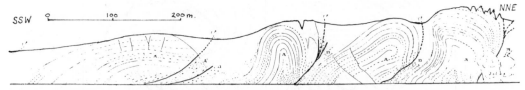

FIG. 4. Ice-thrust structures at Møens Klint, Denmark, consisting mainly of overturned anticlines of Upper Cretaceous chalk (A), over rising thrust planes, resting on late Pleistocene till (B), locally with chalk breccia zones (A') between (Slater, 1927a).

Basin region, Washington and Idaho," *Bull. Geol. Soc. Am.,* **55,** 1431–1462.

Mackay, J. R., and Mathews, W. H., 1964, "The role of permafrost in ice-thrusting: a discussion," *J. Geol.,* **72**(3), 378–380 (ref. Kupsch, *ibid.* 1962).

Nichols, R. L., 1953, "Marine and lacustrine ice-pushed ridges," *J. Glaciol.,* **2**(13), 172–175.

Paterson, J. A., 1965, "Ice-push ramparts in the George River Basin, Labrador-Ungava," *Arctic,* **18**(3), 189–193.

Rutten, M. G., 1960, "Ice-pushed ridges, permafrost and drainage," *Am. J. Sci.,* **258,** 293–297.

Rutten, M. G., 1965, "Ice-pushed ridges, permafrost, and drainage: a discussion," *J. Geol.,* **73**(6), 895–896.

Shaler, N. S., 1894, "Pleistocene distortions of the Atlantic seacoast," *Bull. Geol. Soc. Am.,* , **5,** 199–202.

Slater, G., 1926, "Glacial tectonics as reflected in disturbed drift deposits," *Proc. Geol. Assoc, London,* **37,** Pt. i, 392–400.

Slater, G., 1927a, "The structure of the disturbed deposits of Møens Klint, Denmark," *Trans. Royal Soc. Edinb.,* **55,** Pt. ii (No. 12), pp. 289–302.

Slater, G., 1927b, "Structure of the Mud Buttes and Tit Hills in Alberta," *Bull. Geol. Soc. Am.,* **38,** 721–730.

Slater, G., 1929, "Quaternary Period," in *Handbook of the Geology of Great Britain,* Chap. 13, London, Murby.

Weeks, W. F., and Anderson, D. L., 1958, "Sea ice thrust structures," *J. Glaciol.,* **3**(23), 173–175.

Woldstedt, P., 1954–65, "Das Eiszeitalter," Stuttgart, Enke Verlag, 3 vols.

Woodworth, J. B., and Wigglesworth, E., 1934, "Geography and Geology of the region including Cape Cod, the Elizabeth Islands, Nantucket, Martha's Vineyard, No Mans Land, and Block Island," *Harvard Coll. Mus. Comp. Zoölogy Mem.,* **52,** 338pp.

Cross-references: *Ablation Moraine; Esker; Fluvioglacial Processes; Glacial Spillways and Proglacial Lakes; Moraines; Permafrost; Stagnant Ice Melting; Washboard Moraines.* Vol. VI: *Glacier Geophysics; Ice Sheet; Till.*

ICE WEDGES—*See* PERIGLACIAL LANDSCAPES

INCISED MEANDER

A meandering river valley that has cut down its bed into the bedrock, because of uplift or lowered base level, is called incised, intrenched, entrenched, inclosed or ingrown. It is characteristic of antecedent drainage systems. Finer distinctions are recognized by some authorities. Thornbury (1954) proposed that *incised* or *inclosed meanders* are terms appropriate to all sorts of meanders cut down into bedrock, and that two sub-types should be identified:

(a) *Intrenched or entrenched meanders* are those cut down with symmetrical valley sides, i.e., due to rapid down-cutting; and

(b) *Ingrown meanders* (Rich, 1914) are those with a pronounced asymmetry of cross section, which would normally develop under slower incision.

Experiments at the United States Waterways Experimental Station at Vicksburg have shown that the shape of the incised meander should not always be taken as strictly "inherited," e.g., from an antecedent pattern, where a "free" meander system could develop. As down-cutting proceeds, modifica-

FIG. 1. Incised meanders: (A) intrenched meanders; (B) ingrown meanders (Sparks, 1960). (By permission of Longmans, Green & Co., London.)

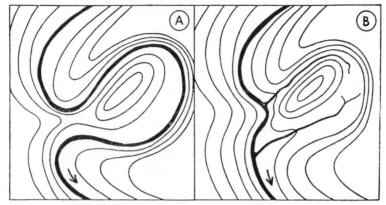

Fɪɢ. 2. Formation of abandoned incised meander (Sparks, 1960). (By permission of Longmans, Green & Co., London.)

tion of the stream course can evolve into (a) lithologically conditioned meanders or (b) structurally controlled meanders.

An additional modification (a climatic type) suggested by Troll (1954) is the "slip-off meander" often found at the head of "*trumpet valleys*" (q.v.). These valleys are cut in the steeply sloping proglacial outwash fans of Alpine type. Downcutting in this unconsolidated material and meander development proceed very rapidly as the glacier recedes.

Where double ingrown (asymmetric) meander becomes cut-off, a compound *slip-off slope* (q.v.)

remains, the high point of which forms a small butte. This is called a "pembina" by Crickmay (1960) after an example on the Pembina River of Alberta, Canada.

Rʜᴏᴅᴇs W. Fᴀɪʀʙʀɪᴅɢᴇ

References

Blache, J., 1939–40, "Le problème des méandres encaissés et les rivières lorraines," *J. Geomorphol.,* **2,** 201–212; **3,** 311–331.

Cole, W. S., 1930, "The interpretation of intrenched meanders," *J. Geol.,* **38,** 423–436.

Fɪɢ. 3. Incised meanders at "The Goosenecks" on the San Juan River in southern Utah. Cut in resistant limestones to a depth of 260 meters, one of the meanders here measures 14 km in a loop that brings it back to 1 km from itself. (Photo: R. W. Fairbridge)

Cole, W. S., 1937, "Modifications of incised meanders by floods," *J. Geol.*, **45,** 648–654.

Cotton, C. A., 1952, "Geomorphology," sixth ed., New York, John Wiley & Sons, 505pp.

Crickmay, C. H., 1960, "Lateral activity in a river of northwestern Canada," *J. Geol.*, **68**(4), 377–391.

Davis, W. M., 1906, "Incised meandering valleys," *Geog. Soc. Philadelphia, Bull. 4.*

Dury, G. H., 1959, "The Face of the Earth," London, Penguin, 223pp.

Dury, G. H., 1960, "Misfit streams; problems in interpretation, discharge, and distribution," *Geog Rev.,* **50,** 219–242.

Miller, A. A., 1935, "The entrenched meanders of the Herefordshire Wye," *Geogr. J.*, **75,** 160–178.

Rich, J. L., 1914, "Certain types of stream valleys and their meaning," *J. Geol.*, **22,** 469–497.

Sparks, B. W., 1960, "Geomorphology," London, Longmans Green and Co.; New York, John Wiley & Sons, 371pp.

Thornbury, W. D., 1954, "Principles of Geomorphology," New York, John Wiley & Sons, 618pp.

Troll, C., 1954, "Über Alter und Bildung von Talmäandern," *Erdkunde,* **8,** 286–302.

Wooldridge, S. W., and Morgan, R. S., 1959, "An Outline of Geomorphology," Second ed., London, Longmans, Green & Co.

Cross-references: *Drainage Patterns; Rivers; Rivers— Meandering and Braiding; Slipoff Slope; Trumpet Valley.*

INDICATOR BOULDER

An indicator boulder is an erratic used in glaciology or glacial geology for determining the source area and distance of travel for any given till complex. *Provenance* of boulders may become a form of intellectual guessing game and indeed geological practice. In Germany there was formerly a *Zeitschrift für Geschiebeforschung*—a journal dedicated to the erratic boulder enthusiasts, that has subsequently expanded to take in all the fascinating aspects of Quaternary Ice-Age and postglacial research. In North America the various divisions of the "Friends of the Pleistocene" share the same interests on a less formal level.

Indicator boulders frequently display a very broad dispersion and the expressions *boulder train* and *indicator fan* are appropriate. The critical feature of the indicator boulder is its distinctive appearance, unique mineral assemblage or characteristic fossils. In Ireland the discovery of rock suites

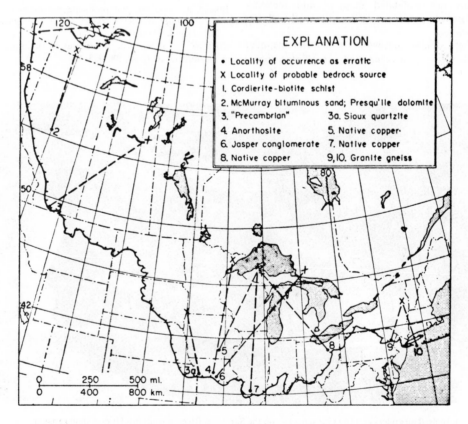

FIG. 1. Apparent paths of selected far-traveled indicators in North America, compiled from several sources (from Flint, 1957). (By permission of John Wiley & Sons, N.Y.)

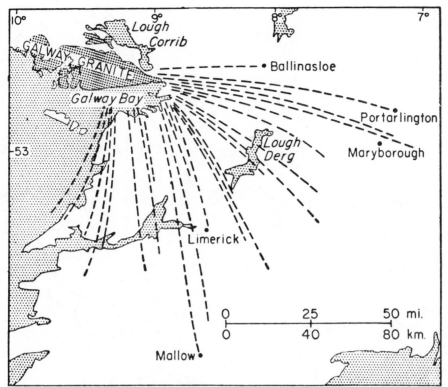

FIG. 2. Fanlike dispersal of indicators of Galway granite, across central Ireland. Inferred paths of travel (dashed lines) parallel other evidences of direction of glacier movement (after Charlesworth; from Flint, 1957). (By permission of John Wiley & Sons, N.Y.)

unique to the Oslo region of Norway proved that the ice had at one stage crossed not only the region of the North Sea but also the North of England and Irish Sea as well. Ailsa Crag is a uniquely distinctive granitic boss in the Firth of Clyde, Scotland, and its boulders or pebbles are found all down the east coast of Ireland and the west of Britain. Such boulders are usually characteristic of one till but not another and are thus used for correlation purposes.

In the southern Great Lakes region of North America, rare diamond pebbles have been found from Wisconsin to Ohio; vectors suggest a source in northwestern Ontario or adjacent Quebec, but so far it has not yet been discovered (Hobbs, 1910).

RHODES W. FAIRBRIDGE

References

Charlesworth, J. K., 1957, "The Quaternary Era," London, Edward Arnold, 2 vols.

Donner, J. J., 1965, "The Quaternary of Finland," in (Rankama, K., editor), "The Quaternary." New York, Interscience (John Wiley), Vol. I, 199–272.

Flint, R. F., 1957, "Glacial and Pleistocene Geology," New York, John Wiley & Sons, 553pp.

Hobbs, W. H., 1910, "The cycle of mountain glaciation," *Geograph. J.,* **36,** 146–163, 268–284.

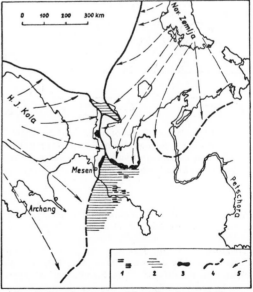

FIG. 3. Meeting point of Scandinavian and Novaya Zembla ice during the last glaciation in the Kanin Peninsula. (1) Marine deposits, (2) same postulated, (3) end moraines, (4) ice margins, (5) ice movement (after Rudovitz, 1947; from Woldstedt). (By permission of Ferdinand Enke Verlag, Stuttgart.)

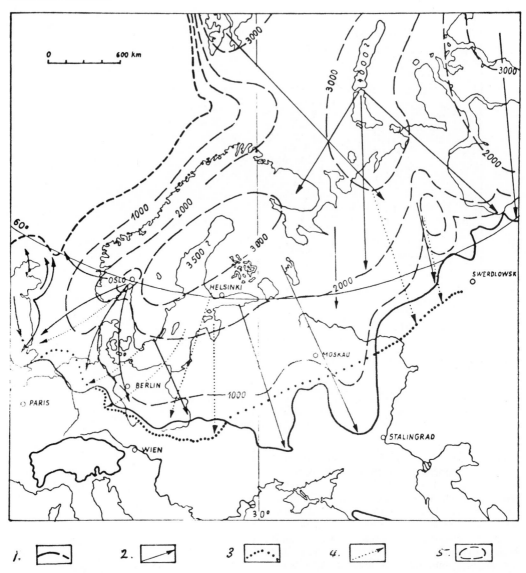

FIG. 4. Borders and ice movement (derived in part from indicator boulders) of the Saale (Riss = Illinoian) and Elster (Mindel = Kansan) ice in Europe. (1) Border of Saale ice, (2) Saale Movement direction, (3) Elster border, (4) Elster movement, (5) elevation contours of Saale ice (after S. A. Jakowlew, 1956; from Woldstedt). (By permission of Ferdinand Enke Verlag, Stuttgart.)

Milthers, V., 1936, "Geschiebeuntersuchungen und Glazialstratigraphie," *Z. Deut. Geol. Ges.,* **88,** 115–120.

Trefethen, J. M., and Harris, J. N., 1940, "A fossiliferous eskerlike deposit," *Am. J. Sci.,* **238,** 408–412.

Woldstedt, P., 1954–65, "Das Eiszeitalter," Stuttgart, Enke Verlag, 3 vols.

Wright, W. B., 1937, "The Quaternary Ice Age," Second ed., London, Macmillan, 478pp.

Cross-references: *Erratic Block; Glacial Geology; Great Lakes (North America); Quaternary Period.*

INDURATION

Induration is the process of hardening rocks through cementation of soil or porous rock, as one of the processes of diagenesis and lithification (see pr Vol. VI), or as a secondary effect of weathering (Merrill, 1897, p. 254); the latter is sometimes referred to as "case hardening." It is this aspect of induration that is particularly important in geomorphology. This near-surface induration is called "*epidiagenesis*" by the writer (Fairbridge, 1967). The term induration is also applied to the hardening that results from baking of sedimentary formations at igneous contacts by the heat of the intrusion (involving metasomatism and recrystallization as well as cementation: see *Petrology* in Vol. V of this series).

The chemical role of weathering involves principally the selective solution of material and the transport of those mobilized ions away in solution. This transport may be downward or laterally in the groundwater, resulting in a loss of mass and generally a loosening of individual grains near the surface. On the other hand, particularly in climatic belts where the potential evaporation exceeds precipitation, at least for certain parts of the year, the ions initially transported downward return to the surface by capillarity; then the water evaporates and precipitation occurs interstitially in the near-surface material (soil or weathered rock) forming a resistant crust, the *duricrust* (of Woolnough, 1927). Later on, further downward solutions add a veneer on the upper side of the crust. Local induration also occurs in some places where mineral-rich groundwater escapes, e.g., under artesian head as at mound springs.

Three chemical compounds are principally involved in induration: $CaCO_3$, Fe_2O_3 and SiO_2. Three important types of duricrust are thus formed, and they have received a large number of local names; this is possibly because they are essentially unknown in the mild temperate climates of classical geology in northwestern Europe and northeastern United States, whereas in the semiarid regions they are almost universal. In rare instances, the cement

FIG. 1. Subaerial and intertidal induration of eolian calcarenite. The upper level, a typical calcrete (caliche or soil travertine) conforms to the topography of the original calcareous sand dunes (Pleistocene). It is punctuated by calcrete-lined (karst) solution pipes, now exposed by differential weathering. A wide intertidal platform is exposed at low tide, and the soft eolianite indurated here by daily exposure and covering by the ocean; in this zone alternate induration and solution occur (see *Limestone Coastal Weathering*). Traces of a 3-meter mid-Holocene marine terrace, cut and indurated about 5000 years ago are also exposed, but partly obscured by landslides from the upper calcrete horizon. Example: Garden Island, Western Australia (The "Organ Pipes," Point Atwick).

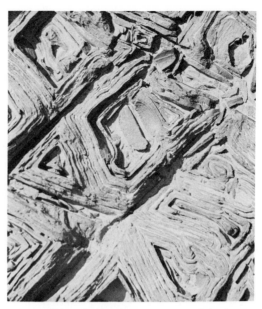

FIG. 2. Boxwork of ferricrete induration, following the joint pattern in a ferruginous sandstone of Permian age, Noonkanbah Station, Kimberley Div., Western Australia (Photo: R. W. Fairbridge).

is $CaSO_4 \cdot 2H_2O$, gypsum, or even $BaSO_4$, barite. Besides diverse mineralogy, the duricrusts have diverse structural forms: veneer crusts (built from above), capillary crust (built from below), scattered large concretions, soil pisolites, breccias ("soil pavements"), tubes and pipes, pseudomorphs after roots (rhizomorphs, rhizoconcretions) and so on. The chief induration rocktypes are as follows:

(a) *Calcrete* (Lamplugh, 1902), mainly of calcite, $CaCO_3$, also known as *calc-crust, soil travertine, tufa, caliche* (U.S. southwestern districts), *tepetape* (Mexico, an Aztec name), *nari* (Arabic), *kunkar* or *kankar* (India), etc.; another type of *caliche* from the desert regions of Peru and Chile is nitrate-rich. (These recementation features for carbonates are described in some detail in the article on *Corrosion*, q.v.; see Blank and Tynes, 1965; Bretz, 1960; Brown, 1956; Choubert, 1948; Gigout, 1960; Moseley, 1965; Ruhe, 1961, 1965; Rutte, 1958; see also Fig. 1.)

(b) *Ferricrete* (Lamplugh, 1902), and thus *ferri-crust*, mainly hematite, Fe_2O_3, but often associated with opaline silica, as well as the hydrated sesqui-oxides of iron and aluminum, limonite, goethite, gibbsite, etc. In the formerly French parts of North Africa, the term *ferralite* is used, to stress the mixture of iron, aluminum, and sometimes manganese and titanium as well (Auber, 1963). Merrill (1897, p. 256) mentions a North African crust that carried 37% Fe_2O_3, 31% MnO_2, 9% Al_2O_3, and 8% SiO_2. The metallic blackish stain often seen on *desert varnish* (q.v.) or as a patina marking the flood

FIG. 3. Silcrete surface of a Permian sandstone in the St. George Range, Kimberley Div., Western Australia. The dip is nearly horizontal and an earlier rectangular jointing (quartz filled) is intersected by vertical columnar jointing.

levels of the Nile and other semiarid-region rivers is mainly due to an iron-manganese oxide mixture. The geomorphically important crust on the land surface is often referred to by the French as the "*cuirasse de*

fer" (Maignien, 1958; Termier, 1961), the suit of armor, since it plays such a role in protecting the landscape from mechanical erosion and is indeed a major factor in differentiating subtropical pediplanation from humid peneplanation. The ferricrete crust most often crowns a weathering profile of laterite, but not necessarily. In some of the earlier literature, the crust is simply called "laterite" which is not good practice; a lateritic crust is essentially a *paleosol*, and reflects a polycyclic regime, usually as a result of repeated alternation of hot, humid conditions developing laterite, with dry, evaporating conditions favoring crust development. In transition zones (especially monsoon climates) there may be seasonal alternation of the two conditions.

Ferruginous sandstone tends to develop a very remarkable ferricrete induration along its normal joint planes, in the manner of a concentric "boxwork." This was illustrated by Merrill (1897, opposite p. 258, Pl. 20, No. 4). The writer discovered some parallel examples in northwestern Australia (Fig. 2). The successive layering is somewhat reminiscent of *liesegang rings* (see pr Vol. IV). Merrill (1897) also illustrates a zonally banded argillite, which appears to be the same phenomenon in a fine-grained claystone.

(c) *Silcrete* (Lamplugh, 1902), and thus also *silcrust*, quartz, often chalcedonic, SiO_2; or opal, the hydrated form. Sandstone formations primarily of quartz enjoy extreme durability in low latitudes, because frost action is their only important erosion agency. Quartz is relatively insoluble in tropical

FIG. 4. Hard carapace of indurated crust (reddish yellow in color from iron-stained silica) on a vertical Ordovician sandstone at Ayers Rock, central Australia. Here and there the crust has been eroded to expose the softer interior material to honeycomb or alveolar weathering (see also figures in *Inselberg, Tafoni,* and *Granite Landforms*).

FIG. 5. Alveolar weathering ("Tafoni") in the early Quaternary Bandelier Rhyolite Tuff, in the Bandelier National Monument, Frijoles Canyon, a branch of the Rio Grande, west of Santa Fe, New Mexico. Width of section shown in picture, about 4 meters. (Photo: R. W. Fairbridge).

rainwater, but when that water becomes enriched with respect to the alkaline salts (either brought in as "cyclic salts" from the sea or by solution of other minerals), a very high pH is developed in thin films of dew or interstitial water; at this high pH (9–10), the solubility of quartz rises to several hundred parts per million. Surface solution occurs, but since the dew or sporadic rain is rapidly evaporated once more, the silica is reprecipitated to form a crust of extraordinary durability. Many of the residual hills, inselbergs and mesas of central Africa and Australia are capped or coated by this quartzitic silcrete, and it seems to have protected them in some cases at least since the Mesozoic (Stephens, 1964; Mabbutt, 1965). The homogeneous silicification of some surfaces is so thorough that polygonal columnar jointing develops (Fig. 3). After this sort of induration, individual sand grains become almost welded together and the rock develops a conchoidal fracture, thus a true quartzite (defined as fracturing *across* the grains). A similar conchoidal fracture develops also in silicified shale crusts, the resultant rock being called a *porcellanite*.

In softer formations of quartz sands, groundwater has apparently been responsible for the formation of concretionary layers of silcrete. Under altered climatic conditions, the less competent beds erode away leaving these concretions scattered about the landscape. Since they are often about the size of old-fashioned woolsacks and are grayish white, they are popularly known (in Britain, Australia, western United States) as *graywethers* (greywethers), or *gray billy* (wethers = sheep, billy = slang for "billy goat"). If the silica-rich waters drain locally into a swamp, the result is often a site of magnificently preserved *fossil wood, opalized wood* or

"petrified forest," with even the finest cell structure faithfully represented. Patches of silcrete, found here and there around Salisbury Plain, England (where Eocene sands overlap the chalk) and in the west of France, were employed by Neolithic and Bronze Age Man to build dolmens, menhirs, megaliths and giant structures like Stonehenge. The reason for using these rocks was because they are flat and not too thick (about 1–1.5 meters) and cleave often into rectangular blocks. They are known in England as "sarsen stones" (from "Saracen," a term dating from the time of the Crusaders and implying "stranger," i.e., exotic to the area, Geikie, 1903, p. 464). Similar indurated blocks, but composed of aragonite-cemented calcarenite, originally *beachrock* (q.v.), were used by early Polynesians for the construction of "trilithons" and other megalithic structures on the island of Tonga-tabu and elsewhere in the South Pacific.

Two additional terms of less common induration cements are *gypcrete* (a gypsum cement, seen in some playa lake beachrock environment in very hot country), and *salcrete* (a sea salt or halite cement, usually of ephemeral significance, observed on beaches, Yasso, 1966; also on *sabkha*, q.v.).

In the weathering of granite, the chemical breakdown of feldspars liberates silica which then tends to form an iron-stained induration crust over the rest of the granite surface. The result is often the curious anomaly of hollow depressions (see *Tafoni*), "honeycomb" or "alveolar weathering," alternating with extremely hard carapaces. Merrill (1897, p. 255) mentions that the nature of this process was probably first recognized by Choffat in Portugal (1896). This same principle applies to the development of the alveolar weathering in *volcano-karst* (q.v.; see also Fig. 4).

Another major cause of induration is the modification of the solution chemistry by a change in the groundwater regime. For example, the replacement of (or precipitation on) limestone by chert at depth, with silica liberated in alteration of montmorillonite to kaolinite (Altschuler, Dwornik and Kramer, 1963).

RHODES W. FAIRBRIDGE

References

Altschuler, Z. S., Dwornik, E. J., and Kramer, H., 1963, "Transformation of montmorillonite to kaolinite during weathering," *Science*, **141**, 148–152.

Auber, G., 1963, "Soils with ferruginous or ferralitic crusts of tropical regions," *Soil Sci.*, **95**(4), 235–242.

Blank, H. R., and Tynes, E. W., 1965, "Formation of caliche *in situ*," *Bull. Geol. Soc. Am.*, **76**(12), 1387–1391.

Bretz, J Harlan, 1960, "Bermuda: a partially drowned, late mature, Pleistocene karst," *Bull. Geol. Soc. Am.*, **71**, 1729–1754.

Brown, C. N., 1956, "The origin of caliche on the

north-eastern Llano Estacado, Texas," *J. Geol.*, **64**, 1–15.

Choffat, P., 1896, "Sur quelques cas d'erosion atmospherique dans les granite du Minho," *Comm. Dir. Trab. Geol. Portugal*, **3**(1), for 1895–96, 17.

Choubert, G., 1948, "Au sujet des croûtes calcaires quaternaires," *Compt. Rend. Acad. Sci. Paris*, **226**, 1630–1631.

Fairbridge, R. W., 1964, "The Importance of Limestone and its Ca/Mg Content to Palaeoclimatology," in "Problems in Palaeoclimatology," pp. 431–477, New York, Interscience Publishers.'

Fairbridge, R. W., 1967, "Phases of Diagenesis and Authigenesis," in (Larsen, G., and Chilingar, G. V., editors) "Diagenesis," Amsterdam, Elsevier, 19–89.

Geikie, A., 1903, "Text-book of Geology," London, Macmillan, 2 vols. (First ed., 1882).

Gigout, M., 1960, "Sur la genèse des croûtes calcaires pléistocènes en Afrique du Nord," *Compt. Rend. Somm. Soc. Géol. France*, 8.

Lamplugh, G. W., 1902, "Calcrete," *Geol. Mag.*, **9**, 575 (letter).

Mabbutt, J. A., 1965, "The weathered land surface in Central Australia," *Z. Geomorphol.*, **9**(1), 82–114.

Maignien, R., 1958, "Le cuirassement des sols en Guinée, Afrique occidentale," *Mem. Serv. Carte Geol. Alsace Lorraine*, **16**.

Merrill, G. P., 1897, "A Treatise on Rocks, Rock-weathering and Soils," New York, The Macmillan Co., 411pp.

Moseley, F., 1965, "Plateau calcrete, calcreted gravels, cemented dunes and related deposits of the Maallegh-Bomba region of Libya," *Z. Geomorphol.*, **9**, 166–185.

Roth, J., 1879, "Allgemeine und chemische Geologie," Berlin, Hertz, 2 vols.

Ruhe, R. V., 1965, "Quaternary Paleopedology," in (Wright, H. E., Jr., and Frey, D. G., editors) "The Quaternary of the United States," pp. 755–764, Princeton, N.J., Princeton University Press.

Ruhe, R. V., Cady, J. G., and Gomez, R. S., 1961, "Paleosols of Bermuda," *Bull. Geol. Soc. Am.*, **72**, 1121–1141.

Rutte, E., 1958, "Kalkkrusten in Spanien," *Neues Jahrb. Geol. Palaeontol., Abhandl.*, **106**, 52–138.

Stamp, L. D. (editor), 1961, "A Glossary of Geographical Terms," London, Longmans, Green, 539pp.

Stephens, C. G., 1964, "Silcretes of Central Australia," *Nature*, **203**, p. 1407.

Termier, H., and Termier, G., 1961, "L'Evolution de la Lithosphere: III Glyptogénèse," Paris, Masson & Cie, 471pp.

Woolnough, W. G., 1927, (I) "The chemical criteria of peneplanation. (II) The duricrust of Australia," *J. Roy. Soc. N.S. Wales*, **61**, 1–23, 24–53.

Yasso, W. E., 1966, "Heavy mineral concentration and sastrugi-like deflation furrows in a beach salcrete at Rockaway Point, New York," *J. Sed. Petrol.*, **36**(3), 836–838.

Cross-references: *Beachrock*; *Corrosion*; *Desert Varnish*; *Duricrust*; *Granite Landforms*; *Inselberg*; *Limestone Coastal Weathering*; *Playa*; *Sabkha*; *Tafoni*; *Volcano-Karst.*   Vol. II: *Capillarity.* pr Vol. IV: *Liesegang Rings.* pr Vol. V: *Petrology.* pr Vol. VI: *Caliche*; *Diagenesis*; *Groundwater*; *Laterization and Rubefication*; *Paleosol*; *pH-Eh Relations*; *Salts—Cyclic.*

INSELBERG

Residual uplands which stand in isolation above the general level of the surrounding plains in tropical regions are called *inselbergs*. Inselbergs display considerable morphological variation, but whether they take the form of extensive ridges, ranges or isolated hills, they project starkly, abruptly and dramatically above the flatness of the surrounding plains: hence their name. Unquestionably the most spectacular inselbergs are the dome-shaped monoliths known as *bornhardts* (q.v.), of which examples are known from every continent save Antarctica but which are best developed, and most clearly and abundantly displayed, in the tropical lands.

Inselbergs have been sculptured from a variety of rock types. In central Australia, for instance, in the areas adjoining the border between the Northern Territory and South Australia, many ridges, ranges and massive monolithic rocks protrude above the vast sand and gibber plains. Some, such as the Indulkana Ranges are built of tilted or subhorizontal sedimentary rocks; others, like the western Everards are underlain by granitoid complexes or, as in the Musgraves, by complexes of igneous and metamorphic crystalline rocks. There are three justly famous isolated inselbergs in the southern part of the Northern Territory each standing over 1000 feet above the central plain level. Mt. Conner is a flat-topped hill formed of gently dipping quartzites; to the west is Ayers Rock ("the biggest single gibber in the world") which is a massive, monolithic flattish-topped dome of arkosic grit; and still further westward is perhaps the most fantastic and strange of them all, the Olgas, a group of weirdly shaped domes composed of massive conglomerate.

Although inselberg ridges and ranges are underlain by a wide variety of resistant rock types, domed inselbergs are especially common in granitic terrain (though as has been indicated they have formed also on other lithological types). Examples have been described from such diverse areas as Newfoundland and Lapland; the American West and Southwest, Georgia and New England; the deserts of northern Chile and the humid coastlands of Brazil; Korea, Siam and Corsica; and many climatically contrasted regions of the African continent.

Inselbergs were first named from arid Africa, and the "sugarloafs" of the Rio area of coastal southern Brazil are renowned. In the United States, the Yosemite region is famous for its granitic domes; Stone Mountain, Georgia, and Looking Glass Rock, North Carolina, are other well-known domed mountains. In part, the reason for the widespread occurrence of the form on granite is that it is a common and extensively outcropping constituent of the continental areas, but the

FIG. 1. Ayers Rock, Central Australia, Precambrian, steeply dipping arkosic sandstone. Mount Olga, with gigantic spheroidal weathering forms stands above the sand dune-covered etchplain in the background. (Courtesy South Australian Tourist Bureau, Adelaide.)

structure of granite also renders it especially prone to inselberg development. The morphology and development of granite inselbergs illustrates many general points which are true of non-granitic forms also.

Although they are dome shaped and give the impression of roundness in plan, many granite bornhardts are in fact composed of a single, or of a number of, massive rectangular or rhomboidal blocks bounded by major joints. In South Australia it has been shown that major joints, which deter-mine the outlines of the domes in plan, but which are not the only joints in the rock mass, run parallel to certain regional tectonic trends called *lineaments*, which always represent the major structural lines of every continent. Joints paralleling lineament trends also play a significant part in determining the detailed sculpture of the domes. Viewed from the side, the morphology of many domes is determined by the development of several more or less concentric and massive rock sheets or shells, which vary in thickness between

FIG. 2. Steepened basal slopes of granite inselberg caused by subsurface weathering and subsequent exposure of the weathering front. Pildappa Hill, South Australia. But note double concavity of steepened slope. Low wall was built to direct runoff from the hill into a storage tank. Area now has a temperate climate. (Photo: C. R. Twidale.)

FIG. 3. Steepened basal slope of inselberg at Ucontitchie Hill, South Australia. (Photo: C. R. Twidale.)

one and several scores of feet. These shells impart a dome-like form in section to many of the bornhardts. Many workers believe that the shells have developed as a consequence of offloading or release of vertical pressure by erosion; others see in the shells a manifestation of vertical and lateral pressures, i.e., of tectonism.

Some of these thick massive shells have broken down to more or less rectangular joint blocks; and on the upper surface and flanks of the domes weather pits or *gnammas*, caverns or *tafoni*, and grooves or gutters are developed by weathering and erosion. Many of these features, large and small, are typical of granitic outcrops, but they are not confined to them. The outline of Ayers Rock, for example, is apparently determined by major joints; caverns, gnammas and gutters are developed in profusion on its surface, and the same is true of the Olgas.

Inselbergs are not the tropical equivalents of the monadnocks of humid temperate lands. Certainly some residuals termed inselbergs are morphologically identical with monadnocks, and it is confusing, to say the least, to differentiate forms merely on the basis of present climatic regions. However typical inselbergs rise more abruptly from the plains than do typical monadnocks. The abruptness of the hill-plain junction is thus critical to any understanding of inselbergs. The cause of the sharp, in some cases angular, transition from plain to upland is partly structural. Granitic rocks are subdivided into joint blocks, but whereas some are closely jointed, in others the joints are widely spaced. As ground water penetrates primarily along joint planes, weathering of closely jointed masses is much more rapid and intense than areas that are but sparsely jointed. The rock tends to be

weathered compartmentally: some areas are disintegrated and decayed; other, joint-bounded areas remain virtually fresh. Thus when erosion occurs, the weathered areas remain untouched and form upstanding masses bounded by major joints and hence are usually steep sided—inselbergs. It is important to appreciate that the rocks of the inselbergs and those underlying the plains or valleys may well be mineralogically and texturally identical, but the structure and, particularly, the joint spacing of the respective areas differ markedly. In the Tomkinson Ranges, of the far northwest of South Australia for instance, the basic crystalline rocks of the ranges are the same as those of the valley floors, but whereas the former are merely well jointed, the latter are much shattered and traversed by numerous joints and faults.

A second reason for the abrupt hill-plain junction is to be found in the topographic distribution of weathering in arid lands particularly. The greatest amount of weathering (hydration and hydrolysis) occurs low on the topography and especially adjacent to uplands. Hence, these piedmont areas are susceptible to intense dissection, and in this way steep escarpments tend to be maintained. A third reason for the sharp break of slope between hill and plain is that plains and valleys in arid lands are commonly blanketed beneath considerable thicknesses of consolidated detritus which masks the bedrock floor and laps up against the bounding rock walls. The valleys of the Musgrave Ranges are buried to a depth of up to 150 feet of unconsolidated alluvium, colluvium and eolian debris. A similar situation obtains in the Gawler Ranges in southern South Australia.

Thus, several factors contribute to this distinctive feature of inselbergs, but whereas burial and the differential weathering of lower slopes are restricted to arid lands, structural effects recognize no climatic boundaries. Also, climates know few geographic limits. The fact that bornhardts have been described from every climatic region, including the Arctic and Subarctic (Lapland and Newfoundland), is a measure of the significance of the structural factor in the development of the inselberg form, as well as of the importance of climatic mobility.

C. R. TWIDALE

References

Birot, P., 1958, "Les dômes crystallins," *Mem. Doc. C.N.R.S.*, **6**, 9–34.

King, L. C., 1949, "A theory of bornhardts," *Geograph. J.*, **112**, 83–87.

Twidale, C. R., 1964, "Contribution to the general theory of domed inselbergs. Conclusions derived from observations in South Australia," *Trans. Papers Inst. Brit. Geogr.* **34**, 91–113.

Wilhelmy, H., 1958, "Der Klimamorphologie der Massengesteine," Braunschweig, G. Westermann, 238pp.

Cross-references: *Alluvium; Bornhardt; Colluvium; Etchplain; Gibber; Granite Landforms; Monadnock; Solution Pits and Pans; Spheroidal Weathering; Tafoni; Tropical Weathering and Relief.*

INSEQUENT VALLEY, STREAM—*See* DRAINAGE PATTERNS; RIVERS

INSTRUMENT CONTOUR DIAGRAMS

Early twentieth century exploration of mineral concessions was a complex undertaking often involving large areas which formed significant fractions of continents. Exploration of the Antarctic during recent years has been much more complex, expensive and demanding than earlier explorations, requiring multi-man, multi-vehicle systems. Current explorations of the solar system by unmanned systems, and increasingly by manned systems dwarfs the expenditures for the study of the Antarctic continent and its environment (Ehrick, 1968). The International Geophysical Year may be the last major exploratory effort planned almost exclusively by panels and specialists.

The concept of instrument contour diagramming (Hovnanian, 1966) was devised to aid formalized space mission planning. It is very useful when trade-off studies are necessary on unmanned or manned planetary fly-by, planetary orbit, or planetary landing missions. Such vehicles may be equipped with sensors which range through men, cameras, cosmic particle counters, micrometeorite counters, radars, lasers, electric field detectors, mass spectrographs, etc. A sensor could deal with such complex results

as the analyses of chemical and geophysical measurements along complex traverses, and even gravitational perturbations of a vehicle's path.

Instrument contour diagrams indicate the degree of resolution possible for any mode of sensing, including field, photon, wave energy, bulk-messenger, or hapatic (see the article on *Signature Theory*) as a function of the instrument's resolving power. The resolving power of the instrument is further conditioned by the path of the platform which carries the sensor, noises and interference along the path of information transfer, and distance of the observed object. Resolution is still further conditioned by rates of movement of the observer and the observed (Miller and Enzmann, 1966).

Instrument contour diagrams can be used to indicate the ability of Electromagnetic sensors in orbit to distinguish what are essentially features of a planetary surface and ability of particle sensors on the surface to distinguish external features. Diagrams indicating the resolvability of lithospheric (planetary crust), endospheric (planetary interior), hydrospheric (oceanic), and atmospheric features, look very similar. The diagrams indicate, at a glance, approximately what may be expected of an instrument in a fly-by mode, in orbit about a planet, in flight in a planet's atmosphere, or traversing the planet's surface (Enzmann, 1968).

ROBERT DUNCAN ENZMANN

References

Ehrick, K. A., 1968, in "Second conference concerning planetology and space mission planning," *Ann. N.Y. Acad. Sci.* (in press).

Enzmann, R. D., 1968, "Use of Space Systems for Planetary Geology and Geophysics," American Astronautical Society, Technology Series (in press).

Hovnanian, H. P., 1966, "Biotic signatures," in "Planetology and space mission planning," *Ann. N.Y. Acad. Sci.*, **140**(1), 294–306.

Miller, R., and Enzmann, R., 1966, "Space mission planning," in "Planetology and space mission planning," *Ann. N.Y. Acad. Sci.*, **140**(1), 586–591.

Cross-references: *Geomorphology—Expanded Theory; Signature Theory; Terrain.*

INTERFLUVE

An interfluve is, in *sensu strictu*, the land between two rivers (Latin *inter.* between, *fluvius*, rivers). In the "Glossary of Geographical Terms" (L. D. Stamp, editor), it is noted that the term has slipped into common usage without ever having been precisely defined. W. M. Davis (1899) in what is apparently the earliest geomorphic use refers to "... the interfluviatile strips..." in the dissection of young coastal plains.

Many geomorphologists today use the term for

the interstream area to imply a discrete landscape or geomorphic unit, composed of uni- or polycyclic slope facets. Interfluve almost always appears in a phrase explicitly or implicitly denoting its dissection. Kendall, Glendinning and MacFadden (1958) represent the extreme form of this approach and refer to interfluves as youthful, mature and old-age interfluves.

DAVID S. SIMONETT

References

Davis, W. M., 1899, "The drainage of cuestas," *Proc. Geol. Assoc. London*, **16**, 75–93.

Kendall, H. M., Glendinning, R. M. and MacFadden, C. H., 1958, "Introduction to Geography," Second ed., pp. 194–196, New York, Harcourt, Brace and Company.

Stamp, L. D. (editor), 1961, "A Glossary of Geographical Terms," London, Longmans, Green & Co., 539pp.

Cross-references: *Cycles, Geomorphic.*

INTERNATIONAL GEOGRAPHICAL UNION —See INTERNATIONAL ORGANIZATIONS FOR GEOMORPHOLOGY

INTERNATIONAL ORGANIZATIONS FOR GEOMORPHOLOGY

International organizations which serve the science of geomorphology tend to be numerous because of the interdisciplinary nature of the subject and because of regional affiliations. For example in North America, geomorphology is largely studied and taught by geologists; only a handful of universities or colleges offer sophisticated courses in geomorphology within departments of geography. In Europe, in contrast, the situation is largely reversed and the rigorous centers of geomorphic training are almost always under the auspices of geography. Further, where there are separate faculties of arts, science and engineering, the geography school is usually on the arts side, the geology with science or engineering. Those planning curricula to embrace a proper scientific background for geomorphology (in this writer's opinion, for one) should include at least twelve (twelve-week) terms of geology, four of chemistry, four of physics, as well as some biology, soil science and engineering (cartography, soil testing, hydraulics). Since soil science may only be offered in an agricultural school, there are further difficulties. An organization that provides the right background for this sort of discipline is thus faced by almost schizophrenic problems.

The historical fact is that of the various international bodies offering shelter to geomorphology, the *International Geographical Union* has furnished the longest record of service. The Union itself was organized in Brussels in 1922, but long prior to that, since 1871, there have been International Geographical Congresses, which now meet concurrently with the Union approximately every four years (see Meynen, 1960).

The Union publishes a regular *I.G.U. Newsletter*, while the Congress abstracts and reports are usually published independently by the host countries and the commission reports are usually published or circulated privately by commission presidents and secretaries.

I.G.U. Commissions

Of particular interest to geomorphologists are the large number of commissions of the I.G.U. devoted to their special problems. While these vary from time to time, as does their personnel, the following list may serve to guide the reader to what is in progress and who are some of the specialists:

Commission on Karst Phenomena
Chairman: H. Lehmann; A. Bögli, J. Corbel, N. A. Gwozdeckij, G. Morandini, J. Roglic, G. T. Warwick. Corresponding members: F. Bauer, S. Gilewska, G. Nangeroni, B. Smyk, M. Sweeting, P. Z. Szabo, H. Trimmel, H. T. Verstappen, J. Zötl, A. Gerstenhauer. (It may be noted that there are furthermore several national and international organizations that promote congresses and publications in *Speleology* and *Karstology*.)

Commission for the Study of the Evolution of Slopes
Chairman: P. Macar; J. P. Bakker, P. Birot, H. Mortensen, A. N. Strahler, S. A. Huzzayin, L. C. King, D. L. Linton, L. C. Peltier, L. Solé-Sabaris. The latest (third) report of this commission has appeared as "Neue Beiträge zur internationalen Hangforschung" edited by H. Mortensen [*Nachr. Akad. Wiss., Goettingen, Math.-Physik. Kl., II* (1963) 293pp.]. Following a symposium organized at Liège in 1966 P. Macar edited "L'évolution des versants" (Liège, *Lab. Géogr. Phys.*, 374pp).

Commission on the Arid Zone
Chairman: P. Meigs; D. H. K. Amiran, H. Awad, J. Dresch, E. M. Murzaev, R. F. Peel. An important outcome of their recent activity was a statement on recommended methods of classifying the geomorphology of arid lands prepared by a subcommittee headed by F. Dixey [*I.G.U. Newsletter*, **14**(1), 5–11 (1963)]. The arid zone, in particular, receives a great deal of attention from geomorphologists because of its physical problems for human settlement, and UNESCO allocates a large budget to its study, including the publishing of an extensive *Arid Zone Research* series of volumes, as well as a periodical newsletter *Arid Zone*. The commission sponsors international meetings, usually with the support of UNESCO and of the governments concerned. The one in Crete (1962) dealt with geomorphology and land use in Mediterranean semiarid lands; and one in Peru (1967) dealt with coastal deserts of the world: climate, the effects of

runoff on terrain, and land use. The papers from the Crete meeting were published in two volumes: geomorphology in *Bulletin de la Société hellénique de Géographie*, ser. 3, vol. 4, Athens (1963), 203pp; and land use in *Arid Zone Research*, vol. 26, UNESCO, Paris (1964), 170pp. (The papers from the Peru meeting are expected to be published in the UNESCO series.) Another volume, on the geography of coastal deserts, has been published by P. Meigs, *Arid Zone Research*, vol. 28, UNESCO, Paris (1966), 140pp. So much attention has been given to coastal deserts because the recent improvement in desalination of sea water makes these deserts more habitable.

Commission on Periglacial Geomorphology

President: J. Dylik. Secretary: R. Raynal. Regular members: A. Cailleux, L. Hamelin, K. K. Markov, T. L. Péwé. Corresponding members: J. Alexandre, R. F. Black, B. Bout, C. Capello, A. Corte, P. Cotet, A. Dylikowa, R. W. Galloway, F. Gullentops, G. Hoppe, A. Jahn, L. Kádár, K. Kobayashi, G. C. Maarleveld, P. Macar, H. Mensching, T. Morariu; G. Nangeroni, A. Popov, H. Poser, A. Rapp, J. Sekyra, L. Sole-Sabaris, J. Tricart, A. Washburn, R. S. Waters, K. Wiche. A subcommission on terminology has been formed.

An important publication in this field that appears regularly, edited by J. Dylik in Poland, is the *Biuletyn Peryglacjalny*; the bulk of its papers are in English and French.

Commission on National Atlases

Chairman: K. A. Salichtchev; C. P. Barnes, S. P. Chatterjee, E. Imhof, S. Rado, O. C. Tulippe. Corresponding members: O. Hedbom, R. Joly, I. du Jonchay, J. Kondracki, K. Kuchař, E. Lehmann, A. Libault, N. L. Nicholson, Y. Ogasawara, T. W. Plumb, F. Vasquez Maure, E. Willats.

Formed in 1956, this commission has played an important role in stimulating and coordinating the production of regional and national atlases, a large number of which are now in preparation. Most of those that have appeared to date carry useful geological and geomorphological maps. Numbers of these atlases issue sheets one by one, to be added to a peg binder or similar system. One of the interesting features of each I.G.U. congress are the colorful exhibits of the new maps.

Commision for the Study and Correlation of Erosion Surfaces (around the Atlantic)

Chairman: F. Ruellan; Marguerite Lefevre, O. Ribeiro, E. Brown, M. G. S. Ganichine, R. W. Fairbridge. Since 1960 an attempt has been made to extend the commission work to the *islands* of the Atlantic, and further to the Mediterranean, the North Sea and the Baltic. Attention is also given to (now) submarine erosion surfaces and to the problem of cartography (Ruellan, *Ann. Géogr.*, **70**, 481–485).

Commission of Coastal Geomorphology

Originally called the Commission on Coastal Sedimentation (1952), the present name was adopted in 1960.

Chairman: A. Schou; C. Kidson, A. Guilcher, R. J. Russell, V. P. Zenkovitch. Corresponding members: I. Asensio, H. Awad, A. Ayala-Castañares, J. P.

Bakker, R. Battistini, J. B. Bird, E. C. F. Bird, J. Chebataroff, T. R. Cordini, K. Darmojuwono, J. Davidsson, J. V. Eade, A. Farrington, M. Feio, H. Fuenzalida, A. O. Fuller, B. Fristrup, R. Galon, H. G. Gierloff-Emden, O. Granö, F. Gullentops, H. Holtedahl, M. Hukku, H. Inandik, F. Karim Khan, S. Massip, F. Ottmann, N. Panin, J. C. Pugh, H. O'Reilly Sternberg, H. Reinhardt, Ali Ibne Hamis Rizvi, J. Roglić, E. Romero, A. V. Roshdestvensky, I. Schattner, A. Sestini, N. Stephens, D. R. Stoddart, B. Swann, W. F. Tanner, S. Thorarinsson, H. Valentin, S. K. El Wakeel, T. Yoshikawa, J. I. S. Zonneveld.

One of the most helpful activities of this commission is a series of very comprehensive bibliographies on coastal geomorphology. The one for 1959–63, issued by the Geographical Institute, University of Copenhagen, as *Folia Geogr. Danica*, **10**(1), (1964), 68pp. That for 1964–68 is being edited by A. Guilcher. In addition, numbers of local conferences and field meetings have been organized. This field is particularly complicated by problems of interdisciplinary interests, since there are similar commissions in the *International Union of Geodesy and Geophysics* (Association of Physical Oceanography; Nearshore Oceanography, chairman, V. P. Zenkovitch) and in the *International Union for Quaternary Research* (Shorelines Commission chairman: R. W. Fairbridge). Different aspects, however, are stressed, and duplication of effort is avoided by some exchange of data. A related organization of engineers is the *Council for Wave Research* of Berkeley, California.

Commission for Applied Geomorphology

Chairman: J. Tricart; secretary, H. T. Verstappen. Subcommission for Geomorphological Mapping: chairman, M. Klimaszewski. Subcommission for Fluvial Dynamics: chairman, L. B. Leopold; J. P. Bakker, N. Nielsen. Corresponding members, 31.

The commission meets annually to consider current problems and treatments, especially dealing with urban sites, conservation, irrigation, transport routes, and also interdisciplinary questions concerning pedology, agronomy, photointerpretation, city planning, and rural engineering.

Geomorphic mapping is a relatively new science (see separate article in this volume), but notable advances have been made in recent years toward an agreed, international system, largely due to cooperation between workers in Poland, Hungary, U.S.S.R., France and Canada. Numbers of other countries are now beginning to take an interest in this important field. Stress is being laid on mapping at 1:50,000 scale or better. The work has been reported in "Problems of Geomorphological Mapping" issued by the Polish Geographical Institute (1963, Prace, No. 46, 179pp.). Small-scale geomorphic maps of all major regions and continents in the world may now be found in the Russian "Physico-Geographical World Atlas" (Moscow, Akad. Nauk, 1964), a translation of which has been issued by the American Geographical Society.

A further area of concern for this commission is *fluvial dynamics*, especially through the UNESCO organization, the *International Hydrological Decade* (q.v., Vol. VI). The question of hydrological mapping is closely related to that of geomorphic maps. UNESCO issues a periodical newsletter *Nature and Resources*.

Other Commissions of I.G.U. This is not the place for a complete review of I.G.U. activities, but worth noting are some other commissions of possible interest to certain geomorphologists:

Commission on a World Land Use Survey.
Commission on the Teaching of Geography in Schools.
Commission on a World Population Map.
Commission on Early Maps.
Commission on Medical Geography (see pr Vol. VI).
Commission on the Classification of Books and Maps in Libraries.
Commission on Methods of Economic Regionalization.
Special Commission on Humid Tropics.
Special Commission on Cartography.

Other Organizations That Include Geomorphology

(1) International Union of Geological Sciences. For about a century the International Geological Congresses, and now since 1960 the I.U.G.S., have attended to the international coordination of geological matters. While important geomorphological papers are often found in the congress proceedings (available in most of the better libraries), there is rarely much attention paid to geomorphology as such. On the other hand, the Geological Union is clearly responsible for matters dealing with the chronology and stratigraphy of the Quaternary Period, i.e., approximately the last two million years, the time during which much of the present landscape was molded. Thus, for example, at the Eighteenth Congress (London, 1948) there was a special discussion with a proceedings volume (part 9 of the Report) on "The Pliocene–Pleistocene Boundary," and at the Twentieth Congress (Copenhagen, 1960) there was a special volume (part 4) on "Chronology and Climatology of the Quaternary."

The Union also maintains an *International Commission of Stratigraphy*, which is extremely active. A major service is performed by the *Subcommission on the Stratigraphic Lexicon* (under J. Roger) which has issued dozens of regional stratigraphic lexicons for all parts of the world and every period. Those volumes including the Quaternary should be closely consulted by geomorphologists who are concerned with any chronological matters.

The Union also maintains a subcommission on the *Quaternary Stratigraphy*, but this group has largely referred its activities to the INQUA (see below).

(2) International Union for Quarternary Research (INQUA) This Union (from its inception in 1928 to 1965 an "Association") has as its purpose the co-ordination and encouragement of international interdisciplinary research on the Quaternary Epoch. It is governed by an International Executive Committee of seven (current president: G. M. Richmond, U.S.A., secretary treasurer: S. van der Heide, Netherlands) and by an International Council consisting of one representative from each member nation. Congresses are held every four years at the invitation of, and under the organization of a host country. INQUA adheres to the International Union for Geological Sciences (IUGS) and adherence to the International Geographical Union (IGU) is pending. INQUA also maintains liaison commissions with the International Union of Biological Sciences (IUBS) and the International Union of Prehistoric and Protohistoric Sciences (IUPPS).

INQUA does not represent all interests of any single discipline, but rather the common interest in the environment and history of the Quaternary Epoch of each of many disciplines. Major disciplines represented include archaeology, climatology, ecology, geomorphology, glaciology, limnology, paleontology, palynology, physical geology, Quaternary geology, oceanography, soil science, and volcanology.

The history of INQUA Congresses has been as follows:

INQUA

I	1928	Copenhagen
II	1932	Leningrad
III	1936	Vienna
IV	1953	Rome and Pisa
V	1957	Madrid and Barcelona
VI	1961	Warsaw
VII	1965	Denver, Colorado
VIII	1969	Paris

INQUA maintains a number of temporary research commissions:

1. Quaternary shorelines (chairman: R. W. Fairbridge, U.S.A.), with five regional subcommissions.
2. Nomenclature and correlation of the Quaternary (chairman: F. Gullentops, Belgium). Subcommissions: (a) Lower boundary of the Pleistocene (chairman: V. P. Gritchuk, U.S.S.R.). (b) The Holocene (chairman: B. P. Hageman, Netherlands), (c) The loess stratigraphy of Europe (chairman: J. Fink, Austria), (d) Stratigraphy of ocean sediments (chairman: C. Emiliani, U.S.A.).
3. Neotectonics (chairman: N. I. Nikolaev, U.S.S.R.).
4. Origin and lithology of Quaternary deposits (co-chairmen: E. V. Shanzer, U.S.S.R., and B. Krygowski, Poland).
5. Absolute age of Quaternary deposits (chairman: E. H. Willis, U.S.A.).
6. The Quaternary map of Europe (chairman: P. Woldstedt, Germany).
7. Quaternary regional maps (chairman: G. M. Richmond, U.S.A.). Subcommissions: (a) Quaternary map of N.W. Africa (chairman: H. Alimen, France), (b) Paleogeographical atlas of the Quaternary (chairman: K. Markov, U.S.S.R.).
8. Tephrochronology (chairman: K. Kobayashi, Japan).
9. Paleopedology (chairman: I. P. Gerasimov, U.S.S.R.).
10. Quaternary biology (chairman: W. Mullenders, Belgium). Commission is also liaison body with IUBS.
11. Man in the Quaternary (chairman: L. Balout,

France). This Commission is also liaison body with I.U.P.P.S.

At the meetings a great deal of attention is given to geomorphological problems, and this organization must now be regarded as the primary world body for geomorphology.

RHODES W. FAIRBRIDGE

References

Dylik, J. (editor), 1965, *Report of the VIth International Congress on Quaternary, Warsaw,* 1961, Lodz, 4 vols.
Meynen, E., 1960, "Orbis Geographicus 1960," Wiesbaden, F. Steiner Verl.; also 1964/66, ditto (lists of societies, institutes, agencies and personal addresses, worldwide).
Watson, J. W. (editor), 1967, *Twentieth International Geographical Congress (U.K.),* London, Nelson, 401pp.

Cross-references: *Geography: Concept, Growth, and Status; Geomorphic Maps; Holocene; Loess; Neotectonics; Quaternary Period.* Vol. VI: *International Hydrological Decade; International Union of Geological Sciences; Medical Geography; Medical Geology.*

INTERNATIONAL UNION OF GEOLOGICAL SCIENCES—*See* pr Vol. VI

INTERNATIONAL UNIONS AND CONGRESSES (of the Earth Sciences)—*See* pr Vol. VI

INTERSECTING PENEPLAINS—*See* EXHUMED LANDSCAPE; MORVAN

INTERTIDAL ZONATION—*See* pr Vol. VI, LITTORAL SEDIMENTATION

INVERSION (OF TOPOGRAPHY, RELIEF)

The more any rock formation is uplifted, the more rapidly it is liable to be eroded. Hard and soft sedimentary alternations tend to develop a contrasting relief. Thus anticlines, domes, upthrown sides of fault blocks, etc., are liable to become eroded down, so that the part which was formerly highest, becomes progressively worn down the most. A structural feature also favors this process. There is a tendency for joints and small fractures to open up over an anticline, facilitating deep weathering, while in a syncline they tend to become wedged tightly together and to resist erosion. We have thus the phenomenon of anticlinal valleys and synclinal ridges ("perched synclines"), dissected domes, with circumferential cuestas or hogbacks. A graben structure may lead to a resistant cap-rock being depressed below the graben floor; after deep erosion the cap-rock of the floor may become the topographic "high," while the shoulders are eroded away.

A remarkably widespread form of topographic inversion found in regions of youthful volcanic flows is caused by the filling of a preexisting stream valley with lava. The locus of the stream is shifted to one side or the other and new downcutting sets in along the margins of the flow; eventually a "cast" of the old valley preserved in lava is left as a platform, with the surrounding country reduced to a lower base level. Thornbury (1954, Fig. 22.7) illustrates a fine example of a Tertiary lava flow causing inversion in Table Mountain, near Sonora, California. Further examples are rather common in eastern Australia, from Queensland to Tasmania (Fairbridge, 1949). Valuable placer gold ores (called "deep leads") are found there in many of the old channels (Hills, 1940).

Drainage patterns tend to reflect the inversions. In dome structures, in both igneous and salt domes, the initial *quaquaversal dips* (centrifugal drainage) are replaced by centripetal patterns. In volcanic calderas, the inversion is structurally, not geomorphically, controlled; nevertheless the initially radial volcanic drainage is often replaced by centrifugal drainage. Complex systems of longitudinal and transverse drainage tend to develop, with extensive *stream capture* (q.v.).

RHODES W. FAIRBRIDGE

References

Barré, O., 1903, "L'Architecture du Sol de la France," Paris, A. Colin, 393pp.
Cotton, C. A., 1952, "Geomorphology," Sixth ed., New York, John Wiley & Sons, 505pp.
Davis, W. M., 1889, "The rivers and valleys of Pennsylvania," *Natl. Geogr. Mag.,* **1,** 183–253 (also in Geographical Essays," New York, Dover reprint, 1954).

FIG. 1. Erosion of two comparable anticlines, the one on the left having a positive relief at the axis, that on the right being negative (i.e., inversion) (from Barré, 1903).

FIG. 2. Relief inversion controlled by a single resistant bed, with trace of intermediate erosion surface. The result is the preservation of plateaus in the synclinal belts, broad valleys in the anticlinal belts (de la Noë and de Margerie, 1888).

Fairbridge, R. W., 1949, "Geology of the country around Waddamana, Central Tasmania," *Papers Proc. Roy. Soc. Tasmania, 1948,* 111–149.

Hills, E. S., 1940, "The Physiography of Victoria," Melbourne, Whitcombe & Tombs, 292pp.

Lobeck, A. K., 1939, "Geomorphology," New York, McGraw-Hill Book Co., 731pp.

Louis, H., 1961, "Allgemeine Geomorphologie," Berlin, Second ed. W. de Gruyter, 355pp.

Martonne, E. de, 1950, "Traité de Géographie Physique," Paris, A. Colin, Vol. 1, 496 pp.; Vol. 2, 1057pp.

Noë, G. de la, and Margerie, E. de, 1888, "Les Formes de Terrain," Paris, Impr. Nat., 4°, 105pp.

Thornbury, W. D., 1954, "Principles of Geomorphology," New York, John Wiley & Sons, 618pp.

Von Engeln, O. D., 1942, "Geomorphology," New York, The Macmillan Co., 655pp.

Cross-references: *Drainage Patterns; Lava-displaced Drainage and Deep Leads; Stream Capture, Piracy; Structural Control in Geomorphology.*

ISLAND ARCS, GENERAL

There are several thousand islands in the oceans of the world, many of them are part of groups or chains of islands. If these island chains describe segments of an arc which are generally convex outward from the continental areas and are part of the major globe-encircling active orogenic belt systems, they are called *island arcs*.

General Distribution and Description

Island arc systems are morphologic indications of tectonic activity found roughly along two mutually perpendicular great circles (Fig. 1). According to Wilson (1954), they are parts of two vast and complex zones of fracture about the earth. These zones include the major mountain chains of the continental areas and the major island arc systems of the oceanic areas. One of the major orogenic systems, the "Eurasian-Melanesian Belt", or "Mediterranean—Tethyan Belt", includes the Atlas, Alpine, Turkish, Persian, Himalayan, and Burmese Mountains, and the island chains of Indonesia, New Guinea, the Solomons, New Hebrides, and New Zealand. The other, the "East Asian-Cordilleran Belt" or "circum-Pacific Belt", surrounds the Pacific Ocean; its members extend from Indonesia to the Aleutian Islands, and from there to West Antarctica.

Some of the island arc systems are relatively simple and form a *single island arc* which consists of a single chain of volcanic islands. Prominent examples (see Fig. 2) are the Aleutian, the Kurile and the Mariana Island groups. With further tectonic development, *double island arcs* may be formed. These consist of an outer arc of sedimentary islands and a parallel inner arc of volcanic islands. Most of the single island arcs contain submerged or scattered traces of a second line (Brouwer,

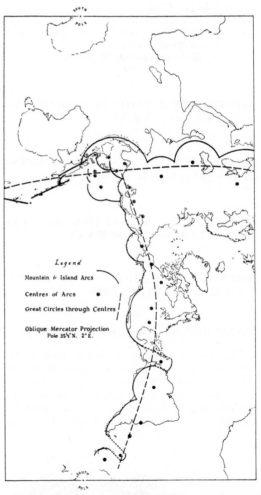

FIG. 1. Distribution of the active orogenic belts (from J. T. Wilson, 1954). (By permission of The University of Chicago Press.)

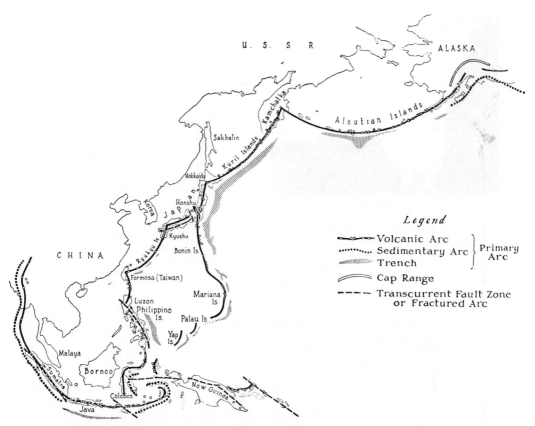

Fig. 2. Distribution of island arcs in the northwest Pacific Ocean (from J. T. Wilson, 1954). (By permission of The University of Chicago Press.)

1951; Hobbs, 1925). Double island arcs are not as numerous as the single island arc systems, but an excellent example is found in the northeast Indian Ocean. Here the Andaman and Nicobar Islands form an outer arc of sedimentary islands and there is an inner volcanic trend which manifests itself in two isolated volcanic islands and a chain of submarine volcanoes (see *Andaman Sea*, Vol. I). Less obvious examples are Kodiak Island, part of a sedimentary arc, and the volcanic trend on the Alaska Peninsula. In this latter case, the clear arcuate trends of the single arc systems are less well defined, since a portion of this double arc system is part of the continent itself.

Certain single and double island arcs exhibit large transcurrent (or strike-slip) fault zones which suppress the ideal arcuate pattern. These island arcs are called *fractured island arcs*. Typical examples of these are the Melanesian arcs from the Philippines to New Zealand.

Morphologic Associations

There are several fundamental morphologic relationships between the island arcs themselves and the sea floor from which they rise.

In case of the relatively simple single island arcs, the chain of volcanic islands is characteristically associated with a deep-sea trench on its convex side. Whereas the island arc–deep sea trench system may be several thousand kilometers in length, the width of the system is generally only a few hundred kilometers. Many of the volcanoes on the islands have elevations of 1–2 km above sea level, and the adjacent deep-sea trench may reach depths exceeding 10 km. The greatest depth surveyed in the Mariana Trench is approximately 11 km. Thus, together with the cordilleran-trench combinations (e.g. Andes–Peru Trench) with relief in excess of 15 km, the island arc–deep sea trench systems represent the maximum relief features found on the earth's surface.

Moving toward a single island arc from the open ocean, the deeper ocean basin, which may have an average depth of 4–5 km, becomes shallower at first (by approximately 1 km), then dips with increasing steepness into the deepest portions of the trench (Fig. 3). The ocean floor rises somewhat more sharply on the inner wall of the trench, up to the island platform itself. The shallower part of the deep-sea floor seaward of the trench is called the

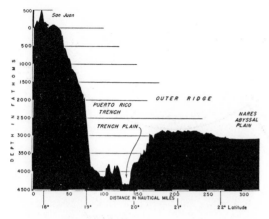

FIG. 3. Cross section of the Puerto Rico Trench (after Ewing and Heezen, 1955). Vertical exaggeration: 50 to 1.

TABLE 1. ISLAND ARCS

	Name		Oceans
Single Island Arcs	Antillean Arc	Puerto Rico Trench	Atlantic
	Sandwich (Scotia) Arc	South Sandwich Trench	Atlantic
	Aleutian Arc	Aleutian Trench	Pacific
	Kurile Arc	Kurile-Kamchatka Trench	Pacific
	Japan Arc (including Bonin)	Japan Trench	Pacific
	Palau Arc	Palau Trench	Pacific
	Yap Arc	Yap Trench	Pacific
Double Island Arcs	Ryukyu Arc (Nansei Shoto)	Ryukyu Trench	Pacific
	Mariana Arc	Mariana Trench	Pacific
	Kodiak-Alaska Peninsula	Aleutian Trench	Pacific
	Indonesian Arc	Java Trench	Indian
Fractured Island Arcs	Philippine Arc	Philippine Trench	Pacific
	Solomon-New Hebrides Arc	New Britain and New Hebrides Trench	Pacific
	Tonga-Kermadec Arc	Tonga-Kermadec Trench	Pacific

outer ridge, and it is generally an area of rugged (but relatively small-scale) bottom relief features and a complex crustal structure. The insular slope of the island arc is also riddled with canyons and sharp, usually small-scale, topographic depressions and elevations. However, as contrasted to the outer ridge, the insular slope frequently shows benches and ridges which can be followed parallel to the island arc sometimes for several hundred kilometers. Menard (1964) says: "Almost everyone who sees an echogram of the side benches and bottom troughs of trenches believes that they are produced by normal faulting. That is, the benches are the upper surfaces of fault blocks which have moved down into the trenches and been rotated away from the trenches so they are excellent traps for sediment. Likewise, the troughs in the center can hardly be anything but grabens." Studies of the Aleutian Arc (Gibson and Nichols, 1953; Gates and Gibson, 1956) showed that several canyons, sharp depressions, and ridges are connected to known fault zones mapped on the islands. Location of volcanic necks, plugs and dikes were found to be connected to tensional faulting on several islands of the Aleutian Arc (Knappen, 1929; Coats, 1950).

Well-developed double island arcs are less common than the single arcs and consist of two generally parallel arcuate trends (Fig. 4). As recognized half a century ago by Brouwer, the inner arc consists of volcanic islands or, when the islands themselves are not present, a drowned ridge or a zone of submarine volcanoes. The volcanoes are characteristically steep cones of the explosive, andesitic type. On the outer, convex side of this andesitic volcanic arc there is another island chain composed chiefly of sedimentary rocks (limestones, tuffs, greywackes, shales, cherts). These are cut in places by ultrabasic and serpentine intrusions. The greywacke–chert–serpentine facies is the so-called Steinmann Trinity, characteristic of axial orogenic belts. These forma-

tions are involved in complex overthrust or nappe-klippe tectonics, directed outward (ideally exposed, for example, on Timor). The length of the double island arcs, similarly to the single arcs, may reach several thousand kilometers, the overall width of the double arc–trench system is approximately 500 km.

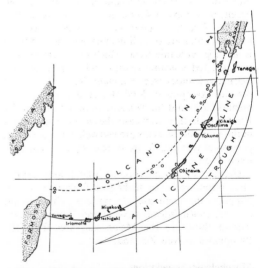

FIG. 4. The Ryukyu (Riukiu or Nansei Shoto) island arcs, including both a volcanic line (poorly developed), anticlinical belt (Cenozoic limestones, etc.), and a contemporary trough or trench (from Hobbs, 1944).

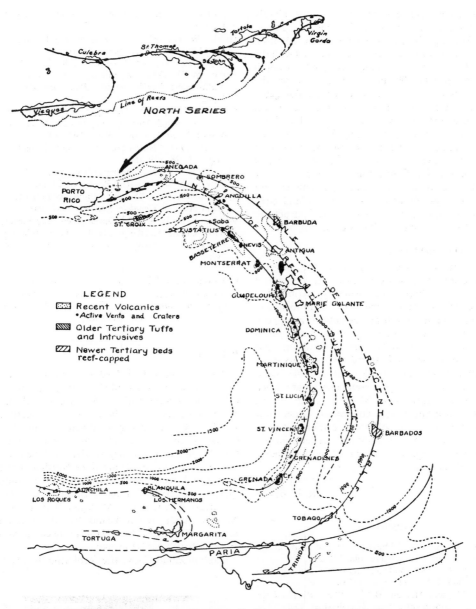

FIG. 5. The Antillean island arc, in the eastern Caribbean (West Indies), including the Leeward and Windward Islands. Outer, nonvolcanic arc is very poorly developed. Northern and southern borders are complicated by gigantic strike-slip faults and "drag" structures (from Hobbs, 1944).

The depth and height relationships and the topography of the walls of the outer sedimentary arc are generally similar to those of the single island arcs. However, the characteristic deep-sea trench of the single island arc system is generally not quite so deep in the double island arcs. Two prominent double arc sectors (Kodiak-Kenai, Andaman-Nicobar) have what appears to be an infilled trough which is an extension of the axial

trend of the major trench (Aleutian Trench, Java Trench) of the associated arc systems.

A listing of the principal island arcs is shown in Table 1. (Some of those marked as "single" show the beginnings of a double row.)

Tectonic and Geophysical Associations

In addition to the general morphologic relationships, the island arcs, as one of the primary features of the earth's active orogenic belts, are closely related to seismic activity which occurs along these belts. Although there is some scatter in distribution, shallow earthquakes (25 km) are associated with the area of the trench and outer arc, medium depth earthquakes (100-300 km) are located under the volcanic island ridge, and deep earthquakes (400-700 km) are located farther toward the continent. The rugged topography of the island arcs is related to present-day volcanism, young fractures and the earthquake activity. Vertical movements of extreme youth are shown by coastal terraces that in places (e.g., Timor, New Guinea) may be traced to over 4000 feet above sea level. Gravity anomalies and other geophysical attributes of the island arc–trench systems, and the basic crustal structures associated with them are discussed in Vol. V.

Development and Origin

The origins of island arcs and of the orogenic belts are still subjects of geological and geophysical debates. The earthquakes are generally attributed to an inclined fracture zone, but compressional, tensional and strike-slip movements all have been suggested for the nature of this fracture system (Fig. 5). It is generally agreed, however, that during the course of a hundred million years or so the single island arcs develop into double island arcs and then into marginal mountain ranges. Rock suites, similar to those of island arcs, can also be found deep inside several continents. These show the location of mobile belts in the earlier geological history of the earth and suggest that the development of continents occurred through the marginal addition of island arcs.

GEORGE PETER
R. E. BURNS

References

Brouwer, H. A., 1951, "The movement of island arcs," *Quart. J. Geol. Soc. London.* **106,** 231–239.

Coats, R. R., 1950, "Volcanic activity in the Aleutian Arc," *Bull. U.S. Geol. Surv..* **974-B,** 35–49.

Ewing, M., and Heezen, B. C., 1955, "Puerto Rico Trench Topography and Geophysical Data," in (Poldervaart, A., ed.), "Crust of the Earth," 255–267, *Geol. Soc. Am. Spec. Paper* **62.**

Fisher, R. L., and Hess, H. H., 1963, "Trenches," in in "The Sea," Vol. 3, pp. 411–436, New York and London, Interscience Publishers.

Gates, O., and Gibson, W. M., 1956, "Interpretation of the configuration of the Aleutian Ridge," *Bull. Geol. Soc. Am.,* **67,** 127–146.

Gibson, W. M., and Nichols. 1953, "Configuration of the Aleutian Ridge, Rat Islands-Semisopochnoi I. to west of Bouldir I.," *Bull. Geol. Soc. Am.,* 1173–1181.

Hawkes, D. D., 1962, "The structure of the Scotia Arc," *Geol. Mag.,* **99,** 85–91.

Hess, H. H., 1939, "Island arcs, gravity anomalies and serpentine intrusions: A contribution to the ophiolite problem," *Rept. Int. Geol. Congr. (U.S.S.R.) 1937,* **17,** 263–283.

Hobbs, W. H., 1925, "The unstable middle section of the island arcs," Gedenkboek Verbeek, *Verh. Geol.-Mijn. Gen. Ned. en Kol., Geol. Ser.,* **8,** 219–262.

Hobbs, W. H., 1944, "Mountain growth, a study of the southwestern Pacific region," *Proc. Am. Phil. Soc.,* **88,** 221–268.

Knappen, R. S., 1929, "Geology and mineral resources of the Aniachak District," in "Mineral Resources of Alaska," *Bull. U.S. Geol. Surv.,* **797,** 161–223.

Lake, P., 1931, "Island arcs and mountain building," *Geogr. J.,* **78,** 149–160.

Menard, H. W., 1964, "Marine Geology of the Pacific," New York, McGraw-Hill Book Co., 271pp.

Sykes, L. R., 1966, "Seismicity and deep structure of island arcs," *J. Geophys. Res.,* **71,** 2981–3006.

Wilson, J. T., 1954, "The Development and Structure of the Crust," in (Kuiper, G. P., editor) "The Earth as a Planet," Chicago, University of Chicago Press, 749pp.

Cross-references: *Islands; Mountain Systems; Submarine Geomorphology.* Vol. I: *Andaman Sea; Bathymetry; Ocean Bottom Features; Trenches.* Vol. V: *Island Arcs—Geophysics and Tectonics.*

ISLANDS

An island may be defined as "a relatively small body of land surrounded entirely by water" (*Columbia Encyclopedia*, 1963 ed.), but there is some confusion as to how much is "relatively small." The Australian continent is sometimes known as the "island continent." More conventionally, however, the largest island is taken to be Greenland (a structural part of the North American continental mass), after which come New Guinea (part of the Australian mass), Borneo (part of the Southeast Asiatic mass), Madagascar (part of the African mass), Baffin Island (North America), Sumatra (Southeast Asia), Honshu (eastern Asia), and the British Isles (Europe).

Captain James Cook, after exploring the Pacific,

FIG. 1. Continental-type islands (ancient): example in the Great Barrier Reefs, Queensland, Australia—Lizard Islands, of ancient gneiss and schist, with a fringing coral and incipient barrier reef with lagoon. (Photo: R. W. Fairbridge).

FIG. 2. Continental-type island (of Tertiary age): the maturely dissected island of Viti Levu (Fiji), part of the now-submerged Melanesian "lost continent," showing "two-stage" coastal planation surface and late mature river (the Rewa), navigable for 60 miles up from its mouth near Nasori, in foreground. (Courtesy Fiji Govt.)

identified two types of island: "high islands" and "low islands," the former being of continental or volcanic rocks and the latter of coral material. An "oceanic island" is any island that rises from the deep sea floor. However, it is customary today to

recognize several more types:

(a) **Continental Islands.** These may be of any dimensions from subcontinental sizes (Greenland, New Guinea, etc.) down to small rocky outposts, the essential characteristic being their continental-

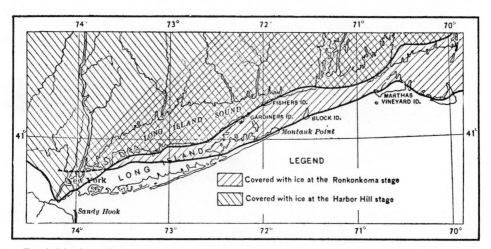

FIG. 3. Islands consisting largely of moraines and outwash sands: Long Island, Block Island, Martha's Vineyard, Nantucket. Sketch map showing relative positions of the ice during the Ronkonkoma and Harbor Hill stages of the Wisconsin period (U.S. Geological Survey).

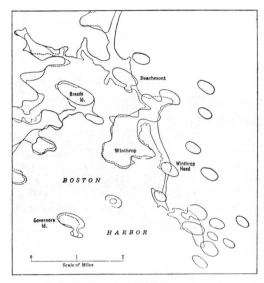

FIG. 4. Restoration of initial drumlin shore line of the Winthrop region, Boston Harbor. Broken lines show present form of shore line. In center of map is a glacial delta plain on which the village of Winthrop is located (Johnson, 1925). (By permission of John Wiley & Sons, N.Y.)

type rocks and their history showing a former land connection to an adjacent continent (Figs. 1 and 2). An extreme case is that of the *Seychelles* (q.v., in pr volume VIII) in the northwest Indian Ocean; it is totally isolated today, but in Mesozoic and possibly early Tertiary time it was connected to Madagascar (as part of the former *Gondwanaland*, q.v., in pr volume VII). Several important islands off New England (Long Island, Martha's Vineyard,

Nantucket, etc.) and in the Baltic are remnants of Pleistocene moraines, and off the coast of Massachusetts there are numerous islets that are drowned drumlins (Figs. 3 and 4). Sandy islets result from outwash sands and their reworking (Cameron, 1965). Small rocky islands and rocky reefs are often known as *skerries* (Norway, Scotland, Arctic Canada). These examples were all "drowned" segments of the continent, submerged and cut off by the rapid postglacial eustatic rise of sea level. A small continental island may become reunited with the mainland by the building of a sandspit, or multiple spits, known as a "*Tombolo*." An offshore example may become an "attached island" due to tectonic uplift, such as postglacial isostatic rebound (e.g., coasts of Sweden, Finland: Hurtig, 1965).

(b) Volcanic Islands. In single ones or complex groups, volcanic islands are generally rather small (1–100 km across) but often very high (500–3000 meters or so). They are generally in irregular clusters (Kerguelen, Fiji), in subrectangular patterns (Azores), in a complex mass (Iceland), in long lines (Hawaii, Society Islands, etc.), or in arcuate loops, festoons or "*island arcs*" (Aleutians, Banda Arc, etc.). Non-volcanic island arcs (continental rocks) are locally parallel to the volcanic belts (on the ocean side). The volcanic rocks may date back to early Tertiary or even Mesozoic times, but more often, they may be entirely Quaternary in age. New volcanic islands are constantly being created (off Hawaii, south of Japan, southwest of Tonga, off Iceland, Azores, etc.), as described by Lyell and others (see Figs. 5–11).

A special type of extrusive material is provided by *sedimentary volcanism* (q.v., in pr volume VI) leading to small, ephemeral mud-volcano islands

FIG. 5. Oblique air photograph of Bandaneira (in the Banda Sea, East Indies), showing on the right a large remnant of the caldera wall, elsewhere destroyed by explosions, and the new cone in the center. The physiography may be compared with Santorin (Thera) in the Aegean and with Bogoslof in the Aleutians (see Fig. 10).

FIG. 6. Volcanic island in mid-Pacific: youthfully dissected island of Moorea, seen from Tahiti. Note characteristic afternoon cumulus of the trade-wind belt. (Photo: T. W. Collins, Auckland, N.Z.)

or mud-lumps (e.g., off Burma, Pakistan, Timor, or the mouth of the Mississippi; see figure of Foul Island, off Burma, in *Craters*).

(c) **Low Coral Islands.** These appear either as accumulations of coral sand and shingle on the surface of a coral reef (Figs. 12–14) or as a slightly emerged limestone platform of formerly living coral not more than 3 meters above mean low water today (i.e., of mid-Holocene, eustatic origin; several varieties are known, see *Coral Reefs— Morphology and Theories*). Small sand accumulations (cay, key, cajo) may be ephemeral, and liable to destruction by hurricanes (Stoddart, 1965). Mature cays develop beachrock, beach ridges, mangrove and general vegetation (Teichert and Fairbridge, 1948). Oceanic *atolls* (q.v.) often contain extensive lagoons, but the island rims may be interrupted due to collapse by submarine landsliding down the steep, offshore slopes.

(d) **Emerged Coral Islands.** Constructed of coral and algal limestones, often dolomitized and partly phosphatized (by leached guano), emerged coral islands may date back to mid- or early Tertiary. The shape of former atoll reefs, modified by terracing and ice-age karst erosion, is often preserved (Figs. 15–17). Examples of pure raised atolls are rare and scattered in isolated occurrences (Christmas, Nauru, Ocean, Minami Daito, etc.).

Examples of reef-capped and rimmed islands in the mobile "island arcs" are, on the other hand, quite common (e.g., East Indies, New Guinea, Palau Islands, Loyalty Islands). Certain reef foundations gained a veneer of eolian calcarenite or calcareous "eolianite" (lime-rich dune rock) owing to Pleistocene dune building (e.g., the Houtman's Abrolhos Islands, Western Australia).

(e) **Barrier Islands.** Constructed entirely of terrigenous or bioclastic sands, barrier beaches are built up by longshore drift on continental coasts, probably first as offshore bars, and gradually gaining size and stability by eustatic oscillations, dune building and vegetative fixation (e.g., Friesian Islands of North Sea—"Wadden Islands," "Halligs"; the east coast barrier islands of North America from Long Island to Florida, and those of Texas; West Africa; southern Queensland). In the last-named, the quartz-sand dunes reach over 300 meters in height (Moreton Island, Stradbroke Island, Great Sandy Island.) A special type of barrier beach is that built largely of calcareous sands and developed into coastal dunes during stillstands in Quaternary sea level oscillations; pluvial conditions led to the consolidation of the sands into calcarenites and subsequent rise of sea level led to isolation as islands and reefs (e.g., Bahamas, Bermuda, off southwest Africa, and off

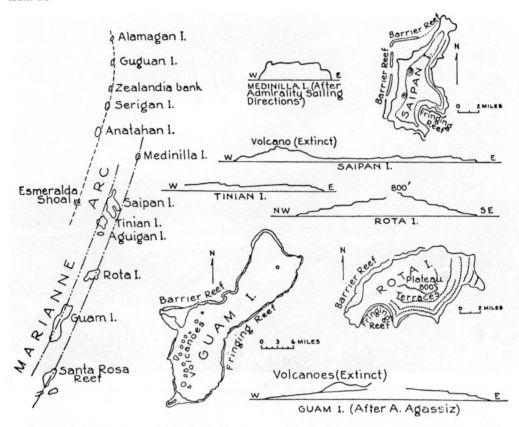

FIG. 7. Relationship of a youthful volcanic island arc to a belt of uplifted coral and ancient volcanic islands. The juxtaposition of youthful volcanic inner arcs and older nonvolcanic arcs is found in several belts bordering the great oceans, but never within those oceans. Example: the Marianna (Marianne) Islands, Western Pacific (Hobbs, 1944).

western and southern Australia). Calcareous beach-rock may also form a barrier, as in the great Sandstone Reef of Brazil originally described by Darwin.

(f) **Nonmarine Islands.** For the sake of completeness, one should add various types of islands found in nonmarine settings. These may be classified as *fluviatile islands*, due to cutoff meanders; also ephemeral islands built up from gravel, sand and mud bars, delta islands of the same sort, and various *lacustrine islands*, which include volcanic cones rising within crater and caldera lakes.

Biogeographic Questions

The plant and animal populations of offshore islands have long stimulated the attention of both biologists and geologists. Darwin was early attracted to the problem of the finches and other fauna of the Galápagos. A classical work was the book "Island Life" by Wallace (1880), who found a curious line of division running through the East Indian Archipelago, separating Borneo from Celebes (Sulawesi) and Bali from Lombok. West of this line (called *Wallace's Line* by Huxley) the populations were essentially Asiatic; east of it —rather Australian. An analogous line farther east (limiting the more distinctive Australian characteristics) was later called the *Weber Line*, after its discoverer.

Many island populations reach their habitats by floating, as epiplankton, epinekton, etc., or by air through winged spores or bird carriers. Notably widespread through all tropic seas are the floral elements with floating seeds, e.g., the mangroves (the seeds of which are viviparous), the nut-growing palms (e.g., *Pandanus*), and the conifer *Casuarina*. However, the appearance of strictly terrestrial organisms such as reptiles, amphibians, and non-swimming mammals on isolated islands sets up problems that may only have geological explanations in some inherited characteristics or events. The biogeographic question constantly comes up in discussions of Gondwanaland (Fairbridge, 1965), the ancient Melanesian "Continent" ("Tasmantis") and "Atlantis" theories.

Essentially there are four biogeographic access

FIG. 8. Birth of a new volcanic island. The sea boils and the lava steams as volcanic eruptions on Surtsey break the ocean surface. Surtsey (so-named from the Icelandic god of volcanoes) is situated at 63° 18′ N, 20° 36.5′ W off the coast of Iceland, and first began to emerge on November 14, 1963. (Photo: *Timinn*, Reykjavik, Iceland and *Geo-Marine Technology*).

ways for terrestrial organisms to reach offshore islands. These are:

(1) Biologically normal methods, swimming, floating, flying.

(2) Biologically accidental routes, e.g., the penguin floating on an iceberg from Antarctica to southern Australia, the small clam embedded in the mud on a duck's foot, the frog or snake carried in the branches of a floating tree, the domesticated "passenger" traveling with man by canoe and boat. (including cattle, dogs, rats and parasites).

(3) Changes in world sea level (eustasy) that permit dry-land access to islands on the continental shelf. All the Great Sunda Islands of Indonesia were once accessible in this way (Fairbridge, 1961). It should be noted, however, that the Quaternary ice epochs (extending over the last million years or more) were marked by negative oscillations of sea level (± 100 meters), *superimposed* on a general lowering of sea level (due to tectonic deepening of basins) that persisted through the whole period. The mean sea level in the Pliocene was approximately 200 meters higher than today. Thus glacio-

eustatic negative oscillations of 100 meters did not expose the present continental shelf until *late* Pleistocene, possibly only during the Riss (Illinoian) and Würm (Wisconsin). Due to the postglacial rise of sea level, many faunal types have been isolated on offshore shelf islands; an extreme case is where certain primitive Australoid aboriginal tribes in the Gulf of Carpentaria are found to have completely different blood groups on separate islands, having no interisland transportation (Simmons, Tindale and Birdsell, 1962).

(4) Changes in land level due to tectonic changes in the earth's crust. These are restricted to certain orogenic belts if we are considering geologically recent movements, e.g., over the last one million years, but over periods of the order of 10^7 and 10^8 years, continental spreading or drifting may be considered. Great care should be exercised in considering such theories because the geological data are notoriously weak and the urge by some biologists and paleontologists to build "land bridges" is sometimes verging on the messianic. Nevertheless there seems to be a real land bridge that paleontologists have traced from China, through Taiwan, Philippines to the Celebes, permitting ancient man and major mammals (e.g., the *Archidiskodon*, *Elephas* types, etc.) to move dryshod into Indonesia (to the east of the Wallace Line) during the Pleistocene (see *Sunda Shelf*, Vol. I). Connection for early man's entry into Australia from Indonesia and New Guinea was

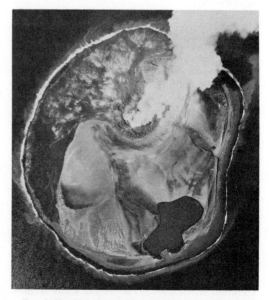

FIG. 9. Vertical air photograph of Surtsey, off Iceland, born November 14, 1963, almost a year old and already showing a quite complex development of lava and cinder cones, landslide effects and coastal erosion. (Photo: *Timinn*, Reykjavik, Iceland and *Geo-Marine Technology*).

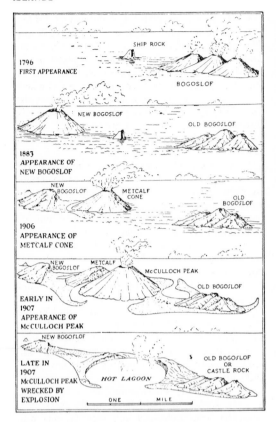

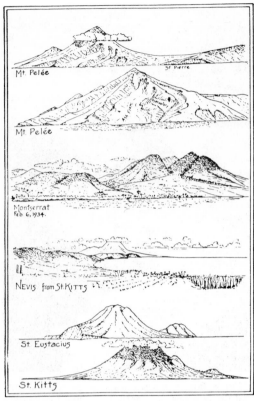

FIG. 10. Successive events in the history of Bogoslof Island (Lobeck, 1939). (By permission of McGraw-Hill Book Co., N.Y.)

FIG. 11. Various stages of maturity among the volcanic islands of the West Indies (field sketches by Lobeck, 1939). (By permission of McGraw-Hill Book Co., N.Y.)

provided by eustatic exposure of the Torres Straits. Rapid vertical movements of the crust in some orogenic belts are illustrated by the discovery of late Pleistocene coral reefs rising up to over 1000 meters in Timor, an uplift rate that could not be much less than 10 mm/yr.

It should be added that there is very strong geological evidence (tectonic, stratigraphic, geophysical) for rejecting all paleobiogeographic theories that call for orogenic crustal changes or continental drift in the central Pacific. Some such theories are still maintained by certain botanists, such as Skottsberg, to account for the pre-human population of Hawaii, Tahiti, etc., but they must be emphatically rejected.

RHODES W. FAIRBRIDGE

References

Cameron, H. L., 1965, "The shifting sands of Sable Island," *Geograph. Rev.*, **55**(4), 463–476.

Fairbridge, R. W., 1948, "Notes on the geomorphology of the Pelsart Group of the Houtman's Abrolhos Islands," *J. Roy. Soc. W. Australia.*, **33** (for 1946–47), 1–43.

Fairbridge, R. W., 1950, "Recent and Pleistocene coral reefs of Australia," *J. Geol.*, **58**, 330–401.

Fairbridge, R. W., 1961, "Eustatic changes in sea level," in "Physics and Chemistry of the Earth," Vol. 4, pp. 99–185, London, Pergamon Press.

Fairbridge, R. W., 1965, "The Indian Ocean and the status of Gondwanaland," *Progress in Oceanography*, **3**, 83–136.

FIG. 12. Oblique air photo of a typical low coral island in the lagoon of the Tijger Atoll (a compound atoll: see *Coral Reefs*), its ring-reef visible in the distance. Beachrock outcrops in right foreground.

FIG. 13. Oblique air photo of Adélie Island, a vegetated cay and sand bank on a platform reef of the Sahul Shelf.

Hinds, N. E. A., 1943, "Geomorphology," Englewood Cliffs, N.J., Prentice-Hall, 894pp.

Hobbs, W. H., 1944, "Mountain growth, a study of the southwestern Pacific region," *Proc. Am. Phil. Soc.,* **88,** 221–268.

Hurtig, T., 1965, "Die Ålandinseln im Gesamtrahmen von geomorphologischen Fragenkomplexen des Ostseeraumes," *Geogr. Z.,* **53**(2/3), 140–161.

Johnson, D., 1925, "The New England-Acadian Shoreline," New York, John Wiley & Sons, 608pp.

Kuenen, P. H., 1933, "Geology of coral reefs," *Snellius Exped.,* **5,** pt. 2, 125pp.

Lobeck, A. K., 1939, "Geomorphology," New York, McGraw-Hill Book Co., 731pp.

Marshall, P., 1927, "Geology of Mangaia," *Bernice P. Bishop Museum Bull.,* **36,** 48pp.

Mayr, E., 1945, "Wallace's Line in the Light of Recent Zoogeographic Studies," in "Science and Scientists in the Netherlands Indies," pp. 241–250, New York (also: in *Quart. Rev. Biol.,* **19,** 1–14).

Mayr, E., (editor), 1952, "The problem of the land connections across the South Atlantic, with special reference to the Mesozoic," *Bull. Am. Mus. Nat. Hist.,* **99**(3), 81–258.

Menard, H. W., and Ladd, H. S., 1963, "Oceanic islands, seamounts, guyots and atolls," in (Hill, M. N., ed.) "The Sea," pp. 365–387, New York, Interscience Publishers.

Millot, J., 1953, "Le continent de Gondwana et les méthodes de raisonnement de la biogéographie classique," *Ann. Sci. Nat., Zoo. Biol., Paris,* Ser. 11, **15,** 187–220.

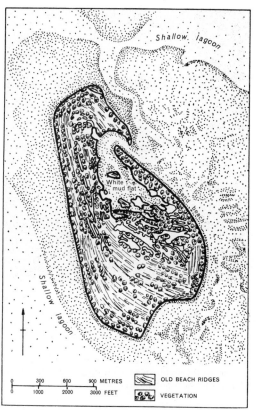

FIG. 14. Map of Adélie Island (shown in Fig. 13) showing truncation of mature beach ridges in the southeast due to coast erosion, in contrast to accumulating spits to the northeast (see Teichert and Fairbridge, 1948).

Neumayr, M., 1886, "Erdgeschichte," Leipzig, 2 vols.

Scott, H., 1933, "General conclusions regarding the insect fauna of the Seychelles and adjacent islands," *Trans. Linnean Soc., London,* Ser. 2 (*Zool.*), **19,** 307–391.

Selling, O. H., 1948, "On the late Quaternary history of the Hawaiian vegetation," *Bernice P. Bishop. Museum Spec. Publ.,* **39.**

Selling, O. H., 1951, "A contribution to the history of the Hawaiian Vegetation," *Svensk Bot. Tidsk.,* **45**(1), 12–41.

FIG. 15. Sketch showing ancient volcanic core and makatea of Mangaia Island, South Pacific. The "makatea" is a former barrier reef, now a rocky wall of limestone, an uplifted barrier, with an emerged lagoon inside, now a depression used for growing taro (root crop). The outer escarpment of the makatea is eroded by an intermediate shore terrace, forming a platform above the modern fringing reef (Marshall, 1927).

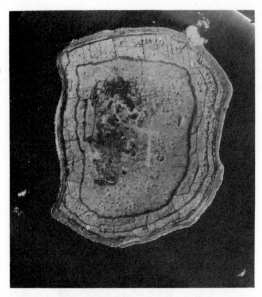

FIG. 16. An uplifted atoll, the island of Minami Diato, south of Japan. Note raised atoll rim, with several intermediate terraces, and central depression, the former lagoon, pock-marked by karst pipes, partly water filled. Bight-shaped cuts in the island's outline, to the east and west, are interpreted as sites of former landslides, this destroying the circular plan of the original volcanic cone. North is to the top. Dimensions: 6 × 8 km.

Simmons, R. T., Tindale, N.B., and Birdsell, J. B., 1962, "A blood group genetical survey in Australian Aborigines of Betinck, Mornington, and Forsyth Islands, Gulf of Carpentaria," *Am. J. Phys. Anthropol.*, **20**(3), 303–320.

Stoddart, D. R., 1965, "British Honduras cays and the low wooded island problem," *Trans. Inst. Brit. Geogr.*, **36**, 131–147.

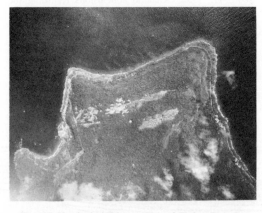

FIG. 17. Vertical air photograph of Flying Fish Cove area of Christmas Island (Indian Ocean, 10° 27′ S, 105° 38′ E), showing phosphate loading point and coral limestone cliffs that mark former sea levels on this uplifted coral island. North is to the top. Width of area shown in picture 5 km.

Teichert, C., and Fairbridge, R. W., 1948, "Some coral reefs of the Sahul Shelf," *Geograph. Rev.*, **38**, 222–249.

Thorarinsson, S., 1965, "Surtsey: island born of the fire," *Natl. Geogr. Mag.*, **127**(5), 712–726.

Verstappen, H. T., 1960, "On the geomorphology of raised coral reefs and its tectonic significance," *Z. Geomorphol.*, **4**, 1–28.

Wallace, A. R., 1860, "On the zoological geography of the Malay Archipelago," *J. Linnean Soc. London*, **4**, 172–184.

Wallace, A. R., 1880, "Island Life," London, Macmillan (Third revised ed., 1902), 563pp.

Wallace, A. R., 1892, "The permanence of the great ocean basins," *Nat. Sci.*, **1**, 418–426.

Weber, M., 1902, "Der Indo-Australische Archipel und die Geschichte seiner Tierwelt," Jena, 46pp.

Wilson, J. T., 1963, "Pattern of uplifted islands in the main ocean basins," *Science*, **130**, 592–594.

Cross-references: *Algal Reefs*; *Atolls*; *Barriers—Beaches and Islands*; *Coral Reefs*; *Crater*; *Crater Lakes*; *Drumlin*; *Eustasy*; *Fringing Reef*; *Great Barrier Reefs*; *Island Arcs*; *Lagoon*; *Makatea*; *Mountain Systems*; *Tombolo*. Vol. I: *Sahul Shelf*; *Sunda Shelf*. Vol. IV: *Phosphates (including Guano)*. Vol. V: *Volcanoes*. Vol. VI: *Eolian Sediments*; *Sedimentary Volcanism*; *Wadden Sea Sediments*. pr Vol. VII: *Biogeography*; *Gondwanaland*. pr Vol. VIII: *Seychelles*.

ISOBASE

"An isobase is a topographic or imaginary contour line on a map, drawn through points of equal elevation in a topographic surface or line, formerly level, but at present deformed" (American Geological Institute, 1960). Isobases are best illustrated in connection with former bodies of water. The surface of a water body is a horizontal (geoidal) surface during its existence. However, it is common that the surface of an extinct water body, as determined by ancient shore-line features, is no longer horizontal. The former water surface has been deformed by some geologic agency, commonly isostatic adjustment due to removal of the burden of water formerly in the lake, or the removal of the load of a formerly adjacent ice cap. On the other hand, some deformation may have been tectonic. The deformed water surface can be visualized as an imaginary surface extending throughout a basin, but this surface can be observed only where traces of former shorelines remain around the rim of the basin. The deformed surface is generally an irregular dome centered on the basin, and the surface of this dome can be defined by a set of contour lines connecting points of equal altitude on the ancient shorelines. *Such contour lines are called isobases.*

Isobases were introduced into geologic method in 1890. G. K. Gilbert produced maps showing the deformation of Pluvial Lake Bonneville in the Great Salt Lake Basin by means of "contours on the deformed surface." Gilbert (1890, p. 368) introduced the term "isogrammic lines" for such contours. At the same time Baron DeGeer introduced the term "isobase" for lines of equal deformation resulting from glacio-isostatic rebound in southern Sweden. DeGeer (1890, p. 72) further defined "isanabases" and "isokatabases" as isobases which indicate uplift and subsidence, respectively. Although the great majority of isobases in present usage are actually isanabases, the latter term is rarely employed. The shorter, more general term "isobase" is nearly universally used.

(Illustration of the usage of isobases may be found in *Postglacial Isostatic Rebound.*)

W. R. FARRAND

References

American Geological Institute, 1960, "Glossary of Geology," second ed.

DeGeer, Gerard, 1890, "Om Skandinaviens niva-förändringar under qvartärperioden," *Geol. Fören. Stockholm Förh.*, **12**, 61–110.

Gilbert, G. K., 1890, "Lake Bonneville," *U.S. Geol. Surv. Monograph*, **1**, 438 pp.

Cross-references: *Geomorphic Maps; Great Salt Lake; Postglacial Isostatic Rebound; Water Loading and Crustal Response.* Vol. II: *"Iso" Terms.*

ISOCLINAL RIDGES AND VALLEYS—*See* RIDGE AND VALLEY TOPOGRAPHY

ISOKINETIC THEORY—*See* WARPING

ISOPLETH—*See* Vol. II

ISOSTASY—*See* POSTGLACIAL ISOSTATIC REBOUND; WARPING; *also* Vol. V

ISOSTATIC DEFORMATION DUE TO WATER LOADING—*See* WATER LOADING AND CRUSTAL RESPONSE

"ISO" TERMS—*See* Vol. II, pr Vol. VI

K

KAME

Kames are mounds of poorly sorted sand and gravel deposited from running water in close association with stagnant glacial ice. Kames form within holes or fissures in the glacier or between the glacier and the land surface. They may appear, after melting of the ice, as a single mound (a kame or moulin kame), groups of closely associated mounds (kame field, kame complex, or kame group) or as a ridge called a *crevasse filling*, if straight, or an *esker*, if long and winding. Bedding within any type of kame is highly irregular, locally cross-bedded, and frequently distorted as a result of collapse of supporting ice. Gravel and sand are the most common components, but at times silt and till may be seen. Eskers and crevasse fillings are formed more regularly, having a more persistent direction of cross-bedding, a smaller variation in grain size, and less frequent bedding distortion than kames.

A *kame terrace* forms as an ice-contact deposit when waters flowing from a glacier find a course between the ice mass and a valley wall. This feature is especially well developed with valley glaciers, but it is not unknown with continental glaciation. A level-topped fill sloping downstream tends to develop in this position, but subsequent collapse of the ice usually leaves behind an irregular-topped terrace. The character of the sediments within a kame terrace is intermediate in complexity between that of an esker and that of a kame.

Kames are frequently associated with terminal and interlobate moraines; locally a terminal moraine may consist entirely of kames (kame moraine). In areas of moderate relief and irregular topography, kames may be scattered throughout the ground moraine area. Noteworthy displays of kames occur in moraines in Wisconsin, Michigan, Indiana, and in Great Britain. Kames not associated with moraines are well developed in northeastern United States as far west as Ohio.

VINCENT C. SHEPPS

References

Brown, T. C., 1931, "Kames and kame terraces of central Massachusetts," *Bull. Geol. Soc. Am.*, **42**(2), 467–479.

Cook, J. H., 1946, "Kame complexes and perforation deposits," *Am. J. Sci.*, **244**, 573–583.

Embleton, C., and King, C. A. M., 1968, "Glacial and Periglacial Geomorphology," London, E. Arnold Ltd., 608pp.

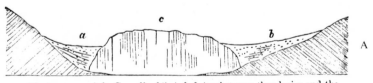

c. Glacier.   *a* & *b*. Gravelly débris lodging between the glacier and the sides of the valley.

a, b. Gravel terraces.

FIG. 1. (A) (*above*). Section of glacier-filled valley in retreat stage: (a, b) Kame terrace gravel; (c) glacier. (B) (*below*). After-melting of ice: (a, b) gravel terraces; these commonly slump after removal of lateral support (original sketches by Jamieson, 1874).

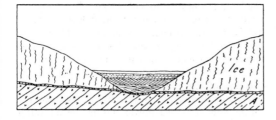

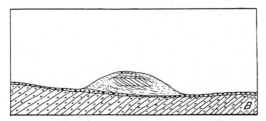

Fig. 2. (A). Kame sediments accumulate in depression or "bay" of the melting glacier. (B) Lone kame left as isolated hill (from Brown, 1931).

Holmes, C. D., 1952, "Kames," *Am. J. Sci.,* **245,** 240–249.

Cross-references: *Crevasse; Esker; Glacial Deposits; Glacial Geology; Glacial Moulin; Glaciation, Glacierization; Moraine; Stagnant Ice Melting; Valley (Mountain) Glacier.* Vol. VI: *Glaciers; Till and Tillite.*

KARA-BOGAZ GULF

The most remarkable natural evaporite basin in the world is the Kara-bogaz Gulf (*Karabogazgöl,* in the Turkmen language; or *Zaliv,* "gulf" in Russian), situated in an isolated embayment off the eastern shore of the Caspian Sea, in the Turkmen Republic of the USSR (41°N, 53°E). Kara-bogaz means "black throat" and used to refer simply to the entrance channel; in older literature, the gulf is referred to as the Adji-Darya (or "salt water"). Evaporation is always so high that the gulf is 4.5 meters below the level of the Caspian (Fig. 1).

Geologists have long been attracted to this remote spot for it is the only place in the world today where natural evaporites are continuously evolving without human intervention; it thus represents an analog (though far from perfect) for appraising the genesis of the great salt deposits of the geological past, which were particularly important in the Cambrian, Silurian, Devonian, Permian and Triassic. Ochsenius (1877, 1905), in developing his "bar theory" (for the Strassfurt deposits), was the first to suggest that the Kara-bogaz Gulf might be the modern counterpart of the ancient evaporites (see also Grabau, 1920).

The *Caspian Sea* (q.v.) of today is a land-locked arm of the ocean, slightly salty, in a region of high evaporation, and largely renewed by the fresh waters of the Volga; levels of the Caspian have fluctuated strongly in response to changes in the evaporation-

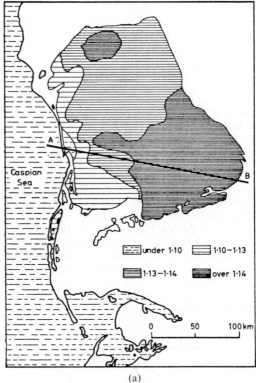

(a)

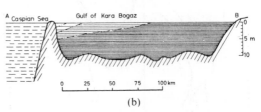

(b)

Fig. 1(a). Map of Kara-bogaz Gulf showing variations in density, i.e., brine concentration, prepared about the turn of the present century. (b) Profile through A–B (adapted from Borchert and Muir, 1964; after W. Stahlberg, 1909). At the present time, the gulf is reduced to about half this size and has shallowed to only 3.5 meters.

precipitation balance in its drainage area (Fig. 2). The Kara-bogaz Gulf is separated from the Caspian Sea by a long sand spit (Fig. 3), cut through by a narrow strait, the Proliv Karabogazsky, some 10 km long and 300 meters wide, and mostly less than 1 meter deep. The flow is always one way, at 1–4 m/sec. During the "high" level of the Caspian Sea in the last century, inward flow to the gulf was maintained by a very high evaporation rate, not counteracted by local precipitation or fluvial dilution. The severe drop in the Caspian in the present century reduced the inflow rate. In the strait there are a pair of waterfalls (like a miniature Niagara, divided by an island), the Kara Kum Falls on the

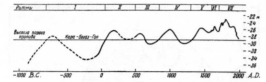

FIG. 2. Curve showing variations in the level of the Caspian Sea (below mean sea level), present level being about 29 meters (Rikhter, 1961). Borings in the Kara-bogaz depression show that over the last 2700 years, there have been seven sedimentary cycles (terrigenous, followed by carbonate, gypsum, and then by mirabilite, halite, epsomite and astrakhanite). These represent regressive phases.

south side and the Mangyshlak Falls on the north. The falls occur over a resistant formation of Khazarian (Middle Pleistocene) age which overlies a Tertiary limestone escarpment dipping gently to the west. The fall in 1966 was 4 meters, while an inner delta (like the *tidal deltas*, q.v., of barrier beach coasts) developed inside the gulf. The delta supports a curious biotic community which feeds on the dead fish and other organisms carried over the fall into the lethally saline waters of the gulf. There are virtually no organisms living in the gulf itself, but in 1897 expeditions under A. Spindler and N. Andrussov found masses of the characteristic salt-lake "shrimp" *Artemia salina* near the inlet, but none are left today. Nevertheless there are huge concentrations of the alga *Aphanothece salina* forming enormous slimy mats, and the flagellates *Dunaliella viridis* and *D. salina* flower during the mirabilite precipitation periods (of winter), amounting to 21×10^6 individuals per cubic centimeter of brine (Zenkevitch, 1963). The shores are scattered with old shells of *Cardium edule* L., but these date from a high-level stage of the Caspian a few thousand years ago, when the Gulf was less saline.

Kara-bogaz Gulf formerly covered about 18,000 km^2 (7000 square miles) and was over 15 meters deep; now it is 10,500 km^2 (4000 square miles) and its maximum depth is 3.5 meters. Large areas are now dry. The inflow of water has dropped from 25 km^3 (6 cubic miles) in 1930 to 10 km^3 (2.5 cubic miles) in 1966. There is a somewhat similar gulf farther south, the Gulf of Enzeli, which resembles Kara-bogaz on a small scale.

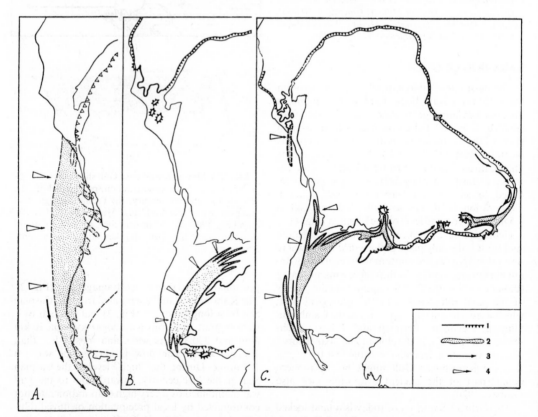

FIG. 3. Evolution of the coastal features of the Kara-bogaz Gulf, in three stages: (A) Low water level stage, growth of bars and barrier ridge across mouth of bay. (B) Early high-level stage, open bay condition, terracing of inner gulf, bar building in south. (C) Late high-level stage with renewed bar building and longshore drift (Leontyev, 1961). Legend: (1) terraced shore or raised beach; (2) sand bars; (3) longshore drift; (4) wave approach.

TABLE 1. COMPOSITION OF BRINES OF VARIOUS TYPES OF EVAPORITE BASINS (BORCHERT AND MUIR, 1964)

Components	I Sea Water	II Lake Assal	IIIa Caspian Sea	IIIb Kara-bogaz	IV Iletzk Lake	V Great Salt Lake
$MgCl_2$	9.4	14.8	5.1	13.9	0.4	5.0
KCl	2.6	5.9	1.1	1.5	—	2.1
$MgSO_4$	5.7	3.4	22.7	18.3	—	6.3
NaCl	78	75.3	62.0	64.6	98.7	85.1
$CaSO_4$	3.6	0.6	8.2	1.4	0.9	1.5
$CaCO_3$	0.4	—	0.9	0.3	—	—
Total salt content, ‰	35	324	13	164*	155	196

[* This is the 1897 figure; latest is 310‰.]

The slightly saline incoming water of the Caspian (13‰) is enriched with sulfates from the Volga (25.6% $SO_4^=$ among its dissolved salts) and becomes concentrated by evaporation in the Gulf to nearly 310‰, saturation level, thus one of the saltiest lakes in the world; it loses 1 m/yr by evaporation. The Dead Sea, by comparison, has a salinity of 250‰, and Great Salt Lake of Utah averages 200‰. In 1897, its salinity was only 164‰. Table I shows a comparison of seawater and some characteristic salt lakes with the Caspian Sea and the Kara-bogaz Gulf. (Lake Assal is in French Somaliland, 9 miles from the Gulf of Aden and 116 meters below sea level. Lake Iletzk is in Kazakstan and famous for its halite deposits.)

The Kara-bogaz salt deposition rate is enormous: formerly averaging 350,000 tons/day, 1.3×10^8 tons annually, but in 1950 it reached 2×10^8 tons. The total evaporite reserve accumulated now exceeds 34×10^9 tons. The order of precipitation is gypsum-mirabilite-halite. The mirabilite (or "Glauber's salt"), $Na_2SO_4 \cdot 10H_2O$, of which the reserve exceeds 10^9 tons, is extracted commercially and baked to drive off the H_2O before export. The halite only began to precipitate in 1939 and grows in volume from year to year (Solovyev, 1954). At the present time, pure mirabilite is no longer formed, but a mixture is co-precipitated, consisting of halite (NaCl), epsomite ($MgSO_4 \cdot 7H_2O$) and astrakhanite ($MgSO_4 \cdot NaSO_4 \cdot 4H_2O$).

Mirabilite is an interesting mineral since it is relatively stable only below 10°C. With rising temperature, its solubility increases very rapidly. It precipitated in winter when the water temperature used to fall into its stability range relative to its concentration. On exposure to the air, it dehydrates and effloresces to become thenardite (Na_2SO_4). Its close relative, glauberite ($CaSO_4 \cdot Na_2SO_4$), is formed locally and only at temperatures above 10°C. In summer, mirabilite was partly taken back into solution. (A solid layer of mirabilite in the bed of Great Salt Lake suggests that this area was once perigla-cial.) Calcium sulfate and calcium carbonate both enter the Gulf in solution, but in the high ionic con-

centration encountered they precipitate immediately as gypsum and calcite near the exit of the channel. Gypsum, especially, is deposited here in consider-able quantity.

RHODES W. FAIRBRIDGE

[Grateful acknowledgment is due to Professor O. K. Leontyev of the Moscow State University, who was kind enough to provide the latest statistics.]

References

Andrussov, N., 1897, "Der Adschi-darja oder Kara-bogaz Busen," *Peterm. Mitt.*, **43**, 25–34.

Borchert, H., and Muir, R. O., 1964, "Salt Deposits: The Origin, Metamorphism and Deformation of Evap-orites." London, D. Van Nostrand Co., Ltd., 338pp.

Dzens-Litovsky, A. I., 1967, "Kara-Bogaz-Gol," Mos-cow, Nedza.

Dzens-Litovsky, A. I., and Vasilyev, G. L., 1961, "Geo-logic conditions of the formation of bottom sediments in Karabogaz-Gol in connection with fluctuations of the Caspian Sea level," *Izv. Akad. Nauk, USSR*, No. 3 (in Russian).

Garbell, M. A., 1963, "The sea that spills into a desert," *Sci. Am.*, **209**, 94–100.

Grabau, A. W., 1920, "Principles of Salt Deposition," New York, McGraw-Hill Book Co., 435pp.

Leontyev, O. K., 1961, *Akad. Nauk USSR, Trudy Inst. Okean.*, **48**, 34–66.

Ochsenius, C., 1877, "Die Bildung der Steinsalzlager und ihrer Mutterlaugensalze," Halle, 172pp.

Ochsenius, C., 1888, "On the formation of rock-salt beds and mother liquor salts," *Proc. Acad. Nat. Sci. (Philadelphia)*, 181–187.

Ochsenius, C., 1905, "Karabugas," *Z. Prakt. Geol. Berlin*, **13**.

Rikhter, V. G., 1961, *Biulleten M. O-VA Isp. Prirody, Otd. Geol.*, **36**, 115–126.

Solovyev, V. F., 1954, *Priroda (Moscow)*, **43**, 89–91.

Stahlberg, W., 1909, *Naturw. Wochenschr.*, **20**, 689.

Zenkevitch, L. A., 1963, "Biology of the Seas of the U.S.S.R.," New York, Interscience Publishers, 955pp. (translated by S. Botcharskaya).

Cross-references: *Barriers—Beaches and Islands*; *Caspian Sea*; *Dead Sea*; *Great Salt Lake*; *Tidal Delta*. pr Vol. VI: *Evaporites*.

KARST

The term karst is derived from the German form of the Slav word, *krs* or *kras*, meaning rock. The original use of the word was as a regional name for the area of massive limestone country to the north and south of the port of Rjeka in Yugoslavia, a district of many rocks, sinkholes and underground streams. The term is now more widely used to denote a type of terrain with a distinctive and unique assemblage of landforms. This assemblage is the result of one dominant erosion process, namely solution. The main characteristic of a karst area, or a karstland, is its possession of predominantly vertical and underground drainage, resulting in the complete absence of surface streams. In all other types of terrain, surface drainage is normally integrated into streams which flow along the contours of the ground and which do not disappear into it. The Adriatic coastal areas of Yugoslavia from Istria to Kotor were the first karstlands to be described in a scientific manner by European writers (Cvijić, 1893). Many other parts of the world also possess assemblages of landforms dependent upon the development of underground drainage, notably in the Kwangsi area of southern China, in Jamaica and Puerto Rico, in parts of the High Calcareous Alps, in Israel and many other parts of the Mediterranean region, and in the Mammoth Cave area of Kentucky, and Carlsbad Caverns, New Mexico.

For a karst to develop fully or for an area to become karstified, the region must possess the following set of features:

(a) There must be a considerable thickness (preferably some hundreds of feet) of rock which is to some extent soluble in the slightly acidulated water of ordinary rainwater or soil water. The rock should be well bedded and jointed and fractured to allow the easy passage of water through it. The rock must also be of the massive type and possess strength. Any type of geological structure from horizontal bedding to contorted folds and highly faulted country may be involved.

The most abundant rock type which fits the above specification is limestone, which is massively bedded, pure, hard, consolidated and crystalline. Non-crystalline and amorphous limestones, such as chalk, are mostly too soft to give rise to a well-developed karst relief. Underground drainage and karst landforms also develop upon soluble rocks such as dolomite, gypsum and salt, but these rocks are not widely distributed. Hence, a karst area normally means an area of pure and massive limestone.

(b) There should be a moderate to heavy rainfall since solution of the rock cannot take place without adequate water. In humid regions, the presence of dense vegetation assists the solution caused by rainwater. In desert and semiarid regions, karst landforms are poorly developed and may be absent altogether.

(c) The "available relief," or the height of the area above sea level, should preferably be some hundreds of feet; this enables the free circulation of underground water and the full development of the karst landforms.

Solution

When water collects in hollows of the surface of such an area, solution of the rock takes place particularly along bedding planes, joints and other lines of weakness. The most important single factor in the solution of limestone is the concentration of carbon dioxide, either as free CO_2 or as the complex ion HCO_3^-. Some of the problems concerning the complex chemistry of limestone solution are dealt with by Trombe (1952). The lines of weakness in the rock become enlarged and surface water disappears into the ground. Instead, therefore, of a normal stream pattern appearing on the surface, a series of hollows or pits develops absorbing the drainage into the ground. It is then known sometimes as *kryptorheic* ("hidden drainage").

Doline

These hollows are known as *dolines* or *dolinas* (from the Serbian, a little valley or dale, Cvijić, 1893; spelling "doline" is from the French), or in English as *sinkholes*. Dolines give to the karst landscape its pitted or "wannen" character, and despite the fact that they are absent in some areas, they may be considered as the fundamental landforms of

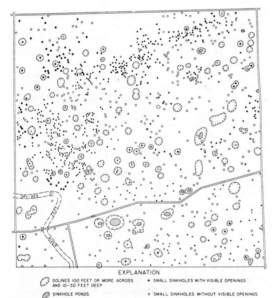

EXPLANATION

⬡ DOLINES 100 FEET OR MORE ACROSS • SMALL SINKHOLES WITH VISIBLE OPENINGS
AND 10-30 FEET DEEP

⬭ SINKHOLE PONDS ∘ SMALL SINKHOLES WITHOUT VISIBLE OPENINGS

FIG. 1. Map of the sinkholes and dolinas in 1 square mile southwest of Orleans, Indiana. There are 1022 sinkholes shown (after C. A. Malott; from Thornbury, 1954). (By permission of John Wiley & Sons, N.Y.).

Fig. 2. Karst fluting in Devonian limestones of the Napier Range, Kimberley Division, Western Australia. (Photo: Geological Survey of Western Australia)

karst regions. Dolines are of variable size and morphology. In size they may vary from a meter or so in diameter to over 1000 meters and from a few centimeters to over 300 meters deep. In temperate climates, the slopes of the dolines are not usually more than 20 or 30°, and the ratio of the depth to the diameter is of the order of 1:3. Figure 1 shows a portion of a doline covered area in Indiana.

Many factors control the development of dolines, the most important of which may be summarized as follows: (a) the geological structure of the limestones, such as the inclination of the beds, lines of faulting; asymmetrical dolines develop on dipping beds for instance; (b) the relief of the land; dolines are less conspicuous on steep slopes, because of the greater rapidity of surface runoff; (c) variations in the water level within the limestones; violent and rapid fluctuations in the water level as occur in some tropical humid areas cause massive collapse of the rock and change the relatively gentle funnel-like shape of the doline into a steep rock-walled "cockpit" (Versey, 1959); (d) climatic factors such as the duration of snow cover in an area; active solution of the limestone is important under a snow cover, and snowy regions often have intensive doline formation; (e) the nature of the vegetation cover. Trees and other vegetation in hollows can contribute by accelerating solution to the formation and enlargement of dolines.

Usually, though not necessarily, the deeper and wider dolines in any one limestone have taken longer to form. Dolines may enlarge until only a narrow divide separates one from another, and may coalesce to form *uvalas*. In some semiarid and arid karst regions, with steep relief, runoff is so rapid that doline formation does not occur and a normal network of surface drainage channels is present. Examples of this type of karst relief are found in the Fitzroy Ranges of northwest Australia (Fig. 2), and in the Guadalupe Mts. of southern New Mexico.

Caves, Blind Valleys

Though not all karst areas possess well-developed dolines, all possess underground caverns. Water enters the limestone by means of joints and dolines; it percolates underground and, if it still contains sufficient carbon dioxide, dissolves more of the rock. Movement of water in limestones is controlled largely by lithological variations and by joints and fault lines. Underground water can be conveniently divided into two zones; in the upper zone or *vadose zone*, the water is freely circulating; in the lower or *phreatic zone*, water is circulating under hydrostatic pressure and all the fissures and joints are filled. In both zones, water tends to collect into fairly well-defined channels and to move as a body underground. Solution and abrasion cause the formation of caverns which are important and significant landforms in a karst terrain.

Caves (see *Speleology; Limestone Caves*) tend to be located where massive limestones are bordered by other rock types. Ordinary streams developed on the insoluble rocks disappear into caves on reaching the limestone; these caves are known as caves of engulfment, and the disappearing valleys are known as *blind valleys* (q.v., blinden Taler, vallées aveugles, Cvijić, 1893). Caves also tend to occur at the base of a limestone series, where channels of water issue at the junction of the limestones with the other rocks; these caves are called caves of debouchure. Cave passages are of two main types, horizontal galleries, and vertical passages (sometimes called pitches or avens). The world's longest cave is claimed to be at Hölloch in Switzerland, and is over 70 km long, and the world's deepest cave is the Gouffre Grotte Berger, near Grenoble, France, which is over 1000 meters deep. Local solution and collapse of the limestone may produce cave chambers of enormous size, as for instance in the Postojna Cave in northern Yugoslavia, where one cavern alone is over 46 meters high, and in the Big Room of Carlsbad Cavern in New Mexico, which is over 1 mile in circumference, and 200 feet high.

In many caves, evaporation of water and loss of carbon dioxide take place; calcium carbonate dissolved from the limestone is redeposited in a variety of ways, particularly in the form of dripstones, i.e., *stalactite* and *stalagmite* (q.v.; see also *Speleothems*). Dripstones, except for stalactites, are rather poorly developed in caves in colder climates; massive stalagmite deposits are characteristic of caves in tropical climates. The finest dripstone deposits probably occur in caves in warm temperate humid areas. It is possible that studies of dripstone could elucidate some of the problems associated with climatic change, and this has been attempted in studies of caves in Central Europe (Kunsky, 1958).

It is probable that most of the caves of the world have been formed by solution and abrasion caused by movements of underground water at the level of the water table, the fluctuating and irregular surface between the vadose and phreatic zones (Swinnerton, 1932; Lehmann, 1932). Carlsbad Caverns in New

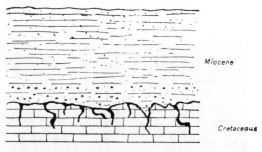

FIG. 4. Paleokarsts in Tunisia, where the cavernous Cretaceous limestone (below) offers an excellent aquifer beneath the thick cover of Miocene formations (from Castany, 1963).

Mexico are an exception to this and were most probably formed by solution of a well-defined body of water in the phreatic zone (Bretz, 1949). The roofs of large caverns may occasionally collapse forming both natural bridges and steep-sided cliffed hollows, sometimes known as collapse dolines (*Einsturzdolinen*; Cvijić, 1893).

Karst Hydrology

In a well-developed karst area, underground water tends to become integrated into a few large underground channels. This means that when the water issues at the surface, it is in the form of large springs; springs of great volume and depth are characteristic of karst regions. A good example is the spring at Ombla near Dubrovnik in Yugoslavia. The springs may be relatively quiet upwellings of water in more or less flat country, when they are sometimes known as "Blue Holes" or "Bottomless Pits," or they may issue from deep rock channels, like the Fontaine de la Vaucluse in southern France, when they are called "*Vauclusian Springs*"; such springs are under considerable hydrostatic pressure. Large springs are found in almost every karst area.

It is clear therefore that karst regions develop their own type of hydrology (Fig. 3). It is frequently asserted that because of the irregular fissuration of the rock and their highly cavernous nature, karst areas do not possess a water table in the ordinary geological sense. Local water levels are, however, very common. Furthermore, the vertical drainage of a karst terrain frequently becomes impeded by reason of the occurrence of less soluble beds or by the narrowing of the limestone fissures; such impeded drainage gives rise to local flood levels or "*Vorfluter*" (Lehmann, 1960). The flood levels become the sites of lakes, which are usually temporary or seasonal. Buried karst surfaces ("*paleo-karsts*") are often excellent aquifers (Fig. 4).

Polje Basins

Long-continued solution of the limestones by lake waters may form abraded rock platforms by

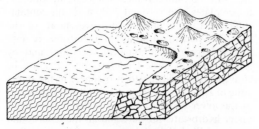

FIG. 3. Contrast between hydrologic regimes in impervious terrain (1) and limestone country (2). Note the formation of a *polje* with surface drainage, ending in a *blind valley* (q.v.), in the sinkhole covered karst (Roglič, 1960).

FIG. 5. Sketch of cone and cockpit karst up to 300 meters high in Permocarboniferous limestones (in the foreground) with tower karst (background) rising from an alluvial plain behind Faitsilong Gulf (left) in the Bay of Halong, North Vietnam (from air photograph by H. von Wissmann; Lehmann, 1954). One may observe the rounded concave shape of drowned uvalas around some of the towers.

means of a process of solution abrasion. Such abraded rock floors give rise to the locally leveled basins which become alluviated and are a feature of the chief karst regions of the world; they are known as *poljes* (q.v., from the Serbian, a flat field; Cvijić, 1893). Poljes are particularly well developed in the karstlands of Yugoslavia where both the complex geological structure and the seasonal flooding caused by the Mediterranean rainfall regime have assisted the development of the polje basins. Poljes are always associated in some way with impeded drainage and are not now considered to be a stage in the development of the landforms of a karst area; they are also not now thought to be necessarily unique to karst regions.

Surface Modeling

In addition to solution of the limestone by underground water, superficial solution of the rock by rain or soil waters also takes place. This superficial solution gives rise to a whole range of micro-landforms, which are important in almost all karst areas and which are of very varied morphology. In the Alps, where several different types of these

micro-landforms have been recognized, they are usually known by the general name of *karren* or *lapiés* (q.v.); here the most usual types of karren are those known as *Rillen-karren* and *Rinnen-karren* and these may vary in length from a few centimeters to about 20 meters (Bögli, 1960). The morphology of karren is probably dependent upon the rate and type of chemical reaction affecting the waters and the limestones; for instance, solution of limestone beneath a vegetation cover produces different types of micro-landforms from those formed from the action of intensive rain showers upon a bare limestone surface (see *Limestone Coastal Weathering*). Karren therefore tend to be of different types in the different climatic zones.

Erosion Rates

Calculations have frequently been made to assess the rates at which limestones are dissolved in different climatic and vegetational belts. Where there is little or no vegetation, the rate of solution of the limestone is probably more rapid in colder climates than in warmer climates, as figures from Corbel (1959) indicate. However, the role of CO_2 and hence vegetation in the solutional process of limestone is an important one; Adams and Swinnerton have shown that the adsorbed CO_2 in the soil can be up to 15 times that in the atmosphere and the solution of densely vegetated limestones can be very rapid (Sweeting, 1958). The solution rate of limestones in desert regions is very slow, but dew is effective in causing solution and reprecipitation on "oriented pebbles."

In tropical humid areas active surface solution by vegetable acids is also accompanied by rapid evaporation, and redeposition of the limestone takes place. In this way, large deposits of tufa are formed which are common in tropical areas; tufa deposits are also important in some Mediterranean areas, where they seem to be associated with the activities of calcareous algae and bryophytes. Redeposited or secondary limestone can frequently be harder than the limestone which was originally dissolved. Hence, relatively soft limestones may acquire a hard outer casing of tough redeposited limestone, a process which has been called case hardening; this can be shown to have affected the

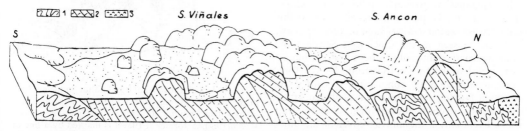

FIG. 6. Diagrammatic section through the Sierra de los Organos in Cuba (Lehmann, 1954). (1) Pizarras formation; (2) Lower Cretaceous and Jurassic Limestones; (3) Serpentine. On the left, the coastal plain karst of Vinales.

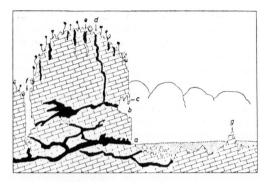

FIG. 7. Section through one of the tower-karst hills (*Turm karst*, German) of the Sierra de los Organos of Cuba (Lehmann, 1954). (a) "Foot case." (b) "Half cave." (c) Stalactite overhang. (d) "Yama" (sinkhole). (e) Rudimentary "yama." (f) Karst slot. (g) Isolated clint (*Karrenstein*).

Aymamóm Limestones of Miocene age in Puerto Rico (cf. "*Duricrust*").

Variations in the landforms of karst areas depend first upon the structure and lithology of the limestones. Thus the most complex cave systems occur in areas of Alpine-type folding, and poljes tend to be most developed in folded and faulted regions since the level of the "Vorfluter" is frequently structurally controlled. Secondly, variations are also dependent upon the major climatic differences of the world, and it is arguable that these climatic differences are of greater significance in the production of the total assemblages of karst landforms than purely geological considerations. This statement is perhaps best supported by the changes which take place in the morphology of dolines when they are subjected to the greater fluctuations in the level of the floodwater in karst areas in the humid tropics.

Cone Karst

The transformation of the dolines into steep-sided cockpits (named after the "Cockpit Country" of Jamaica) gives rise to a completely different assemblage of landforms in the humid tropics from those in temperate areas. A landscape with funnel-like hollows is replaced by a very much more dissected one consisting of a succession of cone-shaped hills separated by irregular hollows or cockpits (Figs. 5 and 6). Tropical karst terrain such as this is known as *cone karst* (*kegel karst* or *karst à pitons*), and can be seen in the Goenoeng Sewoe (now Gunung Sevu) country of southern Java, in Indonesia, as well as in Jamaica (Sweeting, 1958). Moreover, modification of cone karst is caused by recurrent flooding and alluviation of the cockpits; this process steepens further their already steep walls. Eventually if the alluvial cover of the limestone becomes considerable, limestone cliffs or towers are left standing above flat alluviated floors.

This form of landscape is known as *tower karst* (*turm Karst* or *karst à tourelles*) and reaches its finest development in southern China and in the Hanoi region of northern Vietnam (Wissmann, 1954). In some of the Caribbean islands (Cuba and Puerto Rico), such groups of steep-sided limestone towers (Figs. 7 and 8), situated in the midst of an alluviated flat limestone floor, are known as *mogotes* (q.v.) on the large scale, or *pepino hills* on a smaller scale. In some trade wind areas, the mogotes may be asymmetrical due to differences in weathering on their windward and leeward sides. Many geomorphologists believe that cone karst landforms similar to those now found within the humid tropics were formed in Europe during the Pliocene period, when warm humid climates were far more widespread than at present. "Paleokarsts" are known in which an ancient (e.g., Paleozoic) karst landscape has been buried and is now re-exposed.

Dry Valleys and Mero-karst

In many karst areas, landforms occur which are the relics of former fluvial erosion before vertical drainage was established. Such landforms are not true karst features, and the most important are *dry valleys*. Occasionally a river entering a karst terrain is of sufficient volume to maintain its flow and does not disappear entirely underground; deep limestone gorges are thus formed as in the Tarn Gorge in France and in the gorge of the Yangtse-Kiang in China. In areas where there are important impermeable beds within the limestones or where the limestones have been affected by recent glacial deposition, many traces of fluvial landforms occur; such terrains are known as *mero-karst*, one of the best examples being the Jura Mountains. Where a relatively thin cover of non-limestone rocks iies above a limestone series, collapsed dolines may appear in the cover rocks. Such dolines are caused by the development of cavities in the limestones

FIG. 8. Isolated tower-karst hill about 85 meters high in the Bay of Halong, North Vietnam, showing sharp intertidal undercut (cf. illustrations in *Limestone Coastal Weathering*). A former sea level is marked by a line of erosion of sea caves about 25 meters above mean sea level (Lehmann, 1954).

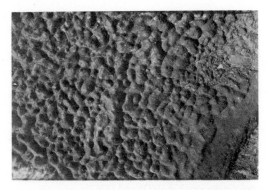

FIG. 9. Cone karst with numerous pepino kills, in the Lluidas Vale area of Jamaica (see sheet G, 1:50,000 map series). Vertical air photo (by kind permission of the Survey Dept., Jamaica).

into which the surface rocks collapse. This type of terrain is known as a *covered karst* and is well represented in New Mexico, near Santa Rosa, where thick Permian limestones are covered by Triassic sandstones.

Karst Residuals

In well-developed karstlands, it is possible that such traces of fluvial erosion may never have existed. But in time, by the solution and collapse of the limestone, and by the integration and coalescence of sinkholes, the less soluble rocks underlying the limestone series become exposed. Normal fluvial erosion begins to be established, and eventually, only residuals of limestone (known as *Hums*, q.v., in Yugoslavia; Cvijić, 1893) are left standing upon the non-limestone rocks below. Thus although karst landforms and karst processes are very distinctive, they normally form only a phase in the total geomorphic development of an area.

Non-calcareous Karsts

Certain other types of solution phenomena that lead to relief and microrelief forms due to solution, but not related to limestones, are also recognized. These may be concerned with ice freeze-melt processes in permafrost country (*thermokarst*, q.v.), to salt or gypsum solution (*salt karst*, q.v.), or to solution of unstable minerals in volcanic deposits such as tuffs (*volcano-karst*, q.v.).

M. M. SWEETING

References

Bögli, A., 1960, "Kalklösung und Karrenbildung," *Z. Geomorphol.*, *N.F. Suppl.*, **2**.
Bretz, J H., 1949, "Carlsbad Caverns and Other Caves of the Guadalupe Block, New Mexico," *J. Geol.*, **57**, 447.
Castany, G., 1963, "Traité Pratique des Eaux Souterraines," Paris, Dunod, 657pp.
Corbel, J., 1959, "Erosion en terrain calcaire," *Ann. Géog.*, **68**, 97–120.
Cvijić, J., 1893, "Das Karst Phänomen," *Penck's Geogr. Abh.*, **5**(3).
Cvijić, J., 1918, "Hydrographie souterraine et évolution morphologique du Karst," *Rec. Trav. Inst. Géogr. Alpine* (Grenoble), **6**(4), 56pp.
Kunsky, J., 1958, "Karst et Grottes," translated from the Czech by J. Heinz, for the *Bureau de Recherches Geologique*, Paris.
Lehmann, H., 1954, "Der tropische Kegelkarst auf den Grossen Antillen," *Erdkunde*, **8**, 130–139.
Lehmann, H., 1960, "La Terminologie Classique du Karst pour l'aspect critique de la morphologie climatique moderne," *Rev. Géogr. Lyon*, **35**, 1–6.
Lehmann, O., 1932, "Die Hydrographie des Karstes," *Enzykl. de Erdkde.*, Leipzig and Vienna.
Roglić, J., 1960, "Das Verhältnis der Flusserosion zum Karstprozess," *Z. Geomorphol.*, **4**(2), 116–128.
Sweeting, M. M., 1958, "The Karstlands of Jamaica," *Geograph. J.*, **124**, 184–199.
Swinnerton, A. C., 1932, "Origin of limestone caverns," *Bull. Geol. Soc. Am.*, **43**, 663–693.
Thornbury, W. D., 1954, "Principles of Geomorphology," New York, John Wiley & Sons, 618pp.
Trombe, F., 1952, "Traité de Spéléologie," Paris, Payot.
Versey, H. R., 1959, "The hydrologic character of the white limestone of Jamaica," *Trans. Second Caribbean Geol. Conf. 2nd, Mayaguez, P.R.*, 59.
Wissmann, H. von, 1954, in (Lehmann, H., editor) "Das Karstphänomen in der verchiedenen Klimazonen," *Erdkunde*, **8**, 112–122.

Cross references: *Biological Erosion of Limestone Coasts; Blind Valley; Cone Karst; Cycles, Geomorphic; Dolina; Dry Valleys; Duricrust; Hum; Lapiés; Law of Declivities; Limestone Caves; Limestone Coastal Weathering; Mogote; Polje; Relict Landforms; Salt Karst; Sink, Sinkhole; Speleology; Speleothems; Stalactite and Stalagmite; Thermokarst; Uvala; Volcano-karst. pr Vol. VI: Groundwater; Hydrology; Phreatic Water; Tufa; Vadose Water.*

KETTLE

Kettle is an old Anglo-Saxon term that is applied both to a domestic pot or basin and to a geomorphic feature, a depression or hollow of small dimensions, often as *"kettle hole."* In early geological literature it has at least five meanings: a fluvial *pothole* (q.v.), a glacial *moulin* (q.v.), a karst *dolina* (q.v.), a *moraine hollow* and an *outwash depression*. It is only in the last two senses that it is currently in use. The hollow is frequently water filled, so that it forms a *kettle lake, kettle pond* or swamp.

A detailed description of *moraine kettles* is provided by Fuller (1914, pp. 38–44). They usually "mark the depressions between two accumulations" of till of different stages (e.g., between the Harbor Hill and Ronkonkoma moraines on Long Island), "rather than the sites of buried or projecting ice blocks." The kettles of ordinary till moraines are usually small, only 30–300 meters across and up to 10 meters deep.

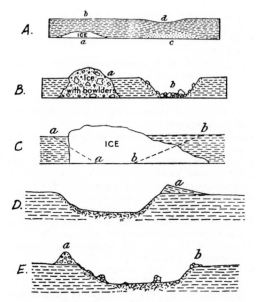

FIG. 1. (A) Section illustrating the formation of a kettle from a buried ice mass: (a) buried ice mass; (b) original outwash surface; (c) structureless sands occupying space of melted ice mass; (d) resulting kettle. (B) Same, but projecting ice mass, with boulders. (C) Showing relation between the slopes of kettle sides and the shape of melted ice mass: (a–a) steep kettle side resulting from steep ice face; (b–b) gentle kettle side resulting from sloping ice face. (D) Profile of kettle with outwash rim (a). (E) Section illustrating: (a) till rim; (b) boulder rim (Fuller, 1914).

The kettles on stratified till, especially in push-moraines, are more generally depressions left by melting ice blocks, usually with steep sides but in all shapes and sizes from less than 5 meters to more than 500 meters across, and varying from round basins to branching valleys.

Kettles in outwash deposits include perhaps the simplest and smallest forms, but they range up to several kilometers in width and up to 30 meters in depth. In some cases, the ice block was clear and merely led to a general subsidence when it melted; in others, the ice was heavily charged with boulders and these now form the floor of the kettle [Fig. 1(A), (B) and (C)].

Terraced kettles are marked by small, flat benches in their sides at intermediate levels. These are due, for the most part, to melting of irregular and projecting ice masses, in some cases to partial melting and redeposition, and in a third type to erosion during partial melting. Elevated kettle rims are sometimes formed by radial deposition or slumps from projecting ice [Fig. 1(D) and (E)].

Double and triple kettles and *kettle chains* are quite common in some areas, and on Long Island, for example, there are extensive outwash plains closely dotted with kettles. These are called *pitted outwash* plains. Thwaites (1935, p. 42) has described them as follows:

"Pitted outwash is formed only within the area occupied a comparatively few years before by ice. Isolated blocks of ice persist longest in preexisting depressions such as the kettles of buried terminal deposits and preglacial or interglacial valleys. In many places outwash must have been deposited on top of a more or less continuous sheet of stagnant ice of variable thickness. Deposition of sand and gravel went on so rapidly that it buried the ice masses or sheets in whole or in part thus retarding their melting. Thus the presence of pitted outwash in front of a moraine is positive proof that it is not the end moraine of the glacial stage in which it was deposited and that the moraine was not formed by a readvance after a long lapse of time. Some of the ice masses were not buried but stood above the adjacent outwash plain. When these melted, their contained debris was deposited as a *kettle rim* which locally contains till and boulders. Kettles formed by projecting ice masses can also be recognized by the fact that they (a) expose some of the underlying drift topography which there escaped burial by outwash, (b) contain more or less till and boulders once contained in the ice mass, or (c) both. The melting ice masses formed small terraces around their sides in favorable spots. In some places melting

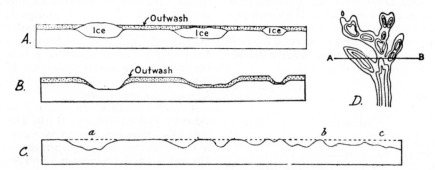

FIG. 2. (A) Residual ice masses partly buried by outwash. (B) Same, after melting of ice masses. (C) Pitted outwash or kettle plain: (a) isolated kettle; (b) divide between kettles rising just to level of plain; (c) kettle surface with no remnants rising to surface of plain. (D) Kettle valley system, as illustrated in profile A (Fuller, 1914).

occurred before the streams had finished depositing sediments. Then the resulting kettle was filled with silt, clay and deltaic deposits. The foreset beds of the latter are deeper than those of the normal outwash. Many ice masses were completely buried. Those which were small and deeply covered made slight sags in the plain. Larger ones left deeper kettles the sides of which slope at the angles of repose for wet sand and gravel. Kettles of this type commonly do not contain many boulders except those (a) normally present in outwash sediments or (b) eroded by the streams from nearby high spots in the underlying drift. Adjacent to kettles or pits the strata are commonly disturbed as a result of slump, but such disturbance is less than might be expected. In fact one geologist has suggested that many pitted plains were formed subglacially when the waters lifted large parts of the thin edge of the ice. In areas of outwash which were deposited on top of a large stagnant mass of ice and let down by melting extreme disturbance of the bedding should be expected. The writer, however, has never found good cuts which demonstrate this fact. The abundance of kettles reaches a maximum where only relatively small holes in the ice received sediments. Kettles are especially common at the contact with adjacent drift deposits.

"The occurrence of elongated valley-like kettles and long lines of kettles has puzzled several geologists. Such are the reflection of buried drainage lines, valleys in which the ice lasted longer than elsewhere. These valleys might be either preglacial or interglacial in age. That chains of kettles are not valleys blocked by morainal deposits is evident from the character of the sediments on the banks of and between the pits. It is not uncommon to find that kettle chains lead up to breaks in a moraine older than the plain through which the waters from the pitted plain escaped. The history of such is probably this: (a) during the time that the ice front stood at the older moraine a subglacial stream escaped through a low spot in the moraine, (b) the subglacial stream eroded or kept open a valley in the underlying drift, (c) during retreat of the ice stagnant masses of ice filled this valley, (d) those masses persisted during the time the waters from the wasting ice escaped through the low spot of the older moraine and formed the outwash plain, (e) after cessation of glacial drainage the ice masses melted leaving pits in the bottom of the outlet valley.

"Much outwash seems to have been deposited when the ice stood near to or at its maximum. This is explicable because it was then that conditions were stable for a time in general longer than during either growth or decay of the ice sheet."

Kettles are also associated with fluvioglacial sediments, but those formed subglacially are known too (Rice, 1961). They are much less common and are occasionally associated with kames (q.v.).

In areas long used for agriculture, it is often difficult to distinguish kettles from man-made pits of various sorts: sand, gravel, clay and marl pits. For example, in the English county of Norfolk alone, over 27,000 pits were counted (Prince, 1962). Some are undoubtedly also periglacial thaw sinks (Wolfe, 1953). Numbers of *pingo* depressions (q.v.) and *suffosion* craters (q.v.) are known in various places, and these can also lead to confusion. It seems inevitable also that a hypothesis of small meteorite craters is proposed for them from time to time.

Relict pingo depressions such as have been recognized in the Netherlands and elsewhere in western Europe, may often be recognized by their periglacial setting and stratigraphy. They have been referred to as *pseudo-kettles* (Gravenor and Kupsch, 1959).

RHODES W. FAIRBRIDGE

References

Fuller, M. L., 1914, "The geology of Long Island, New York," *U.S. Geol. Surv. Profess. Paper* **82.**

Gravenor, C. P., and Kupsch, W. O., 1959, "Ice-disintegration features in western Canada," *J. Geol.,* **67,** 48–64.

Prince, H. C., 1962, "Pits and ponds in Norfolk," *Erdkunde,* **16,** 10–31.

Rice, R. J., 1961, "The glacial deposits at St. Fort in north-eastern Fife: a re-examination," *Trans. Edinburgh Geol. Soc.,* **18,** 113-123.

Thwaites, F. T., 1926, "The origin and significance of pitted outwash," *J. Geol.,* **34,** 308–319.

Thwaites, F. T., 1935, "Outline of Glacial Geology," Ann Arbor, Michigan, Edwards Bros., 115pp.

Wolfe, Peter E., 1953, "Periglacial frost-thaw basins in New Jersey," *J. Geol.,* **61,** 133–141.

Woodworth, J. B., 1893, "An attempt to estimate the thickness of the ice blocks which gave rise to lakelets and kettle holes," *Am. Geologist,* **12,** 279–284.

Cross-references: *Dolina; Glacial Geology; Glacial Lakes; Glacial Moulin; Kame; Outwash Plain; Periglacial Landscape; Pingo; Pothole; Suffosion and Tundra Craters.*

KLIPPE—*See* STRUCTURAL CONTROL IN GEOMORPHOLOGY

KNICKPUNKTE—*See* NICKPOINT

KOPPIES—*See* BORNHARDT; TOR

L

LAG GRAVEL, DEPOSITS—*See* **DEFLATION**

LAGOON

A lagoon is an elongated body of water lying parallel to the coastline and separated from the open sea by barrier islands. Usually, it lies athwart the mouths of one or more streams (estuaries) (Fig. 1). As a consequence, the quiet water behind the barrier island is an ideal site for the deposition of stream-contributed sediment.

Lagoons are commonly shallower than estuaries, so the lagoon floor is subjected to reworking by waves. The turbulence developed by the waves may lift the bottom sediments into suspension, as well as keep much of the river-borne material in suspension, so that the finer sedimentary particles are carried to sea through inlets between the barrier islands. Even so, deposition is normally the dominant process in lagoons (Shepard, 1953).

Most lagoonal systems are compound in that they adjoin one or more estuaries. The environment is complicated, therefore, and each lagoonal-estuarine system has variations in its environment which are unique. The extensive lagoons of the Atlantic and Gulf coasts of the United States (Fig. 1) are good examples of such complexes.

Physiographic Factors

Lagoons have been considered as evidence of emergence of low-lying coastal areas (Johnson, 1919). They may also form along coastlines of submergence, however, and in some areas, the offshore barrier island has been constructed by longshore currents where neither submergence nor emergence has taken place within the life span of the lagoon.

Lagoons are most common along coasts bordering lowlands. The relief of the landward shore is negligible, therefore, as is that of the seaward barrier island. Sand dunes may form on the islands to heights of 300 meters, but more usual are dunes of from 3–10 meters.

Entrances. The entrance of a lagoon is restricted by the narrow tidal inlets through the barrier islands and the complex of sand bars which form on both the lagoonal and seaward side of the inlet. The inlet is usually kept open by tidal currents, but the longshore currents, developed by waves on the seaward shores of the barrier islands, may move or close the inlet. Storms may also close the

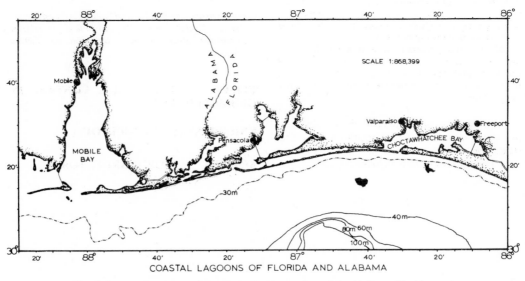

FIG. 1. Lagoonal and estuarine systems along a portion of the Alabama-Florida coast.

inlet or cut new inlets through the dune ridges on the barrier islands.

A large volume of water must pass through the entrance of a lagoon during each tidal cycle. The entrance is sometimes the deepest part of the lagoon. In most cases, the entrance is entirely through sediment so that the depth is in equilibrium with the volume of the tidal flow. Only slight deposition or erosion occurs from the action of the tidal currents.

Because the dominant action within a lagoon is deposition, the lagoon fills over a long period of time. The entrance gradually shoals because the amount of tidal water that must pass through the entrance is diminished. It still remains the deepest part of the lagoon until the basin is completely filled with sediment.

Sediment carried by longshore currents may be deposited in or on one side of the inlet. Where the longshore current is stronger than the tidal currents, the inlet tends to be filled and a "tidal delta" is formed on the lagoonal side of the entrance (van Straaten, 1950).

Substrate, Tidal Flats. Most of the bottom materials in lagoons are unconsolidated muds and sands in various combinations. Mud (mainly silt with varying percentages of clay-size particles and sand) is characteristic of regions of reduced current action. Such areas are in those parts of the lagoon farthest from the entrance. Near the tidal inlet, sand is dominant in the channel. Rocky surfaces are rare in a lagoon and, when present, are normally in the entrance where the currents keep the rock swept clean of sediment.

Tidal flats line the shores of lagoons and eventually fill them. The flats consist mostly of mud, except near the lagoonal entrance. Their surfaces are intertidal and thus are periodically exposed to air and then covered by water. Nearly all the water which covers the flats at high tide travels through tidal channels. The large channels are fairly straight, but the smaller ones, which act as both tributaries and distributaries, meander tortuously.

The meanders of the tidal channels follow characteristic patterns. Near the mouths of large channels, they have a cuspate shape, with the outside of the bends broadly concave and the inside pointed. Farther into the tidal flat, where a lesser volume of water passes than near the channel mouth the pattern becomes sinuous with nearly equal radii of curvature of both sides (Emery and Stevenson, 1957). Within marshes bordering the tidal flats, the channels may wind around among roughly circular patches of vegetation.

The winding channels may migrate through the tidal flats, and their patterns can be detected from aerial observation where former flats and marshes are completely filled.

Natural levees are common along the edges of the larger channels. Where the meanders are extremely tortuous, the levee may nearly completely enclose a marsh which then has a smaller pond in its center.

Water Characteristics and Currents

The tide is usually the most important ecological factor in a lagoon, because it is the agent which effects the exchange of water, and its vertical range determines the extent of tidal flats exposed and submerged during each tidal cycle. Where the tidal amplitude is low, as along the Gulf Coast of the United States, the wind is, at times, a more important agent than the tide in effecting water motion. The wind effect is most dramatic during violent storms and hurricanes. Water levels in the lagoon behind Padre Island, Texas, rose 8 meters above normal during Hurricane Carla in 1961. Even the passage of the usual winter cold fronts results in water movements in Texas lagoons which are more dramatic than the tide action. Lagoonal water is commonly encountered more than 50 km from the shore during the winter months.

The periodic changes in water level within a lagoon, which are produced by the tide, subdivide the area into ecological zones having horizontal boundaries. The height of the zones varies with distance from the tidal inlet. In most lagoons, the tide range decreases away from the entrance until at the upper reaches it is zero.

Currents. The currents in a lagoon are usually related to the tide. In the open sea the tidal current reaches its maximum at high and low tide. In the narrow entrance of a lagoon, the friction may be great enough to cause the water to be largely held back until a hydraulic head develops. In this case, the maximum current velocity is at mid-tide, or when the water level is changing fastest.

There are varying phase relationships of tidal height and current velocity which depend on degrees of closure of the lagoon and the volume of the lagoonal basin. At the upper reaches of a lagoon, the flooding and ebbing currents are zero at high tide and low tide. The currents in tidal-flat channels may have velocities of 2–3 knots. In the lagoon, velocities are much lower than in the channels, usually less than 1 knot, but in the inlet, velocities may reach 5 knots under a suitable combination of tide and wind conditions.

In hypersaline lagoons, slow currents are produced by the excessive evaporation within the shallow waters. The loss by evaporation is replaced by water from the open sea. A well-known example is in the Gulf of Kara Bogaz, Caspian Sea, into which water flows continuously from the open sea.

Where lagoons lie between an estuary and the open sea and receive more water from stream runoff than they lose by evaporation, the excess of water may leave in the form of a continuous seaward current. More commonly, however, the excess river water merely modifies the tidal currents within the lagoon, decreasing the rate and duration of the flood current and increasing the rate and duration of the ebb.

Temperature. The layer of water in a lagoon, and especially that over the tidal flats, is relatively thin. As a consequence, it follows the temperature variations of the air more closely than does the water of the open sea. The waters are, therefore, much colder in the winter and warmer in the summer than the adjacent sea. The diurnal variation in temperature is also great, especially where the water has flowed over previously exposed tidal flats. The water near lagoonal entrances is nearly the same temperature as that of the open sea, while greater departures occur with increasing distances from the entrance.

There are also vertical temperature variations, but they are not as pronounced as in estuaries because of the shallow depths common to the lagoonal environment. Cold surface water may form, temporarily, in response to short periods of cold winter weather. In the summer, solar radiation in the absence of winds (and thus, wind waves) may cause high temperatures in the surface layers. Where summer heating and evaporation are great, the warmed surface water may become so saline as to sink and flow out the entrance beneath cooler incoming seawater.

Salinity. On the basis of salinity, lagoons may be regarded as brackish, marine or hypersaline. Such designations may change with season, so that the terms are not usually suitable for classification.

Where normal estuaries enter lagoons, the lagoonal waters are brackish near the estuarine mouth and grade toward marine conditions near the tidal inlet. If the river discharge is low, or there is no entering estuary and the climate is temperate, the waters have mainly the salinity characteristics of the adjacent sea (Stevenson and Emery, 1958).

Lagoons in regions where evaporation exceeds precipitation and runoff have hypersaline waters. Evaporation increases the salinity of the surface waters which sink to the bottom and may flow seaward, to be replaced by incoming surface water from the open sea. This results in a salinity gradient which increases with depth and with distance from the lagoonal entrance.

Salinities in hypersaline lagoons may exceed 100 parts per thousand, as in the Sivash in the Black Sea (Fig. 2), which is three times that of normal seawater. Especially high concentrations occur in lagoons where the entrance is restricted by a bar or shallow sill, as in the Laguna Madre, Texas (Fig. 2). When salinities are as high as in the Sivash and Laguna Madre, salt is deposited on the shallow flats, and even on the lagoon floor.

In most lagoonal environments, the various salts are in different ratios than in the open sea. Where there is a significant runoff from the land, there is a higher ratio of carbonate and sulfate to chloride and of calcium to sodium than in normal seawater. In hypersaline lagoons, the ratios are reversed.

Oxygen and Carbon Dioxide. For oxygen and carbon dioxide content, see article on *Lagoon Sedimentation* (in pr Vol. VI).

Lagoonal Sediments

The coarsest sediment in most lagoons is on the barrier island and is composed of sand or even cobbles (as in many cases in southern California, New England, and Great Britain). Such material is normally too coarse to have been transported across tidal flats and has come from erosion of a sea cliff followed by longshore transportation. Sand on the barrier islands is well sorted, with few silt or clay-size particles, due to the turbulence of wave action.

If the flat floors of lagoons are deeper than about 6 meters, they are generally covered with sediment that is finer in the deeper waters. The sediment distribution in shallower lagoons is more complex, but usually follows a systematic pattern. Most of the flowing water is confined to channels that slowly migrate over the tidal flats. The finer grains are swept out and a residual deposit of coarse shell and sand is left in the channel (Stevenson and Emery, 1958). The tidal flats between the channels consist of poorly sorted mud that is finer with distance from the channels.

Manner of Deposition. The inorganic constituents of the sediments are derived from entering rivers, the outside sea floor, and from reworking of marsh and other recent deposits. Most comes from the inflowing rivers.

Deposition normally takes place at or beyond the end of the distributaries, thus prograding the tidal flats. Where there is fresh (or brackish) water entering the lagoon, it flows out on top of the denser seawater and carries with it a load of suspended silt and clay-size particles. The silt is deposited directly from suspension in the quiet lagoonal basin. Clay sizes, however, are mainly deposited through flocculation. Bourcart (1939) has noted that much sediment travels down the Seine River in large floccules. When these settle to the bottom, they stick there by capillary action.

Some sediment is swept into the entrances of lagoons by flooding tidal currents, but most of it remains near the inlet. During storms, additional material may be transported across the barrier island into the quiet lagoon, although most barrier islands are too large for such transportation to be common.

Lagoons are sites of continuous deposition. The average rate of deposition is far greater than in the open sea because most of the sediment contributed

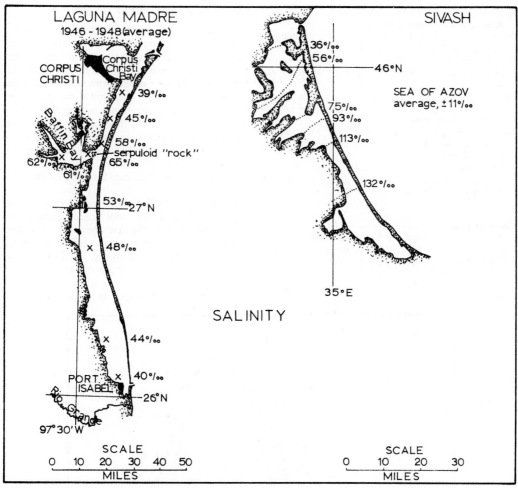

FIG. 2. Hypersaline lagoons in Texas and Russia (modified from Hedgpeth, J. W., 1957, "Biological aspects," in "Estuaries and lagoons," *Geol. Soc. Am. Mem.*, **67**, 1).

to the open sea comes from rivers which must first pass through the quiet settling basins provided by estuaries and lagoons. The fastest rate is atop the tidal flats and is a function of supply, height of the flat, and rate of subsidence as a result of compaction, diastrophism and eustatic changes of sea level. Along the Texas coast, there has been an average shoaling of 20 cm from 1875–1936 in spite of a general subsidence of the region of about 30 cm in the same period (Shepard, 1953).

Organic Constituents. The remains of all phyla of animals are buried in the sediment, but few may be preserved as fossils. So much organic debris is contributed from rivers, the open sea and the lagoonal waters, that Bourcart (1942) has termed the mud a biological milieu. Even though the remains are scattered and destroyed, they still have enriched the sediment in organic matter, calcium carbonate, silica, nutrients and other constituents.

In lagoons where evaporation is less than precipitation, the sediments have an organic nitrogen content up to 0.6 per cent. In hypersaline lagoons, organic nitrogen is much less (0.04–0.2 per cent). The value of 0.2 per cent organic nitrogen corresponds to 1.7 per cent organic carbon.

Phosphorus, like nitrogen, is abundant in normal lagoonal sediments (0.1–0.4 per cent in the Clyde Estuary, England). Calcium carbonate is highly variable because of the presence or absence of shells and of solution induced by low pH. Generally, there is an increase in calcium carbonate content from temperate to tropical lagoonal environments.

R. E. STEVENSON

References

Bourcart, J., 1939, "Sur l'origine des vasiéres de la Seine maritime," *Acad. Sci. Paris, Compt. Rend.*, **208**, 758–760.

Bourcart, J., 1942, "La vase, milieu biologique," *Soc. Biogéographie, Compt. Rend.*, 1–5.

Emery, K. O., and Stevenson, R. E., 1957, "Estuaries and lagoons," *Geol. Soc. Am. Mem. 67*, **1**, 673–750.

Johnson, D. W., 1919, "Shore Processes and Shoreline Development," p. 584, New York, John Wiley & Sons.

Shepard, F. P., 1953, "Sedimentation rates in Texas estuaries and lagoons," *Bull. Am. Assoc. Petrol. Geol.*, **37**, No. 8, 1919–1934.

Stevenson, R. E., and Emery, K. O., 1958, "Marshlands at Newport Bay, California," *Allan Hancock Foundation Publ. Occas. Paper 20.*

van Straaten, L. M. J. U., 1950, "Giant ripples in tidal channels," *Tijd. Kon. Nederl. Aard. Genoot.*, (*Waddensymposium*), 76–81.

Cross-references: *Barriers—Beaches and Islands*; *Coastal Plains*; *Delta Dynamics*; *Estuary*; *Kara-Bogaz Gulf*; *Lake Maracaibo*; *Levee, Natural*; *Mangrove Swamp*; *Tidal Inlet.* Vol. I: *Mean Sea Level*; *Ocean Currents*; *Tides.* pr Vol. VI: *Estuarine Hydrology*; *Estuarine Sediments*; *Lagoon Sedimentation*; *Swamp, Marsh and Bog*; *Tidal Flats.*

LAGOON (CORAL-REEF TYPE)

A coral reef lagoon is that body of water that lies within an atoll (annular) reef or within a barrier reef. It is generally assumed that an appreciable depth of water is maintained within the lagoon, say 5–50 meters. Those reef platforms which have some shallow pools a few feet deep that show up especially at low tide have sometimes been called *pseudo-atolls* or *pseudatolls*, and their pools thus "pseudo-lagoons" or "miniature lagoons," but these terms are not recommended. The miniature lagoon of a *faro* (q.v.) is termed a "velu." The terms "moat" or "lagoonlet" are often used for pools on platform reefs.

The floor of the lagoon in some areas may be largely free from living coral heads, pinnacles, or patches. This is often the case where there is a plentiful local source of terrigenous sediments, which tend to make the lagoon murky, the floor muddy, and in general inhibit coral growth. In other cases, the lagoon floor may become almost blocked by vast growths of coral patches. In the deeper lagoons,

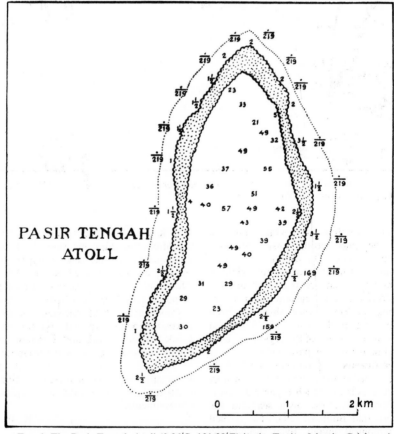

FIG. 1. The Pasir Tengah Atoll (0.26′S, 121.38′E) in the Togian Islands, Celebes. A perfect example of the complete ring-shaped, island-less atoll reef, enclosing a lagoon of moderate depth, but entirely surrounded by deep water. (All depths in meters. On hydrographic charts the conventional dot-bar figure indicates depths "greater than . . ., in this case over 219 meters or 100 fathoms.)

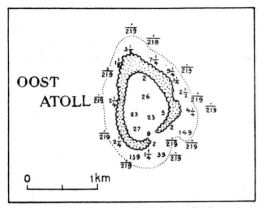

FIG. 2. The Oost (East) atoll in the Togian group (Indonesia). Influence of northwest winds is shown by horseshoe shape, and opening to lagoon in southeast.

below about 20 meters, one is below the depth limit for vigorous reef coral growth, and so such lagoons tend to remain permanently open; the pinnacles and coral patches now actively growing had their initiation between 10,000 and 15,000 years ago when the lagoon floor was appreciably shallower (before and during the postglacial eustatic rise).

In the case of shelf atolls, e.g., in the Great Barrier Reef lagoon, small lagoons similar to velus develop, but the ratio of depth to sediment accumulation rate is low and the interiors fill up, converting such reefs into platforms (Fairbridge, 1950). The growth and eventual filling of a lagoon is sometimes called the "*lagoon cycle.*"

The floors of coral reef lagoons ("*lagoon floors*") are normally well aerated, and the carbonate sands or *lagoon muds* (later to become *lagoon limestones*) are white in color; those barrier reef lagoons backing on to non-carbonate hinterlands display gray to reddish terrigenous muds and silts, e.g., the Australian Great Barrier Reefs, the insular barrier reefs of New Caledonia, Tagula (New Guinea), the "Great Sea Reef" of Fiji and the smaller reefs of Tahiti, etc. These lagoons are well ventilated due to the presence of so-called "openings," "passes" or "channels" that cut the barriers here and there. Such passages are as deep or deeper than the lagoon floor, although often extremely narrow, and date back to the late Pleistocene glacial period when a −100 meter sea level caused subaerial streams to cut narrow gorges through the borders of the reef foundations. Post-glacial growth of reef corals on the rim was favored by the post-glacial eustatic rise, but has been inhibited in passes owing to excessive depth or to muddy currents.

A constant current system is maintained in many coral reef lagoons, the incoming water breaking over the reef margins at all exposed points, and passing out through the openings. In oceanic regions, tides are generally small, but even so the out-

going current at ebb tide may make inbound navigation difficult. Off some of the mainland coasts, with tidal ranges of 5–12 m, e.g., the coral-lined passes of the northwest Australian coast, ebb tides set at up to 10 knots, thus constituting a severe navigational hazard.

In somewhat rare instances the lagoon of an atoll is totally closed. Cases are known in the Maldives (Sewell, 1935), in the East Indies (Umbgrove, 1947), off northwestern Australia (e.g., Seringapatam Atoll: Teichert and Fairbridge, 1948). In such cases, the lagoon floor is stagnant and the normally white carbonate mud is black and, when sampled, smells of H_2S. There is no benthonic population, apart from the bacteria.

The mean levels of lagoon floors tend to be rather constant (see Fig. 5). This uniformity precludes any possibility that they should be random depths. Daly (1910) made a systematic study of the figures (Table I) and prepared numerous profiles across typical examples (Daly, 1934). Since the development of precision echo sounding, however, it has been possible to show that many lagoon floors are not smooth, as previously thought, but are covered with small knolls and in places even have deep "sinkholes." Some examples of such deep pipes or holes have long been known in the Bahamas (where the reef is mainly eolianite) and are called "ocean holes." Examples of the knoll-studded lagoon floor are well illustrated at Eniwetok (Emery, Tracey and Ladd, 1954), and the reef full of holes or pipes is well exemplified by the Houtman's Abrolhos (Fairbridge, 1948). In both cases the features are inherited. The knolls are usually nonliving coral heads and pinnacles, "drowned" by the rapid rise of sea level about 10,000–6000 B.P. The pipes and holes, on the other hand, are karst solution effects (dolinas, etc.) dating from the last glacial period (mainly about 25,000–15,000 B.P.).

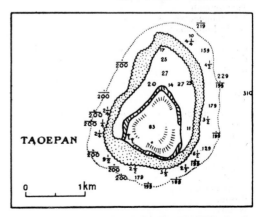

FIG. 3. Taupan Island (0.35′S, 121.37′E) in the Togian Group. Here there is a high rocky island in the center, bordered by fringing reef, lagoon and barrier reef. It shows the intermediate stage of subsidence between an island with a fringing reef and a true atoll.

TABLE 1. DEPTHS OF LAGOON FLOORS (from Daly, 1910, unrevised)

	1 Maximum Depth (fathoms)	2 Mean Depth in Deeper Part (fathoms)	3 Extreme Width (miles)	4 Extreme Length (miles)	5 Exposure to Waves (quadrants)
Great Barrier, Australia					
10–12° S latitude	32	15	72	—	2
12–14 ,,	27	15	35	—	2
14–16 ,,	34	20	33	—	2
16–18 ,,	37	20	35	—	2
18–20 ,,	36	22	65	—	2
20–22 ,,	37	25	100	—	2
Fiji Group					
Viti Levu, North West coast, barrier	46	35	30	—	2
,, ,, East ,, ,,	42	22	15	—	2
Vanua Levu, South West ,, ,,	49	35	15	—	2
,, ,, North ,, ,,	46	35	25	—	2
Wakaya, barrier	35	30	4	—	2
Mbengha. ,,	32	20	12	12	3
North Astrolabe Reef, barrier	18	10	3	4	4
Great ,, ,, ,,	31	20	6	10	3
Ngau, barrier	26	25	4	—	2
Nairai, ,,	26	18	3	5	3
Ringgold islands, atoll	52	40	6	30	4
Exploring islands, barrier	101[a]	40	10	25	3
Reid reef, atoll	20	18	6	7	4
Southern Argo reef, atoll	36	30	5	9	4
Hao, atoll (Paumotu group)	31	30	10	35	4
Gambier islands, barrier	38	18	6	7	2
Society Islands					
Tahiti, East coast, barrier	31	20	1.5	—	2
,, Taiaropu, ,,	30	25	1.5	—	2
Tahaa, barrier	27	20	2	—	2
Raiatea, ,,	33	20	2	—	2
Murea, ,,	27	20	1.5	—	2
Bora Bora, ,,	25	18	2	—	2
Huaheine, ,,	28	20	1.5	—	2
Tonga Group					
Nomuka group, plateau ca.	48	40	20	25	4
Haapai ,, ,, (Southern part) ca.	50	40	16	25	4
Vavau ,, ca.	65	55	12	25	4
Vavau island, barrier	50	40	—	—	—
Funafuti, atoll (Ellice group)	30	25	9	14	4
Arhno, atoll (Marshall islands)	32	22	10	20	4
Truk islands, barrier (Carolines)	36	30	35	35	4
Maldive Group					
Ihavandiffulu, composite atoll	34	30	6	12	4
Tiladummati, ,, ,,	29	20	12	30	4
Miladummadulu, ,, ,,	32	28	18	54	4
North Molosmadulu ,,	31	24 ⎫	—	—	—
Middle ,, ,, ,,	26	20 ⎬	20	60	4
South ,, ,, ,,	36	30 ⎭	—	—	—
Fadiffolu, ,, ,,	32	28	18	24	4
North Male, ,, ,,	38	33	20	24	4
South Male, ,, ,,	37	30	10	20	4
Felidu, ,, ,,	40	35	14	28	4
Ari, ,, ,,	43	35	15	48	4
North Nilandu, ,, ,,	37	30	14	18	4
South ,, ,, ,,	39	30	12	20	4
Mulaku, ,, ,,	42	35	15	25	4
Kolumadulu, ,, ,,	45	40	24	27	4
Suvadiva, ,, ,,	48	40	33	50	4
Makunudu, atoll	17	10	6	18	4
Horsburgh, ,,	23	20	4	9	4
Gaha Faro, ,,	22	20	4	7	4
Rasdu, ,,	23	18	4	5	4
Wataru, ,,	21	18	3	4	4
Addu, ,,	36	30	7	10	4
Haddumati, ,,	42	38	13	20	4
Great Chagos Bank	50	40	60	90	4

[a] At a local, very narrow trough in the lagoon.

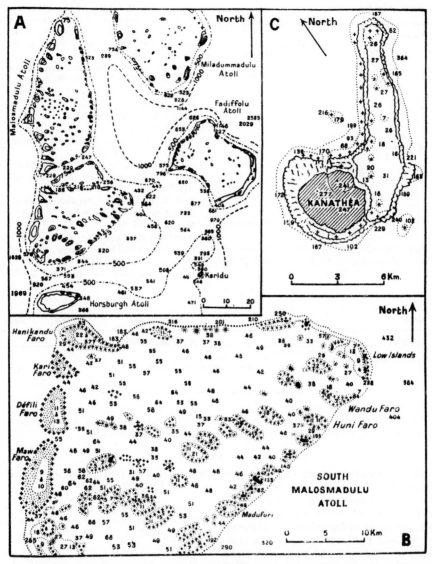

FIG. 4. Lagoons of compound type. (A and B) Minor lagoons within shelf atolls and faros within major complex atolls, in the Maldive-Laccadive Islands. (C) Combined barrier and atoll-type lagoon adjacent to a volcanic island, Kanathea, in the Fiji Islands (Guilcher, 1958). (By permission of Methuen & Co., London.).

Secondary lagoon features of atolls include the *lagoon beach*, the sandy fringe on the inner, protected side of the rim islets (if present); next comes the *lagoon flat*, the nearly horizontal reef flat lagoon-ward of the lagoon beach. It may consist of an old abraded reef rock, but more often is of newly grown coral heads and patches joined together with an in-filling of calcareous sand and coral mud; frequently, there are shallow pools with clusters of living coral communities. On the seaward side of the lagoon is the *lagoon scarp* or lagoon cliff (underwater), usually an abrupt boundary to the interior of the annular reef or an intermediate lagoon terrace (Fig. 6).

The outer margin of the lagoon is generally more abrupt and sharply defined than its inner margin. The term "lagoon island" (an outdated term), is mentioned by Charles Darwin as synonymous with "atoll"; but in a composite atoll or major barrier reef lagoon, there are many scattered islets, rising from within the lagoon, generally marking former shore-line (fringing) reefs that grew up with the postglacial eustatic rise, and these are also known as *lagoon islands*.

In the larger barrier reef lagoons, e.g., that of northeastern Australia, there are serried belts of inner reef platforms or patches. These reflect former

597

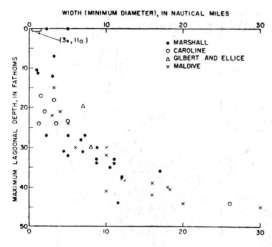

FIG. 5. Plot of 61 well-sounded oceanic atolls showing relationship of depth and diameter for atoll lagoons (Emery, Tracey and Ladd, 1954).

of the Pelsart Group of the Houtmans Abrolhos Islands," *J. Roy. Soc. West. Australia*, **33**, 1–43.

Fairbridge, R. W. and Teichert, C., 1948, "The low isles of the Great Barrier Reef: a new analysis," *Geogr. J.*, **111**, 67–68.

Fairbridge, R. W., 1950, "Recent and Pleistocene coral reefs of Australia," *J. Geol.*, **58**, 330–401.

Guilcher, A., 1958, "Coastal and Submarine Morphology," London, Methuen, 274pp, (translated by Sparks, B. W., and Kneese, R. H. W.).

Ladd, H. S., Tracey, J. I., Wells, J. W., and Emery, K.O., 1950, "Organic growth and sedimentation on an atoll," *J. Geol.*, **58**, 410–415.

Murray, J., 1880, "On the structure and origin of coral reefs and islands," *Proc. Roy. Soc. Edinburgh*, **10**, 505–518.

Sewell, R. B. S., 1935, "Studies on corals and coral-formations in Indian waters," *Mem. Asiatic Soc. Bengal*, **9**, 461–540.

Teichert, C. and Fairbridge, R. W., 1948, "Some coral reefs of the Sahul Shelf," *Geogr. Rev.*, **38**(2), 222–249.

Umbgrove, J. H. F., 1947, "Coral reefs of the East Indies," *Bull. Geol. Soc. Am.*, **58**, 729–778.

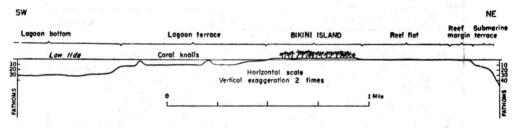

FIG. 6. Generalized cross section through the windward reef of Bikini island. Figure shows profile of island and reef, seaward and lagoon terraces, and lagoon bottom (Emery, Tracey and Ladd, 1954).

fringing reef foundations and are therefore associated with specific bathymetric contours. Between these belts there are generally open waters, which are usually marked out for navigation. They are technically referred to as *lagoon channels* (Murray, 1880). In the Great Barrier Reef they have a complete service of lighthouses and markers to make the channel continuously serviceable for over 1000 miles; it is often referred to as the "Ship Channel" or "Steamer Channel."

RHODES W. FAIRBRIDGE

References

Daly, R. A., 1910, "Pleistocene glaciation and the coral reef problem," *Am. J. Sci.*, 4th ser., **30**, 297–308.

Daly, R. A., 1934, "The Changing World of the Ice Age," New Haven, Yale University Press, 271pp.

Darwin, C., 1842, "The Structure and Distribution of Coral Reefs," First ed., London, 214pp.

Davis, W. M., 1922, "The barrier reef of Tagula, New Guinea," *Ann. Assoc. Am. Geograph.*, **12**, 97–151.

Emery, K. O., Tracey, J. I., Jr., and Ladd, H. S., 1954, "Geology of Bikini and nearby atolls," Pt. 1, *U.S. Geol. Surv. Profess. Paper* **260-A**.

Fairbridge, R. W., 1948, "Notes on the geomorphology

Wood-Jones, F., 1910, "Coral and Atolls," London, Lovell Reeve, 392pp.

Cross-references: *Atolls; Barriers—Beaches and Islands; Coral Reefs; Eustasy; Faro; Fringing Reef; Great Barrier Reefs.*

LAGOON DYNAMICS—*See* COASTAL LAGOON DYNAMICS

LAGOON GEOCHEMISTRY—*See* pr Vol. IV

LAGOON SEDIMENTATION—*See* pr Vol. VI

LAHAR—*See* MUDFLOW; *also* CRATER LAKES

LAKES

In the latter part of the last century Forel, the famous Swiss limnologist, defined a lake as a mass of still water situated in a depression in the ground without direct communication with the sea. Geologically speaking, they are temporary bodies of water which are usually formed rapidly and decay quickly, sometimes leaving only scant evidence of their existence in the geological record.

Today lakes are universally distributed; they are more abundant in high rather than low latitudes and are numerous in mountain regions. They are particularly abundant in those areas which have been recently glaciated. Lakes are common alongside rivers with low gradients and wide valley floors where they are obviously connected with changing river channels. Low lying areas bordering the sea may also have many lakes.

The waters of lakes may be fresh or saline, this condition being primarily controlled by climatic conditions. The source of lake waters today is direct precipitation and runoff; in some cases the water originally may have been seawater.

Lakes possess a marked individuality in physical, chemical and biological features; these are related to the isolation and position of any lake. Consequently, it is not possible to make too many generalities on this subject.

Classification of Lakes

Any lake may be formed by one or a number of agents. Various authorities have classified lakes in different ways—Davis (1882) and Penck (1882) adopted a classification based on the agencies which may have produced basins and have grouped them into *constructive*, *destructive* or *obstructive*. Others have grouped lakes as *rock basins*, *barrier basins* and *organic basins*. Both these systems can be criticized because they cut across natural regional groupings. For the limnologist who is concerned with a group of lakes, it is better to consider the agencies which led to their formation. Hutchinson (1957) puts forward such a scheme, and a simplified version of his classification is presented here.

Origin of Lakes

Tectonic Basins. (*a*) *Lakes Formed by Gentle Crustal Movements.* (i) Relict seas isolated from the sea by epeirogenetic earth movements, e.g., Caspian Sea and the Aral Sea. (ii) Uplift of the sea floor allowing irregularities to become lakes, e.g., Lake Okeechobee, Florida. (iii) The gentle tilting of an existing land surface leading to the reversal of drainage, e.g., Lake Kioga in East Africa (see Fig. 1). (iv) The gentle upwarping of the margins of a region resulting in a central basin, e.g., Lake Victoria (see Fig. 1).

(*b*) *Lakes Formed by Uplift of Peneplains during Orogenic Movements.* Here peneplains have been uplifted and now appear as intermontane basins, and lakes may occupy part of these depressions. In some cases local faulting may delineate the limit of the lakes. Examples of lakes of this type are found in the Altiplano of the Andes and include Lake Titicaca.

(*c*) *Lakes in Basins Formed by Folding.* A syn-

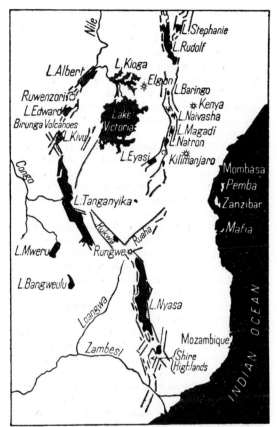

FIG. 1. Lakes of East Africa, showing lake due to reversal of drainage (Lake Kioga), lake in depression due to upwarping of margins of a region (Lake Victoria), and lakes in grabens.

clinal basin formed by folding is the site of Fählensee, Switzerland. In this case the synclinal basin is blocked by an anticline thrust across its lower end.

(*d*) *Lake Basins Formed by Faulting.* Lake basins formed by faulting and tilting, or by block faulting resulting in grabens, form an important category of lakes. Many of the world's great lakes fall into this category, e.g., Lake Baikal and Lake Balkhash of Central Asia, the lakes of the African Rift Valley (see Fig. 1), and the lakes of the Great Basin and the Sierra Nevada of North America.

Lakes Associated with Volcanic Activity. (*a*) *Lakes in Modified or Partially Modified Craters.* E.g., the lake in Crater Butte, California and the *maars* of the Eifel District of Germany.

(*b*) *Lakes in Calderas.* E.g., Crater Lake, Oregon, Medicine Lake, California, and Lago di Bolsena in the Roman Campagna.

(*c*) *Lakes in Modified Calderas Where Preexisting Faults are Important.* E.g., Lake Toba, Sumatra.

(*d*) *Lakes on Collapsed Lava Flows.* E.g., Myvatn, Iceland, and Yellowstone Lake, Yellowstone National Park.

(e) *Lakes Formed by Barriers of Lava, Volcanic Mud or Volcanoes.* Lake Kivu, East Africa, lakes around Bandaisan, Japan, and Lake Bunyoni, East Africa, are respective examples.

Lakes Formed by Landslides. Lakes in this category are usually extremely short-lived. Lake Sarez in the Pamirs is held by a rock slide and is quite stable. Some lakes, e.g., Lac de St. Andre, Mt. Granier, develop in irregularities on the surface of landslides.

Lakes Formed by Glacial Activity. Lakes formed by glacial agencies constitute a special category since they were formed during a very limited period of the earth's history. However, the Pleistocene glaciation has produced far more lakes than all the other agencies combined.

(a) *Lakes Held by Ice.* E.g., Märjelensee, Switzerland, against the Aletsch Glacier, or some Greenland lakes which are held by the Greenland ice-sheet ("Proglacial" or "Ice-dammed" lakes).

(b) *Lakes in Glacial Rock Basins.* (i) Cirque, Corrie or Cwm Lakes formed at about the snow line in glaciated valleys, e.g., Llyn Glaslyn, Wales, Blea Tarn, English Lake District, Iceberg Lake, Glacier National Park. (ii) Valley rock basins formed below the snow line by glacial erosion, e.g., the larger lakes of the English Lake District, the fjord lakes of Norway, such as the Nordfjord lakes, and many of the lakes in Alpine valleys. (iii) Lakes in basins produced by continental ice sheets scouring on an enormous scale, e.g., the Great Slave Lake and the Great Lakes of North America. (iv) Lake basins formed by glacial corrosion of planes of weakness on mature surfaces. Such lakes are usually small in size.

(c) *Lakes Held by Glacial Deposits.* Glacial moraines (often combined with glacial overdeepening) cause many lakes. Examples include the Italian lakes south of the Alps, Green Lake and the Madison lakes of Wisconsin which are held by terminal moraines, the Finger Lakes of New York State which are held by moraines at each end, and Lac de Barterand in the Jura which is held by a lateral moraine.

(d) *Drift Basins.* Kettle hole lakes, lakes filling depressions formed by the melting of blocks of ice trapped in glacial drift, are extremely common but are usually of small dimensions. Linsley Pond, Connecticut is an example of this type of lake. Other basins in drift may have been caused by erosion of ground moraine by subglacial streams, e.g., Jelserseen, North Germany. In permafrost regions of the present day, areas of local melting give rise to small lake basins. Examples of this type of lake occur in Alaska.

(e) *Pingo Lakes.* Pingo depressions, roughly circular depressions surrounded by rings of unconsolidated glacial debris, may be filled with water and thus give rise to Pingo lakes and ponds. These depressions are formed by the repeated slipping of morainic material off a partially buried mass of stagnant ice. The slipped material gives rise to concentric rings of debris. With the final melting of the ice a central depression may be formed. Pingo depressions have been described in the Paris Basin, the Low Countries and Wales.

Solution Lakes. (a) The solution of limestone by water can give rise to roughly circular depressions. These may be filled by water to give *doline* lakes, e.g., Deep Lake, Florida, while a fusion of dolines can give rise to *uvala* lakes, e.g., Muttensee, Switzerland.

(b) Lakes may be formed by solution in tectonically determined basins, i.e., *polje* lakes, e.g., Lake Scutari in the Karst region of Yugoslavia.

(c) Lakes formed by subsidence after natural solution underground of soluble salts, e.g., Mansfeldersee, Saxony, and possibly some of the lakes in the Landes region of France.

Lakes Due to Fluviatile Action. (a) *Fluviatile Erosion.* E.g., Falls Lake and Castle Lake which were plunge pools created by the falls in the Grand Coulee, Washington State, when it was a diversion channel in Pleistocene times.

(b) *Fluviatile Deposition.* (i) Alluvial fans and deltas divide existing lakes, e.g., Derwentwater and Bassenthwaite in the English Lake District and Loch Geal and Loch Lomond in Scotland. (ii) Levees of a main river which dam tributaries, e.g., along the Yangtzekiang, the Danube, or levees which create basins between the river and the scarp defining the flood plain, e.g., Catahoula Lake, Louisiana, or basins between levees in a delta, e.g., Lake St. Catherine in the Mississippi Delta. (iii) Basins formed by abandoned channels in mature flood plains, e.g., oxbow lakes.

Lakes Associated with Shore Lines. Lakes are often formed behind bars, spits and tombolos. Their formation is favored by a rise in sea level, causing the drowning of estuaries, followed by a fall in sea level, thus stabilizing the bars. Examples include some of the lakes in the Landes region of France, and many lakes bordering the Gulf of Mexico.

Lakes Formed by Wind Action. (a) *Lakes in Basins Dammed by Windblown Sand.* E.g., Moses Lake, Washington.

(b) *Lakes between Dunes.* E.g., lakes found in the Tarim Basin of Central Asia and in Cherry County, Nebraska.

(c) *Deflation Basins Formed by Wind Action.* Found in arid, or previously arid regions, examples of lakes in this type of basin occur in Australia, northern Texas and South Africa.

Lakes Formed by the Accumulation of Organic Matter. This class of lake includes those dammed by dense growths of plants, such as Silver Lake, Nova Scotia, and the lake on Washington Island in the Central Pacific which is in a coral atoll basin raised above sea level.

Lakes Formed by Meteorite Impact. Ungava or Chubb Lake, Quebec, is believed to have been formed in this way. The bay lakes of the southeast coast of North America have been claimed to have been formed in this way, but opinion is firmly divided on this point.

Lakes Produced by the Complex Behavior of Higher Organisms. This class of lake includes lakes caused by beaver dams and reservoirs, water-filled excavations and subsidence hollows created by man.

Size of Lake Basins

Only the area, volume and depth of some of the greatest lakes are given here.

Area:

(1) Caspian Sea: Tectonic (epeirogenetic) basin; saline: 436,400 km^2.

(2) Lake Superior: Glacially eroded basin; fresh: 83,300 km^2.

(3) Lake Victoria: Tectonic (epeirogenetic) basin; fresh: 68,800 km^2.

Volume:

(1) Caspian Sea: Tectonic (epeirogenetic) basin; saline: 79,319 km^3.

(2) Lake Baikal: Tectonic (graben) basin; fresh: 23,000 km^3.

(3) Lake Tanganyika: Tectonic (graben) basin; fresh: 18,940 km^3.

(4) Lake Superior: Glacially eroded basin; fresh: 12,000 km^3.

Depth:

(1) Lake Baikal: Tectonic (graben) basin; fresh: 1741 meters.

(2) Lake Tanganyika: Tectonic (graben) basin; fresh: 1470 meters.

(3) Caspian Sea: Tectonic (epeirogenetic) basin; saline: 946 meters.

Many lake floors are far below sea level:

(a) Tectonic basins: e.g., Lake Baikal—1279 meters; Dead Sea—793 meters; and Caspian Sea—972 meters.

(b) Excavated basins: e.g., Hornindalsvatn (fjord) lake) Norway—461 meters; and Loch Morar (glacial basin) Scotland—301 meters.

(c) Volcanic basins: Tazawako, Japan—175 meters.

Some lake surfaces are below sea level: e.g., Dead Sea—396 meters; and the Caspian Sea—25 meters.

Shape of Lake Basins

The shapes of lakes vary considerably and are often related to their modes of origin. Some examples are given here.

Circular: volcanic crater, doline and wind formed. *Sub-circular:* Cirque and kettle-hole basins. *Elliptical:* possibly meteorite basins. *Rectangular and sub-rectangular:* grabens and overdeepened valleys. *Dendritic:* flooded valleys. *Lunate:* oxbow lakes. *Triangular:* drowned valleys behind bars. *Irregular:* areas of glacial scouring and combined lakes.

Life History of Lakes

From the moment of their formation all lakes begin to disappear. In *humid regions* this is brought about by the erosion of the barrier at the exit of the lake and the deposition of detrital and organic matter as deltas and bottom deposits. No marked change in the chemistry of the lake waters is likely in their short history. In *arid regions* lakes disappear because of evaporation and the deposition of wind- and water-borne sediments. Because of evaporation many lakes in arid regions become increasingly saline though the ancestral lake may have been fresh, e.g., the Great Salt Lake and possibly the Dead Sea. Lakes which are descended from trapped seas usually become more saline, e.g., the Aral Sea. The Caspian Sea is a special case because its waters have become less saline; the reason for this is that the Gulf of Karabogaz on the eastern side of the

TABLE 1. ANALYSES OF LAKE WATERS

Constituent Salt	1	2	3	4	5	6	7[d]
CO$_3$	29.96	26.94	53.21	0.09	t	0.66	—
SO$_4$	11.93	38.35	5.29	6.68	0.28	23.70	17.36
Cl	9.96	0.57	0.87	55.48	66.37[a]	41.67	53.28
Ca	19.15	29.65	33.74	0.16	4.37	3.01	—
Mg	1.32	2.27	1.99	2.76	13.62	5.97	16.01
Na	8.32	0.64	0.75	33.17	11.14	24.44	11.51
K	4.00	0.38	0.74	1.66	2.42	0.53	1.83
SiO$_2$	13.93	0.71	2.37	—	t[c]	0.02	—
Al$_2$O$_3$ + Fe$_2$O$_3$	1.45[b]	0.49[b]	1·04[b]	—	—	—	—
Others	—	—	—	—	1.80	—	—
Total:	100.00	100.00	100.00	100.00	100.00	100.00	99.99
Salinity, ppm	27	270.5	122	203,490	226,000	12,670	163,960

[a]Includes 1.78 % Br.
[b]Includes traces of Mn.
[c]t = trace.

[d]See newer statistics under separate articles. N.B. For explanation see page 602.

Caspian Sea is the site of intense evaporation and consequently has led to the removal of salts from the waters of the Caspian Sea.

Lake Water

(*a*) *Composition of Lake Water.* The amount of dissolved salts in lake waters varies considerably, e.g., The Great Salt Lake contains 238.12 g/liter whereas Lake Geneva contains only 0.1775 g/liter.

The salts which are present in solution in lake waters are the result of the original composition of the ancestral lake, the salts in the waters entering the lake and the rate of evaporation (Table 1).

(1) Lac de Champs, Switzerland: fresh water derived from igneous and metamorphic rocks (Clarke, 1924; recalculated from Boucart).

(2) Lac Noir, Switzerland: fresh water derived from geosynclinal sediments (Clarke, 1924; recalculated from Boucart).

(3) Lac Taney, Switzerland: fresh water derived from calcareous sediments (Clarke, 1924, recalculated from Boucart).

(4) Great Salt Lake, Utah: saline (Hutchinson, 1957).

(5) Dead Sea: saline (Hutchinson, 1957).

(6) Caspian Sea: trapped sea water, reduced salinity (Russell, 1895).

(7) Gulf of Karabogaz, Caspian Sea: Saline-water drawn from Caspian Sea (Russell, 1895).

(*b*) *Movement of Lake Water.* The movement of water in lakes is usually turbulent, i.e., at any point in a lake, in addition to any average directional flow, variable movements in any direction may be observed. The turbulence permits the transfer of material and heat in any direction and increases the apparent viscosity. This last point helps explain the importance of wind-driven currents. Without this viscosity such currents would only have a shallow effect. The main currents are (i) the movement of water from influents to effluent (this is rarely important); (ii) tidal currents, as yet little studied and not believed to be important; (iii) density currents—these are important bottom sweeping currents caused by cold and/or sediment laden waters moving under the main body of lake water; and (iv) wind drift which leads to a piling of water at the down wind end of the lake and creates a return current. When the piling of water by wind ceases, the water flows back; since in the process the momentum is not lost, a new flow starts from what was the old upwind end. In this way in particular, a periodic rocking motion or *seiche* is produced. Uneven atmospheric pressure over a lake can also produce a seiche. The period of seiches is determined by the shape of a lake.

(*c*) *Temperature of Lake Water.* The temperature of lake water varies with the season and from place to place in the lake. Insolation, atmospheric temperature, inflow of rivers and rain all play a part in controlling the temperature of a lake. The varying temperature of lake water can lead to the stratification of the waters of a lake. (Stratification can also be caused by differences in the salinity and the amount of suspended sediment.) Lakes which are not *holomictic* (wholly circulating) are divided into an upper region of more or less uniformly warm circulating, fairly turbulent water, the *epilimnion*, and a lower relatively undisturbed region, the *hypolimnion*. The two regions are separated by a plane of rapid temperature change, the *thermocline*.

Stratification can be destroyed when the surface waters of the lake become cooler, and thus more dense, than the lower waters. When the cooled surface water sinks the lake waters are said to *turnover*. Turnovers tend to be seasonal. In those lakes where the temperature of the surface waters does not fall below 4°C (the temperature at which fresh water is most dense), there will be one turnover in the autumn. In those lakes where the temperature of the surface waters falls below 4°C there is a possibility of two turnovers annually.

Sediments in Lakes

Saline and freshwater lakes have markedly different deposits. Those of saline lakes may be predominantly evaporites interrupted by clastic sediments brought into the lake in periods of sudden flooding. The composition of the evaporites precipitated depends greatly upon the composition of the rocks in the catchment area, the climatic conditions, and the degree of evaporation, and the position in the lake in relation to the inflow. Organically formed sediments may be rare in such lakes since very few forms of life can be supported in the saline waters.

The sediments of freshwater lakes vary considerably in response to a host of factors. These include the nature of the origin of the lake basin, the character of the rock and soil around the basin and in the drainage area, the size and depth of the basin, the extent of shallow water near the shore lines, the relief and amount and type of vegetational cover of the drainage area, the climatic conditions, and the organisms dwelling in the lake. The deposits in any lake tend to be characteristic of that lake only; even closely adjacent lakes may have different deposits. Recent deposits in most freshwater lakes contain a high percentage of organic matter. Organic sediments range from recognizable plant and animal remains, sometimes called *Förna*, down to finely divided plant and animal matter of colloidal dimensions, which, when composed of unstable protobitumins, may be called *äfja*. *Gyttja* is a deposit formed from äfja under oxidizing conditions. The terms förna, äfja and gyttja were proposed by Wasmund (1930). These highly organic deposits may accumulate rapidly in the still waters of some lakes. Over 5 meters of such deposits have accumulated in Windermere, English Lake District, in about 8000 years. Many lake deposits can be dated accurately by a study of pollen and macroscopic plant remains trapped in the sediments. Such remains may also indicate changes in climatic conditions during the history of deposition in a lake. In recent years more accurate dating of organic sediments has been possible by the carbon-14 method.

Marked changes often occur in lake deposits soon after deposition, bacteria being particularly important in this respect. All newly deposited sediments are subjected to reworking by micro- and macro-organisms.

Studies of lake sediments have been largely confined to those in existing lakes. Some attention has been paid to sediments which predate the organic sediments described above. Particularly interesting are the *varved* sediments which occur in lakes which receive or have received at some time in their history, waters from melting ice sheets. A varve is the product of an annual cycle of sedimentation. The rapid melting of glacial ice during the spring and summer thaw leads to a high volume of water discharge. This carries into the lake relatively coarse-grained sediments giving rise to a coarse grained layer, while in winter, when freezing reduces or stops the inflow and when the freezing of the lake waters stops all water agitation, the finest sediments, which would normally be kept in agitation or swept out of the basin, are deposited. The winter layer is sharply separated from the succeeding summer band above but usually grades down into the preceeding summer layer. The pair makes an annual deposit and as such have been used to establish a late and postglacial time scale (Antevs, 1953).

ALEC J. SMITH

References

Antevs, E., 1953, "Geochronology of the Deglacial and Neothermal ages," *J. Geol.*, **61**, 195–230.

Clarke, Frank W., and Washington, Henry S., 1924, "The composition of the earth's crust," *U.S. Geol. Surv. Profess. Paper*, **127**, 117pp.

Davis, W. M., 1882, "On the classification of lake basins," *Proc. Boston Soc. Nat. Hist.*, **21**, 315–381.

Hough, Jack L., 1958, "Geology of the Great Lakes," Urbana, University of Illinois Press, 313pp.

Hutchinson, G. Evelyn, 1957, "A Treatise on Limnology," Vol. 1, New York, John Wiley and Sons, Inc., 1015pp.

Penck, A., 1882, "Die Vergletscherung der Deutschen Alpen, ihre Ursachen, periodische Wiederkekr und ihr Einfluss auf die Bodengestaltung," Leipzig, J. A. Barth, 483pp.

Russell, I. C., 1895, "Lakes of North America," Boston and London, Ginn & Co., 125pp.

Twenhofel, W. H., and McKelvey, V. E., 1941, "Sediments of fresh-water lakes," *Bull. Am. Assoc. Petrol. Geol.*, **25**, 826–849.

Wasmund, E., 1930, "Bitumen, Sapropel and Gyttja," *Förh. Geol. Fören. Stockholm*, **52**, 315–350.

Cross-references: *Aral Sea; Caspian Sea; Crater Lakes; Dead Sea; East African Lakes; Finger Lakes; Glacial Deposits; Glacial Lakes; Glacial Spillways and Proglacial Lakes; Graben; Great Lakes (North America); Great Salt Lake; Karabogaz Gulf; Kettle; Lagoon; Lake Atitlán; Lake Baikal; Lake Balaton; Lake Balkhash; Lake Chad; Lake Eyre; Lake Geneva; Lake Maracaibo; Lake Titicaca; Lake Toba; Lake Urmia: Lava-displaced Drainage and Deep Leads; Moraine; Oxbow Lake; Pluvial Lakes; Salton Sea.* Vol. I: *Baltic Sea; Black Sea; Seiche.* pr Vol. VI: *Lacustrine Sedimentation.* pr Vol. VII: *Palynology; Varve Chronology.*

LAKES, EAST AFRICAN—*See* EAST AFRICAN LAKES

LAKE AGASSIZ AND OTHER PLEISTOCENE LAKES — *See* GLACIAL LAKE AGASSIZ; GLACIAL LAKES

LAKE ATITLÁN

One of the world's most beautiful lakes, Lake Atitlán, is situated in the middle of Guatemala (14°40′S, 91°10′W), about 60 km west of Guatemala City. It is geologically a caldera depression in the Central American belt of late Tertiary and Quaternary volcanics. The last major, large-scale eruptions of ash and pumice [distributed further by lahars, or volcanic *mudflows* (q.v.) and *avalanches* (q.v.)] have been dated by radiocarbon in charcoal at 31,000 B.P. (Bonis *et al.*, 1966). The caldera has a diameter of 19 km (12 miles), and the lake is about 18 by 8 km (11 × 5 miles), covering roughly 120 km² (50 square miles). It is up to about 300 meters deep. It is 1562 meters (5124 feet) above sea level.

The southern border of the caldera is blocked off by three magnificent volcanic cones: Atitlán—3537 meters (11,603 feet); Tolimán—3158 meters (10,256 feet) and just north of Atitlán, San Pedro—3020 meters (9966 feet) just west of a little gulf and the town of Santiago Atitlán. On the slope of Tolimán, near the lake shore, there is a classical lava dome Cerro de Oro.

Hydrologically, the lake has only a small intake area and no surface outlet, but with tropical rainfall it remains fresh. There is probably underground leakage, because appreciable variations in level occur, and there are traces of several former terrace levels. To the south of the southern border of volcanoes, at the foot of the abrupt fall-off to the Pacific coastal plain, there are numerous springs which in part may represent leaking from the lake.

The monomictic lake waters appear to be fully circulating in the dry season, but Deevey (1957) found that in August the temperature at the surface is 24°C versus 20°C at the bottom.

RHODES W. FAIRBRIDGE

References

Atwood, R. S., 1933, "Lake Atitlán (Guatemala)," *Bull. Geol. Soc. Am.*, **44**, 661–668.

Bonis, S., Bohnenberger, O., Stoiber, R., and Decker, R., 1966, "Age of pumice deposits in Guatemala," *Bull. Geol. Soc. Am.*, **77**, 211–212.

Deevey, E. S., 1957, "Limnologic studies in Middle America, with a chapter on Aztec limnology," *Trans. Conn. Acad. Arts Sci.*, **39**, 213–328.

Ocana, D., 1933, "Descripción de la Laguna de Atitlán," *Anales S.G.H. (Guatemala)*, **11**(3), 297–302.

Williams, H., 1960, "Volcanic history of the Guatemalan highlands," *Univ. Calif. (Berkeley) Publ. Geol. Sci.*, **38**, 1–64.

Cross-references: *Avalanche; Caldera; Crater Lakes; Lakes; Mudflow.*

LAKE BAIKAL

The (true) freshwater lake with the greatest depth and the greatest volume of water in the world is Lake Baikal in the Buriat-Mongol Republic in Siberia (approximately 53°N, 108°E), with a depth of 1741 meters, a length of 674 km, a breadth of 74 km, embracing an area of 31,500 km² and a volume of 23,000 km³. Its surface is 462 meters above mean sea level. (The Caspian Sea is of course much larger but tectonically is a land-locked arm of the sea and partly salty. Lake Baikal is almost as large volumetrically as all the "Great Lakes" of North America put together; they have a collective volume

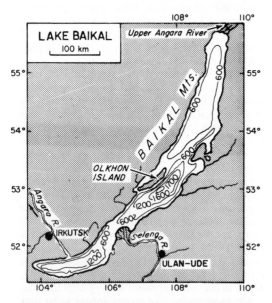

FIG. 1. Map of Lake Baikal, the world's deepest lake (adapted from Hutchinson, 1957). Note principal inflows: Upper Angara River in the northeast and the Selenga River in the southeast. In the southwest, through Irkutsk, is the outflow of the Angara River, which eventually joins the Yenisei River (depths in meters).

of 24,620 km³.) Its name in Mongolian is *Dalai-Nor*; in Turkish *Bai-Kul*.

In origin, Lake Baikal is a graben parallel to the Paleozoic and Precambrian structures southeast of the Anabar (Angara) Shield; however, its own history probably does not go back beyond Paleocene or late Cretaceous, but later tectonic revival has occurred. Nevertheless it is one of the oldest known lake basins that is still unquestionably a lake. Structurally it has an arcuate shape (northeast-southwest swinging in the north to NNE-SSW), parallel to the old structures but with three subdivisions. The northern part is divided by an oblique ridge (northeast-southwest), and the southern by the Selenga Delta infilling from the southeast (Fig. 1). Suslov (1947) mentioned that part of this delta collapsed catastrophically in 1861, so that it is likely that there are extensive turbidites on the lake floor. There is a small delta at the northeast end where the Angara River debouches. The drainage area of the lake is 650,000 km², from which it receives 163 km³ of water per year. Its width-to-depth ratio is 32:1, which is comparable to Lake Tanganyika (20:1) and other "taphrogeosynclines." Hutchinson (1957, p. 191) points out that like some other important structural lakes, Baikal is a "crypto-depression," i.e., much of the bottom is below sea level, in this case − 1279 meters, which is deeper than the bottom of the Dead Sea (− 793 meters), and thus the world's deepest continental rift.

On a large water body like this, an important seiche develops (oscillating over a 38-day period), but the true astronomic tide is limited to less than 1.5 cm. According to Vereshchagin (1937), Lake Baikal's dimictic thermal structure is more complicated than any other lake on account of its depth. In the surface waters down to 100 meters, there is a normal seasonal cycle, reaching a maximum of 19.1°C in the Selenga Delta in summer, though at that season the open water mean is only 9.0°C. Regular northwest winds cause a cold upwelling on that shore, rising from considerable depth. At 200–300 meters there is a mesothermic maximum of highest density about 3.7°C, below which is the "perennial zone" of little change in which the temperature varies no more than 3.38–3.16°C in over 1000 meters. Since the bottom is reasonably oxygenated (9.12 mg/l near the bottom), Hutchinson suggests that there is a slow convective overturn driven by terrestrial heat flow. This is in spite of a winter ice cover every season to a mean thickness of 92 cm from December to May.

The meteorologic effect of Lake Baikal on the area in the wintertime is extraordinary, raising the mean temperature by over 10°C, while in summer it lowers the regional temperature by 5–7°C, giving a summer heat income of about 100 cal/cm²/day (Fig. 2).

The lake is plentifully populated with fish, including some marine elements which may have mi-

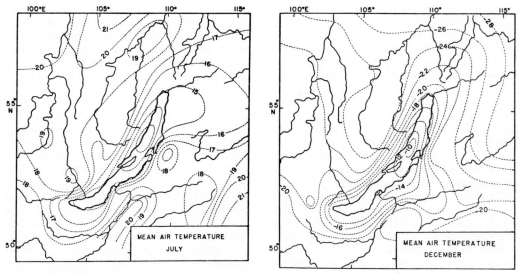

FIG. 2. Isotherms of mean ground level temperatures in July (left) and December (right). Note tempering effect of large volume of lake water, warming in winter, cooling in summer (Hutchinson, 1957). (By permission of John Wiley & Sons, N.Y.).

grated up the Lena, possibly under the pressure of glacial adversity in the Arctic Ocean. Most extraordinary is a deep-sea fish *Comephorus baikalensis*. There is also a seal (*Phoco foetida sibirica*).

RHODES W. FAIRBRIDGE

References

Hutchinson, G. E., 1957, "A Treatise on Limnology," Vol. 1, New York, John Wiley & Sons, 1015pp.

Suslov, S. P., 1947, "Fizicheskaia geografia SSSR: 'Zapadniia Sibir', vostochniia Sibir', Dal'ni Vostok, Sredniaia Asia," Leningrad and Moscow, 544pp. (in Russian).

Vereshchagin, G. Y., 1937, "Études du lac Baikal. Quelques problèmes limnologiques," *Verh. int. Ve. Limnol.*, **8,** 189–207.

Cross-references: *Caspian Sea*; *Cryptodepressions*; *East African Lakes*; *Graben*; *Great Lakes*; *Lakes*; *Pluvial Lakes*. Vol. I: *Seiche*.

LAKE BALATON

The largest lake in western or central Europe, the Balaton (*Platten See* in German), is situated in the western part of Hungary (46°50′N, 17°40′E). It is shaped like a slightly curved elongate rectangle, 77 by 13 km (48 × 8 miles), covers 600 km² (230 square miles), and stands at 106 meters above sea level.

The lake is fed by many small streams and one fairly large river, the Zala, which rises in the extreme west of the country. The lake overflows from the southeast, at Siófok, with the Sió River which even-

tually joins the Danube. Precipitation in the hills averages 700–1000 mm, but the lake, being rather shallow, has a fairly high evaporation. The average depth is only 2 meters, with a maximum of 12 meters. Its chemical composition is quite exceptional: CO_3 38.8, SO_4 21.5, Cl 2.9, Ca 8.9, Mg 12.8, Na 6.1, K 3.3, SiO_2 4.5, Al_2O_3 0.8, and Fe_2O_3 0.3 $\%_{00}$. It is described as a "sulfato-carbonate lake."

The Balaton is oriented ENE-WSW and lies along the southern margin of the Bakony Hills (the Hungarian "middle mountains") that separate the Great Hungarian Plain (Nagy Magyar Alföld) and the

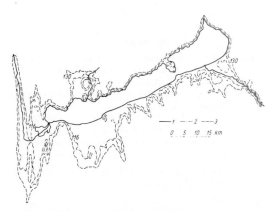

FIG. 1. Limits of abrasion activity at the presumed highest water level of the ancient Balaton (late Pleistocene) according to B. Bulla (from Pécsi, 1964). (1) Present-day beach line of Lake Balaton. (2) Evidenced limit of abrasion activity (116 meters above sea level). (3) Presumed limit of abrasion activity (132 meters above sea level).

Transdanubian Hilly Region (Dunántúli dombság) from the Little Hungarian Plain (Kis Alföld). Its southern margin is low and merges with the Somogy hilly region. The Bakony slopes consist of a foundation of block-faulted late Paleozoic metamorphic rocks and early Mesozoic sediments, with much limestone and dolomite, capped by outpourings of Tertiary volcanics. One cone, the Tihany, forms a striking peninsula midway along the north shore. It also controls the position of an interesting cuspate bar that attracted the attention of Johnson.

Cholnoky in 1897 reported a uninodal seiche for Lake Balaton, with a period of 690 minutes, which is quite unusual (Hutchinson, 1957).

The Somogy hilly region to the south consists of Pliocene sediments (Pannonian clays and Astian sands), often over 1000 meters thick. Late Pliocene epeirogeny caused general upwarping with marine regression, at the same time as block faulting and volcanic revival occurred in the Bakony. An almost continuous ENE–WSW fault trough developed across Hungary, and its slow subsidence caused the development of the Balaton depression. In the late Pleistocene, the southern borders of the Balaton lay 1–3 km farther south, and the cold epochs are marked by extensive solifluction colluvium from the hills, mixed or interstratified with wind-transported loess, and *grèzes litées* (stratified slope loesses). Further subsidence continued right into the late Würm, giving the lake a polygenetic structural origin. There were high lake levels in the interglacials, in the Alleröd and early Holocene (6–8 meters above present). Emerged clifflines, sand bars and peat swamps are common along the southern shore. During the Atlantic substage, 5000–6000 B.P., the lake almost dried up. (Basic surveys by Loczy, Cholnoky, Bulla, Kéz and Zólyomi are summarized in English by Pécsi, 1964.)

RHODES W. FAIRBRIDGE

References

Anon., 1891–1916, "Resultate der wissenschaftliche Erforschung des Balatonsees," *Ungar. Geogr. Gesell.*, Vienna, 1897 (Hölzel, editor), 3 vols.

Bulla, F., 1943, "Über die Ausbuildung und das Alter des Balaton Sees," *Földt. Közl.*

Hutchinson, G. E., 1957, "A Treatise on Limnology," Vol. 1, New York, John Wiley & Sons, 1015pp.

Pécsi, M., 1964, "Ten Years of Physico-geographic Research in Hungary," Budapest, Akad. Kiadó, 132pp.

Cross-references: *Holocene*; *Lake Balkhash*; *Lake Chad*; *Lake Eyre*; *Quaternary*.

LAKE BALKHASH

Situated in Kazakstan, USSR (46°30'N, 75°00'E), Lake Balkhash is interesting geologically as being the first place where modern dolomites were found in the process of formation. The lake is known as Ala-Denghiz in the Kazak language and Se-Hai in Chinese. It is 700 km long, 50–80 km wide, and 275 meters above mean sea level, extending northeast-southwest in a convex shape (like Lake Baikal), but in contrast to the latter is no more than 12 meters deep. While its area, 17,575 km^2, is close to the figures for Lake Ontario or Lake Chad, its depth is so slight that it is more comparable to the latter than the former. It is situated in an alluviated structural downwarp, possibly a true graben (Leuchs, 1937). Debouching into it is the large delta of the Ili, a river which rises in the Tien Shan. However, there is no outlet to the lake.

The level of Lake Balkhash has tended to rise and fall rather interestingly over the last century, not in phase with the Caspian which is fed mainly from the north, but rather like the Aral Sea which is fed, like Lake Balkhash, from the melting snow in mountains of central Asia (Altai, etc.). The record was as follows: 1859–93 falling, 1893–1910 rising, 1910–30 falling (by 2–8 meters), subsequently rising (Domratschev, 1933).

Chemically, the lake waters are essentially fresh; their salts are *athalassohaline*, that is to say, unlike the ions of sea-water. According to Byrstein and Beliaev (1946), they are rich in potassium, which they believe is responsible for a depauperated fauna. The planktonic and fish life is the poorest in any of the major Asiatic lakes. Around the shallow shores, however, there are immense growths of swamp vegetation, and following Lamb's observations on Lake Chad, the opinion has been expressed by Ochsenius (1904) that they act as salt concentrators, keeping the lake fresh in a region where the high evaporation would normally lead to hypersaline conditions.

It was on the shores of this lake which are periodically swamped by change of meteorological conditions and then dried out, thus simulating tidal action, that Strakhov (1953) found the first contemporary dolomites, after geologists had been looking for them for over a century. Subsequently, in littoral, supersaline lagoons and swamps, modern dolomites have been found in South Australia (the Coorong), the Persian Gulf, the Dutch West Indies (Bonaire) and in Florida, all marine or partly so; another dolomitic lake deposit has yet to be recorded. From the point of view of the Precambrian dolomite problem, it is interesting that Lake Balkhash is essentially a *fresh*water lake, i.e., lacking high ionic concentration and notably poor in sodium chloride, which might make it an interesting model for the Precambrian "ocean."

RHODES W. FAIRBRIDGE

References

Berg, L. S., 1950, "Natural Regions of U.S.S.R." New York, The Macmillan Co., 436pp. (translated by G. A.

Titelbaum from second Russian ed., 1938; Morrison, T. A., and Nikiforoff, C. C., editors).

Byrstein, J. A., and Beliaev, G. M., 1946, "Deistvie vody Ozera Balkhash na Volgo-Caspiiskikh bezpozvonochnykh (The action of the water of Lake Balkhash on the Volga-Caspian invertebrates)," *Zool. Zh.*, **25**, 225–236.

Domratschev, P. F., 1933, "Materialien zu einer physikalisch-geographischen Charakteristik des Sees," *Serv. hydrometeorol. USSR, Inst. Hydrol. Explorations des lacs de l'USSR*, **4** (Balkhash Exped.), Russian text, 31–53; German summ., 54–56.

Halbfass, W., 1922, "Die Seen der Erde," *Petermanns Mitt.*, Erganzungsheft 185, 169pp.

Leuchs, K., 1937, "Geologie von Asiens," Vol. 1, T.2, "Zentralasien," in (Krenkel, E., editor) "Geologie der Erde," Berlin, Borntraeger, 317pp.

Lotze, F., 1957, "Steinsalz und Kalisalze," Second ed., Berlin, Borntraeger, I, 465pp.

Ochsenius, C., 1904, "Hebungen und Verhinderung des Versalzens abflussloser Becken," *Z. Deutsch. Geol. Ges. (Berlin)*, **56**, 35–40.

Siegel, F. R., 1965, "High pH and primary dolomite," *Sedimentology*, **5**(3), 255–261 (with reply by Chilingar and Bissell).

Strakhov, N. M., 1953, "Diagenesis of sediments and its significance for sedimentary ore formation," *Izv. Akad. Nauk. S.S.S.R.*, **5**, 12–49.

Cross-references: *Aral Sea*; *Caspian Sea*; *Great Salt Lake*; *Lake Baikal*; *Lake Chad*; *Lake Eyre*; *Lakes*.

LAKE BONNEVILLE AND LAKONTAN—*See* GLACIAL LAKES; PLUVIAL LAKES

LAKE CHAD

Lake Chad (225 × 145 km; altitude 282 meters) is situated on the southern edge of the Sahara Desert, partly in the states of Chad, Nigeria, Cameroun and Niger (Fig. 1). It lies in the south-central part of a large, irregular sedimentary basin which reaches its lowest point in the Bodele Depression (altitude about 200 meters). The lake covers 22,600 km² (8700 square miles) of which 68 % is open water, the rest being covered by floating papyrus (*Cyperus papyrus*) rafts and anchored vegetation about the shores. The increasing salinity of the lake from south to north restricts vegetation mainly to the area of the lake south of the Baga peninsula. The western shore north of Baga is a uniform sandy beach with some vegetation. It is backed by a series of high linear sand ridges and these are broken by the small delta of the Yobe River. South of Baga the shore is irregular and formed of low, sandy islands with surrounding clay flats which are seasonally flooded and heavily vegetated. The southern shore is formed by a large compound delta of the Chari and Ebedji (El Beid) River systems which is being actively extended today. The eastern shore is very complex and is formed of hundreds of small linear sand ridges separated by clay flats (Fig. 2).

The lake is shallow, having an average depth of 3–5 meters in the south and 4–8 meters to the north. The floor is irregular and formed of parallel ridges. The lake level is lowest in July and August. The time of maximum rainfall in the catchment area is August and the lake rises rapidly in October and November, reaching its peak in late December. The annual rise is variable, between 65 and 130 cm, and the maximum level varies from year to year. Records have been kept since 1901 but are not strictly comparable. During the period 1901–57, thirty years had a peak value of less than 281.95 meters, 25 years between 281.95 and 283.15 meters, and only three years higher than 283.15 meters. However, a small rise in the peak flood causes a broad zone to be flooded.

The catchment basin extends further than the sedimentary basin (Fig. 1). Water is received directly from only three river systems, the Chari-Logone, the Ebedji and the Yobe. There may be slight seepage from the southerly clay plains which receive water from the Alo and Yedseram rivers which no longer reach the lake. Many north bank tributaries of the Yobe River are now dry, as is the Dillia river system in Niger, though there may be subsurface seepage to the lake. Rainfall over the lake surface has a mean annual value of between 180 and 400 mm.

Only the Chari River flows throughout the year in all years. The Ebedji and the Yobe may be reduced to a series of surface pools for two and four months, respectively. The total annual flow of the Yobe River reaching the lake is estimated at 0.131×10^9 cubic meters, with peak flow during September and October. The Ebedji River has an annual flow of 1.6×10^9 cubic meters, with peak flow in December when it may receive spill water from the Logone system. Annual flow is variable, but the degree of variation is not known. The Yedseram and Alo Rivers flow to the limits of their deltas for only two months of the year. In contrast, the Chari river has a flow of 38×10^9 cubic meters, representing approximately 95 % of the water received by the lake. The peak flood is in October or early November.

Figure 2 shows the concentration of sodium salts during April-May, 1957 (Bouchardeau, 1958). The dominant salt is sodium bicarbonate. The proportion of the soluble ions may be seen from the following example;

Ca	Mg	Na and K	Cl	SO$_4$	CO$_3$	Total
1.8	1.8	6.0	Trace	Trace	9.6	19.8 meq/liter

The total concentration will vary however throughout the year. Off Keronawa (Nigeria) the values for March, June and August, 1959 were 273, 383 and 164 ppm, respectively. Salt efflorescence (natron) occurs at the northern end of the lake.

The mean annual precipitation over the Chad

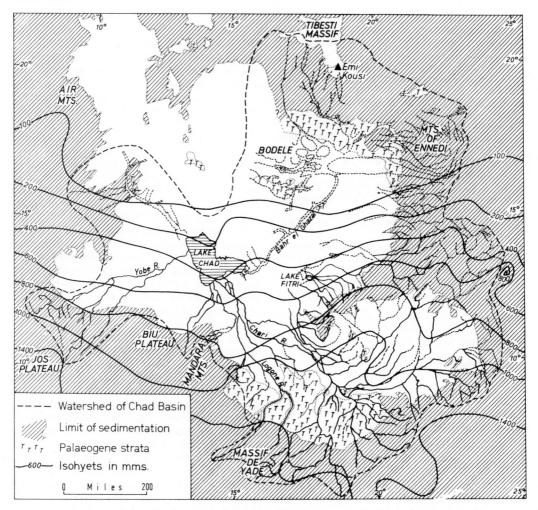

FIG. 1. The Chad basin.

basin is shown in Fig. 1. It has been estimated that evaporation-transpiration losses from the lake are 2000 mm/yr and seepage losses 260 mm/yr. A piche evaporimeter has recorded an annual loss of 3419 mm at Nguigmi.

In 1964 the Chad Commission was created, consisting of the four interested republics Chad, Niger, Cameroun and Nigeria, to coordinate and pursue research on Lake Chad and the Chad Basin. A UNESCO hydrological survey is in progress.

Evolution of Lake Chad

The Chad Basin is one of several major downwarps of the Precambrian crystalline Basement Complex of western and central Africa. It is closely paralleled by the Middle Niger Basin to the west, which was breached by an overflowing lake during the Late Pleistocene and has maintained this flow as the Niger River. It is possible that a similar breach

occurred in the Chad Basin and the waters of Paleo-Chad escaped via the Logone to the Benue. The basin is underlain by gently warped Cretaceous marine and fluviatile sediments which were deposited in several deep broad troughs trending WSW-ENE. Sedimentation of the basin started in the Paleocene with the sandy clay deposits of the "Continental terminal", but these appear to have been mainly at the basin edges. During the Pleistocene, however, over 800 meters was deposited in an essentially lacustrine environment at the centre of the basin. This sedimentation, which continues today, has been interrupted by arid periods. The sediments are mainly clays or sandy clays, but bores have proved three predominantly sandy sequences at depths of 30–90, 200–260 and 430–500 meters at Maiduguri, Nigeria (Barber, 1965). The middle sequence is a major acquifer and provides artesian water in a zone some 82 km wide about the lake in

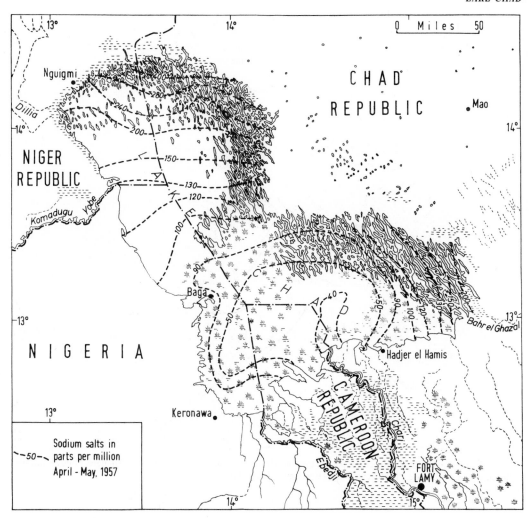

Fig. 2. Lake Chad.

Nigeria. Diatomite beds are also found between 270 and 310 meters deep. Diatomite beds from various localities have been described from Niger (Faure *et al.*, 1963), and C[14] dates of between 9000 and 6900 B.P. and one of 15,000 B.P. are recorded. These deposits imply that a lake, with a maximum depth of 180 meters and covering 1 million km[2] existed during the Late Paleolithic (Aterian) period. The lake represents a major pluvial period and can be correlated with the erosion of the Nile terraces and lacustrine deposits in the Hoggar Mountains.

An arid period represented by linear dunes aligned NNW-SSE has been recognized from deposits on the pre-Pleistocene land surface (Fig. 3), and was succeeded by the Aterian Lake. This lake was severely reduced in size during a subsequent arid period. As the lake retreated, a series of sandy deposits masked the clays, and these were formed into a series of seif dunes trending NNE-SSW (the

great erg of Hausaland; Grove and Pullan, 1963). A return to more pluvial conditions followed, the dunes were flooded in the central part of the basin, and a major beach ridge or offshore bar (Bama ridge) was formed along the southwestern shore, stretching for 480 km, with only minor breaks where it has been breached by rivers (Pullan, 1964). The ridge represents a lake at 320–332 meters. It has also been traced for 645 km from Massenya to Koro Toro in Chad. This lake, which was bounded by the Falaise d'Angama ("continental terminal" strata) in the north, may be represented by low ridges near the frontier of Chad and Niger, and formed the well-developed Cordon du Tal near Nguigmi. Montmorillonitic clay plains are associated with this lake stage. Its age is not known, but it can be tentatively correlated with the Neolithic, subpluvial period (5000–2400 B.P.), which has been recognized in the Nile Valley (Monod, 1963).

609

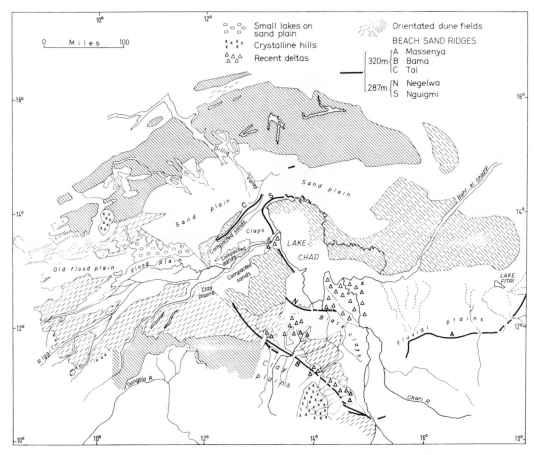

FIG. 3. Land forms in the south central part of the Chad basin. Elevation of Lake Chad: 282 meters. Note elevations of beach ridges of the late Pleistocene/early Holocene "pluvial lakes."

The lake subsequently retreated from the 320-meter stage, and a minor arid period followed with the formation of a small area of dunes aligned NNW–SSE. They have been described in detail from the area immediately east of the lake and reach a height of 50 meters at Mao. This dune field appears to have confined the lake to its present site and ensured the drying out of the lower Bodele depression which had no inflowing rivers. Lake Chad and the Bodele depression are joined by the valley Bahr el Ghazal which has well-developed but fossilized river meander patterns. It is probable that the lake overflowed into this valley during a minor rise in the lake level which flooded the edges of the NNW-SSE dunes and formed the Negelwa beach ridge in Nigeria at 287 meters. This ridge may be correlated with ridge fragments within the Ebedji and Chari deltas, such as at Bir Kerala, and with the multiple ridges running close to the present lake shore north and south of the Yobe delta. Small overflows have been reported since 1953.

C^{14} dates from a settlement mound south of this ridge on the clay plains indicate they were not waterlogged by 2400 B.P. (Connah, 1967). It is probable that this minor lake extension also led to the extension of Lake Fitri and the area of Ter Baro, which is a seasonal marsh today.

Alluviation continues today not only in the lake deltas but in many small deltas passing through the Bama ridge onto the clay plains which are seasonally flooded by rain and river floodwater.

R. A. PULLAN

References

Barber, W., 1965, "Pressure water in the Chad Formation of Bornu and Dikwa Emirates, North-eastern Nigeria," *Geol. Surv. Nigeria Bull.*, **35,** 138.

*Bouchardeau, A., and Lefevre, R., 1958, "Monographie du lac Tchad," Paris, O.R.S.T.O.M.

Connah, G., 1967, "Progress report on archaeological work in Bornu, 1964–66," Northern History Research Scheme, Second interim report, Zaria, Nigeria, pp. 17–31.

Faure, H., Nanguin, E., and Nydal, R., 1963, "Formations lacustres du Quaternaire superieur du Niger oriental: diatomites et ages absolus," *Bull. Bur. Res. Geol. Min.*, No. 3, 41–63.

Grove, A. T., and Pullan, R. A., 1963, "Some Aspects of the Pleistocene Palaeogeography of the Chad Basin," in (Howell, H. C., and Bourliere, F, editors) "African Ecology and Human Evolution," Viking Fund Publications in Anthropology No. 36, pp. 230–245.

*Monod, T., 1963, "The Late Tertiary and Pleistocene in the Sahara and Adjacent Southerly Regions," in (Howell, H. C., and Bourliere, F., editors) "African Ecology and Human Evolution," Viking Fund Publications in Anthropology No. 36, pp. 117–229.

Pullan, R. A., 1964, "The recent geomorphological evolution of the south central part of the Chad Basin," *J. West Afr. Sci. Assoc.*, **9**, 115–139.

* Additional bibliographic references may be found in this work.

Cross-references: *Beach Ridges*; *Delta*; *Floodplain*; *Pluvial Lakes*.

LAKE EYRE

Lake Eyre is the focus of a centripetal system of rivers which drain an area exceeding 1,300,000 km² of central and northeastern Australia (Fig. 1). The lake bed lies in the lowermost section of a vast tectonic depression of great complexity and antiquity; because the depression is tilted, both the locus of drainage and the river pattern are likewise asymmetrical. Lake Eyre is located in the far southwest of the drainage basin and lies some 14 meters below sea level; rivers such as the Diamantina, Thomson and Barcoo which flow to the lake from the northeast and east are much longer than those like the Macumba, Frome and Neales which run from the west or south.

Despite the extent of its catchment, Lake Eyre belies its name and is at present essentially a dry salina. Not only is the catchment as a whole hot and dry, but the salina itself lies in the most arid part of the arid continent. The annual rainfall averages less than 125 mm, with a mean variability of more than 50%, a value well above the world average. In a typical year, there are only 25 rainy days. Moreover temperatures are high, especially in summer. Marree, the nearest official recording station (Fig. 1), has a January mean maximum of 36.7°C and a minimum of 20.0°C; the values for July are 18.9°C and 4.4°C. This heating causes extreme desiccation: the potential evaporation is 305 cm/yr.

In these circumstances it is hardly surprising that the lake bed only rarely receives water from its contributary streams. Still more exceptionally is it covered by water. Observations over the past two decades suggest that although the short western rivers flow fairly frequently, their contribution to the lake is small. The shorter streams entering the

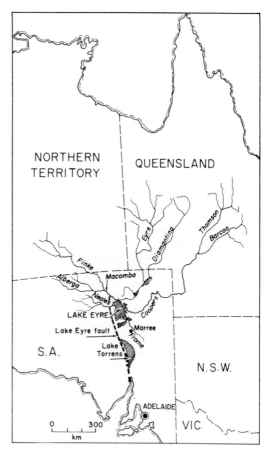

FIG. 1. The Lake Eyre drainage basin (eastern Australia). (On map, for "Macomba", read Macumba.)

lake basin from the south and east have a similar status. It is the great rivers which rise in the higher-rainfall regions of the eastern uplands and in the far north which determine the hydrology of Lake Eyre from year to year. These rivers—the Diamantina, the Thomson and the Barcoo—frequently flow in their headwater regions, but for the runoff to attain the distant bed of Lake Eyre, special circumstances must prevail. The rainfall must be extraordinarily high and widely distributed. In particular, heavy precipitation in the headwater catchments must be accompanied by substantial rains closer to the lake, in southwest Queensland and the northeastern part of South Australia.

The great flood of 1949–50 has been closely studied, and the peculiar conditions which obtained then may be taken as typical of those necessary for waters to reach the lake in sufficient quantity to cover the bed. During 1949, February and March rains averaged 220–250 mm over the Cooper and Diamantina catchments, compared to the long-term averages of 100–120 mm. More significantly, the rainfall in these two months over the South Austral-

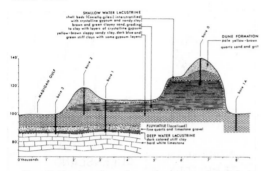

FIG. 2. Section through southeast margin of Lake Eyre (after D. King).

ian sections of the two drainage basins varied from 200–380 mm, or three to six times the normal. Floodwaters from the headwaters of the Cooper and Diamantina river systems are usually lost in a vast distributary network in the lower reaches, but with this area saturated by the abnormal February and March rains, the rivers scoured the channels near the lake and breached the massive sand drifts blocking the waterways, so that in June 1949, water flowed into the lake. Rainfall in late 1949 and early 1950 was again well above average in northeastern South Australia, and in the central Queensland catchments was markedly above normal, with most stations registering the heaviest totals on record, 750–1250 mm. With the downstream distributary areas saturated, and with the channels still open after the 1949 flood, the 1950 rains and run-off filled the lake. It has been estimated that more than 25 million acre-feet of water reached the lake during 1949 and 1950.

The Lake Eyre salina occupies an area of 9300 km². The sedimentary record shows, however, that this ephemeral water body is but the shrunken remnant of a huge lake, which, because of the long continued subsidence of the region, persisted through most of later Cenozoic times. This larger water body of the recent geological past is often referred to as *Lake Dieri*, after an aboriginal tribe of the area.

In common with many other parts of Australia, much of northern South Australia by the early Mesozoic had been reduced to a land surface of low relief. Exhumed remnants of this ancient plain form a significant element of the modern land surface at the eastern border of the Shield, to the west of Lake Eyre. The Jurassic and Cretaceous saw the spread of the sea over much of Australia, and widespread and massive deposition of marine sediments in the Lake Eyre basin. Toward the end of the Cretaceous and the earliest Tertiary, lacustrine and riverine conditions represented by the *Winton Formation* prevailed in the region. Winton sediments are the oldest penetrated by bores put down beneath the bed of Lake Eyre. Over most of the broader Lake Eyre basin, Winton and older strata were subjected

to prolonged erosion and weathering, culminating in the development of a siliceous duricrust (*silcrete*) as a pedogenic horizon during the Miocene. This old duricrusted surface was warped along old established tectonic axes during the late Tertiary.

The silcrete is not encountered, however, beneath the bed of the Lake Eyre salina. Possibly it once extended over the area and has since been removed by erosion. In view of the negative tectonic character of the region, it is more likely that the persistence of lacustrine conditions even through this widespread and prolonged phase of subaerial denudation prevented the development of the duricrust.

Following the accumulation of the silcrete, there were widespread lacustrine conditions which continued through the later Cenozoic. The most important deposit related to this period is the *Etadunna Formation*, which is primarily dolomitic though it includes pyritic and carbonaceous clays. It contains fish teeth and bones, a few foraminifera and occasional ostracodes, is about 40 meters thick and of late Tertiary age. Beneath Lake Eyre, the Etadunna Formation is succeeded with strong erosional disconformity by about 10 meters of Quaternary lake sediments, mainly silt, clay and salt. The salts consist primarily of sodium chloride, magnesium sulfate and magnesium chloride (in that order), with minor amounts of calcium carbonate, calcium sulfate and sodium sulfate. The details of Quaternary history, and particularly the origin of the Lake Eyre salina itself, are still controversial.

One view is that the depression occupied by the salina is a vast deflation hollow created by wind erosion during the late Pleistocene. This dating derives from evidence described from the southeastern margin of the lake (Fig. 2). Here, the dunes adjacent to the lake are of windrift type. The cores of the dunes are formed by eroded lake sediments in which occur shells of *Coxiella gilesi* which according to C[14] analysis are almost 40,000 years old. Organic materials from beneath the nearby lake bed have been dated as almost 20,000 years old. The deflation may have lowered the lake bed to 18 meters below

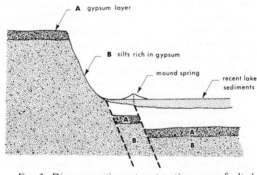

FIG. 3. Diagrammatic west-east section across faulted western margin of Lake Eyre salina.

sea level, and 4 meters of sediment have accumulated over the older depositional surface.

Evidence concerning late Pleistocene and recent climatic changes in the nearby Simpson Desert suggests an alternative explanation. The dune sands form merely a veneer (maximum thickness less than 40 meters), overlying strata of various ages but including fossiliferous fluvial and lacustrine sediments no more that 10,000 years old. Thus the aridity to which the modern dune fields are related is a Holocene phenomenon. It may be, of course, that there was an earlier late Pleistocene desiccation also, but the sedimentary record of the adjacent regions argues against it. Moreover, evidence from the western side of Lake Eyre strongly suggests that the salina depression is due to downfaulting in the late Pleistocene (Fig. 3).

The evidence for faulting at the western margin of the lake bed is as follows:

(a) The western margin of the bed is a steep escarpment which, though dissected in detail, is in broad view rectilinear in plan, running virtually north-south.

(b) The western margin is seismically active.

(c) Mound springs on the lake bed close to the western margin are not randomly distributed but occur in distinct zones trending north-south.

(d) The escarpment is capped by massive crystalline gypsum which is underlain by gypsiferous silts; a similar sequence is intersected below the most recent lake sediments beneath the bed of the lake.

(e) The fault zone suggested by these features conforms to the regional pattern of major faults or lineaments and in particular can be projected to join up with the prominent fault zone which delineates Lake Torrens on its western side (Fig. 1).

Thus, Lake Eyre appears to be a tectonic depression (either a sag feature or a down-faulted block) superimposed upon a broader tectonic subsidence. About 4 meters of sediment have been deposited on the lake bed since the down-faulting in the late Pleistocene, and during rare fillings of the lake (a study of the 1949–50 floods and an examination of relevant meteorological records suggest that it may be filled perhaps three times each century), wave trimming caused the development of steep, though low, cliffs in the unconsolidated sediments exposed at its margins.

C. R. TWIDALE
BRUCE MASON

References

Bonython, C. W., et al., 1955, "Lake Eyre, South Australia: The Great Flooding of 1949–50," Report of Lake Eyre Committee, Adelaide, 75pp.

Bonython, C. W., and Mason, B., 1953, "The filling and drying of Lake Eyre," *Geogr. J.*, **119**, 321–330.

Johns, R. K., and Ludbrook, N. H., 1963, "Investigation of Lake Eyre," *Geol. Surv. S. Aust. Rept. Invest*, No. 24, 104pp.

Wopfner, H., and Twidale, C. R., 1967, "Geomorphological History of the Lake Eyre Basin," in (Jennings, J. N., and Mabbutt, J. A., editors), "Landform Studies from Australia and New Guinea," Ch. 7, pp. 119–143, Canberra, Austr. Nat. Univ. Press, 434pp.

Cross-references: *Aral Sea*; *Holocene*; *Lake Balkhash*; *Lake Chad*; *Lakes*; *Quaternary*; Vol. II: *Evaporation*.

LAKE GENEVA

The Lake of Geneva, or Lac Léman (*Lacus Lemanus*, in Latin), is the most important lake in Switzerland (46°27′N, 8°50′E). It measures 72 by 13 km (45 × 8 miles), with an area of 580 km² (224 square miles). Its elevation is 375 meters (1230 feet). Part of the south shore belongs to France (with the town of Evian).

The lake is fed by the Rhône and drained by its continuation, rising high in the Alpine snow fields and debouching into the Mediterranean. The lake's shape is arcuate, extending from the east and swinging to the southwest. The inflow of the Rhône near Villeneuve, in a phenomenon called *La Bataillère*, is normally yellow with sediment, but this load is rapidly dropped and the lake is normally a clear blue. The exit near Geneva is likewise of clear blue water, but on the edge of the city it is joined by the River Arve, which brings in an impressively turbid load; the two contrasting waters flow side by side for some distance before mixing. The level of the lake is high from May through October, corresponding to the thaw season in the Alps.

The seiches of Lake Geneva have long attracted attention, especially because of the funnel effect of the constriction at the southwest end, precisely at the city of Geneva, where the water level rise can be dangerous. Many theories have been proposed to explain them: sudden rush of meltwater, atmospheric pressure effects, electric charge effects during thunderstorms, and so on (Hutchinson, 1957); it was Forel (1876) who developed the basis for modern seiche theory here (see Vol. I: *Seiche*). Classical studies of the *mirage* (*q.v.*, Vol. II) or *fata morgana* were also made here by Forel (1897, 1912).

Geologically, the origin of the Lake of Geneva—along with most other Alpine lakes—has been a subject of some controversy. Lyell, Heim and others favored a tectonic origin, and there is no doubt that several of the lakes are oriented along preexisting structural lines. In contrast, numbers of other geologists, e.g., Ramsay, Penck and Brückner, prefer a glacial scour origin. In favor of the second hypothesis are the transverse character of many of the lakes and the presence of morainic dams at their exits. This seems to be the true explanation. In comparing these mountain lakes to those in broad depressions like the Great Lakes of North America, it should be recalled that the scouring possibilities of long, narrow valley glaciers under a high relief potential are likely to be appreciably greater than for the far more extensive but more sluggish continental ice sheets.

Sediment deposited by the Rhône at the eastern end of the lake forms a big subaqueous delta which is channeled by an important sublacustrine canyon extending at least 8 km. Turbidites are constantly discharged down this channel, just as in the ocean (Forel, 1892), and there is a miniature "abyssal plain." Slumps also occur from time to time, even displacing the shores of the lake; Heim analyzed those that occurred at the village of Horgen in 1875 and 1877 (summarized in English by Grabau, 1913).

RHODES W. FAIRBRIDGE

References

Dussart, B., 1966, "Limnologie," Paris, Gauthier-Villars, 678pp.

Favre, J., 1935, "Histoire malacologique du lac de Genève," *Mém. Soc. Phys. Hist. Nat. Genève*, **41**(3), 295pp.

Forel, F. A., 1873, "Les taches d'huile connues sous le nom de fontaines et chemins du lac Léman," *Bull Soc. Vaudoise Sci. Nat.*, **12**, 148–155.

Forel, F. A., 1876, "Le formule des seiches," *Compt. Rend.*, **83**, 712–714; Also *Arch. Sci. Phys. Nat.*, **57**, 278.

Forel, F. A., 1880, "Températures lacustres: recherches sur la température du la Léman et d'autres lacs d'eau douce," *Arch. Sci. Phys. Nat.*, Ser. 3, **3**, 501–515.

Forel, F. A., 1885, "Faune profonde des lacs suisses," *N. Denkschr. schweiz. Ges. Naturw.*, **29**(4), 234pp.

Forel, F. A., 1892, "Le Léman: monographie limnologique," Vol. 1, "Géographie, Hydrographie, Géologie, Climatologie, Hydrologie," Lausanne, F. Rouge, 543pp.

Forel, F. A., 1895, "Le Léman: monographie limnologique," Vol. 2, "Mécanique, Chimie, Thermique, Optique, Acoustique," Lausanne, F. Rouge, 651pp.

Forel, F. A., 1897, "Réfractions et mirages. Passage d'un type à l'autre, sur le lac Léman," *Bull Soc. Vaudoise Sci. Nat.*, Ser. 4, **32**, 271–277.

Forel, F. A., 1901, "Handbuch der Seenkunde: allgemeine Limnologie," Stuttgart, 249pp.

Forel, F. A., 1912, "The Fata Morgana," *Proc. Roy. Soc. Edinburgh*, **32**, 175–182.

Grabau, A. W., 1913, "Principles of Stratigraphy," New York (Dover reprint, 1960).

Hutchinson, G. E., 1957, "A Treatise on Limnology," Vol. I, New York, John Wiley & Sons, 1015pp.

Joukowsky, E., and Buffle, J. P., 1938, "Constitution physique et chimique des sédiments du lac de Genève," *Mém. Soc. Phys. Hist. Nat. Genève*, **41**(4). 415–466.

Lüdi, W., 1939, "Analyse pollinique des sédiments du lac de Genève," *Mém. Soc. Phys. Hist. Nat. Genève*, **41**(5), 467–497.

Cross-references: *Finger Lakes; Glacial Lakes; Glacial Scour; Great Lakes; Lakes.* Vol. I: *Abyssal Plains; Seiche.* Vol. II: *Mirage, Fata Morgana.*

LAKE MARACAIBO

Situated at 9–10.4°N latitude, 71–72°W longitude, on the Caribbean coast of Venezuela, Lake Maracaibo has an area of 5500 square miles (142,000 km^2). Its maximum depth is 115 feet (35 meters).

The geosynclinal basin in which Lake Maracaibo lies has been slowly sinking and has accumulated some 16,000 feet of post-Eocene sediments which support a major oil field. The depression in which the lake lies has had nearly the same size and shape since the Oligocene, but its connection with the sea has varied so that the sediments alternate between marine, brackish, freshwater, and terrestrial deposits (Sutton, 1946). The lake is connected with the Caribbean Sea, via the Gulf of Venezuela and Tablazo Bay by a strait some 50 feet (15 meters) deep. The topography suggests that the Strait of Maracaibo represents the course of a river which once drained a freshwater lake and which has been flooded by the postglacial rise in sea level (Redfield, 1958).

Tides and Currents

The tides of Lake Maracaibo and its approaches are attributable to standing waves produced by the tidal waves of the Gulf of Venezuela and their reflection from the head of the lake. A node for the semidiurnal constituents occurs in the northern part of the lake, and an antinode is present in Tablazo Bay. The presence of the antinode is indicated by the fact that when the tide is rising, the current flows into the bay southward from the Gulf

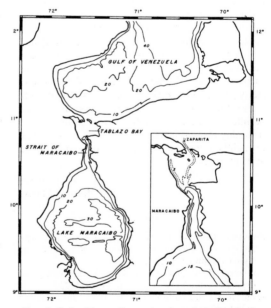

FIG. 1. Lake Maracaibo and approaches. Depths in meters.

of Venezuela and northward from the lake. The reduced velocities at the antinode appear to be responsible for the accumulation of sediments in Tablazo Bay, which is very shallow (about 10 feet or 3 meters).

The range of tide decreases along the approaches, from 3 feet (0.92 meter) in the Gulf at Zaparita to 0.7 feet (0.22 meter) at Maracaibo. In the northern part of the lake, the tidal range is reduced to about 0.05 feet (1.5 cm) but is somewhat greater along the southern shore (0.2 feet or 6 cm). The lake is subject to temporary seiches set up by the wind, which obscure the astronomical tides.

The semidiurnal currents in the approaches to the lake reach maximum velocities of 0.6 knot (or 30 cm/sec) at Maracaibo. Within the lake, the water circulates in an anticlockwise direction with velocities which approach 0.7 knot (35 cm/sec) presumably as the result of the prevailing wind system. Along the shore, the astronomical tides cause this circulation to vary in velocity but do not result in a change in direction (Redfield, 1961).

Salinity

In spite of the lake's connection with the sea, about 95% of its water is derived from precipitation on its watershed and on the lake surface. The northern part of the lake lies in a semiarid region but the southern end falls within the tropical rain belt. Freshwater reaches the lake from the Catatumbo River and minor tributaries along the southern shore. The salt water which enters from the Strait of Maracaibo causes the lake water to be brackish to a degree which varies with the balance between the outflow of lake water and the inflow of seawater. During the wet season (summer), the outflow of lake water becomes so great that very little salt water can enter along the approaches and the result is a slight reduction in the salt content of the lake water. Long periods of exceptionally high or low rainfall produce more pronounced changes in the salt content of the lake. Prior to 1956, the chloride concentration of the surface water of the lake fluctuated about a value of 750 ppm. An exceptionally dry period from 1947–1950 led to an increase in chloride concentration to 1100 ppm. An exceptionally rainy period in 1955–1956 was followed by a decrease in lake chlorides to 400 ppm. A similar drop was recorded in 1938. Deepening of the navigation channel across Tablazo Bay, completed in 1956, has been followed by an increase in lake chlorides which now appear to have become relatively stable at 2000–2200 ppm.

The saline water which enters the lake from its approaches is more dense than the lake water and, consequently, tends to sink to form a layer above the bottom, having a chloride content which may exceed 3000 ppm. This layer is devoid of oxygen and contains hydrogen sulfide. The counter-clockwise circulation of the lake causes this more saline water to rise toward the surface near the center of the lake and, as a result, the surface waters are slightly more saline at the center. During periods of heavy rainfall when the seawater entering the lake is greatly reduced, the deep water of the lake becomes oxygenated and can no longer be recognized by its high chloride content (Redfield and Doe, 1964).

Temperature

The temperature of the lake water is quite uniform except for a′ slight warming of the surface during the day. It ranges from 29°C in February to 31°C in September. The deep water which enters the lake from the strait is somewhat cooler, having temperatures of 28–29°C.

Sediments

The sediment of the bottom of Lake Maracaibo is a soft blue mud which is unconsolidated to depths as great as 30 feet (10 meters). The content of organic carbon is high. Around the margin of the lake where the bottom water is oxygenated, the organic carbon content is about 1 or 2%. It increases to more than 5% near the center where anaerobic conditions usually prevail. Evidently, large quantities of incompletely oxidized organic matter are incorporated into the sediment in the anaerobic area. The sediments of Tablazo Bay, the Strait of Maracaibo and along the northwestern shore of the lake are sandy (Redfield, 1958).

Biology

Lake Maracaibo is exceptional in providing a relatively large and stable environment of low salinity. The phytoplankton of the lake consist of freshwater forms which tolerate the low salt content, while the animals present are for the most part marine forms adapted to low salinities. During the period when the chlorinity of the lake has increased to above 1000 ppm, shipworms and barnacles have appeared in the lake in numbers which have caused serious damage to the oil installations. In recent years, a shrimp fishery, yielding more than a million dollars annually to the fishermen, has developed in the Gulf of Venezuela, Lake Maracaibo and their connecting waterways. About a third of this comes from the shallow waters along the northern part of the lake, from Tablazo Bay and the Straits, and from the adjacent coastal regions of the Gulf (Ewald, 1964).

Gessner has stated that Lake Maracaibo may well be the richest in plankton of all the waters of the earth. Undoubtably it supports an exceptionally rich flora of phytoplankton. The plant nutrient content of the water, as judged from its phosphate content, is not exceptional as compared with ocean water. The high fertility of lake water appears to depend upon the rapid recycling of nutrients set free by the decomposition of plants in the deeper water combined with the favorable conditions of high temperature and strong sunlight associated with the tropical position of the lake (Redfield, 1958).

ALFRED C. REDFIELD

References

Ewald, J. J., 1964, "The shrimp fishery in Western Venezuela," *Proc. Gulf and Caribbean Fisheries Institute,* Nov. 1964, 23–30.

Redfield, A. C., 1958, "Preludes to the entrapment of organic matter in the sediments of Lake Maracaibo," *Habitat Oil Symp.* Am. Assoc. Petrol. Geologists, June 1958, 968–981.

Redfield, A. C., 1961, "The tidal system of Lake Maracaibo," *Limnol. Oceanog.,* **6,** 1–12.

Redfield, A. C., and Doe, L. A. E., 1964, "Lake Maracaibo," *Verhandlungen Internationalen Vereinigung theoretische u. angewandte Limnologie,* **15,** 100–110.

Sutton, F. A., 1946, "Geology of Maracaibo Basin, Venezuela," *Bull. Am. Assoc. Petrol. Geologists,* **30,** 1621–1741.

Ziegler, J. M., 1964, "The hydrography and sediments of the Gulf of Venezuela," *Limnol. Oceanogr.,* **9**(3), 397–411.

Cross-references: *Estuary; Lagoon; Lakes.* Vol. I: *Fertility of the Oceans; Ocean Currents; Primary Production; Salinity in the Ocean; Seiche; Tides;* pr Vol. VI: *Estuarine Hydrology; Estuarine Sedimentation.*

LAKE TITICACA

The largest lake in the Andes, Lake Titicaca, is partly in Bolivia and partly in Peru. It is roughly 210 by 56 km (130 × 35 miles), covering 9000 km^2 (3500 square miles). Its elevation is 3812 meters (about 12,507 feet), thus the highest of the world's major lakes. It is fed by numerous streams from perennial snows in the Eastern Cordillera of the Andes, though the trough where it lies is largely a rain shadow area and semiarid. There are more than 30 islands in the lake which reaches a maximum depth over 400 meters (1300 feet). The shore is highly indented and the lake is divided into two parts (Lakes Chucuito and Uinamarca, respectively, the larger in the northwest), being separated by the Yunguyo and Achacachi promontories; the connecting Tiquina Strait is in places only about 1.5 km (1 mile) in width.

The lake overflows to the southeast, into the Desaquadero River, which degenerates into salinas and the saline Lake Poopó (Lake Pampa Aullagas). Titicaca is quite fresh, being fed by snow waters, and the intake exceeds evaporation. Lake Poopó, up to 100 km long, the second largest in Bolivia, is in contrast highly saline; the incoming waters filter through the pervious sands and gravels of the lake floor; its average depth is only 2 meters, and the shores are marshy and indistinct.

There are no major cities around Lake Titicaca, but there are numerous Indian settlements (mostly fishing villages) and two towns—Puna (in Peru, at the northwest end) and Guaqui in Bolivia. There are also extensive traces of Inca stone constructions (especially on Titicaca Island, or "Island of the Sun") and of pre-Inca megalithic people dating to about 4000 B.P. The latter are particularly on Coati Island and at Tiahuanaco, some distance south of the present lake. There are successive terraces of older and higher lake levels, which correspond to evidence of progressive down-cutting of the Desaquadero River.

Geologically, Lake Titicaca lies in the complex graben-faulted Altiplano, the Andean structural equivalent of the Basin-Range Province of North America and the various *Zwischengebirge* (median mass) structures of the Alpo-Himalayan orogenic belts. The Eastern Cordilleran side consists of much-folded Paleozoic geosynclinal sediments faulted against Cretaceous and other Mesozoic formations (Newell, 1949). According to Newell, there were giant low-angle overthrusts, but Arnold Heim (1947) and subsequent workers believe that folding is more significant in this complex. Gerth (1955) could find no trace of low-angle thrusts. There was late Tertiary vulcanism, mainly in the Western Cordillera, on a vast scale, accompanied by major uplift and the block faulting of the present Altiplano. There has been claimed to be some old erosion surfaces (pediplains?) that may have been much lower in the Pliocene, so that the rate of uplift (as demonstrated elsewhere in the Andes) must have been extraordinary, averaging, say, 1 mm/yr for 4 million years. Garner (1963) and others doubt this.

The Altiplano depression is largely filled with late Tertiary and Quaternary lake deposits, volcanic deposits and, later, extensive alluvial fans. Steinmann (1929) believed that the Pleistocene snow line was lowered here by 600–700 meters. Both Troll (1937) and Heim (1951) have stressed the role of the vast uplift in amplifying the effects of Quaternary cooling. Glaciation provided extensive outwash gravels, e.g., in the Pampa de Junin. Locally the lake clays are covered by outwash, but elsewhere they may be contemporary.

Two former and more extensive lakes have been described from the present Lake Titicaca depression:

(a) *Lake Ballivian,* about 40 meters above the present lake level and apparently early Holocene in age.

(b) *Lake Minchin,* covering a vastly greater area, the whole central and southern part of the Altiplano, reaching its maximum in the late Pleistocene. Relics of this lake are still preserved in some of the salt lakes and playas of the present day: Poopó, Coipaza and Uyani.

There are outstanding Quaternary mammalian fossils associated with these lake beds, the *Ulloma Formation,* largely sands and gravels.

RHODES W. FAIRBRIDGE

References

Agassiz, H., 1876, "Hydrographic sketch of Lake Titicaca," *Proc. Am. Acad. Arts Sci.*, **11,** 283–292.

Agassiz, A., and Garman, S. W., 1871–76, "Exploration of Lake Titicaca," *Bull. Mus. Comp. Zool. Harvard Coll.*, **3,** 273–286.

Bandelier, A. F., 1910, "The Islands of Titicaca and Koati," New York, 358 pp.

Bowman, I., 1909, "The physiography of the central Andes," *Am. J. Sci.*, **28,** 197–217, 273–402.

Bowman, I., 1914, "Results of an expedition to the central Andes," *Bull. Am. Geogr. Soc.*, **46,** 161–183.

Garner, H. F., 1963, "Mountains from Molehills," *Bull. Geol. Soc. Am.*, **74,** 195–196.

Gerth, H., 1955, "Der Bau der Südamerikanischen Kordillere," Berlin, Gebrueder Borntraeger, 264pp.

Gregory, H. E., 1913, "Geologic sketch of Titicaca Island and adjoining areas," *Am. J. Sci.*, **36,** 187–213.

Gresswell, R. K., and Huxley, A., 1965, "Standard Encyclopedia of the World's Rivers and Lakes," New York, Putnam's, 384pp.

Heim, A., 1947, "Estudios tectónicos en la Región del Campo petrolifero de Pirin, lado N.W. del Lago Titicaca," *Bol. Direcc. Min. Petról.*, (*Lima*), **79.**

Heim, A., 1951, "On the glaciation of South America as related to Tectonics," *Eclogae Geol. Helv.*, **44**(1).

Neveau-Lemaire, M., 1906, "Les lacs des hauts plateaux de l'Amerique du Sud," Paris.

Newell, N. D., 1949, "Geology of the Lake Titicaca region, Peru and Bolivia," *Geol. Soc. Am. Mem.*, **36,** 111pp.

Steinmann, G., 1929, "Geologie von Peru," Heidelberg, Winter, 448pp.

Troll, C., 1937, "Quartäre Tektonik und Quartärklima in den Quartären Anden," *Frankf. Geogr. Hefte*, **11.**

Cross-references: *Holocene*; *Lakes*; *Playa*; *Quaternary*. Vol. V: *Zwischengebirge*. pr Vol. VIII: *Basin-Range Province*.

LAKE TOBA

The largest lake in southeast Asia, Lake Toba (Danau Toba), is situated on the island of Sumatra, 45 miles south of Medan (2° 30′ N, 90° 00′ E). It is 88 by 29 km (55 × 18 miles) and covers 1130 km² (37 square miles). Its elevation is 910 meters (2985 feet). The maximum depth is about 450 meters. It is particularly unusual because the middle part of the lake is occupied by a very large island, Samosir Island, which is 43 by 19 km (27 × 12 miles).

The lake has a limited catchment area high in the median mountain spine of Sumatra. It overflows into the Asahan River which drains to the north into the Strait of Malacca and the Andaman Sea.

The lake water body is stratified, thus oligomictic. It has a well-marked epilimnion, with a poor metalimnion at 25–50 meters, the temperature dropping in the deep water from 26.4 to 23.9°C (Ruttner, 1931).

The Lake Toba depression lies in a strike-slip fault belt that runs along the entire length of the

FIG. 1. The volcano-tectonic sink of Lake Toba, Sumatra (after van Bemmelen). The island of Samosir is a tilted block of the former chamber roof.

Barisan Mountain chain of Sumatra. The depression complex itself is the largest caldera in the world (Van Bemmelen, 1930, 1949), constituting a volcano-tectonic depression. It lies in an early Tertiary geosynclinal and orogenic belt, capped by late Tertiary volcanics. Paroxysmal eruptions occurred covering the surrounding country for 20,000 km² with a blanket of ash up to 600 meters thick. The expulsion, under gas pressure, of such an immense volume of material led to an emptying of the magmatic reservoirs and a gravitational collapse of the former roof materials. An alternative interpretation favors downwarping and block faulting (see discussion by Cotton, 1962; Verstappen, 1961, 1964).

The Toba volcanic depression at first filled up with water and then broke out along the lines of a preexisting valley, the Asahan River, cutting deeply into the fill. The lake level was thus lowered and the inflow streams also cut down in small canyons to match the lowered base level. A renewed volcanic phase produced an island of several cones in the middle of the lake. A second collapse cut this island in two; the major portion, forming part of the old chamber roof, is tilted somewhat to the south, and a small volcanic cone near the caldera border fault has now built a small isthmus to join this island (Samosir) to the shore.

RHODES W. FAIRBRIDGE

References

Cotton, C. A., 1962, "The volcano-tectonic theory of block faulting no longer tenable," *New Zealand Sci. Rev.*, **20**(3), 48–49.

Ruttner, F., 1931, "Hydrographische und hydrochemische Beobachtungen auf Java, Sumatra und Bali," *Arch. Hydrobiol. Suppl.*, **8**, 197–454.

Van Bemmelen, R. W., 1930, "The origin of Lake Toba," *Proc. Pacific Sci. Congr. Pacific Sci. Assoc. 4th Java, 1929*, **2A**, 115–124.

Van Bemmelen, R. W., 1949, "The Geology of Indonesia," The Hague, Government Printing Office, 2 vols.

Verstappen, H. Th., 1961, "Some 'volcano-tectonic' depressions of Sumatra, their origin and mode of development," *Proc. Koninkl. Nederl. Akad. Wetenschappen*, ser B., **64**, 428–443.

Verstappen, H. Th., 1964, "The geomorphology of Sumatra," *J. Trop. Geogr.*, **18**, 184–191.

Williams, H., 1941, "Calderas and their origin," *Bull. Dept. Geol. Univ. Calif.*, **25**, 239–346.

Cross-references: *Base Level*; *Caldera*; *Crater Lakes*; *Lake Atitlán*; *Lakes*. Vol. I: *Andaman Sea*.

LAKE URMIA

The largest lake in Iran, Lake Urmia (Urumiah; also known as Lake Rezaiyeh) lies west of Tabriz in Azerbaijan, in the western part of the country, on the borders of Armenia (38°N, 45–46°E). It is roughly 145 by 48 km (90 × 30 miles) and covers about 6000 km² (2300 square miles) at high water. Its elevation is about 1297 meters (4353 feet). The lake takes its name from the town of Urmia (now Rezaiyeh) on its western side.

Lake Urmia is fed mainly by the Talkeh River and by the Zarineh River. It has no outlet. The lake is shallow, less than 6 meters deep, and evaporation is high. The waters are very salty, with up to 23% dissolved material, thus about 60% as salty as the Dead Sea, and cannot support normal life. There is a marked annual rise and fall of lake level due to meltwaters from snow mountains, and at the low stage Shahi Island becomes joined to the shore. There are about fifty of these rocky islands in the southeast. At low water the lake's area drops by about one-third (De Morgan).

Structurally, Lake Urmia lies in the block-faulted median mass (*zwischengebirge*) between the Zagros chain to the south and the Elburz chain to the north. It is thus in a tectonically controlled endorheic depression analogous to that of the Great Salt Lake in Utah.

RHODES W. FAIRBRIDGE

References

de Mecquenem, R., 1908, "Le Lac d'Ourmiah," *Ann. Geogr.*, **17**.

de Morgan, J., 1894, "Mission scientifique en Perse," Paris.

Günther, R. T., 1899a, "Contributions to the geography of Lake Urmi and its neighbourhood," *Geogr. J.*, **14**.

Günther, R. T., 1899b, "Contributions to the natural history of Lake Urmi, N.W. Persia, and its neighbourhood," *J. Linn. Soc. London Zoo.*, **27**, 345–373.

Kaehme, K., 1923, "Beiträge zur physische Geographie des Urmija-Beckens," *Z. Gesell. Erdk.* (*Berlin*), 104–132.

Cross-references: *Dead Sea*; *Great Salt Lake*; *Lakes*.

LAND MASS AND MAJOR LANDFORM* CLASSIFICATION

On a gross scale, the land areas of the earth are classified first of all into *continents*, seven in number: North and South America, Europe, Asia, Africa, Australia and Antarctica (for statistics see *Continents and Oceans*). In the past, there has been some discussion as to the justification for separating Europe and Asia along the line of the Urals and the Caspian Sea. Curiously enough, recent paleomagnetic dating by Russian and Chinese geologists on the two sides of this barrier suggests that, in fact, these two continental areas were formerly up to 3000 km apart and, by approaching each other, have closed an old Ural waterway once wider than the Mediterranean, so perhaps the boundary is not a bad one after all.

The earth's continents for a long time were separated by two seaways, now converted into semicontinuous, linear, mountainous belts; these zones are accompanied today by intimately related belts of volcanicity, seismicity and gravity anomalies. These mountains are commonly known as the *Alpine Fold Belts* (Fig. 1) and constitute about 90% of the great mountain zones of the earth today: (a) the *Circum-Pacific Belt*, strongly asymmetric, with numerous marginal sea basins; (b) the *Mediterranean–Himalayan* Belt (the former *Tethys* Seaway), largely symmetric with mountain belts along opposite sides of a long series of plateaus, plains and subsided basins (western Mediterranean, Pannonian Plain, Aegean Sea, Anatolia, Iran, Tibet).

The ancient nuclei or shields and platforms of the earth's crust are found with representatives on every single continent which are thus on the one hand united by the young fold belts, but on the other, separated into two groupings whose geological histories are remarkably distinctive:

(a) *Laurasia*, in the northern hemisphere, consisting of *Laurentia* (the stable lands of North America, including Greenland) and *Eurasia* (the stable lands of northern Europe and Siberia);

(b) *Gondwana*, largely in the southern hemisphere, consisting of South America, Africa, India, Australia and Antarctica. These correlations were long ago recognized by E. Suess (1885–1909), well before the widespread development of theories of continental spreading or drift. Their significance is very profound for the earth's paleogeography (see Vol. V and pr Vol. VII of this series).

The geometric patterns of the major land mass boundaries and their prominent features (mountain belts, fault zones) have long attracted attention.

* "Landform" is given as one word by some specialists, in two by others; in Britain it is often hyphenated [Ed.].

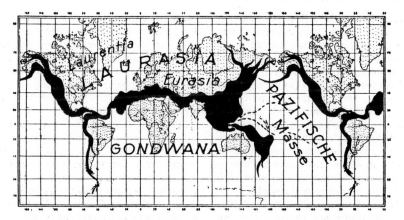

FIG. 1. The great mountain belts of the world today, as represented by Staub (1928): (a) the *Circum-Pacific Belt* surrounding the Pacific Ocean (the "Pacific mass;" the margins of the Pacific are still one of the great enigmas of geology); (b) the *Mediterranean (Alpine)-Himalayan Belt* which separates the two great ancient land masses of Laurasia and Gondwana, now separated in an east-west sense by the phenomenon of continental spreading. It should be noted, however, that the extension of the orogenic belt across the mid-Atlantic proposed by Staub is not supported by recent exploration. His *Pazifische Masse* (Pacific Block) was long regarded as a submerged continent, for which there is also no evidence at all. (By permission of Gebrüder Borntraeger, Stuttgart.)

Suess and his successors have applied distinctive names to *trends* which evolved over specific geological epochs, thus the "Caledonide," "Hercynide" and "Alpide" trends. Within limited regions, the trend directions show concordant patterns, though as long ago as 1847, J. D. Dana wisely warned that "the trend of ridge is not independent evidence of its age." The basic pattern of intersecting fracture and fold lines across the face of the earth ("lineaments") is widely attributed to fundamental shear networks

inherited from the earliest history of the earth and locally revived or reexposed in different regions at different epochs. Such lineaments ("rhegmagenesis" of Sonder, 1956) may well be related to ancient polar shifting (Vening Meinesz, 1947). Harmonic analysis (see Chevallier, 1952) and various statistical treatments of global features (e.g., Brock, 1956; Matschinski, 1964) have been offered from time to time.

As recognized long ago by Penck and later by Kossinna (see *Continents and Oceans*), the hypso-

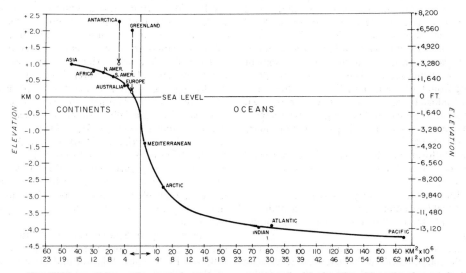

FIG. 2. The world's continents and oceans: area compared with elevation. Note the abnormal elevations of Greenland and Antarctica due to thick layers of continental ice. (Courtesy Ned Ostenso.)

619

graphic curve of the earth is distinctly bimodal, genetically separating these two great crustal categories. What is perhaps less well-known is the rather uniform curve of area versus elevation that may be drawn through both types (Fig. 2). This suggests perhaps that continents can be converted into oceans and vice versa. Antarctica and Greenland are recognizably displaced from the curve because of their 1–2 km thick caps of continental ice. It may be concluded, therefore, that there are fundamental inherited geological and geophysical similarities between all of the continents (as well as between the oceans), and thus we may reasonably suspect that there is a fundamental basis for a uniform classification of superficial major landforms across those same continents, provided that due allowance is made for such latitudinal factors as climate.

Methods of Classification of Major Landforms

Below the scale of continents, the land surface is divisible into major categories, the broadest of which are simply *mountains* and *plains*.

In a review of classification procedures, Howard and Spock (1940, see Table 1) noted at least six different methods (and there are others): gross topography, superficial shape, microrelief, size, geological structure, active processes, inherited features, degree of erosion (stage) and so on. Howard and Spock (1940) define a landform (which they write as one word) as "any element of the landscape characterized by a distinctive surface expression, internal structure, or both, and sufficiently conspicuous to be included in a physiographic description." Scale is thus involved, and in this classification we are only considering major landforms. Minor genetic features ("morphotexture" of Gerassimov), climatic attributes (see *Morphostructure*), are dealt with in more detail under such headings as *Periglacial Landscape*, *Tundra Landscape* and *Savanna Landscape*. In terms of scale, landform units fall into seven convenient orders of magnitude (Cailleux and Tricart, 1956) ranging from the "myriametric" down to the "kilometric," added to which there are microforms, down to what may be called "micro-geomorphology," which treats phenomena involving less than 1 square meter (see Table 2).

The landform can also be considered in several dimensions (as indicated by Howard and Spock, 1940), thus:

(a) Linear dimension (e.g., a shoreline),

(b) Areal (two) dimensions (e.g., a peneplain),

(c) Solid (three) dimensions (e.g., fold mountains).

To these one might well add a fourth dimension, the historical or inherited characteristics (e.g., in an etchplain or a resurrected surface). In the major landforms, only the third category is considered, for the first is merely a transient feature of a coastal plain, while the second must be related to its underlying structure if only to be identified.

In the science of sedimentary petrology, it has been found appropriate to devise for classification of sedimentary rocks a trinomial nomenclature—the key name being based usually on a measurable *geometric parameter* (granulometry), e.g., sandstone, siltstone, claystone; this is then generally modified by *compositional* and *genetic adjectives*, e.g., a "polymictous fluvioglacial sandstone." Numbers of "shortcuts" are used, such as "calcarenite" for calcareous sandstone; in the case of dominantly calcareous rocks, the geometric character is less important in general field work than the compositional, so the term "limestone" is preferred. Let us consider how this convenient system of labels can be applied to geomorphology (Davis long ago recommended the use of selected adjectives in this manner): A major landform is primarily a geometric feature, a unit or category of relief. To describe a surface feature, it should not be necessary to go immediately underground to work out its deep-seated character, and to make an "educated guess" as to its structural genesis; nor should it be necessary in a geometric classification to identify its contemporary geomorphic process or to work out its inherited or historical record.

It must be stressed that a three-dimensional *geometric system* is the safest and most trustworthy, because it identifies something on a directly measurable or mappable relief basis; interpretation is not involved. However, it has limitations, so one turns naturally to the third dimension in depth—*geological structure*; since mountains are cut by valleys and even plains may be locally dissected, this view in depth is still largely observable without introducing undue interpretation. Strahler (1960; also see Fig. 3) illustrates how unequivocally the gross geological structures can be identified. One may next turn to geomorphic process, the identification of the contemporary genetic agency that is modeling a particular landform. Here we are on more dangerous ground; in microrelief it is often clear, but for major landforms the question of inheritance arises (e.g., a mid-latitude land surface can be dominated by glacially striated pavements; see discussion under *Geomorphology—Principles*; *Landscape Types—Genetic*; and *Morphogenetic Regions*). Finally, there is the highly subjective classification *stage* (of development), so much stressed by W. M. Davis, which is no doubt a very helpful "modifier" in any geomorphic characterization, but not one that can always be subjected to very rigorous definition.

As pointed out by Strahler (1946), a feature of the classification of landforms proposed by Davis and followed by Douglas Johnson and certain others of that school, was the term "mountain"; this referred to *disturbed structures* regardless of whether the topography was rugged or of only moderate

TABLE 1. COMPARISON OF LANDFORM CLASSIFICATION SYSTEMS (Howard and Spock, 1940)

Authors	Basis and Major Divisions	Remarks
J. D. Dana (1863)	*Topography:* (1) Lowlands (2) Plateaus or elevated table lands (3) Mountains	Limits of each division indefinite, a weakness recognized by Dana. No recognition of landscape features of smaller dimensions. Not genetic. Probably proposed merely as an aid in physiographic description.
W. M. Davis (1884)	*Structure and amount of erosion:* A suggested basis, but not elaborated upon. "Horizontal structure" is used as an example and subdivided on the basis of accumulation, elevation, and deformation.	The suggested scheme is incomplete, so that little room for discussion exists. However, the complexities which must attend the use of subsequent erosional and diastrophic history as bases of classification have already been alluded to in the text. Davis, himself, acknowledged this weakness in a later article (1907) in which he suggested that adjectives be used to complete the picture brought to mind by the "generic nouns" representing the landforms. The main bases of the present classification are not genetic. It is also to be noted that some features recognized as landforms, as the peneplain, are distinguished by no particular rock structure. In this paper Davis first uses the term "destructional" with reference to "destructional characteristics" which develop as land evolution progresses.
J. W. Powell (1895)	Genesis { Volcanism, Diastrophism, Gradation } Plains, plateaus, mountains, valleys, hills, cliffs, stream channels and cataracts, fountains, caverns, lakes, marshes, coast forms and islands.	The "classification," which may have been proposed solely to simplify physiographic description, is merely a list of landforms not grouped under the major genetic headings, hence failing to show the relations between the landforms themselves. The landforms are further subdivided, however, on a genetic basis.
W. M. Davis (1899)	*Genesis:* Horizontal structure Deformed structures	The forms of the land are attributed to their internal structure, the destructive processes operating on them, and the stages of degradational development. Structure is held to be the "foundation of all geographical classifications in which the trio of controls is recognized." Only forms due to deformation and uplift are considered, one group including forms of horizontal structure, the other group consisting of forms of disordered structure. The destructive processes are described, but the forms developed by them are not mentioned. The classification is not elaborated further.
W. M. Davis (1900)	*Genesis*	Davis herein proposed the substitution of the terms "initial," "sequential," and "ultimate" for "constructional" and "destructional," suggesting that the latter terms had previously been applied to landforms. The terms "initial," "sequential," and "ultimate" were probably presented as aids in description, not as a classification of landforms.
D. W. Johnson (unpublished notes, 1904)	*Genesis:* Constructional Destructional	The terms "constructional" and "destructional" incorporated in a comprehensive classification. Johnson defines constructional landforms as those produced by constructional forces (diastrophism, volcanism) which tend to build up the continents; destructional landforms are defined as those produced by destructional forces (weathering, stream action, glacial action, etc.) which tend to tear down the continents. He subdivides the latter group into erosional, residual and depositional forms.
A. J. Herbertson (1911)	Four classifications submitted: (I) *Superficial covering*	The classification is based on the assumption that the agency shaping a surface marks it with characteristic surface forms "both of accumulation and denudation." This is not always true. Inasmuch as a definite grouping of landforms is not submitted, further judgment is impossible.
	(II) *Structure:* (1) Mass or accumulation lands (igneous). (2) Lands underlain by sedimentary rocks.	The classification takes no cognizance of areas of mixed rock types, or of the numerous minor land forms. Volcanoes find no place in the classification.
	(III) *Superficial shape:* Plain, mount, ridge, table, hollow, furrow or trough, depression, col or pass, cavern.	Not genetic.
	(IV) *Genesis:* Table-lands, scarp lands, mountain lands, eruptive accumulation lands, tectonic mountains, denudation highlands, plain lands, forms of the coastal belt, islands, forms of oceanic margins.	The classification is only partly genetic, and there are many inconsistencies. Only tilted rocks are included under scarp lands. Other headings overlap. Forms subdivided sometimes genetically, sometimes empirically.
H. R. Mill (1912)	*Surface forms:* Plain, plateau or table land, hollow, cliff or scarp, mountains and hills, valley.	Not genetic. Prepared for use of geographers who are mainly interested in the influence of landforms on climate, vegetation, animal life and human activity.
R. D. Salisbury, H. H. Barrows, and W. S. Tower (1913) also R. D. Salisbury (1919)	*Size:* First order Second order Third order	Not genetic. Difficult to set size limits.
J. F. Unstead and E. G. R. Taylor (1929)	*Genesis:* (1) Structural (2) Sculptured	Structural landforms are those formed by movement of great masses of the crust; sculptured forms are those fashioned by erosion and accumulation. The subdivision and treatment of structural forms is good, except that the restriction of structural plateaus to broad, anticlinal arches is unusual. After the treatment of structural forms, the classification breaks down to a list of forms, some of which may clearly be structural in origin, others sculptured, and still others of either origin. The inclusion of "accumulation" forms under "sculptured" seems inappropriate inasmuch as deposition is not a sculpturing process in the popular sense of the word.
A. K. Lobeck (1939)	*Genesis:* (1) Constructional (2) Destructional	D. W. Johnson's classification slightly amplified.

TABLE 2. SCALE OF UNITS IN GEOMORPHOLOGY
(modified after: Tricart, 1952, and Cailleux and Tricart, 1956)

Magnitude	Size Km²	Duration Years	Examples (in three categories)	Basis
1st	10⁷	500 Million	1. Continental masses, ocean basins	Different categories of varied geo-dynamic origin, i.e. 1, geophysical; 2, geotectonic; 3, climatic.
		100 Million	2. Geosynclines, continental platforms	
"Myriametric scales"		Tert. = 65 Million Quat. = 2 Million	3. Morphoclimatic zones, e.g. tropical zone.	
2nd	10⁶		2. Scand. Shield, Russian Platform, Hercynian Belt	Subdivisions of categories 2 and 3.
			3. Savanna, rainforest ("major division" of Linton, 1948)	
3rd	10⁵		2. High Plateau, High and Anti-Atlas ("province" of Linton, 1948)	Structural units. Geomorphic effects of single climatic zones not recognizable at this scale.
4th	10⁴		2. Paris Basin, Central Massif ("section" of Linton, 1948)	Structural units, of limited regional character. Single physiographic process usually dominant.
5th	10³		2. Chalk of Picardy–Normandy ("tract" of Linton, 1948)	Tectonic and often lithologic individuality. Lower limit of isostatic compensation. Single relief type.
6th	10²		Individual anticlines, synclines in folded ranges. cuestas, fault-blocks ("stow" of Linton, 1948)	Lithology important, influences tectonic style and operation of exogenic processes. No isostatic compensation. Repetition of relief features.
7th "Kilometric scales"	10	10⁴–10⁵	Local relief, pediments, inselbergs, consequent gaps, etc.; ("site" of Linton, 1948)	Tectonics subordinate, Exogenic processes and lithology dominant. Microclimates and biotopes influence process.
Microforms Less than 1 km² Hectometric Decametric Metric Microgeomorphology		Map scale 1:100,000 1:10,000 1:1,000	Mudflows, torrent ravines, slope facets, goletz, barchans, solifluction lobes, soil polygons, thufurs, terracettes, lapiés, dreikanter, ripplemarks.	Exogenic processes, marked by discontinuity of phenomena in place and time (requires statistical treatment). Susceptible to experimental approach.

relief (the German system *Gebirge*). On the other hand, areas of horizontal sediments became "plains" or "plateaus," regardless of relief, while flat country of complex underlying structure was automatically classified as "mountains." Much confusion resulted. Therefore in the classification adopted here, the ordinary topographic dictionary connotations are retained and the Davisian scheme is rejected. Nevertheless, the Davisian concept of "stage" (youth–maturity–old age) is found to be exceptionally valuable (used in a relative sense) and is employed extensively.

For plains, the classification adopted by Mescherikov (see *Plains*) has been used but somewhat

simplified. Davis took "structure" in geomorphology to mean something quite distinct from "structure" in tectonic geology. Since many landforms are controlled by tectonics, ambiguity is inevitable and the result is vastly confusing. Under "structure," Davis included two classes of landform: (a) *initial* or *constructional*, and (b) *sequential* or *destructional*, but these clearly cut across many of the categories commonly recognized. Thus, a concordant plain is constructional and a discordant plain is destructional, while a collapse caldera would seem to be 50:50. Evidently this scheme of Davis' has value as a modifier, but not as a good basis for primary classification. It was

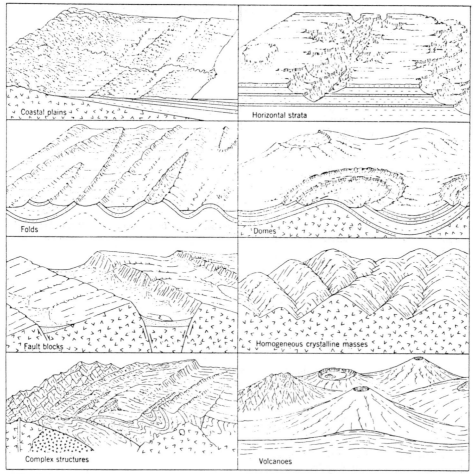

FIG. 3. Land masses can be classified according to the groups illustrated here. Classification is based on variety, attitude and structure of rock (Strahler, 1960). (By permission of John Wiley & Sons, N.Y.)

adopted nevertheless by Douglas Johnson and systematically reorganized by Howard and Spock (1940; see Table 3). This constructional-destructional approach has merit in that it is logical and all inclusive. The difficulties in using it, apart from those noted above involving the constant need of subjective interpretation, include the fact that probably more than 90% of the earth's surface falls into the first category ("diastrophic"), while the fraction of this which is constructional or destructional must be qualified by question marks. The system therefore applies much better to minor landforms—morphotextures, such as yardangs and features of that scale. Within the destructional type, the recognition of *reduction forms* as distinct from *residual forms* is very commendable.

The basic criterion adopted here, therefore, is *topography* (geometric description), but we are using specific *genetic* labels where they help to identify the category.

Major Landform Classification

Within each continent the following major geomorphic landforms are recognized (partly after Strahler, 1946):

(1) Undisturbed Structures (Plains and Plateaus). Exogenic forces are dominant.

(*a*) *Coastal Plains.* These pass seaward into continental shelves with little or no break. This combined zone is, from the crustal standpoint, true continent, but because of periodic shifts in sea level, the whole zone is at times under the sea, while at other times it is all land.

(*b*) *Lowland Plains.* These usually conform to the structure of underlying sedimentary basins, but sometimes correspond to erosion surfaces discordantly crossing ancient folded foundations. Regionally, they may be modified with glacial stage veneers: till plains, outwash plains.

(*c*) *Upland Plains.* These are usually discordant to the underlying structure, which is not expressed

623

TABLE 3. A GENETIC LANDFORM CLASSIFICATION (Howard and Spock, 1940)

	Constructional		Destructional		
Processes	Forms	Reduction Forms	Residual Forms	Processes	
Diastrophic	Plains and plateaus, grabens, fault mountains, down-warped basins, dome mountains, fold and complex mountains	?	?	Diastrophic	
Volcanic	Lava plains and plateaus, volcanoes	Calderas?	?	Volcanic	
Weathering and soil movements	Talus, rock glaciers, landslide accumulations	Landslide scars	Exfoliation domes	Weathering and soil movements	
Depositional — Fluvial	Plains and plateaus, fans, cones, deltas, floodplains, precipitation forms	Valleys, straths, peneplains	Monadnocks	Fluvial	Erosional
Glacial	Moraines, drumlins, outwash plains	Troughs, cirques	Arêtes, horns	Glacial	
Eolian	Loess plains, dunes	Deflation hollows	Yardangs	Eolian	
Littoral	Offshore bars, beaches, embankments	Sea cliffs, wave-cut terraces	Sea stacks	Littoral	
Lacustrine	Lake plains, precipitation forms	?	?	Lacustrine	
Terraqueous	Cones, terraces	Sinks	Natural bridges (in part)	Terraqueous	
Impact	?	Meteor scars	?	Impact	
Organic	Coral reefs	?	?	Organic	

in the topography, except as relict hills or "fossil" land surface areas. Less commonly, they are conformable on existing flat-lying formations (e.g., Great Plains, western U.S.).

(*d*) *Plateaus.* These consist of horizontally bedded rocks (sediments) elevated to anomalous altitudes, e.g., the 2000-meter Colorado Plateau. Alternatively, they may be high interior basins with discordant foundations and borders, as the Alti Plano of Mexico and Bolivia, the high plateaus of Anatolia, Iran and Tibet. Thirdly, they may be high discordant plains (as extensively developed in East and South Africa); finally, they may be exhumed peneplains (or other erosion planes, relict landscapes), as in the Spanish Meseta.

(2) **Disturbed Structures**. Endogenic forces are dominant.

(*A*) *Youthful, Early-mature, or Rejuvenated Stage*:

(a) *Fold Mountains*—Singly or in chains, sedimentary, Jura type, or Appalachian Valley and Ridge.

(b) Fold-thrust-nappe Complexes—Alpine-type mountains, mixed sedimentary sheets and crystalline sectors.

(c) Domes—Singly as in laccoliths or plutons, or in complex uplifts, like the Black Hills or Ozarks.

(d) Fault Blocks—Include both troughs and horst-type mountains or ranges, e.g., Rhine Graben, or Basin-Range Province of Nevada, etc.

(e) Belted Metamorphic Mountains—In well-dissected younger mountain belts or rejuvenated ancient belts, e.g., Laurentians of Quebec.

(f) Ancient Crystalline Mountains—Always rejuvenated, sometimes with monoclinal flanks, e.g., some of the Wyoming and Colorado Rockies.

(g) Batholithic Crystalline Complex Mountains—Relatively youthful complexes, combining any of the above, e.g., Sierra Nevada.

(*B*) *Old-age Stage*. The endogenic origin is almost suppressed by exogenic modeling. All of the disturbed structures mentioned above may be reduced to late-mature or old-age landscapes, to constitute:

(a) Lowlands—Disturbed structures, now degraded; thus degraded mountain roots, degraded metamorphic belts, e.g., Hudson River Lowlands of strongly folded Ordovician rocks, Pennsylvania Slate Belt.

(b) Lowland or Upland Hills—Disturbed structures of any category reduced to irregular topography of subdued relief, hills (less than 600 meters). These are thus intermediate between highlands and lowlands, e.g., Appalachian Piedmont, Southern Uplands of Scotland, Hunsrück of Germany.

(c) Highlands—Disturbed structures of any sort deeply dissected and reduced to moderate relief, marked by more mature slopes, but with absolute relief in the mountain category, e.g., Scottish Highlands (mean height *ca.* 1000 meters), Hudson Highlands, N.Y., Black Forest, Polish and Hungarian "Mittelgebirge," French Massif Central. Linear developments may be termed *highland ridges, highland ranges* or *highland chains* in the sense of reduced mountains. A problem may arise over the degree to which some highlands represent exhumed landscapes, category 1 (*d*). The decisive criterion is simply a question of dominance—the more striking plateau characteristics or the hilly relief characteristics.

(3) **Extrusive Structures (Endogenic Effusives)**. Landforms derived from eruptive sources depend primarily on the geochemistry and thus the viscosity of the magma. High volatile content leads to lower temperatures of flow, and initially low viscosity, but, because of rapid loss of volatiles, there is more rapid congealing, resulting in steep-sided cones; there is also a higher explosion potential (Pacific suite). Low-volatile, high-temperature alkali basalts (Atlantic suite), in contrast, tend to flow further and form gently sloping domes or plateaus.

(*A*) *Youthful, Early-mature or Revived Stage*:

(a) Volcanic Cones—"Central volcanoes," usually disposed in long belts, ranging from small cinder cones (and maare), such as Paracutin (Mexico) and small spatter cones up to elegant symmetrical cone mountains of mixed ash and lava components (strato-volcanoes); e.g., Fuji Yama, Japan; Mt. Egmont, New Zealand; Popocatepetl,

Mexico; Mts. Hood, Shasta and so on of Pacific Northwest, U.S.

(b) Volcanic Domes—Also "central volcanoes" and ranging in size from small "mamelons" up to that of Mauna Loa on the "big island" of Hawaii, characterized by gentle slopes and large size. They may be isolated or in belts.

(c) Lava Fields—Related to fissure eruptions or small cones, characterized by assuming the topography of existing land surfaces, especially valleys, often leading to displaced streams; common in New Mexico, southeastern Australia, etc.

(d) Lava Plateaus—Complex regions of multiple fissure eruptions, bringing about a regional plateau form, though locally very rough in microtopography, e.g., Columbia Plateau, Oregon, Washington, Idaho; Deccan Plateau, India; Ethiopian Plateau, Africa; Icelandic Plateau.

(e) Calderas—Related to extremely viscous lavas and gas explosions, ranging from diatremes to explosion craters, to explosion calderas, to collapse calderas, the last due to gravitational subsidence into the magma chamber after evacuation by gas. In topography, they are usually marked by ring-shaped depressions, often occupied by lakes up to 25 km in diameter.

(*B*) *Old Age* (*Extrusive Structures*). All of the above categories may be found as degraded landforms, following long extinction of volcanicity. Craters are often filled by *crater lakes*, and central volcanoes are reduced to simple *necks, spines* or *plugs*, representing distinctive circular and resistant hills on the landscape. Plateau lavas tend to hold up erosion, leading to development of high escarpments, steep-sided box *canyons* and impressive *waterfalls* (q.v.).

RHODES W. FAIRBRIDGE

References

Brock, B. B., 1956, "Structural mosaics and related concepts," *Trans. Geol. Soc. South Africa,* **59,** 149–197.

Cailleux, A., and Tricart, J., 1956, "Le problème de la classification des faits géomorphologiques," *Ann. Géogr.,* **65,** 162–186.

Chevallier, J. M., 1952, "Analyse harmonique du relief terrestre. Essai d'interprétation mécanique," *Rev. Géomorph. Dynam.,* **3,** 219–242.

Dana, J. D., 1847, "Origin of the grand outline feature of the earth," *Am. J. Sci.,* Ser. 2, **3,** 381–398.

Dana, J. D., 1863, "Manual of Geology," Philadelphia, Th. Bliss & Co.

Davis, W. M., 1884, "Geographic classification. Illustrated by a study of plains, plateaus and their derivatives" (abstract), *Proc. Am. Assoc. Advan. Sci.,* **33,** 428–432.

Davis, W. M., 1899, "The Geographical Cycle," *Geograph. J.,* **14,** 481–504 (also "Geographical Essays," New York, Dover Publ., reprint, 1954).

Davis, W. M., 1900, "Physiographic terminology with special reference to landforms" (abstract), *Science,* **11,** 99.

Haggett, P., Chorley, R. J., and Stoddart, D. R., 1965, "Scale standards in geographical research," *Nature*, **205**, 844–847.

Howard, A. D., and Spock, L. E., 1940, "A classification of landforms," *J. Geomorphol.*, **3**, 332–345.

Linton, D. L., 1948, "Delimitation of morphological regions," *Trans. Inst. Brit. Geogr.*, **14**, 86–87, also, 1951, in "London Essays in Geography," London, Longmans, Green and Co.

Lobeck, A. K., 1939, "Geomorphology, An Introduction to the Study of Landscapes," New York, McGraw-Hill Book Co., 731pp.

Matschinski, M., 1964, "Die Erdoberfläche und die Gesetze ihrer Formen," *Z. Geomorphol.*, **8**(2), 163–188.

Mill, H. R. (editor), 1912, " The International Geography," New York, D. Appleton, 1088pp.

Powell, J. W., 1895, "Physiographic Features," *Natl. Geogr. Mono.*, **1**, 33–64.

Salisbury, R. D., 1919, "Physiography," Third ed., revised, New York, H. Holt & Co., 676pp.

Salisbury, R. D., Barrow, H. H. and Tower, W. S., 1913, "Modern Geography for High Schools," New York, H. Holt & Co.

Sonder, R. A., 1956, "Mechanik der Erde," Stuttgart, Schweizerbart, 291pp.

Stamp, L. D., and Unstead, J. F., 1937, "Classification of regions of the world" (Rept. Comm. Geogr. Assoc.), *Geography*, **22**.

Staub, R., 1928, "Der Bewegungsmechanismus der Erde," Berlin, Borntraeger, 270pp.

Strahler, A. N., 1946, "Geomorphic terminology and classification of land masses," *J. Geol.*, **54**(1), 32–42.

Strahler, A. N., 1960, "Physical Geography," New York, John Wiley & Sons, Inc., 534pp.

Suess, E., 1885–1909, "Das Antlitz der Erde," Vienna, F. Tempsky (English translation "The Face of the Earth," Oxford, Clarendon Press, 1904–1924).

Tricart, J., 1952, "La géomorphologie et la notion d'échelle," *Rev. Geomorph. Dyn.*, **3**, 213–218.

Unstead, J. F., and Taylor, E. G. R., 1929, "General and Regional Geography for Students," Eleventh ed., London, Philip & Sons.

Vening Meinesz, F. A., 1947, "Shear patterns of the Earth's crust," *Trans. Am. Geophys. Union*, **28**, 1–61.

Cross-references: *Basin and Range Landscape; Caldera; Coastal Plain; Continents and Oceans; Crater Lakes; Dome Mountain; Endogenic Dynamics; Etchplain; Exhumed Landscape; Exogenic Dynamics; Geomorphology; Graben; Horst; Hypsographic Curve; Landscape Types—Genetic; Morphogenetic Regions; Morphostructure; Mountains; Outwash Plain; Paleogeomorphology; Peneplain; Periglacial Landscape; Plains; Plateaus; Process-Structure-Stage; Relict Landforms; Savanna Landscape; Tectonic Landscapes; Tundra Landscape; Volcanic Landscapes; Volcanic Necks and Diatremes; Waterfalls; Yardang; Youth—Maturity—Old Age.* Vol. I: *Continental Shelf.* pr Vol. VII: *Gondwanaland; Paleogeography.*

LANDSCAPE ANALYSIS

Landscape may be defined as a stretch of country as seen from a particular vantage point. The landscape is made up of rock with its "mantle" of weathered material (saprolite) and soil, together with any vegetation cover and any streams, rivers, lakes, snow or ice that may be present. There can be a tremendous range of variation from one place to another. In the humid tropics, an aerial view will be restricted to the canopy of the dense tropical rain forest. In deserts, the landscape may be dominated by bare rock, while lowlands which have just been deglaciated may be dominated by small lakes and erratic blocks.

Just as the landscape is highly variable, so may be the vantage point. This may be a point on a high hill, perhaps from an aircraft, or it could be virtually at the limit of resolution as in the case of the view from a satellite.

Landscape analysis is the subdivision of landscape for some purpose or other. It may be for some scientific study such as the nature and origin of the landforms, or to determine the best way of modifying or exploiting the landscape to the advantage of man. Studies in this second category have become very important since World War I.

There are many methods of carrying out landscape analysis, these being largely controlled by the purpose of the survey, the resources available for carrying it out, and the accessibility of the area. In most cases, landscape analysis involves the use of maps or aerial photographs in place of, or as a supplement to, field work. Usually the best way to keep down costs and yet to obtain reasonably accurate results is to use a combination of all three methods. On the other hand, field work by itself can be most time consuming and costly. In northern Canada, Alaska and Antarctica, as well as in some tropical areas, helicopters or light aircraft may be used to overcome the lack of roads and inaccessibility of the terrain. Lack of ground checks tends to produce inaccuracies, though this depends on the type of work.

Landscape analysis may be carried out on vastly different scales. For some purposes, small-scale maps of the key features of the landscape of entire continents are required. At other times, details of variations within 1 km² or less are the object of the study. Obviously very different mapping units and methods will be used in these extreme cases. For convenience, we will therefore divide landscape analysis into three scales of study: detailed, regional and continental. It will also be convenient to examine each of these from various viewpoints, e.g., landforms, vegetation, soils and drainage.

Landscape Analysis of Small Areas

There are two main kinds of studies—scientific and applied. These differ only in the purpose of the study. Most studies of small areas have been academic studies, i.e., studies designed to find out what precisely is there. It is a common technique in the better-studied areas of the globe for concentrating attention on certain points that may need reexamination where previous work has been inadequate. Such select studies are also basic for the eventual understanding of landscapes of larger regions.

The early studies of landscapes were almost entirely descriptive or physiographic. As time went by, observers began to ask themselves questions about the origins of the landforms and so the subject of geomorphology developed. It was soon found that some degree of order of arrangement occurred in landforms. Uplift of the crust from beneath sea level would produce a new block of land upon which the exogenic agencies of denudation would immediately become active. From this initial condition, the landscape would pass through a series of sequential stages to a "final" form consisting of a plain at or close to sea level. W. M. Davis (1899) has described these stages in his "Geographical Cycle". Any landform was regarded as being a function of structure, process and time. *Time* controls the stage in the sequence, *process* refers to the nature of the forces of denudation, while *structure* (of Davis) encompasses the lithology, permeability, dip and strike of individual beds, etc., of the underlying rock. Erosion by streams in a humid temperate environment was regarded as being due to "climatic accidents." Rejuvenation by a new phase of uplift of the land causes a new cycle.

This cyclic concept of Davis has been widely followed. Johnson and Cotton have subsequently applied it to shorelines and other features, and it is still widely used in teaching. However, it is also clear that this is an oversimplification (see, for example, discussion by Chorley, 1962). Davis assumed that the whole cycle worked in a closed system; i.e., the mountain building forces were inactive after the initial uplift. We now know that conditions are constantly changing. The climates of the world have not stayed constant for more than a few centuries and certainly not for geologically long periods of time (see *Palaeoclimatology* and *Ice Age Meteorology*, Vol. II). Climatic conditions change from season to season and year to year so that there is a great variability in the processes acting within the so-called humid region. Thus in a mid-latitude continental environment such as southern Ontario, localized polygon formation and widespread solifluction alternate on a seasonal basis with subhumid tropical weathering.

Erosion in streams is controlled by *base level* (q.v.), i.e., usually the ocean, or the altitude at which the stream joins a lake or river. Any change in the base level leads to widespread changes working upstream. Thus a rise in base level reduces the amount of material that can be removed by the rivers and thus causes deposition of material in the lower portion of the stream course. Lowering of the base level causes intensified downcutting at the mouth of the stream. Traces of both these effects can be found along the courses of most rivers around the world. Evidently the closed system concept is an oversimplification.

Not the least of the problems is the fact that the response of a stream to a change in external conditions is not always shown in the longitudinal profile of the stream. Thus increased *runoff* at a constant load may lead to one or another of two reactions by the stream. Either the stream channel can steepen or else it can increase its cross-sectional area. Seasonal modifications of this type are well documented. *Load* is an additional variable which changes together with flow along a stream wherever it is joined by a tributary. Thus the picture in detail is much more complicated than that suggested by the geographical cycle of Davis. The closed system concept must be replaced by that of an open system.

Curiously enough, this was recognized by C. K. Gilbert (1880) well before the time of Davis' work. An open system of this type tends to make adjustments within the system itself, e.g., by the local widening of the stream channel, rather than by comprehensive modification (i.e., the erosion of a new deepened channel along the bulk of its course).

The routine topographic and engineering surveys over the last one and a half centuries permit the use of quantitative studies to develop or illuminate geomorphological theories. Examples of this use include graphs of long profiles of streams, diagrams of heights of terraces, and tables of volume and load characteristics of streams. Recently, advanced mathematical treatment has come much more to the forefront. Quantitative methods are excellent for checking theories and showing the relative importance of the various processes of denudation operating in a given area. To get the best out of them, the method of study must be carefully chosen so as to deal effectively with the problem.

Detailed geomorphic investigations of small areas have been most fruitful in other studies of landscapes. They are often very helpful in the study of the structural relationships between different rock formations. Mapping of the lithology in the field may be supplemented by the application of geophysical methods and by photo interpretation. Most such studies are genetic and usually involve the collection and laboratory study of many rock samples.

Vegetation is most useful as an indicator of the geochemical composition of the country rock, soils and drainage of an area, besides forming a study in itself. Certain plants grow only on certain soils or under certain drainage conditions. Traces of some chemical elements in the soil cause the leaves of certain species of plants to be discolored. This geobotanical information can help in landscape analysis, besides warning the agriculturalist of potential trouble in crops or with livestock. Where vegetation is studied for its own sake, the botanist may be interested primarily in collecting different species and so compiling a flora, or he may be concerned with the ecology of the plants. In the latter case, he will try to sort out the nature of the plant successions and climaxes in the area. Photo interpretation can be very useful in this case, but basic field work is still essential.

Soils (see pr Vol. VI) may be studied by either the botanist or the geomorphologist in their obvious relationships to plant growth and to landform evolution. Primarily they are the object of study of the pedologist. In each case, it is necessary to determine the variation in the soils with variations in topography and with the other factors of the landscape. Soil formation and its modification often constitute an index of variations in these environmental factors. These studies are mainly carried out in the field (with augering or trenching) since the surface appearance seen on aerial photographs is inadequate for proper description of the soil. The all-important variations beneath the surface usually do not show save in exceptional cases. Laboratory study of selected samples is generally essential.

Drainage is generally one of the easiest features to read in the landscape. Its effects are apparent in the distribution or absence of plant communities, streams and lakes. Even water quality and seasonal variability of precipitation can usually be discerned.

Besides these primarily scientific studies, much work is carried out in applied landscape analysis. These are essentially special studies treating some commodity aspect important to man. Here we may be dealing with water or soil conservation, studies of usable forest reserves or grazing lands, finding potential irrigable areas, or finding minerals or rocks of economic importance. The workers in these fields use modifications of the methods described above, but their primary attention is slanted toward the planned use of the area. Often this involves the study of a combination of subjects such as slope, vegetation cover, soils and distribution of potential irrigation water, as would be appropriate in the case of the search for irrigable areas. Additional factors such as climate and agronomy also come in here, although these are only indirectly related to landscape analysis.

Landscape Analysis of Moderately Large Areas

Geomorphologists have been carrying out landscape studies for too short a period to have covered much of the total land surface of the earth using detailed methods. Our knowledge of the nature of the landscape of this globe is based chiefly on reconnaissance-type studies augmented by detailed surveys of small key areas. The results of these studies of the small areas are then extrapolated into the surrounding areas. Scale is all important, and generally only enough work is carried out to ensure that no large areas could have been wrongly classified on the map.

The limits of the region to be surveyed depend on the reason for the survey. It may be an obvious natural boundary such as the limits of a *physiographic region*, or else an arbitrary limit such as a geographic grid or a political boundary. The latter are particularly common in the case of surveys by government departments. Applied studies more often take in a tract of land with some natural boundary, such as a drainage basin.

Mapping units are invariably more generalized than in detailed surveys. Thus, whereas a detailed geological map would show all the main lithological units in a rock formation, a map of a large area (say, at 1:500,000) would show only the chronostratigraphic systems or major units. In forest maps one would only expect to find the generalized forest types and not the distribution of climax forests and successional units.

In applied studies, such as land use, many different items may be plotted on the same map. Thus a pasture survey map of Cyprus (Jones *et al.*, 1958) showed soils, principal crops, limit of flood irrigation, pasture boundaries and forest areas, as well as a pasture-use classification. In Australia, a rapid method of small-scale survey is essential for this rapidly developing continent, and a technique has been developed for mapping *land systems* (q.v.). These are landscape types with a recurring pattern of landforms, soils and vegetation (Mabbutt and Stewart, 1963). As in most recent surveys of this kind, the mapping is carried out primarily on air photographs. The different patterns on the air photographs are checked on the ground by a team consisting of a geomorphologist, a pedologist and plant ecologist, together with any other specialists deemed necessary. The vertical air photography should be new and on a scale of 1:40,000 to 1:80,000. The field checks are carefully chosen so as to reduce traveling distance, and observation points are approximately 10 km apart. Where necessary, a small detailed study may be made at the observation station. On return to headquarters, the mapping is completed on air photographs, showing such features as lithology, weathering, dissection, relief, soils and vegetation. These categories are mapped in *land units*. Usually several boundaries are common to more than one feature, so the land units can be combined into land systems. They are the result of three interacting controls, namely, regional lithology, past and present regional climates, and geomorphic evolution. Thus the land system approach attempts to express the integration of all elements of the land complex, recognizing the causal link between them through the genesis of the land system itself. From the land system maps, specialist maps such as land surface, surface drainage, etc., can be constructed.

Analysis of Major Regions and Continents

The method of approach in this case is similar to the studies of moderately large areas. The main difference lies in the type of information that can be plotted. Thus in the case of geology, only the distribution of tectonic belts, folded mountain chains or rocks of the main eras can be shown. With landforms—the main topographic units—mountains, plateaus, hills and plains—alone are mapped. For vegetation, only the main formations such as Boreal Forest, Steppe Grassland, etc., or the Hylea can be plotted. For comparative purposes, these maps are excellent because they are simplified to an extent where all the data can be readily comprehended and compared. They form the basis of many fundamental studies in the geography of large areas and can be used to bring out the main principles of the relationships between the various landscape factors.

Continental-scale analysis can be appreciated by examining the new Russian World Physical Atlas which is the only work so far that compares on the same scale the geology, tectonics, geomorphology, pedology, vegetation, climate, etc., for every single continent.

Organization of Applied Landscape Analysis

From the above discussion, it will be clear that considerable cooperation is necessary in landscape analysis. Normally in Europe or North America each government department or agency will survey a given area independently. This is very convenient since it prevents squabbles by two related agencies over the nature of the survey or details of field work, but it is also rather expensive and may lead to awkward anomalies in classification and mapping. In the end, some coordinating or planning group usually has to take the various reports and integrate them, carrying out any additional work that may be necessary.

One of the first attempts to integrate applied studies was in Holland in the case of the empoldering and development of the Zuider Zee which was begun in 1920 (Herweijer, 1965) and in recent decades with the Delta Plan. Since World War II, the United Nations (through its Food and Agriculture Organization) has organized many integrated applied studies in underdeveloped countries. The Arid Zone researches have been particularly significant.

Some governments have started to follow this example. In Australia, the land system studies began in 1953 and are now being carried out at an ever-increasing rate. In Britain, a complex hierarchy has been established to achieve a similar end, in spite of the strength of the various government agencies. This seems to be the pattern for the future; applied landscape analysis will come to play a more and more important role in regional development work.

STUART A. HARRIS

References

Chorley, R. J., 1962, "Geomorphology and general systems theory," *U.S. Geol. Surv. Profess. Paper* **500B,** 10 p.

Davis, W. M., 1899, "The geographical cycle," *Geogr. J.,* **14,** 481–504.

Gilbert, C. K., 1880, "Report on the geology of the Henry Mountains," Second ed., U.S. Govt. Printing Office, Washington, D.C., 170 pp.

Herweijer, S., 1965, "Problems of Regional Planning and Development (Netherlands)," in "International Conference on Regional Development and Economic Change," pp. 101–110, Department of Economics and Education, Toronto.

Jones, D. K., Merton, L. F. H., Poore, M. E. D., and Harris, D. R., 1958, "Report on Pasture Research, Survey and Development in Cyprus," Govt. of Cyprus, 88 pp.

Mabbutt, J. A., and Stewart, G. A., 1963, "The application of geomorphology in resource surveys in Australia and New Guinea," *Revue de Géomorphologie Dynamique,* **14,** 97–109.

Cross-references: *Base Level; Cycles, Geomorphic; Desert and Desert Landforms; Drainage Patterns; Geomorphic Maps; Land Mass and Major Landform Classification; Land Systems; Open Systems—Allometric Growth; Physiographic or Landform Maps; Process—Structure—Stage; Quantitative Geomorphology.* Vol. II: *Climatic Variations—Historical Record; Ice Age Meteorology; Paleoclimatology.* pr Vol. VI: *Geologic Maps; Geologic Surveys; Pedology; Photogeology; Photo Interpretation; Vegetation Markers and Landscape.*

LANDSCAPE, BASIN-RANGE—*See* BASIN AND RANGE LANDSCAPE

LANDSCAPE, EXHUMED—*See* EXHUMED LANDSCAPE

LANDSCAPE, GEOGRAPHICAL

The term "landscape," as used in the earth sciences, has been confused with the term "region" to such an extent that a restatement of the scope and definition of this term is needed.

As will be mentioned below, "landscape" is a geographical unit of relatively small size, but still large enough to be a representative part of the earth's surface. Any unit smaller than a "landscape" is not representative.

Passarge (1921) gives the following definition:

"A natural landscape is a district which so far as possible represents a unit according to its climate, vegetation cover, modelling of the surface, geological structure and soil. Generally all these characteristics do not coincide; some must however agree to unity, if a landscape is to result.

"Actually, natural landscapes are not made up by a single oneness. On the contrary, they are broken down according to relief forms and structure, according to their waters, soils and vegetation mantle into subdivisions which are called *sectional landscapes*. Landscapes and sectional landscapes must have sufficient size and consist of a combination of individually uniform *landscape sections*. One could take these small landscape sections as the 'building stones' of the landscape."

Passarge points out that the nomenclature of such landscape sections may prove a problem, and also that distinction between landscapes, sectional landscapes and landscape sections may be difficult. Only the smaller uniform entities (whether based on landforms, structure, soil, waters or plant cover) are incontrovertible. How to group them into larger landscape sections or sectional landscapes or landscapes is a matter for the individual scholar.

Toniolo (1950) defines landscape as "a collective manifestation of forms which tend to become organized, at a given moment, with a certain balance and appearance, which evolve in time, and are reciprocally linked by some relationship." Thus the concept *time* is introduced. Toschi (1952) in adopting Toniolo's definition stresses the differences between panoramic view, landscape and region. A panoramic view may encompass a whole landscape in the geographical sense; in most cases, however, it is only part of a whole landscape which extends beyond where the eye can see.

Men and animals are dependent on the environment, which, taken comprehensively, is a landscape section.

The environment of an individual, however, is not synonymous with landscape section, because not every aspect of the landscape section is likely to affect the individual. To an ecologist preoccupied with the study of an individual organism in its ecological niche, the landscape section may be distractingly crowded with irrelevant elements. To the geographer, the landscape section is one integrated entity. "Area" is no synonym—it does not include the atmosphere above.

Perhaps because of its complexity, "landscape" is a relatively recent concept in the history of civilization. Ancient Greeks and Romans had no term for "landscape"; the Romans used *ager* (field) or *pagus* (district, region) but did not show an interest in the integration of the various elements into one concept. Only relatively late (Trajan column, some frescoes at Pompeii) was there any attempt at representing some aspect of landscape views. From *pagus* came the early medieval *pagensis* which, by the tenth century, had given rise to the French *païs* (later *pays*) for the smallest recognizable unit of a landscape type—a highly geographical concept which still permeates rural France, where the peasant infallibly detects the characteristics of the various *pays* within his experience. The concept of landscape, however, remained unknown to the Byzantine, Celtic and Gothic cultures.

The Arabs were forbidden by their religion to make any image, but they showed a remarkable understanding of landscape in their development of irrigated orchards and gardens, which they introduced to southern Europe. Whereas the Romans had been structural architects, the Arabs proved to be landscape architects.

The most profound "landscape feeling" is, however, reflected in Chinese and Japanese art, from early age to the present day.

The first viable, if highly stylized, European landscapes are shown in the paintings by the Sienese forerunners of the Renaissance, especially Duccio and the Lorenzetti brothers, and above all by the Florentine Giotto (1267?–1337). The earliest-known minutely realistic landscapes form the background to paintings and miniatures by Hubert van Eyck (1365?–1426), who gave this characteristic to Flemish painting and illumination. Frequency of recognition of the individuality of landscapes by the painters of the Italian Renaissance increased during the fifteenth century, culminating with the luminous and real landscape backgrounds painted by the Venetian Giovanni Bellini (1430–1516). The French painter Jean Fouquet (1415?–1485) sojourned in Italy between 1440 and 1447, and returned to Tours with such an appreciation of the significance of landscape that the work of his school showed "a masterly understanding of French landscape" (Bradley, 1905).

The importance of landscape continued to remain proportionally greater in the Flemish art, becoming predominant with Patinir (1490–1545?), and it was as the Flemish or Dutch *landschap* that the term came to England, where it altered to "landskip" (1598), later evolved to *landscape*. At the time it still referred to the subject of paintings but almost immediately (1602) acquired a generic meaning as well. Thus the history of the term, both in the Romance and the Germanic languages, shows that it refers to an anthropocentric view. The kinds of landscape available to European writers and painters would, moreover, to a great extent be anthropogenous as well.

The origin of the term has thus contributed to its ambivalence in most European languages, ambivalence which has greatly worried many a leading geographer (cf. discussion and bibliographical references in Hartshorne, 1939, pp. 149–158), but it seems in fact to be unavoidable. A landscape, unless specifically defined "natural" or "primeval" as opposed to "human" or "cultural," i.e., "man-made," includes all those aspects, forms and organisms that are present in it. Such aspects, forms or organisms may be conspicuous, noticeable, subdued, latent; the geographer may exercise a choice and, for the sake of generalization or brevity, eliminate those in the last categories. Some aspects may be relatively permanent, others transient, others may have passed on leaving more or less effaced traces of their former presence. The historical geographer and the paleogeographer may pay particular, almost exclusive, attention to these traces, which other geographers may ignore. The physical geographer may wish to exclude anthropogenous forms and aspects from the landscape, but he may have to become an historical geographer in order to discover what man has done to the original landscape, and a paleogeographer to allow for the factor time.

The most controversial point is the inclusion, or otherwise, of intangible phenomena, such as language or religion. Some geographers (Penck, Passarge, Waibel, Granö) adhere to the original meaning of the term and specifically limit the landscape to what is visible; others (Lautensach, Maull) include every aspect of it. Broek (1938) describes the landscape as "an abstract landscape free from time bounds and place bounds of the observer and supplemented by invisible, but, nevertheless, significant data."

Considerable confusion has arisen because of the indiscriminate use of the term landscape, especially in Germany, to signify distinct areas of any size. In fact, there is a whole hierarchy of terms, arranged in order of magnitude, but all referring to the one basic concept of an integrated view of a telluric space. These terms are:

(a) Zone (*Landschaftsgürtel* of some German writers);

(b) Region (*Landschaftstyp* of some German authors, *domaine* of some French authors);

(c) Landscape (the fundamental unit);

(d) Landscape section (Passarge's *Landschaftsteil*, Unstead's *Stow*).

A *zone* is not dissimilar from the ancient Greek *klimata*; it consists of the largest space in which basic geographical characterization is possible— usually because of differential insolation, e.g., the polar caps or the equatorial belt. Where emphasis is on the graduality of zonal variation, *transition zones* may be singled out. The concept of zone was revived by the Russian soil scientists of the last century, beginning with Dokuchaev, and has found its way into soil science and biogeography; it remains of course fundamental in climatology.

A *region* (q.v.) is a unit of lesser magnitude, differentiated from nearby regions not only or primarily because of insolation, but because of other factors such as *continentality* (q.v., Vol. II); this was at the root of the regional units recognized by some Arab geographers in the Middle Ages. The regions recognized in modern climatology, although distinguished by various criteria which may range from the most unsophisticated climatic averages to the most elaborate synoptic combinations, are basically of this nature. Marginal and transitional belts may also be recognized. It is unfortunate that so many geographers have confused "region" with "landscape" and have

weakened the foundations of what promises to be a powerful method of geographical analysis.

A *landscape* is a unit of lesser magnitude still, but large enough to be of telluric significance (larger, therefore, than *locality* and *landform*) and small enough to be within the scope of more direct and immediate human experience than the region. The landscape differs from its neighbors because of zonal and regional characteristics and other characteristics as well, e.g., topography, drainage, land use, type of settlement. Some of these characteristics may be uniform throughout the landscape unit (e.g., house types), but this does not mean that a landscape must be uniform in all or even several of its aspects; it is the combination of these aspects that gives individuality to the landscape. Furthermore, this individuality is intrinsic to the very existence of that given landscape, and any further, (i.e., more minute) subdivision would alter it (perhaps causing the recognition of two or more landscape units where one had previously been recognized).

The basic concept of landscape and a practical outline of landscape surveying were given by Unstead (1916), who suggested

".... considering the effects rather than the elements of climate, for example, to note what vegetation, natural and artificial, can exist in particular areas, and similarly to estimate the combined effect of structure, relief, accessibility, climate and natural resources by observing the distribution of men, their characteristics and their activities.

"Indeed it may be put forward as a general proposition that, in view of the essentially correlative nature of geographical science, the best method of discovering geographical regions is not to bring together on separate maps certain analyzed factors, such as relief, structure, temperature, rainfall, natural vegetation, etc., and to compare these elements, but to take their combined effects as they work themselves out, i.e., to take the actual complex of physical and human conditions, to regard this as a closely interrelated whole, to observe the predominant characteristics of this complex in different parts, and so, by a synthetic rather than an analytic method, to arrive at the determination of regions with common characteristics ....

"The idea of *natural* regions in which a number of physical factors have been combined marked a further advance, and this points to the more completely synthetic study of *geographical* regions. Somewhat similar divisions have been made of relatively small areas ....

"... The work should proceed from small districts to large regions, and not begin by dividing up the world as a whole. In each small district [i.e. landscape section, J.G.] the survey should include the relief and structure, ... noting not only landforms but soil conditions and mineral deposits. It should include also the climate ... also noting the synthetic effect of the climatic factors in making possible certain associations of natural and cultivated plants. It should consider, also as a factor of independent importance, the natural vegetation ... and ... the distribution and relative importance of artificial pastures and crops ... should be taken into account .... Industries should be considered ....

TABLE OF LANDSCAPE TYPES

Landscape Type	Typical Landscapes and Number of Examples Quoted
I. Polar:	
1. Polar cap plateaus	2 (Greenland, Antarctica)
2. Glaciated mountain landscapes	20 (Spitsbergen, Iceland . . . Sierra Nevada, Cascade Mts., N.Z. Alps, East Africa's giant volcanoes . . .)
II. Subpolar:	
1. Lowland tundras	5 (Kola . . . N. Siberian, N. Laurentian lowlands, North American Arctic Archipelago . . .)
2. Highland tundras	7 (Lapland . . . Labrador Highlands . . .) [above the upper limit of mountain forests]
3. High-mountain meadows	
4. Cold high-mountain steppes	4 (Pamir . . . Tibet . . . Puna)
5. Cold high-mountain deserts	2 (W and N Tibet)
6. Subpolar meadow islands	7 (SW Greenland, Iceland, Faeroes, NE Newfoundland, Aleutians . . .)
7. Subpolar forested plains	5 (N Sweden . . . N Russian Lowland, Canadian Conif. Forest Belt)
8. Oceanic subpolar forested mountains	8 (N Scandinavian mountains . . . Alaska, Newfoundland mountains . . . Tierra del Fuego . . .)
9. Continental subpolar forested mountains	4 (Forested Urals . . . Canadian Cordillera)
III. Lands with a warm season:	
1. Oceanic forested plains	9 (German, French, E English, Irish plains . . . coastal plains of New England)
2. Oceanic forested mountains	
(a) cool temperate	8 (German, French, British central mountains . . . Appalachians . . . British Columbian mountains, Andes of S central Chile)
(b) warm temperate	10 (Galicia . . . mountains of Oregon and Washington, Cascade Mts . . . Tasmania)
3. Continental forested plains	2 (Central Russian-W Siberian plain, N Laurentian Basin)
4. Continental forested mountains	8 (Carpathians, Balkans . . . Altai . . . Tien-Shan, Rocky Mts.)
5. Winter-cold monsoon forested mountains	4 (Kamchatka, Amur Mts., N Japan . . .)
6. Summer-hot broadleaf forested plains and basins	6 (N Italian plain . . . SW Caucasian foreland, Ohio basin, S. Laurentian basin)
7. Forest-steppe plains a.b.	10 (SW and central German basins . . . N Ukrainian meadow-steppe . . . Manchurian steppe, Wisconsin Plateau . . .)
8. Winter-cold steppe plains	9 (Podolian, Bessarabian . . . E Gobi, Canadian prairie, Missouri prairie, Columbia tableland)
9. Winter-cold, summer-hot basin steppes	4 (E Turkestan . . . W Gobi . . .)
10. Winter-cold, summer-hot salt steppes	2 (Aralo-caspian, W Turkestan)
11. Winter-cold, summer-hot desert basins	4 (E Turkestan, Mongolian deserts . . . deserts of N Iran)
IV. Ever-warm lands:	
1. Etesian coasts with sclerophylls	9 (coasts of S European peninsula, etc., . . . Atlas, Canary Is., SW Cape Province, SW Australia . . .)
2. Etesian highland steppes	9 (Castillas . . . Tripoli area . . . steppes of Israel, Syria, etc.)
3. Hot alluvial steppes	3 (Nile, Mesopotamia, Punjab)
4. Hot continental highland steppes	3 (Central Arabia, Kalahari, central Australian steppes)
5. Hot peripheral steppes	7 (NW African coast, Erythrea, Somali coast . . . W Australian marginal steppe, Californian Gulf steppe)
6. Hot continental deserts	
(a) Desert mountains	3 (Taureg highlands, Tibesti . . .)
(b) Desert lowlands, etc.	7 (Libyan, etc., deserts . . . Thar . . .)
7. Warm coastal deserts	2 (Atacama, Namib)
8. Warm highland steppes	9 (Andes of Ecuador, Bolivia, Peru, Mexican highlands . . . Madagascar mountain savannas)

TABLE OF LANDSCAPE TYPES (continued)

9. Hot savanna lands with gallery and riverain forests	9 (Menam, Mekong savannas ... Sudan ... Llanos, Campos of Brazil ... savannas of N Australia)
10. Warm grassland plains	2 (Pampas, Murray-Darling basin)
11. Temperate-warm grassland plateaus	2 (Patagonia, highlands of Transvaal ...)
12. Hot savanna highlands with dry forest	9 (Mountains of Yemen, Guinea ridge, Sudan-Congo ridge ... Guiana mountains, Coatingas, W Antilles, Yucatan)
13. Subtropical mountains with monsoon rain forest	4 (Vietnam, S China, S Himalaya ...)
14. Subtropical rainforest mountains	7 (Natal, S Appalachains, Mexican coastal mountains, S Brazil ... Hawaii, SE Australia)
15. Subtropical rainforest lowlands	5 (S Mississippi lowland, Florida ...)
16. Tropical mountains with monsoon rainforest	5 (peripheral mountains of Dekkan ... mountains of Formosa, Ceylon, E Africa)
17. Tropical plains with monsoon rainforest	2 (Hindustan, Burmese coastal plain)
18. Tropical rainforest mountains	14 (Indonesia, Malaya, Philippines, E Madagascar ... Lesser Antilles, Central America, SE Brazil ... New Guinea, Melanesia, NE Australia)
19. Tropical rainforest lowlands	5 (basins of Amazon and Congo, coastal plains of Mozambique, Guiana, deltas of tropical rivers)
20. Tropical mangrove littorals	10 (coastlines of Guinea, E Africa, E and N Brazil, etc.)
21. Tropical and sub-tropical coral islands	3 (Polynesia, Micronesia, Bahama)

"The general character of the district [landscape section] having been ascertained, the question would arise as to the extent of the area to be included; this would be determined by finding how far in each direction the country continued to bear the same general character, and so the particular method of delimitation would depend upon the particular characteristics of each district ....

"When the boundaries of a particular district [section] have been provisionally drawn, the neighbouring districts [sections] would be similarly dealt with .... A reconsideration might be necessary where on one side of a line one criterion ... was taken, while on the other side another criterion ... was employed. The position of a boundary would seldom be quite definite, for sudden and definite changes seldom occur .... It would frequently be found that the actual boundary would depend ultimately upon ... relief (i.e. height, slope and exposure), the soil conditions ... more often than the climatic factors which change very gradually.

"To a considerable extent the characteristics of the regions [of any magnitude] are capable of quantitative expression ....

"... these geographical units of the first order [landscape sections] would be combined with others adjoining them to obtain larger areas [landscapes], geographical units of the second order, which though necessarily less uniform would yet have many features in common .... As a rule, there would be little hesitation about combining those regions [landscape sections] whose precise delimitation presented the greatest difficulty during the first survey, for the slight and gradual transitions which caused that difficulty may indicate broad similarities.

"... The boundaries of the larger units [landscapes] would, of course, never cut across the smaller units already determined to be of an essentially uniform character.

"... racial, linguistic, and religious factors change but slowly; ... very slow change is also to be predicated of climatic conditions ...; in other words, it is the rate rather than the existence of change that makes the problem .... One of the objects of geographical science should be to observe this evolution .... If the geographical regions take into account the factors which undergo relatively rapid change they will, of course, have to be reconsidered and reconstituted at intervals .... And, after all, a reconsideration of regions ... must be periodically undertaken as our knowledge of facts and our powers of analysis and interpretation increase."

Passarge (1919) wrote the only systematic handbook of landscape analysis. He suggested that each landscape should be studied in its

1. Constant aspects:
    (a) Topography (mountains, valleys, etc.)
    (b) Hydrography (rivers, lakes, etc.)
    (c) Plant formations
    (d) Influence of animals (burrows, trails, etc.)
    (e) Human influence (settlements, fields, etc.)
2. Variable aspects:
    (a) Regularly variable, e.g., seasonal aspects, i.e., ice and snow cover, incidence of rain and drought, river regime, leaf growth and fall, grass fires, harvests, migrations of animals and men.
    (b) accidental, e.g., volcanic eruptions, earthquakes, tornadoes, hail, floods, desertification through overstocking, etc.

For each major aspect Passarge gave a guide to detailed description, e.g., 4 different colors of the sky, 4 colors and 3 states of the horizon, 11 aspects of light, 6 effects of extraneous entities, such as fog, shadows of mountains, cloud shadows. As to clouds, their color, pattern and behavior must be described, besides the usual cloud type and height. In all, over 500 possible aspects or criteria were suggested. The enormous mass of material to be analyzed proved too much in the end; and Passarge's later work was much more general and limited to increasingly anthropocentric studies of geographical zones and regions.

Landscape units are now studied in Australia under the name of *land systems* (Christian and Stewart, 1953) for the purpose of planning the most rational utilization of underdeveloped areas.

The very large number of landscape units recognizable on the earth's surface has made it necessary to group them in some systematic way. This was achieved very effectively by Hassinger (1933, pp. 181–184) with his *landscape types*, which in fact are major *natural regions*:

In all, Hassinger recognizes 43 types of landscapes, and quotes 269 examples, some of which are multiple, e.g. "deltas of tropical rivers" or "peripheral mountains of...."

Unfortunately, Hassinger only gives a small map showing 4 major "types" [i.e., zones]. Credit must be given to Biasutti (1962) for the most detailed map of the earth's landscapes, showing 128 units, obtained by the analytical method proposed by Herbertson in his elaboration of *regions* (q.v.) but based on recent and detailed "element" maps and thus constituting an excellent basis for further research, verification and synthesis.

It is obvious that with the introduction of plant cover and topography as criteria, each landscape becomes unique, even though it may belong to a type which includes many other individual examples. This uniqueness becomes even more pronounced when human aspects are included.

J. GENTILLI

References

Biasutti, R., 1962, "Il Paesaggio Terrestre," Torino, Unione Topografica, 586pp.

Bradley, J. W., 1905, "Illuminated Manuscripts," London.

Broek, J. O. M., 1938, "The concept landscape in human geography," *C.R. Congr. Intern. Géogr. Amsterdam*, **2**, Section IIIA, 103–109.

Christian, C. S., and Stewart, G. A. 1953, "Survey of the Katherine–Darwin Region, 1946," *C.S.I.R.O., Australian Land Res. Ser.*, No. 1.

Gallois, L., 1908, "Régions naturelles et noms de pays," Paris.

Hartshorne, R., 1939, "The Nature of Geography," Lancaster, Pa.

Hassinger, H., 1933, "Die Geographie des Menschen," in (Klute, F., editor) "Handbuch der Geographischen Wissenschaft," Potsdam.

Krebs, N., 1938, "Le concept paysage dans la géographie humaine" (report on eight papers) *C.R. Congr. Intern. Amsterdam*, **2** (rapports), 207–213.

Marsh, G. P., 1874, "The Earth as Modified by Human Action," London.

Passarge, S., 1919–1921, "Die Grundlagen der Landschaftskunde," Vols. 1–2, Hamburg, L. Friederichsen & Co.

Schwenkel, H., 1957, "Die Landschaft als Natur und Menschenwerk," Stuttgart.

Sherlock, R. L., 1931, "Man's Influence on the Earth," London, Butterworth, 256pp.

Toniolo, A. R., 1950, "Compendio di Geografia generale," Milano.

Toschi, U., 1952, "Tipi di paesaggi e paesaggi tipici in Puglia e in Emilia," *Ist. Geogr. Univ. Bari Mem.*, **15**.

Unstead, J. F., 1916, "A Synthetic Method of Determining Geographical Regions," *Geograph. J.*, **48**, 230–249.

Unstead, J. F., 1948, "A World Survey from the Human Aspect," London.

Waibel, L., 1928, "Beitrag zur Landschaftskunde," *Geograph. Z.*, **34**, 475–486.

Cross-references: *Geomorphology; Landmass and Major Landform Classification; Landscape Analysis; Landscape Types—Genetic; Land Systems; Morphogenetic Classification; Morphogenetic Regions, Natural and Geographical; Mountains; Plains; Plateau; Terrain Analysis; Terrain, Terrane.* Vol. II: *Climatic Classification; Climatology; Continentality.*

LANDSCAPE, LIMESTONE—See DOLINA; KARST; LAPIÉS; LIMESTONE CAVES; MOGOTE; SPELEOTHEMS

LANDSCAPE, MOUNTAIN GLACIER—See MOUNTAIN GLACIER LANDSCAPE

LANDSCAPE, PERIGLACIAL—See PERIGLACIAL LANDSCAPE

LANDSCAPE, SELVA—See SELVA LANDSCAPE

LANDSCAPE, STEPPE—See STEPPE LANDSCAPE

LANDSCAPE, TAIGA—See TAIGA LANDSCAPE

LANDSCAPE, TUNDRA—See TUNDRA LANDSCAPE

LANDSCAPE TYPES: GENETIC

A genetic analysis and classification of the physical landscape can be considered primarily from two points of view: the *geophysical causes*—energy sources and processes, and the *historico-geological causes*—denudation chronology and accumulation history. The biologic-humanistic aspects of landscape are not considered in this analysis (see *Landscape—Geographical*). Details of each physical process are treated elsewhere in this Encyclopedia (see cross-references at end of this article). For the different categories of landforms, see the article *Land Mass and Major Landform Classification*, with further discussion under *Morphogenetic Regions*. Here we may summarize the key headings:

(I) Geophysical Causes

(See also Vol. V of the *Encyclopedia of Earth Sciences Series*.) The best general introduction to this aspect is probably Walther Penck's celebrated "Morphological Analysis of Land Forms," published in 1924 in German, and unfortunately unavailable in English translation until 1953. Its influence on English-speaking geomorphologists was thus seriously delayed, although a few writers attempted to pass on some of its message (e.g., Von Engeln, 1942). This recommendation of Penck's analytic approach should not be construed as a wholesale approval of his interpretations, many points of which are still controversial (see Symposium, 1940). Two major dynamic categories are identified:

(A) Endogenic Dynamics. These have energy sources stemming from within the earth itself. They include heat flow, volcanism, magmatism, earthquakes, tectonic activity such as folding (orogenesis), faulting (taphrogenesis) and general warping (epeirogenesis), including various manifestations of isostasy. A landscape dominated by the effects of one or more of these internal dynamic phenomena would be called "structurally controlled" (see *Structural Control in Geomorphology* and *Morphotectonics*).

(B) Exogenic Dynamics. Energy sources operating at or near the earth's surface and in the most part derived ultimately from the sun, moon and planetary motions in general are classified as exogenic. Solar heat is transferred into various forms of kinetic and potential energy at the surface of the earth mainly by the agency of the *hydrologic cycle*, though direct solar energy is involved in *exfoliation*, for example. Both *physical and chemical weathering* are critical factors; *biological weathering* is generally a secondary one. *Soil formation* (see also pr Vol. VI) is the direct effect at the earth's surface. The oceans are derived ultimately from endogenic sources (volcanic volatiles), but their energy effects are mainly generated by planetary winds and *wave action*, which are strictly exogenic.

Creep, avalanche and landslides are all in the general category of *mass movement* (q.v.) generated by gravity, another planetary energy source. Running water, rainwash, rivers, waterfalls, and so on involve additionally the hydrologic cycle, as does ice motion (see *Glaciation*). The work of *wind*, *ablation*, *sand dunes*, etc., also has a meteorological cause, but is most effective in the absence of humidity.

One may speak therefore of landscapes dominated by hydrologic controls, by eolian features, by glacial or periglacial processes, by gravitational phenomena.

A modifying role may be played by the *lithology* of the area. Granite weathering tends to favor inselberg landscapes, limestone is immediately identifiable with karst landscapes, sandstones favor escarpments or ridge and valley landscapes, till (boulder clay) generally contributes to the arheic drainage and kettle lakes of the moraine landscape. These are all lithologic or facies controls. What is commonly regarded today as the critical overriding control is exercised by *climate* (see *Morphogenetic Classification*), and the introductory article on *Geomorphology* (q.v.) stresses this new approach, but not without a fourth dimension, the historical approach.

(II) Historico-geological Causes

A review of the stratigraphic and tectonic foundations of a given area can be expressed as a sequential history that for the most part ceases at the moment the area emerges above sea level and its denudational history begins. *Denudation* (q.v.) implies two things: erosion on the one hand, and deposition on the other. The earliest hills to be destroyed by erosion may have left no traces whatever, but the depressions are likely to have trapped some of the resultant debris.

An observed denudation chronology can start as soon as, and provided that, some traces of the early landforms remain. In this way, a landscape that has been continuously above sea level say, since the Cretaceous is liable to contain a vast complexity of different minor features, whereas a newly erupted volcanic ash cone can, for a few weeks, appear to be utterly virginal.

Fundamental Law of Morphology

From the above classification, a primary deduction can be made. Walther Penck (1953, translation, p. 11) called it the *fundamental law of morphology:* "the modelling of the earth's surface is determined by the ratio of the intensity of the endogenetic to that of the exogenetic displacement of material." (*Note:* The difference between endogenetic and endogenic is semantic; most writers today regard them as synonyms and prefer the shorter form, though others see a distinction.)

It was assumed by W. M. Davis that any erosion cycle began with rapid uplift and was followed by a long sequential history of denudation, i.e., brief and violent endogenic primary cause, followed by long and secular exogenic modification. This is confirmed in principle by Penck and others, but it was oversimplified (see discussion below). Penck remarks: "Generally speaking, the origin of any outstanding elevation, any mountain mass, is bound up with the assumption that mountain building is more successful., i.e., works more rapidly, than denudation. . . .

635

The one consistent feature, however, common to every region, is that the activity of exogenetic happenings is subordinate to that of endogenetic processes. This ... forms the basis of morphological analysis."

There is thus a second empirical law, that *the intensity of denudation increases with absolute height*. This is explained by the fact that the processes of denudation tend to increase in intensity with the gradient, as required by the laws of mechanics and hydraulics (see *Law of Declivities*).

From this general law evolves an important deduction for the general relief of the earth's surface —the *Principle of flattening*. In Penck's words (*op. cit.*, p. 121): "No part of any surface on the earth, no matter how denudation works upon it, can ever thereby become as a whole steeper. It can only become flatter. The most important law obeyed during the development of denudational forms is this principle of flattening." A critical phrase here is "as a whole," because in detail, for the microrelief, the opposite is true. Because in fluvial erosion the rate is proportional to the velocity times the load, at the highest point the stream is represented by the merest trickle which has very little erosive potential. Thus we must state that in homogeneous materials *the steepest relief is found at the highest relative elevations* which is required by *Surell's law* (q.v.).

At first glance, this increasing relief would appear to contradict the law of flattening. The paradox is resolved when one considers the scale; it is stressed that the steepest relief rule applies only to the detail, as in the jagged peaks in the high Alps, while the ultimate truth of the law of flattening can be appreciated on the undulating terrain of the Canadian Shield, where individual belts long ago passed through alpine stages. The critical factor is *time*. The jagged relief of the Alps has taken about 4×10^6 years to develop and is still *increasing* as the Alps are rising at about 1 mm/yr while their *mean* denudation rate is about 0.1 mm/yr (see *Continental Erosion* and *Denudation*). Ultimately we predict that these mountains will become reduced to the degree of flattening of the great shields. At 0.1 mm/yr, this denudation would take 40 million years. Even so, as Schumm (1963) has pointed out, progressive isostatic revival means that the story is going to be very long drawn out. In the case of the once-Alpine Appalachians, where absolute dating shows the principal mobilization and uplift to have been about 3.5×10^8 years ago, there was violent revival in the Appalachian orogeny, about 2.8×10^8 years ago and periodic isostatic rejuvenation since then so that the belt continues to represent a subdued mountain belt today.

Because of the progressive epeirogenic upwarping of the Appalachians since Cretaceous times (1×10^8 years), when a near state of planation had been achieved, we have the apparently paradoxical situation that in this intervening time the local relief has been gradually becoming more rugged. Geodetic releveling shows that they are still rising slowly today. They have thus a finer and more deeply dissected microrelief today than at any time since the Mesozoic. Yet the long-term history of every mountain system shows that for the gross relief over the course of major eras (10^8–10^9 year periods), the law of flattening is ultimately valid.

Profile of Equilibrium

In the early nineteenth century, studies of fluvial hydraulics (hydromechanics), particularly in France and Italy, brought about a conviction that there was probably an ideal shape in the longitudinal profile of any stream, the *profile of equilibrium* (q.v.), essentially derived from *Surell's law* (q.v.). Davis (1915) preferred to call it the condition of *grade* (q.v.)—the equilibrium condition between degradation and aggradation. Attempts to establish empirical rules, however, have been less than successful and the explanation of this failure comes readily into view when one considers the historical record. Unless one treated a totally homogeneous lithology drained by a stream-net under constant climatic conditions and totally static tectonics, one could hardly expect an ideal profile to emerge. On the short-term micro-relief scale, an equilibrium profile may be established, but inhomogeneities in space and time normally prohibit such a state. We must therefore consider the genetic history in detail.

Genetic History

A division of landscapes into four types on the basis of their fundamental genetic history—rather than material, stage, cycle, etc.—has been offered by Horberg (1952). With some explanatory suggestions, these are:

(1) *Simple, monocyclic landscapes* that conform directly to an idealized cycle. Such landscapes can have experienced no important climatic changes, but since no stable parts of the earth's crust can have avoided several such changes in regime during the last 10,000 years or so, a simple monocyclic system can only be established (a) on a microrelief scale, or (b) on a newly established land surface such as freshly erupted volcanic slopes or a section of sea floor violently uplifted by a recent seismic event.

(2) *Multicyclic (polycyclic) landscapes* which represent a synthesis of past structural and climatic events that in some cases go back to the Archean. A peneplaned surface to a geomorphologist is simply an unconformity to a stratigrapher.

(3) *Compound landscapes* in which a mantle of youthful material fails to obscure the dominant features of an underlying landform. Thus a post-glacial soil in no way effaces the identity of a late glacial moraine; nor does a coastal dune always obscure the presence of barrier beaches or beach ridges.

(4) *Exhumed or resurrected landscapes* which have been buried stratigraphically and subsequently re-exposed as relicts or "fossil" erosion surfaces, slightly remodeled in the contemporary cycle (see *Relict Landforms*).

Horberg emphasized that the geological history of the *Quaternary* (q.v.), essentially the last 2–3 million years, plays a decisive role in geomorphology for many reasons, including (a) mutual concern of stratigraphers and geomorphologists with glacial landscapes, (b) topographic control of Quaternary glaciation, (c) glacio-eustasy, (d) accelerated Quaternary diastrophic and volcanic activity (as compared with the Tertiary), and (e) mutual interest in absolute dating. As pointed out by Kirk Bryan (1941), dynamic geology is the study of present-day processes, but it frequently cannot explain landforms without considering the inherited aspects ordinarily embraced by geomorphology. The sedimentological concept of *facies* (including biofacies and lithofacies), the integration of environment and stratigraphic sequence or historical relationships, is essential for understanding landscape.

Three axioms were thus laid down by Horberg:

(1) Most landscapes are complex and contain relict features;

(2) Such inherited features mostly date from the Pleistocene;

(3) Complex landscapes are best correlated on the basis of Quaternary climatic fluctuations.

In terminology, the relative degree, dominance or otherwise, of the inherited features needs to be brought out. Thus we have (a) *dominantly inherited landforms* and (b) *subordinate relict forms* with contemporary dynamics dominant, impressed on the ancient surfaces.

A serious weakness of the Davisian school of geomorphology (and indeed, most modern textbooks) is their insistence on the inductive, and later the descriptive dynamic approach, not a true historical approach; the assumption that almost everything in the landscape is to be explained in terms of present-day landforms and events and the backward projection of the "normal" fluvial cycle. Both Davis and Johnson assumed the inherent stability of sea level, whereas the opposite is true. The landscape simply cannot be explained in terms of contemporary physical geography. In fact, most landscapes show traces of numerous earlier cycles and epicycles, often pertaining to quite contrasting climatic regimes (Fig. 1; see, e.g., Mabbutt, 1966). This may explain in part why traces of periglacial morphology (today well-developed in Iceland and Spitzbergen) are only just beginning to be recognized in New Mexico and North Africa; why desert sands are widespread in the Congo basin, partly overgrown by jungle trees, yet never mentioned in textbooks; why many soils just do not seem to "make sense" when considered in the light of present climate regimes; why most coastal features cannot be adequately

FIG. 1. Linear dunes in the Simpson Desert, Australia (oblique air view). Overgrown and largely stabilized by vegetation.

explained without detailed consideration of world eustatic history.

The paleoclimatological approach to the "new geomorphology" has been stressed by a number of workers in North America (Bryan, Smith, Horberg), but has been more integrated into the whole discipline overseas, in France by Tricart and Cailleux (1955) and in Germany by Büdel (author of *Geomorphology—Principles* in this Encyclopedia). In North America and Britain, the quantitative and dynamic approach (Strahler, Chorley) is very helpful for understanding the microterrain, but is difficult to apply with precision to the major landforms which invariably lead us back into geological history.

More and more examples are being observed of climatically conditioned landforms, from late Pleistocene dunes in Nebraska (H. T. U. Smith, 1965) to periglacial solifluction in the Appalachians (Peltier, P. B. King). In the semiarid Southwest, traces of formerly wetter and formerly still drier epochs are being worked out (partly in cooperation with the archeologists). It is in the transitional period between purely geological observations (essentially the Pleistocene and earlier) and the contemporary period of instrumental, quantitative dynamics, that collaborative work between geologists and archeologists is richly rewarding. In the Nile Valley, for example, the writer learned that historical and archeological data provided a record of tropical rainfall, that controls river siltation or erosion, back for over 5000 years. With C^{14} dating of records of Late Paleolithic man, the record has now been pushed back more than 25,000 years. An astonishing and unexpected discovery during this work, of worldwide importance to meteorology, paleoclimatology and geomorphology, was that during the Wisconsin epoch the Nile almost completely dried up; this was corroborated later by similar reports about the Congo, the Niger and the Senegal. It then emerged that the great dune-building periods of the world correlated with cold epochs, when sea level was low; the fossil dunes are found also below sea level on the continental shelves. This makes sense meteorologically, because the evaporation of ocean moisture during the cold epochs would be at least 20% lower than now (Flohn, 1963). Conversely, the high solar radiation epochs, as in the early Holocene, are marked by heavy tropical rains, which caused much of the vast sand dune covered areas of central Africa to become vegetated and brought savanna conditions into the northern Sahara; thus petroglyphs by Neolithic man in the mid-Sahara depict all sorts of game animals no longer seen in the barren desert (Fairbridge, 1964).

It is to be stressed that here was a discovery that has confirmed the geomorphic ideas of Cailleux and Tricart, and has far-reaching significance for geomorphology. It was only possible because of an integration of the data from archeology, paleontology, stratigraphy, geochemistry, pedology, oceanography, meteorology and climatology as well as dynamic geomorphology.

In genetic landscape analysis there is a constant danger of identifying a certain paleoclimatic indicator, such as river gravels as an indication of rainfall, and then assuming a particular climatic regime. Precipitation and temperature are not necessarily correlatives, positive or negative. As a common rule in mid-latitudes (40–20°) it can be said that an increase of summer rains indicates increased solar radiation, while a decrease in the latter results in more winter rain coupled with an equatorward shift of the westerlies and their principal jet streams. But there are many complicating factors such as the orographic effects, ocean currents, continentality and so on. An interesting example of this complementary effect may be seen in the record of inland sea and lake levels. Two such water bodies are the Caspian and the Aral Sea, the levels of which are strikingly out of phase; the former is fed from the north and thus dominated by winter precipitation (from the westerlies) and the latter is fed by summer melting of mountain snows.

The genetic approach to landscape studies is therefore urged as a guiding principle in geomorphology. While many of its techniques and conclusions are already included within the working procedures of the practical geomorphologist, much remains to be accomplished, especially in the area of integrated correlation.

RHODES W. FAIRBRIDGE

References

Bryan, K., 1941, "Physiography," in "Geology, 1888–1938," pp. 1–5, Fiftieth Anniversary Volume, New York, *Geological Society of America.*

Bryan, K., and Albritton, C. C., Jr., 1943, "Soil phenomena as evidence of climatic changes," *Am. J. Sci.,* **241**, 460–490.

Büdel, J., 1959, "The periglacial-morphologic effects of the Pleistocene climate over the entire world," *Intern. Geol. Rev.,* **1**, No. 3, 1–16 [translation of German original in *Erdkunde,* **7**, 249–266 (1953)].

Büdel, J., 1963, "Die pliozänen und quatären Pluvialzeiten der Sahara," *Eiszeit. Gegen.* **14**, 161–187.

Davis, W. M., 1915, "The principles of geographical description," *Ann. Assoc. Am. Geogr.,* **5**, 61–105.

Fairbridge, R. W., 1964, "African Ice-age Aridity," in "Problems in Palaeoclimatology," pp. 357–363, London, John Wiley & Sons.

Flohn, H., 1963, "Zur meteorologischen Interpretation der pleistozänen Klimaschwankungen," *Eiszt. Gegen.* **14**, 153–160.

Horberg, L., 1952, "Interrelations of geomorphology, glacial geology, and Pleistocene geology," *J. Geol.,* **80**, 187–190.

Howard, A. D., and Spock, L. E., 1940, "Classification of landforms," *J. Geomorphol.,* **3**, 332–345.

Mabbutt, J. A., 1966, "Landforms of the Western Macdonnell Ranges. A Study of Inheritance and Periodicity in the Geomorphology of Arid Central Australia," in (Dury, editor) "Essays in Geomorphology," pp. 83–119, London, William Heinemann, Ltd.

Peltier, L., 1950, "The geographic cycle in periglacial regions as it is related to climatic geomorphology," *Ann. Assoc. Am. Geog.,* **40**, 214–236.

Penck, W., 1953, "Morphological Analysis of Land Forms," London, Macmillan & Co., 429pp. (translation by Czech, H., and Boswell, K. C., of 1924 edition).

Schumm, S. A., 1963, "The disparity between present rates of denudation and orogeny," *U.S. Geol. Surv. Profess. Paper* **454-H**, 1–13.

Smith, H. T. U., 1965, "Dune morphology and chronology in central and western Nebraska," *J. Geol.,* **73**(4), 557–578.

Symposium, 1940, "Walther Penck's contribution to geomorphology," *Ann. Assoc. Am. Geogr.,* **30**(4).

Tricart, J., and Cailleux, A., 1955, "Cours de Géomorphologie, Introduction à la Géomorphologie Climatique," Paris, Cent. Doc. Univ., 222pp.

Von Engeln, O. D., 1942, "Geomorphology," New York, The Macmillan Co., 655pp.

Cross-references: *Aral Sea; Caspian Sea; Continental Erosion; Dead Sea; Denudation; Endogenic Dynamics; Exfoliation; Exhumed Landscape; Exogenic Dynamics; Geomorphology—Principles; Glaciation; Grade, Graded Stream; Granite Landforms; Holocene; Lake Balkhash; Landscape, Geographical; Land Mass and Major Landform Classification; Law of Declivities; Mass Movement; Morphogenetic Classification; Morphogenetic Regions; Morphotectonics; Morphostruc-*

ture; *Periglacial Eolian Effects*; *Pluvial Lakes and Terraces*; *Profile of Equilibrium*; *Quantitative Geomorphology*; *Quaternary Period*; *Relict Landforms*; *Structural Control in Geomorphology*; *Surell's Law*; *Tropical Weathering and Relief*; *Wind Action*. Vol. I: *Wave Action*. Vol. II: *Climatic Change in American Pre-History*; *Climatic Variation*; *Paleoclimatology—Astronomic Cycles*. Vol. V: *Geophysics*. Vol. VI: *Hydrological Cycle*; *Soil Genesis*. pr Vol. VII: *Paleoclimatology*.

LANDSLIDES

Landslides are perceptible downslope movements of rock, soil or artificial fill (see *Mass Movement*). The motion may be either that of a slide, flow or fall, acting singly or together. All are forms of slope failure arising from a high shearing stress along a potential surface of rupture which exceeds the shearing resistance along that surface (see Varnes, 1958).

Regions of High Shearing Stress

Landslides are especially important agents of denudation in tectonically active zones subject to earthquakes and regional tilting, in mountains, in humid lands (notably the wet tropics), in semiarid landscapes, in cliffed coastal belts, and in those areas where new cycles of erosion are oversteepening slopes.

In all these environments, high shearing stress arises through such agencies as the component of horizontal acceleration of earthquakes; under cutting at the toe of a slope by stream action; prolonged rainfall or snowfall, producing over-

loading, saturation, and/or rise of the piezometric surface (Terzaghi, 1950); profound alternations of wetting and drying; fluctuations in depth of water bodies, and progressive attack by storm surges along actively degrading coastlines.

Quite the most landslide-prone regions of the world are the mountains girdling the Pacific and similar regions of active mountain building, where many of the above factors operate in conjunction.

Geologic Conditions Favoring Low Shearing Strength

Even in regions of modest shearing stress, however, there are certain lithologies, weathering states and dispositions of strata which make for very low shearing strength and thus are usually unstable. Among the more important of these are:

(a) *Lithologies*: sedimentaries composed substantially of layered clay minerals—clays, shales, mudstones; porous volcanics—tuff and breccia; material either loosely coherent or marked by disordered arrangements of clays such as "sensitive" clays with some thixotropic qualities (the capacity of suddenly turning from a solid to a liquid under transitory stress) (see *Quickclay*, pr Vol. VI), platy or foliated rocks, including talc, phyllite, schist and serpentine.

(b) *Weathering States*: progressive reduction of cohesion through deep chemical weathering of crystalline rocks in subtropical and tropical regions; long run changes in hydration; the genesis of expanding lattice clay minerals at the weathering interface; the presence of allophanic constituents in weathered volcanic ash and many soils of the humid tropics; soil clays carrying substantial percentages of hydrophylic cations (Na^+ and K^+)

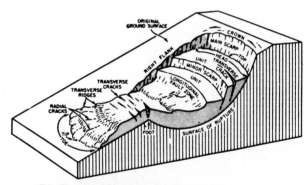

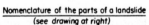

Nomenclature of the parts of a landslide
(see drawing at right)

MAIN SCARP- A steep surface on the undisturbed ground around the periphery of the slide, caused by movement of slide material away from the undisturbed ground. The projection of the scarp surface under the disturbed material becomes the surface of rupture.

MINOR SCARP- A steep surface on the disturbed material produced by differential movements within the sliding mass.

HEAD- The upper parts of the slide material along the contact between the disturbed material and the main scarp.

TOP- The highest point of contact between the disturbed material and the main scarp.

FOOT- The line of intersection (sometimes buried) between the lower part of the surface of rupture and the original ground surface.

TOE- The margin of disturbed material most distant from the main scarp.

TIP- The point on the toe most distant from the top of the slide.

FLANK- The side of the landslide.

CROWN- The material that is still in place, practically undisturbed, and adjacent to the highest parts of the main scarp.

ORIGINAL GROUND SURFACE- The slope that existed before the movement which is being considered took place. If this is the surface of an older landslide, that fact should be stated.

LEFT AND RIGHT- Compass directions are preferable in describing a slide, but if right and left are used they refer to the slide as viewed from the crown.

FIG. 1. Nomenclature of the parts of a complex rotational landslide (after Varnes, 1958).

639

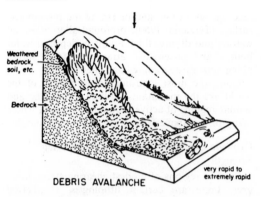

FIG. 2. Debris avalanche movements are very common in mountainous areas (after Varnes, 1958).

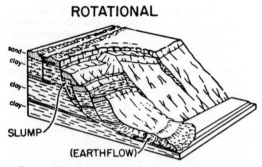

FIG. 4. The characteristic form of a rotational land-slide (slump) with a spoon-shaped surface of rupture. These slides may occur on both steep and gentle (6–8°) slopes (after Varnes, 1958).

on the exchange complex; and fragmentation of mudstones, slates, shales and clays through repeated cycling of wet-dry rhythms.

(c) *Disposition of Strata*: rocks subject to much fine jointing, fissuring and brecciation; interbedded permeable and impermeable strata; sediments dipping towards an unloaded face; and massive beds (jointed limestone) overlying incompetents (shale).

Landslide Types

Though many landslides are complex, one of three major types of movement (fall, slide, or flow) is normally dominant. These movements form the basis for the classification developed by Sharpe (1938) and modified by Varnes (1958) which is used here. However, many classifications have been developed, and for certain complex slides some authors have preferred to refer to type examples (see Sokolov in Popov and Kotlov, 1961).

Falls embrace rock fall and soil fall in which the movement of the segments is largely independent of one another. The surface of rupture is often a near-vertical joint plane. Slides may be grouped

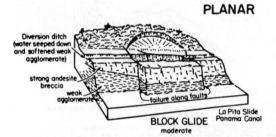

FIG. 3. Block glide landslides are common in sedimentary rocks gently dipping toward an unloaded face, undercut by a river, wave-cut coastline or canal (after Varnes, 1958).

depending on the degree of deformation of the moving mass. Relatively undeformed slides include *slumps*, characterized by cycloidal shear, backward rotation, spoon-shaped slump walls, sag-ponds at the head of the slide and repeated movements. These are prominent in shales and occur on all ranges of slopes from gentle to steep. Also included in the relatively undeformed group are *block glides*, marked by planar motion, normally along a bedding plane and without rotation. These may continue slowly over centuries or be very rapid. Often they occur on very gentle slopes.

Profoundly deformed slides include (a) *rockslides* and *debris slides* which are usually rather shallow and take place on steep slopes, and (b) *failure by lateral spreading*, which takes place on gentle slopes as soft clay spreads beneath an overburden usually in response to a rise in pore-water pressure along silt or clay partings. "The movement is usually complex involving translation, breaking ..., some slumping and some liquefaction and flow" (Varnes, 1958). *Flows* typically are more moist than slides, though (a) *dry flows* may occur in silt, sand and loess, particularly under seismic stress, and dry rockfall avalanches of great size behave as density currents and flow at very high velocities; (b) *wet flows* include *debris avalanche* and *debris flow* which involve the relatively thin weathered mantle of steep slopes. They cut long narrow swathes in mountainous valleys, destroying all trees in their path, and may be triggered by protracted rainfall or by earthquakes. A variety of rock types are involved but igneous and metamorphic rocks figure prominently.

Earthflows and mudflows contain more liquid than the above group and represent a gradational sequence from relatively dry and slow to very wet and rapid. A special class of mudflows are those developing in *quick clays* which spontaneously liquefy and may flow readily on very gentle slopes, rafting houses, roads and trees appreciable distances.

Landslides as Agents of Denudation

Observations by Wentworth (1943) in the Honolulu watershed on Oahu, Hawaii, show that soil avalanches on basalt lower the surface one foot every 400 years.

Recent unpublished studies by this contributor indicate denudation rates at least as high as one foot every 200–300 years on a variety of sedimentary and igneous rocks in highly seismic areas of New Guinea. In many areas, aerial photographs taken at different times may be used to detect landslides and quantify their contribution to denudation.

Where large numbers of slides occur, aerial photographs at a scale of 1:10,000 to 1:30,000 at time intervals of 10 years may be used for detailed evaluation of such items as denudation rates, relation to earthquake shock, and to delimit areas of especial hazard in road-making operations.

Landslides and Climatic Change

Landslides in many regions are relict, or at least the conditions under which they were formed are relict. Shifts in temperature, and amount, distribution and intensity of rainfall during the climatic fluctuations of the Pleistocene have left their impress in landslides showing clear age and weathering differences in such widely separated regions as Arizona and New Mexico (Ahnert, 1960), coastal New South Wales (Walker, 1963), coastal Brazil (Bigarella *et al.* 1965) and the Crimea (G. S. Zolotarev, in Popov and Kotlov, 1961).

DAVID S. SIMONETT

References

Ahnert, F., 1960, "The influence of Pleistocene climates upon the morphology of cuesta scarps on the Colorado Plateau," *Ann. Assoc. Am. Geogr.*, **50**, 139–156.

Bigarella, J. J. *et al.*, 1965, "Processes and environments of the Brazilian Quaternary," Curitiba, Univ. Parana Press, 71pp.

Kayser, B., 1963, "L'erosion par franes en Lucanie," *Mediterranée*, **4**(1), 93–100.

Popov, I. V., and Kotlov, F. V., 1961, "The Stability of Slopes," Transactions of the F. P. Savarenskii Hydrogeology Laboratory, Vol. 35; Translation, 1963, New York, Consultants Bureau.

*Sharpe, C. F. S., 1938, "Landslides and Related Phenomena," New York, Columbia Univ. Press (Pageant Books reprint, 1960).

Terzaghi, K., 1950, "Mechanism of Landslides," pp. 83–123, Geological Society of America, Berkey Volume.

*Varnes, D. J., 1958, "Landslide Types and Processes," in (Eckel, E. B., editor) "Landslides and Engineering Practice," Highway Research Board, Special Report 29, Washington, D.C.

Walker, P. H., 1963, "Soil history and debris-avalanche deposits along the Illawarra scarpland," *Australian J. Soil Res.*, **1**, 223–230.

Wentworth, C. K., 1943, "Soil avalanches on Oahu, Hawaii," *Bull. Geol. Soc. Am.*, **54**, 53–64.

* Additional bibliographic references may be found in this work.

Cross-references: *Avalanche*; *Denudation*; *Mass Movement*; *Mass Wasting*; *Mudflow*; *Relict Landforms*; *Rock Glacier*; *Solifluction*; *Talus, Scree*; *Weathering*. Vol. VI: *Quickclay*; *Slope Stability*; *Thixotropy*.

LANDSLIP—*See* LANDSLIDES; MASS MOVEMENT

LAND SYSTEMS

A *land system* is an area or group of areas with a recurring pattern of landforms, soils and vegetation. The concept of land systems was defined by Australian scientists engaged in reconnaissance land resource inventories (Christian and Stewart, 1953). Land systems have many uses but are particularly valuable (1) as units for summarizing and mapping resources, landforms, soils, vegetation, geology or any other feature of the earth's surface, and (2) as conceptual devices which achieve an integrated overview of the relationships between geologic and climatic history, landforms, soils, and ecology. Use (1) is primarily technical, i.e., land systems constitute a methodological tool which provides a relatively easy way of summarizing a vast amount of otherwise disparate information. Use (2) is primarily scientific, i.e., land systems are a conceptual device which requires a scientist to look at the landscape as an entity in which all components are interrelated.

Land system patterns are the result of three interacting controls (which are generally expressed on a scale suited to reconnaissance survey):

(1) Regional lithology and structure,
(2) Past and present regional climates,
(3) Geomorphic evolution.

The interaction of these three factors tends to give rise to a characteristic assemblage of landforms and soils, which in turn combine with climate to produce a typical pattern of natural vegetation (Fig. 1). The land system approach attempts to express the integration of all elements of the land complex, recognizing the causal links between them through an understanding of the *genesis* of the land system itself.

From a methodological point of view, the land system concept is essentially a synthetic approach to air photo interpretation. As Fig. 1 shows, close relationships exist between geology, geomorphology and vegetation. Field observations confirm that soil characteristics also can be related to air photo pattern. Standard techniques of air photo interpretation are used to delineate various areas of similar landforms and vegetation (i.e., to describe land systems). Field surveys are then made to determine the

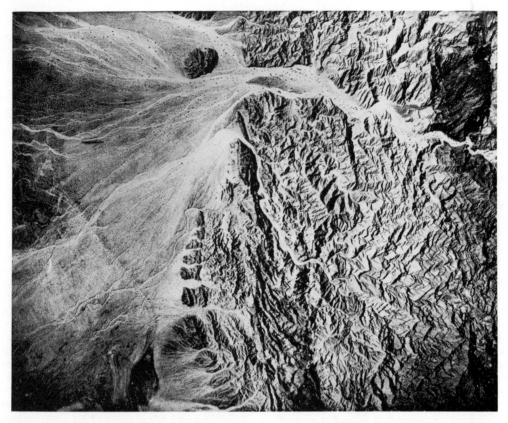

FIG. 1. Aerial photograph in Basin and Range Province, western United States. Two distinct land systems are shown: a mountainous terrain consisting mainly of erosional slopes with minor valley alluvium, and an alluvial fan terrain consisting of channels, interfluves and occasional inselbergs. Each land system is characterized by differing topography, vegetation, soils and history.

validity of land system mapping and to provide detailed descriptions of each land system. A report is published describing the general characteristics of the area mapped (climate, soils, vegetation, geology, geomorphology, agriculture, mineral resources and other data) and also providing summaries of characteristics of each land system (Fig. 2). A land system map is also published; this sheet is often accompanied by subsidiary maps showing geology, vegetation, soils, water resources, etc., for the entire area mapped. Such subsidiary maps are derived directly from the land system map by combining land systems which have similar geology, vegetation and so forth.

Difficulties in actually mapping and describing land systems occur. These often relate to the scale used in mapping, the fact that the mapped area may be very complicated, or to problems in correlating land surface characteristics with air photo patterns. However, once these problems are overcome, the final map and report provide an extremely useful summary of earth surface characteristics which is of value to many different scientific disciplines (geo-

morphology, ecology, and pedology, in particular), and to all those interested in analyzing and developing the resource potential of the area mapped [for a detailed description of this use of land system surveys, see Christian and Stewart (1964)].

As all ecologists (as well as many geographers, pedologists and some geologists) are aware, there is usually a very well-developed interrelationship between geologic and climatic history, bedrock, landforms, drainage, vegetation, soils and human activity. The concepts of the *ecosystem, soil catena, geographical cycle*, all illustrate this point.

The primary value of the land system approach to regional reconnaissance mapping is that it forces the mapper(s) to analyze *all* the factors which produce a given landscape and to integrate these factors. Thus, the forester can understand the distribution of trees in terms of slopes, drainage, soils and climate. For the geomorphologist, the great advantages of land system mapping are:

(1) Land system maps are geomorphic maps which, while not detailed, are very useful and relatively easy to make.

Lynne Land System (250 sq. miles)

Stony plateaux with open mulga, in the centre and north-east of the area.

Geology. Partly weathered, gently dipping Upper Proterozoic quartzite, sandstone, and feldspathic grit (Nullagine "system").

Geomorphology. Surfaces formed by dissection of the old plateaux—sandstone plateaux: strike belts up to 4 miles wide, with plateaux and bevelled ridges, rocky slopes, and narrow, flanking lowlands; occurring as parallel ridges separated by strike valleys with alluvial flood-plains, or as single ridges with a radial pattern of incised valleys; relief up to 150 ft.

Land Use. Hill pastures with stunted mulga shrubland: ephemeral growth in units 1–3 after rain should be stocked; palatable pastures in units 1 and 4 should be preserved by controlled stocking; drought resistance moderate; unit 4 subject to severe water and wind erosion; a little stock water in unit 4, but commonly saline.

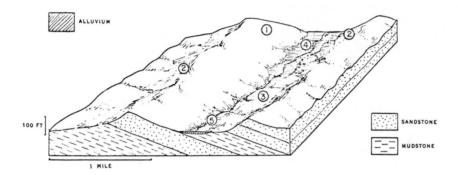

Unit	Approx. Area (sq. miles)	Land Form	Soil and Soil Association	Vegetation
1	60	Summits: up to 150 ft high, in strike belts up to 1 mile wide; gently sloping or rounded surfaces with slopes less than 5%; very stony, with many rock outcrops.	Outcrop and shallow stony soils. Rock outcrop and 2.	Open mulga and other *Acacia* spp. with moderately dense inedible shrubs and palatable and unpalatable perennial grasses: *Acacia aneura* (mulga) sub-alliance (33).
2	70	Hill slopes: mainly 5–20%, with ledges and upper breakaways up to 20 ft high formed by quartzite or silicified strata; dissected into rounded spurs up to 50 ft high and ¼ mile wide, with marginal slopes up to 15%		Stunted mulga with sparse shrubs, forbs, and short annual grasses: *A. aneura* sub-alliance (29, 30).
3	70	Lower slopes: concave, 0·5–3·5% and mainly up to ½ mile long; stony surfaces with minor rock outcrops and extensive colluvial mantles; locally dissected to 5 ft.	Shallow, stony soils on rock, locally on hard-pan crusts. 4b.	As in unit 2, but increasing in density downslope.
4	30	Flood-plains and tributary alluvial drainage floors: up to 500 yd. wide, gradients 1 in 250 to 1 in 1000; levees up to 1 ft high, with back slopes about 0·5%; severely scalded surfaces with multiple shallow runnels, either throughout or in central zones up to 100 yd wide.	No records; probably mainly texture-contrast soils. 6b	Very sparse mulga with shrub layers of saltbush and bluebush and with forbs and succulents: *A. aneura-Kochia pyramidata* (bluebush) alliance (60)
5	20	**Channels**: up to 50 ft wide and 5 ft deep.	Bed-loads mainly sand, with low banks of pebble gravel.	Dense fringing community of *Acacia* spp with some tall eucalypts and shrubs: 72; also 60.

FIG. 2. Tabular summary of the characteristics of the Lynne Land System, Western Australia [as published in C.S.I.R.O. Land Research Series, No. 7, (1963), Melbourne, Australia]. Note that general characteristics of the entire land system are given, including total area of system and land use. A block diagram showing landform relationships and geology is included; in some land system descriptions, a geomorphic map replaces the block diagram. Detailed descriptions of landform-vegetation-soil assemblages within the land system are also given. References within these (e.g., 4b for the soil of unit 3) refer to more complete descriptions within the text of the published report. Specific descriptions contain details commensurate with detail of real assemblages. In this example, the landforms are complicated and hence are described at some length, whereas the soils are relatively uncomplicated and are described very briefly.

(2) It is possible to relate closely different geomorphic aspects of the landscape (e.g., see Fig. 2) and to relate landforms to geologic and climatic controls.

A team of scientists is generally required to produce a land system map. The contribution of the geomorphologist to this team (Mabbutt and Stewart, 1963) includes: (1) analysis of *morphology*, i.e., relief, slope, drainage characteristics; (2) delineation of land systems on the basis of such geomorphic factors as a *common source*, such as lithology and structure in erosional land systems, or of a common formative process as in the case of flood plains; (3) determination of the *relative ages* of the land surfaces which make up the mapped area; (4) mapping on the basis of *landscape dynamics*, especially mode and rate of landscape change (e.g., stable versus active flood plains).

LEE WILSON

References

*Christian, C. A., and Stewart, G. A., 1964, "Methodology of integrated surveys," Conference on Principles and Methods of Integrating Aerial Survey Studies of Natural Resources for Potential Development, U.N.E.S.C.O., Toulouse, France, 1964, 145pp.

Mabbutt, J. A., and Stewart, G. A., 1963, "Application of geomorphology in integrated resources surveys in Australia and New Guinea," *Revue de Géomorphologie*, **14**(7–9).

Perry, R. A., *et al.*, 1962, "Lands of the Alice Springs Area, Northern Territory," Melbourne, C.S.I.R.O., Land Research Series No. 6.

Perry, R. A., *et al.*, 1965, "Lands of the Wabag-Tari Area, Papua, New Guinea," Melbourne, C.S.I.R.O., Land Research Series No. 15.

* Additional bibliographic references mentioned in the text may be found in this work.

Cross-references: *Climatic Geomorphology*; *Cycles, Geomorphic*; *Drainage Patterns*; *Equilibrium in Geomorphology*; *Geomorphic Mapping*; *Landscape Analysis*; *Morphogenetic Regions*; *Slopes*. Vol. II: *Climate and Geomorphology*; *Climatology*; *Vegetation Classification and Description*. pr Vol. VI: *Hydrology*; *Lithology*; *Pedology*; *Photo Interpretation*; *Vegetation Markers and Landscapes*. pr Vol. VII: *Ecology*; *Paleoclimatology*.

LAPIÉS

The term "lapiés" refers to a rill-like erosional form of limestone solution in the karst landscape. The term *lapié* is French, stemming from the type locality, *Lapiaz*. The term *lapiésation* was proposed for the process by Wray (1922). The equivalent word in German is *Kar* (plural *Karren*), and the area is called *Karrenfeld*, which is used occasionally in English. The terms *clint* and *grike* or *gryke* are often

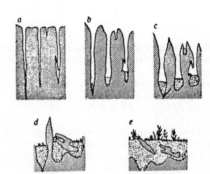

FIG. 1. Evolution of a series of Lapiés (from Eckert, 1902; in Louis, 1961).

FIG. 2. Lapiés formed in limestone covered by residual clay. In a quarry near Generalski Sto, on the railway line Zagreb-Rijeka, in Croatia. When the lapié ridges are destroyed, a dolina will be formed, filled with clay (Cvijić, 1924).

used in the north of England. "Clint" is of Scandinavian origin and refers to the bare rock surfaces, while "grike" (from "gric" in Yugoslavia) refers to the vertical channels and fissures.

Where there is no soil cover, or soil has been stripped off, the limestone surfaces and joint planes are etched, pitted and transected by rills, grooves and flutes, ranging from a few millimeters to several meters in depth. The corrosion is largely "biological weathering," due to carbonic acid and humic acids in soil and around the roots of lichens and mosses (Jones, 1965). The micro-lapiés are called *Rillensteine* in German, or *rock-rills* in English. The limestone base is always secondarily cemented and

FIG. 3. Development of pipe-like lapiés (grikes) at Keld Bank, Yorkshire, England (Jones, 1965).

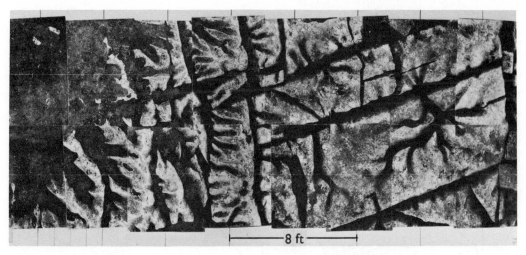

FIG. 4. Pattern of lapiés (grikes) following joints in Carboniferous limestone, near Malham Cove, Yorkshire, England. A vertical photo-mosaic (Jones, 1965). Note also patterns of dendritic rills; areas of bare rock (clint) lie between.

becomes intensely hard. Deep crevices are often filled with *terra rossa* (see Vol. VI). Well developed lapiés with pinnacles standing up to 5 meters high are common in emerged limestone reefs, particularly in the South Pacific (Marshall, 1930).

Analogous surface texture erosion features are often seen in certain easily corroded volcanic tuffs and sometimes even in granite (see *Granite Landforms*). In Hawaii, they were observed in basalt (Palmer, 1927). The terms are equally appropriate for solution forms in evaporites, notably halite and gypsum. They have been termed "*pseudokarren*" in the German literature (by Klaer, 1956; see discussion in Louis, 1961).

Cvijić (1918, 1924), who described and illustrated the classical karst regions of Dalmatia (Yugoslavia), pointed out that the lapiés were essentially a youthful or first stage in karst evolution, being most common in tilted rocks, whereas horizontal rock normally favored the deeper weathering forms, sink holes and cryptorheic drainage.

RHODES W. FAIRBRIDGE

References

Bögli, A., 1951, "Probleme der Karrenbildung," *Geogr. Helvetica,* **6,** No. 3, 191–204.

Cvijić, J., 1918, "Hydrographie souterraine et évolution morphologique du karst," *Rec. Trav. Insts. Geog. Alpine, Grenoble,* **6**(4), 56pp.

Cvijić, J., 1924, "The evolution of lapiés," *Geograph. Rev.,* **14,** 26–49.

Jones, R. J., 1965, "Aspects of the biological weathering of limestone pavement," *Proc. Geol. Assoc.,* **76,** 421–433.

Louis, H., 1961, "Allgemeine Geomorphologie," Berlin, Gruyter, 355pp.

Marshall, P., 1930, "Coral reef rock," *Proc. Pacific Sci. Congr. Pacific Sci. Assoc.,* **2B,** 863–867.

Palmer, H. S., 1927, "Lapiés in Hawaiian basalts," *Geograph. Rev.,* **17,** 627–631.

Thornbury, W. D., 1954, "Principles of Geomorphology," New York. John Wiley & Sons, 618pp.

Wray, D. A., 1922, "Karstlands of western Yugoslavia," *Geol. Mag.,* **59,** 392–409.

Cross-references: *Granite Landforms; Karst; Volcano-Karst.* Vol. VI: *Terra Rossa.*

LATERIZATION—*See* pr Vol. VI

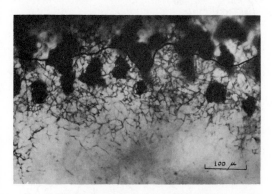

FIG. 5. Photomicrograph of endolithic lichen growths in slice of carboniferous limestone (Yorkshire). Black line marks weathered surface, penetrated by large tubes (up to 50 μ) and fine hairlines ("hyphae") of the lichens.

LAVA-DISPLACED DRAINAGE AND DEEP LEADS

Volcanic activity has a marked effect, sometimes catastrophic, on preexisting drainage. If only small

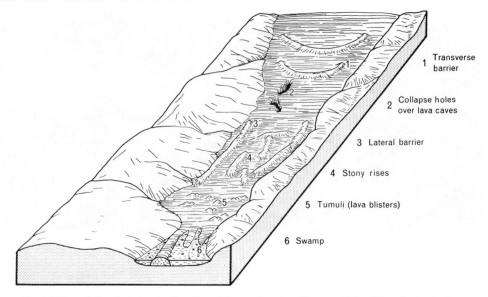

FIG. 1. Minor surface features on a lava flow. Diagram based on Harman Valley, Victoria, Australia. The river that once occupied this valley has been completely diverted so there is no lateral stream (Ollier, 1967).

cones and flows are involved streams may flow around them, but with large-scale lava eruptions all preexisting topography may be obliterated (Fig. 1) and a completely new drainage pattern initiated on the volcanic cones and lava plains. Some immense lava flows are known, such as the one that partly filled the Crooked River, Oregon, for 30 miles and then flowed up the Deschutes River for over 4 miles from its mouth, where it is 900 feet thick. In Iceland, the Skaptár Jökull eruption of 1783 filled one valley for 50 miles and another for 40 miles with lava up to 600 feet deep.

Lakes Formed by Volcanic Damming

When volcanic products pile up in a valley, they may create dams that block drainage and produce lakes (*les lacs de barrage*, in French).

On a very large scale, an entire drainage system may be blocked by an extensive volcanic field, for example, Lake Kivu in East Africa which occupies a high valley that originally drained north into the Nile. The eruption of the Birunga volcanic field, still active in places, created a vast barrier to this northern drainage, dammed back the water to form Lake Kivu, and now the drainage flows to the south through an older and lower volcanic barrier, eventually to reach Lake Tanganyika.

On a much smaller scale, a single small volcanic cone may block a valley, as Le Tartaret in the Auvergne (Massif Central of France) blocked the river Couze during the late Pleistocene to form the Lac de Chambon, today only 5.8 meters deep. At least a dozen small lakes in the Puys-de-Dôme are blocked by Pleistocene lava streams (Fig. 2); some

larger lake basins are today completely filled by sediment (Fig. 3).

More lakes are dammed back by lava flows than by cones. A main valley may be blocked by lava flows along its course forming a single lake like Bunyoni, Uganda, on the upstream side, or lava may flow down a main valley, blocking tributary valleys, and thus create many lakes. On complex initial topography, more elaborate lakes may be formed, an example of which is provided by Lake Lanao on

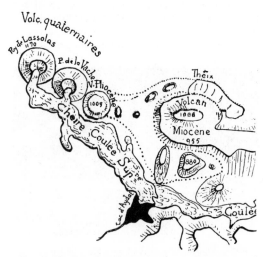

FIG. 2. The Lac d'Aydat in the Puy-de-Dôme area of the French Massif Central, which was formed by a blockage of the older drainage by Pleistocene lava flows (Glangeaud, 1913).

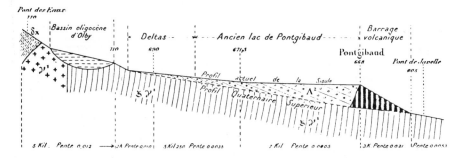

FIG. 3. A now infilled Pleistocene lake produced by a lava dam. Profile through the 14-km-long old lake Pontgibaud, France, now filled with sediment (A^2; Glangeaud, 1913).

Mindanao in the Philippines. Here, the initial topography was an upland plateau cut by a ravine. Lava subsequently dammed the ravine causing flooding of the valley and part of the plateau, so the lake has a trough about 300 meters deep near the lava dam, with a large expanse of water only 4 to 10 meters deep over the former plateau.

Lakes may be produced in valleys blocked by volcanic mud-flows as at Bandaisan, Japan. Both lava and ash from Fujiyama have combined to cut off five attractive lakes around its northern margin.

Ponding may also be due to river aggradation, as in the Waikato valley, New Zealand. Great eruptions of pumice fragments added easily transportable material to the Waikato River, which rapidly aggraded its bed over an area of 500 square miles. Tributary valleys, not supplied with volcanic fragments, were unable to build up their beds to the same level, and so formed shallow lakes.

Volcanic activity is frequently accompanied by tectonic movements, and lakes may be caused by a combination of both effects; they are known as volcano-tectonic lakes (see also *Calderas*). In New Zealand there is a large complex of volcano-tectonic depressions in the North Island, containing Lakes Rotorua and Taupo. Lake Toba in Sumatra, Indonesia, is of similar origin, and the many lakes of the Valley of Mexico are probably also volcano-tectonic.

The surfaces of lava flows may have many minor

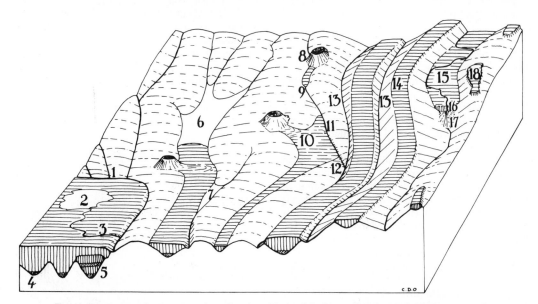

FIG. 4. Diagrammatic representation of various kinds of drainage diversion and subsequent erosion.

(1) Completely rerouted stream at edge of lava plain.
(2) Insequent lake on surface of lava plain.
(3) Insequent stream on surface of lava plain.
(4) Deep lead.
(5) Inter-basaltic alluvium.
(6) Lake on main river caused by lava damming.
(7) Lake on tributary valley caused by lava damming.
(8) Stream blocked by volcano.
(9) Spring due to sub-basaltic seepage.
(10) Simple lava flow diverting drainage.
(11) Lateral stream.
(12) Stream diverted into the next valley.
(13) Twin lateral streams and valleys.
(14) Inverted relief with valley flow on ridge.
(15) Insequent drainage on lava flow.
(16) Waterfall.
(17) Alluvial cone.
(18) Remnants of old valley flow.

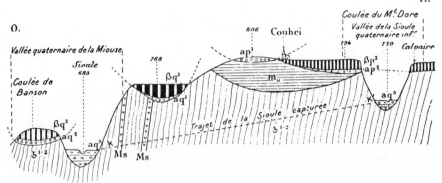

FIG. 5. Profile through multiple (polycyclic) stream channels in the Mont Dore area of the Massif Central, France. The valley of the Sioule has been progressively displaced since the Upper Pliocene, when alluvium ap^1 and ap^2 was laid down, to be overwhelmed by basalt βp^2. In the adjacent valley of the Miouse, progressive alluvial fills, aq^1, aq^2 and aq^3 were in part covered by Pleistocene basalts βq^1, βq^2 (Glangeaud, 1913).

features and irregularities, as shown in Fig. 1, and the drainage on some flows is insequent or almost random, with many small and shallow pools in irregularities of the surface. The volcanic plains of western Victoria, Australia, contain many such lakes. Occasionally, large but shallow lakes are maintained on the surface of lava flows, e.g., Yellowstone Lake in Yellowstone Park, Wyoming, and Myvatn in Iceland which has an area of 27 km² and a maximum depth of only 2.3 meters.

Lava-displaced Drainage

Lava often displaces rivers from their beds, and the water they carried must be transported elsewhere. Lakes may be formed as described above, but unless evaporation removes water (forming a salt lake such as Lake Baringo in the Kenya Rift, on the site of the much larger, lava-dammed Pleistocene Lake Kamasai), the water will overspill along some other channel.

Many lava flows are slightly convex upward in cross section, so that a shallow trench exists where the lava meets the old valley wall. This is commonly the place where diverted water flows, in what is then called a lateral stream. When a lava flow occupies a broad valley with tributaries on each side, lateral streams may develop on both sides of the flow, making twin lateral streams.

Thick flows of lava may reach or overtop the old interfluve ridges, and streams may then be displaced entirely from their old valleys. Thus the Plenty River near Melbourne, Victoria, flowed for some distance as a lateral stream on the east side of a lava flow, but eventually it was diverted into a neighboring valley, from which point it flows in a gorge it has excavated in Silurian bedrock.

Very large sheet flows of basalt may divert rivers completely from their course so that they flow for

many miles around the lava edge. The River Wannon in Victoria provides an example. In some circumstances, the direction of flow may be completely reversed, usually in association with lake formation. The example of Lake Kivu has already been given. In New Zealand, the upper Waitangi valley has been dammed by lava to form Lake Omapere, which has a westward over-flow now, although the original Waitangi drainage was to the east. In Nicaragua, volcanoes have ponded drainage so that it now flows eastward across a former continental divide.

Rivers that have been displaced from their courses may meander irregularly over the lava for some distance, depositing alluvium here and there in patches (accounting for the non-basaltic minerals found in many "basalt" soils), but eventually a distinct stream forms again, which proceeds to erode

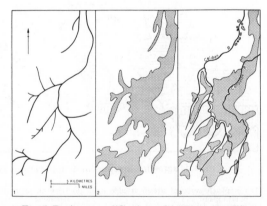

FIG. 6. Drainage modifications of the Campaspe River, Victoria. (1) A map of the original drainage pattern as indicated by deep leads. (2) The maximum extent of lava. (3) The present-day drainage.

new valleys, gorges or canyons. Lateral streams cut down at the side of lava flows and often erode valleys with floors much deeper than the original stream, so that the valley-fill lava is left as a ridge or plateau edge (Fig. 4). This is an example of *inversion of topography or relief* (q.v.). The lava may be further eroded into a series of separate lava-capped hills as shown in Fig. 5.

The changes in drainage that accompany volcanic action and the repeated damming and downcutting of rivers lead to the formation of multiple alluvial and lacustrine terraces. Where a diverted stream returns to its old channel, the sudden decrease in gradient causes deposition of an alluvial fan, which is itself destroyed as the river cuts down by vertical erosion.

Alluvial deposits in former valley bottoms that have been buried beneath lava flows are known as "deep leads," and in gold-bearing areas they are of obvious importance for placer deposits. They are especially common in California and in Victoria (Australia), and the intense investigation that went into their mining has provided much information about the pre-volcanic topography in such areas. The lava has been responsible for the preservation of the gold-bearing alluvium in the leads, which otherwise would probably have been carried away long ago.

The area in Victoria shown in Fig. 6 was originally drained by the Campaspe River and by the small Coliban River in the north. The old courses can be traced from the deep leads. After the valleys were filled with lava, no tributaries from the west were able to cross the basalt to join the Campaspe; they were diverted north as a lateral stream and eventually joined the Coliban which as a result became much larger and cut deeply through its lava fill. The Campaspe, deprived of its tributaries, failed to cut down very much and still flows over the basalt surface in most of its upper reaches, only here and there crossing onto bedrock.

Lava diversion and stream incision may be repeated many times in areas of continuing volcanic activity, as exemplified by the Snake River in southern Idaho. The Snake River first cut a canyon at least 400 feet deep. Then came the Malad basalt, entirely filling the canyon for at least 9 miles of its length and displacing the river southwestward. The river then cut a canyon about 200 feet deep, which was interrupted by the outpouring of the Thousand Springs basalt and caused further displacement to the southwest. The next canyon was eroded to a depth of over 500 feet and was then blocked by three further flows. The river flowed around the southwest end of the barrier and tumbled back into its old course at Thousand Springs.

Groundwater as well as surface water is affected by volcanic activity. Deep leads become sub-basaltic aquifers, and in the McKenzie Valley, Oregon, a small flow created a lake on the up-

stream side that drains away beneath the basalt and emerges as a spring at the downstream end. Basalt itself is often highly jointed and permeable, especially at the base of flows, and layers of alluvium or paleosols between flows also provide aquifers (see *Groundwater in Volcanic Terrain*, pr Vol. VI). For this reason, surface drainage is usually scarce on lava plains. For 200 miles along the northern edge of the Snake River Plain, Idaho, all the rivers descending from the mountains sink into the porous lava, and at the end of the plain great springs discharge groundwater from the old lava-filled canyons. The water table in lava plains is generally very flat but may be influenced by an impermeable pre-lava landscape beneath. In Victoria, Australia, some volcanic lakes fluctuate with the regional water table, but others are isolated groundwater patches with independent behavior, and lakes only a few hundred yards apart can have completely different salinities.

Drainage can be disrupted catastrophically during actual eruptions. A lake that occupied the crater of La Soufrière, St. Vincent (West Indies), was thrown out of the crater during the first phase of the eruption of 1902, producing extensive hot mudflows that rushed down the mountain into the sea. The crater lake in Kelut, Indonesia, used to be similarly displaced during eruptions producing a dangerous *lahar* or mudflow, but this danger was overcome by tunneling to reduce the size of the lake. In Iceland, there is an ice-covered lake kept liquid by volcanic heat in a depression in the Vatnajökull icecap During eruptions, the lake is destroyed and up to 10 km³ of meltwater may be discharged beyond the icecap where the flood or glacier burst completely devastates the landscape.

CLIFF OLLIER

References

Cotton, C. A., 1952, "Volcanoes as Landscape Forms," second ed., Christchurch, Whitcombe & Tombs, 416pp.

Glangeaud, P., 1913, "Les régions volcaniques du Puy-de-Dôme. II. La chaîne des Puys," *Bull. Serv. Carte Géol. France*, **22**, (135).

Hutchinson, G. E., 1957, "A Treatise on Limnology," Vol. 1, New York, John Wiley & Sons, 1015pp.

Ollier, C. D., 1967, "Landforms of the Newer Volcanic Province of Victoria," in (Jennings, J. N., and Mabbutt, J. A., editors) "Landform Studies from Australia and New Guinea," Ch. 14, Canberra, A.N.U. Press.

Stearns, H. T., 1942, "Hydrology of Volcanic Terranes," in (Meinzer, O. E., editor), "Hydrology," Ch. 15, New York, McGraw-Hill Book Co.

Cross-references: *Calderas*; *Drainage Patterns*; *Interfluve*; *Inversion of Topography*; *Lakes*; *Lake Toba*; *Louderback*; *Mudflow*; *Volcanic Landscape*. pr Vol. VI: *Groundwater in Volcanic Terrain*.

LAW OF ACTUALISM—*See* pr Vol. VI, **ACTUALISM**

LAW OF DECLIVITIES, LAW OF STRUCTURE AND LAW OF DIVIDES

Three laws of fluvial erosion were enunciated by G. K. Gilbert (1877) in his classic Henry Mountains monograph.

(1) *The law of declivities* states that "erosion is most rapid where the slope is steepest" being related in part to the velocity of the flow (p. 96). "Weathering is not directly influenced by slope, but is reached indirectly through transportation.... The rapid, but partial, transportation of weathered rock accelerates weathering, but the complete removal of its products retards weathering" (p. 97). Upon this law depend the two *laws of Surell*, previously established (q.v.). An addendum, that "declivity bears an inverse relation to quantity of water" (Gilbert, *op. cit.*, p. 102) was identified further by McGee (1891) as the *law of river gradation* but usually this is taken simply to be part and parcel of the *law of declivities*.

(2) *The law of structure* "controls sculpture" and "hard masses stand as eminences and soft are carved into valleys.... In the structure of the earth's crust hard and soft rocks are grouped with infinite diversity of arrangement ... and from these forms are carved an infinite variety of topographic reliefs" (Gilbert, *op. cit.*, p. 110).

(3) *The law of divides* states that "mountains are steepest at their crests. The profile of a mountain if taken along drainage lines is concave outward.... The nearer the watershed or divide the steeper the slope" (Gilbert, *op. cit.*, p. 110). However, in soft materials, as in the *badlands* (q.v.), and mature landscapes, rather generally, there is what seemed to him to be an exceptional condition: The divide summit is convex. This, in fact, is the normal profile for rainwash on unvegetated surfaces (as well as for *solifluction*, q.v.) and the acute ridge is a consequence of mass wasting (landslides, etc.).

(*Note:* in early American and British usage, divide and watershed are synonyms for "water parting" or "boundary between drainage basins," and Gilbert used them so. However, since 1874, according to O.E.D. there has been a tendency in the United States to use "watershed" for catchment area; this leads to much confusion.)

The combination of the second and third laws controls the earth's erosional relief. Following Gilbert (*op. cit.*): "Declivities are steep in proportion as their material is hard; they are steep in proportion as they are near the divides. In some places the first of the two conditions is the more important, in others the second. In the bed of a stream without tributaries the grade depends on the structure of the underlying rocks. In rock which is homogeneous and structureless all slopes depend on the distribu-

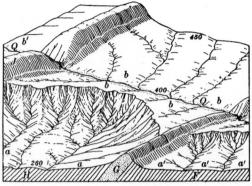

FIG. 1. Illustrating three of Gilbert's laws (Davis, 1912, Fig. 89). In the amphitheater, lower left, rapid erosion is causing a fine-textured relief and steep declivities (law 1); transportation is facilitated in stream basin H (elevation 260 m) more than in stream Q (local elevation 400 m) thus leaving greater relative relief.

In the two ridges (G and J), hard quartzitic sandstones provide structural control, with low erosive potential (law 2).

In the divide between stream basins F, H, and Q, the tributaries of F and H steepen to the divide (law 3), while those of Q flatten to the divide (the mature or old age condition of slopes b, b, b; also seen in the lower slopes of F, H, as a, a, a and a', a', a').

tion of divides and drainage lines. The relative importance of the two conditions is especially affected by climate, and the influence of this factor is so great that it may claim rank as a third condition of sculpture." Gilbert was also one of the first to recognize that erosion is not favored by increasing rainfall so much as by decreasing vegetation; maximal erosion may therefore be expected at some midpoint between the two extremes, later empirically determined by Langbein and Schumm (1958) at about 30 cm or 12 inches of rainfall under a mean annual temperature of 50°F.

RHODES W. FAIRBRIDGE

References

Davis, W. M., 1912, "Die erklärende Beschreibung der Landformen," Leipzig, B. G. Teubner, 565pp.

Gilbert, G. K., 1877, "Report on the geology of the Henry Mountains, Utah," *U.S. Geol. Surv. Rocky Mtn. Reg.*, 160pp.

Langbein, W. B., and Schumm, S. A., 1958, "Yield of sediment in relation to mean annual precipitation," *Trans. Am. Geophys. Union*, **39**, 1076–1084.

McGee, W J, 1891, "The Pleistocene history of northeastern Iowa," *U.S. Geol. Surv., Ann. Rept.*, **11**, 189–577.

Cross-references: *Badlands; Denudation; Erosion; Grade, Graded Stream; Mass Wasting; Profile of Equilibrium; Slopes; Solifluction; Structural Control in Geomorphology; Surell's Laws; Watershed.*

LAW OF UNEQUAL SLOPES

This "law" states that a divide separating asymmetric slopes ("declivities") will migrate *away* from the steeper of the two slopes. It assumes more or less homogeneous lithology and may be nullified by certain overriding structural controls. The principle was first established by G. K. Gilbert (1877) in his celebrated monograph on the laccolithic Henry Mountains of Utah.

If constant lithology and meteorologic controls (see *Asymmetric Valleys*) are assumed, the stream on the steeper side will flow faster and erode more rapidly than the more sluggish streams on the gently sloping side. Thus, for example, in a terrain of gently homoclinal dips, differential erosion will develop marked asymmetry, until the dip slopes consist largely of the ridge forming lithologies, and beneath the fronts of the escarpments or cuestas the weaker formations will outcrop; the scarp or local divide will migrate gradually in the down-dip direction (Gilbert, 1877, p.134). Longitudinal streams will help undercut the steep slope and keep it active (see *Slipoff Slope*).

On the regional scale this law is generally valid, and we usually observe that streams from coastal mountains flowing directly to the sea are generally more vigorous and gradually shift their divides inland, while the interior-directed streams are less active. A progressive loss of the former interior-directed tributaries occurs by *stream capture* (q.v.) to the coastward rivers.

In the Appalachians this was brought out especially by Thompson (1949). It is a striking feature also of coastal Brazil, the Drakensberg in South Africa and the Dividing Range of eastern Australia.

On the smaller scale and in microrelief, the law of unequal slopes is rather commonly invalidated, at least in mid- and high latitudes, by meteorologic and related factors. These are controlled by insolation, prevailing winds, vegetation and soil factors (see *Asymmetric Valleys*).

RHODES W. FAIRBRIDGE

References

Gilbert, G. K., 1877, "Report on the geology of the Henry Mountains, Utah," *U.S. Geol. Surv. Rocky Mtn. Reg.*, 160pp.

Thompson, H. D., 1949, "Drainage evolution in the Appalachians of Pennsylvania," *Ann. N.Y. Acad. Sci.*, **52**, art. 2, 31–62.

Thornbury, W. D., 1954, "Principles of Geomorphology," New York, John Wiley & Sons, 618pp.

Cross-references: *Asymmetric Valleys; Law of Declivities, Law of Structure, Law of Divides; Slipoff Slope; Stream Capture, Piracy.*

LEACHING—*See pr Vol. VI*

LEVEE—NATURAL

Alluvial streams flowing on flood plains commonly develop natural levees. Each levee is a low, wide ridge located immediately adjacent to the channel. Along many flood plain streams the natural levees are so small that they cannot be seen, if indeed they are present at all.

A stream which develops large natural levees generally also aggrades its bed so that the resulting channel is no deeper than the pre-levee channel: it is merely located at a higher elevation. That is, the channel bed may be almost as high as, or higher than, the surface of the adjacent flood plain. Such a stream flows on a mid-valley ridge. It is sometimes described as a "*poised stream*" (but this term also has another meaning, with much wider usage). The lower courses of the Mississippi River in the United States, the Maas–Lek system in Holland, and the Po in Italy, are good examples of poised streams.

An initial natural levee may be built first during an overbank flood. According to this theory, silt-laden water passing from the deep channel to the adjacent (shallow) flood plain is retarded and deposits some of its load adjacent to the channel wall. This is not, however, the way in which the natural levee is augmented. In fact, once a system of natural levees is established, overbank floods commonly do not inundate them, but instead breach them locally and spread out behind them onto the flood plain.

A breach in a natural levee may become a full-size flood-time channel and, in some cases, may even develop into a new permanent channel. More commonly, however, only a small amount of water spills over a low place on the levee crest, cutting a small gully known (along the lower Mississippi) as a *crevasse*. The mechanical load picked up during the cutting of the crevasse, plus the load already in the water, is deposited lower down the flank of the levee, thereby building it higher. As deposition continues on the back slope, old cre-

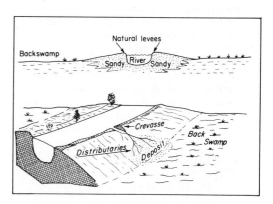

FIG. 1. Natural levee.

vasses are healed and new ones formed. As a result, the back slope angle is kept low, while the levee is built upward and outward.

In areas where the flood plain is marshy or swampy, agriculture is restricted essentially to the low-angle back slope of the natural levee. Prior to the advent of modern highways, most roads (in such areas) were built along natural levees, which were also the preferred sites for houses and villages.

An excellent example of a natural levee, with a crevasse system arrested in mid-development, can be seen along the southwest bank of False River, an oxbow lake which was at one time part of the Lower Mississippi River channel. The details can be seen along Louisiana State Road 1, and adjacent roads, between Oscar and Lakeland, in Pointe Coupee Parish, northwest of Baton Rouge, Louisiana.

W. F. TANNER

References

Leopold, L. B., Wolman, M. G., and Miller, J. P., 1964, "Fluvial Processes in Geomorphology," San Francisco, W. H. Freeman and Company, 522pp.

Thornbury, William D., 1954, "Principles of Geomorphology," New York, John Wiley & Sons, 618pp.

Cross-references: *Deltaic Evolution*; *Flood Plain*; *Oxbow Lake*.

LIMESTONE CAVES

Most caves are in limestone, and this is so because no other rock equally abundant at the surface is so readily dissolved. Ground water containing dissolved carbon dioxide is an effective solvent for the mineral calcite ($CaCO_3$), the chief constituent of limestone. In gently dipping limestone beds, which contain most of the world's large caves, the water begins its work along the principal joints in the limestone, which intersect nearly at right angles. The cave passages consequently form a network whose plan is somewhat like that of the streets of a city, though because of irregularities in the jointing, it resembles that of an ancient city rather than a modern one (Fig. 1).

The action of ground water on limestone is not simple solution, for calcite is almost insoluble in pure water. Dissolved carbon dioxide, combining with water to form carbonic acid, plays an indispensable part in the following double reaction, which converts part of the calcite to soluble calcium bicarbonate:

$$CO_2 + H_2O$$

carbon $\downarrow$ water
dioxide $\downarrow$

$$H_2CO_3 + CaCO_3 \rightarrow Ca^{+2} + 2HCO_3^{-1}$$

carbonic calcite calcium bicarbonate
acid solution

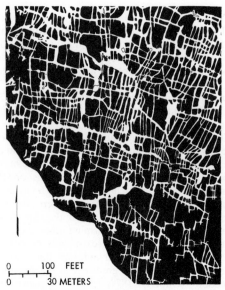

0   100   FEET
0   30 METERS

FIG. 1. Part of Anvil Cave, Alabama, a typical network in which the passages follow a system of intersecting joints in the limestone (after W. W. Varnedoe).

Some of the necessary carbon dioxide could be taken up by rainwater falling through the air, but since in ordinary air, which exerts a pressure of 1 atm, the partial pressure of carbon dioxide is only 0.0003 atm, rainwater that has been exposed only to the air is not sufficiently acidic to form caves. Water takes up a great deal more carbon dioxide, however, if it passes through soil that contains decaying humus, for the air in soil of that character may contain more than 0.1 atm of carbon dioxide—over 300 times as much as the air above it. The water passing through soil rich in humus may, therefore, become strongly acidic, and it is by such water that most caves in limestone have been formed.

Caves are formed just below the water table by water that may move as slowly as 10 m/yr. One evidence that this water generally moved very slowly is that cave walls are generally smooth.

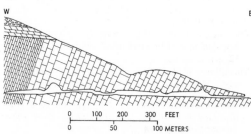

FIG. 2. Cave-passage networks are typically horizontal, as shown by this profile of Lehman Caves, Nevada. They are thought to have formed just below a horizontal water table.

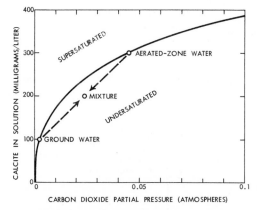

FIG. 3. The mixing of downward-percolating water with groundwater at the water table invariably results in an undersaturated solution, even if both waters were initially saturated with calcite. This is believed to be the reason why most caves were developed directly below the water table.

Where a fast stream flows on limestone, either on the surface or below it, the rock becomes indented with small solution pits known as *scallops*. Their absence in most caves proves that the caves were not formed by underground streams, and where such streams do exist today, we infer that they penetrated the caves late in their history.

The characteristic network pattern of cave passages is further evidence that caves are formed in the saturated zone below the water table, for a downward-cutting underground stream would tend, like one on the surface, to develop a dendritic pattern, so that larger and larger passages finally would join a master passage containing a trunk stream. But cave passages do not have such a pattern, and they are usually horizontal even where the limestone beds dip steeply (Fig. 2); cave passages in steeply dipping limestone extend without deviation through various limestone layers that differ greatly in their resistance to solution by ground water. All this goes to show that solution went on close to a level that remained stable for a very long period.

The reason that most caves develop just below the top of the saturated zone, rather than at random depths within this zone, is believed to be due to a nonlinear relation between calcite solubility and the partial pressure of carbon dioxide (see Fig. 3). As a consequence, the mixing of any two waters, either saturated or undersaturated with respect to calcite, will always produce an undersaturated solution capable of dissolving more calcite. Dissolving would therefore go on continually in the zone just below the top of the water table, where downward-percolating water constantly mixes with slowly moving ground water.

The ages of some limestone caves can be estab-

lished by noting whether their originally horizontal passages have been tilted during mountain-building deformations of known ages. Wherever such determinations have been made, the caves have proved to be less than about 5,000,000 years old. Such a maximum age for open limestone caves is also indicated by the rate of solution calculated from the calcium bicarbonate content of streams draining cave regions.

GEORGE W. MOORE

References

Bögli, A., 1964, "Mischungskorrosion—ein Beitrag zum Verkarstungsproblem," *Erdkunde*, **18**, 83–92.

Davis, S. N., 1966, "Initiation of ground-water flow in jointed limestone," *Natl. Speleol. Soc. Bull.*, **28**, 111–118.

Ek, C., 1961, "Conduits souterrains en relation avec les terrasses fluviales," *Ann. Soc. Géol. Belg. Bull.*, **84**, 313–340.

Ford, D. C., 1965, "The origin of limestone caverns: a model from the central Mendip Hills, England," *Natl. Speleol. Soc. Bull.*, **27**, 109–132.

Gradziński, R., 1962, "Rozwój podziemnych form krasowych w południowej części Wyżyny Krakowskiej" (Origin and development of subterranean karst in the southern part of the Cracow upland), *Soc. Géol. Pologne Annales*, **32**, 429–492 (in Polish).

Jennings, J. N., 1967, "Some Karst Areas of Australia," in (Jennings, J. N., and Mabbutt, J. A., editors) "Landform Studies from Australia and New Guinea," pp. 256–292, Canberra, Australian Natl. Univ. Press.

Moore, G. W., (editor), 1960, "Origin of limestone caves—A symposium with discussion," *Natl. Speleol. Soc. Bull.*, **22**, pt. 1, 84 pp.

Moore, G. W., and Nicholas, G., 1964, "Speleology," Boston, D. C. Heath and Co.

Cross-references: *Blind Valley*; *Dolina*; *Karst*; *Polje*; *Stalactite and Stalagmite*. Vol. VI: *Groundwater*.

LIMESTONE COASTAL WEATHERING

All types of limestone, being composed of calcium carbonate, are soluble in CO_2-rich rainwater and slightly soluble in surface seawater (Fairbridge, 1948; Revelle and Emery, 1957). Limestone coasts are not very common in high latitudes but are extremely frequent in the tropics. Two limestone types are predominant: (i) *coral reef limestones*, hermatypic corals being very widespread between latitudes 30°N and 30°S; sea level was several meters higher than at present, during both the mid-Holocene and the Pleistocene interglacials, so that fossil coral reef coasts are very numerous; (ii) *eolian calcarenites* ("eolianites"), derived from coastal dunes that are usually calcareous; during the Quaternary period of important climate changes and sea level oscillations, such dunes developed in

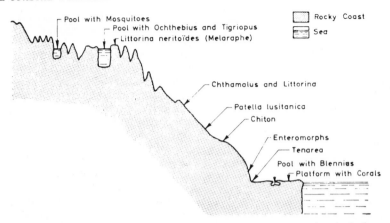

FIG. 1. The limestone littoral zone of Algeria, showing the wave-cut bench platform with Corallines (after L. G. Seurat, 1935; from Termier and Termier, 1963). (By permission of D. Van Nostrand Co., Princeton, N.J.)

enormous belts along the more arid coastlines, notably latitudes 15–45°N and S.

Types of Weathering

Several weathering mechanisms are recognized along limestone coasts—partly subaerial, partly submarine and partly transitional. These include:

(a) Subaerial Chemical Weathering. Rainwater normally has a pH below 7 and effectively develops Karst-type features on bare cliffs. Pits, pans and deep solution pipes develop.

(b) Subaerial Biological Weathering. Because of growth of lichens and spray-moistened algae, a network of fine threads and holes develops that

gives the rock a strikingly hackly surface; the white limestone quickly gains a blackened appearance from this organic layer, which at a depth of 1–2 mm is often green. (Similar organic etching is observed inland; see *Lapiés*.)

(c) Intertidal Chemical Weathering. For many years, there has been controversy as to whether seawater or its spray could effect strictly chemical erosion, because theoretically tropical seawater is supersaturated in $CaCO_3$ and therefore could not dissolve more. However, Fairbridge (1948) and Revelle and Emery (1957) carried out extensive pH and other chemical tests which demonstrated the probability that slow complexing under diurnal

FIG. 2. Limestone cliffs at Vavau, Tonga Islands. Note subtropical vegetation and karst in supralittoral, deep mesolittoral undercut and absence of intertidal platform (steep-to coast). (Photo: Scripps Institution of Oceanography. *Capricorn* Expedition).

FIG. 3. Weathered coral limestone blocks, Mango in the Lau Group (Fiji), showing clear intertidal notch (Agassiz, 1899).

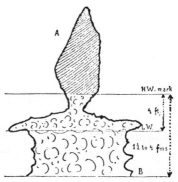

FIG. 5. Pinnacle (A) of calcareous eolianite from Bermuda (Agassiz, 1895, p. 264), showing intertidal notch as well as submarine undercuts (B).

heating and cooling takes place, rendering the surface seawater (especially in pools and spray) nocturnally undersaturated with respect to $CaCO_3$. Daytime saturation leads to interstitial cementation and crusting, so that the remaining rock is extraordinarily hard (See *Induration*).

(d) **Intertidal Biological Weathering.** The intertidal zone of the tropics is one of the most vigorous ecologic belts on the face of the earth, supporting an enormously varied biota. Particularly, limestone boring and scouring organisms include crabs, sipunculids, chitons, sponges, echinoids, gastropods (*Patella, Littorina, Marinauris,* etc.), and a variegated flora of algae. The observational fact is undisputed that in the intertidal belts of the tropics the sea forms deep undercuts; in places, it seems to "saw" horizontally into the limestone cliffs. But how much is due to biological agents and how much to purely chemical erosion is very hard to establish (see *Biological Erosion of Limestone Coasts*).

(e) **Infratidal Mechanical Weathering.** No sign of physico-chemical corrosion is to be seen below the low-tide mark, but there is abundant evidence of mechanical weathering (*corrasion, abrasion,* q.v.) below about mean sea level, provided that there is a supply of sand or pebbles. The latter constitute the "armament" of the waves, and without sand the evidence of abrasion (polishing, rubbing) is

absent. The contrast of smooth, polished surfaces compared with the corrosion-etched, jagged, hackly texture a little higher up is very striking indeed. A second type of mechanical weathering, limited to exposed coasts only, is *hydraulic fracturing*; under heavy surf action, air is trapped in undercuts and blowholes and powerfully compressed by successive surges. The resultant hydraulic pressure buildup may be tremendous, enough to break off 10–20 ton blocks and throw them up into the reef or shore platform (see *Negroheads*).

(f) **Infratidal Biological Erosion.** While very much inferior in importance to intertidal erosion, there is a continuance of biological activity below tide limits that is sometimes quite striking (Fig. 5). The scraping and browsing organisms of the intertidal zone are less important here, but the deep borers may be very vigorous: sponges, echinoids, pholad pelecypods, etc. In some Pleistocene emerged limestone cliffs, certain evidence of former submergence is seen in the form of pholad holes; Lyell used the pholad borings in the limestone columns of the Roman "temple" (market) of Serapis, near Naples, to demonstrate the rapidity of crustal oscillations on a volcanically active coast.

FIG. 6. Contemporary platform in eolian calcarenite on the coast of Lebanon at Ras el Kalb (Photo: H. Fleisch).

FIG. 4. Undercut islet from southeast coast of Kamaran Island in the Farsan Islands, Red Sea (Macfadyen, 1930).

FIG. 9. Contemporary platform in eolian calcarenite on the coast of Lebanon near Tabarja, stepping up to the platform of 75 cm (believed to be about 900 years old). Modern platform has cut it back by about 19 meters (10 mm/yr). (Photo: H. Fleisch).

FIG. 7. Intertidal platform with low algal rim at north end of Garden Island, Western Australia, seen at low tide.

Zonation of Limestone Coastal Weathering

Broadly speaking, the rocky coastal belt may be subdivided into three zones:

(a) **Supralittoral Zone**. This is characterized by subaerial and spray weathering, both physico-chemical and biological. The physiographic effect is an extremely jagged, honeycomb effect ("*alveolar* weathering"), with numerous *lapiés* (q.v.), pits, pans and pipes, in fact a littoral *karst* (q.v.). W. von Zahn (1909) called this the *Spritzzone* (spray zone) or *Brandungskarrenzone* (littoral karst zone).

(b) **Mesolittoral Zone**. This refers to the belt of maximal wave action, often the site of vigorous organic growth, alternating (where sand and gravel are present) with powerful abrasion which produces in limestone a well-rounded and polished effect, strikingly smooth after the jaggedness of zone (a).

FIG. 8. Very deep notch in west point of Waaf in Indonesia (Kuenen, 1933).

This zone tends to develop a distinctive profile: a *flat platform* at about mean low tide (Figs. 6 and 7), an *undercut notch* or nip at about mean sea level, and a *cliff* or *overhanging visor* somewhat above mean high tide level. On some coasts, there is a smooth ramp (slope about 10°) from the platform to the supralittoral level. On steeply cliffed coasts, the undercut may reach 10–20 meters back into the cliff, as Kuenen (1933) has described in the East Indies, like a giant "saw-cut." Undercuts dating from earlier, lower stands of sea level, 2 or 3 meters below the present level, may lead to collapse features, and the present undercut may also cause rock falls. The ramp zone may, in areas of abundant sand supply, be plastered with *beachrock* (q.v.).

(c) **Infralittoral Zone**. This is the belt just below the limits of low tide which is momentarily exposed as swells break and recede. It can be best explored by Scuba methods. Traces of earlier sea levels can often be observed in the forms of former undercuts and beachrocks. Today these features are evidently no longer in active course of erosion for they are plastered by small corals, calcareous algae, worm tubes, sipunculids and so on, which would be killed if abrasion were in progress.

Rates of Intertidal Limestone Erosion

Careful experiments by Hodgkin (1964) on eolian calcarenite coasts, together with longer-term historical data, demonstrate that the mean rate of recession of the intertidal notch is about 1 mm/yr, and since the undercut is generally 1–3 meters in depth, a period of 1000–3000 years of erosion at or about this level is indicated during the last 6000 years, the length of time that sea level has been within reach of the present shore. An appreciable part of this time, therefore, has been with mean sea level well below (1–3 meters) or above (1–3 meters) the present level. Traces of correspondingly

FIG. 10. Cut stone blocks in the foundation of a Roman building at Sabratha, Tripoli (Libya) exposed to intertidal action for about 1000 years. Slot in middle was occupied by a metal cross-tie. (Photo: R. W. Fairbridge)

higher or lower notches match these other levels (Fig. 9). Some near tideless areas (with little vertical cutting, or overburden) recede at up to 10 mm/yr.

Hodgkin's measurements were made only on the calcarenite coasts, but since the notches are very similar on coral limestone coasts, the erosional rates there are deemed to be comparable. However, the extremely hard Mesozoic limestones of the Mediterranean show very reduced intertidal erosion, and recession rates are probably less than 0.1 mm/yr. The writer has observed only a minor degree of erosion of massive limestone building blocks at Sabratha, a Greco-Roman city in Tripoli, which was partly drowned by the rise of sea level about A.D. 400 and shows irregular pitting only during an exposure to spray for over 1000 years (Fig. 10).

RHODES W. FAIRBRIDGE

References

Agassiz, A., 1895, "A visit to the Bermudas in March, 1894," *Bull. Museum Comp. Zool. Harvard Coll.*, **26**, 205–281.

Agassiz, A., 1899, "The islands and coral reefs of Fiji," *Bull. Museum Comp. Zool. Harvard Coll.*, **33**, 1–167.

Cotton, C. A., 1963, "Levels of planation of marine benches," *Z. Geomorphol.*, **7**(2), 97–111.

Emery, K. O., 1946, "Marine solution basins," *J. Geol.*, **54**, 209–228.

Fairbridge, R. W., 1948, "Notes on the geomorphology of the Pelsart Group of the Houtman's Abrolhos Islands," *J. Roy. Soc. W. Australia*, **33**, 1–43.

Fairbridge, R. W., 1950, "The geology and geomorphology of Point Peron, Western Australia," *J. Roy. Soc. W. Australia*, **34**(3), 35–72.

Fairbridge, R. W., 1952, "Marine erosion," *Proc. Pacific Sci. Congr. Pacific Sci. Assoc. 7th, New Zealand, 1949*, **3**, 347–359.

Guilcher, A., 1953, "Essai sur la zonation et la distribution des formes littorales de dissolution du calcaire," *Ann. Geogr., Paris*, **62**, 161–179.

Guilcher, A., 1958, "Coastal corrosion forms in limestones around the Bay of Biscay," *Scot. Geogr. Mag.*, **74**, 137–149.

Hodgkin, E. P., 1964, "Rate of erosion of intertidal limestone," *Z. Geomorphol.*, N.F. **8**(4), 385–392.

Kaye, C. A., 1959, "Shoreline features and Quaternary shoreline changes, Puerto Rico," *U.S. Geol. Surv. Profess. Paper* **317-B**, 49–140.

Kuenen, P. H., 1933, "Geology of coral reefs," in "Snellius Expedition," Leiden, E. J. Brill.

Macfadyen, W. A., 1930, "The undercutting of coral reef limestone on the coasts of some islands of the Red Sea," *Geograph. J.*, **75**, 27–37.

North, W. J., 1954, "Size distribution, erosive activities, and gross metabolic efficiency of the marine intertidal snails, *Littorina planaxis* and *L. scutulata*," *Biol. Bull.* **106**, 185–197.

Pérès, J. M., and Picard, J., 1952, "Les corniches calcaires d'origine biologique en Méditerranée occidentale," *Trav. Station Marine d'Endoume, Fac. Sci. Marseille*, fasc. 4, bull, 1.

Prat, H., 1935, "Les formes d'érosion littorale dans l'archipel des Bermudes et l'évolution des atolls et des récifs coralliens," *Rev. Geogr. Phys. et Geol. Dynam.*, **8**, 257–283.

Purdy, E. G., and Kornicker, L. S., 1958, "Algal disintegration of Bahamian limestone coasts," *J. Geol.*, **66**(1), 97–99.

Revelle, R., and Emery, K. O., 1957, "Chemical erosion of beach rock and exposed reef rock," *U.S. Geol. Surv. Profess. Paper* **260-T**, 699–709.

Stephenson, W., 1961, "Experimental studies on the ecology of intertidal environments at Heron Island. II. The effect of substratum," *Australian J. Marine Freshwater Res.*, **12**, 164–176.

Termier, H., and Termier, G., 1963, "Erosion and Sedimentation," Princeton, N.J., D. Van Nostrand Co., 433pp.

von Zahn, W., 1909, "Die zerstörende Arbeit des Meeres an Steilküsten," *Mitt. Geogr. Gesell. Hamburg*, **24**, 193–284.

Wentworth, C. K., 1944, "Potholes, pits and pans," *J. Geol.*, **52**, 117–130.

Cross-references: *Abrasion; Beachrock; Biological Erosion of Limestone Coasts; Corrasion; Eustasy; Induration; Karst; Lapiés; Negroheads; Organisms as Geomorphic Agents; Solution Pits and Pans; Tafoni.* Vol. I: *Mean Sea Level Changes, Long Term.* pr Vol. VI: *Weathering—Chemical; Weathering—Organic.*

LIMESTONE LANDSCAPE—See **DOLINA; KARST; LAPIÉS; LIMESTONE CAVES; MOGOTE; SPELEOTHEMS**

LIMNOLOGY—*See* pr Vol. VI

LITHOLOGY—*See* pr Vol. VI

LITHOSPHERE—*See* Vol. V

LITTORAL PLATFORM, BENCH, TERRACE—
See **PLATFORMS**

LITTORAL PROCESSES—AN INTRODUCTION

Geomorphic processes of the littoral belt are perhaps the most varied and among the most vigorous of any on the face of the earth. They include *erosion, sedimentation* and *transport* (see *Coastal Geomorphology*). The littoral zone of ecologists is strictly the intertidal zone, between mean high tide and mean low tide, but geologists frequently employ the term *littoral belt* to extend from the approximate lower limit of vigorous wave-generated turbulence (10–20 meters) to the beach and then the back-beach to the front of the littoral sand dunes, beach ridges or cliff line. Zenkovich (1967) sets the outer limit at a depth corresponding to one-third of the wavelength at storm maxima. All of this sequence of subparallel zones is involved in complex interacting processes, the energy and equilibrium of which are liable to (a) predictable disturbances (e.g., tides, seasonal storms and wind incidence), (b) less predictable catastrophic events (e.g., hurricanes, landslides, etc.) and (c) varied secular events (e.g., eustatic rise and fall, geodynamic changes in wind and current systems, crustal tectonic rise and fall). Any one measurable parameter, e.g., the establishment of *mean sea level* (q.v., Vol. 1), must therefore be interrelated to all the other parameters.

It is to be stressed that world mean sea level today is about 75 mm higher than it was at the turn of the century and is constantly oscillating, in addition to which there are numerous local secular trends, which may amplify or offset world eustatic controls (Fairbridge, 1962; Fairbridge and Krebs, 1962). The position of mean sea level today is simply an accidental datum at this instant of geologic time; during glacial maxima that datum lay 100–130 meters lower (i.e., the coast lay near the outer edge of the continental shelf), while before the Quaternary and during interglacial warm epochs the shore line was higher on the *coastal plain* (q.v.), leaving "raised beaches" and *terraces* (q.v.). The littoral zone of the last 5 million years has thus shifted like a shutter effect from shelf margin to the inner limits of the coastal plain, and traces of older littoral zones may be studied both offshore by oceanographic techniques and inland by standard geomorphic and stratigraphic methods.

The width of the littoral belt at any one time depends upon the primary relief of the coastal region; thus it is wide in regions of low relief and narrow in areas of high relief. It is further controlled by tidal range, which may vary from a few centimeters (as in the Mediterranean) to 15 meters or more (Bay of Fundy; Northern Australia, etc.).

The stability of a coast at any one moment (and its related geomorphic features) can be written mathematically in terms of an energy budget in which the component masses removed over a given period are equated against the materials transported into the system during that same period. The principal components and agencies are outlined below.

Materials

(a) Hard-rock Shores. There are either mechanically resistant or chemically resistant rock types, e.g., a coral limestone is mechanically very strong, but chemically weak (see *Biological Erosion; Corrosion; Limestone Coastal Weathering*). Even some both mechanically and chemically strong rocks like granite or basalt contain less durable components such as certain feldspars, which permit etching and pitting, especially under intertidal and spray conditions (see *Solution Pits and Pans*). The expansion of crystallizing salt, "fretting," may be important (see *Salt Weathering*). Unloading and weathering along joint systems of certain massive igneous rocks favor large-scale exfoliation, and *wave quarrying*, especially by hydraulic pressure effects, may be important (see *Granite Landforms*).

In a general way, mechanical wave erosion (notably *Abrasion*, q.v.) is secondary to the rotting of weathered rock under groundwater conditions in the middle and low latitudes (see *Denudation; Regolith and Saprolite*); rock rotting is dependent upon humidity and soil acids generated largely by bacterial activity which is positively temperature dependent. In polar latitudes *ice push* is an important mechanical effect (see *Ice Thrusting*), and hard rocks are prepared for littoral attack by *frost riving* (q.v.). Hard-rock shores in general are necessarily those in the process of erosion and *denudation* (q.v.); in any one cycle of relatively stable sea level and tectonic conditions, hard rock indicates a *retreating coastline*.

(b) Soft-rock Shores. Since soft rocks by definition are in discrete particles, loosely consolidated or poorly cemented, the question of their chemical erosion rarely arises in geomorphology, because mechanical breakdown is often rapid or effectively instantaneous. Such shores include sandy coasts, low cliffed coasts of glacial debris, mudbanks of deltaic regions and mangrove coasts. The basic equilibrium landform of the soft-rock shore is the *beach* (q.v.), most often composed of sandy material and less commonly of silts or mud. The particle components are commonly *quartz* sands along a mature coast, with local concentrates of long-stable, "heavy sands" (black or red minerals like ilmenite, magnetite, zircon, rutile, monazite, garnet); then there are *calcite* or *aragonite* sands on coral islands or eolian calcarenite coasts (limited to middle and low latitudes); further, there are mixed minerals and rock fragments on glaciated coasts, and black rock ("lithic") fragments on volcanic coasts.

On soft-rock shores only can one often speak of a

balanced equation of erosion versus accumulation, in short, a steady-state equilibrium, when viewed on an annual basis. The establishment of a sandy beach in front of a "*fossil cliff*" in fact protects and stabilizes that sector. Unless man-made interference occurs or an important secular trend of geodynamic nature is involved, the beach budget tends to be balanced over the twelve-month cycle.

It is rather exceptional to find either a sedimentary excess or deficiency over a given sector. Thus a *prograding shoreline* (q.v.) is to be expected only in the vicinity of (a) excessive sediment supply, e.g., near deltas, or (b) in a tectonically or oceanographically unstable area involved in a positive net geodynamic shift. Equally well, a soft-rock *retrograding shoreline* (q.v.) is to be expected only where a normal supply of sediment is cut off (a common result of man-made obstructions) or where there is a negative net geodynamic shift. It is quite possible to have a retrograding sector and a prograding sector side by side. For example, many of the immature coasts of Quaternary moraines of New England, Long Island, Martha's Vineyard or similar ones in Denmark possess headlands that are retreating, supplying abundant sediment to adjacent prograding spits and *bars* (q.v.); in such a case, one may say that the retrograding, cliffed sectors are reacting to a post-glacial crustal phenomenon— marginal subsidence, while the spits are prograding under excess sediment supply.

Coastal classification (q.v.) has in the past been based largely upon structural or genetic factors (real or fancied!). The most impressive component of the multicomponent system is often selected on a highly subjective basis. Thus Johnson (1919) recognized *submergent* and *emergent coasts*; since most coasts have been submerged after the last glacial stage, emerged after mid-Holocene, and have submerged during the last 50 years, how does one say which effect is most important? Valentin (1952) offered a system that grouped *advancing coasts* with progradation and emergence, contrasting with *retreating coasts* marked by erosion and submergence, but this suffers from the same weakness. Shepard (1952) in contrast recognized *primary coasts*, nonmarine (e.g., volcanic), that were equated with youth, and *secondary coasts*, shaped by marine processes, that are also usually complex and mature, but since the great bulk of all coasts are in the latter category, this system too has shortcomings. Long ago, Suess (1885–1909) distinguished between "Pacific" coasts that were parallel to the tectonic trend, and "Atlantic" coasts that were cut off abruptly. Other structural categories were proposed by von Richthofen, Cotton (1952) and others, but a completely satisfactory scheme has not yet been forthcoming. Some observers, after a simple division perhaps into hard-rock and soft-rock coasts, or by relief into steep-to coasts and low relief favor a nomenclature based on genetic features, e.g., *fjord* (q.v.), *fjärd*

(q.v.), *rias* (q.v.), morainal coast, mangrove coast, barrier island coast, fringing reef coast and so on.

Cumulative Features

It was postulated by Johnson (1919) that an offshore bar would eventually build up to become a vegetated *barrier island* (q.v.). High-energy conditions of exceptional nature (such as hurricane incidence) are now widely regarded as necessary for building up such features; the writer feels that an additional energy source is required, such as the small eustatic sea level oscillations of the last 6000 years. In the Black Sea, for example, there are no hurricanes, but excellent barrier islands; they have been test-bored and trenched to disclose cores of high mid-Holocene beaches. Off some low-energy coasts, traces of the lower-than-present Holocene sea levels are still preserved in soft sediments (Tanner, 1965). In hard rocks, the old coastal platforms, now submerged, may be preserved in limestones (Carrigy and Fairbridge, 1954) but hardly in more resistant rock types, which do not develop coastal benches rapidly enough.

Over a low-relief shore under prograding conditions multiple lines of *beach ridges* (q.v.) are found in many parts of the world. Some 50–100 ridges have built up in some areas over the time span of about 6000 years. Frequently they are divided into three or more groups which the writer interprets as due to major interruptions caused by sea level drops about 3000, 1900 and 700 years ago (Fairbridge, 1961), but this is a controversial matter. The building of a new individual ridge is attributed by Savage (1959) to a steepened wave system; such a condition is usual for offshore winds and is usually seasonal, but the new bar-beach system is destroyed by the normal succeeding onshore winds. To obtain sequences of new ridges, a longer-than-annual periodic energy buildup under favorable winds is needed, alternating with periods of lower-energy conditions. In the opinion of the writer, based on C^{14} datings of beach-ridge series (Schofield, 1961), the periods involved may be of the order of 10–100 years; long-term sea level oscillations of this order do occur and likewise long-term shifts in the prevailing wind patterns, but it seems unlikely that a satisfactory analysis can be achieved until appropriate detailed, long-term studies are made. A correlation between sedimentation in Guiana mangrove swamps and the sunspot cycle has been offered by Choubert (see *Sunspots and Sedimentation*, Vol. I).

Complicating factors in the interpretation of beach ridges, because of their long-term characteristics, include not only eustatic and climatic factors, but also the tectonic stability question. In the case of a broad belt of beach ridges in a highly stable shelf region (e.g., the Malayan coast—Nossin, 1965; Western Australia—Fairbridge, 1950), it is found that innermost series of ridges (usually dated mid-Holocene) are 2–3 meters higher than the contemporary belt, which suggests some eustatic control. On the other hand, in a subsiding area such as the Mississippi delta, successive beach ridges ("*cheniers*") are found prograding across lagoonal mud flats (McFarlan, 1961); in spite of this abnormal setting, the beach ridges are found in sheaves that date, curiously enough, from about the times of the principal Holocene eustatic oscillations (although no such correlation has been suggested by the local geologists).

In favorable regions, beach ridges are augmented by back-beach sand dunes. These dunes do not contribute to deserts, except in very arid zones; in the humid belts, they tend to be limited to a few hundred meters of the coastal belt, although in areas of very abundant sand supply a broad belt of parabolic or even barchan dunes may develop for certain periods, after which they generally become stabilized by vegetation.

Vegetation plays an important role in stabilizing soft-rock coasts. In the middle latitudes, this vegetation is generally of the salt marsh type, with *Spartina* and so on. Usually the colonization is limited to mudflats of lagoonal and bay areas (e.g., coastal New England; the Fens of England, the Watten of Germany, Holland and Denmark; see *Wadden Sea*, pr. Vol. VI); there is often a protective barrier spit or island. The accumulations of peat form a resistant "mattress" against tidal currents and storm wave conditions. In the low latitudes, various species of *mangrove* take over, and because of their remarkable stilt roots and other features, they may play an important role in helping the progradation of muddy coasts or building a sedimentary cover over the inner parts of some *coral reefs* (q.v.; see also *Organisms as Geomorphic Agents*). As with marine peat swamps, the mangrove usually requires some sort of barrier to protect it from the full force of wave action, such as a wide reef, some offshore islands or bars.

In high latitudes, the soft beaches are modified not only by ice push, like the rocky shores, but by *thermokarst* (q.v.) and are often marked by frost wedges, polygons, ventifacts and so on. They may contain ice-rafted materials, ice lenses and deep-frozen or desiccated fossils, and may terminate abruptly against ice margins, past or present (Nichols, 1961).

Agents

(a) **Chemical Agents.** Numerous chemical agents are involved in littoral processes. Above mean sea level, rainwater is the principal solvent, aided by soil bacterial modification (usually with the addition of CO_2 or "humic acids," which lower the pH). Capillary action, evaporation and supersaturation play roles in reprecipitation of cements, e.g., in the calcareous hardening of *eolianite* (see *Induration*) and of *beachrock* (q.v.). Between tide limits, the chemical agencies are mainly biochemical, aided by the mechanical boring potential of numbers of marine organisms (see *Biological Erosion of Limestone*). Below low-tide limits, the role of chemical agents is extremely small except in the microenvironments of the borers' immediate ecotope (niche) and in fresh, fine-grained sediments rich in organic debris where a vigorous bacterial population is maintained (for details, see various articles in Vol. IV and pr Vol. VI).

(b) **Mechanical Agents.** These are even more varied than chemical ones in the littoral belt. The various wave types (see below) develop *turbulence* (q.v., Vol. 1) and hydraulic pressures (see *Fluid Mechanics*, Vol. II). The transported sand develops a potential for *abrasion* (q.v.) that is dependent on velocity, time and supply. Thus a breaking wave on an algal-covered coral reef has little erosive potential (in spite of tremendous hydraulic pressures) because of its lack of abrasive "armament," i.e., sand or boulders which, if present (e.g., island beaches), may render much more effective the smaller waves of a lagoon.

The *beach* (q.v.) develops a characteristic profile for any given energy situation (Le Méhauté, 1961; see also *Littoral Processes—Quantitative*)—but a small shift of relative sea level transposes this profile up or down, accompanied by appropriate erosion and filling. The theoretical formulation by Bruun (1962) has been subjected to experimental and field confirmation by Schwartz (1965). Besides the cross profile, a longitudinal "wave" of particle dynamics has been established for sand drift along the beach (wavelength: 100–500 meters). A short-wavelength, longitudinal undulation of the beach face leads to the development of *beach cusps* (Russell and McIntire, 1965) but an adequate explanation is still awaited. A systematic mathematical approach to an analysis of overall shape of the coastline has been begun by Grijm (see *Coastlines—Theoretical Shapes*). An analysis of net sediment transport directions for the entire world coastline was completed by Silvester (1962; see also *Sediment Transport— Long-term Net Transport*) who showed that it is the persistent swells, not storms, that determine the net sand transport. According to the "Lewis Law," the beach tends to elongate in a direction normal to the maximum fetch (Lewis, 1938). According to the wave energy, sand supply and other factors, the net annual shift ranges from about 100,000 cubic meters (e.g., Gulf of Mexico) to 1,000,000 cubic meters (e.g., U.S. Pacific Coast).

Littoral Energy Sources

Many different energy sources interact in the littoral belt, and waves themselves are driven by different mechanisms, long-term swells (major atmospheric pressure phenomena), local wind waves, tsunamis and so on (see articles in Vol. 1: *Waves*;

Tsunamis; etc.). *Oscillatory waves* begin to "feel the bottom" on exposed shores at 10–20 meter depth, becoming *waves of translation*, developing breakers which are amplified by local winds. The waves set up an orbital motion that may cause bottom erosion. Swell, generated at a considerable distance from the coast, tends to transport the sand up the beach to the *swash* limit; back-swash then operates under gravity. In the turbulence of inshore wave activity, sand is held in suspension, so the wave refraction and geostrophic currents ($\pm$ tidal components) combine to set up local longshore drift, providing a major avenue of *sediment transport* (q.v.). Under certain wave conditions, essentially a nearly symmetric (90°) onshore approach, water level tends to build up near the beach, resulting in a strong longshore set for a short distance turning to a high-velocity *rip current* (q.v.) which carries sand out of the local system, only to be returned under heavy storm activity.

Above sea level the same planetary atmospheric pressure fields that control most wave action are now dominant. Hence, the wind is a major energy source and is the principal modelling agent, but without the long-distance (swell) component that water waves develop. There is, on the other hand, an additional local component in the energy spectrum—the effects of rainfall. These are relatively minor in dune areas since the high porosity of the sand permits almost direct passage of the rain to the groundwater table. On any back-beach areas and hinterland of reduced permeability, rainfall is likely to lead to sheetwash and some stream erosion. The effects of stream outlets may be to keep beach drift to limited sectors or to shift the locus of principal longshore drift from the beach, and immediately offshore, to the outer periphery of a fan or belt of offshore bars. Fresh water may also inhibit coral reef growth and lead to a gap in an otherwise continuous fringing reef; an inherited feature of the same origin is observed in the radial passes or "passages" in barrier reefs and atoll rings. Fresh water also plays a chemical role in causing solution of carbonate sands and leading to cementation of eolianites.

For contemporary energy sources, the ever-present potential of the earth's gravity field is seen as a primary force in tsunamis (giant sea waves associated with seismic shocks), a major factor in wave break, the dominant factor in backwash, likewise in the slip-off slopes of dunes. While gravity-dependent glaciers and ice age river valleys are in no way products of littoral processes as such, their activities predetermine the postglacial shapes of *fjords, fjärds, estuaries* and *rias* (q.q.v.). Solar energy drives the atmospheric circulation and hence both principal wind and wave systems, as well as controlling rainfall.

For secular shifts of the littoral energy budget one must generally look to planetary causes. These are in part (a) *external causes*; in the case of long-term shifts of climate and mean sea level the most likely cause is the complex of variations in celestial mechanics taken into consideration by the *Milankovitch theory* (see Vol. II, *Time and Astronomic Cycles*, the tilt, ecliptic and precession cycles). For the (b) *endogenic causes*, there are the great long-term geotectonic events connected with the rise and collapse of orogenic belts, the subsidence of intracratonic basins, the collapse of quasicratonic marine regions, the isostatic uplift of the coasts immediately behind collapse sectors, the rapid postglacial elastic rebound and the slower plastic transfers, and shifts in the earth's axis due to uneven loading. Shifts in crustal loading may be due to ice accumulation, deglaciation, sedimentation, vulcanism and so on.

Littoral Stability

The field procedures for measuring *coastal stability* (q.v.) are numerous and still await serious integration:

(a) *Long-term Tide Gauge Record Analysis*: Both climatic and crustal trends are involved but cannot be easily dissected from the record. Only short runs are available for the most part and the resultant record has an essentially local characteristic. Nevertheless, the tide records are strictly quantitative and thus offer interesting potentials.

(b) *Geodetic cadastral survey network analysis*: In this case, the triangulation nets have been generally standardized assuming that the principal tide gauge stations were stable, which is palpably incorrect. Geodetic markers are also notoriously liable to disturbance by frost action, human interference, compaction and so on, so that systematic reoccupation of triangulation networks is fraught with difficulties; nevertheless, certain trends are emerging and more skillful analysis is bringing unexpectedly valuable information (see *Crustal Movements—Contemporary*; *Neotectonics*). The great advantage of cadastral records over tide gauge data is that they can disclose true crustal changes (in part), without the confusion of climatic trends.

(c) *Geomorphic Analysis*, both inland and offshore, is bringing to light evidence of secular trends in coastal shift. As with tidal records, the geomorphic data are complicated by the mixing of crustal and climatic components. But they do possess the great advantage that, at least within the range of precision C^{14} dating (about 50,000 years), a long-term trend can be established, and with other newly developed dating systems, the record is currently being extended back several million years. Since multiple processes of different periodicities (and often contrasting mathematical sign) are always overprinted on one another, the analysis is far from simple.

In conclusion, it may be said that the study of littoral processes, in all dimensions, presents one of the most fruitful areas of study for understanding planetary dynamics.

RHODES W. FAIRBRIDGE

References

Bascom, W., 1964, "Waves and Beaches," New York, Doubleday & Co., 267pp.

Bruun, P., 1962, "Sea level rise as a cause of shore erosion," *J. Waterways Harbors Div., Am. Soc. Civil Engrs.*, **88**, 117–130.

Caldwell, J. M., 1966, "Coastal processes and beach erosion," *J. Soc. Civil Engin. (Boston)*, **53**, 142–156.

Carrigy, M. A., and Fairbridge, R. W., 1954, "Recent sedimentation, physiography and structure of the Continental Shelves of Western Australia," *J. Roy. Soc. W. Australia*, **38**, 65–95.

Cotton, C. A., 1952, "Geomorphology," Sixth ed., New York, John Wiley & Sons, 505pp.

Dolan, R., and McCloy, J., 1965, "Selected Bibliography on Beach Features and Related Nearshore Processes," Baton Rouge, Louisiana State University Press, Coastal Studies Ser. 11, 59pp.

Evers, W., 1964, "The problem of coastal genesis with special reference to the strandflat, the banks, or grounds, and deep channels, of the Norwegian and Greenland Coasts," *J. Geol.*, **72**, 681.

Fairbridge, R. W., 1950, "The geology and geomorphology of Point Peron, Western Australia," *J. Roy. Soc. W. Australia*, **34**(3), 35–72.

Fairbridge, R. W., 1961, "Eustatic Changes in Sea-level," in "Physics and Chemistry of the Earth," Vol. 4, pp. 99–185, London, Pergamon Press.

Fairbridge, R. W., 1962, "World sea-level and climatic changes," *Quaternaria*, **6**, 111–134.

Fairbridge, R. W., and Krebs, O. A., Jr., 1962, "Sea level and the Southern Oscillation," *Geophys. J.*, **6**, 532–545.

Guilcher, A., 1958, "Coastal and Submarine Morphology," London, Methuen & Co., 274pp. (translated by B. W. Sparks and R. H. W. Kneese).

Guilcher, A., and King, C. A. M., 1961, "Spits, tombolos and tidal marshes in Connemara and West Kerry, Ireland," *Proc. Roy. Irish Acad., Sect. B*, **61**(17), 283–338.

Harrison, W., Pore, N. A., and Tuck, D. R., Jr., 1965, "Predictor equation for beach processes and responses," *J. Geophys. Res.*, **70**(24), 6103–6109.

Ingle, J. C., Jr., 1966, "The Movement of Beach Sand," Vol. 5, Amsterdam, Elsevier (series: *Develop. in Sed.*), 221pp.

Johnson, D. W., 1919, "Shore Processes and Shoreline Development," New York, John Wiley & Sons, 583pp.

Johnson, J. W., 1956, "Dynamics of nearshore sediment movement," *Bull. Am. Assoc. Petrol. Geologists*, **40**, 2211–2232.

King, C. A. M., 1959, "Beaches and Coasts," London, E. Arnold, 402pp.

Le Méhauté, B., and Brebner, A., 1961, "An introduction to coastal morphology and littoral processes," Kingston, Ontario, Queen's Univ., Civ. Engin. Res. Rept., No. 14, 46pp.

Lewis, W. V., 1938, "The evolution of shoreline curves," *Proc. Geologists Assoc. Engl.*, **49**, 107–127.

McFarlan, E., Jr., 1961, "Radiocarbon dating of Late Quaternary deposits, South Louisiana," *Bull. Geol. Soc. Am.*, **72**, 129–158.

Nichols, R. L., 1961, "Characteristics of beaches formed in Polar Climates," *Am. J. Sci.*, **259**(9), 694–708.

Nossin, J. J., 1965, "Analysis of younger beach ridge deposits in eastern Malaya," *Z. Geomorphol.*, **9**, 186–208.

Otros, E. G., Jr., 1964, "Observation of beach cusp and beach ridge formation on the Long Island Sound," *J. Sediment. Petrol.*, **34**, 554–560.

Russell, R. J., and McIntire, W. G., 1965, "Beach cusps," *Bull. Geol. Soc. Am.*, **76**(3), 307–320.

Savage, R. P., 1959, "Notes on the formation of beach ridges," *Bull. Beach Erosion Board*, No. 13, 31–35.

Schofield, J. C., 1961, "Sea level fluctuations during the last 4000 years as recorded by a chenier plain, Firth of Thames, New Zealand," *New Zealand J. Geol. Geophys.*, **3**(3), 461–485.

Schou, A., 1945, "Det Marine forland," *Folia Geogr. Danica*, **4**, 1–236.

Schwartz, M., 1965, "Laboratory study of sea-level rise as a cause of shore erosion," *J. Geol.*, **73**(3), 528–534.

Shepard, F. P., 1952, "Revised nomenclature for depositional coastal feature," *Bull. Am. Assoc. Petrol. Geologists*, **36**, 1902–1912.

Shepard, F. P., 1963, "Submarine Geology," Second ed., New York, Harper & Row, 557pp.

Silvester, R., 1962, "Coastal processes," *Nature*, **196**, 819–920.

Suess, E., 1885–1909, "Das Antlitz der Erde," Vienna, F. Tempsky (English translation "The Face of the Earth," Oxford, Clarendon Press, 1904–1924).

Tanner, W. F. and Bates, J. D., 1965, "Submerged beach on a zero-energy coast," *Southeastern Geol.*, **7**(1), 19–24.

Valentin, H., 1952, "Die Küsten der Erde," *Peter. Geogr. Mitt*, 246.

Wells, D. R., 1967, "Beach equilibrium and second-order wave theory," *J. Geophys. Res.*, **72**(2), 497–504.

Zenkovich, V. P., 1967, "Processes of Coastal Development," London, Oliver & Boyd, 738pp.

Cross-references: *Abrasion; Atlantic and Pacific Type Coasts; Barriers—Beaches and Islands; Bars; Beach; Beach Erosion and Coastal Protection; Beach Ridges; Beachrock; Biological Erosion of Limestone Coasts; Coastal Classification; Coastal Geomorphology; Coastal Plain; Coastal Stability; Coastlines—Theoretical Shapes; Coral Reefs; Corrosion; Crustal Movements—Contemporary; Denudation; Eolian Transport; Estuary; Fjärd; Fjord; Granite Landforms; Holocene; Ice Thrusting; Induration; Limestone Coastal Weathering; Littoral Processes—Quantitative; Mangrove Swamps; Neotectonics; Organisms as Geomorphic Agents; Prograding Shoreline; Quaternary; Regolith and Saprolite; Retrograding Shoreline; Rias; Rip Currents; Salt Weathering; Sediment Transport; Solution Pits and Pans; Terraces; Thermokarst; Vol. I: Continental Shelf; Mean Sea Level; Sunspots and Sedimentation; Tsunami; Turbulence; Waves. Vol. II: Time and Astronomic Cycles; Atmospheric Circulation; Fluid Mechanics; Winds. pr Vol. VI: Coastal Vegetation Types; Wadden Sea.*

LITTORAL PROCESSES—FIELD METHODS

The nearshore (or littoral) zone encompasses, according to modern geomorphological ideas, the space between the swash line reached during high-tide storm surges and the seafloor out to a depth corresponding approximately to one-third of the storm wavelength. Waves and currents within the limits indicated are capable of changing the bottom relief as well as orienting and displacing the sandy sediments. Together with the contemporaneous accumulations on the coast, the cliffs and landslide belt are also considered as parts of the littoral zone.

Evolutionary processes of the underwater slope and the shore itself are mutually interdependent and indivisible. This is because they are going on under the action of a single factor, namely, wave motion in the water and the currents which are induced by the waves (and in some places also the tides).

The structure of the littoral zone depends not only on its geological composition and tectonic characteristics, but in the first place on the position and relative width of the abrasional and depositional subzones and local features of the submarine slope, as well as the land itself. Of great importance also is the thickness and composition of recent sediment cover.

Cutting across the boundaries of several different scientific disciplines—geology, geomorphology and oceanography—the study of the shore zone is a distinct branch of science and borrows the methods of all three. Thus, there are three main directions for shore studies: hydrodynamic, geomorphologic and lithologic, appropriately modified and interrelated.

Preliminary analysis of the relief and structure of the shore zone is carried out by means of a study of large-scale maps and charts, geological materials and air photo surveys. It is particularly important to use the navigational charts with depth soundings and isobaths. On this basis, one may prepare a plan of field work aimed at learning all the details needed for an explanation and proper up-to-date appraisal of the shore zone dynamics and its developmental history.

The first investigations to be undertaken involve the preparation of a series of sections showing the relief and inclination of both the submarine slope and the subaerial part of the shore. This marine work may be carried out using a cutter with a shallow draught or an amphibious vehicle ("duck"; Bascom, 1964). A surf boat may also be used, but it is less convenient. The sections must be oriented perpendicularly to the shore line. The best technique for sounding operations is the use of the self-recording echo sounder, although the usual lead line is enough in some simple cases. If a cutter or duck is available for the investigator, it is the most con-

Fig. 1. Lowering of the vibro-piston corer from the ship.

venient for taking specimens of sediments at the same time the soundings are being made (during the reverse course). The starting point of each section must be related to some fixed geodetic mark. Simultaneously, the sea level has to be established precisely by tide gauge. The leveling profiles on the land must run across the beaches, aggradational terraces (beach ridges) and barrier islands, if present. In the last case, the lagoon floor should also be investigated.

The sediment sampling is accomplished at the bottom surface by using a grab or by scuba diving. The cores are best obtained with a special device called the *vibro-piston core sampler* (Nieviessky, 1958; Zenkovich, 1962). It is 5 meters long (Fig. 1) and easily takes the coarse, nearshore sediments (shells, gravel, pebbles); it is effective down to water depths of 300 meters as well as on the land (from a truck mounting). Recently, in the USSR, a 10-meter model has been tested.

The internal composition and stratification of thick sediment cover (up to tens of meters) may be revealed using special devices based on the echo-sounding technique or low-frequency seismic principles (*sparker, geolocator, seismoprofilograph,* of various designs).

For each of the marine profiles, the direction and the sampling points must be carefully established. The course is oriented along a line connecting two high and extremely visible poles on the shore. The traverse points must be taken by two theodolites set up on opposite sides of the line. Signals are communicated by the theodolite observers to the boat crew by radio ("walkie-talkie" type).

Distances between the sections and their position depend on the shape of the shore. The more it is dissected (complex), the more closely must the sections be spaced. In the Soviet investigations, the separation varies from 1–10 km.

Comparison and analysis of all the data obtained enables one to draw up a comprehensive description of the shore zone composition for the sector under consideration. This description is a basis for the further investigations of the coastal dynamics, i.e., up-to-the-minute changes of the shore zone both in profile and outline. This is necessary in turn for making predictions as to future developments and inferring certain comparative geographical conclusions. With this aim, the investigation must include not only the changes themselves, but also the processes going on and the action of many other factors.

The best means of finding out the relief changes of the shore zone is to make repeated measurements over certain time intervals. It is recommended that one choose some representative sectors for investigation and establish the detailed relief by compiling a large-scale plan (scale up to 1:200), taking panoramic photos and making some profile sections (submarine part included) as precisely as possible. For long stretches of shore, a repeated air photo survey is of major importance, particularly because one can distinguish the forms of submarine meso-relief down to depths of about 20 meters.

Special hand drilling operations may be undertaken to establish an abrasion-rate for certain points of cliffed coast and for rock bench surfaces. Holes of about 5-cm depth and 5-mm diameter have been made in the solid rock and filled with plasticene to avoid chemical decomposition. After some time, the depth of the holes is measured again. The difference shows the thickness of the rock layer worn down for the time unit (some millimeters per year).

There is also a means of defining a rate of accumulation on the surface of marshes. It was suggested by N. Nielsen (see Moller, 1964) that one should spread a thin layer of any stable, colored substance (heavy dye, mineral sand, etc.) over the surface. After some years, one must take cores on the spot and determine the sediment layer accumulated above the marked horizon (see also Steers, 1964, p. 526). The same technique is suggested for underwater conditions in bays or lagoons sheltered against any strong wave action. Longer-term determinations using C^{14} have been employed by Redfield (1962) and others.

Data on recent retreating or aggrading shore lines may be obtained from the comparison of maps of different dates and from the study of historical and archaeological evidence.

The most important process to be studied in the littoral zone is the drifting of sediment, both transverse and longitudinal to the shore line. This process creates rapid and temporary changes of bottom and beach relief. It also causes long-lasting and large-scale alterations of huge parts of the littoral zone. This is why this process deserves a careful study under different conditions.

An idea of the strength and direction of this process may be obtained by comparing successive surveys near "hydrotechnical" (engineering) constructions such as moles, breakwaters, groins, etc. (Wiegel, 1964). However, as the main purpose is the prediction of sediment deposition in some places or abrasion and destruction in others, one set of measurements should be taken on a natural stretch of shore not yet affected by artificial constructions.

The hydrodynamic conditions of a given sector of the littoral zone are among the most important factors to be studied during stationary observations. This is necessary in any chosen place because the existing observation stations do not gather the detailed data needed. Self-registering wave gauges of some type should be placed along one bottom section at different depths. With all existing devices, one can obtain the maximum wavelength and period. For observing the direction of wave propagation, three planks or buoys must be anchored, creating a triangle having dimensions comparable to those of the mean wavelength. The direction of wave propagation is determined by noting the time in which the crest of the same wave passes under every buoy.

Nearshore currents (their speed and direction at various depths) are measured using floats (superficial or those with a counterweight of appropriate length). The same is possible with a dye creating a visible stain on the sea surface. All measurements must be carried out at specific time intervals (three or four times daily).

Hydrodynamic observations are necessary for analyzing results of repeated relief measurements and data on the sediment bottom and beach drifting. To obtain the most valuable data, storm measurements are desirable. In some countries (Japan, the United States and the USSR), suspended cableways or lines of stakes have been constructed for this purpose.

Hydrometeorologic observations, repeated soundings and experiments with sediment tracers have to be made synchronously for a long time.

There are two kinds of tracer techniques for sediment drifting studies. The first uses luminescent dyes; the second radio isotopes. Both have some advantages and disadvantages. In the USSR, the "luminofore method" (invented by Soviet scientists) is preferred. The natural sand taken from the spot to be studied is subjected to special treatment. After drying, it is covered by a thin film of colloidal matter (e.g., agar-agar) mixed with dye. The several colors and different coarsenesses of the sand may be used as indicators. In either method, the colored sand is dumped on the bottom. The amounts needed depend on the scale of the experiment (from several kilograms to 1 ton or more). Usually the time of dumping is chosen just before an expected storm. The depth and location of dumping points may vary for different colors.

During or after the storm the specimens are sampled along some sections by divers (or from the boat with special devices) taking short cores of superficial layers only. Samples, after drying, are observed under the luminoscope (the simplest model uses windows penetrable by "black light," i.e., ultraviolet) and the luminescent grains are counted. The operation is much facilitated if there is a photo-electric self-registering apparatus for different colors.

Plotting the results (for a square unit or a specimen weight) on the map, one obtains a figure of the drifting speeds and directions for different grain diameters and bottom depths. The areas of distribution also may be obtained showing the combinations of transverse and longshore sediment displacement (Fig. 2; also Zenkovich, 1962; Aybulatov, 1966; Ingle, 1966).

Luminofores have been used for tracing pebble material also, but USSR scientists believe that for these experiments the common oil paints are more convenient.

The operation of the radioisotope method is quite different (Cummins and Ingram, 1963). Artificial sand must be produced using glass containing the isotope needed. Then it is activated in an atomic reactor. (In some cases, it is also possible to activate natural sand.) Transporting the activated sand to the seashore is a rather difficult operation considering the danger of gamma rays to the personnel.

After placing a portion of the radioactive sand at the selected point on the sea bottom, the surface of the surrounding bottom is examined several times using a Geiger counter dragged across the sea bed (impulse frequency). The duration of the experiment depends on the half-life of the isotope chosen. After some set measurements, it is possible to draw maps with lines of equal radiation intensity. The last set shows the net direction or the area of sediment transport and distribution.

The only essential advantage of the isotope method is that the material may be crushed very finely and therefore used to imitate movements of silt and mud sediment. At the same time, it is not as laborious as the luminofore method. However, there are some drawbacks to the isotope method: (a) The preparation of the indicator is rather expensive. (b) Only one experiment may be carried out during a single field season at one point. (c) It is impossible to determine the drifting of sand of varying coarseness from several points simultaneously.

By the methods enumerated above it is possible to study single, unidirectional sediment shiftings during one set of waves. But it is more important to determine the properties of so-called sediment streams (net transport), i.e., total drifting over a long time (a year or more), these properties being direction, length, capacity and load. The direction may be obtained from the outlines and asymmetry of some accumulative features of shore lines (Silvester, 1962), from river mouth deflections and from the sequential arrangement of abrasional and accumulative stretches of the shore.

More trustworthy is the lithological method, which gives not only the direction but also the length of a sediment stream. The specimens taken from the beach and submarine slope are subjected

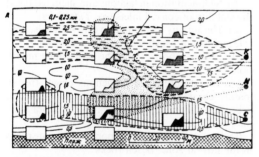

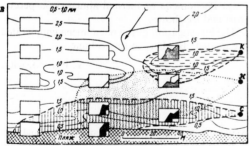

Fig. 2. Two selected sketch maps showing the results of a series of experiments using three luminescent colors: red (K), yellow (H), and blue (C). Mixture of four sand fractions (0.1–0.25 mm, 0.25–0.5 mm, 0.5–1.0 mm and 1.0–2.0 mm) have been painted in every color. Dump points indicated as three black circles. The places of specimen gathering are in the centers of the rectangles. In the same rectangles the appearance time and amount of colored grains of different colors are depicted. The horizontal axis corresponds to the experiment duration (1 hour); vertical—amount of grains. Spreading areas of different sand colors have a distinctive shading. Depth contours are given in meters. The arrow shows direction of the wave approach. Current flows from right to left side.

to laboratory analysis to determine and count the percentage of different minerals or kinds of rocks (shingle beaches).

Then the composition of specimens is compared for different parts of the shore under investigation, as well as with river alluvium and solid rock outcrops which are possible sources of material. In many cases, if there are any specific minerals or rocks delivered to the shore from only one source, it will be clear where and in what relative quantities they are moved along the shore. The same conclusions can sometimes be obtained by comparing the differences in coarseness and rounding of the particles and sorting of the sediment as a whole. In any case, it is necessary to keep a certain order as to frequency and position of the specimens gathered to be sure that the material is representative enough (Krumbein and Slack, 1956).

The load of the sediment stream is determined approximately if there are any engineering constructions which control the accretion or retreat of shore lines after their creation. The same result may be obtained by measuring the amount of sediment dredged from the harbor channels (Wiegel, 1964).

Until recently, the only means of determining the sediment-stream capacity were the indirect calculations of so-called drifting ability of the waves and currents. The first method was suggested by Munch-Petersen (1936) and was later improved. In the USSR, the "energy" method is in common use (Zhdanov, 1951), based on wave observations during a long period.

The study of recent and contemporaneous vertical movements of the coast is of much importance (see *Crustal Movements—Contemporary; Neotectonics*). One should remember the method suggested by D. Johnson (1919): a leveling of relative heights of different age series of *beach ridges* (q.v.) on the surface of wide accumulation terraces. The study of sediment stratification in long cores taken at sheltered estuaries with permanent bottom accumulation is also reliable.

If the period of the last few millennia, or even centuries, is considered, the ancient maps, historical documents and archaeological findings may be of great help in solving these problems. For the long periods of Quaternary time, one should study ancient high marine *terraces* (q.v.) as well as submarine ones. The same materials are also useful in judging the changes of shore outlines. These investigations are carried out by using the well-known geomorphologic methods.

Shore-line evolution may be studied deductively, but the analysis of ancient beach ridges (the pattern of generations of different age) is of great help in the reconstructions suggested (Fig. 3).

A comprehensive littoral zone study should also include the many local phenomena and processes which are as follows:

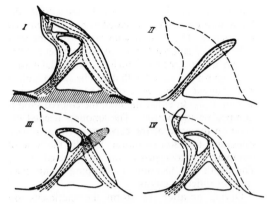

FIG. 3. Evolution of complex accumulative morphology with several series of beach ridges. I: recent outlines; II–IV: reconstruction of successive stages of growth and erosion (Cape Amjak foreland on the Bering Sea, after A. Ionin).

(a) The vegetation associations of tidal marshes and their influence on land accretion;

(b) Sedimentation in lagoons and sheltered bays; the stability of coastal inlets (see *Tidal Inlet*);

(c) The activity of submarine canyon heads, their role as traps of beach sediments (Emery, 1960);

(d) Eolian processes and the shore dune migrations;

(e) The structures of biogenous origin (reefs), mainly coral ones, their growth and destruction processes, the influence of reefs on the shore morphology;

(f) Dissolving and lithification of carbonate rocks in the littoral zone, beach rocks;

(g) Phenomena of thermal abrasion on permafrost and ice shores.

The investigation of the phenomena enumerated are treated elsewhere in this volume.

V. P. ZENKOVICH

References

Aybulatov, N. A., 1966, "Investigation of the Sand Bottom Drifting in the Seas," Moscow, Ed. "Nauka" (in Russian).

Bascom, W., 1964, "Waves and Beaches," New York, Anchor Books, Doubleday & Co., Inc., 267pp.

Budanov, V. I., 1964, "Field Investigation Methods of the Shore-Zone of the Seas," Moscow, Ed. "Nauka" (in Russian).

Cummins, R. S., and Ingram, L. F., 1963, "Tracing sediment movement with radio isotopes," *Military Engr.*, **55**, (365), 161–164.

Emery, K. O., 1960, "The Sea off Southern California," New York, John Wiley & Sons, Inc., 366pp.

Ingle, J. C., 1966, "The Movement of Beach Sand," Amsterdam and New York, Elsevier Publishing Co., 221pp.

Johnson, D. W., 1919, "Shore Processes and Shoreline

Development," New York, John Wiley & Sons, 583pp.

King, C. A. M., 1959, "Beaches and Coasts," London, E. Arnold, Ltd., 403pp.

Krumbein, W. C., and Slack, H. A., 1956, "Relative efficiency of beach sampling methods," *U.S. Beach Erosion Bd. Tech. Memo.*, **90**, 43pp.

Moller, J. T., 1964, "Accumulation and abrasion in a tidal area," *Denmark, Collected Papers for XXth Intern. Geogr. Congr.*

Munch-Petersen, T., 1936, "Über Materialwanderung an Meeresküsten," *5th Hydr. Conf. der Baltischen Staaten, Helsinki.*

Nieviessky, E. N., 1958, "Étude des sédiments marine littoraux à l'aide du tube à piston vibreur," *Bull. Inform. Comité Centr. Océanographie, Paris*, **X**, 6.

Redfield, A. C., and Rubin, M., 1962, "The age of salt marsh peat and its relation to recent changes in sea level at Barnstable," *Proc. Natl. Acad. Sci. U.S.*, **48**, 1728–1735.

Sanders, J. E., and Imbrie, J., 1963, "Continuous cores of Bahamian calcareous sands made by vibrodrilling," *Bull. Geol. Soc. Am.*, **74**, 1287–1292.

Silvester, R., 1962, "Sediment movement around the coastline of the world," *Inst. Civil Engrs.*, No. 14.

Steers, J. A., 1964, "The Coastline of England and Wales," Cambridge, The University Press, 750pp.

Wiegel, R. L., 1964, "Oceanographical Engineering," Englewood Cliffs, N.J., Prentice-Hall, 532pp.

Yasso, W. E., 1962, "Fluorescent coatings on coarse sediments: an integrated system," *Tech. Rpt., Project NR 388–057, Contract Nonr 266(68), Geogr. Branch, Off. Naval Res.*, **1**, 48pp.

Zenkovich, V. P., 1962, "Some problems and methods of shore dynamics investigations in the U.S.S.R." (and other papers), *De Ingenieur, Holland*, NN 13, 15, 17.

Zenkovich, V. P., 1967, "Processes of Coastal Development," London, Oliver & Boyd, 738pp.

Zhdanov, A. M., 1951, "The determination of the energetical resultant value of the wave regime," *Proc. Acad. Sci. USSR, Geogr. Geodet. Series*, No. 1 (in Russian).

Cross-references: *Barriers—Beaches and Islands; Beach; Beach Erosion and Coastal Protection; Beach Ridges; Beachrock; Coastal Geomorphology; Coastal Lagoon Dynamics; Coral Reefs; Crustal Movements—Contemporary; Eolian Transport; Lagoon; Neotectonics; Permafrost; Platform; Quaternary Period; Sediment Transport; Terraces—Marine; Tidal Inlet.* Vol. I: *Ocean Currents; Ocean Waves; Scuba as a Scientific Tool; Sounding; Storm Surge; Tides.* pr Vol. VI: *Coastal Vegetation Types; Lagoon Sedimentation; Tracer Techniques.*

LITTORAL PROCESSES—QUANTITATIVE TREATMENT

(I) Origin of Beaches and Coastal Material

A beach occupies the zone on a coast between the highest wave uprush and the lowest level at which material may be moved by storm waves. A beach is a temporary deposit for material coming from the land in its active transit along the shore or on and off the shore. This material eventually ends up in deep water offshore (Fig. 1).

Apart from broken shell particles, coastal material originates from coastal or river erosion. Coastal material may be classified as follows:

(a) Pebbles, cobble, shingle and gravel have a diameter larger than 2 mm. They consist of hard rocks (quartzite, granite, basalt) and are rounded in shape by continued impact caused by wave action.

(b) Sand (between 2 and 0.06 mm) is a mixture of quartz, feldspar, heavy minerals, broken shells.

(c) Ooze or silt consists of very fine particles readily moved in suspension and deposited in very still areas such as harbors and estuaries. Ooze is made of silt (0.06–0.002 mm), clay (below 0.002 mm), and also organic particles and colloidal matter found only under certain condition of salinity frequently encountered in estuaries.

Particles in shore regions may be moved by currents and waves in different ways. Sand starts to be moved by wave motion when

$$U_b \geq 0.37 d^{1/4} (\delta - 1)^{2/3} T^{3/8} \qquad (1)$$

where

U_b = the near bottom velocity expressed in centimeters per second,

d = the sand diameter in centimeters,

$\delta - 1$ = the relative density $\cong 1.6$,

T = the wave period in seconds.

When the size of sand particles is smaller than the thickness of the laminar boundary layer, currents and waves on a sandy bottom cause ripple marks, averaging about 1 inch high and 4 inches apart. The distance between ripple marks increases when the water velocity increases and then tends to disappear, giving way to a larger sand transportation.

A large amount of deposit moves by rolling, slipping or jumping in the boundary layer near the bottom. This is *bed load* transportation. The lightest particles are moved from the bottom by *turbulence* and have a confused motion before depositing far from their origin by this means. This is transport by *suspension*. Between these two modes of transportation is transport by saltation. In saltation, particles jump from the bottom but fall again not far from their original position.

These three kinds of motion obey statistical laws, the concentration of solid particles increasing from the free surface to the bottom and increasing also with the water velocity, the state of wave agitation and the rate of turbulence. The rate of turbulence is particularly high in a breaking wave.

(II) Two-dimensional Wave Motion Affecting Beaches

(A) In the case of a wave arriving perpendicularly to the shoreline, the bottom fluid velocity is, as a first approximation:

$$U_B = \frac{\pi H}{T} \frac{\cos(\sigma t - kx)}{\sinh kd}$$

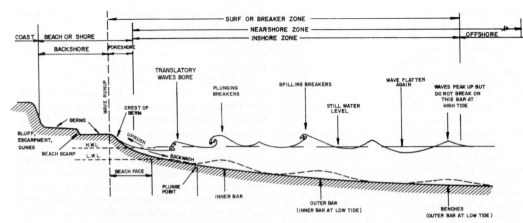

FIG. 1. Terminology of littoral features.

i.e., increasing considerably when the depth d decreases. H is the wave height, T the wave period and L the wavelength;

$$k = \frac{2\pi}{L}, \quad \sigma = \frac{2\pi}{T}, \quad \left(L = \frac{gT^2}{2\pi}\tanh\frac{2\pi d}{L}\right).$$

The application of this formula and the previous formula giving the critical speed of erosion shows that the sand is easily moved at a depth of 300 feet by the longest swell. The formation of ripple marks at such a depth is an evidence of sand motion (but not necessarily by swell; geostrophic and tidal currents are also involved).

This wave motion component, however, is without net mass transport. In order to explain the balance with gravity action on a sloped beach or the net forward (or backward) motion, other phenomena must be considered. First of all, the perviousness of the sandy bottom permits a slight vertical component in the boundary layer. Particles are slightly raised under the wave crest and move quickly forward. Then they are pressed down by the water motion under the wave trough in a part of the boundary layer where the horizontal velocity component is almost zero.

Also, the water motion at the bottom around a fixed point is not symmetrical but has generally a net forward component which increases as the depth decreases. The corresponding force is balanced by the gravity component. This partly explains why beaches usually have a curvature upward (concave up). This asymmetric motion is explained through mathematical development:

(1) By the nonlinear terms due to convective inertia forces, as evidenced by the wave theories at higher order of approximation. For example,

$$U_B = \frac{\pi H}{T}\frac{\cos(\sigma t - kx)}{\sinh kd}$$
$$+ \frac{3\pi^2 H^2}{4LT}\frac{\cos 2(\sigma t - kx)}{\sinh^4 kd} + \cdots$$

(2) By the rotationality induced by bottom friction. In the case of viscous boundary layer

$$\left(U_B\sqrt{\frac{T}{v}} < 280\right),$$

the net forward motion at the bottom is

$$U = 1.25\frac{T}{L}(U_{B\max})^2$$

The vertical distribution of mass transportation depends upon d/L as shown by Fig. 2 and is also very strongly influenced by the wind. Moreover, the wind induces turbulence into the water and the transportation of sand by suspension seaward above the boundary layer. The overall effect is a depletion of the beach when the deep water wave steepness $H_0/L_0 > 0.03$ (storm wave) resulting in a "winter beach profile" and an accretion when $H_0/L_0 < 0.03$ (swell) resulting into a "summer beach profile" (Fig. 2).

The turbulence generated in the breaking zone is the main cause of transportation by suspension. According to various theories, the waves break when (subscript b refers to breaking conditions).

$$\frac{H_b}{L_b} = 0.14\tanh\frac{2\pi d_b}{L_b} \quad \text{or} \quad \frac{H_b}{d_b} = 0.78$$

Also, in practice:

$$\frac{H_b}{H_0} = 1 + 0.003\frac{L_0}{H_0} \quad \left(\frac{H_0}{L_0} < 0.03\right)$$

$$\frac{d_b}{H_b} \cong 1.14 + 4.5\frac{H_0}{L_0}$$

The lightest particles of sand are moved from the breaking zone by suspension. At the end of a storm, this material flows seaward as density currents, replaced near the free surface by clear water. Consequently, the average particle size decreases as the distance from the shore increases. This is another

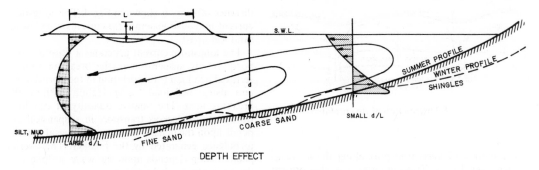

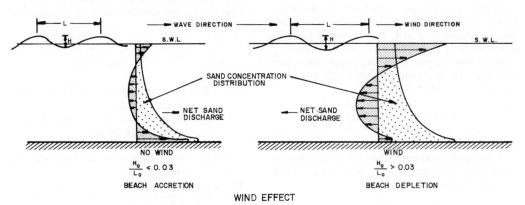

FIG. 2. Vertical distribution of mass transport.

reason why the beach profile has a curvature upward, shingle or cobbles keeping a steeper equilibrium slope under wave action than fine particles of sand. Off the breaking zone, equilibrium profiles of beaches are approximately defined by

$$\frac{d(x)}{L_0} = K\left(\frac{x}{L_0}\right)^m$$

where x is the distance from the shore line. K and m are functions of the sand size, their density and the wave steepness. The average slope given as function of the size of material is:

Mean diameter, mm	0.2	0.3	0.4	0.5	0.7
Average slope, %	1–5	5–10	10–15	12–15	15–20

An equilibrium profile under the action of a given sea state rarely exists because the variation of the beach profiles are always lagging with respect to the sea state. Moreover, coastlines are usually subject to migrating humps, bars and undulations generated by local erosion and river floods. These irregularities travel slowly along the shore under the influence of currents and waves arriving at an angle.

(III) Waves at an Angle and Currents Affecting Beaches

Two-dimensional motions are but a mathematical fiction. Waves approaching the shore tend to carry a large amount of water shoreward at the bottom and near the surface. Because of instability due to the interaction of the sea bottom and wave action, the return flow is often concentrated in cells by "*rip currents*" (q.v.). Rip currents are from 200 feet to 1 mile apart, distributed at random or fixed near a special feature such as groynes (groins) perpendicular to the shore (Fig. 3). Because of their speed, as high as 3 ft/sec, they are dangerous to swimmers. "*Beach cusps*" are a series of low mounds of beach material separated by crescent-shaped troughs, averaging 10 feet apart. They are also due to a phenomenon of instability resulting from the interaction of flow motion and movable bed.

The most important three-dimensional effect is due to the fact that in most cases, the waves reach the shore at an angle. The angle of breaking wave crest with the shoreline, α_b, is related to the angle of incident wave in deep water, α_0, by the relationship:

$$\alpha_b \cong \alpha_0\left[0.25 + 5.5\frac{H_0}{L_0}\right]$$

Water in the breaking zone moves approximately in the direction of the incident wave shoreward and on returning in the back-flow, in a direction given by the line of steepest gradient of beach. Thus the motion in this region is serrated and there exists a

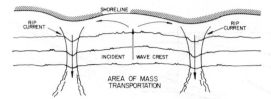

FIG. 3. Distribution of rip currents.

component of mass transport along the shore as seen from Fig. 4. This component is also present before breaking because of the mass transport of water by waves escaping driftward. The wind has also an important effect on the mass transportation effect as shown by Fig. 4. The motion of particles before breaking is roughly a helicycloidal curve.

The average longshore velocity component V_L can be estimated from various semiempirical formulas in terms of α_0 or α_b. For example,

$$V_L \cong c' \left[\frac{sgH_0^2}{T} \sin 2\alpha_0 \right]^{1/3}$$

where c' is a friction coefficient between 1.5 and 3.5 according to bottom roughness, and s is the average beach slope. It is seen that V_L is maximum when $\alpha_0 = 45°$. Again, in terms of α_b:

$$\frac{V_L}{\sqrt{gd_b}} \cong \frac{1}{2} \frac{H_b}{d_b} \sin \alpha_b$$

The variation of longshore velocity current V_L with distance offshore is shown in Fig. 4. This longshore current may also generate rip currents a few thousand feet apart.

The longshore current generates a littoral transportation by suspension in the breaking zone, a serrated bed load transportation in the uprush zone and also a bed load transportation offshore the breaking area. The relative quantity of bed load transportation *versus* transport in suspension depends upon the density and size of material and the turbulence generated by the breaker. The overall phenomenon depends upon the wave steepness as shown qualitatively by Fig. 5.

The total alongshore littoral transport in cubic feet per day is approximately given by the empirical formula (best line of fit)

$$Q = 0.88E^{0.91}D^{0.59} \left(\frac{\rho_f}{\rho_s - \rho_f} \right)^{0.41}$$

where

$E =$ the "alongshore energy" in foot-pounds per day,

$E = E_i \sin 2\alpha_0$ where E_i is the incident wave energy per day,

$D =$ the diameter of sediment in feet,

ρ_f and $\rho_s =$ the density of the fluid and of sand, respectively.

The discharge of sand is also a function of the distance from a fixed obstacle such as capes, headlands, islands, estuaries, groynes and breakwaters.

In most general cases, the shoreline appears as a succession of beaches between obstacles. Between these fixed obstacles, the shoreline changes (to a

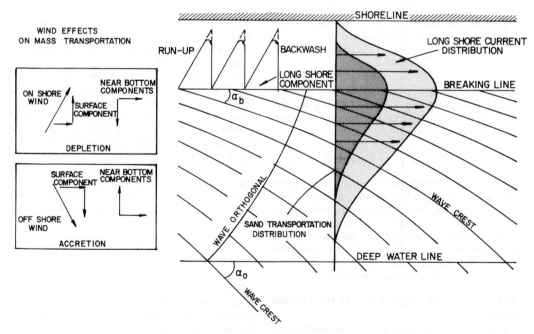

FIG. 4. Longshore transport.

LITTORAL DRIFT
DISCHARGE Q_S

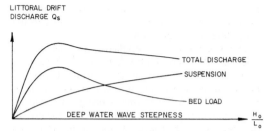

— TOTAL DISCHARGE

— SUSPENSION

— BED LOAD

DEEP WATER WAVE STEEPNESS $\frac{H_o}{L_o}$

FIG. 5. Relationship of bed load to suspension.

geological time scale, a human time scale or a daily scale) with the variation of quantity of material accreting or eroding between such obstacles. Under a given *sea state* (see Vol. I) in a fixed direction, the shoreline evolution is governed by the classical one-dimensional heat equation:

$$\frac{dy}{dt} = KE\frac{d^2y}{dx^2}$$

where K is a constant. The axes ox and oy are parallel and perpendicular to the initial shoreline, respectively.

By imposing boundary conditions (such as due to the construction of groynes perpendicular to the shoreline, for example), the integration gives the shoreline evolution as function of E (Fig. 6).

Many cases of shoreline evolution can be studied by this method, such as due to the sudden dumping in a given point, dunes and benches evolution, erosion or accretion between obstacles, provided α_0 remains smaller than $45°$; beyond that the theory is not valid.

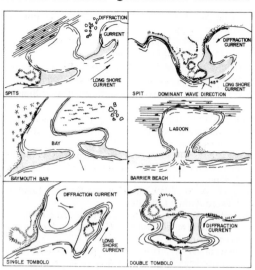

FIG. 7. Typical "singularities" in littoral physiography.

The analysis of other phenomena such as spit, tombolo, is mostly empirical and based upon field observations and laboratory experiments. Figure 7 illustrates some typical singularities which can seldom be subjected to mathematical analysis.

BERNARD LE MÉHAUTÉ

References

Bagnold, R. A., 1946, "Motion of waves in shallow water," *Proc. Roy. Soc. London, Ser. A.*, **187.**

Bascom, W., 1953, "Characteristics of natural beaches," *4th Conf. Coastal Engineering.*

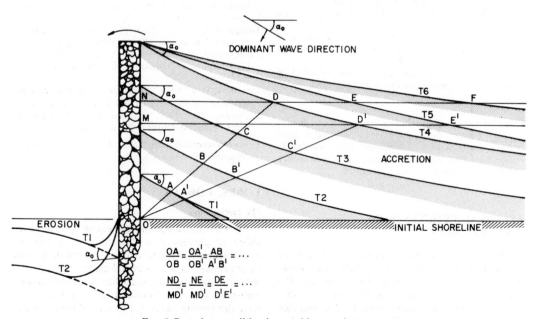

FIG. 6. Boundary condition imposed by a groin (groyne).

Bascom, W., 1964, "Waves and Beaches," Doubleday Anchor, 267pp.

Bruun, P., 1954, "Migration sand waves or sand lumps," *5th Conf. Coastal Engineering.*

Grant, U. S., and Shepard, F. P., 1943, "Waves as a sand transportation agent," *Am. J. Sci.,* **241**(2), 117–123.

I.G.U. Comm. on Coastal Geomorphology, "Bibliography 1959–1963," *Geogr. Danica,* **10**(1), 68pp.

Johnson, J. W., (editor), *Proc. Conf. Coastal Engineering,* Council on Wave Research, University of California (various dates).

Keulegan, G. H., 1948, "An experimental study of submarine sand bars," *U.S. Beach Erosion Bd., Tech. Rpt.,* **3**, 40pp.

King, C. A. M., 1959, "Beaches and Coasts," London, Edward Arnold Ltd., 403pp.

Krumbein, W. C., 1944, "Shore currents and sand movement on a model beach," *U.S. Beach Erosion Bd. Tech. Mem.,* No. 7.

Krumbein, W. C., 1944, "Shore processes and beach characteristics," *U.S. Beach Erosion Bd. Tech. Mem.,* No. 3, 35pp.

Larras, J., 1957, "Plages et Côtes de Sables," Paris, Eyrolles.

Le Méhauté, B. and Koh, R. C. Y., 1967, "On the breaking of waves arriving at an angle to the shore," *J. Hydraulic Res.* No. 1, 67–88.

Longuett-Higgins, M. S., 1953, "Mass transport in water waves," *Proc. Trans. Roy. Soc. London, Ser. A,* **245**, No. 903.

Munk, W. H., Putnam, J. A., and Traylor, M. A., 1949, "The prediction of longshore currents," *Trans. Am. Geophys. Union,* **30**(3), 337–345.

Munk, W. H., and Traylor, M. A., 1947, "Refraction of ocean waves: A process linking underwater topography to beach erosion," *J. Gepl.,* **55**(1), 1–26.

Steers, J. A., 1957, "How are beaches supplied with shingle?" *6th Conf. Coastal Engineering.*

U.S. Beach Erosion Board, Corps of Engineers, *Technical Memorandum,* No. 4, 1961, "Shore protection planning and design."

Van Straaten, L. M. J. U., 1961, "Directional effects of winds, waves and currents along the Dutch North Sea coast," *Geol. Mijnbouw,* **40**, 333–346.

Watts, G. M., 1954, "Laboratory study of effect of varying wave periods on beach profiles," *U.S. Beach Erosion Bd., Tech. Mem.,* No. 53.

Cross-references: *Barriers—Beaches and Islands; Beach; Beach Erosion; Bed Load; Cuspate Foreland or Spit; Rip Current; Sediment Transport; Tombolo.* Vol. I: *Sea State.* Vol. II: *Laminar Flow, Laminar Boundary Layer; Turbulence.*

LITTORAL PROCESSES IN TIDELESS SEAS

There are no essential differences between the littoral processes in tideless and tidal seas. However, in details the following may be noted. The constant water level results in the better development of submarine ridges (*bars,* or *low and ball structures*). Around the Baltic Sea, for instance, they number up to six and extend out to a depth of 9 meters. Sometimes they run strictly parallel to the shore line and to each other.

The beach profile is simplified at the tideless seas. The foreshore berm (ebb tide level) may be absent altogether. The short-term and abrupt changes of beach during storms are not as pronounced as in tidal seas; a narrower zone is being reworked by waves and currents. Benches in tideless seas do not possess the marked steps at the spring and neep tides; also no ramparts have been observed.

Abrasion (q.v.) goes on at a more rapid pace during the youthful stage, because the strongest wave action is confined to a narrow zone. This difference is eliminated, however, at the mature stage of development.

There are no marshes and mud flats around the tideless seas, but in shallow places storm tides create small features which are almost similar, as is the case in the Baltic and Caspian Seas (Leontyev, 1961).

There are no such characteristic features as troughs due to tidal bottom scour in narrow inlets and at the bay mouths.

The investigation of sediment drifting and hydrodynamic processes is, however, made much easier in tideless seas because some of the complications are eliminated. This is why certain new principles of this kind have been established by Soviet scientists working on the littoral zones of the Black Sea, the Caspian Sea and the Baltic Sea (Longinov, 1963).

V. P. Zenkovich

References

Bird, E. C. F., 1965, "A Geomorphological Study of the Gippsland Lakes," *Aust. Nat. Univ., Dept. Geol. Publ. GD1.*

Hough, J. L., 1958, "Geology of the Great Lakes," Urbana, University of Illinois Press, 313pp.

Leontyev, O. K., 1961, "Basis Principles of Sea Shore Geomorphology," Moscow, Moscow University Press (in Russian).

Longinov, V. V., 1963, "Shore-zone Dynamics of Tideless Seas," Moscow, Acad. Sci. U.S.S.R. (in Russian).

Zenkovich, V. P., 1967, "Processes of Coastal Development," London, Oliver & Boyd, 738pp.

Cross-references: *Abrasion; Bars; Beach; Coastal Lagoon Dynamics;* Vol. I: *Tides.*

LOBES, LOBATION

(1) Definitions

Both terms are used in connection with large ice sheets or glaciers of continental size. A *lobe* or, more properly, a *glacial lobe* is a curved projection or appendage of a continental glacier or ice sheet. Whereas the main ice sheet has areal dimensions measured in a few thousand miles, glacial lobes have dimensions measured in several tens of miles or a few hundred miles. Lobation is the development of a lobate form of the ice sheet border as it deploys over a non-mountainous land surface during expanding or advancing stages. This lobate pattern is commonly retained during the shrinking or retreatal stages of the ice.

(2) Use of the Terms

The terms glacial lobe, ice lobe, or lobe are applied to marginal portions of the ice sheets that covered about 30% of the earth's land surface during the "Ice Age" or the Pleistocene Epoch which began about two million years ago. Glacier lobes are not conspicuous features of either the Greenland or Antarctic ice sheets because conditions at their margins are not conducive to their development. Where the borders of these ice sheets roughly coincide with coastal mountain ranges, the ice spills through them in the form of ice rivers called outlet glaciers or ice tongues. In other cases, the ice borders of the Greenland and Antarctic ice sheets terminate as ice cliffs in the ocean or as broad floating ice shelves. Neither condition produces lobation of the ice margin. Incipient lobation probably exists in both Greenland and the Antarctic, but actual lobation will not develop until the ice border withdraws to a position inland, away from the seacoast and coastal mountains, at some unknown future time.

(3) Recognition of the Lobate Margin of Pleistocene Ice Sheets

Scratches and grooves on rock surfaces in areas formerly covered by continental glaciers are evidence that the glacier ice was moving. This deduction has been verified many times by measurements on existing glaciers. While moving, glaciers transport rock fragments and loose earth, some of which becomes lodged at the base of the glacier and some of which is carried to the glacier margin where it is heaped into a belt of mounds and ridges known as an end moraine. Because they are more or less coincident with past ice borders, end moraines permit the reconstruction of the glacier margin since they remain as identifiable topographic features long after the ice has retreated to a new position or has disappeared entirely. The extent and the distribution of the borders of the various lobes of the Pleistocene ice sheet in North America, Europe, and Asia have been determined for different stages of ice retreat. The geographical positions of end moraines plotted on a map (Fig. 1) disclose the size and configuration of the lobes that produced them.

(4) Causes of Lobation

Controlling factors of lobation in Pleistocene ice caps according to Horberg and Anderson (1956) were (a) the preglacial topography over which the ice spread; (b) the configuration of the ice sheet; (c) deflections by adjacent ice lobes. The terrain over which the continental ice sheets spread during the

Pleistocene had been subject to a long erosional history which, in the Great Lakes area and the northeastern states, may have lasted for over 100 million years. The bedrock configuration of the preglacial land surface shows a close correspondence between the glacial lobes and bedrock lowlands. In the late nineteenth century, the American geologist T. C. Chamberlin (1888) recognized ". . . that a broad depression, reaching well backward along the lines of glacial movement, was effective in producing prolongation of the ice. . . ." The effect of ice cap configuration (i.e., thickness, centers of snow accumulation, surface topography of the ice) and deflections by adjacent ice lobes are difficult, if not impossible, to evaluate because both factors are dependent on conditions that no longer prevail.

(5) Glacial Lobes and the Origin of the Great Lakes

The coincidence of major Pleistocene glacier lobes with the basins of the Great Lakes (Fig. 1) led some geologists to the conclusion that the lake basins themselves were the product of profound glacial scour. Others believed that the major depressions containing the lakes were produced by Tertiary stream erosion and that scour by glacial lobes was only of secondary influence in their origin (see Wayne and Zumberge, 1965, for a discussion of the evidence bearing on this problem).

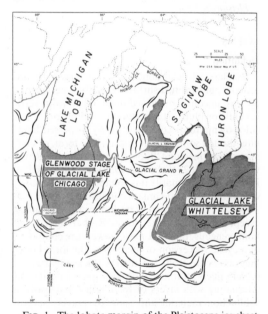

FIG. 1. The lobate margin of the Pleistocene ice sheet about 13,000 years ago and the end moraines (heavy black lines) which show earlier positions of the ice margin. Glacial Lakes Chicago, Saginaw, and Whittlesey occupied areas formerly covered by the Lake Michigan lobe, Saginaw lobe, and the Huron-Erie lobe (Wayne and Zumberge, 1965). (By permission of Princeton Univ. Press.)

Thick layers of glacial debris discovered on the bottom of Lake Superior show that the Superior lobe actually deposited material in the depression occupied by the lake rather than deepened it by scour. Whether similar evidence exists in other lakes is not yet known.

J. H. ZUMBERGE

References

Chamberlin, T. C., 1888, "The rock-scorings of the great ice age," *U.S. Geol. Survey, 7th Ann. Rept.,* 155–254.

Flint, R. F., 1957, "Glacial and Pleistocene Geology," pp. 131–133, New York, John Wiley & Sons.

Flint, R. F., Colton, R. B., Goldthwait, R. P., and Willman, H. B., 1959, "Glacial Map of the United States East of the Rocky Mountains," Geological Society of America.

*Horberg, L., and Anderson, R. C., 1956, "Bedrock topography and Pleistocene glacial lobes in central United States," *J. Geol.,* **64,** 101–115.

Wayne, W. J., and Zumberge, J. H., 1965, "Pleistocene Geology of Indiana and Michigan," in "Quaternary of the United States," Part I, pp. 63–84, Princeton, N.J., Princeton Univ. Press.

* Additional bibliographic references may be found in this work.

Cross-references: *Glacial Scour; Great Lakes (North America); Moraine.* Vol. II: *Ice Age Theory.* pr Vol. VI: *Glaciers; Glaciology; Ice Sheet.* pr Vol. VII: *Pleistocene Epoch.*

LOESS

Definition

By classical definition, loess is a largely homogeneous, unstratified silt. It is usually a permeable, porous, unconsolidated sediment apt to form vertical cliffs or bluffs. It is commonly yellow or buff in color owing to its content of finely dispersed limonite, though sometimes it is gray. The term, of German origin, meaning "loose" was used in the Rhine valley about 1821 (Scheidig, 1934) and employed by Lyell in 1834. Primarily it is eolian, and is associated with proglacial arid climate conditions.

Today this definition is no longer fully accepted except for typical (true) loess. Rather than being homogeneous, the thick *loess packets* are composed of a cyclic succession of members. The loess layers themselves are from 1–5 meters thick, unstratified or very finely stratified, with loess-like deposits and alternating with layers of fossil soil ("paleosols"), solifluction material and sand or gravel. Several variants and facies of the loess are known also regionally, which together constitute the *loess series.*

Lately, the term "(typical) loess" has assumed a double meaning in its geological sense, for it implies both a well-defined lithology and a well-defined genesis, whereas in engineering practice the lithological interpretation is meant without any genetic connotation. Whichever way it is defined, loess is unquestionably an ice age facies. No pre-Pleistocene loess is known.

Grain Size Distribution

In typical loess, which is only moderately well sorted, loosely coherent grains from 0.01–0.05 millimeters in diameter form the dominant grain size fraction which is also called "loess fraction." Grain size analyses by various methods gave 40–50% as the mean abundance of this fraction. Further it may contain 5–30% of clay-size particles (below 0.005 millimeter) and 5–10% of sand particles (above 0.25 millimeter). In loess-like deposits, either the clayey or the sandy fraction or both may be enriched at the expense of the loess fraction.

The origin of this grain size distribution peculiar to loess is attributed by different schools of thought to: (1) sorting by the depositing medium, which may be either air or water, (2) the coagulation of clay particles, (3) the comminution of rock debris down to a certain grain size limit. The formation of a certain amount of the loess may further be due to pedogenic processes such as podzolization.

The particles of the loess fraction consist mostly of quartz grains and are largely due to comminution by insolation and frost. These processes produced particularly large volumes of dust in the regions of both hot and cold arid climates; in most cases, this dust was then transported and redeposited once more (or repeatedly) by exogenic processes. In the various loess areas, the proportion of quartz grains to clay particles that are coagulated to form silt-size grains, differs widely as a function of the mechanical and climatic conditions of accumulation as well as of the nature and abundance of the cementing material. Aggregates of clay particles are quite naturally likely to predominate in loesses containing abundant clay. The coagulation of the clay particles may take place either in the course of deposition or during diagenesis or epigenesis (epidiagenesis); it is promoted by the presence of Al and Fe, and to a lesser degree, Ca and Mg cations.

The *mineralogical composition* of loess is fairly uniform all over the world, local deviations being due to differences in grain size and area of origin. The main constituents are quartz, ranging in abundance from 40–80%, with a mean of about 65%; feldspar, from 10–20%; and calcium and magnesium carbonates, from 0–35%. The sand fraction (above 0.25 millimeters) consists largely of quartz; the silt fraction is composed of quartz, feldspar, carbonates and heavy minerals, whereas in the finest fractions the clay minerals tend to outweigh the clastic element. As a result of various combinations of physico-chemical and colloidal processes, clay minerals can form authigenically in the loess either simultaneously with or subsequent to the deposition.

The heavy-mineral assemblage of loess provides us with information as to the nature of the area of origin of the silt fraction. Accordingly, if the parent rock of the heavy minerals lies a considerable distance away, the heavy-mineral association may be quite exotic; alternatively it may be quite close by, or even within the loess area.

To explain the substantial fraction of *carbonates* in loess, various hypotheses have been put forward: (1) the abundance of carbonates is primary, in either the accumulated dust or the underlying formation; (2) they are due to geochemical or organic processes; (3) there has been a combination of various factors acting at different times during the evolution of the loess deposit.

$CaCO_3$ and $MgCO_3$ may be present in a variety of forms such as concretions of various size, typical nodules (so-called *Loess Kindchen, Männchen, Pupen*), layers of lime accumulations such as limestone bands, and *caliche*, underlying fossil soil horizons or overlying impermeable layers, further in incrustations and membranes, granules and powdery spots, etc. All the above-mentioned forms are secondary, being due to the concentration of migrating lime-bearing solutions. Primary forms of lime include minute grains, incrustations on silt-size grain aggregates and snail shells.

The carbonate content of loess and the forms in which it is present are mainly functions of geographical environment, particularly of precipitation and relief. In dry regions, the lime content is generally higher, and there are more horizons of lime accumulation than in the loess areas with heavier rainfall, whereas the clay mineral content exhibits a contrary trend. In some loess areas, the carbonates may have been removed by subsequent leaching.

The porosity peculiar to loess is believed to be due to a number of factors such as the electrical charge of the grains about to be deposited, the activity of animals and plants, the distribution and redistribution of carbonates, and finally, but not least to frost action.

Distribution and Occurrence of Loess

Loess and loess-like deposits form a blanket 1–100 meters thick over about one-tenth of all land surfaces in the world, being particularly widespread in the marginal semiarid zones of the great deserts, e.g., in Asia, as well as in the temperate zones and the adjacent areas e.g., in North America and Europe. Particularly excluded are the equatorial tropics and those continental regions which were covered by inland ice during the last glacial period.

The particular importance of loess in economic geography rests on the fact that most of the world's best agricultural soils are developed over loess-type deposits, and further in its soil mechanical behavior which makes it something of a problem in foundation engineering.

Loess occurs over a variety of relief forms. It is most widespread in *plains* (q.v.), both of abrasion and accumulation, e.g., the North American prairie belt, the Russian Plains, the basins of the Mississippi, Hoang Ho, La Plata and Danube valleys, etc. According to the geographical environment, various sandy and clayey types of loess, such as the flood plain, alluvial-fan and plateau types of loess, may alternate both horizontally and vertically with true loess. A similar alternation of loess with wind-blown sand is fairly often observed. Interfluve ridges and flat-topped divides as well as the terraced valley flanks of *pediment regions* are also typical areas of loess accumulation.

Loess and loess-like deposits on mountain slopes, in intramontane basins, on valley flanks and pediments exhibit a considerable variety with regard to both composition and vertical distribution, i.e., absolute altitude. The loess blankets of hills and mountains tend to increase in thickness toward the bottom of the slopes and to split into several (cyclic) units, each containing layers of different genesis and grain size distribution. A further observation of fairly general validity is that the abundance of both the clayey fraction and coarse detritus (the latter occurring in well-defined layers or randomly scattered) tends to increase from the basin toward the mountains, at the expense of the true loess or silt fraction.

The percentage of the finer loess particles and clay mineral grains tends to increase toward the more elevated parts of the loess-covered region on the one hand, and with increasing distance from the source of the dust, on the other. This phenomenon is attributed to the gradual decrease of the carrying capacity of the wind with increasing distance from the area of deflation. However, other factors may also be involved: e.g., loess tends to grow finer from the semiarid zones toward the more humid regions, owing to the enrichment of the clay fraction in the wetter environment. This is particularly evident in closed basins such as the Columbia River Basin of the American northwest or the Carpathian Basin of central Europe, where sandy loess or typical loess is predominant in the central part of the basin, but changes into the adobe and clayey varieties toward the basin margin.

Classification and Genesis

Loess has been classified according to several different points of view, but a comprehensive system is still lacking.

The most comprehensive classification is that according to *grain size distribution*. On this basis, *typical loess* is distinguished from *loess-like deposits* such as sandy loess, loess loam or adobe, clayey loess, etc. These terms bear no genetic connotation. Loess and loess-like deposits are fairly often classified according to their genesis, mostly in some combination with the classification according to grain size.

A further basis of classification may be the distinction between the "fossil," Pleistocene *glacial loess* which covers most of the loess areas, and Recent dust accumulations, the so-called *continental loess*.

According to their orographic position and particular lithologic associations, *plains loess, platform loess, hill loess* and *mountain loess* are sometimes distinguished.

A prerequisite to any genetic classification is the knowledge of the origin of loess which has, however, been a much-discussed subject for over a century.

Opinions as to the processes bringing about the formation and accumulation of the dust fraction forming the basic material of loess are widely divergent. Most authors agree, however, that the process of evolution which turns the dust into loess is a diagenetic one. The diagenetic process is interpreted in a number of different ways: Some consider it a siallite-carbonate type of weathering process leading up to a loess loam enriched in alkali cations which then turns into loess owing to steppe-type pedogenic processes involving leaching of Na and K and enrichment of Ca and Mg carbonate. The diagenesis is contingent upon certain environmental conditions. Optimum conditions of loessification are considered to prevail in the steppe zone marginal to the deserts and to have prevailed in the cold-steppe and wooded-steppe zones of the Pleistocene periglacial regions. This is borne out by periglacial phenomena, plant and animal remains, human artifacts, etc., preserved in the loess, and is compatible with the paleoecological conditions reconstructed from all the available evidence. Under any conditions that differ, more or less, from the steppe environment, the original dust material became turned into a *loess-like deposit* such as mountain loess, a loam or adobe, clay, etc., rather than a true loess.

Whenever the optimum conditions of loess building deteriorated, the epidiagenetic alteration of the loess took over. In this way, the layers of loess formed over numbers of episodes (semiarid, cold cycles) in the Pleistocene periglacial regions, and today constitute complex loess profiles, having been repeatedly altered and redeposited under a succession of different climatic phases. Their original characteristics are thus understandably difficult to reconstruct.

This is why the usual statement that typical loess is unstratified and eolian in origin cannot be taken as an unambiguous generalization. For a number of loess-like loams it is impossible to tell today whether these formations represent a syngenetic type of regional connotation or an epidiagenetic facies of loess.

The various theories put forward to explain the origin of loess and particularly the accumulation of its basic material number at least fifty. The divergences between the views are largely due to differences between the loess areas studied by the authors. The most generally favored hypotheses are the following.

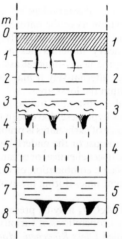

FIG. 1. Generalized profile of the phases of loess and slope deposit formation between two fossil soil horizons of the last glaciation (PÉCSI). (1) Fossil steppe soil (chernosem) from whose lower part a polygonal pattern of lime-filled cracks extends down to a depth of 1.5 to 2 meters. (2) Rhythmically stratified slope loess or sandy loess. Sediment deposited from slopewash. Little precipitation in early summer, considerable amount of snow, periodically frozen subsoil. (3) Finely stratified slope loess, with a slightly cryoturbated structure. Deposited by solifluction in the course of a wet cold "atlantic" spell of climate. (4) Unstratified typical loess. Deposited out of the air in the driest, coldest spell of the continental climate. (5) Stratified slope loess, substituted locally by likewise stratified loessy slope wash soil (loessy semipedolite). The deposition occurred by pluvionivational slope wash at the beginning phase of the cold stadial. (6) Fossil forest soil (or wooded steppe soil). Developed under a warm humid forest climate. The forest was exterminated by the gradual cooling of the climate. In the upper part of the forest soil traces of cryoturbation are locally observed. (Profiles like this may be repeated up to 10 times, within the same section in certain favored spots, e.g., in Moravia).

(1) *The eolian theory*: A majority of the authors consider loess a formation of largely eolian origin, transported and deposited by the wind. The eolian theory was developed by Virlet d'Aoust, F. von Richthofen and V. A. Obruchev.

Winds during glacial times undoubtedly played a major role in the transportation of the dust and sand-size grains; in the Pleistocene periglacial periods, this eolian activity covered much larger regions than today. This is confirmed also by the widespread wind-blown sand dunes, innumerable ventifacts and thin layers of volcanic ash. However, although the loesses formed by eolian accumulation, particularly the typical loess of the plateaus, cover fairly vast regions, there is abundant evidence for accumulation by other sedimentary processes. These other facies occur intercalated in the loess series as well as independently in space.

(2) On the slopes of hilly or mountainous areas,

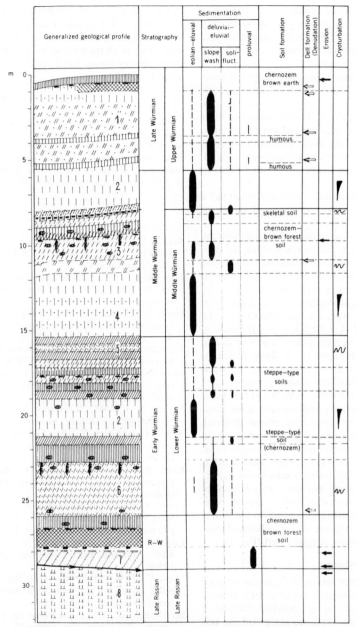

FIG. 2. Generalized profile showing the division of Upper Pleistocene loess deposits (Pécsi, 1965). ⇒—areal denudation, phases of derasional valley scooping; →—linear dissection, phase of erosional valley sculpture; ∿ — processes of solifluction; ▼—probable episodes of frostwedge and frost-crack formation;⊸⨍⊸⨍—animal burrows, wasp holes; 1—Sandy slope loess, loamy in places; 2—Loess; 3—Slope loess; 4—Sandy loess; 5—Semipedolite; 6—Sandy slope loess; 7—Proluvial sand; 8—Old loess.

the dusts deposited from the air were, in the opinion of several workers, reworked and deposited into their present position by *sheetwash* and *meltwaters*. This type of loess which exhibits a rhythmic stratification parallel to the slope of the topography is held to be of *niveolian* (*eolian-nivational*) or *eolian-pluvionivational* origin. Such loesses are sometimes categorized under the title *deluvial loess* (Pavlov). Several authors are of the opinion that the loess-like deposits redeposited by solifluction over a frozen subsoil should also be classed here.

(3) On suitable slopes, a loess-like *colluvium* might have accumulated by downslope creep and have gained a loess-like aspect by diagenesis according to the opinion of R. J. Russell.

(4) Sandy and clayey loess-like deposits cover appreciable areas on valley straths, flood plains and alluvial fans. Detailed studies have proved beyond doubt the fluvial origin of these formations. Their widespread distribution prompted some workers to develop the *theory of the fluvial origin of loess* (e.g., Willis). It would, however, be erroneous to generalize this idea to explain the origin of other kinds of loess deposit.

(5) It was a similar consideration which had half a century earlier led to the *fluvioglacial theory* of Lyell.

(6) The *pedogenic-eluvial theory* is based upon the irrefutable fact that in most loess profiles, the products of pedogenic processes, ranging from vague traces to well-developed fossil soil horizons, may be recognized. In this line of reasoning, loess is a dry, periglacial or warm, semiarid steppe soil, the latter of the brown-earth type. The accumulation of the dust fraction could thus be taken as the result of various processes, but it could just as well be due to eluvial comminution *in situ* (L. S. Berg, R. Gannsen). However, this leaves unexplained the thick and complex loess blankets of some regions.

(7) According to the *polygenetic theory*, the basic material of loess may have accumulated as the result of any of the following processes: eolian, deluvial, fluvial, proluvial, fluvioglacial, gravitational, eluvial and pedogenic. In different areas and periods, these processes may have acted in different combinations. The dust fraction constituting a substantial part of the thick loess blankets and consisting largely of typical loess was transported into its present position by eluvial and deluvial processes. In the course of loessification, pedogenic and geochemical processes have undoubtedly played a part (Fig. 1).

Chronological Subdivision

Radiocarbon dating has in the last few decades lent considerable impetus to the evolution of loess chronology, although the radiocarbon method is limited to dating the loess· sequences of the last glaciation only. The detailed stratigraphic analysis of the loess profiles incorporating the largest number of fossil soil horizons and the greatest variety of loess types has revealed that, both in Eurasia and North America, the loess series can relatively easily be subdivided in two main sequences: the *younger loess series* which does not show traces of any appreciable alteration, and the underlying *older loess series* of substantially altered dark-yellow or reddish loess-like adobe. The younger series constitutes the larger part of the loess blanket. It is of Last Glacial age, whereas the older series represents an incomplete sequence of earlier Pleistocene formations. Up

to ten such cycles have been demonstrated in Moravia (Kukla, Ložek and Zaruba, 1961, etc.). The older series may attain considerable thickness locally and is characterized by numerous reddish-brown clayey-loamy fossil soil horizons which are almost coalescent.

MÁRTON PÉCSI

[*Note*: In Europe, the term *eluvium* refers to rotted rock (saprolite) or sometimes just to the leached "A" horizon; *deluvium* is slope material, creep deposits, talus, etc., usually transported under periglacial conditions; *proluvium* is applied to mudflow and flash flood deposits of a bajada-type alluvial fan. R.W.F.]

References

Berg, L. S., 1964, "Loess as a Product of Weathering and Soil Formation," Jerusalem, I.P.S.T., 207pp., (translated from Russian).

Flint, R. F., 1957, "Glacial and Pleistocene Geology," pp. 181–194, 352–354, 408–411, New York, John Wiley & Sons.

Ganssen. R., 1922, "Die Entstehung und Herkunft des Löss, *Mitt. Laborat. Preuss. Geol. Landesanst. Berlin*, **4.**

Gerasimov, I. P., 1962, "Lessoobrazovanie i pochvoobrazovanie," *Izv. Akad. Nauk SSSR Ser. Geol.*, No. 2.

Gerasimov, I. P., 1964, "Loess genesis and soil formation," *Rept. VI Int. Congr. Quaternary (Warsaw*, 1961), **4,** 463–468.

Kriger, N. I., 1965, "Less, yego svoystva i svyaz' s geograficheskoy sredoy," Moscow. Nauka, 295pp.

Kukla, J. and Ložek, V., 1961, "Loesses and related deposits," *Instytut Geologiczny, Warszawa, Prace*, **34**(1), 11–28.

Kukla, J., Ložek, V., and Záruba, Q., 1961, "Zur Stratigraphie der Lösse in der Tschechoslovakei," *Quartär (Bonn)*, **13,** 1–29.

Ložek, V., 1965, "The relationship between the development of soils and faunas in the warm Quaternary phases," *Anthropozoikum (Praha)*, **3,** 7–51.

Lugn, A. L., 1962, "The origin and sources of loess," *Univ. Nebraska Studies (Lincoln, Neb.)*, N.S. **26,** 105pp.

Lyell, C., 1834, "Observations on the loamy deposit called "Loess" of the basin of the Rhine," *Edinburgh New Philosoph. J.*, **17,** No. 33–34.

Merzbacher, G., 1913, "Die Frage der Entstehung des Lösses," *Pet. Geogr. Mitt. Gotha*, **59.**

Obruchev, V. A., 1945, "Loess types and their origin," *Am. J. Sci.*, **243**(5).

Pavlov, A. P., 1888, "Geneticheskie tipy materikovykh obrazovaniy lednikovoy i poslelednikovoy epokhi," *Izv. Geol. Kom. Moscow*, 243–263.

Pécsi, M., 1965, "Genetic classification of the deposits constituting the loess profiles of Hungary," *Acta Geol. Hung., Budapest*, **9**(1–2), 65–84.

Richthofen, F., 1877, "China," Vol. I, Berlin.

Russell, R. J., 1944, "Lower Mississippi valley loess," *Bull. Geol. Soc. Am.*, **55,** 1–40.

Scheidig, A., 1934, "Der Löss und seine geotechnischen Eigenschaften," Dresden–Leipzig, Th. Steinkopf, 233pp.

Willis, B., 1907, "Quaternary Huang-tu formation Northwestern China," in "Research in China," Vol. I, Part 1, Washington.

Cross-references: *Cryopedology, etc.; Deflation; Glacial Spillways and Proglacial Lakes; Nivation; Periglacial Eolian Effects; Plains; Quaternary Period; Terraces—Fluvial; Wind Action.* Vol. II: *Ice Age Meteorology.* Vol. VI: *Adobe; Caliche; Diagenesis; Engineering Geology of Loess; Grain-size Studies; Paleopedology; Podzol.*

LONGITUDINAL VALLEYS, STREAMS—*See* DRAINAGE PATTERNS; RIVERS; STRUCTURAL CONTROL IN GEOMORPHOLOGY

LONGSHORE DRIFT—*See* BEACH; BEACH EROSION

LOUDERBACK

The louderback, or, more precisely, the louderback lava flow, is a term proposed by W. M. Davis (1930) for a lava flow isolated from its source by faulting, such as is seen in numbers of places in the block-faulting of the Basin-Range Province of Nevada, Utah, Arizona, and adjacent states. An older topographic surface is preserved by the flow itself, and where base level has been lowered, the louderback stands out as a special type of lava-capped mesa, coulee or abutment. Since the original flow would normally have filled a valley, the louderback is usually also a form of inverted topography, for the old valley is now on the mesa and the present valley system represents a diversion to one side or the other.

The name "louderback" was proposed by Davis (1930, p. 299) in recognition of George D. Louderback whose work (1923) first brought out the special relationship of the lava flows to block-faulting in the Basin-Range and Great Basin areas. (The block-faulting, early recognized by Gilbert and Powell, had been denied in the early part of the century by Keyes and others.) Referring specifically to the Humboldt Range, Louderback (1923, p. 349) wrote: "It is important to note that the distribution and relation of the basalt prove that the block-faulting which has accompanied the uplift of these ranges and produced the scarps whose dissection yielded the present mountain fronts was entirely post-basaltic." On the other hand, Douglas Johnson (1930) sketches a basalt flow that is unquestionably younger than the faulting, but older than the resurrection of the fault-line scarp.

FIG. 1. One of the small louderbacks at eastern base of Peacock Range, looking south (Davis, 1930).

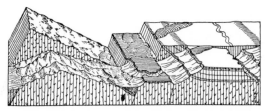

FIG. 2. Block diagram of the Peacock Range, Arizona showing potential forms of the Peacock Range tilted fault block, evenly uplifted Truxton fault block and western part of Arizona plateau in background, and their actual forms in foreground. Louderbacks are seen in the mid-foreground (Davis, 1930).

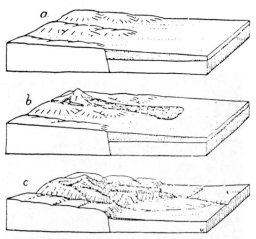

FIG. 3. An unfaulted example of a resurrected basin-range lava stream (Johnson, 1930).

Thornbury specifically lists louderbacks as one of the diagnostic criteria for fault scarps. A fine oblique air photo of a louderback is reproduced in Thornbury (1965, p. 481).

RHODES W. FAIRBRIDGE

References

Davis, W. M., 1930, "The Peacock Range, Arizona," *Bull. Geol. Soc. Am.*, **41**, 293–313.

Johnson, D. W., 1930, "Geomorphologic aspects of rift valleys," *Intern. Geol. Congr., 15th, South Africa, 1929, Compt. Rend.*, **2**, 354–373.

Louderback, G. D., 1923, "Basin-Range structure in the Great Basin," *Univ. Calif. Publ., Geol. Sci.*, **14**(10), 329–376.

Thornbury, W. D., 1965, "Regional Geomorphology of the United States," New York, John Wiley & Sons, 609pp.

Cross-references: *Fault Scarp; Inversion of Topography.* pr Vol. VIII: *Basin-Range Province.*

LOW AND BALL—*See* BARS

LYNCHET—*See* TERRACETTE

M

MAAR

The term *maar*, from the Rhineland dialect, refers to the volcanic craters of the Eifel, Germany, area. A maar, however, is a special type of volcanic crater which originates by repeated, intermittent gas venting and coring (Shoemaker, 1956; Reeves and DeHon, 1965). Lakes in maare may be termed

FIG. 1. Crater lake of youthful cinder cone within the large maar lake basin of Zuni Salt Lake, 120 miles west-south-west of Albuquerque, New Mexico. It carries 36‰ Na and 54‰ Cl, presumably leached from Permian salt in the basement. (Photo: R. W. Fairbridge.)

FIG. 2. Zuni Salt Lake, New Mexico. A maar depression or diatreme, complicated by gravitational collapse, exposing crater walls of Cretaceous sandstone and shale. A later (Quaternary) eruptive phase introduced two cinder cones into the depression. Pluvial lake (freshwater) deposits rise to 15 meters above present lake floor. (Photo: R. W. Fairbridge).

"maar lakes," but the term maar does not come from the lake even though *ubehebe* has been proposed for maare without interior lakes (Cotton, 1952).

The developmental history of a maar begins with an initial explosive venting which creates a diatreme (Daubrée, 1891). The brecciated pieces of country rock and volcanic debris fall as a low, narrow encircling rim. Intermittent gas venting and coring of decreasing intensity enlarge the crater and build the surrounding rim, lahars occurring because of slope, predominance of fine-grained clastics, and condensation of the volcanic gases. Slumping of the maar walls, combined with normal erosive backwasting, contemporaneously destroy the tuff rim and enlarge the crater. A final stage of lava extrusion or cinder cone development within the maar may occur. Maare therefore characteristically exhibit: (1) rims of cross-bedded volcanic ejecta with accretionary lapilli and large blocks of country rock, and (2) related lava flows and/or cones.

Maare sometimes resemble calderas, but calderas originate mainly by subsidence of a volcanic pile rather than by the combination of intermittent extrusion and slumping of the crater-wall rock. A late phase subsidence is, however, characteristic of some maare. Maare are smaller than calderas, diameters generally ranging from several hundred

to several thousand feet, depths from rim crests to the central lakes or playas usually of a few hundred feet. The inner walls tend to be steep, especially if associated lava flows are present, but the outer rims imperceptibly merge with surrounding topography.

For authoritative studies of ancient maare and related features see Viete (1952, Libya), Shoemaker (1956, Arizona), Hopmann, Frechen and Knetsch (1956, Eifel, Germany), and Jahns (1959, Mexico). Müller and Veyl (1957) have documented the actual origin and formation of a maar. Reeves and DeHon (1965) and DeHon and Reeves (1966) illustrate the association of maare in southern New Mexico and northwestern Chihuahua, Mexico, with regional tectonics.

C. C. REEVES, JR.

References

Cotton, C. A., 1952, "Volcanoes as Landscape Forms," New York, John Wiley & Sons, 416pp.

Darton, N. H., 1905, "The Zuni Salt Lake," *J. Geol.*, 13(3), 185–193.

Daubrée, A., 1891, "Recherches expérimentales sur le role possible des gaz a hautes températures, doués de très fortes pressions et animés d'un mouvement fort rapide, dans divers phénomènes géologiques," *Bull. Soc. Géol. France*, **19**, 313–354.

DeHon, R. A., and Reeves, C. C., Jr., 1966, "A maar origin for Hunts Hole, Dona Ana County, New Mexico", *Texas J. Sci.* **18**, 296–316.

Hopmann, M., Frechen, J., and Knetsch, G., 1956, "Die vulkanische Eifel," Bonn, W. Stollfuss Verlag, 143pp.

Jahns, R. H., 1959, "Collapse depressions of the Pinacate volcanic field, Sonora, Mexico," *Arizona Geol. Soc. Guidebook*, **2**, 165–184.

Müller, G., and Veyl, G., 1957, "The birth of Niahue, a new maar type volcano at Rininahue, Chile," *XX Intern. Geol. Congr. Rept., Sec. 1*, 375–396.

Reeves, C. C., Jr., and DeHon. R. A., 1965, "Geology of Potrillo Maar, New Mexico and northern Chihuahua, Mexico," *Am. J. Sci.*, **263**, 401–409.

Schoemaker, E. M., 1956, "Occurrence of uranium in diatremes on the Navajo and Hope reservations, Arizona, New Mexico, and Utah," in "Contributors to the geology of uranium and thorium by the U.S. Geological Survey and Atomic Energy Commission for the United Nations International Conference on Peaceful Uses of Atomic Energy, Geneva, Switzerland, 1955," *U.S. Geol. Surv. Profess. Paper* **300**, 179–183.

Shoemaker, E. M., 1962, "Interpretation of Lunar Craters," in (Kopal, Z., editor) "Physics and Astronomy of the Moon," New York, Academic Press, 538pp.

Viete, G., 1952, "Geologie und Mondoberfläche," *Bergakad*, Freiberg, **4**, p. 470–482.

Cross-references: *Caldera; Crater; Crater Lakes; Mudflow; Volcanic Landscapes; Volcanic Necks and Diatremes.*

MAKATEA

A "makatea" means an annular rocky wall around an unusual type of coral island, encountered only in a few places in the Pacific Ocean. The word is Polynesian, meaning "white rock". Specifically, geologists use the term makatea to mean an uplifted atoll or high barrier reef ring around an uplifted island; loosely it may apply in the South Pacific to any white, karst-affected limestone surface.

One particular island (situated at 15°50′ S, 148°16′ W, in the Tuamotu group 130 miles northeast of Tahiti) is called Makatea (or Aurora) and may be taken as the prototype of an uplifted reef island. It is shaped like a crescent, 5 × 3 miles across. It lies on a peculiar great circle line of uplifted islands, extending WNW–ESE across the Pacific. The oldest exposed rocks on Makatea seem to be Eocene (Wilson, 1963, p. 593). The island rises on all sides from very deep water with a fringing reef about 300–900 feet wide, bounded in the inner side by an abrupt or overhanging cliff of ancient coral limestone, which forms a bare rocky terrace around the island. To the inside again, there is a second cliff, 60–80 feet high, and a second rocky terrace. Within this ring-wall is a moat-like depression, occupied by a rich soil, encircling the central part of the island which is a steep flat-topped hill rising to about 600 feet, with a hard volcanic clay on top.

Another example of a makatea is at Mangaia (21°55′ S, 157°55′ W, in the Cook Islands), where there is a similar emerged limestone terrace, 70 feet high, locally with some intermediate steps. The terrace surface is a deeply etched karst ("karrenfeld"), with pinnacles 15 feet high, alternating with deep crevices, partly filled with red soil, all overgrown by tropical jungle. This terrace borders a depression that seems to be an emerged lagoon, which in turn surrounds an extinct volcanic cone. The elevated rim was denied to be of barrier origin by Hoffmeister (1930), but comparison with other examples supports the first interpretation.

Yet another example is at Atiu (20°2′ S, 158°7′ W, also in the Cook Islands) where the first makatea ring averages 3500 feet across, but not over 20 feet in height. It then rises gently to 70 feet and subsequently drops off gently to a swampy "moat" about 0–20 feet above sea level; this is the rich soil belt again and is used for taro cultivation (Marshall, 1930).

A fourth example is in the northwestern Pacific,

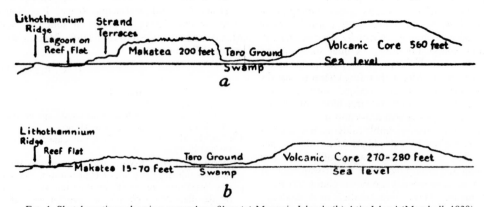

FIG. 1. Sketch sections showing general profiles: (a) Mangaia Island; (b) Atiu Island (Marshall, 1930).

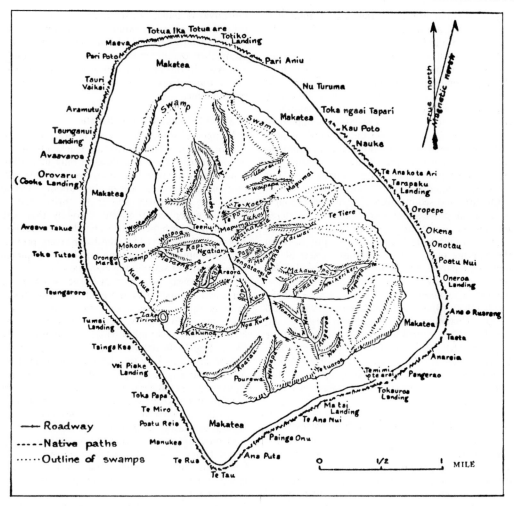

FIG. 2. Map of Atiu Island: outline survey by H. M. Connal (1911); physiographic features by Patrick Marshall (1927).

where Kita Daito Jima (25°56′ N, 131°18′E) represents a perfect uplifted atoll lagoon (now dry) fringed by an annular terrace in several steps. With it, constituting the Kita Oagari or Borodino Islands, are Minami Daito Jima and Okino Daito Jima, which are similar. The entire rock surfaces are pockmarked by karst depressions, those in the former lagoons being partly waterfilled (Saplis and Flint, 1949; Fairbridge, 1950).

RHODES W. FAIRBRIDGE

References

Fairbridge, R. W., 1950, "Landslide patterns on oceanic volcanoes and atolls," *Geograph. J.,* **115,** 84–88.

Hoffmeister, J. E., 1930, "Erosion of elevated fringing coral reefs," *Geol. Mag.,* **67,** 549–554.

Marshall, P., 1927, "Geology of Mangaia," *B. P. Bishop Mus. Bull.,* No. 36, 48pp.

Marshall, P., 1930, "Geology of Rarotonga and Atiu," *B. P. Bishop Mus. Bull.,* No. 72, 75pp.

Saplis, R. A., and Flint, D. E., 1949, "Ramparts on the elevated atoll of Kita Daito Jima," *Bull. Geol. Soc. Am.,* **60,** 1974 (Abs.).

Wilson, J. T., 1963, "Pattern of uplifted islands in the main ocean basins," *Science,* **139,** 592–594.

Cross-references: *Atoll; Coral Reef; Islands; Limestone Coastal Weathering.* Vol. I: *Pacific Ocean.*

MANGROVE SWAMPS: GEOLOGY AND SEDIMENTOLOGY

Mangrove swamps are tidally submerged coastal woodlands. They are the modern counterpart of the marine and brackish-water coal swamps that covered vast areas of the continents during the latter part of the Paleozoic era.

Geological studies of modern mangrove swamps are important because they provide information on the development of ancient coastal swamps and criteria for the recognition of their sedimentary deposits. However, owing to the remoteness (tropical shores) and complexity of mangrove swamps and the difficult working conditions (e.g., malodorous mud, high humidity and air temperature, biting insects, tropical diseases, impenetrable swamp vegetation), mangrove swamps have not received the attention their importance warrants.

Quantitative sedimentological and geochemical data on mangrove swamps are sparse and scattered throughout zoological, botanical, ecological and geological literature. There is no synoptic work on the geology of mangrove swamps. A few of the important papers which treat and give additional references to the geology and sedimentology of mangrove swamps are those by Freise (1938), Davis (1940), Brelie and Teichmuller (1953), Weyl (1953), Chapman and Ronaldson (1958), and Scholl (1963, and 1964/65). Additional data can be found in Hedgpeth (1957). Useful but more biological papers are those by Watson (1928), Thorne (1954), West (1956), and Tabb, Dubrow and Manning (1962). West (1956) cites extensive bibliographies.

Geological History and Geographical Distribution

Mangrove trees had evolved by the Middle Cretaceous and hence have fringed tropical shores for the last 120,000,000 years. Mangroves existed throughout most of the Cenozoic around the Gulf of Mexico and the Caribbean (Davis, 1940). Some comments on fossil mangrove swamps have been made by Weyl (1953).

In general, mangrove swamps do not occur in latitudes higher than the thirtieth parallels since mangroves are killed by frost. Details of the global pattern are given by Guppy (1906), and Ridley (1930), who also discuss the special dispersal characteristic (viviparous seed separation, etc.). The global distribution of mangroves is shown on maps by West (1956) and McGill (1958).

Botany

Mangroves are trees, although some shrubs are also called mangroves. All mangroves are salt tolerant (halophytic). In large mangrove forests, trees measuring 100–120 feet high and 2–3 feet in diameter are not uncommon; however, most swamps are composed of smaller trees.

Mangroves of the western hemisphere are composed of about six species that belong to four major genera; these genera are *Rhizophora*, the red mangrove; *Avicennia*, the black mangrove; *Laguncularia*, the white mangrove; and *Conocarpus*, the

buttonwood mangrove. In contrast, twenty species of mangroves are common to swamps of the eastern hemisphere, which, in size and maturity, attain their maximum development around southeast Asia. In this area, species of *Avicennia*, *Bruguiera*, *Carapa*, *Ceriops*, *Rhizophora* and *Sonneratia* predominate.

Physical Setting and Characteristics

Mangrove swamps form only in protected areas or along open coastlines that are reached by waves of low energy. They also develop only in shallow water areas because the young trees cannot take root in water that is deeper than about 2 feet at low tide. Mangroves appear to thrive best in brackish-water environments, though they can grow in fresh or hypersaline water; hence, estuaries, especially those served by mud-laden rivers, provide the optimum physical setting for the development of mangrove swamps along many coasts.

Along coasts where river-borne sediment is deposited in mudbanks and mud flats, a coastwise or fringing mangrove swamp up to several miles wide may develop. Mangrove swamps extend inland up to 20–40 miles wherever there are tidal rivers (Fig. 1). In deltaic regions, the shape of the swamp is dictated by the shape of the delta itself. Along many coasts, mangroves develop in lagoonal regions behind barrier bars and reefs. The locations of tropical mangrove swamps are, therefore, largely controlled by coastal geomorphology and by the pattern of coastal sedimentation.

Geologic factors favoring the development of a broad fringing belt of coastal mangroves are (1) high tidal range, (2) large supply of detrital sediments, (3) low coastal relief, and (4) low coastal wave energy.

Large mangrove swamps are rarely more than 500 square miles in area. Some of the world's largest are found along the southwest coast of Florida, along the Pacific coast of Colombia, in the Guayaquil estuary of Ecuador, along the west coast of Malaya, and along the northern coast of Borneo. In the Philippines, mangrove swamps occupy almost 2000 square miles of coastal area. About 10,000 square miles of earth are covered by large mangrove swamps; this is about 1% of the area estimated to be covered by swamps of all types.

The floor of a mangrove swamp is entirely submerged at times of extreme high tide, but interior portions may not be submerged by the average high tide. At low tide, large areas of the mangrove forest are subaerially exposed. Meandering tidal channels penetrate the forest as do the sinuous and branching tidal creeks of salt-grass marshes and mud flats. Bays or intra-forest lagoons and pools may lie within the forest, connected to the coast by tidal channels (Fig. 1).

A distinctive characteristic of the swamp is the entanglement of vegetation at and just above the

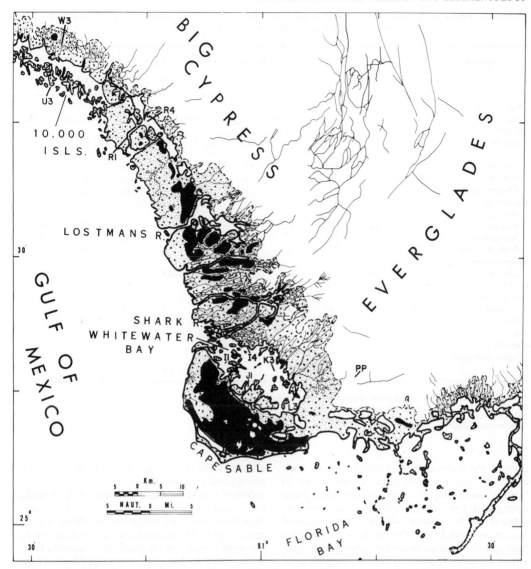

FIG. 1. Physiobotanic map of the coastal mangrove swamps of southwestern Florida. Stippled area is mangrove forest; dark areas within forest are marshlands. Big Cypress and Everglades are freshwater swamps overlying the mainland of Florida. Approximate boundary between mangrove swamps and these freshwater swamps is delineated by a dashed line.

floor of the forest. This is especially true of forests of the red mangrove (species of *Rhizophora*); this tree has prop-roots that arch outward from the base of the tree like the legs on a tarantula. In addition, the upper branches drop aerial stilt-roots that descend to the ground and intermesh with the prop-roots. Other species, in particular those of *Avicennia* and *Sonneratia*, have spike-like pneumatophores that project several inches to a foot or more above the mud and peat forest floor surrounding the trees. Many investigators believe this entanglement of roots and trunks serves as a sedi-

mentary weir, thereby promoting the seaward growth of the swamps through sediment entrapment. Evidence that this is not always the case is discussed below.

Sediments and sedimentation

Mangrove swamp sediments form beneath stands of trees or accumulate in the tidal channels. Some of the physical, chemical and mineralogical properties of clastic mangrove sediments from southwestern Florida are given in Table 1.

Clastic sedimentation over the forest bed,

TABLE 1. PHYSICAL, MINERALOGICAL AND CHEMICAL PROPERTIES OF CLASTIC SEDIMENTS (EXCLUSIVE OF PEAT) FROM THE MANGROVE SWAMPS OF SOUTHWESTERN FLORIDA[a]

Properties of Surface Sediments	Station Numbers (see Fig. 1 for locations)									
	U3	W3	R1	R4	J1	I1	I4	K3	L3	PP
Median grain size, mm	.089	.041	.185	.096	.165	.700	.264	.410	.006	.006
Trask's So.	2.20	4.66	1.68	4.47			17.3			1.85
Porosity, %		77		60	80	61	77	86	81	
%										
Quartz	60	56	75	60	15	7	16	6	24	3[d]
CaCO₃	37	20	22	32	54	85	68	68	62	90[d]
Organic matter[b]	3	24	3	8	31	8	16	26	14	7[d]
Carbonate fraction, %[c]										
Calcite	27	11	25	27	24	48	29	40	93	99
Aragonite	55	89	60	73	76	52	71	60	7	1
High-Mg calcite	18	0	15	0	0	0	0	0	0	0
Moisture content, dry-weight %	57	160		58	192	58	140	252	176	270
Ca/Mg ratio[c]	23	20[d]	20[d]	19	57	65	51	86	48	78
Sr/Ca ratio[c] × 1000	5.4	5[d]	4[d]	4.4	3.9	9.5	4.2	2.9	3.9	2
C/N ratio	23	38		28	30	19	28	27	33	
pH	7.4	6.9				7.7	6.8	7.1		
Interstitial water chlorinity, ⁰/₀₀	11	12		4	16	13	13	12	11	.6

[a] Data from Scholl (1963), and from unpublished information in author's files.
[b] Computed as 1.7 × % organic carbon.
[c] Data from Taft and Harbaugh (1964).
[d] Estimated, based on values for nearby sediments.

through the accumulation of mineral grains, shell debris, or transported organic matter, tends to build its surface higher. Accumulation takes place during slack water at high tide. Clastic detritus contributed to the coastal swamps from seaward sources is carried into the swamps by flooding tides and storm surges. Sediment coming from landward sources is deposited by rivers during seasonal floods. The floor of the forest is also built up by the emplacement of *in situ* or autochthonous organic matter (peat).

Sediments of mangrove swamps differ little from those encountered in salt-grass marshes which, in higher latitudes, occupy the same sedimentological environment as mangrove swamps. The most typical sediment of mangrove swamps is a soft, organic-rich (peaty), sandy to clayey mud. This type in south Florida is very shelly (Table 1). Along the bottoms of tidal channels are found coarser shelly sands and sandy silts. Silty, fibrous peat forms beneath the forest in areas somewhat distant from sediment-transporting tidal channels or along coasts receiving little fluvial sediment.

Although mangroves aid in trapping sediment and thereby promote land buildup, they do not significantly increase the rate of seaward or lateral growth of the coast. Lateral accretion of sediment along a coast is a function of such factors as coastal sediment supply, strength of sediment-distributing forces and relative sea-level changes. Too much importance has been placed on the ability of mangrove trees to bring about coastal progradation by sediment entrapment (Watson, 1928; Thorne, 1954; West, 1956). In fact, sediment trapped within the forest may actually lead to a slowdown of coastal progradation as less sediment is thereby available for lateral or seaward accretion. The mangrove swamp and forest advance seaward only where sedimentary processes have prepared shallow-water areas suitable for the establishment of new mangrove growth. This explains why the location and shapes of mangrove swamps are strongly influenced by the pattern of coastal sedimentation, which is a function of the several factors mentioned above.

The mineralogy of the sediments of mangrove swamps is principally that of the clastic detritus supplied to the coastal area by rivers or biologically formed in the coastal waters by shell-forming organisms. Along coasts served by rivers draining interior lowlands, the swamp sediments are rich in clay minerals. Within the protected lagoons of organic reefs, the sediment is substantially composed of biologically precipitated calcite and aragonite.

Owing to sulfate reduction by bacteria, mangrove sediments are rich in H_2S and other malodorous gases derived from the decay of organic matter. *In situ* precipitated pyrite is typically abundant; it commonly occurs embedded within or attached to plant remains. Gypsum and organic salts, such as calcium oxalate dihydrate (weddellite), develop in *stored* samples of mangrove sediments. The sediments of some mangrove swamps (e.g., those along the western side of Andros Island, Bahamas, and along the southwestern coast of Florida) are very rich in fine-grained calcareous matter. This fine calcareous debris may be formed inorganically or by the action of algae and bacteria.

Classification by Sediments

Mangrove swamps can be grouped into three principal types based on their dominant mode of sedimentation: (1) autochthonous, (2) allochthonous, and (3) mixed. Autochthonous swamps are those formed largely by *in situ* sedimentation, e.g., by peat deposition or, more rarely, by the precipitation of carbonate mud within the environmental framework of the swamp. Allochthonous swamps are those with dominant clastic sedimentation; i.e., sediments largely derived from outside the environmental framework of the swamp. The mixed type, of course, is a blend of the first two.

Examples of autochthonous peat swamps occur on the southwestern coast of Florida. This is chiefly due to the scarcity of clastic sediments. Extensive mangrove swamps along the western side of Andros Island, Bahama Islands, have developed in an area of carbonate mud precipitation; they may be regarded as autochthonous carbonate swamps. However, the precipitation of the carbonate mud may have little to do with either the presence or the absence of the mangrove trees.

Allochthonous mangrove swamps are common along tropical shores that receive an abundant supply of river-borne terrigenous (clastic) sediment. This type of mangrove swamp is exemplified by many along the west coast of Malaya (Watson, 1928). The mixed type develops in areas having an intermediate to low supply of sediment with respect to the productivity of the mangrove forest (peat formation). Examples are represented by swamps fringing the Pacific coast of Colombia (West, 1956).

Because the dominant mode of sedimentation may change during the development of a mangrove swamp, the type may change from one to another. This may be caused by an overall change in the pattern of coastal sedimentation, or a sedimentological succession may have taken place within the swamp. For example, a prograding coast may increasingly isolate an earlier-formed portion of an allochthonous mangrove swamp from seaward

sources of clastic detritus and, thereby, bring about a transformation of its isolated inner portion to an autochthonous peat swamp.

Mangrove swamps can be further classified according to geomorphological criteria. As an example, allochthonous swamps may be broken down into deltaic, estuarine, lagoonal-barrier, or open coast subtypes. The other types may be treated similarly. The swamps of southwest Florida would therefore be referred to as open coast autochthonous peat swamps. Perhaps with increasing knowledge, the historical development of a mangrove swamp can be taken into account as an augmenting classification.

DAVID W. SCHOLL

References

Brelie, G. v. d., and Teichmuller, M., 1953, "Mikroskopische Beobachtungen an Mangrove-Sedimenten aus El Salvador," *Neues Jahrb. Geol. Paleontol., Monatsh.*, No. 6, 244–251.

Chapman, V. J., and Ronaldson, J. W., 1958, "The mangrove and salt-grass flats of the Auckland Isthmus," *New Zealand Dept. Sci. Ind. Res. Bull.*, **125,** 79pp.

Davis, J. H., Jr., 1940, "The ecology and geologic role of mangroves in Florida," *Carnegie Inst. Wash. Publ.*, **517,** 303–412.

Freise, F. W., 1938, "Untersuchungen am Schlick der Mangrovkust Brasiliens," *Chem. Erde*, **2,** 333–355.

Guppy, H. B., 1906, "Observations of a naturalist in the Pacific between 1896 and 1899," Vol. II, "Plant Dispersal," London, Macmillan and Co., Ltd., 627pp.

Hedgpeth, J. W. (editor), 1957, "Treatise on Marine Ecology and Paleoecology," Vol. I, *Geol. Soc. Am. Mem.*, **67,** 1296pp.

McGill, J. T., 1958, "Map of coastal landforms of the world," *Geog. Rev.*, **48,** 402–405.

Ridley, H. N., 1930, "The Dispersal of Plants Throughout the World," L. Reeve and Co., Ltd., 744pp.

Scholl, D. W., 1963, "Sedimentation in modern coastal swamps, southwestern Florida," *Bull. Am. Assoc. Petrol. Geol.*, **47,** 1581–1603.

Scholl, D. W., 1964/65, "Recent sedimentary record in mangrove swamps and rise in sea level over the southwestern coast of Florida," Parts 1 and 2, *Marine Geology*, **1,** 344–366; **2,** 343–364.

Tabb, D. C., Dubrow, D. L., and Manning, R. B., 1962, "The ecology of northern Florida Bay and adjacent estuaries," *Florida Tech. Ser.*, **9,** 81pp.

Taft, W. H., and Harbaugh, J. W., 1964, "Modern carbonate sediments of southern Florida, Bahamas, and Espiritu Santo Island, Baja California: A comparison of their mineralogy and chemistry," *Stanford Univ. Publ. Geol. Sci.*, **8,** 133pp.

Thorne, R. F., 1954, "Flowering plants of the waters and shores of the Gulf of Mexico," in "Gulf of Mexico, its origin, waters and marine life," *U.S. Fish Wildlife Serv., Fishery Bull.*, **89,** 193–202.

Watson, J. G., 1928, "Mangrove forests of the Malay Peninsula," *Malayan Forest Records*, **6,** 274pp.

West, R. C., 1956, "Mangrove swamps of the Pacific

coast of Colombia," *Ann. Assoc. Am. Geogr.*, **46,** 98–121.

Weyl, R., 1953, "Lithogenetische Studien in den Mangroven der Pazifik-Kuste," *Neues Jahrb. Geol. Paleontol., Monatsh.*, No. 5, 202–218.

Cross-references: *Coastal Geomorphology*; *Coral Reefs*; *Estuary*; *Lagoon*. Vol. II: *Vegetation Classification*. pr Vol. VI: *Fluvial Sediment Transport*; *Peat Bog Deposits*; *Salt Marsh Sedimentology*; *Tidal Flat Geology*; *Vegetation Markers and Landscapes*.

MANTLE—*See* **REGOLITH AND SAPROLITE;** *also* Vol. V

MAPPING—*See* pr Vol. VI, **TOPOGRAPHIC MAPPING AND SURVEY**

MAPS AND MAP PROJECTIONS—*See* pr Vol. VI

MARACAIBO—*See* **LAKE MARACAIBO**

MARINE DENUDATION, EROSION—*See* **BEACH EROSION; LIMESTONE COASTAL WEATHERING; PLATFORMS—WAVE-CUT; STACK**

MARINE MARSH—*See* **MANGROVE SWAMP;** *also* pr Vol. VI, **SALT MARSH SEDIMENTOLOGY**

MARINE SEDIMENTS—*See* pr Vol. VI, **ENGINEERING PROPERTIES OF MARINE SEDIMENTS**

MARINE TERRACES—*See* **TERRACES—MARINE**

MARSH—*See* pr Vol. VI, **SWAMP, MARSH, BOG**

MASS MOVEMENT

The crust of the earth is raised or depressed with respect to the geoid by endogene phenomena associated with epeirogeny and orogeny. These large-scale crustal movements come within the province of tectonics and are not considered here. The surface layers of the crust are subject in addition to the action of exogene processes, largely controlled by climate, of which weathering, mass movement and mass transport are the chief. These interact with the endogene processes to produce surface form.

Weathering results in most cases in a weakening of a surface zone of the crust, rendering it more susceptible to downward movement under the influence of gravity. Mass movement comprises all such gravity-induced movements except those in which the material is carried directly by transporting media such as ice, snow, water or air, when the process is termed mass transport. In nature, the two processes merge into each other and in intermediate cases the distinction becomes arbitrary.

Mass movements exhibit great variety, being affected by geology, climate and topography, and their rigorous classification is hardly possible. Here the various types are subdivided mainly by mechanism, insofar as this is known, and morphology. Consideration is also given to the rate of the movement and the nature of the material involved. A primary division is made between mass movements occurring on slopes and those involving only a sinking of the ground surface.

Mass Movement on Slopes

In every slope, gravity-produced shearing stresses exist which increase with slope inclination and height, and with unit weight of the slope-forming material. Within the surface zone, the processes of freezing and thawing, shrinkage and swelling and thermal expansion and contraction produce further shearing stresses.

The response of the slope to these imposed stresses is controlled by the resistance to shear deformation currently exhibited by its component materials, itself closely dependent on the pressure exerted by the groundwater which generally occupies the soil pores. Very slow, largely irreversible deformations termed *creep* begin as soon as a "critical" strength is exceeded, which may be considerably lower than the strength at which shear failure occurs (Haefeli, 1953). As the imposed stress approaches the average shear strength, the rate of creep increases until eventually some form of relatively rapid failure takes place, to which the generic term *landslide* is applied (Terzaghi, 1950).

The various forms of mass movement on slopes are listed in Table 1 and described below.

Creep. In this context, the term "creep" has been used rather loosely to describe any very slow, permanent deformation of a slope, regardless of the mechanism causing it. It is useful to distinguish between seasonal, or mantle creep, the more continuous mass creep (Terzaghi, 1950; Haefeli, 1953), and a phenomenon which may be referred to as progressive creep.

(1) *Shallow, Predominantly Seasonal Creep; Mantle Creep.* This type of creep is largely confined to the weathered surface zone of fluctuating ground temperature and moisture content. Viscous move-

TABLE I. MASS MOVEMENT ON SLOPES

CREEP	(1) Shallow, predominantly seasonal creep;
	    (a) Soil creep
	    (b) Talus creep
	(2) Deep-seated continuous creep; mass creep
	(3) Progressive creep

FROZEN GROUND PHENOMENA	(4) Freeze-thaw movements
	    (a) Solifluction
	    (b) Cambering and valley bulging
	    (c) Stone streams
	    (d) Rock glaciers

LANDSLIDES	(5) Translational slides
	    (a) Rock slides; block glides
	    (b) Slab, or flake slides
	    (c) Detritus, or debris slides
	    (d) Mudflows
	        (i) Climatic mudflows
	        (ii) Volcanic mudflows
	    (e) Bog flows; bog bursts
	    (f) Flow failures
	        (i) Loess flows
	        (ii) Flow slides
	(6) Rotational slips
	    (a) Single rotational slips
	    (b) Multiple rotational slips
	        (i) In stiff, fissured clays
	        (ii) In soft, extra-sensitive clays; clay flows
	    (c) Successive, or stepped rotational slips
	(7) Falls
	    (a) Stone and boulder falls
	    (b) Rock and soil falls
	(8) Sub-aqueous slides
	    (a) Flow slides
	    (b) Under-consolidated clay slides

ments contribute little to the net downslope creep.

(a) Soil Creep. This affects the surface zone of the soil mantle and is especially active in regions with a wide seasonal variation in climate. Annual downslope surface movements tend to increase with slope angle and soil colloid content and vary in order of magnitude from less than 1 mm to several centimeters. On the more clayey slopes, the greater part of the creep is likely to result from volume changes caused by wetting and drying. Observations suggest that soil creep movements diminish progressively with depth and are most marked in a surface layer less than a meter thick.

The effects of soil creep are well revealed by the downslope deflection of weathered outcrops of stratified rock in hillsides. The slow and largely seasonal downhill movement of isolated boulders or blocks on slopes, for example, of as little as 5° would seem also to be a manifestation of creep in the underlying soil. The use by Sharpe (1938; see reference in Terzaghi, 1950) of the term "rock-creep" to describe these two phenomena is unfortunate. It is better reserved for the mass creep of rock at depth.

(b) Talus Creep. This involves the very slow downslope movement of the surface layers of the slopes of rock fragments or scree which typically occupy the foot of steep cliffs. Such material, with some exceptions, is predominantly frictional, rather coarse and well drained and in the steeper talus slopes stands at inclinations, often of around 35°, which approach its angle of internal friction. In general, recurrent expansion and contraction from temperature fluctuations probably make an important contribution to talus creep. In periglacial regions, talus creep is probably stimulated by freeze-thaw processes. Rates of talus creep of as much as 10 cm/yr have been observed in such a climate by Rapp (1961).

(2) *Deep-seated Continuous Creep; Mass Creep.* This type of creep can be expected to occur in all soils and rocks which are subjected to shear stresses in excess of the critical. It is probably the result of viscous movements and has a much lower order of magnitude than the other forms of creep mentioned in Table 1. It is therefore of chief significance when acting alone, below the zone of mantle creep. Mass creep in rock slopes is mentioned by Terzaghi (1953; see reference in Haefeli, 1953). There is, as yet, scarcely any direct field evidence for its existence.

(3) *Progressive Creep.* Creep movements of this type occur in slopes which are approaching failure. They are thus characterized by a stress level near to that at which failure takes place and by gradually increasing and relatively high rates of movement. Such movements frequently arise through, and hasten, a progressive deterioration in strength, particularly in slopes of heavily overconsolidated, argillaceous sediments. A well-documented case record of progressive creep in a slope of such material at Kensal Green, London, is given by Skempton (1964). The total movement there during the year preceding failure was approximately 20 cm. In heterogeneous slopes, progressive creep deformation of the less rigid strata can effect a further reduction of the overall stability by bringing about the fracture of more rigid, overlying beds.

Frozen Ground Phenomena. Phenomena resulting predominantly from the natural processes of freezing and thawing of ground moisture are widespread and in both their active and their relict forms are currently much studied. Only those involving significant downslope mass movement are mentioned below:

(4) *Freeze-thaw Movements.* (a) Solifluction. This involves the slow, downslope movement of surface material under the influence of freeze-thaw processes. In periglacial environments, solifluction is one

of the main agents of denudation (Rapp, 1961) and varies between general, creep-like movements and localized, more active forms which grade into the Alpine type of mudflow (Sharpe, 1938). It is most active when shallow thawing of the slope, generally to a depth of less than a meter, produces saturation of the surface layer above the impermeable, still-frozen subsoil. Frost heaving soils are particularly susceptible.

Solifluction deposits are characteristically unsorted and are limited in source to the higher parts of the slope, which may be inclined as little as 2° (Flint, 1957; see reference in Menard, 1964).

(b) Cambering and Valley Bulging. These related features were first clearly recognized in 1944 by Hollingworth, Taylor and Kellaway (see reference in Terzaghi, 1950) in the Northampton Ironstone field of central England, where they are believed to have a Late Pleistocene origin. The ironstone occurs in the near-horizontal and relatively thin Northampton Sands, which are the uppermost solid rocks in the neighborhood. These are underlain, conformably, by a great thickness of the Lias, into which shallow valleys, typically 1200–1500 meters wide and 45 meters deep, have been eroded. Excavations for dam trenches in the valley bottoms have shown the Lias there to be thrust strongly upward and contorted, while opencast workings in the Northampton Sands occupying the interfluves reveal a general valleyward increase of dip of "camber" of this stratum, often passing into dip and fault structure, suggesting corresponding downward movements along the valley margins. In adjusting to these movements, the rigid cap-rock has been dislocated by successive, regularly spaced fissures which parallel the valley and are known as "gulls". Similar features have been recognized in other parts of England and in Bohemia. The mechanisms by which cambering and valley bulging have been formed remain to be established.

(c) Stone Streams. Also called stone rivers, these are linear concentrations of boulders on slopes and valley floors. Related to solifluction deposits, they reach lengths of more than 1 km and thicknesses of several meters. Stone streams are abundant in formerly glaciated areas of Europe and North America. Most are now inactive. Although these features are not fully understood, it seems likely that the majority represent the residue of solifluction deposits from which the fines have been washed out (Flint, 1957).

(d) Rock Glaciers. Also called rock streams, these are glacier-like accumulations of angular rock waste which in their lower parts frequently exhibit successive lobate ridges, suggesting flow. They may exceed 1 km in length and have a thickness of 30 meters or more. Rock glaciers seem to be confined to currently glaciated terrain, generally contain interstitial ice at depth, and are sometimes genetically connected with true glaciers (Haefeli, 1953; Flint, 1957). The origin of these features and the mechanics of their motion is still in dispute. While creep may contribute to the movement of some rock glaciers, it seems that the majority, especially the more active, move predominantly through ice flowage and are better regarded as a form of mass transport.

Landslides. Landslides are relatively rapid movements involving failure. In further contrast to mantle and mass creep movements, where there is generally a continuous gradation between the stationary and the moving material, the movement in landslides takes place characteristically on one or more discrete surfaces which define sharply the moving mass. (The strain distribution in progressive creep movements is likely to be transitional between these two extremes.)

(5) *Translational Slides.* Landslides of this type are usually fairly rapid and involve shear failure on a fairly plane surface running roughly parallel to the general slope of the ground. The movements of the slide masses are therefore predominantly translational and relatively shallow, the depth to the slip surface being as a rule less than one-tenth of the distance from toe to rear scarp of the slide.

Translational slides are characteristic of slopes of largely frictional material, in which the rapid increase of shear strength with depth inhibits the development of a deeper, rotational type of failure. They are also widespread in cohesive soils in which the failure surface is predetermined by a marked heterogeneity, such as a sharp transition from soft to hard material with depth, or the presence of an adversely located weak layer within the slope.

(a) Rock Slides or Block Glides. These are the most clear-cut type of translational failure. The rock mass involved may move as one or break up to produce a multiple failure. In either case, movement is generally fairly rapid. The slip surface is commonly formed by a bedding, cleavage or joint plane, frequently occupied by an argillaceous filling. In the rock slide of 1806 at Goldau, Switzerland, failure occurred on a bedding plane in stratified marly sandstone, dipping approximately parallel to the valley side at about 25°. The volume of rock involved is estimated to have been about 15×10^6 cubic meters (Terzaghi, 1950; Haefeli, 1953).

(b) Slab Slides. These are similar in form to rock slides, but involve uncemented materials. The landslide at Jackfield, Shropshire, described by Henkel and Skempton in 1954 (see reference in Skempton, 1964), exemplifies a failure of this type in the moderately deep weathered zone of hard, Upper Carboniferous clays. That at Furre, Norway, reported by the writer in 1961, was determined, in contrast, by the presence of a thin layer of quick clay, interbedded in silty Post-glacial deposits and dipping at an average inclination of about 6° beneath the slope foot. In both of the slides, the failing mass moved predominantly as a single unit. Multiple slab slides also occur. These are usually retrogressive, but progressive forms are also known.

(c) Detritus or Debris Slides. These slides are characterized by the tendency of the slide material to behave as a more or less cohesionless mass, suffering considerable distortion during movement. They generally occur on fairly steep slopes, typically between about 15 and 40°, and are frequently fairly rapid. The depth of the movement and the degree of distortion involved is influenced largely by the cohesion of the slide debris. At one extreme, heavily weathered clay debris may approach the nature of a *slab slide*; at the other is the *sand run* in slopes of dry, cohesionless material, in which the movement involves only the grains in a thin surface layer.

Extremely rapid debris slides often result from sudden heavy rainfall, particularly in the tropics. In cold mountainous regions, significant mass movements are brought about by dirty snow avalanches, as pointed out by Rapp (1961). Both these types of movement clearly grade into mass transport.

(d) Mudflows. These form an important group of mass movements, and again, in their wetter manifestations, involve a strong element of mass transport. They are typically glacier-like in form, with surface slopes ranging from about 25° to less than 1° and normally consist of poorly sorted, weathered rock debris in a soft, clayey matrix. Their movements are commonly highly seasonal and vary widely in rate between the different types of flow.

(i) Climatic mudflows develop characteristically beneath steep, bare slopes of deeply weathered, fissured or jointed rock, which serve as a debris source. If, upon wetting, a sufficient amount of the accumulated debris breaks down to a clayey paste, mudflowing will begin. This cycle is naturally favored by climates which alternate between stimulating the production of rock and soil debris and providing a fairly plentiful supply of water.

That such conditions are not limited to the semi-arid and Alpine environments recognized by Sharpe (1938) is illustrated by the widespread occurrence of mudflows in southern England. These "temperate mudflows" develop on outcrops of over-consolidated clays and are currently most active on the coast, where their tongues are subject to marine erosion. Summer drying and shrinkage in the steep upper cliffs lead to falls of hard clay fragments which, particularly in fissured clays, supply much of the debris. This is supplemented by frost spalling and shallow slides during the winter, when the chief mudflow movements occur. An alternative supply mechanism, which affects both fissured and intact clays, is the undermining of clay beds by seepage erosion in an underlying fine sand. The mudflow margins are generally sharply defined and slickensided. The movements of a mudflow in the London Clay have recently been observed by the writer to approximate *plug flow*.

The term *seepage erosion* is employed when groundwater discharges at a free face and the seepage drag may be large enough to dislodge individual particles of the soil, thus permitting their removal. This phenomenon is largely confined to soils in the coarse silt to fine sand range. It occurs typically at the base of a free face of water-bearing, fine cohesionless material underlain by an impermeable bed. The resultant back-sapping tends to undermine the superincumbent strata and produce their eventual collapse (Terzaghi, 1950).

(ii) Volcanic mudflows or lahars occur in association with explosive eruptions and arise from the sudden supersaturation of great accumulations of volcanic dust and ashes. The necessary supply of water may be derived from the ejection of crater lakes, the condensation of steam clouds or the melting of snow banks. Mudflows of this type are frequently terribly destructive and may owe some of their mobility to included gases. In 1929, Scrivenor (see reference in Thornbury, 1964) described a Javanese volcanic mudflow which, in threequarters of an hour, overwhelmed a tract of land extending over 38 km from the crater and having a width of up to 4 km. (See *Lahar*, pr Vol. VI.)

(e) Bog Flows or Bog Bursts. These consist of the predominantly translational, downhill movement of masses of saturated peat. They are confined to ombrogenous mires and are common in the rainy, mountainous areas of Ireland and north-west England. Many examples are described in the *Scientific Proceedings of the Royal Dublin Society*.

The most catastrophic bog bursts are associated with raised bogs, which consist typically of a domed mass of soft peat enclosed within a perimeter of firmer material. On receiving a sudden access of water, it appears that such a bog may swell until some form of failure releases the inner, semifluid peat. In a burst of this type in the Knocknageeha bog, County Kerry, Ireland on December 28, 1896, nearly 5×10^6 cubic meters of peat were discharged.

Bursts in blanket bog, which forms on slopes up to about 15° in wet, mountainous areas of north-west Britain, are more limited in extent. In the deeper blanket bogs, on slopes as flat as 3 or 4°, failures typically involve areas of the order of 4×10^4 square meters and are accompanied by a discharge of semifluid peat. On the steeper slopes, of about 6–15°, the blanket bog is generally thinner and the whole peat profile may be fairly firm. Failures in such situations are more limited in extent and are better described as bog slides.

(f) Flow Failures. These originate through the collapse of metastable structure in certain loose, predominantly non-cohesive silts or fine sands, which are generally also saturated. Such collapse usually results from a sudden disturbance and probably gives rise to transient, high pore pressures in the failing material which give it briefly a semi-fluid character.

(*i*) Loess flows, although not yet closely investigated, appear to involve the failure of virtually dry deposits. Collapse is usually caused by earthquake shock, probably through breaking of the weak intergranular bonds. The mobility of the resultant flows suggests that pore-air pressures may be generated within the flow masses. Loess flows in Missouri and Kansu, China, are referred to by Terzaghi (1950).

(*ii*) Flow slides occur chiefly in subaqueous environments (see Section 8). Flow slides have also been initiated in saturated, or nearly saturated, metastable deposits above free water level by slip movements, pile driving, explosions and earthquakes. Artificial sand fills and industrial waste deposits, particularly where placed hydraulically, have been fairly frequently involved.

(6) *Rotational Slips*. Rotational landslips occur principally in slopes largely formed of, or underlain by, a fairly thick and relatively homogeneous deposit of clay or shale. Failure takes place, usually fairly rapidly, by shearing on a well-defined, somewhat curved, slip surface. This, being concave upward, imparts a degree of backward rotation to the slipping mass which produces sinking at the rear, heaving at the toe and back-tilting of the slipped strata. Elongated pools commonly collect in the depression formed behind the slipped mass. Failures of this type are as a class more deep-seated than translational slides.

The main types of rotational landslip are illustrated in Fig. 1. Further subdivision is made below:

(a) Single Rotational Slips. These are characterized by the presence of a single, concave slip surface upon which the slipping mass moves as a virtually coherent unit (Fig. 1). They have received much

attention in the geotechnical literature as they are of frequent occurrence in cuttings. A typical landslip of this type is that in Lodalen, Norway, described by Sevaldson (1956; see reference in Skempton, 1964).

(b) Multiple Rotational Slips. Under certain circumstances retrogression of single rotational slips can occur, producing two or more slipped blocks, each with a curved slip surface tangential to a common, generally deep-seated, slip sole (Fig. 1). Clearly, as the number of units increases, the overall character of the slip becomes more translational, though in failing, each block itself rotates backwards. Two widely different types of multiple rotational slip can be recognized.

(*i*) One type occurs in *stiff, fissured clays*. Prerequisites for the occurrence of multiple rotational slips in such clays appear to be fairly high relief, the presence of a considerable capping stratum of well-jointed but otherwise competent rock, a relatively thick layer of underlying clay or shale, and active and continuing erosion at the foot of the slope. In Britain the most well-developed landslips of this type are found on the coast and appear to have a Post-glacial origin. Long intervals seem to have elapsed between the failure of consecutive blocks, and contemporary activity generally comprises chiefly a renewal of movement in the old slipped masses.

A well-investigated multiple rotational landslip is that at the Folkestone Warren on the south coast of England. This involves a 45 meter thick bed of Gault clay capped by over 120 meters of Chalk, and was described by Toms in 1953 (see reference in Bishop and Bjerrum, 1960).

Multiple rotational slips rarely occur in cliffs formed entirely of stiff, fissured clays. In the absence of a competent cap rock, the rear scarp formed by the initial slip is degraded so rapidly by shallow slips, soil falls and mudflows that unless erosion at the toe of the protecting slip masses is exceptionally severe, the general level of imposed stresses does not again rise high enough to bring about a further deep-seated failure.

(*ii*) The other type is found only in *soft, extrasensitive clays*. Retrogressive failures in deposits of quick clay form a distinctive category of multiple rotational slip, to which the Late- and Post-glacial marine clays of Norway and east Canada are particularly prone. A good example is the landslip at Ullensaker, described by Bjerrum in 1954 (see reference in Bishop and Bjerrum, 1960). Such failures generally begin with a single rotational slip in a bank produced by fluvial incision in a near-horizontal surface of the clay deposit. The slip movements remold the quick clay forming the lower part of the initial slip to the consistency of a heavy liquid. This runs out of the slide cavity, carrying with it flakes of the stiff, weathered crust which normally forms the upper few meters of the

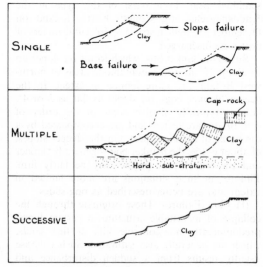

FIG. 1. Main types of rotational landslip.

deposit. The steep rear scarp is thus left un-supported, and a further rotational slip is induced. This, in turn, is largely remolded and flows out of the cavity, and retrogressive failures continue until a stable scarp is attained. The retrogression is ex-tremely rapid, consecutive slips following each other in a matter of seconds. Lateral spread of the failure is usually more marked in the deposits re-mote from the river than in the more weathered, somewhat stronger material forming the river bank. This gives these slips their characteristic bottle-necked shape in plan and their Scandinavian name of "bottle-neck slide" in quick clay. Either this name or that of "clay flow" suggested by Terzaghi and Peck (1948; see also Terzaghi, 1950) is pref-erable to the term "flow slide" sometimes used, as the latter has long been applied to liquefaction failures in loose noncohesive deposits (see Sections 5 and 8).

(c) Successive or Stepped Rotational Slips. Slopes of stiff, fissured clay that are approaching their angle of ultimate stability frequently exhibit repeated, shallow rotational slips. [The angle of ultimate stability is discussed by Skempton and DeLory, 1957 (see reference in Skempton, 1964), who conclude it to be about 10° for the London Clay.] Each rotational slip is of limited extent in a direction down the slope but of considerable extent across it, thus forming a succession of cross-slope steps or terraces (Fig. 1). Typical successive rota-tional slips, with terrace widths between 9 and 12 meters and rear scarps about 1.5 meters high, occur on 35-meter high slopes of approximately 12° inclination in the London Clay.

Some of the features known as *terracettes* may represent a miniature form of stepped rotational slip. Investigations of terracettes by Ødum are referred to by Sharpe (1938). They seem to occur chiefly on relatively steep slopes in somewhat fric-tional soils.

7. *Falls.* Falls comprise the more or less free descent of masses of soil or rock of any size from steep slopes or cliffs. As Rapp (1961) has empha-sized, on a slope steep enough to be subject to falls, no significant protective mantle of rock waste can accumulate and mass movement can proceed as fast as the weathering and disintegration of the parent mass permits.

(a) Stone and Boulder Falls. These involve dis-turbance of the equilibrium of rock bodies which, already physically separated from the cliff, are merely lodged upon it. They are thus relatively limited in magnitude.

(b) Rock and Soil Falls. These are characterized by a frequently protracted phase of progressive separation of a mass from its parent cliff which eventually leads to its abrupt collapse. The separa-tion is effected initially by the growth of tension cracks: the final release of the rock mass commonly occurs through shear failure of the root of the mass.

These failures are confined to the surface zone of rock in which the effects of pressure release and of seasonal variations in temperature and cleft-water pressure are most significant. In Norway, a wide-spread, well-marked annual peak of rock-fall intensity in the spring suggests thawing following frost-bursting to be a relevant mechanism (Rapp, 1961).

8. *Subaqueous Slides.* The processes of weathering and erosion, which under subaerial conditions are the chief promoters of mass movement, are largely absent from subaqueous milieus, where deposition and consolidation naturally predominate and relief is generally more subdued. Fossil structures result-ing from submarine slumping have long been known, however, and recent oceanographic in-vestigation has established firmly that contempo-rary submarine slides and resultant turbidity currents are widespread and extensive (Menard, 1964).

In shallow, coastal waters, the bottom sediments are subject to disturbance by waves and tides, and submarine slides are frequent, particularly in areas such as large river deltas where the rate of sedi-mentation is high. The volume of such sublittoral slides ranges from 10^4 to at least 3×10^8 cubic meters (Menard, 1964). Two main types can cur-rently be distinguished:

(a) Flow Slides. Under certain conditions, masses of cohesionless or slightly cohesive silts or fine sands are deposited underwater with a metastable struc-ture (see Section 5). A subsequent slight disturbance may be sufficient to cause a collapse of this structure, which can lead, through the generation of transient high pore-water pressures, to a flow slide (Terzaghi, 1957; see reference in Menard, 1964).

(b) Underconsolidated Clay Slides. Terzaghi (1957) has suggested that under submerged condi-tions in which predominantly clayey sediments ac-cumulate fairly rapidly upon a slope, excess pore-water pressures will build up within the deposit through a lag in consolidation. Under-consolidated clay slides may then result, even on very gentle slopes, without further external stimulus. The nu-merous grooves which descend the Mississippi delta front are believed to be the scars of this type of slide.

The abyssal plains of the ocean basin floor are often blanketed by great thicknesses of fine-grained deposits brought in by turbidity currents, which were themselves probably initiated by slides on the continental slope (Gorsline & Emery, 1959; see reference in Menard, 1964). Investigations of the continental slope so far carried out suggest that, as in the sublittoral zone, submarine slides occur chiefly in localities having a high rate of sedimentation. Most of these slides of the deeper sea bed are thus believed to originate, recurrently, in the heads of the submarine canyons which notch the continental slope and form natural sediment traps (Moore, 1961; see reference in Menard, 1964).

The largest submarine slide yet reported is that generated by the 1923 Kwanto earthquake in Sagami Wan, off Japan. This had a volume of 7×10^{10} cubic meters (Menard, 1964). The nature and mechanics of these failures are still obscure though their initiation is often associated with earthquakes.

Mass Movement Involving Sinking of the Ground Surface

In contrast to those on slopes, mass movements involving sinking take place by the predominantly vertical, downward movement of superficial parts of the earth's crust which are confined on all sides. Although less widespread than slope movements, they can be more deep-seated. A distinction is drawn between the relatively rapid *subsidence*, resulting from roof breakdown in subsurface macrocavities such as caves, and the generally more gradual *settlement*, arising from a reduction in volume of soil microcavities or pore spaces. The various categories are listed in Table 2 and described below.

TABLE 2. MASS MOVEMENT INVOLVING SINKING OF THE GROUND SURFACE

MASS MOVEMENT INVOLVING SINKING	(9) Subsidence caused by
	(a) Mining
	(b) Marine erosion
	(c) Subsurface erosion, or piping
	(d) Subsurface solution
	(e) Melting of ground ice
	(f) Chemical changes
	(g) Outflow of lava
	(h) Old land movements
	(10) Settlement caused by
	(a) Consolidation
	(i) Surface loading
	(ii) Lowering of ground-water level
	(iii) Underdrainage
	(b) Collapsing grain structure

9. *Subsidence.* The many forms exhibited are subdivided according to the process by which the subsurface cavity is produced:

(a) Mining. Extensive subsidence has been brought about artificially by the mining of coal, salts and metalliferous ores. Examples are given by Sharpe (1938).

(b) Marine Erosion. Subsidence may result from roof collapse in caves formed by the sea. Falls of the inner parts of such caves in Cornwall, England, have led to the curious "blow holes" there.

(c) Subsurface Erosion or Piping. Under conditions where susceptibility to seepage erosion is accompanied by a tendency to "roofing," the progressive removal of fine material on a limited front may lead to the formation of a subterranean con-

duit of considerable length. Several cases in which large sinkholes were produced by the roof collapse of conduits eroded in fine sands are reported by Terzaghi & Peck (1948). Related subsidence into erosion channels located at the base of deep, blanket peat occurs in the English Pennines.

(d) Subsurface Solution. In limestone and dolomite regions, the drainage tends to sink underground and produce a system of subterranean solution channels. Widespread subsidences of very variable form, termed *sinkholes*, result from the solution and fall of cavern roofs and from the collapse of overlying unconsolidated deposits (Thornbury, 1964). These features are among those which characterize karst topography. Related phenomena, referred to generally as *solution subsidence*, occur in chalk, gypsum, anhydrite and halite terrain (Morgan, 1941; see reference in Thornbury, 1964). Artificial solution subsidence has been produced in Cheshire, England, by brine pumping from Triassic halite deposits.

(e) Melting of Ground Ice. A common form of this type of subsidence is the kettle hole, which is generally produced by the melting of a mass of dead ice buried in glacial deposits. Less widespread are the features referred to as *thermokarst*. These consist of depressions, termed thaw lakes and thaw sinks, which have been reported from Alaska and are ascribed to subsidence following the thawing of perennially frozen ground (Flint, 1957; p. 204).

(f) Chemical Changes. Certain subsurface ore bodies suffer volume reductions as a result of oxidation, which lead to surface subsidence similar in appearance to that produced by mining. An example of oxidation subsidence in Arizona is described by Wisser (1927; see reference in Thornbury, 1964), and cases of appreciable and continuing subsidence resulting from the burning of seams of coal or lignite are mentioned by Sharpe (1938). The lowering of the surface of peat mires as a result of drainage is a complex phenomenon, but in many instances a significant part of the total loss in level is due to decomposition of the drained peat.

(g) Outflow of Lava. Some volcanoes exhibit steep-walled depressions known as *volcanic sinks*. These are formed predominantly by collapse following withdrawal of magma from below and may have a width of over 5 km. Mokuaweoweo, on the summit of the Mauna Loa lava dome in Hawaii, is a good example (Thornbury, 1964). Various smaller-scale forms of subsidence in lava fields, including roof collapse in lava tunnels, are described by Cotton (1944; see reference in Thornbury, 1964).

(h) Old Land Movements. Landslides, or cambering movements, can give rise to deep fissures, aligned along the affected slope and usually located in the neighborhood of its crest. Superficial unconsolidated deposits may mantle these, particularly if the fissures were ancient, and the collapse of this loose cover may eventually produce a locally severe, characteristically linear subsidence.

10. *Settlement*. (a) Consolidation. In a saturated soil, the superimposed load is carried partly by the soil structure and partly by the fluid, usually water, which fills the pore spaces. As the pore water is relatively incompressible in comparison with the soil structure, any load increment is carried, initially, by the liquid phase of the soil-water system. The excess pore-water pressures, which are thus set up, initiate a drainage process which effects their gradual dissipation, at a rate controlled largely by the permeability of the loaded soil. This transfers an increasing proportion of the incremental stresses to the soil structure which compresses accordingly, producing a surface settlement. This process, which is termed consolidation, is of chief importance in soils, such as soft clay, with a highly compressible structure (Terzaghi & Peck, 1948). It is most frequently brought about in the following ways:

(*i*) By far the most widespread and extensive consolidation takes place as a result of the surface loading, through continuing deposition, of sea and lake bed deposits. On land, consolidation of this type is brought about by the loading imposed, for instance, by ice sheets and their outwash deposits. It is also frequently caused by man-made structures and fills.

(*ii*) Lowering of groundwater level results in an increase in the effective weight of the mass of soil situated between the initial and final positions of the water table. This causes a corresponding additional consolidation of this mass and the deposits underlying it. Extensive consolidation of this type has taken place in soft, marine clays raised above sea level by the isostatic recovery of regions which were previously heavily glaciated. Consolidation settlements of similar nature but smaller scale are often caused by artificial drainage (Terzaghi & Peck, 1948).

(*iii*) Underdrainage, or the reduction of pore-fluid pressures at depth, is a related form of loading resulting chiefly from either the extraction of oil or water at depth or the fortuitous drainage of a confined aquifer by excavation or tunnelling. Heavy pumping of water from beneath soft, clay deposits has led in about 13 years to consolidation settlements of up to 1.2 meters in the Santa Clara valley, California (Terzaghi & Peck, 1948), and even the stiff clay beneath London has settled several centimeters through abstraction of water from the underlying Chalk.

It appears that considerable reduction of pore-fluid pressures in sands located at great depth can lead to unexpectedly large surface settlements, which seem to derive from the sand layers rather than from the overlying strata. Laboratory studies on the sands suggest that the settlements are produced by *grain crushing* at high effective pressures.

(b) Collapsing Grain Structure. Certain loose, dry deposits of fine sand or coarse silt exhibit considerable settlement on wetting. This is generally only large when the deposit is wetted under a superimposed load, but in some very high-porosity deposits, settlement can occur under the self-weight of the soil alone. The settlement results from a collapse of the metastable soil structure following weakening by the water of clay bonds which may be present at grain contacts, and its destruction of intergranular capillary tensions. The rate of collapse seems to be below that necessary for flow slides to develop (see Sections 5 and 8). The phenomenon is well documented in the loess of Europe and the United States and is reported from residual granite soils in South Africa and slightly clayey, marine sands in Angola (see papers in the *Proceedings of the Fifth International Conference on Soil Mechanics and Foundation Engineering*, Paris, 1961). Relatively flat deposits of such soils which suffer structure collapse under earthquake shock exhibit large regional settlements, apparently unaccompanied by flow failures.

J. N. Hutchinson

References

*Bishop, A. W., and Bjerrum, L., 1960, "The relevance of the triaxial test to the solution of stability problems," *Proc. of the Research Conference on Shear Strength of Cohesive Soils, Boulder, Colo.*, 439–501.

Embleton, C. and King, C. A. M., 1968, "Glacial and Periglacial Geomorphology," London, E. Arnold Ltd., 608pp.

*Haefeli, R., 1953, "Creep problems in soils, snow and ice," *Proc. Intern. Conf. Soil Mech. Found. Eng., 3rd, Switzerland*, **3**, 238–251.

Hutchinson, J. N., 1967, "The free degradation of London Clay cliffs," *Proc. Geotech. Conf. Oslo 1967*, **1**, 113–118.

*Menard, H. W., 1964, "Marine Geology of the Pacific," New York, McGraw-Hill Book Co., 271pp.

*Rapp, A., 1961, "Recent development of mountain slopes in Kärkevagge and surroundings, Northern Scandinavia," *Geograf. Ann.* **42**, 71–200.

Skempton, A. W., 1964, "Long-term stability of clay slopes," *Géotechnique*, **14**, 77–101.

*Terzaghi, K., 1950, "Mechanism of landslides," *Geol. Soc. Am. Eng. Geol.*, 83–123.

*Terzaghi, K. and Peck, R. B., 1948, "Soil Mechanics in Engineering Practice," New York, John Wiley & Sons, 566pp.

*Thornbury, W. D., 1964, "Principles of Geomorphology," New York, John Wiley & Sons, 618pp.

Watanabe, T., 1966, "Damage to oil refinery plants and a building on compacted ground by the Niigata earthquake and their restoration," Tokyo, *Soil and Foundation*, **6**, 86–99.

* Additional bibliographic references may be found in this work.

Cross-references: *Denudation*; *Exogenic Dynamics*; *Frost Action*; *Landslide*; *Mudflow*; *Rock Stream, etc.*;

MASS MOVEMENT OF CLAYS—*See* pr Vol. VI, QUICKCLAY

MASS WASTING

Wasting of the earth's crust on a massive scale by gravity-controlled movement of materials, important though it is, is less commonly emphasized than sculpture of the earth by the gradational processes of streams and the work of ground water, glaciers, winds, waves, and currents. A broad designation, the term *mass wasting* has been used to encompass "... a variety of processes by which large masses of earth material are moved by gravity either slowly or quickly from one place to another." (AGI Glossary of Geology and Related Sciences, 1957, p. 179). Mass wasting may be very effective as an erosional agent even where other erosional agents are less active or absent. The term could be used to designate the sum total of gravity-controlled wastage over small or large areas. Sheetwash should be covered by the term, and certainly underwater mass wasting phenomena should be included.

Mass movement is often used interchangeably with mass wasting, but mass movement probably should be reserved for movement of large masses as a *unit*, for example, "landslides or landslips." Mass movement has been defined as: "Unit movement of a portion of the land surface as in creep, landslide or slip" (AGI, *op. cit.*).

Confusion in terminology may stem from the classification of gravity-induced movement on the basis of either velocity or the size of the material involved. According to the definition of mass movement, it is incorrect to include such things as talus accumulation, solifluction (soil flowage), or surficial creep of fine rock materials under this term. It is confusing also to classify a unit mass movement like a landslide in the same category as the flow or creep of rock materials. And yet, as will be explained later, the mechanics of all kinds of gravity-induced movement are probably similar.

Terzaghi (1950, pp. 84–87) emphasizes the difference between landslide and creep. It is more than a difference in velocity. Landslides occur as the result of sudden mass movement of weak-to-strong materials along a surface of shear, because the load per unit area exceeds the compressive (rupture) strength of the materials involved. Smaller loads may start the process of creep (or flow) in similar materials by exceeding the "fundamental strength" (elastic limit), but not exceeding the rupture strength of the materials involved. Creep may be plastic deformation. Unfortunately, it is often virtually impossible to draw a clear-cut boundary between different kinds of movement or to determine the relative velocity of movement after the event has taken place.

In this entry, *mass wasting* (including mass movement) is considered a general process of gravity-controlled, subaerial or subaqueous, slow-to-sudden, downward, or downward and outward fall, slide, flow, creep or subsidence of small-to-large masses of dry-to-wet, or frozen rock or rock materials, including soil or snow. Ranging from free fall to subsidence, basically, all mass wasting may be compared to fluid motion, either laminar or turbulent flow of fluids (Fig. 1). In terms of effective volume, mass wasting is perhaps the most important

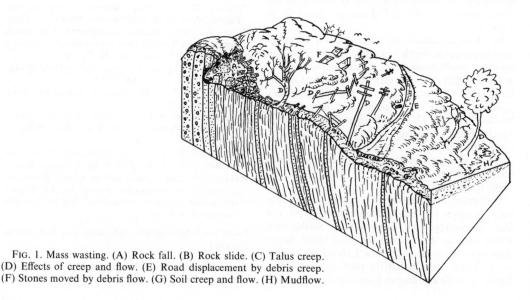

Fig. 1. Mass wasting. (A) Rock fall. (B) Rock slide. (C) Talus creep. (D) Effects of creep and flow. (E) Road displacement by debris creep. (F) Stones moved by debris flow. (G) Soil creep and flow. (H) Mudflow.

among the agencies that sculpture and reduce the earth's surface.

In terms of effect upon mankind, such movement may cause great loss of life or produce millions of dollars worth of damage every year. Mass wasting frequently destroys highways, buildings, dams, and bridges, while valuable resources such as forests, soils, mineral deposits, and water supply may be ruined by such phenomena (Savage, 1951).

Original rock materials may be subject to mass wasting because of their composition. Materials with low bearing strengths such as schist, tuff, loose sand, gravel, silt, loess, cinders, ash, shale, marl, clay, soils, muds, and oozes are easily sheared permitting fall, slide, flow, creep, or subsidence. Also of low bearing strength are rocks that contain soft and platy mineral components such as mica, talc, tremolite, serpentine, glauconite, and others. Organic materials (peat and coal) also tend to be unstable under stress.

The original texture and structure of materials may also be conducive to mass wasting because of poor compaction or a high degree of rounding of fragments. Movement may take place along planes of structural weakness such as bedding planes, foliation, cleavage, incipient fractures, joints, brecciated zones, unconformities, faults, and gouge zones. Breaks and fractures developed by previous natural and artificial shearing stresses often prepare the way for later and more widespread instability.

Changes in environmental conditions, including climatic factors, vegetative cover, and artificial changes within or adjacent to potentially unstable areas of rock material may result in mass wasting. New sets of environmental conditions may (1) reduce the basic shearing strength of the materials themselves or (2) produce higher internal shearing stresses. A complex of forces is usually involved in mass wasting; one set may affect the shearing strength and the internal shearing stresses of the materials, and another set of forces may promote or increase the effects of other forces. The total result may be a combination of spectacular rock fall or slide as unit masses, surficial creep, flow, or subsidence.

Reduced shearing strength is brought about by weathering, physical and chemical changes, or by structural changes. Some structural changes may be produced by the activities of man. Weathering and physical and chemical reactions favor mass wasting through granular disintegration, hydration and expansion, saturation and loss of compactness (increased buoyancy) or cohesion, drying and

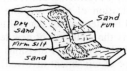

FIG. 2. Dry sand flow (Eckel, 1958).

FIG. 3. Slump slide and earth flow (Sharpe, 1938). (By permission of Columbia Univ. Press, N.Y.)

cracking, and removal of soluble components (see *Quickclay*; Vol. VI).

The role of water in the reduction of shearing strength is a major one. It is particularly important through the introduction of intergranular forces by pore water pressure (piezometric or hydraulic pressure), and the buoyant effect of water. Fine-grained materials on a gentle slope may move by slow-to-rapid flow because they become saturated with water and lose their cohesive strength. Formerly it was thought that water served as a lubricant; except under very special conditions, this is now known to be untrue. The presence of water in rock materials may actually produce cohesion and increase their resistance to some kinds of mass wasting. However, the fact that rapid mass wasting frequently occurs during or following heavy precipitation, rapid melting of snow cover, or the breaking of water mains, does dramatically emphasize the effect of water upon gravity movement. Furthermore, undesirable mass wasting may be slowed, stopped, or prevented by proper control and removal of ground and surface water (see *Electrokinetics*, Vol. V).

In addition to the above-described effects of changes in shearing strength, the stage may be set for mass wasting by an *increase in shearing stresses*. This may be accomplished through the erosional, depositional, and solvent effects of the natural geologic processes, principally through the removal of lateral or vertical support, and by loading. Already mentioned, the work of surface and subsurface waters, waves, currents, winds, and ice (including glaciers, frost, and snow) may accomplish these changes in stress. Less obvious, but important, are increased shearing stresses that may result from internal crustal strain such as tilting, folding, and faulting (including earthquake movements). All these natural processes both *aid*—and *are aided by*—mass wasting.

Mass wasting brought about artificially through the increase of shearing stresses by the activities of animals, including man, merits special attention. Wasting processes occur as the result of excavating (including mining), filling, grading, building, blasting, trampling, burrowing and grazing.

Frequently, the immediate cause of mass wasting

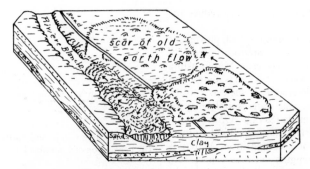

Fig. 4. Earth flow (near St. Thuribe, Quebec 1898; Sharpe, 1938). (By permission of Columbia Univ. Press, N.Y.)

can be related directly to changes in shearing stress brought about by (1) increase in the weight of materials, (2) withdrawal of support, or (3) earth tremors; these causes may be either natural or artificial in origin. For example, major slide, flow, creep, or subsidence may occur as the result of loading by stream deposition or through the activities of man, or by the accumulated weight of excess ground water. The lateral or underlying support of rock materials may be withdrawn as the result of the removal of materials by any agency. New unstable slopes are caused by previous mass wasting; removal of soluble material; mining; expansion and contraction because of freezing or hydration; washing out of granular materials; failure in massive or compact materials resting above less competent materials; the lowering of stream, pond, and sea levels; lowering of the water table; or outward and upward movement of ground water (pore water pressure or buoyancy) (Figs. 1–4). Experience has demonstrated that earthquake shocks may not only be *caused* by sudden movement of unstable masses, but such shocks may also *initiate* mass wasting (Heezen and Ewing, 1952).

Much of our present knowledge of mass wasting has been derived largely from the study of actual landslide types of mass movement, and a considerable body of literature has been accumulated that

deals with both the engineering and geological aspects of these gravity-controlled phenomena. The foregoing discussion reflects this fact. However other mass wasting processes such as slow creep, flow, and subsidence are volumetrically important and merit further attention. Surficial creep, for example, is commonly attributed to the effects of (1) freezing of rock material, (2) expansion perpendicular to a slope, and (3) thawing and contraction, or subsidence with downslope movement (Fig. 5). However, these may not be the only factors producing creep.

Flow of rock materials should be more carefully studied also; presumably, such flow should be a process governed by hydraulic principles. This kind of movement in finely subdivided rock materials occurs when water saturation produces fluidity, and in combination with gravity starts a downslope flow. However, dry flow is not uncommon when a slope is unstable and the angle of repose for particular materials is exceeded. Subsidence or sinking of rock or rock materials is principally the result of compaction or the removal of support; for example, ground subsidence may occur because of the removal of salt, sulfur, coal, petroleum, ground water, or ore. The compaction of materials by natural or artificial loading may also cause landslump. Sinks are produced by the collapse of material above a soluble rock, for example, limestone.

Eckel and others (1958), among many things, deal with the subjects of recognition of potential areas of landslide movement, and preventive and remedial measures to be taken where mass wasting is unwanted. Sharpe (1938) was one of the first to prepare a definitive discussion and classification of mass wasting. Various systems of nomenclature and classification have since been devised (Ladd, 1935; Savage, 1951; Eckel, *et al.*, 1958).

The classification of mass wasting phenomena here included is intended for general use, while its format permits the inclusion of new terms not yet devised (Table 1). The main divisions are descriptive of the type of movement involved: (*a*) landfall, (*b*) landslide (landslip), (*c*) landflow, (*d*) landcreep,

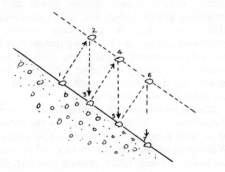

Fig. 5. Expansion and contraction movement on slope.

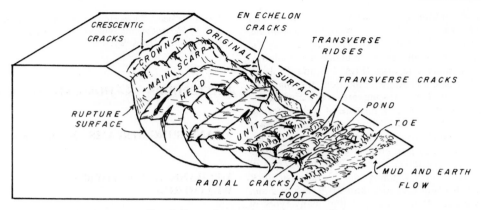

Fig. 6. Successive rotational or slump slide.

TABLE 1. CLASSIFICATION OF SUBAERIAL MASS WASTING OF LAND[a]

Landfall	Landslide[b]	Landflow	Landcreep	Landslump
Free fall	*Wet, dry, or semi-frozen unit planar slide*	*Dry flow*	*Wet, dry, or semi-frozen impercepti-ble flow*	*Wet, dry, or semifrozen slow-to-fast subsi-dence*
Rock fall		Rock-, scree-, or talus flow or rock stream		
Soil fall	Rock-, slab-, scree-, or talus slide; block slide or glide		Rock-, scree-, or talus creep; rock glaciers; stone rivers, -stripes, or -runs	Rock, soil, or debris -slump depression, -compaction depres-sion, -settlement -subsidence, -wal-low, or -sink
Debris fall		Soil flow (silt-, loess-, or sand flow; sand run)		
Debris avalanche	Soil slide			
	Debris slide (earth slide)	Debris flow (gravel flow)	Soil creep or soil terrace	
	Debris avalanche		Debris creep (terra-cettes, animal paths, or cat steps)	
		Wet flow		
	Wet, dry or semi-frozen unit rota-tional slide	Soil-, mud-, slum-gullion-, quick clay flow		
	Rock slump slide			
	Soil slump slide	Debris-, earth sheet-, or overland flow; debris stream		
	Debris slump slide (successive-, pro-gressive-, and retrogressive slump slide[c])			
	Debris avalanche	*Wet or semi-frozen flow in permafrost or cold climate areas*		
		Rock flow, protalus ramparts, or niva-tion ridges		
		Solifluction (soil lobe-, tundra mud-, lobate-, or terrace flow)		
		Debris avalanche		

[a] Classification is based chiefly on relative types of land movement and on kind and relative size of rock material. Climatic factors are generally recognized. As herein used, *rock* is considered to be any angular-to-rounded fragment or block of solid mineral matter ranging from 0.079 in. or 2 mm up to many cubic yards (a block) in diameter. *Soil* is considered to be finely subdivided, somewhat weathered rock material and foreign matter with particles no larger than 0.079 in. diameter. *Debris* is understood to be a mixture of rock and soil. *Avalanche* implies relatively rapid movement and the presence of snow and perhaps ice particles. *Earth* is essentially the same as debris.
[b] Equivalent to European "landslip."
[c] Complexes of self-initiated rotational slides developed successively down- or upslope following the first slide.

and (e) landslump. All these terms have been used to describe overall mass wasting phenomena. Specific terms that have been applied to the various types of movement fit under one or another of these main categories (Figs. 1–6 and Table 1). In all cases, excluding vegetation, the materials involved in mass wasting are considered to be natural, rock, soil, or a mixture of rock materials, snow, and ice, called "debris." An attempt is made in this classification to distinguish generally between only two size groups: (1) blocks and fragments of rock larger than 0.079 inch or 2 mm in diameter, and (2) grains and particles or rock materials ("soil") smaller than 0.079 inch or 2 mm in diameter. It is recognized that many types of mass wasting involves all sizes of material or debris. When a distinction is to be made, it may be necessary to classify on a general percentage-volume basis. The term avalanche implies the presence of snow and perhaps ice particles. Solifluction is essentially soil flow in a region of permafrost, that is, flow of soil in the upper portion of thawed ground.

Attention is called to the fact that many words used in the classification are joined by custom to form one word, for example, rockfall, rockslide, soilflow, mudflow, etc. There is no reason why this should not be done when the word is not awkward. In the classification given here, to be consistent, none of those words are joined. It is sincerely hoped that this classification will make it easier to understand and to classify mass wasting for those concerned with such phenomena.

C. N. SAVAGE

References

Eckel, E. B., *et al.*, 1958, "Landslides and engineering practice," *Highway Res. Board Spec. Rept. 29, Natl. Acad. Sci.—Natl. Res. Council Publ.*, **544**, 232pp.

Heezen, B. C., and Ewing, Maurice, 1952, "Turbidity currents and submarine slumps, and the 1929 Grand Banks Earthquake," *Am. J. Sci.*, **250**, 849–873.

Ladd, G. E., 1935, "Landslides, subsidence, and rockfalls," *Am. Ry. Eng. Assoc. Bull.*, **37**, 72pp.

Savage, C. N., 1951, "Mass wasting, classification and damage in Ohio," *Ohio J. Sci.*, **51**, No. 2, 299–308.

Sharpe, C. F. S., 1938, "Landslides and Related Phenomena," New York, Columbia University Press, 136pp.

Terzaghi, Karl, 1950, "Mechanism of Landslides," in "Application of Geology to Engineering Practice," Berkey Volume, pp. 83–123, Geol. Soc. America.

Varnes, D. J., 1950, "Relation of Landslides to Sedimentary Features," in (Trask, P. D., editor) "Applied Sedimentation," pp. 229–246, New York, John Wiley & Sons.

Cross-references: *Anthropogenic Influences in Geomorphology; Avalanche; Frost Action; Landslides; Mass Movement; Mudflow; Organisms as Geomorphic Agents; Permafrost; Soil Creep; Solifluction; Talus*

Fan or Cone; Terracettes, Lynchets; Weathering. Vol. V: *Electrokinetics.* Vol. VI: *Engineering Geology; Groundwater; Quickclay.*

MATTERHORN—*See* HORN, MATTERHORN

MEANDERING STREAMS—*See* RIVERS

MECHANICAL WEATHERING—*See* WEATHERING

MESA AND BUTTE

A term of Spanish origin, mesa was first introduced into geological literature in the American southwest, and is now universally applied to flat-topped hills and mountains, cut off on one or more sides by steep escarpments or "breakaways." Generally they occur in flat-lying structures, or where a complex (e.g., Precambrian) basement has developed a duricrusted soil (silcrete or lateritic ironstone, "ferricrete"), and base level has been lowered as in multiple pediplanation surfaces.

The diminutive form *mesita* is sometimes used, but it is rare. It is not to be confused with *meseta* which is used for semiarid high plains or tablelands in general and, in particular, by French geomorphologists for a peneplaned (or pediplaned) ancient complex of plateau or high-plain character (such as the central Meseta of Spain).

Mesas are sometimes rendered in English as tabletop mountains or hills (German, *Tafelberg*). Beyond the marginal escarpment there are often erosional outliers (*buttes*; French, *buttes-témoins*; German, *Zeugenberge*). The escarpment is often referred to as a cuesta (French, *côte*) in the earlier literature, but the latter is now exclusively applied to homoclinal, asymmetric ridges (see *Cuesta*). Lahee distinguished the butte that was formerly part of a mesa as a *mesa-butte*, in order to distinguish it from small volcanic cones, diatremes, etc. (such as the Hopi buttes of Arizona); however, the term is rarely used.

"Butte" seems to have been first used in American literature by Fremont in 1845 (see A.G.I. *Glossary*) and was applied on a worldwide basis after its general use by Powell, Gilbert and others. Sometimes knob, cerro (Spanish), kopje (Afrikaans) are used in synonymy.

The term *tepee butte* was applied in Colorado and elsewhere to large earth pillars, pyramids or hoodoo hills of small conical nature (Gilbert and Gulliver, 1895).

RHODES W. FAIRBRIDGE

FIG. 1. A mesa in subdesertic savanna; Mt. Conner, Northern Territory, Australia. The cap rock is a Precambrian quartzite, of subhorizontal attitude. (Photo: C. R. Twidale)

References

Baulig, H., 1956, "Vocabulaire Franco–Anglo–Allemand de Géomorphologie," Paris (Publ. Fac. Lettres Univ. Strasbourg, No. 130), 230pp.

Gilbert, G. K., and Gulliver, F. P., 1895, "Tepee buttes," *Bull. Geol. Soc. Am.,* **6,** 333–342.

Lahee, F. H., 1916, "Field Geology," New York, McGraw-Hill Book Co. (sixth ed., 1961).

Cross-references: *Cuesta*; *Duricrust*; *Earth Pillars*; *Pediplanation*.

METEORITE CRATERS—*See* Vol. II, **ASTROBLEMES AND METEORITE CRATERS; EXPLOSION CRATERS**

MICROATOLL

A microatoll is a ring-shaped organic reef commonly found within the intertidal belt in relatively warm seas, where the mean daily temperature does not drop below about 15°C. The organisms constituting or contributing to these reefs may be single colonies of large madreporarian corals, e.g., *Porites*; they may also be annular growths upon a basis of preexisting rocks (coral or eolianite limestones as a rule) of serpulids; encrusting pelecypods, e.g., *Mytilus*; or encrusting calcareous algae, e.g., *Lithothamnion, Porolithon.*

The dimensions of the microatoll normally range from 1–6 meters across. They are often found scattered across a reef flat or erosional platform every 100 meters or so. The serpulid reefs of Bermuda are the best known, having been described by R. J. Nelson in 1837, and others, notably A. Agassiz

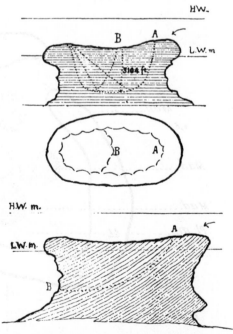

FIG. 1. Serpulid microatolls from Bermuda (from Agassiz, 1895). Above illustrates example constructed on horizontal eolianite bedrock, and below one on steeply dipping dune rock, which may lead to a horseshoe plan. Note relative positions of H.W.M. (high water mark) and L.W.M. (low water mark).

Fɪɢ. 2. Mytilid microatoll at Point Peron, Western Australia (from Fairbridge, 1950).

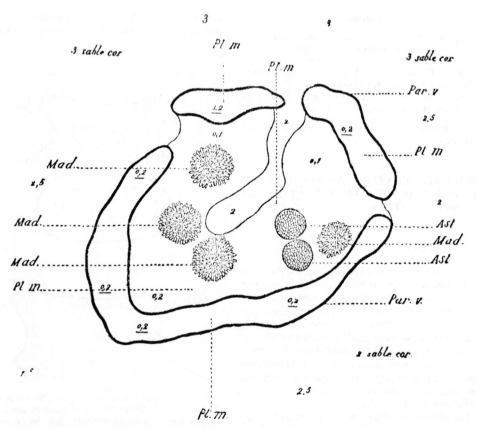

Fɪɢ. 3. Plan of Porites microatoll from Vietnam (from Krempf, 1927), 1.6 meters across. Depths in meters. Pl. m. = plateforme morte, i.e., rim-rock, fringed by growing *Porites* (Par. v.) and micro-lagoon floor. Mad. = growing Madrepora; Ast. = growing Astraea.

(1895), who remarked that they are among the most interesting structures there, "constituting miniature atolls, and barrier and fringing reefs, apparently formed by the upgrowth of serpulae" (but also algae, corallines, barnacles, mussels, etc.). Agassiz found, on hammering the rim away, "that the vertical walls were not built up, as is generally believed, of serpuline limestone, but were composed of eolian rock, and ... that in many cases the elevated rim was protected by the hard ringing crust so characteristic of limestones exposed to the action of the sea, and ... that the coating of serpulae, of algae, of corallines, and of nullipores was quite superficial.... Some of the serpuline atolls are circular and quite regular in outline, others crescent-shaped, while others are apparently formed by the accrescence of two or three atolls." The atoll rim here may be 5–50 cm high and 20–150 cm wide, sometimes leaving only a small hole in the center. The central depression may vary from 15–200 cm in depth. The serpulid crust may be 30–50 cm thick (Fig. 1).

It is apparent that the centers of microatolls are eroded out while the rims grow and protect the underlying rock. Hodgkin has demonstrated that the rate of intertidal limestone erosion in general averages 1 mm/yr. Agassiz (1895, p. 258) believed that microatolls represented the microcosm for all atolls. The organisms concerned grow upward and outward during submersion by high tides, but at low tides, a pool of water is trapped, remaining behind as a miniature lagoon (see Fig. 2). This example is from the coast of Western Australia at Point Peron, where the same type of calcareous eolianite is found as in Bermuda, though the encrusting agent is a mytilid, *Brachyodontes erosus* (Fairbridge, 1950).

The term microatoll was apparently first used by Krempf (1927) in describing fine examples along the coast of Vietnam (Hon Kohé, Annam). However, there, in the warm waters of the South China Sea, Krempf found that the principal reef builder was the colonial coral *Porites*. He pointed out that

one does not normally see the middle of corals being eroded or dissolved away below low tide level. He found instead, in one example (Fig. 3), that there was a degrading reef limestone platform about 20 cm below low spring tide level, evidently cut by solution weathering during a sea-level regime that was just that much lower than the present; this intertidal erosional phenomenon in limestones is strictly limited by the low spring tide level. Almost bisecting the *plateforme morte* as he called it, is a cleft that descends to −2 meters; we would interpret this as the trace of a subaerial drainage channel that developed during brief exposure of the microatoll stump to rainfall erosion. A period of −2 meters eustatic sea level is recorded for Roman times about 1800–2000 years ago, and another brief exposure period occurred some 700 years ago.

As this degraded platform was subsequently slowly submerged by a rising sea level, the *Porites* grew up in an annular shape to form a uniformly raised rim today that is 20 cm above low springs and approximates low neap tides. The inner measurement of the rim is thus 40 cm high. Within this pool, there are scattered colonies of *Madrepora* and *Astraea*, growing up to the level of low springs (Fig. 4).

There is a close parallelism between this interpretation of the microatoll and the full-scale oceanic atoll, as visualized in the McNeil model and demonstrated experimentally by Hoffmeister and Ladd (see *Atoll*).

In the mid-Pacific the microatolls are generally represented by coral heads with raised rims and dead centers, generally the *Porites* and *Astraea* types. However, Wells (1957) mentions "larger, less compact microatolls consisting mostly of the thickly and stoutly branching *Acropora palifera*."

In the Bahamas, east of Andros, Newell *et al.* (1951, p. 23) remark "Immediately behind the barrier at several localities are irregular oval, or ring-like patches of gorgonians and corals surrounded by nearly uninhabited sand floor. These

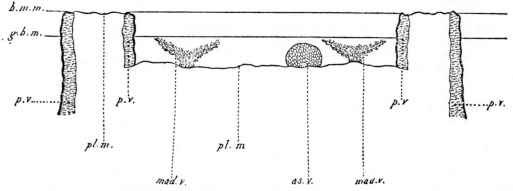

FIG. 4. Section of Porites microatoll, shown in Fig. 3. Pl. m. = plateforme morte, h.m. = high tide level, b.m.m. = mean low water neaps, g.b.m. = low spring tide level, p.v. = living veneer of *Porites*.

FIG. 5. Coralline-algal microatolls from Yucatan, Mexico (from Boyd *et al.*, 1963).

patches range in diameter from about 30 to 100 meters, and growth is most vigorous at the periphery where food and oxygen are most available. They resemble the microatolls of Bikini (Ladd, Tracey, Wells, and Emery, 1950, p. 415)." Comparison may be made also with some small reef patches (not true microatolls) off Madagascar (Guilcher, 1960).

Coralline algae (*Lithothamnion, Porolithon, Goniolithon,* etc.) form the rims on terraces in favorable places, like miniature barrier reefs 10–30 cm high, in many parts of the world and in all oceans. Some of the most spectacular examples are reminiscent of volcanic sinter-rimmed terraces and can be seen on the south coast of Tongatabu in the Southwest Pacific (Lister, 1891). Most reefs, where there is appreciable wave action, have at least a simple rim. The famous algal rim or "Lithothamnion Rim" of Charles Darwin, a feature of every exposed coral reef (of high wave energy), is simply a large example of the same phenomenon; the essential requirement for the algal growth is constant wetting by surf or spray. This requirement enables the rim builder to achieve a considerably higher elevation than is possible for true corals, and in the South Pacific, the rim may reach 2 meters elevation above the mean level of the reef flat (about low spring tide level).

Fine examples of coralline algal microatolls have been described by Boyd, Kornicker and Rezak (1963) off the coast of Yucatan, Mexico (Fig. 5). They rest on the eroded surface of a preexisting limestone. Each rim is about 15 cm wide and reaches 10 cm above an annular platform 50–150 cm wide,

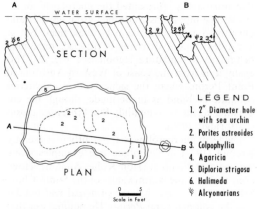

LEGEND
1. 2" Diameter hole with sea urchin
2. Porites astreoides
3. Colpophyllia
4. Agaricia
5. Diploria strigosa
6. Halimeda
Ⅴ Alcyonarians

FIG. 6. Section and plan of Yucatan microatoll (from Boyd *et al.*, 1963).

approximating low spring tide level (Fig. 6). Diameters are 4–8 meters across. The "microlagoon" is 1–50 cm deep. The floor is unknown, being possibly bedrock or earlier microatoll algal or coral growth.

RHODES W. FAIRBRIDGE

References

Agassiz, A., 1895, "A visit to the Bermudas in March, 1894," *Bull. Museum Comp. Zool. Harvard Coll.,* **26,** 205–281.

Boyd, D. W., Kornicker, L. S., and Rezak, R., 1963, "Coralline algal microatolls near Cozumel Island, Mexico," Texas A. & M. Univ., *Contrib. to Geology,* **2,** 105–108.

Fig. 7. Microatoll of calcareous algae, produced by differential erosion of eolianite, as in Bermuda, on sandstone reef flat at the mouth of the Murchison River, Western Australia.

Fairbridge, R. W., 1950, "The geology and geomorphology of Point Peron, Western Australia," *J. Roy. Soc. W. Australia*, **34** (for 1947/48), 35–72.

Guilcher, A., 1960, "Les récifs coralliens à petits lagons multiples de la baie Ramanetaka (côte nord-ouest de Madagascar)," *Bull. Soc. Geol. France, Ser. 7*, **1** (1959), 337–340.

Hodgkin, E. P., 1964, "Rate of erosion of intertidal limestone," *Zeit. Geomorphol.*, **8**(4), 385–392.

Krempf, A., 1927, "La forme des récifs coralliens et le régime des vents alternants," *Trav. Serv. Océanog. Indochine, Mém.*, No. 2, 33pp.

Ladd, H. S., Tracey, J. I., Jr., Wells, J. W., and Emery, K. O., 1950, "Organic growth and sedimentation on an atoll," *J. Geol.*, **58**, 410–425.

Lister, J. J., 1891, "Notes on the geology of the Tonga Islands," *Quart. J. Geol. Soc. London*, **47**, 590–617.

Nelson, R. J., 1837, "On the geology of the Bermudas," *Trans. Geol. Soc., London, Ser. 2*, **5**, Pt. 1, 103–123.

Newell, N. D., *et al.*, 1951, "Shoal-water geology and environments, eastern Andros Island, Bahamas," *Am. Mus. Nat. Hist. Bull.*, **97**, 1–29.

Wells, J. W., 1957, "Coral reefs," in "Treatise on marine ecology and paleoecology," Vol. 1, *Geol. Soc. Am., Mem. 67*, 609–632.

Cross-references: *Algal Reefs*; *Algal Rims*; *Atolls*; *Barriers—Beaches and Islands*; *Coral Reefs*; *Fringing Reef*; *Lagoon*; *Limestone Coastal Weathering*.

MICROGELIFRACTION—See PERIGLACIAL LANDSCAPE

MICRORELIEF

Relief refers to relative height, while microrelief refers to small-scale differences in relief. Microrelief consists of any minor undulations on the surface of the land, usually of a scale which would not show on a normal topographic map. They are common in all parts of the land areas of the world.

Microrelief can be produced by any of the endogenous processes. Thus solution in limestones produces many small depressions, while landslides cause an undulating surface to be produced both in the source area and in the final resting place. Deposition of boulder clay when the ice melts is usually uneven, while ridges occur on most benches parallel to the shore. Likewise erosion by wind or ice tends to form undulations often corresponding to the variations in ease of erosion of the underlying materials.

In polar regions and in areas which were formerly glaciated, *striations* and *glacial grooves* have usually been cut in the underlying rocks by loose blocks of rock dragged along by the ice movement. In currently cold regions, *patterned ground* with stone polygons and stone stripes are common where snow is blown off the surface of the ground. In wet alluvial soils, freezing of the groundwater produces *pingos*—rounded steepsided mounds with a core of ice rising up to a maximum of 230 feet (70 meters) above the surrounding flood plain. *Tors* (angular rocky peaks) may be formed on steeper slopes. Where the underlying permafrost has melted, it often causes uneven settling called *thermokarst*, due to the similarity between its appearance and that of a true limestone region. *Solifluction*, the mass movement of soupy topsoil over a frozen subsoil, is widespread even on gentle slopes and produces marked microrelief.

The polygons extend well into temperate humid regions at suitable sites. Thus, polygons have formed on the shales of the Kettle Point formation exposed on the foreshore of Lake Huron at Kettle Point. These have taken no more than three years to form since the site was covered by Lake Huron until 1961. More usual microrelief is the result of trees being overturned with resulting disturbance of the soil by the roots. Animals burrowing in the ground can likewise produce microrelief, e.g., rabbit burrows, ant hills and mole hills. Solution of limestones commonly produces microrelief while earth pinnacles capped by boulders, and abandoned stream meanders, are only two of many forms produced by flowing water. Avalanches, landslides and mudflows add their contribution.

In the humid tropics, worm casts are a major source of microrelief and these features may be two feet (60 cm) high. Tracks of animals and mounds left by the roots of fallen trees add to the unevenness. In cases of organic surface materials, natural or man-made fires cause patchy burning of the organic matter lying above the water table. This can cause appreciable microrelief in swamps.

Tropical and semitropical arid regions may show a variety of phenomena. Apart from karst microrelief, wind erosion can also produce uneven deflation hollows. Wind transporting sand can erode and cause flutings in the rocks over which it passes, while the surfaces of wind-deposited materials are notoriously uneven, especially where the vegetation consists of clumps of grasses or other plants. Deposition round these clumps produces coppice mounds. These same clumps, which are characteristic of savanna areas also cause patchy water or wind erosion since they protect only part of the surface of the ground.

Large animals such as the bison roll in the dust and make dustpits in grasslands where wind erosion can then erode a hollow. Such small hollows are widespread in the prairies and in the plains of Eastern Europe and are characterized by special soils, e.g., the solodized-solonetz and solod. Termites may produce colossal mounds in grassland areas, and these are very numerous in parts of Africa. Finally there is a whole range of phenomena due to alternate seasonal wetting and drying of soils causing heaving and the production of microrelief. There are a large number of names used in different areas, e.g., hog-wallows, hush-a-bye, Bay of Biscay, etc. Most, if not all, of these are local names for the gilgai microrelief first described in detail from Australia. Until more work has been carried out, the definite equivalence of all these remains in doubt.

Thus, microrelief can be quite diverse under apparently similar topography, even within one climate. Man, of course, adds his share of features. Accidental dropping of matches in dry marshes and swamps in summer, disturbance of the permafrost causing it to melt, planting of hedges parallel to the contour to arrest soil creep, underground mining operations causing cave-ins, deforestation causing landslides and avalanches, and irrigation of dry desert producing *gilgai* (q.v.), or of gypseous beds

causing karst features, are all examples of man's contributions.

STUART A. HARRIS

References

Rapp, A., 1960, "Recent developments of mountain slope in Kärkevagge and surroundings, northern Scandinavia," *Geog. Ann.,* **42,** No. 2–3.
Sharpe, C. F. S., 1938, "Landslides and Related Phenomena," New York, Columbia University Press, 137pp.
U.S. Department of Agriculture, 1951, "Soil survey manual," *U.S.D.A. Handbook 18,* 156–158.

Cross-references: *Anthropogenic Influences in Geomorphology; Earth Pillars or Pyramids; Frost Action; Gilgai; Karst; Organism as Geomorphic Agents; Patterned Ground; Pingos; Prairie Mound; Scabland; Solifluction; Striae, Striated Pavement; Thermokarst; Tor; Wind Action.*

MIMA MOUND—*See* PRAIRIE MOUND

MISFIT STREAM

This term is used for a stream whose size and form suggest that it did not erode the valley in which it is found (Lake and Rastall, 1910, p. 47). Thus, for example, during the melting of glaciers in Northern Europe and North America great volumes of meltwater flowed across the peripheral lowlands. These rivers derived most of their water from the ice and eroded deep U-shaped valleys which had the unusual characteristic of being of nearly uniform size from their source to their point of discharge. After the ice melted, some of these valleys were left without any streams in them, while others carried rivers. All these represent examples of misfit streams. The valleys are obviously of a different form to those cut by postglacial streams since the non-glacial river-eroded valleys are much smaller and shallower and they also decrease in size in proportion to decrease in volume of flow in the stream.

Johnson (1932, p. 487) has rightly emphasized that differences in meander radius between present-day streams and the scars on the river terraces are ideal evidence. However this presupposes that the valley has reached the stage of development of having meanders, a flood plain and terraces. This may not always be so.

The most commonly recognized case of a misfit stream is the *underfit* river, i.e., one which is too small to have eroded the valley in which it flows.

Davis (1913) also recognizes *overfit* streams where the river is too large to always have had the same volume and have occupied its present valley, i.e., the valley is too small for the present size of the river. Examples of both these types are common where *river capture* has occurred.

STUART A. HARRIS

References

Davis, W. M., 1913, "Meandering valleys and underfit streams," *A.A.A.G.*, **3**, 3–28.

Dury, G. H., 1964, "Principles of underfit streams," *U.S. Geol. Surv., Profess. Paper* **452-A-B-C.**

Johnson, D. W., 1932, "Streams and their significance," *J. Geol.*, **40**, 481–497.

Lake, Phillip, and Rastall, R. H., 1910, "Textbook of Geology," London, Edward Arnold, 520pp.

Cross-references: *Glacial Spillways and Proglacial Lakes; Rivers; Stream Capture; Streams—Underfit.*

MOBILITY PRINCIPLE (OF PENCK)

In his studies of erosion, Walther Penck (1927) became most impressed by the idea that *base level* (q.v.) of erosion was not the only controlling factor in the formation of the thalweg of a stream. Here he was directly contradicting the views of Davis (1899) who based his model of the normal cycle of *erosion* (q.v.) on the concept of erosion down to a given stable base level.

Why was there this difference of opinion? Davis had worked on the Atlantic seaboard of the United States where a series of erosion surfaces suggested to him that there had been long periods of degradation in which peneplains were produced, separated by relatively abrupt periods of tectonic movement. In some of the cases, the movements would lead to a long period of marine deposition, while at other times sudden uplift would initiate a fresh cycle of erosion. His evidence was clear and so was his concept of a cycle of erosion.

Penck lived and worked primarily in Central Germany. There, he observed many areas of block faulting with independent movements taking place in the case of each small mountain range. Unlike much of North America, the rocks are of widely differing ages and the distribution of mountains and plains, hills and valleys, lacks the regional uniformity which is found over broad areas of North America. Penck, looking at the evidence from his region, concluded that base level was only part of the story. He pointed out that base level is only a theoretical level, not a point or an actual surface. Thus the level of the North Sea is the ultimate level of the erosion occurring along the River Rhine. However, he doubted whether changes in this base level affected areas further upstream than the Rhine Rift Valley. In the rift itself, it is the tectonic history of the Rhenish Schiefergebirge that controls the levels of erosion. Terraces traced across this mountain zone rise up as they reach the mountain, then follow a level parallel to the present valley floor and then descend at the far end of the mountain to a lower position. Clearly then we are dealing with the effect of a *local base level of erosion.* Similarly Penck argued that the erosion along the Neckar Valley was controlled, first by the movements of the Odenwald block, then by the Rhine Rift valley and only finally by the North Sea.

He regarded local base levels as being of two kinds, one being found at the confluence of a tributary stream with a major stream and one being where there is a break of gradient at any other point. The former is fairly well defined in position horizontally, whereas the second type works its way upstream. Examples of the latter are waterfalls and rapids. Both types have since been well documented [see the ideas of Wager and Baulig in Sparks (1960) and the discussion of waterfall recession in Holmes (1965)].

As we have come to know more about stream action, other cases of sudden modification of river valleys have been discovered. An increase in runoff also causes valley deepening with the consequent development of a nickpoint in the affected part of the valley. This nickpoint works its way back upstream, as is to be seen in many of the valleys of the western United States. The cause was destruction of vegetation by man, i.e., there was not even a climatic change involved in this particular case.

It is interesting to contrast the effect of these concepts on workers in the various countries. The work of Davis, written in English, became the standard for others to follow in most of the English-speaking world. Cotton, Wooldridge, Johnson and others strived to show the value of the work of Davis, and the ideas of the latter are still widely accepted with only limited comment.

In Germany and in areas of Germanic influence, i.e., South Africa, the ideas of Davis were never really given great weight, the mobility concept of Penck being the cause.

Through the recent work of King in South Africa, Penck's views have been modified and refined to a point where they are now accepted as being nearer the truth than those of Davis. This had one other very important effect; it caused Büdel and others to concentrate more attention on the relationship between climate and geomorphology (see Holzner and Weaver, 1965) which has been rather neglected in the English-speaking world. (*Note:* "Mobility principle" should not be confused with Penck's old "mobility concept" which is now abandoned.)

STUART A. HARRIS

References

Davis, W. M., 1899, "The Geographical Cycle," *Geograph. J.*, **14**, 481–504.

Holmes, A., 1965, "Principles of Physical Geology," Second edition, London, Thos. Nelson & Co., 1288pp.

Holzner, L., and Weaver, G. D., 1965, "Geographic

evaluation of climatic and climatogenetic geomorphology," *Ann. A.A.G.*, **55**, 592–602.

Penck, W., 1927, "Die morphologische Analyse," Stuttgart.

Penck, W., 1953, "Morphological Analysis of Land Forms," London, Macmillan (translated by H. Czech and K. C. Boswell), 429pp.

Sparks, B. W., 1960, "Geomorphology," London, Longmans Green & Co., 371pp.

Cross-references: *Base Level; Climatic Geomorphology; Degradation; Erosion; Geomorphology—Principles; Grade, Graded Stream; Nickpoint; Piedmont Landform; Thalweg.*

MODELS—*See* Vol. II

MOGOTE

A mogote is a large residual hill of limestone associated with a karst erosion landscape. It is circular in plan and nearly vertical sided, often riddled with caves. The name comes from western Cuba (Spanish) where mogotes in great number in the highlands of Pinar del Rio (Sierra de los Organos) rise 300 meters above the surrounding flat areas (Bennett, 1928). They are known only in regions of tropical or subtropical rainfall. Gigantic examples are a characteristic of the karst country of Tonkin (North Vietnam) and south China (Klimaszewski, 1964). Their nearly vertical sides, rising abruptly from lush paddy fields, and with tops sometimes hidden in the clouds, have long been an inspiration to Chinese painters; to western

eyes such mountains have often been taken to be figments of the imagination, but the classical painters often captured the feeling of the scenery better than the modern photographers.

In other classical karst regions, the residual limestone hills are often present (e.g., in Yugoslavia, see *Hum*; in the French Causse districts of Massif Central, "buttes témoines"; in Puerto Rico, "*Pepino hills*," "hay-stack hills"; in the Philippines, "Tit hills"; in southern Java and Celebes, "kegelkarst," etc.). General terms for extensive landscapes of this sort are also numerous: *Karstinselberglandschaft, Kegelkarst* (German), *karst à pitons* (French). "*Cockpit Landscape*," a term coming from Jamaica, is almost the converse of haystack hills, but is more characterized by multiple dolinas, rather than residual hills.

RHODES W. FAIRBRIDGE

References

Bennett, H. H., 1928, "Some geographic aspects of Cuban soils," *Geograph. Rev.*, **18**, 62–82.

Klimaszewski, M., 1964, "The karst relief of the Kueilin Area (South China)," *Geographia Polonica*, **1**, 187–212.

Lehmann, H., Krömmelbein, K., and Lötschert, W., 1956, "Karstmorphologische, geologische und botanische Studien in der Sierra de Los Organos auf Cuba," *Erdkunde*, **10**(3), 185–203.

Meyerhoff, H. A., 1938, "Texture of Karst topography in Cuba and Puerto Rico," *J. Geomorphol.*, **1**, 279–295.

Wissmann, H., 1954, "Das Karst der Lumiden-heissen und sommer-Leissen Gebiete Ostosiens," *Erdkunde*, **8**, 122–130.

FIG. 1. Mogotes near Kueilin (Kwangsi), China.

Fig. 2. An isolated mogote in the city of Kueilin. (Photos courtesy Mieczyslaw Klimaszewski).

Cross-references: *Cone Karst* (*Pepino Hills*); *Dolina*; *Hum*; *Karst*.

MONADNOCK

A monadnock is an isolated mountain representing an erosional residual (peak or knob). The penultimate stage of the geomorphic cycle developed under humid temperate conditions is the peneplain, which the innovator of the term, W. M. Davis (1895), himself described as a region of "broad swells of gentle convexity between wide valley floors." The reduction of the land surface to low relief is, however, never complete, and residuals called *monadnocks*, after Mt. Monadnock in New Hampshire, stand above the general peneplain level. The type example is moderately glaciated, but this is not an essential criterion. The German term is *Härtlinge*.

As is the case with inselbergs, the steep-sided equivalent landform in arid and semiarid regions, monadnocks may take the form of hills, ridges or ranges; the essential feature is that they stand in isolation above a given peneplain level, the last remnants of former, higher land mass. Although in theory such monadnocks may be interpreted as representing the final remnants of *circumdenudation*, there is most commonly a structural reason for their survival, for they are underlain by rocks which are particularly resistant to weathering and erosion by virtue of either their lithology or their structure. Quartzites, for instance, are composed essentially of quartz which is chemically almost inert, and so quartzites and quartzitic sandstones commonly form upstanding masses. Likewise, massively jointed igneous rocks offer few avenues by which water and other weathering agents can gain entry to the rock mass and these too tend to form residual uplands.

C. R. TWIDALE

References

Davis, W. M., 1909, "Geographical Essays," New York, Dover reprint, 1954, 777pp. (reprint of 1895 article, p. 591).

Stamp, L. D., 1961, "A Glossary of Geographical Terms," London, Longmans, 539pp.

Von Engeln, O. D., 1942, "Geomorphology," New York, The Macmillan Co., 655pp.

Cross-references: *Bornhardt*; *Cycles, Geomorphic*; *Inselberg*; *Peneplain*.

MONOCLINE—*See* STRUCTURAL CONTROL IN GEOMORPHOLOGY

MORAINES

(1) Definition

Moraines are characteristic glacial land forms, and also features built of clastic glacigene sediments. The latter are transported by moving ice (especially by mountain glaciers or continental ice sheets) and are deposited during both growth and recession (shrinking) of the ice. This picks up rock debris ranging from clay to large block size and of heterogeneous origin, at its base, along its flanks and over its surface. This debris thus is transported beneath, beside, on, within and in front of the ice, and so travels into other parts of the continent (sometimes far removed from its source) or into the ocean where it is deposited as "marine till."

Moraines provide important paleoclimatic evidence: widespread distribution indicates general or continental glaciation, while local distribution during any one period occasionally suggests only mountain glaciation.

(2) History

The name "moraine" is French and comes from the Western Alps (Alps of Savoy and Valais). In this region, it means "hill" or "rubble heap" as well as "rubble" (pebbles). Thus, from the beginning the word "moraine" had not only a morphologic but also a sedimentological meaning. H. Besson ("marème"), W. Coxe and H. B. de Saussure ("moraines") used it in 1779–1780. J. v. Charpentier

(1841) adopted the term "moraine" in scientific geological literature. Flint (1957, p. 130) remarks that the term moraine is sometimes used in European literature as a synonym for till, i.e., the sediment; in North America, the term is more strictly geomorphic. In this article the broader use is followed.

(3) Distribution

The limit of moraines indicates the approximate extent of the glaciated areas. However, in a landscape formerly covered by ice, much of the area at the present time is marked by meltwater deposits (especially till) or bedrock. Table 1 gives the most probable areas of Quaternary glaciation in the world, according to Penck (1933, figures limited to continents; cf. v. Klebelsberg, 1948, p. 472) and Flint (1957, p. 51, 53) respectively. The column "Maximum Pleistocene" contains the ice area at the time of the greatest glacial extension in the Pleistocene, the column "Last Maximum" shows only the area at the maximum of the last glaciation (Würm/Wisconsin). The last column shows the ice-covered areas in present time.

(4) Development and Classification

Moraines can be classified either by their *sediment* or by their *morphology*. Thus, according to the local development, any combinations of the two classifications are possible.

(a) Sedimentological Classification. (*i*) *Surface*

TABLE 1. GLACIATED AREAS (in KM²)

Region	Penck (1933) Maximum	Flint (1957)		
		Last Maximum	Maximum Pleistocene	Existing Ice
North America (without Greenland)	16,700,000	14,825,000	15,735,000	230,197
Greenland	3,000,000	2,160,000	2,160,000	1,802,600
Europe	6,600,000	4,935,590	6,349,890	81,213
Asia	10,200,000	4,859,487	7,714,315	179,083
Northern Hemisphere	36,500,000	26,780,077	31,959,205	2,293,093
South America	⎫	830,000	940,000	25,000
Africa	⎬ 3,800,000	465	515	30
Australasia	⎭	58,000	66,500	1,015
Antarctica	14,500,000	13,210,000	13,210,000	12,653,000
Southern Hemisphere	18,300,000	13,268,465	13,277,000	12,679,045
World total	54,800,000	40,048,542	45,236,220	14,972,138

Moraine. A surface moraine is comprised of debris falling on the surface of the ice as a consequence of frost weathering, falling boulders, rock slides, avalanches, slumps, mudflows and the like. According to Hess (1904), a granite mountainside of 1 hectare (10,000 square meters) produces 5 tons of dust for every 300 frost-thaw oscillations. It is sometimes known as "ablation moraine" and after melting has been called "superglacial till"; neither term is favored by the writer. The rock material is angular and consists of pieces of all grain sizes up to thousands of cubic meters. It does not show glacigene working (such as striations). The finer-grained material (clay, silt and sand) can be carried away from the ice surface by meltwater (fluvioglacial erosion), while the coarser material can be broken up further by frost working. A surface moraine appears only where mountains rise above the glacier surface. When the ice melts the surface moraine drops onto the ground moraine (see below).

The *englacial moraine* is a development of the surface moraine. In the catchment basin of a mountain glacier, the falling debris is repeatedly covered by snow, season after season. Thus the surface moraine becomes englacial (intraglacial). In the ablation area, it is eventually melted out, and the englacial moraine is joined again by the youngest surface moraine. A recognizable englacial melt can result only from stagnant ice. Other kinds of debris within the ice are sometimes also included in the englacial moraine (e.g., ground moraine, transverse moraine and the like). So-called *rock-slide moraines* can be created by rock slides, transported talus; scree can lead to so-called *scree moraine*. The scree accumulating on the surface of the ice during ablation is called *ablation moraine*. If the surface of the ice is densely covered with blocks, one may speak of a rock glacier, but, in North America, "rock glacier" does not necessarily involve ice.

(*ii*) *Ground Moraine* (*Subglacial Moraine or "Basal Till"*). This term includes sediment resulting from grinding (scouring) of boulders in the bottom part of the ice as it moves across solid bedrock. The material shows considerable variation in degree of roundness and grain size. Generally, however, clay- and silt-size particles predominate. Blocks are rare. Meltwater activity is not detectable, and the rocks always appear to be unsorted. The bedrock is worn away by scouring, scratching, and polishing of the rock, and by plucking of rock fragments; the material removed from the bedrock is incorporated in the ground moraine. Here, the softer rocks are reduced to clay, silt and sand-size by the continuous motion, frost and pressure of the ice load. Rocks of greater resistance are abraded and become more rounded on their way to the front of the glacier. The harder minerals (notably quartz) carve glacial striae into less resistant rocks. The boulders also develop facets. Rocks thus worked are called *faceted* and *striated pebbles*. They are an important

characteristic of ground moraines. Continually reoriented in the ice during transport, the pebbles can show different striations one over the other in different directions, and on several faces.

Occasionally a certain orientation of the boulders and a banded structure of the ground moraine are detectable (see "Petrofabrics" sect. 5c) as a result of the motion of the glacier. Ground moraine appears in all former glaciated areas of large extent, particularly just inside the most advanced terminal moraines [see 4a(iii)]. Often the thickness of ground moraines is overrated. The thickness of the ground moraines of piedmont glaciers seldom amounts to more than 5 meters and commonly is only a few decimeters. The thickness of ground moraines developed by continental ice sheets, however, sometimes reaches 10–20 meters.

If ground moraine reaches the surface of the ice through fissures (especially transverse fissures), it is called *transverse moraine*. Here it unites with the surface moraine, or at the front of the glacier with the terminal moraine [see 4a(iii)]. By melting of the ice or by ablation, the englacial and surface moraines are superimposed upon the ground moraine.

As the ice border recedes over the ground moraine area during the melting period, its surface is often covered by a considerable overlay of fluvioglacial material or reworked into these meltwater sediments. These characteristic sediments of the ice border can be distinguished from true ground moraine material by their degree of roundness and sorting. Ground morainal material can become incorporated into terminal moraines at the front of the ice (see below).

Ground moraine containing a matrix of clay or marl is a type of *till* (q.v. Vol. VI) often called *boulder clay* [in Central Europe, the term "boulder loam" is used for weathered boulder clay]. By diagenesis or metamorphism a solid rock, i.e., *tillite*, can develop, especially in the case of the Permo-Carboniferous and Precambrian glaciations. However, the geomorphic relations are rarely discernable.

(*iii*) *Terminal* (*or End*) *Moraine*. This is debris shoved together or melted out from the advancing glacier along its terminal face or "front." Similar material is also found at its sides in the lateral moraines. Collectively they are sometimes called *border moraines*. This material occupies an intermediate position between the surface moraine, passively transported on the ice, and the ground moraine, heavily worked under the ice. This follows clearly from its situation within the moving ice: underneath the ice, it joins the ground moraine; on the surface, it joins the surface moraine. Thus the material may consist of silt, sand, gravel and blocks. True clay is generally less common, if there has been no chemical weathering.

The different grain sizes are completely unsorted, and the various components show no preferred orientation. During the growth of the ice, the border debris is constantly relocated and disturbed.

Morainal sediments consisting of local rock material are occasionally called *local moraine*. Morphologically distinct types of border moraine are *frontal moraine, lateral moraine* or *bank moraine, end moraine* (*lateral* and *frontal moraine*) and *medial moraine* (see paragraph 4b below).

Owing to the seasonal rhythm of the ice supply, during a cycle of general ice retreat so-called *winter moraines* can develop (1–3 meters high). Hundreds of these ridges may be counted as annual terminal moraines or *washboard moraines*. Small, low annual border moraines are heaped up or pushed together by the ice every winter or spring, while the ice stagnates and melts during the summer. This sequence is exhibited by varves and by some glaciers still existing. If the ice terminates in the sea, *submarine moraines* can develop.

Moraine dispersal is the result of the moraine covering being washed away from the slopes to a great extent ("strew moraine"). Weathering over a long period of time can reduce the morainic covering of a plain to a layer of loose bouldery material of allochthonous character (i.e., from other regions). Single boulders of larger size (*Findlinge*) are final relics of former morainic covering.

(b) Geomorphic Classification. (*i*) *Border Moraines, Terminal or End Moraines* (*in Europe often called Wall Moraines*). Horseshoe-like walls may encompass still-existing or former ice tongues as distinct, individual ridges, which are commonly 10–30 meters high, several kilometers long, and 100–1000 meters broad. They consist of border moraine debris, ground moraine, and bedrock sediments pushed up and together by the ice. They are the most conspicuous indicators of former glacial distribution. The most advanced chain of terminal or wall moraines of a glaciation (especially of the last glaciation) can often be followed over hundreds of kilometers along the former ice border because of their particularly distinct shape. According to their situation in the former or present glacial formation, the different end moraines have special names. The ice is surrounded by *bank moraines*, which are divided into *frontal* and *lateral* moraines. Occasionally the term bank moraine is also used to mean lateral moraine. The *medial moraine* lies between two ice streams and is formed upon intersection of two lateral moraines.

Lateral moraines of valley glaciers commonly are found plastered high onto the flanks of the valley. In this case, they are occasionally called *stuck* or *perched moraines* (*angeklebte* in German) or, when looking like terraces, *moraine terraces*. In the so-called *moraine amphitheatres* the terminal moraines achieve their finest geomorphic expression, e.g., near the southern border of the Alps at Lake Garda. There the walls stand 200–250 meters above the meltwater apron ("sandur"). If an unglaciated side-

valley or some other depression is dammed up by the ice, this lateral wall moraine is sometimes called *dam moraine.*

The so-called *ice-pushed* (*Stauch-*, in German) *moraines* and the *ice-pushed end-moraines* are another special form: ice has ploughed up (so-called exaration) the older bedrock by its motion (commonly between two neighboring ice lobes) and has buckled the debris into considerable folds or walls (cf., Woldstedt, 1954, illustration p. 106), or the debris is dislodged and sometimes shifted a considerable distance (e.g., Møens Klint, Denmark). Ice-pushed moraines can be best seen along the Baltic coast, (e.g., Rügen), as they are laid bare, by surf action, in cliffs over 100 meters high.

(*ii*) *Cover Moraine; Ground Moraine, sensu lato.* This is a collective name for the morphologically less-striking moraine forms in the back country, behind the terminal moraines. There they cover with variable thickness large areas of the older substratum. Essentially the ground or cover moraine consists of the sediments of the ground moraine, (*sensu stricto*), englacial moraine and surface moraine. These have been deposited one above the other during the final retreat; together they form the cover moraine. The term "ground moraine" is generally used in a loose sense for this material, but it is really too narrow a term and technically incorrect. Therefore it seems advisable to use it only for the sediment. Cover moraine is commonly reworked or covered by meltwater sediments of the receding ice.

The classification of moraine terminology is still rather confused. A system commonly used, and still widespread, since the Glacier Conference in 1899, involved classification into (a) *modern active moraines*; and (b) *ancient accumulated moraines*. However, there is no reason to label moraines differently according to age when they have evidently developed in the same way.

(c) Moraine Landscapes. Besides the most advanced moraine of a glaciation, there are commonly several other terminal or wall moraines, in some regions dozens of them (*terminal or wall-moraine belt*); when covering large areas they are spoken of as *terminal-* or *wall-moraine landscape*, also called end-moraine landscape, e.g., the Baltic Ranges (Woldstedt, 1954, illustration p. 102). Farther up the basin, the wall moraines become less closely spaced so that the cover moraine and the meltwater formations of the shrinking ice period are prevalent. This normally fairly flat and monotonous landscape, with relief of only a few meters, is called *ice-recession landscape*, formerly "ground-moraine landscape" (cf. Woldstedt, 1954, illustration p. 96). Its level is generally lower than that of the wall-moraine landscape; here and there it is marked by eskers, drumlins, kettles, channel lakes, ice-tunnel valleys and the like. Where the deposits of the ice-recession landscape are mainly a result of their melting out of the ice, one speaks of a *stagnant ice* or *thawed-out landscape* (Gripp), while the term *meltwater landscape* is used where the meltwater influence (fluvioglacial sediments) dominates the moraine landscape.

Shallow depressions reaching beneath the ground-water level were commonly filled up with peat in the Holocene. The still extant river courses in this landscape show considerable meandering and still have unmodified primary features. Where the solid bedrock is pushed into successive folds by the moving ice, the ice-pushed moraine walls can form a *glacial fold-landscape* (cf. Woldstedt, 1954, illustration p. 106).

The *preglacial relief* (landscape before the beginning of the glaciation) is considerably transformed by the ice. In the *terminal basin* the old surface is eroded, while it is buried at the end of the ice stream (where scouring ceases). Old buried valleys can be important for ground-water storage or can lead to development of postglacial waterfalls (e.g., Niagara Falls, Rhine Falls).

(5) Sedimentology and Origin

(a) Origin and Transport. Morainal sediments commonly contain pebbles that are traced to source areas which are limited to small districts.

Using such pebbles as indicators, the origin and route of the ice movement and its moraines can be reconstructed (see Fig. 1). Transfer of the ice-borne debris into river systems can be proved only by indicators, except for geomorphologic indications. Normally, however, the ice route (especially that of a continental ice sheet) varies during the sequence of glaciations. Further difficulties arise from peripheral meltwater accumulations along the ice border. By this process, sediments of two or more ice tongues are mixed. During the next advance of the ice, the pebbles of the secondary deposit are taken up again by the ice and transported farther. Thus, the direct connecting line between the place of origin and the place of final deposition is not necessarily the pebbles' true transport route. *Analysis of indicators (Geschiebeanalyse, in German)* involves the examination of all the boulders and pebbles of a moraine sediment in order to determine the source area. Only a small percentage of pebbles can be traced to their precise place of origin. The others appear over extensive areas, or their place of origin is now destroyed or covered by the sea. The pebble counts change further owing to weathering and fluvioglacial transport (which causes a relative increase of quartz). *Heavy-mineral analysis* is also employed to study the pebbles and their postulated

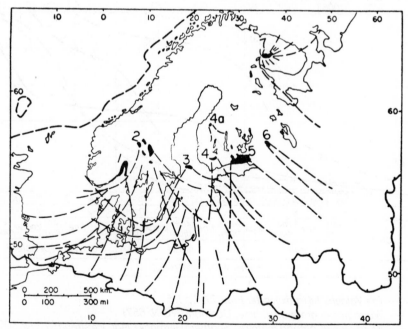

FIG. 1. Dispersal of indicator boulders and pebbles by the Scandinavian Ice Sheet. Only the lateral limit of the indicator fans and a few representative inferred paths within them are shown (after Flint, 1957, p. 125).

Key to Rock Types: (1) Oslo district bedrocks, (2) Dala porphyries, (3) Åland Island Rapakivi granites and quartz porphyries, (4) Satakunta olivine diabase, Hameenlinna uralite porphyry, (4a) Lappajärvi karnaite, (5) Viipuri Rapakavi granites, (6) Lake Ladoga Rapakivi granites, (7) Umptek and Lujavr-Urt nephelite syenite.

areas of origin. In boulder clay, it enables one to discriminate stratigraphically between formations of different ages or between several areas of origin of one formation (facies areas).

Glacial striae or scratches of the bedrock also indicate direction of transport. They are formed by hard boulders and pebbles of the ground moraine. The different directions, which can vary over 180°, are distinguished by the depth of the striae and cross-cutting relationships.

In piedmont (mountain) glaciers, lateral wall moraines give a geomorphologic clue as to the direction of the ice flow, as they mark the place where the ice passes from the mountains into the plain. The distal ends of medial moraines and drumlins point in the same direction.

(b) Grain Size of Morainic Sediments. The grain size of morainic sediments varies from clay-size to large boulders and blocks (sizes up to 100 cubic meters) in different places. It depends mainly on the rock composition of the area of origin and the resistance of the rocks to mechanical abrasion. The resulting great variation in grain sizes is shown

in Fig. 2. Other sediments, with grain sizes within the range of morainic grain sizes (fluviatile gravel, alluvial loam, dune sand, loess and the like), differ from them by a steeper *cumulative percentage curve*, i.e., a higher degree of sorting and smaller variation in the average grain sizes. The *rounding index* of erratic boulders is smaller than that of gravel. There are several methods for the morphological analysis of erratic boulders and gravel, which unfortunately take much time, as many pieces must be measured and many calculations must be made in order to permit correct statistical evaluation.

During growth of the ice, terminal moraines receive fluviatile and fluvioglacial gravel of the piedmont, together with varied marine, lacustrine and eolian sediments derived from the country rock. Frequently in this case, only the examination of the entire rock succession permits clear identification. Some cumulative percentage curves of morainic sediments bear a striking resemblance to those of fluvioglacial sediments, particularly those within the area of the terminal moraine—the outwash apron or *sandur* (Icelandic word = plural—sandar;

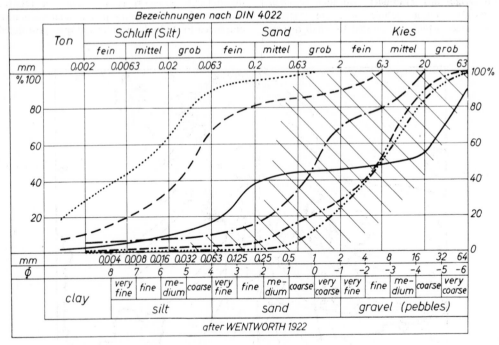

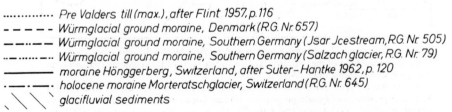

.... Pre Valders till (max.), after Flint 1957, p. 116

– – – – – Würmglacial ground moraine, Denmark (R.G. Nr. 657)

—··—··— Würmglacial ground moraine, Southern Germany (Jsar Jcestream, R.G. Nr. 505)

··—····—·· Würmglacial ground moraine, Southern Germany (Salzach glacier, R.G. Nr. 79)

————— moraine Hönggerberg, Switzerland, after Suter–Hantke 1962, p. 120

·—·—·—· holocene moraine Morteratschglacier, Switzerland (R.G. Nr. 645)

\\\ glacifluvial sediments

FIG. 2. Cumulative percentage curve for moraine and fluvioglacial sediments (after German, 1964).

also given as sandr). In such regions, water erosion causes a natural transition from one type of sediment to the other.

(c) Petrofabrics. In ground moraine material, there is to be observed macroscopically an alignment of erratic boulders, and microscopically an alignment of grains in oriented samples (see *Till*, Vol. VI). Provided that possible disturbances caused later on by ice-push, solifluction, melting phenomena and weathering are taken into account, the motion of the ice can be reconstructed by means of *petrofabric analysis*. The petrofabric of ground moraines is controlled by the orientational forces working upon the bedrock during the moving of the ice (cf. shear planes in the basal part of the ice).

(d) Weathering. Weathering of morainic sediments starts with removal of chalk, limestone and dolomite (decalcification). The weathered (decalcified) form of boulder clay in Central Europe is called *boulder loam*. In the weathering zone some of the striated pebbles may lose their glacial striae. The depth of the weathering zone depends on the climate of the region concerned, the topography, and the time of exposure. When the chalk and limestone percentage varies very much in a horizontal direction, the depth of the weathering zone can alter abruptly within a few meters (depth proportions up to about 1 : 20). Normally the depth of the weathering zone does not vary much within the same region, and amounts to about 0.5–1 meter in ground-moraine material of the last glaciation in temperate zones with 750 mm (30 inches) of rainfall. In deposits of the penultimate (Riss) glaciation, the depth of the weathering zone may increase to twice that amount.

A special kind of ground-moraine weathering leads to the formation of *earth pyramids*. These are steep columns or pinnacles, sometimes several meters in height, capped by erratic boulders. The erratic boulder protects the loose material beneath from erosion until it collapses and the boulder falls. The conditions necessary for formation of earth pyramids are relatively low rainfall and steep slopes which let the water flow off quickly (so that the loose material does not become saturated). As a result of water erosion, the loam columns occasionally collapse and the boulder tumbles down; this sometimes marks the beginning of another earth pyramid cycle. Classic examples are seen in the Tyrol.

(6) The Glacial Series (see Fig. 3; also Penck and Brückner 1909, Fig. 1)

Moraines and meltwater sediments appear in a specific arrangement. This regular succession of sediments and geomorphic landforms, occurring in all glaciated areas, was called the *glacial series* by A. Penck. This term is very important for the stratigraphy of the Quaternary (see especially the discussion of Penck with *Ampferer* and *Knauer*).

The glacial series consists of glacigene sediments, of ground and terminal moraines, and of the fluvioglacial meltwater sediments. Decisive for the geological interpretation of these sediments is the interrelationship of their ages, their different facies, and their mutual transitions.

When the ice is advancing two kinds of processes are to be distinguished: (a) scouring at the base of the ice and (b) accumulation from meltwater in front of the ice border.

The sedimentation of meltwater deposits takes place along the whole ice front. Scouring by the ice depends mainly on the morphology of the bedrock. If the foreland rises steadily, as for instance in the

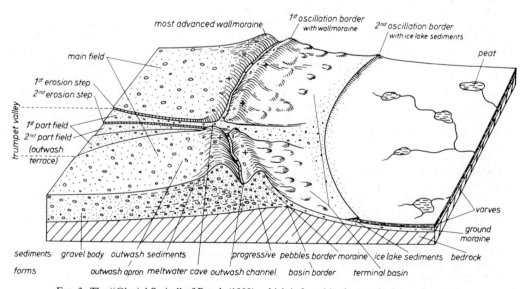

FIG. 3: The "Glacial Series" of Penck (1909), which is found in the terminal moraine areas.

most advanced part of the terminal basin, the vectorial force of the ice motion is directed straight into the bedrock, so that there is considerable scouring (formation of terminal basins by glacial denudation). The meltwater sediments are picked up again by lateral and ground moraines. Where the foreland of the ice tongue slopes down slightly (e.g., outside the terminal basin), the ice does not abrade the bedrock as much (vectorial force more horizontal). Here the meltwater sediments are less disturbed. Only the part nearest the surface is picked up again by the ice. Such coarse fluvioglacial sediments, accumulated by the growing ice and then overrun by it, are called *progressive gravels* (*Vorstoss-Schotter*, in German). As coarse sediments, they may be followed beneath the end moraine and beneath the outwash apron extending in front of it, and pass down the valley into the Main Glacial gravel bed (there is thus a connection between the progressive gravels and the main gravel bed). Thus, progressive gravels are outwash aprons from the ice-growth period arranged one after or above the other, which are continually covered with sediments and overrun by ice. The difficulty of their interpretation lies in the fact that the connection of moraine sediments with the main gravel bed can seldom be observed though it actually occurs (indentation of moraine and gravel bed at the upper end of the outwash apron; several oscillations in Fig. 2). In a few places, the lateral moraine seems to lie discordantly upon the gravel bed, which appears to pass undisturbed underneath the lateral moraine. This has led to an incorrect classification of the sediment sequence of a glaciation developed over short intervals (e.g., division of the last glaciation into two or three substages).

Sequence Determination. The deposition of a Penckian "glacial series" in the Main Glacial (of the Würm) took place within a relatively short time span (particularly when compared with the duration of the whole glaciation). This minor time difference being ignored, the sediments (especially lateral moraines and progressive gravels) deposited at the time of sedimentation of the most advanced moraine are merely different facies of the same subepoch. Farther up the valley, the ground moraine naturally thins out. There, however, it is slightly older than the Late Glacial ice-lake sediments from the time of recession, which cover it in a few places.

The formation of the "glacial series" ended together with the Main Glacial stage of the Würm. The following initiation of the melting stage is inappropriately called the "retreat," or "recession" stage. The term gives somewhat wrong ideas. Since the ice is still moving forward, and the melting time can be interrupted by oscillation, the expressions "retreat" and "recession" apply only to the terminal moraine fronts and perhaps ought to be replaced by a term such as *ice-shrinking*. The Late Glacial stage is characterized by erosion outside the most advanced moraines and by accumulation inside the terminal basin. The "glacial series" in its most advanced parts is intersected by the sinking of its base level of erosion, by which process reentrant, trumpet valleys (*Trompetentäler*) can be developed (Troll, 1924). Distally within the zone of the terminal moraines, little outwash channels develop, and in the terminal basin, ice-lakes are created, whose level depends on the level of the other end of the trumpet valley. Deposited here are fluviolacustrine sediments, locally quite thick, with cut-and-fill stratification (see Fig. 3).

(7) Related Landforms and Moraine-like Sediments (Pseudo-moraines)

Various landforms in glacially controlled landscapes may look like terminal moraines, but may be of quite different origin (e.g., esker, glacial till). Besides these, there are landforms, particularly in the ground-moraine landscape, the origin of which is closely connected with the development of ground-moraine sediments and which used to be included among them (drumlins, kettles). As landforms, however, they are quite distinct and so are their sediments. Moraine-like sediments (pseudo-moraine material) normally show angular debris, irregular distribution of grain sizes, hardly any erosion, and no sorting. Rarely do they contain striated pebbles. Pseudo-moraines often develop in temperate climates, where they commonly show traces of soil. On the evidence of their situation, distribution, and morphology, they can mostly be classified with other sediments. The most important kinds of pseudo-moraines are: earthflow, mudflow, rubble of landslides and floods, talus, soil creep, rockslide, rockfall, blockfield, solifluction debris.

(8) Submarine Moraines

Until recently, all morainic studies were restricted to land areas, but the resurgence of polar and subarctic exploration has brought attention to the widespread subglacial moraines being formed today beneath the great ice-shelves of Antarctica (Carey and Ahmad, 1961) as well as beneath smaller glacial snouts, e.g., in Alaska (Miller, 1953). It seems likely that much of the Permo-Carboniferous and Precambrian morainic material preserved is of this submarine nature.

R. GERMAN

References

Agassiz, L., 1840, "Études sur les Glaciers," Neuchatel, 346pp.
Bohm, A. v., 1901, "Geschichte der Moränenkunde," *Abhandl. Geogr. Ges. Wien.*, **3**(4), 334pp.
Carey, S. W., and Ahmad, N., 1961, "Glacial marine sedimentation," *Proc. Intern. Symp. Arctic Geol. 1st*, **2**, 865–894.
Charlesworth, J. K., 1957, "The Quaternary Era," London, Edward Arnold, 1700pp.

*Flint, R. F., 1957, "Glacial and Pleistocene Geology," New York, John Wiley & Sons, 553pp.

German, R., 1964, "Korngrössen-Untersuchungen an glazigenen und glazifluvialen Sedimenten," *Neues Jahrb. Geol. u. Paläont.*, **7**, 388–390.

Hess, H., 1904, "Die Gletscher," Braunschweig, F. Vieweg & Sohn, 426pp.

Klebelsberg, R. v., 1948, "Handbuch der Gletscherkunde und Glazialgeologie," Vienna, Springer-Verlag, 2 vols., 1028pp.

Miller, D. J., 1953, "Late Cenozoic marine glacial sediments and marine terraces of Middleton Island, Alaska," *J. Geol.*, **61**, 17–40.

Penck, A., and Brückner, E., 1909, "Die Alpen im Eiszeitalter," Leipzig, Tauchnitz, 3 vols., 1199pp.

Troll, K., 1924, "Der diluviale Inn-Chiemsee-Gletscher," *Forsch. dt. Landes Volkskunde,* **23.**

Woldstedt, P., 1954, "Das Eiszeitalter. Grundlinien einer Geologie des Quartars," Vol. I, "Die allgemeinen Erscheinungen des Eiszeitalters," Second ed., Stuttgart, F. Enke, 374pp.

*Additional bibliographic references may be found in this work.

Cross-references: *Ablation Moraine*; *Drumlin*; *Earth Pillars or Pyramids*; *Erratic Block*; *Esker*; *Fluvioglacial Processes*; *Frost Action*; *Glacial Geology*; *Glacial Scour*; *Glaciation*; *Holocene*; *Indicator Boulder*; *Kettle*; *Mudflow*; *Outwash Plain, Fan, Terrace, Sandur*; *Quaternary*; *Soil Creep*; *Solifluction*; *Stagnant Ice Melting*; *Striae, Striated Pavement*: *Talus Fan or Cone*; *Trumpet Valley*; *Valley (Mountain) Glaciers*; *Washboard Moraines*; *Weathering.* Vol.V: *Petrofabrics.* Vol. VI: *Glaciology*; *Ice Sheet*; *Till*; *Varves*.

MORPHOGENETIC CLASSIFICATION

The concept of a *morphogenetic region* is that under a certain set of climatic conditions, particular geomorphic processes will predominate and hence will give to the landscape of a region characteristics that will set it off from those of other areas developed under different climatic conditions (Thornbury, 1954, pp. 60–63). Morphogenetic regions are conceptual devices by which a geomorphologist may relate climate, process, landforms and regions.

The morphogenetic concept does not directly recognize those aspects of the landscape which reflect factors other than process and climate. Thus landforms whose genesis is largely tectonic, volcanic, structural, lithologic etc. are not considered under *morphogenetic classification*, but are discussed under the general heading of *morphostructure* (q.v.). Also excluded are landforms which reflect processes that are relatively independent of climate (e.g., wave-produced features, meanders) and landforms which may be largely controlled by the passage of time (e.g., steep versus gentle slopes, degree of dissection). However, landforms which reflect the existence of *past climates* (e.g., fossil dunes, relict periglacial features) clearly must be considered in any morphogenetic study.

To date, most authors who have discussed "mor-phogenetic regions" have not completely followed the concept outlined above, but have been concerned only with relationships between climate and process, without reference to resultant landforms or to regions where these climates and processes may actually exist. Therefore it seems appropriate to introduce a term for these idealized relationships between climate and process: The term suggested is *climate-process system* (where the word "system" is used to mean "a set of related objects or ideas"). Examples of climate-process systems are given in Figs. 3, 5 and 9. Idealized relationships between climate, process and landforms are considered under the term (and concept) of *morphogenetic systems*. Only when dealing with climate, process, landforms *and* actual regions on the earth's surface is it appropriate to speak of morphogenetic regions. A *paleomorphogenetic region* is any given region in which the landforms largely reflect past climatic conditions. Most modern landscapes reflect both contemporary and past climate regimes (see Table 1 for a summary of this terminology).

Climate and Geomorphology

The influence of climate upon geomorphic processes and forms has long been recognized (see *Climatic Geomorphology*). For example, Davis recognized that "climatic accidents" modify the "normal" cycle of erosion. Many writers have been concerned with the influence of climate on landforms, including A. Penck, C. A. Cotton, K. Bryan, and others (for discussion and references, see Peltier, 1950; Holzner and Weaver, 1965). A few geomorphologists, notably L. C. King, hold that landforms are essentially independent of climate, since the physical nature of processes is independent

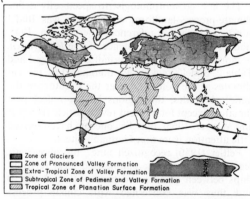

Zone of Glaciers
Zone of Pronounced Valley Formation
Extra-Tropical Zone of Valley Formation
Subtropical Zone of Pediment and Valley Formation
Tropical Zone of Planation Surface Formation

FIG. 1. "Climato-morphologic" zones (morphogenetic regions) of the world (after Büdel, 1963). These zones, which are discussed in Table 2, are regions of specific landform assemblages which have been formed by processes related to present and past climates. Note that these zones represent the interpretations of Büdel and are not necessarily recognized by all other geomorphologists.

TABLE 1. DEFINITIONS OF TERMINOLOGY OF MORPHOGENETIC CLASSIFICATION

Term	Definition	Example: Qualitative Statements
Climate-process system (introduced here)	Concept relating climatic factors to geomorphic processes	Wind action is largely limited to dry climates. The arid climate-process system occurs where precipitation is low and evaporation is high. It is characterized by wind action, desiccation processes (such as salt crystal growth), and very rare but intense rainstorms.
Morphogenetic system (used by Cotton, 1958)	Concept relating climate, process and landforms	Dry climates are typified by wind action which produces dunes and deflation basins. The arid morphogenetic system occurs where precipitation is low and evaporation is high. It is characterized by wind action, desiccation processes and infrequent rainstorms. The landscape is characterized by dunes, deflation basins, desert pavement, salt pans, rock shattered by salt crystals, cavernous weathering, arroyos, patterned ground (polygonal mud cracks, for example), and many other features.
Morphogenetic region (used by Peltier, 1950)	Actual area where landforms reflect present climate and processes	The Sahara Desert is an area where the arid morphogenetic system operates today. It has the climate and landscape characteristic of the arid system.
Paleomorphogenetic region (introduced here)	Area where landforms reflect past climate and processes	Much of the Congo Basin was an arid morphogenetic region during glacial maxima as is indicated by the existence of fossil dunes whose age may be radiometrically dated.

of climatic factors. This viewpoint is valid but overlooks the demonstrable climatic control of the *relative effect* of different processes (e.g., Fig. 8). It would seem that any geomorphic analysis must consider past and present climates in addition to other parameters (structure, lithology, tectonic history, time). It must be recognized that it generally is impossible to isolate completely climatic control of landforms from other controlling factors.

History of the Concept

The first geomorphologist to specifically define climate-process-landform assemblages was Büdel (1963, and earlier references therein). In 1945, Büdel recognized the existence of five *formkreisen*, or morphogenetic regions, as indicated in Fig. 1 and Table 2. Büdel's regions are dominated by present climates at the poles and near the equator; in the middle latitudes, the regions largely reflect past climates. Except for a recent review article (Holzner and Weaver, 1965), Büdel's concepts have received little attention from non-German writers.

Peltier (1950) recognized nine "morphogenetic regions." However, he emphasized ideal relationships between climate and process (Fig. 2 and 3) and thus was concerned with climate-process systems.

Other morphogenetic classifications have been proposed by Tanner (1961) and Leopold *et al.* (1964); see Figs. 4, 5 and 6). Cotton (1958) was the first to state that the actual morphogenetic regions of today are the result of the action of alternating morphogenetic systems during the Pleistocene.

Specific morphogenetic studies have been frequent in recent years. For example, Common (1966) applied the concept of morphogenetic regions to the specific problem of slope failure. Of special interest and importance are the ever increasing number of quantitative field studies throughout the world in which actual correlations are made between climatic factors, magnitude of specific geomorphic processes and the resultant nature of the landscape.

Important Assumptions and Problems

When discussing morphogenetic regions it is important to have in mind several fundamental assumptions and to realize the problems inherent in the basic concept.

(1) The relationship between climate, process and landforms are poorly known and understood. There are individual forms (e.g., moraines) that are known to be caused by processes which in turn are controlled by climate. Conversely, there are many landforms (e.g., pediments) whose genesis is poorly understood, both in terms of process and climate (see *Pediment*; *Slopes*). Quantitative correlations between climate and process are difficult to establish; moreover, such correlations are usually gradational and only rarely does a process cease to function completely. A further problem is that climatic effects are often manifested indirectly; for example erosion is related to climate in many ways, the most important probably being via vegetative cover.

(2) In morphogenetic classification, a very broad

TABLE 2. CHARACTERISTICS OF CLIMATO-MORPHOLOGIC ZONES (MORPHOGENETIC REGIONS) OF THE WORLD[a]

Zone	Present Climate	Past Climates	Active Processes (Fossil Processes in Parentheses)	Landforms
(1) Zone of glaciers	Glacial (cold; wet)	Glacial	Glaciation	Glacial
(2) Zone of pronounced valley formation	Polar, tundra (cool; wet, dry)	Glacial, polar, tundra	Cryogenic processes Stream erosion Mechanical weathering (Glaciation)	Box valleys Patterned ground Glacial forms
(3) Extratropical zone of valley formation	Continental (cool, temperate; wet, dry)	Polar, tundra, continental	Stream erosion (Cryogenic processes) (Glaciation)	Valleys
(4) Subtropical zone of pediment and valley formation	Subtropical (warm; wet, dry)	Continental, subtropical	Pediment formation (Stream action)	Planation surfaces and valleys
(5) Tropical zone of planation surface formation	Tropical (hot; wet, wet-dry)	Subtropical, tropical	Planation Chemical weathering	Planation surfaces and laterite

[a] This table is based upon the writings of J. Büdel. Zones 3 and 4 are transitional between zone 2 (where seasonal stream action and cryogenic processes, especially frost-induced weathering, combine to form deep valleys) and zone 5 (where chemical weathering and sheet-floods combine to produce planation surfaces such as pediplains and etchplains).

concept of *process* is used. An example is the process of mechanical weathering. Actually the term "mechanical weathering" covers many different mechanisms of the physical breakdown of rock: e.g., frost action, salt crystal growth, desiccation-induced shrinkage, organic activity (animal and plant), and others. There is no simple way of relating all these processes to climate since each occurs (or dominates) under differing regimes. Any diagram [e.g., Fig. 7(a)] which purports to relate mechanical weathering to climate is very generalized and idealized. Another problem is that many processes are relatively enhanced by the presence of certain rock types, independent of climate. For example chemical weathering activity is strongly influenced by whether the rock type is susceptible to a given reaction (e.g., limestone, solution; granite, hydrolysis) or not. Morphogenetic analysis largely ignores constructional processes.

It is, of course, possible to *attempt* to relate every specific process (including deposition) to climate. The present state of geomorphic knowledge would not seem to warrant the time and effort involved in such an attempt.

(3) The morphogenetic concept assumes that landscape is climatically controlled. In actuality, however, much topography is structurally controlled. Moreover, landforms reflect relief, time and other factors. Therefore, when postulating that a certain climate will produce a specific landscape it is necessary to assume a certain lithology, relief

and stage of erosion. Since morphogenetic analysis is concerned primarily with erosion, the "ideal" landscape should be one in which erosion is dominant, i.e., a landscape in maturity, with moderate to maximum relief. Furthermore, the bedrock is assumed to be shale, granite (and other crystalline rocks) and those sandstones which are not pure quartz. Quartzites and limestones are excluded because they are essentially monominerallic and are not affected by chemical attack in the same way as other rock types. Volcanic rocks are excluded because they almost always give a strong structural aspect to the landscape. Ultimately, morphogenetic analysis must be expanded to include all kinds of structures, rocks and other factors.

(4) No natural phenomena can be classified without ambiguity. Most classification systems rely upon the fact that there are certain distinct types of natural phenomena. However, these distinct types merge into one another through transition zones which are often broad and which may be as important as the main types. For example, desert and equatorial regions have distinct climates and landforms but they merge in many places (e.g., savannas, monsoonal areas, subtropical regions). Morphogenetic classification is further beset by the lack of quantitative data which relate climates, process and landforms. Without such data it may be impossible to separate landforms which are in dynamic equilibrium with the present climate-process system from those forms inherited from past climatic regimes.

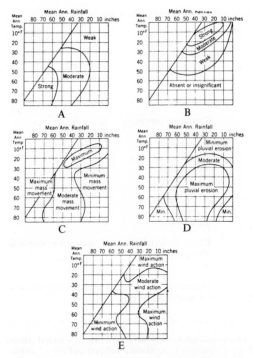

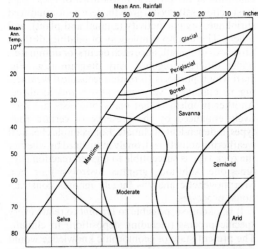

FIG. 2. Diagrams suggesting the relative importance of certain geomorphic processes under varying climatic conditions: (A) chemical weathering; (B) mechanical weathering; (C) mass movement; (D) "pluvial erosion" (erosion by all forms of running water); (E) wind action. Diagrams are by Peltier (1950) as redrawn by Thornbury (1954, p. 58, 60). Compare with Figs. 5 and 7; note that in Fig. 2 cold, dry climates are in upper right corner of diagram. Metric units of temperature and precipitation are given in Fig. 7.

In summary, morphogenetic classifications are subjective, qualitative and artificial. Such classifications constitute, essentially, a geomorphic *model* which must be used with care and understanding!

Previous Classifications

Peltier (1950) proposed nine climate-process systems on the basis of qualitatively conceived geomorphic controls exerted by temperature and rainfall on geomorphic processes. Figure 2 shows correlations between processes and climate, while Fig. 3 combines the various graphs of Fig. 2 in order to establish nine climate-process systems (summarized in Table 3). The type of reasoning which underlies graphs such as Fig. 2 will be discussed later.

Tanner (1961) stated that "for the geomorphologist there are four main climatic types, ... sub-types should be examined after these four have been firmly established." The four types listed by Tanner were: wet (selva), warm dry (arid), cold dry (glacial, tundra) and temperate (moderate humid). Figure 4 is a generalized diagram showing the boundaries of these four climate types. Note that Tanner used potential evaporation and precipitation as climate parameters.

Leopold, Wolman and Miller (1964, pp. 40–46) discussed the classification of "morphogenetic regions" (climate-process systems). Figures 5 and 6 summarize their conclusions. Note that, like Peltier, Leopold *et al.* have used temperature and precipitation as climatic parameters but have reversed the directions of the coordinates and changed the orientation of the graphs. Note also that the terminology used in Fig. 2 and 5 is deliberately qualitative. The relative lack of sharp boundaries in Fig. 6 reflects the subjective nature of morphogenetic classification.

For this article, the author has prepared a new morphogenetic classification. Modifications of, and additions to, prior classifications include: (1) changes in climate parameters; (2) reassessment of climate-process relationships; (3) introduction of the concept of "simple" and "compound" climate process systems; (4) production of a tentative table of morphogenetic systems *and* regions. A fifth modification concerns introduction of a considerable amount of new terminology (e.g., Tables 1 and 4). It should be realized that this terminology is ultimately unimportant; it is the concept which is of great concern to the geomorphologist. In any case, the terms used, though lengthy, are very simple and can be expressed with symbols.

FIG. 3. Diagram indicating possible climatic boundaries of climate process systems as determined by Peltier (1950, p. 222; redrawn by Thornbury, 1954, p. 65). Compare with Figs. 6 and 9. In Peltier's article, the term "morphogenetic region" is used in place of climate-process system. However, Peltier's use of this term was inconsistent with his definition thereof, hence the revision of terminology in this article. (By permission of John Wiley & Sons, N.Y.)

TABLE 3. CHARACTERISTIC CLIMATE AND GEOMORPHIC PROCESSES OF THE NINE CLIMATE-PROCESS SYSTEMS PROPOSED BY PELTIER (1950, p. 215; as listed in Thornbury, 1954, p. 64)[a]

Morphogenetic Region	Estimated Range of Average Annual Temperature (°F)	Estimated Range of Average Annual Rainfall (in.)	Morphologic Characteristics
Glacial	0–20	0–45	Glacial erosion Nivation Wind action
Periglacial	5–30	5–55	Strong mass movement Moderate to strong wind action Weak effect of running water
Boreal	15–38	10–60	Moderate frost action Moderate to slight wind action Moderate effect of running water
Maritime	35–70	50–75	Strong mass action Moderate to strong action of running water
Selva	60–85	55–90	Strong mass action Slight effect of slope wash No wind action
Moderate	38–85	35–60	Maximum effect of running water Moderate mass movement Frost action slight in colder part of region No significant wind action except on coasts
Savanna	10–85	25–50	Strong to weak action of running water Moderate wind action
Semiarid	35–85	10–25	Strong wind action Moderate to strong action of running water
Arid	55–85	0–15	Strong wind action Slight action of running water and mass movement

[a] Compare with Table 2. Note that "morphologic characteristics" as used by Peltier refers only to geomorphic processes, not land forms.

Climate Parameters

When trying to formulate a climate-process-land form relationship, an immediate problem is the choice of climatic parameters. Most graphs permit the use of only two parameters. Most geologists would use temperature and precipitation, since these

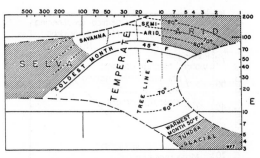

FIG. 4. Generalized classification of climates with approximate boundaries indicated (Tanner, 1961). The class labels represent a geomorphic interpretation. Vertical axis is logarithmic scale of annual potential evaporation; horizontal axis is logarithmic scale of total precipitation (annual).

variables are easily envisaged and measured. However, it should be noted that other possibilities exist. For example, temperature may be used indirectly by means of potential evapotranspiration, a variable which is closely related to vegetation density.

A further problem results from the nature of climatic data. All previous morphogenetic classifications have used data for mean annual precipitation and temperature; in other words, no consideration has been given to seasonality of climate or to other short-term variations. Clearly many geomorphic phenomena are affected by short-term variations in climate. For example, it is known that frost action is more intense under a regime of diurnal freeze-thaw than under a regime of continual freeze, even at very low temperatures. Peltier, Leopold *et al.* and others have considered the problem of seasonality but have not incorporated

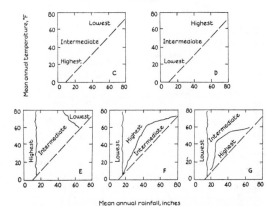

FIG. 5. Diagrams illustrating the relative importance of certain geomorphic processes in various climates (from Leopold, Wolman, and Miller, 1964, p. 42): (C) mechanical weathering; (D) chemical weathering; (E) wind action; (F) mass wasting; (G) running water. Compare with Figs. 2 and 7. (By permission of W. H. Freeman and Co., San Francisco.)

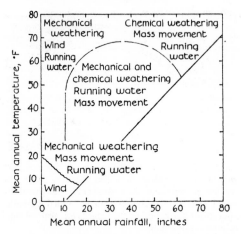

FIG. 6. Hypothetical climate-process systems based on process relationships in Figs. 5 (from Leopold, Wolman and Miller, 1964, p. 45). The possible relative importance of specific processes is indicated by the order in which they are listed. Compare with Figs. 3 and 9. (By permission of W. H. Freeman and Co., San Francisco.)

it into their classifications. A preliminary attempt to use short-term climate variations is discussed later. The climate parameters used in this article are summarized below:

(1) Temperature and precipitation are used since the use of more sophisticated parameters might imply a state of knowledge which in fact does not exist.

(2) Figures 7 and 9 use mean annual data. These diagrams are extended to include very wet and very cold regimes. Note that not all known climatic stations appear within the confines of the graph.

(3) Figure 12 uses monthly data in an attempt to illustrate landscapes which are influenced by more than one climate. Figures 10 and 11 (from Common, 1966) illustrate some further climatic parameters which are of interest to the geomorphologist.

Climate—Process Relationships

Figure 7 illustrates idealized relationships between climate and various geomorphic processes (see also Figs. 2 and 5). When considering these relationships, it is important to remember that they are extremely qualitative, based on a minimum of actual data, subjective, and idealized for a landscape of moderate relief underlain by rocks such as shale or granite, and relatively devoid of tectonic influence (see previous discussion on problems of analysis).

Figure 7(a) indicates combinations of temperature and precipitation where, other things being equal, mechanical weathering is relatively enhanced or suppressed. The major premise underlying Figs. 7(a), 2(b) and 5(c) is that two major climatic requirements for mechanical weathering are alternating freeze and thaw and the presence of moisture. Hence mechanical weathering should be intense in cold moist regions and less intense where: (1) freezing rarely occurs, (2) thawing rarely occurs and (3) moisture is rare or absent. This argument is almost certainly valid, but it actually concerns only

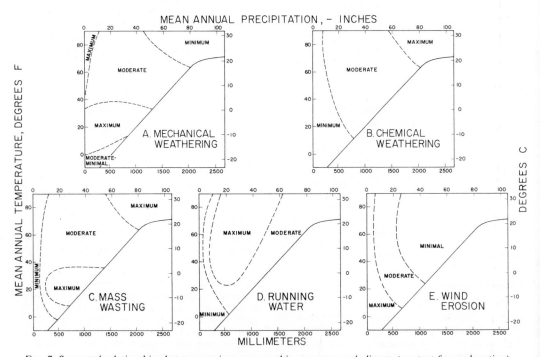

FIG. 7. Suggested relationships between various geomorphic processes and climate (see text for explanation).

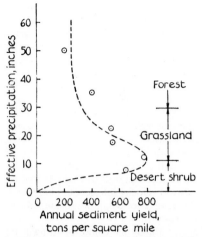

FIG. 8. Variation of sediment yield with precipitation as determined from records at sediment-measuring stations (from Langbein and Schumm, 1958). Effective precipitation is derived by extrapolation from runoff values at gauge stations; graph is calibrated for values obtained at 50°F and does not necessarily apply for hotter or colder temperatures. This graph is very general and does not reflect important factors such as seasonality.

those mechanical processes commonly included under the heading *frost action* (q.v.).

It is becoming increasingly clear that much mechanical disintegration occurs outside of frost climates. Of particular importance are those processes related to desiccation in dry, hot climates. For example, the growth of salt crystals in dry climates promotes many features which are similar to those produced by ice crystal growth. Wetting and drying of clay minerals may produce patterned ground and other features. In hot, wet climates, the abundance of organisms (especially plants) causes or abets rock disintegration. Other mechanical processes such as expansion and contraction of rocks due to heating and cooling must be considered. Very little quantitative data exist regarding mechanical weathering. Figure 7(a) is based on the unproved assumption that freeze-thaw and desiccation promote maximum mechanical weathering whereas climates lacking freeze-thaw and desiccation are associated with relatively minimal mechanical weathering.

Figure 7(b) outlines the general importance of chemical weathering relative to temperature and precipitation. There are a multitude of chemical reactions; no one graph could summarize their relation to climate. Since both limestone and quartzite are excluded from consideration (see earlier discussion), it is possible to ignore the process of solution, at least in order to make some first approximations. If this is done, it is possible to base Fig. 7(b) [also Figs. 2(a) and 5(d)] on the fact that most weathering reactions involve water as an active or catalytic agent; also it is known that the

rate of most chemical reactions increases with increasing temperature, everything else being constant. Thus chemical weathering should be relatively intense in hot, humid regions (i.e., the tropics) and least in arid regions, with progressive variation in between. As pointed out by Peltier (1950, p. 217), tropical regions have dense vegetation which produces organic acids which further promote chemical decay. Recent studies indicate that chemical weathering is much more important in dry climates than has been thought. Evidently the presence of water, even in small quantities, is sufficient to promote considerable decomposition of rock.

Nonetheless, the general relationship indicated by Fig. 7(b) is probably broadly correct. If solution reactions are considered, the situation is more complicated. Carbonate solution is maximum in cool, wet environs, whereas silicate solution is highest in hot, wet regions. Caliche formation seems most important in fairly dry, warm regimes with irregular or seasonal rainfall. Thus Fig. 7(b) holds only for reactions which do not concern solution or reprecipitation. If the latter reactions are included, the figure may still be *broadly* correct; however, there are few data presently available which can resolve this problem.

Figures 7(c), 2(c) and 5(f) illustrate the probable importance of mass movement relative to variations in climate. There are considerable differences between these figures, but all three indicate that mass movement is favored in wet climates, especially those which are relatively hot or cold. Such climates promote maximum weathering (mechanical or chemical) and hence promote accumulation of movable debris. Also most mass movements are favored by the availability of moisture. Leopold

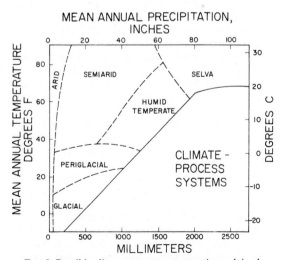

FIG. 9. Possible climate-process systems. As explained in the text, six climatic groups can be recognized, each of which should be associated with a distinctive assemblage of geomorphic processes.

et al. (1964, p. 44) suggest that "a relatively even distribution throughout the year rather than a concentration of heavy precipitation should favor mass wasting processes over those of surface runoff. Thus there might be expected some dominance of mass wasting as a geomorphic agent in wet regions having relatively even distributions of precipitation." However, concentrated precipitation is important in promoting "rapid" mass movements such as landslides, earth-flows and mudflows. Even creep may be promoted by alternate wetting and drying. Quantitative measurements are too few to determine whether mass wasting, as a whole, is favored by steady or concentrated precipitation.

Figure 7(d) outlines the variation of erosion by running water with climate; the figure differs appreciably from Figs. 2(d) and 5(g). It is generally recognized that running water is the most important of the earth's subaerial erosional agents and that action by running water is a major agent even in very dry climates. However, it is clear that the relative effectiveness of stream and overland flow depends in part upon the amount of water available. All other things being equal (infiltration, for example), fluvial erosion should increase with increasing precipitation. However, climatic conditions which produce dense vegetation covers (e.g., the tropics) should not produce maximum water erosion, since vegetation resists such erosion and also utilizes much of the available moisture. Hence, stream erosion should be at a maximum where runoff is high and vegetation is sparse. Conversely, where vegetation is dense or where precipitation is scarce, there will be minimal erosion by flowing water. Langbein and Schumm (1958) showed that for mean temperatures of about 50°F (10°C) an annual precipitation of 15 inches (38 cm) produces maximum sediment yield (Fig. 8). Erosion decreases rapidly as precipitation decreases. As precipitation increases above 15 inches annually, erosion gradually decreases due to increase in vegetative cover. For higher temperatures, the graph in Fig. 8 would be displaced upward, i.e., maximum erosion occurs with higher precipitation in warmer climates (due to the effect of evapotranspiration on vegetation density).

From Fig. 8 it would seem that maximum stream action occurs in climates of a semiarid or subhumid nature. Possibly the zone of maximum erosion extends to frost climates where vegetation is sparse and seasonal runoff can be quite high due to storage of precipitation as snow and ice. Mechanical erosion by running water is at a relative minimum in very dry and very hot, wet regimes. In the latter, chemical load is of extreme importance. However, if chemical stream load is considered to be related to chemical weathering, then Fig. 7(b) may crudely account for this factor.

Figure 7(e) illustrates the relationship between wind erosion and climate. Figures 2(e), 5(e) and 7(e) are essentially in agreement in placing maximum wind erosion in dry climates. Wind action is most effective where vegetation is sparse; hence, wind erosion is most important in very arid regimes. As precipitation increases, vegetation increases, and the effect of wind rapidly decreases. Even in dry climates, wind erosion may not be the most important agent, as was once thought. Cold climates should promote wind action since such climates are characterized by relatively open vegetation and relatively high wind velocities. Conversely the equatorial doldrums should show little effects of wind activity except in localized situations (e.g., coasts). Figure 7(e) does not take latitudinal variation of wind velocity into account but merely shows the progressive lessening of erosion with increased precipitation

Further diagrams could be drawn for other processes. For example, a graph relating glacial action to climate would show maximum glacial erosion in cold, wet climates and minimum (i.e., no) glacial erosion in warm climates. Miller (1964) has prepared a tentative morphogenetic classification of glaciers from which it may be possible to relate glacial landforms to climate.

Climate—Process Systems

Figure 9 illustrates six climate-process systems. As indicated previously, a climate-process system is merely an idealized statement or concept relating climate and geomorphic process. Table 4 summarizes both the climatic and the geomorphic aspects of the six systems of Fig. 9.

Figure 9 is equivalent to the diagrams of "morphogenetic regions" which have been published by Peltier and by others (Figs. 3 and 6). All such diagrams are obtained by superposing graphs of specific processes versus climate. The choice of boundaries is generally arbitrary (see discussion below). Some systems are quite straightforward, assuming that the climate-process relationships of Fig. 7 are essentially valid. Certainly it is valid to imagine a concept of a glacial climate-process system in which a cold, wet climate acts to induce glacial, cryogenic and eolian activity and ultimately a "glacial" landscape. The arid system is characterized by wind action, desiccation processes and the minimal activity of other agents. The selva system has intense chemical weathering, much mass wasting and moderate activity of other agents. Wind and frost action are absent under a selva regime.

The remaining systems are less clear-cut, partly because they are less extreme. The periglacial regime is generally recognized and is characterized by intense frost action coupled with much solifluction and the moderate activity of many other processes. The humid temperate regime is a true amalgam of nearly all the important landscaping agents except wind and ice. In a semiarid (or subhumid) climate, the action of running water is supreme. Most other

TABLE 4. SIMPLE MORPHOGENETIC SYSTEMS

System Name		Equivalent Koppen Climates[a]	Dominant Geomorphic Processes[b]	Landscape Characteristics[c]
Glacial	EF	Icecap	Glaciation	Glacial scour
			Nivation	Alpine topography
			Wind action (freeze-thaw)	Moraines, kames, eskers
Periglacial	ET	Tundra	Frost action	Patterned ground
	EM		Solifluction	Solifluction slopes, lobes,
	D-c	Humid microthermal	Running water	terraces
				Outwash plains
Arid	BW	Desert	Desiccation	Dunes, salt pans (playas)
			Wind action	Deflation basins
			Running Water	Cavernous weathering
				Angular slopes, arroyos
Semiarid	BS	Steppe	Running water	Pediments, fans
(subhumid)	Cwa	Tropical savanna	Weathering (especially mechanical)	Angular slopes with coarse debris
			Rapid mass movements	Badlands
Humid temperate	Cf	Humid mesothermal	Running water	Smooth slopes, soil covered
	D-a		Weathering (especially chemical)	Ridges and valleys
			Creep (and other mass movements)	Stream deposits extensive
Selva	Af	Tropical	Chemical weathering	Steep slopes, knife-edge ridges
	Am	Monsoonal	Mass movements	Deep soils (laterites included)
			Running water	Reefs

[a] Equivalents are approximate, and not exhaustive.
[b] Processes are listed in order of relative importance to landscape (not in order of absolute magnitude). List is abbreviated.
[c] Both erosional and depositional forms are included. List is neither comprehensive nor definitive, merely suggestive.

processes operate, to greater or lesser degree.

The choice of names for the six climate-process systems is somewhat arbitrary and involves semantic inconsistencies. The terms arid, semi-arid, glacial and humid temperate refer to fairly specific climatic types. The term *selva* (q.v.) refers to a vegetative type (tropical rain forest) but by extension has become associated with most aspects of the humid tropics. The term periglacial refers to *areas* peripheral to glaciers but by extension is often used to include any *climate* characterized by *frost action* (q.v.).

Boundaries

Many criteria can be used to help determine the subjective and arbitrary boundaries of climate-process systems. The best criteria are those directly relating climate to process. Among geomorphic relationships which might be used are: climatic limit of glaciation and glacier formation, limit of permafrost, limit of laterite formation, maximum precipitation under which dune migration normally occurs, relationship between precipitation and erosion (Fig. 8), and many others. The criteria used by climatologists in classifying climates may be useful also. Table 4 includes possible relationships between climate-process systems and climates as

classified by Köppen. Indeed, the boundaries drawn in Fig. 9 are based in part on these relationships. This unfortunate situation reflects the difficulty of making general, quantitative statements about climate-process relationships. Should any classification of climate-process systems become generally accepted (which is unlikely in the near future), it will become important to define system boundaries. However it should always be recognized that such boundaries are really artificial and represent transitions from one clearly identifiable system to another. Figures 10 and 11 give additional boundary criteria.

Seasonality

Figure 9 does not completely correspond to actual climatic conditions in the world. This is because it uses annual data as a basis whereas most actual climates show a considerable seasonal (or monthly, weekly, etc.) variation from the annual average. Thus on Fig. 9 there is no way to distinguish between a semiarid region in which a modest amount of precipitation (e.g., 15 inches) is distributed evenly throughout the year and a semiarid region in which the same amount of precipitation falls during a few months, the remaining months being dry. Moreover, there is no way of telling whether a dry season corresponds in time to high

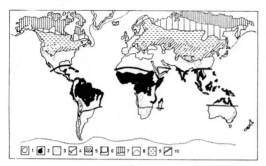

FIG. 10. Temperature data which appear to be important to the geomorphologist and which could be used to help determine morphogenetic boundaries (from Common, 1966). (By permission of Heinemann Educ. Books, London.)

(1) Average actual temperatures below 32°F all the year.

(2) Average actual temperatures above 70°F all the year.

(3) Poleward limit of average actual 70°F isotherm.

(4) Equatorward limit of average actual 32°F isotherm.

(5) Zone of overlap between 32 and 72°F isotherms.

(6) Approximate position of average actual 32°F isotherm in April and October.

(7) Approximate limit of general permafrost.

(8) Approximate limit of pack ice.

(9) Extensive microthermal zone particular to the northern hemisphere.

(10) Land areas where diurnal range of temperature is greater than annual range.

Note how in the northern hemisphere the length of the frost period or the range of average actual temperatures must be morphologically significant over considerable areas. The intertropical area where diurnal ranges are important extends over much of the land area in the southern hemisphere.

temperatures (as in India) or to relatively low temperatures (as in Manitoba).

Seasonal variations are of considerable geomorphic importance. For example *laterites* (q.v. pr Vol. VI) do not form under a strictly selva regime but only where a hot climate is characterized by strongly seasonal variation in precipitation (i.e., monsoonal or savanna climates). Furthermore, if one studies the actual climates of the world, it soon becomes apparent that there are virtually no simple semiarid climates—all such dry climates involve considerable seasonality of precipitation (and often seasonality of temperature as well). Similarly, there are few simple periglacial climates.

A first attempt to introduce seasonality into morphogenetic classification is made in this article. Rather than analyze the infinite possible combinations of geomorphic variables, it has been deemed best to look at actual climates and to describe a minimum number of basic types (seasonal and nonseasonal) which characterize most of the world.

These types can then be correlated with the systems outlined in Fig. 9.

Use of a simplified climate classification proposed by Strahler (1965) makes it possible to recognize seven basic climate types which are directly related to the major air masses of the world (see Fig. 12 and Table 5). Three of these climates correlate fairly nicely with the systems of Fig. 9. Equivalent regimes are: equatorial—*selva*; desert—*arid*; polar—*glacial* (climate-process systems are italicized). The middle-latitude equable climate of Strahler corresponds roughly to the *humid temperate* system outlined in Fig. 9, although in polar latitudes this climate is somewhat periglacial.

The remaining three regimes of Strahler are strongly seasonal, and thus do not correlate with the systems of Fig. 9. The tropical wet-dry and Mediterranean climates show seasonality in precipitation and actually represent regimes which *oscillate* between humid temperate and selva conditions, on the one hand, and arid and semiarid conditions, on the other. Areas subjected to these climates should show a combination of the landscape characteristics of these systems and, in addition, should have some morphological features peculiar to seasonal precipitation (e.g., laterite, caliche). The seventh regime described by Strahler, *continental*, is seasonal in temperature (and, to some extent, precipitation) and oscillates between glacial and periglacial conditions, on the one hand, and semiarid and humid temperate conditions, on the other. It too should show a composite of landscape features, e.g., talus produced by frost action in the cold winter and grus weathered out chemically during the summer.

Table 4 summarizes the seven regimes and indicates the control of these climates by air mass dynamics. The nonseasonal regimes are those dominated by a single air mass throughout the year. Such regimes produce *simple* climate-process systems. Where more than one air mass dominates during the year, a seasonal regime occurs, and a *compound* climate-process system results. Compound systems are characterized by seasonal climates and the resultant composite landscape.

Summary

Morphogenetic analysis is a subjective technique by which correlations are made between climates and landforms. In the simplest analysis, there are three geomorphically significant climates: glacial, dry, wet. More generally, there are probably about seven dominant climate-process systems; arid (desert), glacial, selva and humid temperate systems occur under the year-round dominance of a single air mass. Where air masses vary throughout the year, seasonality results. Three systems are seasonal: continental (periglacial winter, semiarid or humid temperate summer), mediterranean (alternating semiarid and humid temperate conditions), and

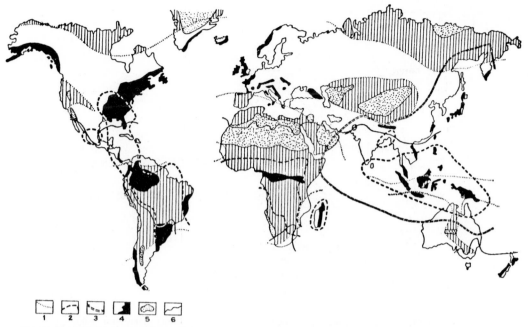

FIG. 11. Precipitation regime data which appear to be important to the geomorphologist and which can be used to help determine morphogenetic boundaries (from Common, 1966). (By permission of Heinemann Educ. Books, London.)

(1) Areas essentially outside temperate and tropical storm tracks.
(2) Thunderstorm zones of importance.
(3) Areas with monsoon type of climate.
(4) Areas with at least 2 inches of precipitation in January, April, July and October.
(5) Areas with less than 5 inches of precipitation per year.
(6) General equatorward limit of snowfall.

The basic pattern of the precipitation regime suggests that arid zones separate three humid areas.

TABLE 5. SIMPLIFIED CLASSIFICATION OF CLIMATIC REGIMES BASED ON AIR
MASS DYNAMICS (AFTER STRAHLER, 1965) AND COMPARISON WITH
CLIMATE-PROCESS SYSTEMS[a]

Climatic Regime	Air Mass Dominance	Relation to Climate-Process Systems
Polar	cA (year round)	Same as glacial; locally periglacial
Desert	cT (year round)	Same as arid
Equatorial	mT (year round)	Same as selva
Middle latitude equable	mP (year round) mT (wet season)	Same as humid temperate; locally periglacial or semiarid
Tropical wet-dry	cT (dry season) MT (wet season)	Seasonal oscillation between selva and semiarid-arid; locally humid temperate
Mediterranean	cT (dry season) mT (wet season) mP (wet season)	Seasonal oscillation between humid temperate and semiarid-arid
Continental	mT (warm season) cP (cold season)	Seasonal oscillation between glacial-periglacial and semiarid-humid temperate.

[a] Air masses: c = continental, m = maritime, P = polar, A = arctic, T = tropical.

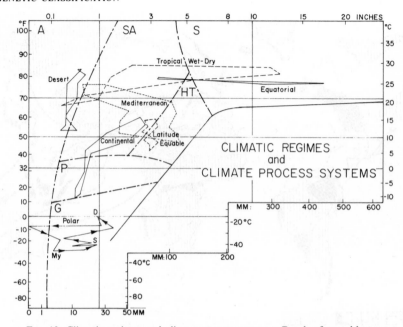

FIG. 12. Climatic regimes and climate-process systems. Graph of monthly precipitation and temperature data derived by Strahler (1965) and termed a thermohyet diagram. Temperature scale is proportional to fourth power of temperature in degrees Kelvin, while precipitation scale is proportional to square root of precipitation depth. Distortion of scales results in emphasis of dry climates. Boundaries of climate-process systems are given by dash-dot lines; each system is labeled by one or two letters indicative of name (A = arid etc.). Climatic data from stations typical of each of the seven dominant climatic regimes are plotted and labeled. For example, the Polar regime data is from McMurdo Sound, Antarctica. December values (labeled D) are about 1 inch precipitation at a temperature just below 0°F. Monthly variations follow line (note arrows) so that May values (My) are 0.1 inch precipitation at −30°F. Stations used for other regimes are: equatorial—Padang, Sumatra; tropical wet-dry—Calcutta, India; desert—William Creek, Australia; Mediterranean—Izmir, Turkey; continental—Winnipeg, Manitoba; middle-latitude equable—Dunedin, New Zealand, indicated in figure as "latitude equable." (Regime diagrams courtesy John Oliver, Columbia University.)

tropical wet-dry (alternating selva and semiarid-arid conditions).

Each of these systems should produce a distinctive suite of landforms, all other things being equal (structure, relief, etc.). Possible landform characteristics are indicated in Table 3 for the nonseasonal systems (including two nonseasonal systems, semi-arid and periglacial, which seldom exist in a pure state in nature). Seasonal systems should produce landscapes combining features of their simple constituents, plus a few features characteristic of seasonality (especially soils).

Examples of each dominant system can be given. Such examples are true morphogenetic regions, i.e., regions in which physiography reflects climatic controls, Examples include: arid—Sahara, selva—Congo Basin, glacial—Antarctica, humid temperate—lowlands of New Zealand, Mediterranean—Southern California coast, tropical wet-dry—India, and continental—Wyoming. Of course, each of these areas contains some landforms no longer

in climatic equilibrium, and are partly paleomorphogenetic regions.

Examples of pure paleomorphogenetic regions are more difficult to cite. Terrain completely modified by glaciation and now ice free, is perhaps the best example of a landscape totally unrelated to today's climates.

While morphogenetic analysis is still rather speculative, it represents a major aspect of geomorphic activity. One goal of geomorphology should be the quantification of climate-process-landform relationships and the further analysis of existing landscapes in terms of climate and paleoclimate.

LEE WILSON

References

Büdel, J., 1963, "Klima-Genetishe Geomorphologie," *Geographische Rundschau*, **15,** 285–286 (English summary).

Common, R., 1966, "Slope Failure and Morphogenetic

Regions," in "Essays in Geomorphology," pp. 53–82, New York, American Elsevier.

Cotton, C. A., 1958, "Alternating Pleistocene morphogenetic systems," *Geol. Mag.*, **95**, 125–136.

Holzner, L., and Weaver, G. D., 1965, "Geographic evaluation of climatic and climatogenetic geomorphology," *Ann. Assoc. Amer. Geog.*, **55**, 592–602.

Langbein, W. B., and Schumm, S. A., 1958, "Yield of sediment in relation to mean annual precipitation," *Trans. Am. Geophys. Union*, **39**, 1076–1084.

Leopold, L., Wolman, M. G., and Miller, J., 1964, "Fluvial Processes in Geomorphology," pp. 40–46, San Francisco, W. H. Freeman.

Miller, M., 1964, "Morphogenetic classification of Pleistocene glaciations in the Alaska-Canada Boundary Range," *Proc. Am. Phil. Soc.*, **108**, 247–256.

Peltier, L., 1950, "The geographical cycle in periglacial regions . . . ," *Ann. Assoc. Amer. Geog.*, **4**, 214–236.

Strahler, A. N., 1965, "Introduction to Physical Geography," pp. 111–116, New York, John Wiley & Sons.

Tanner, W. F., 1961, "An alternate approach to morphogenetic climates," *Southeastern Geol.*, **2**, 251–257.

Thornbury, W. D., 1954, "Principles of Geomorphology," pp. 58–65, New York, John Wiley & Sons.

Cross-references: *Climatic Geomorphology; Erosion; Frost Action; Geomorphology—Principles; Geomorphology—Statistical Analysis; Land Mass and Major Landform Classification; Morphogenetic Regions; Morphostructure; Pediment; Periglacial Eolian Effects; Quantitative Geomorphology; Selva; Slopes; Weathering.* Vol. II: *Climatic Classification; Climate and Geomorphology; Evapotranspiration.* pr Vol. VI: *Laterite; Runoff.*

MORPHOGENETIC REGIONS

According to Peltier (1950, p. 217) morphogenetic regions are those geomorphic areas that are characterized by *climatic regimes* "within which the intensity and relative significance of the various geomorphic processes are . . . essentially uniform." They can be defined broadly in terms of *temperature* versus *rainfall*, and nine such regions were so designated. Peltier (*op. cit.*) also defined the principal *geomorphic agents* in the same terms, indicating climatic fields of weaker or stronger action (see detailed discussion, figures and table 3 in *Morphogenetic Classification*).

W. M. Davis (1899), taking the "normal" cycle of geomorphology to be appropriate to the temperate humid climatic regions, described the geomorphic phenomena of other environments as "climatic accidents." While he recognized youth-maturity-old age within any geographic cycle, this was morphology viewed only within the present instant of geologic time, ignoring the long and varied historical preparation of the landscape. A wider view was developed by the European school, Albrecht and Walter Penck, de Martonne, Passarge, and more recently Visher (1941), Büdel (1948), and Tricart and

Cailleux (1955). Thus a particular geological formation of uniform lithology may respond quite differently if it is affected in different areas of outcrop by distinct climatic regimes.

A further complication is added by the multicyclic or polygenetic history (see Fig. 1) of most landforms resulting from the march of climatic belts north and south with every successive glacial/interglacial phase (see *Landscape Types—Genetic*).

We now recognize that the influence of those great climatic oscillations is worldwide. No polar nunatak or equatorial selva was unaffected. In this way, morphogenetic regions should have an inheritance factor. It will not be constant. For example, in the northern hemisphere, the northern border of a subtropical arid zone morphogenetic region will bear traces of cool humid westerly (pluvial) and periglacial regimes. On the southern border, this same region will show an "overprint" of inherited features of an earlier warm humid (monsoon pluvial) regime.

Büdel (1944, 1948) described the unit of this integration of genetic processes as a "landform association" (*Formkreis*, pl. *Formenkreise*). The importance of the inherited features is particularly stressed in recent papers (e.g., Büdel, 1963, p. 286): "Almost everywhere . . . fossil landforms occupy a far greater area than the landforms developed by currently active processes."

An important distinction by Hartshorne (1939; also Büdel, *op. cit.*, Holzner and Weaver, 1965) is made between (a) *climatic geomorphology*, the currently active aspect, providing us with a *morpho-climatic classification*, and (b) *climato-genetic geomorphology*, which offers a *morphogenetic classification* (q.v.). (Some confusion may result in Peltier's use of "morphogenetic" where "morphoclimatic" was implied. He recognized the role of inheritance but paid only lip service to it).

Mapping Morphogenetic Regions

The concept of the morphological or physio-

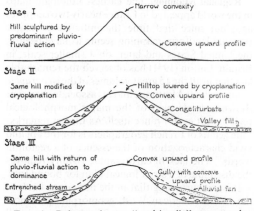

FIG. 1. Polygenetic or "multicyclic" topography (Peltier, 1950).

graphic region especially as a mappable unit of the land surface has evolved gradually from a simple categorization of mountain belts, highlands, plateaus, uplands, hill country and plains (which are basically relief or *terrain types* (q.v.)), to geomorphologic regionalization on a sophisticated, genetic basis. This is distinct from *geomorphic cartography* (see *Geomorphic Maps*), which is detailed mapping of landforms.

Armin K. Lobeck, that master of geomorphologic illustration, saw his landscape in an almost stylized geometric light; he had been trained as an architect which might explain some of that skill. Nevertheless he was a geologist and his "physiographic diagrams" of each of the continents included also inset maps of the geomorphic regions (see *Physiographic Maps*). The writer, in company with J. Gentilli, a skilled climatologist and human geographer, was asked by Lobeck to prepare such a descriptive and cartographic regionalization for Australia. Again and again the question came up: Where do we draw the boundary between a regional unit characterized, say, by a structural border (such as a mountainous belt cut off by a distinct fault zone) and an adjacent unit characterized, say, by a morphoclimatic landscape (such as desert dunes)? Clearly, we were mixing the immiscible; yet we wanted a geomorphic map that was genetic, that told more than the relief analysis of a military terrain study. We came to the conclusion that in striking contrast to the methods of stratigraphy (which considers the positive historical sequence in the accumulation of strata), we should work back from the present. Thus the geomorphic units would be selected on two criteria:

(a) *Terrain type*, unified by common genesis and environmental (mainly paleoclimatic) history.

(b) *Sequence*, negative, going backwards from the present. To revert to the fault boundary/desert dune paradox, mentioned above, the dune cover is younger; therefore the dune boundary wins and the fault boundary only appears in those sectors that were not overlapped by the dunes.

Regional Mapping. The earliest lithologic maps in the world appeared in France nearly two centuries ago, but since that time the initiative in major regional landform mapping seems to have been in the United States and later, on a smaller scale, in Britain. Linton (1951) has observed the remarkable fact that in all the 15 great volumes of the *Géographie Universelle*, de Martonne and his associates have not shown a single map of the major morphological regions, not even France itself. As Linton remarks: "the genius of French geographers is for the apt and vivid characterization of the essence of a region in words." The lack of cartographic rigidity removes the discipline of a strict logical plan for boundaries.

It is not surprising that in the new, open lands of the North American West, geomorphic provinces were first really appreciated. These were, and still are, often called "*natural regions*," but morpho-logical considerations are almost always paramount in their delimitation. In the United States, the principal regions so defined were worked out by Powell (1896), Davis (1899), Bowman (1911), Blackwelder (1912) and others (see summary, with 1/50 million maps, by Joerg, 1914). While there were disagreements over the ranking of some subdivisions, there is a gratifying uniformity in the selection of most of the boundaries. As Fenneman (1914) remarked, the purpose of this regionalization was twofold: (a) morphologic ("as much geologic as geographic") and (b) as a basis for plotting human and economic geographic data. It was clear, therefore, that the latter was no criterion; the only criteria for mapping were geomorphologic, although he did not use that term, rather the old-fashioned sounding term "physiographic" (see discussion in *Physiography*). When one studies the criteria in detail, it emerges that the pioneers were using essentially the same kind of arguments that we employ today, though with more emphasis on the general geological history rather than the paleoclimatic record which now emerges as paramount (though not exclusive, of course).

Fenneman rightly insisted on boundaries that were "visible in the field," thus exactly the same requirement that the stratigrapher makes in mapping a formation. This is quite different from a climatic boundary which is statistically derived. A Physiographic Committee of the U.S. Geological Survey cooperated with Fenneman in preparing a standard map of the physiographic boundaries of the United States (1915; Third ed., 1928), with divisions in three orders of magnitude: *major divisions*, *provinces* and *sections*. The basis of division was on the "highest common factor" (HCF) in the morphology. With each reduction in order, the HCF embraces more and more detail.

In considering the question of lower orders of magnitude of regional units, such as would be needed in a country the size of Britain for example, Linton (1951) finds a stage at which the common physiographic (i.e., morphogenetic) history ceases to be a unifying factor. Areas of identical climatic history may then be further subdivided on a basis of relief, structure, lithology or soil. He points out that many small-scale geomorphic units in Europe possess *noms de pays*, thus "Lothian" and "Moray" in Scotland, the "Weald" in England. Unstead (1933) recognized thus two minor divisions: *tracts* and finally *stows* (his lowest order of regional mapping). Linton (1951) added a final end-point, the *site*. ("Site" is etymologically a single unit spot; a "stow" is Anglo-Saxon for a stockaded place, e.g., within which animals might be herded for protection; a "tract" is a more extended parcel of land, comparable with a large farm or estate.) Unstead (*op. cit.*) cites the North or South Downs as a "tract" in his scheme, while within these he would identify various water gaps, wind gaps, coombes and dry valleys as "stows." A "site" would be an individual terrace, for example.

There is here offered a complete hierarchy of seven regional morphologic units: *continent, major division, province, section, tract, stow* and *site*. Terms such as "landscape" are omitted (in the same manner as "sequence" in stratigraphic hierarchy) which keeps them free for general use.

The modern mapping, on a regional basis, of morphogenetic regions has been developed particularly in Australia, under the title of "*land systems*" (q.v.). This methodology aims at a total integration of landforms, lithology, relief, climate, soils, vegetation and so on. Since inheritance is implied, though not forced, the land system becomes an ideal morphogenetic unit.

RHODES W. FAIRBRIDGE

References

Blackwelder, E., 1912, "United States of America," in (Steinmann and Wilckens, editors) *Handb. d. regional Geol., Heidelberg,* **8**(2), No. 11, 258pp.

Bowman, I., 1911, "Forest Physiography: Physiography of the United States," New York, John Wiley, 759pp.

Büdel, J., 1948, "Das System der klimatischen Morphologie," *Verhandl. Deut. Geographentag,* **27.**

Büdel, J., 1963, "Klima-genetische Geomorphologie," *Geogr. Rundschau,* **7,** 269–286.

Davis, William, 1899, "The geographical cycle," *Geogr. J., London,* **14,** 481–504 (also "Geographical Essays," New York, Dover reprint, 1954).

Fenneman, N. M., 1914, "Physiographic boundaries within the United States," *Ann. Assoc. Am. Geogr.,* **4,** 84–134.

Fenneman, N. M., 1915, "Physiographic divisions of the United States," *Ann. Assoc. Am. Geogr.,* **6,** 19–98.

Gentilli, J., and Fairbridge, R. W., 1951, "Physiographic Diagram of Australia," New York, Geogr. Press, Columbia University (now Hammond Map Co.).

Hartshorne, R., 1939, "The nature of geography," *Ann. Assoc. Am. Geogr.,* **29**(3–4).

Holzner, L., and Weaver, G. D., 1965, "Geographic evaluation of climatic and climato-genetic geomorphology," *Ann. Assoc. Am. Geogr.,* **55,** 592–602.

Joerg, W. L. G., 1914, "Natural regions of North America," *Ann. Assoc. Am. Geogr.,* **4,** 55–83.

Linton, D. L., 1951, "The delimitation of morphological regions," in "London Essays in Regional Geography," 199–217.

Peltier, L., 1950, "The geographic cycle in periglacial regions," *Am. Assoc. Am. Geog.,* **40,** 214–236.

Powell, J. W., 1896, "The Physiography of the United States," New York, American Book Company, Nat. Geogr. Soc. Monog. 1 (Physiographic processes, pp. 1–32; Physiographic features, pp. 33–64).

Tricart, J., and Cailleux, A., 1955, "Cours de Géomorphologie, Introduction à la Géomorphologie Climatique," p. 222, Paris, Cent. Doc. Univ.

Unstead, J. F., 1933, "A system of regional geography," *Geography,* **18,** 175–187 (Herbertson Memorial Lecture).

Visher, S. S., 1941, "Climate and geomorphology," *J. Geomorphol.,* **4,** 56–64.

Cross-references: *Geomorphic Maps; Geomorphology—Principles; Landscape Analysis; Landscape Types—Genetic; Land Systems; Morphogenetic Classification; Nunatak Theory; Physiographic or Landform Maps; Physiography; Regions, Natural and Geographical; Terrain Types.*

MORPHOMETRY—*See* HYPSOMETRIC ANALYSIS; QUANTITATIVE GEOMORPHOLOGY; ALTIMETRIC FREQUENCY CURVE

MORPHOSCULPTURE—*See* MORPHOSTRUCTURE

MORPHOSTRUCTURE

Morphostructure consists of those forms of the earth's surface which are produced by the interaction between endogenetic and exogenetic forces, the endogenetic factor being predominant in the tectonic movements of the earth's crust. The morphostructure consists mainly of the major forms of earth's relief (mountain ranges, intermontane basins, plateaus, lowlands, etc.). However, morphostructures are also relatively smaller forms of relief, which are formed directly by tectonic movements, such as anticlines, basins, domes, arches, faults, and other topographic elements.

The term morphostructure was introduced in 1946 by I. P. Gerasimov, who proposed to subdivide all forms of earth's relief into three main genetic categories for geomorphological analysis: (1) elements of geotexture, (2) morphostructures and (3) morphosculptures. Elements of *geotexture* comprise the largest features of earth's relief (continental massifs, oceanic basins, and others), the formation of which is connected with manifestation of world-wide processes. The elements of *morphostructure* complicate the forms of geotexture. The morphostructures are in turn complicated by even smaller forms—the morphosculpture forms.

The analysis of morphostructural relief elements is a special science of *structural geomorphology*. Structural geomorphological investigations, as well as the concept of morphostructures, are now very popular among the geomorphologists of the Soviet Union and some European countries. The analysis of morphostructures is used both in the solution of theoretical problems of structure and evolution of earth and in the geomorphological interpretation of geological structure. The latter studies are of practical importance in prospecting for petroleum, natural gas, and other mineral deposits. The concepts of morphostructure and morphosculpture are used in geomorphological mapping. The geomorphological maps of the Soviet Union, the world, the continents, and the sea floor in the physical-geographical atlas of the world (Moscow, 1964) were prepared using this classification.

The morphostructural elements of the surface of continents are of various morphology, age, and origin. In a very general aspect, two kinds of morphostructures can be distinguished (1) plains regions in platforms, and shield, and (2) the morphostructures of mountain (orogenic) regions. *Plain-platform regions* can be subdivided into: (a) the basement plains and plateaus of *ancient shields;* (b) plateaus and plains of *ancient platforms;* (c) plains, lowlands, and hilly areas of *young platforms.* Ancient platforms are subdivided into *medium-altitude plains* of the Russian and North American type and the *high-altitude plains* of eastern Siberian and South African type. *Mountain* structures are subdivided into (a) *young mountains* belonging to the Cenozoic orogenic belts (Alps, Kamchatka Mountains, mountains of Japan), and (b) *regenerated mountains* which formed in peneplaned folded regions by the later orogenic movements (Tien Shan, Sayans, Rocky Mountains). There are regenerated mountains formed within the Precambrian orogenic belts, Paleozoic orogenic belts, and Mesozoic orogenic belts. This classification reflects the most important features in structure and evolution of mountain lands.

The young mountains are predominantly folded, while the rejuvenated mountains in regions of Precambrian orogenic belts are predominantly block-faulted mountains. The older is the folded belt within which developed a later orogeny, the more prominent are the movements of blocks along the faults.

Elements of earth's morphostructure of various ages are characterized by various relations between the orohydrography and the geological structure. The closest correlation exists between the major land forms and the elements of geological structure of young (Cenozoic) mountains and young platform regions, where the lineaments are dominant. Within the ancient platforms and rejuvenated mountains of ancient platforms and shields, there are frequently various discordances between relief and the geological structure. These are called *inverted* or *discordant* morphostructures.

The distribution of various morphostructural elements of the earth's relief depends considerably on the geological and structural features of the earth's crust. However, the major morphostructural features of relief depend not only on the ancient geological structure, but also on the later deformations of the earth's crust, those which are best outlined by the geomorphological studies. The investigations have demonstrated that in the general concept of morphostructure, the structure must be considered not as a passive substratum, but as an actively developing element. Tectonic movements which developed during the latest geological periods—the Neogene and Quaternary periods (see *Neotectonics*)—are of great importance in the formation of Recent morphostructural elements of the earth's surface.

However, as is shown by accurate studies, many major morphostructural elements started to form before the *neotectonic stage.* An important boundary in the history of evolution of structure and relief of earth is at the end of Paleozoic—Early Mesozoic time. This marked the development of present deep oceanic troughs and highly uplifted continental blocks, enormous systems of regenerated mountains, and the high plains and low plains. The post-Paleozoic earth's history should be considered to be an independent *geomorphological stage* which may be compared with the pre-geological and geological stages of earth's history. The term "geomorphological stage" stresses the specific importance of geomorphological methods (analysis of orography, morphostructure of peneplaned surfaces, terraces, etc.) in the study of this period in the earth's history.

I. P. GERASIMOV
J. A. MESCHERIKOV

References

Gerasimov, I. P., 1946, "Experience with geomorphological interpretation of the general scheme of geological structure of Soviet Union," *Probl. Fizicheskoy geografii,* **12** (in Russian).

Gerasimov, I. P., 1959, "Structural features of the earth's surface relief in the territory of Soviet Union and their origin," *Akad. Nauk SSSR* (in Russian).

Gerasimov, I. P., and Mescherikov, J. A., 1964, "Morphostructure and morphosculpture of earth's surface," *Sovrem. Probl. Geografii* (Scientific contributions of Soviet geographers to the XX International geographical congress, London) (in Russian).

Gerasimov, I. P., and Mescherikov, J. A., 1964, "Geomorphological stage in the evolution of earth," *Izv. Akad. Nauk SSSR Ser. Geograficheskaya,* **6** (in Russian).

Mescherikov, J. A., 1960, "Morphostructure of the plains and platform regions," *Akad. Nauk SSSR* (in Russian).

Mescherikov, J. A., 1963, "Major cycles in the development of the relief of platform plains," *Izv. Akad. Nauk SSSR,* **2**, 3–13 (English transl. in *Sov. Geogr.,* 1963, **4**(6), 3–16).

Mortensen, H., 1959, "Russische Geomorphologische Konferenz 1958," *Z. Geomorphol.,* **3**, 248–251.

Cross-references: *Continents and Oceans; Endogenic Dynamics; Exogenic Dynamics; Holocene; Inversion of Topography; Land Mass and Major Landform Classification; Morphotectonics; Neotectonics; Peneplain; Plains; Plateau; Quaternary; Structural Control in Geomorphology; Terraces.*

MORPHOTECTONICS

As the Greek roots of the term imply, *morphotectonics* (form, plus building) refers to the structural foundations of geomorphology. Kober (1928, p. 23) used it to cover the gross and major relief features of the earth. In the first order there is the distinction between continents ("epeirogenic") and ocean basins ("oceanogenic"). For the same features the writer has emphasized the crustal differences, thus *epeirocraton* and *thalassocraton* (Fairbridge, 1955). In any case, the relief contrast is statistically proven by the bimodality of the *hypsographic curve* (q.v.), and the geophysical contrast between the 30–50 km thick continental crust and the 5 km thick oceanic crust is now well known. Mean altitudes of continents show a statistically close relationship to areas, if due allowance is made for ice-covered areas (Matschinski, 1952).

Within the epeirocratons are recognized the following second-order morphotectonic units: the ancient *shields* (*cratons*), younger *orogenic chains* or fold *mountain belts*, and older orogenic belts—now block mountains or *massifs*. Very ancient (Precambrian) fold belts, for the most part, have little morphotectonic expression, but simply merge with the shield complexes. Finally there are *basin-ranges* (block-faulted belts), *rift systems* (taphrogenic zones) and *basins* of many sorts.

In the orogenic belts, there are two fundamental regional zones: (*a*) the *Circum-Pacific* and (*b*) the *Mediterranean-Alpine-Himalayan*. Very striking from the morphotectonic viewpoint is the generalization that most of the Circum-Pacific belt "faces" the Pacific Ocean and tends to be fronted by deep trenches, and in places is associated with rising shears (marked by deep-focus earthquakes). In contrast, the Mediterranean-Alpine-Himalayan belt is

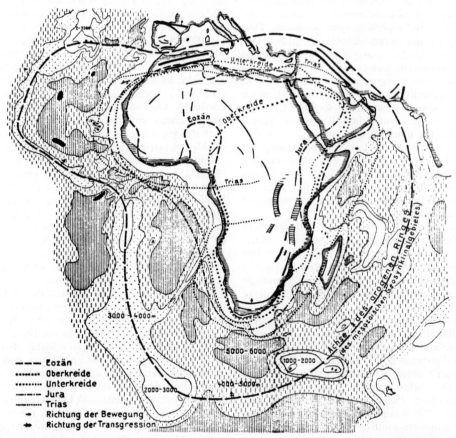

Legend:
- — — Eozän
- ········ Oberkreide
- ········ Unterkreide
- —·—· Jura
- ··········· Trias
- → Richtung der Bewegung
- ⇥ Richtung der Transgression

FIG. 1. Example of a first-order morphotectonic unit with outlines of former shore lines (Kober, 1928). Note that former shore lines surround the African continent, together with Arabia, an integral part of the morphotectonic unit, but not within the usual geographic limits of Africa. Kober showed considerable prescience in recognizing an "orogenic ring" surrounding the continent along the site of the mid-oceanic ridge, that was not to be really discovered until thirty years later. It is now known that it represents the locus of rifting that began in the Mesozoic. (By permission of Gebruder Borntraeger, Stuttgart.)

double sided, the folds tending to be overthrust against *forelands* (a concept developed especially by Suess, 1904–24) both to the north and to the south, while in between lie block-faulted collapsed regions known as median masses (or *Zwischengebirge*, following Kober's expression).

Within the orogenic belts, Kober recognized that there were generally two zones: an inner belt or series of nuclei of ancient rocks with younger igneous material, the *Internides*, that have quite distinctive mountain scenery (massive rock and metamorphic features); they are sharply separated from the parallel folds and overthrusts in youthful unmetamorphosed sediments, the *Externides*. The particular phase in orogenesis that sees the emergence, uplift and development of true mountain relief has been called a *morphorogenic phase* (see Schieferdecker's glossary).

Major Morphotectonic Units

While continents constitute a first-order category, the structurally coherent units do not always coincide neatly with the physiographic continents. Thus *Africa* as a major morphotectonic unit takes in also Arabia; the Red Sea is only a youthful fissure and the paleogeographic history of the whole unit shows old shore lines swinging around the margins of Arabia for much of the recorded history (best known in Mesozoic and Tertiary times, see Fig. 1). *Eurasia* lies together as a unit today, although perhaps it represents the union of two ancestral units that drifted together in the late Paleozoic along the suture of the Urals. The *Indo-Australian* complex, on the other hand, may well have been closely joined in the Paleozoic, only to split apart, leaving the scattered Indonesian archipelago as partial and drawn-out remnants.

The concept of "Gondwanaland" in the southern hemisphere, embracing South America, Africa, India, Australia and Antarctica, evolved in the late nineteenth century (Blanford, Suess) on the basis of extraordinarily similar morphotectonics, as much as from common features of stratigraphy, paleontology and paleoclimate (e.g., the Permo-Carboniferous glaciation). The phenomenon of the dismemberment and drifting apart of Gondwanaland during the Mesozoic and Tertiary is one of the marvels of geology (Fairbridge, 1965; see also Vols. V and VII).

Wegener's concepts of continental drift led him back to the conclusion that there was once one great proto-continent, *Pangaea*, that later broke apart (Wegener, 1924). In contrast, Staub (1928) could find little trace of north-south connections and proposed two proto-continents: *Laurasia* (North America plus Eurasia) and *Gondwana* (the southern units). The fact that there had formerly been a great east-west seaway has long been established, and was named *Tethys* by Von Mojsisovics in 1893 (see discussion in Suess, *op. cit.*, Vol. 3, p. 19). In recent times, with the development of paleomagnetic analysis, enormous east-west displacements have been suggested for this belt, in addition to the north-south jostling proposed by Staub.

Morphotectonic boundaries are essentially those of geotectonics, but the most important of all often fall in zones of such extreme complexity that they are not always easy to recognize. There is undoubtedly a major east-west suture that separates northern from southern Europe, not through the Mediterranean, but through the southern Alps (Insubric-Tonale-Judicaria Line), Vardar Line in Yugoslavia, Anatolian Fault in Turkey, Brahmaputra Line in Tibet, and so on into southeast Asia. This intercontinental suture was called an *Epeirophoresis* (a parting of continents) by Salomon-Calvi (1930).

Small-scale Morphotectonic Units

Kober pointed out how the river valleys of the world tend to pick out the morphotectonic lines. Machatschek (1955) has provided the world treatment (e.g., Fig. 2). During World War II, E. S. Hills had charge of an army project to prepare a full-scale relief model, on the scale of 8 miles to 1 inch (1:500,000), of the entire continent of Australia. From this work he was able to "read out" many of the fundamental traits of a vast area. Lineaments, fold belts, domes, basins, etc., emerged with remarkable clarity, because geology and relief could be combined. One studies thus the external forms simultaneously with the internal structure. Particularly striking is the way in which Hills was able to establish the structural controls of subsiding basins within a geotectonic framework, which he called "framed basins." Uplift areas are much more accentuated of course, and a great variety of *inherited* landforms can here be identified. *Resurgent tectonics* apply to fold belts, domes, faults, etc., of all ages, and the role of "neotectonics" can often be read straight off the field data (Mescherikov, 1959).

Some broad attention has been given to some other continents in this light, but the work has been scattered. In America, W. H. Hobbs (1911) established some basic ideas, but most of the studies in this field both in America and Europe have avoided the actual term, morphotectonics. In Africa, Krenkel (1925) and Cloos (1937) laid out the broad lines, followed in North Africa by the highly dynamic surveys of Caire (1965), but up till now only one attempt has been made at a detailed world survey of morphotectonics and that is by Machatschek (1955), an impressive two-volume work but regrettably only in German, and thus unavailable for the bulk of world readers (only about 5% of the world's geologists read German). The only English language textbook to date that carries even a chapter on morphotectonic principles is that of Hills (1963). Closely approaching this field from a dynamic structural base has been the "Morphology of the Earth" of L. C. King (First ed., 1962; Second ed., 1967).

As Hills (1961, p. 88) remarked, morphotectonics

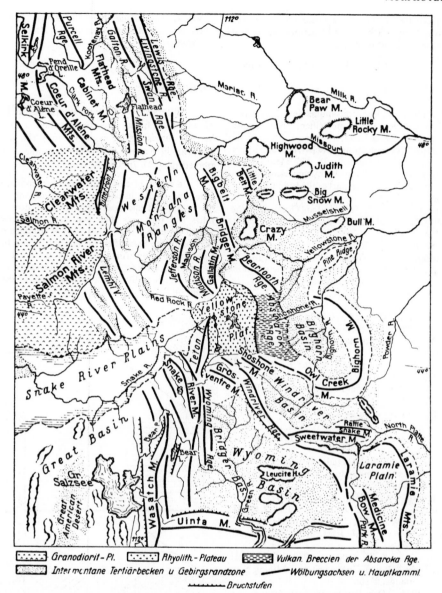

FIG. 2. Morphotectonic sketch map of the Northern Rocky Mountains (Machatschek, 1955), showing second- and third-order features such as fold belts (solid black lines), fault zones (ticked lines), Cenozoic intermontane and piedmont basins (dotted), volcanic breccia belt (Absaroka Range, broken line pattern), rhyolitic plateau (Yellowstone, crosses), basaltic plains (Snake River plains, horizontal lines), granodiorite batholithic mountains (Clearwater, Salmon River Mountains, Idaho). (By permission of Gebruder Borntraeger, Stuttgart.)

offers the key for understanding the present dynamic state of the earth's crust:

"Geological studies in themselves are strictly limited by the requirement that we must have rocks to observe and for the most part we study regions of deposition, old and new. It is geomorphology that can tell us most about regions affected by erosion. The two lines of work are wedded in morphotectonics, and a further link, of in-creasing practical importance, comes through study of superficial deposits of all kinds, which require the appli-cation of physiographic concepts for their understanding. Quaternary geology, physiography and soil science to-gether afford a scientific basis for investigations of surfi-cial phenomena, and all of them must use a genetic ap-proach, since it is only on a sound basis of genetic under-standing that we can appreciate the effects of past changes—changes induced by geological mobility, by climatic fluctuations and by varying vegetation—and can thus venture to modify by our own actions the natural state of the earth as we now find it."

RHODES W. FAIRBRIDGE

References

Caire, A., 1965, "Morphotectonique de l'autochtone présaharien et de l'allochtone tellien," *Rév. Géogr. Phys. Géol. Dyn.*, **7**, 267–275.

Cloos, H., 1937, "Grosstektonik Hochafrikas und seiner Umgebung," *Geol. Rundschau*, **28**, 333–348.

Fairbridge, R. W., 1955, "Some bathymetric and geotectonic features of the eastern part of the Indian Ocean," *Deep-Sea Res.*, **2**, 161–171.

Fairbridge, R. W., 1965, "The Indian Ocean and the status of Gondwanaland," *Progress in Oceanography*, **3**, 83–136.

Hills, E. S., 1956, "A contribution to the morphotectonics of Australia," *J. Geol. Soc. Australia*, **3**, 1–15.

Hills, E. S., 1961, "Morphotectonics and the geomorphological sciences with special reference to Australia," *Quart. J. Geol. Soc.*, London, **117**, 77–89.

Hills, E. S., 1963, "Elements of Structural Geology," New York, John Wiley & Sons, 483pp.

Hobbs, W. H., 1911, "Repeating patterns in the relief and in the structure of the land," *Bull. Geol. Soc. Am.*, **22**, 123–176.

King, L. C., 1962, "Morphology of the Earth," Edinburgh, Oliver & Boyd, 726pp. (Second ed., 1967).

Kober, L., 1928, "Der Bau der Erde," Second ed., Berlin, Borntraeger, 499pp.

Krenkel, E., 1925, *Geologie Afrikas*, Berlin, Borntraeger, **1**.

Machatschek, F., 1955, "Das Relief der Erde," Berlin, Borntraeger, 2 vols.

Matschinski, M., 1952, "Altitude moyenne des continents et forces géodynamiques," *Revue Géomorphol. Dynam.*, **2**, 157–165.

Mescherikov, J. A., 1959, "Contemporary movements in the earth's crust," *Intern. Geol. Rev.*, **1**, 40–51.

Salomon-Calvi, W., 1930, "Epeirophoresis, Pt. 1," *Sitzber, Heidelberg Akad. Wiss. Math. Naturw. Kl. Abhandl.*, **6**, 26pp.

Schieferdecker, A. A. G. (editor), 1959, "Geological Nomenclature," Royal Geological and Mining Soc. of the Netherlands, 521pp.

Staub. R., 1928, "Der Bewegungsmechanismus der Erde," Berlin, Borntraeger, 270pp.

Suess, E., 1904–24, "The Face of the Earth" (*Das Antlitz der Erde*), Oxford, Clarendon Press, 5 vols.

Wegener, A., 1924, "The Origin of Continents and Oceans" (*Die Enstehung der Kontinente und Ozeane*), London and New York, Dutton (translated by J. G. A. Skerl). (See also Dover translation, 1967, of German 1929 ed.)

Cross-references: *Basin and Range Landscape*; *Continents and Oceans*; *Dome Mountain*; *Hypsographic Curve*; *Mountain Systems*; *Neotectonics*; *Physiography*; *Quaternary Period*; *Rift Valley*; *Structural Control in Geomorphology*. Vol. I: *Red Sea*; *Trenches and Related Deep-sea Troughs*. Vol. II: *Earth—Geology of the Planet*. Vol. V: *Geotectonics*; *Lithosphere*; *Orogenic Belt*; *Shield*; *Taphrogeny*; *Tethyan Torsion Zone*; *Zwischengebirge*. Vol. VI: *Pedology*. pr Vol.

VII: *Gondwanaland*; *Laurasia*; *Tethys*. pr Vol. VIII: *Geology of Africa*; *Geology of Asia*; *Geology of Europe*.

MORVAN

The intersection of two peneplains, at least one of which is tilted, has been called a *morvan* by W. M. Davis (1911, p. 115), after the district of Morvan in France, where an example is well displayed (Fig. 1). In Davis' words:

". . . a region of composite structure, consisting of an older undermass, usually made up of deformed crystalline rocks, that had been long ago worn down to small relief and that was then depressed, submerged, and buried beneath a heavy overmass of stratified deposits, the composite mass then being uplifted and tilted, the tilted mass being truncated across its double structure by renewed erosion, and in this worn-down condition rather evenly uplifted into a new cycle of destructive evolution."

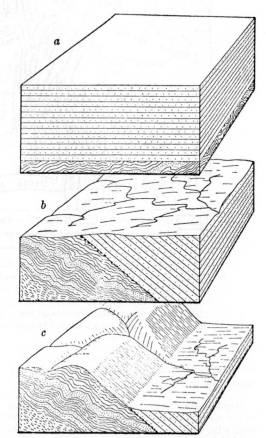

FIG. 1. Development of morvan-type peneplain intersection (Johnson, 1925). (By permission of John Wiley & Sons, N.Y.)

The Mesozoic Fall Zone Peneplain, recognized by H. S. Sharp (1929, 1956) is described as intersected by the Schooley Peneplain (pre-Oligocene age) along a fulcrum close to the Fall Zone of the U.S. Atlantic Coastal Plain; to the interior, that peneplain is lower than the Fall Zone surface, but seaward it overlaps and truncates the Cretaceous formations of the coastal belt. It was classified as a morvan by Renner (1927). A similar example is noted by Thornbury (1954) at the Colorado Front Range where a partly exhumed pre-Pennsylvanian erosion surface is intersected by the Tertiary Rocky Mountain Peneplain (or pediplain).

RHODES W. FAIRBRIDGE

References

Davis, W. M., 1912, "Relation of geography to geology," *Bull. Geol. Soc. Am.,* **23**, 93–124.

Johnson, D. W., 1925, "The New England-Acadian Shoreline," New York, John Wiley, 608pp.

Renner, G. T., Jr., 1927, "The physiographic interpretation of the fall line," *Geograph. Rev.,* **17**, 278–286.

Sharp, H. S., 1929, "The Fall Zone Peneplane," *Science,* **69**, 544–545.

Sharp, H. S., 1956, "Resurrected peneplanes of the Eastern United States," 8th Rept. Comm. Study and Correlation of Erosion Surfaces around the Atlantic, Int. Geogr. Union, pp. 10–21.

Thornbury, W. D., 1954, "Principles of Geomorphology," New York, John Wiley & Sons, 618pp.

Cross-references: *Coastal Plains; Exhumed Landscape; Fall Line; Peneplain.*

MOULIN—*See* GLACIAL MOUTIN, MILL OR POTHOLE

MOUNTAINS

According to the Oxford English Dictionary (also quoted by Dudley Stamp in his "Glossary of Geographical Terms," 1961), a mountain is "a natural elevation of the earth surface rising more or less abruptly from the surrounding level, and attaining an altitude which, relatively to adjacent elevation, is impressive or notable." The O. E. D. adds: "Down to the 18th c. often applied to elevations of moderate altitude," whereas the Encyclopedia Britannica writes "the term properly connotes height superior to that of a hill." For the item "hill," the Shorter O. E. D. writes "formerly the general term, including mountain; but now restricted, e.g., in Great Britain, confined to heights under 2000 feet." Rather generally, the term mountain is applied to relative relief over about 2000 feet (or 700 meters).

Whatever its lower altitudinal limit may be, it is now agreed that a mountain, compared with a hill, is defined by both its greater height and its greater area, i.e., by its volume; thus an inselberg is not a mountain, but a hill. The term mountain may also be contrasted to the term plateau, a plateau being an elevation with a flat top, whereas a mountain has an irregular surface. Nevertheless it may be observed that when the *relative elevation* over the surrounding country is great, a plateau is generally eroded and dissected so that its even surface cannot remain intact for a long time (geologically speaking).

Blache (1928) pointed out that "a hill (in French, *une colline*) is not a small mountain," because the processes of erosion are not the same, not only in scale but in nature, the volume of a mountain being charged with an "erosional potential" which is, on the contrary, negligible on the slopes of mere hills.

A second meaning of the word mountain has been discussed by Strahler (1946) as disturbed geologic structures independent of their relief. A complicated structure may never have given rise to a topographic mountain, e.g., the thrust structures which form the hills of Basse Provence in southern France, which have been strongly folded but not much uplifted (only two short ridges exceeding 3000 feet).

Thus the word mountain can be used in two different ways: the common language and topographic meaning refers to the salient volume, the geological one insists on a complicated structure. As regards the history of mountains, the same may be said in other words: one may distinguish the origin of complex structures (*tectogenesis*) and the origin of relief (*orogenesis*).

The relief of a mountain (its mountainous volume) is due to a relatively recent uplift, whatever the age of the folding may be. Thus the disturbed structure may be of any age. Almost any stretch of country which has not undergone a post-Pliocene uplift has now been more or less eroded to a gentle relief and consequently may be a "geological mountain," not a "topographic" one. Thus after a few million years a mature surface is produced, *unless revived.* For instance, a mountain of Laramide uplift (late Cretaceous) or Pyrenean folding (mid-Eocene) is no longer a mountain in the topographic sense if it has not been rejuvenated by new movements, as was the case in the Rockies and the Pyrenees. *A fortiori,* a Hercynian (late Paleozoic) or Caledonian (mid-Paleozoic) mountain is only a low peneplain if it has not been lately redistrubed; e.g., the Appalachians are a geologically old mountain system, but a topographically youthful (rejuvenated) mountain; it could be said it is a young mountain system of old folding.

Therefore, it is important, when speaking of mountains, to consider three different aspects:

(a) The origin and age of the materials (which are partly older than the mountain building, partly contemporaneous with it; e.g., Alpine-type flysch or syntectonic granites);

(b) The type and age of the main folding;

(c) The history of the mountain after the main folding, including stages of partial or total reduction of the relief and stages of rejuvenation (refolding, retilting, block-faulting and uplift).

Tectogenetic Classification of Mountains

From the above reasoning, it appears that every mountain has its own history, its own "biography" as Birot has noted (1958) so that it is often difficult to distinguish every type with precision. However, we shall first consider the origin of materials and folding and try to classify the mountains according to their tectogenesis; we shall then introduce the consequences of later stages of mountain building.

In our classification of mountains according to tectogenesis, we shall follow the theories of J. Aubouin (1961a, 1961b, 1965). The origin of folding and thrusting will not be discussed here, nor will the part played by either gravity or compression (see *Tectonics* and *Tectogenesis*, Vol. V).

(1) *Intracontinental* or *intracratonic chains* (a craton is a geotectonic unit made of stable materials but may be partly drowned, as in the Hudson Bay or Baltic Sea). In intracratonic chains the tectonic events may take place at two different levels:

(a) At the basement level, causing broad warpings known as *"plis de fond"* (following Argand)—Such a *pli de fond* (a deep-seated warp) is often formed of a number of smaller rigid blocks separated by faults and sometimes by fault troughs filled with sediment. It may be complicated by compression or gravity movements causing folding (type: Pyrenees, Tian-Shan).

(b) At the level of the superficial covering strata—in that case, the strata either just conform themselves to the undermass (*plis de revêtement*) or fold independently from the undermass, becoming "un-stuck" (décollé), i.e., detached from it and sliding on a lubricant layer such as Triassic evaporites, shales or flysch (type: Jura).

(2) *Geosynclinal chains.* The term "geosyncline" is here applied exclusively to mobile troughs located along the margins but not within the cratons (i.e., Stille's "orthogeosynclines" only); they are characterized by frequent development of overthrusts and simatic magmatism (ophiolitic "greenstone" submarine eruptions). Generally, such a geosyncline is not a single trough but is divided into several ridges and furrows; the furrows are grouped in two main deeps: the "internal" or eugeosyncline (the only one with ophiolitic syntectonic eruptions) and the "external" one, also called miogeosyncline. Mountain building progresses from the internal toward the external zone. Thrust sheets also migrate in the same direction. (Great care should be taken with the interpretation of the terms "internal" and "external"; the former is *not* "internal" with respect to the continent, but merely close to the axial zone of the geosyncline.)

Two mountain belts may evolve at the same time from two orthogeosynclinal systems in a related sense; in one case they may have their backs to each other (centrifugal symmetry) and in another, may face each other (centripetal symmetry). For instance, the Appenine and the Dinaric chains are arranged in a centripetal symmetry, on both sides of a zone running through the northern Adriatic Sea and the Molise province of Italy [the "heel" of the Italian Peninsula (Apulia) being structurally a part of the Dinaric Chain]. The sense of growth of the mountain building, as well as that of the migration of thrust sheets is from the Tyrrhenian Sea to the northeast on one hand, from the Thessaloniki region of Greece toward the west on the other, converging in a central zone of "encounter" or axis of symmetry.

After the phases of folding and thrusting in the growth of such mountains, there is a phase of post-tectonic faulting, often associated with post-tectonic basaltic volcanism, quite different in character from the syntectonic ophiolitic stage. This faulting may cause parts of the mountain to collapse (e.g., the Pannonian Plain, Po Valley). Such post-tectonic subsidence generally happens at the expense of the internal zones. Concurrent uplifts may also cause the old basement rock to appear in the central belts of the mountains (e.g., Mont Blanc).

The shape of the mountain arcs on the maps are not always coincident with that of earlier geosynclines. The patterns are mainly the result of late-tectonic or post-tectonic faults which sometimes submerge parts of the system (e.g., Po Valley) and sometimes produce new folding ("accretion" of new-born chains such as in the Pacific island arcs).

The tectonic style of external zones is generally not very different from that of the superficial folding (décollement) of the covering strata sliding over their basement in the intracratonic chains (the Prealps may be compared with the Jura), and may be either autochthonous or allochthonous. Internal zones, on the other hand, are made up of flysch belts or metamorphic belts, with ophiolites.

Mountain Relief

The aspect of small-scale units within mountain systems depends not only upon their place in the above classification but also on the rocks affected by the mountain building and on the type of small-scale folding. Thick, rigid limestone formations give rise to massive fault-fold structures and karstic relief, as in the Dinaric Alps and the Lebanon; a different geomorphic type is in the regular ridge and valley undulations of those parts of Jura along the Swiss-French border or in the Appalachians; volcanoes are another distinctive type of mountain here; the Circumpacific chains are particularly characterized by syntectonic plutonic intrusions, generally in the anticlines. Each part of the world offers distinctive types.

To understand the appearance of mountains, the whole succession of events from initial sedimentation to present-day erosion must be taken into account. For instance, the relief of the Bighorn Range (Wyoming) is explained by the fact that the mountain was initially eroded after the main folding period (Precambrian), then uplifted again (Meso-zoic-Cenozoic), worn down again and revived once more. All so-called old mountains are actually up-lifted and tilted old peneplains on which erosion now works again, usually carving out the weaker formations into erosional furrows leaving the resistant rocks to stand out as ridges (the Appalachians or the Armorican folds of southern Brittany). The last events in the history of a mountain give rise to a new cycle of erosion, reworking old structural lines and producing the present landforms.

Effects of Marked Relief

Whatever the structure of a mountain, the great altitudes and high relative relief have the following consequences:

(1) *Erosion is more vigorous* than in the surrounding country. Such phenomena as torrents and land-slides are frequently observed. The streams have a greater rate of flow, carry more waste, of coarser size, than in the plains. The aggradation near the foot of mountains is characterized by coarser sediments than in plains (conglomerates, e.g., the Montserrat Conglomerate deposited in response to the Pyre-nean uplift in northern Spain).

(2) The *morpho-climatic system of erosion* in a mountain chain is different from that of the adjacent plain. It is marked by greater (orographic) precipitation (exceptions are noted in some high equatorial mountains) and a colder temperature. At low latitudes, ferrallitic ("lateritic") alteration ceases on the mountain slopes; at medium and high latitudes, gelifraction (frost-riving) is an overwhelming agent (see article *Insolation*, Vol. II). The result is a typical denudation into rocky slopes and crests which gives the mountains a saw-toothed aspect, debris being accumulated at the foot in huge talus and alluvial sheets. "High mountain" may be defined by the preponderance of gelifraction on other erosional processes, and consequently by the extension of jagged crests and frost-riven rocks. Its lower limit varies from about 4000 meters (13000 feet) in the southern Rockies and Mediterranean countries, to 2800 meters (9000 feet) in the northern Rockies and Alps, and 700 meters (2300 feet) in Alaska, Iceland and northern Norway or Labrador. At higher latitudes, speaking of "high mountain" has no sense, all elevations being in the category of "high mountains" even if near sea level (for instance, Spitsbergen or the coasts of Greenland and Antarctica).

The Quaternary glaciations have affected many now unglaciated mountains, so that glacial relics are wide-spread. The topography is, of course, quite different in mountains which have suffered glaciation (cirques, U-shaped valleys, etc.) and those which have not (long V-shaped valleys). Such recent events may have ceased only a few thousand years ago and may play their part in the total geomorphology of mountains just as much as the type of folding or the succession of tectonic and planation stages.

Max Derruau

References

Aubouin, J., 1961a, "Propos sur les Géosynclinaux," *Bull. Soc. Géol. France*, 7 series, **3**, 629–702.

Aubouin, J., 1961b, "Propos sur l'orogénèse," *Bull. Trim. Serv. d'Inf. Géol. B.R.G.M.*, No. 52, 1–21; No. 53, 3–24.

Aubouin, J., 1965, "Geosynclines," Amsterdam, Elsevier Publishing Co., 335pp. (translated by Express Translation Service).

Birot, P., 1958, "Morphologie Structurale," Vol. 2, p.334, Presses Univ. Fr., 2 vols.

Blache, J., 1928, "Volume montagneux et érosion fluviale," *Revue de Geographie Alpine*, 457–497.

Stamp, L. D., 1961, "Glossary of Geographical Terms," London, Longmans, Green and Co., 539pp.

Strahler, A. N., 1946, "Geomorphic terminology and classification of land masses," *J. Geol.*, **54**, 32–42.

Cross-references: *Cirque; Climatic Geomorphology; Denudation; Erosion; Inselberg; Island Arcs; Land Mass and Major Landform Classification; Landslides; Mountain Glacier Landscapes; Mountain and Hilly Terrain; Mountain Types; Plateau; Quaternary Period; Ridge and Valley Topography; Slopes; Snowline; Terrain Analysis; Warping.* Vol. II: *Climate and Geomorphology; Insolation; Radiation.* Vol. V: *Craton; Tectogenesis; Tectonics; Volcanoes.* Vol. VI: *Flysch; Laterite.*

MOUNTAIN GLACIER—See VALLEY (MOUNTAIN) GLACIER

MOUNTAIN GLACIER LANDSCAPES

Truly "alpine" mountain forms are of glacial origin whether they occur in association with existing glaciers or not. Many mountainous regions now ice-free have been glacier-clad in the glacial ages and still bear the scars of late Pleistocene glacial erosion. Where glaciers have melted away, land-forms thus developed are in the "relict" category.

Characteristic alpine features make up the glacially "fretted upland," an unmistakable assemblage of cirques, arêtes, and horns. Commonly in association with such summit forms—but only where the glaciers have been extensive enough to thrust tongues down to lower levels—valleys are of U-shaped (catenary) or even trough-shaped cross section and have uneven floor gradients with steep descents at irregular intervals and even with reversals of slope that have impounded lakes; steps are present also, making hanging or discordant junctions, where valleys branch or receive tributaries.

The contrasts between mountains displaying such features and those that have been sculptured entirely by rain-and-river erosion are very striking. The facts of continuity of slopes and accordance of stream junctions were recognized long ago as proof that land slopes and river gradients so characterized had been shaped by running water to suit its own flow. Their conspicuous absence from alpine landscapes calls for a special explanation, and this has been found in the hypothesis of glacial erosion, which makes, however, a basic assumption that the change to a glacial climate is a climatic "accident" that has supervened, so that glacial erosion has modified and reshaped previously existing erosional landscapes, rather than itself beginning the dissection of originally tectonic forms or of features due to accumulation (with the exception of some glacial erosion on volcanoes).

Alpine Summit Forms

Vertical corrasion or actual wearing away of the bedrock as it is overridden by moving ice armed with grit and rock fragments is the dominant process in glacial sculpture and has left its marks on hundreds of thousands of square miles of the earth's surface, but the conspicuous summit forms of alpine topography are shaped in quite a different way by the process of cirque development. "Cirques" are steep-walled, often bowl-shaped hollows that are formed at the heads of glaciers both large and small —including a great many perched, or hanging, glaciers of small dimensions that have no down-valley continuation as ice streams (glacier tongues) and are therefore engaged in vertical corrasion only

to a minor extent. Perched cirques are sometimes distinguished as "corries," while another usage is to restrict the name "cirque" to them, excluding "valley-head" cirques. Large and small cirques are so much alike in many respects, however, that the mechanism of their development must be very much the same.

Enlargement of a cirque takes place by retreat of the bounding walls behind it and at each side, the process being related in some way to the presence of glacier ice in the hollow. The initial form of the hollow may have been a feature of the hill- or mountainside as it existed before glacierization (occupation by glaciers) took place. Such recesses which may become the sites of snowfields and embryonic glaciers are common in mountains which, like the Himalayas and the Southern Alps of New Zealand, have been already sculptured and dissected to a fine texture by running water.

On the broad-shouldered slopes of mature mountains of coarser texture, such as are common in Europe and parts of North America and occur also in southwestern New Zealand, the initiation of the cirque form has been attributed to accumulation of banks of snow in accidental dimples of the surface. These snow accumulations are thin at first and are without movement, but they develop deeper and steeper-sided hollows as a result of frost activity (alternate thaw and freeze) at the receding margins of the snowbanks during summer. This process has been termed "nivation," and it results in the formation of "nivation cirques" which, when they become deep enough, can accommodate small glaciers. A deep accumulation of snow converted by

FIG. 1. Bowl-shaped cirques, one above another. The lake in the lower cirque over-flows as the Sutherland Falls (1904 feet), southwestern New Zealand.

its own weight into névé (granular ice) is potentially a glacier. When a thickness of 100–150 feet of névé is present, it will begin to move forward down a moderate slope; it has become a glacier.

Though the mechanism of flow, which implies abrasion under the ice, accounts for some hollowing out of the floors of incipient cirques, thus making room for thicker glaciers, it does not explain the enlargement of cirques by retreat of their back and side walls. During this retreat, the walls have remained very steep, or have been steepened, becoming in many cases nearly vertical, thus giving cirques their bowl-like form (Fig. 1). The retreat of cirque walls has not taken place as a result of abrasion. The walls have been kept steep and caused to retreat by the collapse of unsupported rock faces as they have been undercut by the process of glacial "sapping." This sapping has obviously been due to the presence of the cirque glaciers, for when these have melted away the sapping has ceased; a cirque no longer containing a glacier loses the original steepness of its walls, which become buried at the base under accumulations of talus derived from their own disintegration.

The explanation of sapping appears to be found in rending and disintegration of rock by the freeze-and-thaw process. Some of this takes place in crevices of the rock wall, especially near its base, behind the cirque glacier (Lewis, 1940). The water necessary to keep this process in operation comes from melting of snow in summer; it trickles down between the rock wall and the glacier, sometimes opening a cleft between them. According to the "bergschrund hypothesis," announced by Matthes as long ago as 1892, the freeze-and-thaw process is most active in a crevasse (the bergschrund) that persistently remains open along the rear margin of the cirque glacier.

Explored to a depth of 150 feet (Matthes, 1900), such a crevasse was found to be walled on one side by rock, which was thus exposed to the atmosphere and was wet. Such walls are subject to frequent freezing and thawing of meltwater. Rock rending by frost at the bottom of a bergschrund does not by itself fully explain sapping, for such crevasses do not apparently exist at a sufficient depth to expose the rocks of the deepest parts of the walls bounding very large cirques. Some such walls are 2000 feet and more in height and are nearly vertical throughout.

The near-vertical upper part of the cirque wall extends down in some cases only to a "schrund line" (Gilbert, 1904), which perhaps marks the bottom of the bergschrund, or alternatively, this is a level above which water has seeped out of the rock wall and has thus been available for freeze-and-thaw activity. Below the schrund line, where there is one, the cirque floor begins as a slope that bears marks of glacial abrasion. If there is no schrund line, the near-vertical back wall may extend down to the lowest part of the cirque floor, which is perhaps occupied by a lake.

The cirque floor is normally of solid rock, which shows evidence (in the form of polished and scored surfaces) of the passage of ice over it carrying rock fragments that have abraded the rock, deepened the cirques and, in the case of bowl-shaped cirques, dug out hollows behind thresholds. As a hollow develops, the ice of the glacier becomes thicker towards the rear, bearing therefore with greater weight on the rock floor, so that the excavating potential increases. Most of the differential scour-

FIG. 2. Expanded cirques (still containing shrunken glaciers) with arêtes between them, on the flank of Mount Cook (12,349 feet), Southern Alps, New Zealand.

FIG. 3. A typical horn, Mount Aspiring (9975 feet), the "Matterhorn" of New Zealand.

ing that deepens a cirque is probably due, however, to extrusion flow, a squeezing out of the ice under its own weight that speeds up movement along the floor. This accounts also for efficient removal from the cirque of rock debris derived from retreat of the back wall.

Especially where cirques are close together, their retreating walls must intersect; the cirques inosculate. Unconsumed residuals of a preglacial mountain or plateau surface survive between cirques in some regions that have been only lightly glaciated and also on the fringes of areas of more intense mountain glaciation. It is the intersection of expanding cirques, however, that has produced alpine mountain forms. Steep cirque walls back to back have between them the characteristic sharp arêtes, or "comb ridges" (Hobbs, 1912) of alpine landscapes, the teeth of which are "gendarmes" (Fig. 2).

Where three (or more) large cirques or cirque-headed glacial valleys head against one another in a preexisting mountain, generally a monadnock of the preexisting landscape, the arêtes between them ascend to the unconsumed but sharpened summit of the mountain, which becomes a "horn," such as the Matterhorn, in Switzerland, for example, or Mount Aspiring, in New Zealand (Fig. 3).

Valley Forms

To the geomorphologist, the most characteristic feature of glaciated valleys is an irregularity of the longitudinal profile that contrasts strongly with a continuity of slope generally exhibited by non-glaciated (river-made) valleys of comparable size. To the traveler, however, who makes his first acquaintance with strongly glaciated mountain scenery, undoubtedly the most striking, in some cases astonishing, thing about the valleys is their U-shaped cross section, which when exaggerated is a trough form. This may be associated with complete absence of interlocking valley-side spurs and of

minor valley windings such as are seen in valleys that rivers have shaped for themselves. This valley form is especially striking where valleys are occupied, as are many major glaciated valleys, by elongated lakes or by fiords.

The change of valley form to the U-shaped or trough-shaped cross section as a result of glaciation —which may be assumed to have transformed a normal (river-sculptured) landscape—is attributable to two processes, of which one or the other may be dominant. One is "overdeepening" and the other spur truncation.

Vertical corrasion of the rock floor by a glacier as a result of its down-valley movement, its weight, and the abrasive action of the load of rock fragments it drags along with it proceeds unchecked to produce overdeepening—deepening that is not controlled by base level as is vertical corrasion by run-

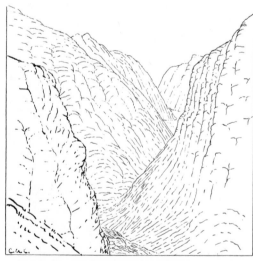

FIG. 4. A wall-sided glacial trough. View down the Clinton Valley, southwestern New Zealand.

FIG. 5. Valley-side shoulders above an inner, wall-sided glacial trough. Routeburn Valley, southwestern New Zealand.

ning water. It has excavated some lake floors and the floors of fiords far below sea level. Very powerful glaciers, like those that overran the southwestern part of New Zealand in the glacial ages, cut deep and steep-sided trenches through even the hardest crystalline rocks (Fig. 4), the walls in such rocks being "oversteepened" because of the relative slowness—indeed insignificance—of valley-side grading processes as compared with the speed of dominant vertical corrasion, and remaining nearly vertical till the present day, because of the negligible amount of postglacial modification of steep faces and slopes on these rocks. Some winding valleys that have been converted into deep troughs by overdeepening retain their winding form (Fig. 5). Valleys so deepened are wall-sided, receiving no tributaries at floor level or even at less than perhaps 2000 feet above the floor. In southwestern New Zealand, there are many such valleys from which exit is impossible for many miles (Figs. 4 and 5) except by the use of aircraft.

Many U-shaped glaciated valleys, especially overdeepened valleys, have shoulders above the steep lower walls. In some cases, especially in lightly glaciated regions and near the fringes of glaciation, the valley sides above the shoulders are unmodified or little modified preglacial slope forms, but in other cases they preserve the appearance of the sides of a U-shaped valley or shallower trough, as though the valley forms had been developed in separate stages of glacial erosion (Fig. 5).

The rock floors of overdeepened troughs remain bare in parts but may be diversified by scanty morainic mounds (*infra*) or covered in parts by modern gravels (Figs. 4 and 5), in some cases outwash from glaciers of reduced size that still occupy valley heads (Fig. 8). Thus innumerable irregularities of rock-floor gradient due to glacial erosion are buried and hidden under aggraded valley plains.

Overdeepening is responsible for the production of numerous lakes, some of very large size, which characterize glaciated regions. The rock debris carried in large quantities by glaciers (originating from rock slides that fall from oversteepened walls as well as from the scouring and plucking activities of the moving ice) is released as the glacier ice melts at a terminal face when it has reached a low level. Much of this is carried away as outwash by rivers of meltwater, but some is dumped in heaps on valley floors as "moraines." Some glacial lakes are impounded either wholly or in part by barriers formed by moraines, but the largest—and innumerable smaller ones as well—lie in basins walled by solid rock. These have been excavated in glacial troughs by overdeepening. The hollowing out of rock basins is one of the manifestations of the law of adjustment of cross sections (see *Glacial Valley*), the deepest parts of basins having been formed under the thickest parts of glaciers (i.e. their middle parts) for towards their terminal faces they have been thinned by ablation.

Many rock basins in overdeepened valleys no longer contain lakes, for their deeply excavated rock floors have been buried under thick late-glacial and postglacial accumulations of gravel that now form plains. The filling-in of large lakes is still in progress, as deltas grow at the lake heads.

Spur truncation, which also contributed to shap-

FIG. 6. Truncated spurs forming trough-wall facets. East side of Hawea Valley, southwestern New Zealand. The low hills in the foreground are moraines.

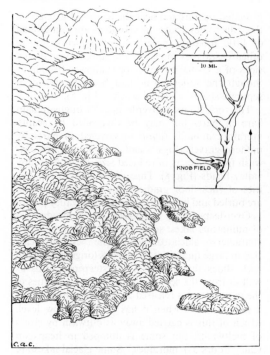

FIG. 7. Knob field at the base of a large truncated spur at the junction of former glaciers in two arms of Lake Te Anau, southern New Zealand. Inset map: Lake Te Anau; arrows show directions of glacier flow.

even right-angle bends. Where the tapering spurs of winding valleys of the preglacial landscape jut out, however, from a valley side, or spurs lie between confluent glaciers, the ice streams, being many times greater in depth and cross section than equivalent streams of water, override their distal ends and vertical corrasion proceeds to saw or grind off the spur ends. Given a lapse of sufficient time before another change of climate has caused glaciers to melt away, spur ends have been entirely removed down to the level of the valley floor. In cases where this process has not been accompanied by conspicuous overdeepening, great gable-end facets replace former spurs along straightened valley sides (Fig. 6).

At places where truncation of spurs has not been complete, relics of former spurs project from valley floors as fields of rounded and sometimes grotesquely shaped rock knobs, among which there may be scoured-out rock-basin lakes (Fig. 7).

Some of the "roches moutonnées" which are characteristic features of glaciated landscapes are relics of truncated spurs. In general these are salients of solid rock rounded and scoured smooth by glacial abrasion on the upstream side but commonly jagged on the lee side owing to the plucking action of the ice stream. ("Scour" and "pluck" together account for most glacial erosion. Plucking takes place where glacier ice passes over projecting parts of an uneven floor; it is due to refreezing of meltwater that has momentarily been produced by change of pressure, which allows the ice to adhere to and drag away joint-bounded blocks.)

Steps and other irregularities in the profiles of glacier-valley floors are due for the most part to vertical corrasion by thick and heavy ice streams together with the operation of the law of "adjustment of cross sections," an empirical law embodying the observed fact that narrow glacier channels have been deepened while those of less restricted

ing the trough form and has done so even in valleys that are not appreciably overdeepened, cuts off preglacial valley windings and rounds off sharp bends (Davis, 1954). This straightening is not due entirely to lack of mobility in the flowing streams of ice. Beneath a superficial layer of brittle ice, glaciers flow like viscous fluids and have sufficient mobility to turn corners, so that glaciated valleys exhibit

FIG. 8. Hanging valley near Mount Cook, New Zealand, viewed across the Tasman Valley, which is infilled and floored by outwash gravel from the Tasman Glacier.

width remain shallower. This explains, for example, the abrupt deepening of a valley to become a trough, at the "trough end," where ice that has collected in widely spread snowfields contained in convergent cirques has become concentrated into a valley glacier, or "glacier tongue."

There is commonly also a step down in the floor of a trough just below the point at which a trunk glacier is joined by a large secondary or tributary glacier, giving it a sudden accession of volume. Such steps as are explicable by adjustment of cross sections have been breaks in the profile only of the floor under the glacier. The ice of such a glacier has not cascaded down the steps as "ice falls" but has had an evener surface gradient analogous with that of a graded river.

So also has the junction of a tributary glacier with the main commonly been accordant, but when such glaciers have melted away, exposing the rock floors of their valleys, there is a steep descent from the floor of the (shallower) tributary to that of the (deeper) main. The junction is a hanging one, and the smaller side valley as viewed from the floor of the main valley is a "hanging valley" (Fig. 8)—one of the most characteristic features of the glaciated landscape, the discordance amounting commonly to many hundreds of feet.

There are also some hanging junctions of non-glaciated side valleys with glacial U-shaped valleys, but these are due simply to the process of vertical glacial corrasion, active wherever a glacier tongue occupies a valley, even where such a tongue streams down into an otherwise non-glaciated landscape. This is also true in regions where glaciation has been light or moderate, so that a condition of adjustment has not been attained; vertical glacial corrasion has exposed rocks of varying resistance. Thus some steps and other irregularities of the valley floor have been developed by differential erosion, roches moutonnées remain unconsumed, and partly worn-down cross-valley bars of resistant rock ("riegels") remain, impounding lakes, though these have commonly been drained by rivers that have cut gorges through the riegels since the melting of the glaciers.

Some passes through mountain ranges are troughs or U-shaped valleys deepened by ice streams that have been fed by ample snowfall on one side but have spilled over to the other side of a range. In some cases also, glacier valleys have become so full of ice that it has overflowed across divides and new glaciers so formed (by "diffluence") have then cut deeply incised valleys. Diffluence may take place even between cirque glaciers, the ice from a higher-level cirque spilling over into one at a lower level through a gap formed by the recession and intersection of cirque walls. Such gaps among mountain peaks may be scoured by the overflowing ice, assuming the U shape and becoming "cols."

C. A. COTTON

References

Cotton, C. A., 1947, "Climatic Accidents in Landscape-making," pp. 157–299, New York, John Wiley & Sons; Christchurch, Whitcombe and Tombs.

Davis, W. M., 1954, "Glacial erosion in France, Switzerland, and Norway," reprinted from *Proc. Boston Soc. Nat. Hist.*, **29**, 273–322 (1900) in "Geographical Essays," 635–689, New York, Dover Publications.

Gilbert, G. K., 1904, "Systematic asymmetry of crest lines in the High Sierra of California," *J. Geol.*, **12**, 579–588.

Hobbs, W. H., 1912, "Earth Features and Their Meaning," pp. 367–382, New York, The Macmillan Co.

Johnson, D. W., 1904, "The profile of maturity in alpine glacial erosion," *J. Geol.*, **12**, 569–578.

Lewis, W. V., 1940, "The function of melt-water in cirque formation," *Geograph. Rev.*, **30**, 64–83.

Matthes, F. E., 1900, "Glacial sculpture of the Bighorn Mountains, Wyoming," *U.S. Geol. Surv. Ann. Rept.*, **21**(2), 167–190.

Cross-references: *Bergschrund; Cirque; Col; Corrasion; Fjord; Frost Action; Glacial Lakes; Glacial Plucking; Glacial Scour; Glacial Stairway; Glacial Valley; Glaciation; Grade, Graded Stream; Hanging Valley; Horn; Landscape, Geographical; Moraine; Nivation; Playfair's Law; Relict Landforms; Roche Moutonnée; Slopes; Snow; Metamorphism of Deposited Snow. Vol. VI: Ablation; Glacier Geophysics.*

MOUNTAIN AND HILLY TERRAIN

Some 36% of the land area of the earth is said to be terrain of mountains, highlands and hill country. Such terrain is appraised on the basis of *relative relief* and *roughness* (a morphologic criterion), specifically, the relative spacing of the slopes. The usual rule of thumb puts hills below 2000 feet (about 700 meters) and mountains above that in relative relief, but not in absolute relief (a hypsographic criterion); this means that a low relative relief on a high plateau would normally not be classified as mountains, but as hills. The terms *highlands* and *uplands* are usually applied to dissected plateaus and mountain complexes of rather irregular, nonlinear character, often equivalent to the German *Mittelgebirge* (mountains of intermediate height). The term *alpine relief* is generally applied to relative relief over 3000 feet (1000 meters), while the German *Hochgebirge* is applied to "high mountains" over 5000 feet (1500 meters) of absolute elevation.

Mountains normally are accompanied by an ecologic zoning which repeats the order of physical geographic and vegetational zones normally correlated closely with latitude. Mountains play an important role in climate, leading to updraught of moist air, often experiencing higher rainfall than the surrounding country ("*orographic precipitation*," q.v. Vol. II), while to the lee side, away from

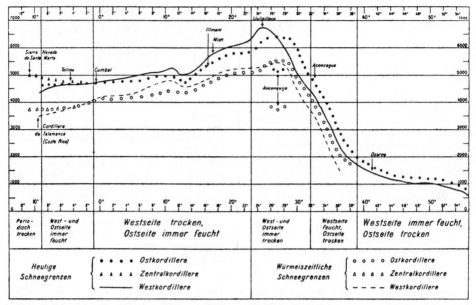

FIG. 1. Curve showing the present-day and Wisconsin (Würm) glacial-stage snow lines in the central Andes (Wilhelmy, 1957). Numerous erosion features of high mountain terrain are inherited from the last glacial stage, even in the tropics. (Explanation: Heutige Schneegrenzen = present-day snow line; Würmeiszeitlichen . . . = Würm glacial; Ost-, Zentral-, West-Kordillere = Eastern, Central and Western Cordillera; Peridisch Trocken = periodically dry; West- und Ostseite immer feucht = west and east sites always humid.)

the prevailing winds, there are commonly found *rain-shadows*, and possibly even rain-shadow deserts. A type of warm dry wind developing on such lee slopes is the *foehn* of the Alps, or the *chinook* of the Rocky Mountains.

Mountain, highland and hill relief has a rich terminology (ridge, hogback, cuesta, dome, cone, inselberg, kopje, monadnock, nunatak, etc.) which has developed on the basis of several factors:

(a) Primary geological structure: massive, volcanic, folded, flat-lying but faulted, etc.; the closer the diaclastic network (joint and fault pattern), the closer is the erosive dissection and the roughness index.

(b) Primary lithology: initial hardness or erodibility, depending on rock types, cementation, etc.

(c) Climatic history and resultant soil development: depth of weathered rock ("regolith"); a long warm-wet history preceding a semiarid one will lead to extreme dissection, even badlands, while a long semiarid evolution will lead to total stripping of all loose soil and the emergence of rather stark, steep but simple relief. Glacial evolution tends to parallel the semiarid, except that gelifraction (frost-riving), solifluction and other distinctive structures and textures disclose its special history. The lowering of the Pleistocene *snowline* (q.v., in Vol. VI) on tropical mountains, often by more than 1000 meters, had profound effects (Fig. 1).

(d) Present vegetative cover: mountain tundra,

mountain meadow, forest to semiarid and total arid environments—each has its characteristic effect on the relief.

TABLE 1. THE MOUNTAIN PEAKS OF THE WORLD OVER 8000 m HIGH (BASED ON FIGURES PREPARED BY G. O. DYHRENFURTH; FROM KOSSINNA, 1933)

Mountain Peak	Height (m)	Region
(1) Mount Everest or		
Chomolungma	8882	E. Himalaya
South Peak or Lhotse	8501	
(2) Kanchendjunga		E. Himalaya
main peak	8603	
south peak	8479	
west peak	8400	
(3) Mt. Godwin Austen		
(Chogo Rioder K 2)	8591	Karakorum
(4) Makalu	8488	E. Himalaya
(5) Broad Peak, main peak	8270	Karakorum
(6) Dhaulagiri	8172	E. Himalaya
(7) Cho-Oyu	8154	E. Himalaya
(8) Peak XXX	8125	E. Himalaya
(9) Nanga Parbat	8114	W. Himalaya
(10) Morhiadi (Peak XXXIX)	8075	E. Himalaya
(11) Gasherbrum No. 1 (K 5		
or Hidden Peak)	8068	Karakorum
(12) Gasherbrum No. 2 or K 4	8035	Karakorum
(13) Gosain Than		
(Shisha Pangma)	8014	E. Himalaya

(e) Stage and rate of erosional history: all things being equal, the rapid, deep dissection of a mountain terrain, still in the youthful stage of V-shaped valleys, may have a greater relative relief than a moderately dissected terrain, with a greater roughness index. The drainage history, whether consequent or antecedent, also plays an important role.

Absolute Relief

Following the trigonometric survey of India's work of 1852, it was recognized that the highest mountain in the world was Mt. Everest in the Central Himalayas (on the borders of Nepal and Tibet). No less than 13 independent peaks are now recognized at over 8000 meters elevation, all in the Himalayas or Karakorums (see Table 1). With the exception of Antarctica (because of ice cover), the world's continents have mean heights that are proportional to their areas. It is thus not surprising that the largest land mass also embraces the highest mountain system (see *Continents and Oceans*).

RHODES W. FAIRBRIDGE

References

Cotton, C. A., 1952, "Geomorphology," sixth ed., New York, John Wiley & Sons, 505pp.

de Martonne, E., 1951. "Traité de Géographie Physique," Vol. 2, Paris, Colin, 1057pp. (relief).

Kossinna, E., 1933, "Die Erdoberfläche," in (Gutenberg, B., editor) "Handbuch d. Geophysik," Vol. 2, pp. 869–954, Berlin, Borntraeger.

Penck, A., 1894, "Morphologie der Erdoberfläche," Stuttgart, Engelhorn, 2 vols.

Supan, A., 1930, "Grundzüge der physischen Erdkunde," seventh ed., Vol. II, Pt. 1, Berlin, De Gruyter.

Tricart, J., Cailleux, A., and Raynal, R., 1962. "Les particularités de la morphogenèse dans les montagnes," Paris, Cent. Doc. Univ., 136 pp.

Troll, C., 1941, "Studien zur vergleichenden Geographie der Hochgebirge der Erde," *Ber. 23 Hauptvers. Ges. v. Freunden d. Univ. Bonn.*

Wilhelmy, H., 1957, "Eiszeit und Eiszeitklima in den feuchttropischen Anden," *Petermanns Geogr. Mitt.*, Erg. **262** (Machatschek Festschrift), 281–310.

Cross-references: *Badlands; Continents and Oceans; Cuesta; Dome Mountain; Drainage Patterns; Frost Riving; Hogback; Hypsographic Curve; Inselberg; Monadnock; Mountain Glacier Landscape; Mountains; Nunatak; Plateau; Process-Structure-Stage; Regolith and Saprolite; Relict Landforms; Solifluction; Terrain Analysis.* Vol. II: *Ice Age Meteorology; Orographic Precipitation, Rain Shadow; Winds.* Vol. VI: *Snowline; Vegetation Markers and Landscape; Zonation of Terrestrial Ecologic Belts.*

MOUNTAIN SYSTEMS

Mountains are commonly classified in physical geography according to scale and continuity, without reference to genesis. Nevertheless, the geologist finds it difficult to resist recognizing a common genesis on the basis of common scenery (i.e., geomorphology). In rising dimensions, one may distinguish:

(a) *Mountain:* a singular isolated feature or a feature outstanding within a belt or mass of mountains. Its culmination is a *peak*. Steep-sided pyramids (usually three or four distinct slopes) are known technically as *horns* (q.v.), with the Matterhorn of Switzerland as a typical example. Sharp-pointed needles are called *aiguilles* or *dents* (French) and serrated ridges *sierras* (Spanish).

(b) *Mountain range:* a linear topographic feature of high relief, usually in the form of a single ridge, i.e., possessing only two distinct slopes on opposing sides, although these may be complicated by valley cutting. The plural form "*ranges*" is often applied to a series of such ridges of more or less parallel arrangement or persistent trend. Geologists (e.g., J. W. Gregory) have often insisted that a range must be a mountainous belt or group "formed by one cause" or related by a common history. Thus, they would clearly differentiate a mountain of volcanic nature situated in the middle of a folded range. The term mountain range is also applied in some cases to the steeply rising margin of a high plateau. In this case, it is essentially an asymmetric, one-sided mountain, and is more accurately considered as a plateau border or escarpment (e.g., Western Ghats of the Deccan of India, Darling Range of Western Australia, or coastal escarpment of Brazil). Prince Kropotkin (1904) applied the term "*border ranges*" to the many examples of this sort in Central Asia.

Note: The term "range" is also used sometimes in economic geology for a mineralized belt that may or may not carry a topographic connotation (e.g., Iron Range, Mesabi Range, in the Lake Superior region). Further, the term "range" is used in the United States in the public land surveys to denote north–south strips marked by meridians 6 miles apart; a "township" is a square of 6×6 miles, subdivided into 36 "blocks" of 1 square mile each.

(c) *Mountain chain:* again applied to linear topographic features of appreciable relief, as in "range" or "ranges," but usually given to major features that persist without important interruptions for hundreds or even thousands of miles. They are usually related by common history but not so closely as in the case of "range." The terms "belt" and "zone" are often used in a less precise way. The term *cordillera*, of Spanish origin, is widely applied in both North and South America to the rather youthful (and thus distinctively linear and rugged) mountain chains of the Pacific coasts.

(d) *Mountain mass, massif, block or group:* a term applied to irregular regions of mountain terrain which are not characterized by simple linear trends, but by block-faulted "accidents," *basin-range landscape* (q.v.), volcanism or revived uplift of complex structures of crystalline rocks, batholiths and metamorphic areas. The term "median mass" (German *Zwischengebirge*) is often applied to broad regions *between* distinct mountain systems or ranges, e.g., Basin-Ranges of the United States, Alti Plano of Mexico and Peru, interior basins of Anatolia, Iran and Tibet.

(e) *Mountain system:* the major category of mountain terminology, "system" is reserved for the greatest continent-spanning features. They invariably have complex histories and comprise subdivisions of varied ages and types, thus chains, ranges and masses.

Suess (1885, and later) applied the suffix *ide* to denote mountain systems of distinctive age and trend. Great emphasis was initially laid upon the *trend* of linear mountains, an inherited feature which is now recognized as often going back to ancient Precambrian fracture patterns, regardless of the age of the principal diastrophism.

World Mountain Systems

Outstanding mountain systems of the world are broadly distinguished in two quite distinct planetary zones:

(a) The Circum–Pacific Orogenic Belt;
(b) The Alpo–Himalayan–Indonesian Orogenic Belt. (Also: "Mediterranean—Alpine—Himalayan").

These are the Mesozoic–Cenozoic fold belts of the world. Relatively few mountain systems are found outside these zones, and even these have currently been subject to relatively recent epeirogenic revival. As pointed out by Suess (English ed., 1908, Vol. 3, p. 4), "the folding force was once active over the whole globe" (at one time or another), "but is restricted at present to particular regions." The task of the geotectonicist is largely to work out *the plan of the ancient trend-lines* "written by nature on the face of the earth" (Suess, *ibid.,* p. 3). In outline, the world systems are:

(a) **North America.** (*i*) *Appalachian–Ouachita System*. This is a series of arcs extending from Newfoundland, through New England and the eastern United States, to Texas. Orogenies: mid-Paleozoic ("Taconic") and late Paleozoic ("Acadian" and "Appalachian"); block faulting and revival in Triassic ("Palisades") and upwarp in Cenozoic. Trends northeast–southwest; in Ouachitas east–west (connection obscured in Mississippi Embayment).

(*ii*) *Rocky Mountain System*. This refers to a series of three complexes: the *Canadian or Northern Rockies* and *Mackenzie Mts.,* an almost continuous cordillera in the north (some authors separate the Mackenzie Mts. from the Canadian Rockies); the *Middle Rockies,* an interrupted group of major chains in Montana and Wyoming; the *Southern* or *Colorado Rockies* in Colorado and New Mexico, also somewhat interrupted by high intermontane basins. Orogenies: mid-Precambrian; block-fault-

ing and taphrogenic revival in late Mesozoic ("Laramide") and Cenozoic. Trends: orogenic, northeast–southwest; taphrogenic, northwest–southeast to north–south.

(*iii*) *Sierra Madre Orientale*. This is a strongly folded arcuate cordillera that forms the eastern border of the Mexican plateau. Orogeny: late Mesozoic–Cenozoic. Trend: northwest–southeast.

(*iv*) *Alaskan Rockies*. The Alaskan Rockies (Brooks Range and other ranges of Alaska) diverge in a fan westward, to be carried on in part across the Bering Sea into eastern Siberia. The ranges are increasingly open and block-faulted to the west in the intermontane plateaus, as in the middle part of the Rocky Mt. System. Orogenies: Paleozoic–Mesozoic. These are the *Alaskides* of Suess. Trends: east–west, northwest–southeast and northeast–southwest.

(*v*) *Pacific Coast Mountain or Western Cordilleran System*. This comprises a number of important chains extending from the *Coast Mountains of Canada* and the *Selkirk Mts.,* to the Idaho Ranges, then a broad loop through southern Oregon to the Klamath Mts. Here in northern California, a division into two chains occurs, the granitic *Sierra Nevada* to the east and the folded *California Coast Ranges* to the west, separated by the Great Valley. The two are displaced in steps eastward in the *Transverse Ranges,* in southern California, while the outer belt continues south in the *Peninsular Range,* the Cordillera of Baja California and then the *Sierra Madre del Sur.* The inner belt continues through Sonora, east of the Gulf of California, and forms the western border of the Mexican Plateau in the *Sierra Madre Occidental,* here largely drowned by Tertiary volcanics. The Pacific Mountain belt is here and there divided or separated from the Rockies by plateaus and basin-ranges, e.g., the Columbia Plateau, Great Basin, Basin-Range Province, Colorado Plateau, Central Plateau (Altiplano) of Mexico. Orogenies: mid-Mesozoic to Cenozoic (Batholiths mainly 100 ± 10 million years). Trend: northwest–southeast.

(*vi*) *Aleutian Arc–Alaskan Range*. This is a northwesterly continuation of the Pacific Coast System, marked by extensive youthful revival and vulcanism. West of the Bering Sea, it continues through the Koryak–Kamchatka System to the Kuriles and Japan. Orogenies: late Mesozoic to Cenozoic. Trend: arcuate east–west to northeast–southwest, in west swinging to northwest–southeast.

(b) **Central America.** (*i*) *Caribbean Arc*. This embraces the larger Caribbean islands, Cuba, Hispaniola and Puerto Rico, and extends through the Virgin Islands and the Leeward Islands to Trinidad. The only example of an island on the usual outer non-volcanic belt of island arc systems is Barbados. An inner branch connects Hispaniola through Jamaica with the Sierra Madre of Mexico. Orogenies: mid-Mesozoic to Cenozoic. Trends: east–

west (northeast–southwest in the west, swinging in a 180° loop in the east, though north–south to east–west again in Trinidad).

(*ii*) *Central American Cordillera*. These are largely volcanic mountain chains connecting Guatemala with Panama and so to a branch of the Andes in South America. Orogeny: Cenozoic. Trends: northwest–southeast (sectors north–south to east–west).

(**c**) **South America.** (*i*) *Venezuelan Cordillera and Caribbean Ranges*. These continue the Caribbean arcs through Trinidad and are displaced by large strike-slips (east–west) to join the main Andes in Colombia and Peru. Orogeny: Mesozoic to Cenozoic. Trend: east–west, swinging north–south.

(*ii*) *Coastal Cordillera of Andes*. These extend from Colombia to Tierra del Fuego, occupying the entire west coast of South America. Orogeny: Mesozoic–Cenozoic. Trends: north–south to northwest–southeast.

(*iii*) *Eastern Cordillera of Andes*. These are of similar length to (*ii*) but separated from (*ii*) by discontinuous sectors of high plateaus and basin-range provinces (*altiplanos; Zwischengebirge* in German). Orogenies: middle and late Paleozoic; later revival. Trends: north–south with virgations to northeast in north and southeast in south.

(*iv*) *Buenos Aires Ranges of Argentina*. These are very subdued ranges, important only for their correlation with the Cape System of South Africa. Orogeny: late Paleozoic. Trend: northwest–southeast.

(**d**) **Europe.** (*i*) *Caledonian System*. This system extends through Scotland, northern Ireland, western Scandinavia, Spitsbergen and also northeastern Greenland. Principal orogeny: mid-Paleozoic ("Caledonian"). Caledonide trend: northeast–southwest. Local revival with intense Tertiary basaltic volcanism (Britain–Iceland–Greenland).

(*ii*) *Hercynian or Variscan System*. This central European system includes most notably the Harz Mts., Bohemia, the Ardennes, the Massif Central of France, the Armorican Mts. (Brittany), Devon, Cornwall, southern Ireland, and most of the Iberian Peninsula. Principal orogeny: late Paleozoic ("Hercynian" or "Variscan"). Hercynide trend: northwest–southeast. Tertiary volcanism and taphrogeny in northnortheast–southsouthwest lines (Oslo graben–Rhine–Rhone).

(*iii*) *Alpine System*. This extends from the Alps of southeast France, Switzerland and Austria, to the Carpathians and Rhodope Mts. of southeastern Europe and also the Pyrenees. A southern series is found in the Betic Cordillera of Spain, the Apennines of Italy and the Dinaric chains of Yugoslavia, Albania and Greece. Principal orogeny: late Cretaceous to mid-Tertiary. Alpide trend: east–west (note that the younger systems loop and swing, trending here and there parallel to earlier developed trends; thus the Apennines and Dinaric chains are more generally northwest–southeast, "Dinaride"

trend of Suess). Suess noted in the Alpides also "posthumous Altaids" to indicate that there were nuclei of Hercynian orogenic belts with the same east–west trend as the Altaides.

(**e**) **Africa.** (*i*) *Atlas System*. This system is found in Morocco, Algeria and Tunis. (It is actually an extension of the Betic Chains of Spain in the west and the Apennines of Italy and Sicily in the east.) Principal orogeny: "Alpine," i.e., late Cretaceous to mid-Tertiary. Alpide trend: east–west.

(*ii*) *Cape System*. These are found in the Cape of Good Hope, South Africa. Principal orogeny: "Hercynian," i.e., late Paleozoic. Trend: east–west.

(**f**) **Asia.** (*i*) *Baikal System*. The "Baikal Vertex" of Suess, an arcuate belt of ancient mountains (Precambrian–Paleozoic), borders the south and west of Angara Shield (Anabar Block, etc.). Orogeny: Proterozoic–Cambrian ("Baikalian" of Obruchev). Trends: northwest–southeast, east–west to northeast–southwest.

(*ii*) *Ural System*. This system of the Europe–Asia boundary is located at the border of European Russia and western Siberia. Loops extend into Novaya Zemlya, the Taimyr Belt and Severnaya Zemlya. Principal orogenies: mid-Paleozoic and late Paleozoic. Uralide trend: (Stille, 1928) north–south.

(*iii*) *Tien Shan—Altai—Nan Shan Systems*. This central Asian system also includes many other chains extending into western China and Mongolia. Suess spoke of the great "Vertex" of central Asia. Principal orogenies: mid-Paleozoic and late Paleozoic (mainly Hercynian); some Mesozoic and Cenozoic revival. Altaide trend: northwest–southeast to westnorthwest–eastsoutheast. Tienshanide trend: east–west. (The term "Altaide" has rather a weak foundation according to Gregory (1915), for it refers only to the Russian Altai and not the greater or Mongolian Altai.)

(*iv*) *Southeast Asian Systems*. These extend from China into Indochina, into Malaya, Borneo and the Philippines. Principal orogenies: late Paleozoic and Triassic. Suess (1908, p. 198) called these the eastern *Altaides*, and although northwest–southeast trends are common, numerous recurved loops complicate the pattern.

(*v*) *Hindu Kush–Pamir–Karakorum–Kunlun System*. This forms an outer loop for the Himalayas from Afghanistan to western Tibet, the "Pamir Knot" or "Syntaxis" of Suess, or *Pamirides* of Mushketov (1935). Principal orogeny: Alpine (southwest—east–west—southeast), some Hercynian inclusions.

(*vi*) *Alpo–Himalayan System*. This is actually an extension of the Alpine System of Europe and northern Africa, represented by a series of double loops in Anatolia, the Crimea and Caucasus, the Elburz–Zagros chains of Iran, Kopet Dag, the multiple chains of Baluchistan and Afghanistan, including the Kirthars and Sulaiman Ranges; Stille (1928) continued his "Carpathides" as a term for the entire northern belt and the "Dinarides" for the southern and they are doubtless continuous, but the extension of the original terms is not usually followed. The northern belt then merges into the Pamirs and Karakorums, but with only a revived role. The southern belt continues in the Himalayas proper, the Arakan Yoma and other chains of Burma. Principal orogeny: late Cretaceous to mid-Tertiary. Alpide trend: east–west (note, as in Europe, there are complex loops and swings in these younger chains, which may even trend north–south in places, as in Hindu Kush and Arakam Yoma).

(*vii*) *Indonesian System*. This constitutes a further extension of the Alpo-Himalayan System, between the northeast Indian Ocean (Sunda-Banda Arcs), with recurving loops joining up with the Western Pacific (East Asian Arcs), in Sulawesi (Celebes) and Halmahera. Principal orogenies: Mesozoic and Cenozoic. Trends: east–west (northwest–southeast in the northwest; complete recurving in Banda Arc through 180°; north–south in Sulawesi and Halmahera).

(*viii*) *Verkoyansk—East Siberian System*. This system occupies a great loop encircling the shield of eastern Siberia (Kolima Block and Omolon Block), with the Verkoyansk arc in the west, swinging round along the north coast to the Oloy Basin and the Anyny-Chukota Fold Belt (joining on to northern Alaska and the Rockies). Principal orogenies: late Mesozoic to Cenozoic. Suess called them the *Anadyrides*, trends east–west, northwest–southeast to north–south.

(*ix*) *Sikhote–Alin–East Mongolian Arcs*. These mountains lie south of the Sea of Okhotsk and occupy a shelf converging in part from the eastern Altaides but largely paralleling the younger Pacific coast belts. Principal orogenies: late Paleozoic to Mesozoic. These are the *Ochotides* of Suess, with trends northeast–southwest to northnortheast–southsouthwest.

(*x*) *Koryat–Kamchatka System*. This mountain system of easternmost Siberia represents an extension from the Aleutian–Alaskan Range structures and continues through the Kuriles to Japan. Principal orogenies: late Mesozoic to Cenozoic. Trend: northeast–southwest.

(*xi*) *Western Pacific Arcs*. Forming a series of impressive arcs, but scarcely mountains, these are largely submarine, in distinctive loops, like those of the Alpo-Himalayan System. They form mountainous islands in Japan, Formosa (Taiwan) and the Philippines. Principal orogenies: mid-Paleozoic to Cenozoic. Trends: basically north–south to northeast–southwest.

(**g**) **Australia and Southwest Pacific.** (*i*) *Adelaide–Flinders–Macdonnell System*. This is an interrupted belt that runs through central Australia to South Australia. Principal orogeny: late Cambrian. Trends: east–west in central Australia, swinging north–south in Flinders Range and northeast–southwest at the south coast (including Kangaroo Island). Traces of this system are found in westernmost Tasmania.

(*ii*) *Eastern Australian System*. This is a heterogeneous belt that extends from east of Cape York Peninsula to Tasmania. Principal orogenies: mid-Paleozoic and Late Paleozoic (especially "Tabberaberan"). Trend: northnorthwest–southsoutheast. Taphrogenic revival occurred in Triassic times (with dolerites in Tasmania) and in Tertiary times (with basalts) along the entire belt, culminating in "Kosciusko" uplift, which continued into the Quaternary.

(*iii*) *Papua—New Caledonia—New Zealand Arc*, a largely drowned island arc chain, that was called "Second Australian Arc" by Suess. Orogenies: late Paleozoic and Mesozoic. Trend northwest-southeast; swings east-west in New Guinea and "Sula Spur." Extensive Tertiary and Quaternary revival.

(*iv*) *New Guinea–New Britain–Solomons–New Hebrides–Fiji–Tonga–New Zealand Arcs*. This complex series of youthful arcs forms the outermost borders of the Australasian lands against the open Pacific Ocean ("Third Australian Arc" of Suess); the outer limit is known as the "Andesite Line," corresponding also to the outer boundary of the circum-Pacific "Girdle of Fire," the andesite volcanic belt. Orogenies: Cenozoic (in part, still in action). Trends: northnortheast–southsouthwest (Tonga–New Zealand; New Hebrides); westnorthwest–eastsouthwest (Solomons–Melanesia Border Plateaus), with recurved loops (New Britain, Fiji).

(**h**) **Antarctica.** (*i*) *Victoria Land System*, a belt running diagonally across the continent forming the border of East Antarctica, passing close to the South Pole in the Queen Maud Mts. Principal orogeny—late Cambrian (cf Adelaide System in Australia). Trend (in Victoria Land) NNW-SSE. Taphrogenic activity in Mesozoic and Tertiary (so-called "Antarctic Horst").

(*ii*) *Marie Byrd Land System*, a zone of discontinuous mountains, largely obscured by continental ice, from the Ross Sea to the Antarctic Peninsula. Orogenies—Mesozoic to Tertiary. Trends, generally E–W, fanning out at both ends, with respectively NW and NE trends.

(*iii*) *Scotia Arc*, discontinuous mountainous islands, submarine ridges and the Antarctic Peninsula (Graham and Palmer Lands); connects with Andes and the Marie Byrd Land System, but contains younger elements farther east. Orogenies—Mesozoic to Quarternary. Trends—east-swinging hairpin loops.

RHODES W. FAIRBRIDGE

References

Gregory, J. W., 1915, "Suess's classification of Eurasian mountains," *Geograph. J.*, 497–513.

Lee, J. S., 1929, "Some characteristic structural types in Eastern Asia . . .," *Geol. Mag.,* **66,** 358–522.

Lee, J. S., 1934, "The framework of eastern Asia," *Intern. Geol. Congr. Washington, 1933, Rept. XVI,* Preprint.

Kober, L., 1928, "Der Bau der Erde," second ed., Berlin, Bortraeger, 499pp.

Kropotkin, Prince, 1904, "Orography of Central Asia," *Geograph. J.,***23,** 179–207, 331–361.

Mushketov, D., 1935, "Modern conceptions of the tectonics of central Asia," *Intern. Geol. Congr. Washington, 1933, Rep. XVI,* 885–894.

Powell, J. W., 1876, "Types of orographic structure," *Am. J. Sci.,* ser. 3, **11,** 414–428.

Shatzki, N. S., and Bogdanoff, A. A., 1959, "Explanatory notes on the tectonic map of the U.S.S.R. and adjoining countries," *Intern. Geol. Rev.,* **1,** 1–49 (translation of 1957 Moscow ed.).

Stille, H., 1928, "Über europäisch-zentralasiatische Gebirgszusammenhänge," *Nachr. Gesell. der Wissen. zu Göttingen,* 173–201.

Stille, H., 1944, "Geotektonische Probleme des pazifischen Erdraumes," *Abh. Preuss. Akad. Wiss., Math.-Physik. Kl.,* No. 11, 77pp.

Stille, H., 1945a, "Die tektonische Entwicklung der hinterindischen Festlands und Inselgebiet," *Geotektonische Forschungen, Berlin,* No. 7/8, 34–153.

Stille, H., 1945b, "Die tektonische Entwicklung der neoaustralischen Inselwelt," *Geotektonische Forchungen, Berlin,* No. 7/8, 210–260.

Stille, H., 1945c, "Die zirkumpazifische Faltungen in Raum und Zeit," *Geotektonische Forschungen, Berlin,* No. 7/8, 261–323.

Suess, E., 1885–1909, "Das Antlitz der Erde," Vienna, F. Tempsky (English translation "The Face of the Earth," pp. 1904–1924, Oxford, Clarendon Press).

Cross-references: *Basin and Range Landscape; Escarpment; Horn; Island Arcs; Morphogenetic Regions; Mountains; Mountain Types; Structural Control in Geomorphology; Volcanic Landscape.* Vol. V: *Orogenic Belt; Taphrogeny; Zwischengebirge.* pr Vol. VIII: *Basin-Range Province; Colorado Plateau Province.*

MOUNTAIN TYPES

Historical Introduction

Several simple geomorphic classifications of mountain types have been proposed. The philosophy adopted is generally to employ a nomenclature which recognizes the *dynamic process* that conditions the gross geometry of the relief, rather than using the geometry itself, which is not very informative.

James Geikie (1898) recognized:

(a) *Mountains of Accumulation*: those produced by igneous (volcanic) outpourings on the earth's surface, and "epigene" types—glacial and eolian.

(b) *Mountains of Elevation*: those produced by structural uplift, typically fold mountains.

(c) *Mountains of Circumdenudation*: those iso-

FIG. 1. Volcanic, accumulation, mountains. Note characteristic radial symmetry of structural origin (extrusive accumulations derived from single vertical pipe; Mt. Agung, Bali).

lated by erosion, by implication generally a structural outlier (i.e., a prominence of younger stratified rock, isolated, and rising above a surrounding area of older formations).

Archibald Geikie (1903) identified (a) *Volcanic Mountains,* (b) *Tectonic Mountains,* (c) *Outlier*

FIG. 2. Air view of cluster of volcanic mountains, ranging from extreme youth (center bottom) to late mature (top left). Note "nesting" of craters in center; youthful fault scarp on right. Width of picture—12 km (Rabaul, New Britain).

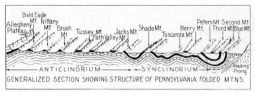

GENERALIZED SECTION SHOWING STRUCTURE OF PENNSYLVANIA FOLDED MTNS.

FIG. 3. Simplified section across the Paleozoic fold mountains of the northern Appalachians in Pennsylvania (the deeper structure contains some low-angle faults not indicated here). Note that the tops of these folds are evenly beveled off by Mesozoic peneplanation. Compare with Fig. 4, which are younger folds, and the absence of peneplanation is striking (sketch by Lobeck).

Mountains, (d) *Denudation Mountains.* Gilbert (1875, p. 21) found another significant type: *Mountains of Dislocation* (i.e., fault or block mountains). A further type added by W. M. Davis was *Dome(d) Mountains.* Credner (in the German literature) gave a rather similar series, respectively (a) *Vulkangebirge,* (b) *Tektonischgebirge* [(i) *Bruchgebirge,* (ii) *Faltengebirge*], (c) *Erosionsgebirge.*

Later, J. Geikie (1914) and likewise Supan (1930) felt that all types should be reduced basically to two forms—structural ("original" or "tectonic") and denudational ("subsequent" or "relict"), and this concept has considerable merit.

Genetic Classification

Today a simple genetic system of mountain types may be taken to include:

(I) *Structural, Tectonic or Constructional Forms*
    (a) Volcanic Mountains
    (b) Fold and Nappe Mountains
    (c) Block Mountains
    (d) Dome Mountains
    (e) Erosional Uplift or Outlier Mountains
    (f) Structural Outlier or Klippe Mountains
    (g) Polycyclic Tectonic Mountains ("Alpinotype")
    (h) Epigene Mountains
(II) *Denudational, Subsequent, Destructional or Sequential Forms*
    (a) Differential Erosion-Relict Mountains
    (b) Exhumed Mountains
    (c) Igneous (Plutonic) and Metamorphic Complexes
    (d) Polycyclic Denudational Forms

In more detail, these will be discussed briefly below (though some categories, as indicated, have been given separate treatment in this Encyclopedia):

(I) Structural, Tectonic or Constructional Forms. (a) *Volcanic Mountains:* of more or less radial symmetry; sometimes isolated, sometimes in clusters or in rows (see *Volcanic Landscapes;* also see Figs. 1 and 2).

(b) *Fold and Nappe Mountains:* of linear, often with more or less bilateral, symmetry, except in recumbent folds and nappes; may be mono-anticlinal or poly-anticlinal, straight or arcuate. Belts

of folds or nappes are often broadly arched into anticlinoria or synclinoria (Figs. 3–6).

(c) *Block Mountains; Also Horst, Fault, Fault-block, or Fault-fold* ("*Dislocation*") *Mountains* (see *Block Mountains*): linear but asymmetric in profile, rarely symmetric as *hogback* or *cuesta* (qq.v.) related to monoclines; fault-fold mountains have monoclinal borders, which pass downward or longitudinally into faults (Figs. 7 and 8).

(d) *Dome Mountains* (q.v.): simple, intrusive, as in stripped laccoliths (e.g., Henry Mts., Utah) or plutons; or complex, as in an exhumed domal uplift (such as the Black Hills, S.D.), including domal *inliers* (as in the Ozark uplift, or Nashville dome), or purely sedimentary, tectonic domes.

(e) *Erosional Uplift or Outlier Mountains:* characteristic of simple horizontal structures uplifted (possibly with faulted borders) and regionally dissected; they may represent simply the margin of a little dissected plateau, and may equally well be composed of flat-lying sediments or basaltic lava fields (Fig. 9).

(f) *Structural Outlier or Klippe Mountains:* rather rare tectonic phenomena where a mountain of older rocks has been thrust (or gravitationally slipped) in front of a tectonic belt and may or may not have been further isolated by erosion (Figs. 10 and 11).

(g) *Polycyclic Tectonic Mountains* ("*Alpinotype*"): often marked by intense metamorphism and nearly vertical dips, characteristic of the core or axial regions of major orogenic belts, structurally separated from the overlying (little metamorphosed) fold and nappe mountains, often by a major unconformity. The near-vertical dips of the axial zone help give the sharp-pointed *aiguilles* and *dents*, so characteristic of the Alpine landscape. The terms "alp," "alm," and "albe" simply mean an upland pasture, but "Alpine" is used variously to designate, for example, a type of mountain glacier and its associated landforms; it also denotes the geological revolutionary time, the Alpine orogeny, 50–100 million years ago, as well as other attributes (Stamp, 1961). L. Kober (1928) designated the fold and nappe belt in a complex orogenic belt as "externides" and the polycyclic axial mountains as "internides." In some Alpinotype mountains, the unmetamorphosed nappe formations can be traced back to members of the metamorphosed axial region, then called the "*Root Zone*." In the Alps, most of the axial region consists of igneous and metamorphic rocks of the Hercynian orogeny (Paleozoic), and thus antedate the Alpine orogeny by 100–200 million years, there being a major unconformity below the Permian. This unconformity is strongly deformed in many places (Figs. 12 and 13).

(h) *Epigene Mountains:* a division proposed by J. Geikie, as "epigene mountains of accumulation," to embrace the categories of *glacial accumulation* (moraines and related "drift" or till deposits) and

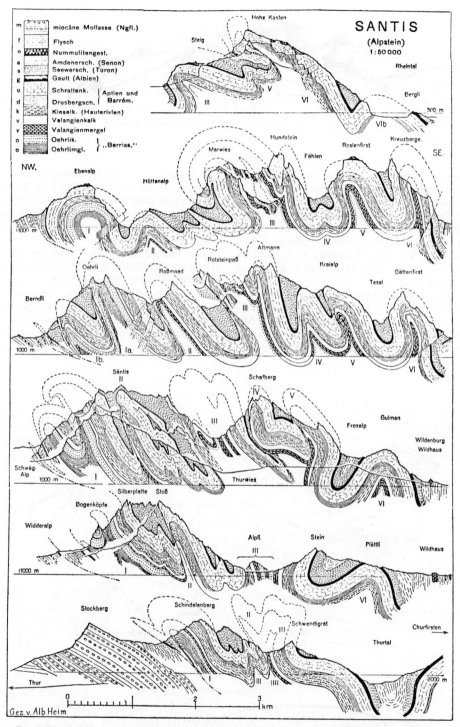

FIG. 4. Plastic folding in Cretaceous and early Tertiary limestones and shales in the Säntis Mountains of Switzerland. Typical fold mountains of the younger (Alpine) orogenic belts. (Heim, 1919).

eolian accumulations (dunes). While these accumulations normally form only hills and rarely build features of over 1000-foot elevation, there are exceptional dunes of Pleistocene age (southwest of Shark Bay, Western Australia and forming islands along the Queensland coast,—Moreton Island, etc.)

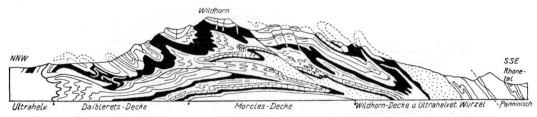

FIG. 5. Typical Alpine nappe-structures in the Wildhorn section (profile after M. Lugeon; simplified from J. Cadisch, 1953).

that are very impressive. Also the "Sand-sea" dunes of the Rub-al-Khali in Saudi Arabia are approaching mountainous dimensions.

(II) Denudational, Subsequent, Relict, Destructional or Sequential Forms. (*a*) *Differential Erosion-Relict Mountains*: the tectonic structure of this category has had little or nothing to do with its present existence, which is an isolation due to epeirogenic uplift, revival and differential weathering, so that a more resistant formation or intrusion has become instrumental in preserving or developing its mountainous character (Fig. 14). Mt. Monadnock, N. H., is the type example; although the precise nature of its isolation—e.g., pediplana-

tion to inselberg—is highly controversial, it is unquestionably an erosion relic. For a whole complex, the Precambrian Laurentian Mts. of Quebec Province reflect perfectly differential weathering of a broad upwarp, though a certain degree of exhumation is possible (see below).

(*b*) *Exhumed Mountains*: structures of ancient origin, are to be found in the St. Francis Mountains of the Missouri Ozarks, where Precambrian mountains were buried (before peneplanation) during Paleozoic and Mesozoic, to be stripped and re-exposed as mountains today. In most cases, however, burial only occurred after peneplanation and later block faulted in different trends, uplifted

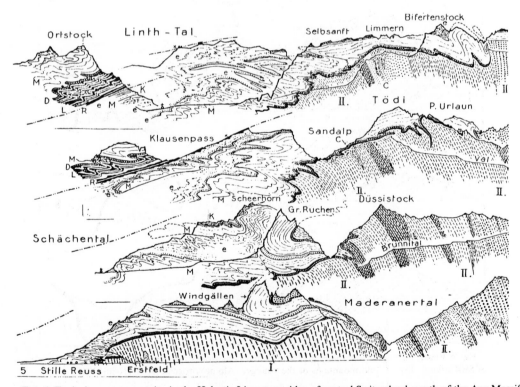

FIG. 6. Typical nappe mountains in the Helvetic Limestone Alps of central Switzerland, north of the Aar Massif (metamorphic Paleozoic rocks of the axial region; see also Figs. 12 and 13). Note contrast (unconformity) between nearly vertical dips in the latter (I, II) and the plastic, low-angle folding of the overriding nappes. Soles of upper nappes marked x—x. Length of section 12 km (Heim, 1919).

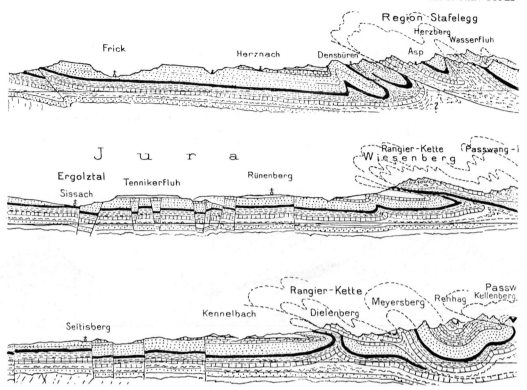

FIG. 7. Block Mountains (on the left, the "Plateau Jura") overridden partly by folds and thrusts of the "Folded Jura" (on the right). The folds have become "unstuck" (décollement) from their basement of peneplaned Hercynian crystalline rocks and have slid across it from right to left (south to north). Length of section, 12 km (Heim, 1919).

again and re-exposed with *stripped surfaces*. Examples are the Harz Mts. of Germany, the central Massif of France or the principal Precambrian mountain ranges of the Colorado and Wyoming Rockies. The older grain commonly runs obliquely to the new trends. As Supan observed, these are physiographically destructional forms, but from their internal morphology, structural forms (*Rumpf-*

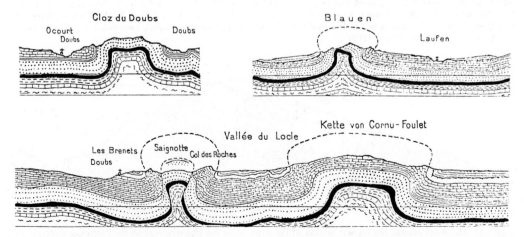

FIG. 8. Typical "box folds" in the Swiss Jura. Note that the cores of the folds are filled with Triassic salt while the overlying Jurassic limestones have buckled up into "square" folds, locally with fault folds (faulted margins), thus transitional to block mountains. Length of section, 12 km (Heim, 1919).

FIG. 9. Denudational mountains in horizontal rocks: Castle Group from the west (Carboniferous sandstones), in the Elk Mountains, Colorado (Hayden, 1876).

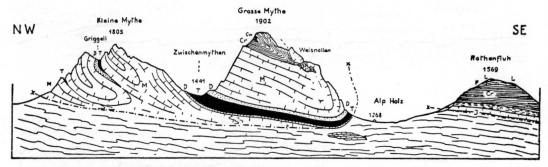

FIG. 10. Section of the Mythen Klippen, giant blocks of Triassic, Jurassic, and Cretaceous formations (700 meters high) resting on a floor of Older Tertiary Flysch ("Ultrahelvetic," partly wild-flysch with its own exotic blocks). These are strictly "mountains without visible roots," i.e., structural outliers or klippes. (Cadisch, 1953; after Heim *et al*.). (By permission of Wepf & Co., Basel, Switzerland.)

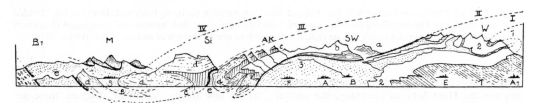

FIG. 11. Structural setting of the Mythen Klippen (M, close vertical shading). A profile through the Helvetic Limestone Alps (central Switzerland), south on the right. Note: Paleozoic axial core region of Aar Massif (1), overlain by Jurassic (2) and early Tertiary Flysch (3), in turn overthrust by several nappes (II, III), the highest (IV) coming from far to the south supplying the giant blocks of the Mythen. Localities, left to right: B_1 = Bannegg, S = Schwyz, Si = Sissikon, Ak = Axen Chain, F = Fluelen, A = Altdorf, B = Burglen, SW = Schächtentaler Windgälle, E = Erstfeld, A_1 = Amsteg, W = Gr. Windgälle (see detail in Fig. 6, bottom profile). Letters a, b, c, d, e = Mesozoic and Tertiary formations (Heim, 1919).

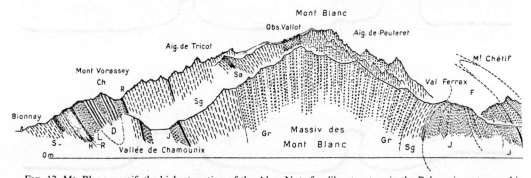

FIG. 12. Mt. Blanc massif, the highest section of the Alps. Note fan-like structure in the Paleozoic metamorphic rocks which form the axial region. Although the orogeny that caused this metamorphism was produced by an earlier revolution, further structural disturbance occurred in the Alpine orogeny, and uplift of the mountains is still going on today, several millimeters each year (Heim, 1919)

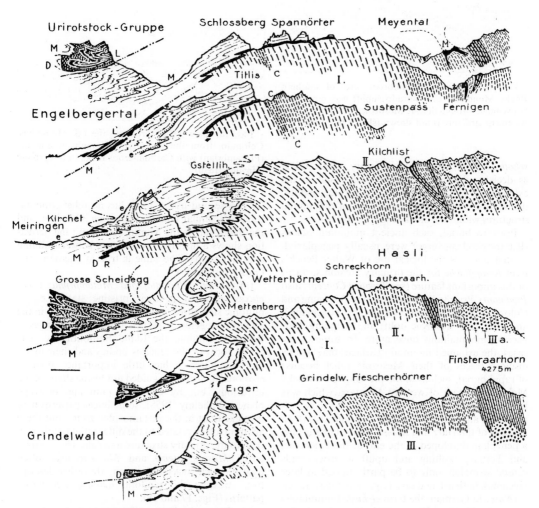

R e u s s t a l

Urirotstock-Gruppe   Schlossberg Spannörter   Meyental

Engelbergertal

Titlis

Sustenpass   Fernigen

Gstellih   Kilchlist

Kirchet
Meiringen

Grosse Scheidegg   Wetterhörner   H a s l i
Schreckhorn
Lauteraarh.

Mettenberg

Finsteraarhorn
4275m

Eiger   Grindelw. Fiescherhörner

Grindelwald

FIG. 13. Axial region of the Alps along the northern part of the Aar Massif; culmination in the Finsteraarhorn, 4275 meters. Note great angular unconformity on these Paleozoic metamorphic rocks (schist and gneiss), the unconformity being seriously contorted in places by the Alpine orogeny which led to the sliding of several overlying nappes to the north (left) (Heim, 1919).

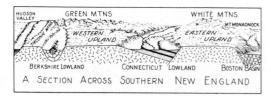

A SECTION ACROSS SOUTHERN NEW ENGLAND

FIG. 14. Differential erosion-relict mountains in New England (Taconic Mts., Green Mts., White Mts., including Mt. Monadnock). Note that the younger structures—Hudson Valley, Berkshire Lowland, Connecticut Lowland (Triassic) and Boston Basin (Late Paleozoic) are not related to the mountains. Multiple erosion surfaces (traces of peneplains or terrace systems) are traced across the uplands (sketch by Lobeck).

FIG. 15. Section across the Vosges and Black Forest. (1) Hercynian granite, gneiss, etc; (2–7) Mesozoic Strata; (8–9) Tertiary and Quaternary of Rhine Graben. Pre-Mesozoic peneplain is locally exhumed (after A. Penck).

757

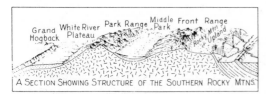

FIG. 16. Exhumed Precambrian cores of southern Rocky Mountains of Colorado; uplift was repeatedly rejuvenated through the late Mesozoic and Tertiary eras. Basement structure is not shown (sketch by Lobeck).

FIG. 18. Snow Mass Group in the Elk Mountains, Colorado, from the west; typical granite weathering (Precambrian) with Carboniferous rocks in foreground (Hayden, 1876).

schollengebirge). The surface history is here taken as decisive. Youthful exposure will result in the exhumation of the former eroded surface; mature denudation will see the etching-out of differential structures within the block (Figs. 15 and 16).

Prior to burial, such ancient mountain blocks (Rumpfschollengebirge) were usually peneplaned, so that one sees the logical use of Walter Penck's term *Rumpffläche* for the primary erosion surfaces of this important feature (see *Treppen Concept*; also *Piedmont*). Prior to the Paleozoic, the Wyoming and Colorado mountains were thoroughly peneplaned, and after late Mesozoic uplift and stripping, they became mountainous once more. In some of the cases, the exhumed mountain surfaces may locally disclose traces of their Mesozoic relief because of rapid burial, such as in the pre-Oligocene Rocky Mountain terrain of western Montana which was buried by enormous showers of mid-Tertiary volcanic ash and other pyroclastics (Wolfe, 1964). In the case of the Harz and Massif Central of Europe, a peneplain developed at the end of the Paleozoic, and Tertiary faulting and uplift in new trends caused stripping, only to be partly buried in later volcanics, both ash and lava (e.g., in the Auvergne).

(*Note*: In German, the term *Gebirge* (mountains) has a double meaning in geology, not only for features of high relief, but also for features of complex structure, e.g., *Grundgebirge* (basement complex), *Zwischengebirge* (median mass or complex); in English, the term "complex" is often preferred

for this second usage, for it has no relief connotation. In a similar analogy, *Bergman* is a miner, and the *Bergschule* is the Mining Academy: the derivation shows a historical correlation between mining and mountains. The same is true in Russian—the Gorny Institut.)

(*c*) *Igneous* (*Plutonic*) *and Metamorphic Complexes*: exposed in their pristine state (i.e., as plutonic structures, not exhumed mountains) in the younger orogenic belts such as the Coast Ranges of British Columbia, the Idaho Batholith, etc. The actual form of the igneous bodies and their metamorphic aureoles has little importance because erosional dissection is guided not by the shape of the intrusions, but by countless joint and cleavage planes (Wilhelmy, 1958); some linear patterns may be picked out in the metamorphic zones, but these are more often related to the differential weathering than to the primary structure as a rule. The German terms *Massengesteine* and *Massengebirge* often used for such rocks and terrain are rather descriptive, stressing the random, massive weathering patterns (Figs. 17 and 18).

(*d*) *Polycyclic Forms*: The relatively simple criteria specified in the above categories (I and II) make no provision for the polycyclic (or multicyclic) mountain that shows revival or multiple revival along old or new structural lines. Practically all mountains show some sort of rejuvenation or

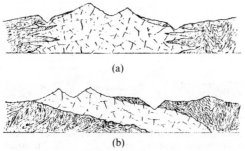

(a)

(b)

FIG. 17. (a) Batholith intrusive into preexisting strata, partly stripped of its sedimentary cover. (b) Batholithic or lopolithic sheet in similar setting (Geikie, 1914).

FIG. 19. Differential erosion of several characteristic land forms in a north-south profile through central United States: superposed differential erosion of a peneplaned fold bed (Ouachitas); dissection of a plateau to give erosion relics (Boston Mountains); stripping and exhumation of Precambrian St. Francis Mountains (sketch by Lobeck).

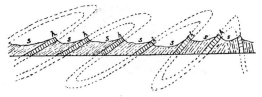

FIG. 20. Steeply-inclined isoclinal strata giving rise to narrow escarpments and ridges. Valleys are cut in weak formations (Geikie, 1914).

FIG. 21. Sections through isoclinal valley; synclinal on left, anticlinal on right (Heim, 1919).

revival. It is impossible to avoid a polynomial terminology, just as in stratigraphy, for example, one might say: "a late Cretaceous, finely bedded, blue-gray, marine, calcareous sandstone," thus treating age, structure, appearance, genesis, petrographic description.

Thus, almost any mountain type that is Mesozoic or older, is liable to require some adjectival modifier reflecting its polycyclic history. Take a well-known problem in mountain terminology: the Ridge and Valley Province of the Appalachian System. It is a fold mountain belt of (1) mainly late Paleozoic folding, (2) Mesozoic–Tertiary planation, and (3) further upwarping and differential erosion. One might, therefore, label the chain: "a fold mountain belt, showing polycyclic revival." The Piedmont Province in contrast could be labeled: "a degraded mountain root belt, including denudational remnants forming differential weathering relict mountains such as the Blue Ridge Mts. of Virginia, and locally affected by Triassic taphrogeny (with fault-block differential uplift and subsidence)." Naturally the individual ranges within this complex chain can be dealt with more expeditiously (Fig. 19).

Primary and Secondary Forms

In the case of the *structural* mountain categories listed above, it is the tectonic process rather than structural geometry that has played a *primary* role. In the *denudational* categories, the epeirogenic uplift of the region is implied and evidently tectonics must play the primary role, but the various classes of denudational mountains, exhumed, igneous-metamorphic complex, and so on, are in each case so totally characterized by the *secondary* denudational events that the primary epeirogenic history can only be inferred.

Third Order Forms

There is a large number of minor (third-order) modulations that will shade or vary the character of a mountain (Figs. 20 through 25); these largely concern *climatic history* (e.g., glacial, arid) and *lithology* (sandstone, limestones, shale, slate, flysch, till, igneous and metamorphic types). Nevertheless, mountains are frequently of mixed lithologies and the climatic veneers in most cases are multicyclic, so that the primary (structural) or secondary (denudational) categories must be paramount.

It is evident that the larger the mountain system, the more numerous are the structural or denudational types represented likely to be. Thus a pure type is probably to be found only within a single mountain, or within a genetically unified range, and as the scale of the mountainous terrain increases to chain and system, so will the number and complexity of the mountain types increase.

Structure-Process-Stage

The classical Davis trilogy has its place here, except that the *dominant genetic role* or *dynamic process* is chosen for the descriptive label. Davis would call the first group of mountain types "Initial" or "Constructional" and the second group "Destructional" or "Sequential," both aspects of his concept of *structure*. He used *process* for the geomorphic modifier, essentially *climate* (equatorial, arid, temperate, glacial), which is here regarded as of superficial character in a geotectonic, genetic classification.

Stage, on the other hand, is highly significant, because only *Youthful* and early *Mature* erosional forms can be classified as mountains, in any accepted sense, e.g., having more than 700 meters or 2000 feet of relative relief (see *Mountains; Mountain and Hilly Terrain*). Davis, unfortunately, had no satisfactory term for degraded, formerly mountainous terrain;

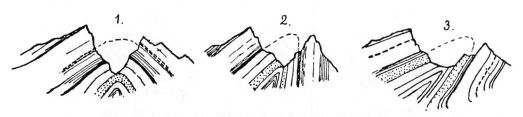

FIG. 22. Sections through anticlinal valleys; note inversion of relief due to lithology (Heim, 1919).

FIG. 23. Anticlinal ridges, controlled by resistant beds of quartzite on massive limestone (Heim, 1919).

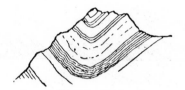

FIG. 25. Synclinal ridge (Heim, 1919).

the complex folded slates of the Hudson Valley or Great Valley of Pennsylvania–Virginia or the deeply weathered metamorphics of the Piedmont Province had to be classified somehow as "mountains." Strahler (1946) pointed out the nonsense of this, and suggested that in a structural geomorphic classification all land masses that were not undisturbed (flat-lying) structures or volcanic complexes should be classified as "disturbed structures" of various sorts. When one applies Davis' own *stage* analysis to such "disturbed structures," it emerges immediately that the ones in the youthful and early mature stages are likely to be mountains while those in the old-age stage cannot be mountains. One may apply to the "old-age disturbed structures" of the eastern Appalachian Piedmont, an explanatory phrase such as a "belt of degraded mountain roots," implying the former presence of mountains, because such "disturbed structures" are characteristic of mountains today, permitting the deduction of their former existence in this belt. This scheme does not prevent a mature to old-age landscape being revived or exhumed; the revived uplift cycle simply resets the clock to youth (see *Relict Landforms*).

RHODES W. FAIRBRIDGE

References

Cadisch, J., 1953, "Geologie der Schweizer Alpen," Basel, Wepf & Co., 480 pp.

Credner, H., 1912, "Elemente der Geologie," Leipzig, Engelmann, 811pp.

Davis, W. M., 1909, "Geographical Essays," New York (Dover reprint, 1954), 777pp.

Fenneman, N. M., 1931, "Physiography of the Western United States," New York, McGraw-Hill Book Co., 534pp.

Geikie, A., 1903, "Text-book of Geology," London, Macmillan and Co., 2 vols. (First ed., 1882).

Geikie, J., 1898, "Earth Sculpture, or the Origin of Land-forms," London and New York, Putnam, 397pp.

Geikie, J., 1914, "Mountains, Their Origin, Growth and Decay," Princeton, N.J., D. Van Nostrand and Co., 311pp.

Gilbert, G. K., 1875, "U.S. Geographical and Geological Survey West of the 100th meridian," Vol. 3, p. 21, Washington.

Gilbert, G. K., 1877, "Geology of the Henry Mountains," *U.S. Geol. Surv. Rocky Mt. Region*, 160pp.

Hayden, F. V., 1876, "Annual Report of the U.S. Geological and Geographical Survey of the Territories (for 1874)," Washington.

Heim, A., 1919, "Geologie der Schweiz," Leipzig, Tauchnitz, **1**, 704pp.

Kober, L., 1928, "Der Bau der Erde," Second ed., Berlin, Borntraeger, 499pp.

Obst, E., 1914, "Terminologie und Klassifikation der Berge," *Petermanns Mitt.*, **1**.

Penck, A., 1894, "Morphologie der Erdoberfläche," Stuttgart, Engelhorn, 2 vols.

Penck, W., 1953, "Morphological Analysis of Land Forms," London, Macmillan and Co., 429pp. (translated by H. Czech and K. C. Boswell).

Rice, W. N., 1905, "The classification of mountains," *8th Intern. Geog. Congr. (Washington)*, 185–190.

Stamp, L. D. (editor), 1961, "A Glossary of Geographical Terms," London, Longmans, 539pp.

Strahler, A. N., 1946, "Geomorphic terminology and classification of land masses," *J. Geol.*, **54**(1), 32–42.

Supan, A., 1930, "Grundzüge der physischen Erdkunde," Vol. 2(1), "Das Land" (Allgemeine Geomorphologie), Berlin–Leipzig, de Gruyter.

Thompson, W. F., 1964, "How and why to distinguish

FIG. 24. Isoclinal ridges; a single resistant formation is the "ridge former" (Heim, 1919).

between mountains and hills," *Prof. Geographer,* **16**(6), 6–8.

Wilhelmy, H., 1958, "Klimamorphologie der Massengesteine," Braunschweig, G. Westermann, 238pp.

Wolfe, P. E., 1964, "Late Cenozoic uplift and exhumed Rocky Mountains of central western Montana," *Bull. Geol. Soc. Am.,* **75**, 493–502.

Cross-references: *Block Mountain* ; *Cuesta*; *Dome Mountain*; *Hogback*; *Morphogenetic Regions*; *Mountains*; *Mountain and Hilly Terrain*; *Piedmont*; *Process-Structure-Stage*; *Relict Landforms*; *Ridge and Valley Topography*; *Structural Control in Geomorphology*; *Treppen Concept*; *Volcanic Landscape*; *Youth-Maturity-Old Age.*

MUD CRACKS

Mud crack polygons [i.e., *mud cracks*; synonymous with, (1) *regular mud cracks,* (2) *desiccation cracks,* (3) *polygonal soil cracks,* (4) *shrinkage cracks*] are convex, concave or flat polygonal surfaces (1–0.05 meter in diameter) limited by down tapering *soil-shrinkage,* visible flaws in fine-grained *argillaceous muds* and/or *ooze.*

Mud cracks form largely because of *solar radiation.* They are cellularly assembled on *playas, floodplains, deltas* and *tidal flats,* differing genetically from other *patterned ground* features (i.e., *giant soil cracks,* or *king-size mud cracks* on *playas,* etc. ; *ice-wedge polygons* in *permafrost,* and *columnar jointing* in basalts); nevertheless, all the tensional type polygons have similar breadth/ depth/spacing and secondary cracking relations (Lachenbruch, 1961).

In nature, according to Bucher, by far most mud cracks start as three-pronged stars, clearly reflecting competing random centers of shrinkage. If the drying mud were absolutely uniform in grain shape and size, water content, etc., a hexagonal pattern would result, comparable to the cells in a honeycomb. But because of inhomogeneities, the centers of shrinkage are spaced randomly, and as the cracks meet, they produce irregular polygonal outlines ranging from three or four sides to dominant five and six sides, with few of larger number of sides (Fig. 1).

Differential *soil moisture* content and drying rates influences the soil *cracking patterns:* parallel arrays of mud crack cells tends to form on an evenly sloped-barren-soil surface (e.g., *river banks*), concentric ones on shallow depressions (e.g., *pools of ephemeral channels*).

Mud cracks could form *pre-* or *early-diagenetically* in different environments: Krynine (1935) postulates preservation of mud cracks under humid conditions; Twenhofel (1925) reported the forma-

Fig. 1. Top view of playa mud cracks showing primary and secondary cells resembling a deformed honeycomb.

Fig. 2. Contemporary mudcracks showing curling of individual polygons (photo: J. J. Bigarella).

tion of mud cracks on clay pools under water cover, and Kindle (1923) followed up the development of mud cracks during the desiccation of *calcareous ooze*. Moreover mud cracks are also present at any latitude/elevation soils (e.g., *playas, tundras*, etc.).

Preserved mud cracks could be of assistance as *top-and-bottom* and *paleocurrent* indicators. For instance, if *wind-blown sand* covers a layer of mud cracks, *soil lithification* might lead to a sedimentary *top* having on its base a series of ridges (i.e., the *cast*) combined with a sedimentary *bottom* retaining on its upper surface the shape of the original cracks (i.e., the *mold*); and if a *sheetflood runoff* transports a mud-cracked soil layer, depositing it with sand, the lithified sediment might retain the *mud crack chips* (i.e., *clay galls*).

Well-preserved mud cracks on *sandstones* and *limestones* are found in photographs of many geology textbooks (e.g., Dunbar and Rodgers, 1957); however, frequently the poorly preserved mud cracks are omitted and/or erroneously identified. For instance, the *deformed mud cracks* of Precambrian quartzites described by Wheeler and Quinlan (1931) have been recently—according to Barnes and Smith (1964)—equivocably interpreted as fossil *metazoans* in Canadian outcrops.

Soils are natural aggregates of *organic/inorganic matter* consisting of three phases: *solids, liquids* and *voids. Muds* are water-saturated soils (i.e., two-phase systems: solids and liquids). Unlike *structural materials, soils* and *muds* undergo active changes; development of mud cracks is one of them. The integral understanding of this process is complex and comprises more than one discipline. *Geology*, a pioneer, gives environmental and descriptive data on mud-crack patterns, provides mineralogical/chemical composition of soil ingredients, and associates features of *tensional cracking* origin with mud cracks. *Soil Mechanics* furnishes data encountered from experimental studies of *soil-phases* and/or engineering practice; and finally the fracture studies on *artificial materials* add partial understanding to mud-crack propagation phenomena.

TABLE 1. APPROXIMATE WATER-HOLDING CAPACITY OF SOILS (DATA FROM LYERLY AND LONGENECKER, 1962)

Types	Moisture Held at Field Capacity*
Sands	1.0–1.4
Sandy loams	1.9–2.3
Loams	2.5–2.9
Silt loams	2.7–3.1
Clay loams	3.0–3.4
Clays	3.5–3.9

* Expressed as inches of water per foot of soil.

In principle, if a clay mud loses water, it shrinks more than a sandy mud; hence, more cracks per unit area develop in the clay soil. Empirically the *shrinkage/swelling* values of soil types are derived by comparing their *water-holding capacities* as expressed in inches of water per foot of soil (Table 1).

A quantitative evidence of soil shrinkage/swelling values could be obtained by comparing computed *Poisson ratio* values (i.e., ratio of lateral contraction to stretching) derived from the measurements of *dynamic moduli* of *elasticity* and *rigidity* of mud in the laboratory (Corte and Higashi, 1960).

Genetically the process of mud-crack formation must take into account Terzaghi's (1920) principle of negative tension set-up in the mud's *pore water*, because there is a *water diffusion* loss during mud desiccation and cracking.

Furthermore, the type of clay and *ionic substitution* affects *soil volumetric changes* also. For example, the *wet-dry ratio of montmorillonite* is four times larger than *kaolinite* (Chilingar and Knight, 1960) and Li^+, Na^+, and Ca^+ ions increase the *swellability* of *trioctahedral* clays more than *dioctahedrals*.

To date, few experiments on mud cracks have been carried out in the laboratory. Kindle (1917) concluded that the desiccation of fresh water mud forms *curling-up mud cracks*; high salinity of the slurry not only delays cracking but also causes a downward inclination of the polygonal edges of the mud. Twenhofel (1925) observed the development of mud cracks beneath water after flocculating a colloidal suspension with salts; recently, the follow-up experimentation of Corte and Higashi (1960) shows a series of geometric relations for mud-crack patterns and, more significantly, that mud cracks begin to form from the center of the soil layer propagating to the surface or bottom of the layer with a nonuniform speed. (See also Cegla *et al.*, 1967.)

In general, mud-crack formation is due to polygenetic nature like most patterned ground features. It appears that although *non-confining pressure* laboratory experiments on soils could provide data on *cracking propagation* as well as pattern/geometric relations, the origin of *fracture nuclei* and the nature of early growth into mud cracks are still largely unknown.

RAYMUNDO J. CHICO

References

Barnes, W. C. and Smith, A. G., 1964, "Some markings associated with ripple-marks from the Proterozoic of North America," *Nature*, **201**(4923), 1018–1019.

Bucher, W. H., 1920–1921, "The mechanical interpretation of joints," *J. Geol.*, **28**, 707–730; *ibid.*, **29**, 1–28.

Cegla, J., Dzulinski, S. and Kwiatkowski, S., 1967, "Fractures resulting from liquid infiltration into dry powdered materials," *Bull. Acad. Polonaise Sci.*, géol.-géogr., **15**, 83-88.

Chilingar, G. and Knight, L., 1960, "Relationship between pressure and moisture content of kaolinite, illite, and montmorillonite clays," *Bull. Am. Assoc. Petroleum Geol.*, **44**(1), 101–106.

Corte, A. E., and Higashi, A., 1960, "Experimental Research on Desiccation Cracks in Soil," Research Report 66, U.S. Army Snow Ice and Permafrost Research Establishment, Corps of Engineers, 48pp.

Dunbar, C., and Rogers, J., 1957, "Principles of Stratigraphy," New York, John Wiley & Sons, 356pp.

Kindle, E. M., 1917, "Some factors affecting the development of mud cracks," *J. Geol.*, **25**, 135–144.

Kindle, E. M., 1923, "Notes on mud crack and ripple mark in recent calcareous sediments," *J. Geol.*, **31**(2), 138–145.

Krynine, P. D., 1935, "Formation and preservation of desiccation features in a humid climate," *Am. J. Sci.*, 5th ser., **30**(176), 96–97.

Lachenbruch, A. H., 1961, "Depth and spacing of tension cracks," *J. Geophys. Res.*, **66**(12), 4273–4292.

Lyerly, P. and Longenecker, D. E., 1962, "Salinity control in irrigation agriculture," *Bull. Agricultural and Mechanic College of Texas*, **876**, 20pp.

Neal, J. T., Langer, A. M. and Kerr, P. F., 1968, "Giant desiccation polygons of Great Basin playas," *Bull. Geol. Soc. Am.*, **79**, 69–90.

Terzaghi, C., 1920, "New facts about surface friction," *Phys. Rev.*, new series, **16**(1).

Twenhofel, W. H., 1925, "Significance of some of the surface structures of central and western Kansas," *Bull. Am. Assoc. Petroleum Geol.*, **9**(7), 1061–1070.

Cross-references: *Floodplain; Patterned Ground; Playa.* Vol. VI: *Clay; Soil Mechanics; Tidal Flat Geology.*

MUDFLOW

A mudflow is a flowing mass of predominantly fine-grained earth material that possesses a high degree of fluidity during movement. The degree of fluidity is revealed by the observed rate of movement or by the distribution of the resulting deposit. If more than half of the solid fraction of such a mass is material larger than sand size, the term "debris flow" is preferable (Sharp and Nobles, 1953; Varnes, 1958).

Mudflows are intermediate members of a gradational series of processes characterized by different proportions of water and rock debris. The water

FIG. 1. Volcanic mudflows of Pleistocene age exposed in the Sandy River Valley east of Portland, Oregon. The two mudflows are separated by a thin horizontal bed of silt and clay 3 feet above the man's head. Note the crude upward size gradation in the upper mudflow from coarse to fine; it is overlain by horizontally bedded sand and silt.

content of mudflows ranges from 10–60% according to various measurements. With an increase in water content, mudflows grade into loaded and clear streams; with a decrease of water, they grade into earthflows and dry landslides.

The large component of fine-grained material contributes mobility to mudflows because each particle attracts an envelope of water. Curtis (1954) suggested that in a mudflow "each lubricated fragment, like a ball bearing in a wheel, helps mobilize the mass and may be considered a part of the fluid; hence it does not move appreciably faster or slower than the mass as a whole, nor does it sink or float because of its size." Many observers have compared the movement of a mudflow to that of wet concrete.

Mudflows possess a remarkable ability to transport very large masses of rock; this ability is in large part due to a relatively high specific gravity, which ranges from less than 2 to at least 2.4. Some mudflows no more than 4 feet thick have transported blocks having dimensions of $9 \times 11 \times 16$ feet, and thicker mudflows have carried rock masses measuring at least $20 \times 30 \times 40$ feet.

The velocity of mudflows has been reported to range from less than 1 to about 55 mph, and they generally move down-valley in a series of waves or surges which succeed each other at intervals of a few seconds to several hours. Mudflows seem to have limited erosional ability; materials such as grass, loose volcanic ash, and forest litter have been overriden by mudflows without being removed.

Some common features of mudflow deposits are lobate form, distribution confined to valley floors, poor size sorting, lack of stratification, vertical size gradation upward from coarse to fine, abundant voids in the matrix, and content of angular to subangular stones, some of which may be very large (Fig. 1) (Sharp and Nobles, 1953; Mullineaux and Crandell, 1962; Bull, 1964). Mudflows have a great range in size; they include masses that have not moved more than a few feet and flows that have moved many tens of miles.

Mudflows occur most frequently in environments that provide an abundant source of incoherent fine-grained rock debris, steep slopes, a large but intermittent source of water and sparse vegetation (Sharpe, 1938). These conditions are typically found on mountains in arid regions, on parts of mountains above timberline in humid regions, and on the flanks of active volcanoes. In arid and semiarid regions, mudflows usually accompany periods of intense widespread rainfall or local cloudbursts, and are derived from accumulations of loose rock debris on steep slopes (see examples and references in Bull, 1964).

In humid alpine environments, mudflows usually result from the saturation of glacial debris by water from melting snow; enormous mudflows have been observed in the Himalayas. However, they can also be caused by heavy precipitation and can originate in other kinds of materials that have a fine-grained component. Mudflows also form in humid lowland environments where there is a copious supply of moisture and unconsolidated or poorly consolidated clay-rich material.

Some of the largest and most devastating mudflows of historic time have accompanied or followed volcanic eruptions and have been caused by such phenomena as the ejection of a crater lake, heavy rains on loose volcanic ash, and avalanching of great masses of rock debris. Volcanic mudflows, which are also known by the Indonesian word *lahar*, commonly travel distances of many tens of miles. Because of their high rate of speed and long distance of movement, mudflows have cost thousands of lives within the last century in regions adjacent to active volcanoes in Japan, Indonesia and elsewhere in the world.

Dwight R. Crandell

References

*Bull, W. B., 1964, "Alluvial fans and near-surface subsidence in western Fresno County, California," *U.S. Geol. Surv. Profess. Paper* **437-A**, 71pp.

Curtis, G. H., 1954, "Mode of origin of pyroclastic debris in the Mehrten Formation of the Sierra Nevada," *Calif. Univ., Dept. Geol. Sci. Bull.*, **29**, 453–502.

Mullineaux, D. R., and Crandell, D. R., 1962, "Recent lahars from Mount St. Helens, Washington," *Bull. Geol. Soc. Am.*, **73**, 855–870.

*Sharp, R. P., and Nobles, L. H., 1953, "Mudflow of 1941 at Wrightwood, southern California," *Bull. Geol. Soc. Am.*, **64**, 547–560.

*Sharpe, C. F. S., 1938, "Landslides and Related Phenomena," New York, Columbia University Press, 137pp.

*Varnes, D. J., 1958, "Landslide types and processes," in (Eckel, E. B., editor) "Landslides and engineering practice," *Highway Res. Board Spec. Rept.*, **29**, 20–47 (232pp.).

*Additional bibliographic references may be found in this work.

Cross-references: *Avalanche*; *Mass Movement*; *Mass Wasting*.

MUSICAL SANDS—*See* SINGING SANDS

MUSKEG—*See* TAIGA LANDSCAPE

N

NATURAL BRIDGES

Natural bridges, which are often associated in origin with natural tunnels, are topographic features, whose human interest greatly exceeds their geologic importance. Not necessarily different in origin from natural arches, they are more likely to bridge streams and chasms than are arches. Often they are closely related in origin to natural tunnels and caverns.

Generally speaking, natural bridges do not occur, or are very uncommon, in areas underlain by metamorphic or intrusive igneous rocks. They are not unusual features, however, in regions of recent volcanic activity such as the Hawaiian Islands and parts of the Columbia River Lava Plateau. Here they are caused by the collapse of all but a small

section of the ceiling of a lava tunnel. Such tunnels form underneath a solidified crust of lava, when the still molten material beneath the surface flows on leaving an elongate empty chamber. Indian Tunnel Bridge, the largest lava bridge in Craters of the Moon National Monument, Idaho, has a height of 60 feet and a span of 75 feet bridging a former lava tunnel of approximately these dimensions.

Most of the renowned and magnificent natural bridges of the world occur in regions of sedimentary rock, usually horizontally bedded sandstone or limestone. In the United States, famous bridges in this class are the Rainbow Bridge of Utah and the Natural Bridge of Virginia. Rainbow Bridge, in an until recently remote part of southeastern Utah, was first seen by white men in 1909. This graceful arch, called Nonnezoshie by the Indians, has a

FIG. 1. Natural bridge created by a tunnel in basaltic lava; Dimmuborgir region, Iceland. White line is a measuring tape. (Photo: Jack Green).

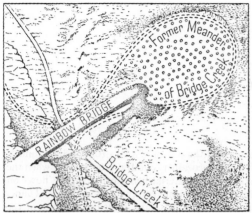

FIG. 2. Sketch map of Rainbow Bridge, Utah, the origin of which is attributed to meandering of Bridge Creek (from Holmes, 1965). (By permission of Ronald Press, N.Y. and T. Nelson & Sons, London.)

FIG. 4. Another natural bridge in Utah. An important aspect of these Utah bridges is that they are mostly formed in the Jurassic Navajo Sandstone, which develops large exfoliation arches, without the aid of streams. (Photo: H. J. Bissell).

span of 278 feet and rises 309 feet above Bridge Creek. It typifies those bridges formed by streams flowing in deep valleys with extremely sinuous meanders. When the stream cuts through the narrow neck of such a meander loop without causing collapse of the top, it takes the short cut resulting and flows under a natural bridge of its own making. Other large bridges of the same origin occur nearby.

The Natural Bridge of Virginia exemplifies those formed by solution in limestone country. This bridge, once owned by Thomas Jefferson and attributed by him to "a great convulsion of nature," is 90 feet long and rises 195 feet above Cedar Creek. It serves the practical purpose of supporting an important highway. Once attributed to collapse of a solutional tunnel formed by waters flowing underground through the neck of an entrenched meander of Cedar Creek, its origin is now generally believed

to be somewhat more complicated. Evidence suggests that underground drainage originating some miles to the northwest took a southeasterly direction along the present course of Cedar Creek to the James River. Eventually all but a few feet of the ceiling of this underground passage collapsed; the remnant is Natural Bridge.

Natural bridges of other origins also occur such as the wave-cut arch seen in Percé Rock at the end of the Gaspé Peninsula. Well-known wave-cut arches are found also in the south of England (Dorset), the west of Ireland, Australia and elsewhere. The rock material may range from limestone

FIG. 3. A natural bridge at the Arches in Southeastern Utah. (Photo: H. J. Bissell).

FIG. 5. Natural Bridge, Virginia; the rock is limestone and the bridge is attributed to solution and collapse. (Photo: F. A. Broedel).

FIG. 6. Wave-cut natural bridges at "London Bridge," Port Campbell (Victoria), Australia.

to granite. A natural bridge of a silicified tree trunk is known from Arizona (the "Onyx Bridge," see figure in Holmes, 1965).

All natural bridges are ephemeral features subject to collapse at any moment. Geologic processes, however, will construct new ones.

HENRY S. SHARP

References

Cleland, H. F., 1910, "North American natural bridges, with a discussion of their origin," *Bull. Geol. Soc. Am.*, **21,** 314–338.

Holmes, A., 1965, "Principles of Physical Geology," New York, Ronald Press; London, T. Nelson & Sons, 1088pp.

Wilson, B. E., 1958, "Arches and Natural Bridges—National Monuments (Utah)," in *Intermountain Assoc. Petrol. Geol., Guidebook*, 9th Ann. Field Conf., 16–18.

Woodward, H. P., 1936, "Natural Bridge and Natural Tunnel, Virginia," *J. Geol.*, **44,** 604–616.

Cross-references: *Coastal Geomorphology*; *Exfoliation*; *Karst*; *Stack*; *Weathering*.

NATURAL REGIONS—*See* REGIONS, NATURAL AND GEOGRAPHIC

NECK—*See* VOLCANIC NECKS AND DIATREMES

NEGROHEAD

Large blocks of coral or coral limestone are found along the margins of many great coral reefs; they become coated by unicellular boring algae, which reach in to depths of 1–2 mm but quickly die when exposed to long periods of drying and then turn black. Most exposed coral cliffs in the intertidal or spray zone develop this black appearance, though dead coral is normally a glistening white. The blackened lumps of dead coral on the reef thus readily earned the name *negro heads* (and inevitably also the colloquial name, without malice, *nigger head*). Both terms are also commonly, but not scientifically, applied to growing coral heads, "brain corals" and so on; these dome-like living corals are properly referred to simply as *coral heads*.

The term negro head is found throughout the literature of coral reefs. They have also been referred to as *storm-tossed boulders, jetsam debris, coral horses, bommies, tête de negre* and *chapeiro*. Matthew Flinders in 1814 wrote: "The negro heads were lumps which stood higher than the rest (of the reef); and being generally dry, were blackened by the weather; but even in these, the forms of the different corals, and some shells were distinguishable." Other early descriptions were provided by J. D. Dana (on the Wilkes Expedition), J. B. Jukes (of H.M.S. *Fly*), Semper, A. Agassiz and Wood-Jones. Hedley (1906) wrote: "nigger heads stand out against the sky like tombstones in a cemetary ... doubtless washed up by heavy gales."

There are two quite distinct theories as to their origin. Agassiz (1898) attributed them to the solution and dismemberment of a former reef platform. At Rose Atoll, Samoa, Mayor (1924) described them as being all uniformly 5.5 feet in height, evidently part of a once-continuous reef now emerged; in many places the remnants are undercut to form *mushroom rocks*, sometimes supported on "so slender a pedicel that it would seem as if the next storm must cause it to topple over." Long, flat-topped examples are

Fig. 1. Flat-topped negro heads on the outer reef of Pelsart, Houtmans Abrolhos Islands, Western Australia. Note heavy swell breaking on reef margin, in distance. (Photo: R. W. Fairbridge).

widespread in the Maldives and Laccadives where they have always been termed "coral horses" according to Seymour Sewell (1935).

The second explanation was that the negro heads were coral colonies that had been torn off from the front of the reef during hurricanes and thrown up onto the reef flat. Saville-Kent (1893) thus described them as "jetsam." Hedley and Griffith Taylor (1908) found that they were exclusively thrown up in the Great Barrier Reefs on the sides exposed to hurricanes.

It is interesting that in the East Indies between latitudes 10°N and 10°S hurricanes are unknown, and there are also no negro heads, although the monsoon winds may blow with considerable force. Umbgrove (1931) noted, on the other hand, that after the Krakatoa eruption of 1883 with its cataclysmic tsunamis, large numbers of negro heads were thrown up along the coast of the Sunda Strait.

From his studies in the Indian Ocean, Gardiner (1931) concluded that there were in fact two quite distinct types of negro heads. The writer has confirmed this; the flat-topped (or flat-sided, if they have been undercut and tilted) varieties are remnants of former mid-Holocene reef tracts while the randomly shaped and colony units have been thrown up as jetsam.

RHODES W. FAIRBRIDGE

References

Agassiz, A., 1898, "A visit to the Great Barrier Reef of Australia in the steamer 'Croyden' during April and May, 1896," *Bull. Mus. Comp. Zool. Harvard Coll.*, **28**, 93–148.

Flinders, Matthew, 1817, "A Voyage to Terra Australia," Vol. 2, p. 88.

Gardiner, J. S., 1931, "Coral Reefs and Atolls," London, Macmillan and Co., 181pp.

Hedley, C., and Taylor, T. Griffith, 1908, "Coral reefs of the Great Barrier, Queensland," *Rept. Aust. Assoc. Adv. Sci. (Adelaide) 1907*, **11**, 397–413.

Mayor, A. G., 1924, "Rose atoll, American Samoa," *Carnegie Inst. Washington, Publ. 340*, Pap. Dept. Mar. Biol., **19**, 73–91.

Saville-Kent, W., 1893, "The Great Barrier Reef of Australia," London, W. H. Allen, 387pp.

Sewell, R. B. S., 1935, "Studies on coral and coral formations in Indian waters," *Mem. Asiatic Soc. Bengal*, **9**, 461–540.

Umbgrove, J. H. F., 1931, "Note on 'Negroheads' (coral boulders) in the East Indian Archipelago," *Koninkl. Ned. Akad. Wetenschap. Proc.*, **34**, 485–487.

Cross-references: *Coral Reef*. Vol. I: *Tsunami*. Vol. II: *Tropical Cyclones*.

NEOTECTONICS

(1) Definitions

The term "neotectonics" was originally proposed by V. A. Obruchev to mean the section of the earth sciences which is devoted to the movements of the earth's crust that have taken place during the late Tertiary (Neogene, i.e., Miocene and Pliocene) and Quaternary periods, and which played a decisive role in the formation of the contemporary topography. The time of occurrence of these movements marks a special Neotectonic Stage of the earth's development, with which is connected the evolution of the present topography and structure of continents and ocean floors.

The extent of the idea "neotectonics" is still not completely defined. Some investigators narrow this concept and limit it to the Quaternary (or Pliocene–Quaternary) movements. Other investigators broaden the concept and attribute to the neotectonic stage all movements which played a role in forming the contemporary topography, although the initial stages of many major elements of topography go back to the beginning of the Tertiary period and even to the Mesozoic (the Gondwana shields and platforms, likewise of Laurasia–Canada, Fennoscandia, Siberia). With the compilation of neotectonic maps of the U.S.S.R. it was accepted by a majority of workers that the beginning of the neotectonic stage would be taken as the Miocene, i.e., the boundary between Paleogene and Neogene.

Contemporary movements of the earth's crust are distinguished as an independent category of neotectonic movements. They are movements closest to the present time, which yield to direct observation with the help of geodetic and other precise survey methods (see *Crustal Movements—Contemporary*).

(2) Survey of Investigations

Comparatively recently, until the 1920's and 1930's, a common assumption was that no marked tectonic movements or deformation of the earth's crust took place in Recent (Holocene) geological time, except in highly seismic areas. This was a prevalent view although varied signs of continuing tectonic activity (the uplift of Fennoscandia, the subsidence of the Netherlands) were known for a long time. In his great work on "The Face of the Earth," E. Suess, summing up the investigations of the nineteenth century, came to the conclusion that disregarding local movements, the continents were absolutely stable. Suess explained the advances and retreats of the ocean by *eustatic oscillations* of the sea level. In more recent times, Baulig developed the idea of glacio-eustatic oscillations of sea level which had a controlling influence on the development of modern land forms. At the end of the nineteenth century, the concepts of epeirogeny (Gilbert), isostasy (Airy, Pratt) and cycles of erosion (Davis) were less acceptable than the Suess theory of eustatism. Gradually, however, under the influence of accumulated data, investigators began to associate the important transgressions and regressions not so much with the eustatic oscillations, but with the *orogenic and epeirogenic movements* of the earth's crust. The works of W. M. Davis, W. Penck, E. de Martonne, V. A. Obruchev and their followers, both geologists and geomorphologists, played an important role in this connection.

During the 1930's it became clear that the topography of the earth's surface was and is still being developed on a mobile substratum. At the Third Conference of the International Association for the Study of the Quaternary Period (INQUA), G. F. Mirchink, on the basis of surveys in the U.S.S.R., showed that intensive movements of both orogenic and epeirogenic nature took place in the Quaternary period. H. Stille (1936) came to the conclusion that the Quaternary period is characterized by an intensification of orogenic movements and general tectonic activity of the earth. S. S. Schultz (1939), in a paper at the Seventeenth International Geological Congress, suggested the term "newest tectonics" for designating the movements which have produced the contemporary topography. In 1948, V. A. Obruchev introduced the term *neotectonics*. Bourcart (1950) outlined a theory of continental flexure based on the argument that the boundary of continental shelves and oceanic basins separates distinct parts of the earth's crust with contrasting tendencies toward uplift (continents) and subsidence (the floor of the oceans). I. P. Gerasimov (1946) introduced an idea of *morphostructure* expressed in the topography by tectonic structures, as having actively developed in most recent times. Nikolaev (1949, 1962) published summary works about the neotectonics of the U.S.S.R., in which he showed the general appearance of youthful movements of the earth's crust and distinguished a particular, neotectonic stage of the earth's development as distinct from the Alpine stage.

In 1960, a summary map of neotectonics of the U.S.S.R. (editors, N. I. Nikolaev and S. S. Schultz) was published at a scale of 1:5,000,000. The map characterizes quantitatively (with the help of isolines) the amplitudes of crustal uplifts and depressions over the Neogene-Quaternary period. V. E. Khain and E. E. Milanovsky (1956) gave a summary of the neotectonics of the world; L. King (1950, 1962), on the basis of studies and correlations of the erosion surfaces of the whole world, came to the conclusion that there was a particular type of movement (cymatogenic) which represented oscillations of wide portions of the earth's crust (hundreds of miles in diameter) with vertical displacements of hundreds of feet.

The study of neotectonics constitutes one of the main research topics of the International Association for the Study of the Quaternary Period (INQUA), which has a special commission on neotectonics (president—N. I. Nikolaev). An international neotectonic map of Europe on a scale of 1:2,500,000 is being compiled.

(3) Methods of Investigation

There are various indications of neotectonic movements; they are revealed in the geomorphology, in the composition of sediments, and in the tectonic structure. One should employ every technique in the study of neotectonics in order better to control the results.

For the study of regional subsidence and accumulation, the same *geological methods* which are used for determining old movements may be employed. These include the analysis of the surface structure of the subsidence, the conditions of occurrence, etc. For regions of uplift and denudation, the critical data are acquired by *geomorphological methods*: the tracing of river terraces, planation surfaces, old coastlines of seas and lakes, and other geomorphological levels and evidence of their deformations. A study of the elements of topography must be accompanied by a *sedimentologic analysis* of the deposits connected with it. (For example, an analysis of river terraces must be accompanied by a study of the thickness and composition of the fluvial deposits of each terrace.) For establishing effectively neotectonic deformation of broad areas, the study of *polygenetic erosion surfaces* is necessary (see *Morphogenetic Regions; Plains*). Each of these levels includes the denudational surface and the corresponding accumulation area (plain), formed by simultaneous erosion and deposition (Fig. 1).

Indications of neotectonic deformation may be given by: morphometric construction; the study of old glaciations, including the position of snow lines and boundaries of permafrost; the history of the development of karst, etc. For the study of younger deformation and contemporary movements, archeological indicators may be used also, as well as the repeated geodetic leveling and astronomical deter-

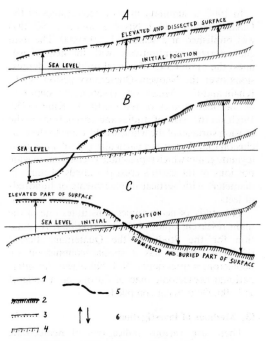

FIG. 1. Polygenetic surfaces of planation: some types of deformation.

(A) General uplift along continental flexure (subsidence seaward of continental shelf margin).

(B) Deformation with the preservation of general plan of distribution of erosional and accumulation areas (shelf subsiding).

(C) Deformation with the inversion of tectonic conditions.

Key: (1) Original position of polygenetic (erosion and accumulation) surface. (2) Erosional surface. (3) Accumulation plain (or continental shelf). (4) Mixed (erosional and accumulation) part of the surface. (5) Contemporary position of deformed polygenetic surface. (6) Amplitude of deformation (uplifts and depressions).

minations of the point coordinates (see *Crustal Movements—Contemporary*).

(4) Basic Characteristics of Earth's Neotectonics

(a) **General Information.** According to Obruchev (1948), neotectonics should fully explain the chief features of the contemporary topography of the entire globe. Demonstrations of neotectonics are general; they embrace both orogenic and platform regions, the land surface and the floor of the oceans and marginal seas (see Vol. 1, *Encyclopedia of Oceanography*). The predominant movements have been uplifts in the continental regions and subsidences in the oceanic regions, notably in marginal seas.

For the continental platform regions, the amplitude of neotectonic deformation (uplift or depression) is usually measured in the tens or few hundreds

of meters (as in the Eastern European Plain), with a maximum value of 1–1.5 km (Colorado Plateau, Eastern Siberian Plateau, African plateaus). In the orogenic region of continents, amplitudes of neotectonic movements are measured in kilometers, with maximum values of 5–8 km (Alps, Himalayas, Andes). In areas of oceans and internal seas, amplitudes of neotectonic movements (subsidences) may range from 1–3 km, in relatively stable (quasicratonic) regions of platform type, to 8–10 km in active geosynclinal troughs. Orogenic regions differ from platform ones, not only in the greater amplitude of their neotectonic movements but also in their higher gradients and greater degree of differential movement.

In comparison with the vertical movements of Neogene-Quaternary time, the horizontal movements on the whole have received less study. However, the presence of youthful movements along some faults is well-known (the San Andreas Fault, California; Talasso-Fergan Fault, Central Asia; both transcurrent, strike-slip faults).

(b) **Principal Types of Neotectonic Structures.** The movements of the earth's crust in the Neogene-Quaternary period led to the formation of *neotectonic structures* (domes, depressions, anticlines, synclines, horsts, grabens, etc.) which, to a great extent, are reflected in the contemporary topography (see *Morphostructure*). Many neotectonic structures are *inherited* from older ones (see *Morphogenetic Regions*); other neotectonic structures were formed on their own, according to a new plan, uninherited from old structures (*superimposed neotectonic structures*).

As a whole, the *young mountains* which developed from geosynclines of Alpine age (the Alps, Caucasus, Andes) are characterized by an inherited sequential development. In quite recent times, there were also formed extensive chains of *regenerated* (epiplatform) mountains which arose in areas of ancient peneplaned folded zones of varying ages (Central Rocky Mountains, Tien-Shan, Baikal mountain region, East African uplands and other "regions of tectonic reactivation," according to V. V. Beloussov). A major role in the formation of the regenerated mountains and primarily of those involved in block movement (taphrogenic), is played by the variously directed movements of blocks of the earth's crust along the faults (often "lineaments") which often cut the old folded structures. The formation of the regenerated mountains is connected with widespread deformation of a general planetary nature (Fig. 2). According to V. E. Khain, the regenerated mountains are subdivided into two groups:

(1) *Peri-oceanic regenerated mountains* arose primarily along the borders of the continents. The formation of these mountains may be connected with compensational uplifts of the marginal parts of the continents in relation to the sinking of the quasicratonic oceanic depressions and with the corresponding displacement of subcrustal masses toward

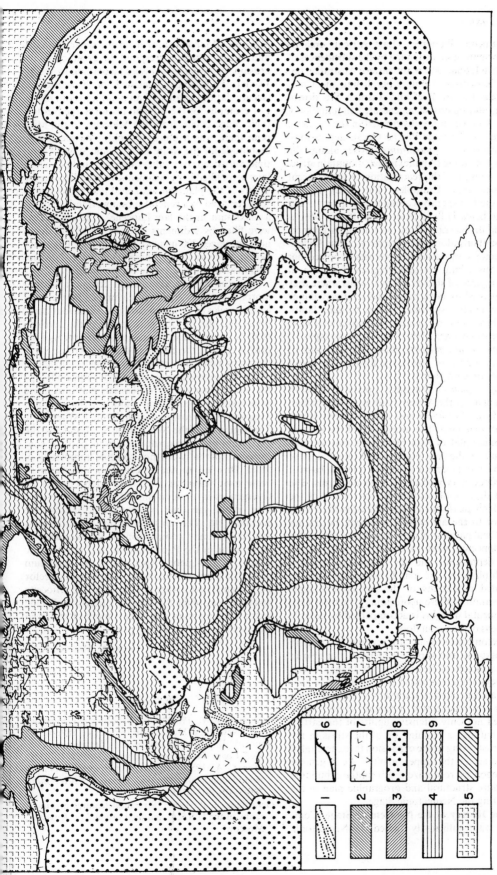

Fig. 2. Basic elements of the morphotectonics of the earth. (1) Young mountains (Alpides, mountains of contemporary geosynclinal regions). (2) Regenerated mountains of peri-oceanic type. (3) Regenerated mountains of peri-orogenic type. (4) High platforms, border and median-mass lowlands (in regions of dry land and continental shelf). (6) Border of continental masses (continental flexure type). (7) Transitional zone between continents and oceans. (8) Ancient oceanic depressions (primary). (9) Later oceanic depressions (secondary) and depressions of inland seas. (10) Mid-oceanic ridges and rises of the oceans.

the continents. Examples: East African uplands whose formation was attended by the subsidences of the western Indian Ocean, the eastern Australian uplands ("Kosciusko Uplift") paralleling the Coral Sea, Great Barrier Reef and Tasman Sea downwarping, and chains of regenerated mountains of Eastern Asia which are distributed in the "zone of influence" of the huge Pacific Ocean depressions.

(2) *Peri-orogenic mountains* arose along the periphery of young (Alpine) folded mountain structures as a result of the reactivation of the adjacent peneplaned area. Examples: The Black Forest, Vosges, the Rhine graben along the periphery of the Alps, the Black Hills in front of the Rocky Mountains, and the Sierra de Cordova and other regenerated mountains along the periphery of the Andes.

Neotectonic movements have been reported not only in disturbing orogenic regions, but also in "quiet" regions of shields and platforms where they are manifested by both major and relatively minor structures (arches, synclines, domes, troughs, faults, etc.). In broad outline, neotectonic movements have led to the subdivision of platforms into two types:

(1) *Low, or intermediate plains* (a major part of the North American plains, the Eastern European plain, the Amazon plain).

(2) *High plains*—plateaus, uplands (Eastern Siberian plateau, the African platform, the Brazilian highland, the Colorado and other western North American plateaus). The amplitude of the general neotectonic uplift of high plateaus is two to three times that of the low platforms. A great deal of fracturing and magmatic extrusion (plateau basalts, cinder cones) is typical of the high platforms. The different degrees of neotectonic movement of the high and low platforms are not related to their early history or to the age of the basement, but rather reflect global patterns of deformations of the earth's crust connected with the active growth of the oceanic depressions and the continental regions. The high platforms are mainly associated with the regenerated mountains of the peri-oceanic type. The formation of these neotectonic structures near the continental margins is accompanied by notable depressions of the ocean floor.

Neotectonic movements are revealed not only in the topography and surface structures, but also in the deep structure of the earth's crust (thanks to seismic surveys and gravimetry). A comparison of neotectonic and geophysical data shows that in the high platform and regenerated mountain regions there have been not only intensive uplifts of the earth's surface, but also a building up of the stress in the earth's crust owing to the expansion (broadening) of the material of the upper mantle. As a general phenomenon we recognize a substantial rebuilding of the entire structural and orographic plan of the earth during the Neotectonic Stage.

(c) **The History of the Neotectonic Stage.** Complex and still insufficiently studied, the Neotectonic Stage is undoubtedly broken up into separate phases and cycles which correspond to great cycles of erosion, or *geomorphic cycles* (according to W. M. Davis). Each cycle consisted of a subsidence (accumulation) phase and an uplift (erosion) phase. For example, for the Russian platform, the Neotectonic Stage begins from the Miocene. In the Miocene there was a phase of uplift, the greatest in amplitude for the entire Neotectonic Stage. At this time, very deep river valleys were scoured out which later were filled in by sediments. In the Pliocene, the uplifts of the platform weakened and subsequently were replaced by a general subsiding trend (reaching a maximum in the late Pliocene). The old valleys were filled by sediments (150–200 meters in thickness, in places 300 meters). During the Quaternary period, there was a new phase of uplift, but it did not reach the amplitude of the earlier phase.

A picture of the alternating tectonic and geomorphic cycles is made more complex by the presence of cycles of various orders (and of various durations), and also by local peculiarities of the development of individual structures. In several parts of the earth's crust in the course of the Neotectonic Stage there was a complete rebuilding of the tectonic plan, and superimposed structural forms appeared; e.g., the Volga upland on the Russian platform arose as a result of neotectonic uplift on the site of a Mesozoic–Cenozoic synclinal basin ("syneclise"). The beginning of the Neotectonic Stage and also the maximum phase of uplift on various parts of land surface apparently did not coincide completely in time. This led to the so-called *metachronism of neotectonic movements* [to this are related in part the divergences in opinion among different investigators, about the time of neotectonic events—see Section (1)]. The metachronism appears most distinctly in any comparison of the sequence of movements in the Pacific and in the Indo-Atlantic sectors of the globe. Apparently, the maximum neotectonic movements in the Indo-Atlantic sector were manifested earlier (basically in the Miocene and beginning of the Pliocene), whereas in the Pacific sector the maximum movements more often fall in the late Pliocene-Quaternary period.

YURI A. MESCHERIKOV

References

Beloussov, V. V., 1962, "Basic Problems in Geotectonics," New York, McGraw-Hill Book Co., 809pp.

Bourcart, J., 1950, "La theorie de la flexure continentale," *Congr. Intern Geogr. Lisbonne, 1949,* **2,** 167–190.

Cotton, C. A., 1955, "Aspects géomorphologiques de la flexure continentale," *Ann. Soc. Geol. Belg. Bull.,* **78B**(8–10), 403–418.

Gerasimov, I. P., 1959, "Structural features in topography of the U.S.S.R. and their origin," (in Russian), Moscow.

Khain, V. Ye., 1962, "Fundamental stages in the evolution of the crust, recent continental regions" (in Russian), *Bull. Nat. Soc. Moscow (Geol.)*, **37**, 8–24 (translated *Intern. Geol. Rev.*, **6**, 439–449).

Khain, V. Ye., 1964, "General geotectonics" (in Russian), Moscow, Izdatelstvo Nedra, 477pp. (review by Burgunker, *Intern. Geol. Rev.*, **7**, 2223, 1965).

Khain, V. E., and Milanovsky, E. E., 1956, "Main features of the Earth's topography and neotectonics," (in Russian), *Bull. Mosk. ob-va ispytatelej prirody, otd. geologii*, **31**(3, 4).

King, L. C., 1962, "The Morphology of the Earth; A Study and Synthesis of World Scenery," Edinburgh, Oliver & Boyd, 699pp. (Second ed., 1967.)

King, P. B., 1965, "Tectonics of Quaternary Time in Middle North America," in (Wright, H. E., Jr., and Frey, D. G., editors) "The Quaternary of the United States," pp. 831–870, Princeton, N.J., Princeton University Press.

Kukkamäkt, T. J., 1965, "Second symposium of the International Commission on Recent crustal movements (CRCM) held in Aulanko, Finland, August 3–7, 1965," *Bull. Géodésique*, No. 78, 311–315.

Lubimova, E. A., 1964, "Heat flow in the Ukrainian Shield in relation to recent tectonic movements," *J. Geophys. Res.*, **69**(24), 5277–5284.

Mescherikov, Yu. A., 1959, "Contemporary movements in the earth's crust," *Intern. Geol. Rev.*, **1**(8), 40–52.

Mescherikov, Yu. A., 1961, "Recent crustal movements, erosion and aggradation, the northwest portion of the Russian Plain" (in Russian), *Moscow, Acad. Sci. U.S.S.R. Geogr. Inst.*, 88pp. (review by Burgunker, *Intern. Geol. Rev.*, **5**, p. 363).

Mescherikov, Yu. A., 1965, "Structural Geomorphology of Plainlands," (in Russian), Moscow, U.S.S.R.

Mirchink, M. F., 1955, "Geotectonic development of platforms and the nature of tectonic movements" (in Russian), *Neft. Khoz.*, **23**(6), 42–50 (translated T.C.T., Philadelphia).

Nickolaev, N. I., 1949, 1962, "Neotectonics of the U.S.S.R.," (in Russian) Moscow, U.S.S.R.

Nikolaev, N. I., 1953, "Some structural characteristics of mobile tectonic belts" (in Russian), *Izv. Akad. Nauk SSSR, Ser. Geol.*, No. 2 [translated in *Intern Geol. Rev.*, **1**, 50–64 (1959)].

Obruchev, V. A., 1948, "Osnovnyje certy kinetiki i plastiki neotektoniki," *Izv. Akad. Nauk SSSR Ser. Geol.*, No. 5.

Rantsman, E. Ya., 1965, "Quaternary horizontal movements along the Talas-Fergana fault," *Dokl. Akad. Nauk SSSR, Earth Sci. Sects.* (in translation), **149**(1–6), 57–59.

Schults (Schultz), S. S., 1939, "Sur la tectonique récente du Tian-Chan," *Intern. Geol. Congr., Moscow, 1937, Rept. 17th Session*, **2**, 615–621 (English abstract, see *Add. Abs.*, 12–13).

Schults (Schultz), S. S., 1948, "Analysis of newest tectonics and topography of Tian-Shan," (in Russian), Moscow, U.S.S.R.

Stille, H., 1936, "The present tectonic state of the earth," *Bull. Am. Assoc. Petrol. Geologists*, **20**, 849–880.

Stille, H., 1948, "Ur- und Neuozeane," *Abhandl. Deut. Akad. Wiss., Berlin, tl. Math. Allgem. Naturur.*, **1945–46**, No. 6, 68pp.

Wegmann, E., 1955, "Lebendige Tektonik, eine Übersicht," *Geol. Rundschau*, **43**(1), 4–34.

Cross-references: *Continental Flexure; Crustal Movements; Cycles, Geomorphic; Cymatogeny; Eustasy; Holocene; International Organizations for Geomorphology; Morphogenetic Regions; Morphostructure; Plains; Postglacial Isostatic Rebound; Quaternary Period; Warping*. Vol. V. *Taphrogeny. See also* Vol. I, "Encyclopedia of Oceanography."

NÉVÉ—See MOUNTAIN GLACIER LANDSCAPES; SNOW: METAMORPHISM OF DEPOSITED SNOW

NICKPOINT (KNICKPOINT)

The *nickpoint* is the name applied to the point of interruption of the graded longitudinal profile or *thalweg* (q.v.) at the head of a second cycle valley derived according to the *treppen concept* (q.v.) of Penck (1927). The supporters of the *geographical cycle* of Davis would regard the nickpoint as being a synonym for "*knickpoint*" (or "*Knickpunkte*") i.e., points of abrupt change in the longitudinal profile of streams due to a change in base level. Penck introduced "Knickpunkte" as being a special kind of nickpoint formed due to the influence of a change in a local base level, not due to sea level changes as envisaged by Davis.

It now appears as though both Penck and Davis were wrong in certain details (Howard, 1965). Nevertheless both authors also put forward ideas in this connection which are substantially correct. Breaks in the thalweg can indeed be induced by factors other than change in base level, contrary to the ideas of Davis. An example is the downcutting of the arroyos in the western United States due to

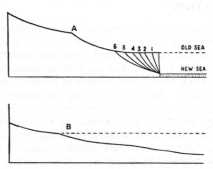

FIG. 1. Nature of nick points. On a steep-to coast a drop of sea level means the formation of a steep cliff (A). Headward erosion is rapid at this point and the waterfall is slowly flattened out by the erosion of the river so that the profile occupies successively the positions 1 to 6. When the nick point has receded a considerable distance upstream, it will have a much gentler form, comparable with A, which represents the head of an earlier rejuvenation. The more usual condition is a gently sloping coast (B), where the nick point migrates inland in a less abrupt manner (Sparks, 1960). (By permission of John Wiley & Sons, N.Y.)

destruction of vegetation by the European settlers and the consequent local increase in stream discharge. A possibility which has not been considered in the literature is that the term "nickpoint" should still be used for such breaks in the thalweg not induced by sea level changes. Such a term is certainly needed to support modern theory. This usage would be essentially the same as that for which it was first suggested, though whether the exact cause was the same as that envisaged by Penck is rather doubtful.

STUART A. HARRIS

References

Brush, L. M., Jr., 1957, "Laboratory study of knickpoint behavior in noncohesive material," *Bull. Geol. Soc. Am.*, **68**(12)AGs.

Howard, A. D., 1965, "Geomorphological systems—equilibrium and dynamics," *Am. J. Sci.*, **263**, 302–312.

Penck, W., 1927, "Die morphologische Analyse," Stuttgart (translated as "Morphological Analysis of Land Forms," London, Macmillan, by H. Czech and K. C. Boswell, 1953).

Sparks, B. W., 1960, "Geomorphology," New York, John Wiley & Sons, London, Longmans, 371pp.

Stamp, L. D., 1961, "A Glossary of Geographical Terms," London, Longmans, 539pp.

Cross-references: *Base Level*; *Cycles, Geomorphic*; *Thalweg*; *Treppen Concept*.

NIEVES PENITENTES—*See* pr Vol. VI, SNOW AND ICE FORMS

NIVATION

Nivation is a term proposed by F. E. Matthes (1899) for a mass-wasting phenomenon of periglacial, i.e., subpolar latitudes and high mountain landscapes. Quoting from his original description: "We know that stream erosion is arrested under the *névé*, . . . the effects of the occupation by quiescent *névé* are thus to convert shallow V-shaped valleys into flat U-shaped ones and to efface their drainage lines without material change of grade. These *névé* effects . . . are wholly different from those produced by glaciation . . ." Such effects he described as the result of *nivation*. Lewis (1939), and others, have called it "snow patch erosion"; according to him a *nivation hollow* is a periglacial phenomenon, a "snow nitch" or "amphitheatre" where snow patches tend to "dig themselves in," in short, the first stages of cirque formation. Maximum erosion is always in the upper semicircle of the snow patch.

The process has been generally described as a combination of freeze-and-thaw with mass-wasting, marked by deep penetration by meltwater, and frost wedging at the periphery due to nocturnal freezing. There is therefore at the margins an up-and-down movement due to crystallization expansion followed by melting and a small vectoral motion owing to gravity. However, a transition from a small snow patch to a large firn bank to ice means the initiation of a mechanism like that of a *cirque glacier* (q.v.) with concomitant flow motion.

The term "cryonivation" has been proposed by Guillien (1949) for periglacial phenomena in general (see article: *Cryopedology* . . .).

RHODES W. FAIRBRIDGE

References

Berger, H., 1964, "Vorgänge und Formen der Nivation in den Alpen," *Buch Ser. Landesmus. f. Kärnten, Klagenfurt*, **17**, 1–88.

Cailleux, A., 1948, "Etude de cryopédologie," Paris, C. Doc. Univ. (*Exp. Pol. Fr., Miss. Victor*), 8pp.

Guilcher, A., 1950, "Nivation, cryoplanation et solifluction quaternaires dans les collines de Bretagne Occidentale et du Nord du Devonshire," *Rev. Géomorphol. Dynamique*, **1**, 53–78.

Guillien, Y., 1949, "Gel et dégel on sol: les méchanismes morphologiques," *L'Information Géogr.* (Paris) **13**, 104–116.

Lewis, W. V., 1939, "Snow-patch erosion in Iceland," *Geogr. J.*, **94**, 153–161.

Matthes, F. E., 1900, "Glacial sculpture of the Bighorn Mountains, Wyoming," *U.S. Geol. Survey 21st Ann. Rept.*, 1899–1900, Pt. 2, 167–190.

Nichols, R. L., 1963, "Miniature nivation cirques near Marble Point, McMurdo Sound, Antarctica," *J. Glaciol.*, **4**(34), 477–479.

Russell, R. J., 1933, "Alpine land forms of western United States," *Bull. Geol. Soc. Am.*, **44**, 927–949.

Troll, C., 1948, "Der Subnivale oder Periglaziale Zyklus der Denudation," *Erdkunde*, **2**, 21pp.

Cross-references: *Cirque*; *Cirque Glacier*; *Cryopedology, Cryonivation, Cryoplanation, Cryoturbation*; *Frost Action*; *Periglacial Landscape*.

NUNATAK

A *nunatak* is an isolated hill or mountain peak rising above the level of a continental ice sheet and alpine-type icecap. It is an Eskimo word introduced by A. E. Nordenskiöld [*nuna* = lonely; *tak* = peak; also nanatag; pl. *nunatakker* is purely a Swedish modification (Charlesworth, 1957)].

Nunataks were first described from the regions bordering the Greenland ice sheet, and subsequently have been extensively noted and photographed from the Antarctic continent (see, for example, photo in Flint, 1957, p. 42).

A hypothesis known as the "Nunatak Theory" concerns hypothetical *"Glacial Refuges"* (q.v.) during glacial periods.

RHODES W. FAIRBRIDGE

References

Charlesworth, J. K., 1957, "The Quaternary Era," London, Edward Arnold, 2 vols.

Cotton, C. A., 1942, "Climatic Accidents in Landscape-making," Christchurch, N.Z., Whitcombe & Tombs, 354pp.

Flint, R. F., 1957, "Glacial and Pleistocene Geology," New York, John Wiley & Sons, 553pp.

Cross-references: *Glacial Refuge* (*"Nunatak Theory"*); *Monadnock*; pr Vol. **VI**: *Ice Sheet*.

O

OBSEQUENT VALLEY, STREAM—*See* **DRAINAGE PATTERNS; RIVERS**

OMBILIC—*See* **CIRQUE**

OPEN SYSTEMS—ALLOMETRIC GROWTH

Geomorphologists conceive of a river as an open system (Strahler, 1950, p. 676; Leopold and Langbein, 1962; Chorley, 1962; Howard, 1965) which is defined as a set of interrelated parts through which flow energy and matter. A characteristic of open systems is that they tend to achieve a time-independent steady state if average inflows and outflows are balanced and remain relatively constant (see *General Systems Theory; Equilibrium*). In the case of channel flow, the geometry of a graded stream system remains relatively constant through time (Strahler, 1964, pp. 4–41).

It is also recognized that open systems may change form or grow in size, depending on imbalances of flows through the system, or changing relations of the parts with the system. This type of growth has been termed allometric growth by biologists and was first formulated as a general principle by Huxley (1924; Reeve and Huxley, 1945; von Bertalanffy, 1960). Recently Nordbeck (unpublished) and Woldenberg (1966) have applied the term allometric growth to the changing geometry of river systems. The concept may well be usefully applied to other geologic open systems.

The law of allometric growth applied, for example, to an animal states that the specific rate of growth of an organ is a constant fraction of the specific rate of growth of the whole organism.

Thus if y is a measure of the size of the organ and x is a comparable measure of the size of the entire organism,

$$\frac{dy}{y} \cdot \frac{1}{dt} = b \frac{dx}{x} \cdot \frac{1}{dt}$$

multiplying by dt and integrating,

$$\int \frac{dy}{y} = b \int \frac{dx}{x}$$

$$\log y = \log a + b \log x$$

where a and b are constants and a is always positive. Taking antilogs,

$$y = ax^b$$

This equation indicates that paired observations for y and x, when plotted on double logarithmic paper, yield a straight line or are best fitted by a straight line. As a corollary, it might be inferred that if each of two parts of a system is related allometrically to the whole system, then they are related to each other by a power function. Hence, regression of any one of the geometrical characteristics of a river system in dimensions of length, area, volume or weight upon another geometrical characteristic of the system will also yield a straight line on double logarithmic paper (Fig. 1).

Relating stream order as defined by Strahler (1952, p. 1120) to some geometrical characteristic of a river system will also yield a straight line. This apparently semi-log graph has been shown to be actually a double logarithmic graph because each integer stream order represents a logarithmic increase of absolute magnitude to the base of the bifurcation ratio (Woldenberg, 1966; see Fig. 2).

Log–log regressions yielding a straight line result from random processes and reflect situations of

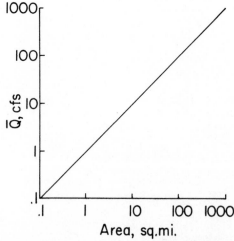

FIG. 1. Discharge versus area on double logarithmic paper. Both scales are read in arithmetic values. Data hypothetical (see Woldenberg, 1966).

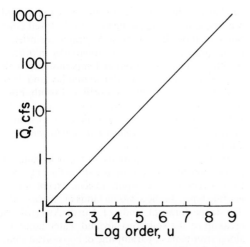

FIG. 2. Discharge versus stream order. $\log_{R_b} x = u - 1$, where x is a variable of stream geometry or flow, R_b is the bifurcation ratio and the base of $\log x$, and u is stream order as defined by Strahler (1952). The ordinate is read in arithmetic values and the abscissa is read in logarithmic values.

maximum probability (Simon, 1955). Simon considered only the Yule distribution which describes a system growing allometrically by the addition of variates. An example of this in fluvial systems would be the addition of basins through headward erosion. Actually many alternative distributions may be substituted for the Yule distribution as an explanation or description of log–log regressions because the tails of many distributions are similar and indistinguishable.

Up to this point, the discussion has implied that allometric growth is only positive. Steady state may be thought of as zero allometric growth. While the number of basins may not be changing, it is also obvious that their physical location cannot be changing or the condition of invariant geometry in steady state would be violated. Negative allometric growth might occur as a land surface approaches base level. Small basins, once present in early maturity, will tend to disappear.

Double logarithmic graphs of variables of river geometry which yield a straight line are actually expressions of maximum probability and hence maximum entropy possible under conditions of flow. In such an open system which tends to equilibrium even while growing, the free available energy tends to be distributed evenly throughout the system (Leopold and Langbein, 1962, pp. 2, 6, 11).

In the equation, $\log y = \log a + b \log x$, $\log a$ is the intercept on the ordinate and b is the slope of the line. If $\log a$ were to change, this would signify a change in scale of the system (White and Gould, 1965). Such would be the case if, for instance,

vegetation were stripped off a land surface, exposing that surface to intensified erosion, resulting in a badland topography with first-order basins diminished in size while the shape of basins of all orders might be modified. Conversely, reforestation may serve to increase the size of the first-order basin and change the shapes of basins of all orders, perhaps to the original condition.

The slope of the regression line, b, is dependent on the ratio of the dimensions of the two geometrical variables being compared (von Bertalanffy, 1960, pp. 198–208). If the ordinate has the same dimension as the abscissa, $b = 1$. If the abscissa has the dimension L^2, while the ordinate has the dimension L^3, then the slope $b = 3/2$.

The concept of allometric growth has potentially wide application in the physical, biological, and social sciences. This should not be surprising since allometric growth and steady state reflect most probable states of open systems.

MICHAEL J. WOLDENBERG

References

Chorley, R., 1962, "Geomorphology and general systems theory," *U.S. Geol. Surv. Profess. Paper* **500B.**

Howard, Alan D., 1965, "Geomorphological systems—equilibrium and dynamic," *Am. J. Sci.*, **263,** 300–312.

Huxley, J. S., 1924, "Constant differential growth-ratios and their significance," *Nature*, **114,** 895–896.

Leopold, Luna B., and Langbein, Walter, 1962, "The concept of entropy in landscape evolution," *U.S. Geol. Surv. Profess. Paper* **500A.**

Reeve, E. C. R., and Huxley, J. S., 1945, "Some Problems in the Study of Allometric Growth," in (Clark, W. E., Le Gros, and Medawar, P. B., editors) "Essays on Growth and Form". Presented to D'Arcy Wentworth Thompson, Oxford, Clarendon Press, 408pp.

Simon, Herbert, 1955. "On a class of skew distribution functions," *Biometrika*, **42,** 425–440.

Strahler, A. N., 1950, "Equilibrium theory of erosional slopes approached by frequency distribution analysis," *Am. J. Sci.*, **248,** 673–696, 800–814.

Strahler, A. N., 1952, "Hypsometric (area-altitude) analysis of erosional topography," *Bull. Geol. Soc. Am.*, **63,** 1117–1142.

Strahler, A. N., 1964, "Quantitative Geomorphology of Drainage Basins and Channel Networks," in (Chow, Ven Te, editor) "Handbook of Applied Hydrology: Compendium of Water Resources Technology," Ch. 4, pp. 39–76, New York, McGraw-Hill Book Co.

von Bertalanffy, Ludwig, 1960, "Principles and Theory of Growth," in (Nowinsky, Wiktor, editor) "Fundamental Aspects of Normal and Malignant Growth," Amsterdam, New York, Elsevier, 1025pp.

White, John F., and Gould, Stephen Jay, 1965, "Interpretation of the coefficient in the allometric equation," *Am. Naturalist*, **99,** 5–18.

Woldenberg, Michael J., 1966, "Horton's laws justified in terms of allometric growth and steady state in open systems," *Bull. Geol. Soc. Am.*, **77,** 431–437.

Cross-references: *Cycles, Geomorphic; Equilibrium in Geomorphology; General Systems Theory; Quantitative Geomorphology; Stream Orders.*

ORGANISMS AS GEOMORPHIC AGENTS

"Organisms" considered here exclude man and his domesticated animals, in their roles as agents of soil erosion, forest modification, swamp filling, coastal control, and so on. Independently of these *anthropogenic influences* (q.v.) there are many organic agents of profound importance. They play two contrasting roles, either as superficial, modeling, marking or eroding agents, or as constructive, sediment-builders.

(A) Modeling Agencies

One of the minor, yet delightful works of the founder of modern natural science, Charles Darwin, was his classic "The Formation of Vegetable Mould, through the Action of Worms..." (1881), in which it emerged that earthworms acted as organic ploughs. bringing soil from lower horizons to the surface, in such a way that archeological sites such as Roman ruins and so on were always deeply buried under some feet of soil, without the agency of floods, rainwash or sheet erosion, soil creep, solifluction, etc. Darwin observed that earthworms could build up a topsoil 25 cm thick within a few decades (see also Lobeck, 1939).

Ants, in more arid regions, play a similar role to the earthworm in the cool, humid latitudes. Broad anthills up to 2 meters across and 30 cm high are not unusual. The ants frequently concentrate rings of coarse quartz grains around their nest entrances. Even more impressive "anthills," or better *termite mounds* (*termitaria*), are built by termites, in mud brought up to the surface from several meters depth (Fig. 1). Such termite mounds are up to 4 meters high. Since they are most common in the lateritic

FIG. 1. "Anthill" or termite mound in the spinifex country south of the Cape Range, Western Australia. (Photo: M. E. Johnstone).

soil belts of the tropics and subtropics, the mounds are frequently of an orange-red to dark-red color. Some of those in Northern Australia are oriented rather precisely north-south, apparently in order to maintain maximum internal temperatures; in the tropics, the sun is always high at midday, and therefore the coolest aspects are north and south. Fossil remains of termite mounds and tunnels are found in Pleistocene paleosols and provide rather useful indications of former *savanna-type landscapes* (q.v.) and climates (see Vol. II).

Among the major animals, in the wild state, the population densities are not usually sufficient to lead to appreciable geomorphic effects, except for the herding types. In the savanna lands of Africa, and in the steppe (prairie) lands of North America, the breakup of the soil crust around water holes and along river banks by trampling of hooves can sometimes be an appreciable aid to agents of erosion. In swampy areas, certain mammals (from pig to buffalo and hippopotamus) habitually scoop out wallows, leaving circular depressions in the landscape (Passarge, 1904); many hollows attributed to "*buffalo wallows*" by Darton (1915) and others are, however, nowadays believed to be due to periglacial deflation and other inorganic processes (Judson, 1950). Elephants play a role akin to wind blow-down in pulling out trees by the roots, thus breaking up the soil surface; in duricrust regions this can be important in facilitating additional vertical circulation.

Probably most important of all organic agents are the *bacteria* and similar unicellular organisms. These play a key role in controlling soil acidity and thus in the "rotting" of most rock-forming minerals. Were it not for bacteria, rainfall (initially "acid" with pH 4.5–6.5) would rapidly be neutralized in the soil and no further chemical erosion would occur.

Certain organisms are also very helpful as horizon indicators, particularly of the zonation between high and low mean sea level. Ecologists have long noted the precise (and narrow) ranges of many sessile intertidal organisms, both fauna and flora. For the geomorphologist, it is particularly helpful to establish the sea level relationships of certain easily recognized organisms, such as *Ostrea, Patella* or various balanids (Steers, 1930; Stephenson, 1949, 1950). One may then essentially "read off" the height of mean sea level and calculate the tidal range characteristics, provided that due allowance is made for exposure, swash effects and so on.

(B) Constructive Agents

We have mentioned above only those organic agents that erode, model or in some way mask the land surface. In contrast, there are also numbers of organisms that create permanent physical structures or formations. These fall into two major categories again:

(1) Animal Builders. (*a*) *Corals*. First and fore-

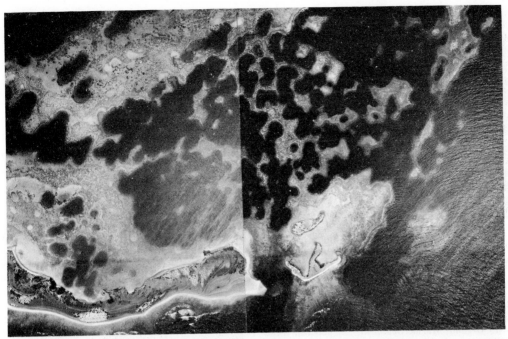

FIG. 2. Vertical air photographs of northeast end of Pelsart Island, Abrolhos Group, Western Australia, showing a Pleistocene karst, overgrown by corals, calcareous algae and related organic associations. Note that patch reefs are normally rounded coral clumps, while in this case round pipes or dolinas are encrusted in coral facing inward (area known appropriately as "The Maze"). Pelsart Island is partly of old (pre-Würm) coral and lagoon limestones, overlain by beach ridges of coral shingle and sand. The direction north is diagonally to the top-right. Width of mosaic 2.2 km (see also *Atolls*; *Coral Reefs*).

most, these are the most impressive animal building agents, leaving enormous coral reefs of calcium carbonate in any suitable shallow area of the warmer oceans (mean temperature above about 18°C). Apart from continental shelves and ocean plateaus, volcanic foundations afford the only suitable sites for most open ocean reefs (see *Atolls*; *Barriers*; *Coral Reefs; Fringing Reefs*). It should be stressed that corals only play the role of frame building in these complex ecologic communities, to which very important contributions are made also by mollusca, echinodermata, bryozoa, foraminifera and calcareous algae (Fig. 2).

(b) *Other Organic Reef Builders of Animal Origin.* These are usually limited to smaller structures, but some may extend for miles. They include *oyster reefs* (q.v.), *bryozoa reefs*, *serpulid reefs*, *Mytilus* (*mussel*) *reefs*. A number of these are in the form of *micro-atolls* (q.v.). In rare cases, *sponge banks* accumulate

FIG. 3. Pleistocene coral reef, exposed in a low cliff south of Geraldton, Western Australia. Note how the coral (radiating structure) is coated by successive layers of massive white algal limestone, thus protecting and binding the more fragile corals together. (Photo: R. W. Fairbridge).

FIG. 4(a). Algal-rimmed shore platform at Point Peron, Western Australia. Surge of wave causes a small waterfall over the inner side of the algal rim.

quite extensive deposits of siliceous spicules (spongolite or sometimes "spiculite").

(*c*) *Organic Marine Sediments.* In general, these sediments such as foraminiferal ooze, pteropod ooze (calcareous) and radiolarian ooze (siliceous) are almost worldwide in modern oceans but can hardly be regarded as geomorphically important because no distinctive structures are built (see Vol. I, "*The Encyclopedia of Oceanography*").

(2) Plant Building. (*a*) *Algal Reefs.* Algal reefs often play a symbiotic role with corals, since the waste products of the former include O_2, for example, which is advantageous to the latter; further-

FIG. 4(b). The same algal rim shown in Fig. 4(a), seen at the moment of wave withdrawal, when the shore platform is covered by only a shallow layer of water (about 20 cm deep). The rim thus protects the shore platform, cut in soft eolian calcarenite, which in some areas may thus reach a width of 100 meters or more (see also *Limestone Coastal Weathering*; *Platforms—Wave-cut*).

FIG. 5. Tangle of roots of the mangrove *Rhizophora*, evidently an effective trap for mud and organic debris; this may be an important factor in building up land on certain protected shores. Example from Low Isles, Great Barrier Reefs, Queensland. (Photo: R. W. Fairbridge).

more, calcareous algae help to weld together the massive but loosely packed coral and thus they also play a very important auxiliary mechanical role (Fig. 3). In addition, calcareous algae form independent but small reefs, generally in marginal areas, unsuitable for corals.

(*b*) *Algal Rimmed Pool Builders.* These construct relatively miniature features, yet they are of great interest, particularly in the intertidal zone of the ocean, where they have strict vertical limits and thus afford interesting geomorphic tide-level markers. *Lithothamnion* and *Porolithon* are important genera. Splash and spray from breakers must be adequate to keep the pools filled, while spillover must be maintained almost continually in the tropics or else the algae would be killed by exposure (Fig. 4).

Algal rimmed pools are also found in continental regions in some hot-spring areas [both travertine (calc-sinter) and siliceous sinter], the most celebrated being the famous pink travertinous sinter terraces of Lake Rotomahana in New Zealand, destroyed by the earthquake of 1886. Some extant examples occur in the Yellowstone National Park, Wyoming; here at Mammoth Hot Springs, algae from the genera *Leptothrix* and *Mastigonema* contribute to extensive terrace building. In cold-water carbonate springs, there are also celebrated traver-

FIG. 6. Young *Rhizophora* mangrove colonizing and simultaneously fixing the inner edge of an advancing spit of coral shingle on Low Isles, Great Barrier Reefs, Queensland. (Photo: R. W. Fairbridge).

tine deposits (as at Tivoli, near Rome: see Geikie, 1903, p. 611), but the deposition of the $CaCO_3$ is often due to the sudden release of CO_2 and not necessarily to organic agency.

(c) *Fresh-water Lake Deposits.* These deposits are often precipitated by plant agencies, and since such

lakes are likely to be ephemeral, these lacustrine formations may soon become part of the landscape. In lime-rich areas the small *Chara* may form massive deposits. Lakes in quartz sandplain areas are often siliceous and then favor the formation of *diatomaceous earth* (tripolite, "kieselgur"). Trees growing

FIG. 7. Mangrove lining (and fixing) the meandering course of a river at Morning Inlet, Gulf of Carpentaria. Note barren mudflats away from the tidewater. (Oblique air photo: F. W. Whitehouse).

FIG. 8. Mangrove lining the tidal estuary sector of the Flinders River below Inverleigh, Queensland. (Photo: F. W. Whitehouse).

FIG. 9. Centrifugal drainage from meander levees toward the dry mud flats, marked and fixed by mangrove. Smithburne River, Queensland. (Photo: F. W. Whitehouse).

around the shores of these silica-rich lakes or swamps are readily replaced by opaline silica after they die, to give rise to extensive "petrified forest" accumulations. In higher latitudes (e.g., Sweden) iron-precipitating bacteria contribute a limonite-rich deposit known as "bog iron ore," formerly extensively exploited.

(*d*) *Peat Swamps.* Both freshwater and marine ("salt marsh") peat swamps play a very important role in the landscape. Both establish regimes of very low pH, more so in the land areas (pH 3–5), whereas the marine (intertidal) peat is constantly "buffered" (to pH 6.5) by alkaline seawater (pH 8). As a result, the peat is preserved from rotting and not only is a landscape feature, but also is fairly easy to date (by

FIG. 11. Vertical air photo of the coast of Horn Island, near Cape York, Torres Strait, Australia. A fringing reef is largely veneered by sediment (note mud patches where creeks cross it). Its inner margin is marked by a dark belt of mangrove (*Rhizophora*), behind which is a white sand beach. To the interior again is a partly freshwater (brackish) swamp with inner mudflats. The coast is thus paralleled by four distinct organically controlled geomorphic belts. Width of area shown in photo: about 1000 meters.

FIG. 10. Traces of centrifugal drainage and former meanders in an alluviated sector. Albert River below Burketown, Queensland. (Photo: F. W. Whitehouse).

C^{14}) and preserves pollen in a fresh state; finally, and by no means least in importance, the marine peats form excellent high-tide markers. For dating old shore lines and working out the climatic history of the last 100,000 years or so, these peat formations have been of enormous value; much of the science of *palynology* (see pr volume VII of this series) depends upon them. Upland peat swamps tend to act as gigantic sponges, and the high acidity results in deep rotting of the underlying sediments and rock, the combination sometimes producing a mud reservoir that bounces as one walks across it and occasionally bursts out (see *Suffosion*) and even leads

FIG. 12. Coastal dunes, largely fixed by vegetation but partly affected by channel-like "blow-outs" and deflation hollows. Example near 12° 30′ S latitude near Cape Weymouth (Cape York Peninsula, Queensland). Although the climate is wet in summer, there is a long dry (winter) season. (Photo: F. W. Whitehouse).

to catastrophic mudflows; one such mudflow at Kinalady, Ireland, on June 25, 1821, spread out destruction over an area of 13 km^2; another at Knocknagehan Moor in Killarney, beginning December 28, 1896, flowed continuously for five days.

(*e*) *Mangrove Swamps.* These are essentially the equatorial and subtropical equivalents of the salt marshes of higher latitudes; they occupy the same intertidal ecologic niche but, in contrast, grow to full-sized trees in vast profusion. The various genera, *Rhizophora*, *Avicennia*, *Sonneratia*, *Bruguiera*, etc., are few in species and almost worldwide in distribution since their seeds are distributed by ocean currents. Geomorphically, the mangrove swamp leads to two opposing consequences: The stilt roots and tangle of pneumatophores ("breathing roots"), air roots (direct from branches to mud), and general debris unite to trap mud and thus build up the land along a low coast (Figs. 5 and 6) as, for example, on the west side of Florida. In contrast, the inner parts of many fringing coral reefs became veneered by mud and then populated by mangrove, but now the mangrove roots and rotting vegetation lower the pH (to 4–6), resulting in the *corrosion* (q.v.) of the calcium carbonate of the reef; the inner parts of the reef thus become pockmarked and later dissolved away by the same agency that elsewhere may be building up the coast. Several mangrove species live under a broad range of salinity (i.e., are euryhaline), and thus they tend to line the edges of tropical estuaries and deltas, extending sometimes dozens of miles inland. In parts of northern Australia, the interior may be semiarid, so there is a striking contrast in vegetation just at the water's edge from bare, dry mud flats to a

narrow band of rich and lush thickets kept damp by the daily rise and fall of the tide. The inner salt flats are inundated only seasonally, when there are onshore monsoon winds, periodically somewhat amplified by spring tides; further inland again, there is the normal halophytic vegetation of the interior (Figs. 7–11).

Mangrove, peat and other swamps are seen by paleontologists as the present-day analogs of Carboniferous and Permian coal swamps. Studies of these show that there were similarly varied types of vegetation, ranging from massive trees (palms, tree ferns, giant horse-tails, etc.) to spore (pollen) accumulations. Burial by sediment, followed by long periods of *diagenesis* (see pr Vol. VI), was necessary for conversion to coal. Those deposits that formed in the swamps themselves are known as "autochthonous," and those that accumulated from floating debris ("biological rafts") are classified as "allochthonous."

(*f*) *Dune-fixing Vegetation.* This type of vegetation is active in two distinctive regions—coastal belts and continental interiors. Coastal dunes tend to be progressively stabilized as they grow by various halophytic and xerophytic plants, which include the long-rooted grasses such as marram grass, *Psamma* (formerly *Ammophila*) *arenaria*, the sea couch grass (*Agropyrum junceum*), and creepers such as *Mesembryanthemum* (Van Dieren, 1934, Steers, 1946). The freshwater table lies as a thin layer over the salt "wedge" near the shore, so that once the roots reach the freshwater level, a general fixation of the dune results from the spread of vegetation and further sand accumulation tends to fill in the hollows; there are some coastal dunes that build to over 1000 feet (Fig. 12).

Interior dunes do not readily stabilize unless there is a climate change. Much of central Africa and Australia is covered by vegetated dunes of the last (Wisconsin) ice age when general desiccation occurred in middle and low latitudes (Fairbridge, 1964). These dune ridges became fixed by a general expansion of the savanna and equatorial vegetation, resulting from a progressive increase in the seasonal rains. The time of this fixation is now established by C^{14} dating at between 12,000 and 7000 years ago. In many places, especially in the Sahara, there has since been a drop in rainfall and many dunes have become remobilized; the cutting up of thin soil crusts by hooves of animals (and lately, jeep tracks) has contributed to the reversal.

Where dune stabilization is important for human economy, as in populated coastal areas or along desert margins, e.g., in Libya and Egypt, systematic encouragement of the local vegetation and planting of imported species (e.g., Australian eucalypts to North Africa) have had remarkably encouraging results.

RHODES W. FAIRBRIDGE

References

Benninghoff, W. S., 1952, "Interaction of vegetation and soil frost phenomena," *Arctic*, **5**(1), 34–44.

Bouillon, A. (editor), 1966, "Etudes sur les Termites Africains," Paris, Masson et Cie, 414pp.

Boyer, P., 1959, "De l'influence des termites de la zone intertropicale sur la configuration de certain sols," *Rev. Géomorphol. Dyn.*, **10**, 41–48.

Chapman, V. J., 1944, "Cambridge University expedition to Jamaica. Pt. 2, A study of the botanical processes in the development of the Jamaican shore-line." *J. Linnean Soc. London*, **62**, No. 346, 407–447.

Darton, N. H., *et al.*, 1915, "Guidebook of the western United States, Pt. C, The Santa Fé route," *U.S. Geol. Surv. Bull.*, **613**, 194pp.

Darwin, C., 1881, "The Formation of Vegetable Mould, through the Action of Worms, with Observations on Their Habits," London.

Davis, J. H., 1940, "The ecology and geologic role of Mangroves in Florida," *Carnegie Inst. Wash. Publ.*, No. 517, *Papers from Tortugas Lab.*, **32**(16), 303–412.

Emerson, A. E., 1952, "The biogeography of termites," *Bull. Am. Museum Nat. Hist., N.Y.*, **99**(3), 217–225.

Erhart, H., 1953, "Sur les cuirasses termitiques fossiles dans la vallée du Niari et dans le massif du Chaillu (Moyen-Congo, A.E.F.)," *Compt. Rend.*, **237**, 431–433.

Eyre, S. R., 1963, "Vegetation and Soils," Chicago, Aldine, 324pp.

Fairbridge, R. W., 1964, "African Ice-age Aridity," in (Nairn, editor), "Problems in Palaeoclimatology," London, Interscience Publishers, 357–363.

Geikie, A., 1903, "Text-book of Geology," London, Macmillan, 2 vols. (first ed., 1882).

Goodland, R. J. A., 1965, "On termitaria in a savanna ecosystem," *Can. J. Zool.*, **43**, 641–650.

Grassé, P. P., and Noirot, C., 1959, "Rapports des termites avec les sols tropicaux," *Rev. Géomorphol. Dyn.*, **10**, 35–40.

Hesse, P. R., 1955, "A chemical and physical study of the soils of termite mounds in East Africa," *J. Ecol.*, **43**, 449–461.

Judson, S., 1950, "Depressions of the northern portion of the southern High Plains of eastern New Mexico," *Bull. Geol. Soc. Am.*, **61**, 253–274.

Julien, A. A., and Humphreys, E. W., 1911, "Local decomposition of rock by corrosive action of preglacial peat bogs," *J. Geol.*, **19**, 47–48.

Lobeck, A. K., 1939, "Geomorphology," New York, McGraw-Hill Book Co., 731pp.

Passarge, S., 1904, "Die Kalahari," Berlin, Dietrich Reimer, 823pp.

Phillips, O. P., 1903, "How the mangrove tree adds new land to Florida," *J. Geogr.*, **2**, 10–21.

Pia, J., 1933, "Die rezenten Kalkstein," *Z. Krist., Min. Petr.*, **B**, 1–420.

Schimper, A. F. W., 1903, "Plant Geography," Oxford (translated by W. R. Fisher).

*Schimper, A. F. W., and von Faber, F. C., 1936, Third ed., "Pflanzengeographie auf physiologischer Grundlage," Jena.

Stamp, L. D., 1940, "The southern margin of the Sahara; comments on some recent studies of desiccation in West Africa," *Geograph. Rev.*, **30**, 297–300.

Steers, J. A., 1930, "A geographical introduction to the biological reports," *Brit. Mus. Nat. Hist. Great Barrier Reef Exped., 1928–29*, **3**, 1–15.

Steers, J. A., 1940, "The cays and the Palisadoes, Port Royal, Jamaica," *Geograph. Rev.*, **30**, 279–296.

Steers, J. A., 1946, "The Coastline of England and Wales," Cambridge, The University Press, 644pp.

*Stephenson, T. A., and Stephenson, Anne, 1949, "The universal features of zonation between tide-marks on rocky coasts," *J. Ecol.*, **37**, 289–305.

Stephenson, T. A., and Stephenson, Anne, 1950, "Life between tide-marks in North America, I. The Florida Keys," *J. Ecol.*, **38**(2), 354–402.

Taylor, B. W., 1955, "The flora, vegetation and soils of Macquarie Island," *Australian Nat. Antarctic Res. Exped., Ser. B*, **2**, 192pp.

Termier, H., and Termier, G., 1961, "L'évolution de la lithosphère, III. Glyptogénèse," Paris, Masson & Cie, 471pp.

Twenhofel, W. H., 1932, "Treatise on Sedimentation," Second ed., Baltimore and London, Williams & Wilkins; reprint, 1961, New York, Dover, 2 vols.

Van Dieren, J. W., 1934, "Organogene Dünenbildung," The Hague, Martinus Nijhoff, 304pp.

Watson, J. G., 1928, "Mangrove forests of the Malay Peninsula," *Malayan Forestry Records*, No. 6, 275pp.

* Additional bibliographic references may be found in this work.

Cross-references: *Algal Reefs*; *Algal Rim*; *Anthropogenic Influences in Geomorphology*; *Atoll*; *Barriers*; *Coral Reefs*; *Corrosion*; *Fringing Reef*; *Limestone Coastal Weathering*; *Mangrove Swamps*; *Microatoll*; *Oyster Reefs*; *Platforms—Wave-cut*; *Prairie Mound*; *Savanna Landscape*; *Suffosion and Tundra Craters*. Vol. 1: *Marine Sediments*. Vol. II: *Equatorial and Tropical Climates*. pr Vol. VI: *Coal*; *Diagenesis*; *Peat Bog Deposits*; *Spongolite*; *Swamp, Marsh and Bog*; *Weathering—Organic*. pr Vol. VII: *Palynology*.

ORIENTED LAKES

The term *oriented lakes* is applied to groups and regional spreads of lakes and lake basins with a common oval shape and long axis orientation, as in the "Carolina Bays" (Melton and Schriever, 1933) and to lakes that are initially squarish or elongate-rectangular with the opposing long sides having a common orientation, as in the Beni Basin, Bolivia (Plafker, 1964). Oriented lakes are best known for the elliptical and elongate-oval forms. Conceivably, initially triaxial lakes of the Beni type may occur.

Many of the basins have marginal beach-ridge or foredune rims which may be multiple or single, or only partly margin the basins. The rims are of sand, silt or silty organic sediment and upward of 20 feet high. Some deep basins have foredunes as high as 100 feet in their bottoms bordering a shrunken lake. The basins are excavated in unconsolidated Quaternary sediments, some containing Pleistocene fossils. Other small basins are still being formed today in some oriented groups.

Oriented lakes are known from a variety of environments on at least three continents. In many cases, groups of unoriented lakes occur with them.

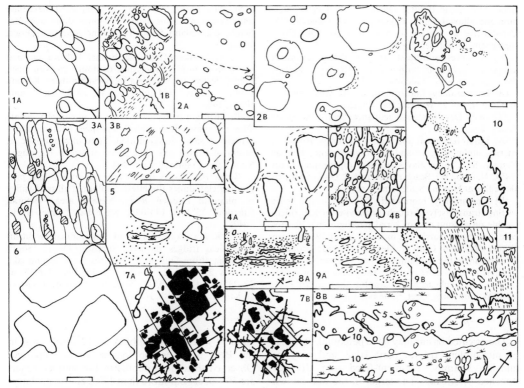

FIG. 1. Developmental forms of oriented lakes. North is upwards, except in sketches 3B, 8A, and 8B. Lakes of sketches 3B, 5 and 6 are reassembled but in true orientation.

Sketch 1: Carolina Bays in humid forest. Two alignments with same orientation.

(A) Long axis aligned with swales of Pleistocene longitudinal dunes about 7 miles northwest of Elizabethtown, Cape Fear River valley, Bladen County, North Carolina. Scale bar, 3000 feet (Prouty, 1952).

(B) Marshy Bays, large and small, with short axes aligned with beach ridge swales of Pleistocene cuspate foreland (dashed lines). Many smaller Bays not shown. About 4 miles from coast, Brunswick County, North Carolina. Scale bar 1 mile. Sketched from aerial photo (Prouty, 1952).

Sketch 2: Developmental stages, unfilled playa basins, semiarid grassland, Llano Estacado plateau, Southern High Plains. Scale bars 2 miles (see Figs. 41 and 81; also Price, 1958).

(A) Small to medium sized basins, 10–60 feet deep. Long axes aligned with swales of degraded and etched longitudinal dune field. Runningwater Creek in a swale or etched trough.

(B) Large "mature" basins, aligned as in A, 50–60 feet deep, crossed here by, and aligned on, short axes with transverse fractures of Amarillo arch; in Randall County, Texas. Amarillo is at north edge of Figure.

(C) Guthrie Lakes, Tahoka, Lynn County, Texas, 60–150 foot series. Asymmetrical sedimentation in eastern end caused retrograde migration of playa, with reorientation of small residual lakes. Broken line, approximate outer margin of basin and fill. Steepening of walls at northwest, with gullying (from field mapping by Price).

Sketch 3: Developmental series, oriented lakes, arid

arctic coastal plain, Barrow Region, Alaska. Scale bars 1 mile (see Figs. 2 and 3).

(A) Present small lakes (cross-lined) with filled and partly drained basins (Carson and Hussey, 1962; see also Fig. 2).

(B) Reassembled sequence: thaw ponds elongated along interdune swales at west. Reorienting intermediate forms in center. Small lakes in regional orientation at east (from Black and Barksdale, 1949). Along outcrop of sandy zone in Quaternary Gubic Formation (Black, 1951).

Sketch 4: Oriented lakes in tundra, arid Pleistocene coastal plain east of Mackenzie delta, Northwest Territories, Canada.

(A) Shore lines, broken line; submerged inner basins, full line. Scale bar 1 mile (Mackay, 1963).

(B) Former shore lines, broken line. Lakes as mapped, full line. Scale bar 2 miles. Stanton topographic sheet at 130° 15'W, 70° 00'N (Mackay, 1963).

Sketch 5: Heart-shaped and clam-shaped playas, subhumid grassland Refugio County, Texas, reassembled from Refugio topographic sheet in true orientation. Eolian beach ridges of playas dotted. Outer rim of northeast basin, broken line. Scale bar 1 mile (Price, 1958; see also Fig. 7).

Sketch 6: Savanna marsh lakes with bilateral orientation in transverse fracture pattern, subhumid tropical Beni Basin, Bolivia, 13–17°S, 63–67°W. Typical forms reassembled in true orientation (Plafker, 1964). Scale bar 1 mile.

Sketch 7: Lakes with bilateral orientation in four-axis drainage network. Lineations shown by added straight lines. Arid arctic tundra, Old Crow Holocene inter-montane alluvial plain, Yukon District, Canada. Old Crow River at northwest in each figure. Old Crow topographic sheet (see Fig. 9).

(A) Northwest–southeast and northeast–southwest lake-shore lineations, with a few northeast–southwest drainage lineations. Scale bar 2 miles.

(B) Four drainage lineation directions. West-center is at 67°50′N, 139°25′W. Scale bar 4 miles.

Sketch 8: Developmental sequence, bean plain swale ponds, Texas coast.

(A) Initial rectilinear and lanceolate forms, Holocene barrier, subhumid grassland. St. Joseph Island, Aransas County, St. Charles Bay southwest topographic sheet (28°02′N, 96°52′W). Beach ridges dotted. Gulf of Mexico shore line at bottom. Scale bar 0.2 mile.

(B) Incompletely reoriented "young" ovals, some cutting transversely through coastwise beach ridges (visible on ground and in aerial photographs). Pleistocene Ingleside barrier, Chambers County between Trinity Bay and Gulf of Mexico. Humid; probably forested in native condition. Parallel lines of marsh symbols in lower part of figure show spacing of swales there. Lake Stephenson topographic sheet at 29°34′N, 91°42′W. Contours, 5 feet. Scale bar 1 mile.

Sketch 9: Elongate-oval playas of stabilized and etched transverse sand dune field of banner dune complex. Semiarid grassland, South Texas sand plain (*erg*) (Price, 1958).

(A) Swale lakes of stabilized banner. Full line, mapped shore lines inside depression contours (broken line). Dunes dotted. La Sal Vieja topographic sheet, Kenedy County, Texas, 26°42′N, 97°55′W. Scale bar 1 mile (Price, 1933).

(B) Diagram of typical banner dune complex. Swale lakes not shown. Bare central sand sheet, with migratory transverse sand dunes dotted. Spot blowout lake at origin of banner and divergence of lateral lag ridges. Scale bar 0.25 mile (Price, 1958).

Sketch 10: Playas (pans) oriented by (dotted) pro-grading clay dunes (lunettes). Subhumid alluvial valley or plain of Ludden River, Kerang area, Victoria, Australia, 35°45′S, 143°05′E. Scale bar 2 miles (Hills, 1940).

Sketch 11: Swale playas of longitudinal (windrift) dune field (ridges dashed). Simpson Desert, South Australia, (from Oodnatta sheet No. 3343, second ed.). Area is 25–57 miles north of Lake Eyre North, at 27–28°30′S, 137–137°30′E. Scale bar 10 miles (*Courtesy D. King*).

The oriented basins may have perennial, seasonal or intermittent (playa, pan) lakes and may be marshy, swampy, sediment-filled and dry, or trenched by streams. The larger of the well-known spreads includes the estimated half-million Pleistocene "Carolina Bays" in an area 700 miles by more than 100 miles in size and the hundreds of thousands of rectangular to spade-shaped Holocene basins of the 45,000 square miles of the Beni Basin of Bolivia. Small groups of closely spaced to widely scattered basins may also show group or regional orientation, as along the Texas coast.

Long diameters of 2–4 miles are common in some lakes of oriented assemblies. A 12.4-mile oval in the Beni Basin is the longest so far reported. Observed maximum depths in the simpler basins are 50–70 feet but more than 150 feet in some large, complex playa basins of the Llano Estacado (High Plains of New Mexico and Texas). Axial ratios range from 1 : 1 in squarish forms to 7 : 1 in some elongate ovals.

Initial Forms

Developmental series of oriented lakes studied show that they have originated as random, serially aligned, or aligned and initially oriented ponds.

TABLE 1. INITIAL DEPRESSIONS OF ORIENTED LAKES[a]

(1) Swale ponds of ridged terrain of beach plains and dune fields (Price, 1958, pp. 62–69, 72, 73). Fig. 1, sketches 3B, 8A and 11 show early stage.

(2) Thaw ponds of permafrost randomly distributed or in aligned depressions of Types 1, 4 and 6 (Obruchev, 1938, 1940; Bostock, 1948; Black and Barksdale, 1949; Mackay, 1956, 1963; Plafker, 1964). Initial forms described by Hopkins (1949).

(3) Drainage channels and alluvial plain lakes oriented by clay dunes (Harris, 1939; Hills, 1939, 1940; Stephens and Crocker, 1946; Price, 1958, p. 85, Fig. 16).

(4) Local depressions in elevated Pleistocene lagoon plains, after hypothesis of Cooke (1934), but his published examples of Bays are of Type 1, including Bays of drowned terrain (Cooke, 1954, Pls. 41 and 43); Fig. B, Pl. 4, of Black and Barksdale (1949), although an oblique view, seems to show oriented lakes developed from a lagoon.

(5) Eolian spot blowouts randomly distributed (Price, 1958, p. 52, S Fig. 7; see also Fig. 1, sketch 9B).

(6) Slump basins over subsiding square or quadrangular fracture-enclosed blocks (Bostock, 1948; Plafker, 1964) known among and on the continental flanks of active young mountain chains. Initial and mature forms associated (see Fig. 9).

(7) Second-generation lakes in some cases poorly oriented are reshaped remnants of shrinking larger oriented lakes (Fig. 1, sketch 2C; also Prouty, 1952, Figs. 3, 7 and 14A; Pl. 2, Fig. 1; Pls. 8 and 10).

[a] Authors are cited in Tables 1–3 variously as having proposed an hypothesis or a part of it, or merely for illustrations used as examples.

TABLE 2. PROCESSES OF BASIN ENLARGEMENT AND SHORE LINE CURVATURE DURING LONG-AXIS ORIENTATION

---

(1) Deflation (wind excavation) of bottoms and sides of basins in dry phases of intermittent lake (pan, playa) stage, some eolian sediment escaping, some forming lee dunes and sheets (Evans and Meade, 1945; Price, 1958, pp. 63, 65, 72, 73).

(2) Leaching of walls, sidewall wash and slump during dry stages (Judson, 1950) facilitating deflation under No. 1. Some elongation, some deltaic deposition by inflowing swale drainage.

(3) Leaching of fines and soluble materials into an underlying aquifer with nearby scarp-spring discharge, with some cementation of subbottom and wall beds (Judson, 1950, and observations of Llano Estacado playas and subbottom cores by Price and others).

(4) Lowering of basin bottoms by melting of permafrost ice, overflow, and deposition of some organic debris outside basins as beach ridges, including ice-push and wave-built varieties (Bostock, 1948; Black and Barksdale, 1949; Carson and Hussey, 1960, 1962). For latter type see No. 5.

(5) Basin enlargement requires Nos. 1 (with 2 and 3) or 4. Building of water-laid storm beach ridges is not an enlargement process, but accompanies prograding of shore line and retrograde basin migration.

(6) Alternations of preceding processes with changes in climate.

Thereafter, the ponds are enlarged and oriented, or an initial orientation is either preserved during enlargement or reoriented by long-axis rotation. Reorientation may occur at any stage.

The recognized types and some of their developmental form sequences are shown in Fig. 1.

Meteor Craters?

Melton and Schriever (1933) suggested that the Carolina Bays might be meteor craters, but this view is now untenable, as are other early hypotheses of the origin of the "Bays," The high degree of terrain selectivity of the distributional pattern denies these hypotheses (Fig. 1, sketch 1). Intercomparisons between the many oriented lake occurrences now known, with the study of evolutionary series of forms, and extensive field and laboratory work by several writers make possible the analysis here given. The results are outlined here (Tables 1–4) and under *Carolina Bays* (q.v.).

Open Situations (Wind)

Except for a few in forest areas, all the oriented lake assemblies now well known lie on treeless, wind-swept, poorly drained plains of grassland, marsh or tundra. Trees now lining a few lakes have not prevented their development in step with the associated treeless lakes. Wind is found to be the primary agent of basin enlargement and orientation, wind waves and leaching acting in wet stages, whereas deflation of walls and bottoms take place in dry stages. Wind and wind waves have enlarged and oriented a variety of initial basin forms (Table 1). Subsidiary processes and factors are listed in Table 2.

It was first thought that oriented lakes were elongated in the direction of the strongest wind (Raisz, 1934). Schou (1945), however, showed that shore lines tend to become straightened perpendicular to the direction of the strongest onshore wave attack. Carson and Hussey (1960, 1962) found by detailed field studies of the Alaskan tundra thaw lakes (Black and Barksdale, 1949) that *lakes become elongated and oriented along an axis perpendicular to the mean direction of the resultants of two opposing systems of flank winds and that all shore lines tend to become rounded by the action of longshore currents* (Figs. 2 and 3; Fig. 1, sketch 3A). It was also found that an asymmetry in the opposing wind spreads *tends to make one end of a basin tapered or narrower than the other*. Mackay (1956) contributed to the development of these conclusions.

In the Alaskan lakes, Carson and Hussey show that oriented lakes develop in permafrost only where a thaw season has opposing strong resultant

TABLE 3. SOME LAKE AND BASIN ALIGNMENTS NOT CLASSIFIED AS ORIENTATIONS

---

(1) Meteor craters aligned in a narrow zone along a trajectory of a disintegrating meteor or a small meteor swarm (Cassidy *et al.*, 1965). The craters are characteristically initially round; a few reported oval may or may not have been reshaped in a lake stage.

(2) Groundwater geyser basins aligned along an earthquake rift line (Price 1933, Fig. 8). Basins lie along what was then interpreted as former creek channel between Oso Creek and Flour Ridge. Basins round except as elongated by inflowing drainage along rift depressions.

(3) Limestone karst lakes (term "caliche karst" formerly used by the writer for Llano Estacado lakes is abandoned). No instances of areal assemblies of lakes with rectilinear alignment in hard limestone have come to the writer's attention. Johnson's (1942, Fig. 44) illustration from a Florida locality has not been fully investigated and is not said to be on limestone.

(4) Belts of oxbow lakes along a stream valley (see *Oxbow Lake*).

Table 4. Stages of Development and Orientation

Stages and Shapes		Critical Activities, Initial Environment, Origin, Form	Initial Shoreline Curvature	Initially Oriented Forms	Some Reoriented	Filled, Dormant or Near-Dormant in Forest
(I) Initial Stage (A) Wind and wave action not yet effective in lake	(1) Random	Permafrost thaw ponds and unknown	X	—	—	—
	(2) Round	Aligned along swales of beach plain or dune field	—	X	—	—
	(3) Rectilinear		—	X	—	—
	(4) Square; open plain	Fault-block subsidence	—	X	—	—
	(5) Square; in forest	Fault-block subsidence	—	X	—	X
(B) Wind acts	(1) Oval	Eolian spot blowouts; Stages I and II are penecontemporaneous	X	X	—	—
(II) Development Stage	(1) Young	Shore line curvature; enlargement	—	—	X	—
	(2) Mature	Oval elongation, ends curved or tapered, enlargement continues	—	—	X	X
	(3) Senescent or arrested	Sedimentary filling; second generation lakes form	—	—	X	X
(III) Terminal Stage	(1) Extinct	Filled with sediment (dry or marshy), including second generation basins	—	—	—	X

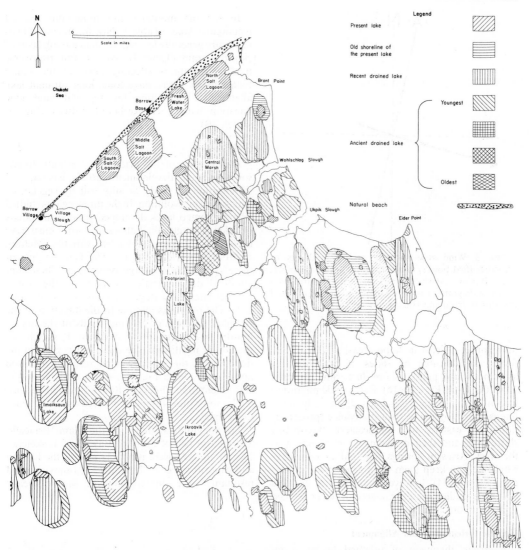

Fig. 2. Oriented permafrost tundra thaw lakes, terraced area, coastal lake belt, arid arctic coastal plain, Barrow, Alaska. Short-axis alignment indicates strong initial coastwise depression influence swales or possibly lagoons in development of closely spaced thaw lakes. Northeast diagonal pattern lines, present lakes; others drained. East–west pattern lines, former shore lines. Single lakes upward of 2.6 miles long. North is to the top (Carson and Hussey, 1962; see also Fig. 1 sketch 3).

winds, and that the straightened flanks develop dynamic equilibrium profiles with shallow, barred terraces, leaving deep water along the axis and at the ends. Undercutting and melting at the ends elongate the basin while rounding the shore lines there. Erosion of permafrost, marshy organic debris, or clay makes a shore line irregularly jagged in detail while the overall conformation is straight (Black and Barksdale, 1949, Pls. 2–5).

Preventing or retarding of lake enlargement by forest is seen in (1) the almost entire preservation of the initial squarish forms of the Beni Basin lakes in

narrow forested belts in contrast with the abundance of elongated spade-shaped and oval basins (Fig. 1, sketch 6) in the main open-marsh area (Plafker, 1964, Pl. 1); (2) the Carolina Bays which, although having reached a mature elliptical form, are mostly extinct as lakes or senescent, with shrinkage by sedimentation the major net change and only very minor changes of form now reported as taking place (Wells and Boyce, 1953; Frey 1954); (3) probably also the slow development of swale lakes in humid forest in Chambers County, Texas (Fig. 1, sketch 8B). Shrinkage is shown by the

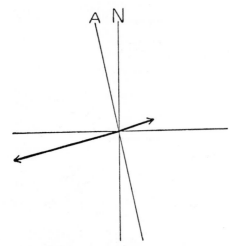

FIG. 3. Wind rose showing vector resultants of velocities (first power) of all winds of June–September, Point Barrow, Alaska. Winds directed outward from center of diagram. A is direction of lake orientation and tapering (Carson and Hussey, 1962).

dominance, at least in some areas, of Bay-in-Bay forms, as indicated by series of concentric or asymmetrically placed shore line rims (Prouty, 1952, Pls. 8–16, Figs. 14–16). Retrograde migration within, and in some cases beyond, an early shore line is shown by the westward advance (progradational) of eastern and southeastern Bay-in-Bay shore lines and their crowding or intersection at the west. Artesian springs reported in two lakes would help to keep them open against sedimentation. Frey (1954), however, reports that in lakes which he studied the only source of water seemed to be from precipitation.

Genetic Orientation and Alignment

A linear alignment of oriented basins is an indicator of origin and developmental history (Fig. 4). Initially rectilinear ponds of ridged sandy land of dune fields (Fig. 5; Fig. 1, sketches 1A, 2A, 9A and 11) and beach plains (Fig. 1, sketches 1B, 2 and 8) are aligned in parallel series along their long axes. These axes may be rotated without a change in wind regime by more sediment being deposited in one end of the basin than in the other (Fig. 1, sketches 2C, 5 and 10) or, as in some dune-swale permafrost thaw lakes, by their becoming interconnected by fracturing, thaw and slump combined with the action of orienting wind waves and currents. The final result is reorientation on the regional long axis and alignment on a short axis which is parallel with the interdune swale (Fig. 7 and Fig. 1, sketch 3B). In a cuspate foreland, a short-axis alignment will follow the curvature and offsets the cusp, while the long axes remain parallel to each other (see *Carolina Bays*).

In the intermontane and mountain-bordered rectangular lakes (Table 1, No. 6), fracture alignments are generally less precise than among lakes of ridged terrain (Table 1, No. 1). But transverse fracture lineations affecting parts of the Llano Estacado, of Texas, have some long, straight lake alignments intersecting the regional inter-ridge lineation with a checkerboard pattern (Fig. 1, sketch 2B).

Stabilization

Preservation of the oriented lakes until today, some after long development periods, has required stabilization of sandy or silty soil by vegetation, with some soil evolution. In the three regions studied where oriented lakes developed from swale ponds of fields of longitudinal dunes, the latter must have been of the hairpin and windrift varieties (Melton, 1940) of semiarid grassland. The paired ridges of these types may converge downwind. These longitudinal dune varieties originate as the paired parallel lateral lag ridges of migrating spot blowouts. The blowouts migrate in the direction of the resultant of the sand-moving winds of the dry or hot-dry season. In Fig. 6 and Fig. 1, sketch 3B, previously mentioned, the dune ridges grew in the direction of the summer wind resultant (Carson and Hussey, 1962, Fig. 14), which is 90° from the lake orientation direction. Reworking and reshaping by some dune ridges is reported as taking place there today.

The longitudinal dunes of the Llano Estacado and interior belt of Carolina Bays (Fig. 1, sketches 2A, 2B and 1A) were probably also of the hairpin and windrift varieties. If so, the sand-moving wind resultants were directed toward the southeast,

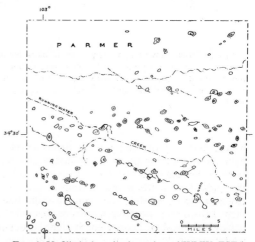

FIG. 4. Unfilled playa basins oriented WNW–ESE in 10- to 60-foot series. There is parallel swale drainage in an area of downweathered longitudinal dune field. Semiarid grassland, Llano Estacado, Palmer County, Texas. Scale bar 5 miles long (see Fig. 1, sketch 2A).

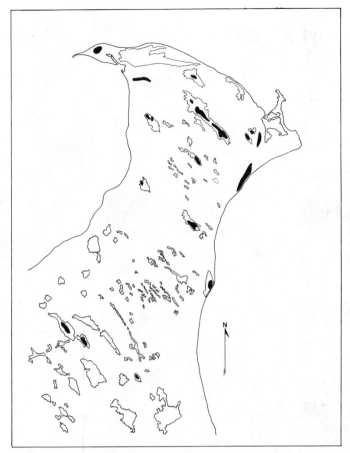

FIG. 5. Swale lakes of stabilized longitudinal dune field in initial rectilinear and lanceolate forms. Ingleside Pleistocene barrier, Live Oak Point, Aransas County, Texas. Age of dunes unknown. Stabilizing grassland invaded in last century by live oak forest. From aerial photograph (Price, 1958, Fig. 17). See Rockport topographic sheet. North arrow 0.5 mile long.

while present-day sand-moving winds blow from the southwest in the Bays region and from south–southwest and south–southeast along the Llano Estacado plateau margins (Melton, 1940; also field observations of Price).

Crowding

In the single photograph seen which shows the Alaskan dunes (Fig. 6), swale pond origin has not produced the crowding characteristic of the Carolina Bays (Fig. 1, sketch 1). However, cases of lateral crowding in the interior belt of the Alaskan region are shown on the small-scale base map (Fig. 2, and Fig. 1, sketch 3A), and crowding of enlarging oriented lakes has produced intersections and mergings in most of the regions studied. In some areas, lakes of one or more generations have formed within the filled basins of earlier lakes Fig. 1, sketches 2C and 3A).

Reorientation

Lee *clay dunes* (q.v.) of some Australian (Harris, 1939, p. 56, Fig. 4; Hills, 1939, Fig. 5 and 1940, Figs. 1 and 2; Stephens and Crocker, 1946, Fig. 1) and Texan (Price, 1958, Fig. 16 and other lakes) playas have built outward toward the basin in front of the initial foredunes which border the shore line (Fig. 1, sketch 10). The later ridges built against the first tend to turn normal to the onshore, warm-season, dune-making wind resultant, becoming transverse clay dunes. This prograding rotates the long axis of the playa without a change in wind regime having occurred.

The westwardly tapered "clam-shaped" Willow Lake basin of Texas (Johnson, 1942, Fig. 46) shown in Fig. 7, was produced by reorientation and reshaping of a NNW–SSE swale pond of a longitudinal dune field, accompanied by beach ridge progradation (outbuilding), at the south under

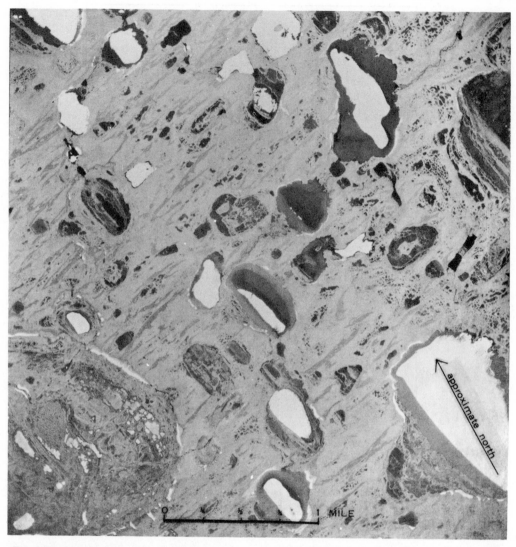

FIG. 6. Vertical air photograph of sand dunes and oriented lakes of Alaskan arctic coastal plain showing effects of wind and wind waves. The dunes appear to be of east–west longitudinal (windrift?) type. Thaw ponds in interdune swales have enlarged to form small rectilinear to lanceolate swale lakes and these have been reoriented into the regional orientation elongation direction. Forms intermediate between the two orientations are seen in intermediate sizes (after Black and Barksdale, 1949, pl. 3B and personal communication from Black; see also Fig. 1, sketch 3B) (Photograph: U.S. Air Force).

imperfectly opposed flank wind resultants (from the north and the southeast). This lake, 28°26′N, 97°17′W, is associated with other tapered ("clam-shaped" and "heart-shaped") lakes with the same orientation along the south Texas coastal plain (Fig. 1, sketch 5). Middens with spear blades of the Angostura culture some 6000–8000 years old have been found at a number of these lakes including the large Sharps Lake. The reorientation of these lakes may have been associated with a wind change that occurred before 8000 B.C.

Llano Estacado Lakes

Probably in middle to late Pleistocene, a field of longitudinal dunes developed on a sheet of eolian sand which covered the cap rock complex of the Llano Estacado, or most of it (Price, 1944; 1958, Figs. 4, 10–15). The ridges trended WSW–ESE and some northwest–southeast; only a ridge-and-swale topography, its parallel drainage, and a series of oriented swale lakes now show the former dune field pattern. Prolonged deflation has stripped the sand off a southwest marginal zone of the

FIG. 7. Willow Lake, Refugio County, Texas. Tapered clam-shaped lake. Semiarid grassland, south Texas coastal plain. Initial northerly axis of dune-swale basin rotated with building of beach plain in south end (see Fig. 1, sketch 5 and Johnson 1942, Fig. 46). North is at top. Figure is 4.4 km wide. (Courtsey Edgar Tobin Aerial Surveys.)

plateau, leaving a cap rock *scabland* (q.v.) and has probably thickened the eolian blanket to the east. The swales have become broad troughs leached into the caliche at the west (Harper and Smith, 1932). The playa basins increase in size and simple elliptical orientation eastward from this southwest area, reaching maximum depths of 60 feet. In a middle zone, the basins reach lengths of a mile and have small, entrenched bottom pond depressions reoriented in directions from northeast–southwest to northwest–southeast (Figs. 4 and 8; Fig. 1, sketch 2A), and the latter tendency occurs also in the bottom ponds of larger, simpler basins to the east (Fig. 1, sketch 2B; also Price, 1944, 1958, pp. 62–69, Figs. 4, 10 and 15). The eastern ellipses are as much as 2–3 miles long and are closely similar to the Carolina Bay basins but without the extensive lacustrine filling of the latter. There are no satisfactory morphological maps or air photographs for this eastern region, the soil maps being the best seen (Price, 1958, Fig. 14). The series of basins from west to east in the dune field represent a developmental series from small to large; however, their sizes are in part related to the thickness of soil and eolian sediments.

In parts of the northeast third of the plateau, there are numerous straight NNE–SSW and northeast–southwest alignments among the 10- to 60-foot playas which cross the normal regional WNW–SSE alignment, producing a diagonal checkerboard pattern (Fig. 1, sketch 2B). The northeast–southwest lineations are developed transversely across

the eastern lengths of two large buried WNW–ESE structural arches. These are the Amarillo and Matador arches. In some parts of the northeast region, however, only the NNE–SSW alignments are developed.

Scattered over the Llano Estacado Plateau there are large deep basins up to 10 miles across and 150 feet deep, or more, that are reoriented, migratory, multiphased, and terraced, with early Pleistocene fossils in wind-and-lake deposits (Evans, and Meade, 1945). The bottoms of most basins are sunk to impervious Cretaceous strata and have brine ponds oriented from northwest–southeast to northeast–southwest. The original orientation of these large basins is in most cases obscured but may have been roughly east–west. Among them are basins which seem to have originated in stream courses and not to have been strongly reoriented. Reeves (1966) has commented on these stream-course alignments.

Besides the oriented playas described, there are many small, shallow basins, 10 feet or less in depth (shown in Fig. 1, sketches 2A and 2B) that trend on northerly axes like those of the central ponds of the middle and eastern playas of Fig. 1, sketches 2A and 2B. The northerly trend in small ponds is general and may be related to the present sand-moving winds from south–southwest and south–southeast.

Discharge into the underlying porous Ogallala Sandstone can take place only when the water stands above a clayey bottom deposit commonly present in the small basins. Loss of water from the basins is normally almost entirely by evaporation. However, it was reported that when many basins

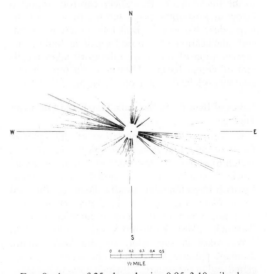

FIG. 8. Axes of 35 playa basins 0.95–3.10 miles long of 10- to 60-foot series, Llano Estacado, with axes of 21 bottom ponds 0.25–0.7 mile long (from Price, 1958, Fig. 15B).

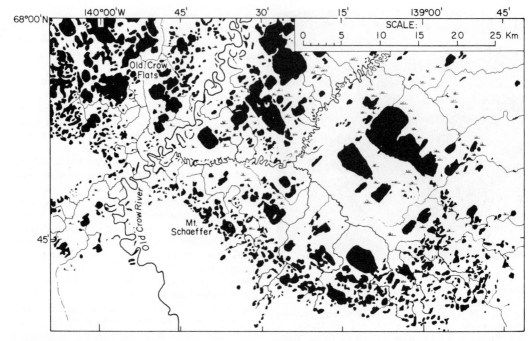

FIG. 9. Fault-block slump lakes, arid arctic tundra. Sides northwest–southeast and northeast–southwest with drainage network with these and east–west and north–south lineations. Oval basin shape developing toward southeast ends. Largest lake 6.5 miles long. Old Crow Holocene alluvial basin, Old Crow topographic sheet, Yukon District, Canada (see Fig. 1, sketch 7).

were brimful during the exceptionally heavy rains of 1940–42, the water "drained out" and recharged the partly depleted aquifer being developed for irrigation. This drainage into an aquifer that discharges in springs on plateau scarps may have led to the thickening of the caliche cap rock reported below at least some playa basins. In some of the large, deep basins (like Bull Lake) there is a west-end silicification of exposed Ogallala bluffs. The reorientation of the deep, migratory lakes recalls that of similar basins of Western Australia inadequately explained by Jutson (1934, pp. 223–227).

Lakes of Beni Basin Savanna Marsh and Old Crow Tundra

Plafker's (1964) interpretation of the squarish forms of the initial *Beni Basin marsh lakes* (Fig. 1, sketch 6) as due to subsidence over fault or fissure blocks is supported, as he noted, by the similar squarish-to-rectangular tundra lakes of the Old Crow Plain (Fig. 9; Fig. 1, sketch 7) an intermountain basin of the Yukon District, Canada (Bostock, 1948). Fault-block origin for the Old Crow lakes is supported by the large square drainage patterns with which the lakes are associated and in the squares of which most of the lakes lie. River flood plains within the nearby mountains have belts of randomly shaped and oxbow lakes showing no group orientation and with only an

occasional oval lake having the Old Crow orientation. However, the drainage in the district of the rectangular lakes has been captured by the facture lines.

The Old Crow Lakes of today have been dated by the radiocarbon method as post-4408 B.C. (Hughes, 1966). Contemporary and earlier Holocene faulting is not, of course, unexpected in either the Old Crow Plain or the Beni Basin because of their close association with active, young mountain chains which are folded and faulted.

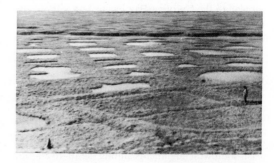

FIG. 10. Checkerboard of bilaterally oriented thaw ponds formed between permafrost soil polygons in arctic tundra. Lena River delta, Siberia. (Courtesy Serge A. Strelkov, USSR Academy of Sciences.)

Mackenzie Delta Area Lakes

Mackay (1956, 1963) has described a large assembly of elongate-oval oriented lakes in the partly glaciated treeless tundra of the Tuktoyaktuk Peninsula of the Pleistocene coastal plain just east of the front of the Mackenzie River delta, Northwest Territories, Canada (Fig. 1, sketch 4). He reports similar lakes to the east, and other similar occurrences (Fig. 10) have been reported from Russian and Siberian arctic coastal plains (Obruchev, 1938, 1940). Many unoriented lakes occur in forested areas adjacent to the Mackenzie delta which have different terrain conditions from the Tuktoyaktuk Peninsula.

Forest-Bound Glaciated Lakes—Unoriented

It is notable that of the millions of lakes of areas glaciated by the younger ice sheets and now in forest, many, probably most, of the lakes have curved shore lines or curved sectors but are not oriented, in the sense of the oriented lakes here studied. Some orientations occur that are controlled by deep grooving or by materials that are not readily eroded and transported. The only oriented lakes—as the term is commonly used—reported in glaciated terrain, which have come to the writer's notice, are in Mackay's Tuktoyaktuk Peninsula area (compare Mackay, 1963, Figs. 3 and 13) and are in treeless tundra in unconsolidated, readily eroded sediments.

W. ARMSTRONG PRICE

References

Black, R. F., 1951, "Eolian deposits of Alaska," *Arctic*, **4**, 89–111.

Black, R. F., and Barksdale, W. L., 1949, "Oriented lakes of northern Alaska," *J. Geol.*, **57**, 105–118.

Bostock, H. S., 1948, "Physiography of the Canadian Cordillera, with special reference to the area north of the fifty-fifth parallel," *Can. Dept. Mines Tech. Surv., Geol. Surv. Can. Mem.*, **247**, 106pp.

Carson, C. E., and Hussey, K. M., 1960, "Hydrodynamics in three arctic lakes," *J. Geol.*, **68**, 585–600.

Carson, C. E., and Hussey, K. M., 1962, "The oriented lakes of arctic Alaska," *J. Geol.*, **70**, 417–439

Cassidy, W. A., *et al.*, 1965, "Meteorites and craters of Campo del Cielo, Argentina," *Science*, **149**, 1055–1064.

Cooke, C. W., 1934, "Discussion of the origin of the supposed meteorite scars of South Carolina," *J. Geol.*, **42**, 88–104.

Cooke, C. W., 1954, "Carolina bays and the shapes of eddies," *U.S. Geol. Surv. Profess. Paper* **245-I**, iii, 195–207.

Evans, G. L., and Meade, G. E., 1945, "Quaternary of the Texas High Plains," *Texas Univ. Publ.*, **4401**, 485–507.

Frey, D. G., 1954, "Evidence for the recent enlargement of the 'Bay' lakes of North Carolina," *Ecology*, **35**, 78–85.

Harper, W. G., and Smith, L. H., 1932, "Soil survey of the Lovington area, New Mexico," *U.S. Bur. Chem. and Soils, Ser. 1932*, No. 2, 21pp.

Harris, W. J., 1939, "The physiography of the Echuca District," *Proc. Roy. Soc. Victoria*, **51**, Pt. 1, 45–60 (see p. 56, Fig. 4).

Hills, E. S., 1939, "The physiography of northwestern Victoria," *Proc. Roy. Soc. Victoria*, **51** (N.S.), Pt. 2, 296–323.

Hills, E. S., 1940, "The lunette, a new land form of aeolian origin," *Australian Geographer*, **3**, 15–21 (see Figs. 1 and 2).

Hopkins, D. M., 1949, "Thaw lakes and thaw sinks in the Imruk Lake Area, Seward Peninsula, Alaska," *J. Geol.*, **57**, 119–131.

Hughes, O. L., 1966, "Old Crow River, Yukon. GSC-372. Geological Survey of Canada radiocarbon dates V," *Radiocarbon*, **8**, 116.

Johnson, D. W., 1942, "The Origin of the Carolina Bays," New York, Columbia University Press, 341pp.

Judson, S. S., Jr., 1950, "Depressions of the northern portion of the Southern High Plains of eastern New Mexico," *Bull. Geol. Soc. Am.*, **61**, 253–274.

Jutson, J. T., 1934, "The physiography of Western Australia," *Geol. Surv. W. Australia, Geol. Bull.*, **95**, 223–227.

Mackay, J. R., 1956, "Notes on oriented lakes of the Liverpool Bay area, Northwest Territories," *Rev. Can. Géographie*, **10**, 169–173.

Mackay, J. R., 1963, "The Mackenzie delta area, Northwest Territories (Canada)," *Can. Dept. Mines Tech. Surv. Can. Geogr. Branch Mem*, **8**, 202pp.

Melton, F. A., 1940, "A tentative classification of sand dunes, its application to dune history in the southern High Plains," *J. Geol.*, **48**, 113–174.

Melton, F. A., and Schriever, William, 1933, "The Carolina 'bays'—are they meteorite scars?" *J. Geol.*, **41**, 52–66.

Obruchev, S. V., 1938, "Shakhmatnye (ortogonal'nye) formy v oblastiákh vechnoĭ merzloty (The checkerboard orthogonal forms in permafrost regions), Vses. Geograficheskoe Obshchestvo Izv.*, **70**(6), 737–746.

Obruchev, S. V., 1940, "Obshcheie merzlotovedeneie (General Frozen Ground Science)," *Akad. Nauk, SSSR* (unpublished abstract of Ch. ix by I. V. Poire, February 1947).

Plafker, Geo., 1964, "Oriented lakes and lineaments of northeastern Bolivia," *Bull. Geol. Soc. Am.*, **75**, 503–522.

Price, W. A., 1933, "Role of diastrophism in topography of Corpus Christi area, south Texas," *Bull. Am. Assoc. Petrol. Geologists*, **17**, 907–962.

Price, W. A., 1944, "Greater American deserts," *Texas Acad. Sci., Proc. and Trans., 1943*, **27**, 163–170.

Price, W. A., 1958, "Sedimentology and Quaternary geomorphology of south Texas," *Trans. Gulf Coast Assoc. Geol. Soc.*, **8**, 4i–75 (abstract in *Geoscience Rev.*, 1959, 1–1630).

Prouty, W. F., 1952, "Carolina bays and their origin," *Bull. Geol. Soc. Am.*, **63**, 167–224.

Raisz, E. J., 1934, "Rounded lakes and lagoons of the coastal plains of Massachussets," *J. Geol.*, **42**, 839–848.

Reeves, C. C., Jr., 1966, "Pluvial lake basins of West Texas," *J. Geol.*, **74**, 269–291.

Schou, Axel, 1945, "Det marine forland," *Folia Geog.*

Danica, **4**, H. Hagerups Forlag, 236pp (English summary, pp. 213–224, also, 1950, *Medd. Skalling Lab.*, **9**, H. Hagerups Forlag).

Stephens, C. G., and Crocker, R. L., 1946, "Composition and genesis of lunettes," *Trans. Roy. Soc. S. Australia*, **70**, 302–312.

Tedrow, J. F. C., 1965, Letter to W. A. Price (November 23, 1965).

Wells, B. W., and Boyce, S. G., 1953, "Carolina bays: additional data on their origin, age and history," *J. Elisha Mitchell Sci. Soc.*, **69**, 119–141.

Cross-references: *Beach Ridges*; *Carolina Bays*; *Clay Dune*; *Crater Lakes*; *Deflation*; *Glacial Lakes*; *Karst*; *Oxbow Lake*; *Pingos*; *Playa*; *Scabland*.

OUTWASH PLAIN, FAN, TERRACE, SANDUR

An outwash deposit is one laid down under fluvioglacial conditions around the margin of an ice sheet or beyond the snout of a glacier, fed by subglacial streams. The physiographic feature is variously termed *outwash plain, terrace, fan, apron, train,* or *sandur* (also sandr, sander), an Icelandic term that has obtained widespread international use (also plural form, sandar, originally meaning simply sandy ground).

According to Wooldridge and Morgan (1959): "The meltwater from the ice escapes as a stream or a series of streams which breach the terminal moraine, and redistribute its material downward along the valley in more or less distinctly stratified deposits known as *valley trains, outwash plains* or *frontal aprons*."

Outwash sediments, as suggested by the nature of their waste-born origin (with streams of high energy), are usually in cross-bedded units of sharply alternating grain sizes. Typically, they are gravels closest to the glacial margin passing into extensive belts of sand, silts and clays carried away into the ocean. In piedmont areas, the distribution tends to be linear (i.e., literally a "valley train"); in regions of low relief, e.g., coastal plains like the southern half of Long Island, Cape Cod, or the western Denmark–North German Plains, the sand deposits fan out to form almost flat plains. An extreme case was the valley train of the Mississippi which in glacial times carried fine sand some 700 miles south of the glacier front to the delta region (Flint, 1957, p. 138).

Outwash plains tend to great smoothness and gentle gradients (0.5%), but when confined, as in valley trains, they may be 1–7%. Symptomatic of the high gradients are certain outwash trains which are slightly humped in cross section (highest in the middle).

Occasionally large boulders would be carried by floating ice along major meltwater streams and thus deposited far from the limit of glacial erratics. Blocks of floating ice would tend to be carried down until they grounded and would eventually melt out, producing the phenomenon of small kettles or basins, a *pitted outwash plain* (Thwaites, 1926). Extreme pitting may indicate deposition over stagnant ice of irregular thickness (see photo

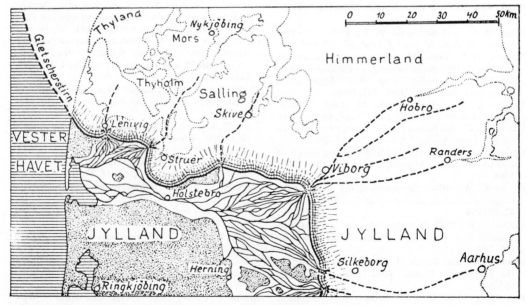

Fig. 1. Outwash plain (sandur) in western Denmark (after Ussing, 1903), as reconstructed near the maximal limit of Würm ice sheet (about 17,000 years B.P.).

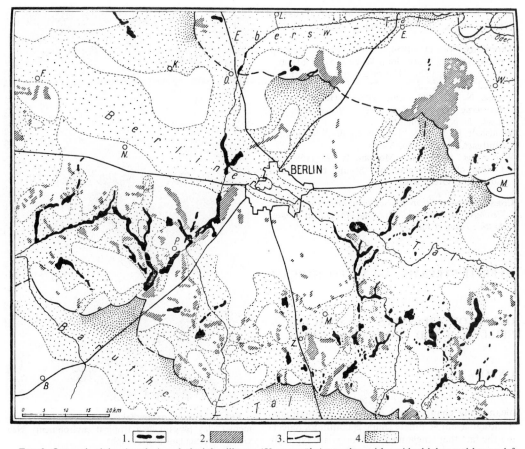

FIG. 2. Outwash plains (sandur) and glacial spillways (*Urstromtäler*) together with residual lakes and kanes, left by the last glaciation around Berlin, Germany (Woldstedt, 1954). (By permission of Enke Verlag, Stuttgart.) Key: 1. Lakes. 2. Kames. 3. Main Ice Borders. 4. Outwash plains and glacial spillways.

FIG. 3. Pleistocene glacial outwash gravels and moraines, Pukaki River, New Zealand. (Airphoto: S. N. Beatus, N.Z. Geological Survey.)

in Thornbury, 1954, p. 394). Many outwash plains are also terraced. Most of them are *recessional outwash plains*, but outwash material is found to be overridden in a number of places, thus giving rise to the term *advance outwash*; nevertheless recession with its rapid melting more readily leads to an outwash stage. *Outwash deltas* also built outward into periglacial lakes.

RHODES W. FAIRBRIDGE

References

Flint, R. F., 1957, "Glacial and Pleistocene Geology," New York, John Wiley & Sons, 553pp.

Fuller, M. L., 1914, "The geology of Long Island, New York," *U.S. Geol. Surv. Profess. Paper,* **82,** 231pp.

MacClintock, Paul, 1922, "The Pleistocene history of the lower Wisconsin River," *J. Geol.,* **30,** 673–689.

Peltier, L. C., 1949, "Pleistocene terraces of the Susquehanna River, Pennsylvania," *Penn. Geol. Survey,* Ser. 4, Bull. G, **23,** 158pp.

Penck, A., and Brückner, E., 1909, "Die Alpen im Eiszeitalter," Leipzig, Tauchnitz, 1100pp.

Shaw, E. W., 1911, "High terraces and abandoned valleys in western Pennsylvania," *J. Geol.*, **19,** 140–156.

Thornbury, W. D., 1954, "Principles of Geomorphology," New York, John Wiley & Sons, 618pp.

Thwaites, F. T., 1926, "The origin and significance of pitted outwash," *J. Geol.*, **34,** 308–319.

Ussing, N. V., 1903, "Om Jyllands Hedersletter og Teorierne om deres Dannelse," *Ofvers. Dan. Vid. Selsk. Forh.*, Copenhagen.

Woldstedt, P., 1954/65, "Das Eiszeitalter," Second ed., Stuttgart, Enke Verlag, 3 vols.

Wooldridge, S. W., and Morgan, R. S., 1959, "An Outline of Geomorphology," Second ed., London, Longmans, Green & Co.

Cross-references: *Esker*; *Fluvioglacial Processes*; *Glacial Geology*; *Glacial Spillways and Proglacial Lakes*; *Kettle*; *Trumpet Valleys*.

OVERFIT STREAMS—*See* MISFIT STREAM

OVERFLOW CHANNELS—*See* GLACIAL SPILLWAYS AND PROGLACIAL LAKES

OXBOW LAKE

An oxbow lake is a lake located in an abandoned meandering channel, and hence on a floodplain. Although a simple lunate shape is common, reflecting the fact that single meander loops are typically isolated, there is no requirement that limits a cutoff to a single loop. In some cases rather long stretches of meandering channel have been cut off from the main stream, by either natural processes or human activity, leaving serpentine lakes (e.g., "The Serpen-

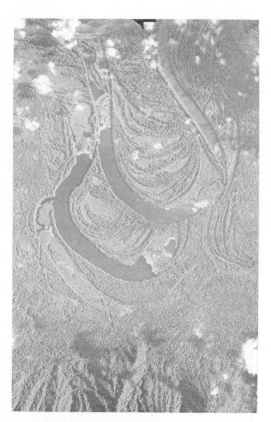

FIG. 2. Multiple oxbow lakes, in part infilled by sediment ("clay plugs") in a tropical environment—New Guinea (vertical air photograph).

tine," Hyde Park, London). A similar feature in Australia is known as a "billabong."

The natural process whereby a meander loop is abandoned is generally either a flood-time re-arrangement of a short reach of channel or a slowing of the downstream migration rate of one loop so that an upstream bend can overtake it. Because only two loops are involved in most cutoffs, oxbow lakes commonly have only a single direction of curvature.

Shortly after cutoff takes place, the stream flows through two channels simultaneously: the old and the new. The new channel is shorter, and therefore steeper, and hence a preferred route, providing maximum velocity. The two entrances to the old channel represent local widenings, in which eddy currents develop. These currents are relatively slow and therefore contribute to the silting up of the two entrances.

Overbank floods may add clay and silt to the water in the oxbow lake, thereby ultimately filling it and converting it to a marsh. Because clay and silt have been concentrated in the lake, compared with the sandier deposits around it, the marsh constitutes a *clay plug*: a tough and resistant (but

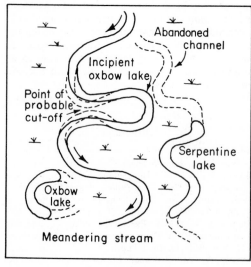

FIG. 1. Oxbow Lake.

not hard or brittle) mass of sediment into which the future channel of the stream cannot cut very well. Hence, old clay plugs tend to deform the meander pattern, making it much more complex than it would be on a floodplain underlain by uniform sediment.

Inasmuch as the *thalweg* (q.v.) of a meandering river does not have a constant slope (it is deeper in bends and shoaler in crossovers or straight segments), the ordinary oxbow lake does not have a constant depth. The silting up of the two ends generally contributes to the slope of the lake bottom.

Geologists commonly say that all oxbow lakes are concave toward the channel from which they were derived. This is not necessarily true, although it is a good workable rule of thumb. Where a serpentine lake is left by isolation of a chain of meander bends, silting of the abandoned channel may leave a lake which is convex toward the stream from which it was derived. Many oxbow lakes and clay plugs are more readily identified on air photos than on topographic maps.

W. F. TANNER

References

Fisk, H. N., 1947, "Fine-grained Alluvial Deposits and Their Effects on Mississippi River Activity," Vicksburg, Corps Engineers Waterways Exper. Station, 2 vols.

Kolb, C. R., *et al.*, 1967, "Geological investigation of the Yazoo Basin," Vicksburg, Miss., *U.S. Army Engineers Waterways Exper. Station, Tech. Rept.* No. 3-480.

Leopold, L. B., Wolman, M. G., and Miller, J. P. 1964, "Fluvial Process in Geomorphology," San Francisco, W. H. Freeman and Company, 522pp.

Thornbury, William D., 1954, "Principles of Geomorphology," New York, John Wiley & Sons, 618pp.

Cross-references: *Flood Plain*; *Rivers—Meandering and Braiding*; *Thalweg*.

OYSTER REEFS

Description and Scope

Among organic reefs, those of the geologically young oysters are now second in size and distribution only to the coralline reefs. They may develop not only bioherms but also biostromes (see discussion under *Coral Reefs*). The modern genera are the estuarine *Ostrea* and *Crassostrea*, and the marine *Pycnodonte* (Hopkins, 1957). Only three of the many species of these genera are reputed to have built conspicuous reefs: the European *O. edulis*, the American *C. virginica* and the Japanese *C. gigas*. The American reefs are reported to be much larger than the European reefs were before cultivation obscured their native condition. Oyster

FIG. 1. A natural oyster reef (living), at Isle Derniers, Louisiana (see also Fig. 4). (Photo: Texas A. & M. Research Foundation).

banks of Heligoland, flourishing in the last century, have now disappeared and have been replaced by *Nucula nucleus* (Caspers, 1950).

Tertiary and Pleistocene oyster reefs are known, but the information in hand permits detailed discussion only of the post-Flandrian Holocene reefs of *C. virginica* from New Jersey to Texas. This species—the edible American oyster—is a cool-water one and ranges from humid to marginal semiarid climates.

It is said that more biological research has been done on the oysters than on any other molluscan group. Information on their reefs, however, is scattered. Grave's classical hypothesis of reef origin (1901, 1905) dealt with a limited group (Price, 1954) and is not supported by later work, which now throws light on the genetic problem.

The minute spat of oysters—0.8 mm ($\frac{1}{32}$ inch)— are carried widely by estuarine currents and settle in great profusion on all kinds of bottoms. Growth to maturity occurs only on firm to slowly yielding bottoms such as rock, shells, roots, sandy clay, stiff clay and even some muds. Oysters also grow on artificial structures such as piling and sea walls.

Oyster communities consist of scattered clusters, densely populated beds, elevated patch reefs ("tow heads"), tabular bodies ("bottoms"), and oval to linear reefs ("bars," "banks"). The tops of reefs range from the intertidal zone (Fig. 1) to depths in some deep Atlantic coast channels of 40 feet below sea level. Reefs in shallower waters, as on the coast of the Gulf of Mexico, commonly rise to intertidal levels, the tops of the higher ones being dead. Texas reefs bored and sampled (Fig. 2) seem to have steep sides and are based on sand or shell beds buried as deep as 24 meters (80 feet) below sea level and 21 meters (68 feet) below bay bottom. C^{14} datings on shells indicate growth toward the surface for as long as 9800 years (Shepard and Moore, 1960, pp. 136, 141, Figs. 16–18). These data show that the deep-seated reefs, which are located in the central parts of the bays of today

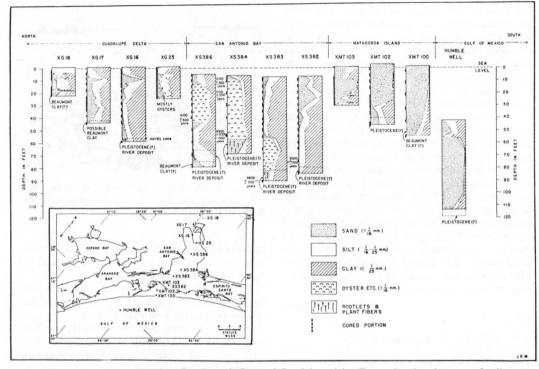

FIG. 2. North-south section along San Antonio Bay and Guadalupe delta, Texas, showing character of sediments in the borings (from Shepard and Moore, 1960, Fig. 18; by kind permission of the American Association of Petroleum Geologists).

began to develop when the rising sea of the Flandrian transgression first drowned the entrenched stream valleys. Oyster reefs and chains of reefs as long as 16–40 km (10–25 miles) occur along the northern Gulf coast.

In 1905, Grave (p. 259) wrote:

"Oyster reefs are . . . long, narrow ridges of mud and shells, the tops usually covered with a dense growth of badly shaped oysters known as 'coons' . . . . The reefs are considerably higher than the surrounding areas . . . . A living reef is . . . made up of clusters of oysters, each rooted in a substratum of soft organic mud mixed with shells and shell fragments. Between the clusters, numbers of mussels, crabs, and worms are also usually present . . . The individuals of a cluster assume a vertical position, with mouth uppermost, and, crowded on all sides by their neighbors, they can grow only in the remaining direction—from their free ends."

Factors and Conditions of Reef Development

Optimum conditions for reef growth include the following locations: (1) in and preferably across the course of a spat-and-food-carrying current; (2) away from stream mouths where the water may be too fresh and silt may settle too rapidly, making the water murky and excluding light; (3) away from estuary mouths and tidal inlets where seawater favors oyster enemies and storm destruction may occur; (4) where ranges of temperature and salinity are favorable and do not fluctuate too rapidly or strongly; (5) on stable to relatively stable bottoms, not too soft and not subject to strong erosion, as on sandy beaches; such bottoms must be "clean," i.e., not fouled with organic sludges.

Optimum temperature ranges for the oyster are said to be from 15–25°C (59–77°F); optimum salinities occur in the central parts of bays and other estuaries midway between stream mouth and oceanic opening. Observed salinity ranges are from 10–30‰ NaCl, with reefs present at or near both extremes. This range applies also where "brackish" conditions in the sea permit reef growth a few miles offshore. Optimum conditions for reef growth are limited also by differences in habitat requirements for spawning, spat distribution, adult development and long-period occupation. The 9000-year-old reefs of Texas required a remarkable stability of habitat within the ranges of oyster survival. Also, the rate of upward growth was potentially at least as great as the rate of sea level rise.

Many observers have commented on the importance of current as a factor in oyster growth and reef development. Lund's (1957) experiments confirm this concept and show that the rate of feeding

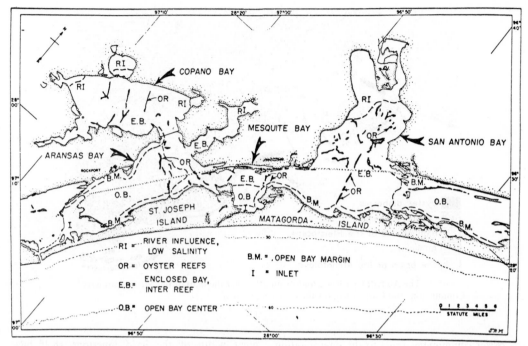

Fig. 3. Areal distribution of macrofaunal assemblages, Rockport, Texas, region (from Parker, 1960, Fig. 10; by kind permission of the American Association of Petroleum Geologists).

increases with the speed of the food-bearing current. The shallowing of the water as a current passes over a reef increases the speed. The roughness of shell growth also develops turbulence which removes some of the fine-grained sediment that settles on a reef. Lund (1957) also studied the voiding by the oyster of silt ingested with the water and food that the current brings. This "self-silt" is voided in pellet form and mixed with organic matter. The oyster thus adds to the fine-grained sediment that accumulates on the reef, and the increase in particle size and cohesiveness tends to resist removal by currents. The oyster protects itself from the accumulating deposit by squirting the water out so as to preserve a dimple in the surface of the "self-silt".

Origin and Development of Reef Form

To explain the common occurrence of reefs that jut out at 70° to 90° from a shoreline, Grave (1901, 1905) postulated that, among clusters of oysters forming along a shore, those that were initially longer than adjacent clusters acquired a forward-growing advantage that let them continue to elongate, but starved out the initially shorter ones. He thought the advantage began when some valves of dead oysters fell forward and some laterally. In the reoccupation of the valves, the forward shells tended to deflect the passing current outward, thus acquiring a feeding advantage over the lateral

oysters. Eventually, by this process, the elongation led to the starvation of the intervening short reefs.

Grave's lateral-pauperization hypothesis has received no support from other biologists and seems never to have been tested experimentally. The hypothesis required that the transverse reefs develop their own linearity and ridge shape. In Grave's day, the ridge-shaped reefs that run longitudinally with a current were explained for some middle Atlantic states by their having developed along the edges of the drowned valley channels of the estuaries, which are there unfilled with sediment (Dean, 1892; Moore, 1910).

For the reefs that jut out transversely from a shoreline (Fig. 3) there is now a simple explanation. The patterns of these reefs are now seen to be those of sand spits whose shapes and positions have been shown by Zenkovitch (1959) to be formed by long-shore currents. Currents flowing dominantly in one direction build diagonal spits. Reversals of current direction develop symmetrical perpendicular spits which attain, in some cases, lengths of several miles. Where such spits develop in opposed pairs, they tend to segment an estuary, even forming midbay barriers (Price, 1947). Zenkovitch's explanation is now widely accepted. The process can be seen in operation on the Texas coast when aerial photographs taken at intervals are closely compared.

The common and widespread occurrence of the transverse sand spits where they are not occupied

801

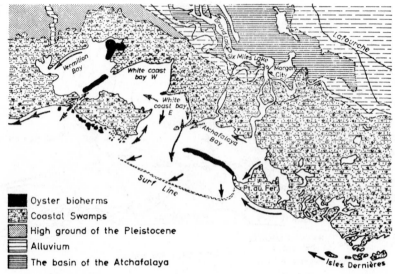

Oyster bioherms
Coastal Swamps
High ground of the Pleistocene
Alluvium
The basin of the Atchafalaya

FIG. 4. The Atchafalaya River and its mouth (after the map of the Mississippi River Commission, and Cary, 1906, for the oyster bioherms).

by oyster communities leads to the interpretation that oyster reefs elsewhere of the same habit of occurrence were formed by the oysters occupying already formed spits and bars where the bottoms were relatively stable and the oysters were not killed out by storms. Occupation by oysters would have made the ridges still more stable. In support of this origin is the seating on sand of reefs bored in Texas and of one seen by the writer in Pleistocene sediments of a bay bluff. There are many reefs, however, including some shown in Fig. 3, the initial orientations of which are now obscure because of their probable long histories and because of the geomorphic and sedimentary changes that would have occurred since they were formed. Oyster reefs are liable to sink under their own weight (Thompson, 1955), so that the base may be convex down.

Reefs Offshore

Reefs of *C. virginica* are found along the coasts of the Gulf of Mexico situated as far as 5 miles out in the Gulf. Two such rare occurrences are known. In both cases, brackish "estuarine" conditions exist in the Gulf because of large volumes of fresh water which dilute the seawater and, to a smaller extent perhaps, because they are protected from strong wave attack and from damaging sand deposition.

Thus, large numbers of linear reefs occur along 125 miles of the northwestern drowned-karst coast (Dawson, 1955; Price, 1956) of the peninsula of Florida (Crystal Bay to Apalachee Bay). The longest is Suwannee Reef, 14 miles long. Fresh water is discharged from streams and from springs in the shelf limestone. The gentle offshore gradient and

great width of the hard limestone shelf have protected the nearshore zone from strong wave activity (Price, 1956), and there is little sand carried alongshore.

Also, the increasingly large volumes of Mississippi River water that have been discharged during the past century through the Atchafalaya distributary have driven the zone of oyster reef deposition from inside to outside Atchafalaya Bay. Thompson's (1955) borings and fathometer survey showed an inner and an outer baymouth oyster reef barrier extending 25 miles west from Pointe Au Fer. The older is now buried in silt and the outer, emergent but dead. Abundant live oysters have been seen on a line of patch reefs developing 5 miles out in the Gulf off the Pointe Au Fer reef. The environment of Atchafalaya Bay is notably scarce in sand (Thompson, 1955), and the coast is one of medium wave energy (Price, 1956; Fig. 4).

Geologic Role of Oysters and Oyster Reefs

In summary, oysters furnish shells for organic sand and shingle, forming sedimentary beds and appearing as constituents of estuarine and (reworked from submerged deposits) of oceanic beaches. The shells stabilize spits and possibly some bars, forming reefs and protecting these sediment baffles from erosion. Oysters deposit "self-silt," but the reefs concentrate current flow over them, increasing both erosion and the volume of self-silt.

Oyster reefs have a narrower range of occurrence than the oysters themselves, both reefs and the species being paleogeographic and environmental indices.

Industrial use of reef shell is competing with the use of the oysters as food material.

W. Armstrong Price

References

Carriker, M. R., 1951, "Ecological observations of the distribution of oyster larvae in New Jersey estuaries," *Ecol. Monographs*, **21**, 19–38.

Caspers, H., 1950, "Die Lebensgemeinschaft der Helgoländer Austernbank," *Helg. Wiss. Meeresunters.*, **3**, 120–169.

Cullen, D. J., 1962, "The influence of bottom sediments upon the distribution of oysters in Foveaux Strait, New Zealand." *N.Z. J. Geol. Geophys.* **5**, 271–275.

Dawson, C. E., Jr., 1955, "A study of the oyster biology and hydrography at Crystal River, Florida," *Publ. Inst. of Marine Sci., Univ. of Texas*, **4**(1), 281–302.

Dean, Bashford, 1892, "The physical and biological characteristics of the natural oyster-grounds of South Carolina," *Bull. U.S. Fish Comm.*, **10**, 335–361.

Frey, D. G., 1946, "Oyster bars of the Potomac River," *Fish and Wildlife Serv., Sp. Sci. Rept.*, **32**, 93pp. (mimeo).

Galtsoff, P. S., 1964, "The American Oyster *Crassostrea virginica* G melin," *Bull., Fish and Wildlife Serv.*, **64**.

Grave, Caswell, 1901, "The oyster reefs of North Carolina. A geological and economic study," *Johns Hopkins Univ. Circular No. 151*, 9pp.

Grave, Caswell, 1905, "Investigations for the promotion of the oyster industry of North Carolina," *Rept. U.S. Fish Comm.*, **29**, 247–341.

Hopkins, S. H., 1957, "Oysters," Annotated Bibliographies in (Hedspeth, J. W., editor) "Treatise on marine ecology and paleoecology," *Geol. Soc. Am. Mem. 67*, 1129–1134.

Lund, E. J., 1957, "Self-silting, survival of the oyster as a closed system and reducing tendencies of the environment of the oyster," *Publ. Inst. Marine Sci. Univ. of Texas*, **4**(2), 313–319.

Moore, H. F., 1910, "Condition and extent of the oyster beds of James River, Virginia," *Rept. U.S. Fish Comm. 1909*, **729**, 83pp.

*Moore, H. F., 1913, "Condition and extent of the natural oysters beds and barren bottoms of Mississippi Sound, Alabama," *U.S. Bur. Fish., Doc. 796*, 61 pp.

Parker, R. H., 1960, "Ecology and distribution patterns of marine macro-invertebrates, northern Gulf of Mexico," in (Shepard, F. P., et al., editors) "Recent Sediments, Northwest Gulf of Mexico," pp. 302–337, *American Association of Petroleum Geologists*.

Price, W. A., 1947, "Equilibrium of form and forces in tidal basins of coast of Texas and Louisiana," *Bull. Am. Assoc. Petrol. Geologists*, **31**, 1619–1663.

Price, W. A., 1954, "Oyster reefs of the Gulf of Mexico. Gulf of Mexico, its origin, waters and marine life," in (Galtsoff, P. S., editor), *Fish Bull. 89 U.S. Fish and Wildlife Service*, **55**. 491(401) (*Contr. 27, Dept. Oceanography, A & M Coll. Texas*).

Price, W. A., 1956, "The low energy coast and its new shoreline types on the Gulf of Mexico," *Actes, IV Congres Assoc. Intern. Quaternaire (INQUA), Rome–Pisa 1953*, 159–166 (*Contr. 44, Dept. Oceanography A & M Coll. Texas*).

Ranson, G., 1943, "La vie des huitres. Hist. Naturelles —I," Third edition, Paris, Librairie Gallimard, 261pp.

Shepard, F. P., and Moore, D. G., 1960, "Bays of Central Texas Coast," in (Shepard, F. P., et al., editors) "Recent Sediments, Northwest Gulf of Mexico," pp. 117–152, *American Association of Petroleum Geologists*.

Thompson, W. C., 1955, "Sandless coastal terrain of the Atchafalaya Bay area, Louisiana. Finding Ancient Shorelines," Symposium with Discussions, *Soc. Econ. Paleontologists Mineralogists, Spec. Publ.*, **3**, 52–76.

Zenkovitch, V. P., 1959, "On the genesis of cuspate spits along lagoon shores," *J. Geol.*, **67**, 269–277.

* Additional bibliographic references mentioned in the text may be found in this work.

Cross-references: *Coral Reefs; Estuary; Holocene; Microatolls; Organisms as Geomorphic Agents.*

P

PALEOGEOGRAPHY—*See* pr Vol. VII

PALEOGEOMORPHOLOGY

Definition

Paleogeomorphology is that subscience of geomorphology which deals with all buried ("fossil") geomorphic phenomena which are recognizable in the subsurface and in outcrops of previously buried and newly exhumed formations. Hence, paleogeomorphology is the science of buried relief features of the earth. This includes both buried landscapes and buried submarine features, such as fossil submarine canyons, fossil reefs and fossil volcanic islands.

Term

The term *paleogeomorphic maps* was first used by Kay in 1945. Paleogeomorphology was further defined by Thornbury, Martin, Harris and McKee. A comprehensive study of the subject, with references, can be found in Martin (1966).

Practical Applications

Paleogeomorphology is of practical importance insofar as many accumulations of oil, gas, certain ores and fresh water are related to buried relief features. Analysis, interpretation and especially extrapolation of such features must emphasize their three-dimensional shape or *form*. However, a proper interpretation of this form is not possible without an understanding of the *process* which created the form, especially if subsurface data are sparse and scattered. It is possible to make certain deductions from the study of buried relief forms which lend themselves to geomorphological interpretation. Since geomorphology depends on a great number of factors, many of which cannot be accurately determined and are of purely local character, no exact mathematical rules can be formulated and only average parameters can be established. However, once these averages have been determined within reasonable limits of accuracy, they can be used in the reconstruction of buried relief forms from a limited number of control points. Such a reconstruction may then serve as a basis for further exploration.

To the petroleum geologist in particular, paleogeomorphology is important since *paleogeomorphic traps* for oil and gas rank in importance with the classical two other trapping mechanisms, *structural traps* and *stratigraphic traps*. Accumulations may take place both below and above (or against) a morphological surface (Figs. 1 and 2). They may be direct or indirect. In the latter case, the trapping mechanism is due to secondary processes related to the buried morphology but not to the buried landform itself.

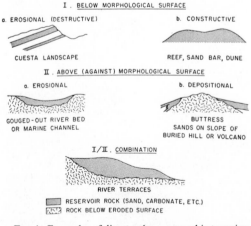

FIG. 1. Examples of direct paleogeomorphic trapping of hydrocarbons.

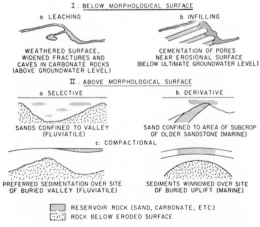

FIG. 2. Examples of indirect paleogeomorphic trapping of hydrocarbons.

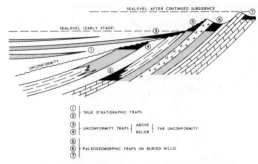

FIG. 3. Relationship between buried hills and different stages of basin formation.

Relationship to Geomorphology

Geomorphological processes may be subdivided into *constructive* and *destructive*. The first group includes all processes whereby material is added to a previously existing surface, e.g., by sedimentation, reef buildups, offshore bars, barrier beaches, point bars (fluviatile), dunes, glacial deposits, volcanoes, etc. The destructive geomorphic processes remove material from preexisting surfaces, and include weathering (chemical and molecular), mass wasting (gravitational processes) and erosional processes (action of running water, ice, wind, waves, marine currents and submarine erosion).

Because of the emphasis on *form* in the exploration for commercial deposits, the geomorphological processes that have received the most attention in the study of paleogeomorphology relate to the formation and morphology of organic reefs, buried erosional landforms, submarine canyons, weathering and underground solution, point bars and barrier beaches.

Buried Erosional Landforms

Buried erosional landforms are widely known from the Paleozoic and Mesozoic of the midcontinent area of the United States and western Canada, as well as from younger formations and other continents. Paleotopographic relief of up to 1000 feet has been observed in surface outcrops of the Precambrian and Lower Ordovician surfaces, and buried relief forms of many hundreds of feet elevation have been encountered in the course of drilling for oil and gas on the buried surfaces of the Ordovician, Devonian and Mississippian, and for fresh water on Tertiary and sub-Recent surfaces. For a complete analysis of a buried landscape it is necessary to determine the climate that prevailed at the time of its formation, the lithology and structure of the rocks involved, and all the geomorphological parameters that determined the final shape of the landscape. The latter include the drainage pattern, drainage density, slope angles, valley gradients, summit levels and other factors.

(1) Time of Formation. Buried landscapes are naturally most prevalent at those levels which correspond to the times in geological history which followed major periods of mountain building. As a result of these orogenic movements, vast areas that previously were part of sedimentary basins were uplifted to positions well above the prevailing base level of erosion (see Fig. 3). A further worldwide lowering of this base level occurred whenever a period of extensive glaciation followed a major orogeny, withdrawing large amounts of water from the oceans. This places the greatest extent of buried landscapes at the end of the Precambrian, the Silurian, the Mississippian and the Tertiary. Additional lesser episodes of landscape formation occurred at the end of the early Ordovician, the Ordovician, the Devonian, the Permian, the Triassic, the Jurassic and the Cretaceous. Paleogeomorphological evidence indicates that these periods of landscape formation were as important as the intervening periods of sedimentation. This is not to say, however, that the one started as the other ended. As the land area expanded, the sea retreated, and vice versa; at any given time there must always have been, as there is at present, contemporaneous denudation of the land and deposition in the sea. The major breaks in the sedimentary record merely correspond to the times of greatest expanse of dry land.

(2) Location. Other factors limit the occurrence of buried landscapes in space. It has been found that the areas in which they occur generally are bounded on the basinward side by a structural hinge line. Beyond this line, the inclination of the strata involved toward the basin center tends to increase markedly. The hinge line also may be associated with one or more boundary faults and commonly (but not everywhere) coincides with the shore line of at least one post-unconformity sequence. On the landward side, the locus of buried landscapes is limited by the shore line of the maximum subsequent transgression. Because the slope of the old landscape, before the time of renewed basin subsidence and transgression, was in most cases no more than a few feet per mile, the width of the denuded area buried by younger sediments may amount to many hundreds of miles.

(3) Paleoplains. The experience gathered from the analyses of certain "fossil" landscapes indicates that the nature of the process of planation, as retained or "frozen" in the shape of these buried landscapes, is not exactly as envisaged by Davis (1889) or by Penck (1924). According to Davis, a landscape passing from youth through maturity to old age finally would be denuded to a peneplain approaching base level. At most, some scattered monadnocks, or disconnected hills, would be left on this surface. Davis did not claim that a peneplain had to be flat: he mentions residual hills of 200–300 feet in height. Hill (1901) introduced the term *paleo-*

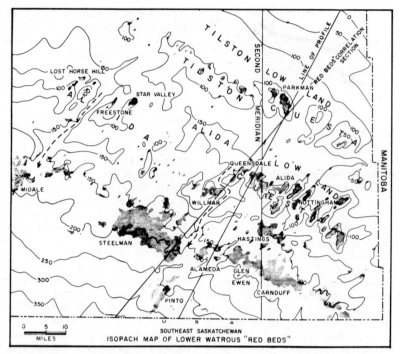

FIG. 4. Southeast Saskatchewan. Isopach map of Triassic (?) Lower Watrous Formation "Red Beds." Thin isopach values correspond to high elevations of the underlying buried Mississippian landscape. Tinted areas = oil fields.

plain, or buried peneplain, for the buried pre-Cretaceous landscape of the Wichita Falls, Texas, area. Studies by the writer of buried landscapes in Western Canada have shown that such a paleoplain still contains all the elements of the preceding mature landscape. There is a recognizable drainage pattern of valleys at a fair gradient, separating a coherent system of ridges that are by no means isolated "monadnocks." Paleogeomorphological data thus might appear to lend support to the theories of Penck (1924), who believed that a slope, once formed, retains its original angle and therewith its identity, while responding to the forces of erosion by gradually retreating parallel with its previous position and losing some of its height. At the foot of such a slope, a "footslope" or *pediment* develops, which maintains the minimum slope consistent with the local erosion facies. Eventually, when the steep scarps on either side of an uplifted area have retreated to the point where the ridge between them is obliterated and the pediments from adjoining valleys meet, a *pediplain* results which is not really very different as an ultimate landform from Davis's peneplain, but which has reached this end form by very different means. However, the buried landscapes of Western Canada definitely have not been reduced to such a pediplain. There is a pronounced difference in slope between the dip slopes and the scarps or "face" slopes. Yet, the steep scarps of

Penck are gone; the inclination of a buried Mississippian surface that was studied in considerable detail ranged from only 15–233 ft/mile.

Thus, the slopes, instead of retaining the same angle at all times, do become reduced to 3° or less, as predicted by Davis. At the same time, as predicted by Penck, the framework of the landscape as a whole retains its general shape, instead of becoming a featureless peneplain. It appears that Hill's term *paleoplain* is well suited to the definition of such a buried landscape. The practical importance of such paleoplains lies in the fact that they have retained sufficient relief to be an important trapping factor

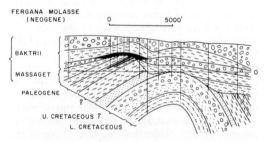

FIG. 5. Cross section of South Alamyshik field, Uzbek S.S.R., Turkestan, U.S.S.R. (after Khutorov), showing buried escarpment on the flank of an anticline.

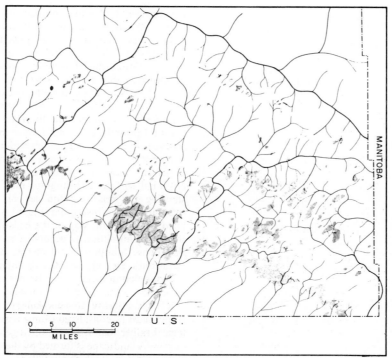

FIG. 6. Southeast Saskatchewan. Drainage system on the Mississippian erosion
surface. Tinted areas = oil fields.

in the accumulation of hydrocarbons, ores, fresh water, etc.

(4) Buried Cuesta Landscapes. Most paleoplains studied in detail to date have retained all or most of the aspects of a cuesta landscape (Fig. 4). Cuesta landscapes are not necessarily typical only of coastal plains, as suggested by Davis (1899b) and subsequent authors. A cuesta landscape will develop on the homoclinal flank of any subsiding basin as the tilted strata on its periphery are eroded into parallel, outward-facing, "belted" escarpments. The formation of cuestas is a logical corollary to new basin subsidence after a period of epeirogenic uplift. This is not to say that buried landscapes have not also been developed in areas where structural deformation has taken place on a noticeable scale. In this case, more complex landscapes have resulted than those which will be described in the subsequent paragraphs (e.g., see Fig. 5). Typical buried cuesta landscapes surround the flanks of various basins on the North American and other continents, as well as some well-known large uplifts. In the latter case, the beds, of course, dip away from the uplift into the surrounding low areas. Cuestas forming such a buried landscape will slope at a slightly smaller angle than the dip of the erosion-resistant beds which form them.

Consequent streams that cut the cuestas flowing down the original topographic slope toward the basin, in the buried Western Canadian landscape studied by the writer (Fig. 6), had a gradient of 2 feet 4 inches per mile, which compares with that of the present Missouri River. At right angles to these are subsequent stream valleys, which parallel the cuestas. The cuestas themselves are dissected by

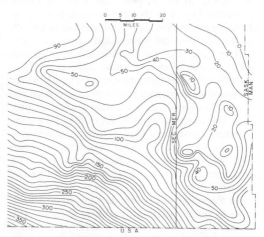

FIG. 7. Summit level of the Mississippian erosional surface, southeast Saskatchewan ("Red Beds" isopachs). The lowest isopach values correspond to the highest summits of the buried Mississippian topography.

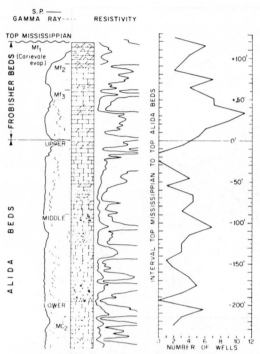

FIG. 8. Mississippian-type log and frequency distribution of levels resistant to erosion, area between Queensdale and Freestone fields, southeast Saskatchewan.

obsequent and resequent tributaries to these subsequent valleys.

(5) **Summit Level.** The highest points of a buried landscape may often be at a comparable original elevation. A plain that touches these highest points may be called a summit level. Summit levels are not necessarily flat, but show a tendency to be lower in the vicinity of the deepest valleys of the buried landscape (Fig. 7). In the original concept of Davis (1899a), a summit level represents a peneplain which has been uplifted and subsequently dissected. Later workers have held that a regular drainage pattern will eventually result in a rather uniform height of the hills, as long as the formations that underlie the landscape are of relatively uniform composition and texture. The buried landscapes that qualify as paleoplains are essentially equivalent to Davis' peneplain. If therefore a summit level were a dissected peneplain, then a paleoplain could not have a summit level. Because it does, it is concluded that a summit level is an essential and contemporaneous part of the paleoplain.

(6) **Resistance to Erosion.** In a cuesta landscape, rocks of lesser resistance to erosion alternate with resistant layers. This results in alternating escarpments and valleys. However, only a few of the escarpments develop into the cuestas that separate major subsequent valleys. Other, subsidiary escarpments form short strike ridges on the spurs that lie

between pairs of either obsequent or resequent valleys. Where particularly well developed, such strike ridges may give these spurs the shape of "hammerhead" hills. To analyze a buried landscape in an area from which it is not known, e.g., from the construction of cross sections, which are the erosion-resistant beds, a statistical method of approach may be used, provided that the area has been explored by completely random drilling. By correlating the formation below the erosional surface in detail in all the wells in which it was penetrated, and by determining in each well how much stratigraphic section is present between a given marker bed and the erosional surface, a histogram may be prepared showing the relative frequency of, say, 10-foot intervals. Such a histogram (Fig. 8) is easily correlated with the lithology of the beds that make up the eroded formation. In general, it may be observed that dense limestones, anhydrites, well-cemented sandstones, etc., are resistant to erosion, whereas shales, dolomites, clayey sandstones, etc., will tend to be less resistant and to form valleys.

(7) **Quantitative Geomorphology.** Buried landscapes must be considered from a true geomorphological rather than from a limited geological point of view. A landscape is formed by the interaction of climatic factors (such as rainfall) and the geological framework. Flowing water may adapt itself to geological factors, but first of all is controlled by hydrophysical laws. These laws and the nature of the underlying geology together determine the ultimate shape of the drainage pattern. Horton (1945) has formulated quantitative geomorpho-

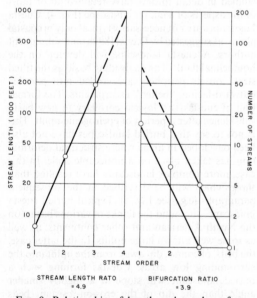

FIG. 9. Relationship of length and number of pre-"Red Beds" streams of different orders, southeast Saskatchewan. Stream orders 1–4 refer to streams of increasing length.

logical laws which are extremely useful in the analysis of buried landscapes. One of these refers to the concept of *drainage density*. It may be assumed that this factor is about the same for similar rock types under the same climatic conditions. Thus, if in a portion of a buried landscape which is known in detail through drilling, the spacing between obsequent streams averages *x* miles, then it may be assumed that the same average applies to unexplored portions of the same general area. This is of considerable importance in the interpretation of the paleotopography of buried landscapes for which subsurface data are sparse and scattered.

According to the *law of drainage composition*, the number and average length of tributary streams vary in geometrical progression with the *stream order* (Fig. 9). Buried landscapes can be interpreted in many different ways, often depending on the personal taste of the geologist, and Horton's law offers an opportunity to check on the validity of any one such interpretation. The two factors affected by the law of drainage composition are the *bifurcation ratio* and the *stream length ratio*. These ratios may be established in densely drilled portions of a buried landscape and then be used to check the interpretation of areas in which the data are sparser. The correctness of such an interpretation would be subject to doubt if the number of tributaries, lengths of streams and channel slopes were not within the limits that are consistent with geomorphological principles. The quantitative approach to geomorphology leads to the concept of *dynamic equilibrium* (Strahler, 1950; Hack, 1960).

(8) Other Principles. Additional principles observed in buried landscapes involve the *law of alternating obsequent and resequent interfluve spurs*, and that of the *oblique angle of entry* of subsequent tributaries into a consequent valley. The latter involves "jumping" of a subsequent valley from the outcrop of one nonresistant horizon to the stratigraphically next higher one. The former principle states that where resequent or obsequent drainage is established on one side of a cuesta, the drainage on the opposite side tends to avoid draining the same part of this ridge. As a result, valleys on one side of the cuesta are opposite spurs on the other side, and vice versa.

Geology of the Eroded Landscape

The main types of nondynamic interference with the forces of denudation with which geomorphology is concerned are related to the geological nature of the landscape on which these forces act. Interference takes the form of (1) differences in resistance to erosion of the underlying rocks, which was discussed earlier, (2) faults and fractures (a compound form results when a fault separates rocks of different resistance to erosion), and (3) karst-type drainage in carbonate rocks. The geomorphic parameter most strongly influenced by geological factors is the drainage density. In an area of relatively simple geology, the drainage density should be fairly constant.

(1) Fault and Fractures. Where the rocks underlying the area that is being subjected to erosion dip at such a low angle that the development of cuestas, representing successive erosion-resistant beds dipping toward the basin center, is not consistent with the hydrophysical demands of drainage density, other geological flaws such as zones of structural weakness exert an important influence on the formation of the drainage system. Such an area will become a tableland or mesa landscape, in which stream valleys tend to follow fault or fracture zones, instead of outcrops of weak rocks as in a cuesta landscape. A stream valley following a fault or fracture zone may deviate locally from its direction for reasons of a subsidiary nature.

(2) Underground Drainage in Carbonate Rocks. Intraformational breccias (caused by roof collapse) and sand-, clay- or conglomerate-filled cavities may indicate the presence of underground drainage during a period of erosion that resulted in the formation of a buried landscape. Karst topography will also be accompanied by the formation of sinkholes. The fill that is encountered in buried sinkholes and caves will give a clue to the time when this type of erosion took place. Many buried landscapes have been subjected to more than one period of erosion, some of which may have been humid and others arid.

Fossil Climates and Weathering

In humid areas, the cover of vegetation restricts erosion and reduces the rate of runoff, resulting in gentle, more or less rounded landscape forms. In an arid climate, on the other hand, steep escarpments can develop freely. When a landscape is subjected to erosion over a considerable period of time, several climates may succeed each other and result in compound landscape forms. The transgressive sediments overlying a buried landscape may give some clue to the climate that prevailed during and, by inference, immediately prior to their deposition. However, unless the last erosion cycle has destroyed or altered completely the effect of all preceding ones, knowledge of the climatic conditions during the final stage of erosion will be insufficient for an understanding of the total buried landscape. In the case of carbonate rocks, for example, limestone tends to act as a "weak" rock in humid regions due to its susceptibility to solution; in arid regions, on the other hand, it will commonly be "strong." The development of plant life in the course of earth history has an important bearing on this problem. Several authors have pointed out that the low forms of plants that covered the earth in earlier times could have created only incipient soils, so that older landscapes generally should have been of the semiarid type even where a plant cover existed.

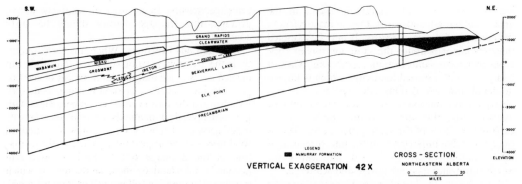

FIG. 10. Southwest-northeast cross section of the Athabasca Bituminous Sands area, northeastern Alberta.

(1) Fossil Soils ("Paleosols"). Weathered surfaces occur on many buried landscape surfaces, but not nearly as frequently as one might expect. Their apparent absence may be the result of removal of the weathering products either by flowing water while the land was still exposed, or by wave and current action during subsequent marine transgression. The coarser weathering products would be expected to collect in low places on the old surface and to become mixed with sediments of the transgressive environment. Some fossil soils are important as reservoir rocks for oil and gas, especially if they are of the eluvial or residual type from which the finer weathering products have been removed.

(2) Cap Rock. Weathering may also lead to the enlargement of pore spaces and fissures that were originally present in carbonate rocks. Subsequent infilling of such secondary porosity by calcite, anhydrite, silica or other minerals will result in the formation of a dense "cap rock."

Sand Deposition in Buried Valleys

Sandstones and other clastic rocks (principally clay) accumulated in the valleys of past landscapes in similar fashion as they do now. Without filling these valleys from ridge to ridge, such deposits may nevertheless be of sufficient thickness and horizontal extent to create economically valuable traps for hydrocarbons, ores and fresh water.

(1) Meanders. Close to their source area, the sands may be so abundant that they fill the valleys completely (Fig. 10). In their lower reaches, however, clay begins to play an important role (as a seal to commercial accumulations) as streams lose velocity. In meanders, especially, sand accumulated on the inside of one stream curve (point bar) will be cut off from the sand bar in the next (opposite) curve by a clay "plug" representing the final stage of the water course. Since each sand body represents a long period of accretion, its final shape will rarely be reminiscent of a river channel. Many such point bars will be cut off on one side by the old river, on the other by a more recent meander cutoff, thus further destroying the original image.

(2) Valley Width and Sedimentation. Where a valley crosses an erosion-resistant ridge or cuesta, it will tend to narrow, with a consequent increase in stream velocity. Sand deposits may be found both upstream and downstream from such strictures, but will tend to be absent within them.

(3) Confluence Sands. Where one stream joins another, sands are frequently deposited at the confluence, i.e., at the upstream side between the two streams.

(4) Terraces. Terraces will form when a stream cuts down into its own previous sandy deposits (Fig. 11). This may be due to a lowering either of the base level of erosion or of the headwaters area of the stream. The latter was the case in a portion of Saskatchewan, Canada, which was subject to salt solution in the rocks underlying the upper reaches of a Cretaceous drainage system.

(5) Palimpsest Drainage. This occurs when two different or partially different landscapes were carved in succession into the same or practically the same buried surface. Between the two periods of ero-

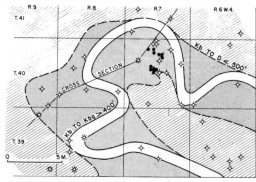

Fig. 11. Lower Cretaceous Mannville Group paleotopography, Hughenden area, Alberta. Meanders of a late basal Cretaceous stream have cut into "Basal Quartz" sands deposited in a broad post-Paleozoic valley.

sion, there was a period of subsidence, and the landscape was covered with a thin layer of new sediments. After renewed uplift, a second landscape started forming; when renewed erosion reached the base of the younger sediments, the old landscape was uncovered. This allowed the new streams in part to start following the old valleys.

Barrier Beaches

It is virtually impossible in the stratigraphic column to recognize beaches that have formed at the foot of an erosional coast as separate morphological entities. Barrier beaches and spits, on the other hand, are built up as discrete units, flanked by the open sea on one side and calmer waters, with or without tidal flats, on the other. They are usually straight or only slightly curved, and extend over distances of many miles. In the language of the oil man, fossil barrier beaches are known as "shoestring sands" (Fig. 12). Their straight, narrow shape and great length make them easily distinguishable from the short, curved point bars of fluviatile origin. In oriented cores, beach sands will show depositional bedding toward the sea, i.e., at right angles to the trend of the bar. River sands, on the other hand, are cross-bedded in the direction of the stream, i.e., in the same direction as the trend of the point bar.

Fossil Dunes

In no fossil dunes, or very few of them, is the original shape expected to have survived the strong

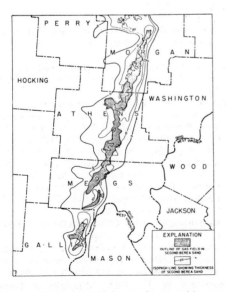

FIG. 12. Outline and thickness of gas pool in second Berea sand in southeastern Ohio. Buried topography is reflected here, for the gas field is outlined by an ancient offshore bar (after J. F. Pepper *et al.*; from W. D. Thornbury). (By permission of John Wiley & Sons.)

erosional force of the wave front of subsequent transgressive seas. The evidence for dune sands in the geologic column therefore involves primarily their lithology, structure and general character, rather than their morphology. Dunes formed inland in desert areas probably had a greater chance of being morphologically preserved than coastal dunes, but nevertheless no unmistakable evidence of dune morphology has been presented in the literature.

Submarine Canyons

Some buried erosional topography is not of subaerial, but of submarine origin. Buried submarine canyons occur exclusively in marine sediments originally deposited relatively close to the edge of the continental shelf. Such canyons commonly are several thousand feet deep and many miles wide, and usually are filled with shale and only partly with sandstone (Fig. 13). Several examples are known from the Tertiary of the Gulf Coast and California (see references in Martin, 1966).

Buried Glacial Landscapes

Evidence of past glaciations comparable to or exceeding the Pleistocene ice age in intensity has been recognized in many localities and at half a dozen stratigraphic levels. The principal criteria for recognizing such ancient glaciations are: fossil moraines (tillites), abraded (rounded, polished and striated) bedrock pavements, stratified (varved) glacial drift, erratic blocks, U-shaped valleys and closed bedrock basins. There has been much discussion about cases in which it is hard to determine whether a given "diamictite" (randomly variegated pebbly mudstone, or polymictous conglomerate) is the result of ancient landslides or a true tillite. With the help of one or more of the other criteria, however, it has been possible to establish that extensive glaciation covered either both or one of the circumpolar regions a number of times during the history of the earth.

The oldest known Precambrian (Archean) traces of glaciation date back more than 2000 million years (Canada). One of the earth's greatest ice ages occurred more than 1000 million years ago (early Algonkian of North America and Southwest Africa); another dates from some 740 to 620 million years ago in the same continents and Australia. A fourth important glacial period is known as the Eocambrian (late Precambrian) and may have extended into the Cambrian; its tillites have been reported from northern Europe, east Asia, Australia, southern Africa and South America. This makes this one of the most widespread glaciations in earth history. Much better known, on the other hand, is the Permo-Carboniferous glaciation, evidence for which has been discovered in all the continents which at that time formed the ancient "Gondwanaland" (South America, Southern Africa, India, Australia). Less well established is an ice age of late Silurian

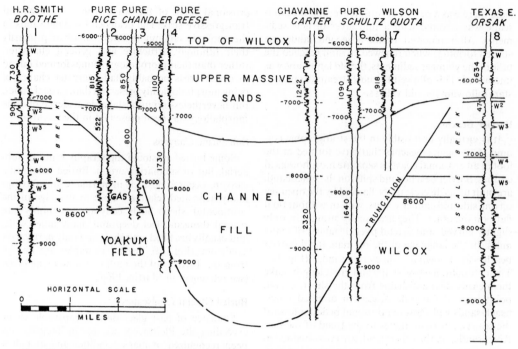

FIG. 13. Erosional channel in the Middle Wilcox (Eocene) near Yoakum, Lavaca Co., Texas (after W. V. Hoyt).

age; striated glacial pavements of that age have been reported from the central Sahara (where paleomagnetic vectors point to the location of a pole at that time) and elsewhere.

These ancient glacial landscapes prove that very remarkable changes have taken place in the pattern of the world's climates since some of the oldest times of which a record exists in the rocks. The alternation of cold with hot climates half a dozen or more times during earth history represents some of the most extraordinary changes in the nature of our planet that geology has disclosed. Thus paleogeomorphology and related subsciences have played a particularly significant role in deciphering the history of geology.

RUDOLF MARTIN

References

Davis, W. M., 1889, "Topographic development of the Triassic formation of the Connecticut Valley," *Am. J. Sci.,* 3d Ser., **37,** 423–434.

Davis, W. M., 1899a, "The peneplain," *Am. Geologist,* **23,** 207–239; also 1909, "Geographical Essays," pp. 350–380, New York, Dover Publications, 777pp. (reprinted 1954).

Davis, W. M., 1899b, "The drainage of cuestas," *Proc. Geol. Assoc.,* **16,** Pt. 2 (May), 75–93.

Hack, J. T., 1960, "Interpretation of erosional topography in humid temperate regions," *Am. J. Sci.,* **258-A,** 80–97.

Hill, R. T., 1901, "Geography and geology of the Black and Grand Prairies, Texas, with detailed description of the Cretaceous formation and special reference to artesian waters," *U.S. Geol. Surv.,* 21st Ann. Rept., Pt. 7, 362–380.

Horton, R. E., 1945, "Erosional development of streams and their drainage basins; Hydrophysical approach to quantitative morphology," *Bull. Geol. Soc. Am.,* **56,** No. 3 (March), 275–370.

Kay, G. M., 1945, "Palaeogeographic and palinspastic maps." *Bull. Am. Assoc. Petrol. Geologists,* **29,** 426–450.

Martin, R., 1966, "Paleogeomorphology and its application to exploration for oil and gas (with examples from Western Canada)," *Bull. Am. Assoc. Petrol. Geologists,* **50,** No. 10 (Oct.), 2277–2311.

Penck, W., 1924, "Die morphologische Analyse. Ein Kapitel der physikalischen Geologie," *Geogr. Abh.,* 2 Reihe, H. 2; "Morphological Analysis of Land Forms, a Contribution to Physical Geology," 1953. London, Macmillan and Co. Ltd., 429pp. (translated by H. Czeck and K. C. Boswell).

Schwarzbach, M., 1963, "Climates of the Past," London, D. Van Nostrand Co., 328pp.

Strahler, A. N., 1950, "Equilibrium theory of erosional slopes approached by frequency distribution analysis," *Am. J. Sci.,* **248,** No. 10, 673–696; No. 11, 800–814.

Thornbury, W. D., 1954, "Principles of Geomorphology," New York, John Wiley & Sons, 618 pp.

Cross-references: *Barriers; Base Level; Buried Valleys and Channels; Climatic Geomorphology; Cuesta; Denudation; Drainage Patterns; Erosion; Exhumed*

PALEOSOL, PALEOPEDOLOGY—*See* pr Vol. VI, **PALEOPEDOLOGY**

PANPLANATION

The term "panplain" was proposed by Crickmay (1933):

"...planation by lateral corrasion which begins with the first grading of the streams and can continue long after active deepening has ceased, must assume a dominant role in the late stages of the erosion cycle, causing the prevalence of broad flood plains, thinly veneered with sediment. In the limit growing flood plains become confluent, giving a surface much flatter than that of a true peneplain.... This plain, formed of flood plains joined by their own growth, may be called a panplain.... The essential difference between panplanation and peneplanation is that the former starts from the lower flood plains of rivers and grows laterally in all landward directions, whereas the latter is of universal occurrence" (Crickmay, 1933, p. 345).

Homologues of panplains in a desert are "the rock-floors of the desert, known as pediments and panfans" (Crickmay, 1933, p. 345).

Some authors use the spelling panplane instead of panplain (Lobeck, 1939, p. 163), but this is an error, akin to "peneplane," since a physiographic

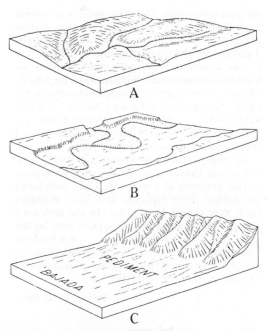

FIG. 2. Diagrams to suggest the differences in the modes of origin of (*A*) a peneplain, (*B*) a panplain, and (*C*) a pediplain (drawing by William J. Wayne; Thornbury, 1954). (By permission of John Wiley & Sons, N.Y.)

"plain" is involved, not a geometric "plane" (assumed by Johnson).

King (1947, pp. xxvi–xxviii) considered that "the essential condition of a panplain is wide areas of river-cut plain" and he wrote of "savanna with wide panplains." Wooldridge (in Taylor, 1951, p. 170) defined panplanation as "...the integrated product of long-continued lateral corrasion by rivers."

Crickmay's panplain is formed essentially by lateral corrasion (Crickmay p. 339), and its occurrence and extent depend on the interpretation of

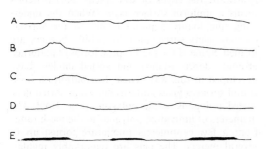

FIG. 1. Sections through landscapes produced under different types of erosion-cycle (some after C. A. Cotton) (A) Arid (sharp scarps and benchlands). (B) Semiarid. Moderately rugged between wide pediments. (C) Savanna with wide panplains. (D) Humid with convexly rounded hillslopes. (E) Etchplain, clearly marked bevels separated in general level by the depth to which weathering attains (King, 1947).

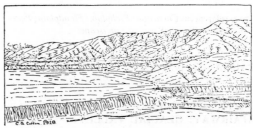

FIG. 3. The Maniototo Plain, New Zealand, a plain of lateral planation slightly modified by renewed erosion. The rear boundary of the plain is defined by the fault-boundary of the northern highland of Otago, which is composed of relatively very resistant rocks (Cotton, 1939).

the term flood plain. Thus "the process of carving away the rock so as to produce an even surface and at the same time covering it with an alluvial deposit, is the process of planation.... The surface of this deposit is hence appropriately called the flood plain of the stream" (Gilbert, 1877, pp. 126–7). "Pediments are essentially compound graded flood plains excavated by ephemeral streams" (Blackwelder, 1931, p. 137). Later Melton (1936, pp. 594–6) included braided streams and plains of lateral corrasion as types of flood plains.

The term panplanation has not been widely used, and neither Crickmay nor later writers have given specific examples of a panplain. Until both terms are defined more explicitly and more examples cited, they should be avoided. In the reviewer's opinion, one example of a panplain may be the Maniototo Plain in New Zealand " ... that has been formed by the coalescence of valley plains of lateral planation developed by a group of subparallel streams" (Cotton, 1939, 231B–232B).

BRYAN P. RUXTON

References

Blackwelder, E., 1931, "Desert plains," *J. Geol.*, **39**(2), 133–140.

Cotton, C. A., 1939, "Lateral planation in New Zealand," *New Zealand J. Sci. Technol.*, **20**, 231B–232B.

Crickmay, C. H., 1933, "The later stages of the cycle of erosion," *Geol. Mag.*, **70**(7), 337–347

Gilbert, G. K., 1877, "Report on the geology of the Henry Mountains, Utah," *U.S. Geol. Surv. Rocky Mtn. Reg.*, 160pp.

King, L. C., 1947, "Savanna with wide panplains," *Trans. Proc. Geol. Soc. S. Africa*, **50**, xxvi–xxviii.

Lobeck, A. K., 1939, "Geomorphology," New York, McGraw-Hill Book Co., 731pp.

Melton, F. A., 1936, "An empirical classification of flood-plain streams," *Geograph. Rev.*, **26**(4), 593–609.

Thornbury, W. D., 1954, "Principles of Geomorphology," New York, John Wiley & Sons, 618pp.

Wooldridge, S. W., 1951, in (Taylor, editor) "Geography in the Twentieth Century; A Study of Growth, Fields, Techniques, Aims and Trends," p. 170, London, Methuen.

Cross-references: *Corrasion*; *Etchplain*; *Floodplain*; *Pediplanation*; *Plains*; *Savanna Landscape*.

PARNA—*See* pr Vol. VI

PATERNOSTER LAKES—*See* **GLACIAL STAIRWAY: GLACIAL VALLEY**

PATTERNED GROUND

Patterned ground is a relatively new term, introduced by A. L. Washburn in 1950, to describe "more or less symmetrical forms, such as circles, polygons, nets, steps, and stripes, that are characteristic of, but not necessarily confined to, mantle subject to intensive frost action." They correspond to microrelief forms of the earth surface and to structures also known as "structure ground" or "soil structures."

All these forms chiefly occur in polar or subpolar regions, in the arctic desert and tundra zones in particular. Patterned ground forms are, therefore, characteristic of microrelief of periglacial zone (see air photographs, e.g., in Thornbury, 1954). They are common in Alaska, in northern Canada, Canadian Arctic Archipelago; they surround the inland ice-sheet of Greenland and are also found in Spitsbergen, in the tundras of northern Europe, in islands of the Soviet Arctic and in Siberia. In the southern hemisphere patterned ground occurs in the rocky surfaces of Antarctica and in the subantarctic islands surrounding it. It is also common in high mountain zones, above the timber line, in many parts of the world. The earliest descriptions of patterned ground come from Spitsbergen and northern Scandinavia (Lapland). Examples from these areas served as a basis of B. Högbom's monograph on frost as a geological factor (1914).

Favorable, though not necessarily indispensable, conditions for formation of patterned ground are provided by permafrost, i.e., polar ground deeply frozen all year round. In summer, permafrost thaws in its surface layer (0.5–1.5 meters). It is this active layer that is the home of patterned ground and its structures. The absence of vegetation as well as the saturation by melt water of the soil further stimulates the development of patterned ground.

The sorting of soil material under the influence of frost action is the principal process involved. Repeated freezing and thawing of soil (multigelation) brings about a movement of its coarser elements, such as the shifting of stones and soil blocks towards the freezing surfaces, i.e., upward or laterally toward the edges of soil cracks. Sorted debris forms a uniform surface layer. When the underlying fine loamy material comes to the surface, circular islets surrounded by pebbly borders are formed. Some of the most typical forms of patterned ground—débris islands and sorted circles—have developed in this way. Their distribution on horizontal surfaces gives patterns known as sorted nets, sorted polygons, stone polygons [Fig. 1(A)]. The diameters of individual polygons in the mesh range from a few centimeters (miniature forms) up to several meters. The nets are remarkably regular. Some early explorers could not believe that this regularity might have been due to natural processes; they were apt to ascribe their origin to human activity.

Fully developed polygons are characterized by well-sorted stone borders and a central area which is free from coarser material. As regards structure,

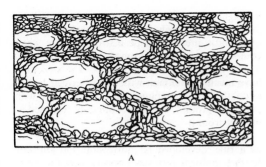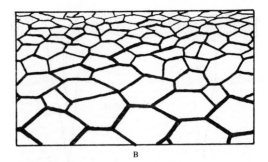

FIG. 1. Sorted (A) and nonsorted (B) polygons.

two types can be distinguished—one in which stone borders reach as deep as the base of the summer thaw of the soil (Type "A", see Fig. 2) and another in which stone borders are shallow and tend to be confined to the surface (Type "B", see Fig. 2). The central area of sorted polygons made of finer material tends to be convex in developing forms and concave in declining ones.

Frost cracking of the ground is another process resulting in the formation of patterned ground. Ice contracts at low temperatures (below $-10°C$), and frozen ground splits and cracks are formed. This process has been described as "thermal contraction." Cracks may run perpendicular to one another with resulting tetragonal forms, or they may intersect at an angle of about 120°, thus forming pentagonal or hexagonal cells [Fig. 1 (B)]. The size of these forms depends on temperature: the lower the temperature, the more dense is the net of frost

cracks. Polygons may be up to a dozen meters in diameter. When they are small, they are called fissure and mud polygons. Large forms are known as tundra polygons; A. L. Washburn (1956) groups them as "nonsorted polygons."

In summer, the cracks of the net are filled with water. When water is frozen, they form ice wedges (Fig. 3). Patterned ground of this sort is termed "ice-wedge polygons." Wedges can renew and expand sideways almost every year. Layers of ground adjoining active wedge walls are lifted. A classical description of ice wedges was provided by E. K. Leffingwell, an explorer of Alaska (1919).

Empty frost cracks may be filled with sand instead of ice, and then sand wedges, analogous to ice wedges, are developed. This happens particularly in winter. Ice-wedge polygons occur in the continental variety of periglacial climate in Alaska and Siberia ("Taimyr polygons"), while sand-

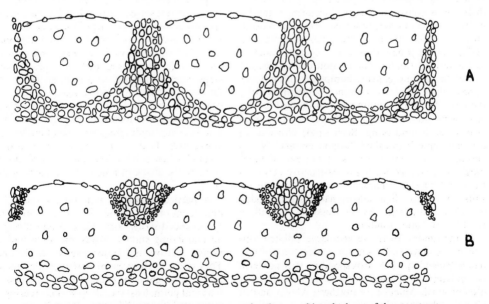

FIG. 2. Section of sorted polygons. Type A—stone borders reaching the base of the structures; type B—"floating" stone borders.

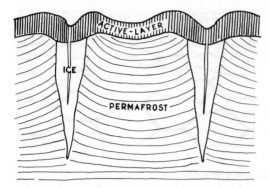

Fig. 3. Ice wedges and related structures of lateral pressure.

wedge polygons are very common in Antarctica.

A peculiar type of patterned ground is formed in fine materials (clay, loam) when they are covered with vegetation. These forms have been generally described as "nonsorted" (circles, polygons, nets) in the Washburn classification. A corresponding Russian term is *bugors*, and an Icelandic one, *thufur*, is also current. They refer to earth hummocks, either single or in groups, largely covered with vegetation. For the most part, vegetation fills in the troughs separating the hummocks. Their height usually ranges from 10–70 cm or so. Siberian bugors may be as high as 1.5 meters. On the other hand, typical forms of northwest Alaska, known as "tussock rings," are no higher than 7.5–15 cm.

These vegetated periglacial forms are characterized by the presence of peat or ice lenses inside the hummocks. Peat may also fill in the troughs in between the hummocks ("peat rings"). In general, these forms constitute a typical element of tundra microrelief. As opposed to sorted forms which occur on bare surfaces, the nonsorted ones are developed owing to frost penetration under vegetation and/or turf mantle of tundra. The tension due to freezing makes the mantle convex, humps and hummocks appear, their regular occurrence being marked by the term "cemetery hummocks." If the turf mantle is broken, the nearly liquid, clayey interior mass erupts like a mudspring. Such single effusions of clay are sometimes called "tundra craters." When vegetation covering the tops of the net of hummocks is destroyed (owing to destructive action of frost and wind), a characteristic phenemonon results—a mesh of light clayey patches surrounded by turf, which is called by the Russians "medallion tundra" or "spot tundra."

In the tundra, there are also large isolated hills which are universally known under the Eskimo name "*pingo*" (q.v.). A corresponding Russian term is "bulgunyak." Pingos occur in continental tundras of north America, in northern Alaska and in Canada; they are also quite common in northern Siberia. They range from a few to a dozen meters

in height; the highest pingo in northeast Alaska is over 100 meters high. Pingos are developed due to hydrostatic pressure in permafrost. As the water comes up, pure ice is formed inside pingos and makes the ground surface convex. The structures have much in common with forms termed hydrolaccoliths. Although pingos may be associated with patterned ground, they are commonly regarded as distinct from it.

Forms of patterned ground discussed so far are, as a rule, developed on horizontal, flat surfaces. Surface gradient provides opportunities for modification of these forms. It has been found that at a gradient of 2° or higher, the microrelief of periglacial slopes develops in a specific way. There appear longitudinal downslope stripes, as well as terraces and steps transverse to the slopes. Such a surface morphology is an effect of the process described as "*solifluction*" (q.v.) or "*congelifluction*". The process involves a two-fold movement of earth masses: (a) due to the action of freezing and thawing, separate particles are displaced down the slope surface; (b) soil saturated with water (the substratum being impervious permafrost) slips down under gravity especially in spring when snow is melting or in summer after rainfall.

The action of solifluction is especially evident in elongate soil strips, separated from each other by parallel lines of stones and debris, which are known as "sorted stripes" (A. L. Washburn), "stone stripes" or "striped soil." There is no question but that they are related to sorted circles and polygons. Sorting may accompany solifluction movement or else precede it.

The action of solifluction is also apparent in slope terraces and steps. These may contain either sorted or nonsorted material. With the former, on the slopes there appear steps made of coarse stones, not infrequently resembling garlands ("stone garlands"). Nonsorted material may form similar terraces, since vegetation, turf, and peat brace the steps. Such forms are, as a rule, an effect of solifluction on tundra slopes covered with compact vegetation; as the soil mass is being displaced downslope, under its mantle of vegetation, the surface becomes undulating with resulting terracelike convexities. Both striped and terrace forms are created when solifluction masses slide down the slope in the shape of long earth tongues or muddy rills.

A particular type of patterned ground, largely dependent on the action of frost, is represented by the so-called string bogs. These are peat bogs with an undulating surface. Folds and steps with intervening furrows are transverse to the inclination. They occur in the zone of boreal coniferous forests and are thought to be connected with permafrost or seasonal permafrost (i.e., deep winter freezing of the ground). Either solifluction downslope movement of earth masses or their cracking due to thawing of permafrost may be responsible for formation of this kind of peat-bog surface. Its dry ridges, alternating with furrows full of stagnant water, create contrasting ecological conditions. They are thus overgrown with diverse plant communities, which make the difference between particular peat-bog forms still more outstanding.

String bogs and similar phenomena are forms of the so-called thermal degradation of permafrost. The latter usually contains veins and lenses of pure ground ice. As the climate warms up and permafrost declines, the surface of the ground becomes rough, the ups and downs being an effect of melting of ground ice. The phenomena of this type are termed "thermokarst". Sometimes it is difficult to distinguish "live" forms of patterned ground from thermokarst examples.

Patterned ground forms are the typical microrelief of the periglacial landscape. They also existed in the periphery of the ancient ice caps which covered vast areas of Europe and North America during the cold stages of the Pleistocene. The evidence of these ancient forms is still preserved today in some characteristic fossil structures in sediments, such as involutions or crenulations of sandy layers, wedges and solifluction structures.

ALFRED JAHN

References

Embleton, C. and King, C. A. M., 1968, "Glacial and Periglacial Geomorphology," London, E. Arnold Ltd., 608pp.

Högbom, B., 1914, "Über die geologische Bedeutung des Frostes," *Upsala Univ. Geol. Inst. Bull.*, **12**, 257–389.

Leffingwell, E. de K., 1919, "The Canning River Region, Northern Alaska," *U.S. Geol. Surv. Profess. Paper* **109**, 251pp.

*Troll, C., 1944, "Strukturböden, Solifluktion und Frost-Klimate der Erde," *Geol. Rundschau*, **34**, 545–694.

*Washburn, A. L., 1956, "Classification of patterned ground and review of suggested origins," *Geol. Soc. Am. Bull.*, **67**, 823–866.

Thornbury, W. D., 1954, "Principles of Geomorphology," New York, John Wiley & Sons, 618pp.

*Additional bibliographic references may be found in this work.

Cross-references: *Frost Action*; *Periglacial Landscape*; *Permafrost*; *Pingo*; *Solifluction*; *Suffosion and Tundra Craters*; *Thermokarst*; *Tundra Landscape*.

PEDESTAL ROCKS—*See* DEFLATION; EARTH PILLARS; EXUDATION

PEDIMENTS

In arid, and especially in semiarid, lands the transition between hill and plain tends generally to be more abrupt than in humid regions. The plains

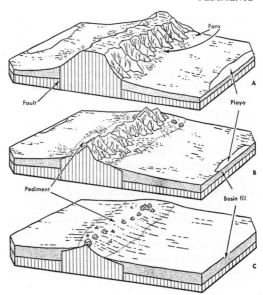

FIG. 1. Three stages in the sculptural evolution of a mountain range and two basins, originally created by faulting, in an arid climate (from Longwell and Flint, 1962). (By permission of John Wiley & Sons, N.Y.)

are but little dissected, gently sloping at angles between 1 and 7°, and smooth of surface. Lines of concentrated drainage are few in number. There may be a veneer of detritus overlying the bedrock, but where present, this cover is thin and the plains are considered essentially to be erosional bedrock features. Such plains, called *pediments*, are commonly faintly concave in longitudinal section, though rectilinearity is common and convexity is not unknown. The critical and abrupt transition between pediment and backing scarp is called the piedmont angle. In enclosed basins, pediments are blanketed in their lower sections by thick wedges of sediments that occupy the lower parts of such depressions, but where there is a more-or-less integrated drainage system, only a veneer of alluvium in the immediate vicinity of the stream channel covers the pediments. *Pediplains* are formed by the coalescence of numerous pediments.

Pediments were first described for the American southwest but have since been reported in many parts of the world. It is generally agreed that pediments are forms typical of arid and semiarid lands but a small number of workers, principally the South African L. C. King, consider that all plains molded by running water are of this type. It must also be noted that some investigators consider that not all plains of the desert and semi-desert regions are pediments. Many workers now consider that a complex of processes—weathering, rill wash, sheet wash and sheet flow—are responsible for the molding of pediments, which, it can be shown, erode regressively and gradually consume uplands.

The distinction between pediplains and pene-plains, between pediments and catenary valley-side-slopes, rests basically upon the nature of the junction between plain and backing upland. Other differences are of degree rather than type. The abruptness of transition between pediment and escarpment varies considerably from place to place. In some places the piedmont angle is so sharp that one can literally place a finger upon the angular contact. Some granite landscapes and semiarid tropical karsts display such junctions admirably. Elsewhere, and more generally, the junction is not as sharp as it appears from some little distance for there is very commonly in reality a gradual change of slope, a smooth concavity or steep curve. This is restricted to a relatively narrow zone, and the transition from plain to upland is in arid regions commonly more abrupt than in, say, humid temperature regions.

Several hypotheses have been advanced in explanation of the piedmont angle. Early workers in the American southwest considered that the sharp break of slope owed its origin to tectonism, that the angular junction is coincident with fault traces. However, in reality, the piedmont angle, even in faulted areas, is not coincident with fault planes; in any case, abrupt hill-plain junctions are known from many areas not subjected to faulting. Structure, through lithology, is however important, for escarpments capped by resistant strata tend to maintain very steep profiles and thus the transition to the plains below is necessarily quite abrupt. Others have sought an explanation of the piedmont angle in the behavior of streams leaving mountainous areas. Streams debouching from uplands deposit much of their solid load; in the piedmont zone, they are subject to autodiversion and the development of a distributary habit, but not to marked meandering as has been suggested. In the immediate vicinity of such distributary streams, undercutting of the scarp wall may well contribute to the development of an abrupt break of slope, but the piedmont angle occurs all along the mountain front in many instances and is not restricted to the vicinity of major stream outlets, so that this can be only a local and contributory factor.

L. C. King has argued that the different gradients of scarp and pediment are due to the prevalence of contrasted processes. He points out that on escarpments, turbulent flow, resulting in concentrated linear erosion, takes place; on smooth pediments, however, laminar flow occurs. The piedmont angle develops at the point of transition from one type of flow to the other. Though laminar flow is known in the laboratory, it is dubious whether it can occur to a significant extent on the surface of pediments which, though smooth in broad view, are in detail quite rough. In any case, even if it is consistent with the present situation on pediments, this explanation scarcely explains how the present morphology evolved.

As for the piedmont angle, this probably results from selective weathering and erosion. Many backing escarpments are maintained by a capping of resistant rock (either a resistant primary rock or a resistant product of weathering or erosion such as silcrete, laterite, kunkar or hamada), and this in itself must lead to a sharp scarp foot change of gradient. Further, in granite terrain, especially sharp breaks of slope have been developed at structural junctions, and particularly at the junction of coarsely and finely jointed areas, which are of strongly contrasted susceptibility to weathering and hence to erosion. Finally, it has lately been recognized that in arid and semiarid lands, marked differential weathering of lower hillslopes and the adjacent plain areas commonly occurs. This leads to strong erosion in this zone, to the regrading and steepening of escarpments, and hence to the development of a sharp break of slope at the hill-plain junction.

C. R. TWIDALE

References

Denny, C. S., 1967, "Fans and Pediments," *Am. J. Sci.*, **265**, 81–105.

Hadley, R. F., 1967, "Pediments and pediment-forming processes," *J. Geol. Ed.*, **15**(2), 83–89.

King, L. C., 1949, "The pediment landform: some current problems," *Geol. Mag.*, **86**, 245–250.

King, L. C., 1953, "Canons of landscape evolution," *Geol. Soc. Am. Bull.*, **64**, 721–752.

King, L. C., 1962, "Morphology of the Earth," Edinburgh, Oliver & Boyd, 699pp. (Second ed., 1967.)

Longwell, C. R. and Flint, R. F., 1962, "Introduction to Physical Geology," New York, John Wiley & Sons, 504pp.

McGee, W J, 1897, "Sheetflood erosion," *Geol. Soc. Am. Bull.*, **8**, 87–112.

Tator, B. A., 1952–3, "Pediment characteristics and terminology," *Assoc. Am. Geogr. Ann.*, **42**, 295–317; **43**, 37–53.

Cross-references: *Arid Cycle*; *Haldenhang*; *Panplanation*; *Sheet Erosion, Sheetwash, Rainwash, Sheetflood*; *Slopes*.

PEDIPLANATION

Pediplanation, the standard mode of cyclic landscape evolution by scarp retreat and pedimentation, is widely found in most parts of the world. The individual landforms developed under the cycle may differ considerably according to local types of bedrock and the manner in which geomorphic processes act upon the terrain, but the general operation of the pediplanation cycle is that it tends to reduce uplifted land, whatever its form, ultimately to a landscape of low relief through a series of intermediate stages during which the hillslopes retreat more or less parallel to themselves, leaving at

FIG. 1. Showing how, under pedimentation and the generation of scarps, local uplift beyond a "critical height" may produce apparently two surfaces in a single cycle of pedimentation graded to a single base level (from King, 1967). (By permission of Oliver & Boyd, Edinburgh.)

reduced level ever broadening pediments which reach from the foot of each hillslope to a nearby stream or river bed (Figs. 1 and 2).

Pediplanation operates to a general continental base level which, under the Davisian concept, is generally regarded as the hypothetical continuation of sea level beneath the land, but local base levels are also valid within the concept.

Broadly, the theory of pediplanation, which owes much to the vision of W. Penck (1953), comes into operation after the rivers and streams of an area have incised themselves following substantial tectonic uplift. The narrow valleys, in their early stages when the rivers are cutting down strongly, are primitively steep sided (steeper than the strength of the local earth materials may warrant). Rill and gully cutting, sheet wash, and mass movement by slide, slip and creep, act to reduce the declivity of these valley sides until an approximate balance is achieved between the production of land waste by weathering upon the slope and the quantity removed from the slope by water wash and mass movement to be carried away by the streams and

rivers. A graded hillslope of stable declivity then results, and reduction of slope steepness disappears from the pediplanation cycle until the final stages when, low relief only existing, it may be resumed once more.

As the hillslopes retreat parallel to themselves (a feature sometimes indicated by close agreement of hill declivities throughout an entire district), they reduce the areas of interfluves upon which relicts of the pre-uplift topography may remain perched even for long periods with little or no alteration, either as broad residual plateaus or as ridges with accordant smooth skylines (Fig. 3). Outliers of plateaus, perhaps only a few acres in extent, are sometimes found spectacularly scores of miles from main developments of cyclic plateaus; these serve to illustrate the former extent and uniformity of some of the older (especially early Cenozoic) surfaces of planation.

The manner in which hillslopes retreat is a matter for detailed study in the field, with due consideration for the several variables of bedrock type, rate of retreat, spacing of rivers and streams (texture of dissection) and the various geomorphic processes in superficial operation. Frequently the cutting of rill channels and gully heads is by far the most active process operating upon the steeper slopes and is the process primarily responsible for the retreat, especially upon hard rocks. Mass movement is proportionately more active upon weak rocks and where flat-lying sedimentary sequences provide overhanging scarp makers.

The phenomenon of parallel scarp retreat is, however, equally well displayed upon major cyclic continental scarps such as the Drakensberg (King, 1963) or in miniature upon the sides of gullies and dongas (Schumm, 1962). Evidently the relative strengths of bedrock and processes are comparable within the reliefs exhibited in the natural experiment.

The forms of individual hillslopes differ very much according to the nature of the bedrock: from the steep, bare rock faces of massive granite-gneiss bornhardts to low-angle ramps in materials such as marls, mudstones and friable sandstones that are too weak to maintain anything but gentle declivity. But always the steepest mid-to-upper section of the hillslope (scarp and debris slope) is that most actively in retreat.

As the steeper parts of the hillslope retreat, they

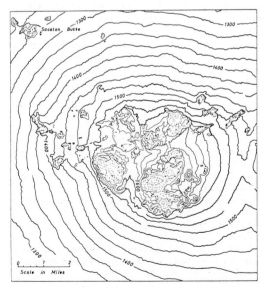

FIG. 2. Pediments and pediment passes in the Sacaton Mountains, Arizona (from King, 1967). (By permission of Oliver & Boyd, Edinburgh.)

FIG. 3. Older cyclic bevel being destroyed by scarp retreat with the formation of a newer pediplain, Odzi Valley, Southern Rhodesia (from King, 1967). (By permission of Oliver & Boyd, Edinburgh.)

leave at the base a relatively flat pediment (declivity $\frac{1}{2}$–7°) which extends as a sloping apron from the foot of the steeper hillslope elements to the neighboring streams. A longitudinal profile through the pediment from hillslope to stream is a concave hydraulic curve, showing plainly that the agent dominantly responsible for its fashioning is running water. Along the foot of the hillslope the inner edge of the pediment falls toward the points where small streams debouch from the hill country behind—a feature which distinguishes pediments from rock fans, with which they should not be confused.

Pediments are commonly veneered with rock waste or soil in transit from the steeper hillslope elements to the transporting streams that remove it entirely from the district. Beneath the waste mantle, the bedrock is often smoothly carved, showing that pediments are truly cutrock land features, but equally often the upper part of the bedrock may be weathered, showing that waste sometimes lies upon the pediment for considerable periods without disturbance. Occasionally a pediment or part of a pediment is devoid of a transported waste mantle, when the bedrock may be either fresh or weathered.

Pediments, though found in all parts of the world, are usually best developed in semiarid regions where rain falls as infrequent heavy thunderstorms. The amount of precipitation to be shed in a short interval of time is at a maximum, and the pediment, which permits broad sheet flow over most of its area, is the landform best calculated to achieve this. Broad, laminar sheet flow, nonerosive in quality, has actually been observed on pediments in Africa, as has deeper, highly erosive *sheetflood* in which turbulent linear flow in sheet form is dominant. Under extremely concentrated rainfall (cloudburst) measured in inches per hour, wave trains have been observed to develop upon the sheets of water, and these may have almost catastrophic erosive effect.

By these means, considerable modification of the pediment surface (or at least the waste mantle upon it) sometimes takes place in periods of time as short as a few hours or minutes, though otherwise the surface may persist without significant alteration for decades.

Minor channeling, seldom absent from pediments, is probably a response to linear erosion during periods of less intense rainfall. As with the steeper hillslopes above, close analogy subsists between broad, even miles-wide pediments of advanced cyclic landscapes and miniature pediments within such small-scale features as gullies (Schumm, 1962). This probably follows, as before, from relative comparisons between the strengths of the earth materials involved and the energies of the processes operating upon those materials.

At old age in the cycle, when virtually all steep-sided residuals have been eliminated under scarp retreat, the landscape consists far and wide of concave pediments—an actual or theoretical pediplain. But as the relief is low, for reasons connected with the "critical heights" of earth materials, scarp retreat fails and waste tends to collect in the landscape. This waste moves more and more by soil creep so that a measure of convexity may be introduced into some of the landforms, thus developing a morphological similarity with the Davisian peneplain concept, which however has an entirely different origin through a theory of downwearing only. It is likely, however, that if a true peneplain existed anywhere it was derived not through a vigorous geomorphic cycle of development, but with small gradations from a landscape already reduced to relatively low relief by other agencies.

L. C. KING

References

King, L. C., 1962, "The Morphology of the Earth," Edinburgh and London, Oliver & Boyd, 699pp. (Second ed., 1967.)

King, L. C., 1963, "South African Scenery," Third ed., Edinburgh, Oliver & Boyd, 308pp.

Mulcahy, M. J., 1966, "Peneplains and Pediments in Australia," *Australian J. Sci.*, **28**(7), 290–292.

Penck, W., 1953, "Morphological Analysis of Land Forms," London, Macmillan, 429pp.

Schumm, S. A., 1962, "Erosion on miniature pediments in Badlands National Monument, South Dakota," *Bull. Geol. Soc. Am.*, **73**, 719–724.

Cross-references: *Base Level; Cycles, Geomorphic; Escarpment; Rock Fan; Sheet Erosion, Sheetwash, Rainwash, Sheetflood; Slopes.*

PEMBINA—*See* **INCISED MEANDER**

PENEPLAIN

The term *peneplain*, almost a geographical plain, was coined by that great systematizer of geomorphology, W. M. Davis. He first employed the concept of the peneplain in 1889 but only gave it a clear definition in his paper on the "Geographical Cycle" (1895) where he wrote: "an almost featureless plain (a peneplain), showing little sympathy with structure, and controlled only by a close approach to base level, must characterize the penultimate stage of the uninterrupted cycle." He viewed it as the final stage of a fluvial erosion cycle. As Thornbury comments in his "Principles of Geomorphology" (1954), "the concept has had a rather controversial history which continues down to the present; probably more has been written pro and con regarding it than about any other geomorphic idea."

The idea of the peneplain was not original with Davis; he only invented the name; the concept itself came from the pioneer work of Powell and Dutton. Powell (1875) introduced the concept of *base-level* (q.v.) for the level below which dry lands cannot be eroded, an essential preliminary to the definition of the peneplain.

Dutton gave greater precision to the base-level idea and paved the way for Davis to take the next step when he wrote, "All regions are tending to base-levels of erosion, and if time be long enough, each region will, in its turn, approach nearer and nearer and at last sensibly reach it" (Dutton, 1882). This goal is the peneplain state.

Some confusion over the spelling of the term was created by Douglas Johnson who suggested that it should be *peneplane* (1916). This has received little support and should be dropped, principally because an essential part of the peneplain concept is that the morphometry of its surface is that of an undulating geographical plain with variations in height amounting frequently to two or three hundred feet and not that of a geometrical plane. However, the verb coined to describe the process of plain formation is spelt "peneplanation" rather than "peneplaination," since the process is one of planing, though not precisely as a carpenter's plane.

Davis described peneplains in two radically different situations. In the first, the peneplain is buried beneath later deposits and is, therefore, synonymous with the geological unconformity as seen, for instance, in the discordant junction between the Cambrian Tonto formation and the underlying Precambrian rocks in the walls of the Grand Canyon. He vigorously propounded the view that the erosion of the even surface across the lower strata, evident at the unconformity, was due to subaerial processes and not to the work of the sea in which the unconformable upper layers were deposited.

The second situation is found where the peneplain has been uplifted, perhaps warped, and then incised by rivers so that it appears in the landscape as an upland plain or plateau. Examples of such plateaus are legion, among the first described were the Rocky Mountain and the Schooley peneplains, the latter uplifted and tilted from west to east in the Pennsylvania and New Jersey Appalachians where it forms the remarkable ridge top surface beveling the structures of the Ridge and Valley province.

It is one of the criticisms frequently made of the peneplain concept, that its adherents cannot give examples which slope down towards the present base level. Their defense is that modern sea level has only been attained in the last 5,000 years and the time available has clearly been too short for peneplanation to occur. There are however extensive areas on weak rocks such as the Eocene clays of the London Basin and the Cretaceous clays of the Weald of southeastern England which have been reduced to the peneplain form during the past 1 million years.

The principal criticism leveled at the peneplain concept attempts not so much to prove that peneplains do not exist, but to seriously question their supposed mode of origin. Davis saw them as the end products of a cycle of erosion during which the land forms passed through youthful, mature and old-age stages. Eventually, during the latter, the peneplain state was attained, largely by the gradual flattening of slopes to produce a surface on which convex slopes dominated. Walter Penck (1927) postulated that what he called the "Endrumpf" was created by the backwearing of slopes, leaving behind concave waste slopes which coalesce to form a planation surface characterized not by convexity, but by concavity of slope. This view has been elaborated into the *pediplain hypothesis* by Lester C. King (1962), who envisages the creation of plateau surfaces of low relief, such as those in Africa, created by the headward retreat of scarps and scarp foot pediments.

Investigation has shown that such planation surfaces do not occur singly but are often arranged in tiers one above the other separated by scarps. This is the "Piedmonttreppen" form of Penck, which he took to be the normal expression of subaerial erosion on an expanding dome. Davis explained them in terms of periodic falls in base level induced by epeirogenic uplift of the land in a manner described by Suess (1904) or, as later became fashionable, by eustatic falls of sea level as championed by Baulig (1935). An alternative hypothesis envisages lateral erosion by rivers creating ever-widening and coalescing flood plains which collectively form a panplane. But this idea of Crickmay's has not proved widely acceptable (1937). Whatever the mechanism involved, the planation surfaces, be they peneplains or not, are often characterized by erosion residuals left standing above the surface. These are Davis' *Monadnocks* and Penck's *Inselberge*. They may be of two kinds, those which owe their eminence to superior rock resistance, the *Hardlinger* of the German school, and those which remain because they are in areas furthest removed from base level —the *Restlinger*.

Peneplains may be recognized from a combination of characteristics. In the first place, they truncate the geological strata which underly them. Surfaces coincident with structural plains may be peneplains or exhumed versions of peneplains, but they are not necessarily related in any way to contemporary base level. Peneplains occur on soft and resistant rocks alike, although if they are uplifted they will be most readily lowered on the weaker rocks first. This may produce a planation surface at a lower level on the weaker rocks which is not really a second distinct stage in peneplanation but only a lowered version of an originally more widespread surface. This may be the origin of the low Piedmont developed on limestones below the high Piedmont on crystalline rocks. It is the explanation of the Harrisburg peneplain offered by Ashley. Faults and folds may also be truncated, thus further substantiating the existence of the peneplain.

Most peneplains are today only represented by an accordance of summit flats, e.g., the Schooley peneplain of the Appalachians; uplift and dissection has destroyed the continuity of the surface form. The surviving fragments betray their erstwhile unity in their general accordance of summit level. Multiple planation surfaces, possibly peneplains, have been deduced from statistical analyses of the elevations of summits above sea level where they fall into well-defined altitudinal groupings. This technique has been criticized on the grounds that accordance of isolated summits may arise from other causes, e.g., the incidence of severe frost shattering above the tree line which will tend to reduce an initially irregular series of summits to a rough accordance of level. This is the *Gipfelfur* concept. By the same token, it will be difficult to recognize tilted peneplains when they have been dissected to the extent of becoming mere accordances of summit heights and when no extensive fragments of the surface remain.

Peneplains are also characterized by topographic breaks above and below them. Slopes significantly greater than those which characterize the peneplain itself rise above them in the form of monadnocks or a scarp which leads up to the next tread in a staircase of partial peneplains. Below the peneplain, more recent incision creates valleys whose upper edges are sharply distinguished from the even surface of the peneplain itself.

The prolonged period of weathering necessary to produce a peneplain should be indicated by the presence of a deep residual soil. Patchy remnants of such regoliths are in fact sometimes found. The clay with flints on the chalk plateau of southern England is in large measure such a peneplain deposit and comprises the insoluble residue of clay and flints from the chalk and the once overlying Eocene strata. In tropical climates with alternating dry and wet seasons, duricrusts are characteristic of peneplain surfaces. These carapaces of aluminous and ferruginous lateritic material on feldspathic rocks, siliceous crust upon argillaceous and arenaceous rocks, and calcareous and magnesian travertine and caliche on lime rich rocks are formed by the dry-season capillary movement of solutions formed in the wet seasons.

It was a corollary of Davis' views on the cycle of erosion and the peneplain that the drainage network gradually became, through the process of river capture, more and more adapted to the geological structure across which it flowed. In Davis' terms, the subsequent streams became dominant over the consequents. In theory, on the peneplain the streams should be entirely adapted to structure. It is not difficult to show that this is in fact not so because proximity to base level is a powerful agent preventing the capture of some consequent streams in spite of the structural advantages of a would-be capturing subsequent river. Nevertheless, a high degree of adaptation is a diagnostic characteristic of a peneplain.

It is not difficult to recognize planation surfaces, which may be peneplains, in the field, whether or not they are uplifted and dissected. Complications arise in tracing their extent which is best carried out, where there is more than one peneplain, by mapping each one independently, rather than by mapping the sequence of surfaces in one locality, then in a second, and afterwards trying to correlate the two.

E. H. Brown

References

Baulig, H., 1935, "The changing sea level," *Institute of British Geographers, Publ. No.* 3.

Crickmay, C. H., 1937, "The later stages of the cycle of erosion," *Geol. Mag.*, **70**, 337–47.

Davis, W. M., 1889, "The rivers and valleys of Pennsylvania," *National Geographic Magazine*, **1**, 81–110.

Davis. W. M., 1895, "The geographical cycle," *Geograph. J.*, **14**, 481–504.

Dutton, C. E., 1882, "Tertiary history of the Grand Cañon District," *U.S. Geol. Survey Mem.*, **2**, 76.

Johnson, D. W., 1916, "Plains, planes and peneplanes," *Geograph. Rev.*, **1**, 443–447.

King, L. C., 1962, "Morphology of the Earth," Edinburgh, Oliver & Boyd, 699pp. (Second ed., 1967.)

Penck, W., 1953, "Morphological Analysis of Land Forms," London, Macmillan & Co. (transl. by H. Czech and K. C. Boswell of 1924 German edition), 429pp.

Powell, J. W., 1875, "Exploration of the Colorado River of the West and Its Tributaries," Washington, 291pp.

Suess, E., 1904–24, "The Face of the Earth," Oxford, Clarendon Press, 5 vols.

Thornbury, W. D., 1954, "Principles of Geomorphology," p. 177, New York, John Wiley & Son.

Cross-references: *Base Level*; *Corrasion*; *Cycles, Geomorphic*; *Gipfelflur*; *Monadnock*; *Pediplanation*; *Slopes*; *Treppen Concept*.

PEPINO HILLS—*See* CONE KARST (PEPINO HILLS)

PERCHED BLOCK, BOULDER

Following an old reference (Campbell, 1865, Vol. 2, p. 9), "Perched blocks are wandering blocks, placed upon hilltops or hill-shoulders, or balanced one upon another, or on 'tors' and ridges, on points where they must have been gently placed by something strong enough to lift them, and carry and lay them down."

It is often assumed that the perched block is exclusively glacial, i.e., an *erratic* (q.v.), but many genetic types are known:

(1) *Glacial Erratic:* This is generally identifiable by its characteristic striations and by its exotic (nonlocal) lithology. Some erratics are local, but others, often randomly distributed along with the local ones, evidently have traveled great distances. Erratics of over 10,000 tons are known (Flint, 1957).

(2) *Differentially Weathered Erratics:* These are equally derived by glacial transport, but they were originally scattered within a till, esker or kame deposit, which has subsequently been removed by erosion, leaving the perched blocks as a "lag deposit." They may occupy the tops of *earth pillars* or *pyramids* (q.v.) as "pedestal rocks" (Bradley, 1940).

(3) *Landslip Blocks:* These may be transported

FIG. 2. Perched block of Bluff Sandstone (Upper Jurassic) resting on Somerville Formation, due to slumping, followed by slope retreat on the Dakota Rim, San Juan Valley, Utah. (Photo: R. W. Fairbridge)

by massive landslips or mudflows and later may be isolated by differential erosion, a removal of the fine material in which they were embedded. A more or less local origin is always observed.

(4) *Exotic Blocks:* These are transported by tectonic means, either as parts of, or within, a nappe

FIG. 1. Perched boulders of glacial origin (erratics), lying on a rock pavement, in the "Glacier Garden," Lucerne, Switzerland. Note the lunate scars and small moulin (pothole, left).

FIG. 3. Perched boulders of granite forming desert tors at Yellowdine, Western Australia. Note development of silicified crust on top and exudation features of "tafoni" type below. (Photo: R. W. Fairbridge)

FIG. 4. Perched block in granite tor, modified by frost splitting, on Mount Kosciusko, N.S.W., Australia. (Photo courtesy N.S.W. Government.)

subaerially or in a submarine setting (as in the *Wildflysch* of Alpine tectonics). By differential erosion, the perched block is left in an anomalous position. Its source may be traceable hundreds of kilometers, e.g., the exotic blocks of Mala Johar, in the Himalayas.

(5) *Tors:* A tor is a typical product of granite weathering (see *Exfoliation*, and *Spheroidal Weathering*) initially in a deep, subtropical weathering profile, i.e., chemical weathering, exposed later to mechanical erosion, slope wash, eolian action, and stripped of its enclosing regolith (Fig. 3). Thermal

FIG. 5. The rocking stone of Tandil (near Buenos Aires, Argentina), a weathered granite boulder, showing subtropical inheritance (modified after a sketch by R. Kettner, from photo by J. Walther).

FIG. 6. A rocking stone in the granite tors of Dartmoor, England. (Photo: C. R. Twidale.)

and frost effects (see Fig. 4) may further modify the blocks, eventually leaving some perched or otherwise in anomalous positions. A special type is the *rocking stone* or *balanced rock* (German, *Wackelstein*) in which the stone is in an unstable position; often of considerable size, up to several tons in weight, it may sometimes be rocked by a touch of the hand (see Fig. 91 in Walther, 1924, of one at Tandil, near Buenos Aires). Rocking stones are also known as "logan stones", "logging stones" or "cheesewrings" in the tors of Devon and Cornwall in southwestern England.

Almost any geomorphic or structural feature in an anomalous position may be described as *perched;* thus, a syncline in an inverted relief is a *perched syncline;* a hydrologic example is a *perched water table*, due to accident of dip, faulting or porosity; a *perched spring* may emerge from it; a *perched sinkhole plain* is one above the usual level of surface karst solution features. A *perched dune* is one related to a former sea or lake level, now no longer active.

RHODES W. FAIRBRIDGE

References

Bradley, W. H., 1940, "Pediments and pedestals in miniature," *J. Geomorphol.,* **3,** 244–255.

Campbell, J. F., 1865, "Frost and Fire," 2 vols.

Flint, R. F., 1957, "Glacial and Pleistocene Geology," New York, J. Wiley & Sons, 553pp.

Matthes, F. E., 1930, "Geologic history of Yosemite Valley," *U.S. Geol. Surv., Profess. Paper* **160.**

Meinzer, O. E., 1923, "Outline of ground-water hydrology," *U.S. Geol. Surv., Water Supply Paper* **494.**

Veatch, A. C., 1906, "Fluctuations of the water level in wells, Long Island," *U.S. Geol. Surv., Water Supply Paper* **155.**

Walther, J., 1924, "Das Gesetz der Wüstenbildung," Fourth ed., Leipzig, Quelle and Meyer, 421pp.

Cross-references: *Earth Pillars; Erratic Block; Exfoliation; Spheroidal Weathering; Striae, Striated Pavement; Tafoni; Tor.*

PERIGLACIAL EOLIAN EFFECTS

These consist primarily of *sand dunes* and *loess* as accumulation land forms, while *corrasion* and *deflation* provide erosional forms (see individual entries for specific attributes). This article will consider the "where" and the "why" of periglacial eolian phenomena.

Since early in the last century there has been a tendency among ice age specialists to correlate glaciation with "pluvial" conditions, i.e., stages of heavy rains, on the presumption that increased precipitation in cold areas was necessary to produce glacial expansion. Thanks to the work of Ahlmann and others, it is now known that longer cold seasons (or conversely shorter melt seasons) are required to cause general ice accumulation, the precipitation values having only local significance. On the other hand, the continental glacierization of North America and northern Europe caused a southward displacement of the westerly wind belts that did lead to some increase in rainfall in parts of the central and southern Rocky Mountains and the Mediterranean. This was true probably just at the beginning and end of certain stages of each glacial oscillation. At the cold maxima, the lowering of world ocean water temperatures resulted in such a severe drop in evaporation that arid conditions were introduced over the periglacial regions, as well as almost everywhere else (see *Quaternary Period; Terraces; Morphogenetic Regions; Tropical Weathering and Relief*).

Evidence of widespread arid conditions around the borders of the Pleistocene continental ice sheets can be independently established without using the circular argument that dunes or loess are the proof. There is paleontological and sedimentological evidence, as well as meteorological theory. This "outside" evidence is needed because dunes by themselves do not prove aridity. There are active coastal dunes today in regions of heavy tropical rainfall, as in parts of Queensland (Bird, 1965; Jennings, 1965) and in southern Brazil. Coastal dunes form today in Oregon, Washington and Alaska in cool humid climates, and likewise on the shores of Lake Michigan, Cape Cod, Sable Island and elsewhere on the east coast of North America. They are well known in the Moray Firth (Steers, 1964) in Scotland, in the province of Jutland in Denmark and in many other coastal sites. On the upper Mississippi, Cooper (1935, p. 108) showed their relation to river-borne sands especially where stream entrenchment locally lowered the water table.

The above data beg the question, however, of widespread interior dunes that are now no longer active, and which are stratigraphically tied to periglacial sedimentary sequences (in many cases now controlled further by C^{14} dating). There are two fundamental criteria for inland dune development: (a) *arid or semiarid climates* or at least extended dry seasons; (b) *a vast supply of sand.*

Both these conditions are met on certain beaches, where onshore winds, favorable currents, loose uncemented country "rock" and other factors combine to supply a large and continuing source of clastic debris. The porosity of sands is such that a few weeks of dry weather may be enough to produce the necessary "arid" condition. For interior regions, these conditions are not so readily established. Country rocks are not frequently found in an uncemented condition. Rivers may build temporary sand banks and dissection can lower the water table, but the alluvium is protected by vegetation unless broken up by man-generated disturbances such as overgrazing.

The special condition that glaciation produces is the development of enormous outwash plains ("sandur") radiating from glacier snouts. Here is met the requirement of a *continuing* supply of immense sources of uncemented clastic material. In humid areas today, these sandur plains quickly become vegetated, so that if we find them generating extensive interior dune fields in the Pleistocene, it is evidence of aridity. Once a dune area is established, however, its very porosity and mobility are factors that maintain it, even though rainfall may rise to 300–500 mm. Mobility, in particular, operates as a "feedback" mechanism since it retards soil and humus accumulation and greatly hinders root development.

With fine-grained silts and clay-sized particles, the eolian processes are not restricted to saltation, and turbulent suspension takes over. The "fallout" of these finer grain sizes is *loess*. There is little doubt that the source areas of loess are the outwash plains, but the geographic separation of the loess and the suspected source has posed some problems. Also, the climate and environment of the accumulation area are still subjects of some controversy. In Europe, it has long been recognized that the loess is commonly associated with prairie-type organisms such as rodents and snails (which crawl only during the brief grass-growing season), and it is usual to equate it with a steppe environment (Penck, 1936). [In and below the chernozems (black, steppe soils) that are often found in loess profiles, there are usually numerous *crotovinas*, or soil-filled burrows (Russian for "mole holes").] There are other loess deposits that get trapped in pockets in hilly country or carried down by streams, so that today there are several clearly recognizable loess varieties (Pécsi, 1964). Extensive river-borne loess deposits are found in the valleys of the Mississippi, the Danube, the Dnieper, the Don and the Huang-Ho (Yellow River). Much purely eolian loess is found in quite humid regions today, such as New Jersey, Long Island, New England (Flint, 1933; Smith and Fraser, 1935) and western France (Brittany).

The thick accumulations of loess in Brittany are strong evidence for glacial anticyclonic winds (from the northeast), because there were certainly no source areas to the west, the direction of the prevailing winds today. Such winds would certainly be dry winds, lacking sources of moisture over the cold ice sheets or continental interiors. The same argument was applied to the loess of northern China (Movius, 1944), where the present monsoon climate is far too moist to permit continued dust transport.

Thanks to its paleoclimatic significance, to its contained fauna, and its relationships to fluvial terraces (see *Terraces, Fluvial—Environmental Controls*), the loess provides one of the best ways of working out a climatic/stratigraphic continental history for the periglacial regions. The INQUA (*International Union for Quaternary Research*) accordingly has a Subcommission on Loess Stratigraphy in Europe (chairman: J. Fink) for its detailed study.

Ventifacts, Corrasion and Deflation

Wherever loess or dunes overlie moraines or till sheets there is frequently evidence of deflation prior to the eolian accumulation; i.e., the finer materials of the till were removed, leaving a *pavement* or *lag gravel* of pebbles and boulders. Both in Central Europe and in North America, these are frequently sculptured into elegant *ventifacts*, *dreikanters* and so on (Bryan, 1931; Poser, 1948). The writer has noticed that such pebbles are often veneered by a ferruginous *patina* known as *desert varnish* (q.v.), a product of dew associated only with climates of extreme aridity (precipitation often less than 50 mm). The widespread discovery of such ventifacts, which commonly form today only in the Sahara and other "total" deserts, is clinching evidence of ice age aridity in periglacial regions.

Hard rock outcrops marked by sand blasting (*corrasion*, q.v.) are best preserved in arid country (Bryan and Albritton, 1942). They are less commonly observed in periglacial regions because under present humid conditions the rock surfaces fret away and the distinctive eolian groovings are usually lost. However, on certain rocks (e.g., the Precambrian granites in Wyoming, silicified quartzites in France and so on), very distinctive surfaces are still well preserved. Again, these are only to be seen actively forming today in such places as the Sahara and Arabia.

Numerous hollows or small closed basins observed in the western plains of the United States, as far south as Texas, are attributed to *deflation*. Just as with the accumulation forms, there are two basic criteria for deflation: dry climates and loose materials. To this one may add that very high katabatic winds could be expected in the foothills of the Rocky Mountains and the high plains during cold epochs because of very great thermal and pressure contrasts. In North Africa the *shott* depressions of Tunis and Algeria are caused by deflation according to Gautier (1953), scoured out by similar winds coming down from the Atlas Mountains. The

enormous Qattara depression of Egypt probably represents an old deltaic fan of the Nile, that was excavated by deflation, for despite extended surveys (mainly by the oil geologists) no tectonic control could be established. Deflation hollows inherited from glacial times are also widespread over the drier parts of South Africa, Australia and central Asia.

Sedimentological Evidence

Close examination of thousands of sand samples by sedimentary petrographic methods (*granulometry*) enabled Cailleux (1942; see also review by Wright, 1946) to establish that well-sorted, frosted grains of distinctly eolian characteristics may be recognized in many periglacial regions. Indeed it was his university thesis that played an important role in proving periglacial aridity over large parts of western Europe, in some cases a thousand kilometers or more from the continental ice fronts. While certain other conditions (soil acids, for example) may lead to a pseudo-frosting effect, absolute confirmation of eolian frosting can now be achieved by electron microscopy (the work of Krinsley; see *Texture—Sand Surfaces*, Vol. VI).

Dune Orientation

Some confusion has been caused in the past because the periglacial dunes did not always have the orientation that one might expect from present-day wind roses. The interpretation of even modern dune forms has been controversial until quite recently (Smith, 1949; McKee, 1966). Air photography and wind analyses, followed up by minute sectioning of dunes, have combined to disclose the principal characteristics. Basically there are several varieties:

(a) Parabolic or "blow-out" dunes, of varying form, lunate, boomerang and hairpin, singly or in multiples, but always U-shaped in the direction of the wind;

(b) Transverse or "megaripple" dunes, which are low ridges normal to the prevailing direction, often crowned by transitions into (a) or (c);

(c) Barchan or crescentic dunes, oriented with the "horns" downwind;

(d) Longitudinal or "seif" dunes, oriented parallel to the wind direction;

(e) Pyramidal dunes, without permanent orientation, and only found in regions of alternating winds, as in the "Sand Sea" dune mountains of the Rhub al Khali in Saudi Arabia.

The dune forms are largely related to the shape of the underlying ground, the quantity of sand available and the wind velocity and stability. Parabolic dunes are clearly associated with line sources, such as beaches and river banks, and vegetation helps to separate them; they may pass distally into seif dunes. Barkhans require a flat floor, e.g., playa lake bottoms and only modest sand supplies. With greater supplies they join together in transverse megaripples. The latter pass abruptly into seif dunes at a critical point, the meaning of which is not clear; arguments for a critical velocity factor or an inheritance factor (from ancient transverse dunes) have not been satisfactorily established. Indeed, the seif dunes are by far the most widespread in the great deserts, always exactly parallel to the prevailing wind.

"Fossil" Dunes and Eolianites

The best-known fossil dunes are perhaps the coastal ones that are frequently composed of $CaCO_3$ sands (in whole or in part $CaCO_3$, up to about 30% being effective), whose composition leads to cementation into relatively stable rocks. They have been well described from Bermuda (Sayles, 1931; Bretz, 1960), from the Bahamas, Hawaii, the Canary Islands, Morocco, Egypt, Lebanon, southern Arabia, India, South Africa and Australia (Fairbridge and Teichert, 1953). In many areas, they form extensive off-shore reefs today and hence must have been formed during cold, low sea level periods. The exposure of the bare sandy continental shelf to wind would be an important factor. Some of these eolianites are found reposing on high interglacial raised beaches, so that an exclusively glacial stage origin should not be assumed. Merely a brief dry episode, when sea level dropped a little, would be sufficient. This same principle may be observed today among Holocene coastal dunes on the coast of humid tropical Brazil; wherever beach ridge building was interrupted by a temporary drop of sea level (say, 2–3 meters), a wide foreshore was exposed long enough to permit a brief period of parabolic dune building, before "fixing" by the encroaching jungle.

Interior dunes have been well studied across the plains of northern Europe (Keilhack, 1918; Högbom, 1923; Dechend, 1937; Allier, 1966) and across the great plains areas of Nebraska and adjacent states (Smith, 1965), and radiocarbon dates confirm several episodes of dune building during the Wisconsin and a brief revival in the Holocene. Interdune soils, alluvium or peat swamps with fossils and datable artifacts provided a fairly extensive chronology even before the advent of C^{14} dating. Most of the dune building so-dated is late glacial or early postglacial (17,000–9000 B.P.), thus corresponding with times of maximum exposure of outwash sands. Interfingering with the rising eustatic sea levels provided Högbom (1923) with a reliable relationship to the deglaciation chronology.

Wind Directions

In northern Europe, Högbom showed that the Fennoscandian dunes formed during deglaciation about 10,000 B.P. reflected the glacial anticyclonic (high) pressure cell over the still-extensive continental ice (as well as the katabatic effect) with outward-blowing winds. Studies of the widespread German and Polish dunes, which are extremely numerous (Romer, Louis, Malkowski, Lehmann, Solger, Tutkowski; see Kádár, 1938; Woldstedt, 1965), suggest that in the ice maximum stage at the end of the Pleistocene, easterly (anticyclonic) winds were dominant. With progressive ice retreat northward across the Baltic, these were gradually replaced by westerlies: at first northwesterlies, then westerlies, then southwesterlies. Traces of the older dunes are often partially effaced by the younger so that interpretation can be very complicated. An ancient complex dune may thus have a layered structure, showing progressive shifts in wind systems. Generally speaking, dunes that are best preserved today are those of the *last* eolian activity, but their sorting may have begun much earlier. The dates of the dunes are therefore systematically younger than those of the loesses, although the ultimate source materials (in multiple cycles) were the same.

These eastern European dunes were mostly parabolic, at least during their late stages, being broken up by patches of vegetation and delimited by the major streams. Some of the earliest dunes appear to have been barkhans and seifs. Recent work in Poland (see review by Galon, 1959) shows that the maximum dune building occurred when these strong westerlies came in during the Boreal time (9800–7500 B.P.). With the warmer climate (about 2°C above today's mean) of the Atlantic stage (7500–5300 B.P.) came a rise of the groundwater table, a growth of vegetation between dunes and general stabilization. With the Subboreal (5300–2300 B.P.), the climate became drier, though still at times warmer than the present but with cooler oscillations, and there was minor renewal of dune building (southwesterly to southerly winds). The Subatlantic (2300–1000 B.P.) saw higher humidity again and renewed stabilization. Since then man-made interference has complicated the picture though at about 500 B.P. a drier phase helped deflation and about 250 B.P. a humid time helped stabilization. Reforestation is now artificially fixing them.

In the United States, the work of Melton (1940) showed three series of dunes in the southern High Plains: (1) recent and active, (2) older, stabilized dunes of somewhat differing wind pattern, and (3) oldest, with wind direction 90° from present. In northeastern Arizona, Hack (1941) mapped now-vegetated dunes, of parabolic, longitudinal (seif) and transverse forms. In Nebraska, by correlation with datable loesses, believed to have a common origin with the dunes, Smith (1965) again recognized three dune generations, (a) Early Wisconsin, (b) Late Wisconsin and (c) Mid-Holocene. The Geological Society of America has issued an excellent map: "Pleistocene eolian deposits of the United States," which illustrates the distribution of these varied deposits.

A historical analysis of the Old Silk Road through central Asia (the old trade route from Europe to

China) suggests that when sea level is believed to have been low, glaciers were more extensive in the Tarim Basin, the snow line dropped, springs were fed, and the caravan route was open (Hoyanagi, 1965). This was the case in the early Han dynasty (206 B.C. to A.D. 8), when vigorous trade was maintained with Rome. With the rise of temperature and sea level during Roman times, there was glacier retreat, general desiccation, blocking of springs by blown sand and closing of certain routes (Chin dynasty, A.D. 265–420). Oscillations from then on seem to correspond roughly with the sea level record (taken to be a "tide gauge" reflecting solar radiation).

Volcanic Ash Showers

A less widespread, but still very helpful, eolian indicator is volcanic ash. Individual ash showers can frequently be dated, either stratigraphically or by absolute dating (mostly K/Ar). The science is known as *tephrochronology* (q.v., pr Vol. VII), the individual ash layers being called "tephra." In the organization of INQUA (see *International Organizations for Geomorphology*), there is a specific commission for tephrochronology (chairman: K. Kobayashi).

Numerous ash showers have thus been traced in the western parts of the United States, Japan, New Zealand and Iceland, as well as extensively in deep-sea cores (e.g., the "Worzel ash" layer in the eastern Pacific). Those of Iceland, during the historic period, are particularly interesting from the Holocene paleoclimatic viewpoint, because they help to establish the position of the Icelandic low and the Arctic front at various stages.

Tropical Dunes

While not strictly periglacial in geographic distribution, immense dune developments occurred in glacial times in Africa, Australia, India and, to a smaller extent, in South America. In Africa, the cold period desiccations were particularly impressive, dunes spreading southward from the Sahara into the now-equatorial forest regions of West Africa, and dunes from Kalahari extending northward right into the Congo basin (Fairbridge, 1964). Both radiocarbon dating and the evidence of dunes passing out onto the continental shelf below present sea level prove the glacial ages of the great dune development. While there are certainly plenty of deserts left, more than 50% of the glacial stage dunes are now stabilized and overgrown with trees (see *Landscape Types—Genetic*).

An important fact to recognize is that even in the mid-tropics the cold-phase snow line was lowered by several hundred meters, in places even more than 1000 meters, thereby introducing humid and periglacial mountain climate conditions to intermediate elevations in regions that are now mild or tropical. Thus in the mountains of the central Sahara (Hoggar, Tibesti, etc.) there were winter rains with a mild Mediterranean flora at midglacials, while the plains below were under full desert (Rognon, 1967). In contrast, the interglacials brought in monsoon rains from the south at all elevations. In the higher slopes and interior basins of the Andes, East Africa, the Himalayas and New Guinea, similar anomalies are observed: In each case the lowered snow line brought increased rains, and in many areas, freeze and thaw conditions appropriate to periglacial latitudes.

RHODES W. FAIRBRIDGE

References

Allier, C., 1966, "Formation et évolution d'une dune continentale en forêt de Fontainebleau," *Rev. Geomorph. Dyn.*, **16**, 101–113.

Bird, E. C. F., 1965, "The formation of coastal dunes in the humid tropics: Some evidence from North Queensland," *Australian, J. Sci.*, **27**(9), 258–259.

Bretz, J Harlan, 1960, "Bermuda: a partially drowned, late mature, Pleistocene karst," *Bull. Geol. Soc. Am.*, **71**, 1729–1754.

Bryan, Kirk, 1931, "Wind-worn stones or ventifacts—a discussion and bibliography," *Nat. Res. Council Rept. and Circ.* No. 98, Rept. Comm. Sedim., 29–50.

Bryan, Kirk, and Albritton, C. C., 1942, "Wind-polished rocks in the Trans-Pecos region, Texas and New Mexico," *Bull. Geol. Soc. Am.*, **53**, 1403–1416.

Büdel, J., 1963, "Die pliozänen und quartären Pluvialzeiten der Sahara," *Eiszeitalter Gegenwart*, **14**, 161–187.

Cailleux, André, 1942, "Les actions éoliennes périglaciaires en Europe," *Mém. Soc. Géol. France*, **46**, 176pp.

Cooper, W. S., 1935, "The history of the upper Mississippi River in late Wisconsin and postglacial time," *Minn. Geol. Surv. Bull.*, **26**, 72–108.

Dechend, Wilfried, 1937, "Untersuchung der Dünen der Frischen Nehrung mit sediment-petrographischen Methoden zur Unterstützung und Ergänzung der Dünenformen," *Phys.-ökom. Gesell. zu Königsberg, Schriften*, **69**, 131–174.

Dylik, J., 1951, "The loess-like formations and the wind-worn stones in Middle Poland," *Bull. Soc. Sci. et Lettre (Lódź)*, III, 3.

Embleton, C. and King, C. A. M., 1968, "Glacial and Periglacial Geomorphology," London, E. Arnold Ltd., 608pp.

Enquist, F., 1932, "The relation between dune form and wind direction," *Geol. Fören. Förhandl.*, **54**, 19–59.

Fairbridge, R. W., 1964, "African Ice-Age Aridity," in (Nairn, editor) "Problems of Palaeoclimatology," 356–360, New York, Interscience Publishers.

Fairbridge, R. W., and Teichert, C., 1953, "Soil horizons and marine bands in the coastal limestones of Western Australia," *J. Proc. Roy. Soc. N.S. Wales*, **86**, 68–87.

Flint, R. F., 1933, "Late-Pleistocene sequence in the Connecticut Valley," *Bull. Geol. Soc. Am.*, **44**, 965–988.

Flint, R. F., 1957, "Glacial and Pleistocene Geology," New York, John Wiley and Sons, 553pp.

Galon, R., 1959, "New investigations of inland dunes in Poland," *Przeglad Geogr.*, **31**, Supp., 93–110.

Gautier, M., 1953, "Les chotts, machines évaporatrices complexes," *35th Colloq. Intern. Centre Nat. Rech. Sci., Act éol. Phén. évap. et hydr. sup. dans rég. arides.*

Hack, J. T., 1941, "Dunes of the western Navajo Country," *Geogr. Rev.*, **31**, 240–263.

Högbom, Ivar, 1923, "Ancient inland dunes of northern and middle Europe," *Geogr. Annaler*, **5**, 113–242.

Hoyanagi, M., 1965, "Sand-buried ruins and shrinkage of rivers along the Old Silk Road region in the Tarim Basin," *J. Geogr.* (Tokyo Geogr. Soc.), **74**, 1–12, 55–75.

Jennings, J. N., 1965, "Further discussion of factors affecting coastal dune formation in the tropics," *Australian J. Sci.*, **28**(4), 166–167.

Kádár, L., 1938, "Die periglazialen Binnendünen des Norddeutschen und Polnischen Flachlandes," *Compt. Rend. Congr. Intern. Géogr.*, Amsterdam, **1**, 167–183.

Keilhack, K., 1918, "Die grossen Dünengebiete Norddeutschlands," *Deutsch. Geol. Gesell., Zeitschr.*, B *Monatsber.*, **69**, 2–19.

Lencewicz, S., 1922, "Les dunes continentales de la Pologne," *Rev. Polonaise Geogr.*, **2**, 12–59.

Maarleveld, G. V., 1960, "Wind directions and cover sands in the Netherlands," *Biul. Peryglac.*, **8**, 49–58.

McKee, E. D., 1966, "Structures of dunes at White Sands National Monument, New Mexico (and a comparison with structures of dunes from other selected areas)," *Sedimentology*, **7**(1), 1–69.

Melton, F. A., 1940, "A tentative classification of sand dunes; its application to dune history in the southern High Plains," *J. Geol.*, **48**, 113–174.

Movius, H. L., 1944, "Early man and Pleistocene stratigraphy in southern and eastern Asia," *Harvard Univ., Peabody Mus., Papers*, **19**, No. 3, 125pp.

Pécsi, M., 1964, "Ten Years of Physico-geographic Research in Hungary," Budapest, Akad. Kiadó, 132pp.

Penck, Albrecht, 1936, "Das Klima der Eiszeit," *Intern. Quartär-Konferenz*, 3d, Vienna, Verh., **1**, 1–14.

Poser, H., 1948, Äolische Ablagerungen und Klima des Spätglazial in Mittel und Westeuropa," *Naturwissenschaften*, **35**.

Rognon, P., 1967, "Climatic influences on the African Hoggar during the Quaternary, based on geomorphologic observations," *Ann. Assoc. Am. Geogr.*, **57**, 115–127.

Sayles, R. W., 1931, "Bermuda during the ice age," *Am. Acad. Arts and Sci., Proc.*, **66**, 381–467.

Smith, H. T. U., 1949, "Physical effects of Pleistocene climatic changes in non-glaciated areas: eolian phenomena, frost action, and stream terracing," *Bull. Geol. Soc. Am.*, **60**, 1485–1516.

Smith, H. T. U., 1965, "Dune morphology and chronology in central and western Nebraska," *J. Geol.*, **73**(4), 557–578.

Smith, H. T. U., and Fraser, H. J., 1935, "Loess in the vicinity of Boston, Massachusetts," *Am. J. Sci.*, **30**, 16–32.

Steers, J. A., 1964, "The Coastline of England and Wales," Second ed., Cambridge Univ. Press, 750pp.

Woldstedt, P., 1954/65, "Das Eiszeitalter," Stuttgart, F. Enke Verl., 3 vols.

Wright, H. E., 1946, "Sand grains and periglacial climate, a discussion," *J. Geol.*, **54**, 200–205.

Cross-references: *Corrasion; Deflation; Desert Varnish (Patina); Glaciation, Glacierization; Holocene; International Organizations for Geomorphology; Landscape Type, Genetic; Loess; Outwash Plain, Fan, Terrace, Sandur; Quaternary Period; Sand Dunes; Terraces—Fluvial; Tropical Weathering and Relief; Ventifacts; Wind Action.* Vol. VI: *Texture-Sand Surfaces.* pr Vol. VII: *Tephrochronology.*

PERIGLACIAL LANDSCAPES

The word "periglacial" was introduced in 1909 by W. Lozinski, the Polish geomorphologist, in order to identify a family of phenomena which are a result of frost-weathering and which have developed in belts of terrain marginal to the Quaternary ice sheets. However, the idea itself is much older. The nineteenth century geologists in Britain had already noticed that frequently the upper part of an outcrop was covered by a mixture of earth and debris, which they called the "head." (The term "head" is also often used in France, but not in North America.) Some geologists had arrived at the idea that the head was a product of a very cold but non-glacial climate. Nevertheless, it was the exploration of the polar areas at the beginning of the twentieth century which disclosed the existence of a special geomorphological milieu. The concept of *solifluction* was explained by Anderson in 1906 in the Falkland Islands, and that of frost-splitting developed by Högbom in Spitsbergen in 1910–11.

This concept of climatic geomorphology was accepted principally by Scandinavian, German and Slav scientists. In the Anglo-Saxon countries, the basic studies by Leffingwell and Eakin, in Alaska, were partly ignored under the influence of the Davisian "normal erosion," and the periglacial landscape was not accepted even as a "climatic accident." This underestimation had a corollary: only microforms were recognized and considered as a product of snow. This was the origin of the *nivation* concept. Actually, snow does not at all favor the development of polygons, ice wedges and so on. On the contrary, the nivation concept must be entirely reoriented.

The first studies of periglacial geomorphology developed from the present subpolar phenomena as well as from the remains of the cold Quaternary climates. As early as 1916, Salomon demonstrated the importance of these phenomena in the physiography of the ancient massifs of Germany. In many countries, such as the Netherlands, Belgium and France, the periglacial concept was introduced through the study of the Pleistocene. Since World War II, however, our knowledge of these phenomena has progressed very rapidly, both in polar countries and in the Quaternary of temperate countries. The International Geophysical Year has played an important role in this development.

Periglacial phenomena are a consequence of the modification of the properties of water when it passes from the liquid condition to the solid state and vice versa:

(a) H_2O is the only compound which has a greater volume when solid than when liquid. The increase is about 10%.

(b) Ice is characterized by a high expansion coefficient, nearly equal to that of steel.

(c) Crystallization of water in soils modifies the

ionic equilibrium and, as a consequence, alters the physical state, i.e. the strength of clays. When thawing, a deflocculation occurs (see *Clays, Strength of* and *Quickclays*, pr Vol. VI).

These properties of water in consequence lead to frost splitting, frost heaving and solifluction. Each of these is dependent on freeze-thaw cycles. We can thus give a dynamic definition of the periglacial concept. The periglacial morphogenetic milieu is that where the influence of freeze-thaw oscillations is predominant. In a glacial milieu, H_2O remains solid and the characteristic feature is the flow of ice. In milder regions, freeze-thaw oscillations become subordinate; this is the case in the forest zone of temperate middle latitudes. The periglacial milieu thus consists of that part of the cold zone where H_2O does not remain in the solid state (nonglacial) and of appropriate mountainous slopes, especially around mountain glaciers. Although the word "periglacial" has been criticized, it can be supported by some justification and, on the whole, is better than the other terms which have been proposed in its place. Furthermore, it is widely used.

The Periglacial Morphogenetic System

(a) **Frost splitting**. This results from the increase of volume of water when freezing. If the holes of the rock are full of water, a high pressure is developed which can break it. One may consider two cases: this water can either be in the joints and enlarge them, or in the pores of the rock, and then have the effect of crushing. In the first case, one may speak of *macrogelifraction*, which gives blocks. In the second, of *microgelifraction*, which results in smaller debris. The end-product of microgelifraction is silt, not clay; the latter is the result of chemical and biochemical processes, which are not intensive under cold climatic conditions.

Each rock has its own characteristic behavior under frost action, but in any case, frost is effective only when the rock is wet. Dry rocks are not affected by frost splitting. Melting snow, which slowly yields its water thus indirectly favors frost action. Lithological factors which are important under periglacial conditions are fissuring and porosity. When climate and slope are adequate, differential erosion results. Fissured rocks give talus slopes, common under cold climates and in mountains. More massive formations are carved into pinnacles or give scarps. Porous rocks are broken down into finer products, sandy or silty. In many cases, macrogelifraction and microgelifraction cooperate and this gives a mixture of blocks and silt ("head," "coombe rock").

(b) **Frost Heaving**. This is a result of volumetric changes in noncoherent rocks soaked with water under the influence of frost. In porous material, water freezing seems to be an osmotic phenomenon. When there are capillary properties, water migrates toward the freezing plane. However, in an heterogeneous soil, penetration of frost is always irregular. Freezing occurs at temperatures under 0°C in impervious clays. A greater amount of cooling is necessary where there is more water in the soil, as in silts. The combination of these various factors leads to the accumulation of ice in certain places, mainly where silt and sand are more abundant. In silty lenses, concentration of ice can be very much greater than the initial volume of the pore spaces (even 50% of total volume).

When freezing, an heterogeneous soil takes on a greater volume, but irregularly. Patterns are developed in the soil which mark the places not yet frozen. Heaving occurs at the surface. When the soil is thawing, a decrease in volume takes place, but it is too irregular. Thawing cannot be regular since the places with more ice need more calories and the conductivity of the soil is a function of its water content (water is a very poor conductor). Places which have been more intensively heaved are not necessarily more depressed on thawing. A rearrangement of the materials occurs in a characteristic style. The particles in the soil migrate quite far, even without slope. This is *geliturbation*, the displacement of soil particles under freezing and thawing. On slopes, of course, the gravity component interferes and geliturbation results in some downslope migration. This is called *gelifluction*, a variety of *solifluction*.

The effectiveness of geliturbation is a function of the grain size (granulometry) of parent rock (when noncoherent) or of the debris (gelifraction debris). The silty fraction is the most favorable, because its capillarity permits the better migration of water when freezing. In alluvial deposits, where silt lenses are interbedded with gravel, one can observe that it is always the silt lenses which have played the active role in the geliturbation patterns, and the gravel has played the passive one. Gravel layers are frequently disrupted and one can observe injections of silt to the gravel layers, etc. On the slopes, the effectiveness of gelifluction is a function of the silt content. The higher the porosity, the lower is the limiting value of the slope which can be so affected. In very silty debris, like that given by the chalk of Champaigne (France), solifluction slopes can be as low as 2–3%. This was enough to enable the slow migration of the sheet of debris under Quaternary periglacial conditions. On the other hand, coarse material without silty fraction gives talus slopes. Under certain climatic conditions, every mixture of coarse material and silty matrix can be affected by solifluction upon slopes which are above a certain threshold value. The debris undergoes gelifraction when transported down the slopes, but the transport may be very slow (a few centimeters per year), so that the proportion of silt frequently becomes higher downslope. This enables a reduction of the slope inclination in its lower section and gives concave profiles. A gradual reduction of the angle of slope is thus possible, but it is limited to a certain value under each climate. When the slope is slightly higher, a parallel recession of slopes occurs. This is frequently the case in talus slopes, where no gelifluction occurs at all.

Geliturbation also affects horizontal surfaces and plays a role in the formation of polygons and sorted soils (patterned ground). Stones are generally upheaved and have a tendency to concentrate at the surface. According to the effectiveness of rearrangement, this movement results in polygons, stone stripes, stone pavements, etc.

(c) Deflocculation of Clays. This is the result of ionic migration under the influence of freezing. Pure water freezes first, so that there is a concentration of the solution in the places which freeze last. A disequilibrium is produced, which breaks up the soil aggregates. When thawing, these are loose and the soil is without cohesion. A liquid mud is produced wherever the rainfall or meltwater is sufficient.

This lack of cohesion everywhere in frost-affected soils with a certain clay content has important consequences. These soils offer a very low resistance to rain splash, and erosion by runoff is easier. In permafrost regions, the persistence of an impermeable frozen layer prevents infiltration of water. Water content, mainly under the influence of concentration developed during freezing, or as a result of melting snow, is often sufficient to enable the soil to become liquid. According to the nature of the material, the water content and the thawing penetration, the results can be mudflows, solifluction lobes or coulees, a pellicular solifluction which co-operates with gelifluction.

(d) Diminution of Volume of Frozen Ground. This occurs mainly when the soil is rich in ice, resulting in contraction cracks, somewhat similar to the shrinking cracks developed under desiccation. They also have a polygonal pattern. They can be well observed in Antarctica, for instance, near McMurdo Sound. These cracks are some millimeters wide and situated from 2–3 meters up to 20–30 meters from one another. They are open during the freeze and may become filled by drifted snow or sand. They tend to form each year in the same place. When thawing occurs, water frequently gets into them and freezes along them, giving ice veins with a pellicular structure, as already explained by Leffingwell. These ice veins can become larger and larger and take on the shape of wedges, with the base of the triangle towards the surface. The higher the ice content of the ground, the greater the contraction is, and the denser the net can become. These ice wedges can occur only under severe climates, with permafrost.

The occurrence of ice in soils is varied. In clays and silts, small crystals form in the material, and when some segregation of ice occurs, ice bands develop up to several millimeters in thickness. In porous material, as in coarse sands, gravel, cobbles, water is always plentiful enough to form an ice conglomerate. Frequently, only a part of the pore spaces are filled with ice, and a good percentage of air remains in it. Naturally, if water penetrates into these spaces when the temperature is below zero, it also freezes, and with a sufficient development of ice, the layer becomes impervious. When this is not the case, the air can still circulate in the ground and the ice crystals are directly evaporated by sublimation. Under cold and dry climates, after a certain period of continuous freezing, a loosening of the ground surface can thus occur. It enables some wind deflation to take place. *Eolian action* is thus possible on frozen ground, but only with high porosity interstitial spaces. A mixture of silt, sand, and snow is frequently blown by the wind and gives *niveolian (niveo-eolian) deposits* (q.v. Vol. VI). When thawing, these are quite different from dunes: the material is not so well sorted, finer on the whole, and the topography is gently undulating.

One can classify ground ice under the following headings according to structure:

(a) *Discontinuous Ground Ice*. This occurs in macroporous material, with possibility of sublimation, when the snow cover is not too thick and the climate is dry enough.

(b) *Compact Ground Ice*. This is found without segregations, mostly in not too porous material or in porous material saturated with water.

(c) *Ice Segregations*. These occur where water is plentiful enough and where the ground is heterogeneous: ice veins, for instance, along joints or shrinkage cracks and ice lenses resulting from segregations.

(d) *Fossil Ice*. This consists of superficial ice buried under sediments, e.g., ponds of a flood plain which have been suddenly covered by high flood waters resulting from an ice break upstream, as in the Mackenzie Delta of Canada. Ice veins can be fossilized too, of course.

Periglacial Regimes

As to regime, one can distinguish the following:

(a) *Seasonal Frozen Soil*. An example of this is in central United States where freezing occurs every winter. The thickness of this seasonal frozen soil depends on temperatures and the amount of the snowfall. A snow cover is a very good protection against soil frost. This is the case in Quebec. If snow falls upon already frozen ground, there is only a hint of frost penetration. Two factors are of importance: depth of freezing and rate of thawing. The thaw period is one of great morphogenetic activity. A slow thawing upon a deep frozen layer, with melting snow or rain, is especially effective: solifluction and runoff are very active.

(b) *Diurnal freeze*. This is a consequence of diurnal oscillations in air temperature. It occurs under temperate conditions in middle latitudes in autumn and in spring and during all of the dry season in high tropical mountains. Under high latitudes, it is hindered by the length of the polar day. Generally, this frost is a result of the loss of heat by radiation, easier at high altitude or in dry air. With a wet soil, especially one with a certain percentage of clay, the air temperature may be below zero when the soil surface is still warm. Needle ice then forms. Soil aggregates and stones can be thus uplifted and fall aside when thawing. This gives a special type of geliturbation, needle-ice solifluction, which is very effective under certain climates. (e.g., in the tropical Andes). It can severely damage vegetation, especially pastures.

(c) *Perennial Frozen Ground* OR *Permafrost* (q.v.) When annual mean temperatures are negative (less than -2 or $-3°C$), in summer, the layer which thaws is thinner than the zone which freezes in winter. One can thus distinguish a thawed layer in summer, the *mollisoil*, and a perennially frozen layer, the *pergelisoil* or permafrost. The limit of the mollisoil-pergelisoil boundary varies from year to year according to the temperature oscillations. When refreezing occurs in the autumn, a layer of not yet frozen ground persists between the pergelisoil and the superficial regelisoil. It suffers severe compression when there is an increase of volume of the soil soaked with water. Severe disturbances can thus occur, which are known under the name of *congelistatic pressure* structures. Under continental climates, as in central Siberia, the mollisoil can be 3–5 meters thick, and forest can grow upon it. Under maritime climates, as in the Canadian Arctic Archipelago, it is only 0.2–0.5 meter thick and only a scanty vegetation can grow.

Climate

With regard to climate, great differences can be seen in the periglacial zone. These differences depend upon temperature and precipitation. Vegetation is more dependent upon summer temperatures: e.g., the northern limit of forest is $+10.5°C$ mean for the warmest month, when permafrost is involved. Precipitation is important, both with respect to total amount and to seasonal distribution. In certain parts of the periglacial zone, there are true arid regions, like McMurdo Sound in Antarctica or Peary Land in Northern Greenland. Northeast Iceland is also semiarid, although without permafrost. In these arid countries, there is very little solifluction. In the case of the McMurdo region, solifluction is decreased too by the insufficient thawing. Eolian processes are active.

Under humid climates, as in southwest Iceland, solifluction is very active, principally where vegetation cover is not too dense. Semihumid climates like northern Canada or Alaska, with continental influences, are covered by tundra. Tundra impedes deep thawing because it is a good insulation in summer, when unfrozen. On the contrary, it is not a good insulation in winter when frozen. Tundra is an obstacle to runoff and wind action. But, where winds are strong enough, they destroy the tundra through blizzard effects which kill off the plants when snow is blown. Under tundra, solifluction gives a chaotical microtopography which is characteristic. But soil movement is slow, impeded by the dense cover of low vegetation.

Each climatic province of the periglacial zone has its own morphogenetic conditions and its own types of microforms. A better knowledge of them is a sound basis for the reconstruction of the climates of non-glaciated areas during the cold periods of the Quaternary. In former years, special attention has been given to the soil polygons, but only large polygons with ice veins are really good indicators of a severe climate, because polygon formation, in this case, is due to contraction. Stone polygons with diameters from some 20 cm to 2 meters are not characteristic of a very cold climate. They form under a combination of a "polygonation" process, which is probably desiccation, either under the influence of drying or of ice segregation, of frost heave, which concentrates the stones on the surface, and of a migration of the stones from the center to the borders; when the center is upheaved, migration seems principally due to needle ice. Many factors interfere with these processes and compensations frequently occur between one and another. These small polygons are found under very different climates—tropical mountains, Iceland, Spitsbergen, Greenland, Alaska, the Alps, Morocco, etc.—and have no definite climatic significance within general periglacial conditions. Ice-vein polygons and congelistatic compression structures are typical of very severe climates. Important solifluction indicates humid climates, with or without permafrost. Eolian features are typical of dry climates; for instance, *loess* is formed at the present time in Alaska with silt blown from flood plains. Its accumulation needs a plant cover which can trap the silty particles. Cold steppe is the most favorable milieu for the thick accumulation of loess.

Between the cold periods of the Pleistocene and the present, some 30–40% of the emerged land area of the earth has been affected by periglacial processes. Knowledge of these phenomena is thus important both for the understanding of present conditions and for the reconstruction of Quaternary climates.

JEAN TRICART

References

Bryan, K., 1946, "Cryopedology—the study of frozen ground," *Am. J. Sci.*, **244**, 622–642.

Brunnschweiler, D., 1962, "The periglacial realm in North America during the Wisconsin glaciation," *Biul. Peryglac.*, **11**, 15–27.

Brunnschweiler, D., 1964, "Der pleistozäne Periglazialbereich in Nordamerika," *Z. Geomorphol.*, **82**(2), 223–231.

Cook, F. A., 1961, "Periglacial phenomena in Canada," *Proc. Intern. Symp. Arctic Geol. 1st* (1960), **2**, 768–780.

Dines, H. G., *et al.*, 1940, "The mapping of Head Deposits," *Geol. Mag.*, **77**, 198–226.

Embleton, C. and King, C. A. M., 1968, "Glacial and Periglacial Geomorphology," London, E. Arnold Ltd., 608pp.

Grave, N. A., 1959, "Main principles of permafrost in the far Northeastern Asia," *Izv. Akak., Nauk SSSR, Ser. Geog.*, **6**, 22–32.

Hamelin, L. E., 1961, "Périglaciaire du Canada: idées nouvelles et perspectives globales," *Cahiers Géog. Québec*, **10**, 141–204.

Matthes, F. E., 1900, "Glacial sculpture in the Bighorn Mountains, Wyoming," *U.S. Geol. Surv., 21st Ann. Rept.*, **2**, 183.

Peltier, L. C., 1950, "The geographical cycle in periglacial regions as it is related to climatic geomorphology," *Ann. Assoc. Am. Geogr.*, **40**, 214–236.

Schenk, E., 1955, "Die Mechanik der periglazialen Strukturböden," *Abhandl. Hess. Landesamtes Bodenforsch.* **12**, 92pp.

Smith, H. T. U., 1962, "Periglacial frost features and related phenomena in the United States," *Biul. Peryglac.*, **11**, 325–342.

Thompson, W. F., 1960, "The shape of New England mountains," *Appalachia*, 145–159, (December 1960).

Thompson, W. F., 1961, "The shape of New England mountains," *Appalachia*, 316–335 (June 1961); 458–478 (December 1961).

Tricart, J., 1963, "Géomorphologie des Régions Froides," Paris, P.U.F., Coll. Orbis, 289pp.

Tricart, J., 1964, "Le modelé périglaciaire. Traité de Géomorphologie," Vol. II, Paris, Sedes.

Cross-references: *Cryopedology*; *Frost Action*; *Frost Riving, etc.*; *Head*; *Loess*; *Nivation*; *Patterned Ground*; *Permafrost*; *Quaternary*; *Slopes*; *Solifluction*; *Thermokarst*. Vol. VI: *Clays*; *Niveo-eolian Sedimentation*; *Quick-clay*.

PERMAFROST*

Definition

Frozen ground can be divided into two general classes: that which thaws annually, "seasonal frost," and that which does not, "permafrost." This rough distinction serves as a precise definition of permafrost if "freezing" and "thawing" are considered to take place at 0°C. That is, permafrost is defined (Muller, 1947) as naturally occurring earth material whose temperature is below 0°C, winter and summer, irrespective of the state of any moisture that might be present. The lowering of the freezing point that can be caused by dissolved solids, intergranular surface forces, or hydrostatic pressure must be considered in many special applications. It is of great practical importance and is the subject of an extensive literature (see for example Tsytovich and Sumgin, 1959; Penner, 1965; Takagi, 1965).

* Publication authorized by the Director, U.S. Geological Survey.

In regions where permafrost exists, the surficial layer that thaws each summer is called the "active layer."

In this brief article, permafrost is discussed from the formal thermal point of view, because it is on the basis of temperature that permafrost is defined. For comprehensive articles on specialized areas of permafrost research and extensive bibliographies, the reader is referred to the Proceedings of the International Conference on Permafrost, 1963, Purdue University, National Academy of Sciences (1965).

Geothermal Conditions and the Formation of Permafrost

If a secular change in surface conditions causes the mean annual ground surface temperature to drop below 0°C, the depth of freezing in winter will exceed the depth of thawing in summer, and a layer of permafrost will grow downward from the base of the seasonal frost. It will thicken progressively with the passage of each succeeding winter. Were it not for the effect of heat escaping from the earth's interior, the permafrost would grow to great depths even when mean ground surface temperatures were only slightly below freezing. Heat flow from the earth's interior, however, normally results in a temperature increase on the order of 1°C for every 100–200 feet of depth. Thus, under a stable surface temperature, the lower limit of permafrost ultimately approaches an equilibrium depth at which the temperature increase due to internal earth heat just offsets the amount by which the freezing point exceeds the mean surface temperature. This is illustrated in Fig. 1(a) for an assumed thermal gradient of 1°C per 100 feet and a mean surface temperature of −10°C. However, heat conduction in earth materials is slow, and the equilibrium configuration might not be approached for thousands of years after a change in the surface regime. The transitional thermal conditions during the growth of permafrost are illustrated schematically in Fig. 2. The effects on permafrost temperature and depth caused by a subsequent increase in mean surface temperature are illustrated in Fig. 3. Surface temperature changes can be brought about by changes in climate or vegetation; by the shifting of shore lines of oceans, lakes or rivers; or by engineering modifications of the surface.

Whereas the position of the bottom of permafrost is determined by the mean surface temperature through processes that act over long periods of time, the position of the top of permafrost is controlled primarily by annual seasonal fluctuations of temperature about the mean. These fluctuations attenuate rapidly with depth. The top of permafrost is that depth at which the maximum annual temperature is 0°C [Fig. 1(b)], or roughly, the depth at which the amplitude of seasonal fluctuation equals the amount by which the freezing point exceeds the mean.

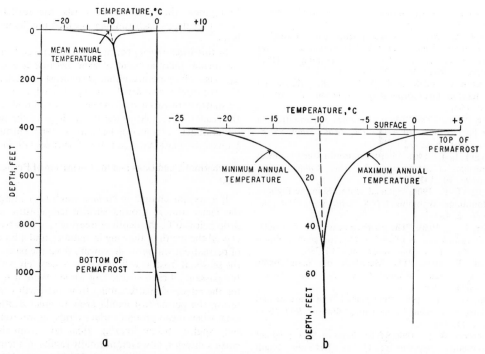

FIG. 1. Relationships between temperature and depth showing how the lower limit (a) and upper limit (b) of permafrost are established. (One-dimensional steady heat flow in a homogeneous medium).

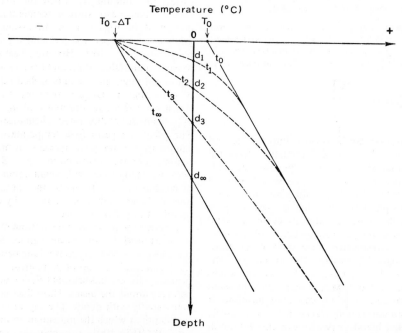

Depth

FIG. 2. Ground temperature at successive times ($t_0, t_1 \ldots t_\infty$) after a decrease in mean ground surface temperature from T_0 to $T_0 - \Delta T$. The initial temperatures are represented by curve t_0. At time t_1 permafrost extends to depth d_1, at time t_2 it extends to d_2, etc. The equilibrium curve, t_∞, is parallel to the initial curve t_0.

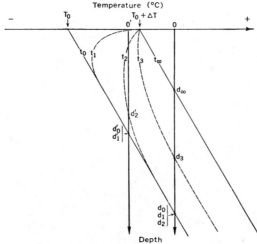

Temperature (°C)

FIG. 3. Ground temperature at successive times $(t_0, t_1 \ldots t_\infty)$ after an increase in mean ground surface temperature from T_0 to $T_0 + \Delta T$. If the final temperature is below 0°C (the case in which 0°C lies at point O), the base of permafrost rises successively from d_0 to d_∞. If the final temperature is above 0°C (i.e., 0°C lies at point O') the permafrost degrades first from the top (curve t_1) then from both top and bottom (curve t_2) and finally vanishes (curves t_3 and t_∞).

Depth of Permafrost

As long as the surface temperature can be considered stable, we might anticipate from the previous discussion that the depth to the bottom of permafrost would be about 100–200 feet multiplied by the negative of the mean annual temperature of the ground surface in degrees centigrade.

This is, in fact, a good rule of thumb at places remote from bodies of water, where the mean surface temperature has not varied too much. Thus on the Alaskan Arctic Slope where the surface temperatures range from -6 to $-9°C$, permafrost depths range from 700–1300 feet (Brewer, 1958, and unpublished). Near the shore on Melville Island, N.W.T., 1800 feet of permafrost is present beneath a surface at about $-14°C$, and somewhat greater depths are probably reached farther inland (Lachenbruch, Green, and Jacobsen, unpublished).

Where surface temperatures are below $-15°C$, the permafrost depths are so great that they are still influenced by little-known climatic changes which occurred at the end of Pleistocene glaciation, and the assumption of climatic stability is questionable. At places where ground surface temperatures are greater than $-6°C$, the rule again may fail because of the large relative effect of the marked climatic warming of the Arctic during the past century. Thus near Cape Thompson, Alaska, 1170 feet of permafrost is present beneath a surface whose mean temperature is near $-5°C$. However the great depth is the result of a mean surface temperature of $-7°C$

which prevailed until about a century ago. The subsequent warming has resulted in temperature changes of the type illustrated in Fig. 3. Present conditions are like those illustrated by curve t_2 with 0°C at point O.

Similarly, near its southern boundary, permafrost sometimes extends to 200 or 300 feet beneath surfaces whose mean temperature today is very close to 0°C. Such permafrost is a relic, and the geothermal gradient within it is practically zero (curve t_2, Fig. 3 with 0°C at point O'). Permafrost may be absent nearby where the material has a lower moisture content and hence responds more rapidly to changing surface temperature (curve t_3, Fig. 3 with 0°C at point O').

Global Distribution of Permafrost

The mean annual temperature of air near the ground is known to vary rather systematically with latitude, altitude, and global climatic patterns. Inasmuch as mean ground surface temperature, and hence depth of permafrost, follow in a very general way the mean air temperature, the depth and distribution of permafrost also have a somewhat systematic geographical distribution. This distribution has been discussed by many authors, the most recent being Brown (1960) and Ferrians (1965).

A useful discussion by Black (1954) is summarized in his map, presented here as Fig. 4. The three intergradational permafrost units—continuous, discontinuous, and sporadic—suggest the large-scale trends in continuity. They are commonly identified with mean ground surface temperatures of $< -5°C$, -1 to $-5°C$, and $> -1°C$, respectively, and with permafrost depths > 500 feet, 0–500 feet, and 0–100 feet.

The exact positions of the zone boundaries are not well defined because of extreme local variability, inadequate observational data, and difficulties with the formal definitions of these intergradational units. Nevertheless, maps such as Fig. 4 provide a very useful perspective. According to Black, 24% of the land area of the earth is in a permafrost zone, and 15% (of which 9% is Antarctica) is in the continuous zone.

The mean ground surface temperature at the southern limit of permafrost is probably very close to 0°C, but the mean air temperature is usually a few degrees lower (the difference is due largely to the insulating effects of winter snow cover). However, the relation between the present surface temperature and permafrost distribution is also complicated by the climatic warming of the last century and by local differences in microclimate and surface properties.

Local Variations in Permafrost Distribution

The greatest departures from the rather systematic patterns of permafrost distribution established by climate, are those caused by the thermal effects

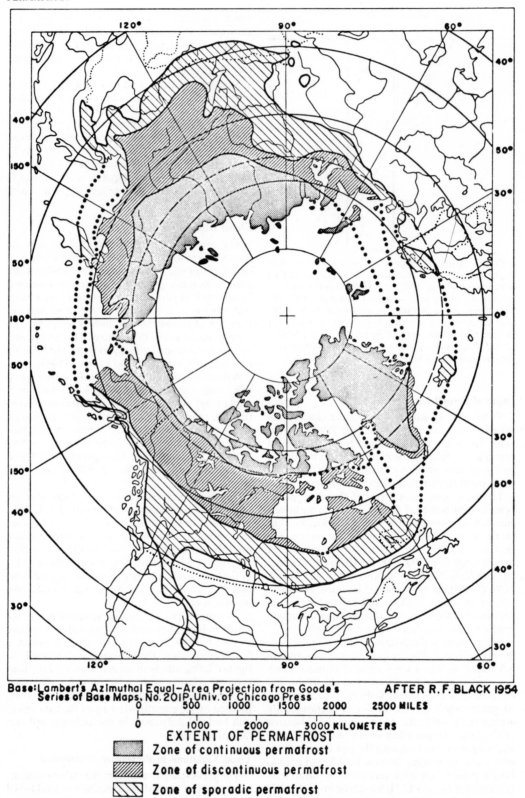

Base: Lambert's Azimuthal Equal-Area Projection from Goode's
Series of Base Maps, No. 201P, Univ. of Chicago Press

AFTER R. F. BLACK 1954

EXTENT OF PERMAFROST

Zone of continuous permafrost

Zone of discontinuous permafrost

Zone of sporadic permafrost

(Eurasia modified slightly from Sumgin and Petrovsky, courtesy of Inna V. Poiré)

FIG. 4. Black's map of permafrost in the northern hemisphere.

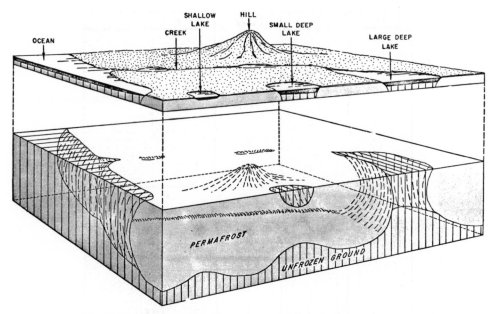

FIG. 5. Schematic representation of effect of surface features on permafrost distribution in continuous permafrost zone.

of bodies of water. Bodies of fresh water that do not freeze to the bottom in winter (those greater than 5 or 6 feet deep, such as the deep lakes of Fig. 5) have mean bottom temperatures greater than 0°C, and minimum bottom temperatures not less than 0°C. Hence they are immediately underlain by perennially unfrozen material. If the minimum horizontal dimension of the water body is more than about twice as great as the local undisturbed permafrost depth, an unfrozen "chimney" through the permafrost generally occurs beneath the body of water (see large deep lake in Fig. 5), unless it was very recently formed. (This convenient rule of thumb is substantiated by heat conduction theory.) A deep body of water with smaller horizontal dimensions is normally underlain by unfrozen sediments enclosed in a perennially frozen basin (see small deep lake in Fig. 5; also see Lachenbruch *et al.*, 1962, and *Pingo* article, this volume).

The blanketing effect of hills and the warming effects of shallow ponds normally cause upward indentations in the lower boundary of permafrost (Fig. 5).

The mean temperature of bottom sediments on the continental shelves in the Arctic Ocean is probably somewhat less than 0°C, and hence these waters are underlain by a thin layer of permafrost, on the order of 100 feet thick or less. Whether or not any ice occurs in these sediments is not known.

Manifestations of Permafrost

Ice-wedge Polygons. Thermal contraction of ice-cemented permafrost in winter often generates tensile stresses that exceed the strength of the material. The resulting tension cracks [Fig. 6(a)] divide the surface into roughly equidimensional blocks, on the order of 30–300 feet across, that resemble the smaller patterns seen in drying mud. Summer meltwater draining into the cracks freezes to form veins of ice [Fig. 6(b)]. The repetition of this annual cycle over centuries results in the growth of wedge-shaped masses of ice Fig. 6(c, d), sometimes tens of feet deep, and many feet wide at the top. The resulting ice-wedge polygons form striking patterns over thousands of square miles of polar terrain, and their growth and deterioration have far-reaching geomorphic and ecologic effects (Black, 1952, 1954; Lachenbruch, 1962).

Surficial Mass Movement. In spite of the aridity of most polar environments, the active layer is often supersaturated with moisture because of the low evaporation rate and impermeability of the underlying permafrost. Hence the surficial layer is commonly very mobile, and evidence of surficial downslope movement abounds in most permafrost terrain. However, profound mass movement of sediments under gravity is virtually absent because of the relative immobility of the underlying permafrost.

Engineering Problems. Engineering problems caused by permafrost have provided most of the impetus for permafrost studies (Muller, 1947; Tsytovich and Sumgin, 1959). These problems are of two fundamentally different types:

(1) Thermal effects of perennially low permafrost temperatures cause environmental problems for buried engineering facilities such as pipelines and

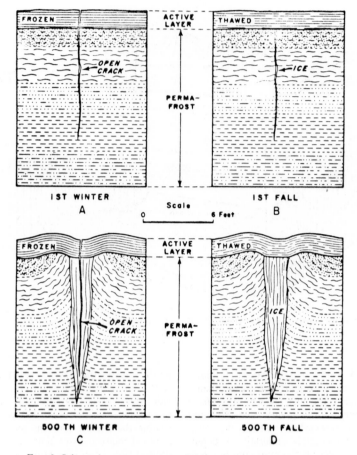

Fig. 6. Schematic representation of the evolution of an ice wedge in permafrost.

sewers. The permafrost temperature and physical properties of the facility determine whether water, oil, or sewage may be transported. Mechanical properties of permafrost, and hence the state of its interstitial moisture, are of only minor importance.

(2) Many other engineering problems result from changes in the mechanical properties of permafrost caused by thawing or freezing of its moisture beneath such structures as roadways or heated buildings. If the strength of interstitial ice cement is necessary for the stability of such a structure, the structure can destroy itself if it upsets the natural thermal regime. It is useful to divide this type of problem into two sub-types: those in which the engineering modification changes the *range* of ground surface temperature from summer to winter, and those in which the modification changes the *mean* ground surface temperature. The first includes most problems associated with the building of roadways and landing fields, where improving drainage and removal or compression of natural organic insulation normally results in a substantial increase in the seasonal range of ground

temperature. This in turn causes a thickening of the active layer and differential settlement of the surface, particularly where ice wedges occur. In this process, which may take several years to approach the destructive equilibrium state, the mean ground surface temperature may either be increased or decreased (Lachenbruch, 1959). The second sub-type includes the effects of reservoirs or foundations of heated buildings, which raise the mean annual temperature of the surface locally, and can cause profound thawing which may take decades or centuries to approach an equilibrium state. The resulting volume reduction or loss of bearing strength can cause differential settlement which may lead to costly maintenance or complete destruction (Lachenbruch, 1957).

ARTHUR H. LACHENBRUCH

References

Black, R. F., 1952, "Polygonal patterns and ground conditions from aerial photographs," *Photogram. Eng.*, **18**, 123–134.

Black, R. F., 1954, "Permafrost—A review," *Geol. Soc. Am. Bull.*, **65**, 839–856.

Brewer, M. C., 1958, "Some results of geothermal investigations of permafrost in northern Alaska," *Am. Geophys. Union Trans.*, **39**, 19–26.

Brown, R. J. E., 1960, "The distribution of permafrost and its relation to air temperature in Canada and the U.S.S.R.," *Arctic*, **13**, 163–177.

Ferrians, O., 1965, "Permafrost map of Alaska," *U.S. Geol. Surv., Misc. Geol. Inv.*, Map I-445.

Lachenbruch, A. H., 1957, "Three-dimensional heat conduction in permafrost beneath heated buildings," *U.S. Geol. Surv. Bull.*, **1052-B**, 51–69.

Lachenbruch, A. H., 1959, "Periodic heat flow in a stratified medium with application to permafrost problems," *U.S. Geol. Surv. Bull.*, **1083-A**, 1–36.

Lachenbruch, A. H., 1962, "Mechanics of thermal contraction cracks and ice-wedge polygons in permafrost," *Geol. Soc. Am. Spec. Paper*, **70**, 69pp.

Lachenbruch, A. H., Brewer, M. C., Greene, G. W., and Marshall, V. B., 1962, "Temperatures in Permafrost," in "Temperature, Its Measurement and Control in Science and Industry," Vol. 3, Pt. 1, pp. 791–803, New York, Reinhold Publishing Corp.

Muller, S. W., 1947, "Permafrost or Permanently Frozen Ground and Related Engineering Problems," Ann Arbor, Edwards Bros., 231pp.

Penner, E., 1965, "Frost Heaving in Soils," *Proc. Intern. Conf. on Permafrost*, 1963 Purdue Univ., Natl. Acad. Sci., 97–202.

Takagi, Shunsuke, 1965, "Fundamentals of the theory of frost heaving," *Proc. Intern. Conf. on Permafrost*, 1963 Purdue Univ., Natl. Acad. Sci., 203–216.

Tsytovich, N. A., and Sumgin, M. I., 1959. "Principles of the Mechanics of Frozen Ground," U.S. Army Snow Ice and Permafrost Research Establishment Translation 19, 288pp.

Cross-references: *Climatic Geomorphology*; *Frost Action*; *Patterned Ground*; *Periglacial Landscape*; *Pingos*; *Solifluction*; *Taiga Landscape*; *Tundra Landscape*. Vol. II: *Climate and Geomorphology*. pr Vol. VI: *Engineering Geology of Permafrost*.

PHILOSOPHY OF GEOLOGY—*See* pr Vol. VI, GEOLOGY, PHILOSOPHY OF

PHOTOGEOLOGY—*See* pr Vol. VI

PHOTOGRAMMETRY—*See* pr Vol. VI

PHYSIOGRAPHIC OR LANDFORM MAPS

The physiographic map or "diagram" or "landform map" (Raisz, 1956, 1962) shows perspective. It is intermediate in style between the old-fashioned hachured topographic map (e.g., see Imhof, 1950) and the modern *geomorphologic map* (q.v.). The former is limited strictly to the depiction of unexplained relief and has largely been replaced today

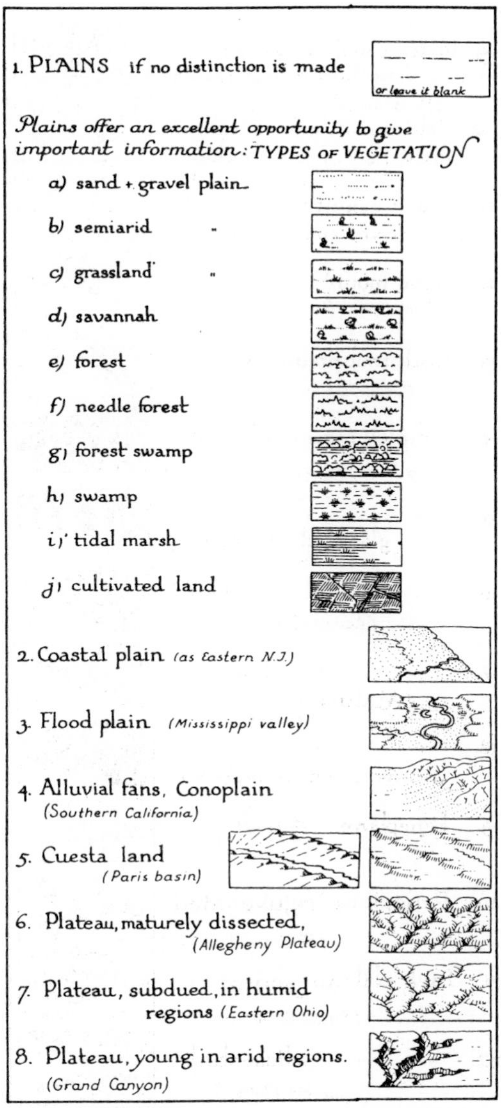

FIG. 1. Physiographic landform symbols (Raisz, 1931).

by contour maps and shaded contour maps, while the latter is a highly analytic and interpretive document, embracing many aspects of the science from slope analysis to denudation chronology. For young people, especially, and some older ones (!), the perspective view is readily understood, whereas the strictly vertical view is often unfamiliar or meaningless to beginners.

Developed primarily by W. M. Davis, D. W. Johnson, A. K. Lobeck and E. J. Raisz from the art of *block diagrams* (q.v.), the physiographic map represents the land forms as from a bird's eye view, but drops the perspective outline employed in block diagrams. For the mapping of large regions of up to continental dimensions, the block diagram is not

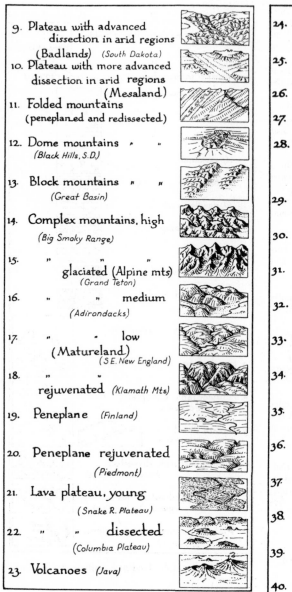

9. Plateau with advanced
   dissection in arid regions
   (Badlands) *(South Dakota)*
10. Plateau with more advanced
    dissection in arid regions
    (Mesaland)
11. Folded mountains
    (peneplaned and redissected)

12. Dome mountains „ „
    (Black Hills, S.D.)

13. Block mountains „ „
    (Great Basin)

14. Complex mountains, high
    (Big Smoky Range)

15. „   „   „
    glaciated (Alpine mts)
    (Grand Teton)

16. „   „   medium
    (Adirondacks)

17. „   „   low
    (Matureland)
    (S.E. New England)

18. „   „
    rejuvenated *(Klamath Mts)*

19. Peneplane *(Finland)*

20. Peneplane rejuvenated
    (Piedmont)

21. Lava plateau, young
    (Snake R. Plateau)

22. „   „   dissected
    (Columbia Plateau)

23. Volcanoes *(Java)*

FIG. 2. Physiographic landform symbols, continued
(Raisz, 1931). (*Note*: The spelling "peneplain" is now
generally preferred to "peneplane.")

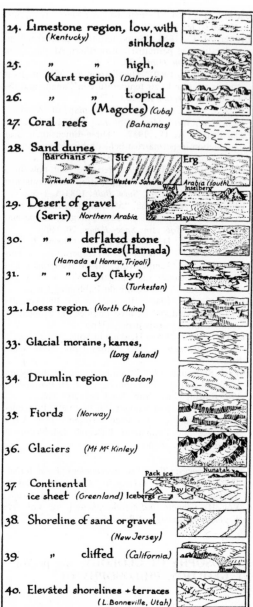

24. Limestone region, low, with
    (Kentucky)   sinkholes
25. „   „   high,
    (Karst region) *(Dalmatia)*
26. „   „   tropical
    (Magotes) *(Cuba)*
27. Coral reefs   *(Bahamas)*
28. Sand dunes
    Barchans   Slf   Erg
    Turkestan *Western Sahara* *Arabia (South)*
                                    Inselberg
29. Desert of gravel
    (Serir) *Northern Arabia*   *Playa*
30. „ „ deflated stone
            surfaces(Hamada)
    (Hamada el Homra, Tripoli)
31. „ „ clay (Takyr)
            (Turkestan)
32. Loess region *(North China)*
33. Glacial moraine, kames,
            (Long Island)
34. Drumlin region   *(Boston)*
35. Fiords *(Norway)*
36. Glaciers *(Mt Mc Kinley)*
37. Continental   Pack ice   Nunatak
    ice sheet *(Greenland)* Icebergs Bay ice
38. Shoreline of sand or gravel
            (New Jersey)
39. „   cliffed *(California)*
40. Elevated shorelines + terraces
            (L.Bonneville, Utah)

FIG. 3. Physiographic landform symbols, continued
(Raisz, 1931).

suitable, but the pictorial view is maintained. Hills
and valleys still appear as hills and valleys, but they
are simplified and the smaller ones are reduced in
number. Scarplands, alluvial fans, plains, dunes,
glaciers and so on are similarly presented in stylized
synthetic sketches. Raisz (1931) has prepared a useful set of "standard" sketches, reproduced here
(Figs. 1–3).

The extraordinary usefulness of continental physiographic maps or diagrams persuaded Lobeck to
prepare (or edit) a series covering every continent.

They were each accompanied by an inset map
naming the physiographic or geomorphic regions
and by brief printed descriptions of each subdivision. Jointly, with J. Gentilli, the writer prepared the
material for Australia; it was a highly instructive
experience, because until one is forced, by cartographic necessity, to choose a definite boundary
between two geomorphic regions, one does not
normally concern oneself about criteria. Does one
give more emphasis to underlying structure, to
absolute relief or to superficial veneer (e.g., sand

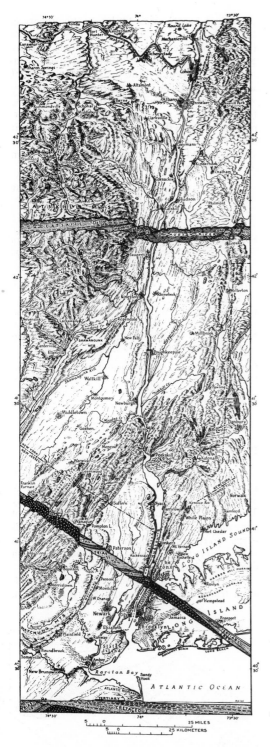

FIG. 4. Physiographic diagram of the lower Hudson region, New York State and New Jersey (Raisz). Note how the sections usually associated with a block diagram can be incorporated into a rectangular map that retains perspective detail.

ridges)? At least the physiographic map itself introduces no such problems. It represents the scenery essentially "as is" and does not interpret. This scenery is structurally understood; cuestas and escarpments are not glossed over but rather emphatically stated; many key features come out rather "larger than life" but interpretation is largely excluded and therein lies part of their secret of success.

The work of Lobeck was carried on further by Raisz, with many very beautiful regional maps. An interesting innovation that appeared for the first time in a basic historical geology textbook was the preparation of *paleogeographic maps* by the physiographic method (see Stovall and Brown, 1954).

The artistic method developed for the continents was first applied to ocean floor morphology in a remarkable series of maps by Heezen and Tharp. Coinciding with the development of precision depth recording and oceanographic surveys on a world scale, it has been possible for Heezen and Tharp to present the newly analyzed data, obtained directly from the echo-sounding tapes of many expeditions, without the intermediary of contoured charts. A slight variation has been offered by Menard for the Pacific Ocean (see example in Vol. I). The usual oceanographic contouring techniques inevitably involve a loss of precision and tend to "smear over" the sharp features depicted on the tapes. The oceanic physiographic map shows the principal features of ocean bottom topography in a clear and vivid way never before conceived by the older techniques.

RHODES W. FAIRBRIDGE

References

Bostock, H. S., 1964, "A provisional physiographic map of Canada," *Geol. Surv. Can. Paper,* 64–25, 24pp.

Davis, W. M., 1908, "Practical Exercises in Physical Geography," Boston, Ginn & Co., 148pp.

Davis, W. M., 1912, "Die Erklärende Beschreibung der Landformen," Leipzig and Berlin, Teubner, 565pp.

Gentilli, J., and Fairbridge, R. W., 1951, "Physiographic Diagram of Australia," New York, Columbia University (Geogr. Press).

Heezen, B. C., and Tharp, M., 1965, "Tectonic fabric of the Atlantic and Indian Oceans and continental drift," *Phil. Trans. Roy. Soc. London Ser. A.,* 90–106.

Heezen, B. C., Tharp, M., and Ewing, M., 1959, "The floors of the oceans. 1. The North Atlantic," *Geol. Soc. Am. Spec. Paper* **65.**

Imhof, E., 1950, "Gelände und Karte," Erlenbach-Zürich, E. Rentsch Verl., 255pp.

Imhof, E., 1965, "Kartographische Geländedarstellung," Berlin, W. de Gruyter, 425pp.

Johnson, D. W., 1921, "Battlefields of the World War," *Am. Geogr. Soc. Res. Ser. No. 3.*

Lobeck, A. K., 1924, "Block Diagrams," New York, John Wiley & Sons, 206pp.

Raisz, E. J., 1931, "The physiographic method of representing scenery on maps," *Geogr. Rev.,* **21**(2), 297–304.

Raisz, E. J., 1956, "Landform maps," *Petermanns Geogr. Mitt.,* **100**(2), 171–172.

Raisz, E. J., 1961, "A new landform map of Mexico," *Internat. Jahrb. f. Kartographie*, **1**, 121.

Raisz, E. J., 1962, "Principles of Cartography," New York, McGraw-Hill Book Co., 315pp.

Stovall, J. W., and Brown, H. E., 1954, "The Principles of Historical Geology," Boston, Ginn & Co., 472pp.

Note: The Lobeck series of physiographic maps of the various continents were published by Lobeck under the name of the Geographic Press, and later taken over by Hammond Map Co., 1 E. 43 St., New York, N.Y.

The Raisz maps were also privately published for the most part and are still obtainable from Dr. Erwin J. Raisz, 107 Washington Ave., Cambridge, Mass.

The Heezen-Tharp series of the ocean floors are available from the Geological Society of America, Colorado Bldg., P.O. Box 1719, Boulder, Colorado, 80302.

Cross-references: *Block Diagrams; Cuestas; Escarpments; Geomorphic Maps.* Vol. I: *Indian Ocean; Submarine Cones; Submarine Plateaus.*

PHYSIOGRAPHY

According to the Oxford English Dictionary, physiography originally meant the "study of nature or of natural phenomena," and the early Webster's concurs, but later usage limits its application to physical geography and then specifically to geomorphology (a procedure adopted by W. M. Davis and widely followed, e.g., by Fenneman, 1938).

In the last century, T. H. Huxley wrote a book entitled "Physiography" (1877) in which he made it clear that physiography referred to causal relationships of natural phenomena, rather than *physical geography*, which he asserted is commonly accused of consisting of "scraps of all sorts of undigested and unconnected information" (p. vi). The Russian geographer aristocrat, the Prince Kropotkin wrote (1893) on the teaching of physiography that "I cannot conceive physiography from which man has been excluded. . . ." A high school text of 1901, Morgan's "Advanced Physiography" said "it includes the main facts and principles of elementary physics, geology, oceanography, meteorology, and astronomy."

Thus from its nineteenth century meaning of something like *earth sciences* in the modern sense, it became remarkably narrowed to the geomorphic physiography of W. M. Davis, R. D. Salisbury and N. M. Fenneman. Loebeck's "Physiographic Diagrams" of each of the continents clearly restricted the term to the description of the relief of the earth's surface and its explanation.

With the 1930's and the post-World War II period came the swing against Davisian physiography and a preference grew up for the term *geomorphology*, suggesting analysis and interpretation, rather than pure description (physiography). For "geomorphology," the O.E.D. quotes *Popular Science Monthly* (April, 1896, p. 815) for its first

use (which hardly seems likely), as "the theory of the conformation of the earth." J. W. Gregory (1899) wrote "veiled by the great variety in topographical details there is some underlying symmetry in continental form, the discovery of which is the main problem of geomorphology," which is what we would normally think of today as "geotectonics." In the mid-twentieth century, geomorphology refers to those "topographic details," their history and their explanation. Physiography at this stage is a dead term, though perhaps there is room for its revival in its initial form.

RHODES W. FAIRBRIDGE

References

Fenneman, N. M., 1938, "Physiography of Eastern United States," New York, McGraw-Hill Book Co., 714pp.

Gregory, J. W., 1899, "The Plan of the Earth," in (Mill, H. R., editor) "The International Geography," London, Newnes.

Huxley, T. H., 1877, "Physiography," London, Macmillan.

Kropotkin, Prince, 1893, "On the teaching of physiography," *Geograph. J.*, **2**, 350–359.

Cross-references: *Geomorphology—General*; *Geomorphology—Principles.*

PIEDMONT LANDFORMS

According to Webster and the Oxford English Dictionary, the piedmont is something referring to, or situated at, the foot of mountains. Thus one may have a piedmont district, piedmont plain, piedmont alluvium, piedmont scarp, piedmont benchlands (steps—*treppen*, Ger.), piedmont lake and piedmont sedimentary facies ("molasse"). The Malaspina Glacier of Alaska is a typical *piedmont glacier*.

The equivalent of piedmont alluvium or "piedmont fringe" (Wooldridge and Morgan, 1937) in

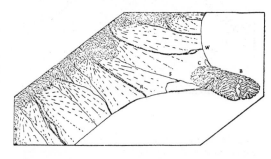

Fig. 1. The Canterbury Plain, a piedmont alluvial plain in New Zealand (Cotton, 1958). (By permission of Whitcombe & Tombs, Christchurch, N.Z.)

FIG. 2. The mountain front at the inner edge of the Canterbury piedmont alluvium plain, New Zealand. It is fed partly by glacial outwash, as by the Rangitata River, illustrated here. Note the braided patterns and the marginal intersecting fans. (Photo: S. N. Beatus, New Zealand Geological Survey).

semiarid lands is the *bajada* (q.v.). The bajada and pediment together, according to W. M. Davis, constitute the "piedmont slope," while Balchin and Pye (1956) speak of it as the "piedmont profile." They call the mountain foot the "piedmont angle." The French use *glacis* in this connection: a *glacis de piémont* (*Berg fussebene* in German) for the whole slope, consisting of a *glacis rocheux* (hard-rock pediment) or *glacis d'érosion* (soft-rock pediment) and a *glacis alluvial*, the bajada, following the advice of Dresch. According to Taillefer (1951), the *piémont* is simply the aggradation cone, in contrast to the rock-cut *pediment* (q.v.). Mensching (1958) feels that the term glacis should be used internationally only for piedmont slopes that have polygenetic origin representing a *complex*, i.e., a succession of morphogenetic features. The piedmont

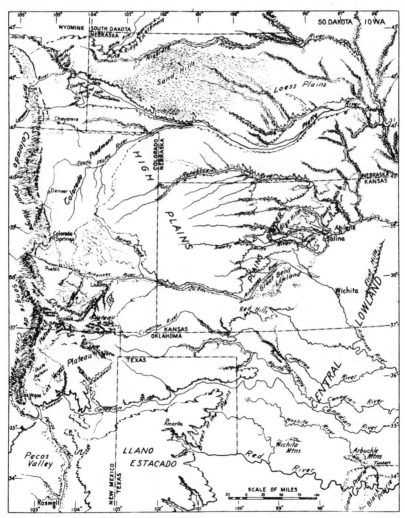

FIG. 3. Piedmont plains and dissected piedmont plateaus along the eastern foot of the Rocky Mountains (by G. H. Smith, from Fenneman, 1931). (By permission of McGraw-Hill Book Co., N.Y.)

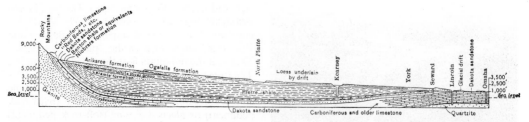

FIG. 4. Geological section from Wyoming to Nebraska, showing successive piedmont facies above the Pierre Shale (Upper Cretaceous). Older rocks were tilted up against the Rocky Mountain front during the Laramide disturbance (Darton, 1919).

alluvial cone (*Schwemmfächer*) of the semiarid regions is distinctive from the fluvial fan of the more humid regions (Czajka, 1958), the former being marked by steeper slope angles and coarse debris at the outer parts of the cone (see *Alluvial Fan, Cone*). The fluvial fans, in contrast, are marked by the familiar, gently diminishing gradient of so-called normal streams (Fig. 5).

Penck (1924, translated 1953) wrote of *Piedmonttreppen* (steps or piedmont benchlands) which are the step-like erosion benches around a progressively elevated massif like the Black Forest or Massif Central. Penck assumed pedimentation around a *continuously* rising dome, but most scientists regard

the "piedmont steps" as evidence of either climate changes or tectonic interruptions (Baulig, 1939). A similar problem was presented in Norway by Evers (see Holtedahl, 1966).

The *Piedmont Province* in the geomorphic divisions of the United States (Fennemen, 1938; Thornbury, 1965) is the older part of the Appalachians that forms a belt of uplands extending from near New York City to Georgia; it is bordered on the east by the "*Fall Line*" (q.v.) and on the west by the "Great Valley" (the beginning of the Ridge and Valley Province). Some writers prefer the term "Crystalline Appalachians" proposed for it by P. B. King (1959). Rocks of the piedmont, now deeply

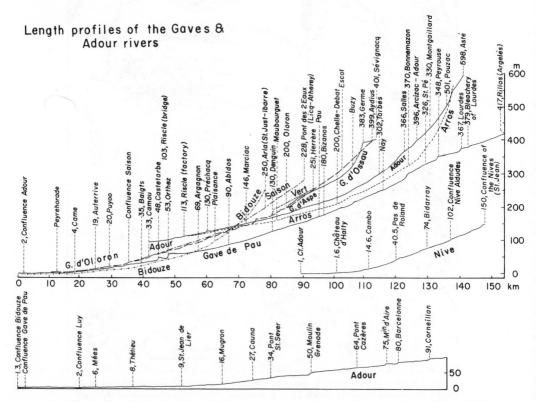

FIG. 5. Typical longitudinal profiles of piedmont streams north of the Pyrenees (after Taillefer, 1951).

weathered for the most part into an impressive saprolite, are of early Paleozoic to Precambrian age (see *Regolith and Saprolite*), with scattered Triassic lowlands conditioned by taphrogenic graben structures. The Piedmont Province is thus an upland area, distinct from the Atlantic Coastal Plain, and secondary in relief to the mountainous zone of the Folded Appalachians (Ridge and Valley Province); from the geotectonic viewpoint, however, it contains the axial zone of the Appalachian orogenic belt (with ultrabasic intrusives, extensive older Paleozoic granitized areas and intensive metamorphism).

RHODES W. FAIRBRIDGE

References

Balchin, W. G. V., Pye, N., 1956, "Piedmont profiles in the arid cycle," *Proc. Geologists Assoc. London*, **66**, 167–181.
Baulig, H., 1939, "Sur les 'gradins de piedmont'," *J. Geomorphol.*, **2**, 281–304.
Baulig, H., 1956, "Vocabulaire Franco-Anglo-Allemand de Géomorphologie," Paris, Soc. d'Editions, 230pp.
Cotton, C. A., 1952, "Geomorphology," Sixth ed., Christchurch, Whitcombe and Tombs, 505pp.
Czajka, W., 1958, "Schwemmfächerbildung und Schwemmfächerformen," *Mitt. Geogr. Ges. Wien*, **100**, 18–36.
Darton, N. H., 1919, "The structure of parts of the Central Great Plains," *U.S. Geol. Surv. Bull.*, **691**.
Fenneman, N. M., 1931, "Physiography of Western United States," McGraw-Hill Book Co., 534pp.
Fenneman, N. M., 1938, "Physiography of the Eastern United States," New York, McGraw-Hill Book Co., 714 pp.
Holtedahl, O., 1966, "The South-Norwegian Piedmonttreppe of W. Evers," *Norsk Geog. Tidsk.*, **20**, 74–84.
King, P. B., 1959, "Evolution of North America," Princeton, N.J., Princeton Univ. Press, 189pp.
Mensching, H., 1958. "Glacis-Fussfläche Pediment," *Z. Geomorphol., NF*, **2**, 165–186.
Penck, W., 1953, "Morphological Analysis of Land Forms," London, Macmillan & Co., 429pp. (translation by H. Czech and K. C. Boswell of 1924 German edition).
Scott, G. R., 1965, "Nonglacial Quaternary Geology of the Southern and Middle Rocky Mountains," in (Wright and Frey, eds.), "Quaternary of the U.S." pp. 243–254, Princeton, N.J., Princeton Univ. Press.
Taillefer, F., 1951, "Le piémont des Pyrénées françaises," Toulouse, E. Privat, 383pp.
Thornbury, W. D., 1965, "Regional Geomorphology of the United States," New York, John Wiley & Sons, 609pp.
Usselmann, P., 1966, "L'évolution géomorphologique de la plaine de Tarbes," *Rev. Géomorphol. Dyn.*, **16**, 145–161.
Viers, G., 1960, "Le relief des Pyrénées occidentales et leur piémont," Toulouse, E. Privat, 604pp.
Von Engeln, O. D., 1942, "Geomorphology," New York, The Macmillan Co., 655pp.
Wooldridge, S. W., and Morgan, R. S., 1937, "The Physical Basis of Geography: An Outline of Geo-

morphology," London, Longmans, Green and Co., 445pp.

Cross-references: *Alluvial Fan, Cone*; *Bajada*; *Fall Line*; *Morphogenetic Regions*; *Mountain Types*; *Pediment*; *Regolith and Saprolite*; *Terraces—Fluvial*; *Treppen Concept*.

PIMPLE PRAIRIE—*See* PRAIRIE MOUND

PINGOS, MODERN

Pingos are dome-shaped hills occurring in regions of permafrost; their growth results from the uplifting of a layer of frozen ground by the pressure of water freezing in the substratum to form large ice lenses. They may rise 50 meters or more above the surrounding terrain. Usually circular or oval at the base, they often measure several hundred meters in circumference. The dominant characteristic is the internal massive lens of clear ice which may have a thickness of 80 meters or more and a diameter almost as great as that of the pingo itself (Fig. 1). The overlying layer of material, varying from 1–10 or more meters in thickness, is frequently ruptured at the top, thus opening the door to decay. The crater may contain a lake.

Pingo is the name given by the Mackenzie delta Eskimos to these features which are numerous in that area, and Porsild (1938) suggested retaining it in scientific usage. The Russian equivalent is *Bulgunniakh*. The genetic term *hydrolaccolith*, which applies to all ice-intrusions, is not just synonymous with pingo. The term pingo is restricted to a perennial intra-permafrost feature, which is distinctly different from seasonal frost mounds, peat hummocks, and winter ice blisters in the active layer or in the ice cover of rivers and lakes.

So far two genetic types of pingos have been distinguished: the open system, East Greenland type, and the closed system, Mackenzie type (Müller, 1959).

The distribution of pingos is related to specific climatic and permafrost conditions which exist predominantly in latitudes 65–75°N, where the permafrost is either discontinuous or continuous but thin. Isolated examples occur in areas of thick permafrost. In Siberia, the pingo belt extends further south. Some 1400 closed system pingos were identified in the Mackenzie delta area. The open system, East Greenland type, pingos do not occur in such large numbers; there are, however, many hundreds of them in the unglaciated parts of Alaska.

Open System Pingos. These occur in areas of discontinuous or thin permafrost where surface water can penetrate into the ground and continue as sub- or intra-permafrost water, circulating in talik. They are found predominantly in mountain-

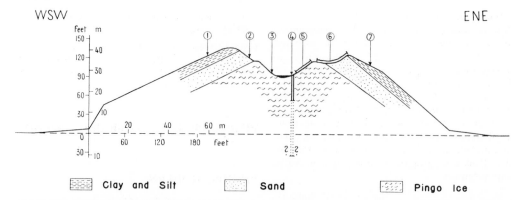

FIG. 1. Schematic cross section through the Ibyuk Pingo in the northeast Mackenzie delta. This section shows the result of the diggings and excavations at locations 1–7. In test hole 4, the ice body was drilled down to a depth of 14 meters. The dotted extension of the drill hole indicates the conjectured thickness of the pingo ice lens. The small crater lake is situated between locations 3 and 4.

ous or hilly regions where hydrostatic pressure, or in some cases hydraulic head, can develop sufficiently to push up the impervious frozen surface layer (Fig. 2). Valley bottoms, particularly broad, gravel-filled riverbeds and the lower, more gentle, valley slopes are favorable locations for this type of pingo which most frequently forms in alluvial material. There are, however, many examples in solid bedrock. Though they most commonly appear as isolated, individual pingos, groups are found consisting of a main pingo with several satellites. Sometimes a new pingo grows inside the remnants of a former one. Intra- or sub-permafrost water has been observed flowing out through the ice body of pingos of this type.

Closed System Pingos. These are found almost exclusively in areas of continuous permafrost, generally in lowlands with thick alluvial deposits and little relief. Most of them are situated in the geometric center of round, shallow lakes or former lake basins; irregularly shaped lake basins may support more than one pingo. There are hardly ever any subsidiary or second-generation pingos. Outflow of intra- or sub-permafrost water is unlikely in this type.

A closed system pingo (Fig. 3) develops where permafrost advances into a lake basin. The hydrostatic pressure generated by the gradual freezing of a confined mass of saturated soil underneath the shrinking lake injects the excess pore water (expelled during the freezing process) into the space beneath the frozen surface layer where it freezes to form the ice lens. The frozen surface layer then yields to this pressure by updoming and frequently rupturing at the stress center, i.e., at the top of the growing pingo.

Pingo Ice. Pingo ice is classed as "injected ice" in contrast to segregated, vein, cave or buried ice. There is little difference in the physical properties of the ice of the two pingo types. In both, it is char-

acterized by translucent, large (up to 10 cm. or more in diameter), simple-shaped crystals and by the scarcity, or more often the complete absence, of internal structures. Colonies of parallel, long-shaped air bubbles roughly perpendicular to the pingo surface indicate the direction of crystallization.

Age. The formation of the existing pingos cannot be related to any single climatic period, but rather it seems that they have formed throughout postglacial times and, in unglaciated areas, even during the Pleistocene. Most of the large pingos are at least hundreds, and more probably several thousands, of years old. Two closed system pingos in the Mackenzie delta area dated by the C^{14} method were found to have ages of about 4000 and 7000–10,000 years, respectively. Some pingos on newly formed land, e.g., in the new Mackenzie delta, appear to be growing today.

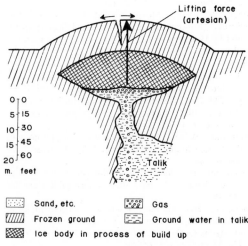

FIG. 2. Hypothetical cross section through a pingo of the open system, East Greenland type.

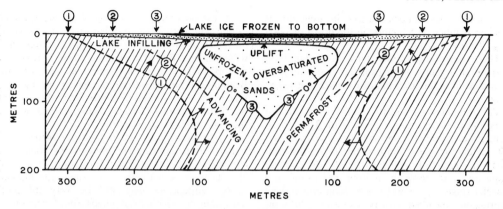

FIG. 3. Diagrammatic sketch illustrating assumed mechanism of the formation of a pingo of the closed system, Mackenzie type. Shallowing of the lake eventually causing the lake ice to freeze to the bottom during the winter months induces aggradation of permafrost, leading to a closed system in which the hydrostatic pressure resulting from the volume expansion of freezing excess water updomes the newly frozen layer in the center of the lake. The ice body forms beneath this uplifted layer. Three successive stages (1, 2, 3) of the decreasing lake and of the associated advance of permafrost are shown.

Relics of former pingos have been identified in the middle latitude lowlands, the periglacial of the Pleistocene.

FRITZ MÜLLER

References

Maarleveld, G. C., 1965, "Frost Mounds," *Mededel. Geol. Stich.*, new ser. no. 17, 3–16.

Mackay, J. Ross, 1962, "Pingos of the Pleistocene Mackenzie Delta area, Canada," *Can. Dept. Mines Tech. Surv., Geograph. Branch. Ottawa, Geographical Bull.*, **18**, 21-63.

*Müller, F., 1959, "Beobachtungen über Pingos," *Medd. Groenland*, **153**, No. 3, 127 pp., Translation by D. A. Sinclair, 1963, "Observations on pingos," *Natl. Res. Council Can. Tech. Translation* **1073**, 177pp.

Porsild, A. E., 1938, "Earth mounds in unglaciated arctic northwestern America," *Geograph. Rev.*, **28**, 46–58.

Wolfe, P. E., 1953, "Periglacial frost-thaw basins in New Jersey," *J. Geol.*, **61**(2), 133–141.

* Additional bibliographic references may be found in this work.

Cross-references: *Periglacial Landscape; Permafrost; Thermokarst.*

PINGOS, PLEISTOCENE

Stoltenberg, in 1935, and Troll, in 1944, drew attention to the resemblance between depressions occupying the sites of pingos and those due to buried masses of dead ice frequently found in areas glaciated in the Pleistocene. They did not, however, produce criteria for distinguishing between these two land forms which are of completely different origin, and it was not until 1955 that Dutch research workers showed that depressions in the north of Holland were in fact due to pingos. They proved that these depressions were formed in the Würm, though ice had not covered the area since the Riss.

Subsequently definite remains of pingos have been found in Belgium (Pissart, 1956), in Germany (Picard, 1961), and in Great Britain (Pissart, 1963). In addition, French writers suggested that the *mares* of the Jura, of the Paris Basin (Cailleux, 1956), of the Bordelais, the "skovmose" of Denmark (Cailleux, 1957), and the "frost-thaw" basins of New Jersey (Wolfe, 1953) might have the same origin, though this has not as yet been confirmed.

At the moment, not many examples of Pleistocene pingos have been published, and a profitable study of their distribution could be undertaken some time.

Form of Pingo Scars

The evidence for pingos is three fold:

(a) *Closed depressions,* like the *mares* of the Paris basin. Their genesis by injection ice is proposed only because no other explanation seems possible.

(b) *Closed depressions surrounded by a rampart* (Fig. 1) found in Belgium, Wales, Norway. The rampart is the most significant feature, for it enables one to distinguish these periglacial basins from those due to melting or to the collapse of underlying material. Its height varies from place to place; on

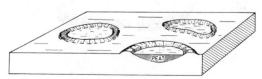

FIG. 1. Block diagram of pingo scars, showing swampy interior and peat accumulation.

the Plateau des Hautes Fagnes in Belgium, it reaches as much as 5 meters; in the north of Norway, 7 meters.

These pingo depressions have been found on horizontal or gently sloping surfaces (less than 5%), on a coastal plain, level plateau surface and valley floor.

The ramparts are mostly circular or oval, but sometimes they are irregular in plan. The largest dimension recorded is 150 meters for circular and 250 meters for oval examples. On slopes, the ramparts are frequently elongated in the direction of slope and pass through intermediate forms into parallel ridges up to 800 meters long. Since these depressions are filled with peat or water, little information is available on the form of floor. Available evidence suggests that the largest depressions are not necessarily the deepest. Borings have shown that basins of about 50-meters diameter are usually about 8 meters deep at their center, to which the bottom slopes regularly.

(c) *Ground structures.* The essential features of the structures described by J. Dylik (1963, 1965) are the deformation of layers which are upwards concentrically with the rim of the depression.

Exposures in the ramparts are very rare and usually show no definite structure, for the solifluctual or morainic material from which they are formed has no obvious bedding. In one case in Wales, however, beds which originally had a horizontal stratification are arched up underneath the rampart, indicating that the ramparts are formed not only by the sliding down of materials lifted up on top of the ice core, but also by thrusting due to the growth of this core.

Age, Origin and Paleoclimatic Significance

Pollen analysis of the peat in the depressions has given some indication of age. In Belgium, they are older than the Pre-boreal and the fresh forms of the ramparts suggest a recent data, probably at the end of the last glaciation. In Holland, Nossin (1961) thinks that the remains of the pingos he has examined were formed at two periods, one just before the Allerød, the other just before the Pre-boreal. In Poland, Dylik (1965) believes the pingos at Józefów developed during the maximum of the last glaciation (Fig. 2).

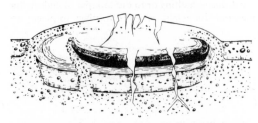

Fig. 2. Reconstruction of the Pleistocene pingo at Józefów in the Łódž region (Poland) (by Dylik).

The origin of these fossil pingos cannot always be established with certainty. However, the pingos of Wales seem to belong to the open system, the water having flowed down the slope between a thin permafrost and an impervious bedrock. In Belgium the pingos were progressively fed by surface water; they cannot be compared with those on the delta of the Mackenzie, which depend on the presence of lakes (Pissart, 1965).

It is necessary to understand the genesis of pingos before drawing any conclusions about the climate at the time of their formation. If a cold climate with permafrost is necessary, the annual mean temperature may still be very different depending on whether the pingos were formed in a closed or open system. A map of their distribution which would be of considerable interest, will probably be feasible a few years hence, for the attention that is being focused on them at present will probably result in their discovery in many areas.

A. Pissart

References

Cailleux, A., 1956, "Mares, mardelles et pingos," *Compt. Rend. Acad. Sci.,* **242,** 1912–1914.

Cailleux, A., 1957, "Les mares du Sud-Est de Sjaelland (Denmark)," *Compt. Rend. Acad. Sci.,* **245,** 1074–1076.

Dylik, J., 1963, "Traces of thermokarst in the pleistocene sediments of Poland," *Bull. Soc. Sci. et Lettres Łodz,* **14,** 2.

Dylik, J., 1965, "L'étude de la dynamique d'évolution des dépressions fermées à Józefów aux environs de Łodz," *Rev. Géomorph. Dynamique,* Paris, **15.**

Maarleveld, G. C., and Van den Toorn, J. C., 1955, "Pseudo-sölle in Noord-Nederland," *Tijdschr. Kon. Nederland. Aardrijksk. Gen.* **72,** 344–360.

Nossin, J. J., 1961, "De Reliefontwikkeling in Zuidoostelijk Friesland," in "Boven-Boorngebied," Publication No. 178 of the Frisian Academy, Drachten, Holland, Laverman.

Picard, K., 1961, "Reste Von Pingos bei Husum/Nordsee," *Schriften Naturw. Ver. Schleswig-Holstein,* **32,** 72–77.

Pissart, A., 1956, "L'origine périglaciaire des viviers des Hautes Fagnes," *Ann. Soc. Géol. Belg.,* **79,** B119–131.

Pissart, A., 1963, "Les traces de pingos du Pays de Galles (Grande Bretagne) et du plateau des Hautes Fagnes (Belgique)," *Z. Geomorphol.,* **7,** 147–165.

Pissart, A., 1965, "Les pingos des Hautes Fagnes. Le problème de leur genèse," *Ann. Soc. Géol. Belgique,* T. 88, B277–B289.

Svensson, H., 1964, "Traces of pingo-like frost mounds," Lund studies in Geography, Sweden, Ser. A, "Physical geography," No. 30, 93–106.

Wiegand, G., 1965, "Fossile Pingos in Mitteleuropa," *Wurzburgen geogr. Arbeit.,* **16,** 152 pp.

Wolfe, P. E., 1953, "Periglacial frost-thaw basins in New Jersey," *J. Geol.,* **61,** 133–141.

Cross-references: *Cryopedology, Cryonivation, etc.; Frost Action; Pingos, Modern; Periglacial Landscape; Permafrost; Thermokarst.* pr Vol. VII: *Palynology.*

PIPING

Piping is subterranean erosion initiated by percolating waters which remove solid particles from clastic (fragmental) rocks to produce tubular underground conduits. Although operating by several different mechanisms, piping does not involve the ion-by-ion solution responsible for caves and true karst topography in limestone. Piping affects materials ranging in size from clay to gravel in alluvium, loess, volcanic ash and soil, as well as bedrock of claystone, siltstone, mudstone and tuff. A worldwide feature of arid and semiarid regions, piping has been noted in Australia, Bolivia, Canada, China, Iran, New Zealand, South Africa and western United States (see Parker, 1963).

Failure of Dams

Civil engineers have studied the theory of piping (originally their term) since 1898 when Colonel Clibborn (see Lane, 1935) predicted the subsequent collapse of the Narora Dam on the Ganges River. Such failures involve rapidly developing underground outlets which are enlarged by rushing waters and immediately collapse. Terzaghi and Peck (1948) recognize two types of piping failure, which both start along a dam's downstream toe. One evolves from seeps that erode headward, tunneling through slightly cohesive materials under the structure until the reservoir is tapped. The other, a quicksand phenomenon, commences with "boiling"—a bulging of earth where hydrostatic pressure of upward percolating water exceeds the earth's effective weight. Although both types produce unstable

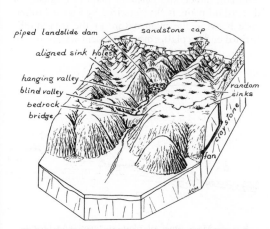

Fig. 1. Badland pseudokarst typical of the Chinle formation in the Arizona Petrified Forest (vertical relief about 100 feet).

ground in which tubes are not preserved, the seep-caving mechanism may apply to some natural piping, and "boiling" might occur in a landslide dam.

Natural Piping

Piping where tubes are preserved occurs either along the margins of recently gullied flats such as floodplains, terraces and loess plains, or in crowns, slopes and channels of badland hills. Both topographic situations allow steep downward percolation and the escape of water along gully bottoms. The necessary permeability reflects either porosity or desiccation cracking in the moderately consolidated materials of gullied flats. Such piped materials characteristically contain montmorillonite, or other swelling clay, which induces deep cracking when dried. Thus, subsequent storm or meltwater penetrates deeply before the ground swells and seals. Badland rocks—often largely montmorillonite—are surprisingly hard and compact beneath their surficial "adobe" mantle produced by alternate wetting and drying. Joints and inherent fractures permit the deep penetration of water into such badland claystones, siltstones and tuffs (Mears, 1963). In flats or badlands, the clays disaggregate readily in downward-moving waters, allowing the removal of solid particles in turbid suspensions. Once initiated by percolation, pipes are rapidly enlarged by scouring storm waters.

Karst-like Topography

Pseudokarsts produced by piping display disappearing streams, sinkholes, blind and hanging valleys, natural bridges, residual hills and caves. These features are far less permanent than comparable forms in limestone, and may be on a smaller scale. However, an Oregon pseudokarst in montmorillonitic tuff and volcanic ash contains Officer's Cave, part of a piping complex 700 feet long, with a room 44 feet wide, 35 feet high and 100 feet long. Parker *et al.* (1964) estimate it has been enlarged by 2700 cubic feet per year since 1900. Wright (1964) attributes hundreds of small depressions and lakes in the Chuska Mountains, New Mexico, to piping—although some disagree. Thus piping, long a problem in engineering and soil conservation, seems of increasing interest to geologists.

Brainerd Mears, Jr.

References

Lane, E. W., 1935, "Security from underground water seepage: Masonry dams on earth foundations," *Trans. Am. Soc. Civil Engineers,* **100,** Paper 1919.

Mears, B., Jr., 1963, "Karst-like features in Badlands of the Arizona Petrified Forest," *Contributions to Geology Univ. of Wyoming,* **2,** 101–104.

*Parker, G. G., 1963, "Piping, a geomorphic agent in landform development of the drylands," *Intern.*

Assoc. Sci. Hydrology, Berkeley, extract pub., No. 65, 103–113.

Parker, G. G., Shown, L. M., and Ratzlaff, K. W., 1964, "Officer's Cave, a pseudokarst feature in altered tuff and volcanic ash of the John Day Formation in Eastern Oregon," Bull. Geol. Soc. Am., **75**, 393–402.

Terzaghi, K., and Peck, R. B., 1948, "Soil Mechanics in Engineering Practice," New York, John Wiley & Sons, 566pp.

Wright, H. E., Jr., 1964, "Origin of the lakes in the Chuska Mountains, Northwestern New Mexico," Bull. Geol. Soc. Am., **75**, 589–598.

* Additional bibliographic references may be found in this work.

Cross-references: *Alluvium*; *Badlands*; *Blind Valley*; *Hanging Valley*; *Karst*; *Limestone Caves*; *Loess*; *Sink*, *Sinkhole*; *Thermokarst*; *Volcano-Karst*. Vol. IV: *Montmorillonite*. Vol. VI: *Engineering Geology*; *Tuff*; *Volcanic Ash Deposits*; *Volcanic Soils*.

PIRACY, STREAM—*See* STREAM CAPTURE, PIRACY

PLACER DEPOSITS—*See* Vol. IV

PLAINS

(1) Definition

The term "plain" has two meanings in geographical and geological literature.

(a) The "plain," in a strict sense, is an area of land surface featuring small differences in topographic elevations and uniform from the geomorphological point of view. The *flood plain* (q.v.), *terrace plain*, *abrasion plain*, *peneplain* (q.v.), and *pediplain* are examples.

(b) "Plain" in a broader sense is synonymous with the flatland or platform plain. The plain lands consist of vast territories and are a combination of plains of various origins. It is even possible that these plains are at various hypsometric levels. The geotectonic connection with shields and platforms is an important feature of plain lands.

Plain lands are analogous to and the counterpart of highlands, which are the geomorphological reflection of orogenic elements of earth's structure, in that the plain lands are the geomorphological image of the platform structures. Examples are: the North American Plain, the Russian or Eastern European Plain, and the East Siberian Plateau.

(2) Distribution

Areas featuring a plain topography occupy about 55% of the earth's continental surface. Plains on the floors of seas and oceans are also very common (shelf plains, abyssal plains of the ocean floors, and others).

There is a definite order or symmetry in the distribution of continental plains (Beloussov, 1962).

The plains are associated mainly with two continental (east–west) belts—*Laurasia*, in the northern hemisphere, and *Gondwana*, in the southern hemisphere. There are thus symmetric pairs of flatlands lying on opposite sides of the equator, one series of plains in the northern, and the other in the southern hemisphere.

In the western hemisphere, such a pair is formed by the North American and South American platform plains. In the eastern hemisphere the Russian and African plains form another pair. The East Siberian and Australian plains may be considered as a third pair. This feature of Recent topography of the continents reflects the distribution of crystalline *shields* and *ancient platforms* making the foundation of plains. The plains of *younger* (*post-Paleozoic*) *platforms* have a tendency to form a framework around ancient platforms and in many cases extend far from the shields. The West Siberian, the Turanian (Kazakhstan), and the various West European plains belong to this type.

(3) Origin of the Surface

The latest studies indicate that the origin of plains is very complex. W. M. Davis (1909) wrote that the Russian plain represents the greatest of all known peneplains. Such a point of view concerning the Russian platform, as well as the other great plains, should be revised. As a whole, the plains cannot be classified simply as peneplains or pediplains, i.e., as surfaces formed by erosion. Within the plains, in addition to traces of peneplains, pediplains and various abrasion surfaces, flat areas formed by the accumulation and stratification of sediments are very common.

The following types of plains are distinguishable (Mescherikov, 1960) on the basis of their geological structure, with the new terms "displain" and "conplain," (Fig. 1).

(A) Displain. Displain (From the Latin *discordare* —to contradict, and *planum*—plain in English), or discordant plain, is characterized by a strong difference between the plain nature of the topography formed under a platform environment and the folded

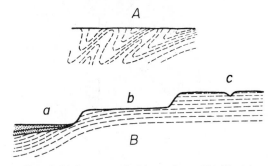

FIG. 1. Main types of plain surfaces. (A) Displain. (B) various types of conplains: (a) sediplain (young); (b) stratiplain; (c) sediplain (ancient, of relict type).

Fig. 2. A "displain" or discordant plain, where a basement of orogenic Paleozoic rocks (Tasman Geosyncline) is overlapped by almost flat-lying Mesozoic sediments, raised by epeirogenic warping to about 400 meters, somewhat reviving the drainage and slope systems. *Note*: Wheat farming, characteristic of such plainlands. Place: Darling Downs, Queensland, Australia. (Photo: Queensland Railways).

nature of the underlying structure produced during the orogenic stage. The formation of a displain is connected with the completion of the orogenic stage of evolution of a given area of the earth's crust and transition to the platform stage. Examples are: Piedmont Belt of the Appalachians, Canadian Shield, Donets Belt, Baltic Shield (see Fig. 2).

(B) Conplain. Conplain (from the Latin *concordare*—to conform), or concordant plain, is characterized by the conformity between the general plain nature of the land surface and horizontal (or warped) bedding of the underlying rock formations. The topography and the geological structure of conplains are both formed during the platform stage in the evolution of a given area in the earth's crust. Among the conplains, the following sub-types of plain surface are distinguishable (see Fig. 1B):

(a) Surfaces coinciding with the uppermost layer of some sedimentary sequence, and having a definite age, are the *sediplains* (from the Latin *sedimentum*—sediment), or sedimentary plain. Widely known are the low accumulation surfaces, usually of Quaternary and Pliocene age—*the younger sediplains*. Examples: lowlands of the Gulf of Mexico coastal region, Caspian Lowlands. *The ancient sediplains* occur in platform regions which were raised by epeirogenic movements. Despite a possibly varied erosion, the ancient sediplains display many features of primary accumulation topography. An example is the high level of the Volga region plateau formed during Paleogene time; also several Tertiary and Cretaceous plains of North Africa and Australia.

(b) Surfaces formed by agents of continental denudation or abrasion at a considerably lower level than the original level at which the accumulation occurred (the sediplain), are *stratiplains* (from the Latin *stratum*—layer) i.e., stripped or stratiform plains. Examples: the Pliocene level of the Volga region plateau and the Miocene–Pontian level of the Paris basin (see Fig. 3).

Surfaces of the displain type make up about 30% of the total area of the flatlands of the world. The larger part (about 70%) of great plains is occupied by various types of conplains—the original flatland surfaces, created and developed under platform conditions.

As a whole, the platform-type plains cannot be classified as peneplains or other types of denudation surfaces. Young and ancient primary flatlands, spared by erosion and created by marine or continental accumulation, are very common within the boundaries of platforms. However, the general flatland nature of platform relief cannot be considered as the product purely of exogenetic agents such as denudation and accumulation. The cause of the flatland nature of platforms is more complex and is founded on geotectonic conditions and the interaction between the endogenetic and exogenetic processes within the platforms. Elevations formed on platforms featuring small vertical movements (upwarping) are compensated for by denudation, while the subsidence of similar magnitude (downwarping) is compensated for by accumulation of sediments.

(4) Planation Surfaces

The compensation for tectonic movements by exogenetic processes is very efficient in the shelf zone and on land directly adjacent to the base level of erosion. This is where there is a development of

Fig. 3. An ancient "stratiplain" (visible to the left) of nearly horizontal Tertiary rocks, interracted by a younger one, a young "sediplain". Place: Murray River, at Nildottie, South Australia. (Photo: South Australian Government).

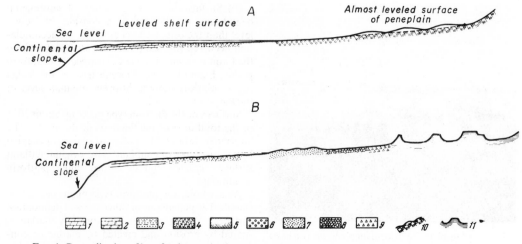

Fig. 4. Generalized profiles of polygenetic planation surfaces.
  A. Profile under humid climatic conditions.
  B. Profile under arid climatic conditions.
  1. Submarine plain (shelf), of organic sediments.
  2. Submarine plain (shelf) of mixed organic and chemical sediments.
  3. Submarine sandy-clay plain (shelf).
  4. Mixed abrasion-accumulation type plain.
  5. Abrasion-type plain.
  6. Deltaic and fluvial plain.
  7. Deltaic and fluvial plain with eolian sand cover.
  8. Playa-type plain.
  9. Proluvium-type plain (Bajada).*
  10. River terraces and peneplain profile.
  11. Denudation surface of pediplain type with relict elevations.

  * *Proluvium* is used in the U.S.S.R. for ephemeral stream-laid deposits in semiarid fans, i.e., *bajada* or *piedmont* types (qq.v.).

polygenetic planation surfaces representing the combination of various denudation-type and accumulation-type plains, having the same age and connected with the same base level of erosion. The general scheme of polygenetic surfaces is as follows:

Subaerial Denudation-type Plains (peneplains, pediplains)	→	Subaerial Accumulation-type Plains (lacustrine, fluvial)	→	Plains of Abrasion and of Marine Accumulation-type (shelf)

The formation of accumulation-type plains depends on the deposition of material removed from areas where denudation is dominant. Variations in structure of polygenetic planation surfaces under conditions of humid and arid climate are shown in Fig. 4.

The polygenetic (denudation–accumulation) type surface may be separated from the main base level of erosion by a general stage of uplift, thus becoming a surface of relict type. The ancient planation surfaces within the platform only undergo deformation of comparatively small magnitude and thus preserve the features of flatland. Lateral erosion

(corrasion) by rivers, parallel recession of the slopes (development of pediments) and general abrasion also contribute to the preservation of the form of ancient surfaces in modern relief. All these forces contribute mainly to lateral erosion resulting in the preservation of monadnocks as well as broad areas where ancient denudation and accumulation levels were both preserved.

It is now recognized that many ancient levels reflecting the relief of flatlands are of polygenetic nature. They include the areas characterized by both denudation and accumulation. Therefore, such surfaces should be more correctly called *planation surfaces*, the more general term (Brown, 1961), instead of erosion surfaces.

(5) Geomorphic Cycles

The surfaces of all great plains feature to some degree a step-like character (see *Treppen Concept*, of Penck). The individual levels making the so-called geomorphological staircase represent the relict platform surfaces of various ages. The steps and ledges separating them are evidence of *geomorphic cycles* (the geographic cycle, according to W. M. Davis) which affected a given territory.

TABLE 1. CYCLIC SURFACES OF SOME GREAT PLAINS (NAMES, ELEVATIONS IN METERS, AGE)

South Africa (L. C. King)	Russian Plain (southeast)	East Siberian Plateau
Gondwana (1200 to 1500), J_1	Mesozoic (350 to 450), J_3–K_{1-2}	Early Mesozoic (500 to 1500), T_2–J_1
African (600 to 900), K_2–Pg_3	Paleogene (280 to 380), Pg_{2-3}	Middle Mesozoic (700 to 800), J_3–K_1
Nossob level (300 to 800), N_1–N_2	Miocene–Pliocene (200 to 240), N_1^3–N_2^1	Late Mesozoic–early Tertiary (300 to 500), K_2–Pg–N_1
Surface and terraces of Congo cycle (180 to 300), N_2(?)–Q	Late Pliocene (110 to 160), N_2^3	Late Pliocene–early Quaternary (200 to 300), N_2^{2-3}–Q_1

N = Neogene (younger Tertiary), Pg = Paleogene (older Tertiary). Subscripts $_{1\,2\,3}$ indicate early, middle or late.

Each cycle includes the *phase of planation* (frequently coinciding in time with phases of the submergence of lands and transgression of the seas), the *phase of dissection* of relief, and the formation of ledges between the steps (in time—phases of marine regression and/or epeirogenic uplifts). According to the terminology by W. M. Davis (1909), almost all geomorphological Mesozoic and Cenozoic cycles within the great plains should be classified as cycles of an interrupted type, because the phases of uplift never allowed the denudation agents to achieve a complete planation of the relief inherited from earlier cycles.

The study of planation surfaces, their dating according to the geological time scale, and determination of the geomorphic cycles during which they formed, is of great importance in the study of geotectonic movements and major climatic rhythms.

The analysis of planation surfaces is the principal means of reconstructing the geological evolution during the Mesozoic and Cenozoic times in regions which developed during long time intervals under subaerial conditions and where almost no marine Mesozoic and Cenozoic sediments are present (South Africa, Eastern Siberia).

As a whole, the cyclic surfaces of planation affecting the flatlands have not up to now been studied sufficiently. At the present time, bibliographic data on cyclic surfaces are only available for a few such plains. Some of these data are included in Table 1.

The inadequate study of cyclic structures of great plains of the world makes it difficult to correlate geomorphic cycles. In 1950, L. C. King introduced the notion of *synchrony* of geomorphological cycles over the entire world during post-Paleozoic history. In contrast to synchrony, the newer data emphasize the *metachronic* (out-of-phase) nature of cycles in some parts of the world.

Thus, in the west of North America, in Eastern Siberia (Fig. 5), and in China, the Miocene phase of uplift did not develop (or was very weak). On the other hand, this phase contributed greatly to the formation of the topography in the Russian platform, Western Europe, Australia and Africa. A phase of intensive uplifts occurred very generally during the Pliocene and the entire Quaternary period. Lack of coincidence in the rhythm of geomorphic cycles in the above-mentioned flatlands may be noted during the early Tertiary and Mesozoic times. It is possible to suggest that the geomorphic cycles and the rhythm of epeirogenic movements in the Indian–Atlantic and the Pacific segments of the globe were of metachronic nature. The peculiarities in rhythm of platform movements in the Indian–Atlantic zone reflect the course of the Alpine stage of diastrophism, while the Pacific zone corresponds to the Mesozoic (Yanshanian) stage of diastrophism.

(6) High and Low Platforms

Each geomorphic cycle represents a stage in the evolution of relief characterized by a definite

FIG. 5. A planation surface in Siberia (Taimyr). Hummocky moss-grassed tundra. (Photo: S. Strelkov).

trend. The evolution of the earth's relief during the Mesozoic and Cenozoic times featured a gradually increasing uplift of the continents, deepening of the oceanic troughs, and a general complication in the earth's relief. The process of gradual uplift and complication in orographic structure also involved the platform plains and established the main trend in the geomorphological evolution of the latter during Mesozoic and Cenozoic eras.

The process of uplift and the increase in altitudes during the Mesozoic and Cenozoic processes differed on various platforms and requires a subdivision into high- and low-level platforms.

The *upland platforms* (South African "high veld" type and East Siberian plateau) and *lowland platforms* (Russian Plain and North American Plain, excluding the Prairies Province) are the two basic morphological types of flatlands. Today the upland plains are more widespread on earth than the lowland plains.

The subdivision of platforms during the Mesozoic and Cenozoic eras into upland and lowland platforms cannot be connected in any way with the early history of those platforms reflected by the age of their folded basement. For example, the Russian and East Siberian platforms are both ancient (Precambrian), but one of them belongs to the lowland type, while the other belongs to the upland-type platforms.

The formation of upland platforms should be considered as a process accompanying the reconstruction of the structure and relief of the earth during the Mesozoic–Cenozoic times, isolation of highly elevated continents, deepening of oceans, and development of rejuvenated orogens. Rejuvenated mountains (of epiplatform type) and high platforms in the zones influenced by the oceanic structures were most active. Thus, the high position of the East Siberian platform is connected with the general uplift of eastern Eurasia adjacent to the Pacific Ocean and the prevalence of rejuvenated mountains in this region. It is possible that the newest intensive uplifts of eastern Eurasia are of a compensating nature, being related to the progressive deepening and increase in width of the Pacific depression accompanied by the flow of the Upper mantle mass transfer under the continent.

The following spatial and genetic connections can be outlined between the major elements of the earth:

(7) Internal Morphostructural Subdivision

During the Quaternary period the plains (platforms) were not limited exclusively to general warping of epeirogenic character. Differential movements of separate blocks and individual structural elements developed in addition to and against a background of these warping movements. These epeirogenic movements continue during the Holocene epoch, as indicated by the results of repeated geodetic measurements (see *Neotectonics* and *Crustal Movements—Contemporary*). At the present time, the concept of mobility of the earth's crust in both the orogenic and the platform regions (where many ancient structures continue to develop) is well established. This idea replaces the old opinion about the tectonic stability of present-day platforms.

The tectonic movements within the platforms are reflected by the relief and are indicated by the structures (*morphostructures*, q.v.) of various orders. During the entire Mesozoic and Cenozoic time, up to the most recent time, the formulation of arches (anteclises), basins (synclises), swells, domes and troughs continued in the platforms. This has been reflected by the topography in the form of elevations and depressions of the plain surface. Faulting of various kinds also continued and is most clearly reflected by stream patterns.

The major (morphostructural) elements of the plains' relief include the marginal and individual accumulation plains (subsiding regions), relict ranges, basement peneplains of crystalline shields, young stratified plateaus, and ancient, eroded escarpments and cuestas.

The most recent deformations of the earth's crust reflected by the plains' relief demonstrate the role of inheritance from more ancient structures, both for the sedimentary cover and for the basement platforms. The marginal and the interior parts of platforms differ substantially because of different inheritance of ancient structures.

Positive, uplift or *Accordance-type* morphostructures are predominant in the *marginal zones*. These morphostructures reflect the inherited movements of basement blocks. Examples: the Gulf of Mexico lowland, the Ozark Plateau, the Caspian coastal lowland, and the Central Russian Plateau.

Inversion-type morphostructures are widely developed in the internal zones. The *inversion* (q.v.) of relief here reflects both tectonic revival and the

TABLE 2. RELATIONS OF MAJOR ELEMENTS

Continental Margin (continental flexure, J. Bourcart) $\longrightarrow$	Rejuvenated Mountains (the activated part of the platforms—*les bourrelets marginaux*, of P. Birot) $\longrightarrow$	Upland Platform Plains $\longrightarrow$	"Stable" Continental Areas, little affected by deformations during the Mesozoic and Cenozoic Eras (low platforms, ancient mountains, and others)

action of erosion. Examples: Michigan Basin, Allegheny Plateau, North Uvaly Plateau, Volga Plateau, eastern Australian "downs". Some major forms of relief developed along the periphery of mountain structures, in the region of foredeeps involved in the uplifts of orogens, also have the inversion-type morphostructure. Examples: Great Plains (of North America); Volhynian–Podolian uplands (of the Russian Platform).

The age of the major topographic elements of plainlands is considerable. Many broad lowlands and uplands in the marginal zones of platforms started to form as early as the pre-Mesozoic time. A series of major relief forms dates from the Mesozoic and early Tertiary. At the same time, the revival of tectonic trends resulting in formation of new major features continues up into the Quaternary period.

(8) Morphoclimatic Zoning

If the distribution of major forms of the plains' relief (*i.e. Morphostructure*) is subject to tectonic processes, then the distribution of minor forms (*i.e. Morphosculpture*) reflects contemporary and ancient climatic conditions. The broad expanses of the great plains where the meridional climatic zonation is most pronounced, supply the best examples of the *latitudinal morphoclimatic zoning*.

The following main morphoclimatic zones (from north to south) can be distinguished according to the *Recent* relief-forming processes in the plains: (a) the *cryogenic zone* with permafrost, commonly featuring thermokarst, polygonal soil pattern, and solifluction associated with rock waste (Fig. 5 and 6); (b) *zone of fluvial relief of temperate latitudes* with intensive formation of gullies and river systems with the process of peneplanation; (c) *zone of semiarid and arid conditions* characterized by considerable eolian activity (deflation, formation of sand dunes and barkhans) with processes of pediplanation; (d) *zone of fluvial relief in the equatorial belt*, dif-

fering from the zone of fluvial relief of temperate zones, the latter receiving a considerable contribution of solifluction during the formation of slopes.

In addition to the landforms that reflect the peculiarities of Recent exogenetic processes and Recent climatic environment, the plains have preserved well the *relict landforms* connected with the Pleistocene glaciation. The distribution of such relict forms exhibits patterns and rules of its own which correspond to the relief of the glacial period. The morphological landscapes of glacial origin are clearly visible as one travels from north to the south. Regions of glacial erosion (scouring), as well as regions of glacial accumulation (moraines and till plains), periglacial regions, regions of Pleistocene pluvial phases, and the intrazonal regions of marine transgressions of glacial and post-glacial epochs are thus exhibited, extending to the equator.

The Recent morphological landscape of plains features super-position of young, actively developing forms, over the more ancient relict forms. Thus, new lines of erosion are superposed over the land forms of glacial accumulation (terminal moraines, eskers, kames and outwash plains), and these in turn are being altered by periglacial processes in northern Siberia and Canada, creating new forms of cryogenic relief, and in the plain of Patagonia—the latest arid forms (deflation, kettles, barkhans). In Recent deserts, the erosional forms, inherited from the pluvial epochs and preserved by the protective desert crusts, are subject to only a very slow alteration by deflation, or are gradually buried by a transgressive sand cover.

In many parts of the plains, the relict forms are dominant in the morphological landscape and determine the aspect of the latter. The morphological forms of the plains thus include forms of various ages and various generations. The age of minor forms (morphosculptures) are not known to be older than Quaternary. This means that the minor forms of plains (morphosculptures) as a rule are younger than the major forms of morphostructure.

Y. A. MESCHERIKOV

FIG. 6. Plainland modified by periglacial phenomena. Landscape in typical tundra subzone, Gydan Peninsula, Siberia. (Photo: S. Strelkov).

References

Beloussov, V. V., 1962, "Basic Problems in Geotectonics," New York, McGraw-Hill Book Co. (translated by P. T. Broneer), 816pp.

Birot, P., 1958, "Morphologie Structurale," Paris, 2 vols.

Brown, E. M., 1961, "Britain and Appalachia: a study in the correlation and dating of planation surfaces," *Publ. Inst. Brit. Geographers*, No. 29.

Büdel, J., 1961, "Morphogenese des Festlandes in Abhängigkeit von den Klimazonen," *Naturwissenschaften*, **48**(9).

Davis, W. M., 1909, "Geographical Essays," Boston (New York, Dover reprint, 1954.)

Gerasimov, I. P., 1959, "Structural Relief Features in

the Territory of the USSR and Genesis of These Features," Moscow (in Russian).

King, L. C., 1950, "The study of the world's plainlands: a new approach is geomorphology," *Quart. J. Geol. Soc. London*, **106**, 101–131.

King, L. C., 1951, "South African Scenery," Edinburgh and London.

King, L. C., 1962, "The Morphology of the Earth. A Study and Synthesis of World Scenery," Edinburgh and London, Oliver & Boyd, 699pp. (Second ed., 1967.)

Melton, F. A., 1959, "Aerial photographs and structural geomorphology," *J. Geol.*, **67**, 351–370.

Mescherikov, Y. A., 1964, "Structural Geomorphology of Plainlands," Moscow (First ed., 1960; both in Russian only).

Cross-references: *Crustal Movements—Contemporary; Cycles, Geomorphic; Denudation; Endogenic Dynamics; Etchplain; Exogenic Dynamics; Glacial Geology; Holocene; Inversion of Topography; Morphostructure; Neotectonics; Peneplain; Quaternary; Relict Landforms; Treppen Concept.* Vol. I: *Abyssal Plains.*

PLANATION SURFACE

G. K. Gilbert (1877, pp. 126–127) wrote: "The process of carrying away the rock so as to produce an even surface, and at the same time covering it with an alluvial deposit, is the process of planation" (see also *Erosion, Pediplanation* and *Peneplain*).

As investigations of base-leveled surfaces have proceeded in differing climatic environments in the ninety years since Powell and Dutton first described them in the American southwest, geomorphologists have felt themselves obliged to propose a number of mechanisms for their fashioning and a variety of names to describe the plains produced. A state of confusion has arisen because of the proliferation of terms and attempts to translate them into other languages, particularly into French and German. The general term "planation surface" is now employed to describe the geographically plain surface which is the end product of all processes of planation by erosion. It is synonymous with the term "erosion surface" frequently employed by British writers, the use of which leads to considerable confusion as many surfaces which may be quite correctly called surfaces of erosion are by no means plane in character. Planation surface is an omnibus term and includes the Davisian *peneplain* (q.v.) or peneplane, the panplane, the pediment and pediplain, the wave-cut platform, etch plains, stripped or structural plains, savanna plains, periglacial pediments, berms and straths.

E. H. BROWN

References

Gilbert, G. K., 1877, "Report on the geology of the Henry Mountains," *U.S. Geol. Surv. Rocky Mt. Reg.* 160pp.

Lobeck, A. K., 1939, "Geomorphology," New York, McGraw-Hill Book Co., 731pp.

Cross-references: *Base Level; Erosion; Etchplain; Pediplanation; Peneplain; Platforms—Wave-Cut.*

PLATEAU

A plateau is "an elevated tract of comparatively flat or level ground," according to the Oxford English Dictionary, a term of French origin (pl., either *plateaux* or *plateaus*; the latter is more usual today). "Literally a *platform*, introduced by the French geographer Bauche ... a table-land or high level region" (David Page, 1864). Dana (1895) recommended an arbitrary lower limit of height of 1000 feet. Fenneman (1916) pointed out that "it may be flat or completely dissected by deep valleys. Hence, it follows that a plateau may also be a plain, or the uneroded part of it may be a plain." Since plateaus of this sort would appear to be upwarped (or faulted and elevated) plains, Powell (1896, p. 39) proposed to call them "*diastrophic plateaus.*"

Some geomorphologists (e.g., Lobeck) reserve "plateau" for high plains of flat-lying rocks. An uplifted massif or complex of ancient rocks, previously peneplaned to a more or less flat erosion surface, such as the Spanish Meseta or the Black Forest, is still regarded as a plateau in the broad sense. French geomorphologists, however, use the term "meseta" in a technical sense for such a massif.

A second use of "plateau" is in oceanography, and if there is any doubt of its application, it should be written *submarine plateau*; sometimes "platform" is used in the same sense—an elevation of the ocean floor with a more or less flat top and steep sides.

Several combinations with "plateau" are found in geologic and geomorphic terminology (see *A.G.I. Glossary*). Thus "*plateau plains* are extensive areas of plain surmounted by a sublevel summit area and bordered more or less completely by

FIG. 1. The Middle Siberian Plateau; valley of the Kotui River. A slightly dissected plateau of subhorizontal Paleozoic rocks overlapping the Anabar Precambrian Massif (the Angara Shield of Suess). (Photo: S. Strelkov).

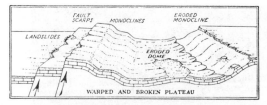

FIG. 2. Warped and broken plateaus, characteristic of the Colorado Plateau (Lobeck, 1939). (By permission of McGraw-Hill Book Co., N.Y.)

escarpments" (Hill, 1900, p. 8). "*Plateau mountain—* the folds of a mountain chain frequently pass abruptly into the horizontal strata of a basalt plateau which, when largely denuded and eroded, may resolve itself into a series of plateau mountains" (Heilprin, 1890). Dana (1895) distinguished two plateau types (a) *marginal plateaus* (as with the Appalachian Plateau) and (b) *intermont(ane) plateaus* (such as the Colorado and Tibet Plateaus and Altiplanos of South America). "*Plateau glacier*" is a term for a special type of mountain ("valley") glacier which occurs in certain high upland regions, e.g., Norway, Spitsbergen.

"*Lava plateau*" (or "vulcanic plateau" of Powell, 1896, p. 40) is a more or less flat-lying high plain or tableland underlain by extensive lava flows and punctuated by volcanic centers, fissures, plugs or cinder cones, of relatively low relief; the lava type is either tholeiitic basalt or olivine basalt types commonly known in petrology as *plateau basalt* or *flood basalt*. Classic examples are the Thulean Province (Brito–Arctic: Scotland, Ireland and Iceland), the Columbia Plateau (of the U.S. Pacific northwest), the Deccan Plateau (of India), the Ethiopian Plateau (Africa).

For many years it has been tacitly assumed that the genesis of plateaus required a widespread upheaval of the earth's crust, upwarping (Argand's *plis de fond*) about a great curvature of arc (radius 500–1000 km or so). Indeed Gilbert (in his famous Lake Bonneville monograph, 1890) proposed the term *epeirogeny* to cover upwarping and downwarping on a continental scale. Quite mysterious forces were involved; nothing being demonstrated,

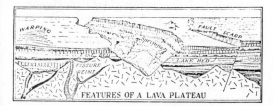

FIG. 3. Lava plateaus, characteristic of the Columbia Basalt region of the Pacific Northwest (Lobeck, 1939). (By permission of McGraw-Hill Book Co., N.Y.)

TABLE 1. MAJOR PLATEAUS AND HIGH PLAINS OF THE WORLD (KOSSINNA, 1933)

	Mean Elevation (in meters)	Area (1000 km²)
German Subalpine Foreland	500	35
Iceland Plateau	600	70
New Castille Plateau	600	60
Old Castille Plateau	700	70
French Massif Central	700	70
Scandinavian Highlands	700	350
Deccan Plateau	800	400
Shotts (Atlas) Plateau	800	80
Nejd Plateau (Arabia)	900	700
Anatolian Plateau (Asia Minor)	1000	500
Kalahari	1000	2100
Tarim Basin	1100	600
Gobi	1100	1650
East African Lakes Plateau	1200	1000
Iranian Plateau	1300	2500
Great Basin (U.S.A.)	1500	600
Colorado Plateau	1800	500
Greenland Ice Plateau	1900	1870
Armenian Highlands	2000	300
Yunnan Highlands	2000	300
Mexican Plateau (Alti Plano)	2000	350
Ethiopian Plateau	2200	450
Antarctic Ice Plateau	2500	12,800
Ecuador Plateau (Alti Plano)	3000	15
Bolivian Plateau (Alti Plano)	3800	350
Pamir Plateau	4000	100
Tibetan Plateau	4500	2000
(including Central Tibet;	4800	600
and West Tibet)	5000	200

the concept of upwelling convection currents in the mantle has sometimes been invoked. But for these too there is also no direct evidence and little theoretical evidence.

Growing acceptance of the hypothesis that the paleomagnetic measurements in ancient rocks may be taken as indicators of polar shift has brought with it the corollary that if the axis of rotation relative to the continental crust is caused to shift from time to time, then after each shift there will be a period of anomalous elevations of the crust corresponding to the relative rise or fall of the oceanic geoid, to conform as closely as possible to the theoretical spheroid (Fairbridge, 1961). In consequence, it has been postulated that the relative motion of the North Pole in the period Cretaceous to Present from eastern Siberia to the north of Greenland, some 30° of arc, should cause a drowning of the central Pacific region. Here, indeed, there is a widespread distribution of guyots and atolls that contain evidence for a rise of water level (or sinking of crust) of the order of 1–2 km. A single secular shift

FIG. 4. A plateau basalt (Tertiary) forming a mesa near Hughenden, Queensland, Australia. (Oblique air photo: F. Whitehouse).

is not proposed but rather a series of short zigzag motions; however, very rapid motions are ruled out because the coral atolls had time to maintain their upward growth, but were interrupted from time to time, which might be when the pole swung back for a short period. This drowning would affect certain quadrants; others would emerge as the sites of potential plateaus.

Areas of either negative or positive elevation anomaly, consequent upon polar shift, would be expected to rapidly adjust themselves isostatically unless something happened that would "fix" their out-of-balance position. Today both the mid-Pacific and the Colorado Plateaus, for example, are gravitationally compensated, yet their crustal elevations are quite anomalous, respectively too low and too high. It is believed that a series of phase changes would take place in the upper 100 km of the mantle, leading to a "lightening" of the sub-plateau material. The seismologists have recently commented on the lower velocities in the subcontinental mantle. Hsu has calculated that a 5% expansion of the mantle's upper 100 km (such as might be due to garnet-olivine transitions) would hold up a plateau 3 km high. Some renewal of mantle material might be necessary (Thompson and Talwani, 1964). Since the energy required to carry out a phase change from the high-pressure to the low-pressure state is very much less than that required for the opposite reaction, it follows that once such a plateau was established it would be a long time before it collapsed. Thus the Colorado

Plateaus (2 km elevation) have been in existence about 50 million years probably slowly gaining in relative altitude. Central Africa and Tibet are greater still but possibly somewhat younger.

No 2–3 km high plateau is found which is cut off abruptly by the ocean. The marginal areas are stepped down with series of fault blocks and monoclinal flexures. It would appear that horizontal support for such plateaus is lacking and that after each crustal adjustment that leads to the building of plateaus, there is a concomitant dropping down of the marginal areas.

RHODES W. FAIRBRIDGE

References

A.G.I., 1960, "Glossary of Geology," Washington, D.C., *Am. Geol. Inst.*, 325pp. + 72pp. suppl.

Dana, J. D., 1895, "Manual of Geology," Fourth ed., New York, American Book Co.

Dutton, C. E., 1880, "Geology of the High Plateaus of Utah," *U.S. Geogr. Geol. Surv. of Rocky Mt. Region*, Washington.

Dutton, C. E., 1882, "Tertiary history of Grand Canyon district," *U.S. Geol. Surv. Mon.*, **2.**

Fairbridge, R. W., 1961, "Eustatic changes in sea level," in *"Physics and Chemistry of the Earth,"* Vol. 4, pp. 99–185, London, Pergamon Press.

Fenneman, N. M., 1916, "Geology of Cincinnati and vicinity," *Ohio Geol. Surv. Bull.*, **19**(4), 202pp.

Gilbert, G. K., 1890, "Lake Bonneville," *U.S. Geol. Surv. Mon.*, **1,** 438pp.

Heilprin, Angelo, 1890, "The principles of geology," *Iconographic Encyclopedia* (Philadelphia), **7.**

Hill, R. T., 1900, "Topographic Atlas of the United States," Folio 3, *Phys. Geogr. of the Texas region.*

Hsu, K. J., 1965, "Isostasy, crustal thinning, mantle changes, and the disappearance of ancient land masses," *Am. J. Sci.,* **263,** 97–109.

Kossinna, E., 1933, "Die Erdoberfläche," in (Gutenberg, B., editor), "Handbuch d. Geophysik," Berlin, Borntraeger, vol. 2, 869–954.

Lobeck, A. K., 1939, "Geomorphology," New York, McGraw-Hill Book Co., 731pp.

Page, David, 1864, "Advanced Textbook of Physical Geography," Edinburgh, W. Blackwood & Sons.

Powell, J. W., 1896, "The Physiography of the United States," New York, American Book Co., *Natl. Geogr. Soc. Monog. 1* (Physiographic processes, pp. 1–32; Physiographic features, pp. 33–64).

Thompson, G. A., and Talwani, M., 1964, "Crustal structure from Pacific Basin to Central Nevada," *J. Geophys. Res.,* **69**(22), 4813–4837.

Cross-references: *Mountains; Plains.* Vol. I: *Submarine Plateau.* Vol. II: *Earth—Geology of the Planet.* Vol. V: *Isostasy; Polar Migration.*

PLATFORMS—WAVE-CUT

The fundamental erosion form of coastal geomorphology is the littoral abrasion feature or wave-cut platform, known under a number of more or less synonymous terms—the platform of marine abrasion, or of marine erosion, the wave-beveled platform, bench or terrace. It is defined in the Schieferdecker "Geological Nomenclature" (1959, section by Van Straaten, Guilcher, Baulig, W. W. Williams and Häntzschel) as "the rock shelf that is produced by the combined action of the direct attack on the cliff base, the to-and-fro motion on the wave base, and the undertow."

The Schieferdecker analysis distinguishes the *wave-cut platform* (as the contemporary feature), from a *marine terrace* ("strip of fossil wave-cut platform, at the landward of which the old cliff is situated...").

The zone of intense wave action is also the "ecotope" of a great variety of marine organisms. Indeed the intertidal belt is often regarded as the site of the most concentrated biologic activity on the face of the Earth. The role of *biologic littoral erosion* is reviewed in another article (see *Biological Erosion of Limestone Coasts*). The wave effect is not limited to the intertidal zone (the *mesolittoral zone*), but reaches also to the range of spray (*supralittoral zone*), while the intense turbulence below low tide level (*sublittoral zone*) provides both sediment scour and biologic aeration.

"Normal" Profile of Equilibrium

The contemporary rock-cut shelf or bench is only part of a general "profile of equilibrium" according to classical workers that approximates to *wave base* (q.v.). The latter was formerly taken to be about −200 meters, but modern studies show that vigorous wave-base erosion is limited to less than 20 meters. Even so, this profile is slowly established and may be seen only in unconsolidated sediments.

In certain rocks on favored coasts may often be seen the result of a smoothing of numerous superposed wave-cut platforms formed at various times of the late Pleistocene and Holocene. This history of multiple attack on rather stable coasts leads to a blurring of the sharp outlines and obscuring of the deeper levels by sediments, so that a pseudoequilibrium profile develops. It should be emphasized that this is only possible on a rocky coast that has been subjected to a long history of eustatic oscillations, covering usually the last Interglacial plus the high Holocene stage, say 20,000 + 6000 years of effective wave action.

Horizontal Platforms

The "pure" wave-cut platform of the contemporary sea level stand is not always easy to distinguish. It requires a rather favored rock type in an uncomplicated area. It does not slope gently out to the continental shelf.

The following notes are largely from a published report (Fairbridge, 1952): The ideal wave-cut platform of today is *steep-to* on the outside edge and is essentially horizontal on the surface. This means that the platform does *not* slope gently outwards to merge into the offshore profile that descends to −200 meters or so, as we would have to believe from textbook figures (e.g., Johnson, 1919-38, Fig. 37). A soft, sandy, or muddy coast may well be endowed with a gently sloping offshore profile, but not

FIG. 1. Contemporary wave-cut notch at the foot of the Pleistocene coral limestone cliffs at Vavau, northern Tonga Is. (southwest Pacific). Traces of elevated marine terraces may be seen at several hundred foot intervals, due to regional uplift.

Fig. 2. Wave-cut platform is steep-to at its outer edge. Tertiary limestone cliffs near Port Campbell, Victoria (Australia), rising 200 ft. above sea level. Note long swells (from the Antarctic) are unbroken owing to the steep off-shore slope. (Photo: Victoria Govt. Railways.)

a rocky coast; in fact, the cliff foot on the average rocky coast is being eaten back more rapidly than is the outer margin of the platform.

Mechanism

The causes of horizontal wave-cut platforms have led to much discussion and controversy. The question is mainly the problem of whether the role of waves is a primary, mechanical one or a secondary one in merely removing debris, rotted by subaerial weathering.

The *theory of marine denudation*, favoring the mechanical role of waves, was first outlined by de la Beche and developed by Ramsay (1846) and by Lyell. It was studied further by von Richthofen (1886) who applied to it the term *abrasion*, in the sense that waves have very little mechanical cutting power unless "armed" by sand, gravel and boulders. A mechanically abraded surface tends to become smooth and polished, while chemical *corrosion* (seen best on limestone coasts) is sharp and jagged. The evidence of mechanical work is most clear on the hard rocky coasts of northwestern Europe and New England (where it was observed by Gulliver, Davis, Johnson and others). The theory was developed by

some to the point of believing that whole continents could be denuded to sea level by wave attack. To quote Johnson (1919): "If a land stands still long enough, the waves will reduce it to an ultimate abrasion platform... no matter how great may have been the original extent of the land." The Johnson school imagined that an entire continent might in time be reduced to a submarine peneplain.

The *theory of chemical denudation* postulated that acid rainwater, soaking through the pore spaces and rock joints, would eventually lead to a general rotting. This is now accepted as the basic principle of weathering and soil formation, but in the last century, it received little notice. Where such a weathered profile is attacked by the sea, a horizontal platform will preferentially appear in the intertide belt. In 1866, G. Maw was struck by "the level surfaces of sea-coast reefs," indicating the base level of rapid coast erosion at sea level; the logical conclusion was that "the sea does no material work below the tidal range," except in certain very exposed places. The general tendency of marine erosion is towards a straightening of a coastline, while drowning institutes indentations formerly occupied by subaerially formed valleys. Maw's accurate description of the normal contemporary horizontal bench or offshore reef in England is a model which today could hardly be bettered elsewhere: "If we examine the sea-bed between high and low water mark, on any cliff-girt shore it is impossible not to be struck with the singularly level disposition of the reef surfaces extending seaward, which once formed the foundations of the old cliffs. Their general height would be a trifle above that of low tide, and any irregularities of surface will not exceed one or two feet. This well-marked lower limit to the erosive action of the sea is not confined to hard rocky coasts, but will be found to hold good in the softest strata."

Fig. 3. Not every rock type develops a wave-cut platform: massive igneous and metamorphic rocks weather most rapidly along joints and spheroidally. Victor Harbour, South Australia. There are traces of an emerged pre-Wisconsin terrace at 8–10 meters. (Photo: South Australian Government.)

FIG. 4. Rainfall and slopewash may cut the cliff back more rapidly than wave action attacks the platform. Rotted debris is removed mechanically by the waves. The sea actually preserves the platform from subaerial weathering. Apollo Bay, Victoria (Australia.)

The same thing was realized, too, by W. Whitaker (1867), who concluded: "The sea, therefore, does not by itself destroy the land, but is largely helped by atmospheric actions." Mellard Reade (1885) agreed, but claimed, in fact, that this was thoroughly understood by Hutton already a century before. Reade remarked: "The chemical agency decomposes the matrix.... The ocean acts merely as a mechanical distributor of matter.... The action of subaerial erosion is ... unlimited, except by sea-level."

It is interesting to quote A. H. Green (1882): "The sea to a very large extent only finishes the work begun for it by subaerial denudating agents" (p. 206). "It must be noted that the destructive action of the sea is confined almost entirely to the belt between high and low water mark. Within that space the rise and fall of the tides and the forces of the breakers grind down any loose matter exposed to their action. These agencies, however, cease to have any effect on the bottom covered by a moderate depth of water, and hence very nearly all the denuding work of the sea is coast denudation. The drifting of the rough sediment over the bottom by under-currents may produce some abrasion, but its amount cannot be very much" (p. 207). Jukes-

Browne stated (1893, p. 135): "Sea-waves can only act along one plane, and its currents, though able to erode soft sands and clays, can make but little impression on more solid rocks." He suggested that low-water mark was the lowest limit of subaerial forces; it was in fact "a line of non-erosion" below which accumulation would normally begin. "On a rocky shore the tendency of these conditions is to produce a horizontal or gently sloping platform, the outer edge of which corresponds to the line of non-erosion, so that its surface is bare at low water" (1884, p. 120).

J. D. Dana (1880, p. 676) said: "The lower limit of erosion is above low-tide level.... The wearing action of waves on a coast is mainly confined to a height between high and low tides." It is not without significance that Dana had traveled the Pacific extensively, including Australia and New Zealand, while Gulliver, Davis, Barrell, Johnson, and others formulated their ideas on the isostatically unstable coasts of New England (which are suffering post-Glacial reactions).

Nansen (1905), recognizing the efficacy of subaerial erosion in Norway, believed that only such loosening and weakening could break down the extremely hard metamorphic (Caledonide) rocks, enabling the waves to move the debris to form the famous "strand-flat." Observations by W. von Zahn (1909) on the rocky coasts of Brittany and Normandy disclosed two distinct zones above and below mean sea level: a "Schliffzone" (smooth zone) below, affected by mechanical erosion, and a "Spritzzone" or "Brandungskarrenzone" (spray-etched zone) above, affected by chemical erosion.

The rather special position of limestone in relation to chemical solution, as indicated above, has long been recognized, though it was exaggerated by Murray, Agassiz, Gardiner, and Crossland. Solution of limestone in ordinary open seawater certainly does not take place beneath the surface. On the other hand, observations by Macfadyen (1930),

FIG. 5. Horizontal platform cut in Jurassic sandstones and siltstones at Apollo Bay, Victoria (Australia), seen at low tide.

FIG. 6. Horizontal platform cut in Triassic sandstones and shales near Illawarra, N.S.W. (Australia). Here, differential erosion plays a part, as well as subaerial rotting. (Photo: New South Wales Dept. of Tourist Activities.)

Kuenen (1933), and Fairbridge (1948) show that chemical erosion of limestone is accomplished by physicochemical and/or biochemical processes of seawater in its few surface inches near the shore. In this way, broad, flat marine benches are eroded, the level of which is at the low-tide limit. Maximum erosion, in protected places—i.e., where the actual sea level is not mechanically raised by wave action —is at mean sea level, and cliffs are deeply undercut at this level. As Kuenen says: "The solvent action is limited between the tidal range. The action of the sea is that of 'sawing' into the limestone."

Apart from the exceptional position occupied by limestone in this broad picture, the weakness of ordinary rocks to subaerial decay and their resistance to submarine mechanical attack has been specially emphasized by workers in New Zealand, where particularly fine examples of various benches were exposed. Noted in very early times by Dana (1849), a thorough explanation appears to have been first suggested by E. de C. Clarke: "Rock benches are developed in many places along the steeper parts of the shore-line, more commonly in the sedimentary rocks, but also in the volcanics. These benches consist of shelves cut out of the solid rock, generally horizontal ... it seems possible to ascribe the formation of rock benches to the cooperation of subaerial weathering, which causes the retreat of the cliffs, with marine transport, which removes the waste so-formed (in Bell and Clarke, 1909, p. 30).

Height of Platform

The precise elevation of the contemporary platform is a matter of importance. From many observations (Macfadyen, 1930; Kuenen, 1933; Fairbridge, 1948), it is claimed that the "normal" platform forms at the level of low-water springs. Excep-

tions are known; preexisting cavities in the rock (karst caverns and holes), lenticles of soft sand in the country rock, collapse structures, and so on, may all cause segments of the reef to be "abnormal." The occurrence of hard rock bands, gently dipping, may institute considerable confusion (Jutson, 1939). Very exposed positions may result in shore "ramps," where the bench slopes gently up on the inside owing to the nature of the swash profile. However, when viewed overall, the "abnormalities" find local explanations.

A problem in this connection was described from New Zealand by Bartrum (1926, 1935), where his "Old Hat" bench was already recognized by Dana and by Hochstetter. Its elevation is just below high-water level. Bartrum assumed that this is a contemporary bench, formed at the present stand of the sea, but in rocks of a particularly favorable sort and in fairly protected places; the rock below high-water level is supposed to be always saturated in protective seawater, while the overlying rock is subaerially weakened and prepared for removal by quite gentle waves. However, the base level of subaerial erosion is not high-water, but low-water springs; also, the role played by intertidal chemical processes should not be forgotten. Indeed, the "Old Hat" type of bench is a perfect example of the 10-feet eustatic platform which was actually formed only about five thousand years ago and is thus preserved in a surprisingly fresh state in favorable locations.

Admittedly, if we had not had the privilege of examining the phenomenon on many occasions under ideal conditions on limestone shores, we might very well have failed to realize that there had been multiple eustatic stands of the sea level during the last few thousand years, which have had the result of producing platforms a few feet above the present one—i.e., at 2–3, 5–6, and 10–11 feet

FIG. 7. Platform cut in steeply dipping Pleistocene eolianite on the west side of Garden Island, Western Australia, seen at low tide. Note undercut cliffs, stacks and boulders, affected by intertidal biochemical action.

FIG. 8. Wave-cut ramp between tide marks, cut in homogeneous calcareous eolianite; small gastropods browse on the algae. A broad flat low-tide platform extends on the seaward side, near Greenough River, Western Australia.

above datum, the present low-water level (see Kuenen, 1933; Fairbridge, 1947a, 1947b, 1948, 1949; Teichert, 1947, 1948).

Emerged Mid-Holocene and Late Pleistocene Platforms

Traces of older platforms can be seen in many parts of the world. Those formed during the last few thousand years are often surprisingly fresh. Even those partly covered by solifluction "Head" from the last glaciation (e.g., in southwest England) are still well preserved. They are difficult to identify from isostatically active areas, as in much of North America (north, northeast and northwest), or from unconsolidated sandy coasts, as along most of the Atlantic seaboard and Gulf coast of the U.S. Ideal areas for observation are the tropics and subtropics, and especially islands where tidal range is small, since a large tidal range tends to destroy traces of higher platforms. On the wave-cut platform in the Bay of Fundy, an excellent example of a high tidal range area, no trace of multiple benches is reported (Klein, 1963).

It would seem to be good policy to keep the words "terrace" or "emerged platform" for the fossil forms and "platform" for the contemporary. However, this raises the controversial question as to just what is contemporary? Mean sea level is constantly changing, and according to modern tide-gauge records, the mean world sea level rose 70 mm between 1890 and 1950 (Fairbridge and Krebs, 1962, p. 542). The longest tide record available is for Amsterdam, going back to 1682. Although a correction has had to be made to allow for the tectonic subsidence, the long-term oscillation of sea level is evident (Fairbridge, 1961). Furthermore, it is believed by some observers that mean sea level has been oscillating through about ± 3 meters during the last 6000 years. Prior to that time, it was rising rapidly during the postglacial melting. There-

fore, it is necessary to appraise the meaning of the term "contemporary" within the range of the last 6000 years.

The controversy that exists over this matter is not merely semantic. Most people who have experience in the coral reef regions have observed the geomorphic traces of reef growth (which is precisely geared to mean low sea level) over this 6000-year period; the reef surfaces suggest an oscillating sea level through ± 3 meters, and C^{14} dates of associated shell beds give a time scale, which is corroborated by a Holocene chronology already established through studies of raised beaches, varve counting, palynology, climatic changes, archeological and historical data (particularly in Sweden).

The opposing viewpoint is held by observers who have their basis of experience in the soft sedimentary areas about the Mississippi delta and elsewhere around the Gulf of Mexico. C^{14} dates in the Mississippi estuarine and deltaic deposits suggest that sea level rose to its present position about 3000–4000 years ago and has remained relatively constant ever since. Allowance has been made for the tectonic subsidence of the delta.

The geomorphic-stratigraphic sequence of the Mississippi does not, however, show a uniform accumulation record. A sequence of important beach-ridge (chenier) systems have built up and each was separated by an appreciable interruption, followed by certain changes in the regime, so that successive chenier belts are slightly unconformable and intersect geographically. With each of these interruptions, there was a major shift in the locus of the delta. A regression is marked by a blanket growth of peat which is then overwhelmed by a marine or brackish transgression. Cheniers tended to be reworked in part. Comparable peats and beach ridges are dated in the Netherlands (Jelgersma, 1966). The principal cyclic oscillations in the Mississippi delta dated for regressions and beginning of new delta growth, in radiocarbon years, appear to be as follows (McFarlan, 1961; Coleman and Smith, 1964; Kolb and van Lopik, 1966):

Mississippi Delta	Date (Before Present)	International Emergence
Peat 5	7500–7000	Late Boreal
Peat 4	6500–6000	Rhine Delta
Peat 3 (Maringouin, Sale, or Cypremort)	5000–4700	Early Subboreal
Peat 2 (Cocodrie)	4300–4000	Bahama
Teche	3300–2800	Pelham Bay
Peat 1 (St. Bernard or La Loutre)	2100–1700	Florida
Lafourche	1500	pre-Dunkerquian III
Plaquemines	700	Paria
Balize	300	Late Medieval

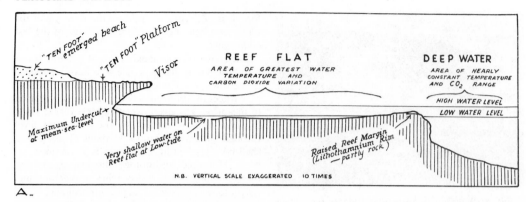

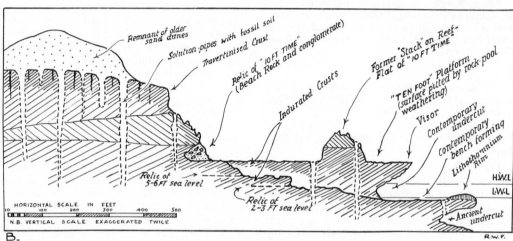

FIG. 9A and B. (A) Idealized section of a limestone reef flat, indicating how extreme physico-chemical conditions over the reef flat may facilitate chemical solution of the limestone down to the level of low-water springs, and operate at a maximum (in protected places) at mean sea-level, producing a deep undercut.

(B) Idealized section of the "coastal limestone" cliffs at Point Peron, Western Australia, showing four post-Glacial bench levels cut by the sea at its various stands. (Fairbridge, 1952.)

It seems scarcely a coincidence that each of these dates corresponds to times when there was evidence from Scandinavia, the Mediterranean or the Pacific of a negative sea-level oscillation. For this reason, the "international" term for each emergence is added in parenthesis (Fairbridge, 1961, see curve on p. 158; also 1962, post-Roman curve, p. 119).

On coastlines lacking consolidated rocks, it is found that Holocene high sea-level stages are often marked by successive belts of beach ridges (as in Louisiana); comparable series have been C[14] dated in New Zealand by Schofield (1962); in Europe (e.g., Landes of Gascony) they are known from historical records. Beach ridges form cyclically, following minor sea-level oscillations, and are interrupted only by important oscillations of 1–2 meters or more. Their peak phases are often merged into belts of coastal dunes that today are vegetated but display 3–4 distinctive bands, representing the "highs" of the Holocene. The major

"swales" or depressions between them correspond to the eustatically low phases (and the beginnings of each of the Mississippi delta stages).

A feature of flat coastlines in civilized regions during the last three millennia has been the construction of salt pans. Salt was a critical item in man's economy prior to modern underground exploitation. During eustatic retreats, broad coastal flats emerged that were ideal for salt evaporation, and prosperity marked the coastal towns. During transgressions, the salt pans were drowned, dikes were overwhelmed and the economy often shifted entirely to inland centers where diapiric salt supplies offered an alternative supply. M. R. Bloch (of the Beersheba Arid Zone Institute) has made a close study of this phenomenon and finds the timing of the archeological data closely matches the eustatic record.

A synthesis of the manifold data on Holocene sea-level changes seems to confirm the record of the wave-cut platforms; emerged platforms reflect the high stands to a maximum of 3 meters, while submerged platforms (recently being explored more and more by divers) reflect low sea levels to above −4 meters.

Independent studies of climatic change, through pollen analysis and historical records, show that in temperate latitudes, each high sea-level stage is warmer than the preceding low stage, but long term trends may be overriding. It should be stressed that the dates are mostly approximate to about ±100–200 years. Elevations in the coral regions are often accurate to better than 0.5 meter, but local tectonics or compaction (more prevalent on mainland coasts) may alter the local figures somewhat.

Names, selected from well-dated examples, have been chosen to designate the stages (Fairbridge, 1961, 1962). (Note: place names are preferable to historic periods, e.g., "Post-Roman" changed to "Haarlem," but "Medieval" is still retained as it is so well known.) High sea-level stages are referred to as "submergences" and low stages as "emergences."

RHODES W. FAIRBRIDGE

References

Bartrum, J. A., 1926, "Abnormal shore platforms," *J. Geol.*, **34**, 793–806.

Coleman, J. M. and Smith, W. G., 1964, "Late recent rise of sea level," *Bull. Geol. Soc. Am.*, **75**, 833–840.

Cooke, C. W., 1930, "Correlation of coastal terraces," *J. Geol.*, **38**, 577–589.

Cotton, C. A., 1963, "Levels of planation of marine benches," *Zeit. f. Geomorph.*, **7**, 97–111.

Evers, W., 1962, "The problem of coastal genesis with special reference to the 'Strandflat,' the 'Banks' or 'Grounds,' and 'Deep Channels' of the Norwegian and Greenland Coasts," *J. Geol.*, **70**, 621–630 (with discussion by Holtedahl, p. 631 ff).

*Fairbridge, R. W., 1952, "Marine erosion," *Proc. Pacific Sci. Congr. 7th, New Zealand*, **3**, 347–359.

Fairbridge, R. W., 1961, "Eustatic Changes of Sea Level," in "Physics and Chemistry of the Earth," Vol. 4, pp. 99–185, New York, Pergamon Press.

Fairbridge, R. W., 1962, "World sea-level and climatic changes," *Quaternaria* (Rome), **6**, 111–134.

Fairbridge, R. W. and Krebs, O. A., Jr., 1962, "Sea level and the Southern Oscillation," *Geophys. J.*, **6**, 532–545.

Grønlie, O. T., 1951, "On the rise of sea and land and the formation of strandflats on the west coast of Fennoscandia," *Norsk Geol. Tidsskrift*, **29**, 26–64.

Hinds, N. E. A., 1929, "Wave-cut platforms in Hawaii," *J. Geol.*, **37**, 603–610.

Jelgersma, S., 1966, "Sea-level changes during the last 10,000 years," in "World Climate From 8000 to 0 B.C.," 54–71, *Proc. International Symposium 1966*, Royal Meteor. Soc.

Klein, G. de V., 1963, "Bay of Fundy intertidal zone sediments," *J. Sediment. Petrol.*, **33**, 844–854.

Kolb, C. R. and van Lopik, J. R., 1966, "Depositional environments of the Mississippi River Deltaic Plain—Southeastern Louisiana," in (Shirley, M. L. and

Ragsdale, J. A., editors), "Deltas," 17–61, Houston Geol. Soc.

Kuenen, P. H., 1933, "Geology of coral reefs," *Snellius Expedition*, **5**, Pt. 2.

McFarlan, E., Jr., 1961, "Radiocarbon dating of Late Quaternary deposits, South Louisiana," *Bull. Geol. Soc. Am.*, **72**(1), 129–158 (discussion, W. Broecker, 159–161).

Schofield, J. C., 1962, "Post-glacial sea-levels," *Nature*, **195**, 1191.

Schou, A., 1956, "Die Naturlandschaften Dänemarks," *Geol. Rundschau*, **8**, 413–423.

Smith, W. S. T., 1933, "Marine terraces on Santa Catalina Island," *Am. J. Sci.*, ser. 5, **25**, 123–126.

Russell, R. J., 1963, "Recent recession of tropical cliffy coasts," *Science*, **139**, 9–15.

* Additional bibliographic references mentioned in the text may be found in this work.

Cross-references: *Abrasion; Beach; Beach Ridge; Biological Erosion of Limestone Coasts; Corrasion; Corrosion; Eustasy; Holocene; Limestone Coastal Weathering; Postglacial Isostatic Rebound; Quaternary; Strandline; Water Loading and Crustal Response; Wave Base.* Vol. I: *Mean Sea Level Changes.* pr Vol. VII: *Palynology; Varve Chronology.*

PLAYA*

Playa (pl. playas) is a distinctive feature within *deserts* but its connotation varies.

Playa—originally a Spanish word meaning "shore" or "beach," now denoting in English the flat-floored bottom of an interior desert basin on which smooth, barren, sun-baked microrelief prevails. It is essentially the dry lake remnant of a former base level of erosion which may be presently active.

The name *playa* can be loosely applied to a dry lake filled periodically with a sheet of water regardless of whether or not the playa depression is a sedimentary/volcanic basin or a basement rock surface partially covered by a thin sheet of clastic sediments (Jutson, 1934).

Geologists know playas as *sebkhas* (Termier and Termier, 1963) or as *sabkas*, which generally refer to former sea inlets, now coastal alkali flats [e.g., the Rann of Cutch, India (Wadia, 1961)].

In America and Australia, playas are known as *salares* or *salinas* (Harrington, 1961; David, 1950). In Africa, playas are regionally known as *chotts* in Tunisia, *solonchach* in the Caspian Sea region, and *shotts* or *sebjas* (Alia Medina, 1956) in the Sahara. For Asia, the designation might vary also; silty flat

* All the photographs of this article were taken by the author in connection with Contract AF 19(628)–1683 Air Force Cambridge Research Laboratories, Office of Aerospace Research, United States Air Force, Bedford Massachusetts (for reference, see Scientific Report, No. 1: "Earth Science Studies of Selected Playas (Lake Beds) (Unclassified), 1963, by Raymundo J. Chico).

FIG. 1. The foreground surface where a soil sample is being taken is the *playa*. The raised slope adjacent to the playa edge is the *bajada* (q.v.), and the area between the mountains and *bajada* is known as the *pediment* (q.v.).

playas and salt encrusted playas of the Arabian Deserts are known respectively as *khabari* and *mamlahah* (Holm, 1960). Playas within cold deserts have not yet been mentioned in geological literature.

Alkali flats, originated by the upwellings of salt waters from subterranean thick salt deposits in Central Europe, should not be classed among playas (Chapman, 1960), nor some ice-free silty-clay hard surfaces common to arctic beaches, nor any lacustrine sedimentary floor which might allow conditions under which degradation always outstrips aggradation (Wallace, 1961).

Most known playas are of Quaternary Age. The Triassic Sidewater series of Barstow area (Mojave Desert) appears to be one of the oldest formations containing playas in California (Oakeshott, Jennings and Turner, 1954). Former playa beds have also been reported from the Furnace Creek Formation (Upper Tertiary) of the Death Valley (Noble and Wright, 1954).

The geometrical shape of playas may or may not depend on regional structures: elongated, fault basins in the Atacama and Death Valley deserts have elliptical playas; low lying deserts of the Sahara, Western Australia, and Mojave Desert have playas of any shape. In the first case, the areal extent of playa surfaces is restricted to the bottom and sides of the valleys; in the second, it could cover from a few hundred square meters to tens of square kilometers.

Playas have been found within active tectonic areas bounded by fault pattern intersections and sinking basins in the Spanish Sahara (Alia Medina,

1956), or within areas where warping and faulting, instead, controlled the formation of basins [(i.e., Mojave Desert (Sharp, 1954)]. Mabey's (1960) gravity work, however, proves that Mojave Desert playas do not always correspond to the basin trough, nor universally to basin regional trend or presence. Elsewhere, playas are within the topographic low land of interior depressions with centripetal drainage and named *bolsones* (Tolman, 1909). The rising slope extending from the playa floor to the surrounding mountains consists of two parts of different origin: (a) immediately adjacent to the playa is the *bajada* (Spanish meaning "gentle slope") of aggradation origin; and (b) the highest part, an eroded rock surface partially covered with alluvium, is called the *pediment*.

Playas have no relief or vegetation, contrasting therefore with the physiography of surrounding *bajadas*, which are molded by badlands, ephemeral gullies, channels, shoreline remnants, and fault scarps.

Vertical airphotographs show playas as a white scar in the desert due to the soil flatness and colors which cause a diffused reflectancy much higher than the albedo of any other desertic feature (Ashburn and Weldon, 1956). The common dark gray tone seen on playa photographs is not always a sign of higher moisture content, as usually accepted, but of compositional variations. The average playa color as determined with the *Munsell notation* ("Munsell Soil Color Chart", 1954) is very pale brown (10YR 8/2), but the hue, value, and chroma may shift to gray, white, and yellow.

FIG. 2. The mud-cracked soil shown above the ruler typically forms within "inorganic clays" of high plasticity. A soil sample from this playa location assayed a Pi (Plastic index) of 28 % and a Li (Liquid limit) of 58 %. By utilizing these values, the mud-cracked polygons with curled perimeter and concave upward shape can be classified as *quick clays* (Meyerhof, G. G., 1957, *Geotechnique*, **7**, 41–49).

FIG. 3. Even though playas are found within dry climatic belts of the earth's surface, water is the main agent changing their microrelief. This photograph shows that the inner ephemeral drainage nets are not only following the classical stream order classifications and laws of Horton or Strahler, but that inner drainage microrelief is of importance for the selection and classification of playa surfaces for trafficability.

Playas are not differentiated from *lakes* on standard topographic maps, because the elevation difference between the lowest sector of a playa and its edge very seldom reaches sufficient variation which could be taken into account for contour gradient representation. The topographic gradient of playas is *ca.* 0.15 m/km; however, each playa surface has its own microrelief or roughness, which together with soil strength is important for determining the use of playa surfaces for aircraft or automotive trafficability.

Mud cracks are the common microrelief feature found on any playa. They vary in size from square centimeters to square meters and even to cracking polygon surfaces of hundreds of square meters. While soil cracking of small magnitude is caused by the effects of solar radiation on playa surfaces, large cracking patterns, called king-size mud cracks,

FIG. 4. Driving along the path of a fourth-order channel is possible, but along adjacent strips, almost impossible.

FIG. 5. An example of a meander belt within a fifth-order channel, and random location of clay-silt patches (measuring 0.10 meter high, 0.15 meter wide, and 1 meter long).

may have originated from subsurface conditions (Wilden and Mabey, 1961; Chico, 1963). Playas appear to be the ideal place to study the genesis of mud cracks in sediments because of the great variety of mud-crack shapes encountered.

Sink holes within the playa surface are depressions of up to 3 meters in depth, formed from the solution of salt beds, stagnant water "*charcos*" (Bryan, 1920), or pools within ephemeral drainage. *Channels,' rills* and *peel-soil covers* are formed by combined erosive effects of raindrop splashing, seasonal

rains, sheetflood runoff, and sedimentation on most of the silty clay, low-saline playa surfaces of the Mojave Desert. Specifically at Rosamond Playa, an inner ephemeral drainage net of up to fifth order has typical *meanders, pools, riffles* and is consistent with Horton's (1945) Laws (Chico, 1963). Occasionally, the playa flatness is partially interrupted by convex, circular *hot spring mounds* 0.60 meters high and 7 meters wide, and elongated *sand bars* rising about a meter above the surface. Deflation of peel-soil covers results in the formation of clay-silt

FIG. 6. Air photograph taken 200 meters above the surface of hot-spring mounds within a playa surface. Notice the variations of soil cracking. For a description and analysis of soil cracks, see articles: *Mud Cracks* and *Soil Cracks—Giant*.

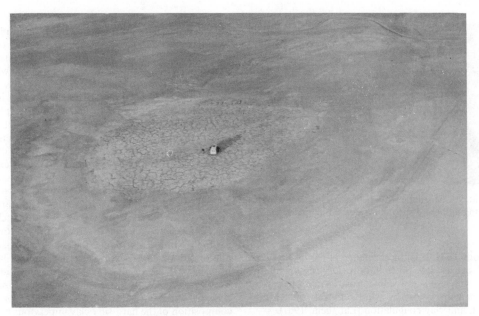

Fig. 7. Similar subject to figure 6, with hot-spring site on playa.

ripples a few centimeters high distributed at random within the playa.

Wherever evaporite minerals are present on the playa surface, typical microrelief results (i.e., *crusts, push-up mud cracks, pinnacles*, etc.). Capillarity rising from a shallow saline water table determines the formation of "*self-risen-ground*" (Thompson, 1929).

After the random study of surface microrelief features and moisture-soil-values Thompson (1924, 1929) empirically, and in order of importance, has classified playas of the western United States into dry playas, salt-encrusted playas, moist playas, clay-encrusted moist playas, compound playas, crystal body playas, lime pan playas, and artificial playas. This nomenclature, by itself indicates first the diversity of playa types and then the affinity between playas, evaporites, and salt lakes of Lotze (1938).

The process of salt formation on playas differs from place to place, but follows the principles of Van't Hoff (1905) and mineral-assemblage separations of Usiglio (1849). Rarely have hypersaline minerals been reported, since the bulk of salts corresponds to saline assemblage.

In general, playa salts originate from precipitation of soluble salts carried into closed lakes since Pleistocene times. Reconstruction of this accumulation of salts is still incomplete, largely due to the lake-volume variations of glaciation stages which were synchronous with strandlines of Lahontan and Bonneville Lakes (Flint and Gale, 1958; Morrison, 1961). Therefore, the reasons for an unequal magnitude of evaporite mineral assemblage formation in playas have not yet been clearly demonstrated.

Theoretically, a closed lake will attain a salinity increase up to a saturation point, and any additional water-volume increase must remain at the same

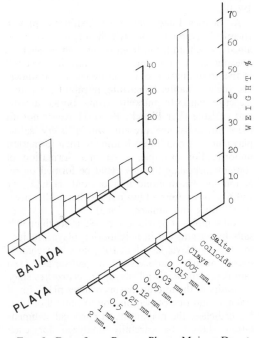

Fig. 8. Data from Rogers Playa, Mojave Desert, California.

869

FIG. 9. Changing microrelief features as shown in this photograph are due to mineralogical differences in the soil.

salinity level. It is the shrinkage of the lake volume that causes salt precipitation. Desiccation of the lake will result in a saline crust formation, part of which will be lost by wind removal, salt entrapment, and clay coagulation (Langbein, 1961).

Repetition of this process, coupled with silt-clay sheetflood deposition, will result in the partial succession of mechanical and chemical sedimentation, as found at Searles Lake. Here the following units are encountered in an 85-meter vertical profile from surface downward: upper mud, upper salt, parting mud, lower salt, bottom mud and "mixed layer" (Flint and Gale, 1958). Contact between the last two units as inferred from C^{14} dating ranges from 100,000–150,000 years old (Hay and Moiola, 1963).

At Searles Lake and other California playas, chemical sedimentation, which might have been aided by salt addition from other sources such as volcanic emanations and hot springs, has resulted in the accumulation of evaporite economic minerals, such as halite, thenardite, mirabilite, gypsum, glaserite, hanksite, burkeite, trona, borax, ulexite, and celestite (Ver Planck, 1958). However not all these minerals are present within every saline playa, nor are conditions leading to their formation uniform. For example, a seasonal formation of sodium carbonate in soils could be formed by reaction of Na-montmorillonite and H_2CO_3 or $CaCO_3$, or by four additional geochemical processes (Whittig and Janitzky, 1963).

Soil samples at Searles Lake yield more than 30% salts by weight, but in neighboring playas, including Rogers Playa, less than 10% salts by weight is found within surface/shallow subsurface soil samples. Genetically all playas are *evaporites* since alkalinity of the interior basins reaches pH 8, Eh of 100 mV, and rate of evaporation to rainfall of 16:1. Nevertheless, the magnitude of chemical sedimentation should be carefully analyzed for each given playa, and in many cases this magnitude is probably less than mechanical sedimentation.

Sediment in Rogers Playa (see Fig. 8) shows an abrupt decrease of particle size toward the playa base-level, with a subtle deficiency in the class 0.12/0.015 mm but a significant net predominance of colloidal material which develops a sol when the playa is covered by shallow floods and when flocculating, hardens the soil surface. The high percentage of colloidal fraction of the playa soils—main criterion for distinguishing playas from common *lake sediments*—apparently derives from the molecularly decomposed bentonite clays which have been formed *in situ* from volcanic ashes and/or tuff (Hewett, 1917), and/or transported to the base level by sheetflood. This theory partially envisaged by Ross and Hendricks (1945) appears to apply well for playas within volcanic regions, such as the Mojave and Atacama deserts, and Basin Range Region. Without excluding the fact that basinal pile of sediments beneath playa surface may have been in part the result of chemical sedimentation (i.e., evaporites), the sedimentation of colloidal clays derived from volcanic rocks accounts for the composition of the hard-silty clay impervious playa surfaces. Widespread occurrence of three-layer silicates, diagenetic minerals derived from volcanic rocks (Droste, 1961; Hay and Moiola, 1963), volcanic glass, bentonite layering, tuffaceous material found within playas, dislocation of playa shapes within interior basin troughs, and varying amounts of salts indicates that a genetic sedimentary gradation exists between a common dry playa (*khabari*) and a typical salt lake (*mamlahah*).

RAYMUNDO J. CHICO

References

Alia Medina, M., M., 1956, "El origen tectónico de las sebjas del Sahara Español," *Intern. Geol. Congress, México*, **20**, 341–346.

Ashburn, E. V., and Weldon, R., 1956, "Spectral diffuse reflectance of desert surfaces," *J. Optical Soc. Am.* **46**, 583–586.

Bryan, K., 1920, "Origin of rock tanks and charcos," *Am. J. Sci.*, 4th Series, **50**, 203–206.

Chapman, V. J., 1960, "Salt Marshes and Salt Deserts of the World," New York, Interscience Publishers, Inc., 392pp.

Chico, R. J., 1963, "Playa mud cracks: regular and king-size," *Geol Soc. Am. Special Paper*, **76**, 306.

David, T. W., 1950, "The Geology of the Commonwealth of Australia," Edward Arnold and Co., **1**, 720pp.

Droste, J. B., 1961, "Clay minerals in the playa sediments of the Mojave Desert, California," *Calif. Div. Mines, Special Report*, **69**, 21pp.

Flint, R. F., and Gale, W. A., 1958, "Stratigraphy and radiocarbon dates at Searles Lake, California," *Am. J. Sci.*, **256**, 689–714.

Harrington, H. J., 1961, "Geology of parts of Antofagasta and Afacama Provinces, Northern Chile," *Bull. Am. Assoc. Pet. Geol.*, **45**, 169–197.

Hay, R. L., and Moiola, R. J., 1963, "Authigenic silicate

minerals in Searles Lake, California," *Sedimentology*, **2**, 312–332.

Hewett, D. F., 1917, "The Origin of Bentonite," *Jour. Wash. Acad. Sci.*, **7**, 196–198.

Holm, A., 1960, "Desert geomorphology in the Arabian Peninsula," *Science*, **132**, 1369–1379.

Horton, R. E., 1945, "Erosional development of streams and their drainage basins," *Bull. Geol. Soc. Am.*, **56**, 275–370.

Jutson, J. T., 1934, "The Physiography of Western Australia," *Geol. Survey Western Australia*, **95**.

Langbein, W. B., 1961, "Salinity and hydrology of closed lakes," *U.S. Geol. Surv., Prof. Paper* **412**, 20pp.

Lotze, F., 1938, "Steinsalz und Kalisalz Geologie," Berlin, Gebruder Borntraeger, 936pp.

Mabey, D. R., 1960, "Gravity survey of the western Mojave Desert," *U.S. Geol. Surv., Prof. Paper* **316-D**, 51–73.

Morrison, R. B., 1961, "Correlation of the deposits of Lakes Lahontan and Bonneville and the glacial sequences of the Sierra Nevada and Wasatch Mountains, California, Nevada and Utah," *in U.S. Geol. Survey*, Research 1961, p. D-122/D-124.

Munsell Color Company, 1954, "Munsell Soil Color Chart," Baltimore, Md.

Noble, L. F., and Wright, L. A., 1954, "Geology of the central and southern Death Valley region, California," *Calif. Div. Mines, Bull.* **170** (1, II), 160–243.

Oakeshott, G. B., Jennings, G. W., and Turner, M. D., 1954, "Correlation of sedimentary formations in southern California," *Calif. Div. Mines, Bull.* **170** (1, III), 5–8.

Ross, C. S., and Hendricks, S. B., 1945, "Minerals of the montmorillonite group, their origin and relation to soil and clays," *U.S. Geol. Survey, Prof. Paper* **205-B**, 23–79.

Sharp, R., 1954, "Some physiographic aspects of southern California," *Calif. Div. Mines, Bull.* **170** (1, V), 5–10.

Termier, H., and Termier, G., 1963, "Erosion and Sedimentation," New York, D. Van Nostrand Co. Inc., 433pp.

Thompson, D. G., 1924, "Some features of desert playas," *J. Wash. Acad. Sci.*, **14**, 56–57.

Thompson, D. G., 1929, "The Mohave Desert region, California," *U.S. Geol. Surv., Water Sup. Paper*, **578**, 579pp.

Tolman, C. F., 1909, "Erosion and deposition in the southern Arizona bolson region," *J. Geol.*, **17**, 136–163.

Usiglio, J., 1849, "Analyse de l'eau de la Mediterranée sur la côte de France," *Ann. Chim. et Phys.* Ser. 3, **2**, 92–172.

Van't Hoff, J. H., 1908, "Zur Bildung der ozeanischen Salzlagerungen," Braunschweig.

Ver Plank, W. E., 1958, "Salt in California," *Calf. Div. Mines, Bull.* **175**, 167pp.

Wadia, D. N., 1961, "Geology of India," New York, St. Martin's Press, 536pp.

Wallace, R. E., 1961, "Deflation in Buena Vista Valley, Pershing County, Nevada," *U.S. Geol. Surv.*, Research 1961, p. D-242/D-243.

Whittig, L. D., and Janitzky, P., 1963, "Mechanisms of formation of sodium carbonate in soils," I. Manifestations of biological conversions," *J. Soil Sci.* **2**, 322–333.

Willden, R., and Mabey, D. R., 1961, "Giant Desiccation fissures on the Black Rock and Smoke Creek Deserts, Nevada," *Science*, **133**, 1359–1360.

Cross-references: *Arctic Beaches; Badlands; Bajada; Bolson; Deserts and Desert Landforms; Great Salt Lake; Lakes; Microrelief; Mud Cracks; Pediment; Pluvial Lakes; Quaternary; Sabkha; Sheet Erosion, Sheetwash, etc.; Soil Cracks—Giant.* Vol. VI: *Bentonite; Diagenesis; Evaporites; Mud Cracks (Contraction Polygons); Quickclays; Soil Salinity and Alkalinity.*

PLAYFAIR'S LAW

A fundamental principle of hydrology and geomorphology is, in Playfair's own words: "Every river appears to consist of a main trunk, fed from a variety of branches, each running in a valley proportioned to its size, and all of them together forming a system of valleys, communicating with one another, and having such a nice adjustment of their declivities that none of them join the principal valley either on too high or too low a level; a circumstance which would be infinitely improbable if each of these valleys were not the work of the stream which flows in it."

Playfair's Law has become the standard norm for appraising a terrain's history. As the "Law of Accordant Functions" it is discussed by Chorley *et al.* (1964, pp. 61–63). Anomalies are observed from which may be deduced departures from the ideal mature pattern. For example, the *hanging valley* of glaciated country reflects former, ice-scour erosion, to which contemporary fluvial erosion is not yet adjusted. Lobeck (1939) has commented on the youthful nature of the Grand Canyon; where an ephemeral tributary stream cascades over the edge, it reflects the non-adjustment of the lateral drainage. A river that rises in a region of heavy precipitation and then passes through a region of light or negligible rain is called allogenous or allochthonous (e.g., the Nile); its mid-course tributaries (dry wadis) are not adjusted to the main stream.

Owing to a change in regime, a small stream may find itself flowing in a broad deeply dissected valley. This is called an *underfit* or *misfit* stream. Such a change in water supply may be due to change in climate or to river capture.

A third example where Playfair's Law is broken is to be seen in almost all coastal regions today. During the last glacial period of the Pleistocene, mean sea level was lowered by about 100 meters or more. River valleys cut down towards a new *profile of equilibrium* (q.v.). With the postglacial rise of sea level ("Flandrian Transgression"), the former lower reaches of the stream became drowned to form *drowned valleys*, or canyons, or the surface of the continental shelf (seen particularly clearly on the

Sahul Shelf: Fairbridge, 1953), where the very low rate of sedimentation has failed to fill them up. Drowned valleys also reach up into land forming *rias* (as in N.W. Spain, southern China, etc.) and *estuaries* in general. These are known as *thalasso-static valleys*, i.e., those modified by eustatic changes of sea level (Zeuner, 1945).

RHODES W. FAIRBRIDGE

References

Chorley, R. J., Dunn, A. J. and Beckinsale, R. P., 1964, "The History of the Study of Land Forms," London and New York, Methuen and John Wiley & Sons, vol. 1 ("Geomorphology Before Davis").

Fairbridge, R. W., 1953, "The Sahul Shelf," *J. Roy. Soc. W. Australia*, **37,** 1–33.

Lobeck, A. K., 1939, "Geomorphology," New York, McGraw-Hill Book Co., 731pp.

Playfair, J., 1802, "Illustrations of the Huttonian Theory of the Earth," Edinburgh; see also reprint by University of Illinois Press, 1956, 528pp.

Zeuner, F. E., 1945, "The Pleistocene. Period." London, Ray Society, 322pp.

Cross-references: *Drowned Valley*; *Estuary*; *Hanging Valley*; *Misfit Streams*; *Profile of Equilibrium*; *Rivers*; *Stream Capture, Piracy*; *Streams—Underfit.*

PLUCKING—*See* BERGSCHRUND; GLACIAL STAIRWAY; ROCHE MOUTONNÉE

PLUG—*See* VOLCANIC NECKS AND DIATREMES

PLUNGING CLIFFS

Plunging cliffs, so called by Davis (1928, pp.151–154, 247, 272–274), are sea cliffs drowned at the base by rapid rise of sea level, which may be due in some cases to sinking of the land, but in most

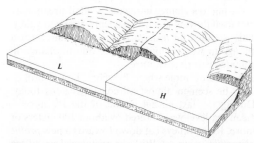

FIG. 1. Plunging cliffs on headlands, Banks Peninsula type. Cliffing at low sea level, *L*, has been followed by drowning at high sea level, *H*, of cliffs that are now plunging. The depth of water is 20 fathoms close to such cliffs on the south side of Banks Peninsula.

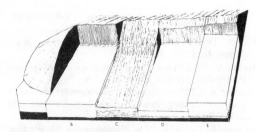

FIG. 2. Plunging continuous cliffs, Auckland Islands type. (A, B, C, D). Successive stages of the development of the cliffs (Fleming, 1965). (E) Finally, drowning has induced the present plunging condition. The depth of water is in places 40 fathoms close to the Auckland Islands cliffs.

cases are the result of postglacial transgression. While this was generally not rapid enough to drown cliffs of soft materials, which would undergo erosion contemporaneously, hard-rock cliffs have commonly become plunging.

Davis included in this category examples in which the cliffs had been reduced in steepness by subaerial processes prior to drowning (Tutuila and Tahiti Islands, in the tropical Pacific). Subsequently to drowning, such cliffs, though initially plunging, have been notched by marine erosion. When, however, unmodified cliffs on rocks so hard that the cliffs are nearly vertical are drowned, the plunging cliffs are immune from attack by the sea at the new level, at any rate under certain conditions.

"It is clear that the persistence or survival of plunging cliffs in the shore line of today implies special conditions leading to postponement of the development of features referable to the current cycle. It is necessary to postulate not only vigorous coastal development and cliff recession in the penultimate cycle, that of low ocean level . . . , but also a virtual moratorium of the same processes since the return of the sea to its present level.

"It is possible, however, to picture conditions that would lead to such a result. Let it be assumed that the submerged part of the cliff is nearly vertical, or is at least too steep to allow waves to break vigorously, thus retaining a primitive steepness unimpaired by slumping or the accumulation of a glacis of material of any kind. From such cliffs, if they descend very steeply to a con-

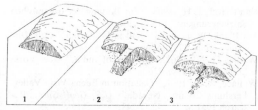

FIG. 3. Successive stages (2, 3) of replacement of a terminal plunging cliff on a headland (1) by a new non-plunging cliff developed by erosion from the sides. Type of headland on Banks Peninsula, New Zealand.

siderable depth below sea level, ocean waves will be reflected instead of breaking (Cotton, 1951, Fig. 7, photograph); and there is, moreover, no resting place below them for the accumulation in shallow water of the rock fragments required for use as ammunition by waves attacking the bases of cliffs. Such small supply of debris as actually becomes detached and falls from the cliffs, or is prised loose by hydrostatic pressure when surging waves enter rock clefts, sinks into deep water, to remain there undisturbed" (Cotton, 1951, pp. 114–15).

Such conditions are satisfied by the plunging cliffs of Banks Peninsula, New Zealand (Davis, 1928, pp. 151–154) (Fig. 1) and of the far southern islands Campbell (Cotton, 1951, p. 117, Fig. 9) and Auckland (Fig. 2), which, like Banks Peninsula, are basaltic domes strongly cliffed at the windward (west) side by marine erosion. The cliffs of Auckland Islands are the subject of a recent discussion (Cotton, 1967).

Plunging cliffs are spectacularly exemplified on numbers of Pacific islands (Banks Peninsula, a volcanic doublet, has been an island). Drowning of cliff bases resulted from the worldwide postglacial rise of sea level. Plunging cliffs occur practically wherever coasts, and especially headlands, of very resistant rocks have been exposed to wave attack and have been cliffed thereby in earlier ages. While the depth of water in front of certain of these cliffs may have been reduced by sedimentation since sea level rose, there are still many local examples fronted by deep water which are immune from wave attack. Of this kind are cliffs of headlands on the coast of Maine, described and figured by Johnson (1925, pp. 88–90), and isolated examples have been recognized on the cliffed coast of Brittany by Guilcher (1954, p. 42).

"Commonly, however, such plunging cliffs will fail to outlast the earliest stages of marine attack.... Debris traveling alongshore, be it sand or shingle, together with that resulting from crumbling and subaerial erosion of the cliffs themselves, for these may intersect any terrain and are not generally endowed with basaltic immunity, will in the majority of cases soon fill in the reentering angle at the now submerged cliff base. Waves breaking on a ramp so formed, which is steep though not steep enough to reflect them, will attack the shore with maximum vigor, so that cliff retreat will go on again and before long all traces of a former plunging-cliff condition will be obliterated" (Cotton, 1952, p. 223).

The cutting of cliffs now plunging is often difficult to date. The Pointe de Raz, Brittany, was cliffed "before the pre-Flandrian regression" (Guilcher, 1948, p. 257), which must mean in some interstadial of the last glaciation (when sea level rose to − 50 ft) and this may be regarded as a probable date for the cutting of many cliffs now plunging. Similar cliffs were noted by Daly (1927, p. 92) on St. Helena, and by Hinds (1930, p. 43) on Kauai (Hawaii), in both cases apparently cut at a lower (late glacial) sea level when the prevailing winds were westerlies,

not easterlies (trade winds) as today. On Kauai there are stupendous cliffs, up to 2000 feet high, on the west (now the lee) side.

The plunging cliffed headlands of a drowned coast (Fig. 1) are temporarily immune from erosion. Nevertheless they are liable to wave attack at the sides, and erosion beginning there may cut right across a drowned spur, shortening it and developing a new end cliff that is not plunging (Cotton, 1952). Two stages of such "resection" are shown in Fig. 3.

CHARLES A. COTTON

References

Cotton, C. A., 1951, "Sea cliffs of Banks Peninsula and Wellington," *N.Z. Geographer*, **7**, 103–120.
Cotton, C. A., 1952, "Cyclic resection of headlands by marine erosion," *Geol. Mag.*, **89**, 221–225.
Cotton, C. A., 1967, "Plunging Cliffs and Pleistocene Coastal Cliffing in the Southern Hemisphere," in "Mélange Tulippe," Liège.
Daly, R. A., 1927, "The geology of St. Helena Island," *Proc. Am. Acad. Arts Sci.*, **62**, 31–92.
Davis, W. M., 1928, "The Coral Reef Problem," New York, American Geographical Society, 596pp.
Fleming, C. A., 1965, "Two-storied cliffs of the Auckland Islands," *Trans. Roy. Soc. New Zealand Geol.*, **3**(11), 171–174.
Guilcher, A., 1948, "Le relief de la Bretagne meridionale," La Roche-sur-Yon, Henri Potier, 682pp.
Guilcher, A., 1954, "Morphologie littorale et sous-marine," Paris, Presses Universitaire de France; English ed., 1958, "Coastal and Submarine Morphology," New York, John Wiley & Sons, 274pp.
Hinds, N. E. A., 1930, "The geology of Kauai and Niihau," *Bernice P. Bishop Mus. Bull.*, **71**, 103pp.
Johnson, W. D., 1925, "The New England–Acadian Shoreline," New York, John Wiley & Sons, 608pp.

Cross-references: *Eustasy; Holocene; Littoral Processes; Platforms—Wave-Cut; Quaternary; Stack; Terraces—Marine.*

PLUVIAL LAKES

Definition

A *pluvial lake* is a lake that has had considerable, and generally periodic, fluctuation in volume (lake level) in the past, primarily in response to climatic changes. All known pluvial lakes are believed to be of Quaternary age.

General Features

The saline lakes and playas of arid and semiarid continental regions commonly show evidence of former periodic large expansions and desiccations during Quaternary time, in the form of abandoned shorelines as well as lacustrine sediments interwedging with units that record subaerial exposure, such as alluvium, colluvium, eolian sand, loess, weathering profiles, and subaerial unconformities. The changes in lake volume typically have ranged through more than one order of magnitude, and the changes in lake level have been many tens of feet for the smaller lakes and hundreds of feet for the larger ones. Lakes with such a history are called pluvial lakes, because they expanded during wetter intervals of the Quaternary, commonly called *pluvial intervals* or "*pluvials*," when precipitation was greater and evapotranspiration was less than now. The times when pluvial lakes were expanded are called *lacustral intervals*. The lacustral intervals were synchronous with glaciations in temperate latitudes (Fig. 4) (and probably at high altitudes in lower latitudes). Between the pluvials, when precipitation was about as low or lower than now (and when the pluvial lakes also were at low levels or dry), were *interpluvial intervals* or *interpluvials*, and likewise, *interlacustral intervals*.

Only the Pleistocene, of all post-Paleozoic time, had sufficiently large and frequent climatic fluctuations to have true pluvial intervals and, consequently, pluvial lakes. The last true pluvial interval was in late Pleistocene (Wisconsin) time; the several precipitation increases during the Recent Epoch have been too small to be considered true pluvials. Pluvial intervals probably existed during the pre-Quaternary glaciations in Pennsylvanian, Permian, and Precambrian time, but no evidence of pluvial lakes has been reported from deposits of these ages.

In common with all lakes, pluvial lakes have occupied closed depressions that have been formed by a wide variety of geologic factors. The amount of closure of the lake basin commonly is much greater for a pluvial lake, however, than for other lakes. The closed basins that held pluvial lakes are of late Pliocene or Quaternary age (or were rejuvenated during the Quaternary), and generally have been formed by crustal deformation, as by block-faulting or warping. Some, however, were created by other geological agencies such as wind scour (deflation) and damming of valleys by lava flows, by landslides, and even by deposition of alluvial fans. Comparatively few lakes of the world meet the requirement of large fluctuations in volume (level) controlled mainly by climatic change to be true pluvial lakes. For example, lakes dammed by ice (proglacial lakes), or occupying ice-scoured or moraine-dammed basins are not pluvial lakes, nor are lakes whose depressions, however formed, are so quickly drained by downcutting of an overflow threshold that they have lasted only brief intervals.

Some pluvial lakes at their higher levels have overflowed their basins, but most have remained without outlet for a considerable time, commonly for all or the greater part of a glaciation of the Quaternary, and some for several glaciations. As long as there is no overflow, the level of a pluvial lake is controlled by changes in precipitation and evapotranspiration (with evapotranspiration controlled chiefly by temperature, but also by cloud cover and wind) in its drainage basin, modified in some instances by stream diversions into or from its drainage basin; thus the lake may persist for long periods. If there is overflow, however, the highest level of a pluvial lake is controlled by the elevation of the overflow threshold, and the lake (like all lakes with outlets) tends to be gradually eliminated as this threshold is corraded and contributory streams infill the lake basin.

Many pluvial lakes have prominent strandlines. The shore terraces, bay bars, spits, deltas, and wave-cut cliffs of Lakes Bonneville and Lahontan (the largest pluvial lakes in the Great Basin of the western United States) commonly rival marine shore features in their magnitude of development. Many smaller pluvial lakes, only a few miles long, also have strongly developed shore features. The stronger strandlines face the dominant storm-wind directions across the wider expanses of the lakes (hence they were exposed to the strongest wave action and longshore currents); generally they are the higher shore lines, unless a resistant overflow threshold has caused a long-lasting stillstand at some lower level. Some strandlines have been intensified by repeated reoccupation during several lake cycles. The chief factors that inhibit formation of prominent strandlines are: the small expanse of a lake (or an arm of it) at any stage; rapid change in lake level, which can be caused by rapid corrasion of an overflow threshold or by diversion of inflow into or from the lake; sheltering by mountains or hills of a shore reach from strong wave action and longshore currents; markedly reentrant sectors; and exposures of resistant rocks at the shore line.

The deposits of pluvial lakes are typically almost entirely clastic sediments, ranging from boulder gravel on shores exposed to strong wave action, to finer gravel and sand in shore and nearshore areas, and to mainly silt and clay in lake-bottom areas. In addition, the successions of some lakes include interbeds of volcanic ash, diatomite, silt and clay rich in organic matter, marl, limestone, tufa, and beds rich in salines such as halite, trona, gypsum, and glauberite. Lake Lahontan is notable for the variety of its tufa deposits; Lake Bonneville for its distinctive "white marl" unit; and ancient Lakes Searles, Panamint, and Manly (Fig. 2), for their saline deposits.

Geographic Distribution

Pluvial lakes are restricted to the relatively arid regions of the world that have had enough late Pliocene and Pleistocene basin-forming activity to interrupt the integrated, through-drainage patterns. Pluvial lakes are concentrated mainly in the desert and semidesert areas of North America and

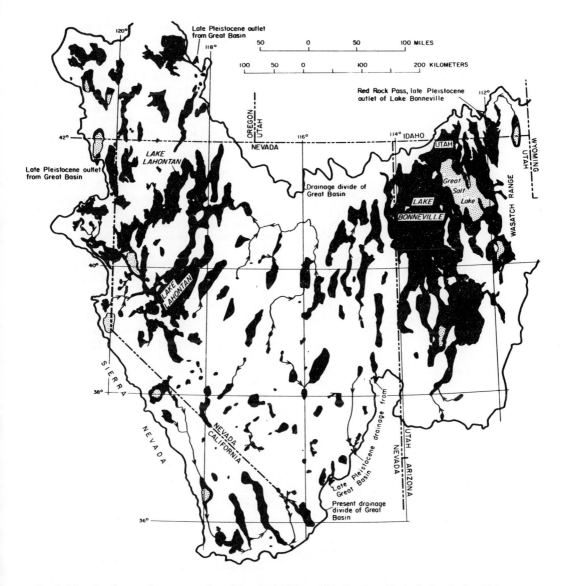

FIG. 1. Map showing maximum expansion of the pluvial lakes within the Great Basin during the late Pleistocene.

Asia, but many are found in Africa and Australia. Humid regions are devoid of pluvial lakes because stream runoff and erosion have remained so great throughout the Quaternary that through drainage was maintained during the slower basin-forming processes. In the relatively rare cases where sudden geologic events such as faulting or volcanism produced local ponding, not only were such lakes generally comparatively transitory, but also they remained filled to the brim and overflowed even during the interpluvials; thus, they did not fluctuate over a wide range as is characteristic of pluvial lakes.

North America. The greatest concentration of pluvial lakes in the western hemisphere is in the Great Basin, in the northern part of the Basin and Range Province. In this huge semiarid to arid region without drainage to the sea are many closed intermontane basins formed by late Pliocene and Pleistocene high-angle faulting. During late Pleistocene time, there were more than 120 pluvial lakes (Fig. 1), including two huge ones, Lakes Bonneville and Lahontan, and the remarkable Lake Russell-to-Lake Manly system (Fig. 2). The late Pleistocene lakes have generally well-preserved shore features and stratigraphic successions. Lakes

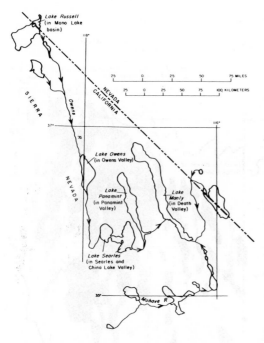

FIG. 2. Lake Russell-to-Lake Manly system of pluvial lakes, showing their maximum extent during the late Pleistocene.

Bonneville, Lahontan, and Searles have been intensively studied (summarized, with numerous references, in Flint, 1957; Morrison, 1965), but most of the other lakes are known only from rapid reconnaissance. Lake Bonneville at its maximum inundated a number of coalescent intermontane basins in Utah, Idaho, and Nevada and had an area of 19,940 square miles (51,700 km²), almost the size of Lake Michigan, and an extreme depth of about 1100 feet (335 meters). Today, the only permanent lakes within its former area are Utah, Sevier, and Great Salt Lakes, whose combined area has fluctuated from about 1000 to 2500 square miles (2600 to 6500 km²) since 1850. Lake Lahontan at its maximum inundated 8665 square miles (22,442 km²) and was about 700 feet (213 meters) deep (at Pyramid Lake). Figure 3 gives past and present interpretations of the history of both lakes.

Pluvial lakes of early and middle Pleistocene age are demonstrated by exposures of lacustrine deposits at a few localities in the Great Basin, but their shore features generally have been obliterated by erosion or concealed by subsequent deposition. Two middle Pleistocene lacustral intervals have been identified in both the Lake Lahontan and Lake Bonneville areas and are correlated with the Kansan and Illinoian Glaciations (Fig. 3).

Pluvial lakes of late Pleistocene and/or earlier age also existed in the portion of the Basin and

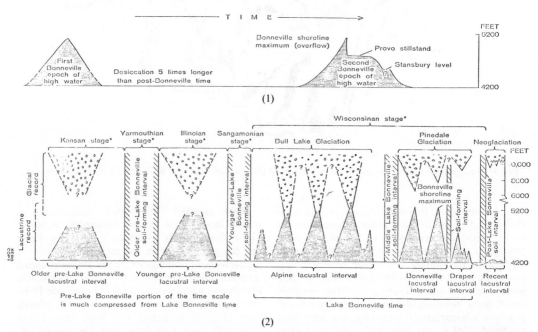

FIG. 3 (a). Classical and modern interpretations of Lake Bonneville history: (1). Classic interpretation (Gilbert 1890); (2). Modern interpretation (Morrison, 1965), and correlations with glacial fluctuations in the Wasatch Range, Utah.*

* Mid-continent time-stratigraphic standard.

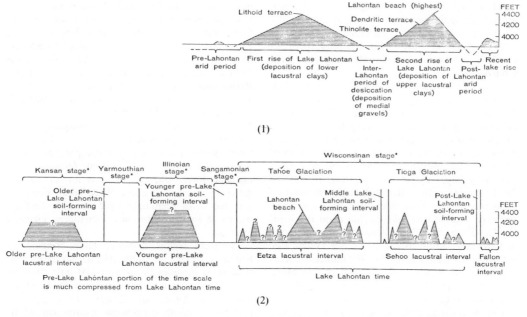

FIG. 3 (b). Classical and modern interpretations of Lake Lahontan history: (1). Classic interpretation (Russel, 1885); (2). Modern interpretation (Morrison, 1965).*

* Mid-continent time-stratigraphic standard.

Range Province south and east of the Great Basin. The ancient lakes are more sparsely distributed than in the Great Basin, because fewer closed basins were formed by Quaternary deformation or other causes. Also, south of latitude 34°N, the amplitude of fluctuation of all the pluvial lakes decreased considerably for given drainage areas, compared with more northerly lakes, because the amplitude of climatic changes decreased markedly with distance from the westerly storm tracks of the temperate zone, and because greater general aridity resulted from the higher mean-annual temperatures of the southerly latitudes. A few pluvial lakes existed in the Mohave Desert (California), Sonora Desert (southwest Arizona and Sonora), and Sacramento Sections (south-central New Mexico; e.g., Lakes Otero and Estancia) of the Basin and Range Province; however, most of the southern lakes are in the Mexican Highland Section, from southern Arizona and New Mexico (e.g., Lakes Willcox, Lordsburg-Animas, San Luis, and Hachita) through the central plateau region of Chihuahua and Coahuilla (e.g., Laguna Guzman and Mayran), and as far south as latitude 20°N, including a former lake in the Mexico City basin and several other basins in central Mexico.

In Baja California, there were a few pluvial lakes (e.g., Lake Chapala). In the semiarid belt east of the Basin and Range Province and Rocky Mountains, there were few large pluvial lakes. The largest, Lake San Augustin, existed in a closed basin at the southeastern edge of the Colorado Plateau Province. The Red Desert area of the Wyoming Basin (south-central Wyoming) held several small pluvial lakes. In the Great Plains from southwest Texas to southeast Wyoming and South Dakota are countless basins formed by deflation during the arid intervals of the Pleistocene. In contrast to many tectonic basins, the deflation basins have small drainage areas and consequently only the larger ones held true lakes even during pluvial intervals. Their maximum development is in the southern High Plains, particularly in the Llano Estacado (Staked Plains) of western Texas —eastern New Mexico.

South America. Not much is known about pluvial lakes in South America. Most of them were in the central-western part of the continent in relatively arid basins formed by deformation in late Pliocene and Pleistocene time, mainly in and near the Atacama Desert and Puna regions of south-western Bolivia, northern Chile, and north-western Argentina. The largest— Lake Minchin— was in southern Bolivia in the basin in which Lagos de Poopo and de Coipasa and Salar de Uyuni are situated. However, a pluvial lake is reported as far north as $4\frac{1}{2}°$ north latitude, near Bogota, Colombia at 8550 feet (2605 meters) altitude. The basin in which Cuzco, Peru is situated held a probably pluvial lake with well-marked shore lines. In the semiarid southern Pampa and Patagonian Desert region of Argentina are numerous lakes in small closed basins (probably many of them formed by deflation) that expanded during the pluvial intervals of the Pleistocene. The large tectonic basin in which Mar Chiquita (between Cordova and Santa Fe) is situated may have held a pluvial lake.

Asia. The extensive steppes and deserts (including the Gobi, Takla Makan, Kara Kum, Thar, Kygye Kum, Dasht-i-lut, and Dasht-i-kavir Deserts), together with the many high mountain ranges (many of them enclosing desert basins) in the interior of this vast continent, provided ideal conditions for pluvial lakes. Many of these lakes were very large; unlike most of those of western North America, they received large amounts of meltwater inflow from extensive glaciers in their drainage areas. These lakes included (in the west) the Dead Sea, the lakes of the Anatolian Plateau, and the huge Aral-Caspian-Black Sea system (see below), and ranged eastward to the numerous lakes on the eastern fringes of the Gobi Desert in Mongolia and Inner Mongolia. Table 1 lists only the larger and better-known pluvial lakes.

The Aral-Caspian-Black Sea system occupied several broad, shallow basins caused by Quaternary warping. All basins received tremendous volumes of glacial meltwater—the Caspian Sea, via the Volga and Ural Rivers, from a large part of the Scandinavian Ice Sheet and glaciers in the Ural Mountains; the Aral Sea, via the Amu Darya (Oxus River) and Syr Darya, from glaciers in the Pamir and T'ien Mountains; and the Black Sea via the Don, Dnepr and Danube Rivers, from much of central and eastern Europe, including the northeastern Alps and much of the Scandinavian Ice Sheet. At least three major and several minor lake expansions are recorded in the Caspian and Aral basins (Flint, 1957). The highest shore lines, 250 feet (76 meters) above the present level of the Caspian Sea, indicate that the maximum lake level was confluent in all three main basins of the system, forming the world's largest pluvial lake. The Aral and Caspian Seas united to inundate an area of 425,000 square miles (1,100,000 km^2) and extended 800 miles (1300 km) up the Volga River from its present mouth. The Caspian intermittently united with the expanded Black Sea (then a lake) through the Mantych Depression. The Black Sea overflowed with large discharge through the Bosporus to the Mediterranean Sea.

Africa. In Africa, pluvial lakes are concentrated in three regions. The northernmost region is along the northern fringes of the Sahara and Libyan Deserts (e.g., the Chott Melrhir Basin of Algeria, the Chott Djerid Basin of Tunisia, and the Kharga and Faiyum Depressions of Egypt). Lake Chad, south of the Sahara, expanded to overflow its shallow basin.

In East Africa there was a group of pluvial lakes with well-preserved late Pleistocene strand-

lines, both on the Abyssinian Plateau (Lake Tanya basin and another basin to the southeast) and in the Great Rift and other rift valleys. Lakes Nakuru, Elmenteita, and Naivasha, in Kenya expanded to form a single great lake, as did Lakes Zwai, Abjata, Langenno, and Shalla in Ethiopia. Lakes Rudolf, Albert, Edward, Kioga, Kivu, Tanganyika, Victoria, and Nyasa (in Tanganyika, Burundi, Rwanda, Uganda, The Congo, Nyasaland, Kenya, Northern Rhodesia, and Mozambique) also all appear to have expanded considerably. The lacustrine history in this region is complicated and to some extent caused by Pleistocene faulting, warping, and local volcanism, and is further complicated by overflow of many of the lakes; nevertheless, the lakes seemingly yield a nearly uniform record of two or three late Pleistocene lacustral intervals.

The third region of pluvial lakes, fringing the Kalahari Desert in South Africa, has been little studied. It includes the 600 by 100 mile (1000 by 160 km) "pan" belt of the Republic of South Africa, South-West Africa, and Eastern Transvaal. The pans are shallow depressions mostly carved by wind erosion, although the basins of certain very large pans (e.g., Etosha Pan, Verneuk Pan, and Makarikari Pans) originated by crustal warping. Many of the larger pans held expanded lakes during the late Pleistocene.

Australia. The vast desert and steppe region of interior Australia had hundreds of large pluvial lakes. Pluvial Lake Dieri in the basin of Lake Eyre covered 40,000 square miles (104,000 km^2), was several hundred feet deep, and overflowed into another pluvial lake which in turn overflowed to the ocean. In the basin of Lakes Victoria and Bonney was pluvial Lake Nawait, 8000 square miles (21,000 km^2) in area. In Western Australia, one pluvial lake was more than 120 miles (200 km) long and another was 400 miles (650 km) long.

Methods of Study

Early studies of pluvial lakes emphasized the ancient strandlines as marked by shore terraces, spits, bay bars, wave-cut cliffs and caves, and deltas. Such geomorphic features, particularly those of late Pleistocene age, commonly are conspicuous. More advanced studies however, have dealt mainly with the stratigraphy of the lacustrine successions, generally in natural and artificial exposures but in some instances from drill cores. Studies based on geomorphic features generally have not yielded nearly as complete and unambiguous information on lake fluctuations as have stratigraphic studies based on detailed mapping and measurement of stratigraphic sections. Lake maxima are determined by mapping the upper altitude limits of the deposits of each lake cycle and observing the relations of these deposits to shore-geomorphic features. Lake recessions,

TABLE 1. IMPORTANT PLUVIAL LAKES OF ASIA

Country (and political subdivision); Name of present lake (or depression) in basin occupied by the pluvial lake	Remarks, including elevation of highest shoreline above present water level and/or areal dimensions during maximum lake expansion (unless stated, the lakes did not, or are not known to have overflowed)
Turkey	
Tuz Gölü (Lake)	75 m
Iznik Gölü (Lake)	55 m; also 2 lower strandlines
Van Gölü (Lake), present area 1453 mi^2	60 m; also 2 lower strandlines
Konya Gölü (double)	
Burdur Gölü	95 m; overflowed; 5 lower shore lines
Israel–Jordan	
Dead Sea	Oldest, 433 m (tilted); younger max. ("main terrace," 400 + m, formed lake 320 km long; 15 recessional shore lines)
Iran	
Daryachen-ye-Reza'iyeh (Lake Urmia) (now 2317 mi^2 at high water)	Expanded to nearly twice its present area
Daryacheh-ye-Sistan	
Lavar Maidan	
Maidan Gil	
Kavir-e-Namak	
Quara chai	
Hamun-i-Jaz Murian	
Namakzar-e-Shahdad and others in Dasht-i-lut Desert	
Daryacheh-ye-Namak and Gavkhanch (in Dasht-i-Kavir Desert)	
Iran-Afghanistan	
Hamun-e-Saberi	
Daryacheh-ye-Namakzar	
Afghanistan	
Daqq-i-Pitargun	
Dasht-i-Daqq-i-Tundi	
Hamun-i-Helmand	
Hamun-i-Puzak	
Ab-i-Istada	
Gaud-i-Zirreh	
Western Pakistan	
Hamun-i-Mashkel (and other lakes in large basin between Siahan Range and Chagai Hills)	
Hamum-i-Lora	
Kashmir	
Wular Lake (and at least 5 other closed basins with pluvial lakes)	
U.S.S.R.	
Aral-Caspian-Black Sea system (see text)	250 ft (76 m) above present Caspian Sea; overflowed to Mediterranean Sea
Tadzhik SSR	
Kara Kul Lakes (2)	Older max., 97 m; younger max., 45 m; lake expansions thought to be related to glacial expansions in adjacent Trans-Alai Mts.
Irkutsk and Buryat ASSR	
Lake Baikal (now 12,162 mi^2, with outlet)	1400 m (questionable); overflowed

TABLE 1. IMPORTANT PLUVIAL LAKES OF ASIA—*continued*

Country (and political subdivision); Name of present lake (or depression) in basin occupied by the pluvial lake	Remarks, including elevation of highest shoreline above present water level and/or areal dimensions during maximum lake expansion (unless stated, the lakes did not, or are not known to have overflowed)
Kirghiz SSR	
Issyk-Kul (now 2395 mi^2)	Expanded at least once; correlated by outwash terraces with glacial expansion in T'ien Shan
Kazakh SSR	
Ozero Balkhash (now 7300 mi^2)	
O. Tengiz	
O. Seletytengiz	
O. Kushmurin	
O. Sarymoin	
O. Aksuat	
O. Karasor	
O. Sasykkol	
O. Alakol	
O. Teke	
O. Markakul	
Mongolian ASSR	
Achita Nuur	
Ubsa Nuur	
Hirgis Nuur	
Hara Usa- Hara Nuur	
Ureg Nuur	
Hobsögöl Dalay	
Sangün Dalay	
Telmin Nuur	
Tolbo Nuur	
Boon Tsagaan Nuur	
Orog Nuur	
Buyr Nuur	
China	
Sinkiang	
Lop Nor	180 m, 600 mi (*ca.* 1000 km) × 125 mi (*ca.* 200 km) (1 or more lakes); 5 lower strandlines
Sairam Nor	60 m
Shor Kul	106 m (older); desiccation; 30 m (younger max.)
Turfan Depression	60 m; 1 lower shore line
Tarim Basin	Lowest part held a very large pluvial lake
Bagrash Köl	
Shona Nor	
Bar Köl	
Ulyungur Nor	
Telli Nor	
Ebi Nor	
Baga Nuur	
Pulunt'o Hai	
Manassu Hu	
Bugur Köl	
Nigsia	
Gashiun Nor	
Chahar	
Tari Nor	
Tsinghai	
Ngoring Nor	

TABLE 1. IMPORTANT PLUVIAL LAKES OF ASIA—*continued*

Country (and political subdivision); Name of present lake (or depression) in basin occupied by the pluvial lake	Remarks, including elevation of highest shoreline above present water level and/or areal dimensions during maximum lake expansion (unless stated, the lakes did not, or are not known to have overflowed)
China—continued	
Tsinghai—continued	
Hala Hu	
Tsaidam Depression	
Toso Hu	
Sukan Hu	
Kotzuk'ulo Hu	
Hait'ung Hu	
Ch'ing Hai (Koko Nor) (now 1630 mi^2)	
Inner Mongolia	
Hulun Ch'ih	
Taerh Hu	
Kashun Noerh	
Hala Hu (and many smaller lakes)	
Tibet	
(more than 100 pluvial lakes, that expanded as high as 133 m above existing lakes)	
Pang-gong Tso Basin	Contained pluvial lakes during at least 2 glaciations
Pangur Tso	Contained pluvial lakes during at least 2 glaciations
Terinam Tso	
Lake Manasarawar	
Lake Nam	
Jiggitai Tsho	
Lake Markham	
Lake Lighten	
Dyap Tsho	
Charol Tsho	
Aru Tsho	
Kashum Tsho	
Lashung Tsho	
Red Salt Lake	
Lake Montcalm	
Nganglaring Tsho	
Rinag Chhutshen	

much more difficult to determine, are represented in the successions by unconformities caused by subaerial erosion, by weathering profiles (soils), by wedges of alluvium, colluvium, eolian sand, or loess between the lacustrine sediments, and even by shore deposits intercalated with deep-water deposits. Such criteria allow determination that a certain lake recession definitely went at least as low as a given altitude.

Various recent studies of Lakes Bonneville and Lahontan (see Morrison, 1965) exemplify modern research on pluvial lakes and the kind of information it affords. Gilbert's (1890) classic interpretation of Lake Bonneville has been considerably modified by recent stratigraphic research [Fig. 3(a)]. Russell's (1885) conclusions on Lake Lahontan are generally confirmed, although many more lake cycles now are recognized within both of his two main lacustrals [Fig. 3(b)]. From the modern investigations, along with finer subdivision of stratigraphic units in the lacustrine successions, has come improved geologic-stratigraphic correlation of these units with successions elsewhere, including glacial ones, which, combined with many radiocarbon dates, led to a better understanding of the absolute and relative chronology of the lake oscillations and the climatic changes that produced them.

Correlation of Lacustrals with Glaciations

The Scottish geologist, Jamieson, theorized in 1873 that pluvial lakes *ought* to expand in unison with glaciation. However, incontrovertible proof, in the form of interstratified till and lake deposits, that lacustral and glacial intervals were contemporaneous is possible (so far as known) in only two places in the world: at the eastern edge of the Sierra Nevada, California, where end moraines of valley glaciers extend below the high shore lines of the pluvial lake in the Mono Lake basin (called Lake Russell), and at the base of the Wasatch Range, a few miles south of Salt Lake City, Utah, where end moraines lie below the highest shore line of Lake Bonneville. Russell (1889) demonstrated in the Mono Lake area that the maximum late Pleistocene expansions of the glaciers and the pluvial lake were virtually contemporaneous. In the Lake Bonneville area, the highest shore line has notched moraines of late Pleistocene age, but the exact relations of the various lake and glacial cycles remained obscure until very recently (Morrison, 1965) [Fig. 3(a)]. On the basis of three separate till units of late Pleistocene age that intertongue and intergrade with sediments of Lake Bonneville, it can be concluded that the glacial maxima represented by these tills were virtually contemporaneous with lake maxima. In various other places in the world, correlations between pluvial lakes and glaciers by indirect means (e.g., by tracing glacial outwash terraces between moraines and lake shore lines, and by detailed analysis of climatic-depositional history recorded by the glacial, alluvial, and lacustrine successions) also suggest that many pluvial lakes fluctuated in unison with glaciers.

The evidence of many more lake cycles of relatively large amplitude than were recognized from the early studies of Lakes Lahontan and Bonneville agrees with recent interpretations of the Wisconsin glacial oscillations in the Midcontinent region, which require a high rate of ice and ice-front movement at times (in several cases during late Wisconsin time, retreats and readvances of the ice front of 100 to several hundred miles within a few hundred years). These lake and glacial oscillations can only be explained by considerable range and rapidity of fluctuation between climatic extremes, even during a single main lacustral-glacial interval.

Evidence on Climatic History

Pluvial-lake successions are potentially among the best records of climatic changes. Certain pluvial lakes, however, provide much better records than others. The stratigraphic successions of Lakes Bonneville and Lahontan contain especially sensitive, complete, and readily available records of late Pleistocene climatically-induced depositional changes in the northern Great Basin. Not only did these lakes have large drainage areas, but they lay in a critical climatic zone. Consequently, the main deep-lake intervals, minor lacustral intervals, and even the interlacustral intervals, are well recorded. South of Lakes Bonneville and

Lahontan, the greater aridity resulted in lakes forming only during the wetter pluvials, so that the climatic-depositional records are less nearly complete. The stratigraphic successions of both lakes give positive evidence of many more fluctuations within a main lacustral-glacial interval than do the glacial successions of the Cordilleran region of western North America.

In addition to providing qualitative data on climatic changes from geomorphic, sedimentologic, paleontologic, and other geologic evidence, pluvial lakes offer means of determining past temperature and precipitation values on a more quantitative basis than is possible from most surficial geologic terrains. For lakes known to have been without outlet, it is possible to calculate either the mean annual temperature or the mean annual precipitation that provided the runoff needed to maintain (against loss by evaporation) the lake at a given stillstand level, if the other factor is known. The temperature during a given lake maximum can be estimated from such criteria as the altitude during this lacustral-glacial maximum of the snow line, of the mean summer freezing isotherm, or of terminal moraines in nearby glaciated areas. Several geologists and hydrologists (cited in Morrison, 1965) have recently appraised, by several closely related methods, the water budgets of various pluvial lakes in the Basin and Range Province between latitude 34 and 43° during their maximum late Pleistocene levels. They all concluded that for each lake, this maximum could only have been attained by *both* higher precipitation and lower evaporation (lower temperature) than now. Estimates of the increase in mean annual precipitation (from present average values over the drainage areas compared with those during the lake maximum) ranged from 7–9 inches (18–23 cm), and for the decrease in mean annual temperature, from 5–9°F (2.7–5°C).

According to some theories, the high levels of pluvial lakes were caused largely by melting of glaciers in their drainage areas; they were not caused by increase in precipitation and (or) decrease in temperature but instead by relatively sudden release of precipitation stored in the glaciers. Nevertheless, many of the world's pluvial lakes obviously did not have glaciers in their drainage areas. For those lakes of western North America that did receive glacial drainage (such as Lakes Bonneville and Lahontan), if the relative volumes of lake water and ice in the tributary glaciers are compared, it is evident that even during maximum melting the glaciers probably contributed only a small percentage of the total water in the hydrologic cycle of the lake.

Inasmuch as pluvial lakes are one of the manifestations of pluvial intervals, it is important to point out certain differences in the time relationships of pluvial, lacustral and glacial intervals.

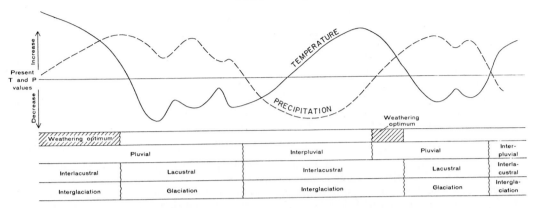

FIG. 4. Typical relations of the fluctuations in temperature and precipitation during the Quaternary in the western United States, and of pluvial-interpluvial, lacustral-interlacustral, and glacial-interglacial cycles.

The pluvial intervals appear to have commenced considerably earlier than the lacustral and glacial intervals that commonly are correlated with them. Modern Quaternary stratigraphic studies clearly show that the pluvials actually began with the intervals of accelerated weathering (soil-forming intervals) during the later parts of the interlacustral-interglacial intervals (Fig. 4), when the climate was both warmer and wetter than now. In the Lake Lahontan area, Nevada (Morrison, 1964), for example, the last three late-Quaternary pluvial intervals started during interlacustral soil-forming intervals that preceded lacustral intervals; precipitation increased considerably during the later parts of the warm interlacustral intervals. The general cyclic pattern of Quaternary climatic change in the Great Basin (Morrison, 1965) has probably been as follows: relatively cool-dry at the start of an interlacustral-interglacial interval, changing to warm-dry and then to warm-wet (during the weathering optimum at the end of an interlacustral-interglacial interval), then during the ensuing lacustral-glacial interval to cool-wet, to cold-wet (during the lacustral-glacial maximum) to cool-moist, and back to cool-dry.

ROGER B. MORRISON

References

Detailed bibliographies on pluvial lakes of the world are given by Flint (1957) and Charlesworth (1957), and for western North America by Hubbs and Miller (1948) and Morrison (1965).

Charlesworth, J. K., 1957, "The Quaternary Era, with Special Reference to Its Glaciation," London, Edward Arnold, Ltd., 2 vols., 1700pp. (see especially Ch. 41 (Vol. 2), "Pluvial Belts," pp. 1112–1145.)

Flint, R. F., 1957, "Glacial and Pleistocene Geology," New York, John Wiley & Sons, Inc., 553pp.

Gilbert, G. K., 1890, "Lake Bonneville," U.S. Geol. Surv. Monograph, 1, 438pp.

Hubbs, C. L., and Miller, R. R., 1948, "The zoological evidence—Correlation between fish distribution and hydrographic history in the desert basins of the western United States," in "The Great Basin, with emphasis on glacial and postglacial times," Utah Univ. Bull., 38, No. 20, 18–166.

Morrison, R. B., 1964, "Lake Lahontan: Geology of southern Carson Desert, Nevada," U.S. Geol. Surv. Profess. Paper 401, 156pp.

Morrison, R. B., 1965, "Quaternary Geology of the Great Basin," in (Wright, H. E. and Frey, D. G., editors), "The Quaternary of the United States," pp. 265–285, Princeton, N.J., Princeton Univ. Press.

Russell, I. C., 1885, "Geological history of Lake Lahontan, a Quaternary lake of northwestern Nevada," U.S. Geol. Surv. Monograph, 11, 288pp.

Russell, I. C., 1889, "Quaternary history of Mono Valley, California," U.S. Geol. Surv. 8th Ann. Rept., 261–394.

Snyder, C. T., Hardman, George, and Zdenek, F. F., 1964, "Pleistocene lakes in the Great Basin," U.S. Geol. Surv. Misc. Geol. Invest., Map I-416.

Cross-references: Aral Sea; Caspian Sea; Dead Sea; East African Lakes; Glacial Geology; Glacial Spillways and Proglacial Lakes; Glaciation; Great Salt Lake; Lake Baikal; Lake Chad; Lake Eyre; Quaternary; Terraces-Lacustrine. Vol. I: Black Sea. Vol. II: Climatic Variations—Historical Record. Vol. VI: Glacier Geophysics. pr Vol. VIII: Basin and Range Province.

POLDER—See pr Vol. VI

POLJE

In the Serbo–Croat language of Yugoslavia, a polje means a cultivated field. In geomorphic literature on the limestone solution areas of the karst landscape, it means a broad sunken area, normally floored by alluvium or residual *terra rossa* soils (hence the name), that have resulted from the collapse of extensive underground cavern systems. They often have vertical walls 50–100 meters high and may cover areas up to 250 km². There may be a central lake and there may be a "disappearing stream" draining the area and passing back into the underground (cryptorheic) system. In the hierarchy of karst solution/collapse features, one may go from *ponor* (sink hole), to *dolina* (a round depression) to an *uvala* (a series of doliny), to the *polje*, the largest of such phenomena.

It has been noted that some poljes are graben depressions (von Engeln, 1942), as are some "ova" depressions of Anatolia (Turkey), but this does not seem to be the original intent of the term. Collapsed walls can of course show slickensides, but these need not be of tectonic origin. Thornbury (1954) believes that "polje" should be reserved for structurally controlled depressions.

In Cuba, the internal (closed basin) poljes are referred to as "hoyos." Their origin has been discussed by Gradzinski and Radomski (1965).

RHODES W. FAIRBRIDGE

References

Gradzinski, R. and Radomski, A., 1965, "Origin and development of internal poljes 'hoyos' in the Sierra de los Organis, Cuba," *Bull. Acad. Pol. Sci., Sér. Sci. Géol., Géogr.*, **13**(2), 181–186.
Salomon-Calvi, W., 1939, "Die Geologie der Lykaonischen Steppentafel," Leipzig, Akad. Verlags.
Thornbury, W. D., 1954, "Principles of Geomorphology," New York, John Wiley & Sons, 618pp.
von Engeln, O. D., 1942, "Geomorphology," New York, The Macmillan Co., 655pp.

Cross-references: *Cone Karst; Dolina; Karst; Sink, Sinkhole; Structural Control in Geomorphology; Uvala.* Vol. VI: *Terra Rossa.*

POLYGONAL GROUND—*See* PATTERNED GROUND

PONOR—*See* SINK, SINKHOLE, SWALLOW HOLE

POPULAR GEOLOGY—*See* pr Vol. VI

POSTGLACIAL ISOSTATIC REBOUND

Only a few years after the theory of worldwide ice ages had been proposed, T. F. Jamieson (1865) saw the implication of such an ice load on the earth's crust. He suggested that the crust should have been depressed under this load and later recovered its original position when the ice was removed. In the 1890's, observations of warped and tilted shore lines around the Great Lakes in North America and in the Baltic area of Europe began to give abundant evidence of the response to glacial loading which Jamieson had predicted. Studies of glacial rebound have intensified in the past several decades in both of these areas, and quantitative as well as geographic data show clearly the genetic relationship of rebound to the previous glacier load. However, a minor dissent is still voiced by those who insist that the uplift of the glaciated tracts of northern North America and of northern Europe is merely the continuing, secular uplift of the Canadian and Fennoscandian Precambrian shields which have been rising more or less continuously throughout geologic time.

Several independent lines of reasoning show the genetic relationship between rebound and ice load:

(1) The outer limit of the area affected by rebound is parallel to, and slightly inside, the outer limit of the last glaciation.

(2) *Isobases* (q.v.) which show the distribution of rebound are concentric to regions believed, on other lines of evidence, to have had the thickest ice, namely, the Hudson Bay area of North America and the Gulf of Bothnia in Fennoscandia. Isobase maps (Fig. 1) show these relationships clearly. Almost 300 meters of rebound are recorded along the eastern rim of Hudson Bay, and perhaps 275 meters in the northern Baltic Sea. Neither of these figures gives the total amount of rebound, however. Rebound is almost universally studied by means of deformed shore lines, and shore lines naturally cannot form until *after* the ice sheet has been melted away from a given locality. From various studies, it is becoming clear that much, perhaps nearly half, of the total rebound took place before complete deglaciation and is therefore not recorded. Nansen has suggested a total of about 530 meters for Scandinavia. And, for North America, by adding the greatest uplifts recorded for Glacial Lake Algonquin and Glacial Lake Barlow–Ojibway, a total of around 2000 feet or 600 meters may be suggested for southern Hudson Bay.

(3) The rates of postglacial rebound are nearly the same for North America, northern Europe and elsewhere. Curves (Fig. 2) relating rebound to time, as determined by radiocarbon dating in North America and by varve chronology in Fennoscandia, show that the observed rates were greatest at the moment of deglaciation. The rate of uplift

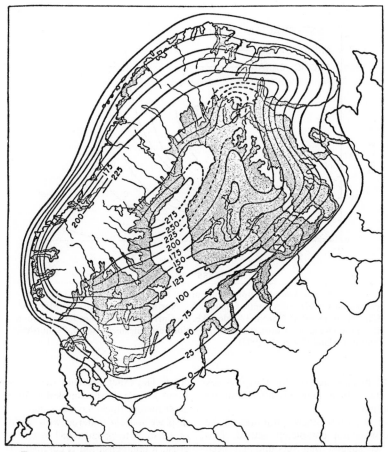

FIG. 1. Map illustrating the depression of Fennoscandia under the weight of its last ice sheet. The curved lines, called "isobases," represent in meters the late glacial and postglacial uplift of the highest strand mark of the ocean. The area covered by the sea at one or other part of late glacial time is shown by stippling. Scale—1:20,000,000 (Daly, 1934). (By permission of Yale University Press, New Haven.)

has decreased progressively to the present day, and it still continues in both of the major glaciated areas. Contemporary rebound ranges from values of about 1 meter per century in central areas to less than 10 cm per century on the periphery of the glaciated tract.

(4) Negative gravity anomalies, indicating a deficiency of mass, presently exist in the former ice centers. This situation is most clearly shown in Canada where a geoidal depression of about −15 milligals encircles the former Hudson Bay ice center (Fig. 3). This deficiency of mass, in the center of a stable shield area, is most logically interpreted as incomplete postglacial rebound.

(5) A final argument is that glacio-isostatic rebound has been observed in every major area which was glacierized during late Pleistocene time, such as Britain, Spitzbergen, Siberia and Patagonia. Even Greenland and Antarctica, which have

suffered only minor retreats of their ice sheets in the past 15,000 years or so, show clearly that rebound accompanied that shrinking.

The rebounding area is separated from the surrounding stable areas by the *isobase of zero uplift* (also called "zero isobase"). The isobases of zero uplift have also been called "hinge lines" because profiles of the deformed shore lines usually show a conspicuous hinging movement where the tilted portion meets the portion which is still horizontal (Sauramo, 1958). The "hinge," however, is very much exaggerated by distortion of the vertical scale in such profiles. In fact, more detailed work usually shows that the tilted portion of the shore line approaches the horizontal portion tangentially, and a discrete hinge does not exist. Internal hinge lines, such as the Great Inner Hinge in Scandinavia (Sauramo, 1958), appear to be areas of rapid change of adjustment and not hinges at all. They are per-

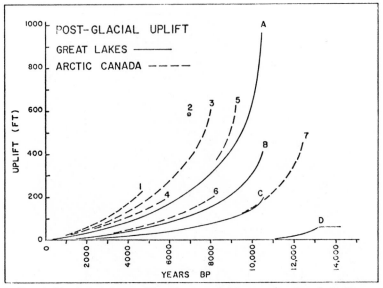

FIG. 2. North American uplift and curves. Solid curves are from Lake Huron; dashed curves are from Arctic Canada. A—North Bay, B—Sault Ste. Marie, C—Cape Rich, D—Port Huron, 1—Igloolike, 2—Carr Lake, 3—James Bay, 4—Southampton Island, 5—Coronation Gulf, 6—Northern Ellesmere Island, 7—northwest Victoria Island (Farrand, 1962).

haps related to preexisting structural weaknesses (fault zones, etc.) which induced differential response to rebound.

The question of pauses or discontinuities in the rebound process is not completely settled. Two lines of evidence suggest that rebound has been continuous and continuously decreasing in rate for the last 10,000 or 12,000 years. The first of these are the uplift curves (Fig. 2); the second is the great number of abandoned shore lines throughout the Canadian Arctic and in many places around the northern shores of the Great Lakes which form a continuous vertical series in which one shore line is not more strongly developed than any other. On the other hand, periods of stability have been postulated to account for shore lines which in some areas are very strongly developed. The strength of a shore line, however, depends not only on the rate of uplift of the land but also on the rate of rise or fall of the water level, which may be controlled independently by eustatic sea-level change, changes in lake outlet, etc. Shore line development reflects the *resultant* of crustal movements and water level fluctuations, which may be in or out of phase. Various combinations may produce rather strong shore lines at certain times without cessation of uplift; an example is the Nipissing shore of the upper Great Lakes.

The mechanism of isostatic adjustment, of which glacial rebound is only one type, is generally agreed to be flowage of the extremely viscous mantle at some depth not far below the base of the crust. The exact depth of the compensating layer is not known. In the simplest analysis, an ice sheet 2500 meters thick having a density of 0.9 should displace mantle material with an average density of 3.3 so as to produce 682 meters lowering of the crust, if compensation is complete. However, both the average thickness of the ice sheet and the density of the compensating layer are poorly known. Other factors such as the shear strength of the crust and viscosity of the mantle also enter into the computation in such a way as to reduce somewhat the value obtained in such a simple calculation (see *Earth—Viscosity*, Vol. V).

In addition to plastic deformation, *elastic* response to the ice load also contributes to rebound. Daly computed that perhaps 50–175 meters of rebound, from the edge to the center of the North American ice sheet, may have been contributed by immediate elastic response. Also, phase changes at the Mohorovičić discontinuity (between the crust and mantle) might account for 40–120 meters of rebound (Broecker, 1962). The postglacial rebound from both of these mechanisms, however, should have been largely dissipated before the complete disappearance of the ice sheet. Therefore, it is largely lost from the geologic record, although the oversteepening of the upper part of the uplift curves (Fig. 2) may possibly be attributable to elastic or phase-change rebound. This leads us to the conclusion that the great majority of postglacial rebound which is recorded by raised shore lines is the result of *plastic* response of the mantle.

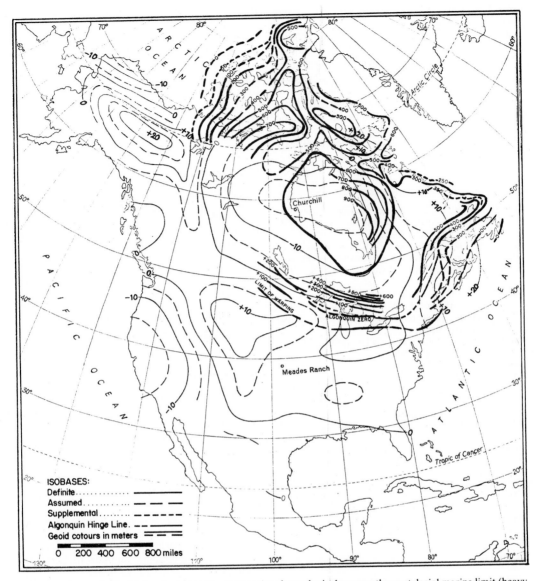

FIG. 3. Postglacial isostatic rebound in North America shown by isobases on the postglacial marine limit (heavy lines, after Farrand and Gajda, 1962) and compared with contours on the geoid surface (thin lines, after Fischer). Note the coincidence in the Hudson Bay area of the greatest uplift and a major depression of the geoid.

A final point concerns the question of a peripheral bulge, lying somewhat beyond the limits of the ice sheets and being the result of the displacement of mantle material away from the ice center. Most geophysicists agree that such a bulge should theoretically exist. It is argued that the viscosity of the mantle is too great and the time period too short for the material displaced to be spread uniformly around the earth. On the other hand, most field geologists can find no unequivocal evidence that such a bulge did exist. Shore lines beyond the isobase of zero uplift have remained horizontal since they were formed. Furthermore, Daly pointed out that the strength of the crust is so great that if a peripheral bulge had been created, it would still exist. It would not be destroyed when the mantle material returned toward the abandoned ice center. Perhaps the crux of this problem rests with the low amplitude of the hypothetical bulge which would require considerably more-precise field measurements than have commonly been made.

One outstanding example of isostatic rebound *beyond the glaciated area* should be mentioned.

887

This is Pluvial Lake Bonneville which occupied the Great Salt Lake basin of Utah. The appearance and disappearance of this large lake (about 200-km diameter) was in phase with the growth and dissipation of Pleistocene ice sheets. The importance of Lake Bonneville is that it provides a rather well-controlled situation in which to test the theory of isostatic compensation. A recent analysis by Crittenden (1963) reveals that the Bonneville shore line is updomed a maximum of 210 feet (64 meters) which represents isostatic compensation of at least 75%, perhaps considerably more.

W. R. FARRAND

References

Broecker, W. S., 1962, "The contribution of pressure-induced phase changes to glacial rebound," *J. Geophys. Res.*, **67**, 4837–4842.

Crittenden, M. D., Jr., 1963, "Effective viscosity of the Earth derived from isostatic loading of Pleistocene Lake Bonneville," *J. Geophys. Res.*, **68**, 5517–5530.

Daly, R. A., 1934, "The Changing World of the Ice Age," New Haven, Yale Univ. Press; London, Oxford Univ. Press (reprinted 1963, New York, Hafner Press), 271pp.

Farrand, W. R., 1962, "Postglacial uplift in North America," *Am. J. Sci.*, **260**, 181–199.

Farrand, W. R., and Gajda, R. T., 1962, "Isobases on the Wisconsin marine limit in Canada," *Geograph. Bull.*, **17**, 5–22.

Gutenberg, B., 1959, "Physics of the Earth's Interior," New York, Academic Press, 240pp.

Jamieson, T. F., 1865, *Geol. Soc. London, Quart. J.*, **21**, 178.

Sauramo, M., 1958, "Die Geschichte der Ostsee," *Ann. Acad. Sci. Fennicae, Ser. A III*, **51**.

Cross-references: *Crustal Movements—Contemporary*; *Great Lakes (North America)*; *Great Salt Lake*; *Isobase*; *Neotectonics*; *Warping*; *Water Loading and Crustal Response*. Vol. V: *Earth—Viscosity*.

POTHOLE

The term *pothole* has a specific meaning in geomorphology which embraces any more or less circular depression worn out by the gyratory abrasion of pebbles or boulders rotated under the energy of moving water, either of streams (Holmes, 1965, p. 507) or of the sea, on abrasion platforms (Wentworth, 1944). The expression "pothole" is also used colloquially for holes which develop in roads and for the sinkholes (ponor) or swallow holes of karst country; neither should be used in geomorphic studies or confusion will result. A special type of pothole is a fluvioglacial phenomenon, usually known as the *glacial moulin* (q.v.).

Hydraulic potholes appear to be favored by granular rocks, usually sedimentary, such as coarse sandstones and siltstones, but also deeply weathered igneous rocks such as granite. The most

remarkable potholes develop in uplift areas where vertical erosion energy has been accelerated and where a supply of boulders is assured. In some places, vertical successions of earlier potholes can be traced (e.g., Watkins Glen, New York: see Von Engeln, 1942, p. 171). Vertical fluting may result from the same process (see Cotton, 1952, p. 13, Fig. 43A).

RHODES W. FAIRBRIDGE

References

Cotton, C. A., 1952, "Geomorphology," Sixth ed., New York, John Wiley & Sons, 505pp.

Elston, E. D., 1917–1918. "Potholes, their variety, origin, and significance," *Sci. Monthly*, **5**, 554–567; **6**, 37–53.

Holmes, A., 1965, "Principles of Physical Geology," Second ed., London, Nelson, 1288pp.

Ives, R. L., 1948, "Plunge pools, potholes and related features," *Rocks Minerals*, **23**, 3–10.

von Engeln, O. D., 1942. "Geomorphology," New York, The Macmillan Co., 655pp.

Wentworth, C. K., 1944, "Potholes, pits, and pans," *J. Geol.*, **52**, 117–130.

Cross-references: *Glacial Moulin*; *Rivers*; *Waterfalls*.

PRAIRIE MOUNDS

Prairie mounds are low, naturally occurring hillocks, randomly distributed over level terrain or more rarely on hill slopes. Mound fields are extensive in Arkansas, eastern Oklahoma, the Gulf Coastal Plain and in places along the Pacific Coast from California to Oregon.

Called "pimples" in Texas and "mima" mounds in Oregon they have been subject to much speculation.

Theories of origin (20 or so) include the idea of human manufacture, (almost perfect symmetry) and other organic agencies. Bretz (1913) and Ritchie (1953) related the mima mounds to periglacial mechanics.

The mounds of Arkansas, however, are far removed from glacial and periglacial areas as well as coastal areas, thus eliminating such explanations here. Nonetheless, similarity in size, shape, orientation, and distribution of prairie mounds, regardless of locality, suggests a common mode of origin and furnishes an explanation of the way in which these mounds are formed.

Mounds range from 20–60 feet in diameter and from 2–8 feet high. They are slightly asymmetrical, somewhat elongated and steepened on the leeward side. All are similarly orientated. The pattern of distribution is random, but in northwest Arkansas, the most abundant mounds, those composed completely of eolian material, occupy flat or level surfaces. Rarer mounds containing coarser materials are located on slopes. Otherwise, the mounds occur

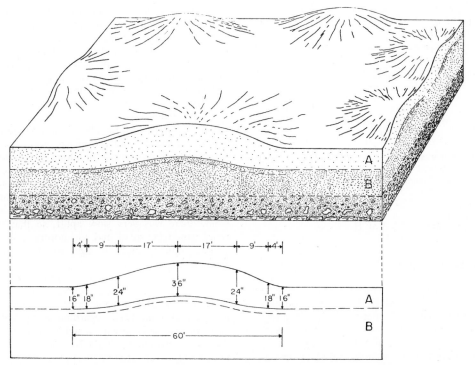

FIG. 1. A group of mounds on University Farm, Highway 112, north of Fayetteville, Arkansas. A refers to the A horizon, B refers to the B horizon. The dashed line below the B unit indicates the base of the loess unit.

in "fields" or groups. Intermound areas are level or, as the mima mounds, contain depressions.

The origin of the mounds in all cases appears to be erosional and/or depositional. Those on level terrain are formed simply by deposition of "A" soil horizon material in clumps of bushes which, under desert conditions, grow in symmetrically rounded patterns. This habit is commonplace for many desert plants simply because maximum mutual protection is provided. Mounds containing rock fragments too large to be moved by the wind are rare and always appear to occur on hillsides. These seem to have formed in areas where erosion by running water lowered the unprotected intermound areas.

The eolian mounds of northwestern Arkansas (Fig. 1) are formed on a blanket of loessal material upon which a soil profile had developed before the mound building began. The dust forming the blanket was removed from arid lands west of Arkansas and deposited wherever vegetation was sufficient to prevent further transportation. After the soil profile had formed, vegetation became discontinuous, "A" horizon material accumulated in suitable places such as clumps of bushes. At the same time, intermound areas were deflated to the A-B interface which is indicated by the uniformity of the surface. Returning humid conditions terminated further activity, and a new soil profile began to form. At present, the A-B interface is approximately 16 inches below the land surface in the intermound areas. Under the mounds, the surface is convex upward and is a subdued replica of the profile of the mounds. A plane connecting intermound surface levels indicates the A-B interface is approximately 4 inches below the plane at the center of the mounds (Fig. 1). Thus, under the centers of the mounds (due, no doubt, to insulation), the A-B interface has been lowered much less than elsewhere.

No fossils or artifacts have been discovered in the mounds, but alluvium on valley floors (possibly related to that composing the mounds) contains artifacts of archaic Indian cultures which may be as much as 3000 years old. On this basis, the soil profile may have formed at a rate of about 0.135 mm/yr, and the mounds themselves furnish clear evidence of a prolonged episode of aridity in areas now humid.

JAMES H. QUINN

References

Bretz, J H., 1913, "Glaciation of the Puget Sound region," *Wash. Geol. Surv. Bull.*, **8**.

Dalaquest, W. W., and Scheffer, V. B., 1942, "The origin of the Mima Mounds of western Washington," *J. Geol.*, **50**, No. 1.

Gravenor, C. P., 1955, "The origin and significance of prairie mounds," *Am. J. Sci.*, **253**, 475–481.

Quinn. J. H.. 1961. "Prairie mounds of Arkansas," *Newsletter of the Arkansas Archeological Society*, **2**, No. 6.

Ritchie, A. M.. 1953, "The erosional origin of the Mima Mounds of southwest Washington," *J. Geol.*, **61**, No. 1, 41–50.

Cross-references: *Arid Cycle; Deflation; Deserts and Desert Landforms; Frost Action; Patterned Ground; Periglacial Landscape.* Vol. VI: *Soil Genesis.*

PRECESSION—*See* Vol. II

PRIMÄRRUMPF

Primärrumpf is a term introduced by Penck (1924) which was translated by Czech and Boswell as "*primary peneplane*" (Penck, 1953). It refers to flattish platforms or benches, corresponding to the remnants of an original, initial structural surface, which have not yet been destroyed by a cycle of erosion (see *Process—Structure—Stage* and *Youth—Maturity—Old Age*). It may be distinguished from, or may be seen as a type of, peneplain resulting from nearly complete erosion of former uplands to a base level because of the fact that it lies substantially above the current base level and its slope tends to increase with the passage of time. For peneplains resulting from erosion to base level of former high land areas, Penck introduced the term *endrumpf*.

Another feature with which it may be confused is an uplifted peneplain produced by an earlier cycle. However, peneplains almost always have monadnocks standing up like islands on their surface, while the "primary peneplain" will be featureless. On the surface of a "primary peneplain," one would expect to find soils developed from the underlying rocks which would show a degree of profile development dependent on the time period which had elapsed since the initial uplift. On the surface of a peneplain might be found material brought in and deposited by the streams that carved the peneplain. Presumably, the soils would be developed on these materials and would show a degree of profile development depending on the age of the incision of the stream in that local area. This would be earliest near the original base level and would become progressively more recent toward the upper parts of the river course.

Primärrumpf would be expected to occur only where the rate of uplift at the beginning of a cycle of erosion was such that erosion failed to destroy the initial surface. Besides rate of uplift, this would depend on the area of land involved, the amount of uplift and the rate of erosion.

Davis in his "Geographical Cycle" had considered the case of rapid erosion following rapid uplift (Davis, 1899). This erosion would quickly destroy the initial surface even though the region uplifted was a large one. Penck emphasized the potentially variable nature of the amount and rate of uplift. Given slow uplift of part of the sea floor to only a small elevation above sea level, destruction of the initial surface would be very slow and the chances of its survival for a long period of time (geologically) as a primärrumpf would be very good.

The concept of an "old-from-birth peneplain" (Davis, 1922) is very similar to the "primary peneplain" concept. Davis used his term for cases where there was very slow uplift, so that local relief would be small and the normal stages of youth, maturity and old age would be inconspicuous.

There has been considerable discussion of the ideas of Penck and Davis (see for example, Thornbury, 1954, pp. 202–203). It would seem that each of the ideas of Penck and Davis regarding the equilibrium between rate and amount of uplift, area involved and rate of erosion would apply in particular cases, none being of universal application. Sauer thought that the summit surfaces of the Mesa Grande and Julian Mesa in the Peninsula Range of California were examples of primärrumpf. However, it is difficult to find any positive criteria to prove this. Sauer merely found no evidence that there had been a cycle of erosion which could have produced this surface, though remnants of dissected peneplains resulting from erosion cycles occur at lower elevations. Difficulty in recognition of the primärrumpf undoubtedly greatly limits the usefulness of this concept (Louis, 1961). Penck appears to have had in mind such features as the revived and stripped peneplains which characterize "Rumpfgebirge" (old basement complexes) of Hercynian, Caledonian and Precambrian age.

STUART A. HARRIS

References

Davis, W. M., 1899, "The geographical cycle," *Geograph. J.*, **14**, 481–504.

Davis, W. M., 1922, "Peneplains and the geographical cycle," *Bull. Geol. Soc. Am.*, **23**, 587–598.

Louis, H., 1961, "Allgemeine Geomorphologie," second ed., Berlin, de Gruyter. 355pp.

Penck, W., 1953, "Morphological Analysis of Land Forms," London, Macmillan & Co., 429 pp. (translation by H. Czech and K. C. Boswell of 1924 edition).

Sauer, C., 1929, "Land forms in the Peninsula Range of California . . . ," *Univ. Calif. Publ. Geogr.*, **3**, 212–215.

Thornbury, W. D., 1954, "Principles of Geomorphology," New York, John Wiley & Sons, 618pp.

PROCESS—STRUCTURE—STAGE

During the last half of the nineteenth century, the explorers, surveyors and geologists in the United States gradually became more and more impressed by the effectiveness of running water as an agent of erosion. It soon became clear that the landforms produced by running water did not occur randomly but were found in categories associated with various stages in the process. This prompted W. M. Davis (1899) to introduce his *geographical cycle* which was essentially a description of a theoretical arrangement of the phenomena of erosion by running water synthesized into a cycle of development of landforms. This theoretical arrangement was sufficiently convincing that it dominated thought in geomorphology in the English-speaking countries for over fifty years (see Holzner and Weaver, 1965).

Davis regarded a landscape as passing from an intitial state via sequential forms to an ultimate state. The three main controlling factors were regarded as being structure, process and time. *Structure* was used to include not only the attitude and relationships of the beds of rock but also such features as their nature, their relative hardness and their permeability. Thus on a very permeable rock, there will be the minimum of runoff, and so erosion by running water will be slower than on an adjacent impermeable material. Obviously soft shales will erode more readily than a massive quartzite, while a bed of limestone or gypsum will also undergo solution by underground water as well as being modified by any surface streams.

Process was used to include the different agents of erosion and weathering, e.g., water, wind, ice and gravity. In actual practice, Davis assumed that climate was an adequate description of the processes actually operating in a given case. A humid climatic condition, as found in the New England states today, was regarded as normal, while arid and glacial conditions were regarded as climatic accidents (Davis, 1909). Modified cycles based on the same structure-process-stage concept were suggested for these. Subsequent studies of paleoclimates suggest that the climates of geological time may have been appreciably warmer and generally rather more humid than at present, except during glacial stages, when, broadly speaking, they were colder and drier. Obviously "process" was and is used in only a qualitative sense.

Time defines the *stage* reached in the cycle. Clearly the more time available, the greater the amount of erosion that will have taken place and the later the *stage* which will be shown by the landforms.

This simple concept has been criticized many times, chiefly because of the assumptions made in the original essays (see also *Cycles, Geomorphic*). Davis had assumed that uplift occurred very rapidly and then ceased for the rest of the period of time in which a cycle would take place. There is ample evidence in the form of river terraces preserved along valley sides, drowned river valleys, and peneplains truncating hill tops, that changes in *base level* (q.v.) do occur during a given erosion cycle. Then there are the climatic changes which have taken place so frequently and over such wide areas in the last million years (see *Pleistocene Climatic Zonation*, pr Vol. VII). Clearly we are dealing with an open system, not a closed system (see *Cycles, Geomorphic*), since we rarely find a cycle going to completion without some environmental changes taking place.

Despite these objections, the cyclic concept remains a very valuable teaching tool due to the fact that it presents the development of landforms in a definite order which can be verified easily in the field. Davis's concept of a closed system may not work in detail, but the concept of process, structure and stage is of fundamental importance in the more practical open system models which are taking its place. This concept also remains of prime importance in the other cycles of landform development which have subsequently been devised, e.g., the cycles of shoreline development.

Stuart A. Harris

References

Chorley, R. J., 1962, "Geomorphology and general systems theory," *U.S. Geol. Surv. Profess. Paper*, **500B**, 10pp.

Davis, W. M., 1899, "The Geographical Cycle," *Geograph. J.*, **14**, 481–504.

Davis, W. M., 1909, "Geographical Essays," New York, Dover Publications, Inc., (reprinted 1954).

Holzner, L., and Weaver, G. D., 1965, "Geographic evaluation of climatic and climato-genetic geomorphology," *Ann. Assoc. Am. Geogr.*, **55**, 592–602.

Thornbury, W. D., 1954, "Principles of Geomorphology," New York, J. Wiley & Sons, 618pp.

PROFILE CONSTRUCTION—*See* pr Vol. VI

PROFILE OF EQUILIBRIUM

The concept of an ideal profile of equilibrium in the *thalweg* (q.v.) of a river goes back to *Surell's Laws* (q.v.), but its development rests largely on the theories and philosophy of William Morris Davis, who lived from 1850–1934. A man like Davis with his basic training as an engineer and early activity in astronomy quite naturally was conditioned to rational deduction. Unfortunately, nature does not always fit the brilliant simplification. Indeed, Davis was loathe to document purely empirical observations. An ideal *must* exist.

Bourdier (1959) in a review of the Davisian ideal quoted Herschel (1832), the astronomer, to the effect that one man lives too short a life to observe the complete growth of an oak tree, but the existence of oak trees of different ages in one and the same forest permit one to reconstruct this growth. In the same way, the astronomer and the geologist observe many individual examples of a particular phenomenon in order to deduce an evolutionary sequence. Thus Davis thought he could construct an ideal fluvial cycle, beginning with a single event, the uplift of part of the earth's crust, to be followed by a relentless cycle of progressive, irreversible and sequential change, from youth to old age, from initial uplift to ultimate peneplain. As Chorley (1965) has pointed out, the basic fallacy was the supposition that from the present landform one can deduce its history. The Davisian ideal profile can scarcely ever be achieved because any fluvial profile is constantly subject to climatic and eustatic changes, as well as isostasy and other tectonic factors.

Davis freely admitted that the "ideal profile" which he preferred to call "*grade*" (q.v.) went back to the engineers and hydrodynamicists of the last century and even earlier, mainly the French and Italians, who were for civic reasons greatly concerned with river control. Chorley *et al.* mention Guglielmini who wrote in 1697 as a noted pioneer. Even Galileo turned his fertile mind to this question. Notable in France were J. A. Fabre (1797), Surell (1841) and Cunit (1855), the history of the idea (with references) being given in some detail by Baulig (1950).

As conceived by Davis, and the early engineers, the ideal profile of equilibrium should be an asymptotic curve, steepest in the headwaters and gently flattening toward *base level* (q.v.). A formula offered by O. T. Jones (1924) is based on a resemblance to a rectangular hyperbola:

$$(x + a)(g + b) = k'$$

where k' is the curve constant, x the distance from origin and g the gradient dy/dx; a and b are constants, a is about 2.4 and b is small, approaching zero. Unfortunately, in the place where the formula was tested there were hanging valley tributaries, rocky steps and nickpoints that upset the smooth ideal. The river profiles published by de la Noë and de Margerie (1888, Pl. XVIII) and by A. Penck (1894, p. 323) show tributaries entering main streams *without* change in slope of the latter— as Jones remarked—"almost certainly not the true relation."

Kimball (1948) has offered formulas for cross section and discharge relations. Despite a vast collection of empirical data, the quantification of the actual subject is still extremely complicated (Leopold, Wolman and Miller, 1964), the reason being the great number of variables and the general refusal of nature to supply a homogeneous model.

What has emerged over the last two decades is the fact that although the longitudinal profile of a river may not be a smooth asymptotic curve, it may still be at grade, i.e., in a state of equilibrium (Mackin, 1948). Some writers (e.g., Langbein and Leopold, 1964; Dury, 1966) prefer "quasi-equilibrium" as a

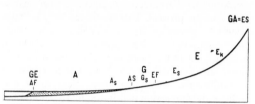

FIG. 1. Theoretical ideal profile of equilibrium (without tributaries), illustrated by Gerber (1957).

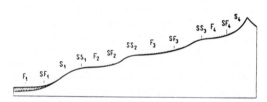

FIG. 2. Ideal profile *with* tributaries in homogeneous rocks, showing stepped reaches.

more accurate expression, since most streams are more or less seasonal, and an equilibrium could only be seen over a period of years. Strahler (1957) and others prefer the term "dynamic equilibrium," which perhaps best describes the open system in a steady state. In it, there is a semicontinuous transport of energy (materials), but the form of the stream is unchanged, as long as the basic parameters remain constant; these would include climate, load, tectonic framework and so on. In Figs. 1–3, three longitudinal valley profiles are represented (Gerber, 1957). Figure 1 shows the so-called normal profile or profile of equilibrium, Fig. 2 the ideal undulating profile in homogeneous rocks, and Fig. 3 the pediment-type *treppen* or stepped profile. Under various conditions of lithology and morphogenetic history, each type can be found to exist in nature.

Illustrated in Fig. 1 is the normal profile or profile of equilibrium. G is the equilibrium point ("grade"). GA is the initial point of the gradient and GE the end. E is the eroding or degrading sector and A the accumulating or aggrading sector. AS is the start, and AF the foot, of the aggradation, and ES is the start of the erosion. E_k is the active downward erosion region, while E_s indicates where sideways or

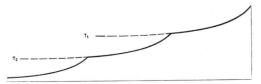

FIG. 3. "Penckian" profile showing erosion steps (*treppen*), due to changes in base level, eustatic or tectonic, and/or changes in regime, due to climate and vegetation.

lateral erosion begins. EF is the foot (end) of the erosional sector, but eventually sideways (lateral) corrasion will reach down to G_s and even to the accumulation sector at A_s. In nature, this profile is approximated in short sectors, but never in long rivers.

Figure 2 shows the ideal stream profile with tributaries in homogeneous rocks. F = flatter reaches; S = steeper reaches (rapids or "riffles"). Beginning from the foot at F, one comes to a steeper flat SF_1, a steep S_1 and steepening SS_1, where F_2 begins. At each F sector there is likely to be some accumulation, but it is only temporary and only at the final sector approaching base level F_1 is the aggradation of a more permanent nature. Each of the above reaches is likely to approach an ideal profile of equilibrium, but it is then upset by the junction of a tributary which will change the stream energy balance. Even in homogeneous materials, the hydrodynamics of the fluvial regime will always tend to maintain this undulating thalweg. In inhomogeneous rocks, there will be narrow gorges alternating with open valley areas, which introduce disturbances to the "ideal" profile analogous to those introduced by tributaries. Notwithstanding all these complications, in modern treatments (of short-term regimes) the entire *thalweg* can be considered to be in dynamic equilibrium.

Figure 3 represents the well-known "Penckian" profile of steps or *treppen* based on the concept of pedimentation and headward migration of *nick points* (q.v.). T_1 is the oldest *treppen* or step and may be interpreted as the remnant of a stream gradient that was related to (a) a higher base level of a former age, (b) a former less energetic erosion cycle, or (c) a resistant horizon in the country rock. The last example (c) has its classic model in the Niagara Falls, which migrate progressively headward. Both (a) and (b) can develop in homogeneous rocks but require a change in the regime (climatic, eustatic or tectonic).

To summarize, then, it may be seen that the nineteenth century concept, a mathematically ideal profile of equilibrium, must remain an ideal, while thalwegs as they really exist may have many forms, with complications ranging from contemporary lithology to inherited features. However, they may be effectively analyzed today on the basis of *dynamic geomorphology* (q.v.).

RHODES W. FAIRBRIDGE

References

Baulig, H., 1950, "La notion de profil d'équilibre," in "Essais de Géomorphologie," *Strasbourg, Publ. Fac. Lettres Univ.*, **114**, 43–86 (reprinted with additions from *Compt. Rend. Congr. Intern. Géorgr., Cairo*, 1925, **3**, 51–63).

Bourdier, F., 1959, "Origines et succès d'une théorie géologique illusoire: l'eustatisme appliqué aux terrasses alluviales," *Rev. Géomorph. Dyn.*, **10**, 16–29.

Chorley, R. J., 1965, "A Re-evaluation of the Geomorphic System of W. M. Davis," in (Chorley, R. J., and Haggett, P., editors) "Frontiers in Geographical Teaching," pp. 21–38, London, Methuen & Co. Ltd.

Chorley, R. J., Dunn, A. J., and Beckinsale, R. P., 1964, "The History of the Study of Land Forms," Vol. 1, London and New York, Methuen & Co., Ltd., and John Wiley & Sons (Geomorphology before Davis).

Davis, W. M., 1909, "Geographical Essays," New York, 777pp. (Dover Reprint, 1954).

Dury, G. H., 1966, "The Concept of Grade", in (Dury, G. H., editor) "Essays in Geomorphology," pp. 211–233, London, William Heinemann Ltd.

Gerber, E., 1956, "Das Längsprofil der Alpentäler," *Geogr. Helv.*, **11**.

Gerber, E., 1957, "Das Längsprofil der Alpenländer und die Steilenwanderungstheorie," in "Geomorphologische Studien" (Machatschek Festschrift), pp. 79–90, Gotha, H. Haack.

Herschel, J. F. W., 1832, "On the astronomical causes which may influence geological phenomena," *Trans. Geol. Soc. London*, **17**, 293–299.

Jones, O. T., 1924, "The upper Towy drainage-system", *Quart. J. Geol. Soc. London*, **80**, 568–609.

Kimball, D., 1948, "Denudation chronology; the dynamics of river action," *Inst. Archaeol, Univ. London, Occ. Pap.*, **8**.

Langbein, W. B., and Leopold, L. B., 1964, "Quasi-equilibrium states in channel morphology," *Amer. J. Sci.*, **262**(6), 782–794.

La Noë, G. de, and Margerie, E. de, 1888, "Les formes du terrain," Paris, Serv. Géogr. de L'Armée, 1 vol. with Atlas, 105pp.

Leopold, L. B., Wolman, M. G., and Miller, J. P., 1964, "Fluvial Processes in Geomorphology," San Francisco, W. H. Freeman & Co., 522pp.

Mackin, J. H., 1948, "Concept of the graded river," *Bull. Geol. Soc. Am.*, **59**, 463–512.

Penck, A., 1894, "Morphologie der Erdoberfläche," Stuttgart, Engelhorn, 2 vols.

Strahler, A. N., 1957, "Quantitative analysis of watershed geomorphology," *Trans. Am. Geophys. Union*, **38**(6).

Cross-references: *Base Level; Dynamic Geomorphology; Grade, Graded Stream; Nickpoint; Quantitative Geomorphology; Rivers; Surell's Laws; Thalweg; Treppen Concept; Youth-Maturity-Old Age.*

PROGLACIAL LAKE—*See* GLACIAL SPILLWAYS AND PROGLACIAL LAKES

PROGLACIAL PROCESSES—*See* FLUVIOGLACIAL PROCESSES

PROGRADING SHORELINE

The definition accepted by Stamp (1961) consists of the following passage from Johnson (1919), "Just so long as the current aggrades (builds up) the seabottom offshore, the waves will prograde (build forward) the shore. Following Davis we may call any shore which is experiencing such a long-continued advance into the sea, a *prograding shore* and distinguish it from the more usual retreating or *retrograding shore*" (Johnson's italics). (Davis does not appear to have used the word "prograde" in print prior to Johnson's definition, "aggrade" being used instead.) The wider meaning within Johnson's definition equates prograding and retrograding with Valentin's (1952) classification of advancing and retreating coastlines, respectively, but as there are several types of advancing coastline, including coral reefs and deltas, the term prograding is perhaps best restricted to the use made by Cotton (1922), i.e., to the first part of Johnson's definition, a prograding shore being a net shift seaward of the shore during which new land is initially formed of a wave-built beach ridge. This is the basic structure for all further land development which, depending on the type of environment, can be divided into three categories: foreland, chenier plain, and spit (Fig. 1) or barrier

island. *Forelands* "if continuous for some distance alongshore are strand plains" (Cotton, 1922). The initial beach ridge is commonly formed at the base of a coastal cliff and all subsequent ridges lie parallel to the first without any intervening major, seawater lagoon being formed. The *chenier plain* (Fig. 2) is "a belted marsh-and-ridge plain," in which the beach ridges are "shallow-based, perched, sandy ridges resting on clay" (Price, 1955). The *spit* (Evans, 1942) and *barrier island* (Shepard, 1952) belong essentially to one geomorphic class that differs from the foreland in enclosing a lagoon or harbor. Whereas the spit (Fig. 3) is tied at one end to the mainland, so that there is only one entrance to the harbor, the barrier island has no such connection. Apart from this there is no morphological and generic difference, longshore and onshore transport of sediments being important in both (Fig. 1).

Factors that control the stability or otherwise of a prograding shore line can be summarized as time, energy, sedimentary supply, organic growth and sea level change. The effects of all these factors, except sea level change, have received fair coverage in textbooks such as those of Guilcher (1958) and King (1959) and thus are only briefly summarized here (see *Retrograding Shoreline*). *Time* permits partial or complete dynamic equilibrium to be

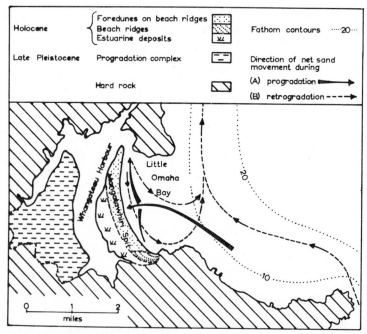

FIG. 1. The directions of sand movements (Schofield) are based on lithological, grain-size and malacological criteria. Surveyed samples were collected from "regular" intervals of 20–30 chains along the beach and in offshore positions, (A) during progradation of the shore in June 1963, and (B) during retrogradation in December 1963. Statistical analyses equal to 50% of total analytical work were made to check reality of results.

FIG. 2. Portion of a chenier plain, north of Miranda, Firth of Thames, New Zealand. (Photo courtesy of the Surveyor-General, N.Z. Department of Lands and Survey.) Here beach ridges of shell, sand and minor shingle separate areas of estuarine mud. The prograded area, about 2000 meters in width, was built during the last 4000 years (Schofield, 1960) and lies seaward of the cliffed hinterland seen on left side of photo. These cliffs were eroded during the rapid post-glacial rise in sea level. (North at top.)

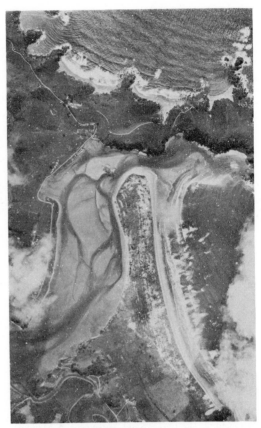

FIG. 3. Prograded spit, Whananaki Inlet, Northland, New Zealand, showing parallel nature of foredune cover on wave-built beach ridges. This mile-long spit, together with the 2½-mile-long spit at Mangatawhiri (Fig. 1) were almost certainly built during the last 4000 years. Note parallel nature of spit to refracted swell pattern. Note also reflected patterns of minor waves. (North at top.) (Photo courtesy of the Surveyor-General, N.Z. Department of Lands and Survey.)

reached between all other factors. The degree of equilibrium can be partly assessed from the shape of coastal outline and sea floor profile; the smoother these are, the higher is the degree of equilibrium. *Energy*, in the form of wind-, wave- and tide-generated currents, controls grain size and direction of sedimentary transport, and speed at which dynamic equilibrium is attained. All other factors being stable, *the rate of sedimentary supply* determines the rate of progradation. *Organic growth* is important in fixing dune sands that are wind-built on top of the wave-constructed beach ridges (see *Retrograding Shore Line*, Fig. 2) and which in turn helps to protect the latter during temporary periods of coastal erosion. It is also important in helping to raise estuarine mud deposits up to high-spring-tide level.

The effects of *sea level change* have received little attention but could be most important as a cause for both prograding and retrograding coasts. Where there is dynamic equilibrium, lowering of sea level produces scouring of the sea floor between the shore and the maximum depth at which sediment is locally transported. Where the net direction of transport is shoreward, and this is normal, the excess sediments will cause progradation. Observations of beaches and offshore sedimentary transport within New Zealand (Schofield. 1967. and work still in progress) suggest good qualitative correlation of progradation with sea level lowering during short and long periods of time (Fig. 4). Quantitative correlation between volumes of sand in prograded

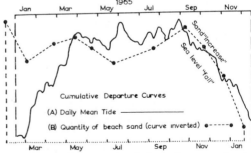

FIG. 4. Preliminary correlation of one year's observations on seven profiles across ocean beach at Mangatawhiri Spit (see Fig. 1) with tidal fluctuations at Auckland, 33 miles to the south. Both the spit and tidal recorder are situated on the east coast of the northern part of the North Island, New Zealand, and are thus in closely similar meteorological and oceanographic areas. Observations are continuing.

areas with theoretical amounts of sand supplied by known amounts of sea level lowering also exists where the period of change has been years, rather than months. Even lowering by an inch can, with sufficient time, cause considerable progradation if the area of sea floor from which the fresh supply of sediment comes is extensive. Certain lags between cause and effect may also be present as has been suggested by Bruun (1962).

J. C. Schofield

References

Bruun, P., 1962, "Sea level rise as a cause of shore erosion," *J. Waterways Harbs Div.*, **88**, WW1 (3065), 117–130.

Cotton, C. A., 1922, "Geomorphology of New Zealand. Part I—Systematic," *N.Z. Board of Sci. and Art, Man. No. 3*, 462pp. 442 figs.

Evans, O. F., 1942, "The origin of spits, bars and related structures," *J. Geol.*, **50**, 846–863.

Guilcher, A., 1958, "Coastal and Submarine Morphology," London, Methuen & Co. Ltd., 274pp.

Johnson, D. W., 1919, "Shore Processes and Shoreline Development," New York, John Wiley & Sons, 584pp.

King, Cuchlaine, A. M., 1959, "Beaches and Coasts," London, Ed. Arnold Ltd., 403pp., 149 figs.

Price, W. Armstrong., 1955, "Environment and formation of the Chenier Plain," *Quaternaria*, **2**, 75–86.

Schofield, J. C., 1960, "Sea-level fluctuations during the last 4000 years as recorded by a chenier plain, Firth of Thames, New Zealand," *New Zealand J. Geol. Geophys.*, 3(3), 467–85.

Schofield, J. C., 1967, "Sand Movement at Mangatawhiri Spit and Little Omaha Bay," *New Zealand J. Geol. Geophys.*, **10**(3), 697–721.

Shepard, F. P., 1952, "Revised nomenclature for depositional coastal features," *Bull. Am. Assoc. Petrol. Geologists*, **36**, 1902–1912.

Stamp, D., 1961, "A Glossary of Geographical Terms," London, Longmans, 539pp.

Valentin, H., 1952, "Die Küsten der Erde," *Peterm. Mitt. Ergänzungsheft 246*.

Cross-references: *Barriers—Beaches and Islands; Beach; Beach Ridge; Cuspate Foreland or Spit; Eustasy; Retrograding Shoreline; Sediment Transport—Long Term.* Vol. I: *Mean Sea Level Changes; Ocean Waves; Wave Refraction; Wave Theory.*

PROTALUS RAMPARTS—*See* **CIRQUE; FROST ACTION; TALUS FAN OR CONE**

PSEUDOKETTLE—*See* **KETTLE; PINGOS**

PUSH MORAINE—*See* **ICE THRUSTING;** *also* **MORAINE**

PUYS

This is a local term used in the Massif Central of France (Auvergne) for any hill or mountain. Puys may be composed of sedimentary rocks, but more commonly they represent parts of old volcanoes. The term was used very early in geological literature since it was in this area that extinct volcanoes and lava flows were first recognized as such by Guettard (see Scrope, 1858). It has come to mean any steep volcanic hill that has been eroded to leave the pipe or neck.

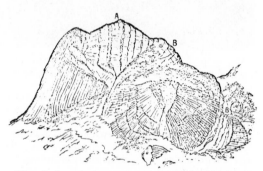

FIG. 1. A typical puys in the Auvergne: the Roche Sanadoire. A = jointed columns, B = stratified tuff bands (disturbed). (Sketch by T. G. Bonney.)

The puys of volcanic origin can be divided into several main groups. In the north are the extinct but essentially intact Quaternary volcanoes of the Puy de Dôme group. These were *Strombolian* or *Péléan* in type (see *Volcanoes*, Vol. V). To the south lies the Mont Dore region where isolated Pliocene cones such as the Puy de Sancy have been fairly severely eroded by streams and by glaciers. The Cantal region consists of an immense Pliocene cone (Puy Mary) of *Hawaiian* type about 40 miles across (Jung, 1946). This has been very thoroughly dissected so that the lava flows from isolated puys exhibiting *inverted relief,* i.e., the former valley bottoms now form the hill crests due to the greater resistance of the lava flow to

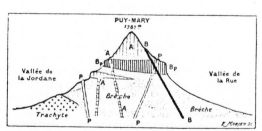

FIG. 2. Section through the Puy-Mary (1787m) in the Cantal group. A = andesite; B = basalt; P = phonolite; Bp = porphyritic basalt. (From Boule and Farge, 1898, "Le Cantal, guide . . .")

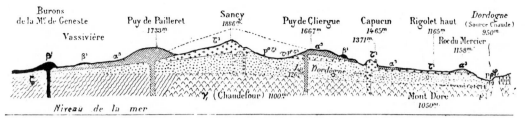

FIG. 3. Section through the Mont-Dore (after Michel Lévy, 1890, *Bull. Soc. Géol. France*). ζ = gneiss; γ = granite; $p\rho$ = rhyolitic ash; φ = phonolite; $p°\tau'$ = andesitic ash; τ' = trachyte porphyroid; α^3 = hornblende andesite; β' = plateau basalts.

erosion. An excellent example of radial drainage is shown by the streams draining the remains of the old cone. Finally there is the district of Le Puy (en-Velay) of Haute Loire, where old volcanic pipes have been left as puys after the rest of the small volcanic cones have been eroded away. The classic neck of Rocher Saint Michel at Le Puy is perhaps the most characteristic puy-type hill.

STUART A. HARRIS

References

Jung, J., 1946, "Géologie de l'Auvergne et de ses confins Bourbonnais et Limousins," Paris, Imprimerie Nationale, 371pp.

Scrope, G. P., 1858, "The Geology and Extinct Volcanoes of Central France," second ed., London, J. Murray, 258pp.

Cross-references: *Inversion (of Topography, Relief); Volcanic Landscapes; Volcanic Necks and Diatremes. Vol. V: Volcanoes.*

Q

QUANTITATIVE GEOMORPHOLOGY*

(I) Introduction

Under the impetus supplied by Horton (1945), the description of drainage basins and channel networks was transformed from a purely qualitative and deductive study to a rigorous quantitative science capable of providing hydrologists with numerical data of practical value. Horton's work was developed in detail by Strahler (1950, 1952, 1956, 1958) and his Columbia University associates (Melton, 1957; Morisawa, 1959; Schumm, 1956).

This section treats quantitative land-form analysis as it applies to normally developed watersheds in which running water and associated mass gravity movements, acting over long periods of time, are the chief agents in developing surface geometry. Emphasis is upon the geometry itself, rather than upon the dynamic processes of erosion and transportation which shape the forms.

(II) Basic Concepts

(A) **Open Systems and Steady States.** Of fundamental importance is the concept of a drainage basin as an open system tending to achieve a steady state of operation. An open system imports and exports matter and energy through system boundaries, and must transform energy uniformly to maintain operation. In a drainage basin, the land surface within the limits of the basin perimeter constitutes a system boundary through which precipitation is imported. Mineral matter supplied from within the system and excess precipitation leave the system through the basin mouth. In a graded drainage basin, the steady state manifests itself in the development of certain topographic characteristics which achieve a time-independent state. Erosional and transportational processes meanwhile produce a steady flow (averaged over periods of years or tens of years) of water and waste from the basin. Potential energy of position is transformed into kinetic energy of water and debris motion or into heat. Considered over a very long span of time, however, continual readjustment of components in the steady state is required as relief

* [Modified from "Handbook of Applied Hydrology" edited by Ven Te Chow. Copyright © 1964 by McGraw-Hill, Inc. Used with permission of the Editor and McGraw-Hill Book Company.]

lowers and available energy diminishes. The topographic forms will correspondingly show a slow evolution.

Where geologic events have brought into being a new land mass not previously acted upon by running water, the steady state is preceded by a transient state in which a new channel system grows and deepens rapidly as the ground slopes are transformed to contribute most efficiently to the drainage network. In the terminology of the earlier, classical descriptive geomorphology, the transient state was referred to as the stage of youth in the cycle of erosion; the steady state, as the stage of maturity.

The validity of the Horton system of fluvial morphometry depends upon the theory that for a given intensity of erosion process, acting upon a mass of given physical properties, the conditions of surface relief, slope and channel configuration reach a time-independent steady state in which morphology is adjusted to transmit through the system just the quantity of debris and excess water characteristically produced under the controlling regimen of climate. Should controlling factors of climate or geologic material be changed, the steady state will be upset. Through a relatively rapid series of adjustments, serving to reestablish a steady state, appropriate new values of basin geometry are developed (Strahler, 1958). In brief, steady state manifests itself by invariant geometry; transient state, by rapid changes in geometry in which new sets of forms replace the old.

(B) **Dimensional Analysis.** Dimensional analysis forms a sound basis for study of the geometrical and mechanical aspects of drainage basins (Strahler, 1958). The fundamental dimensions of length, mass and time, whether used singly or combined as products, suffice to define all geometrical and mechanical properties of a drainage basin. Many of the form elements have the simple dimension of length, e.g., stream length, basin perimeter or basin relief. Measures of area have the dimension of length squared; volumes, the dimension of length cubed. Another class of geometrical properties consists of the dimensionless ratios of one length property to another. Dimensionless ratios describe pure shape, or form, irrespective of absolute size (for tables of land-form parameters and their dimensional properties, see Strahler, 1958, pp. 282–283).

Geometrical similarity is an important concept of dimensional analysis applied to drainage basins.

Systems of landforms evolving from the same geologic processes and materials possess a high degree of geometrical similarity, an attribute that makes possible the recognition and classification of land forms. Figure 1 shows the meaning of geometrical similarity as applied to two drainage basins which differ in size but not in shape. Basins A and B are said to be *homothetic*, because any two corresponding points in the basins lie on the same radius vector from a center of similitude, i.e., are *collinear*.

The points Q' and Q mark the mouths of the basins, at corresponding distances r' and r from the center of similitude. Two other corresponding points are R' and R, collinear and located at distances ρ' and ρ, respectively, from the center of similitude. For reasons that are self-evident from considerations of Euclidian geometry of similar triangles.

$$r' = \lambda r \quad \text{and} \quad \rho' = \lambda \rho \qquad (1)$$

where λ is the linear scale ratio. Consequently,

$$\lambda = \frac{r'}{r} = \frac{\rho'}{\rho} \qquad (2)$$

which is to say that the radius vectors of any two collinear points are always in the ratio λ. Hence, in geometrically similar drainage basins, the distances between corresponding points in the system have the same scale ratio. In geometrical similarity, the tangents to corresponding points on curved lines in the two systems are always equal. In Fig. 1 the tangents of α' and α at the points N' and N are equal, whereas the degrees of curvature at corresponding points on the two figures are inversely related to the linear scale ratio.

In summary, two drainage basins are geometrically similar when all corresponding land-form elements having the dimension of length are in the same ratio λ, when all corresponding measures having the dimension of inverse of length are in the scale ratio $1/\lambda$, and when those of dimension length squared are in the same ratio, λ^2. Furthermore, all dimensionless properties must have identical values in the corresponding parts of both systems. Although perfect similarity is not to be expected in drainage basins, a high degree of similarity has been found over a great size range when planimetric (horizontal) aspects are considered. Lack of similarity among drainage basins may result from strong geologic inhomogeneities which distort the basin shapes.

As applied to scale model studies, the ratio λ is taken as the ratio of length in prototype to length in model. Mechanical (kinematic and dynamical) similarity between basins is not treated here, but would be an essential aspect of model studies.

(C) Statistical Analysis. The application of principles of mathematical statistics to quantitative geomorphology is essential if meaningful conclusions are to be achieved.

Mathematical statistics is concerned with the making of inferences from a small sample about the characteristics of a vast population whose absolute parameters can never be known. Tests are concerned with ascertaining the probability of being right or wrong in stating some hypothesis concerning the relation of one or more samples to the population or populations from which they have been drawn.

In practice, a particular geometric property of a drainage basin, (e.g., the length of stream segments) is sampled by measuring from maps or air photographs or by direct field surveys. When a sample of, say, 50 or 100 measurements is thus obtained, the standard methods of frequency-distribution analysis are used. The individual measurements, termed variates, are grouped into classes, and the nature of the distribution examined. If strongly skewed, a logarithmic transformation of variates may be required. The mean $\bar{x}$, variance s^2, and standard deviation s of the population, as estimated from the sample, are next computed, and serve to describe the geomorphic property in objective and useful terms. Next, the sample frequency distribution is compared with the normal, or gaussian, distribution, and a test is performed to assure that the normal distribution can be assumed. Many geometric properties of drainage basins, particularly those having the dimensions of length, area or volume, are characteristically lognormal in distribution, whereas other properties, particularly dimensionless ratios and angular values, tend to be arithmetically normal in distribution. Melton collected an extensive body of morphometric data on drainage basins and discussed the sample-size requirements for use in statistical tests.

Two or more samples can be compared by statistical tests to reach a decision as to whether the samples are likely to have been drawn from the same or from different populations. Such tests are essential to avoid unwarranted assumptions as to the significance of the observed differences in means and variances of the samples themselves.

The relationship of a dependent variable to an independent variable, as, for example, the influence

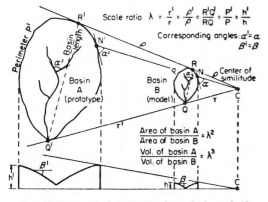

FIG. 1. Geometrical similarity of two drainage basins (Strahler, 1958).

of infiltration capacity upon drainage density, is treated by regression analysis. Linear and nonlinear equations may be used to obtain the best fit of data. The significance of the observed relationship can be evaluated by rigorous tests. Multiple regression, in which the combined effect of several independent variables upon one dependent variable can be considered, has been extensively used in drainage basin analysis. Machine methods of multiple correlation and regression analysis have been introduced.

(D) **Plan of Morphometric Analysis.** A systematic description of the geometry of a drainage basin and its stream-channel system requires measurements of linear aspects of the drainage network, areal aspects of the drainage basin, and relief (gradient) aspects of channel network and contributing ground slopes. Whereas the first two categories of measurement are planimetric (i.e., treat properties projected upon a horizontal datum plane), the third category treats the vertical inequalities of the drainage basin forms. Although not free from inconsistencies, the above plan of morphometric analysis is useful operationally and is followed throughout the remainder of this section.

(III) Linear Aspects of the Channel System

(A) **Stream Orders.** The first step in drainage basin analysis is designation of stream orders, following a system introduced into the United States by Horton (1945) and slightly modified by Strahler. Assuming that one has available a channel network map including all intermittent and permanent flow lines located in clearly defined valleys, the smallest fingertip tributaries are designated order 1 (Fig. 2). Where two first-order channels join, a channel segment of order 2 is formed; where two of order 2 join, a segment of order 3 is formed, and so forth. The trunk stream through which all discharge of water and sediment passes is therefore the stream segment of highest order.

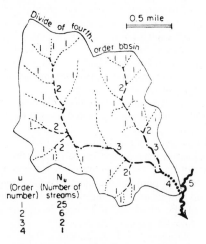

u	N_u
(Order number)	(Number of streams)
1	25
2	6
3	2
4	1

FIG. 2. Designation of stream orders.

The usefulness of the stream-order system depends on the premise that, on the average, if a sufficiently large sample is treated, order number is directly proportional to size of the contributing watershed, to channel dimensions, and to stream discharge at that place in the system. Because order number is dimensionless, two drainage networks differing greatly in linear scale can be compared with respect to corresponding points in their geometry through the use of order number. After the drainage network elements have been assigned their order numbers, the segments of each order are counted to yield the number N_u of segments of the given order u (Fig. 2).

It is obvious that the number of stream segments of any given order will be fewer than for the next lower order but more numerous than for the next higher order. The ratio of number segments of a given order N_u to the number of segments of the higher order $N_u + 1$ is termed the *bifurcation ratio* R_b.

$$R_b = \frac{N_u}{N_{u+1}} \tag{3}$$

The bifurcation ratio will not be precisely the same from one order to the next because of chance variations in watershed geometry, but will tend to be a constant throughout the series. This observation is the basis of Horton's (1945) *law of stream numbers*, which states that the numbers of stream segments of each order form an inverse geometric sequence with order number, or

$$N_u = R_b^{k-u} \tag{4}$$

where k is the order of the trunk segment and the other terms are as previously defined. The law has received verification by accumulated data from many localities (e.g., Schumm, 1956). When the logarithm of the number of streams is plotted against order, most drainage networks show a linear relationship, with small deviation from a straight line.

Calculation on an average value of R_b for a given channel network can be made by determining the slope of the fitted regression of logarithm of numbers (ordinate) on order (abscissa). The regression coefficient b is identical with the logarithm of R_b.

Bifurcation ratios characteristically range between 3.0 and 5.0 for watersheds in which the geologic structures do not distort the drainage pattern. The theoretical minimum possible value of 2.0 is rarely approached under natural conditions. Because the bifurcation ratio is a dimensionless property and because drainage systems in homogeneous materials tend to display geometrical similarity, it is not surprising that the ratio shows only a small variation from region to region.

Abnormally high bifurcation ratios might be expected in regions of steeply dipping rock strata where elongate strike valleys are confined between hogback ridges. The effects of distortions upon maximum flood discharges, assuming precipitation and other controls to be the same throughout, are such that elongate basins with high R_b yield a low but extended peak flow; while rotund basins with low R_b produce a sharp peak.

Horton (1945) shows that the total number of streams of all orders in a network can be computed if the bifurcation ratio R_b and trunk order k are known:

$$\sum_{i=1}^{k} N_u = \frac{R_b^k - 1}{R_b - 1} \qquad (5)$$

(B) Stream Lengths. Mean length $\bar{L}_u$ of a stream-channel segment of order u is a dimensional property revealing the characteristic size of components of a drainage network and its contributing basin surfaces.

The first-order stream channel with its contributing first-order drainage basin surface area should be regarded as the unit cell, or building block, of any watershed. Because first-order drainage basins tend to be geometrically similar over a wide range of sizes, it matters little what length property is chosen to provide the characteristic measurement of size by which systems are compared from region to region. Thus, while length of first-order channel is a convenient and easily obtained length measure, it might be equally valid to select basin perimeter, basin length, drainage density, or the square root of basin area as alternative indices of scale of the unit basin.

As expected, the mean length of channel segments of a given order is greater than that of the next lower order but less than that of the next higher order.

Horton was therefore able to state the *law of stream lengths*, that the mean lengths of stream segments of each of the successive orders of a basin tend to approximate a direct geometric sequence in which the first term is the average length of segments of the first order:

$$\bar{L}_u = \bar{L}_1 R_L^{u-1} \qquad (6)$$

where

$$R_L = \frac{\bar{L}_u}{\bar{L}_{u-1}}$$

If the law of stream lengths is valid, a plot of logarithm of stream length (ordinate) as a function of order (abscissa) should yield a set of points lying essentially along a straight line (Fig. 3). Confirmation of the law seems amply demonstrated by data from many watersheds (e.g., Schumm 1956; Morisawa, 1959).

The verification of Horton's laws of stream numbers and lengths supports the theory that geometrical similarity is preserved generally in basins of increasing order. In other words, a basin of the third order would tend to be geometrically similar to the second-order basins which lie within it, and these in

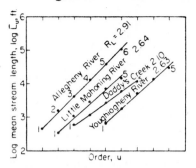

FIG. 3. Regression of logarithm of stream segment length on order for four drainage basins in the Appalachian Plateau Province (after Morisawa, 1959).

turn would be similar to the first-order basins within them. Hack (1957) casts doubt on this theory by finding that stream length (measured cumulatively from the stream head) varies as the 0.6 power of area in basins spanning nearly four orders (0.01–100 square miles). An exponent of 0.5 is required if geometrical similarity is to be perfectly preserved, whereas the observed value of 0.6 requires that basins become somewhat longer and narrower as their size increases.

(C) Length of Overland Flow. Surface runoff follows a system of downslope flow paths from the drainage divide (basin perimeter) to the nearest channel. This flow net, comprising a family of orthogonal curves with respect to the topographic contours, locally converges or diverges from parallelism, depending upon position in the basin. Horton (1945) defined *length of overland flow* L_g as the length of flow path, projected to the horizontal, of nonchannel flow from a point on the drainage divide to a point on the adjacent stream channel. He noted (1945) that "length of overland flow is one of the most important independent variables affecting both the hydrologic and physiographic development of drainage basins."

During evolution of the drainage system, L_g is adjusted to a magnitude appropriate to the scale of the first-order drainage basins and is approximately equal to one-half the reciprocal of the drainage density (Horton, 1945, p. 284).

(IV) Areal Aspects of Drainage Basins

(A) Arrangement of Areal Elements. The perimeters of all first, second and higher orders of basins may be drawn on the topographic map of a watershed. The area A_u of a basin of a given order u is defined as the total area projected upon a horizontal plane, contributing overland flow to the channel segment of the given order and including all tributaries of lower order (Figs. 2 and 4). For example, the area of a basin of the fourth order, A_4, would cumulate the areas of all first-, second- and third-order basins, plus all additional surface elements,

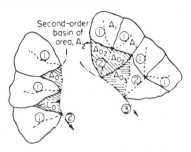

FIG. 4. Interbasin areas contributing runoff directly to second- and third-order channel segments.

known as *interbasin areas*, contributing directly to a channel of order higher than first (Schumm, 1956).

(B) Frequency Distribution of Basin Areas. The areas of drainage basins of a given order can be measured by a planimeter from a map on which the perimeters have been outlined for each order. Frequency distribution of areas has been studied by Schumm (1956, p. 607), who found that a strong right skewness in the distributions could be largely corrected by using the logarithm of area. For a given order, area characteristics can be described in terms of mean variance and standard deviation computed from the sample. Although individual basin areas deviate widely from the mean, the means themselves show a progressive increase with order.

(C) Law of Stream Areas. Horton (1945, p. 294) inferred that mean drainage basin areas of progressively higher orders should increase in a geometric sequence, as do stream lengths. Schumm (1956, p. 606) expressed this relationship in a *law of stream areas*: The mean basin areas of stream of each order tend closely to approximate a direct geometric sequence in which the first term is the mean area of the first-order basin. This law may be written as

$$\bar{A}_u = \bar{A}_1 R_a^{\,u-1} \tag{7}$$

where $\bar{A}_u$ is mean area of basins of order u, $\bar{A}_1$ is mean area of the first-order basins, and R_a is an area ratio analogous to the length ratio R_L. As with stream length, the regression of logarithm of basin area on order is linear.

(D) Relation of Area to Length. Assuming the validity of the laws of stream lengths and basin areas, in which both properties are related in an exponential function with order, length should be related to area by a power function. Morisawa (1959, pp. 12, 58–61) plotted both logarithm of mean stream length and logarithm of cumulative length against logarithm of basin area for each order of representative basins of the Appalachian Plateau Province, obtaining highly linear relationships (Fig. 5).

Absolute stream length, measured headward to the divide from a given point on a stream, plotted against area of watershed contributing to the stream

above the given point, also shows a strongly linear relationship when the logarithms of both variables are used. Hack (1957, p. 64) demonstrated the applicability of the power function relating length and area as thus defined for streams in seven areas of Virginia and Maryland. He used the equation

$$L = 1.4A^{0.6} \tag{8}$$

where L is stream length in miles measured to a point on the drainage divide and A is area in square miles. Hack noted that if geometrical similarity is to be preserved as a drainage basin increases in area downstream, the exponent in the above equation should be 0.5. An observed exponent larger than 0.5 requires that drainage basins change their overall shape in a downstream direction, becoming longer and narrower as they enlarge.

(E) Relation of Area to Discharge. Empirical equations relating stream discharge to basin area have long been in general use in the form

$$Q = jA^m \tag{9}$$

where Q is some measure of discharge in cubic feet per second, such as the mean annual flood; A is the watershed area in suitable areal units; and the constants j and m are derived by fitting a regression line to the available data. The exponent m generally falls in the range 0.5–1.0.

For example, Hack (1957, p. 54) plotted average discharge (cubic feet per second) against drainage area (square miles) on logarithmic paper for all gauging stations in the Potomac River basin and fitted a regression line with an exponent of 1.0. From this, he concluded that studies of relationship of basin area with respect to other variables, such as order, channel slope, channel width and stream length, would apply by direct proportionality to average annual discharge as well.

Leopold and Miller (1956, pp. 23–24) found that for 12 streams of central New Mexico, the discharge-

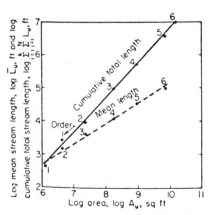

FIG. 5. Relation of stream length to basin area, order for order, for Allegheny River (after Morisawa, 1959).

area relationship can best be described by the equation

$$Q_{2.3} = 12A^{0.79} \qquad (10)$$

where $Q_{2.3}$ is flood discharge in cubic feet per second equaled or exceeded in 2.3 years and A is drainage area in square miles. They were then able to combine the discharge-area graph with an order-area graph to show the relationship of discharge to stream order.

(F) Basin Shape (Outline Form). The shape, or outline form, of a drainage basin, as it is projected upon the horizontal datum plane of a map, may conceivably affect stream discharge characteristics. Quantitative expression of drainage basin outline form can be made through a form factor R_f, which is the dimensionless ratio of basin area A_u to the square of basin length L_b, thus,

$$R_f = \frac{A_u}{L_b^2} \qquad (11)$$

Miller (1953, p. 8) used a dimensionless *circularity ratio* R_c, defined as the ratio of basin area A_u to the area of a circle A_c having the same perimeter as the basin. He found that circularity ratio remained remarkably uniform in the range 0.6–0.7 for first- and second-order basins in homogeneous shales and dolomites, indicating the tendency of small drainage basins in homogeneous geologic materials to preserve geometrical similarity. By contrast, first- and second-order basins situated on the flanks of moderately dipping quartzite strata of Clinch Mountain, Virginia, were strongly elongated and had circularity ratios between 0.4 and 0.5 generally.

Schumm (1956, p. 612) used an *elongation ratio* R_e, defined as the ratio of the diameter of a circle of the same area as the basin to the maximum basin length. This ratio runs between 0.6 and 1.0 over a wide variety of climatic and geologic types. Values near 1.0 are typical of regions of very low relief, whereas values in the range 0.6–0.8 are generally associated with strong relief and steep ground slopes.

The inappropriateness of a circle as the standard figure of reference in comparison with a pear-shaped drainage basin, which has a sharply defined point at the mouth, led Chorley, Malm and Pogorzelski (1957, pp. 138–141) to use as a model a lemniscate function.

(G) Drainage Density. An important indicator of the linear scale of land-form elements in stream-eroded topography is *drainage density* D, introduced into the American hydrologic literature by Horton (1945, p. 283):

$$D = \frac{\sum\limits_{i=1}^{k} \sum\limits_{i=1}^{N} L_u}{A_u} \qquad (12)$$

Thus D is simply the ratio of total channel segment lengths cumulated for all orders within a basin to the basin area (projected to the horizontal). Dimension-

ally, this ratio reduces to the inverse of length, L^{-1}. Horton used units of miles per square mile, and most later workers followed suit. Drainage density may be thought of as an expression of the closeness of spacing of channels.

Drainage density measurements have been made over a wide range of geologic and climatic types of the United States (Fig. 6). The lowest values, between 3.0 and 4.0 miles/square mile, are observed in resistant sandstone strata of the Appalachian Plateau Province. Values in the range of 8–16 are typical of large areas of the humid central and eastern United States on rocks of moderate resistance under a deciduous forest cover. Comparable values are found in parts of the Rocky Mountain region, but in the drier areas of that region values range from 50–100.

Coast ranges of southern California, where strongly fractured and deeply weathered igneous and metamorphic rocks have evolved under a dry summer subtropical climate, show drainage density values in the range of 20–30, but where weak Pleistocene sediments are exposed, values of D rise to 30–40. A still higher order of magnitude of drainage density is observed in badlands, developed on weak clays barren of vegetation. Values of 200–400 have been

FIG. 6. Topographic maps of 1 square mile each, illustrating natural range in drainage density (from maps of the U.S. Geological Survey). (By permission Strahler, "Physical Geography," John Wiley & Sons, Inc., N.Y. 1960.) A. Low drainage density or coarse texture, Driftwood, Pennsylvania, Quadrangle. B. Medium drainage density or medium texture, Nashville, Indiana, Quadrangle. C. High drainage density or fine texture, Little Tujunga, California, Quadrangle. D. Extremely high drainage density or ultrafine texture, Cuny Table West, South Dakota, Quadrangle.

measured in Badlands National Monument, S.D. Schumm (1956, p. 616) measured values as high as 1100–1300 in badlands developed on weak clay at Perth Amboy, N.J.

Factors controlling drainage density are the same as those that control the characteristic length dimension of any group of first-order basins. A complete discussion is not appropriate here. In general, low drainage density is favored in regions of highly resistant or highly permeable subsoil materials, under dense vegetative cover, and where relief is low. High drainage density is favored in regions of weak or impermeable subsurface materials, sparse vegetation and mountainous relief.

The strongest related factor appears to be Thornthwaite's PE index (Melton, 1957).

The average length of overland flow $\bar{L}_g$ is approximately half the average distance between stream channels and is therefore approximately equal to half the reciprocal of drainage density (Horton, 1945).

$$\bar{L}_g = \frac{1}{2D} \qquad (13)$$

In order to take into account the effect of slope of the stream channels and valley sides, Horton (1945, p. 285) refined this generalization to read

$$\bar{L}_g = \frac{1}{2D\sqrt{1 - (\theta_c/\theta_g)}} \qquad (14)$$

where θ_c is channel slope and θ_g is average ground slope in the area.

(H) Constant of Channel Maintenance. Schumm (1956, p. 607) used the inverse of drainage density as a property termed *constant of channel maintenance C*. Thus

$$C = \frac{1}{D} = \frac{A_u}{\sum\limits_{i=1}^{k} \sum\limits_{i=1}^{N} L_u} \qquad (15)$$

This constant, in units of square feet per foot, has the dimension of length and therefore increases in magnitude as the scale of the land-form units increases. Specifically, the constant C tells the number of square feet of watershed surface required to sustain 1 linear foot of channel.

(I) Stream Frequency. Horton (1945. p. 285) introduced *stream frequency* (or *channel frequency*) F as the number of stream segments per unit area.

Melton (1958, pp. 35–54) analyzed in detail the relationships between drainage density and stream frequency, both of which measure the texture of the drainage net, but each of which treats a distinct aspect. He derived the dimensionally correct equation

$$F = 0.694D^2 \qquad (16)$$

and from this the dimensionless number F/D^2, which tends to approach the constant value 0.694, despite vast variations in linear scale.

(V) Relief (Gradient) Aspect of Drainage Basins and Channel Networks

(A) Channel Gradients. (1) *Single-channel Profiles.* The longitudinal profile of a stream channel may be shown graphically by a plot of altitude (ordinate) as a function of horizontal distance (abscissa).

(2) *Cause of Profile Upconcavity.* Single-channel profiles of almost all streams, under a wide range of climatic and geologic conditions, show *upconcavity,* i.e., a persistent downstream decrease in gradient. Causes of upconcavity cannot be treated in detail here. Gilbert (1877, pp. 103–104, 107–108) explained upconcavity as an effect of increasing stream discharge. His *law of declivities* states that declivity (gradient) bears an inverse relation to discharge because, as discharge increases, channel cross section increases, reducing proportionally the frictional losses of the stream and enabling it to carry its bed load on a lesser slope. Others have attributed upconcavity to decreasing caliber (diameter) of bed load particles downstream, (Yatsu, 1955, p. 660–662) using the reasoning that a lesser gradient suffices for the transport of finer bed materials.

(3) *Fitted Regression Functions.* The longitudinal stream profile may be fitted by an equation expressing the statistical regression of elevation Y as the dependent variable on distance X as the independent variable (Fig. 7). Four simple regression equations may be considered:

(1) Simple linear form, in which both altitude and distance are plotted on arithmetic scales. A straight line on such a plot is represented by the regression equation of basic form

$$Y = a - bX \qquad (17)$$

Although useful in providing a visual impression of the longitudinal profile, the arithmetic plot typically

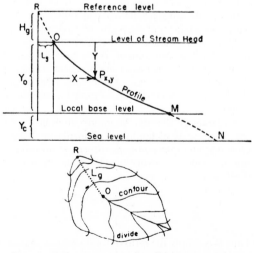

Fig. 7. Reference points in profile plotting (altitude against horizontal distance; after Broscoe, 1959, p. 39).

yields a strong upconcave profile line to which the linear equation is poorly fitted.

(2) Exponential form, in which altitude is on a logarithmic scale while horizontal distance is on an arithmetic scale. A straight line on such a plot is represented by the basic regression equation

$$\log Y = a - bX \qquad (18)$$

(3) Logarithmic form, in which altitude is plotted on an arithmetic scale on the ordinate against distance scaled logarithmically on the abscissa. A straight line on such a plot is represented by the regression equation of the basic form

$$Y = a - b \log X \qquad (19)$$

(4) Power form (log-log form), represented by the basic regression equation

$$\log Y = \log a - b \log X \qquad (20)$$

With appropriate definitions of Y and X, the exponential, logarithmic and power functions are capable of making upconcave profiles more nearly approximate straight lines and therefore minimizing the deviations from the ideal mathematical expression selected for description and prediction.

A discussion of serious problems in plotting the stream profiles in exponential, logarithmic, and power forms has been given by Broscoe (1959).

Numerous different functions have been used with success to describe individual stream profiles. No generalization as to the best description of the single-channel longitudinal profile seems yet warranted in view of divergent observations (see Yatsu, 1955; Hack, 1957; Broscoe, 1959).

(4) *Derivative Functions.* A vexing problem arises in most exponential plots of stream profiles where sea or lake level is taken as the arbitrary reference level. Although sea level is a natural, readily defined geologic feature related to stream development, there are good reasons to think that sea level does not relate dynamically to the control of stream slope in the upper reaches of the stream. Rubey (1952, p. 134) has stated succinctly the reasons for concluding that the level of water body into which a stream flows controls the vertical position of the profile, but not its shape.

(5) *Profile Segmentation.* That the longitudinal profile of a stream channel consists of series of connected segments, "each differing from those that adjoin it, but all closely related parts of one system," has been pointed out by Mackin (1948, p. 491), who states further that "each segment has the slope that will provide the velocity required for transportation of all of the load supplied to it from above, and this slope is maintained without change as long as controlling conditions remain the same." To describe a single-channel profile by one continuous mathematical function is therefore unrealistic in failing to take segmentation into account, but may nevertheless be useful in certain applications.

Abrupt changes in gradient marking the discontinuities between adjoining channel segments may result from changes in discharge-load ratios, in caliber of load or in channel characteristics (Mackin, 1948; Yatsu, 1955).

Considering the convergence of a drainage network into channel segments of increasing order, it is obvious that the formation of a segment of a given order by the junction of two segments of the next lower order will normally mark an abrupt reduction in gradient, for reasons explained by Gilbert's law of declivities, discussed above. Between tributary junctions, the profile may be expected to approach a straight line of uniform slope, discounting the slight upconcavity to be expected from gradual increases in discharge and load from directly contributing valley-side slopes. Actual plots of single-channel profiles do not show obvious segmentation associated with changes from one order to the next (Broscoe, 1959, pp. 44, 72), but the principle is strongly displayed in the composite profiles described below.

(6) *Composite Profiles.* A composite stream profile combines the segments of a given order within the watershed into a single average segment whose vertical drop is the mean drop of all the segments and whose horizontal distance is the mean horizontal length of all the segments (Fig. 8). The average slope of the channel segments of a given order is thus the slope of the hypotenuse of a right triangle defined by the average vertical drop and the average horizontal distance. Triangles for each order are connected in sequence to produce the composite profile shown in Fig. 8.

(7) *Channel Slope as a Function of Order.* The average slope of segments of a given order in a drainage net, measured as described above, will

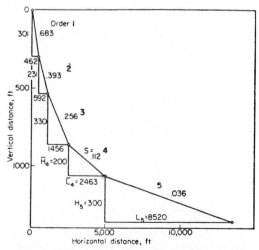

FIG. 8. Composite profile of stream segments of five orders in the Chileno Canyon watershed, California (after Broscoe, 1959, p. 72).

obviously be less than the average slope for the next lower order but greater than that for the next higher order. Horton (1945, p. 295) expressed this relationship in a *law of stream slopes*, an inverse-geometric-series law, which is analogous to the law of stream numbers.

$$\bar{S}_u = \bar{S}_1 R_s^{k-u} \tag{21}$$

where $\bar{S}_u$ is average slope of segments of order u; $\bar{S}_1$ is average slope of first-order segments; R_s is a constant slope ratio, analogous to bifurcation ratio; k is the order of the highest-order segment.

The law of stream slopes has been applied to many watersheds and appears to be generally valid, provided that the geologic materials in which the channels are carved are free of strong inhomogeneities.

(B) Channel Cross-section Geometry. In this section, the channel network has been treated only as a system of branching lines, without consideration of the fact that channels have finite depths and widths and that these parameters change systematically as the channels are followed downstream or with fluctuations of discharge. Detailed treatment given in Leopold and Maddock (1953), Leopold and Miller (1956), Hack (1957) and Miller (1958) constitutes an integral part of the field of quantitative geomorphology of drainage basins and channel systems.

(C) Ground-surface Gradients. (1) *Relationship of Ground and Channel Slopes.* The inclinations, or gradients, of the ground-surface elements of a watershed are closely tied in with its channel gradients and relief (elevation differences). In mountainous regions, where relief is great, erosion intensity is correspondingly high. Steep slopes contribute large quantities of relatively coarse-textured detritus to channels, which must have steep gradients to enable stream flow to transport the debris as bed load through the channel system. In regions of low relief, slopes are gentle and shed relatively small quantities

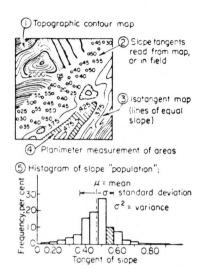

FIG. 10. Construction of isotangent slope map and slope-frequency histogram (after Strahler, 1956, p. 575).

of fine-textured detritus, which in turn requires correspondingly low channel gradients for its transport.

(2) *Maximum Valleyside Slopes.* A significant indicator of overall steepness of ground slopes in a watershed is the maximum valley-side slope θ_{max}, measured at intervals along the valley walls on the steepest parts of the contour orthogonals running from divides to adjacent stream channels.

Maximum valley-side slope has been sampled over a wide variety of geologic and climatic environments. A sample of 50–100 or more slope readings, taken according to a plan of uniformly spaced sample points, may be measured directly in the field with the Abney level or with dividers and scale from topographic maps of suitably large scale and high degree of accuracy. The variates of the sample may then be grouped into classes and treated by standard procedures of frequency-distribution analysis, including calculation of arithmetic mean, variance standard deviation, skewness, and goodness of fit to the normal curve (Fig. 9). These statistics not only serve to describe the slope characteristics of a region, but they may be used in rigorous statistical tests of differences in means and variances between two regions or among several regions.

(3) *Total Surface-slope Distribution.* Slope conditions over an entire watershed may be shown by means of a slope map (Strahler, 1956), which shows distribution of the degree of surface inclination. Procedure is as follows (Fig. 10): (1) A good contour topographic map is obtained. (2) Slopes of short segments of line normal to the contours are determined at many points over the map. Tangent or sine of slope angle may be recorded, depending upon the function desired. (3) The readings are contoured with lines of equal slope (isotangents or isosines).

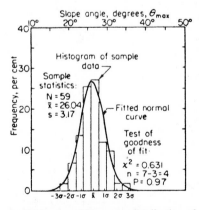

FIG. 9. Histogram of frequency distribution of maximum valley side slope angles fitted by a normal curve and tested for goodness of fit. Field measurements from dissected Santa Fe formation near Bernalillo, N.M. (after Strahler, 1950, p. 683).

(4) The areas between successive slope contours are measured with a planimeter and summed for each slope class. (5) This summation yields a slope frequency-percentage distribution from which mean, variance and standard deviation can be computed.

The construction of slope maps and their areal measurements are extremely time-consuming. Essentially, the same information can be obtained by random-coordinate and grid sampling (Strahler, 1956, pp. 589–594).

(D) Relief Measures. (1) *Relief. Relief H* is the elevation difference between reference points defined in any one of several ways. *Maximum relief* within a region of given boundary is simply the elevation difference between highest and lowest points. *Maximum basin relief* is the elevation difference between basin mouth and the highest point on the basin perimeter, usually stated in units of feet or meters.

Still another means of measuring relief is to take the elevation difference between a point on drainage divide and another on the nearest adjacent stream channel, where both points lie at the ends of a line orthogonal to the contours (e.g., the surface-flow path) (Strahler, 1958, p. 295).

Relief measures are indicative of the potential energy of a drainage system present by virtue of elevation above a given datum. In the absence of information as to the horizontal distances over which the relief measurement applies, however, one cannot directly relate relief to ground and channel slopes.

(2) *Relief Ratios.* When basin relief H is divided by the horizontal distance on which it is measured, there results a dimensionless *relief ratio* R_h (Schumm, 1956, p. 112). Taking vertical and horizontal distances as legs of a right triangle, relief ratio is equal to the tangent of the lower acute angle and is identical with the tangent of the angle of slope of the hypotenuse with respect to the horizontal. The relief ratio thus measures the overall steepness of a drainage basin and is an indicator of the intensity of erosion processes operating on slopes of the basin.

Schumm (1956, p. 112) measured relief ratio R_h as the ratio of maximum basin relief to horizontal distance along the longest dimension of the basin parallel to the principal drainage line. Melton (1957, p. 5) used relative relief R_{hp}, expressed in per cent, as

$$R_{hp} = \frac{100H}{5280P} \qquad (22)$$

where H is maximum basin relief in feet and P is basin perimeter in miles.

The possibility of a close correlation between relief ratio and hydrologic characteristics of a basin is suggested by Schumm (1954), who found that sediment loss per unit area is closely correlated with relief ratio. The significant regression with small scatter suggests that relief ratio may prove useful in

estimating sediment yield if the appropriate parameters for a given climatic province are once established.

Maner (1958) used a relief-length ratio in correlation with sediment delivery rates of watersheds in the Red Hills area of southern Kansas, western Oklahoma and western Texas. This ratio yielded a higher correlation with sediment delivery rate than did relief and length treated together as variables. Moreover, it gave a much closer correlation than did other individually treated geometrical factors of length-width ratio of basin, sediment-contributing area, basin relief alone, or average land slope.

(E) Ruggedness and Geometry Numbers. To combine the qualities of slope steepness and length, a dimensionless *ruggedness number HD* is formed of the product of relief H and drainage density D, where both terms are in the same units. If D should be increased while H remains constant, the average horizontal distance from divides to adjacent channels is reduced, with an accompanying increase in slope steepness. If H is increased while D remains constant, the elevation difference between divides and adjacent channels will also increase, so that slope steepness increases. Extremely high values of the ruggedness number occur when both variables are large, i.e., when slopes are not only steep but long as well. Observed values of the ruggedness number range from as low as 0.06 in the subdued relief of the Louisiana coastal plain to over 1.0 in coast ranges of California or in badlands on weak clays.

The dimensionless property of slope can be introduced into the ruggedness number in the following way. Consider that the horizontal distance between a drainage divide and the adjacent stream channel is equal to about one-half the reciprocal of the drainage density D (Horton, 1945, p. 284) and that local relief H is measured as the vertical drop from divide to adjacent channel. Thus the slope S_g of the ground surface from divide to stream will be related to H and D by the equation

$$S_g = H \times 2D \qquad (23)$$

where S_g is the tangent of the ground slope θ_g in degrees. Then

$$\frac{HD}{S_g} = \frac{1}{2} \qquad (24)$$

Because the geometrical relations of H, D and S_g will not be those of a perfect right triangle, the constant $\frac{1}{2}$ should be replaced by some dimensionless constant, determined empirically, that will differ little from unity, despite a wide range in the ruggedness number (numerator), Strahler (1958, p. 296) computed values of HD/S_g, called the *geometry number*, and found them to fall in the range 0.4–1.0 for six regions differing greatly in the individual components of D, H and S_g. From this it was concluded that the geometry number tends to be conserved about a common value and that a change in any one of the three components is compensated for by changes in one or both of the other two, thus tending to keep the product constant.

(F) Hypsometric (Area-Altitude) Analysis. *Hypsometric analysis* is the relation of horizontal cross-sectional drainage basin area to elevation. It was developed in its modern dimensionless form by Langbein who applied it to large watersheds. Application to small drainage basins of low order has been made by Strahler and others.

Figure 11 illustrates the definition of the two dimensionless variables involved in hypsometric analysis. Taking the drainage basin to be bounded by vertical sides and a horizontal base plane passing through the mouth, the relative height y is the ratio of height of a given contour h to total basin height (relief) H. Relative area x is the ratio of horizontal cross-sectional area a to entire basin area A. The percentage hypsometric curve is a plot of the continuous function relating relative height y to relative area x. As shown in Fig. 11 (lower right), the shape of the hypsometric curve varies in early geologic stages of development of the drainage basin, but once a steady state is attained (mature stage), it tends to vary little thereafter, despite lowering relief. Isolated bodies of resistant rock may form prominent hills (monadnocks) rising above a generally subdued surface; the result is a distorted hypsometric curve, termed the *monadnock phase*.

(VI) Theory of Drainage-basin Dynamics

(A) Statement of Variables. In quantitative studies of geomorphic processes and forms, the relationships between form elements, described above, and causative factors need to be expressed by dimensionally correct rational equations. It has already been noted that drainage basins developed in homogeneous bedrock materials under a given set of climatic conditions tend to develop a characteristic linear scale dimension. Because of the tendency to geometrical similarity of the horizontal, or planimetric, aspects of such systems, one is free to select any property having the dimension of length or a product of length (inverse of length, length squared) to serve as the indicator of characteristic size of the elements in the system. Thus one might select mean length of first-order stream channels, or the mean perimeter of second-order basins, or the mean area of first-order basins. One of the most extensively known scale measures is drainage density D, the length of channels per unit area of watershed. Drainage density has the dimension of inverse of length, L^{-1}, and varies from values as high as 500–1000, where first-order basins are only a few feet across, to values as low as 2–3, where the first-order basins are about a half mile wide. Drainage density is therefore used as the dependent variable in developing an equation relating the horizontal scale of the landform units to a series of independent or controlling

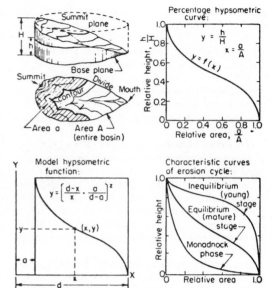

FIG. 11. Definitions and functions in hypsometric analysis of small drainage basins.

variables:

$$D = f(Q_r, K, H, \rho, \mu, g) \qquad (25)$$

All terms of this equation, together with their definitions and dimensional properties, are explained in Table 1.

The first independent variable, runoff intensity Q_r, combines rainfall intensity and infiltration capacity in a single term. Rainfall intensity represents a major climatic control; infiltration capacity, a major physical factor, expresses state of the ground surface and subsoil. Both components have the dimensions of velocity LT^{-1}; runoff intensity is simply the excess of rainfall intensity over infiltration capacity.

The second independent variable is an *erosion proportionality factor K*, defined by Horton (1945, p. 324) as the ratio of erosion intensity to eroding force. Erosion intensity has the dimensions of mass rate of removal per unit area; eroding force, the dimensions of force per unit area. Thus K has the dimensions $L^{-1}T$, the inverse of velocity, and may be thought of as a measure of the erodibility of the ground surface.

Relief H, the third independent variable, represents the vertical dimension of the basin geometry and may vary independently of the horizontal scale. Relief represents potential energy of the system and is directly related to its total erosion intensity. Relief may be measured in various ways, described above, but is most meaningful in the analysis when defined as local, or basin, relief.

The remaining variables—density ρ, viscosity μ, and acceleration of gravity g—are significant properties of a fluid system, introduced here because the

TABLE 1. FACTORS CONTROLLING DRAINAGE DENSITY

Symbol	Term	Dimensional Quality	Dimensional Symbol
D	Drainage density	Length divided by area	$\dfrac{L}{L^2} = L^{-1}$
Q_r	Runoff intensity	Volume rate of flow per unit area of surface	$\dfrac{L^3 T^{-1}}{L^2} = LT^{-1}$
K	Erosion proportionality factor	Mass rate of removal per unit area divided by force per unit area	$\dfrac{ML^{-2}T^{-1}}{ML^{-1}T^{-2}} = L^{-1}T$
H	Relief	Length	L
ρ	Density of fluid	Mass per unit volume	ML^{-3}
μ	Dynamic viscosity of fluid	Mass per unit length per unit time	$ML^{-1}T^{-1}$
g	Acceleration of gravity	Distance per unit time per unit time	LT^{-2}

drainage system is developed by water erosion on slopes and in channels, acting in a force field of gravity. Note that the first four variables involve no mass dimension; hence an analysis limited to these four would include only geometric and kinematic factors of time and length. Introduction of mass through density and viscosity brings force into the analysis and makes possible scale-model comparisons.

(B) Solution by Pi Theorem. The variables of Eq. (25) may be grouped into the functional relationship

$$f'(D, Q_r, K, H, \rho, \mu, g) = 0 \qquad (26)$$

The seven variables in this function may be reduced to four through application of the pi theorem. Solution of the four pi terms, described in detail by Strahler (1958, p. 290), yields a function of four dimensionless groups:

$$\phi\left(HD, QK, \frac{Q_r \rho H}{\mu}, \frac{Q_r^2}{Hg}\right) = 0 \qquad (27)$$

Solving for drainage density gives

$$D = \frac{1}{H} f\left(Q_r K, \frac{Q_r \rho H}{\mu}, \frac{Q_r^2}{Hg}\right) \qquad (28)$$

The term HD is the ruggedness number, previously described as expressing essential geometrical characteristics of the drainage system. It may be replaced by the dimensionless geometry number HD/S_g explained above, without affecting the dimensionless nature of the group. The second term, $Q_r K$, is the *Horton number*, expressing the relative intensity of the erosion process in the drainage basin. The third term, $Q_r \rho H/\mu$, is a form of the Reynolds number, in which Q takes the place of the velocity term and H the characteristic length. The fourth term, Q_r^2/Hg, is a form of Froude number. Reduction of the seven variables into four dimensionless groups focuses attention upon dynamic relationships, simplifies the design of controlled empirical observations, and establishes conditions essential to the

validity of comparisons of models with prototypes.

(C) Steady-state Relationships. Conditions for a steady state within a drainage basin are such that, for a given Horton number (i.e., for a given intensity of erosion process), values of local relief, slope and drainage density reach a time-independent steady state in which basin geometry is so adjusted as to transmit through the system just that quantity of runoff and debris characteristically produced under the controlling climatic regime.

(D) Upsets of Steady State. Consider possible upsets and readjustments of the steady state. If a forested land surface is denuded of its vegetative cover and intensively cultivated, the Horton number will undergo a sharp increase, either through increase in runoff intensity or surface susceptibility to erosion or through simultaneous increase in both. In compensation, basin geometry is altered by gully development to increase greatly the drainage density, to increase channel and ground-surface gradients, but to decrease the local relief (Strahler, 1958, p. 296).

When transformation has been completed, a new set of drainage-basin forms, very much smaller in characteristic length dimension, has replaced the original basins. A new steady state of erosion is achieved on a much higher level of intensity. Thus badlands, from which sediment is produced at a rapid rate, replace the former long, gentle, smooth slopes of the land. Many new channel segments of first, second and third orders have come into existence where formerly a single first-order basin had been (Fig. 12). Steepening of mainstream channel gradients through aggradation is also a characteristic result of the transformation. The various manifestations of accelerated soil erosion are thus seen to be related to a general theory of drainage basin dynamics.

(VII) Observed Complex Relations among Hydrologic and Geometric Properties

(A) Control of Basin Geometry by Climatic Factors. Students of quantitative geomorphology of

TABLE 2. NOTATIONS IN QUANTITATIVE GEOMORPHOLOGY

A	watershed area above gauge or other reference point, square miles	p	constant in lemniscate model of basin shape, dimensionless
A_c	area of a circle of same perimeter as basin, square miles	Q	discharge, ft^2/sec
A_u	area of basin of order u, square miles	Q_r	runoff intensity, ft/sec
$\bar{A}_u$	mean area of basins of order u; square miles	$Q_{2.3}$	discharge equaled or exceeded in 2.3 years, ft^3/sec
A_0	area of interbasin area, ft^2, square miles	R_a	basin-area ratio, dimensionless
A_1	area of a first-order basin, square miles	R_b	bifurcation ratio of stream segments, dimensionless
a	cross-sectional area of basin at a given contour level, square miles; a numerical constant	R_c	circularity ratio, dimensionless
		R_e	elongation ratio, dimensionless
b	regression coefficient, dimensionless	R_f	form ratio of basin, dimensionless
C	constant of channel maintenance, ft^2/ft; a constant of integration	R_h	relief ratio, dimensionless
		R_{hp}	relative relief, dimensionless
D	drainage density, miles/square mile	R_L	length ratio of stream segments, dimensionless
D_u	drainage density of entire basin of order u, miles/square mile	R_{Lb}	ratio of R_L to R_b, dimensionless
D_1	drainage density of first-order basins, miles/square mile	R_s	slope ratio of stream segments, dimensionless
		S_c	channel slope, ft/ft, %
F	stream frequency; channel frequency, No./square mile	S_g	ground-surface slope, ft/ft, %
		S_{st}	equivalent mainstream slope, ft/ft, %
g	acceleration of gravity, ft/sec^2	$\bar{S}_u$	mean slope of stream segments of order u, ft/ft, %
H	basin relief, ft	s	standard deviation, estimated from sample
H_g	elevation difference; stream head to divide reference point, ft	s^2	variance, estimated from sample
		u	a given order of stream segments, a number
$\bar{H}_u$	mean relief of basins of order u, ft	X	horizontal distance downstream from stream head, ft, miles
h	height of given contour above basin mouth, ft		
i	item number in summation	x	relative area of horizontal cross section to basin area, dimensionless
j	a constant, dimensionless	$\bar{x}$	arithmetic mean of a sample
K	erosion proportionality factor, sec/ft	Y	vertical distance downward from stream head, ft
k	highest stream order in a given basin, No.	Y_c	elevation difference between local base level and sea level datum, ft
L	stream length from gauge to point on divide, miles	Y_0	elevation difference between stream head and local base level, ft
L_b	basin length, miles		
L_{ca}	mainstream length from gauge to centroid, miles	y	relative height of given contour above basin mouth, dimensionless
L_g	length of overland flow, ft, miles		
$\bar{L}_g$	mean length of overland flow, ft, miles	λ	linear scale ratio in model analysis, dimensionless
$\bar{L}_u$	mean length of stream segments of order u, miles		
$\sum_{i=1}^{N} L_u$	total length of stream segments of order u, miles	μ	viscosity of a fluid; population mean (statistical)
		ρ	density of a fluid; radius vector in polar coordinates
L_0	interbasin length, ft, miles	σ	population standard deviation
$\bar{L}_1$	mean length of first-order stream segments, miles	σ^2	population variance
		θ	angle of polar coordinates, degrees
m	an exponent, dimensionless	θ_c	gradient of stream channel, degrees
N_u	number of stream segments of order u, No.	θ_g	gradient of ground surface, degrees
P	basin perimeter, ft, miles	θ_{max}	maximum angle of valley-side slopes, degrees

drainage basins have attempted to relate empirically one or more of the geometric elements of drainage basins to several independent variables, including climatic, vegetative and hydrologic factors. Statistical methods of correlation and regression have been applied to observational data on basin geometry, precipitation and runoff, vegetative cover, geologic type, and soils.

Melton (1957) used multiple regression and correlation analysis upon 23 small drainage basins of Arizona, Colorado, New Mexico and Utah. Multiple correlation analyses showed that valley-side slopes and drainage density are related to climate and to properties of mantle and vegetal cover. Slopes were found to be higher with greater values of infiltration capacity and Thornthwaite's precipitation effectiveness index but to vary inversely with soil strength and runoff intensity-frequency. Melton found that drainage density varies directly with per cent of bare area and runoff intensity-frequency, but inversely with precipitation effectiveness index and infiltration capacity, confirming Horton's infiltration theory of erosion. Melton carried his analysis further by examining the correlation structure of morphometric properties of drainage systems and their controlling agents. He classified variable systems by the presence and direction of feedback among the variables.

When relief ratio, circularity ratio and frequency of first-order streams were combined as a product to yield a new T factor, multiple regression for ten of Potter's basins on rainfall intensity and frequency yielded an equation in which the standard error of estimate was considerably reduced and a high correlation was established with peak intensity of runoff.

ARTHUR N. STRAHLER

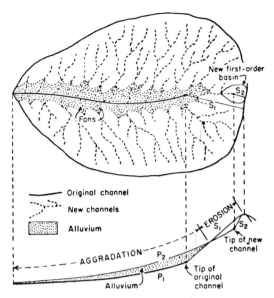

FIG. 12. Drainage density transformation accompanying severe, accelerated slope erosion and development of badlands (after Strahler, 1958, p. 297).

Chorley (1957) attempted to establish the relationship of basin geometry to climate by a comparative study of three areas of similar gross geology but greatly different climate. A climate-vegetation index, combining mean annual rainfall, mean monthly precipitation in 24 hours, and Thornthwaite's precipitation effectiveness index, was computed for each region. The climate-vegetation index was found to be closely correlated with logarithms of stream length, basin area and drainage density.

(B) Relation of Basin Geometry to Stream Flow. Effect of drainage basin characteristics upon unit-hydrograph lag and peak flow has been reported by Taylor and Schwartz (1952), using the data of 20 basins ranging in area from 20–1600 square miles, and located in the North and Middle Atlantic States. Drainage area, length of longest watercourse, mainstream length to centroid of area and equivalent mainstream slope were judged the most significant geometrical variables.

A regression of peak stream discharge upon factors of topography, basin area and rainfall was determined empirically by Potter (1953, p. 69) for 51 basins in the Appalachian Plateau. Potter's T factor, representing basin geometry, is the ratio of longest length of principal stream to square root of average channel slope from head to mouth. The T factor was judged to be significant in multiple regression with basin area measures of rainfall intensity and frequency.

Morisawa (1959, pp. 16–17) substituted other geomorphic properties for Potter's T factor in an effort to explain still more of the observed variance.

References

Broscoe, A. J., 1959, "Quantitative analysis of longitudinal stream profiles of small watersheds," Project NR 389–042, Tech. Rept. 18, Columbia University, Dept. of Geology, ONR, Geography Branch, New York.

Chorley, R. J., 1957, "Climate and morphometry," *J. Geol.*, **65**, 628–638.

Chorley, R. J., Malm, Donald, and Pogorzelski, H. A., 1957, "A new standard for estimating drainage basin shape," *Am. J. Sci.*, **255**, 138–141.

Gilbert, G. K., 1877, "Report on the geology of the Henry Mountains," *U.S. Geographical and Geological Survey of the Rocky Mountain Region*, Washington, D.C.

Hack, J. T., 1957, "Studies of longitudinal stream profiles in Virginia and Maryland, *U.S. Geol. Surv. Prof. Paper* **294-B.**

Horton, R. E., 1945, "Erosional development of streams and their drainage basins: hydrophysical approach to quantitative morphology," *Bull. Geol. Soc. Am.*, **56**, 275–370.

Leopold, L. B., and Maddock, Thomas, Jr., 1953, "The hydraulic geometry of stream channels and some physiographic implications," *U.S. Geol. Surv. Profess. Paper* **252.**

Leopold, L. B., and Miller, J. P., 1956, "Ephemeral streams: hydraulic factors and their relation to the drainage net," *U.S. Geol Surv. Profess. Paper* **282-A.**

Mackin, J. H., 1948, "Concept of the graded river," *Bull. Geol. Soc. Am.*, **59**, 463–512.

Maner, S. B., 1958, "Factors affecting sediment delivery rates in the Red Hills physiographic area," *Trans. Am. Geophys. Union*, **39**, 669–675.

Melton, M. A., 1957, "An analysis of the relations among elements of climate, surface properties, and geomorphology," Project NR 389–042, Tech. Rept. 11, Columbia University, Dept. of Geology, ONR, Geography Branch, New York.

Melton, M. A., 1958, "Geometric properties of mature drainage systems and their representation in an E_4 phase space," *J. Geol.*, **66**, 35–54.

Miller, J. P., 1958, "High mountain streams: effects of geology on channel characteristics and bed material," *New Mexico Bur. Mines Mineral Resources Mem.*, **4.**

Miller, V. C., 1953, "A quantitative geomorphic study of drainage basin characteristics in the Clinch Mountain area, Virginia and Tennessee," Project NR 389–042, Tech. Rept. 3, Columbia Univ., Dept. of Geology, ONR, Geography Branch, New York.

Morisawa, M. E., 1959, "Relation of quantitative geomorphology to stream flow in representative watersheds of the Appalachian Plateau Province," Project NR 389–042, Tech. Rept. 20, Columbia

University, Department of Geology, ONR, Geography Branch, New York.

Potter, W. D., 1953, "Rainfall and topographic factors that affect runoff," *Trans. Am. Geophys. Union*, **34**, 67–73.

Rubey, W. W., 1952, "Geology and mineral resources of the Harding and Brussels Quadrangles, Illinois," *U.S. Geol. Surv. Profess. Paper* **218**.

Schumm, S., 1954, "The relation of drainage basin relief to sediment loss," Intern. Union Geodesy Geophys., Tenth Gen. Assembly (Rome), *Intern. Assoc. Sci. Hydrol. Publ.* 36, **1**, 216–219.

Schumm, S. A., 1956, "Evolution of drainage basins and slopes in badlands at Perth Amboy, New Jersey," *Bull. Geol. Soc. Am.*, **67**, 597–646.

Strahler, A. N., 1950, "Equilibrium theory of erosional slopes approached by frequency distribution analysis," *Am. J. Sci.*, **248**, 673–696, 800–814.

Strahler, A. N., 1952, "Dynamic basis of geomorphology," *Bull. Geol. Soc. Am.*, **63**, 923–938.

Strahler, A. N., 1956, "Quantitative slope analysis," *Bull. Geol. Soc. Am.*, **67**, 571–596.

Strahler, A. N., 1958, "Dimensional analysis applied to fluvially eroded landforms," *Bull. Geol. Soc. Am.*, **69**, 279–300.

Strahler, A. N., 1964, "Quantitative geology of drainage basins and channel networks," in (Chow, V. T. editor), "Handbook of Applied Hydrology," **4**, 39–76, McGraw-Hill Book Co.

Taylor, A. B., and Schwartz, H. E., 1952, "Unit-hydrography lag and peak flow related to basin characteristics," *Trans. Am. Geophys. Union*, **33**, 235–246.

Yatsu, Eiju, 1955, "On the longitudinal profile of the graded river," *Trans. Am. Geophys. Union*, **36**, 655–663.

Cross-references: *Altimetric Frequency Curve*; *Badlands*; *Base Level*; *Drainage Basin*; *Dynamic Geomorphology*; *Grade, Graded Stream*; *Hypsometric Analysis*; *Interfluve*; *Law of Declivities*, etc.; *Monadnock*; *Nickpoint*; *Open Systems—Allometric Growth*; *Profile of Equilibrium*; *Rivers*; *Sheet Erosion, Sheetwash, Rainwash, Sheetflood*; *Slopes*; *Stream Channel Characteristics*; *Stream Orders*; *Surell's Laws*; *Terrain*; *Texture—Topographic*; *Thalweg*; *Watershed*; *Youth—Maturity —Old Age*. Vol. II: *Reynolds, Froude and Other Dimensionless Numbers*. Vol. VI: *Bedforms in Alluvial Channels*; *Runoff*; *Statistical Analysis*.

QUATERNARY FLUVIAL TERRACES—*See* TERRACES—FLUVIAL

QUATERNARY PERIOD

The Quaternary Period, sometimes known as the *Age of Man* or *Great Ice Age*, is the last major division of geological time. It began approximately two million years ago, according to the most recent estimates, and continues at the present time. Detailed consideration of geological time with the principles of stratigraphy and paleontology is reserved for another encyclopedia in this series (Vol. VII), but it is appropriate in this volume to discuss in broad lines the last geological period, because during its history there evolved much of the sculpturing and many of the deposits that mark the present surface of the globe.

The problem has been well summarized by Ray (1949):

"Every landscape bears a wealth of detailed information so complex, so varied, and generally so localized that it is difficult to recognize the major pattern into which the data can be placed. Essentially the problems of Pleistocene stratigraphy are similar to those of earlier geologic times, yet in detail the techniques and methods used in solving the stratigraphic problems differ widely. Many cannot be solved by the geologist alone, but require the coordinated efforts of specialists in widely divergent fields.

"The final solution of the many problems and the establishment of a Pleistocene stratigraphy are only a means to an end—the chronology of events which have led to the physical conditions of the present."

The Quaternary *Period* is a time-stratigraphic term, the equivalent sequence of rocks belonging to the Quaternary *System*. In 1759, Arduino divided geological time into *Primary*, *Secondary*, and *Tertiary*, the "Primary" now being referred to as Paleozoic and the "Secondary" as Mesozoic. The "Cenozoic" proposed by Phillips (1841) as "Caenozoic" (also spelled "Kainozoic") applies to both Tertiary and Quaternary. In scale of complexity (not time) a case could be made for calling these two "suberas" (in the sense of the United States Pennsylvanian and Mississippian as subsystems of the Carboniferous). Some authors, e.g., Charlesworth (1957) prefer to class the Quaternary as an "era." As mentioned above, informally it is also known as "The Great Ice Age" or, in German, *Der Eiszeit*. The formal German is *Quartär* (with an *r*; the common English spelling "Quarternary" is simply an error, derived in part from mispronunciation "Quartnary"; correct pronunciation is "Qua-ternary."

Flint (1957) and Cooper (1958) would abandon the terms Tertiary and Quaternary altogether, an action which requires the passage of an international resolution—a highly improbable eventuality. One simply cannot obliterate a helpful term that has been used for over 200 years. People who want to change nomenclature frequently do so on the basis of logical reasoning, not realizing apparently that the purpose of stratigraphic nomenclature is identification by means of a widely known system of labels.

The term Quaternary was first proposed by Desnoyers (1829) and defined by Reboul (1833) and further by von Morlot (1856) as the period that elapsed since the Pliocene. Von Morlot recognized the following subdivisions:

> Modern Epoch
> Second Glacial Epoch
> Diluvian Epoch
> First Glacial Epoch

The idea of glacial and interglacial subdivisions

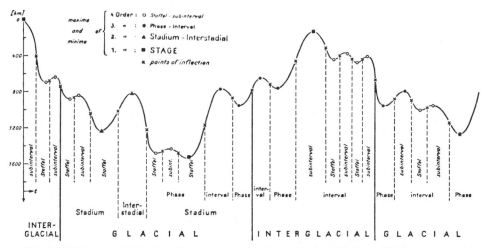

FIG. 1. Arbitrary continental glaciation curve, showing glacial/interglacial oscillation, expressed in terms of distance (km) from ice source area (simplified from Lüttig, 1965). The warmer periods he has called "thermomers" and the colder ones, "kryomers." Names for the categories of glacial advances, proposed by Lüttig, include in descending order: "Glacial," "Stage," "Phase," and "Staffel"; the retreats (warming trends) are: "Interglacial," "Interstadial," "Interval" and "Subinterval." While such sub-divisions of this nature clearly exist, it is rarely possible to establish complete field relationships.

was thus recognized early in France (and England: Ramsay, 1852), though many more oscillations are accepted today. For a long time, there was a minority belief in only one glacial epoch, the so-called monoglacialist school, and a few representatives still survive (see references in Flint, 1957; Alimen, 1967).

In the last century, the terms "Diluvium" and "Alluvium" (first used by Mantell, 1822, see Flint, 1957) were widely applied to the formations that respectively predated and postdated the last de-glaciation (see Vol. VI: *Diluvial Theory*). They are still employed in this manner occasionally in some European countries. They correspond strictly to the *Pleistocene* and *Holocene* of modern usage.

Sir Charles Lyell (1833, p. 52), probably unaware of Desnoyers' term, proposed "*Recent*" for the time that "has elapsed since the earth has been tenanted by man," the post-Tertiary period. Later (1839, p. 621) he introduced *Pleistocene* for those beds that contained more than 70% living species. Going back through time each successive stage of the Tertiary contained progressively fewer living forms. Forbes (1846, p. 402) proposed that "Pleistocene" be reserved for the "Glacial Epoch" and "Recent" for the postglacial, with which Lyell later concurred (1873, p. 3). However, in 1885, the International Geological Congress received a proposal that the youngest epoch should be called "*Holocene*" (wholly recent) and this term is now widely used. The U.S. Geological Survey adopted it in 1967, dropping "Recent." A few authors drop the Recent and refer to the whole Quaternary as "Pleistocene," which would make the "Recent" redundant

(G. F. Kay, 1931; Flint, 1957). This leads to unending confusion, for example, because "late Pleistocene" to one man means the last glacial epoch but to another means the present interglacial epoch. Morrison *et al.* (1957) felt constrained to make a plea for the preservation of the Recent, and the argument can equally well apply for the *Holocene* (q.v.). Those who would drop either evidently fail to appreciate the unique character of the Holocene or the large number of subdivisions already recognized within it. Fairbridge (1961a) indicated some 18 divisions, and palynological work also shows complex variations.

In the USSR there have emerged two "schools" of thought about the Quaternary. The earlier one to emerge favored calling it the *Anthropogene System* (the system marked by the rise of the hominids and *Homo sapiens*) in which they recognized an *Eopleistocene, Mesopleistocene, Neopleistocene* and *Holocene* (Gromov *et al.*, 1960). Another opinion, expressed by Ganespin *et al.* (1961), emphasized the lack of very great paleontological differences from the Tertiary. They recommended, therefore, that Quaternary should be dropped as an independent system and classified as a stage of the *Neogene System* (many European geologists subdivide the Tertiary into Paleogene and Neogene systems); this would make all the above divisions "substages." They rightly pointed out that the International Geological Congress would have to rule on such a proposal.

The writer would like to remind readers that stratigraphic nomenclature is not based on mathematically perfect divisions of the earth's sedimentary

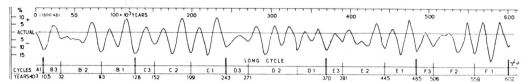

LONG CYCLE

FIG. 2. General curve of winter half-year insolation for 55°N latitude, based on calculations of Milankovich (1941), with numbers of cycles, below, based on the loess stratigraphy of Central Europe (Kukla, in Emiliani, 1968). According to Kukla it is a mistake to take the summer curve of Milankovich, because it is the albedo of winter snow-coverage that mainly controls global cooling, glacial growth and drop of sea level (Fairbridge, 1961a). The latitude 55°N is chosen because this corresponds closely to the mean maximum of global continentality, and also the mean latitude of the great continental ice advances in North America and Europe.

history, but on relatively convenient and somewhat arbitrary "parcels," i.e., on *usefulness*. The names are simply a set of labels established to aid mutual understanding. Furthermore, we should not try to keep the scale exactly constant, since any global consideration should disclose that the earth's crust has grown more and more complex through the passage of time. Therefore, it is reasonable to choose smaller and smaller subdivisions as we approach the present day. Another factor, equally important, is that the younger the epoch, the more it is likely to be preserved. We should, therefore, oppose changes in the nomenclature, unless they are absolutely essential, and we should accept the smaller divisions in stratigraphy for reasons of convenience.

Classifying the Quaternary

The subdivisions of the Quaternary as a whole have presented many difficulties. Stratigraphic nomenclature is controlled internationally by a commission of the International Union of Geological Sciences and by many regional commissions. The American Commission on Stratigraphic Nomenclature publishes its rulings and notes regularly in the *Bulletin of the American Association of Petroleum Geologists*, and the last full code appeared in 1961. "Systems" are defined on the basis of actual rock sequences, preferably marine, appropriately mapped and described, while "periods" are the time equivalents, identified where possible with fossils. In spite of this, there has been a tendency to describe and subdivide the Quaternary on the basis of climatic events. Undoubtedly they are very important, and because of the eustatic drop of sea level that accompanies each glaciation, the desirable marine section is very rarely found, except in deep-sea cores, which are not much use in defining a continental sequence of, say, glacial moraine materials. Nevertheless, the stratigraphic rules are well founded; for instance, if one defined the *time* of an epoch on the basis of a belt of terminal moraines, it could be disastrous, because the ice reached different points at different times and started to retreat from one region before another (see *Holocene* for further discussion).

There has been a strong body of opinion that has favored "special rules" in the stratigraphic nomen-

clature of the Quaternary which would recognize the overriding importance of climate change during this period (see, for example, Leighton, 1958; Lüttig, 1965). It is true that lithostratigraphy (and its officially approved terminology) usually reflects a climate change, but this requires interpretation. The field geologist often uses a synthesis of many types of evidence to deduce such a change, e.g., sediment facies, mammal fossils, palynology, diatoms, foraminifera, oxygen isotopes and absolute altitude of sea level. An application of special rules, notably the overriding control of astronomically determined solar cycles, leads to trouble—the so-called numbers game—unless controlled by absolute dating of an independent nature. The Milankovich theory, for

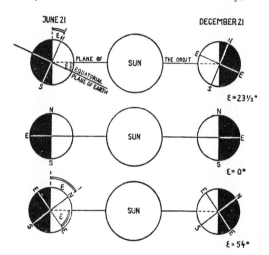

FIG. 3. The principal astronomic basis of the Milankovich theory for explaining the climatic oscillations of the Quaternary. Three diagrams illustrating the influence of the tilt or obliquity of the ecliptic. Cross-section of the orbit with the earth in mid-summer and midwinter, respectively (Zeuner, 1959). (By permission of Hutchinson & Co., London.)

Top: Obliquity (ε) = $23\frac{1}{2}$° (present value).
Middle: Imaginary obliquity, $\varepsilon = 0$°. No seasons, but sharply marked geographical zones.
Bottom: Imaginary obliquity, $\varepsilon = 54$°. Seasons very marked, but geographical zonation reduced to a minimum.

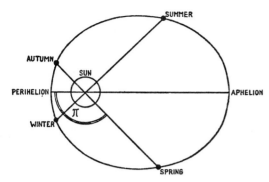

Fig. 4. The second factor in the Milankovich calculations, the precession of the equinoxes. The four cardinal
points move along the orbit. This movement is measured
by the angle π (Zeuner, 1959). (By permission of Hutchinson & Co., London.) Although the precession
cycle, seen from the Earth, is 26,000 years, owing to
the secular shift of the whole orbit the return to the
zero-point occurs every 21,000 years. This factor is more
important in influencing low-latitude climates than those
of high latitudes.

example, after a long period of severe and often ill-
founded criticism, now enjoys a considerable measure of support (Fairbridge, 1961b; Broecker,
1966); however, attempts to apply it to the whole
Quaternary time scale (Soergel, Wundt, Zeuner,
Bacsak, Bernard, and others) produce interesting but
often conflicting "models." While, in the writer's
opinion, the Milankovich scale will ultimately be
found to be very helpful, it must not be used as a
basis for nomenclature or dating. Independent
absolute dating must precede its acceptance. Within
the range of radiocarbon dating the application of
astronomic cycles already offers a very interesting
basis for working hypotheses (Karlstrom, 1961;
Stacey, 1963).

An interesting proposal to find common ground
between stratigraphy and geomorphology in the
Quaternary has been made by Frye and Willman
(1960, 1962) in the form of a "*Morphostratigraphic
Classification.*" It may seem unnecessary to regular
stratigraphers, for it is little more than a lithostratigraphic classification with morphologic additions,
but for field mapping these categories can be very
helpful. Frye and Willman (1962) say:

"The preservation of original or depositional land
forms produced by the emplacement of sediments is a
characteristic of Pleistocene and Recent nonmarine
deposits in many areas. In stratigraphic studies of these
surficial materials, in contrast to studies of rocks of
greater age, these primary depositional land forms have
been widely used. Moreover, in the mapping of late
Pleistocene glacial deposits the surface form has been
used for many years as a criterion, in most cases as the
primary criterion, for recognition of the unit being
mapped.

"Units based on surface form are not everywhere
synchronous in time and can hardly be treated as time-
stratigraphic units. In many cases adjacent units have

similar lithology and cannot be recognized as rock-
stratigraphic units. Such units have in some instances
been treated in a time sense, in others in a rock sense, and
in still others as a hybrid of the two. They generally are
given different unit names than those used for rock- and
time-stratigraphic classification of the bedrock strata.

"In an attempt to recognize the anomalous character
of such units in stratigraphic practice, and at the same
time preserve them for the very useful role they serve in
stratigraphic study of the surficial deposits, Frye and
Willman (1960, p. 7) proposed the recognition of a distinct
category of morphostratigraphic units. The definition
stated: 'A morphostratigraphic unit is defined as comprising a body of rock that is identified primarily from
the surface form it displays; it may or may not be distinctive lithologically from contiguous units; it may or may
not transgress time throughout its extent.'

"It is true that classification on the basis of moraines is
important in a relatively limited geographic region comprising only a few states .... However, the morphostratigraphic unit may be applied also to the classification of
alluvial terrace deposits, alluvial fans, lake plains, beach
ridges, and other such deposits.

"The term 'terrace' has no place in stratigraphic
terminology because literally it means a topographic
bench and therefore is a physiographic term. Clastic deposits that underlie a terrace surface, on the other hand,
are an appropriate element of stratigraphy and have been
treated in different ways by various workers. Commonly,
terrace deposits have been treated as rock-stratigraphic
units, identified on the basis of their supposed age, and
correlated by tracing the terrace form under which they
occurred. In other cases they have been correlated by
their fossil content, but rarely have several terrace deposits of a single valley been differentiated and correlated
primarily on the basis of the lithology of the deposit. In
common practice they are given their identity from the

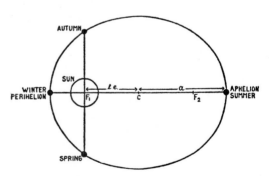

Fig. 5. The third factor in the Milankovich calculations, the eccentricity of the orbit, which influences the
absolute value of the solar radiation reaching the Earth,
reinforcing the second factor, but not itself a seasonal
value (Zeuner, 1959). Sun in one focus (F_1) of the
elliptic orbit. Distance from center (C) to aphelion or
perihelion = half axis major (a). CF_1 = "linear eccentricity" (l.e.). Eccentricity as used in calculation,
e = l.e./a. The period of the eccentricity cycle is 92,000
years. At the present time, the northern hemisphere
winter comes when the earth is nearest to the sun, so that
it is an unfavorable time for glaciation. (By permission
of Hutchinson & Co., London.)

terrace form. It therefore is convenient to name and treat such deposits as morphostratigraphic units."

Plio-Pleistocene Boundary

The lower limit of the Quaternary has also caused much trouble, introducing numbers of interesting problems. Again they rest largely on the fact that the standard sections of the Pliocene are based on marine sections, while the available lower Pleistocene formations are largely continental. Paleontological species are often transitional in development between Pliocene and Pleistocene. Initially, the transition formations, *Calabrian* (marine) and *Villafranchian* (continental), were more often placed in the Pliocene, but after close reexamination of the data, the International Geological Congress (Eighteenth Session, London, 1948; from Ray, 1949) formed a Commission which resolved:

"'that this boundary should be based on changes in marine faunas, since this is the classic method of grouping fossiliferous strata. The classic area of marine sedimentation in Italy is regarded as the area where this principle can be best implemented. It is here too that terrestrial equivalents of the marine faunas under consideration can be determined.' The Commission recommended 'that, in order to eliminate existing ambiguities, the term Lower Pleistocene should include as its basal member in the type area the Calabrian formation (Marine) together with its terrestrial equivalent the Villafranchian.'"

Furthermore, it was "noted that according to evidence given this usage would place the boundary at the horizon of the first indications of climatic deterioration in the Italian Neogene succession' (King and Oakley, 1949; Oakley, 1949)."

Quoting further from Ray (1949):

"The upper boundary, marking the close of the Pleistocene epoch and beginning of the Recent epoch, has been established in a variety of ways by many workers, but none has proved satisfactory (Antevs, 1931; De Geer, 1912; Leverett and Taylor, 1915; Morgan, 1926; Russell, 1940; and others). All are arbitrary, and, while some may be locally useful, none has worldwide application."

Marine transition zones are found in the following areas:

(a) Deep-sea Deposits. The boundary is recognized largely on the basis of foraminifera and other plankton (Ericson and Wollin, 1956; Banner and Blow, 1965; Glass et al., 1967). In a few places relatively deep-water facies are tectonically uplifted and can be studied in the field. One critical area is in southern Italy (Calabria) where the earliest Pleistocene ("Calabrian") is heralded by cold-water foraminifera *Anomalina baltica* (Ruggieri and Selli, 1948). In the northwestern Pacific the first indication of glacial material in cores is established by geomagnetic reversals (see below) as about four to five million years ago, but this in itself is not necessarily to be taken as the base of the Pleistocene. In the southern Indian Ocean, the first ice-rafted glacial debris appears in deep-sea cores also at least four million years ago, though land glaciation there was probably much earlier. In deep-sea cores generally the disappearance of plentiful Discoasters (later appearances here and there are probably reworked) is the most obvious terminal marker of the Pliocene, while the emergence of the *Globoratalia truncatulinoides* among foraminifera (Glass et al., 1967), coupled with various radiolarian lines (Hays and Opdyke, 1967), is now accepted as typical of the early Pleistocene. (Hays has adopted a series of Greek letters for radiolaria zones, omega, at top, going down through psi, and chi, with phi, upsilon and tau going into Pliocene; see Fig. 9.)

(b) Shallow Marine Deposits. In the subsiding, and therefore continuously sedimenting area of the lower Rhine and the southern edge of the North Sea, deep boring and systematic paleontologic studies by

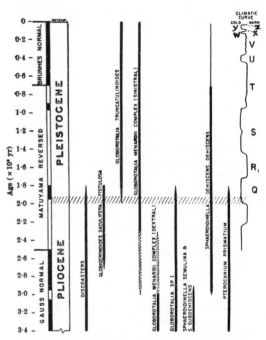

FIG. 6. Correlation of species range, climatic fluctuations and the Pliocene-Pleistocene boundary with magnetic reversals (Glass et al., 1967). The Pliocene-Pleistocene boundary based on the first appearance of *G. truncatulinoides* occurs at the base of the Olduvai event about 2.0×10^6 yr ago. Discoaster, *G.s. fistulosa*, *Globorotalia* sp. 1 and *Pterrocanium prismatium* became extinct near the top of the Olduvai event (about 1.80×10^6 yr ago). *Sphaeroidinella dehiscens* evolved from *S. subdehiscens* at the Mammoth event (3×10^6 yr ago) and decreased in abundance at the Matuyama-Brunhes boundary. The generalized climatic curve is based on the interpretation of Ericson et al. and has been modified to accord with the sequence of geomagnetic reversals. It should be noted that the Ericson et al. curve (right hand column), subdivided into foraminiferal zones (Z, X, Y, W, V, U, T, S, R, Q . . . from the top downward), is presented assuming a uniform sedimentation rate, whereas variable rates between glacials and interglacials are probable.

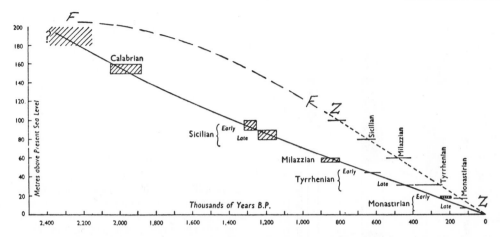

FIG. 7. Diagram suggesting a nearly straight line relation between Pleistocene interglacial sea levels and time (modified from Holmes, 1965). The shorter broken line (Z–Z) on the right represents Zeuner's original diagram (1959) on a shorter time-scale. While at the present time there is no satisfactory dating procedure for choosing which curve is the better, it seems likely to the writer that it has been a steepening curve (F–F).

the Dutch workers have disclosed a detailed sequence of Pleistocene shallow marine facies (Zagwijn, 1963); these are tabulated in Figs. 11 and 12.

In the adjacent coastal areas of Britain, a number of these formations can be correlated in even more nearshore and littoral facies, where they are partially uplifted and rest on marine Pliocene. The first invasion of a cold fauna is seen in the *Red Crag*, and in Holland, in the equivalent horizon, over 70% of the foraminifera consists of *Elphidiella arctica*, a boreal form (Van der Vlerk and Florschütz, 1950). Some equivalent formations are also found on the German side, on the island of Sylt (Wirtz and Illies, 1951).

In the Gulf Coast area, numbers of deep oil bores have been paleontologically studied, the boundary generally being marked by the Willis and Williana silts and shales which pass inland into the Citronelle gravels; the latter has a probable Villafranchian connotation. In the Atlantic coastal plain, e.g., Virginia, the lower Pleistocene is frequently transgressive (with *Elphidium florentinae*: McLean, 1966).

(c) Continental Deposits. Alluvial deposits of Pliocene and early Pleistocene age are widespread in the western United States, in a few areas in southern Europe and in several parts of Asia. The beginning of the Quaternary is marked by *Equus, Bos, Elephas* and other "modern"-looking mammals. However, they are only found in restricted places (e.g., Pilgrim, 1944), so that systematic mapping (on a lithologic basis) is needed. The best-known lower Pleistocene section is the *Villafranchian stage*, the type area being in Val d'Arno, northern Italy. Another important area is the Massif Central of France.

In the western United States, the Plio-Pleistocene boundary formations are largely classified as the *Blancan stage*, being widely associated with mammalian remains. In former prairie areas and fluvial

terrace formations, the high population of rodents is very helpful paleontologically because the teeth are often well preserved and are suitable for close stratigraphic correlation in expert hands (Schultz and Stout, 1948). Nonmarine mollusca (snails, and so on) are also relatively common and may be helpful (Taylor, 1966).

(d) Coastal and Fluvial Terraces. There are traces of rather deeply dissected coastal and river terraces in many areas at various elevations from about 50–200 meters above present sea level that have been classified as "Calabrian" by Gignoux (1936; see English edition, 1955, p. 584). On geomorphic grounds it can be seen that these terraces are older than any other Quaternary levels and also higher, as a rule, but owing to the rather active tectonics of

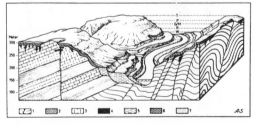

FIG. 8. Block diagram of a typical mature river valley showing progressive lowering of base level through the Quaternary (Schou, 1965; modified after Büdel). Chronology: T = late Tertiary erosion surface; P = Preglacial valley floor; G/M = Günz and Mindel glacial terraces; R = Riss terraces; W = Würm terraces. Lithology: 1 = ancient rocks; 2 = incompetent, younger rocks; 3 = limestones; 4 = red tropical soil of Tertiary age filling karst fissures and caves in limestone; 5 = Quaternary fluvial sediments; 6 = solifluction deposits (in periglacial latitudes); 7 = loess (also periglacial).

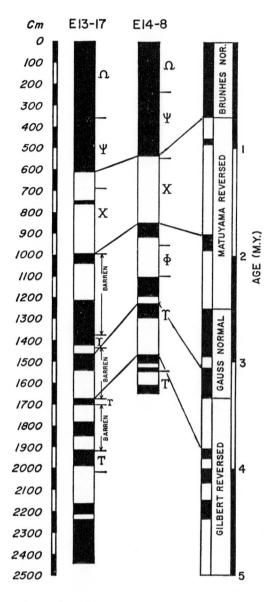

FIG. 9. Typical deep-sea cores penetrating the whole Quaternary red clay sequence and uppermost Tertiary layers (after Hays and Opdyke, 1967). Core depth (in cm) is given on the left. Radiolaria provide zone fossils (Greek letter zones) in the red clays analogous to the foraminifera in the calcareous oozes (see Fig. 6). The paleomagnetic intervals (right hand column) have received designations, named after famous geomagneticists. "Normal" intervals (black) indicate a north-seeking compass needle; "reversed" (white) a south-seeking needle. Brief intervals of opposite sense are designated "events"; the one nearly 2×10^6 years ago is called the "Olduvai Event" from the East Africa ancestral man locality. This event is now taken rather generally as corresponding closely to the beginning of the Quaternary.

many parts of the Mediterranean where they are best known, it is now felt that no reliability can be placed on any purely altimetric reasoning. In western Europe, from southern England to Portugal, there are many traces of a high Pliocene terrace surmounted by Pliocene marine formations. It ranges from below sea level to 1000 meters elevation, but over long sectors it is rather constantly about 200 meters. The Calabrian terrace is clearly old and in a number of places is associated with early Quaternary continental deposits.

(e) Absolute Dating. The beginning of the Pleistocene is far beyond the reach of radiocarbon dating (absolute limit is about 60,000 years) and also beyond the limits of other dating methods that use organic materials or sediments. It is therefore necessary to seek out interstratified ash or lava flows (as in the Massif Central of France, central Italy, Iceland, Hawaii, Japan) or other igneous sources. These may then be handled by potassium/argon and other long half-life isotope methods. With these systems, the younger the age, the greater the relative uncertainty, but the early Pleistocene is old enough to furnish reasonably useful dates. It is unfortunate, however, that some of the best volcanic deposits are in quite remote areas such as the Olduvai Gorge of Tanzania; dates here are most interesting for establishing the age of early man but they do not bear directly on the classic Italian sections. The spread of "reasonable" dates for the Plio-Pleistocene boundary, at the time of writing, seems to fall at about $2.0 \pm 0.2 \times 10^6$ years (Glass *et al.*, 1967).

(f) Paleomagnetism. Systematic measurements of paleomagnetic orientation in Icelandic lava flows by Rutten and Wensink (1960) and in Hawaiian flows by Cox, Doell and Dalrymple (1964) show several significant periods of magnetic reversal during the Quaternary that are now rather well fixed in time (see Fig. 6). Basalts occur also in belts on the sea floor, symmetrically parallel (and as mirror images of each other) everywhere that the *mid-oceanic ridges* (q.v., Vol. I) extend. They are absolutely predictable and have the enormous advantage of being overlain by fossiliferous marine deposits. Thus the base of any given marine sequence can be correlated with its appropriate basement. Magnetic reversals are also recorded within the sediments and these in turn have paleontological zones (see Figs. 6, 9).

Subdivision of the Pleistocene

The upper boundary of the Pleistocene is, *mirabile dictu*, also the lower limit of the *Holocene*, and this is susceptible to precise radiocarbon and *varve* dating (q.v. pr Vol. VI); while still subject to final international agreement, it must lie somewhere between 10,000 and 10,500 years B.P., and may be defined as a time-stratigraphic unit of series rank, viz. the time equivalents of sediments overlying the terminal moraines of the Valders (in North America) or the

Salpausselkä (in Europe) being the last important glacial readvance before the general retreat of the Pleistocene ice sheets. It continues till the present day.

North American Stages. The main subdivision of the North American Pleistocene is on the basis of the great till ("drift") sheets and end moraines of the mid-continent (representing glacial phases) alternating with terrace deposits and *paleosols* (q.v. pr Vol. VI) (representing the interglacial events). Four "glacials"—the *Nebraskan, Kansan, Illinoian* and *Wisconsin*—were recognized (Chamberlin, 1896; and others: see Flint, 1957). Interglacials with paleosols—*Aftonian, Yarmouth and Sangamon*—have been established (Leverett, 1898; and others). A helpful mnemonic for this sequence NAKYISW is "Now Alvin, know your ice sequence well!" An *Iowan* drift originally included is now classed as early Wisconsin; the later Wisconsin being sometimes distinguished today as "*classical Wisconsin.*" Numbers of retreat stages, even with relatively brief readvances, are recognized. Interstadials are observed or suspected in each of the earlier tills. Incidentally, the term "*drift*" is widely used in English-speaking circles, but it is an anachronism dating from the early belief in a great flood with debris carried by ice floes. The continental Europeans often use "moraine" for the same thing, amalgamating the landform ("moraine") with the sedimentary material ("till").

Most of the tills (both major ones and minor readvances) are separated by *loess* (q.v.) horizons. Genetically the loess most likely represents the eolian silts blown from the outwash plains, so that they probably date from immediately after the underlying till. These loess horizons provide a useful correlation with fluvial terrace deposits, and in addition, their paleosols often contain small terrestrial mollusca.

Two particularly helpful and necessary companions to this area are (a) the *Glacial Map of Canada* (published in 1958 by the Geological Association of Canada) and (b) the *Glacial Map of the United States East of the Rocky Mountains* (1959, by the Geological Society of America).

Since each glaciation/deglaciation represents a complete climatic (and sedimentary) cycle, it has been urged by G. F. Kay (1931) that each glacial/interglacial sequence should be regarded stratigraphically as a rock *series* ("epoch," in time), while the distinctive divisions, e.g., Nebraskan and Aftonian should each be classified as a *stage* (or "age," in time). The series names proposed *op. cit.*, though not commonly used, are as follows: *Grandian*, from Grand River valley in southeast Iowa; *Ottumwan*, a small city in southern Iowa; *Centralian* from Centralia, Illinois; *Eldoran* from Eldora, a town in Iowa. Kay was impressed by the relative brevity of each glacial advance (represented by perhaps 10–20 meters of till) and with the great length of time repre-

TIME-STRATIGRAPHIC CLASSIFICATION in the MID-WEST		KANSAS Rock-stratigraphic units used here		TEXAS Rock-stratigraphic and Morphostratigraphic units used here	
RECENT		(Alluvium, dune sand)		(Alluvium, dune sand)	
PLEISTOCENE	WISCONSINAN VALDERAN	Bignell Loess	(Deposits of several terraces, dune sands, basin fills)	Cooke Alluvial Terrace	(Terraces, loess, dune sands, basin fills)
	WISCONSINAN TWOCREEKAN	Brady Soil		Ambrose Alluvial Terrace	
	WISCONSINAN WOODFORDIAN	Peoria Loess			
	WISCONSINAN FARMDALIAN	"Basal zone of Peoria"		Tahoka Fm. Lake Lomax deposits	
	WISCONSINAN ALTONIAN				
	SANGAMONIAN	Sangamon Soil		Sangamon Soil	
	ILLINOIAN	Loveland Silt	(Terrace deposits)	"Cover sands," terrace deposits, dune sands	
		Crete Sand and Gravel			
	YARMOUTHIAN	Yarmouth Soil		Yarmouth Soil	
	KANSAN	Meade { Sappa Mem. Fm. { Grand Isl. M. Kansas Glacial Till Atchison Formation		Hardeman Alluv. Terr. Tule Formation (Terrace deposits, basin fills)	
	AFTONIAN	Afton Soil		Afton Soil	
	NEBRASKAN	Blanco { Fullerton M. Fm. { Holdrege M. Nebraska Glacial Till David City Formation		Blanco Formation (Terrace deposits, basin fills)	
PLIOCENE		"Ogallala climax soil"		"Ogallala climax soil"	
		Ogallala Formation { Kimball Mem. { Ash Hollow Mem. { Valentine Mem.		Ogallala Formation	

sented by each paleosol, at least 100,000 years on the basis of his measurements of weathering profiles (see also discussion by Leverett, 1930; Flint, 1957). He was sharply criticized for this method of estimating ages, and it is true that a soil weathering profile under mild humid conditions forms rather quickly. Although he clearly had swung too far (see absolute dates: Kay, 1931, p. 462), nevertheless his general estimates of the total elapsed time were not so far from the truth.

No satisfactory modern series classification of the Mid-West Quaternary has yet been established, but the stage names are widely employed. In Table 1 (from Frye and Leonard, 1965) there is a useful synthesis, although it should be noted that the "-an" suffixes are not always favored; the "Valderan" of these authors extends up to 5000 B.P. and is accordingly "early Holocene" in most international usage.

Until recently Quaternary glaciation in the Rocky Mountains has not received the same intensive study as in the mid-continent, with only the youngest being at all well known. Mountain glaciers occurred as far south as 37°N latitude; the two Wisconsin substages are named Bull Lake and Pinedale (Richmond, 1965). By potassium-argon dating of associated lavas the earliest glaciation in the Sierra Nevada has now been estimated at about 3 million years (Curry, 1966).

An important fact about the standard North American time scale, based as it is on striking glacial/interglacial oscillations, is that it only covers

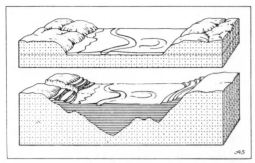

FIG. 10. Block diagrams (by Schou, 1965) comparing a valley floor formed under an equatorial or tropical regime in its middle course (above) and a near coastal mid-latitude regime (below). The equatorial profile reflects a meandering stream with chemical weathering during warm interglacials alternating with braided stream alluviation during semiarid glacial episodes. The lower profile illustrates thalassostatic down-cutting of the thalweg, followed by intense alluviation during a subsequent semiarid stage, and finally progressively deeper terrace incision during a succeeding wetter phase.

the latter part of the Pleistocene, the most strongly glaciated part of the period. Evidence from absolute dating, deep-sea cores, and so on, suggests that the period began with cooling and drying trends, with many minor oscillations, but that extensive till sheets appeared only in the last stages. The early part is represented only by the continental fluvial and piedmont deposits of Blancan age and some younger representations, the close dating of which remains to be achieved (Colbert, *et al.*, 1948).

In the valleys of the Mississippi, Rio Grande and other great southwestern rivers, there are complex terrace accumulations that may contain at least part of the record. It should be noted that in their upper courses, these southern river terraces generally represent the high sediment load to runoff ratio of periglacial and semiarid conditions of the cold epochs, alternating with strong valley cutting during the well-vegetated interglacials (following the Langbein-Schumm rule: see *Continental Erosion*; *Denudation*; *Terraces, Fluvial—Environmental Controls*; *Tropical Weathering and Relief*). Near the mouths

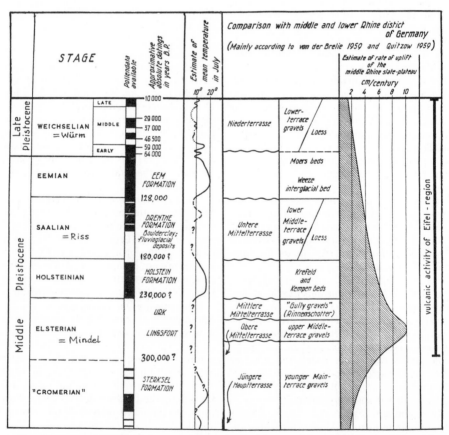

FIG. 11. Late and Middle Pleistocene stages, absolute dates and formations in the Rhine delta area of the Netherlands (left), absolute age, mean summer temperature (middle) and Rhine terrace formations, tectonics and volcanism (right), modified after Zagwijn (1963).

of great rivers, however, the thalassostatic effect, or blocking by high eustatic sea level during interglacials, leads to estuarine terrace building, whereas low eustatic sea level at glacial times leads to deep valley cutting right across the continental shelf (see *Terraces—Thalassostatic*). A third environment of terrace building is found in the Great Basin and middle Rockies where each glacial advance was marked by a southerly shift of the westerly winds, leading to intense pluviation in normally dry areas (discussed in principle by Penck, 1914). Here river terrace building represents drying phases of interglacials and cutting corresponds to the well-watered, well-vegetated early and late glacial phases. Lake terraces, in contrast, built up during these transitional stages (see *Pluvial Lakes*). During the glacial maxima there was almost worldwide desiccation (drop in solar radiation and cooling of ocean water means less evaporation: therefore less cloud: less rain): thus pluvial lake basins filled up during the early and late stages of glaciation, but were cold, dry areas at glacial maxima, alternating with hot, dry areas at glacial minima.

A vigorous campaign of drilling the Quaternary salt lake and playa depressions of the American West has been going on in recent years. The cores are

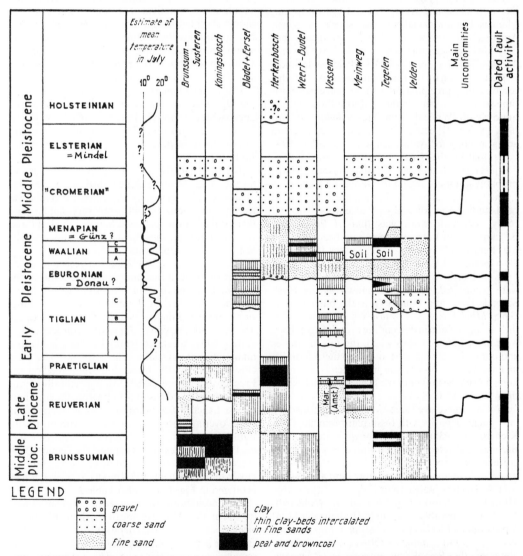

FIG. 12. Pliocene, followed by Early and Middle Pleistocene stages in the Netherlands (simplified from Zagwijn, 1963). Note the mean summer temperatures and the known faulting activity, both of which must have affected the stream energy. Overriding all local features is the widespread deposit of river gravels corresponding to the Elster (Mindel) glaciation with its attendant solifluction and loss of vegetative cover.

studied palynologically and for sediment character, and the upper sections are dated by the radiocarbon method. Key examples have been Great Salt Lake (Pluvial Lake Bonneville) in Utah (Morrison, 1966), Searles Lake in southeastern California (Flint and Gale, 1958), Wilcox Playa (Pluvial Lake Cochise) in Arizona, and St. Augustine Plains and others in New Mexico (Martin and Mehringer, 1965).

Alpine Stages. During the Quaternary the Alps represented a relatively independent orographic center, developing a respectable ice-cap some hundreds of miles long at glacial maxima, alternating with almost totally ice-free conditions during interglacials. It may be noted that with each successive interglacial stage, the high-latitude ice sheets like Greenland and Antarctica did not disappear, whereas the middle-latitude ice sheets of North America and Europe melted away completely, but only after considerable delay (see Vol. II: *Ice Age Meteorology*; *Ice Age Theory*). In their low-latitude, western position on the Eurasian continent, the Alps receive a high precipitation from several close maritime sources and thus build and lose their glaciers quite rapidly. While the time lapse (*climatic retardation*; q.v. Vol. II) between interglacial warming and actual melting for Antarctica must exceed 100,000 years, that for the North American continental ice was just over 10,000 years, and that for the Alps was probably not more than a few thousand years.

Quaternary deposits in the Alpine valleys have been studied now for well over a century. The first really systematic work was that of Penck and Brückner (1909). Later syntheses have been provided by Heim (1919, pp. 197–344), Zeuner (1959) and Charlesworth (1957).

As in North America, four major glacial stages were recognized, sometimes known as the First, Second, Third and Fourth Glacials, but better as *Günz, Mindel, Riss and Würm* (as a memory aid: they are alphabetic in descending order of age). They were named after villages where the tills, moraines and outwash were mapped in the northern foothills in Bavaria. For brevity the interglacials are often known from the initials of the glacials which bracket them: G/M, M/R, R/W.

In Tyrol there are three till stages separated by interglacial deposits with fossil plant remains (Von Klebelsberg, 1935). The best known is the Hötting Breccia, a calcreted colluvium with over 42 warmer-latitude plant species (Penck, 1921), indicating at least 2°C higher mean temperature, and a snow line over 400 meters higher than today. It is probably Mindel-Riss ("Hötting Interglacial" of Woldstedt, 1953). A comparable lignite in the Italian (southern) Alps contains *Elephas* (*Archidiskodon, Mammuthus*) *meridionalis* and *E. antiquus*. Other lignites and peat represent the Riss-Würm interglacial ("Uznach Interglacial" of Woldstedt, 1953).

Penck and Brückner recognized three "retreat stadia" in the Würm retreat phase: *Bühl, Geschnitz*

and *Daun* when the snow line lay 1000, 600 and 300 meters respectively, lower than today. Subdivisions of the Würm are sometimes labeled Würm I, II, III and even IV, but there is some disagreement about exactly to what each number refers. For some time there was a controversy over whether the early Würm was not better called late Riss (equivalent in North America, to the Iowan). Further detailed work has shown that there were probably two or three *stadials* and *interstadials* within each of the great glacial stages and there were additional oscillations within interglacials. Pre-Günz glaciations have also been proved in the eastern Alps, with the *Otto-beuren, Staufenberg* and *Donau* (I, II, III) outwash gravels. It is thus quite apparent that the Quaternary should not be subdivided into four stages, as commonly accepted in textbooks of a few decades ago, but rather is involved in long and complex climato-sedimentary oscillations, as suggested by Milankovich (though probably greatly exceeding the time span contemplated by him).

During the Quaternary's two million years or so, the Alps have also risen tectonically, at a mean rate approaching 1 mm/yr, but modulated by glacial loading and unloading. The mountains would thus appear to have progressively increased in importance.

The Riss had the most extensive icecap; in the northeast, the Mindel reached a little further and the Würm is rather generally less extensive. The mean icecap dimensions though were very similar, and there is really little to choose between the last three. In time, however, these covered probably only the last 10% of the Quaternary.

There is a close correlation between the Alpine glacier outwash trains and the Rhine terraces, the accumulating phases corresponding to the heavy bed loads supplied by the melting ice and solifluction, converting the rivers to *braided streams* (q.v.). The accumulating phases alternated with deep down-cutting when vegetated banks kept bed loads to a minimum (interglacials). The sequence has been closely dated by the potassium/argon method (by Frechen and Lippolt, 1965), using specifically identifiable minerals and basalt pebbles from the eruptions of the Laacher See volcano (near Koblenz). The result overlaps nicely and coincides with protactinium/thorium dates from a deep-sea core (Rosholt *et al.*, 1962). The dates do not support the Zeuner (1959) correlation with the Milankovich curve, but are closer to the Emiliani (1955) model. A revised model is offered in Fig. 11 (see also Table 2).

Paleontologically the river terrace deposits radiating from the Alps are locally rich in diagnostic *mammalian fossils*. The deposits and the ice-free areas are generally also associated with remarkable remains of *Paleolithic man*. The man-made flint artifacts, in general, are as useful in correlation, when competently studied, as are any of the other fossil remains. It is somewhat unfortunate, therefore, that this unique feature (not available in the Americas because of the late arrival of man) has been rather ignored by geologists; the customary treatment of these artifacts as merely study material for archeologists (persons often trained only in the Arts faculties and lacking skills in sedimentology and stratigraphy) has partly denied the proper place of human artifacts as type fossils. The durability of flint tools is at the same time both an advantage and a disadvantage. Not only are they immune from solution in groundwater, but their very toughness results in their being repeatedly reworked and carried down into younger colluvium by solifluction from higher slopes. [An introduction to ancient Man, and to Quaternary mammals is provided in Vol. VII of this series; see also Oakley, 1964.]

Mammalian Faunas

The paleontological classification of the Pleistocene into upper, middle and lower divisions was formerly thought to have some equivalence in time, but today, with the acceptance of a "long" Pleistocene, some 90% of Pleistocene time falls into the lower division. The main European paleontological indicators among the major mammals are as follows (adapted from Alimen, 1967; dates revised according to correlation of recent radiometric dates with the astronomic chronology):

Upper Pleistocene—10,000 back to about 82,800 B.P. (Würm, including several interstadials); *Elephas primigenius, Rhinoceros tichorhinus, Rangifer tarandus* (reindeer).

Middle Pleistocene—About 82,800–355,000 B.P. (Riss and Mindel glacials plus three interglacials: the Cromer (G/M), the penultimate or "Great" Holstein interglacial (M/R) and the last, or Eem (R/W), interglacial; *Elephas antiquus, E. trogontherii, Rhinoceros etruscus, R. mercki, Equus caballus.*

Lower Pleistocene—About 355,000 back to 1.6–2 million B.P. (Günz and earlier glacials, interglacials and preglacial stages); *Elephas meridionialis, Mastodon* spp., *Rhinoceros etruscus, R. mercki, R.* spp., *Hippopotamus major, Trogontherium cuvieri, Equus stenonis, Leptobos* sp.

Early Villafranchian is marked by *Mastodon borsoni, Hipparion, Hyaenarctos* and *Rhinoceros* cf. *megarhinus,* which disappear later.

[*Note*: The terms "Upper," "Middle" and "Lower" are not subject as yet to any international agreement. They are used here following the Netherlands standard (de Jong, 1967). When referring strictly to the time, rather than rock scale, one should use "Late," "Medial" and "Early."]

Because of their capacity to migrate and adapt, the major mammals are better indicators of evolution (age) than environment, simply migrating southward in the cold epochs. However, in numbers of places, the toe of Italy, the Iberian peninsula, and so on, geographic traps exist, which at times led to catastrophic extinctions. Insular isolation also led to rapid speciation and often to extinction. Plant (and insect) fossils, on the other hand, are much better indicators of climate, both leaf and pollen records affording the best records of paleotemperatures.

TABLE 2. TENTATIVE CORRELATION OF THE QUATERNARY GLACIAL AND INTERGLACIAL STAGES OF NORTH AMERICA, THE ALPS AND NORTHERN EUROPE; ABSOLUTE DATING IS BASED ON THE MILANKOVICH–BACSÁK CALCULATIONS (BACSÁK 1955) AND INTERPRETED BY THE WRITER IN THE LIGHT OF Th/U DATING (BROECKER, 1966), THE LOESS PROFILES OF KUKLA (IN EMILIANI, 1968) AND TO THE K/Ar DATING OF RHINE TERRACES (FRECHEN AND LOPPOLT, 1965) (Glacials are in capitals; Interglacials in lower case)[a]

Absolute Dating	North America	Alps	Northern Europe	Poland–USSR
0– 67,000	WISCONSIN (early W. = Iowan)	WÜRM	WEICHSEL (VISTULA) (early W. = Warthe)	VARSOVIAN (VALDAI)
67,000–128,000	Sangamon	Uznach	Eem (Hoxnian)	Masovian I
128,000–180,000	ILLINOIAN	RISS II RISS I	WARTHE (DRENTHE) SAALE	CRACOVIAN (DNIEPER)
180,000–230,000	Yarmouth	Hötting	Holstein	Sandomirian
230,000–300,000	KANSAN	MINDEL I and II	ELSTER	JAROSLAVIAN (Likhvin)
300,000–330,000	Aftonian	−	Cromer	
330,000–470,000	NEBRASKAN	GÜNZ I and II		MENAPIAN
470,700–538,000			Waalian	
538,000–548,000		DONAU II	WEYBOURNE	
− −				
548,000–585,000			Tiglian (Tegelen)	
585,000–600,000		DONAU I	RED CRAG (BUTLEY)	
c. 600,000–c. 2,000,000		Villafranchian		

[a] *Note*: The suffix -ian is added to many of these names to suggest stage formality; many authors refrain from this extension. "Wisconsinan" seems particularly unnecessary.

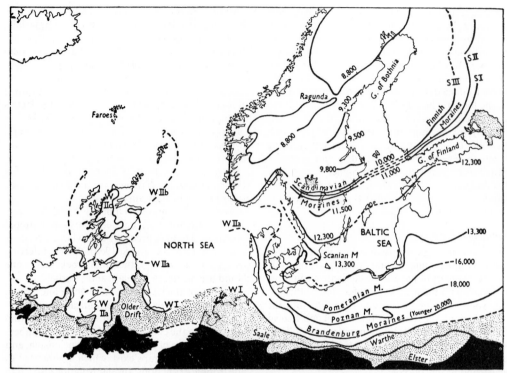

FIG. 13. Map (from Holmes, 1965) (by permission of T. Nelson & Sons, London) illustrating the extent of Pleistocene glaciations over northwest Europe and the British Isles, and the chief moraines and drift borders marking stages in the recession of the last great ice sheet (W = Weichsel and Würm). The Older Drift of Britain corresponds to the Saale (R) and the Elster (M). The Elster front was overrun by the Saale in the Netherlands, but in England reached the site of north London. *Elster* and *Saale* are named after tributaries of the Elbe. *Warthe* is named after a town in Poland on a river of the same name that passes through Poznan on its way to join the Oder. The Warthe front probably corresponds to the outer border of the Newer Drift of Britain, both being here correlated with the maximum spread of W I. In the British area this is the Irish Sea–York–Hunstanton glaciation. W IIa marks the Scottish and Welsh re-advance, and possibly corresponds with the older of the Brandenburg moraines. W IIb is the Highland re-advance, corresponding to the younger Brandenburg and the Poznan, Pomeranian and Scandinavian moraines. W IIc is a British phase of minor cirque and valley glaciers of the same general age as the Scandinavian moraines. Dates are given in years B.P., "before the present." The Pleistocene/Holocene boundary is generally placed between 10,000 and 11,000 B.P., the time of the S (Salpausselkä and central Swedish) moraines.

Northern European Stages. The principal glacial source areas for the continental ice sheets that streamed across the Baltic, the North Sea and northern Europe lay in Scandinavia, Finland and, to a minor extent, Scotland. The sources may be identified rather exactly by petrographic study of the boulders (see *Indicator Boulders*).

In the earliest Quaternary there was no Baltic Sea, just as there were probably no Great Lakes in North America. The basins may have resulted partly from glacial scouring, and partly from crustal warping, but the relative importance of each is hard to establish. The till sheets have received different names, from Britain, Germany, Poland and the U.S.S.R., partly because their continuity was not established at first. The names most widely adopted are those proposed by K. Keilhack: *Elster, Saale* and *Weichsel* (after the German name for the Vistula River in Poland). Subsequently the *Saale* became

correlated with Riss I of the Alps and *Warthe* with Riss II. Of these, the Elster is the most extensive in central Europe (Woldstedt, 1958–65). As in North America, there are extensive loess sheets which help correlate these stages; they probably span the climatic stage from the beginning of each retreat to the steppe grassland stage and eventually to the cool, temperate woodland, when they were succeeded by scattered interglacial deposits with rich plant and mammal fossils. In northern Europe the earliest glacial stages are evidently missing and the closest representatives are the shallow marine members in Britain and Holland (see above). The Alpine Günz (U.S. Nebraskan) is represented only by gravels from the Rhine and the earliest till sheets appear to be Mindel (Kansan) in age.

Non-glaciated Areas of Europe. During the maxima of glacial events in the Alps and northern Europe all of southern Europe came under the

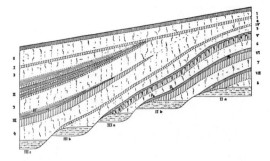

FIG. 14. Fluvial terraces of the Vltava (Moldau) River in Czechoslovakia, especially in the Sedlec Clay-pits near Prague, show successive terrace gravels passing up into loess (diagrammatic profile by Woldstedt, 1958–65, based on the works of Zaruba, and of Prožek and Ložek). Each loess cycle (1–8), has a matching zone of weathering and paleosol with snails (I–VII). Pa = Paleolithic flint implements. BF = Banatica fauna, the warm-latitude fossils of the last (Eem) interglacial. Terraces IIa and b are early Pleistocene; IIIa, b, c, are mid-Pleistocene.

influence of extreme frost action (see *Periglacial Landscapes*; also *Periglacial Stratigraphy*, pr Vol. VII); indeed frost wedges are found at sea level in North Africa, Morocco, Cyrenaica and Egypt. Thus massive solifluction material accumulated on lower slopes and in river valleys at each glaciation. These solifluction wedges are very helpful in working out a stratigraphic record in the non-glacial areas, especially when taken in conjunction with *fluvial terraces* (see *Terraces—Fluvial*) and with *loess* deposits.

Two areas offer unrivaled sections for this study: the Bohemian Basin of the Vltava (Moldau) River in Czechoslovakia, especially because of the work of Zaruba (English summary in Svoboda, 1966), and the Danube Basin of Lower Austria and Hungary (Krivan, 1955; Pécsi, 1964). The Hungarian section, in particular, has been subject to a close correlation with the Milankovich-Bacsák astronomically controlled climatic model. In Moravia no less than ten complete loess cycles have been established by

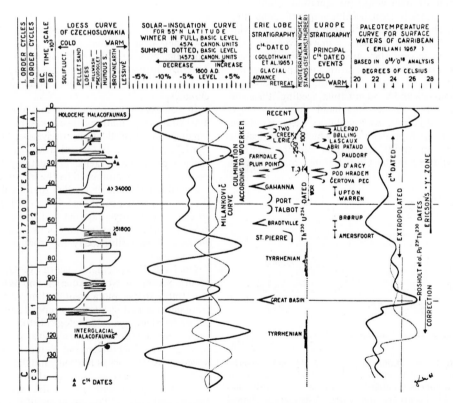

FIG. 15. Comparison of Czechoslovakian loess sections of the last glacial cycle with major isotope-dated Pleistocene events, with winter and summer insolation curves, and with Emiliani's paleotemperature curve (Kukla, in Emiliani, 1968). Definite C[14] dates are marked by a solid triangle, others by an open triangle and an estimate in figures. Sources, other than those indicated above, are Kaufman and Broecker (1965), Leroi-Gourhan (1965), Morisson and Frye (1965), Movius (1960), and Musil and Valoch (1966). (References in Emiliani, 1968, p. 44.) Note: "malacofaunas" = shelly fossils, notably snails.

Kukla (in Emiliani, 1968), and seem to correlate nicely with the astronomic curve.

Czechoslovakia was only marginally touched by the continental ice sheets and had numbers of small mountain centers. The eastern Europeans often refer to the outwash alluvium as proluvium. Cycles of this material with loess, weathering profiles, and fossil horizons are found repeated again and again. The Vltava terraces above Prague were thus never obliterated and probably contain the most complete synthesis of the entire Quaternary in the world, outside of deep-sea sections. Comparable sections are also found in Moravia near Brno.

Non-glaciated Areas of the World. During the cold phases of the Quaternary, the mean oceanic surface water temperature dropped by several degrees, variously calculated on the basis of O^{18}/O^{16} isotope measurements from pelagic foraminifera and on the basis of many biogeographic indicators (Emiliani, 1955; Fairbridge, 1964a). The consequence, deduced by Flohn (1953) on the basis of meteorological data, would be an equatorward displacement of the jet streams (Fig. 16) and a catastrophic drop in world precipitation. Subtropical and equatorial regions became unquestionably much drier. The drop in precipitation was not worldwide, however, because an increase in wind velocities, e.g., in the main westerlies, in spite of lowered temperatures, would raise evaporation and, therefore, precipitation, in areas of maritime climates, e.g., Scandinavia and Scotland, thus "feeding" the growing icecaps. On the other hand, the expansion of these mid-latitude continental ice sheets would set up cold high-pressure cells, which would lead to anticyclonic winds, resulting in cold dry deserts in the Midwest of the United States, many parts of

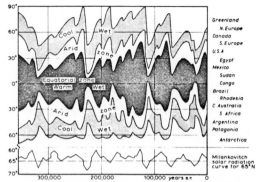

FIG. 17. Displacement of world climatic belts, during warmer and cooler stages of the late Quaternary. The Milankovich curve of solar radiation is given for 65°N, but no correlation with known stratigraphy is offered in view of the uncertainty of the absolute dating except for the last cycle (Würm-Weichsel-Wisconsin). Note that the semi-permanent ice sheet of Antarctica maintains a much more uniform cool level in the southern high latitudes, in contrast to remarkable oscillations in the northern latitudes.

Europe (France, Spain, Czechoslovakia, Hungary, Ukraine), central Asia, China, parts of India, Australia, most of Africa and most of eastern South America. In contrast, interglacial phases were reflected by widespread extensions of humid, tropical climates.

In equatorial deep-sea cores this alternation is marked by an oscillation between kaolinite-gibbsite minerals (interglacial lateritic derivatives) and chlorite-feldspar minerals (glacial arid "mechanical" erosion products). Organic productivity in many marine areas was stimulated by the increased circulation (thermal gradients), rather than inhibited (by the lowering of temperatures). *Coral reefs* (q.v.; also *Atolls*) were greatly restricted and in many places eroded down by low eustatic seas (Daly, 1934). Many of those visible today are products of Holocene upgrowth.

On land the systematic records of Quaternary events outside of North America and Europe are regrettably sparse, but a great deal may be gleaned from general geological survey reports, archeological material and geomorphological studies.

In China and Mongolia, the classical loess descriptions by Von Richthofen and Pumpelly were followed up by the work of Barbour, and the celebrated American Museum of Natural History (of New York) Expedition with remarkable accounts by Morris and Berkey. The discovery of Peking Man added impetus, with studies by Black and Teilhard de Chardin. A good summary is given by De Terra (1941).

In the Himalayas and their foothills, the interesting Siwalik vertebrates of the late Tertiary continued into the Quaternary, and De Terra (with Paterson)

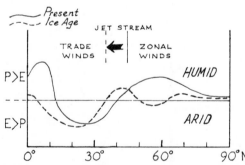

FIG. 16. Meridional displacement of zonal (westerly) winds, principal jet streams, and trade winds during glacial epochs (modified after Flohn, 1963; with additions by the writer). Upper half of diagram is marked "Humid," where P (precipitation) exceeds E (evaporation); lower half is arid, and E exceeds P. In latitudes 50–60° the usual glacial trend is toward aridity, while in latitudes 30–50° (northern fringe of desert) there may be a "pluvial" condition. It seems likely that reduced oceanic evaporation during cold epochs produced a general aridity in low latitudes.

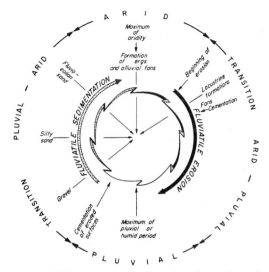

FIG. 18. Diagrammatic representation of a continental sedimentary cycle in the low latitudes (adapted from Chevaillon, 1964; from Alimen, 1965). Note that in the semiarid regions of the subtropics a transition from pluvial (rainy) phase to an arid results in alluviation and eventually the building of sand dunes. In contrast, the transition from arid to pluvial leads initially to fluviatile erosion; in the humid areas, vegetation eventually stabilizes dunes, extends ground cover to reduce runoff and an equilibrium is reestablished. It is believed that in Mediterranean latitudes the pluvials came with each glacial onset, but in low equatorial latitudes, pluvials are now usually regarded as interglacial, although the question is still subject to controversy.

has again furnished a useful summary of the successions. Paterson (1941) attempted also a world synthesis of the Pleistocene.

Australia has a fascinating paleontological record of giant kangaroos, including marsupial *Diprotodon* (which was as large as a rhinoceros) and many others (Gill, 1957). The glaciated areas were limited to small icecaps about Mt. Kosciusko in the southern part of the continent and in Tasmania. However, the soils and continental (fluvial and dune) deposits are of enormous interest and subject to rigorous study (Butler, 1967).

In New Zealand, with its relatively high-latitude maritime climates, there was widespread glaciation in the South Island with an average temperature depression of 6°C (Gage, 1965). On the other hand, the absence of any large continental area kept conditions relatively temperate in both glacials and interglacials, so that the record is largely a pluvial one.

Africa gives the most illuminating picture of Quaternary events outside of the glacial and periglacial regions. It was at first thought that evidence for enormous pluvial lakes indicated increased rains during the glacials, but this was based on a false

assumption; continental glaciation is associated with lowered world temperatures, and usually with decreasing precipitation; only in local areas, e.g., northwestern Europe, was there evidence of heavy precipitation. Deserts were widespread (Beetz, 1938; Van Zinderen Bakker, 1967). In Africa, dunes extended from the Kalahari northward, to cross the Congo. The Saharan sands spread southward into the jungle fringes of West Africa and the northern Congo. The now vegetated dunes of the last arid phase are traceable, as in Australia, deep into what today are tropical jungles (Fairbridge, 1962, 1964b, 1965). The expansion of the great lakes of East Africa were studied in detail by Nilsson (1940) and even today Leakey and others regard them as the product of glacial pluvials, although C^{14} dates show clearly that the last big expansion of lake waters occurred during the early and mid-Holocene *"climatic optimum"* (q.v. Vol. II), a time of worldwide warmth. During the cold arid periods the great rivers like the Nile, Senegal, Niger, and even the Congo, became braided channels and largely dried up with broad swampy areas in their mid-courses (Fairbridge, 1962; Tricart, 1965; Garner, 1967).

In South America (notably Brazil, the Guianas and Venezuela), the great sand sources of Africa were lacking but arid erosion alternated with humid "stabilization" in a most remarkable way. Series of pediments, cutting into each other progressively, are to be seen on all the hills; the pediments have the shape of those forming today in Death Valley, California, but they are now covered by jungle or savanna vegetation and are clearly inactive. These pediments and their associated piedmont fans are graded to about − 100 meters (below sea level) and thus glacial in age. The sediments of the fans are characterized by large angular feldspars (today often rotted *in situ*), minerals that could only be produced by mechanical weathering under arid conditions (Bigarella and de Andrade, 1965; Bigarella and Mousinho, 1966). In the lower valleys one sees the sharp junctions between knife-edged ridges reminiscent of badlands and flat valley floors which are filled from upstream by braided torrent deposits. Again, today, with the heavy vegetative cover (following the Langbein-Schumm principle) the topography is essentially stabilized.

In the high Andes a very interesting picture emerges. Reduced temperatures lowered snow lines, particularly on the windward side of the mountains; in cold stages there was an increase in high-altitude precipitation and stream runoff. In high interior basins like the Bogotá savanna in Colombia there would be a large pluvial lake (glacio-pluvial), and palynological analysis of deep cores shows unquestionably a cold pluvial sequence alternating with dry interglacial conditions (Van der Hammen and Gonzalez, 1964). On the other hand, in the rain shadow areas extreme aridity occurred in the cold periods, so that valleys became blocked by hundreds

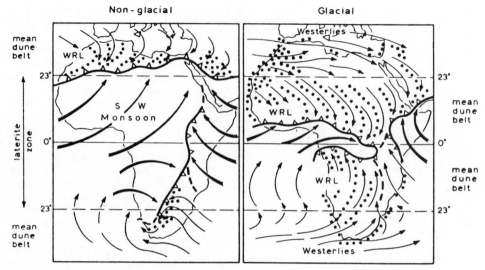

FIG. 19. Generalized wind system maps of Africa, seen for a non-glacial (or interglacial) period and for a glacial maximum (Fairbridge, 1964b). Note that in the former, warm humid conditions accompanied the strengthened monsoons to cover much of the present desert regions, whereas in the glacial time the westerlies were displaced equatorward, the mean temperature of the world ocean dropped several degrees C and the monsoons were severely curtailed. As a result desert dunes (black dots) extended far into equatorial belts; many of these ancient dunes are now overgrown with forest, savanna or even jungle rain forest. WRL = Wheel-round latitude, the mean latitude where the westerlies bend round into the tropical easterlies. (More detailed maps are provided by Van Zinderen Bakker, 1967).

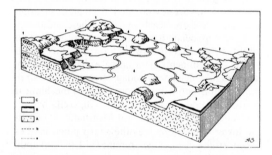

FIG. 20. Block diagram illustrating a non-coastal (upland) fluvial environment in the humid tropic or equatorial regions, after subjection to varying cycles of Quaternary climatic change (Schou, 1965; in part, after Büdel, 1963), based on example in the source region of the Niger River. Key: A = bedrock; B = kaolinite-rich red clay; C = bauxite with lateritic hardpan. a. Tertiary base level; b. Holocene base level.

1. Maturely weathered mountains (*ca.* 1000 meters elevation);
2. Tertiary sheet wash plain (*ca.* 800 meters);
3. Inselbergs;
4. Holocene sheet wash plain, 7–10 km wide, subject to seasonal flooding. Fluvial erosion today is insignificant, because the river carries only a clay fraction, and erosion is strictly chemical. During arid periods, however, reduction of vegetation cover permits coarse sediments to join the rivers, a braided regime replaces a meandering one, and pediments develop on the slopes.

of meters of alluvium. Today these alluvial fills are being progressively carried away (Garner, 1967).

Conclusion

For the geomorphologist, who is not concerned purely with dynamic and statistical studies of present-day phenomena, the significance of inherited features in the landscape hardly needs to be stressed. The rills on the slopes of a volcanic ash cone that erupted ten years ago already contain the inherited record of annual variations of climate during that decade. For much of the earth's surface there are inherited features whose evolution exceeds the two-million-year duration of the Quaternary. Hardly anything survives intact. An ancient landscape is rather like the much-canceled postage stamp on a letter that has been repeatedly forwarded. Some of the earlier printing is pretty difficult to decipher. But if we ignore the extraordinarily variegated history of the Quaternary we would lack even the most elementary working hypothesis. The good geomorphologist must, therefore, be a good Quaternary stratigrapher.

RHODES W. FAIRBRIDGE

References

Alimen, H., 1965, "The Quaternary Era in the northwest Sahara," *Geol. Soc. Am. Spec. Paper,* **84,** 273–291.

Alimen, M.-H., 1967, "The Quaternary of France," in (Rankama, K., editor), pp. 89–238, "The Quaternary," vol. 2, New York, Interscience Publishers.

Bacsák, G., 1955, "Pliozän- und Pleistozänzeitalter im Licht der Himmelsmechanik," *Acta Geol. Acad. Sci. Hung.*, **3**, 305–346.

Balchin, W. G. V., 1952, "The evidence for Late Tertiary eustatic changes of sea-level in western Europe," *Proc. I.G.U., 8th Gen. Assembly, Washington*, 296–300.

Banner, F. T., and Blow, W. H., 1965, "Progress in the planktonic foraminiferal biostratigraphy of the Neogene," *Nature*, **206**, 1164–1166.

Beetz, W., 1938, "Klimaschwankungen und Krustenbewegungen in Afrika südlich des Aequators von der Kreidezeit bis zum Diluvium," Hannover, Geogr. Gesellsch., Sonderveröff. **3**, 172pp.

Bigarella, J. J., and de Andrade, G. O., 1965, "Contributions to the study of the Brazilian Quaternary," *Geol. Soc. Am. Spec. Paper* **84**, 444–451.

Bigarella, J. J., and Mousinho, M. R., 1966, "Slope development in southeastern and southern Brazil," *Z. Geomorphol.*, **2**, 150–160.

Broecker, W. S., 1966, "Absolute dating and the astronomical theory of glaciation," *Science*, **151**, (3708), 299–304.

Broecker, W. S., and Thurber, D. L., 1965, "Uranium-series dating of corals and oolites from Bahaman and Florida Key limestones," *Science*, **149**, 58–60.

Broecker, W. S., et al., 1968, "Milankovitch hypothesis supported by precise dating of coral reefs and deep-sea sediments," *Science*, **159**(3812), 297–300.

Butler, B. E., 1967, "Soil Periodicity in Relation to Landform Development in Southeastern Australia," in (Jennings and Mabbutt, editors) "Landform Studies from Australia and New Guinea," pp. 231–255, Canberra, Australian Natl. Univ. Press.

Charlesworth, J. K., 1957, "The Quaternary Era," London, E. Arnold, 2 vols.

Colbert, E. H., et al., 1948, "Pleistocene of the Great Plains," *Bull. Geol. Soc. Am.*, **59**, 541–630.

Cooper, W. S., 1958, "Terminology of post-Valders time," *Bull. Geol. Soc. Am.*, **69**, 941–945.

Cox, A., Doell, R. R., and Dalrymple, G. B., 1964, "Reversals of the earth's magnetic field," *Science*, **144** (3676), 1537–1543.

Curry, R. R., 1966, "Glaciation about 3,000,000 years ago in the Sierra Nevada," *Science*, **154**(3750), 770–771.

Daly, R. A., 1934, "The Changing World of the Ice Age," New Haven, Yale University Press, 271pp.

Deevey, E. S., Jr., 1949, "Biogeography of the Pleistocene," *Bull. Geol. Soc. Am.*, **60**, 1315–1416.

De Jong, J. D., 1967, "The Quaternary of the Netherlands," in (Rankama, K., editor) "The Quaternary," Vol. 2, pp. 301–426, New York, Interscience Publishers.

Desnoyers, J., 1829, "Observations sur un ensemble de depots marins plus recens que les terrains tertiaires du bassin de la Seine…," *Ann. Sci. Nat.*, **16**, 171–214, 402–491.

De Terra, H., 1941, "Pleistocene formations and stone age man in China," *Inst. Geobiol.* (*Pekin*), No. 6, 54pp.

De Terra, H., and Paterson, T. T., 1939, "Studies on the Ice Age in India and associated human cultures," *Carnegie Inst. Wash. Publ.*, **493**, 354pp.

Emiliani, C., 1955, "Pleistocene temperatures," *J. Geol.*, **63**, 538–578.

Emiliani, C., 1968, "The Pleistocene Epoch and the evolution of Man," *Current Anthropology*, **9**(1), 27–47.

Ericson, D. B., and Wollin, G., 1956, "Micropaleontological and isotopic determinations of Pleistocene climate," *Micropaleontology*, **2**, 257–270.

Fairbridge, R. W., 1961a, "Convergence of evidence on climatic change and ice ages," *Ann. N.Y. Acad. Sci.*, **95**(1), 542–579.

Fairbridge, R. W., 1961b, "Eustatic Changes in Sea Level," in "Physics and Chemistry of the Earth," Vol. 4, pp. 99–185, London, Pergamon Press.

Fairbridge, R. W., 1962, "New radiocarbon dates of Nile sediments," *Nature*, **195**, 108–110.

Fairbridge, R. W., 1964a, "The Importance of Limestone and its Ca/Mg Content to Palaeoclimatology," in (Nairn, A.E.M., editor) "Problems in Palaeoclimatology," pp. 431–477, New York, Interscience Publishers.

Fairbridge, R. W., 1964b, "African Ice Age Aridity," in (Nairn, A.E.M., editor), "Problems of Palaeoclimatology," pp. 356–360, New York, Interscience Publishers.

Fairbridge, R. W., 1965, "Eiszeitklima in Nordafrika," *Geol. Rundschau*, **54**(1), 399–414.

Flint, R. F., 1957, "Glacial and Pleistocene Geology," New York, John Wiley & Sons, 553pp.

Flint, R. F., 1965, "The Pliocene-Pleistocene boundary," in (Wright, H. E. and Frey, D. G., editors), "International studies on the Quaternary," *Geol. Soc. Am. Spec. Paper* **84**, 497–533.

Flint, R. F., and Brandtner, F., 1961, "Climatic changes since the last interglacial," *Am. J. Sci.*, **259**, 321–328.

Flint, R. F., and Gale, W. A., 1958, "Stratigraphy and radiocarbon dates at Searles Lake, California," *Am. J. Sci.*, **256**, 689–714.

Flohn, H., 1953, "Studien über die atmosphärische Zirkulation in der letzten Eiszeit," *Erdkunde* (*Bonn*), **7**, 266–275.

Flohn, H., 1963, "Zur meteorologischen Interpretation der pleistozänen Klimaschwankungen," *Eiszeitalter Gegenwart*, **14**, 153–160.

Forbes, E., 1846, "On the connection between the distribution of the existing fauna and flora of the British Isles, and the geological changes which affected their area, especially during the epoch of the Northern Drift," *Geol. Surv. Gt. Brit. Mem.*, **1**, 336–342.

Frechen, J. and Lippolt, H. J., 1965, "Kalium-Argon-Daten zum Alter des Laacher Vulkanismus, der Rheinterrassen und der Eiszeiten," *Eiszeitalter Gegenwart*, **16**, 5–30.

Frye, J. C. and Leonard, A. B., 1965, "Quaternary of the southern Great Plains," in (Wright, H. E. and Frey, D. G., editors), "The Quaternary of the United States," Princeton, N.J., Princeton Univ. Press, 203–216.

Frye, J. C., and Willman, H. B., 1960, "Classification of the Wisconsinan Stage in the Lake Michigan Glacial Lobe," *Illinois State Geol. Surv. Circ.*, **258**, 1–16.

Frye, J. C., and Willman, H. B., 1962, "Morphostratigraphic units in Pleistocene stratigraphy," *Bull. Am. Assoc. Petrol. Geologists*, **46**(1), 112.

Gage, M., 1965, "Accordant and discordant glacial sequences," *Geol. Soc. Am. Spec. Paper* **84**, 393–414.

Ganespin, G. S., et al., 1961, "Volume, contents and nomenclature of stratigraphic subdivisions of the Quaternary system," *Sov. Geol.*, 3–15 (in Russian, with English abstract).

Garner, H. F., 1967, "Rivers in the making," *Sci. Am.*, **216**, 83–94.

Gignoux, M., 1955, "Stratigraphic Geology," San Francisco, W. H. Freeman & Co., 682pp. (translated from French, Fourth ed.).

Gill, E. D., 1957, "The stratigraphical occurrence and palaeoecology of some Australian Tertiary marsupials," *Mem. Nat. Museum Victoria*, **21**, 135–203.

Glass, B., Ericson, D. B., *et al.*, 1967, "Geomagnetic reversals and Pleistocene chronology," *Nature*, **216**, 437–442.

Gromov, V. I., *et al.*, 1960, "Principles of stratigraphic subdivisions of the Quaternary (Anthropogen) system and its lower boundary," *Rept. 21st. Ses. Norden*, 1960, *Copenhagen*.

Gross, H., 1966, "The so-called Göttweig Interstadial of the Würm glaciation," *Current Anthropology*, **7**, 239–243.

Hays, J. D., and Opdyke, N. D., 1967, "Antarctic radiolaria, magnetic reversals, and climate change," *Science*, **158**(3804), 1001–1011.

Heim, A., 1919, "Geologie der Schweiz," Leipzig, C. H. Tauchnitz, 2 vols.

Holmes, A., 1965, "Principles of Physical Geology," Second ed., London, T. Nelson & Sons; New York, Ronald Press, Co., 1288pp.

Hopkins, D. L., *et al.*, 1965, "Quaternary correlations across Bering Strait," *Science*, **147**, 1107–1114.

Karlstrom, T. N. V., 1961, "The glacial history of Alaska: its bearing on paleoclimatic theory," *Ann. N.Y. Acad. Sci.*, **95**, Art. 1, 290–340.

Kay, G. F., 1931, "Classification and duration of the Pleistocene period," *Bull. Geol. Soc. Am.*, **42**, 425–466.

Kay, G. F., and Leighton, M. M., 1933, "Eldoran epoch of the Pleistocene period," *Bull. Geol. Soc. Am.*, **44**, 669–674.

King, W. B. R., 1950, "The Pliocene–Pleistocene boundary: introduction," *Intern. Geol. Congr. (18th, London, 1948)*, Pt. 9, 5.

Klute, F., 1948, "Die Bedeutung der Depression der Schnee grenze für eiszeitliche Probleme," *Z. Gletscherk.*, **16**.

Krivan, P., 1955, "La division climatologique de pleistocène en Europe Centrale et le profil de loess de Paks," *Ann. Inst. Geol. Publici. Hung.*, **43**, 363–512.

Ku, T.-L., and Broecker, W. S., 1966, "Atlantic deep-sea stratigraphy: extension of absolute chronology to 320,000 years," *Science*, **151**(3709), 448–450.

Kukla, J., Ložek, V., and Záruba, Q., 1961, "Zur Stratigraphie der Lösse in der Tschechoslowakei," *Quartär (Bonn)*, **13**, 1–29.

LeConte, J., 1877, "On critical periods in the history of the Earth and their relation to evolution; and on the Quaternary as such a period," *Am. J. Sci.*, **14**(3), 99–114.

Leighton, M. M., 1958, "Principles and viewpoints in formulating the stratigraphic classifications of the Pleistocene," *J. Geol.*, **66**(6), 700–709.

Leverett, F., 1898, "The weathered zone (Sangamon) between the Iowan loess and Illinoian till sheet," *J. Geol.*, **6**, 238–243.

Leverett, F., 1930, "Relative length of Pleistocene glacial and interglacial stages," *Science*, **72**, 193–195.

Ložek, V., 1965, "The relationship between the development of soils and faunas in the warm Quaternary phases," *Anthropozoikum (Prague)*, **3**, 7–51.

Lüttig, G., 1965, "Interglacial and interstadial periods," *J. Geol.*, **73**(4), 579–591.

Lyell, C., 1830–33, "Principles of Geology," London, J. Murray, 3 vols.

Lyell, C., 1839, "Nouveaux éléments de geologie," Paris, Pitois-Levrault, 648pp.

Lyell, C., 1873, "The Geological Evidences of the Antiquity of Man," Fourth ed., London, J. Murray, 572pp.

Martin, P. S., and Mehringer, P. J., Jr., 1965, "Pleistocene pollen analysis and biogeography of the Southwest, U.S.A., in (Wright and Frey, editors) "Quaternary of the United States," pp. 433–451, Princeton, N.J., Princeton University Press.

McIntyre, A., 1967, "Coccoliths as paleoclimatic indicators of Pleistocene glaciation," *Science*, **158**(3806), 1314–1317.

McLean, J. D., Jr., 1966, "Miocene and Pleistocene foraminifera and ostracoda of southeastern Virginia," *Virginia Div. Mineral Resources Rept. Invest.*, **9**.

Milankovich, M., 1941, "Kanon der Erdbestrahlung und seine Anwendung auf das Eiszeitenproblem," *Acad. Roy. Serbe* (Belgrade), Ed. sp. vol. **133**, Sect. Sci. Math. Nat. no. 33.

Morlot, A. von, 1856, "Notice sur la Quaternaire en Suisse," *Bull. Soc. Vaudoise Sci. Nat.*, **4**, 41–45.

Morrison, R. B., 1966, "Predecessors of Great Salt Lake," in "The Great Salt Lake," *Utah Geol. Guidebook*, **20**, 77–104.

Morrison, R. B., *et al.*, 1957, "In behalf of the Recent," *Am. J. Sci.*, **255**, 385–393.

Movius, H. L., Jr., 1949, "Villafranchian stratigraphy in southern and southwestern Europe," *J. Geol.*, **57**, 380–413.

Nilsson, E., 1940, "Ancient changes of climate in British East Africa and Abyssinia," *Geog. Ann.*, **22**, 1–79.

Oakley, K. P., 1964, "Frameworks for dating fossil man," London, Weidenfeld and Nicolson, 355pp.

Paterson, T. T., 1941, "On a world correlation of the Pleistocene," *Trans. Roy. Soc. Edinburgh*, **60**(11), 373–425.

Pécsi, M., 1964, "Ten Years of Physico-geographic Research in Hungary," Budapest, Akad. Kiado, 132pp.

Penck, A., 1914, "The shifting of the climatic belts," *Scot. Geog. Mag.*, **30**, 281–293.

Penck, A., 1921, "Die Höttinger Breccie und die Inntalterrasse nördlich Innsbruck," *Pruess. Akad. Wiss. (Berlin)*, *Abh. 1920, Phys.-math. Kl.*, No. 2, 136pp.

Penck, A., and Brückner, E., 1909, "Die Alpen im Eiszeitalter," Leipzig, Tauchnitz, 3 vols., 1199pp.

Phillips, J., 1841, "Figures and descriptions of the Palaeozoic fossils of Cornwall, Devon, and west Somerset," *Geol. Surv. Mem. London*, 231pp.

Picard, L., 1965, "The geological evolution of the Quaternary in the central-northern Jordan Graben, Israel," *Geol. Soc. Am. Spec. Paper* **84**, 337–366.

Pilgrim, G. E., 1944, "The lower limit of the Pleistocene in Europe and Asia," *Geol. Mag.*, **81**, 28–38.

Ramsay, A. C., 1852, "On the superficial accumulations and surface markings of North Wales," *Geol. Soc. London, Quart. J.*, **8**, 371–376.

Ray, L. L., 1949, "Problems of Pleistocene stratigraphy," *Bull. Geol. Soc. Am.*, **60**, 1463–1474.

Reboul, H., 1833, "Géologie de la Période Quaternaire, et Introduction à l'Histoire Ancienne," Paris, Levrault, 222pp.

Richmond, G. M., 1965, "Glaciation of the Rocky Mountains," in (Wright and Frey, editors) "Quaternary of the United States," pp. 217–230, Princeton, N.J., Princeton University Press.

Rosholt, J. N., et al., 1962, "P^{231}/Th^{230} dating and O^{18}/O^{16} temperature analysis of core A254-Br-C.," *J. Geophys. Res.*, **67**, 2907–2911.

Ruggieri, G., and Selli, R., 1948, "Il Pliocene e il postpliocene dell "Emilia," *Giorn. Geol. Ann. Museo. Geol. Bologna Ser.* 3, **20** (English summary in *J. Geol.*, **60**, 496).

Rutten, M. G., and Wensink, H., 1960, "Paleomagnetic dating, glaciation and the chronology of the Plio-Pleistocene in Iceland," *Rept. Int. Geol. Congr., 21st Copenhagen*, **4**, 62–70.

Schou, A., 1965, "Klimatisk geomorfologi," *Saertryk Geogr. Tids.*, **64**, 129–161.

Schultz, C. B., and Stout, T. M., 1948, "Pleistocene mammals and terraces in the Great Plains," *Bull. Geol. Soc. Am.*, **59**, 553–588.

Soergel, W., 1919, "Lösse, Eiszeiten und paläolithische Kulturen, Eine Gliederung und Altersbestimmung der Lösse," Jena, G. Fischer, 177pp.

Soergel, W., 1924, "Die diluvialen Terrassen der Ilm und ihre Bedeutung für die Gliederung des Eiszeitalters," Jena, G. Fischer, 79pp.

Stacey, C. M., 1963, "Cyclical measures—some tidal aspects concerning equinoctal years," *Ann. N.Y. Acad. Sci.*, **105**, Art. 8.

Svoboda, J., et al.,1966, "Regional geology of Czechoslovakia. I. The Bohemian Massif," *Prague, Geol. Surv.* (Czech. Acad. Sci.).

Taylor, D. W., 1966, "Summary of North American Blancan nonmarine mollusks," *Malacologia*, **4**, 1–172.

Tricart, J., 1965, "Le modelé des régions chaudes, forêts et savanes," Traité de Géomorphologie, Vol. 5, Paris, Sedes, 322pp.

Van der Hammen, T., and Gonzalez, E., 1964, "A pollen diagram from the Quaternary of the Sabana de Bogota (Colombia) and its significance for the geology of the northern Andes," *Geol. Mijnbouw*, **43**, 113–117.

Van der Vlerk, J. M., and Florschütz, F., 1950, "Nederland in het Ijstijdvak," Utrecht.

Van Zinderen Bakker, E. M., 1967, "Palynology and stratigraphy in sub-Saharan Africa," in (Bishop, W. W. and Clark, J. D., editors), "Background to Evolution in Africa," pp. 371–374, Chicago, Univ. Chicago Press. (See also Clark, J. D., 1967, "Atlas of African Prehistory," Univ. Chicago Press.)

Von Klebelsberg, R., 1935, "Geologie von Tirol," Berlin, Borntraeger, 872pp.

West, R. G., and Wilson, D. G., 1966, "Cromer Forest Bed series," *Nature*, **209**(5022), 297–298.

Wilmarth, M. G., 1925, "Geologic time classification," *Bull. U.S. Geol. Surv.*, **769**, 138pp.

Wirtz, D., and Illies, H., 1951, "Lower Pleistocene stratigraphy and the Plio-Pleistocene boundary in northwestern Germany," *J. Geol.*, **59**, 463–471.

Woldstedt, P.,1953, "Über die Benennung einiger Unterabteilungen des Pleistozäns," *Eiszeitalter Gegenwart*, **3**, 14–17.

Woldstedt, P., 1958–65, "Das Eiszeitalter," Stuttgart, Enke Verlag, 3 vols.

Zagwijn, W. H., 1963, "Pleistocene stratigraphy in the Netherlands, based on changes in vegetation and climate," *Geol. Surv. Neth.*, 173–196.

Zeuner, F. E., 1959, "The Pleistocene Period; Its Climate, Chronology and Faunal Successions," London, Hutchinson & Co., 447pp (Second revised ed. of 1945 work).

Cross-references: *Atolls; Braided Stream; Coral Reefs; Continental Erosion; Denudation; Glacial Lakes; Holocene; Indicator Boulder; Loess; Moraine; Periglacial Eolian Effects; Periglacial Landscapes; Pluvial Lakes; Terraces, Fluvial—Environmental Controls; Terraces —Thalassostatic; Tropical Weathering and Relief.* Vol. I: *Mid-Oceanic Ridge.* Vol. II: *Climatic Optimum; Climatic Retardation; Ice Age Meteorology; Ice Age Theory.* Vol. VI: *Diluvial Theory; Paleosols;* pr Vol. VII: *Anthropology, Geological; Archeology, Prehistoric; Paleontology; Palynology; Periglacial Stratigraphy; Tephrochronology; Varve Chronology.*

QUICKCLAY—*See* pr Vol. VI

QUICKSAND—*See* pr Vol. VI

R

RADAR SCANNING IN GEOSCIENCES—*See* pr Vol. VI

RAINWASH—*See* SHEET EROSION, SHEET-WASH, RAINWASH, SHEETFLOOD; SLOPES

REEF—*See* CORAL REEF

REFUGIA—*See* GLACIAL REFUGES

REGIONS, NATURAL AND GEOGRAPHICAL

The English term *region* has evolved through Old French from the Latin *regio*, which meant at first "direction" but soon was extended to mean "limit" and "area." At present the term means "area" or "space," i.e., it may refer to a two-dimensional or three-dimensional concept.

In geography the term has been used in the sense of "definite area" or "functional area"—almost irrespective of magnitude. The first discussion of the subject is due to Herbertson (1905) who coined the expression "major natural regions," which implies the existence of "minor" regions and also of other regions besides the "natural" ones. The determination of orders of magnitude among regions was recognized as a problem. As to the aspects to be considered,

"Configuration is necessarily the framework, but we must not think of it merely as a more or less irregular surface; we must see it as part of a solid which comprises not merely the soil beneath, but the air above, with relations to other parts of the earth, and also to the influences coming from outside the earth. This gives a movement, a life to the whole. . . .

"The facts of configuration and of climate are of first importance, but the distribution of vegetation, and even of man, may also profitably be examined" (Herbertson, 1905).

Of *configuration*, Herbertson takes the horizontal and vertical extension (lowland to 200 meters, upland 200–1000 meters, highland above 1000 meters, with perhaps a distinction above 2000 meters) and the morphological structure (young folded mountains, tablelands and plat-

forms, denudation highlands and plains, and elevated and lower accumulation lands). Of *climate*, he takes the isotherms of 0, 10 and 20°C for the coldest month and 10 and 20°C for the warmest month. As to rainfall, he obtains

". . . the differentiation of regions which receive sufficient rainfall at none or one or more seasons, and the comparison between those regions where the rainfall is precipitated when temperature conditions are most and least favourable.

"If the existing plant-covering of the earth is mapped, then the influence of man is a third factor, which in most botanic maps is eliminated. . . ."

It is a pity that Herbertson did not proceed to analyze human factors for the purpose of regional classification, even though he was aware of "the importance of the human factor" because "each geographical region has its potentialities as well as its actualities. . . ."

It is an even greater pity that Herbertson limited himself to dividing the earth into *types* of natural regions (15 at first, later increased to 20), most of which in fact are geographical *zones* (q.v. Vol. II). He was aware of the hierarchy of magnitude, even though he was hampered by the lack of a systematic vocabulary, when he wrote that "knowing each of the chief types, it is a simple matter to learn the peculiarities of each variety. . . ."

Herbertson's method was *analytical*—from the study of the geographical distribution of the relevant elements over the globe, through their super-imposition and combination, the regions would result.

Hettner (1908) followed a different approach and recognized 42 distinct regions, mostly based on morphological characters. A similar method was adopted by Banse (1912) who recognized 12 regions comprising 60 subregions. Neither author attempted to show any world pattern in the location of these regions. Unstead (1916) advocated a more minute and deliberately synthetic method, beginning with the study of the smallest geographical units (cf., *Landscape*) which could be grouped to form regions of a higher order of magnitude, but he did not provide any example.

In 1948, however, Unstead produced a small world map in which he showed 12 regional types [zones] comprising 72 actual regions based on climate, morphology and human occupation.

Graphic syntheses of seasonal rhythms are shown for insolation, temperature and rainfall, streams if relevant, vegetation, cultivation of the soil, crops, sowing or harvesting, domestic animals, if any, and hired labor where required.

Biasutti (1962), beginning with climatic zones and adding vegetational and morphological criteria, arrived at 11 climatic regional types subdivided into 34 actual regions and 128 landscapes. His maps form the most detailed series published within one book.

There has been controversy on the use of the term "natural" applied to these world regions. The term is quite apt provided it is understood to mean the complex of natural elements that constitute the physical and biotic environment, i.e., to the exclusion of man-made elements (although not necessarily of "man as an animal"). "Natural" is not synonymous with "primeval"—the simple omission of the human element from a region does not restitute the region to its primeval state, which only painstaking paleogeographical research can hope to reconstruct. In fact, a "natural" region is a theoretical abstraction; it may be very convenient for teaching purposes, as Herbertson, the first propounder of "natural regions," clearly stated in his original (1905) paper. The German antinomy is "natural" and "cultural," and this was widely accepted by geographers in the United States (cf. discussion in Hartshorne, 1939, pp. 250–365). In Britain it was due to Unstead (1916) that the expression "geographical regions" found wider acceptance. (For a fuller discussion of the problems of areal classification, see *Landscape* in this volume and *Zone* in Vol. II).

J. GENTILLI

References

Banse, E., 1912, "Geographie," *Peterm. Mitt.*, **58**, 69ff.

Berg, L. S., 1958, "Die geographischen Zonen der Sowjetunion," Vol. 1, Leipzig.

Biasutti, R., 1962, "Il paesaggio terrestre," Torino.

Hartshorne, R., 1939, "The Nature of Geography," Lancaster, Pa.

Hassinger, H., 1933, "Die Geographie des Menschen," in (Klute, F., editor) "Handbuch der geographischen Wissenschaft," Potsdam.

Herbertson, A. J., 1905, "The major natural regions: An essay in systematic geography," *Geograph J.*, **25**, 300–312.

Herbertson, A. J., 1912, "The thermal regions of the globe," *Geograph. J.*, **40**, 518–532.

Hettner, A., 1908, "Geographishe Einteilung der Erdoberfläche," *Geogr. Z.*, **14**, 1–137.

James, P. E., "The terminology of regional description," *Ann. Assoc. Am. Geogr.* **24**, 78–92.

Unstead, J. F., 1916, "A synthetic method of determining geographical regions," *Geograph. J.*, **48**, 230.

Unstead, J. F., 1948, "A World Survey from the Human Aspect," London.

Cross-references: *Landscape—Geographical*. Vol. II: *Climatic Classification*; *Zone—Climatic*.

REGOLITH AND SAPROLITE

The loose, unconsolidated material on the surface of the earth's crust is popularly referred to as "soil," but agriculturalists and pedologists have developed special definitions of soil (see articles on *Pedology*, in pr Vol. VI) that make it an unsuitable term for precise geomorphic and geological descriptions. Two terms regolith and saprolite, have been proposed with appropriately precise definitions and are properly distinct, though some writers in the past have confused them. The oldest of the two is *saprolite*, a term restricted to rotted or weathered rock (*in situ*), while regolith covers the entire soil mantling material, including saprolite, *colluvium* (q.v.), solifluction material, eolian wedges, paleosol and modern soil. The term "mantle" is often used formally instead of regolith, but this is to be deprecated, because this term is reserved to that part of the earth that lies between the core and the crust; thus "mantle" should *not* be used as a synonym for regolith, although a definition as used above employing the phrase "mantling material" is unobjectionable. In detail, the origin and use of these terms is as follows:

Saprolite

Based upon the Greek *sapros* (rotten) proposed by G. F. Becker (1895), saprolite (or rarely, "saprolith") refers to rock rotted *in situ*, i.e., chemically altered, but coherent and not texturally disintegrated.

The term "saprolith" has sometimes been used for sapropelic rocks, asphaltites and related petroleum (see Pettijohn, 1957, p. 489); this should be avoided. The spelling "sathrolith" of Sederholm (1931) is also undesirable.

The definition of saprolite implies that chemical components have been removed by groundwater during the weathering process (Clarke, 1910), but that interstitial grain relations are undisturbed. Saprolite is often equivalent to the *C-horizon* of pedology. An ideal place to study saprolite is in a long-stable region that has not been glaciated or stripped by sub-tropical rains in a semiarid region; the disintegration process is most apparent in metamorphic and igneous rocks. Climatically such regions are the humid subtropics and equatorial regions. An area of this sort is the Piedmont uplands of the Appalachians (Cady, 1950), where complex bedding, folds and faults with intersecting dikes in the early Paleozoic and Precambrian metamorphic rocks are still faithfully preserved although it is possible to cut the saprolite with a spade or a pocket knife. If its origin can be clearly identified, the residual may be referred to as "granite saprolite," "basalt saprolite," etc. The feldspars and micas are largely reduced to clays, kaolinite and so on, though quartz grains often remain more or less intact. The sequence of chemical weathering in the more common rock-forming silicate minerals is: nephelene, leucite, olivine, sodic feldspars, augite, hornblende, biotite, calcic feldspars, alkali feldspars, muscovite and finally quartz.

Gemstones (e.g., emeralds and rubies in Burma and Ceylon, diamonds in Africa, etc.) are often worked in old saprolites because they are not weathered while their original enclosing rock is now quite soft and easily worked. In the same way, tin (as cassiterite) is contained in the granite saprolites of Malaya, Indonesia and Australia. Often the saprolites have been eroded and the precious (heavy) minerals further concentrated by running water, as alluvial "placer deposits." The term "eluvium" has the meaning of a leached residual and has also been applied to placer deposits due to rock rotting *in situ* (e.g., Purington, 1905), but the term has not found favor because it is so liable to confusion in speech with "alluvium." Other ores sometimes mined in saprolite include: gold, kyanite, graphite, tantalite and monazite. Kaolinite is often sufficiently pure to be dug for china clay.

In the tropics, the thickness of saprolite frequently exceeds 100 meters, and may reach 200 meters. Leopold, Wolman and Miller (1964, p. 124) show "depth of weathering" to 390 feet. The figures are minimal, because the deepest profiles (beneath river-beds) are rarely disclosed. This fact, together with the slight reworking of the soft surface layers and the formation of "iron-bound" crusts, is a major one in keeping tropical regions economically backward because geologists cannot easily map or gain access to the unaltered bedrock.

A classical sketch made by Walther (1924) in the Precambrian shield of Western Australia showed an ancient quartz dike penetrating a laterite, thus proving that this particular laterite was a saprolite, rotted *in situ* (Fig. 1). Considerable controversies have existed about laterites, because some are obviously transported; others are silicified or otherwise recemented as paleosol crusts. The term *laterite* simply refers to a material consisting largely of sesquioxides of iron (and often alumina) with varying quantities of residual, unweathered, quartz grains and other relatively insoluble minerals. It is derived mainly from the weathering of granite, basaltic and metamorphic terrains or shales; quartzose sandstones or pure limestones, because of their composition, do not furnish laterites.

The alumina-rich laterite is bauxite, the principal ore of aluminum and shows the same characteristics. The nickel ores of New Caledonia occur in a *nickeliferous laterite*. Because of the oxidation of iron and alumina in saprolites, the color of these residual rocks is generally red to yellow (Russell, 1889).

FIG. 1. Laterite profile with a hard ferruginous (ferricrete) crust (1), passing down into a ferruginous pisolite or concretionary zone (2), then a "spotted zone" (3) of residual clay, a "bleached zone" (4) of weathered but partially preserved rock, and (5) the fresh crystalline rocks of the Precambrian basement. An ancient quartz dike (6) penetrates the entire sequence and thus proves that the overlying soil is saprolite, rotted *in situ*. A former stream filling (of Tertiary age) with fluvial gravels (7) is also involved in the saprolitic process and subsequent duricrust development (from sketch by Walther, 1924).

Related to saprolite are varied sorts of *residual soil* ("*regosol*" of pedologists). This term usually refers to a soil that is concentrated *in situ*, the best-known example being *terra rossa* which is widespread in regions of Mediterranean-type climates (first applied by Neumayr, 1886, Vol. I, p. 405); transitions into laterite are known. In the classical karst country of the Yugoslav Adriatic, the terra rossa often fills crevices and depressions of the limestone surface. Here it represents the insoluble residues of limestone solution (possibly only 2–5% of the original bulk). In the valleys and piedmont foothills, the terra rossa is washed down as colluvium or alluvium, and is then no longer a residual soil, but a transported soil.

Another important residual is the *quartz sand* that commonly occurs on coastal plains, from which all soluble material such as calcium carbonate shells, calcareous eolianite, beachrock and so on, have been leached; the resultant residual sands may be *in situ*, but lacking cementing media, are liable to removal or redistribution by wind, slope wash, stream and waves, and in consequence often form a residual blanket, the origin of which is hard to designate precisely. Even one clay may be altered to another in this process; thus the montmorillonites of the Pliocene of Florida are being altered to kaolinites (Altschuler, Dwornik and Kramer, 1963). The geomorphic results are important, because there is mass loss, and where the rock is a sandy clay, the quartz sand will eventually be concentrated as a residual.

Regolith

Based upon the Greek *regos* (blanket) and *lithos* (stone), the term regolith embraces the entire mantling cover of unconsolidated material on the surface of the earth's crust regardless of origin. (The spelling "rhegolith" is seldom used.) Regolith was proposed by Merrill (1897, p. 299), who recognized both transported and *in situ* or "sedentary" types, as follows (with comments by the writer):

(a) *Sedentary* or *in situ regolith*: (*i*) Residual Deposits—lag gravels, residual sands and clays, grits, laterite, bauxite, terra rossa. These include, therefore, *saprolite* (though Merrill did not like the term).

(*ii*) Cumulative ("cumulose") Deposits—peaty, humic and swampy soils, organic accumulations (gyttja, dy, etc.); the term "muck" employed by Merrill is highly undesirable for general organic-rich soil since it is commonly applied to agricultural farmyard manure. Lacustrine deposits are not to be included in this group, except on a minute scale.

(b) *Transported Regolith*: (*i*) Colluvial Deposits—scree, talus and cliff debris, avalanche, mudslide, rockslide, and landslide debris; *grèzes litées* (bedded, and partly cemented talus debris and soil); appreciably displaced solifluction material (at the foot of slopes).

(*ii*) Alluvial Deposits—modern alluvium (but not ancient alluvium, which constitutes distinct stratigraphic formations), including such aqueoglacial (fluvioglacial) deposits as outwash sands (sandur) and piedmont gravels.

(*iii*) Eolian Deposits—wind-blown accumulations, sand dunes, parna ("adobe") and loess (each treated separately in this Encyclopedia Series).

(*iv*) *Glacial Deposits* (q.v.)—morainal material, till or boulder clay ("drift"), drumlins, kames, eskers, etc. (each treated separately). A transition from eskers to outwash sand and gravel [see (*ii*)] is often found.

Merrill (1897, p. 300) points out that the upper part of the regolith generally corresponds to the *soil* of agriculturalists, as that part that supports plant life, providing nutrients and foothold; however, long roots penetrate deep into the regolith and pedologists speak of the "C-horizon" which specifically corresponds to saprolite (sometimes called "subsoil") so that there is hardly any part of the regolith that does not as a rule correspond to the soil of pedology. It should be stressed that it is the biological production of CO_2 by plants and soil bacteria that plays a major role in the weathering of the regolith, so that there is a high degree of mutual interdependence.

The term *head* (q.v.) is widely used in England and France for regolith, which, because of its geographic situation, usually contains transported saprolite and solifluction debris.

The term *grus* of German origin is applied there to both rock-rotted debris and mechanical weathering detritus such as products of exfoliation (desquamation), *frost disintegration, salt weathering* (q.v.; see also *Tafoni*); it has sometimes been used in American literature. Also used some-times in the last century was *geest* (a word adopted by de Luc and favored by McGee, 1891, p. 279), another Germanic term referring to high gravelly land (lag gravels), a bouldery till, a saprolite, and thus rather specifically the gravelly or gritty varieties of regolith. The old Celtic word *growan* is sometimes used in Britain, likewise *grouan* in France, generally meaning a fine gravelly grit, without genetic connotation.

RHODES W. FAIRBRIDGE

References

Altschuler, Z. S., Dwornik, E. J., and Kramer, H., 1963, "Transformation of montmorillonite to kaolinite during weathering," *Science*, **141**(3576), 148–152.

Becker, G. F., 1895, *U.S. Geol. Surv., 16th Ann. Rept.*, Pt. III.

Cady, J. G., 1950, "Rock weathering and soil formation in the North Carolina Piedmont region," *Proc. Soil Sci. Soc. Am.*, **15**, 337–342.

Clarke, F. W., 1910, "A preliminary study of chemical denudation," *Smithsonian Misc. Coll.*, **56**(5), 1–10.

Guillien, Y., 1951, "Les grèzes litées de Charente," *Rev. Géogr. Pyrenees S.O.*, **22**, 154–162.

Hosterman, J. W., *et al.* 1960, "Investigations of some clay deposits in Washington and Idaho," *U.S. Geol. Surv. Bull.*, **1091**.

Keller, W. D., 1955, "Principles of Chemical Weathering," Columbia, Mo., Lucas Bros., Publ., 88pp.

Leith, C. J., and Craig, R. M., 1965, "Mineralogic trends induced by deep residual weathering," *Am. Mineralogist*, **50**(11/12), 1959–1971.

Leopold, L. B., Wolman, M. G., and Miller, J. P., 1964, "Fluvial Processes in Geomorphology," San Francisco, W. H. Freeman and Co., 522pp.

McGee, W J, 1891, *U.S. Geol. Surv., 11th Ann. Rept.* (for 1889–90), 189–577.

Merrill, G. P., 1897, "A Treatise on Rocks, Rock-weathering and Soils," New York, Macmillan, 411pp.

Minard, J. P., 1959, "Recent saprolite," *Science*, **129**, 1206–1209.

Neumayr, M., 1886, "Erdgeschichte," Leipzig, Bibl. Inst., 2 vols., (Second ed., 1895).

Pettijohn, F. J., 1957, "Sedimentary Rocks," Second ed., New York, Harper Bros., 718pp.

Purington, C. W., 1905, "Methods and costs of gravel and placer mining in Alaska," *U.S. Geol. Surv. Bull.*, **263**, 273pp.

Reiche, P., 1945, "Survey of weathering processes and products," Albuquerque, *Univ. New Mexico, Publ. Ser. Geol.*, **1**.

Russell, I. C., 1889, "Subaerial decay of rocks and origin of the red color of certain formations," *U.S. Geol. Surv. Bull.*, **52**.

Sederholm, J. J., 1931, "On the sub-Bothnian unconformity and on Archaean rocks formed by secular weathering," *Bull. Comm. Géol. Finlande*, **95**, 1–81.

Trefethen, J. M., 1959, "Geology for Engineers," Second edition, New York, Van Nostrand, 632pp.

Tricart, 1965, "Morphogénèse et pédogénèse. I, Approche méthodologique," *Science du Sol.*, **1**, 69–85.

Walther, J., 1924, "Das Gesetz der Wüstenbildung," Fourth ed., Leipzig, Quelle and Meyer, 421pp.

Cross-references: *Alluvium*; *Colluvium*; *Corrosion*; *Duricrust*; *Exfoliation*; *Frost Action*; *Glacial Deposits*; *Head*, *Eluvium*; *Loess*; *Mass Wasting*; *Moraine*; *Salt Weathering*; *Sand Dunes*; *Solifluction*; *Tafoni*; *Talus, Scree and Cliff Debris*; *Weathering*. pr Vol. IV: *Bauxite*; *Laterite*; *Placer Deposits*. pr Vol. VI: *Paleosol*; *Parna*; *Pedology*; *Terra Rossa*.

REJUVENATION—*See* RIVERS

RELICT LANDFORMS

Relict landforms are those developed by erosive processes (*morphogenetic systems*) no longer operating. In many cases, but not invariably, such development has taken place in a climate no longer prevailing (*paleoclimate*). Generally speaking, relict forms do not make up entirely relict landscapes but survive side-by-side with forms that are currently developing. While French- and English-speaking geomorphologists use the description "relict," most German authors call these forms "fossil." This is an unfortunate usage, as "fossil" implies burial and is strictly applicable only to exhumed forms.

Of all the continents, Africa best exhibits the effects of north and south *secular migration of the climatic zones* (Büdel, 1957, 1963a; Fairbridge, 1964). This has brought extensive regions alternately into the zone of intense chemical weathering, at present limited to an equatorial rain forest belt

of moderate width and the bordering savanna zones with longer annual dry seasons, and into the domain of dominant mechanical weathering and erosion. Though morphogenetic systems dominated by these processes are especially characteristic of cool regions, mechanical erosion is particularly important also in the zones bordering the hot-humid zone of chemical dominance, especially in the hot-dry zones of semiarid pedimentation, but to some extent also in the dry-desert core regions within these. In these last, however, mechanical erosion is slowed down by scarcity of running water, though wind takes the place of water to some extent as a sculpturing agent. As these zones are dominated by contrasting landscape-shaping systems, transference of a region from one zone to another substitutes one system for another, and since transformation of landscapes is generally a slow process, relict land forms and even relict landscapes may be recognizable. Büdel (1963b, p. 286) claims indeed that "almost everywhere ... fossil [i.e., relict] land forms occupy a far greater area than the land forms developed by currently active processes." Overprinting of landscape types will, however, blur the picture considerably if the climate has changed more than once.

In the hot-humid equatorial belt in particular, the morphogenetic system differs in practically every respect from that commonly termed "normal," or rain-and-river erosion. The peculiarities of river behavior in the hot-humid belt result from

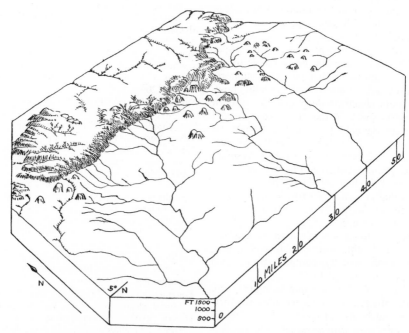

Fig. 1. Landscape of plain and inselbergs in coastal Ghana, bordering a little-dissected ancient plateau (after R. W. Clayton).

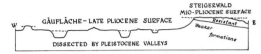

FIG. 2. Two ancient (late Tertiary) upland surfaces in Franconia which are relict forms if they were developed either in "savanna" cycles or by pediplanation. They are dissected by valleys which were initiated by river erosion in the Pleistocene.

very thorough *chemical decay of the regolith* and dominance of chemical weathering over mechanical weathering. Decay of the rocks, while involving removal of material in solution, leaves a solid residue consisting of fine particles, to the exclusion of rock fragments and mineral particles such as would make river gravel and coarse sand, so that running water is deprived of these tools of erosion. Streams fail to corrade laterally and even vertically, and it follows that they remain ungraded. This applies to both small streams and large rivers, which flow alike in sluggish swampy reaches separated by falls and rapids (Tricart and Cailleux, 1965, pp. 16–21). They continue to occupy courses determined in the remote past by tectonic and structural accidents (Tricart, 1956, p. 305). Such are the rivers of the African equatorial zone (and also those of equatorial South America, notably the great tributaries of the Amazon). A contrary view is expressed by Garner (1966), whose explanation of the relief of the land and anastomosing and ungraded courses of rivers in the Orinoco basin invokes active mechanical erosion. Falls and ungraded river courses are, according to him, by no means sempiternal but are being rapidly eliminated. Land relief that conditioned the infantile drainage of a current fluvial cycle, and still survives in relict landscape forms, developed under aridity in the last of a "sequence of alternating arid and humid climates." (See *Tropical Weathering and Relief*.)

Throughout most of Africa, excluding the extreme north and south, an ungraded condition of the rivers persists. In some regions not definitely bounded this state is relict from the Pleistocene or even earlier. These were times when the equatorial zone of dominant chemical weathering was much broader than it now is and bordering climatic zones were poleward of their present positions.

At such times, much development of the "savanna" landscape type took place (plains and inselbergs, Fig. 1) in the extended hot-humid zone, whether by the "wash" mechanism advocated by Büdel (Cotton, 1961) or the "old-from-birth" mechanism of Louis (Cotton, 1962). Being a stable form when once developed, it is now in many places relict. Such planation is developing widely at present throughout the hot-humid monsoon rain forest region of southeast Asia, but in southern India (Cotton, 1947, Fig. 31) the landscape of plains and inselbergs seems to be relict. A far northerly extension of the hot-humid zone of plain-and-inselberg development in the latter part of the Tertiary era is believed by some authors (cf. Büdel, 1963b, p. 279; hypothesis foreshadowed by Jessen and advocated also by Louis) to explain the origin of the summit and other high-level "peneplain" remnants in Europe (Fig. 2), which if so explained are relict features. If, however, as some geomorphologists believe, some are early Tertiary pediplains of semiarid erosion, these also are relict.

If, on the other hand, the later Tertiary "peneplains" are relics of true (Davisian) peneplains that were produced by erosive processes still operating (Baulig, 1957, p. 925), they are not, strictly speaking, relict forms. So also, if such forms have been developed, as Hack (1960) has argued, by secular noncyclic denudation controlled by structure, they result from processes still operating and are not relict.

If any summit "peneplain" remnants are relics

FIG. 3. Progressive replacement of a relict coarse-texture hilly landscape (with low drainage density) by fine-textured dissection (with high drainage density) (as in Hokkaido, Japan) generalized from vertical photographs.

of desert plains developed, as Davis (1905) supposed possible, in the "arid cycle," they are then relict, though criteria for the recognition of such are doubtful. Remnants of other features recognizable as due to former desert erosion, outside the actual deserts of today, are rare because of the destructive activity of the running-water processes now operating, both pediplanation and dissection by rivers. In some arid deserts, however, organized systems of valleys and divides recognizable as due to river erosion are present, notably in the Atacama Desert, South America. These must be relict. In the Ahaggar (Hoggar), the mountainous heart of the Sahara Desert, as Büdel (1955) has shown, remnants of an erosion plain that has been uplifted occur and are relict, for the surface was developed by humid-tropical planation and it still carries, preserved under basalt flows, some of the red regolith characteristically produced by weathering in a hot climate with wet and dry seasons. Its relation to periods of volcanism dates this surface as Tertiary, however. Besides this there are some relict forms that are much younger, being referable to a mid-Pleistocene climatic oscillation toward humidity. These are valley-side debris slopes leading down to valley plains aggraded with sand and silt that have been converted into terraces by relatively modern vertical incision of stream courses.

In the Pleistocene, the semiarid zones characterized by pediplanation moved to and fro across Africa, accounting for relict occurrences of pediments and pediplains, e.g., in the Nubian Desert.

Extensive pediments in Spain are relict forms dating from the late Tertiary, when climatic zones were far poleward of their present positions. Downstepping pediments in northernmost Africa are also regarded as relict, dating, it is believed, from successive glacial ages, when pluvial conditions prevailed in that region, causing a very abundant supply of coarse rock waste.

In high and middle latitudes, swinging of climatic zone boundaries has brought about alternation of humid-temperate and arctic conditions. Features produced by *glaciation*, such as cirques, arêtes, trough valleys, roches moutonnées, eskers, drumlins, and moraines survive as relict forms in

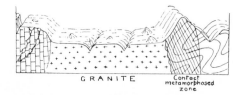

FIG. 4. Advanced stage of differential erosion in a hot-dry climate. Planation on granite while limestone (left) remains in high relief. After a change of climate to humid-temperate the landforms on both granite and limestone will be relict (after P. Birot).

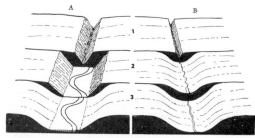

FIG. 5. Stages (1, 2, 3) in the development of a "normally eroded" flat-floored valley (A) contrasted with those of the cryergic-fluvial valleys developing in northeast Spitsbergen and perhaps relict in some middle-latitude regions (B).

some otherwise normally dissected landscapes. So also do the somewhat less spectacular but very common features produced by the periglacial processes, frost weathering (gelivation) and solifluxion. In western Europe and in southern and central New Zealand, periglacial processes have been widespread, rounding the edges of structural escarpments and alluvial terraces and of dolines and other karst forms; and indeed there has been much modification of the slopes on terrains of various kinds of rocks. All are relict from glacial ages when gelivation and solifluxion were the dominant processes. Block fields are relict on plateaus, as also are convex arrested streams (*coulées*, q.v.) of coarse debris that have encroached on valleys. Low-lying parts of the landscape have been built up also by deposition of the finer solifluxion debris that has moved forward down very gentle slopes, making vast sheets and low-angle fans that are now relict in regions subject to normal erosion.

The broad *whaleback hills* characteristic of western Europe, which have too often been assumed to be typical examples of "normal" land forms, have been for the most part shaped and smoothed by *periglacial processes*. The effects of a succession of ice ages have been cumulative because of the slowness or feebleness of dissection by normal erosion in intervening warmer episodes. *Practically the whole landscape is relict* except for a few recently river-cut gorges where changes of drainage have taken place. In New Zealand, on the other hand, while periglacial smoothing processes have been as active as in Europe, a much finer texture of dissection has been maintained by stream erosion in the interglacial episodes, and this still persists. Thus, though relict forms of periglacial origin are common they do not dominate the landscape to the exclusion of stream-eroded forms that are still developing, generally with fine-textured dissection (Cotton, 1958).

In northernmost Hokkaido, Japan, there is a large-scale relict landscape of very coarse-textured dissection on a weak-rock terrain which is in course of replacement by one with very fine-textured dis-

FIG. 6. Relict sea cliffs now separated from the sea by a delta. Wairau Valley, New Zealand (field sketch).

section (Shiro Kaneko, *in litt.* 1965) (Fig. 3). The relict hill forms have been developed by cryergic processes in a glacial age, presumably the last. A similar replacement might be brought about by a change of climate from one of rather low and well-distributed rainfall to one with more concentration of rainfall, either episodic or seasonal, i.e., in the winter, when because of low evapotranspiration, runoff takes place abundantly as proliferating streams which actively branch into headward-eroding gullies (Cotton, 1963a, p. 532).

In certain parts of Europe, active cryergic processes in the glacial ages were particularly effective in producing forms that are now relict. In Champagne, where gelivation was severe, the *chalk terrain* was especially susceptible to it (Tricart, 1951, p. 185). While this process fragments all rocks to some extent, reducing much of the material eventually to fine powder, chalk breaks down readily into a slurry of small fragments and fine debris. Thus, while chalk in districts not strongly affected by the periglacial processes is moderately resistant to erosion—forming escarpments in southeastern England and surviving in Picardy as a plateau dissected by narrow ravines (Tricart, 1953, p. 40)—it was a very weak rock when intensely gelivated. Anti-escarpment-making effects then produced chalk forms, now relict, which defy explanation by "normal" processes.

In Champagne, a large area of gelivated chalk was leveled off in the Pleistocene ice ages by cryoplanation, producing a plain that is now a relict form (Tricart, 1951, p. 200). Even on resistant rocks—e.g., in Wales—the process of cryoplanation has developed flights of terraces (now relict) that replace otherwise smooth slopes.

As regards rocks less susceptible to gelivation than chalk and in general more resistant, Birot (1949) has contrasted the effects of climate on the resistance offered to denudation by limestone and granite. The former wastes away rather rapidly in a hot-*humid* climate, extensive limestone terrains being reduced to plains dotted over with dwindling steep-walled hums (the "needle karst" of the southeast Asian monsoon region). Such forms when found relict indicate change of climate. According to Birot, granite has been rapidly reduced to low relief in hot-*dry* climatic episodes, while limestone

has been much more resistant (Fig. 4). In the cool-humid climate largely prevailing in middle latitudes, granite is more resistant, so that massifs of granite tend to stand out in relief.

The bold theory has been advanced by Büdel (1963) that practically the whole of Germany and much of the rest of northwestern Europe is a relict landscape left over from the Pleistocene glacial ages (Cotton, 1963b). It is sculptured into valleys with flat floors which, according to Büdel, are not, as has been generally assumed, late mature forms developed in the cycle of rain-and-river erosion, for the rivers in them seem now to be misfits and not actively engaged in developing them further. He explains the wide-open valleys as of a special type now relict in this region but to be found in course of development in the frigid climate of northeast Spitsbergen. They may be called *cryergic-fluvial valleys.* The catenary, or broadly U-shaped, cross profile of these valleys in Spitsbergen, where their rate of development has been measured, is present at the earliest stage of incision, and the valleys increase thereafter simultaneously in depth and width (Fig. 5). It is claimed that the German valleys were formed thus in successive Pleistocene ice ages, undergoing little or no significant modification in interglacial episodes or at the present day.

Among other landscapes that are certainly relict

FIG. 7. Relict sea cliffs now plunging and therefore immune from further wave attack. Western side of Campbell Island far south of New Zealand (from a photograph).

are areas of *fixed sand dunes* that are now vegetated and are losing their characteristic forms. In western Nebraska, for example (Smith, 1965), the largest dune area in North America (22,000 square miles) is now almost entirely relict, some of the dunes having been formed in the early, and others in the late, Wisconsinan. Soil has since been formed on them and a consequent drainage system has developed in the relatively humid present-day climate.

Lines of *former sea cliffs* that are no longer undergoing marine erosion come into the category of relict forms (French: *falaises mortes*). Some have been cut off from the sea by growth of deltas or strand plains or by slight emergence that has exposed a narrow coastal plain. An example of such is a relict shore line bordering the delta of the Wairau River, New Zealand (Fig. 6).

Plunging cliffs (q.v.) are also relict forms (Cotton, 1951). Some of the boldest examples are several hundred miles south of New Zealand on the western, exposed coasts of Campbell Island (Fig. 7) and the Auckland Islands. In both these examples, the western slopes of high basaltic islands have been cut back for miles by marine erosion, so that near-vertical cliffs over a thousand feet high descend into the sea. The level of the sea has risen since the last cliff-cutting episode and the cliffs now plunge into deep water. There is no rock platform at the sea margin, and waves are reflected from a vertical wall instead of breaking. Thus the cliffs at present enjoy immunity from marine erosion. Since cutting is no longer in progress, they are relict.

C. A. COTTON

References

Baulig, H., 1957, "Peneplains and pediplains," *Bull. Geol. Soc. Am.*, **68**, 913–930.

Birot, P., 1949, "Essai sur quelques problèmes de morphologie générale," Lisbon, Instituto par alta Cultura.

Büdel, J., 1955, "Reliefgenerationen und plio-pleistozäner Klimawandel in Hoggargebirge," *Erdkunde*, **9**, 100–132.

Büdel, J., 1957, "The Ice Age in the tropics," *Universitas*, **9**, 183–191.

Büdel, J., 1963a, "Die pliozänen und quartären Pluvialzeiten der Sahara," *Eiszeitalter und Gegenwart*, **14**, 161.

Büdel, J., 1963b, "Klima-genetische Geomorphologie," *Geographische Rundschau*, **1963**, 269–288.

Cotton, C. A., 1942, 1947, "Climatic Accidents in Landscape-making," New York, John Wiley & Sons.

Cotton, C. A., 1951, "Sea cliffs of Banks Peninsula and Wellington," *N.Z. Geographer*, **7**, 103–120.

Cotton, C. A., 1958, "Fine-textured erosional relief in New Zealand," *Z. Geomorphol.*, **2**, 187–210.

Cotton, C. A., 1961, "The theory of savanna planation," *Geography*, **46**, 89–101.

Cotton, C. A., 1962, "Plains and inselbergs of the humid tropics," *Trans. Roy. Soc. N.Z. Geol.*, **1**(18), 269–277.

Cotton, C. A., 1963a, "Development of fine-textured landscape relief in temperate pluvial climates," *N.Z. J. Geol. Geophys.*, **6**, 528–533.

Cotton, C. A., 1963b, "A new theory of the sculpture of middle-latitude landscapes," *N.Z. J. Geol. Geophys.*, **6**, 769–774.

Davis, W. M., 1905, "The geographical cycle in an arid climate," *J. Geol.*, **13**, 381–407.

Fairbridge, R. W., 1964, "African Ice-Age Aridity," in "Problems in Palaeoclimatology," pp. 356–360, New York, Interscience Publishers.

Garner, H. F., 1966, "Derangement of the Rio Caroni, Venezuela," *Rev. Géom. Dyn.*, **16**, 54–83.

Hack, J. T., 1960, "Interpretation of erosional topography in humid temperature regions," *Am. J. Sci.*, **258A**, 80–97.

Smith, H. T. U., 1965, "Dune morphology and chronology in central and western Nebraska," *J. Geol.*, **73**, 557–578.

Tricart, J., 1951, "Cours de Géomorphologie, 2: 1, Le modelé périglaciaire," Paris, Tournier & Constans, 271pp.

Tricart, J., 1953, "Les formes d'influence du climat sur le modelé," *Cahiers d'information géographique*, **2**, 39–51.

Tricart, J., 1956, "Types de fleuves ... en Afrique occidentale," Extrait de *Bull. Sec. Géogr. Com. Trav. hist. scient. 1955.*

Tricart, J., and Cailleux, A., 1965, "Introduction a la Géomorphologie climatique," Paris, Soc. d'Edition d'Enseign. Superieut, 307pp.

Cross-references: *Cirque; Continental Erosion; Coulee; Cryology; Cryopedology; Denudation; Drumlin; Esker; Exhumed Landscape; Geomorphology—Principles; Glaciation; Hum; Inselberg; Moraine; Morphogenetic Regions; Pediplanation; Peneplain; Periglacial Eolian Effects; Plains; Plunging Cliffs; Quaternary; Roche Moutonnée; Solifluction; Tropical Weathering and Relief; Weathering.* Vol. II: *Ice Age Meteorology.* pr Vol. VII: *Paleoclimatology.*

RELIEF—*See* MOUNTAIN AND HILLY TERRAIN

RELIEF INVERSION—*See* INVERSION (OF TOPOGRAPHY, RELIEF)

RESEQUENT VALLEY, STREAM—*See* DRAINAGE PATTERNS; RIVERS

RESURRECTED LANDSCAPE—*See* EXHUMED LANDSCAPE

RETROGRADING SHORELINE

Johnson (1919) first used the term retrograding shore when he distinguished it from a *prograding shore* (q.v.). He also used the term retrograding cliff in the same way as Cotton's (1922) "retrogradation—the cutting back of the shore in a line of cliffs." Wooldridge and Morgan (1937) used it

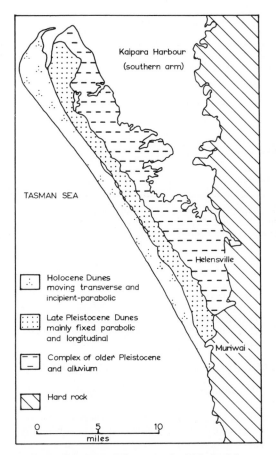

Kaipara Harbour
(southern arm)

TASMAN SEA

Helensville

Muriwai

::: Holocene Dunes
moving transverse and
incipient-parabolic

::: Late Pleistocene Dunes
mainly fixed parabolic
and longitudinal

- - Complex of older Pleistocene
and alluvium

Hard rock

0   5   10
miles

FIG. 1. This prograded area north of Muriwai lies on the west coast of the North Island, New Zealand, where prevailing winds cause dune development far exceeding that on the east coast. Retrogradation has been severe so that instead of preservation of foredunes, as at Mangatawhiri Spit on the east coast (Fig. 1 of *Prograding Shorelines*), the Holocene foredunes have been amalgamated into transverse dunes. Where partially fixed by vegetation these tend toward parabolic structures like those in the older fixed dunes. The Holocene dunes have formed during the fall of sea level that commenced about 4000 years ago. The contact between them and the older dunes consists of a partially buried coastal cliff and ponded-back freshwater lakes. The cliff was almost certainly cut during the rapid postglacial sea-leval rise prior to 4000 years ago.

more as the antithesis of the way in which prograding shore line has been defined, but also accepted its wider meaning. Semantically, retrograde is the antonym of prograde, and furthermore, as gradation implies a close connection between both processes, it is suggested that retrograding shore line be restricted to the reverse movement of progradation, thus, a retreating of the shore line in loose sediments previously deposited by wave action. It follows that the erosion is due primarily to the capabilities of local waves to transport the size of grain present on shore, and this separates shore retrogradation from other forms of coastal retreat due to mechanical abrasion, chemical solution and tectonic subsidence.

During retrogradation, a wide belt of beach ridges with their overlying dunes, if present, may be rapidly removed. The retrograding shore line may cut back at an angle to previously formed ridges, and if there is renewed progradation, this coastal revision is preserved in the form of an angular discontinuity between the directions of the older and younger ridges. New foredunes no longer form to protect those in the hinterland (Steers, 1964) and wide areas of foredunes, previously retaining their typically parallel distribution to the shore, become transformed by wind erosion into a complex of transverse, parabolic and longitudinal dunes (Fig. 1). Retrogradation may remove only a previously formed high-spring-tide berm leaving a temporary cliff, a few inches to a few feet high, at the toe of the foredune. Even less amounts may only partially remove the high-tide berm and flatten the beach profile (Fig. 2). Where progradation is the net movement of the shore, periods of retrogradation may only be temporary. This is the norm at present in tectonically stable areas.

As with progradation, retrogradation is a function of time, energy, sedimentary supply, sea level change and organic growth. *Time* is required to bring about full dynamic equilibrium after a change in one or more of the other factors. *Energy*, as wind-, wave- and tide-generated currents, may increase during storms to speed up retrogradation or produce temporary periods of retrogradation in an area of net progradation. Reduction of *sedimentary supply* in areas where longshore drift or offshore tidal currents are important will have similar results. Presence of *organic growth* on dunes reduces the rate or amount of erosion during temporary retrogradation or during the initial stages of "permanent" retrogradation (for further references to these factors see *Prograding Shoreline*).

The effects of rising sea level on retrogradation has had little attention (Bruun, 1962). Such periods may be temporary as during storms, or they may have different degrees of permanency as during the rise to the postglacial high and subsequent fluctuations (Fairbridge, 1961; Schofield, 1964). During storms, increased steepness of waves is important in causing erosion of the beach and seaward transport of sediment "inside the break point of the waves," but not outside the break point where transport is "practically always in a landward direction" (King, 1959). At the same time, storms promote a local lift in sea level through the piling of water on to the coast assisted by the accompanying reduction in atmospheric pressure. Such a lift must decrease tidal current action on the

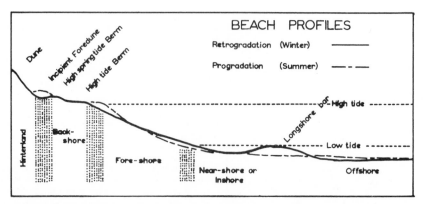

FIG. 2. Beach profiles typical of prograding and retrograding shores—berms and incipient foredunes are not always present. The longshore bar with deepening of the water on the seaward side (Steers, 1964) develops along the breaker zone during storm-produced retrogradation.

sea floor and promote local deposition of sediment removed from the beach. In prograded areas—areas of dynamic equilibrium between sea level and sea floor—these are temporary changes under static sea level conditions, and material removed from shore during storms is rapidly replaced. Following a storm in an area where sea level is rising relative to the land, over and above any temporary lift of sea level due to the storm, some or all of this material may not be replaced on shore and retrogradation becomes more permanent. Thus a continually rising sea level may speed up retrogradation or even change a prograding shore line to one of retrogradation. Nevertheless, a rising sea level favors, but need not cause, retrogradation, as other factors, particularly rate of rise and rate of sedimentary supply, are important.

J. C. SCHOFIELD

References

Bruun, P., 1962, "Sea-level rise as a cause of shore erosion," *J. Waterways Harbors Div.*, **88**, WW1 (3065), 117–130.

Cotton, C. A., 1922, "Geomorphology of New Zealand. Part 1—Systematic," *N.Z. Board of Sci. and Art, Man. No. 3*, 462pp.

Fairbridge, R. W., 1961, "Eustatic Changes in Sea Level," in (Ahrens, L. H., *et al.*, editors) "Physics and Chemistry of the Earth," Vol. 4, pp.99–185, London, Pergamon Press.

Johnson, D. W., 1919, "Shore Processes and Shoreline Development," New York, John Wiley & Sons, 584pp.

King, Cuchlaine, A. M., 1959, "Beaches and Coasts," London, Ed. Arnold Ltd., 403pp.

Schofield, J. C., 1964, "Postglacial sea levels and isostatic uplift," *New Zealand J. Geol. Geophys.*, 7(2), 359–370.

Steers, J. A., 1964, "The Coastline of England and Wales," Second ed., Cambridge, Cambridge University Press, 750pp.

Wooldridge, S. W., and Morgan, R. S., 1937, "Physical Basis of Geography," London, Longmans, 445pp.

Cross-references: *Beach Ridges; Beach; Eustasy; Holocene; Prograding Shoreline; Sediment Transport, Long-term.*

RIA, RIAS COAST AND RELATED FORMS

The term *ria* comes from the Spanish. In northwestern Spain (Galicia and Asturias), there are series of long, mountainous-sided estuaries that are not glaciated, thus not fiords, but are subaerially eroded, former river valleys that have been drowned by postglacial rise of sea level. Examples are the Rio de Vigo, Rio de la Coruna, Rio del Farroll. They are a characteristically funnel or trumpet shape in plan and not so deep as fiords. Similar coasts are seen in southwest Ireland (Kerry), China, and in such places where the structural grain of the country rock is cut off obliquely by the trend of the coast. They are thus typical of the "Atlantic type" coasts of Suess (see *Atlantic and Pacific Type Coasts*).

F. von Richthofen (1886) proposed the term *ria* for this type of coast. He used it in a restricted sense, while Gulliver (1899, p. 220) recommended that it be applied to "all types of subaerially carved troughs, including von Richthofen's fjord, ria, dalman and liman types." W. M. Davis (1915, p. 82) supported this extended definition for "any broad or estuarine river mouth, and not necessarily an embayment produced by the partial submergence of an open valley in a mountainous coast, in the sense that Richthofen originally proposed."

The Gulliver-Davis broadened use was followed also by D. W. Johnson, but it has not been generally adopted by geomorphologists. It appears that most scientists prefer the original application, simply to a non-glaciated, drowned, dissected mountainous coast, fingering out to sea, indeed

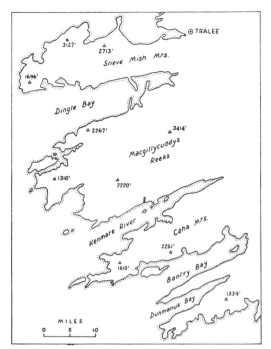

FIG. 1. Southwest Ireland (Kerry); rias parallel to folded structures of Hercynian age on a transverse or "Atlantic" type coast (from Sparks, 1960). (By permission of Longmans, Green & Co., London and John Wiley & Sons, N.Y.)

such as may be seen in Galicia (Baulig, 1956, p. 105). Baulig mentions that rias in Britanny (France) are called "rivières" or "abers" (also in Cornwall and Wales).

Baulig has indicated also the accepted modern usage for the related coastal types:

(a) *Cala or Calanque Coasts* (from *Cala* of the Balearic Islands and *Calanques* of the French coast of Provence): narrow, short, drowned valleys with steep sides, characteristic of some limestone coasts, thus related to rias; somewhat similar also to the *sherm, cherm* (Arabic, pl. sherum) of the Red Sea described by Schmidt (1923).

(b) *Dalmatian-type Coasts* (from Dalmatia, Yugoslavia): as proposed by Von Richthofen, for a drowned mountainous coast consisting of parallel fold ranges, resulting in zigzag channels (*canali* in Italian) parallel and normal to the general coastal trend.

(c) *Liman Coasts* (from Turkish and Russian, for "lagoon," as on the Black Sea): broad valleys cut in a low flat-lying coast, mostly cut off by baymouth bars or barriers. On the Black Sea, without tides, tsunamis or major swell, such barriers can only be built up well above waterline by eustatic drop of sea level (as proposed by O. K. Leontyev) and contributions by fluvial floods and eolian sources. There are also *fluvial limans* which are tributary valleys cut off by fluvial bars built up by the main stream, notably in the Danube delta (Pfan-

FIG. 2. Part of the Tailevu coastline on the eastern side of Viti Levu (Fiji); a typical ria coast on a mature volcanic island in tropical waters. Note the fringing coral reefs and offshore reef patches.

nenstiel). In the eastern United States and the Gulf of Mexico (also Western Australia, West Africa, Brazil, etc.) where tides somewhat modify the pattern, coasts of this sort are often called *barrier island coasts.*

(d) *Estuary Coasts:* E. de Martonne proposed that for coasts of low relief, thus in contrast to the classic rias, where drowning had produced deep, funnel-shaped reentrants, the term *estuary coast* should be used. Fine examples are seen in Chesapeake Bay and Delaware Bay.

RHODES W. FAIRBRIDGE

References

Baulig, H., 1956, "Vocabulaire Franco–Anglo–Allemand de Géomorphologie," Paris (Publ. Fac. Lettres Univ. Strasbourg, No. 130), 230pp.

Davis, W. M., 1915, "The principles of geographical description," *Ann. Assoc. Am. Geogr.,* **5,** 61–105.

Gulliver, F. P., 1899, "Shoreline topography," *Proc. Am. Acad. Arts Sci.,* **34,** 149–258.

Leontyev, O. K., 1965, "Genesis of offshore bars and the Flandrian transgression" (read at INQUA, VII Sess., Boulder, publ. in Russian).

Martonne, E. de, 1950. "Traité de Géographie Physique," Vol. 1, Paris, Colin, 496pp.

Pannekoek, A. J., 1966, "The ria problem," *Tids. v. Het Konin. Nederl. Aard. Genoot.,* **83**(3), 289–297.

Schmidt, Walther, 1923, "Die Scherms an der Rotmeerküste von el-Hedschas." *Petermanns Mitt.,* **69,** 118–121.

Sparks, B. W., 1960, "Geomorphology," London, Longmans, Green & Co.; New York, J. Wiley & Sons, 371pp.

Von Richthofen, F., 1886, "Führer für Forschungsreisende," Hannover, Janecke, 734pp.

Cross-references: *Atlantic and Pacific Type Coasts; Barriers—Beaches and Islands; Estuary; Eustasy; Fjord; Fringing Reef.*

RIDGE AND VALLEY TOPOGRAPHY

In the first attempt at defining the principal physiographic provinces of the United States, J. W. Powell (1896) applied the term *ridge and valley*

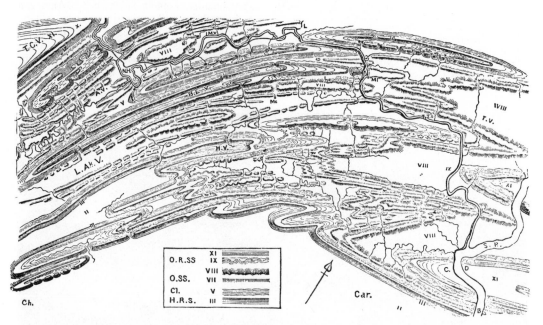

FIG. 1. Early sketch map of the Appalachian Ridge and Valley structures, drawn nearly a century ago by Lesley. Roman numbers: III "Hudson River Shales" or Martinsburg (Ordovician); V "Clinton" (Silurian); VII "Oriskany" (Devonian); XI Upper Carboniferous. S.R. = Susquehanna River; L = Lewistown.

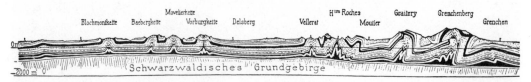

FIG. 2. General profile through the Swiss Jura Mountains (by A. Buxtorf); north to the left; length of section 40 km. Note the "rumpling of the tablecloth" over the previously peneplaned unconformity on the Black Forest. Paleozoic crystalline complex ("Schw. Grundgebirge"). This surface was "lubricated" by a layer of Triassic salt.

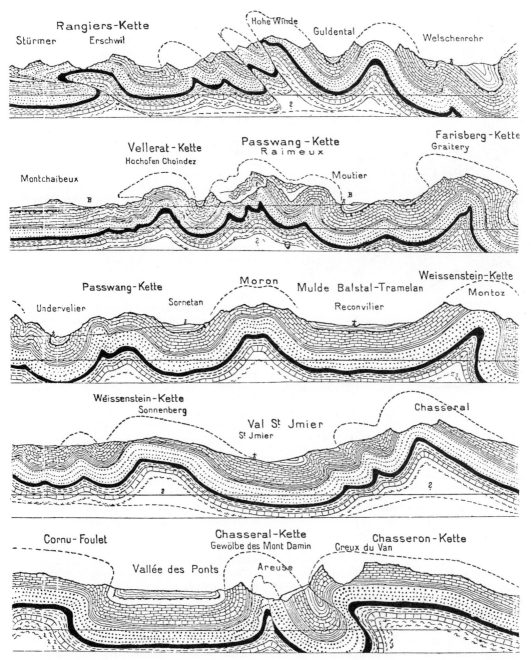

FIG. 3. Typical profiles through the Swiss Jura Mountains (Heim, 1919); length 12 km. Note that some of the ridges are anticlines, but others are "breached" and form valleys; likewise some synclines form valleys while others form ridges.

province to the Newer Appalachian Belt that was deformed in late Paleozoic times and is represented by one of the most strikingly uniform belts of simple, even isoclinally folded sediments known in the world (Fig. 1). The term "folded Appalachians"

is thus often used synonymously in North America with valley and ridge province (Fenneman, 1938).

The folded Appalachians are closely paralleled by the structural pattern of the Jura Mountains of France and Switzerland, a geotectonic style first

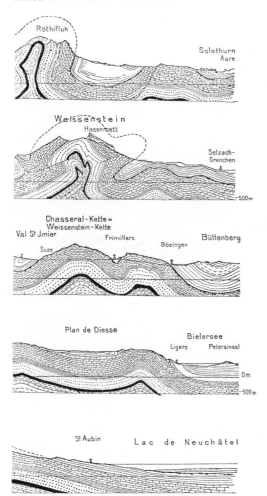

Fig. 4. Profiles through Swiss Jura (continued from Fig. 3).

sandstones and conglomerates (the "ridge formers"), alternating with softer shales and a few limestones. The facies are largely flysch, partly deltaic and paralic, passing upward into a molasse.

Some transverse faulting leads to certain offsets crossing the structural "grain," but parallel fault trends have little topographic expression that is not already established by the lithology.

Of the geomorphology, Fenneman (1938) writes:

"Viewed empirically, the ridge and valley province is a lowland (an assemblage of valley floors) surmounted by long, narrow, even-topped mountain ridges. Either of these elements may predominate, the mountains being widely spaced and isolated, or so closely ranged that the lowlands are disconnected or absent. The valley floor is again trenched by streams. Morphologically the province is one of folded mountains in their second (or later) cycle, in which resistant strata form ridges, and weaker rocks are worn down to lowlands, themselves more or less eroded in a later cycle."

The main steps in the morphogenesis of the Appalachian ridge and valley province were: (a) general peneplanation (Mesozoic); (b) upwarping (repeatedly, in steps); (c) reduction of weaker rocks to erosion surfaces at lower levels; (d) further upwarping and dissection. Differential erosion has brought out a characteristic series of parallel ridges and valleys, except at structural plunges, where "hairpin" ridges (enclosing so-called coves) occur. Trellis drainage is a result of subsequent adaptation, but the main ("master") streams are superimposed.

A considerable controversy has built up around the interpretation of these peneplains and related erosion surfaces, their naming, dating and precise meaning. It is far from resolved as yet, but it is irrelevant in the definition of the valley and ridge type of relief. Similar disagreements have arisen over the dating of the Jura ridge and valley province.

To sum up, the characteristic features of ridge and valley topography are: (a) a province of uniform structural origin; (b) developed in sedimentary rocks; (c) monotonously folded into parallel, symmetric (sometimes isoclinal) anticlines and synclines; (d) peneplaned to give a general summit accordance; (e) subject to subsequent discontinuous upwarping resulting in multiple secondary erosion surfaces; (f) differential erosion that has picked out distinctive lithologies—ridge formers and valley formers—to provide series of parallel mountains and valleys, marked by distinctive trellis drainage pattern.

RHODES W. FAIRBRIDGE

recognized by Buxtorf, and formally designated by Stille (1924) as "Juratype"; while the two are quite different in age, in their structural genesis, they are characterized specifically by planes of décollement, over which the overlying beds have rumpled "like a tablecloth," producing symmetric folds of almost identical dimensions in great number (Fig. 2). Similar sheafs of Juratype fold belts are found along the marginal zones of the great orogenic belts of the world. The detailed structure is illustrated in Figs. 3 and 4.

Thus the ridge and valley topography (as a relief form) has become a standard of general usefulness in geomorphology. The prototype has a length of 2000 km and a width varying from 60 km in New York State to 150 km in Pennsylvania at about the line of the Susquehanna (Fig. 5). The succession of anticlines and synclines are developed in quartzitic

References

Buxtorf, A., 1916, "Prognosen und Befunde beim Hauenstein-basis und Grenchenberg-tunnel, und die Bedeutung der letzteren für die Geologie des Juragebirges," *Verh. Naturf. Ges. Basel,* **27**.

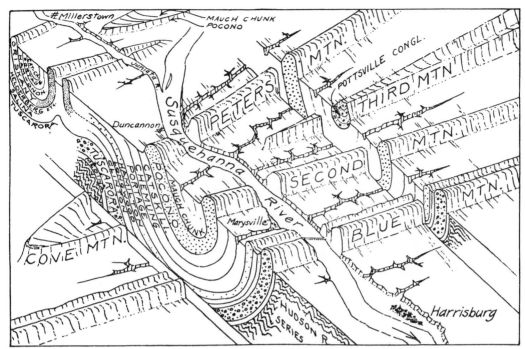

Fig. 5. Diagram showing structure of the Folded Appalachians, Harrisburg, Pennsylvania (Courtesy of A. K. Lobeck). Note strong "ridge formers": Tuscarora (Silurian), Pocono (Lower Carboniferous) and Pottsville (Upper Carboniferous).

Fenneman, N. M., 1938, "Physiography of the Eastern United States," New York, McGraw-Hill Book Co., 714pp.

Geikie, J., 1914, "Mountains, Their Origin, Growth and Decay," Princeton N.J., D. Van Nostrand Co., 311pp.

Heim, A., 1919, "Geologie der Schweiz," Leipzig, Tauchnitz, Vol. 1, 704pp.

Lobeck, A. K., 1939, "Geomorphology, An Introduction to the Study of Landscapes," New York, McGraw-Hill Book Co., 731pp.

Powell, J. W., 1896, "The physiography of the United States," *Nat. Geogr. Soc. Monog.*, **1**, 1–64.

Stille, H., 1924, "Grundfragen der vergleichenden Tektonik," Berlin, Borntraeger.

Thornbury, W. D., 1965, "Regional Geomorphology of the United States," New York, John Wiley & Sons, 609pp.

Cross-references: *Drainage Patterns*; *Landscape Analysis*; *Mountain Types*; *Peneplain*; *Warping*. pr Vol. VI: *Flysch*. pr Vol. VIII: *Appalachian Province*.

RIFT VALLEY

"Valleys of subsidence with long steep parallel walls," as originally defined by J. W. Gregory (1894), rift valleys are evidently the geomorphic equivalents of *fault troughs* or *graben* in structural geology (see discussion by Quennell in *Rift Valley Structure*, Vol. V). Quennell believes that the term "rift valley" should be restricted only to those major features of the earth's crust which accord with Gregory's prototypes in East Africa, where the width of the rift is of the same order of magnitude as the local thickness of the crust, whether continental or oceanic (for oceanic rifts, see *Trench* in Vol. I).

Detailed surveys of rift valleys in Africa, the Middle East and elsewhere show that idealized symmetric graben profiles are rarely seen, that the opposite sides are frequently asymmetric, and that there is often only a single fault. The nature of the shift may be dilatational, with normal faults, or it may have a strike-slip component (as in the Jordan–Dead Sea or Great Glen system). The reverse-fault or ramp theory of Bailey Willis receives no support from field data.

The Rhine Graben is perhaps the best example of the symmetric rift valley as recognized a century and a half ago by Elie de Beaumont. The use of the term "rift" with respect to the San Andreas Fault, a major dextral strike-slip fault, is widely questioned in view of the frequent absence of any fault-controlled valley; the recent movements along the fault may be traced over mountain slopes and across valleys showing intersection of a newly revived fault system with an earlier-established geomorphic landscape pattern that was evidently developed independently of the faulting. The narrow clefts associated with such new fault systems have been called earthquake rifts (e.g.,

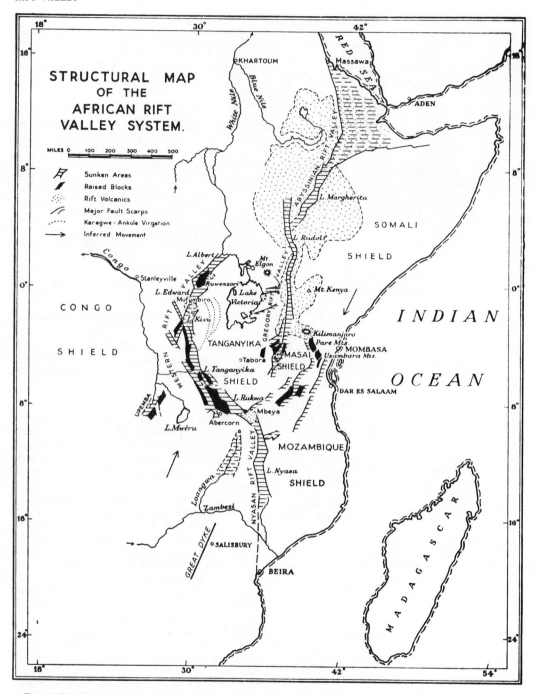

FIG. 1. Distribution of rift valleys in East Africa (from McConnell, 1951). Note that McConnell postulated a certain torsional couple (dextral), to explain some asymmetry in the rift pattern.

Von Engeln, 1942, p. 388), which are distinctive from rift valleys.

Where rift valleys intersect high plateaus, an interesting geomorphic problem arises. In East Africa, an earlier series of erosion surfaces offer one or more "reference planes" for judging the time and degree of relative uplift near the rift. Quennell points out that the "rise to the rift" is not always a concave-up surface, but may become convex-up near the rift or may have an even slope.

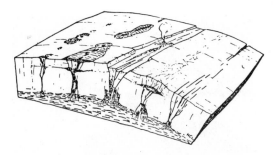

FIG. 2. The "keystone theory" of rift valleys, originally postulated by de Lapparent, and favored by Gregory and by Cloos. Block diagram suggests an explanation also for the associated vulcanism (Cloos, 1939).

The question may then be posed: was the plateau up-domed by endogenic forces, leading eventually to a split crown, or were the margins downwarped from an originally much more extensive high crustal sector. Up-arching, with a down-dropped keystone was first proposed by de Lapparent in 1886. In contrast, Suess (1909) believed there could be no upward epeirogeny, lacking a mechanism, but only downwarping of the margins. The dismemberment of his "Gondwanaland" might well provide such downwarp in the case of Africa.

It has been proposed by Fairbridge that the alteration of the orientation of the geoid following major polar shift (paleomagnetic data) should lead to the emergence of high plateau areas in those parts of the globe formerly closer to the equatorial bulge. Such areas would not be uplifted, but rather left behind when the hydrosphere reacted instantaneously to the newly oriented geoid. Phase changes below such plateaus would maintain their elevation in isostatic equilibrium, but continual spreading would lead to lateral stress

release and collapse. A collapse also of a "keystone," with or without strike adjustment would appear to be compatible with this model. Detailed analysis of the geology and geophysics of rifts is given by Quennell (cf. *Rift Valley Sructure*, Vol. V).

RHODES W. FAIRBRIDGE

References

Cloos, H., 1939, "Hebung-Spaltung-Vulkanismus," *Geol. Rundschau*, **30**, (4A), 405–527.
Dixey, F., 1956, "The East African rift system," *Col. Geol. Min. Res. Bull. London*, Suppl. 1.
Gregory, J. W., 1894, "Contributions to the physical geography of British East Africa," *Geogr. J.*, **4**(4), 289–315.
Gregory, J. W., 1921, "The Rift Valleys and Geology of East Africa," London, Seeley, 479pp.
McConnell, R. B., 1951, "Rift and shield structure in East Africa," *Rept. Int. Geol. Congr. London, 1948* **18**, Pt. 14 (A.S.G.A.), 199–207.
Suess, E., 1909, "The Face of the Earth," Vol. 4, Oxford, Clarendon.
Von Engeln, O. D., 1942, "Geomorphology," New York, The Macmillan Co., 655pp.
Willis, B., 1936, "East African Plateaus and Rift Valleys," Washington, Carnegie Institution, publ. 470.

Cross-references: *Basin and Range Landscape*; *Dead Sea*; *East African Lakes*; *Graben*; *Horst*. Vol. I: *Red Sea*; *Trenches*. Vol. II: *Earth—Geology of the Planet*. Vol. V: *Rift Geophysics*; *Rift Valley Structure*. pr Vol. VII: *Gondwanaland*.

RILL WASH—*See* **SHEET EROSION, SHEET-WASH, RAINWASH, SHEETFLOOD**

RINNENTÄLER—*See* **GLACIAL SPILLWAYS AND PROGLACIAL LAKES**

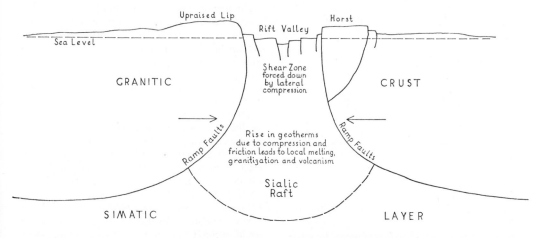

FIG. 3. The "ramp theory" of rift valleys, proposed by Bailey Willis, supported by Bullard, McConnell and others, now generally rejected.

RIP CURRENT

A rip current is a narrow seaward flow of water resulting from the breaking of waves on a beach. They are most strongly developed on long, exposed sandy beaches facing an open ocean. The name rip current was proposed for this phenomenon by Shepard (1936) and now seems to be generally accepted.

When waves run up a beach they eventually break, and the momentum imparted to the water carries it further up the beach to above mean water level. When its energy is spent, the water tries to return under the influence of gravity to mean water level, but often, before it can do so, another wave has broken and more water surges up the beach. The result is an accumulation of water in a quasi-stable position above the level of the sea. The volume of this water increases with the arrival of yet more waves, until at some particular point on the beach the head of stored water becomes greater than the upthrust of the oncoming waves, and water begins to flow seaward at this point from the top of the beach. Once started, this flow reduces the wave effect at that part of the beach and the current gathers momentum as it runs out to sea. The stored water may flow along the top of the beach for as much as several hundred yards, before returning to the sea as a fast narrow current, or rip. As it flows, it hollows out a deeper channel through the beach just as a river cuts its own valley, thereby making its travel easier and establishing itself in that position.

The maximum speed of a rip current can be

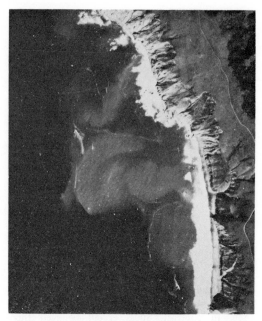

Fig. 2. Examples of three rip currents at McClures Beach near Tomales Point, Marin County, California (air photograph, courtesy Harold Wanless). Largest rip extends just over 500 meters from the beach, to where the offshore depth is 20 meters. North is at the top.

much greater than that of a swimmer; very few accurate measurements have been made, but in moderate conditions with waves having a deep-water height of up to about 10 feet, rip currents on the Cornish coast of England have been observed to reach an average surface speed of nearly 5 knots when measured over several hundred yards (Draper and Dobson, 1965), while Popov (1956) reported 10.6-knot (5.5-m/sec) rips at the surface under severe storm conditions.

The plan of a rip current, as in Fig. 1, looks like a huge tree lying with its roots on the shore, its narrow trunk stretching through the surf zone and its branches spreading out beyond. The width of the central "trunk" of the rip can be quite narrow, perhaps only a few tens of feet, but the effect of the current can sometimes be detected up to a mile or more from the shore.

If waves approach the shore obliquely, the resulting discharge of water up the beach has a longshore component, which results in the establishment of a longshore current in the water at the top of the beach. A pertinent comment concerning such cases was made by Inman and Bagnold (1963): "The waves discharge water into each unit length of the surf zone. So, assuming the resulting longshore current to be so confined, the velocity of the current would, were it not for the existence of outward-flowing rip currents at discrete places, go on increasing indefinitely with distance along the shore.

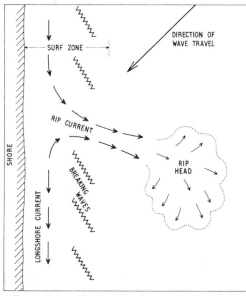

Fig. 1. Schematic representation of waves, longshore current and a typical rip current (adapted from Shepard and Inman, 1950).

On this view the existence of outward rip currents is inevitable." When a longshore current is established, the rip-feeder currents become asymmetrical, as shown in Fig. 1. In some cases, rips may have permanent positions on a beach, because of local topography, but more often it is the direction of approach of the waves on any particular day which governs the positions of the outflows. The flow of water in a rip current may be continuous, particularly under heavy wave conditions, but with smaller waves it may be intermittent, continuing only until the store of water on the beach is exhausted and resuming later when the waves have again piled up enough water for the situation to become unstable.

The carriage of sediment by rip currents means that they are a factor in the shaping of underwater topography. Sand and other materials are swept up from the beach by the swiftly flowing current, and are redeposited out at sea below the area where the current disperses and decays, thereby helping to construct offshore bars.

The distribution of speeds within the rips is imperfectly understood. In some cases it is suggested that the swiftest flow is at the surface, but Popov found the highest speed to be at the sea bed, where it was about twice that at the surface. Where the surface speed was 5.5 m/sec (10.6 knots), it was 10.8 m/sec (20.8 knots) near the bottom.

Rip currents are difficult to identify from a beach, but from a height it is often possible to locate them because the current sweeps up sand which yellows

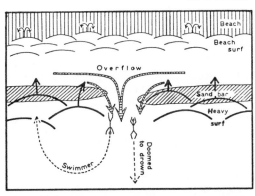

FIG. 4. Breakers with concomitant currents on a sandy seashore with sand-bars (Kuenen, 1955). Note how a swimmer carried out in a rip current should try to go with the current and not against it. (By permission of John Wiley & Sons, N.Y.)

the water and acts as a natural tracer. Also, their presence may be indicated by waves breaking out at sea; if a rip current is present, it can cause a narrow sequence of breaking crests out beyond the normal surf zone as it runs into the oncoming waves.

The name *"undertow"* is commonly used to describe some current which, by implication, runs out to sea from a beach and is entirely below the surface. No such current has been shown to exist, and it seems probable that undertow is a misnomer for either backwash or rip current; another name used in some areas is sea puss.

L. DRAPER

References

Draper, L., and Dobson, P. J., 1965, "Rip currents on a Cornish beach," *Nature*, **206**(4990), 1249.

Inman, D. L., and Bagnold, R. A., 1963, "Beach and Nearshore Processes," in "The Sea," Vol. 3, Ch. 21, pp.529–553, New York, Interscience Publishers.

Kuenen, P. H., 1955, "Realms of Water," New York, John Wiley & Sons, 327pp.

McKenzie, P., 1958, "Rip current systems," *J. Geol.*, **66**(2), 103–113.

Popov, E. A., 1956, "On current surges on the coastal zone," *Tr. Okeanogr. Komis. Akad. Nauk SSSR, 1,* 98–104 (in Russian).

Shepard, F. P., 1936, "Undertow, Rip Tide or 'Rip Current'," *Science*, **84,** 181–182.

Shepard, F. P., and Inman, D. L., 1950, "Nearshore circulation," *Scripps Inst. Oceanogr. Geology Report No. 14.*

FIG. 3. Successive rip current eddies, seen in vertical air photograph; California coast (Courtesy F. P. Shepard).

RIVERS

A river is a large body of flowing water, constrained in a channel. Geologically, the word river is generally used for the main trunk of a drainage system. Rivers have always been the centers of habitation by man. They supply not only fertile fields for cultivation, but also avenues of travel, water power and recreation. Table 1 shows the ten largest rivers of the world, in terms of drainage area, stream length and discharge.

The Hydrology of Rivers

Rivers may sometimes be *ephemeral* (q.v.), i.e., they carry water only during and immediately after a rain; they may be *intermittent*, i.e., they flow part of the year; or they may be *perennial* and flow all year round. Ultimately, all rivers are supplied with water from rainfall. Although this idea was advocated as early as the sixteenth century by Bernard Palissy and others, it was not generally accepted until 1674 when Pierre Perrault measured the amount of precipitation which fell annually in the Paris basin and compared this with the amount of discharge in the Seine. He found that almost six times as much rain fell on the basin as flowed out in the stream. Thus, it is actually only a very small amount of the total rainfall which flows off in stream channels. In most regions of the world, the greater part of the annual precipitation is lost by evaporation (Table 2).

We can express the relationship among the various forms of water as the hydrologic cycle. Water falls on the earth in the form of some kind of precipitation—rain, snow, hail, or sleet. It may be temporarily retained on the surface in glaciers, snowbanks, lakes or ponds, or it may immediately be evaporated back into the air or transpired by plants. Part may be retained in plants, or in soil; part may run off immediately into streams, and part may sink into the ground to reach the stream at a later time as ground-

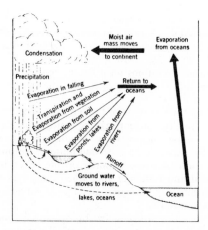

Fig. 1. The hydrologic cycle (after Holtzman; from Strahler, A. N., 1960, "Physical Geography," New York, John Wiley & Sons, 534pp.). (By permission.)

water flow (Fig. 1). Through the rivers, the water reaches the sea, to be evaporated again. This total cycle can be expressed as the hydrologic equation:

$$\text{Rainfall} = \text{Runoff} + \text{Evaporation}$$

Over the world as a whole, 20% of the mean annual rainfall of 40 inches flows off in rivers to the sea. In the United States, approximately 9 of the 30 inches of annual rainfall become runoff. Some typical examples of the amount of evaporation or water loss in drainage basins of the United States are given in Table 3.

However, much of the flow of a river is not from immediate runoff. Part of the precipitation percolates into the ground, moves through the zone of saturation and eventually flows out into a stream. Thus, the flow of rivers is regulated and water is provided to it between rains. Rivers which receive water from the zone of saturation are called

TABLE 1. THE TEN LARGEST RIVERS OF THE WORLD

River (Country)	Discharge (thousand cu ft/yr)	Drainage Area (thousand sq miles)	Stream Length Head to Mouth (miles)
Amazon (Brazil)	7500	2722	3912
Congo (Congo)	1400	1425	2900
Yangtze (China)	770	756	3602
Yenisei (U.S.S.R.)	614	792	2800
Mississippi (U.S.)	611	1244	3872
Lena (U.S.S.R.)	547	1000	2661
Parana (Argentina)	526	890	1500
Ob (U.S.S.R.)	441	1131	3200
Amur (U.S.S.R.)	338	787	2900
Nile (Egypt)	100	1812	4160

(From Encyclopedia Britannica (1965) Book 19, p. 326 and from Leopold, L. B. (1962) "Rivers," *Amer. Scientist,* **50**(4).)

TABLE 2. WORLD DISTRIBUTION OF RUNOFF (from Langbein, after Lvovich)

Continent	Runoff (in.)
Asia (including Japan and Philippines)	6.7
Africa (including Madagascar)	8.0
North America (including West Indies and Central America)	12.4
South America	17.7
Europe	10.3
Australia (including Tasmania and New Zealand)	3.0
Greenland (and Canadian Archipelago)	7.1
Malayan Archipelago	63.0
Total (Average)	10.5

(From Langbein *et al* (1949), "Annual runoff in the United States," *Geol. Surv. Circ.* **52**).

effluent; those which lose water to the groundwater table are called influent. Groundwater replenishment occurs mainly during the spring, and this water flows out into rivers during the dry periods. Thus a steady year-round flow can be maintained by groundwater.

The regimen or habit of a stream depends in great part upon the amount of water supplied to it, i.e., the intensity and amount of rainfall; in part, upon the nature of the soil or rock upon which it flows; and in part, upon the topography of the surface. The first factor, the water supplied to it, is in the realm of hydrology. The chief concern of the hydrologist is the measurement of stream flow and the relationship among the various forms of water in the hydrologic cycle. The U.S. Geological Survey measures stream discharge at over 6000 stations. Discharge, the volume of flow per unit time, is usually expressed as feet per second.

From stream-flow records, hydrographs can be drawn which show the variation of discharge with time. From such graphs, total flow, ground water (or base) flow, and periods of high and low water can be determined. This data is of great use to engineers and hydrologists in the planning of irrigation and power development, drainage systems, water supply and flood forecasting. Storm hydrographs, showing the variation of discharge with time during a particular storm, are of particular interest because they show the dependence of discharge on geologic and geographic characteristics of a river basin. A flashy stream has a hydrograph with a sharp high peak, resulting from high immediate surface runoff with very little absorption of water in the watershed.

In many parts of the world, spring is a time of floods because the flow of rivers is augmented not only by spring rains but also by snowmelt (Fig. 2). It is estimated that rivers generally overflow their banks (flood) at least once every two years. However, the recurrence interval (time between floods) varies from river basin to river basin and varies also with the size of flood. It is thought that floods are very important, not only to man himself because of their danger, but also in changing the morphology of the river.

River Hydraulics

Flow in rivers is turbulent; i.e., the water moves in chaotic, heterogeneous movements with many secondary eddies imposed on the main downstream movement. There are two kinds of turbulent flow: streaming (or tranquil) flow and shooting (or rapid) flow. The type of turbulent flow

TABLE 3. WATER LOSS IN SELECTED RIVER BASINS

Rainfall (in.)	Runoff (in.)	Water Loss (in.)	River
43.0	18.5	24.5	Sudbury River, Framingham Center, Mass.
43.2	23.1	20.1	Delaware River, Trenton, N.J.
38.3	17.6	20.8	Susquehanna River, Harrisburg, Pa.
20.8	0.6	20.3	Red River, Fargo, N.D.
35.3	7.2	28.0	Grand River, Gallatin, Mo.
42.8	9.0	33.8	Neches River, Rockland, Texas

(From *U.S. Geol. Surv. Water Supply Paper* **846**).

FIG. 2. Distribution of the seasonal river regimes of the world (Guilcher, A., 1965, "Precis d'hydrologie," Paris, Masson et Cie, 389pp.). Legend: 1. *Intertropical or subtropical* with two maxima, or concentrations; 2. *tropical* with one maximum; 3. *mediterranean and subtropical* (in part influenced by snow); 4. *subtropical pluvial* of Texas type; 5. *oceanic pluvial* and related types; 6. *pluvio-nival* (or nivo-pluvial) of plains type; 7. *nival* of modified plains type (small secondary maximum in the autumn); 8. *nival* of true plains type (one maximum only); 9. *pluvio-nival* with intense freezing; 10. *pluvio-nival* of monsoon type; 11. *steppe* (*or prairie*) *monsoon* regime (with slight nival component) and Kansan type; 12. *mountain regime* with glacial or nival influence; 13. *regimes without regular flow*. (By permission.)

depends upon the velocity and depth of the river and is defined by the Froude number,

$$Fr = \frac{V}{\sqrt{gD}}$$

where Fr is the Froude number, V is stream velocity, g is the gravitational constant, and D is depth of water. If Fr is less than 1, the river is in the streaming flow regime; if Fr is greater than 1, the river is in the shooting flow regime. If the river has an alluvial bed and is clear, one can tell by looking at the river bed which kind of flow is taking place.

In turbulent flow, the velocity of a river varies from point to point. However, in general, one can say that in profile from top to bottom, the fastest flow occurs slightly below the surface of the water (Fig. 3). The actual velocity distribution in transverse section depends greatly upon the shape of the channel (Fig. 4). The velocity distribution in a map view varies with sinuosity. In a straight stream, the greatest velocity path would be toward the center of the river, but in a meandering river, the path of fastest velocity tends to swing from side to side (Fig. 5).

The velocity of a river depends upon the gradient, volume of water, viscosity of the water, width, depth and shape of channel cross section, and roughness of the bed. Of attempts to quantify

the velocity, the formula most used by engineers is the Chézy formula,

$$V = C\sqrt{RS}$$

where V is velocity, R is hydraulic radius and S is

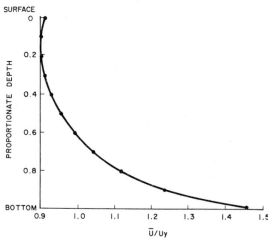

FIG. 3. Velocity profile for Mississippi River, Vicksburg (data from F. B. Toffaleti, 1963, "Deep river velocity and sediment profiles and the suspended sand load," Federal Interagency Sedimentation Conference, Jackson, Miss.).

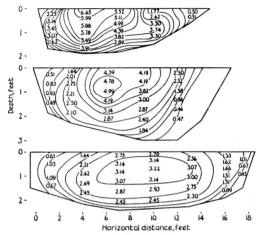

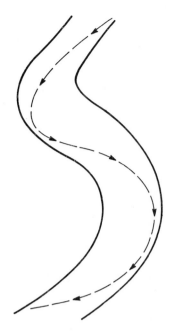

FIG. 4. Velocity distribution in a natural river channel in a straight reach; three examples for the same stream, at different sections within a single reach of a few hundred feet; flow is near bankfull. Lines represent surfaces of equal velocity. (Leopold, Wolman and Miller, 1964.) (By permission of W. H. Freeman and Co., San Francisco.)

FIG. 5. Sketch showing path of maximum velocity in a meandering stream.

gradient. *C* is an empirical constant which depends upon the forces of gravity and friction. Friction in turn depends upon channel roughness, sinuosity and cross-section size and shape.

Transportation and Erosion

Rivers erode the land, carrying particles away as dissolved material, as bed load, and in suspension. They may carry many salts in solution (Table 4); hence corrosion is very important in wearing away the land. Moreover, these chemicals are carried to the sea and contribute to its saltiness.

The solid or debris load of a stream comprises material moving along the bottom of the channel as bed load, and the material supported by the water and moved as suspended load. This bed load is moved along the bottom by rolling or by saltation (jumping). The largest *amount* of a given-size debris that a river can move in traction as bed load is called its capacity. The largest *diameter* of particle that it can carry as bed load measures its competence. Both capacity and competence increase with increased volume and velocity. Hence, any factor which affects velocity, such as gradient, channel roughness, sinuosity, and channel shape, also affects the capacity and competence.

The suspended load is composed of finer particles

TABLE 4. DISSOLVED LOAD OF SELECTED NORTH AMERICAN RIVERS

River	Dissolved Salts (ppm)	Drainage Area (sq mi)
Grand River, S.D.	990	3,120
Clear Fork, Bragos River, Tex.	393	3,974
Yampa River, Colo.	133	3,410
Genesee River, N.Y.	399	2,467
Mohawk River, N.Y.	152	3,456
Ohio River, Ravenswood, W. Va.	312	39,840
Ohio River, Florence, Ind.	306	82,910
Kansas River, Topeka, Kan.	280	56,710
Platte River, Brady, Nev.	477	56,900
Columbia River, Grand Coulee, Wash.	89	74,100
Colorado River, Grand Canyon, Nev.	677	137,800

(From various Water Supply Papers published by the Geol. Survey).

than the bed load, i.e., grains whose settling velocities are less than the turbulent force of the water. Hence, suspended load is in part measured by turbulence. The concentration of the suspended load varies with depth below the water surface. The greatest concentration of grains is near the bottom with the number of grains in suspension decreasing with height above the bed. When suspended sediment discharge is high, stream velocity and volume are high. Hence any factor which changes the velocity will change the suspended load.

The Graded River

Rivers tend to attain, after a time, a condition of equilibrium which is called *grade*. This is a condition of balance in a river where the slope, width, depth and other channel characteristics are adjusted to the prevailing volume of water and load supplied to it. This adjustment enables the river to maintain a long-term equilibrium between erosion and deposition, so that actively it neither erodes nor deposits in its channel. That is, over a long interval of time, a bar that is deposited in the channel at low water is removed during high water. Such a river is said to be in a steady state; the input equals the output. It reacts to any change of environment in such a manner as to offset or counterbalance the effect of the change. For example, increase in the volume of a river which has attained such a steady state, or grade, would result in a change in channel characteristics. Since the river had been adjusted to its former load and volume, it had developed certain channel characteristics of gradient, width, depth, sinuosity, roughness, etc. These characteristics could no longer remain the same, since with a greater volume, the river could carry the same load with a lower velocity. It might, therefore, change the depth, the width and channel roughness, and the slope by eroding. The river might also react by increasing its length and meandering, thus decreasing the slope. The condition of balance is expressed in an equation (amended from Rubey),

$$nSF = \frac{kL^aD^b}{Q^c}$$

where n is channel roughness, S is stream gradient, F is the channel form ratio, L is the amount of load, D is average diameter of the grains in the bed load, and Q is discharge. The graded river, then, maintains a steady state which is required to transport a given load with its discharge. It does this by adjusting its longitudinal profile, its cross-sectional shape and its channel roughness.

Channel Morphology

Quantitative investigation of the morphology of stream channels and river basins has shown the interrelationships of the various geometric factors. To systematize measurements and comparisons among different rivers, a hierarchy of river order was proposed by Horton. His system, as amended by Strahler, is the one generally in use. The fingertip tributaries, or heads, of river systems are designated as first-order streams; two first-order streams unite to form a second-order segment; two second-order stream segments unite to form a third-order, etc. Hence, any two streams of a given order unite to form a river of the next higher order. However, any second-order stream may have any number of first order streams; a third-order river segment must have at least 2 second-order streams and 4 first orders, but, in addition, may have many more of each. (See articles: *Quantitative Geomorphology*; *Stream Orders*).

It has been found that rivers grow according to set laws; i.e., as one proceeds downstream, a river channel widens and deepens in a regular way. The ratio of growth depends upon two main factors: (1) the erosional ability of the stream and (2) the erodibility of the banks and channel bed. The erosional ability, in turn, depends upon the volume and velocity of the water; hence, any factor (such as gradient) which affects these two characteristics will also affect erosional ability. The erodibility of the channel depends upon the type of material through which the river flows and the structure of the material. The mutual interaction of these two main factors, and of the multitude of factors which determine them, results in a given channel form and an orderly development downstream.

Hence, river length, channel width, depth and gradient, and river volume and velocity are related to each other. And, within a given river basin, downstream changes are regular and determinable, so that laws of growth and development can be formulated. Such laws relate river length, number of tributaries, basin area, river gradient and relief of valley to the order of the river. Relationships among the many other geometric characteristics of a river and its basin have also been empirically determined.

Classification of Rivers

A genetic classification of streams was developed by W. M. Davis (see analysis in Stamp *et al.*, 1961) following J. W. Powell's (1875) use of the term *consequent* to denote a river whose course was determined by the original slope of the land surface. Such streams can often be seen on a hillside, all flowing straight down the slope, forming a parallel drainage pattern. A *subsequent* river (so-named by J. B. Jukes in 1862) is one whose direction of flow is controlled by rock structure, i.e., a river which follows a zone of weakness, such as a fault, joint, or thin or easily erodible rock layer. A number of such rivers tend to develop a pattern of drainage which is called trellised or rectangular. A river is said to be *insequent* (Davis, 1894) if there is no discernable reason why it follows the path it takes. Such rivers show a lack of structural control and tend to develop on homogeneous rock, either horizontal sediments or igneous rocks. Drainage patterns of such streams tend to be dendritic, with tributaries branching in all directions. *Obsequent* streams (Davis, 1895) flow in a direction opposite to that of the original consequent slope. *Resequent* rivers (Cotton, 1922) are those which flow in the same direction as the consequent streams, but at a lower level. Rivers which cut across geologic structures such as folded ridges or crystalline mountain ranges can also be classed as either antecedent or superimposed, depending on time of origin in relation to the ridge-building process. If the river was able to keep its course as a mountain range was elevated across its path, it is *antecedent* (Powell, 1875). However, if the folded or crystalline range was covered by horizontal layers upon which the river took its course, not knowing what was below, and then the river eroded its channel until it encountered the underlying structure and cut through it, the river is *superimposed* or *superposed* (Powell, 1875).

Again, rivers may be classified according to Davis, by their stage of development, as young, mature, old or rejuvenated. A young stream is generally characterized by a narrow, deep, V-shaped valley, and a steep, irregular gradient with pools and rapids. It is rapidly deepening its valley and extending its channel headward by erosion. A mature stream is one which has developed an extensive floodplain upon which it flows in a meandering path. It is graded and presents a smooth concave profile from head to mouth. In contrast to a young stream, it predominantly side-cuts into its valley walls. In old age, a river is still predominantly side-cutting and building up its floodplain, which has now grown much wider than the meander belt. As a consequence of the wide valley and low gradient, the floodplain has numerous meander scars, oxbow lakes and natural levees. This cycle of river development may be interrupted at any time by a change in base level towards which the stream is eroding. If base level is lowered (or land uplifted), for example, the gradient of the river will be increased and it will renew its downcutting. Such a river, beginning a new cycle of downcutting, is said to be rejuvenated. It may become entrenched (intrenched, or incised: Cotton, 1922), i.e., its channel is incised into the old floodplain. Or it may become terraced, eroding below its former floodplain to form upper levels along its channel.

Streams whose cycle of erosion is interrupted by a rise in sea level are drowned and are called estuaries. A stream, because of the lowering of its gradient, may deposit its load along the channel as bars and thus become a braided river, with anastomosing waterways threading through the bars.

A current classification of streams is based upon gradient, and rivers are classed as either low or steep gradient. Those with low gradients will tend to have meandering channels, wide and flat floodplains scarred with oxbow lakes, swamps and former channelways. Rivers with steep gradients will generally flow in deep, narrow channels.

It has been suggested by Schumm that rivers flowing on their floodplains rather than on a hard rock channel should be classified in terms of stability; i.e., that streams are stable, eroding or depositing.

M. MORISAWA

References

Hjulstrom, Filip, 1935, "Studies of the morphological activity of rivers as illustrated by the River Fyris," *Univ. Upsala Geol. Inst. Bull.*, **25**, 221–527.

Jukes, J. B., 1862, "Formation of River Valleys in the South of Ireland," *Quat. J. Geol. Soc.*, **18**, 378–403.

Leliavsky, S., 1955, "An Introduction to Fluvial Hydraulics," London, Constable, 257pp.

Leopold, L. B., Wolman, M. G., and Miller, J. P., 1964, "Fluvial Processes in Geomorphology," San Francisco, Freeman, 522pp.

Mackin, J. H., 1948, "Concept of the graded river," *Bull. Geol. Soc. Am.*, **59**, 463–512.

Morisawa, M., 1968, "Streams: Their Dynamics and Morphology," New York, McGraw-Hill Book Co.

*Stamp, L. D., 1961, "A Glossary of Geographical Terms," London, Longmans, 539pp.

Sundborg, A., 1956, "The River Klaralven, a study of fluvial processes," *Geografiska Ann.*, **38**, 127–316.

Troll, C., 1954, "Über Alter und Bildung von Talmäandern," *Erdkunde*, **8**, 286–302.

* Additional bibliographic references mentioned in the text may be found in this work.

Cross-references: *Base Level; Bed Load; Drainage Basin; Drainage Patterns; Ephemeral Streams; Equilibrium in Geomorphology; Estuary; Floodplain; Grade, Graded Stream; Law of Declivities*, etc.; *Levee, Natural; Quantitative Geomorphology; Rivers; Meandering and Braiding; Sediment Transport; Stream Capture; Stream Channel Characteristics; Stream Flow; Stream Orders; Surell's Laws; Youth—Maturity —Old Age. Vol. VI: Bedforms in Alluvial Channels; Fluvial Sediment Transport; Groundwater; Hydrologic Cycle; Runoff.*

RIVERS—MEANDERING AND BRAIDING

Stream channels are either straight, crooked, meandering (sinuous), or braided (anastomosing: separating and rejoining); variations of each of these types are known. Usually, straight channels are engineered (i.e., dredged), or they follow fault or fracture traces, or they are very short. Most natural streams of any appreciable length are either crooked, meandering, or braided.

Many fluid threads (or fluid currents) other than rivers are known to meander. These include the jet stream (in the atmosphere), the Gulf Stream (near the surface of the North Atlantic ocean), countercurrents in the ocean, and tidal currents. Meandering may be, therefore, the normal aspect of a fluid thread, within certain velocity and viscosity limits, unless hindered by some outside influence.

Meandering streams have traditionally been ascribed to fluvial plains and delta plains (e.g., Thornbury, 1954). From statements of this kind has arisen the notion that meandering is limited to large rivers which are mature, in the *Davisian* sense (or supermature, or "old"). This is not correct. Streams of all sizes meander at all altitudes where suitable streams can be observed, with only one proviso: that mobile granular bed materials are present. Braided streams also appear to develop only in the presence of granular sediments. The difference between the two may be that where binding materials are present, mobile grains tend to make a "soft" coherent mass, and a single channel develops; whereas an absence of binding matter means little or no coherence between grains, no steep walls, and hence a wide shallow channel or perhaps even numerous small channels side by side. The binding material most commonly available is clay and fine silt, but organic debris (i.e., from partly decayed vegetation) may be important. The analysis outlined in this paragraph can be summarized as follows:

> Granular bed materials only—Braiding
> Granular materials plus binder—Meandering
> Dominantly clay bed—Crooked or straight
> No mobile bed materials—Crooked or straight

The last category would have characteristics fixed by the nature of the rocks over which the stream flowed.

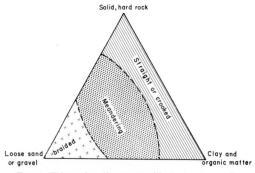

FIG. 1. Triangular diagram to illustrate stream form related to channel material.

Inasmuch as clay is the product of chemical weathering of rather common minerals (such as feldspar and various dark accessory minerals), or the result of erosion of preexisting clays and shales, clay as a binding agent should be limited to regions where fairly wet climates obtain or where considerable sedimentary clay is available. The abundance of braided streams in dry areas (little clay, little vegetation) can be explained on this basis.

Braided and meandering reaches may alternate on the same stream. In some cases, at least, these changes are related to changes in the bedrock (i.e., sandstone or shale) across which the stream flows. Channels cut in coarse materials (i.e., pebbles, cobbles, and boulders) may be either braided or meandering; an outstanding example of the latter occurs on the stream which parallels U.S. Highway 34, in Rocky Mountain National Park, west of the town of Estes Park, Colo., and a good example of the former can be seen on the stream which parallels Canadian Highway 1, in the vicinity of the village of Field, in Yoho National Park, British Columbia.

Hydrodynamically, a single channel in a braided reach can be studied in terms of a single meandering stream. The difference lies in the lack of stability, in the presence of moving water, of loose sand or gravel banks, in the case of a braided stream.

A meandering river is a *graded* stream (i.e., in *equilibrium*); this is true even of those which have many small waterfalls and rapids present throughout meandering reaches. A graded stream is a delicately balanced open system which responds almost instantly to changes in the controlling parameters (for instance, *discharge* and *bed load* grain size). As a graded stream slowly alters its map pattern from roughly straight to meandering, it lengthens its course and reduces its gradient. It also reduces greatly its load carrying ability, for three reasons: (1) the actual bed load in motion is less in a curved channel than in a straight one; (2) the curved channel is also longer than a straight one connecting the same two points; (3) much of the bed load is locked up in alluvial deposits, adjacent to the channel, for long periods of time between passage of successive meander loops. (These considerations apply only in part to *wash load*, very fine particles which move essentially with the water.)

A meandering stream is not free to expand its meander system to any degree whatsoever, as this would imply freedom to reduce its gradient to any arbitrary angle, such as a fraction of a millimeter per kilometer. There is an obscure, but nevertheless effective, relationship between gradient, grain size, amount of binder, discharge, and channel pattern, which prescribes under what circumstances a stream will meander, even though under *almost* identical circumstances a similar reach is braided. In general, braided reaches are steeper than meandering portions of the same stream. This may be related in good part to the fact that the average channel width is greater, and the average depth less, in the braided stretch.

Many streams are two-phase systems, meandering at high water, and being braided at low water, especially if the two pertinent discharges are quite different from each other.

Experience with model streams, in ordinary sand, shows that most straight artificial channels soon develop meanders. Experience with the dredging of natural rivers, such as the Mississippi, shows that very little shortening is achieved even though many meander loops have been eliminated by making artificial cuts; in other words, under the prevailing conditions, a given reach of river requires a given length of channel, and the stream will meander precisely enough to make the necessary adjustments. Therefore, we conclude that meandering is a natural state of affairs, obtained by gradual stages, as the channel departs from a straight line.

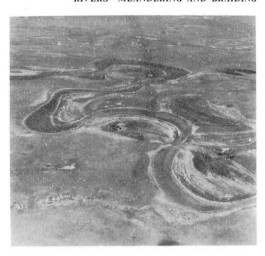

FIG. 3. Completely silted meanders in the delta of the Mitchell River, northern Queensland. (Air photo: F. W. Whitehouse).

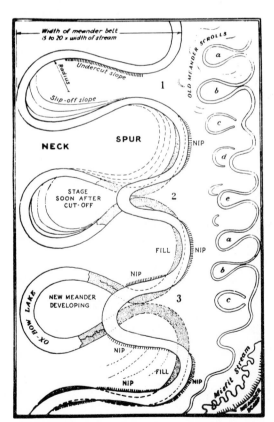

FIG. 2. Terminology of meanders and ox-bow lakes (from Lobeck, 1939). (By permission of McGraw-Hill Book Co., N.Y.)

Many straight currents, in canals, laboratory streams, and natural creeks, exhibit a winding phenomenon which appears to be the forerunner of true meandering. This phenomenon can be made obvious by placing lighted floats on the water surface, at night, and tracking them by means of time-exposure photography. The lines which are obtained in this, or any analogous, manner, show a meander-like pattern (i.e., any single fluid thread meanders, within the confines of straight walls, in these experiments and observations). Furthermore, the channel bed, if made of mobile materials, quickly adjusts so that the deepest water can be found in those parts of the bends where the maximum fluid velocity comes closest to the channel walls. This is also characteristic of meandering streams: the outside bank of each meander loop tends to be deep and undercut ("pool"), and the short "straight" segment between adjacent loops is rather wide and shallow ("riffle"). The pool-and-riffle pattern commonly appears, in the development of a stream, long before surface geometry begins to look like meandering.

Development of a sinuous maximum-velocity thread, and of the pool-and-riffle bottom profile, may be related to the presence of roughness elements (i.e., gravel patches) along the channel walls. A single patch would be adequate to initiate meandering in mobile materials, inasmuch as the first deviation in a channel is sufficient to require an overcompensated counterdeviation, which in turn will lead to a third, etc., as far downstream as the current flows across granular materials. Such a mechanism can work only on a slope, where an initial bend turns the channel so that the fluid thread is no longer moving directly down the

FIG. 4. Well-developed meander, almost at stage of cutoff; the Albert River below Burketown, northern Queensland. (Air photo: F. W. Whitehouse).

slope. Meandering streams, in general, have gradients between about 20 cm/km and about 10 m/km (the lower Mississippi River, below Baton Rouge, flows mostly on clay, has a gradient of about 2 cm/km, but does not meander). This range can be extended from the upper limit in instances where the mobile bed materials are gravel.

It has been known for nearly a century that the maximum velocity thread lies close to the outside (concave) bank in a meander, that convergent and divergent flows occupy definite places in the three-dimensional flow structure, and that the space through which water sinks (acceleration—close to the outside bank) has a much smaller surface area than the space through which water rises (deceleration—between the maximum-velocity line and the inside bank). These facts can be combined only in a system where surface water tends to flow toward the outside bank, whereas bottom water tends to move toward the inside bank. Overturn of this kind has been described, variously, as spiral flow, helical flow or secondary flow, and has been established conclusively in natural streams and many different laboratory experiments.

Recognition of spiral flow in a meandering stream does not answer the question of which comes first, the spiral flow or the meanders. Evidence reviewed in previous paragraphs establishes the fact that meandering is a product of secondary overturn; it is thought that the spiral is the result of differential deceleration due to variability in bottom roughness. A helix in the earth's gravity field *must* have a curved axis, inasmuch as the descending waters will be accelerated relative to ascending fluid.

A spiral cell in a channel carved in granite does

little more than produce interesting flow patterns. A spiral cell in a channel cut across slightly coherent sand results in scour (downflow—acceleration) on the longer side (outside) of the curved axis, and deposition (upflow—deceleration) on the shorter side (inside). In noncoherent sands, where steep banks cannot stand for any significant time in the presence of moving water, a single initial spiral induces second- (and higher) order helices next to it. When a full set of helices has been developed, one can observe that all of the spirals of odd-numbered order (such as first order, third order, etc.) curve in one direction, whereas all the spirals of even-numbered order (second, fourth) curve in the opposite direction. Hence, any two adjacent spirals are either back-to-back (fast, descending current immediately against fast, descending current), or face-to-face (slow, rising current immediately against slow, rising current). Where the adjacent spirals are back-to-back, a deep scour pocket develops. Where they are face-to-face, a diamond-shaped bar forms. The alternation of scour pockets and bars, both across the stream and down the stream, is what is known as the braided pattern. It is sometimes difficult to see, inasmuch as the basic pattern is developed during flood stage but observed only after the waters have subsided, at which time many smaller-scale patterns have been superimposed on the larger one. In model work, however, where water can be kept clean and transparent and where flow can be stopped almost instantly, the diamond-shaped bars show up in relatively systematic checker-board arrangement.

A clear distinction must be made between the behavior of water and the motion of sediment such

FIG. 5. Mature meander, near coast, showing centrifugal drainage of salt flats and fringe of mangrove; the Flinders River below Inverleigh, Queensland. (Air photo: F. W. Whitehouse).

FIG. 6. Braided stream pattern and fluvial plain, South Island of New Zealand. (Air photo: V. C. Browne).

as sand in a meandering stream. The water follows a spiral path, in which the sense of the spiral reverses at each riffle. The sediment behaves somewhat differently because of its greater density (quartz in water has a specific gravity of approximately $2.65 - 1.00 = 1.65$). Scoured out of bank or bottom in a pool, it either moves diagonally across the channel to come to rest on the gentle slope on the convex side, or it travels downstream to the next riffle. If it reaches that shoal area, it may come to rest momentarily, or it may pass on to the next gentle slope (*point-bar*, if built up as a sequence of parallel curved ridges, or *slip-off slope*).

The net result is that the pool migrates laterally (toward the concave bank) and downstream, while the opposite slope shifts in the same direction. The combined effect is meander migration; individual loops appear to slide down the channel, following each other in succession past any given point. This migration buries the sediment coming to rest on any point-bar, which will not be attacked again until the next meander loop shifts into the immediate locality. The period (interval between passage of successive loops) is on the order of 10–100 years; hence most of the sand spends most of its time *not* in motion, and it travels only very slowly toward the sea.

If all soft, mobile, meander-prone materials were uniform, meandering streams might have perfectly symmetrical sinuous channels. However, perfect uniformity of materials in alluvial valleys is almost impossible to achieve. Old abandoned

FIG. 7. Braided pattern ("reticulate drainage") in semiarid environment; McInley River about lat. 21°S, Queensland. (Air photo: F. W. Whitehouse).

oxbow lakes (loops which have been cut off when one reach of the river overtakes another) commonly fill with material having more clay and organic matter than the adjacent alluvium; *clay plugs* of this origin are tough (although not hard) and quite resistant to scour. When, at some later date, a migrating loop impinges against a clay plug, the active channels will be deformed. Other causes of deformation are resistant ledges in the valley wall, resistant ledges in the channel floor, landslide piles, moraines, active faults, tributary streams, patches of well-matted tree or bush roots, lava flows, and (more recently) engineering installations such as bridge pilings, groynes, land-fill, and channel-deflection devices. As a result, streams which appear to have a wide valley flat on which to meander commonly exhibit a large variety of complicated patterns.

One of the clearest examples of meander deformation can be described as stacking (*stacked meanders*). In this example, the gradient of the stream is reduced, slightly, immediately upstream from the deforming influence (such as a clay plug). In the reduced-gradient area, meander migration is slowed, and the first loop which shifts into the area is quickly overtaken by a second. As each new loop arrives, riffles tend to rotate so that the current flow is at right angles to the valley slope, and the curvature in each loop gets progressively tighter. Stacked meanders may collect eight or ten or more tightly deformed loops, with relatively long, straight stretches where short riffles should be.

The geologist is very much interested in deformed meander patterns because they are "anomalous" and therefore provide more information than do perfect meanders. The latter commonly reflect grain size of sediment, relative amounts of granular material and binder, discharge, and hence even perhaps drainage basin characteristics and climate. The former, however, also provide information about either bedrock or other geologic agencies and effects in the area. A careful analysis of meander anomalies (either stacking or other deviations) commonly yields considerable insight into the structure or stratigraphy of the region.

Meandering streams on wide flood plains have, associated with them, many oxbow lakes. These are relics of older channels (ideally observed on air photographs), and therefore they tell something of the history of the stream. Channel widths and arcs of curvature, measured on oxbows, show that in the fairly recent past, meandering streams in many parts of the United States were systematically larger than they are today. That is, the occurrence of oversize oxbows is so widespread that stream *piracy* (diversion of waters of one river into another as a result of a natural accident) cannot be invoked for any appreciable percentage of the known cases. One must conclude that, fairly recently, meandering streams were (in

general) 4–10 times as wide as modern streams in the same area, although they flowed on the same floodplain and down the same gradient. Changes in width can be related to changes in discharge, other factors being held roughly equal, on the following basis:

$$\Delta Q = k(\Delta w)^2$$

where Q is discharge, w is channel width, and k is some constant of proportionality not too far from unity. According to this empirical relationship, a reduction in width by a factor of four would be associated with a reduction in discharge to one-sixteenth its former value. The relationship between discharge and precipitation, again on an empirical basis, is roughly:

$$\Delta Q = k'(\Delta P)^{3.4}$$

where P is average annual total precipitation (rain and snow) and k' is a second constant of proportionality, again not far from one. Combining these two relationships, we obtain the result that a decrease in channel width, by a factor of four, should have followed a reduction in precipitation according to this list:

> From 100 to 40 inches, or
> from 60 to 25 inches, or
> from 40 to 20 inches.

These calculations have omitted a number of pertinent factors, but it is thought that their effects would largely cancel and that the results indicate the extent to which continental deglaciation, accompanied by a change from a wet (pluvial) climate to a subhumid or semiarid climate, altered the sizes of meandering streams.

Oversize oxbows are not the only relics of ice-age pluvial climate. In Oklahoma, for example, a modern meandering stream (Little River, near the center of the state) meanders in a deep valley which also meanders (but on a quite different scale); i.e., present meanders are small enough to develop on the floodplain which exists on the floor of an older, much larger, meandering channel. The old channel is now the valley. Similar "two-level" meander systems have been described from other parts of the United States and the world. Perhaps some meandering valleys can be explained by piracy, but many of them appear to be ice-age relics which give an indication of rainfall even greater than that obtained from oversize oxbows. The reduction in precipitation suggested by studies of these large features might be as great as from 100 to 25 inches.

Entrenched meanders are those which formerly existed on alluvial fill and which have subsequently deepened their channels until now the stream flows through a gorge or chasm cut in bedrock. An excellent example can be found in the *goosenecks* of the San Juan River, northwest of Medicine Hat, in southeastern Utah. A synonymous term for this phenomenon is *incised meanders*. Entrenched meanders are commonly ascribed to *epeirogeny*, although a drop in sea level, or some other process, might have been responsible in some cases. The San Juan River, where it flows through the goosenecks, is not a true meandering stream today, but rather a crooked stream which has inherited a meander-type pattern from a previous stage in its history.

A parameter which has proven useful in studies of meanders is the pure number

$$W = w_{mb}/w_{ch}$$

where w_{mb} is the width of the meander belt and w_{ch} is the width of the channel. This is one kind of *tortuosity ratio;* several others, based on length rather than width, or on curvature, have been proposed. Unfortunately a single universal value for W cannot be given, inasmuch as it depends (in nature) on w_{ch} in a way which does not appear from purely geometrical considerations. A plot of "normal" meandering streams shows that $W = 11.55$ is a limiting case, with $W = 16$ being common on small creeks, and the limiting value being approached only on the largest rivers. The ratio drops to values such as $W_s = 6$ or 8 for stacked meanders, and it rises to as much as $W_e = 95$ for entrenched meanders. Meaningless values for W can be obtained by applying this dimensionless measure to all streams, such as complexly crooked creeks which follow fracture patterns on igneous rocks.

In the Davis system of geomorphology, a stream is young, mature, or old. One of the characteristics of maturity, in that system, is a well-developed meander belt. No acceptable criterion was ever developed, however, to distinguish mature from old rivers. Recent writers on the subject have tended to ignore the problem, to gloss over it (i.e., by lumping channel characteristics with regional characteristics), or to adopt the position that rivers have only two ages in their ordinary development: submaturity (or youth) and maturity. This last position seems to represent a reasonable summary.

W. F. TANNER

References

Bagnold, R. A., 1960, "Some aspects of the shape of river meanders," *U.S. Geol. Surv. Profess. Paper*, **282-E**, 135–144.

Doeglas, D. J., 1962, "The structure of sedimentary deposits of braided rivers," *Sedimentology*, **1**, 167–190.

Dury, G. H., 1962, "Results of seismic exploration of meandering valleys," *Am. J. Sci.*, **260**, 691–706.

Einstein, H. A., and Harder, J. A., 1954, "Velocity distribution and the boundary layer at channel bends," *Trans. Am. Geophys. Union*, **35**, 114–120.

Fisk, H. N., 1947, "Fine-grained alluvial deposits and their effects on Mississippi River activity," Mississippi River Commission, Vicksburg, Mississippi.

Leliavsky, S., 1959, "An Introduction to Fluvial Hydraulics," pp. 92–191, London, Constable, and Co., Ltd.

Leopold, L. B. and Langbein, W. B., 1966, "River meanders," *Sci. Amer.*, **214**(6), 60–70.

Leopold, Luna B., and Wolman, M. Gordon, 1960, "River meanders," *Bull. Geol. Soc. Am.*, **71**, 769–794.

Lobeck, A. K., 1939, "Geomorphology," McGraw-Hill Book Co., 731 pp.

Melton, F. A., 1938, "Underfit meanders of floodplain streams," *Proc. Geol. Soc. Am. for 1937*, 324.

O'Hare, J. E., Carlson, Q. H., and Tamblyn, W. E., 1954, "Some results of a tanker survey of the Gulf Stream," *Trans. Am. Geophys. Union*, **35**, 420–430.

Riehl, H., Alaka, M. A., Jordan, C. L., and Renard, R. J., 1954, "The jet stream," *Am. Meteorol. Soc., Meteorol. Monogr.*, **2**, No. 7, 100.

Russell, R. J., 1947, "Reviews and abstracts of Studies: Stream meanders," *Annals. Assoc. Am. Geogr.*, **37**, 65–67.

Scheidegger, A. E., 1961, "Theoretical Geomorphology," pp. 176–190, Berlin, Springer Verlag, Berlin.

Schumm, S. A., 1960, "The shape of alluvial channels in relation to sediment type," *U.S. Geol. Surv. Profess. Paper 352-B*, 17–30.

Schumm, Stanley A., 1961, "Dimensions of some stable alluvial channels," *U.S. Geol. Surv. Profess. Paper 424-B*, 26–27.

Tanner, W. F., 1955, "Geological significance of "stacked" meanders," *Bull. Geol. Soc. Am.*, **66**, 1698.

Tanner, W. F., 1963, "Spiral flow in rivers, shallow seas, dust devils, and models," *Science*, **139**, 41–42.

Thornbury, W. D., 1954, "Principles of Geomorphology," New York, John Wiley & Sons, 618 pp.

Wolman, M. Gordon, and Brush, Lucien M., 1961, "Factors controlling the size and shape of stream channels in coarse non-cohesive sands." *U.S. Geol. Surv. Profess. Paper 282-G*, 183–210.

Cross-references: *Canyon Cutting; Grade, Graded Stream; Incised Meander; Lava-displaced Drainage; Oxbow Lakes; Rivers; Slipoff Slope; Stream Capture; Stream Channel Characteristics; Stream Table Construction and Operation; Youth—Maturity—Old Age.* Vol. II: *Fluid Mechanics; Hydrodynamics.*

RIVER TERRACES—*See* TERRACES—FLUVIAL

ROCHE MOUTONNÉE

This is a French expression that refers to rocky outcrops in glaciated landscapes, which are round on one side and irregular on the other. The ice has rounded and striated the upstream or "stoss" end (a German expression) and passed over or plucked away at the lee side. Shaler proposed "scour" and "pluck" to the older "push" and "lee" sides and this was recommended by Penck (1905). According to Charlesworth (1957), the term *roche moutonnée* was first used by de Saussure between 1779 and 1796 because these rocks bear a fanciful resemblance to the wavy wigs fashionable in his day and

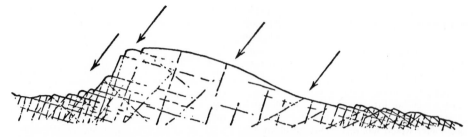

Fig. 1. Longitudinal section of a typical roche moutonnée fashioned by a glacier from an obdurate mass of sparsely jointed granite. The glacier moved from right to left and exerted its force in the direction indicated approximately by the arrows—that is, at a high angle against the back and crown of the hump but at a slight angle away from the downstream face. It consequently subjected the back and crown to vigorous abrasion, leaving them smoothed and gently curved, and it subjected the downstream face to quarrying mainly, leaving it hackled and abrupt. If glaciation had continued until all of the jointed, quarriable rock had been removed from the downstream side, there would have resulted an asymmetric dome, smoothed on all sides but steeper on the downstream side than on the upstream side (from Matthes, 1930).

known as *moutonnées*, being pomaded with mutton tallow. It was widely adopted after its glaciological significance was recognized by Agassiz (1840).

The roche moutonnée may be distinguished from the "crag and tail" in its lack of a streamlined tail of ground moraine ("lodgement till"). It is rather similar to the "rock drumlin," but it is usually reserved for small-scale outcrops, although rock drumlins are not basically different, and Flint (1957) would drop the French term altogether. P. F. Kendall (1924) remarked that "a drumlin is a roche moutonnée expressed in boulder clay."

RHODES W. FAIRBRIDGE

References

Agassiz, A., 1840, "Études sur les Glaciers," Neuchatel, privately published, 346pp.

Bär, O., 1957, "Gesteinsklüfte und Rundhöcker; Untersuchungen im Aare- und Gotthardmassiv," *Geogr. Helv.*, **12**, 1–40.

Carol, H., 1947, "The formation of Roches Moutonnées," *J. Glaciology*, **1**(2), 57–59.

Charlesworth, J. K., 1957, "The Quaternary Era," London, Edward Arnold, 2 vols.

Flint, R. F., 1957, "Glacial and Pleistocene Geology," New York, John Wiley & Sons, 553pp.

Kendall, P. F., and Wroot, H. E., 1924, "Geology of Yorkshire," London, Leeds, 995pp.

Matthes, F. E., 1930, "Geologic history of the Yosemite Valley," *U.S. Geol. Surv., Profess. Paper* **160**, 137pp.

Penck, A., 1905, "Glacial features in the surface of the Alps," *J. Geol.*, **13**, 1–19.

Cross-references: *Crag and Tail; Drumlin; Glacial Geology.*

ROCK COLOR CHART—*See* pr Vol. VI

ROCK FAN

A rock surface shaped in plan as the sector of a circle with apex upslope and arc downslope was named by Davis (1900) a "rock fan." Transverse profiles are convex and profiles along the radii may be concave, straight or convex.

Definitions

". . . Near the base of the mountain front nearly all of the ravines broaden and their floors become distinctly convex, thus imitating the form well-known in alluvial fans, though rarely matched in an eroded surface of solid rock. These convex floors will be called rock fans" (Davis, 1900, pp. 209–210). Rock fans were later defined by Johnson as ". . . forms closely resembling alluvial fans but developed by erosion on bedrock" (1932a, p. 389) and "bedrock surface with the form of a typical fan" (1932b, pp. 658–659).

The bedrock may be weathered rock but not unconsolidated sediments—"rock fan is a bad name

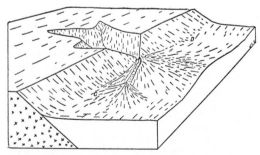

FIG. 1. Development of rock fan. Evolution of topography of a weak-rock area in front of a mountain canyon under conditions of great aridity (J. L. Rich, 1935).

because many are cut on unconsolidated sediments" (Bryan, 1936, p. 771), nor should it be covered by alluvium or fan deposits, "... as long as the cover is present, the visible surface of an (fan-shaped) embayment should not be called a rock fan" (Davis, 1938, p. 1369). Davis' (1938, p. 1347) further restriction of rock fans to "mountain-front embayments" seems unjustified.

Examples

Rock fans, as defined above, are rare (cf. Thornbury, 1954, p. 287). Examples are all on hard massive crystalline rocks (granite, gneiss and quartz-monzonite): (a) from Arizona—the Dragoon Mountains, the Sierrita Mountains (Johnson, 1932, pp. 400–407, Figs. 4 through 9; confirmed by Davis, 1938, p. 1385 footnote), the Little Ajo Mountains (Gilluly, 1937, p. 334; confirmed by Balchin and Pye, 1956, p. 176) and the Coyote Mountains (McGee, 1897, plate 12; cited by Davis, 1900, p. 210; Johnson, 1932, p. 411); (b) from Namaqualand (Mabbutt, 1955, p. 79, Plate 3); (c) from the east-central Sudan and northern Ghana (Ruxton and Berry, 1961, pp. 199–202, Plate 1 A and B, and Fig. 5). Perhaps one exception is the development of rock fans on a homogeneous mudstone in Wyoming, "steep conical pediments ... 20 to 23 degrees ... veneered with quartz pebbles" (Bradley, 1940, p. 251, Fig. 4).

The rock fans described range in area from several acres when steep, 20–26°, to one or more square miles when gentle, $\frac{1}{2}$–7°. Most of them head into a reentrant in the hill or mountain front, though one in northern Ghana is at the foot of a spur, and they may be channeled or unchanneled.

Rock Fans and Coalescing Rock Fans Mantled with Alluvium or Fanglomerate

Rich (1935, p. 1006, Figs. 4 and 6) used the term rock fan for "... a debris-veneered slope at the foot of the mountains having the form of an alluvial apron or a series of fans joining at their sides, but actually being composed of bedrock except for an alluvial veneer." Compare this with Gilbert's (1882, pp. 183, 185) usage of *pediment* for the surface

FIG. 2. Types of dissected rock fans: (A) Sub-conical mass of hills partially blocking canyon mouth, the stream escaping by marginal gorge following contact of fan and mountain front. (B) Inclined rock bench preserved on one side of canyon mouth, representing marginal portion of rock fan largely removed by planation at lower level where new fan of more gentle gradient has been formed (D. W. Johnson).

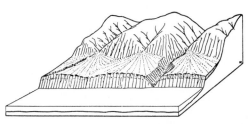

FIG. 3. Truncated fans of the New Zealand coast. Generalized sketch (D. W. Johnson).

of an alluvial fan or cone, and Bryan's (1936, p. 771) comment that "pediments of arid regions are not easily distinguished from alluvial slopes formed of coalescing alluvial fans."

If the alluvial cover is of uniform thickness then alluvial fans and coalescing alluvial fans are underlain by rock fans and coalescing rock fans. Thus the reexamination of Gilbert's "slopes of planation" in the Henry Mountains by Hunt, Averitt, and Miller (1953, p. 2) revealed "a series of confluent rock fans overlain by fanglomerates deposited after the pediments were formed." However, *pediment* and *rock fan* (or *confluent rock fan*) are not equivalent terms as pediments are often not fan-shaped (cf. Bryan, 1936, p. 772) though to many workers alluvial covered rock fans and coalescing rock fans are types of pediment.

The thickness of the alluvial cover is usually about equal to the depth of the flood channel of the streams (Blackwelder, 1931, p. 134; after Gilbert, 1877, pp. 126–127); though some "intersecting low-angle rock fans" in "relatively unchanneled pediment embayments" have only "thin detritus over little weathered rock" (Mabbutt, 1955, pp. 78–80). *A compound, or two-story, rock fan developed on limestone was described from Wyoming by Mackin (1937, Fig. 11).*

BRYAN P. RUXTON

References

Balchin, W. G. V. and Pye, N., 1956, "Piedmont profiles in the arid cycle," *Proc. Geol. Assoc., London*, **66**, 176.

Blackwelder, E., 1931, "Desert plains," *J. Geol.*, **39**(2), 133–140.

Bradley, W. H., 1940, "Pediments and pedestals in miniature," *J. Geomorphol.*, **3**(3), 251.

Bryan, K., 1936, "The formation of pediments," *16th Intern. Geol. Congr., 1933*, **2**, 765–775.

Davis, W. M., 1900, "Fault scarp in the Lapini Mountains, Italy," *Bull. Geol. Soc. Am.*, **11**, 209–210.

Davis, W. M., 1938, "Sheet floods and stream floods," *Bull. Geol. Soc. Am.*, **49**, 1337–1416.

Gilbert, G. K., 1877, "Report on the geology of the Henry Mountains, Utah," *U.S. Geog. G.S. Rocky Mtn. Reg.*, 160pp.

Gilbert, G. K., 1882, "Contributions to the history of Lake Bonneville, Utah," *U.S. Geol. Surv. Ann. Rept.*, **2**, 183, 185.

Gilluly, J., 1937, "Physiography of the Ajo region, Arizona," *Bull. Geol. Soc. Am.*, **48**(3), 323–347.

Hunt, C. B., Averitt, P. and Miller, R. L., 1953, "Geology and geography of the Henry Mountains region, Utah," *U.S. Geol. Surv. Profess. Paper* **228**, 234pp.

Johnson, D. W., 1932a, "Rock fans of arid regions," *Am. J. Sci.*, **23**, 5th ser., 389–416.

Johnson, D. W., 1932b, "Rock planes of arid regions," *Geograph. Rev.*, **22**, 658–659.

Mabbutt, J. A., 1955, "Pediment land forms in Little Namaqualand, South Africa," *Geograph. J.*, London, **121**, 77–83.

Mackin, J. H., 1937, "Erosional history of the Big Horn Basin, Wyoming," *Bull. Geol. Soc. Am.*, **48**(6), 813–893.

McGee, W J, 1897, "Sheetflood erosion," *Bull. Geol. Soc. Am.*, **8**, 87–112.

Rich, J. L., 1935, "Origin and evolution of rock fans and pediments," *Bull. Geol. Soc. Am.*, **46**(6), 999–1024.

Ruxton, B. P., and Berry, L., 1961, "Notes on faceted slopes, rock fans, and domes on granite in the East-Central Sudan," *Am. J. Sci.*, **259**, 194–206.

Thornbury, W. D., 1954, "Principles of Geomorphology," New York, John Wiley & Sons, 618pp.

Cross-references: *Alluvial Fan, Cone; Arid Cycle; Bajada; Deserts and Desert Landforms; Pediment.*

ROCK FLOUR—*See* ABRASION; LOESS; *also* pr Vol. VI, PARNA

ROCK STREAMS, ROCK RIVERS, ROCK GLACIERS

Features of marginal or bare areas of periglacial or mountain glaciation regime, the rock stream, river or glacier (synonymous terms) is a characteristic form of *mass wasting* (q.v.) near the firn limit (French: *coulée de pierres, . . . de blocs;* German: *Blockstrom*). "Rock stream" appeared first in a folio by Cross and Howe (1905), while "rock glacier" appeared in a paper by Capps (1910), although the phenomenon was described earlier by Matthes (1900) and others. They are well known in parts of the Alps, the Pyrenees, Scandinavia and in the Rocky Mountains (especially Montana, Wyoming and Colorado). The components are glacially riven boulders and angular fragments. The shape of these talus trains is rather similar to that of a true glacier, except that ice is normally absent. They are up to a few kilometers wide, 1000 meters long and 50 meters thick. They are lubricated by seasonal penetration by snow and melt water and are constantly in motion

due to freeze and thaw (elevation and constriction). The angle of flow may be quite gentle, less than 5° and may exceed 20° in the mountains (cirques). In plan, the rock glacier may have a talus or scree slope collecting area, a steep middle sector, and a gentle, spreading lower section. Its distal limit may show a succession of lobate ridges or wrinkles 5–30 meters high.

One may determine if the rock stream is in seasonal motion by the presence or absence of lichens growing on the boulders. Some formerly active rock streams are now inactive or very sluggish owing to the climatic amelioration of the last half century. Rock streams above 2400 meters in the Ötztaler Alps of Tyrol photogrammetrically photographed annually over the period 1938–55 showed motions of the order of 1.5 m/yr in the middle, and 3–4 m/yr at the front, but the margins are held back considerably, thus forming a sort of lateral moraine (Pillewitzer, 1957). They appeared to have evolved originally from cirque glaciers; Kesseli (1941) made the same suggestion ("fossil glaciers") for those of the Sierra Nevada, but Sharpe (1938) and others feel they are just another, but more advanced, form of rock creep or "talus creep."

RHODES W. FAIRBRIDGE

References

Capps, S. R., 1910, "Rock glaciers in Alaska," *J. Geol.*, **18**, 359–375.

Cross, W., and Howe, E., 1905, "Geologic atlas of the United States, Silverton Folio, Colorado," *U.S. Geol. Surv.*, Folio 120, 34pp.

Howe, E., 1909, "Landslides in the San Juan Mountains, Colorado," *U.S. Geol. Surv. Profess. Paper* **67**, 58pp.

Kesseli, J. E., 1941, "Rock streams in the Sierra Nevada," *Geograph. Rev.*, **31**, 203–227.

Matthes, F. E., 1900, "Glacial sculpture of the Bighorn Mountains, Wyoming," *U.S. Geol. Surv., 21st Ann. Rept.*, (2), 167–190.

Pillewitzer, W., 1957, "Untersuchnugen an Blockströmen der Ötztaler Alpen," *Abhandl. Geogr. Inst. Fr. Univ. Berlin*, 37–50.

Sharpe, C. F. S., 1938, "Landslides and Related Phenomena," New York, Columbia University Press, 137pp.

Cross-references: *Cirque Glacier; Mass Wasting; Talus.*

ROCKING STONE—*See* PERCHED BLOCK, BOULDER

S

SABKHA OR SEBKHA

Sabkha, with a variety of similar spellings, is an Arabic term for a flat depression, generally close to the water table and covered with salt crust. It is a characteristic feature of coastal lands in North Africa and Arabia (Termier and Termier, 1963, see their Fig. 62 of the Sabkha of Oran, Algeria).

Equivalent features are the *solonchak* salt flats of the Caspian Sea and some *kevir* depressions of Iran and Transcaspia. Certain *salt pans* and *vleis* in South Africa and *playas* in the southwestern United States are of this sort, but the true sabkha depressions are not fed by streams or runoff; they are bordered by sand dunes as a rule. In Algeria, some are fed by groundwater from underground wadis or oueds (Gautier, 1908). The *shotts* of Tunis and Algeria are a special type, being deflation hollows, fed from below by groundwater from the Atlas Mountains. The common feature is periodic flooding and evaporation, resulting in an alternating accumulation of eolian clays and salts. The floor of the sabkha becomes impermeable.

Sabkhas may be covered by rainwater periodically or by high tides in coastal regions. Many coast-sabkhas are somewhat above present sea level (0.5–3.0 meters) and are inherited from short mid-Holocene eustatic oscillations. At the high stands these features were shallow bays, and today the inner margins are lined with raised beaches and vast accumulations of marine shells; extensive examples of this sort may be seen in the Sirte Gulf of Libya and along the south shore of the Persian Gulf.

The seawater temperature and evaporation rates on the Persian Gulf reach an astonishing level in summer (water temperatures exceeding 35°C for several weeks), and contemporary evaporites are formed in the lagoons (fresh gypsum) and by capillary action in the sabkhas. These capillary evaporites include aragonite and calcite, while dolomite, anhydrite, gypsum, celestite and halite occur as early diagenetic products (Evans, Kendall and Skipwith, 1964). The sabkha surface is rather soft, car tires sinking in several inches, and the underlying material is poorly cemented. The water table there is generally at about 1–2 meters. The usual level of the sabkha is high spring tide, but seaward it often passes into the intertidal zone without a very sharp

boundary. Deflation of the surface may occur in the dry seasons.

RHODES W. FAIRBRIDGE

References

Evans, G., Kendall, C. G. St. C., and Skipwith, P., 1964, "Origin of the coastal flats, the sabkha, of the Trucial Coast, Persian Gulf," *Nature,* **202,** 759–761.

Gautier, E. F., 1908, "Sahara algerién," in (Gautier and Chudeau, editors) "Mission au Sahara," Vol. 1, 362pp.

Illing, L. V., Wells, A. J., and Taylor, J. C. M., 1965, "Penecontemporary dolomite in the Persian Gulf," in (Pray, L. C., and Murray, R. C., editors) "Dolomitization and Limestone Diagenesis," *Soc. Econ. Paleontologists Mineralogists Spec. Publ.,* **13,** 89–111.

Termier, H., and Termier, G., 1963, "Erosion and Sedimentation," London and Princeton, N.J., D. Van Nostrand Company, 433pp. (translated by D. W. and E. E. Humphries).

Cross-references: *Eustasy; Lagoon; Mangrove Swamp; Playa.* pr Vol. VI: *Evaporites; Salt Marsh.*

SALCRETE—*See* INDURATION

SALINA—*See* PLAYA

SALTATION—*See* WIND ACTION; *also* SEDIMENT TRANSPORT; *also* pr Vol. VI, BEDFORMS IN ALLUVIAL CHANNELS

SALT KARST

Solution phenomena developed in rock salt (halite, NaCl), in the sulfates (notably gypsum and anhydrite) or in other halogenic rocks have been known for many years. Only in recent years, however, has the term *karst* (q.v.), originally derived from the Karst region of limestone solution in Yugoslavia, been applied to geomorphic effects other than those resulting from $CaCO_3$ solution and landform modification. Thus we have *thermokarst* (q.v.) for solution effects in permafrost and ground ice, and *volcano–karst* (q.v.) for analogous phenomena in tuffs and agglomerates.

The term *salt karst* appears to have been first

proposed by G. V. Korotkevich (1961). As he pointed out, criteria for any kind of karst relief require the following: (1) the rock must be fairly easily soluble in water, (2) there must be groundwater in motion, and (3) the water itself should be a solvent, i.e., it must not be supersaturated in the ions available for solution in the rock in question. The more the rock is jointed and fractured, the more accessible are these waters and the more efficient is the process. An interesting difference between salt karst and limestone karst is that the salt is usually impervious, so that although salt is more soluble than calcite, the initial attack can only be made on the external surfaces, and not from interstitial channels or multiple joint faces. Because of its high flow potential (under the impetus of very small pressure and slight temperatures), salt will rapidly reheal any fracture or joint plane. Most salt mines are perfectly dry. The solubility of rock salt (halite) in distilled water at 10°C is 357.2 g/liter, in contrast to 2.05 g/liter for gypsum and 0.013 g/liter for limestone. If the solubility of calcite is taken as unity, then the respective ratios will be 27,477:1 and 158:1. However with CO_2 in solution, the solubility of calcite rises, and if CO_2 equals the partial pressure in air, then the solubility of $CaCO_3$ rises to 0.055 g/liter. Gypsum solubility is little affected by CO_2. Thus under normal conditions some 7000–8000 times more NaCl can be dissolved in water than $CaCO_3$. Likewise, the rate of NaCl solution in moving water is far higher than that of $CaCO_3$.

In the Solotvina salt dome and in the Dombrov section of the Kalush potassium salt deposits (in the Carpathian foothills, U.S.S.R., formerly part of Polish Galicia), the salts are at depths of 5–30 meters beneath an overburden of alluvial sands and silts with an energetic groundwater circulation. The sides of salt domes and other salt deposits are usually insulated by impervious clays. The top may be partly protected by a cap rock of limestone or anhydrite. Where the cap rock is disrupted for some reason, the karst attack may be quite active.

When the fresh groundwater first reaches the salt face, it rapidly becomes a saturated brine, possessing very high density (20% heavier than fresh water), and its dynamic viscosity (internal friction) increases twofold (the viscosity of distilled water is 1.308 centipoises, of brine 2.60). This brine may then protect the salt surface, unless it is drained off in the groundwater. Only under vigorous circulation will the karst processes evolve rapidly.

Since there are often some clay horizons in the salt deposits, in the absence of a calcareous cap rock, a residual clay cap may develop which in turn serves as a barrier to more rapid solution. Korotkevich speaks of an "anti-karst equilibrium" which is rapidly reached unless a definite lateral pressure gradient develops in the groundwater to maintain a constant hydrologic circulation. In sinks and depressions over the salt surface, the karst attack may well cease. In the Dombrov section, the thickness of the clayey gypsum cap reaches 18 meters which testifies to the amount of total solution; the average insolubles amount to 15% by volume of the salts, so that over 110 meters of potassium salts must have been removed. Presumably, the maximum solution would correspond to the early periods of intense uplift in the diapiric process (due to its flow properties, what Trusheim calls "halokinesis"). Groundwater may penetrate considerable distances (10 meters or more) into the salt body subject to halokinesis along series of microfractures that remain temporarily open, especially in the low confining pressures near the surface. Karst sinkholes, caverns and crevices are leached out under these conditions.

Outside of the U.S.S.R., salt karst is seen in the exposed surfaces of salt domes and salt glaciers that develop and persist for long periods in the arid lands of the Middle East, e.g. Luristan in southern Iran, and Jebel Usdum (Sodom), so-called Lot's Wife at the south end of the Dead Sea. Deep salt lapiés (grikes) and sinkholes are commonplace features.

RHODES W. FAIRBRIDGE

References

Bretz, J Harlen, 1952, "A solution cave in gypsum," *J. Geol.*, **60**, 279–283.

Gansser, A., 1960, "Ueber Schlammvulkane und Salzdome," *Vierteljahresschr. Naturforsch. Ges. Zuerich*, **105**, 1–46.

Harrison, J. V., 1930, "The geology of some salt plugs in Luristan (Southern Persia)," *Quart. J. Geol. Soc. London*, **86**, 463–552.

Korotkevich, G. V., 1961, "Certain characteristics of the development of a salt karst," *Dokl. Akad. Nauk SSSR Earth Sci. Sect.* (in translation, 1962), **136**(1–6), 180–182.

Trusheim, F., 1960, "Mechanism of salt migration in Northern Germany," *Bull. Am. Assoc. Petrol. Geologists.*, **44**, 1519–1540.

Cross-references: *Dome Mountains*; *Karst*; *Lapiés*; *Thermokarst*; *Volcano—Karst*. Vol. IV: *Calcium Carbonate*. Vol. V: *Halokinesis*.

SALT MARSH (MARINE MARSH)—*See* pr Vol. VI, **SWAMP, MARSH, BOG**

SALT WEATHERING OR FRETTING

In special environments, salt fretting, or salt weathering, is the dominant weathering process (Jutson, 1917; Cotton, 1942; Tricart, 1959; Wellman and Wilson, 1965). Surfaces that are being salt fretted are covered by a thin layer of loose material composed of small grains of rock held together by salts. The material is aptly termed "rock meal" (Jutson, 1917; Taylor, 1922) and is diagnostic of the process. Salt fretting can be duplicated in the laboratory, and its physical controls are relatively well understood.

Frost damage to porous rocks is a special case of salt fretting in which ice is the "salt" (Everett, 1961). In general, the damage is due not to the expansion of ice on freezing but to the preferential growth of large crystals as described below.

Relatively hard rocks can be completely broken down into their component particles by soaking them in a salt solution and allowing the salt to crystallize in the interstices (Glaessner, 1948). The chemical free energy of a given mass of solid increases with its surface area. Therefore, any system tends to reduce the area of its interfaces to a minimum (Thomson, 1858, 1859; Verhoogen, 1948), and in a system containing crystals in equilibrium with a saturated solution, larger crystals will grow at the expense of the smaller. It is less obvious why, when the larger crystals entirely fill a pore space, they continue to grow against the constraint imposed by the walls of the pore, expand the pore and fragment the rock. The work which must be done during crystal growth on one face of a crystal is equal to $(P_S - P_L)\, dV$, where P_L is the pressure in the liquid, P_S the pressure in the solid, and dV the increase in volume (Lewis and Randall, 1961). This must equal the work done in extending the surface area, which is equal to $\sigma\, dA$, where σ is the interfacial tension between the crystal face and its saturated solution and dA is the increment of area. Then, since σ is independent of V,

$$P_S - P_L = \frac{dA}{dV}$$

Consider crystallization in a porous solid with large pores and small pores both filled with the saturated salt solution; let water evaporate and escape from the system, or let crystallization be induced by a temperature change. First, the larger

FIG. 1. Salt-fretted granite boulder in Dry Valley, South Victoria Land, Antarctica.

crystals in the large pores will grow at the expense of small crystals in the small pores. Let the process continue until salt crystals completely fill the large pores. Now since $P_S - P_L = \sigma\, dA/dV$, for the crystal to grow down the capillary pores would greatly increase the area of the crystal, but would only slightly increase its volume. The crystal will therefore grow in the large pore until the pressure builds up to such an extent that either mechanical fracture occurs or $(P_S - P_L)/\sigma$ becomes greater than the necessary dA/dV to make the crystal grow down the capillary pore. Thus (for a given crystal and therefore a given σ) whether or not fracture occurs depends on whether $\sigma(1/r - 1/R)$ is greater or less than the tensile strength of the rock, r being the radius of the smaller pores and R the radius of the larger. Thus, for rocks of equal inter-pore tensile strength, those with large pores separated from each other by microporous regions will be the most liable to salt fretting.

The necessary conditions for salt fretting are a supply of salts, sites protected from wind and rain in which salts can accumulate, and cyclic changes in humidity and/or temperature that include the crystallization point of at least one of the salts present. For erosion to occur, as distinct from rock breakdown, an agent such as wind is required to transport the salt-weathered material away. Salt weathering is important in: (1) regions where salts are being concentrated; (2) regions where the concentration of salts is kept high by a rapid rate of supply.

The first is represented by arid regions, and by microenvironments that are protected from rain, such as under ledges, on the insides of caves and parts of buildings. Salts are provided by air-borne salt particles, from rain or snow which everywhere contains small quantities of salts, from chemical degradation of the rocks themselves, and from groundwater percolating to the surface, evaporating and depositing salts. The second is represented by the sea coast in most parts of the world. Salts are provided at a rapid rate by splashing of waves and from sea spray. The rocks most affected are those that frequently become wet and then dry, i.e., in general, those in the zone immediately above the direct reach of waves at high water.

In its attack, salt fretting is similar to most other erosive processes in having a well-defined base level, the water or permafrost level below which it cannot act, but it differs from most other erosive processes by acting most rapidly on the lower rather than the upper side of rock surfaces. It is thus a powerful undercutting agent that constantly tends to steepen slopes to the limit of rock strength.

Cavernous weathering is its most distinctive product, but it plays an important part in the formation of many of those topographic features that are controlled by undercutting such as coastal and desert platforms, some kinds of tors and at least some hills that have been termed inselbergs.

H. W. WELLMAN
A. T. WILSON

References

Cotton, C. A., 1942, "Climatic Accidents," Christchurch, N.Z., Whitcombe and Tombs, Ltd., 354pp.

Cotton, C. A., 1963, "Levels of planation of marine benches," *Zeit. f. Geomorph.*, **7**, 97–111.

Everett, D. H., 1961, *Trans. Faraday Soc.*, **9**, 465, 57.

Glaessner, M. F., 1948, "Principles of Micropalaentology," p. 37, Melbourne University Press.

Jutson, J. T., 1917, "The influence of salts in rock-weathering in sub-arid Western Australia," *Proc. Roy. Soc. Vic.*, **30**, 165–172.

Knetsch, G., 1960, "Ueber aride Verwitterung unter besonderer Berücksichtigung natürlicher und künstlicher Wände in Aegypten," *Zeit. f. Geomorph.*, Suppl. v. **1**, 190–205.

Lewis, G. N., and Randall, M., 1961, "Thermodynamics," Second ed., New York, McGraw-Hill Book Co., 723pp.

Taylor, G., 1922, "The Physiography of the McMurdo Sound and Granite Harbour Region," London, Harrison & Sons; British (Terra Nova) Antarctic Exped., 1910–1913.

Thomson, W., 1858, "On the thermal effect of drawing out a film of liquid," *Proc. Roy. Soc.*, **9**, 255–256; also 1859, *Phil. Mag.*, **17**(4), 61.

Tricart, J., 1959, *Cahiers Oceanogr. du C.O.E.C.*, **11**, 276.

Verhoogen, J., 1948, "Geological significance of surface tension," *J. Geol.*, **56**, 210–217.

Wellman, H. W., and Wilson, A. T., 1965, "Salt weathering, a neglected geological erosive agent in coastal arid environments," *Nature*, **205**(4976), 1097–1098.

Cross-references: *Granite Landforms; Limestone Coastal Weathering; Solution Pits and Pans; Tafoni.*

SALTON SEA

Physical Setting

The Salton Sea is a hydrologically closed saline lake near the southern border of California (Fig. 1). It lies below sea level in the lowest part of an interior valley known as the Salton Trough, and as of 1967 was about 34 miles long and ranges from 9–14 miles in width. The Salton Sea receives the drainage from an area of 8360 square miles that includes the highly developed agricultural areas, Imperial and Coachella Valleys in California and Mexicali Valley in Mexico. Agriculture in all three valleys is dependent on irrigation water diverted from the Colorado River.

History

Geologic evidence indicates that in the geologic past, what is now the Salton Sea was a part of the Gulf of California. The gulf then extended about

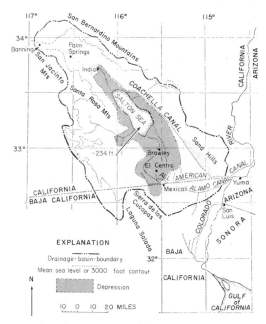

FIG. 1. Salton Sea basin (after Hely and others, 1966). Shaded area indicates region below mean sea level; light dashed line is the 3000 foot contour.

200 miles farther northwest than at present. As a result of the Colorado River depositing its silt load at its mouth year after year, the Colorado delta gradually extended southwestward and divided the old gulf into the present gulf and an inland sea. The river is believed to have discharged alternately into the gulf and into the Salton Sea.

Water probably filled the Salton depression and evaporated from it many times as the meager rainfall and runoff from bordering mountains were greatly exceeded by the evaporation. A clear and definite indication of the last occupancy of the depression by a historically old lake (*Lake Cahuilla*) may be seen in the remarkably well-preserved water line that rims the desert at an elevation of about 40 feet above mean sea level from Indio, California, to the Cerro Prieto in Mexico. The thickness of the calcium carbonate deposits forming the water line indicates that water stood at this elevation for long periods of time. Hubbs and others (1963), using carbon isotopes, dated an inner layer of the deposits at about 13,000 years B.P. and an outer layer at about 1900 years B.P. The date of Lake Cahuilla's disappearance has not been established, but according to Indian legend, the lake existed until about 300 years ago. This seems to be substantiated by a date obtained by Fergusson and Libby (1963) who analyzed the charcoal found associated with the remains of freshwater fish.

During the nineteenth century, the bed of what is now the Salton Sea was a dry lake, or playa, known as Salton Sink. On occasion, water reached the playa as a result of heavier than usual precipitation within the basin, or from high flows from the Colorado River which spread over the part of the delta draining into the Salton Sink. In 1901, irrigation was started in the Imperial Valley with water diverted from the Colorado River, and the present Salton Sea began to form. (Imperial Valley lies between the Salton Sea and the Mexican border.) By 1904, water was 0.2 foot deep on the floor of Salton Sink, at elevation 277 feet below mean sea level, as a result of irrigation drainage. In February 1905, during a flood on the Colorado River, irrigators were unable to control the flow entering their diversion canal, and great quantities of floodwater poured into the Salton Sea. Two years elapsed before this diversion could be brought under control, and during that period the sea rapidly increased in depth and volume until March 1907, when the water surface reached its maximum level of recent times, 195.9 feet below mean sea level. At this level, the sea was 45 miles long, its width ranged from 10–20 miles, and it covered an area of about 520 square miles. After March 1907, the water level gradually receded as evaporation greatly exceeded inflow (Fig. 2). The present levee system and the complex of storage reservoirs in the Colorado River basin make it highly improbable that the Salton Sea will ever again be invaded by uncontrolled floodwater.

Hydrology

The hydrology of the Salton Sea has been described by Hely and others (1966) and by Littlefield (1966). Fluctuations of the water level of the sea reflect the relative magnitudes of evaporation and water supplied to the sea (Fig. 2). Evaporation averages about 5.8 feet annually, but the volume of water evaporated in any year is dependent not only on the evaporation rate but also on the water surface area. The relation of water surface area and volume to water level elevation is shown in Fig. 3.

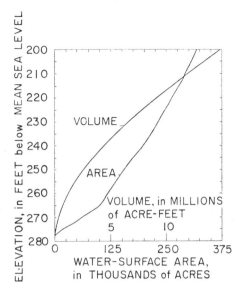

Fig. 3. Area and volume curves for the Salton Sea (after Littlefield, 1966).

Water supplied to the sea includes rainfall on the sea and surface- and groundwater inflow. The average annual rainfall is 2.5 inches, which is roughly equivalent to an average annual volume of 50,000 acre-feet added directly to the sea. Inflow to the sea consists almost entirely of the drainage from irrigation operations; only a small part of inflow is derived from precipitation on the basin surrounding the sea. The great bulk of this inflow is surface water; groundwater inflow is estimated to be only about 50,000 acre-feet per year.

Salinity

The salinity of the water in the Salton Sea has been changing continually since the first significant inflow occurred shortly after the turn of the century. Most of the water in the Salton Sea during the period 1905–07 resulted from large uncontrolled diversions of Colorado River water. Although the river water had an average salinity (total dissolved solids) of less than 800 ppm, the salinity of the water in the sea reached 3550 ppm by June 1907, because of the dissolving of large quantities of salts accumulated on the bed of the Salton Sea during previous centuries. After 1907, the volume of water in the sea decreased rapidly. The loss of water by evaporation, combined with the continued dissolving of salts in the bed of the sea, caused a rapid increase in salinity. By 1920 the salinity had increased to 38,000 ppm, and in 1936 it reached a maximum of about 43,000 ppm. The volume of water in the sea increased greatly during the period 1937–62 as a result of increased irrigation activity; by 1962 the salinity had decreased to 34,000 ppm,

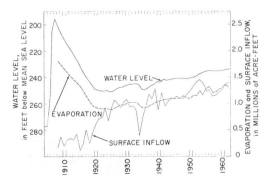

Fig. 2. Annual fluctuations of water level (datum of 1929), surface inflow and evaporation (after Hely and others, 1966).

971

because water of lower salinity had been draining into the sea and had diluted the seawater. By way of comparison, the salinity of ocean water is about 35,000 ppm (36,000 milligrams/liter).

S. E. RANTZ

References

Fergusson, G. J., and Libby, W. F., 1963, "UCLA radiocarbon dates II," *Radiocarbon*, **5**, 6.

Hely, A. G., Hughes, G. H., and Irelan, B., 1966, "Hydrologic regimen of Salton Sea, California," *U.S. Geol. Surv. Profess. Paper* **486-C**, 32pp.

Hubbs, C. L., Bien, G. S., and Suess, H. E., 1963, "La Jolla natural radiocarbon measurements III," *Radiocarbon*, **5**, 260–261.

Littlefield, W. M., 1966, "Hydrology and physiography of the Salton Sea, California," *U.S. Geol. Surv. Hydrol. Inv. Atlas HA-222*, 1p.

Cross-references: *Cryptodepressions*; *Dead Sea*; *Great Salt Lake*; *Playa.* pr Vol. VI: *Evaporation*; *Groundwater*; *Runoff.*

SAND CAY

A sand cay is a low small sandy islet or island, commonly situated on a coral reef platform. The word is based on the Spanish "cajo" (a shoal);

generally in the Pacific and Indian Ocean reef regions it is spelled "cay" and so pronounced, but in the West Indies and Florida the old English spelling "key" persists and the pronunciation is as with the English word "key."

Sand of fine coral debris, mixed with comminuted grains of molluskan shell material, bryozoa, calcareous algae and Foraminifera, is commonly heaped up into a sand bank on the lee side of a coral reef platform. This sand bank is an ephemeral feature at first, moving here and there to different positions on the reef after storms. However, it eventually becomes fixed or semistabilized by the development of *beachrock* (q.v.). Gradually the sand builds above high water level; water-borne vegetation, seeds, etc., arrive and a vegetated sand cay evolves. The sand generally builds up to 5–10 feet above HWM though small dunes may raise it further. Even so, during hurricanes, sand cays are liable to be swept clear of vegetation and may disappear completely in a single storm. The only really safe structures in such environments are stilt-legged lighthouses, with their foundations set right down in the underlying coral rock.

On the windward side of reef platforms, waves commonly heap up "ramparts" of coarse coral debris or "shingle." Within this protective screen, a sand cay, or perhaps an exclusively *shingle cay* may form. The typical regions of sand cays are on

FIG. 1. Green Island, a typical vegetated sand cay in the Great Barrier Reef lagoon, Australia; note situation at northwest end of a coral platform, being in the region of southeast Trade Winds. (Vertical air photo, taken 27 August 1938).

FIG. 2. Same sand cay, seen in oblique air view. (Photo 26 January, 1945, R.W.F.)

the platforms of the Great Barrier Reef lagoon, in the East Indies (notably Spermonde Archipelago, Bay of Djakarta, Thousand Islands), in Florida, Jamaica and elsewhere in the Caribbean. The bulk of the "Florida Keys" are not sand cays but islets of emerged Quaternary reef limestones and so too are most of the atoll islets of the mid-Pacific.

RHODES W. FAIRBRIDGE

References

Fairbridge, R. W., 1950, "Recent and Pleistocene coral reefs of Australia," *J. Geol.,* **58,** 330–401.

Steers, J. A., 1937, "The coral islands and associated features of the Great Barrier Reefs," *Geograph. J.,* **89,** 1–28.

Steers, J. A., 1940, "The coral cays of Jamaica," *Geograph. J.,* **95,** 30–42.

Steers, J. A., Chapman, V. J., Colman, J., and Lofthouse, J. A., 1940, "Sand cays and mangroves in Jamaica," *Geograph. J.,* **96,** 305–328.

Umbgrove, J. H. F., 1947, "Coral Reefs of the East Indies," *Bull. Geol. Soc. Am.,* **58,** 729–778.

Verstappen, H. T., 1954, "The influence of climatic changes on the formation of coral islands," *Am. J. Sci.,* **252,** 428–435.

Cross-references: *Beachrock; Coral Reefs; Great Barrier Reefs.*

SAND DUNES

A sand dune is defined as a topographic feature of eolian origin composed of sand grains deposited downwind from a natural source of sand. Dune size varies greatly, diameters ranging from a few meters to more than several thousand and heights varying from one to several hundred meters. Their shapes also display much variety. There are simple and complex forms, crescentic, sigmoidal, linear, hooked and pyramidal dunes and many complex combinations.

Environment

Sand dunes develop in any environment in which loose rock particles of sand size are exposed to wind action and are free to migrate and accumulate in unconsolidated masses. A student, browsing through the literature on sand dunes, might very well think, from the abundance of papers on coastal dunes, that these were dune regions of greatest importance. The contrary is true. Compared with the vast areas of desert dunes, coastal dunes cover minor areas. In this discussion, the major stress is upon desert dunes because it is only in the broad expanses of desert regions that dunes form freely and without hindrance, in profusion not only of number but of patterns and kinds. Frequent reference will be made to dunes in the Arabian Peninsula and its Rub' al Khali, as this is one of the most completely mapped and explored desert regions of today.

Types of Dune Environments:

    (a) Climatic
        1. Wind Regimen
        2. Precipitation
            (i) Humid
            (ii) Semi-Arid
            (iii) Arid
        3. Temperature
        4. Altitude

(b) Geomorphic
1. Shore and Strand Lines
2. Coastal Plains
3. Riverine Flood Plains and Deltas
4. Periglacial
5. Desert

Climatic Environment. A dry, windy climate favors the formation of dunes. It can be either hot or cold but must be dry and windy for periods sufficient to permit loose surface materials to be picked up and transported by the wind.

Wind Regimen. In most non-desert regions where dunes abound, wind directions are governed by regional factors. Where a dominant wind in a dry season tends to maintain a single direction, dunes will reflect that orientation. Where winds blow from various points of the compass, dune form varies accordingly. Deserts of the trade wind zone are aerated by winds moving toward the equator or away from it, and in Asian deserts the monsoons supply the mode of sand transport. Coastal areas have much wind blowing off an ocean, sea or lake. Regional patterns of dune belts in the great deserts reflect dominant wind paths.

Precipitation. Wet sand grains adhere to each other and thus do not yield readily to eolian movement. Hence, rain, fog and dew retard formation of dunes. Moving air quickly dries the surface of wet sand and permits individual sand grains to be moved. Hence, it is possible for dunes to develop on lake shores or seashores even in relatively humid regions.

Dry seasons are longer and more frequent in semiarid and arid climates. There are extremely arid regions where rains do not fall for years at a time. The infrequent precipitation wets or dampens surface sand, temporarily retarding sand transport by wind.

Temperature. Relative humidity is a function of the temperature and moisture content of the atmosphere. High temperatures and low relative humidity favor transport of sand by wind. Summer desert winds are hot, dry and often of long duration which accounts for transport of great volumes of sand in the Saharan Ergs, the nafuds of Arabia and huge sand concentrations in many of the Asian desert basins.

Altitude. Dunes form at or below sea level and on up into higher plateaus. Sand accumulations usually develop at the lower parts of major topographic basins in arid regions and in other topographic low areas. The Kalahari Desert of Southwest Africa lies in a broad shallow basin as do the Rub' al Khali of Arabia and the Takla-Makan desert of Western China.

Geomorphic Environments. *Shore Lines and Strand Lines.* Dunes are common on shores or strands of seas, oceans and lakes. The Pacific coasts of both North and South America are sites of nu-

merous dune belts. The Atlantic Coast of the United States is graced by many a dune belt from New England to Florida and along the Texas shores of the Gulf of Mexico. A large dune field along the southern shores of Lake Michigan provides a fine recreation area for the neighboring region. Dunes occur in many parts of the western European coasts and in the Baltic region. Waves and currents carry huge volumes of sand to the beaches where the winds sweep it into dunes. Dunes seldom develop on rocky or cliffed coasts, but on low, sandy coasts, they develop freely.

Coastal Plains. Low, coastal plains bordering sandy beaches provide a favorable environment for dunes, in subhumid as well as arid climates. The Sechura Desert of Peru lies on a recently uplifted sea floor, sloping gently upward from sea level to several hundred meters. The floor carries a thin veneer of residual marine sands which have been gathered into scattered barchan dunes, a few dune fields, and several very fascinating multiple dunes one of which is near the village of Sechura. Near the coastal mountain ranges, sand sweeps through passes forming linear dunes and occasionally forms sand sheets nearly burying some of the terrain. Dunes in "chains" are moving inland in Libya and Egypt from the Mediterranean shores. Cooper (1958), in an excellent monograph on the Coastal Dunes of Washington and Oregon, describes some of the dune belts on the Pacific Coast.

Riverine Floodplains and Deltas. The floodplains of many large rivers were formed in arid and semiarid environments. Sand is winnowed from alluvial deposits in the floodplains and from dry river beds, forming dunes in the bed or on the bordering plains. Some of the large dune fields bordering the Caspian Sea were formed from alluvium brought down by rivers from the high mountains. The Sind Desert of West Pakistan is a large sand desert lying east of the Indus River, from which much of the sand in the dunes has been derived. Small dune patches occur in the floodplains of the Columbia, Arkansas, Canadian and Cimmaron Rivers of the United States.

Periglacial Environments. During the ice ages, dunes probably formed about the margins of glacial advances where barren alluvial deposits were swept by winds from the glaciers. The Nebraska Sand Hills are thought by some workers to have formed from the outwash and other alluvial wastes bordering the maximum advances of the continental ice sheets.

Desert Environments. The annual precipitation in most desert environments amounts to less than 10 inches and frequently less than one inch. Being hot, dry, seasonally windy and relatively free of vegetation, a desert favors the development of dunes if an abundant source of sand lies upwind. Continental air masses moving in regular paths across desert regions originate in the trade winds and in the seasonal monsoons. The khamsins of Egypt, shamals of Arabia, and the dry monsoon of Asia, which all blow for days at a time, are the prime manufacturers of desert dunes.

AREAS OF SEMIARID AND ARID LANDS (Shantz, 1956)

	Square Miles	Square Kilometers
Semiarid	8,202,000	21,213,000
Arid	8,418,000	21,802,000
Extremely arid	2,244,000	5,812,000
Total	18,864,000	48,827,000

It is estimated that sand deserts cover about 25–35% of desert regions, of the more arid type. Thus there should be from 2.5–3.5 million square miles of sandy desert. At the present time, many of these are too poorly mapped to determine the areas of sand dunes. Parts of the Saharan Ergs were mapped in reconnaissance by the French. The Arabian Peninsula has been mapped completely in detail using aerial photography, and the sandy regions such as the Rub' al Khali, once more unknown than the Antarctic, are better known than some parts of the United States. The Rub' al Khali has some of the most fascinating dune structures known and a wide variety of dune patterns, in an area of 230,000 square miles of dunes. This will be our guide and source of many examples of dune patterns.

Parts of a Crescentic Dune (Fig. 1)

Upwind, Windward or Back Slope. This has a gentle, convex surface sloping from rear to front at an angle of 5–20°. The summit of the dune is the highest part; for active dunes, the summit and crest of slipface coincide; for waning dunes, the summit forms a rounded surface upwind of the slipface crest.

Lee or Downwind Slope. There are two parts: the slipface and the lee slope on the horns or cusps. The slipface is steep, concave and unstable, forming an angle of about 32° with the horizon. The crest is the top of the slipface, which coincides with the dune summit in an active dune. The horns or cusps continue the convex surface of the back slope downwind, on either side of the hollow bounded by the slipface, and terminate in points or rounded ends. The hollow is usually barren of sand unless wind shifts form eddies to bring fine-grained sand around the cusps into the hollow. In side profile, the whole dune is streamlined. Winds carry sand over the surface by rolling, creep or bouncing (saltation). Sand falls on the slipface by gravity. When the slipface becomes overloaded, it shears and sand slides down the slope. The slipface angle is determined as the angle of repose for dry sand.

Dimensions. Length of a crescentic dune is measured from the most windward to the most leeward point. Width is measured normal to the wind.

Dune Growth

Sand dunes grow by several processes:
(1) Simple laminar accretion on back slope;
(2) Trapping of sand in the slipface;
(3) Overtake of one dune by another.

Influence of Rock Floor Topography on Dune Form

(1) A rise in relief, such as a flat-topped bench in the path of migrating dunes, causes closer grouping of the dunes with possible reduction in size.

(2) An increase in the slope of the floor under dunes causes an increase in wind velocity and quicker deflation or destruction of the dunes. Sand in these dunes is transported downwind to be redeposited as dunes on a falling incline or lower floor.

(3) A hill, butte or outlier in the path of a dune field sets up eddies which deflect the movement of airborne sand around it, with deposition of sand in the wind shadow as a linear ridge. The linear ridge can grow if the sand supply upwind is abundant. If not, the sand ridge will deflate or break up into small, migrating crescentic dunes, probably in the shape of barchans.

The Direction of Eolian Sand Movement in Deserts

Most large sandy deserts have developed in the trade wind zones either side of the equator. But the monsoon of the Arabian Sea and Indian Ocean is steadier and, in general, provides the seasonal winds required to establish the great sandy deserts of Asia. The monsoon blows for half a year from the northeast and for the other half year from the

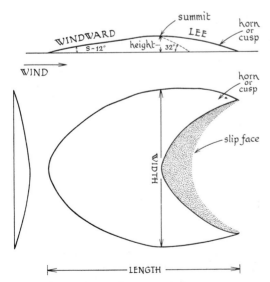

FIG. 1. Parts of a crescentic dune.

southwest. The cause of these winds is the seasonal temperature difference between land and sea areas. Somewhat similar conditions occur in Australia, parts of western, southern and eastern Africa, and parts of North America and Chile.

The large sand deserts we have mentioned show the influence of these seasonal winds, which control the directional flow of sand, by developing an arcuate pattern of dune belts, with the arcs convex to the east. We find the pattern in the Sahara, Arabia, the basins of southern Asia, and Australia.

However, these arcs do not seem to follow the wind directions taken by monsoons. In Fig. 2, a map shows the directions of eolian sand movement in the Arabian Peninsula—the arcs begin in the northwest, swing to the southeast, then south, and finally southwest. Fig. 3 shows that the dune belts are arranged in the arcuate pattern through the central part of the Arabian Peninsula. The winds that work on the Rub' al Khali which forms the huge body of sand in the southeastern part of the Peninsula diverge along the fifty-third meridian and

spread out to the northeast, southeast, south and southwest, carrying dune belts as they spread. Other winds, from the northeast, east and southeast enter the desert from the Arabian Sea and Indian Ocean, pushing sand into the center of the basin and also in a major trend toward the southwest. Southwest winds in Central Najd blow sand toward the north central part of the arc. The southwest margins of the elongated nafuds here show deflation. Sand is piled up in active dune masses along the northeast edges, and then it is carried toward the southeast by the northwest winds.

Sand Dune Terrains

No large sandy desert develops a homogeneous dune pattern. In the majority, several different dune terrains can be distinguished. The mapping of the Arabian Peninsula required distinction of at least four sand dune terrains, which are described in the legend of the excellent maps published by the U.S. Geological Survey for the Saudi Arabian Government. These are:

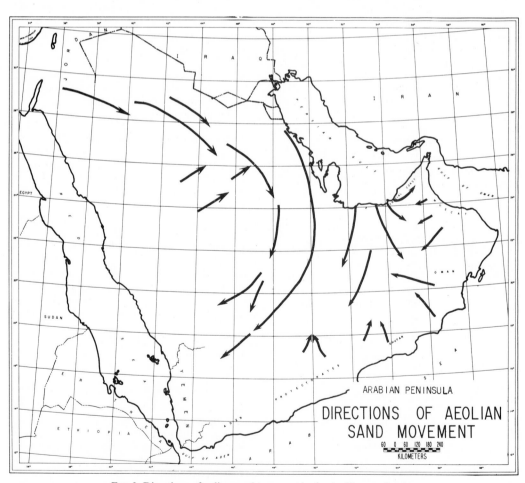

FIG. 2. Directions of eolian sand transport in the Arabian peninsula.

(I) Transverse
(II) Longitudinal, Linear, or Seif dunes
(III) 'Uruq (Arabic for elongated dunes)
(IV) Sand Mountains.

Holm, who carried out detailed dune studies as a part of the mapping program, found that at least five definite sand dune terrains need to be distinguished. These have been outlined on the map in Fig. 3.

Classification of Dunes

Dune patterns may be classified in various ways:
(1) Size
(2) Environment
(3) Growth stages
(4) Origins
(5) Shape
(6) Degree of complexity
(7) Wind directions.

Most of these criteria will be considered as they apply in the dune classification developed below. However, the system developed by Holm and his colleagues is based primarily on dune form and secondarily on wind directions. The degree of simplicity or complexity is of great importance, and the use of terms needs to be defined:

Simple Dunes. Each dune is a unit or individual with distinct, recognizable characteristics. Example: barchan.

Compound Dunes. Two or more dunes of the same kind joined *en echelon*, laterally or in sequence, form a distinct pattern. Example: barchans in transverse ridge.

Complex Dune. Two or more *different* kinds of dunes combined in numbers to form a distinct dune pattern. Example: a complex of sigmoidal and pyramidal dunes.

Dune Complex. Two or more complex dunes or compound dunes combined to form a large dune or dune field or a distinct group pattern. Example: clusters of linear, hooked, and pyramidal dunes such as are found in the southeastern Rub' al Khali.

Two Fundamental Dune Forms. The crescentic and sigmoidal are two fundamental dune forms.

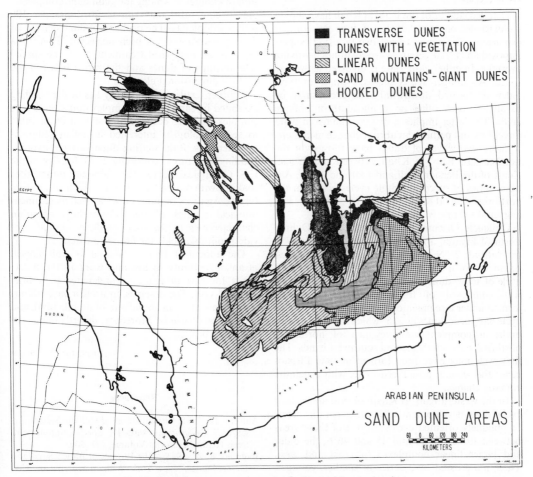

FIG. 3. Sand dune areas and terrains in the Arabian peninsula.

The crescentic is often misnamed "barchan." The barchan is a crescentic dune resulting from the action of unidirectional winds only. There are many varieties of crescentic dune resulting from the actions of winds from various directions.

The sigmoidal dune in its simplest form, is a sinuous, steep-sided, sharp-crested, S-shaped dune ridge, recurved, pointed or rounded at either end, longer than wide and with both slopes increasing in steepness toward a maximum of 32° at the crest. The sigmoidal dune can form from a crescentic dune by the action of opposing, alternating winds plus wind from a quadrant normal to the opposing winds. It is possible to find all gradations between the simple crescentic dune and the simple sigmoidal. However, where the wind regimen holds truly to the three directions required, the sigmoidal dune becomes stable.

Both the crescentic and sigmoidal dune forms are common in many regions. Many of the more complex dunes are derived from these two fundamental dune forms.

Dune Cycles

Detailed studies of the Rub' al Khali have shown the existence of several cycles of dune growth and expansion. There are at least two types: (1) superimposed and (2) successive waves of dunes involving overtake. In either case, time is involved as well as space. A younger set is imposed upon another, older set located downwind. The cycles may be parallel to each other or at an acute or oblique angle. The latter implies a definite change in wind directions and perhaps an abrupt change in climate.

Successive waves of dunes have formed in the northeastern Rub' al Khali between the Trucial Coast of the Persian Gulf and Latitude 23° N. Another series of successive dune cycles occurs in the northwest Rub' al Khali where relief of dunes is low and sand volume is small.

Obliquely Oriented Dune Cycles. In ad-Dahna, north of Riyadh, approximately at longitude 47°E and latitude 26°N, an older cycle of residual dunes, oriented north-south, is crossed by the present cycle of active dunes oriented 325°. The older cycle was composed of transverse ridges probably formed under a regimen of west winds. The current cycle has linear dunes at 325° which have developed under a complex wind regimen of northwest, northeast, east, southeast and southwest winds. The first cycle may have been formed in Late Pleistocene; the second, post-Pleistocene, with a definite climatic change.

In the western Rub' al Khali, several areas show cyclic dune development with either parallel series or obliquely oriented cycles. In one of these areas between 19 and 20°N and 45 and 46°E, the older and larger linear complexes run east and west. These are crossed by a series of smaller, younger, and very active linear ridges at an angle of 45°.

Near Sharqah and Dubai in the Trucial Coast, the older cycles are comprised of broad, linear ridges oriented NE-SW which are crossed by many small, closely spaced, active, sharp-crested sigmoidal ridges oriented 110–120°. The older cycle appears to have developed under a wind regimen of northwest and southeast winds with gentler northeast winds at other seasons. The current cycle seems to be working under a complex wind regimen that includes north-northeast, south, and west winds.

Dune cycles in large sandy deserts may be a valuable source of information on paleoclimates, particularly for the late Pleistocene.

Dune Spacing or Density

Where dunes develop in great numbers, especially with an abundant supply of sand, the spacing of dunes bears an inverse relationship to the size. Tiny crescentic dunes, as individuals or multiples, will be grouped in close array as many as 200 per square kilometer. An adjacent dune field with larger average dune size may have only 100 dunes per square kilometer. Among the giant dune complexes, the spacing ratio may run to 20 dunes per 100 square kilometers. The problem of dune density or dune populations, has been neglected. There is a need for an analytical treatment of all the spatial relationships of dunes and the ratios between the various dimensional elements.

Another fertile area for study lies in the bedding exhibited by sand dunes. Complex dunes have very complex bedding patterns and should be of value to sedimentologists interested in eolian sedimentary deposits. Rain wetting dune surfaces exposes bedding structures beautifully. E. D. McKee of the U.S. Geological Survey has sectioned dunes after soaking with water from tankers, with interesting results. Analysis of dune slopes as well as sedimentological studies of the relationships of grain characteristics to the parts of dunes should provide profitable fields for future research.

The student of dunes is advised to avail himself of an opportunity to live and work in the desert sands for several years, in preference to a brief seasonal visit. The desert is, in itself, a vast laboratory of vast area, an abundance of mobile sand, and a plethora of winds. Moreover, desert dunes possess great beauty.

DONALD A. HOLM

References

Aufrère, L., 1935, "Essai sur les dunes du Sahara Algérien," *Geografiska Ann.*, **17**, Special Supplement, Sven Hedin Memorial Volume, 481–500.
Bagnold, R. A., 1941, "The Physics of Blown Sand and Desert Dunes," New York, William Morrow and Co., 265pp.

*Cooper, Wm. S., 1958, "Coastal dunes of Oregon and Washington," Memoir 72, *Geol. Soc. Am. Mem.* **72.**

Cooper, W. S., 1967, "Coastal Dunes of California," *Geol. Soc. Am. Mem.* **104,** 131pp.

Cressey, G. B., 1928, "The Indiana sand dunes and shore-lines of the Lake Michigan Basin," *Geographic Soc. Chicago Bull.*, **8.**

Geological Society of America, 1952, "Map of Pleistocene Eolian Deposits of the United States, Alaska and Parts of Canada," James Thorp and H. T. U. Smith, co-chairmen.

Hack, John T., 1941, "Dunes of the western Navajo Country, Arizona," *Geograph. Rev.* **31,** 240–263.

Holm, D. A., 1960, "Desert geomorphology in the Arabian Peninsula," *Science,* **132,** 1369–1379.

Madigan, C. T., 1936, "The Australian sand-ridge deserts," *Geograph. Rev.,* **26,** 205–227.

Shantz, H. L., 1956, "The Future of Arid Lands," *Am. Assoc. Advance. Sci. Publ.* no. 43.

* Additional bibliographic references may be found in this work.

Cross-references: *Coastal Plain; Deflation; Deserts and Desert Landforms; Eolian Transport; Periglacial Eolian Effects; Quaternary; Wind Action.* Vol. II: *Monsoons; Trade Winds; Winds—Local.*

SAND SPIT—*See* **BARS**

SANDUR (SANDR)—*See* **OUTWASH PLAIN, FAN, TERRACE, SANDUR;** *also* **MORAINE**

SAPROLITE—*See* **REGOLITH AND SAPROLITE**

SARSEN—*See* **INDURATION**

SASTRUGA—*See* pr Vol. VI, **SNOW AND ICE FORMS**

SAVANNA LANDSCAPE

The term savanna is applicable not only to a type of geomorphic landscape, but also to the vegetation habit, a characteristic climate, soils and so on (see other volumes). The origin of the term is from "zavanna," of the Carib language, thence to the Spanish of Central America, where it has been in the literature since 1535, according to the Oxford English Dictionary. (The spelling savannah is appropriate only to the early English settlements, e.g., in Georgia, and Trinidad; "savana" is used by French writers.) According to Schimper (1903), it is a xerophilous (drought-loving) grassland containing isolated trees. The term *"parkland"* is often

used as a synonym, but it is more suitable for vegetation than geomorphic studies (Küchler, 1947). In Florida and elsewhere, it was the openness of the landscape that struck early travelers after the dense vegetation of the coastal swamp and jungle; however, its application to treeless glades in swampland is a local usage only.

Savanna is a term like selva, steppe, taiga, and tundra, which describes in broad terms a landscape, without morphogenetic overtones. It has no relief implication, and in central Africa the savanna belt occupies a distinct zone on the slopes of the great semi-isolated mountains. Savanna passes in drier regions to steppe or desert, and in wetter areas into savanna woodland.

The term is widely applied in geomorphology to what is sometimes called the *savanna cycle* (Pelzer, 1951), which implies the landscape developed under a climatic regime of subtropical to subequatorial character, typically between latitudes 30 and 10°N and S; the atmospheric pressure is commonly high, and the winds are often related to the subtropical easterlies, the trade winds. Winter seasons are usually dry, and the rainy season comes with the summer monsoon, the shortest seasons being those farthest inland and farthest from the equator. Scattered patches of savanna occur poleward of the great deserts, and here their seasons are reversed, with occasional winter rains.

From the geomorphic, vegetation and soils points of view, these strong seasonal contrasts are of profound importance because they mean a predictable long dry period each year. The vegetation is xerophilous, with wet-season grasses and trees of the narrow-leafed or thorn types (eucalypts, acacias) and adaptive types for water conservation, like the distinctive baobab tree of Africa and northern Australia. Resin secretion is common (e.g., spinifex), as is the canopy of the umbrella type (Eyre, 1963). Some ecologists (e.g., Eyre) say there is no typical savanna climate, as claimed by Schimper and others; some stress the "pyrogenous theory," the importance of fire in maintaining the grass and high canopy contrast. Even though the importance of fire is granted, a strong seasonality is still essential.

In the soil are found tropical red soils with laterites and bauxites; there is downward leaching during the wet season and capillary loss of moisture during the desiccation period, bringing SiO_2 and Fe_2O_3 toward the surface, which results in nodules, hardpans and duricrusts (silcrete and ferricrete). In carbonate-rich areas, $CaCO_3$ may form calcrete crusts, but generally the leaching carries the lime away in solution in the typical savanna. When such a land surface is dissected, these crusts form hard caprocks, leading to escarpments or "breakaways." The result is a type of landform very distinctive from the Davisian rounded, relief reduction (typical of cool-humid and periglacial landscapes) and accords more with the Penckian slope patterns (thus pedimentation rather than peneplanation). In the absence, or after the destruction, of the caprock, local *badland* (q.v.) topography may develop.

Stream development in the savanna is scattered; i.e., much of the surface in the savanna plainlands is arheic (without stream channels), and few through-running rivers exist. Many ephemeral lake depressions evolve, sometimes with pseudo-periglacial patterned ground (see *Gilgai*). In areas of modest relief, dendritic patterns tend to form with ephemeral watercourses (arroyos, wadis, dongas, etc.), which are dry for most of the year. *Gully erosion* (q.v.) may develop where relief and precipitation are suitable. Sediment transport in these fluvial channels is seasonal; silt, sand and gravel bars block the riverbed most of the time, and when the flood comes, this alluvium is shifted some distance downstream as bed load. Its passage toward the local base level and semipermanent accumulation site is in "fits and starts" and may take centuries from source to ocean. Long dry periods in the climatic history lead to a general siltation of these drainage channels, building the alluvium up to form "flood plains" tens or even hundreds of kilometers in width. This is what happened to many of the great rivers in the African and North Australian savannas during the glacial period; the Nile, Congo, Niger and Senegal all went through stages when their middle sectors dried up completely (Fairbridge, 1964). Widespread evidence of coldstage aridity comes also from Brazil (Bigarella and de Andrade, 1965). Much of the Congo was semiarid during the last glacial stage (de Ploey, 1965). Extensive savannas replaced jungle, and desert replaced savannas. A return of wetter conditions causes gully erosion on a grand scale, and new stream channels are carved out of the soft silts in a very brief time (Fairbridge, 1962). Experimental studies with ephemeral streams, admittedly over short periods, illustrate the processes (deduced from the geological evidence) of longer duration (Leopold and Miller, 1956).

Morphogenesis in Some Savanna Regions

Although arheic drainage is characteristic of the bulk of the modern savanna landscape, in areas of mild to moderate relief, runoff (to exorheic or endorheic systems) is the dominant landform process in many parts of savannas. Studies of earlier fluvial deposits in certain savanna regions show that the same morphogenetic systems have been active from time to time (e.g., see the eastern Nigerian studies of Jungerius, 1965). Nevertheless, on a longer time scale, these fluvial systems are often modulating a landscape of degradational nature, an "*etchplain*" (q.v.) or a compound series of pediplains cut down into chemically weathered basement (saprolite), a weathering that requires long warm humid seasons. Many of the world's savannas today are thus on sites of Tertiary or Mesozoic equatorial and subequatorial weathering. Care should be taken not to confuse the inherited morphogenetic features with the contemporary landscape criteria; in this way, many inselbergs and bornhardts are inherited features from more humid epochs, and all hardly related to the present regime. A characteristic organic structure of the tropical savanna is the termite mound ("anthill"); fossil termite tunnels (dating from warm humid interglacial times) can be found in the Sahara at latitudes (e.g., 20–25°) where no rain falls today and termites cannot exist.

RHODES W. FAIRBRIDGE

References

Bigarella, J. J., and de Andrade, G. O., 1965, "Contributions to the study of the Brazilian Quaternary," *Geol. Soc. Am., Spec. Paper*, **84.**

Cole, M. M., 1960, "Cerredo, Caatinga and Pantanal; the distribution and origin of the savanna vegetation of Brazil," *Geograph. J.*, **126**(2).

Dansereau, P., 1957, "Biogeography: An Ecological Perspective," New York, Ronald Press Co., 394pp.

de Ploey, J., 1965, "Position géomorphologique, génèse et chronologie de certains dépôts superficiels au Congo occidental," *Quaternaria*, **7,** 131–154.

Eyre, S. R., 1963, "Vegetation and Soils," Chicago, Aldine, 324pp.

Fairbridge, R. W., 1962, "New radiocarbon dates of Nile sediments," *Nature*, **195,** 108–110.

Fairbridge, R. W., 1964, "African Ice Age aridity," in (Nairn, A. E. M., editor) "Problems in Palaeoclimatology," pp. 356–360, New York, Interscience Publishers.

Jungerius, P. D., 1965, "Some aspects of the geomorphological significance of soil texture in Eastern Nigeria," *Z. Geomorphol.*, **9**(3), 332–345.

Küchler, A. W., 1947, "Localizing vegetation terms," *Ann. Am. Assoc. Geogr.*, **37,** 197–208.

Leopold, L. B., and Miller, J. P., 1956, "Ephemeral streams—hydraulic factors and their relation to the drainage net," *U.S. Geol. Surv. Profess. Paper* **282-A,** 36pp.

Leopold, L. B., Wolman, M. G., and Miller, J. P., 1964, "Fluvial Processes in Geomorphology," San Francisco, W. H. Freeman & Co., 522pp.

Morison, C. G. T., Hoyle, A. C., and Hope-Simpson, J. F., 1948, "Tropical soil-vegetation catenas and mosaics," *J. Ecol.*, **35.**

Pelzer, K. J., 1951, "Geography and the tropics," 311–344, "Geography in the Twentieth Century," New York, Philosophy Library.

Schimper, A. F. W., 1903, "Plant Geography upon a Physiological Basis," Oxford, Clarendon Press (translated by W. R. Fisher).

Cross-references: *Badlands*; *Bornhardt*; *Deserts and Desert Landforms*; *Duricrust*; *Etchplain*; *Gilgai*; *Gully Erosion*; *Inselberg*; *Organisms as Geomorphic Agents*; *Selva Landscape*; *Steppe Landscape*. Vol. II: *Climatic Classification*; *Vegetation Classification*. Vol. VI: *Soils*.

SCABLANDS

The physiographic term "scabland" refers to a poor, scarred fluvioglacial landscape type usually reserved for the so-called *channeled scablands*, southwest of Spokane in the State of Washington. Basic studies of the area by Harlen Bretz (1923, 1928) suggest that this was a region of catastrophic flooding by glacial meltwaters. Bretz proposed a single giant flood up to 800 feet deep that spilled out of an ice-dammed lake (Allison, 1933). Flint (1938) felt that it was not so much a catastrophic flood, but one engendered by the advance of a glacial lobe across the divide from the north, suddenly pouring meltwaters over the preexisting loess plain. Hobbs (1943) even suggested that the channeling was due to abrasion by a lobe of the glacier itself.

The physical character of the Washington scabland is remarkable. The bedrock is part of the Columbia plateau basalts; it was mantled by Pleistocene loess and then channeled, most probably, by intense fluvioglacial action (the Bretz theory), not in a single catastrophe but continuously for some time (the Allison modification). Multiple braiding of interlocking canyons or coulees with multiple spillways are observed, leaving isolated buttes and mesas above the fluvial scoured bedrock. The strong floods carried gravels some 200 miles west of the outlet, leaving a largely rock scoured bed upstream, with sands and silts further downstream. This great fluvioglacial fill was later channeled in turn by the drainage of Glacial Lake Lewis.

RHODES W. FAIRBRIDGE

References

Allison, I. S., 1933, "New version of the Spokane flood," *Bull. Geol. Soc. Am.*, **44**, 675–722.

Bretz, J H., 1923, "The channeled scablands of Columbia River plateau," *J. Geol.*, **31**, 617–649.

Bretz, J H., 1928, "The channeled scablands of eastern Washington," *Geograph. Rev.*, **18**, 446–477.

Cotton, C. A., 1966, "Antarctic Scablands," *N.Z. J. Geol. & Geophys.*, **9**(1–2), 130–132.

Flint, R. F., 1938, "Origin of the Cheney-Palouse scabland tract, Washington," *Bull. Geol. Soc. Am.*, **49**, 461–524.

Hobbs, W. H., 1943, "Discovery in eastern Washington of a new lobe of the Pleistocene glacier," *Science*, **98**, 227–230.

Cross-references: *Fluvioglacial Processes; Glacial Spillways and Proglacial Lakes; Outwash Plains.*

SCARP, ESCARPMENT—*See* CUESTA; ESCARPMENT; FAULT SCARP, FAULT-LINE SCARP

SCIENTIFIC METHOD—*See* pr Vol. VI

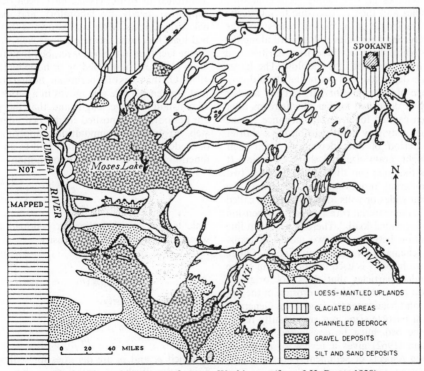

FIG. 1. The scabland area of eastern Washington (from J H. Bretz, 1928).

SCREE—*See* TALUS

SEA ARCH—*See* NATURAL BRIDGE

SEDIMENTS, STRENGTH OF—*See* pr Vol. VI, STRENGTH OF SEDIMENTS

SEDIMENT TRANSPORT—FLUVIAL AND MARINE

The movement of sediments by flowing water is a complex problem. Even in its simplest form, represented by flow in a channel of simple geometrical shape, it reveals a very high degree of unsteady, nonuniform flow condition, because the stream bed changes continuously and thereby influences water, as well as material, flow.

A study of the movement of sand grains along the bed of a straight uniform flume shows that at a certain depth of flow, when the velocity of flow increases to a certain value, some particles move intermittently by sliding and rolling along the bed. With further increase in the velocity, the material movement increases. At the same time, the bed gradually assumes an undulating form consisting first of ripples and then of bars due to increasing velocities. The length of the bars increases with the flow capacity. Sand particles roll upward along the gentle upstream slope of these irregularities and jump out from the crest into the flow. The larger particles are deposited in front of the steep downstream slope of the ripple or bar, but the smaller grains may be deposited farther downstream, after having been carried for a certain distance by the flow, or they may stay in suspension for a shorter or longer period of time depending upon their specific weight, grain size and shape of grains. It thus seems that one can distinguish between two basically different modes of transportation: the material that slides or rolls along the bed is called "bed-load"; the material transported in suspension is called "suspended load." There is no sharp line of demarcation between the two modes of transportation schematically shown in Fig. 1. Often, the term "wash-load" is used for the portion of the fine suspended particles that does not originate from the bed but is derived from erosion of the upstream bed and headwater (storage) area. Generally speaking, all particle sizes, not significantly represented in the bed, must be considered as "wash load." Bruun (1962) gives a review of details in "Engineering Aspects of Sediment Transport."

Bed-load transport starts when the rate of flow

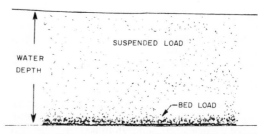

FIG. 1. Schematic representation of bed load and suspended load, beneath the surface of a moving body of water.

has obtained a certain magnitude by which shear stresses transferred by the flow to the bottom push the loose particles along. Du Boys (1879) introduced the idea of "critical tractive force" for the initiation of sediment movement and introduced the formula for movement of bed-load:

$$q_B = C_B \tau (\tau - \tau_c) \tag{1}$$

where

q_B = bed-load transport per unit width and per unit time
C_B = a special "sediment parameter"
τ = shear stress
τ_c = the critical shear stress for start of material movement.

Several other bed-load theories and formulas, as mentioned in Bruun (1962), have been developed, supported partly by laboratory and partly by field experiments. Most well-known is the Einstein bed-load function. Einstein's approach was based on the fact that in the bed layer, bed-load transport takes place by rolling, sliding or hopping (Einstein, 1950). On the basis of experiments, he first concluded that a given particle size moves in a series of steps of constant average length and that the particles are periodically deposited in the bed after such a step. Probability computations, applying results of modern turbulence research, lead to an analytic function for the probability p for motion:

$$p = 1 - \frac{1}{\sqrt{\pi}} \int_{-B_*\psi - 1/\eta_0}^{B_*\psi - 1/\eta_0} e^{-t^2} \, dt = \frac{A_*\phi}{1 - A_*\phi} \tag{2}$$

This is the so-called Einstein bed-load function where bed-load transport intensity

$$\phi = \frac{q_B}{(\rho_s - \rho_f)g} \left(\frac{\rho_f}{\rho_s - \rho_f}\right)^{\frac{1}{2}} \left(\frac{1}{gd^3}\right)^{\frac{1}{2}} \tag{3}$$

and the flow intensity

$$\psi = \frac{\rho_s - \rho_f}{\rho_f} \frac{d}{R_b' S} \tag{4}$$

in which ρ_s and ρ_f are densities for sediment and fluid, respectively; d is the grain size; g is the acceleration of gravity; s is the energy slope of flow; A_*, B_*, and η_0 are universal constants; and R'_b is the hydraulic radius with respect to the grain size as explained in detail in Einstein (1950) and Bruun (1962). If the transport rates of individual mixtures are known, the rate of transport can be readily obtained by summing up these individual rates.

For all practical purposes, the start of movement of particles is extremely important. Lane (1952), in continuation of Shields' (1936) work, has given the following dimensionless expression

$$\tau_c/(\gamma_s - \gamma_f) = C_1 \qquad (5)$$

where γ_s and γ_f are the specific weights of sediment and fluid, and C_1 is a constant for turbulent flow.

Suspended load transport can be considered as a kind of advanced stage of bed-load transport by which particles in saltation are caught by the upward component of the turbulent velocity and are kept in suspension.

The fundamental equation of sediment suspension by fluid turbulence is $cw = -\beta\varepsilon \, dc/dy$, where c is the concentration of suspended load in dry weight per unit volume, w is the settling velocity of the particles, β is the sediment transfer coefficient, ε is the exchange coefficient for suspended load, and y is the vertical distance from the bottom. The quantity ε is not a constant throughout the vertical section but ranges from essentially zero at the bed to a maximum at approximately mid-depth, becoming rather indeterminate thereafter. Using the Prandtl-von Karman relationship for velocity distribution (Einstein, 1950) and the above equation, one gets the following expression:

$$\frac{C_y}{C_a} = \left(\frac{y_0 - y}{y} \frac{a}{y_0 - a}\right)^z \qquad (6)$$

for concentration C_y at a certain distance y from the bottom when concentration C_a is known at distance a from the bed.

$$z = 2.5 \frac{w}{U_*} \quad \text{whereas} \quad U_* = \frac{\tau_0}{\rho_f} \qquad (7)$$

where U_* is the shear velocity at the bed. For details, the reader is referred to Einstein (1950).

As shown by Einstein (1950), it is possible to combine bed-load and suspended load transport formulas in one expression for total load.

With respect to wash-load transport, it seems very difficult to develop any useful overall theory for that mode of transportation. Bogardi (1961) explains that the major difficulty is that sediment transportation in natural streams, to an appreciable extent, is influenced by the hydrological conditions of the watercourse. Widely different hydrological conditions are encountered at various watercourses. Owing to these differences, the theoretical laws governing sediment transportation, that have been derived by considerations of hydrodynamics, or established on the basis of laboratory experiments carried out under more or less ideal conditions, can be used with the greatest conservatism only. Bogardi gives several examples of the effect of hydrological conditions on the sediment transport capacity, on the relationship between discharges and sediment concentration, and on the correlation between the particle diameter and mean velocity.

For information on details and on continued progress of theoretical and practical nature, reference is made particularly to Association Internationale du Recherches Hydrauliques (1959) and Federal Inter-Agency Sedimentation Conference (1963), mentioning recent works by Einstein, Laursen, Kennedy, Brooks, etc., including information on sediment transport and erosion of watersheds (J. S. Rohl, R. L. Fredericksen, C. E. Beer and H. P. Johnson, etc.), problems of sedimentation at reservoirs (G. H. Castle, A. F. Geiger, W. M. Borland, C. R. Ritter, J. M. Jordaan, etc.), and various sediment transportation instruments. Tracing of material transport by radioactive isotopes or by fluorescent tracers (which illuminate themselves if subject to ultraviolet light) is mentioned briefly under littoral drift and in more detail in the article *Tracer Techniques in Sediment Transport*, Vol. VI.

Sediment transport along seashores is called "littoral drift." Comparison of details of sediment transport in rivers with sediment transport on seashores indicates that the main difference lies in the fact that, along the seashore, there is no continuous flow that permits the determination of a representative shear stress such as there is with flow in channels. On seashores, as a result of wave action, the major part of the material motion has its direction at right angles to the shore line.

Waves approaching a straight shore line will tend to shift their direction of propagation, so that the wave crests become increasingly more parallel to the shore line (Fig. 2). This phenomenon is called "wave refraction." Other wave characteristics change simultaneously. The wave-length will be shorter, but wave height will increase, until the wave finally becomes unstable and breaks at a relatively small angle with the shore line. Momentum (mass times velocity) from the breaking will induce a longshore current (Bruun, 1963) by which water, including its sediment placed in suspension by the wave breaking, moves along the coast. In addition to the suspended-sediment load, material is pushed and rolled on the bottom and on the beach itself, in a zigzag motion caused by the wave-induced oscillation of waters and the uprush and backwash on the beach.

The distribution of sediment load along the shore depends upon the shape of the beach and bottom

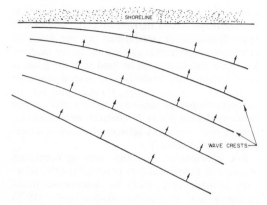

FIG. 2. Wave refraction along a straight shoreline.

profile, wave, current and material characteristics. A quantitative approach to the actual magnitude of drift is mentioned in Bruun (1962). If it is assumed that the littoral drift varies with the longshore component of energy of waves with a given energy content, measured along the crest of the waves, then:

$$M = \tfrac{1}{2}K_1\,We\,\sin 2\alpha_b \qquad (8)$$

where

$M =$ the total amount of sand moved in littoral drift past a given point per year by waves of given periods and direction

$W =$ total work accomplished by all waves of a given period and direction in deep water during an average year

$e =$ wave-energy coefficient at the breaker line for waves of a given period and direction

$\alpha_b =$ angle between wave crests at the breaker line and the shore line

$K_1 =$ factor depending on dimensional units and beach geometry and material characteristics.

The experience from deposits at improved inlets on the New York and New Jersey coasts reveals figures on the order of 500,000 cu yd/yr. On the Gulf coast figures of 100,000 cu yd/yr are probably representative, while on the Pacific 1,000,000 cu yd/yr or more is characteristic (Bruun, 1962).

Some of the most intriguing problems of coastal sedimentation are associated with inlets and estuaries. Many of these may have been improved (dredged and deepened) for navigation and will accumulate material on their updrift side (where material comes from) and cause erosion on their (opposite) downdrift side. Accumulations will take place in the inlet channel which has to be dredged regularly. Bruun and Gerritsen (1960) analyzed

the stability of a great many inlets and found it possible to express the stability of an inlet, "stab," as:

$$\text{"Stab"} = F\left(\tau_s, \frac{\Omega}{M}, \frac{Q_m}{M}\right) \qquad (9)$$

where τ_s is the so-called stability shear stress between flow and bottom; Ω is the so-called tidal prism which is the total amount of water flowing through the inlet in half a tidal cycle, referring to spring tide conditions; Q_m is the maximum-flow quantity passing through the inlet during spring tide; and M is the average amount of littoral drift materials brought to the inlet entrance per year. For further details on inlet hydraulics and stability, the reader is referred to Bruun and Gerritsen (1960) and Bruun (1962).

For many years, methods of tracing sediment transport by following the movement of single grains have been sought. Some rivers deliver natural tracer materials in their sediments in the form of special minerals (California). Modern tracing is based mainly on the use of radioactive material or on coatings which fluoresce with ultraviolet light. Special equipment like geiger counters and machines for counting of tracer grains have been developed, and the technique is still being developed as described in *Tracer Techniques in Sediment Transport*, Vol. VI.

PER BRUUN

References

Association Internationale du Recherches Hydrauliques, 1959, *Compte Rendus*, **4**, Eighth Congress, Montreal.

Bogardi, J. L., 1961, "Some aspects of the application of the theory of sediment transportation to engineering problems," *J. Geophys. Res.*, **66**(10), 3337–3346.

Bruun, Per, 1962, "Engineering Aspects of Sediment Transport," in "Reviews in Engineering Geology," Vol. 1, pp. 39–103, The Geological Society of America.

Bruun, Per, 1963, "Longshore currents and longshore troughs," *J. Geophys. Res.*, **68**(4), 1065–1078.

Bruun, Per, and Gerritsen, F., 1960, "Stability of Coastal Inlets," North Holland Publishing Company, 124pp.

Einstein, H. A., 1950, "The Bed-load Function for Sediment Transportation in Open Channel Flow," U.S. Department of Agriculture. Paper No. 1028.

Federal Inter-Agency Sedimentation Conference, 1963, Proceedings of Sedimentation Conference, Jackson, Miss., including Discussion by J. W. Johnson.

Lane, E. W., 1952, "Progress Report on Results of Studies on Design of Stable Channels," U.S. Bureau of Reclamation, Hyd. Lab. Rept., Hyd-352.

Shields, A., 1936, "Anwendung der Aenlichkeitsmechanik und der Turbulenzforschung auf die Geschiebebewegung," Berlin, *Mitteilungen der*

Preussischen Versuchsanstalt für Wasserbau und Schiffbau, **26.**

Cross-references: *Beach*; *Beach Erosion and Coastal Protection*; *Bed Load*; *Eolian Transport*; *Equilibrium in Geomorphology*; *Littoral Processes*; *Stream Flow*; *Stream Table Construction and Operation.* Vol. I: *Wave Refraction.* Vol. VI: *Fluvial Sediment Transport*; *Tracer Techniques in Sediment Transport.*

SEDIMENT TRANSPORT—LONG-TERM NET MOVEMENT

For the purpose of discussing sediment movement along the coast, waves may be classified as *storm waves* or *swell*. Storm waves are those still being acted upon by the wind in what is known as the *fetch*. Swell is the term for these waves once they have left this generation area and dispersed across the ocean. The two wave types have distinct characteristics (Silvester, 1959) which, in turn, produce different effects upon the beach profile.

Storm waves, because of their intensity, erode material from the beach and place it offshore in the form of a submarine bar. When this is sufficiently large to break subsequent storm waves, further erosion is prevented during that particular storm sequence. The deeper the offshore area, or the higher the water level, the greater is the volume of the bar necessary to effect this protective action. Since storm waves are so infrequent, and arrive generally

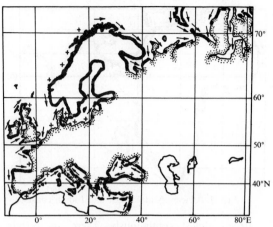

FIG. 2. European and Arctic coasts.

from so many directions, there is little longitudinal movement of sediment, and the material can be considered to be removed directly offshore.

Swell waves return the offshore bar to the beach, swiftly at first as the top is skimmed off and then more slowly. It may take several weeks for a complete refund, after which the floor of the ocean assumes a more or less stable profile, which increases in steepness toward the shore. The wave action shears particles from the bed and throws them continually into suspension. Before they settle, between each wave, they are moved in the direction of any forces existing at the bed level. The major forces, both inside and outside the breaker zone, are those due to wave action and gravity. Currents of tidal or other origin have very little influence within the boundary of water being considered, which is a matter of a centimeter or two from the bottom. Progressive waves produce a net movement of water at the ocean bed in the direction of wave advance known as *mass transport*, which assists in sweeping sediment towards the shore. Gravity is always acting on the particles to pull them seaward, normal to the bed contours. Each particle finds an equilibrium position on the beach profile where the shoreward and seaward forces are balanced. If these are not aligned, as for example when the waves are approaching obliquely to the shore, the grains may oscillate along the coast, tracing a sawtooth path without shifting position with respect to the waterline. This zig-zag motion occurs in the surf zone, with the accompaniment of great turbulence and almost continuous suspension. The material transported alongshore in the surf zone is termed *littoral drift*, but this is only part of the total making its way along the shore.

Storm waves arrive at a beach only when the fetch is adjacent, or in close proximity, to the coast. They are, therefore, of infrequent occurrence. Swell, on the other hand, which has been generated in some storm center or other in the particular ocean

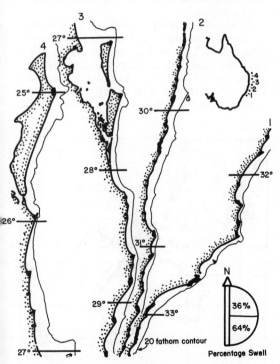

FIG. 1. Equilibrium shaped bays on the east coast of Australia.

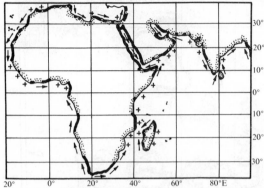

FIG. 3. African, Middle East and Indian coasts.

arrives almost continuously. There are certain oceanic areas where cyclonic centers are stationary for long periods, or follow similar paths each year. The swells from these regions spread to the distant shorelines, in ever-increasing circles whose centers change very little from season to season.

Thus the swell waves reaching any specific coast have a constant direction of approach and may be termed the *persistent swell*. If these waves should arrive at an oblique angle to the shore, they will move materials in one direction only, namely *down coast*. Even when two or more swells arrive from different sources, from either side of the normal to the coast, one is likely to be predominant, or a resultant can be determined.

It is the persistent swell, which arrives day after day, year after year, century after century, that determines the direction of net drift along the coast. Storm waves produce alarming effects upon the beach, but they only place material offshore for the swell to return, probably some distance downcoast. This intermittent transverse motion is not essential to the longshore process, but it certainly does expedite it.

While sediment, being removed from any area, is being replaced by material arriving from upcoast, the profile of the ocean bed remains in equilibrium. However, if the replenishment rate is reduced for any reason, the excess of output over input will result in erosion. This will take place initially in the offshore area beyond the breakers, but will ultimately affect the beach face, probably on the occasion of a storm attack.

If a straight sedimentary coast, which contains headlands at intervals along it, suffers a persistent swell from an oblique direction, it will almost immediately assume a scalloped appearance. Should no replenishment be taking place at the upcoast end, the recession of the beach will take the form of a bay, limited in size by headlands at its extremities. It has been shown by model experiments that the shape of such a bay is that of a half heart (Silvester, 1960) with the curved portion upcoast and the tangent section downcoast.

The sculpturing of an upcoast bay unit will be in advance of that of any unit downcoast, which will still be receiving material from it. Slowly, this first bay will reach an equilibrium shape, by which time the tangent section will be almost parallel to the crests of the incoming swell. Each wave will be diffracting and refracting in the shadow zone of the upcoast headland, such that it will break almost simultaneously around the whole periphery of the bay. When this is accomplished, no longshore drift is then possible. Further sediment may still be removed from the offshore zone, but ultimately this will cease, with the shoreward and seaward forces on the bed particles equal in magnitude and opposite in direction.

While this equilibrium is being approached, the supply of material to the bays downcoast is decreasing. They, in turn, are eroded into deeper forms, each one at a different stage of maturity at any particular time. The greater the volume of sediment being transported along the coast, or the more normal the waves are to the line of the headlands, the milder are the indentations produced.

The half-heart bay features can be observed from prominent vantage points along the coast, but they are more readily verified by studying maps or charts. Admiralty or hydrographic charts, used in navigation, are extremely useful for this purpose since they are available in a variety of scales, depict sedimentary and rocky sections of coast, and include depth measurements as spot values or underwater contours.

The shapes are easily verified, but to prove that the bays are oriented correctly with respect to the persistent swell, a coastline must be chosen where such wave conditions are known. In Fig. 1 is given the example of the eastern Australian coast where a larger proportion of southeasterly swell is known to exist (Monthly Meteorological Charts of the

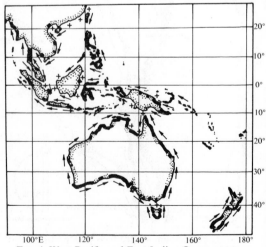

FIG. 4. West Pacific and East Indian Ocean coasts.

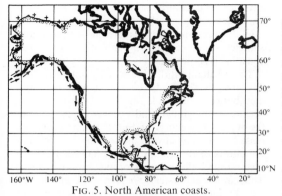

FIG. 5. North American coasts.

Western Pacific, 1956). The bays, which form half of a spearhead, point in a northerly direction, the direction of the net sediment movement.

Where a substantial section of coast is rocky, and the sediment does not protrude above the water surface to form a beach, other criteria must be used to determine the direction of net sediment movement (Silvester, 1962). These include alignment of underwater shoals, the general widening of the bed contours in a downcoast direction, and the swell information in such references as the Monthly Meteorological Charts which are available for all major oceans of the world.

Since swell is produced in specific areas of the oceans, from repetitive meteorological conditions, it arrives on extensive sections of the continental margins from more or less the same direction, certainly within the same quadrant. This results in the net sediment movement being in the same direction over substantial lengths of coastline. These might be termed *physiographic units* in this respect, without implying any similarities of climate, sediment type, wave intensity, or rate of transport along the section. In areas where the waves are nearly normal to the coast, or there is equal swell incidence from opposing directions, little or no longshore movement occurs. These areas are physiographic units in their own right. Thus, the limits of such areas are determined by a change in sediment movement, either from one direction to another, or to none at all.

The angle of approach of the persistent swell may vary greatly throughout the length of a physiographic unit, e.g., due to a change in coastal alignment. The greater the obliquity of the swell, the more easily can the waves transport material along the shore, both within and beyond the surf zone. This is due to the larger longshore component of the wave forces on the particles, the gravitational pull remaining normal to the contours. The grains then follow a flatter sawtooth profile along the coast and so, for the same wave characteristics, will travel faster as the angle to the shore becomes more acute.

For a given total rate of sediment transport, the more oblique swell requires a narrower working profile than do waves more nearly normal to the coast. Contours of the ocean bed therefore vary in spacing around the length of each bay (see Fig. 1), and also more generally along the length of a physiographic unit. If the energy content of the swell should diminish, say due to continued spreading from its origin, the active beach profile must widen if the total rate of transport is to be maintained; otherwise deposition will occur.

Where a sedimentary bed adjoins a rocky section of coast and does not form a beach, the incoming waves are reflected from the steep cliff. This reflection produces standing waves or clapoti which cause excessive horizontal oscillations of the water near the sea bed. This throws sand, and even sizeable boulders, into temporary suspension and so expedites their passage along this section of coast. Here, again, the increased velocity reduces the active margin required to transport a given total rate of sediment.

Besides the universal applicability of bay shapes and related hydrographic criteria as indicators of net sediment movement, one of the greatest advantages in the use of this method is that it integrates the effect of wave action over time. The bays observed have been produced over centuries or even geological eras, with incidental or periodic reversals of drift eliminated from the record. The result of such one-way traffic of material along lengthy sections of continental margins has important implications for geologists studying land forms and engineers concerned with the design of marine structures or the maintenance of navigable channels.

In presenting information on the net sediment movement around the coastline of the world, to

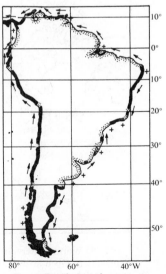

FIG. 6. South American coasts.

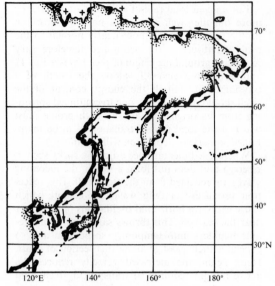

FIG. 7. Northwest Pacific coasts.

the scales available, drastic simplifications have been necessary. In reading Fig. 2 to 7, therefore, the following rules should be observed:

(a) The arrows indicate the direction of longshore drift should sediment be available; no rate of transport is implied.

(b) Net movement is shown, which does not preclude reversals of drift.

(c) Plus signs have been used where drift is substantially retarded or zero; this does not necessarily mean accretion in the area.

(d) The general pattern of sediment motion is illustrated; modifications produced by minor physiographic features, such as islands, have been omitted.

(e) All sizes and types of material—silt, sand and shingle—have been shown stippled: rock or fixed coastline is shown black.

The resultant worldwide pattern obtained from bay analysis should be consistent with the swell distribution observable in swell charts of the oceans, or the global wind systems which generate the waves. Inspection of Fig. 8 will indicate the close correlation between the source of energy and the effects of this energy once it has been distributed around the margins of the several oceans. The major wind systems are seen to occur between the 40 and 50° latitudes in both hemispheres blowing from a westerly direction, but there are other major generation areas such as in the southern Atlantic and the northern Indian Oceans which must be taken into account, as well as the seasonal storms in the enclosed or partially enclosed seas. In the latter, the longshore drift is effected solely by locally generated waves, since swell from distant storm centers cannot penetrate them. Nevertheless, a net sediment movement can result due to the repetitive nature of the meteorological conditions which produce the waves.

R. SILVESTER

References

Bruun, P. and Gerritsen, F., 1960, "Stability of Coastal Inlets," North Holland Publ. Co., 124pp.

Monthly Meteorological Charts of the Western Pacific, 1956, M.O. 484 H.M.S.O., London, reprinted 1956.

Silvester, R., 1959, "Engineering aspects of coastal sediment movement." *Proc. Am. Soc. Civil Engrs.*, **9,** (ww3). 11–39.

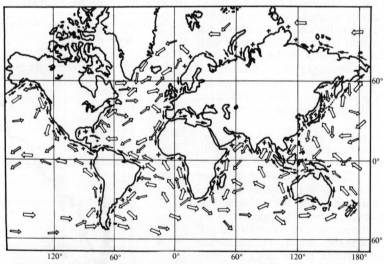

FIG. 8. World pattern of net sediment movement and major wind systems. Explanation: Open arrows, broad = July winds; open arrows, narrow = January winds; solid arrows = net sediment movement; crosses indicate little net transport.

Silvester, R., 1960, "Stabilization of sedimentary coastlines." *Nature*. **185**, 467–469.

Silvester, R., 1962, "Sediment movement around the coastlines of the world," *Proc. 1962 Conf. Inst. Civil Engrs.*, 289–305.

Cross-references: *Bars*; *Beach*; *Beach Erosion and Coastal Protection*; *Littoral Processes*. Vol. I: *Fetch*; *Storm Surge*; *Wave Refraction*; *Wave Theory*.

SEIF—*See* **SAND DUNE**

SELVA LANDSCAPES

The selva, or tropical rain forest, is so intimately related to denudation processes in the humid tropics, that many geomorphologists use the term "selva cycle," as a general descriptor for the forms and processes of denudation and their sequential development through time in the wet tropics.

In the late 1960's, our knowledge of the denudation processes of rain forest areas is based largely on observations by French and German geomorphologists with but a mere handful of papers in English. The most notable single contribution is that of Karl Sapper in his "Geomorphologie der Feuchten Tropen" (1935), but important, sometimes conflicting, contributions have been made by Birot, Thorbecke, Jessen, Freise, Tricart, Lehmann, Sweeting, Wentworth, White, Rougerie, Bakker, and others (listed in Rougerie, 1960). Since the late 1950's, detailed studies in Papua in the Australian Trust Territory of New Guinea by the Division of Land Research and Regional Survey, C.S.I.R.O., Australia, has added much detailed, integrated information on the relationships between topography, soils and vegetation communities, of a type conspicuously lacking in many other studies (Haantjens *et al.*, 1958 *et seq.*).

Distinctive features of the rain forest environment include the following: (1) Knife-edged ridges in both mountainous and low, hilly country, so narrow that in World War II, in New Guinea, companies faced one another two men abreast. (2) Slopes of remarkably uniform declivity especially on igneous and hard metamorphic rocks. These are frequently, but not always, undercut at the base by vigorous stream action. (3) In many areas of low relief, very steep little hillocks with knife-edged ridges may also be found, juxtaposed to gentle, lower valley slopes. Typically, the break of slope between these facets is sharp, very similar to that in arid environments. A tendency to retain steep slopes and knife-edged ridges even in areas with slight relief is evidently in part a function of parent material, for on soft sedimentaries rather lower

FIG. 1. Sketch of typical knife-edge ridges and deeply incised valleys in the humid mountainous tropics. (Sepik District. New Guinea. after W. Behrmann. 1917.) The weathered mantle (commonly 5 to 6 meters deep) is scarred by landslides which lay bare the bedrock at the ridge crests. Streams are incised through the weathered mantle into bedrock. Valley long profiles are irregular and reflect differential rock hardness. much more weakly expressed under the weathered mantle. Up to 2000 meters the entire area from valley to crest is swathed in rainforest.

angles are maintained away from mountainous tracts. On granites and basic igneous rocks, also, there is a tendency for upper slope convexity and lower foot-slope concavity to develop in areas of modest relief. However, particularly in hard metamorphics, the maintenance of straight slopes showing no great evidence of reclining over a wide range of relative relief, is noteworthy. (4) Mountain streams deeply incised and of high gradient. Swept free of fines and floored with boulders and gravel, such streams when they debouch from the mountains, build up great swathes of flanking coarse arkosic deposits. Silts and clays find their resting place some distance from the mountain front. (5) Steep valley slopes typically have a washboard topography, a simple parallel consequent drainage system. This is true even in granitic rocks, which elsewhere show dendritic patterns. (6) Gully action beneath mature rainforest is certainly less than would be expected, based on annual rainfall totals. In short, the drainage net tends to be somewhat coarse. (7) Debris avalanche scars are ubiquitous in igneous, metamorphic and hard sedimentary rock regions. (8) Slump-molded valley heads and valley walls are common, especially in soft sedimentaries. (9) The sediment load of tropical streams is very large, normally from 2–15 times that of temperate streams with a comparable drainage basin. (10) Rain forest is present on all slopes up to 70 or even 80°, and there is an unparalleled urgency of vegetation regrowth on all bared areas.

Rain forests clothe all slopes with an interlocking system of shallow-rooted trees, many exhibiting negative taper, and with a marked surface mass of intertwined surficial roots. The litter of decay (thin to thick depending in part on slope angle) and surface roots, together with the interception of violent tropical rains by the upper stories of the rain forest, helps maintain a relative integrity of the surface soil. Studies by Ruxton in Papua, suggest that at least in that area, more surficial erosion takes place from raindrop action, tree-plowing and trunk trickle than has traditionally been considered to be operative, such that these forms of erosion may in net be more effective under rainforest than temperate forest. Following Sapper and others (given in Rougerie, 1960) it has been widely accepted that surface erosion is limited in the rain forest (i.e., limited in relation to the weathering rate, not necessarily absolute) and this enables relatively deep weathering to take place, for even on steep mountain slopes, under conditions of high temperature, continuous moisture, and abundant humic acids, chemical decay is rapid. Given time, the depth of the weathered mantle may increase to the point where occasional deep-rooted species can no longer anchor the mass to solid rock, and following prolonged periods of heavy rainfall and/or earth tremors, slope failure takes place. Recurrent cycles of avalanching based on variations through time of soil depth, weathering state, and vegetation cover, have been deduced for several areas. Ruxton, however, has vigorously presented an alternative situation in which "a high rate of denudation and shallow, immature weathering mantles are to be expected in the mountains of the humid tropics as in New Guinea." The reconciliation of these different observations and interpretations will represent a major effort for tropical geomorphologists.

Rain forest soils are nearly always saturated, and there is an immediate response to heavy rainfalls in stream flow. Streams rise rapidly and, armed with a coarse bed load, cut deep into bedrock. Consequently, despite the rapidity of weathering, tropical streams carry much unweathered gravels together with the detritus from landslides and mudflows. Rain forest clings to the very edge of the streams, and vertical erosion downward, or Tiefenerosion, is a dominant process.

There are many unresolved geomorphic problems in the selva, including:

(1) Why do very marked differences in depth of weathering occur on steep slopes in the range 30–40 degrees? This contributor has observed granitic saprolite tens of feet thick on steep slopes in portions of New Guinea, yet in others, relatively fresh granite is but thinly veneered with waste products. Some of the divergent views in the literature may merely reflect the differing circumstances in the areas studied.

(2) Are surface raindrop erosion and tree-plowing more important in maintaining uniform slope angles and parallel retreat than many geomorphologists have believed?

(3) How important are subsurface mudflows as denudation agents? Mudflows beneath the surface root-mat have been reported by Sapper, Freise, White, and others, and they attach considerable significance to the phenomena. However, this process raises many further questions and some skepticism as to its universality. How do shallow-rooted trees maintain themselves on steep slopes if subsurface mudflow extends over a substantial portion of a slope? Are mudflows really highly localized features? Do mud ejecta represent primarily end-of-slope, break-of-slope, stream-bank and/or toe-of-landslide phenomena? The literature is not clear on these points.

(4) Is soil creep unimportant, lost in the spectacular denudation rates of avalanching and vertical down-wasting in stream beds?

(5) To what extent are avalanching, slumping, gullying and surface soil erosion continuous, or at least regular, recurrent processes? Are they, rather, episodic, related to unusual seismic events (Simonett, 1967) or profound alternations of wet and dry cycles, and fire damage following long dry spells? Rare, but long, dry periods broken by fire and/or catastrophic rainfalls may introduce marked periodicity in the landslide and the weathering regime in the tropical rain forest. The ubiquitousness of landslides should not, however, lead to the conclusion that they are solely responsible for maintaining slopes at what some observers consider to be the angle of repose of the weathered mantle. Many areas of modest relief still maintain steep slopes even though there is no current evidence of active landsliding, and this, in itself, poses many further questions for study.

(6) The relationship between rock type, weathering process, soil development and erosion mechanisms is very inadequately documented. For example, most writers dismiss soil development as being simply of a latosolic type in the selva. However, juvenile Brown Forest Soils and Podzolics are widespread, and 2 : 1 lattice clay minerals occur in New Guinea much more frequently than studies elsewhere would lead one to expect (Haantjens et al., 1958 et seq., and unpublished data by this author). Knowledge of the soil development and weathering mechanisms lies at the heart of many theories of slope genesis.

(7) Which features of karst development under rain forests are truly unique to this environment, and which are related more to as yet insufficiently documented variations in lithology (Monroe, 1964; Verstappen, 1964)?

The most conspicuous need in further studies of the selva is for detailed, quantified work on slope genesis, development of stream characteristics, landslide frequencies, types of periodicities and surface erosion, mudflow and soil creep magnitudes as influenced by rock type, vegetation cover, climatic regimen, and other variables.

D. S. SIMONETT

References

Haantjens, H. A., Reiner, E., Robbins, R. G., and Saunders, J. C., 1958, "Lands of the Goroka-Mount Hagen area, New Guinea," C.S.I.R.O., Canberra, *Div. Land Res. Reg. Surv., Div. Rept.*, No. 58/1.

Monroe, W. H., 1964, "Lithologic Control in the Development of a Tropical Karst Topography," 20th International Congress, I.G.U., London.

Rougerie, G. 1960, "Sur les Versants en Milieux Tropicaux Humides," Contributions Internationales à la Morphologie des Versants, I.G.U., Commission on the Evolution of Slopes, Supplementband I; 12–18.

Ruxton, B. P., 1967, "Slopewash under Mature Primary Rainforest in Northern Papua," in (Jennings, J. N. and Mabbutt, J. A., editors), "Landform Studies from Australia and New Guinea," Australian National Univ. Press, 85–94.

Sapper. K. 1935. "Geomorphologie der Feuchten Tropen," Leipzig–Berlin, B. G. Teubner.

Simonett, D. S., 1967, "Landslide Distribution and Earthquakes in the Bewani and Torricelli Mountains, New Guinea," in (Jennings, J. N. and Mabbutt, J. A., editors), "Landform Studies from Australia and New Guinea," Australian National Univ. Press, 64–84.

Verstappen, H. Th., 1964, "Karst morphology of the Star Mountains (Central New Guinea) and its relation to lithology and climate," *Zeit. f. Geomorphol.*, N. F., 8(1), 40–49.

Cross-references: *Avalanche; Denudation; Erosion; Gully Erosion; Karst; Landslides; Mass Wasting; Mudflows; Rivers; Soil Creep; Slopes; Tropical Weathering.* Vol. II: *Vegetation Classification and Description.* Vol. VI: *Pedology; Soil Genesis.*

SEMI-ARID REGIONS, HYDROLOGY—*See* pr Vol. VI, **HYDROLOGY IN SEMI-ARID REGIONS**

SERENDIPITY—*See* pr Vol. VI

SHATTER CONES—*See* pr Vol. V

SHEET EROSION, SHEETWASH, RAINWASH, SHEETFLOOD

Sheet erosion is a major process in the denudation of land surfaces. It involves the falling of raindrops and their merging to form a near-continuous sheet which moves down hillslopes, gathering momentum and representing an erosive force of high potential. It is to be distinguished from *gully erosion* (q.v.) and stream erosion which involves concentration of the water flow in surface channels of all dimensions.

Several nearly synonymous terms have been applied to this process: *rainwash, hillwash, sheetwash, sheet flood, rillwash,* in French *ruissellement* (*diffus,* or *en nappe*), in German *Abspülung* or *Flä-*

chenspülung (Cailleux, 1948). Rillwash implies the beginning of very small channels. The term sheet-flood is mostly reserved for the large-scale rainwash briefly observed in semiarid regions during "cloud-bursts" (brief, but severe thunderstorms).

The process has two distinct phases:

(a) The mechanical impact of the raindrop on the weathered rock surface or soil, actually throwing up small particles in the manner of an explosive impact. The nature of raindrop craters occasionally to be seen impressed in a moderately plastic mud is very similar to that of terrestrial or lunar meteorite craters (see *Explosion Craters*, Vol. II). The size of the raindrop is an important factor; the drops are generally largest for the sporadic thunderstorm-type rains of semiarid areas. Thus, although the total rainfall may be low, the erosive capacity is often extraordinarily high. On steep slopes saltation of rain-splattered particles becomes important.

(b) The transport of the liberated particles by the flowing water; the greater the amount of debris, the more vigorous is the erosive capacity of the sheet flow.

Sheet erosion first gained general attention following a classic study by W J McGee (1897) in the subdesertic areas in the American west and northern Mexico, wherein he coined the term *sheetflood erosion*. This process, he believed, was responsible for the planar degradation of desert *pediment slopes* (q.v.). In semiarid regions these slopes, called *Haldenhang* (q.v.) by W. Penck, and *wash slopes* by Meyerhoff, are separated by a distinct nick point (knick point; *Knickpunkte* in German) from an upper, gravity-controlled escarpment or breakaway (the German *Steilwand* and

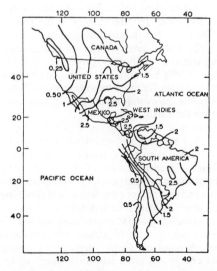

FIG. 1. Isopluvial map of the Americas, showing maximum precipitation for a one-hour interval within any two-year period (Reich, 1963).

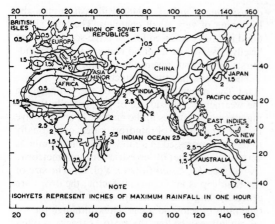

FIG. 2. Isopluvial map of Eurasia, Africa and Australia, showing maximum precipitation for a one-hour interval within any two-year period (Reich, 1963).

Meyerhoff's *gravity slope*). According to Lester King (1957), the mean angles of these slopes, once established, remain essentially constant for a given *rock type* (strength factor) and *available relief*, that is almost independent of climate (excluding the extreme "climatic accident" types—glacial and sandy desert). "As the physical laws of water flow and mass movement are invariable over the land surface of the globe, and as the rock materials of which the upper crust is composed are sensibly the same in all lands, we reach the simple conclusion of a basic homology between the landforms developed under physical agencies the world over." King speaks therefore of the "Uniformitarianism of Hillslopes," as Penck had already suggested, though the role of vegetation in different climatic zones should not be disregarded. Both the density of the vegetation cover and the density of the root mat are distinct factors. In forest-covered country much of the rain fall is directly absorbed or deflected to runoff, over a protective carpet of leaf litter. Cailleux (1950) has pointed out that sheet erosion must have been far more important in pre-Silurian times before the evolution of a general vegetational cover on the earth.

Removal of natural vegetation (see *Soil Erosion*, pr Vol. VI), as is well known, may lead to a duplication of semiarid erosional forms in humid agricultural lands. Intensive studies of the latter have been undertaken for two purposes, (a) to prevent topsoil erosion and thus reduce otherwise severe agricultural losses, and (b) to reduce sediment transport that results in the filling and sedimentation of dams. Thus both soil specialists and hydraulic engineers are involved. A relatively simple method of computing kinetic energy of a given rainstorm and its effect on different soil types has been worked out by Smith and Wischmeier (1957; also Wischmeier and Smith, 1958), who have further provided formulation to quantify the factors of slope length and percent inclination, rainfall, and various elements of man-made disturbance and vegetational cover.

Surveys of sediment sources involved in fluvial transport in humid regions show that "sheet erosion is clearly the dominant source of sediment in most of the watersheds..." but that each watershed is liable to differ in its yield, and the proportion of sediment derived from sheet erosion ranged from 11–100% of the total (Glymph, 1957). In a well-forested area like Ohio, Everett (1963) showed that both sheetwash and rillwash are effective slope erosion agents, but much reduced because of vegetational factors. Mean downslope movements of 8.2 mm/yr were measured. Much more important on exposed faces was "*blow-down*," the exposure of soil to mass-wasting by the uprooting of trees due to wind action.

Experiments in unvegetated badland formations in South Dakota have shown erosion to remove a layer of 2–3 cm/yr from steep slopes and pediments under a rainfall of 800 mm (Schumm, 1956). Although the sheetwash on slopes is maximal at the steepest slopes, the greatest erosion of all was achieved by the soil *creep* on the convex divides and interfluves. Schumm sees the two erosional types as end members of a continuous series.

At the other end of this series, the sheet erosion merges into a fine network of *rills* and some authorities speak of *rillwash* (*ruissellement en filets*), though this was essentially what McGee defined as *sheetflood*. The milder erosion of some humid regions is more appropriate to rillwash. The next step is *gully erosion* (q.v.). If the sheetwash encounters a clay soil, it may well lead to a mudflow (Blackwelder, 1928).

A clear distinction should be made between sheetwash or sheetflood and *streamflood* (Davis, 1938). The latter is characteristic also of semiarid regions, but localized in existing channels, often instituted by an isolated thunderstorm and coming down a preexisting channel (arroyo, wash, wadi, donga) often with a wall-like front. The streamflood may spread out over a broad alluvial fan after leaving a rocky gorge as in *bolson* (q.v.) depressions and thus at times resemble sheetfloods.

RHODES W. FAIRBRIDGE

References

Anonymous, 1964, "Annotated bibliography on hydrology and sedimentation 1959–1962 (U.S. and Canada)," Washington, Bur. Reclam. (*Joint Hydr.-Sed. Bull. 8*).

Blackwelder, E., 1928, "Mudflow as a geologic agent in semiarid mountains," *Bull. Geol. Soc. Am.*, **39**, 465–484.

Cailleux, A., 1948, "Le ruissellement en pays tempéré non montagneux," *Ann. Géogr.*, **57**, 21–39.

Cailleux, A., 1950, "Écoulements liquides en nappes et

aplanissements," *Rev. Géomorphologie Dynamique,*
1, 243–270.

Davis, W. M., 1938, "Sheetfloods and streamfloods,"
Bull. Geol. Soc. Am., **49,** 1337–1416.
Everett, K. R., 1963, "Slope movement, Neotoma
valley, southern Ohio," *Ohio State Univ., Inst. f. Polar
Studies, Rept. 6.*
Glymph, L. M., Jr., 1957, "Importance of sheet erosion
as a source of sediment," *Trans. Am. Geophys.
Union,* **38** (6), 903–907.
Jutson, J. T., 1919, "On the clawing action of rain in
sub-arid Australia," *Proc. Roy. Soc. Victoria,* **32**(1),
20–21.
King, L., 1957, "The uniformitarian nature of hill-
slopes," *Trans. Edinburgh Geol. Soc.,* **17,** 81–102.
McGee, W J 1897, "Sheetflood Erosion," *Bull. Geol.
Soc. Am.,* **8,** 87–112.
Reich, B. M., 1963, "Short-duration rainfall-intensity
estimates and other design aids for regions of sparse
data," *J. Hydrol.,* **1,** 3–28.
Schumm, S. A., 1956, "The role of creep and rainwash on the retreat of badland slopes." *Am. J. Sci.,*
254, 693–706.
Smith, D. D. and Wischmeier, W. H., 1957, "Factors
affecting sheet and rill erosion," *Trans. Am. Geophys.
Union,* **38**(6), 889–896.
Vita-Finzi. C., 1964. "Slope downwearing by discontinuous sheetwash in Jordan," *Israel J. Earth-Sci.,*
13, 88–91.
Wischmeier, W. H., and Smith, D. D., 1958, "Rainfall
energy and its relationship to soil loss," *Trans. Am.
Geophys. Union,* **38**(2), 285–291.

Cross-references: *Badlands; Bolson; Denudation; Deserts
and Desert Landforms; Erosion; Gully Erosion; Haldenhang; Mudflow; Pediment; Slopes; Soil Creep.* Vol. II:
Explosion Craters. Vol VI: *Soil Erosion.*

SHEETFLOOD—*See* **SHEET EROSION,** etc.

SHEETWASH—*See* **SHEET EROSION,** etc.

SIGNATURE THEORY

Observations may be made through the medium
of fields (gravitational, magnetic, electric, nuclear,
weak-field), *photons* (gamma, X-ray, ultraviolet,
optical, infrared, millimeter, radar, radio, VLF,
ELF), *wave energies* (plasma, acoustic, hydrodynamic, seismic), *bulk messengers* (corpuscular,
elements, molecules, particles such as micrometeor-
ites, etc. (Enzmann and Miller, 1966), or hapatic
manipulation (as with simian or human hands).
Signature theory is concerned with observation. The
essence of signature theory is conveyed by the questions: "How well can a particular observer (which
might be a man or a machine) detect or observe
another entity? How well can the specific observer

do this as a function of the mode of detection, the
path over which the information travels, and the
contrast between the observed object and its background, all as functions of time?" These questions
are very pertinent to the "new" geomorphology.

Signature theory is a very rapidly evolving analytical technique. Its systematic beginnings are found
in Shannon's noise and information theory (Shannon, 1948), which originally was concerned with
optimizing information transfer from point to point,
as between telegraph or wireless stations. In nature,
evolutionary processes tend to maximize the ability
of creatures to detect and interpret information
within their action–reaction volumes, and to sub-
due, or occasionally advertise, their presences. The
term "signature," in this sense, is not found in all
dictionaries. The notion was forced by necessity on
radar analysts in the 1950's. They applied it, somewhat informally, to information gained by analysis
of range, amplitude, frequency (Woodward, 1953),
and occasionally polarization and phase characteristics of radar echos. The information was used to
discover the numbers, shapes and hopefully the
masses of echoing objects. With the advent of unmanned and manned space exploration involving
the use of all imaginable means of making observations, singly or in conjunction with each other, a
formal definition of "signature" has evolved (Hovnanian, 1966). In addition, other terms have been
better defined, as outlined in Table 1 (see p. 994).

The foregoing paragraph suggests that the principles of signature theory are relatively simple; they
are. In its more complex forms, signature theory may
be used to maximize both the number and scientific
value of measurements made by information gathering systems. The methods are particularly useful
when used with the expanded theory of geomorphology, and instrument contouring techniques.

ROBERT DUNCAN ENZMANN

References

Enzmann, R. D. and Miller, R. (editors), 1966, "Plane-
tology and space mission planning," *Ann. N.Y. Acad.
Sci.,* **140**(1), 1–163.
Hovnanian, H. P., 1966, "Biotic signatures," in "Plane-
tology and space mission planning," *Ann. N.Y. Acad.
Sci.* **140**(1), 1–163.
Povejsil, D. J., Raven, R. S., and Waterman, P., 1961,
"Airborne Radar," Englewood Cliffs, N.J., D. Van
Nostrand Co.
Shannon, C. E., 1948, "A mathematical theory of com-
munication," *Bell System Tech. J.,* **27,** 379, 623.
Woodward, P. M., 1953, "Probability and Information
Theory with Applications to Radar," New York,
McGraw-Hill Book Co.

Cross-references: *Geomorphology—Expanded Theory;
Instrument Contour Diagrams; Quantitative Geomorphology; Terrain.*

TABLE 1

Detection implies that the sensor is activated when the signal amplitude exceeds a threshold; this protects the system against random noise, preventing a constant state of false alarm (Povejsil, Raven and Waterman, 1961). A system capable of detection and dimensional filtering, would be able to plot the position of a point as a function of time.

An example would be a man's reaction following the breaking of twigs as something passes near him in a dark forest.

Measurement implies that the sensor system has a dynamic range lying between a lower threshold (as found in systems only capable of detection) and an upper threshold. Measurement further implies that the system has a capability to scale between these thresholds (Woodward, 1953).

Examples in the organic world include the human ear that can distinguish a large number of frequencies and a lesser number of intensities over its dynamic range.

Ambiguous signature may be defined as a set of measurements, which may or may not be functions of time. The set of measurements are sufficient to identify an entity as belonging to a set. Ideal filtering is often adapted to securing ambiguous signatures (Enzmann and Miller, 1966).

The footprint seen in the sand by Robinson Crusoe was an unambiguous signature of a human being, but it was ambiguous as to sex, race and individual.

Unambiguous signature implies that the sensor has gained a set of measurements sufficient to unambiguously identify an object or set of objects. In electronics, matched filtering is used to gain unambiguous signatures. The filter is so constructed that it matches the incoming signal. This implies that the sensor knows in advance just what the characteristics of the sensed object are. Mathematically, such signatures may be considered by application of the ambiguity function (Hovnanian, 1966).

A set of fingerprints is almost without exception sufficient information to distinguish one human being in the set of all humans. Perhaps audio-frequency "voiceprints" will also prove to be unambiguous signatures identifying one human in the set of all humans. Notice that in the case of both fingerprints and "voiceprints" the sensor system must have knowledge concerning the object sensed.

Target Language implies a set of unambiguous signatures from an entity which literally traces its life history from conception to death and disintegration. The term may be used somewhat loosely to describe an aircraft, missile, other vehicle, or even a creature during a patterned behavior.

Understanding of target language is used to predict the future behavior of a target. An example might be a hunter's quarry, a hostile aircraft, or even the behavior of the stock market.

SILCRETE—*See* **INDURATION**; *also* pr Vol. VI

SIMPLICITY PRINCIPLE—*See* pr Vol. VI

SINGING SANDS

When in motion, some sands emit sounds that are distinctly audible to the human ear. Such sands have been variously described as *roaring, booming, squeaking, musical* and *singing*, and have been reported from many parts of the world, and from both coastal and desert areas. The phenomenon has been known for many years. European explorers in the Sahara, in Arabia and Afghanistan described roaring sands early in the nineteenth century, but the local inhabitants had recorded accounts much earlier. In the early fifteenth century, for example, the Emperor Baber described sands from which in summer there issued "the sound of drums and nagarets."

Accounts of the precise nature of the noise made by moving sands vary. The explorers Mitchell and Sturt both report hearing "sounds like distant artillery" in the central Australian deserts, and settlers in the Lake Torrens and South East districts of South Australia as early as the eighteen fifties and sixties reported similar noises in the red sandhill country. Hugh Miller (of Old Red Sandstone fame) describes the note emitted by singing sands on the Island of Eigg as shrill and sonorous. The sound emitted is not in the high-frequency range and has been described as

"Somewhat like that produced by a whistling kettle just before the water is thoroughly boiling; something like the rustling of rain on an iron roof or the sound produced by sand falling on to a piece of paper." (Gibson, 1946, p.41.)

The nature of the sound evidently varies according to the velocity and volume of the sand involved. In an early account of sonorous sands from near Kabul, it is described how, on a high slope of some 40° inclination, sand when initially dislodged produced a sound rather like wind blowing through wires, but as it gained momentum downslope, the noise more nearly resembled that produced by drawing moistened fingers over glass. Subsequently, as it neared the base of the slope, the reverberations produced by the sand attained the loudness of distant thunder, and caused nearby rocks to vibrate.

Another account of the occurrence of singing sands has been related by Thesiger, who, during his explorations of southern Arabia, on several occasions encountered sands possessing acoustical properties:

"Next morning while we were leading our camels down a steep dune face I was suddenly conscious of a low vibrant humming which grew in volume until it sounded as though an aeroplane were flying low over our heads. ...The sound ceased when we reached the bottom." (Thesiger, 1959, p.150.)

It was found that the sound could be started and stopped at will simply by stepping on or off the slip face of the dune, and from this it is apparent, as Thesiger himself believes, that the singing is due to one layer of sand slipping over another. Moreover, Miller found that the loudest, sharpest noises were most easily produced where dry, loose sand was underlain, at a depth of some 3–4 inches, by damp, semicoherent sand.

Not all moving sands are sonorous, but there is little to distinguish sands that do, from sands that do not, display acoustical properties when in motion. Singing sands are remarkably well sorted and are sensibly uniform in size, but so are many nonmusical sands. As far as is known, all musical sands are, with one exception (in which the sand grains are about 1 mm in diameter), less than $\frac{1}{2}$ mm in diameter; moreover, the acoustical properties of the sand vary with the size of the particle. For example, various size fractions were taken from a sand from Boston Island, off the coast of southern Eyre Peninsula, South Australia, a sand known for its consistent musical properties, and it was found that the quality of sound varied with the size fraction:

Size (mm)	Sound
Less than 0.251	Poor sound
0.251–0.295	Feeble squeak
0.295–0.353	Good musical sound
0.353–0.422	Sound better than mixture, higher pitch
Greater than 0.422	Sound better than mixture, lower pitch

As far as acoustical properties are concerned, the shape of sand grains is not significant nor are the air pockets occupying the interstitial spaces between sand grains critical in this respect, for it has been demonstrated that musical sand retains its sonorous properties when moved *in vacuo*. Neither heating nor cooling alter the acoustical properties of sand. Most singing sands are of quartz, but sands of coral fragments are reported to sing in Hawaii; the elasticity of sand grains is, therefore, not crucial though experimental work suggests that the grains of musical quartz sands have greater elasticity than those that are acoustically dead.

Sand that sings on the beach will, if kept dry and uncontaminated by dust, retain its properties for a number of years, at least, and probably for an indefinite period. However, if singing sand is exposed to dust and moisture, it quickly loses its ability to make noises. If singing sand is continuously shaken in a container in a dry condition, it gradually loses its sound; however, if the same procedure is followed with the sand mixed with water, the sand subsequently being dried, the musical quality remains unimpaired. The presence of any fine impurities such as shell fragments or chalk seriously interferes with the sound of singing sand, and it is notable that when sand, which was once musical, has been killed by shaking in a dry state and is then washed with water several times, the dust drained off, and the sand dried, the sand is revived. It is not the rounding that causes musical sand to be killed for the shape of singing sands is varied, but the presence of fines between grains does impair the acoustical properties, and it is the production of these by impact during shaking that does the damage. Their removal by washing repairs the situation.

The addition of water destroys the ability to make noises: singing sands are, with a very few exceptions, dry. The addition of 0.05% by weight of water makes little difference to the musical properties of sand, but 0.1% makes a marked difference and 1% permits only a feeble note to be emitted. It has been recorded that roaring sand from the Kalahari was removed from the desert and absorbed 0.2% by weight of moisture and was killed. On the other hand, there is evidence that the loss of moisture kills some singing sands. Nevertheless, most singing sands are dry.

The singing of sands is caused by the impact of sand grains upon other sand grains. The production of sound is favored by the absence of fine particles and moisture which may have a cushioning effect. However, as many writers concerned with singing sands have stated, the ultimate cause of the phenomenon is as yet quite unexplained.

C. R. TWIDALE

References

Bolton, H. C., 1890, "Researches on musical sand in the Hawaiian Islands and in California," *Trans. N.Y. Acad. Sci.* **10**, 28–35.

Bolton, H. C. and Julien, A. A., 1888, "The true cause of sonorousness in sand," *Trans. N.Y. Acad. Sci.*, **8**, 9–11.

Fairchild, H. L., 1920, "Musical sands," *Science*, **51**, 62–64.

Gibson, E. S. H., 1946, "Singing sand," *Trans. Royal Soc. S. Australia*, **70,** 35–44.

Humphries, D. W., 1966, "The booming sand of Korizo, Sahara, and the squeaking sand of Gower, S. Wales: a comparison of the fundamental characteristics of two musical sands," *Sedimentology*, **6**(2), 135–152.

Kegel, W., 1937, "Der Wüstensand 'singt'," *Kosmos*, **34,** 342.

Miller, Hugh, 1858, "The Cruise of the Betsy," pp.58–67, Edinburgh.

Thesiger, W., 1959, "Arabian Sands," p.150, London, New York, E. P. Dutton, 326pp.

Woods, J. E., 1862, "Geological observations in South Australia," p.57.

Cross-references: *Beach; Sand Dunes.*

SINK, SINKHOLE, SWALLOW HOLE

By far the most common feature of limestone solution in karst landscapes, sink or sinkhole applies to any depression ranging from a shallow saucer shape, where runoff water quickly sinks into the ground, to a funnel-shaped or cylindrical pipe that normally gives access to underground caves. Where a stream disappears into the hole, it is usual to call it a *swallow hole* or *ponor* in Serbo-Croat. A deep *karst pipe* leading down into a cavern system is termed a *pothole* in England and a *jama* in Yugoslavia. Explorers of such features are popularly known as "potholers." The depression may contain a pond or lake. Malott (1945) estimated that there are about 300,000 sinkholes within the area of the southern Indiana karst, with up to 500/km².

Thornbury (1954) distinguishes between a depression, lowered by solution beneath a soil cover, ultimately to form a dolina, and the undermining of a cavern that leads to a collapsed sink; this definition seems to run counter to the usual understanding that a collapsed sink is a dolina, and further collapse and extension provide a series: sink-dolina-uvala-polje.

Large sinkholes in Florida and Yucatan, today half filled with water, were formed during the Pleistocene low sea-level stages. In Yucatan these *cenotes* were regarded as sacred by the Mayas in this otherwise waterless limestone platform (Shrock, 1946; Termier and Termier, 1963). Drowned karst holes and pipes are commonly seen in Pacific and Indian Ocean coral reefs that antedate the last glacial drop of sea level, when the ground water table was lowered by over 100 meters (Fairbridge, 1948). They are often seen in calcareous eolianite rocks in Bermuda, Bahamas, South Africa, Western Australia and elsewhere (Fairbridge, 1950). Where large deep examples are found by sounding offshore, as in the Bahamas, they are known as "oceanholes" or "blue holes," in contrast to the green shallows. Small ones in the Bahamas on the land often contain rich soil and are called "banana holes" for that is what is usually planted there. In some early papers, these pipes were mistaken for fossil palmetto trunks. Certainly they are often associated with fossil roots, "rhizomorphs" or "rhizoconcretions" (Northrop, 1890).

Sinks also form sometimes in other soluble rocks such as salt, gypsum and anhydrite.

RHODES W. FAIRBRIDGE

References

Fairbridge, R. W., 1948, "Notes on the geomorphology of the Pelsart Group of the Houtman's Abrolhos Islands," *J. Roy. Soc. W. Australia, **33** (for 1946–47), 1–43.

Fairbridge, R. W., 1950, "The geology and geomorphology of Point Peron, Western Australia," *J. Roy. Soc. W. Australia,* **34** (for 1947–48), 35–72.

Malott, C. A., 1945, "Significant features of the Indiana karst," *Proc. Indiana Acad. Sci.,* **54,** 8–24.

Northrop, J. I., 1890, "Notes on the geology of the Bahamas," *Trans. N.Y. Acad. Sci.,* **10,** 4–22.

Shrock, R. R., 1946, "Karst features in Maya region of Yucatan peninsula, Mexico," *Proc. Indiana Acad. Sci.,* **45,** 111–116.

Termier, H., and Termier, G., 1963, "Erosion and Sedimentation," London and Princeton, N.J., D. Van Nostrand Co., 433pp. (translated by D. W. and E. E. Humphries).

Thornbury, W. D., 1954, "Principles of Geomorphology," New York, John Wiley & Sons, 618pp.

Cross-references: *Dolina; Karst; Polje; Uvala.*

SKERRY—*See* STACK

SLIPOFF SLOPE

There are many causes for the *asymmetry of valleys* such as aspect (insolation and microclimate effect), Coriolis effect, prevailing wind systems and meander development, but structural controls lead to special types of valley asymmetry, and these are known as *slipoff slopes*. In a landscape involved in stream dissection, especially under steady or discontinuous lowering of relative base level, where the stream regime is subsequent, superimposed or antecedent, the downward erosion of the stream bed is likely to be deflected sideways by the stream dynamics or by any tilted structure in more resistant rocks. Such a structure may be provided by a harder sedimentary layer, an interbedded volcanic member, a sill, a tilted unconformity where the basement consists of more resistant rocks, a plutonic intrusive contact, etc. Two types are best known: (a) *meander slipoff slopes*, dynamically developed without structural control by bedrock, and (b) *forced slipoff slopes*, structurally controlled

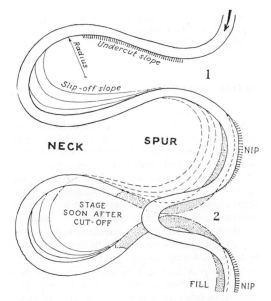

FIG. 1. Non-structural, meander slipoff slope developed in a mature meandering valley still involved in down-cutting. *Note*: undercut slope or nip alternating with and opposite to slipoff slopes. Stage 1 shows a "gooseneck;" stage 2 a "cutoff" (from Lobeck, 1939). (By permission of McGraw-Hill Book Co., N.Y.)

FIG. 2. Valley of the Rhine: Slipoff and undercut slopes (Crickmay, 1959). The view is northward, or down-valley. The town in the foreground is Boppard which lies between Koblenz and Bingen. Here, the river makes its greatest horseshoe bend. The great essentials are the flattish upland some hundreds of feet above river level, and the two contrasting kinds of sloping ground: long, gentle slopes rising from convex shores, and short, steep ones from concave. The long slope in the center of the view is one of the outstanding slipoffs in the world; it was carved by the Rhine as the river cut down from the upland to its present level—at the same time shifting steadily to the left and thereby enlarging the curve of the channel. The steep ones are undercut slopes, made by wasting in response to undermining by the river at their bases. (The illustration was drawn by Mr. G. Picco, Calgary.)

by a tilted bedrock. In both cases a slow uplift or lowering of base level is usually involved, since progressive downcutting of the thalweg occurs.

Meander Slipoff Slopes

These develop in a mature valley where a stream of relatively high energy potential is actively cutting down a meander system by lateral corrasion (Cotton, 1942). Outside slopes become undercut and develop a cliff or nip, while the inside curves are progressively abandoned as the meander swings wider and cuts deeper (Fig. 1). This phenomenon is well displayed by certain river valleys that were not glaciated but which occur in periglacial regions where progressive lowering of base level has occurred from time to time coinciding with episodes of increased stream energy (glacial meltwaters). Well-known examples are the Middle Rhine of Germany (Fig. 2) and the Moldau (or Vltava) of Bohemia. In such cases, the slipoff slopes are partly cut in bedrock with veneered terraces left behind; these are "pointbars," and this term is more appropriate to meanders in old-age reaches where the material is exclusively alluvial.

Forced Slipoff Slopes

This term was proposed by Crickmay (1959) for the type of slipoff controlled by bedrock structure

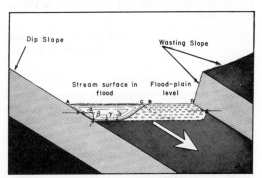

FIG. 3. Dynamics of forced slipoff erosion (Crickmay, 1959), which is essentially the same as "uniclinal shifting" (of Wooldridge and Morgan, 1937). This is a cross section of a strike-trending valley in an area of homoclinal sedimentary formations which alternate with one another in resistance to erosion. The valley bottom is located on a weakly resistant shale, the lowest parts of the valley walls on resistant sandstones. In every possible direction, the river flow A–B exerts erosive forces against its surroundings: four of these forces are represented by the arrows, α, β, γ, and δ. Force α is balanced by an opposing rock resistance force in the sandstone; the lesser force β is also so balanced. But the forces γ and δ are opposed only by weaker resistance forces; consequently, downward cutting may be done by the near-graded stream. The resulting activity of the flow is oscillation across the valley to the position C–D, and downcutting in the direction of the great arrow. Erosion slips off the sandstone at left, but undercuts that at right.

(Fig. 3). An almost synonymous expression, *Uniclinal Shifting*, had been introduced earlier by Wooldridge and Morgan (1937, p. 159) for asymmetrical valleys controlled by bedrock structure. It occurs where alternating hard and soft rocks are tilted at moderate angles (up to about 20°), or against unconformities. Wooldridge and Morgan cited the Lea Valley in southern England as being an example. Subsequently Stamp (1946) suggested that the lower Thames River within the confines of the London Basin (an asymmetrical plunging syncline) is yet another example. In this case, it would seem that the Pleistocene ice advance into the Finchley depression of the northern part of the Thames valley would have helped this process (Lawrence, 1964), though isostatic movements, particularly tilting, may have played some role in this case.

The evolution of a slipoff slope may sometimes be traced by the presence of asymmetric terraces, always stepping down from one side only, and becoming progressively younger from top to bottom. In the case of a classic slipoff slope like that of the lower Hudson in New York State between Poughkeepsie and Manhattan, which has followed the 15–20° west-tilted unconformity between the soft Triassic shales and the early Paleozoic crystalline rocks, there is unfortunately little trace of pre-Holocene terracing, because of the glacial (Wisconsin) gouging that has converted the lower course into a fjord.

RHODES W. FAIRBRIDGE
STUART A. HARRIS

References

Cotton, C. A., 1942, "Geomorphology: An Introduction to the Study of Landforms," Christchurch, Whitcombe and Tombs, Ltd., 505pp.

Crickmay, C. H., 1959, "A Preliminary Inquiry into the Formulation and Applicability of the Geological Principle of Uniformity" (priv. publ.), Calgary, de Mille Books, 50pp.

Harris, S. A., 1968, "Isostatic recovery near ice margins; some evidence from Waterloo, Ontario," *Trans. Symposium on Cold Climate Processes and Environments*, INQUA Congress, Fairbanks, Alaska. August, 1965.

Lawrence, G. R. P., 1964, "Some pro-glacial features near Finchley and Potters Bar," *Proc. Geol. Assoc. London*, **75**, 15–30.

Lobeck, A. K., 1939, "Geomorphology, An Introduction to the Study of Landscapes," New York, McGraw-Hill Book Co., 731pp.

Stamp, L. D., 1946, "Britain's Structure and Scenery," London, Collins, New Naturalist Series No. 4, p. 71.

Von Engeln, O. D., 1942, "Geomorphology," New York, The Macmillan Co., 655pp.

Wooldridge, S. W. and Morgan, R. S., 1937, "The Physical Basis of Geography," London and New York, Longmans, Green & Co., 445pp.

Cross-references: *Asymmetric Valleys*; *Baer-Babinet Law*; *Drainage Patterns*; *Rivers—Meandering and Braiding*; *Slopes*; *Structural Control in Geomorphology*. Vol. II: *Coriolis Force*; *Ice Age Meteorology*; *Insolation*; *Microclimates*.

SLOPE ANALYSIS

The term *slope* in its broadest sense means an element of the earth's solid surface, including both terrestrial and submarine surfaces; it is, therefore, simply an element of the interface between lithosphere and either hydrosphere or atmosphere. Slope elements are assumed to be of small, but unspecified, dimensions. As finite surfaces in space, slope elements may be planar, cylindrical, conical, spherical, or of any other configuration, including highly irregular forms. The science of geomorphology as a whole is concerned with slopes and their history, including slopes produced by exogene (external) processes and endogene (internal) processes of vulcanism, orogeny, and epeirogeny. This discussion, however, is limited to one class of slopes only, namely, those produced in the denudation of the continents by combined processes of weathering, mass-wasting, and flowing water. Such slopes comprise the watersheds of streams and are adjusted to the geometry of the branching channel systems which they supply with water and mineral solids. Slopes produced by glacial ice, wind, and waves are arbitrarily excluded here, but explained elsewhere. Slopes of fluvial denudation treated here are for the most part erosional (e.g., subjected to more or less continuous and progressive removal of mass), although colluvial deposition (sheet-form accumulation at the base of slope) may be locally important.

Slopes of fluvial denudation are most commonly and simply analyzed in terms of a slope profile or a slope belt of unit width extending from a drainage divide at the upper extremity, down to a lower

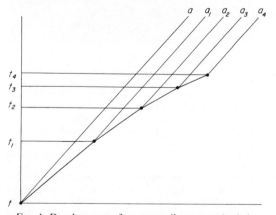

FIG. 1. Development of an upwardly convex, buried-rock slope profile by uniform parallel slope retreat (a through a_4) and slope burial in diminishing increments (t through t_4) (after W. Penck. 1924, Fig. 9B. p. 133).

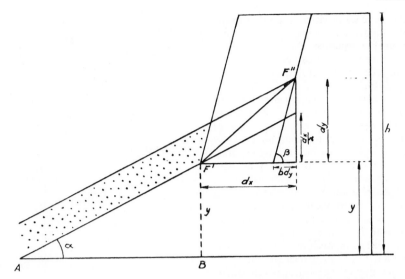

FIG. 2. Geometry, variables, and differential terms postulated by Bakker and Le Heux as the basis of a differential equation of slope development (after Bakker and Le Heux, 1946, Fig. 2).

terminus which is commonly a stream channel, but which may, instead, be a natural discontinuity such as a terrace, pediment, or cliff representing an abrupt change in formative process. A slope profile or belt of unit width is best taken along the down-gradient line, orthogonal to the topographic contours, since this orientation represents the trajectory of fluids and particulate matter moving under the stress of gravity. Ultimately, however, slope analysis must be concerned with the three-dimensional geometry of whole watersheds in which convergences and divergences of the slope orthogonals are taken into account.

Rational Slope Analysis

Schemes of slope-profile analysis may be classified according to whether the approach is *rational* or *empirical*. The rational approach, exemplified in works of Walther Penck (1924) and J. P. Bakker and J. W. N. Le Heux (1946, 1947) proceeds to deduce the geometry of slope profiles and their progressive evolution on the basis of a set of assumptions as to initial geometry and the relative rates of removal and accumulation and of crustal elevation, depression and tilting. Success of the rational method hinges upon the degree to which the assumed conditions and rates of change represent real conditions in nature. Generally, a great deal of simplification of natural processes is required by rational analysis, and confirmation by observation of nature is rendered difficult or impossible because correspondingly simple examples cannot be found. Rational analysis of slope may be *descriptive* or *mathematical*. In the descriptive analysis of Penck (1924), the assumptions, boundary conditions, and

change rates are described in words and illustrated in geometrically precise drawings (Fig. 1). In the mathematical analysis of Bakker and Le Heux (1946, 1947), variables are defined precisely and worked into functional relationships through the setting up of differential equations and their solution to yield profile forms (Fig. 2).

Empirical Slope Analysis

Descriptive. Empirical procedures in slope-profile analysis are based upon direct observation of slopes in nature. Both descriptive and quantitative methods may be used. Over many decades of its evolution, the science of geomorphology was limited to the verbal description of landforms and the processes of their formation. W. M. Davis (1912) and a number of his students applied the explanatory-descriptive method to slope analysis. Slopes were described in terms of qualifying adjectives such as "gentle," "steep," "sigmoid," or "concave" and were referred to a cycle of erosion in stages of youth, maturity, and old age. Conclusions concerning the typical changes of slope with time, e.g., reclining or steepening, were derived from the

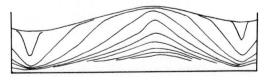

FIG. 3. Stages in the evolution of valley-side slopes. Slopes decrease in declivity as relief is reduced (after W. M. Davis, 1912, Fig. 25, p. 65).

accumulated experience of visual inspection in the field and from topographic maps, as well as from pure deduction. For example, Davis expressed a theory of reclining slope retreat in a composite profile drawing lacking units of measure and without a time scale. (Fig. 3).

Quantitative. Quantitative empirical methods of slope analysis consist of field observations in which measurements of geometry, time rates of change of position and form, and mass transport are taken by instrumental surveys. One group of investigators, exemplified by Robert E. Horton (1945), includes the hydraulic engineers concerned with infiltration and runoff of precipitation and with associated soil erosion. Through appropriate instrumentation, usually in test plots, the processes of slope erosion have been measured, allowing empirical relationships to be established between hydrologic parameters and erosion rates. Such forms of analysis, while adding greatly to the knowledge of dynamics of slope processes, are germane to exceedingly short time spans in the geologic sense and make little direct and immediate contribution to the broader patterns of slope evolution.

Another form of field observation has consisted of the emplacement of strain gauges connecting objects planted in the soil with concrete posts set deeply in bedrock. Rates and distances of soil movement have been continuously recorded. Various forms of traps have been devised to collect the detritus reaching the base of a slope element.

Still another form of quantitative study uses badlands as naturally occurring laboratories in which small-scale models of mountainous terrain evolve rapidly under the eroding force of rainbeat and overland flow (Schumm, 1956). Metal rods are driven deeply into the ground, forming reference points on a slope profile. Removal depths are obtained at annual, or more frequent, intervals by measuring the length of the exposed segments of rods. Not only are erosion rates calculable, but the nature of slope retreat—whether in parallel planes, reclining, or steepening—can be discerned.

Hydraulic Slope Theory

Horton (1945, pp. 315–331) expounded a theory of slope development which combines data of hydraulic field observations with theoretical considerations. His analysis limits itself to the action of overland flow as an eroding and transporting agent; thus, the complex interaction of geologic processes referred to below is ignored in favor of a simple model. Horton shows a slope profile extending from divide to adjacent stream channel (Fig. 4). Rain is shown as falling uniformly on the surface, exceeding infiltration capacity and producing overland flow. Depth of overland flow increases downslope. Within the belt of no erosion, X_c, shear stresses of flow do not exceed resistivity of the surface materials and the flow is clear. At the point a,

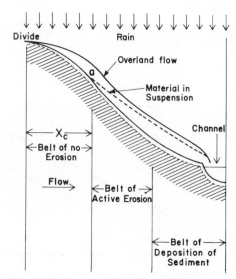

FIG. 4. Profile of a valley-side slope showing zones related to overland flow (after R. E. Horton, 1945, Fig. 14, p. 316).

active erosion sets in and material is carried in suspension in the flow layer. A belt of active erosion is thus produced. A lower zone of deposition is shown where the slope decreases and some of the suspended matter is dropped as a colluvial accumulation. Horton does not explain how the given profile came into existence, nor does he predict its future development in terms of land-mass evolution.

Open Dynamic Slope Systems

To demonstrate the complexity of a complete assessment of slope evolution processes in nature, consider a slope element which is a belt of unit width extending from a drainage divide to an adjacent stream channel. A humid climate of low to middle latitudes is assumed. Let this slope element be bounded on the sides and ends by imaginary vertical planes of reference and extended downward to include a soil layer of arbitrary thickness. The solid figure—a prism—thus produced constitutes an open system, through whose boundaries there is a flux of energy and matter (Fig. 5). Through the upper boundary, or ground surface, the system receives matter in the form of precipitation (and possibly also mineral and organic sediment settled from aerial suspension). Through this boundary also, energy is received from direct solar radiation and from thermal radiation from the air; energy likewise is lost by outward radiation and by conduction and evaporation into the air. Plants, in photosynthesis, produce organic matter which is added to the slope system and acts as a renewable deterrent to erosion. Infiltrating precipitation passes through the slope prism, exiting by the lower boundary and carrying down ions, colloids, and perhaps even mineral particles of clay and silt

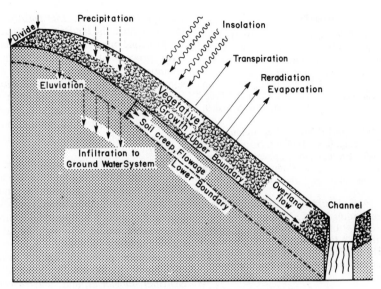

FIG. 5. A slope prism considered as an open dynamic system.

grades, a process generally termed *eluviation*, or simple *leaching*. Removal of such solids from the slope system must result in loss of bulk density and strength, contributing to subsidence and consequent slope retreat. At the same time, the products of eluviation may accumulate in a soil horizon which increases in density and strength. Such deposition is termed *illuviation* and results in hard-pan or laterite zones, which may later resist erosion and thus influence slope development. An opposite process is the upward movement of salts in solution in capillary rise, with subsequent deposition in a soil horizon of accumulation, as illustrated by calcium carbonate nodules and layers (caliche) in semiarid climates.

Water in sheets, films, and shallow rills entrains organic and mineral particles by boundary shear stress. Through the distal or terminal surface boundary of the slope prism, the system loses matter through the passage of overland flow carrying the products of mechanical erosion and chemical decomposition. Through this boundary also passes the slower-moving soil mass engaged in creep and spontaneous flowage. Downslope creep of soil and other unconsolidated overburden resting upon strong bedrock is an inevitable consequence of the numerous forms of soil disturbances. Dilatation through thermal cycles and alternate wetting and drying, spontaneous swelling in mineral hydrolysis, filling of animal borings and burrows, root growth and decay, trampling by animals, and earthquake shocks represent such disturbances. Rearrangements accompanying disturbances and readjustments result in downslope movement because the gravity field exerts a bias upon the force systems and is directed downslope. Spontaneous

movements of soil under the influence of gravitational shear stress, when soil strength is reduced by high moisture content, is a slope development process of general importance in humid climates and of dominant character in arctic regimes (e.g., solifluction).

The slope element under discussion may undergo two basic kinds of change as a geometrical surface in space: it may be translated without rotation through the removal of equal increments of material in a given time throughout its entire length, giving parallel retreat, or it may be rotated to a steeper or less steep attitude by the removal of wedge-shaped increments. Rotation may accompany translation. Pure translation represents the preservation of a steady state in the complex of slope-forming processes, whereas steepening or lessening of slope may reflect adjustments of the steady state to more or less intense states of activity. Slope analysis cannot be divorced from consideration of the action of channelized flow at the slope base. Translation of the slope without rotation implies that stream action removes all material brought to the slope base but does not itself undercut the slope. Undercutting may result in a wave of slope steepening and reflect increased intensity of fluvial action in a region, whereas the accumulation of colluvium because of decreased stream activity may lead to a reduction in slope inclination.

A slope element is thus delicately balanced in its geometry and dynamics with respect to the prevailing regional fluvial activity, and the whole system must be analyzed as a dynamic system if meaningful theories of slope development and valid interpretations of past slope history are to be derived.

ARTHUR N. STRAHLER

References

Bakker, J. P., and Le Heux, J. W. N., 1946, "Projective-geometric treatment of O. Lehmann's theory of the transformation of steep mountain slopes," *Proc. Koninkl. Ned. Akad. Wetenschap.*, **49**, 533-547.

Bakker, J. P., and Le Heux, J. W. N., 1947, "Theory on central rectilinear recession of slopes, I and II," *Proc. Koninkl. Ned. Akad. Wetenschap.* **50**, Nos. 8 and 9, 959-966, 1154-1162.

Davis, W. M., 1912, "Die Erklärende Beschreibung der Landformen," Leipzig, B. G. Teubner, 565pp.

Horton, R. E., 1945, "Erosional development of streams and their drainage basins, hydrophysical approach to quantitative morphology," *Bull. Geol. Soc. Am.*, **56**, 275-370.

Penck, Walther, 1924, "Die Morphologische Analyse," Stuttgart, J. Engelhorns Nachf., 283pp.

Scheidegger, A., 1964, "Lithologic variations in slope development theory," *U. S. Geol. Surv., Circ.*, **485**.

Schumm, S. A., 1956, "The role of creep and rainwash in the retreat of badland slopes," *Am. J. Sci.*, **254**, 693-706.

Cross-references: *Denudation; Erosion; Mass Wasting; Quantitative Geomorphology; Rivers; Sheet Erosion; Slopes; Valley Evolution.*

SLOPE CYCLE—*See* HALDENHANG OR WASHSLOPE

SLOPES

(A) Introduction

The word *slope* has two geomorphic applications. Used in a *general* sense, "slope" refers to any geometric element of the earth's solid surface; the entire landscape is made up of slope elements and thus the science of geomorphology is largely concerned with the study of slopes. There is no genetic or locational connotation to the word "slope"; slopes may be subaerial, submarine (or by extension, lunar, etc.), and may be formed by any process. In a *restricted* sense, "slope" is often used to refer to the angle which any part of the earth's surface makes with a horizontal datum. Better terms for this angle include inclination, slope angle and slope gradient.

Slope elements can be produced under a wide variety of conditions. Slopes can be either endogenetic or exogenetic. *Endogenetic (hypogene) slopes* are those which owe their existence to processes which originate within the earth: *orogeny, epeirogeny, taphrogeny* and *volcanism* (q.v. Vol. V). Each of these processes produces changes in the elevation and orientation of slope elements, and may produce entirely new slopes (see *Structural Control in Geomorphology*). Constructional slopes are not considered *per se* in this entry.

Exogenetic (epigene) slopes result from the action of processes which originate at or near the earth's solid surface. Exogenetic processes (*weathering,*

mass-wasting, erosion, transportation, deposition) tend to reduce the landscape to a *base level* (q.v.), the principal one being mean sea level. The cumulative process of landscape leveling is termed *gradation* (q.v.). Gradation involves both lowering some parts of the land by *degradation* (q.v.) and raising its level by *aggradation* (q.v.).

A third, rare type of slope is produced by the impact of extraterrestrial bodies upon the earth's surface (see *Astroblemes and Meteorite Craters*, Vol. II).

Exogenetic and endogenetic processes interact to produce the features of land surface and sea floor. Without exogenetic processes the landscape would be one of unmodified structural surfaces and volcanic slopes, while without endogenetic processes there would ultimately be a level surface entirely beneath the sea.

Exogenetic processes can act in a number of environments: *subaerial, submarine* (and sublacustrine), *subglacial,* and *subterranean*. Only subaerial slope forming processes will be discussed here. Consideration will be given to slopes produced by gradation due to weathering, mass-wasting and flowing surface water. Processes related to wind, waves and groundwater solution are discussed separately (see *Beach; Beach Erosion; Karst; Littoral Processes; Sand Dunes; Wind Action*).

Two subdivisions of subaerial slopes exist: *aggradational* forms and *degradational* forms (see *Gradation*). The former include alluvial, colluvial and talus slopes and are only briefly mentioned here. Degradational slopes include escarpments, the watersheds of streams, and surfaces eroded directly by streams, e.g., channels and cut terraces. Surfaces originating directly from stream action are discussed elsewhere (see *Stream Channel Characteristics; Terraces*). This discussion is thus limited almost exclusively to those degradational slopes commonly referred to as *erosional escarpments, hillslopes* (including residual landforms) and *valley sides*. Use of the word "slope" in what follows will denote degradational surfaces of these three types, unless otherwise noted. Despite all the other slope types mentioned, these probably dominate the present subaerial landscape, albeit often in combination with other types.

This definition of slope is similar to that of Dylik (personal communication, 1968), who considers the term *hillslope* to be a three-dimensional form, produced by denudational processes of mass wasting and slope wash, and in a very real sense representing the dynamic connection between interfluve crests (hill tops) and valley bottoms (channels). Slope development thus represents the principal effect of denudation, and results in the effacing of endogenetic morphology, as well as the destruction of forms such as those produced subglacially, dunes and so on. Slopes dynamically integrate the landscape by ultimately joining together the entire land surface, be it degradational or aggradational.

The subject of slope form, origin and development is one which has been accorded much discussion but in many cases little more. As Kirk Bryan (1940) aptly put it, the geomorphologist all too often has been like a "complaisant reveler (who) slightly bemused by long though mild intoxication on the limpid prose of Davis's remarkable essays, ... wakes with a gasp to realize that in considering the important question of slope he has always substituted words for knowledge, phrases for critical observation." Many studies of slope over the past thirty (and especially the last ten) years have been field oriented and at least partly quantitative, with the result that knowledge of the nature of slopes is rapidly improving. Nevertheless slope problems present some of the most fundamental questions current in geomorphology. Among these are: (1) the actual form of slopes in profile and plan; (2) variation of slope profiles with climate, lithology, structure, time, tectonism, relief and other factors; (3) parallel retreat of slopes versus slope decline (pediments versus peneplains); (4) retreat of structurally controlled escarpments; (5) importance of various processes upon slope form and slope development; (6) rates of operation of processes and rates of change of slopes; (7) configuration and role of slopes as part of open systems (e.g., *drainage basins*, q.v.).

It is impossible to present a complete synthesis in this article; only the most important and/or prevalent facts and theories will be reviewed.

(B) History of the Study of Slopes

There are not many "classic" studies of slopes. Buffon, in 1785 (see references in Chorley *et al.*, 1964), stated that slopes decline with time and that the erosion of a steep hill is more rapid than that of a gentle hill because erosion is proportional to slope angle. In 1866, Fisher developed a mathematical model for the parallel retreat of a vertical cliff. The still vigorous confrontation between proponents of slope decline and parallel retreat is thus more than a century old.

A major pioneering work was that of de la Noë and de Margerie (1888). This paper contained a number of fundamental statements: (1) Maximum slope inclination is related to rock type. (2) Slopes are continually changing and are controlled by resistance of the rocks, the activity of erosive processes and the duration of the processes. (3) In arid climates slopes are steeper, divides are sharper and there is significant talus, while in humid climates slopes are rounded and flattened. (4) Slopes eroded by rainwash (slope wash) will undergo decline, with the rate of decline being related to the rate and character of weathering, the steepness of the slope, and the amount of rainwash (maximum erosion occurs in rapidly disintegrating bedrock, fine debris, steep slopes, high precipitation and runoff). (5) The limiting angle of slope decline is that angle which will permit flow of water carrying the finest particles.

(6) Basal slopes are gentle due to relatively higher runoff. (7) The ultimate slope profile represents an equilibrium form similar to that of the river profile in which the slope and discharge are *inversely* related (hence steeper slopes in arid regimes). (9) In humid climates vegetation acts to retard erosion. (10) Valley sides may be asymmetrical due to variations in isolation (i.e., their exposure to solar radiation). (11) Alternating lithologies produce complex slopes, but ultimately slope development is independent of stratification.

While each of the above statements is subject to disagreements (most statements on slopes are!), it is remarkable that de la Noë and de Margerie provided a basic summary of much that has been brought out in later writing. Unfortunately, their work has been largely overlooked and is rarely quoted in the literature.

The other major pioneering work on slopes was by Gilbert (1877) who applied the rules of stream transportation to all gradational slopes. Gilbert stated that concave slopes are related to discharge-load relationships. If discharge increases downslope at a relatively faster rate than does load, then slope angles can decrease and still transport all material that flows over them. In addition, the efficiency of transport increases with increasing discharge; this should also promote concave slope profiles. Gilbert mentioned many points which are important, including: (1) Slopes reflect rock type. (2) In humid climates vegetation masks the effect of rock type. (3) Steeper slopes retreat more rapidly than gentler ones. (4) Valley heads are funnel shaped due to the convergence of slope wash toward the beginning of a channel.

Gilbert was especially perceptive in appreciating that slopes are ultimately dynamic equilibrium forms in which "every slope is a member of a series, receiving the water and the waste of the slope above it and discharging its own water and waste upon the slope below." If any part of the slope becomes out of equilibrium there is adjustment throughout the slope; this adjustment is transmitted until the entire slope achieves a new equilibrium.

In the early twentieth century, Davis, Penck and Lawson were among the leading students of slopes. Since the publications of Bryan (1940) and Horton (1945), study of the subject has greatly increased. Considerable impetus to slope study has been supplied by the International Geographical Union through its commission for the study of slopes [see, for example, its 1956 report, and *Supplementband* 1 and 5 (1960, 1964) of Z. *Geomorphol.*].

(C) Slope Dynamics

Another article in this Encyclopedia, *Slope Analysis* (q.v.), presents many important aspects of slope dynamics. The following ideas should be kept in mind while reading subsequent sections of this article. (1) Slopes are complex phenomena resulting

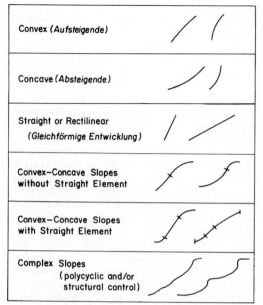

FIG. 1. Elements of slope profiles (German terms in parentheses) and three typical profiles. A quantitative measure of the curvature of concave and convex slopes was given by Savigear (1956): $C = A \pm B/L \times 100$, at the top and bottom of the segment, respectively, and L is the slope length, in meters.

from *interactions* along lithosphere-atmosphere or lithosphere-hydrosphere *interfaces*. (2) Slopes are members of *open systems* and may be graded in a manner similar to rivers. Such slopes may be in *steady state* (unchanging with time) or in growth state (changing with time; see *Open Systems—Allometric Growth*). (3) *Energy* and *material* can enter upon, flow through, and depart from slope elements. (4) The only *natural* boundaries of slopes are the ground surface, channels, divides and solid bedrock. (5) Primary *energy sources* acting on slopes are gravity and solar radiation. (6) Primary sources of *material* are precipitation, bedrock or regolith, and vegetation. (7) Erosion results when *forces of erosion* (e.g., forces related to overland flow, mass-wasting, raindrop impacts, buoyancy of soil particles, loss of soil strength) overcome *forces of resistance* (e.g., intergranular friction, capillary film cohesion, intercrystalline cohesion, shear resistance). (8) Slopes are integral parts of the fluvial system and cannot be fully described without consideration of relationships to drainage basins and channels [see section (I)].

It should be noted that slopes do not always reflect the action of contemporaneous dynamic forces. Historical factors and factors of control by structure or tectonism may be involved.

(D) Slope Form

Slopes may take a variety of forms. A geometrical

terminology appears in Savigear (1956) and in Young (1964). As Fig. 1 shows, slopes may consist of elements which are *concave* upward (angle constantly decreasing downslope), *convex* upward (angle constantly increasing downslope), *straight* or *rectilinear* (unchanging angle), and *complex* (great variation of slope angle in a short distance). Changes from one type of profile to another are termed *breaks-in-slope*.

A commonly observed profile (Figs. 2 and 3) consists of a convex "crest" or "nose," a rectilinear "side slope" or "mid-slope," and a concave "foot-slope." As Leopold *et al.* (1964) point out, there is no statistical evidence to support contentions that this profile (or variations such as convex-concave profiles without the straight portion) is the one most frequently found in nature. Figure 2(B) shows three possible types of slope change.

Until recently, few studies have investigated the question of slope form in *plan view* (Fig. 4). Hack and Goodlett (1960) found that for certain first-order drainage basin hillslopes in Virginia, the following is generally true (Fig. 5): crest slopes are convex in plan *and* profile, valley side slopes are rectilinear in plan *and* profile, and footslopes (mostly channelways) are concave in plan *and* profile. Sparks (1960) and others have noted that slope plan must control the nature of debris and runoff convergence and divergence, and hence must be a critical factor in slope development [see section (I)].

Drainage basin slopes can be considered as making up basin *interfluves* (q.v.). Interfluves often consist of divides which are rounded in cross-profile with fairly straight side slopes (e.g., Fig. 5). This is

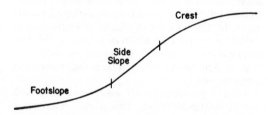

FIG. 2(a). Terminology of a commonly observed slope profile.

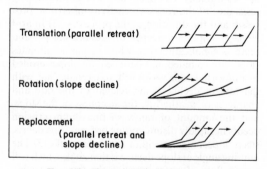

FIG. 2(b). Types of slope change.

(A)

(B)

FIG. 3. Convex-concave hillslope profiles. (A) Born-hardt in Precambrian granite near Bald Head, Western Australia. Profile curvature is slight but distinctive. There is little or no straight segment in the profile. (B) Tumut Valley, New South Wales, in early Paleozoic metamorphic rocks. Most erosional valley side slopes are straight with convex crests. Interfluve profiles are concave as are some slopes adjacent to channels. Note interlocking spurs and pyramidal nature of interfluves (see Fig. 6) and the facet-like character of slopes grading directly to the higher order main stream. Such facets are developed in the course of "normal" drainage basin erosion and do not necessarily indicate uplift or change in base level. (Photographs: R. W. Fairbridge)

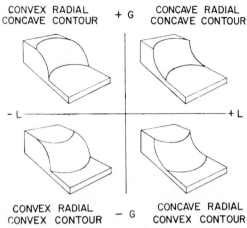

CONVEX RADIAL CONCAVE CONTOUR $+$ G CONCAVE RADIAL CONCAVE CONTOUR

$- $ L $\qquad$ $+$ L

CONVEX RADIAL CONVEX CONTOUR $-$ G CONCAVE RADIAL CONVEX CONTOUR

FIG. 4. Illustrations of the four combinations of con-cavity and convexity of slopes (from Troeh, 1965). "Radial" refers to slope profile; "contour" refers to slope plan. G and L are from equations fitted to ideal forms. G is positive if slope plan is concave, while L is positive if slope profile is concave. According to Hack and Goodlett (1960; see also Fig. 5 of this article) and other authors, natural slopes are generally convex radial and contour, or concave radial and contour (for recti-linear radial and contour). A concave radial convex contour pattern would characterize many residual hills (monadnocks, inselbergs, bornhardts). Convex radial concave contour patterns are probably rare.

especially true in areas of moderate and high relief where concave slopes are rare and are mainly limited to channel areas. *Divides* (see *Watershed*) are concave in long profile in a very close relationship to the channels which they parallel. Drainage basins of second or higher order contain slopes which grade directly to second- or higher-order channels. The result (Fig. 6) is that, taken as a whole, inter-fluves have the form of *triangular pyramids* (Lawson, 1932), with two sides graded to streams which parallel the interfluve and the third side graded to a higher-order stream.

King (1957, and references therein), following Wood (1942), has described a profile distinctly different from those discussed above. This profile (Figs. 7 and 8) consists of a convex *waxing slope*, rectilinear *free face*, rectilinear (on the surface) *debris slope* (q.v. *Haldenhang*), and slightly concave *pediment*. While King regards this profile as being virtually universal, others disagree (e.g., Frye, 1959). This profile may be limited to regions of well-stratified (not necessarily horizontal) rocks and is probably the typical profile developed on erosional escarpments. Certainly, slopes developed upon well-layered rocks often approach this form (Fig. 8). Mountain fronts frequently have this form but may also be largely rectilinear. Drainage basins devel-oped on nonstratified rocks do not usually show this profile, in the opinion of this author. Even when

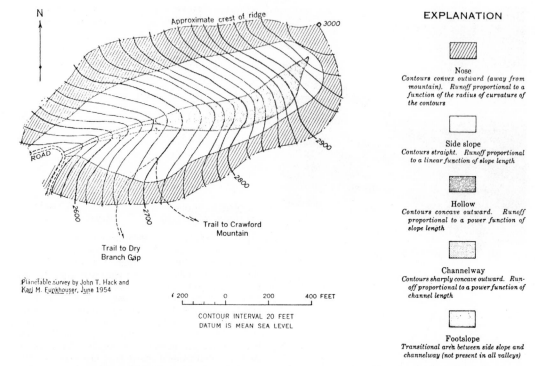

N

Approximate crest of ridge

3000

EXPLANATION

Nose
Contours convex outward (away from mountain). Runoff proportional to a function of the radius of curvature of the contours

Side slope
Contours straight. Runoff proportional to a linear function of slope length

Hollow
Contours concave outward. Runoff proportional to a power function of slope length

Channelway
Contours sharply concave outward. Runoff proportional to a power function of channel length

Footslope
Transitional area between side slope and channelway (not present in all valleys)

ROAD

2900

2800

2600 2700

Trail to Crawford Mountain

Trail to Dry Branch Gap

Planetable survey by John T. Hack and Karl M. Funkhouser, June 1954

200   0   200   400 FEET

CONTOUR INTERVAL 20 FEET
DATUM IS MEAN SEA LEVEL

FIG. 5. Contour map of first-order drainage basin on the west side of Crawford Mountain, Virginia, showing five slope classes studied by Hack and Goodlett (1960). In this paper, the terms *nose* and *side slope* are used as shown in this figure; the term foot slope is used to refer to all slopes which are concave in plan and profile and includes "hollow," "channelway" and "footslope."

drainage basin slopes are developed on stratified rocks, the form of Fig. 7 is not always seen (see Fig. 5, for example).

As sections (E) through (J) will show, many controlling factors of profile and plan form have been cited. It should be stressed, however, that profiles are seldom simple. In particular, the influence of inhomogeneous lithology and/or tectonic and climatic changes produces slopes which are complex and often polycyclic in origin.

Methods of describing and determining slope forms are numerous. Descriptive methods include the use of many terms (e.g., curvature, azimuth, hypsometric curve) and techniques (e.g., isosine and isotangent maps, use of terrain analogs, detailed profile surveys). Many of these techniques are discussed by Strahler (1956, 1964).

In addition to real profiles, many authors have studied slopes by means of mathematically generated profiles. Taylor (1875; see reference in Chorley *et al.*, 1964) sought to identify binomial curves in hillslopes and derived a mathematical model which involved parallel retreat of slopes. More recently, many workers have applied statistical and other techniques to describe or analyze landforms mathematically [see discussions and references in Troeh (1965) and Chorley (1966)]. Several workers have

used mathematical models to predict slope evolution or to idealize profiles characteristic of certain structures (e.g., Fig. 9, p. 1013).

Attempts to classify slopes on the basis of form have largely been confined to using the terms discussed above. A different approach was used by Strahler (1950); he divided erosional slopes into three types based upon the angle of repose of typical

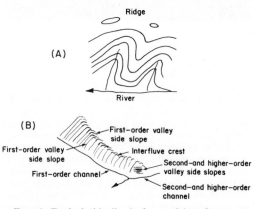

Ridge

(A)

River

(B)

First-order valley side slope
Interfluve crest
Second-and higher-order valley side slopes
First-order valley side slope
First-order channel
Second-and higher-order channel

FIG. 6. Typical (idealized) form of interfluves: (a) contour map (b) perspective sketch.

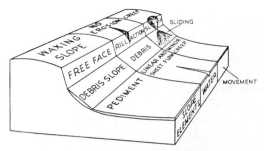

FIG. 7. Diagram (King, 1957) showing the four elements present in a fully developed hillslope profile, according to Lester King. Predominant processes on each element are also shown. This profile is best developed on layered rocks and on escarpments and is seldom found in areas of isotropic bedrock.

noncohesive earth material (about 34° for coarse sand). Erosional slopes at the angle of repose (*not* talus slopes) are called *repose* slopes. Steeper slopes are termed *high-cohesion slopes* and usually develop on resistant bedrock or on dry, compacted clay. Gentler slopes are termed *slopes reduced by wash and creep*.

Another system is that of Miller and Summerson (1960) in which slopes are divided into four categories based upon a mathematical function. The categories seem (by chance) to have some correlation with natural slopes (Table 1).

Other attempts toward using slope angles in slope studies have not produced results which can be easily generalized. Many authors refer to the "characteristic" (mean) slope of a given lithology, climate or area; however, this angle is subject to so many environmental controls that it is difficult to use except locally (see study by Seret, 1963). Use of

"maximum" slope angle has met with more success (see Strahler, 1964).

(E) Slope Processes

Slopes (as well as other landforms) must be studied from three basic points of view, namely, process, structure and stage, where each of these terms is used in the broadest possible sense (see *Process—Structure—Stage*). Structures provide inhomogeneities which can be provisionally disregarded when dealing with "ideal" (no structural control) slopes. Stage primarily involves the relative changes in rates of processes with the passage of time (e.g., due to lowering of relief). A study of slope processes is thus the first step in an analysis of slope form and development. Complexities introduced by structure, tectonism, and/or paleoclimates will be discussed in subsequent sections.

While nearly all geomorphic processes act upon slopes, those of most significance to this discussion are *weathering, mass-wasting, surface runoff, groundwater*. These processes will be evaluated here only as regards their effect upon slopes.

Weathering (q.v.), both chemical and physical, supplies the material which makes up virtually all the debris lying upon and being transported down slopes. Chemical weathering involves complex phenomena which tend toward the decomposition of bedrock coupled with the production of clay minerals and the liberation of soluble ions. Chemical weathering is a function of climate, being important in all but extremely arid climates. Chemical weathering is more dependent on the properties of the parent material, especially texture and chemistry. Vegetation is also a controlling factor, through its influence on soil pH, and because decaying vegetation supplies chemically active organic acids.

TABLE 1. CLASSIFICATION OF SLOPES BASED ON MILLER AND SUMMERSON (1960). CLASSIFICATION IS BASED UPON FOUR EQUAL DIVISIONS OF MATHEMATICAL FUNCTION $\sqrt{\sin A}$ WHERE A IS THE SLOPE INCLINATION. COLUMN 4 (OCCURRENCE) IS BASED ON SPECULATION BY THIS AUTHOR, IN PART FOLLOWING MILLER AND SUMMERSON (FOR PROFILES SEE FIGS. 2, 7 AND 10

Slope Class	Slope Angle	$\sqrt{\sin A}$	Occurrence
1	0°–3° 35′	0–0.25	Waning slope (Wood, 1942) Waxing slope (Wood, 1942; King, 1957) Noses and crests Most fluvial aggraded slopes
2	3° 36′–14° 29′	0.25–0.50	Most fans, pediments Lower part of constant slope (Wood)
3	14° 30′–34° 14′	0.50–0.75	Upper limit of repose of non-cohesive material (debris slope of King) Reduced slopes (Strahler, 1950)
4	34° 15′–90°	0.75–1.00	Free face (King) Escarpments High cohesion slopes (Strahler, 1950)

FIG. 8. Delaware water gap, looking across Delaware River from Pennsylvania to New Jersey. Waxing slope, free face and debris slope well shown. Profile corresponds to that of King (Fig. 7) and is often characteristic of slopes developed on layered rock. Here a Paleozoic quartzite dips westward. (Photo: Alan R. Epstein)

Physical weathering occurs in several ways. In particular, processes related to freezing or desiccating conditions are important (see *Frost Action; Salt Weathering or Fretting*). Physical weathering may also occur because of unloading, hydrolysis, organic activity and differential expansion of minerals (e.g., due to wetting, drying, heating or cooling). Physical weathering generally produces sand and larger-sized particles, and is primarily a function of climate and parent material (especially texture, jointing).

Both forms of weathering are time dependent. Both are related to slope properties such as inclination, orientation and depth of regolith, which in turn are dependent variables (often controlled by the weathering itself!). The question of rate of degradation of slope will be discussed below. Quantitative estimates of the rate of weathering *per se* upon slopes show a wide variation. Textbooks frequently state that it takes 10,000 years for 1 inch of soil to form, but this is a gross generalization. Kellogg (1941) states rather that the building of

1 inch of soil may take anywhere between 10 minutes and 10 million years. We are more interested, however, in the formation of erodable debris by weathering than in the rate of soil production. Based upon data given by Schumm (1963), and assuming that most eroded material is weathered prior to entrainment, it is possible to make crude estimates of rates of weathering. A mean rate for a temperate humid region may be about 1 inch (2.5 cm) every 400–500 years, or about 0.2 mm/yr. Climate and relief are the prime causes for variation in rates. In very arid regions, the mean rate may be one or two orders of magnitude less. In rugged humid regions, weathering may be an order of magnitude greater.

In summary, the prime role of weathering on slopes is the production of debris which is ultimately eroded; a frequent intermediate step is the formation of regolith. Theories of etchplanation and savanna planation [section (I)] are dependent upon the formation of saprolite (residual material, weathered regolith). Other theories (e.g., those of Baulig and Birot) are also based upon assumptions regarding weathering. Recent studies by Ruxton (1958) and Ruxton and Berry (1961) help illustrate the variety of slope features ascribed to weathering. In the first reference, the maintenance of certain breaks in slope is shown to be due to accelerated weathering of granite in zones of high seepage. In the second study, facets on granite residuals are shown to be controlled by unloading. Linton (1956) has provided a bibliography of field studies (mostly in Great Britain) on rock weathering, while Birot (1956) lists French experimental studies on this subject.

Mass wasting (q.v.) provides one of the two main mechanisms for downslope movement of weathered debris. Two classes of mass movements affect slopes: (1) surface mass movements which simply transfer debris downslope in a layer overlying the bedrock (e.g., creep, slump, solifluction) and (2) deep-seated mass movements which affect and alter the bedrock surface (e.g., rockfalls and landslides). Each type of movement is a function of slope angle, nature of debris, climate and vegetation (see *Landslides; Soil Creep; Solifluction; Mass Movements; Mass-wasting*).

On slopes with saprolite and other regolith, *soil creep* (q.v.) may occur. Soil creep is an imperceptible flow of debris downslope. Rates of movements, based on data from many sources, indicate values in the range of zero to a few centimeters per year, with most values in the range of a few millimeters per year. Creep seems to be promoted by steep slopes, fine-grained regolith and moist climates; moreover, rate of creep may show a seasonal variation in one area with maximum values occurring when the soil is unfrozen and/or when the soil is saturated with moisture.

Gilbert (1909) explained convex hilltops and ridges by appealing to creep and analogous processes (such as downslope movement of particles disturbed by rainbeat). He deduced that slope angle must increase downslope in order to transmit the material eroded from above. In detail Gilbert's reasoning was as follows: (1) Gravity promotes downslope movement of regolith. (2) We will assume that regolith creeps as a continuous layer (otherwise creep would induce "piling up" of material). (3) The amount of material passing through a given slope element is the product of the cross-sectional area of the element multiplied by the velocity of movement of the material (this is the basis of the *law of continuity*, $Q = AV$). (4) The farther downslope a slope element is situated, the more slope there is above it and hence the more material it receives from above. (5) The cross-sectional area of the slope element does not change (this is an assumption). (6) Hence, in order that all the material be transported (i.e., in order to preserve equilibrium), the velocity of creep must increase downslope; this increase in creep velocity will satisfy the law of continuity and permit the transport of larger amounts of material farther downslope [see step (4)]. (7) Increase of velocity of creep requires greater effect of gravity upon the material and hence steeper slopes. (8) Thus slopes must steepen progressively in a downslope direction in order to transport all the creeping material; in other words, the slopes must be convex. (9) This mechanism is effective throughout the slope, but on lower slopes it is masked by the influence of overland flow, which produces straight or concave slopes.

Numerous objections to this hypothesis have been raised. Lawson (1932) stated that creep could not account for all convex slopes because: (1) Creep cannot affect slopes with thin or absent regolith. (2) Creep cannot round summits, since summits are areas with no downslope gravitational vector. (3) Creep can produce unequal thicknesses of debris; hence, velocity and slope need not change.

Other writers simply have applied alternate explanations for convex slopes. Possibilities include: rounding of summits due to greater exposure to weathering processes; convex slopes formed by overland flow whereas concave slopes are due to flow in rills or gullies (see below); convex slopes due to tectonic activity [see section (H)]. Theoretical observations by Horton (1945) lend support to the Gilbert hypothesis. Quantitative field studies give conflicting results (e.g., Schumm, 1956; White, 1966).

Other types of mass wasting on slopes are generally of localized importance. Of widespread importance are (1) *solifluction* (q.v.), which is a prime factor in formation of slopes under a periglacial climatic regime [see section (F)] and (2) *rockfalls* which are important in the development of escarpments and vertical cliffs [see section (H)]. Recent comprehensive discussions of the roll of mass wasting in the erosion of certain slopes include Rapp (1960) and Jahn (1964).

The action of *water* upon slopes takes two main forms: (1) Some water infiltrates into the ground and flows as *groundwater* (q.v. pr Vol. VI) to channels. Groundwater flow can transport material both in solution and mechanically. (2) *Overland flow* of water begins as discontinuous surface flow, grading into sheet flow, rills and gullies as it moves downslope. Overland flow is also capable of chemical and mechanical transport.

Much has been made of the control of slopes by running water. Gilbert (1877) described concave profiles of streams and slopes as being due to the basic principles of hydraulic flow, namely that as discharge increases downslope it becomes increasingly more efficient; hence velocity (and slope) can decrease downslope and still permit transport of all supplied load. Fenneman (1908) considered convex slopes to be the result of the action of rillwash which concentrates downslope to produce gullying and concave slopes. Gilbert's paper (1909) by implication discounted this hypothesis, but Lawson (1932) revised it in altered form. Lawson agreed that the transition from convexity to concavity represented a change in the nature of flow of water but felt it to be due to a change from *eroding flow* to *aggrading flow*. He felt that the intervening straight profiles found on many slopes represent either (a) an equilibrium between erosion and deposition, or (b) a zone along which occurs seasonal oscillation of the point of change from one type of flow to the other.

Baulig (1940) placed great emphasis on the nature of regolith as the fundamental factor controlling slope development (see next section). He felt that, due to changes of permeability in a downslope direction, slope wash becomes concentrated into rills; the change in nature of flow is represented by the change from convex to concave profiles with seasonal oscillations of changeover producing straight slopes. Baulig accepted Gilbert's creep hypothesis as a partial explanation for convex slopes. Birot (1949) agreed with Baulig except that he related concavities to diffuse wash on impermeable debris rather than to rill wash. Schumm (1956) presented field evidence showing that slope wash can produce rather straight slopes, while in the absence of wash, creep can produce convex forms.

A quantitative and experimental study of the nature of overland flow and its influence upon slopes is found in a classic paper by Horton (1945). In extremely condensed form, Horton's observations were as follows: (1) *Overland flow*, Q_s (surface runoff), equals precipitation minus both infiltration and surface retention of water. (2) *Infiltration rate* is extremely important in controlling the amount of runoff and the nature of slope development (see next section). (3) When *surface runoff* occurs, it may take three forms: sheet flow, flow in rills and flow in channels (where channels are defined as being bounded by slopes which grade to them). (4) The depth of surface runoff depends on several variables. If d is the depth of runoff, a is a constant, L_g is the length of the slope upon which the runoff has occurred, Q_s is the surface runoff. and $\bar{V}$ is the velocity of turbulent hydraulic flow, then:

$$d = \frac{aL_gQ_s}{\bar{V}} \tag{1}$$

In this equation, $\bar{V}$ is defined as:

$$\bar{V} = \frac{b}{n}R^{2/3}S^{1/2} \tag{2}$$

where b is another constant, n is Manning's number for roughness, R is the hydraulic radius of the channel of flow, and S is slope inclination (usually expressed as a sine function). (5) For *sheet or overland flow*, R is equal to d, b/a can be set to equal a constant c, and thus:

$$Q_s = d^{5/3}\left(\frac{cS^{1/2}}{L_gn}\right) \tag{3}$$

which reduces to:

$$Q_s = kd^m \tag{4}$$

where k represents the parenthetical expression of Eq. (3) and m is an exponent related to flow characteristics (for turbulent flow m is $\frac{5}{3}$). (6) For *laminar flow*, m is 3.00 while for "*subdivided flow*" (as on grass) m is 1.00. (7) As *discharge increases*, surface depth of flow increases [this follows directly from Eq. (3)]. (8) Hence, contrary to the assumptions of Gilbert and others, an increase of discharge of overland flow requires *no increase in velocity* of flow, nor is there any necessary increase of eroding stress with discharge. However, increased depth of flow may be accompanied by increased velocity. (9) As discharge increases, *other types of flow* (with higher velocity and eroding stress) may occur. These include *surge flow*, which occurs when minute dams pond water, then break and release the water. Another type of flow is rain wave trains which are a form of *kinematic waves* and occur only during very high-intensity storms. (10) *Eroding stress* is related to the unit weight of water, depth of surface runoff and angle of slope. (11) *Resisting forces* are related to cohesion of regolith, size of particles to be eroded and other factors (Horton, 1945, p. 317). (12) Erosion will occur on a slope only when available *eroding force exceeds the resistance* (R_i) of the slope material to erosion. Eroding force generally increases downslope from the divide (due to increased runoff changing the pattern of flow and to increasing slope because of effects of creep and rainbeat). Hence there will be a distance, x_c at which eroding force becomes equal to R_i and erosion begins. Between the divide and the critical length, x_c, there will be no erosion due to running water. (13) If ϕS is a function of *slope angle* (with maximum value at 40°) then:

$$x_c = \frac{R_i}{Q_s \, \phi S \, n} \qquad (5)$$

(14) Hence it follows that *slopes consist of three parts*, an upper part between the divide and x_c where slopes are convex due to rainbeat and creep, a middle concavity due to erosion by sheet flow, and a lower concavity where the slope debris is accumulating.

Horton's theory has not received universal acceptance (e.g., White, 1966) but remains an authoritative explanation for many slope phenomena. Moreover, it gives quantitative expression to many prior qualitative observations. For example, it has long been observed that slopes developed in chalk are broadly convex without concavities. This is probably due to high infiltration into the chalk, with the result that Q_s is nil and x_c is essentially infinite. Therefore, overland flow and concave slopes do not occur.

Leopold *et al.* (1966) have shown that for certain basins in a semiarid area, the dominant erosion process is overland flow in the form of sheet erosion. Schumm (1956) concluded that both creep and overland flow (rainwash) are probably important in determining hillslope form.

Erosion by *groundwater* is not well understood. Much of the effect of groundwater is related to weathering processes outlined above. Groundwater is also important in that it represents water unavailable for surficial erosion. The primary control of the amount of water which filters into the ground is the *infiltration capacity* of the regolith (see next section). Locally, subsurface erosion may be a significant process. Subsurface erosion by piping along an interface between materials of differing permeability has caused significant erosional modification of some slopes in New Zealand. The enlargement of these pipes or subsurface tunnels and the collapse of their roofs form deep gullies on the middle section of the slopes and cause development of a broadly concave slope segment (Gibbs, 1945).

The relationship between the action of the above-mentioned processes and the angle of the slope is a subject of controversy. Strahler (1952) holds that rates of runoff and creep are proportional to slope angle, while Leopold *et al.* (1964) state that slope angle is proportional to rates of runoff and creep. Young (1960) found that rate of creep does not necessarily depend upon slope angle, but that soil texture and moisture are also important. Baver (1956) states that total soil loss through erosion (E, in tons per acre) is related to slope inclination (S, in per cent) as follows:

$$E = 0.065 S^{1.49} \qquad (6)$$

As slope length increases, the overall amount of erosion also increases, as is expected (Smith and Wischmeier, 1962). However longer slopes have less erosion per unit length of slope. This probably is a result of deposition on the lower part of long slopes,

and also reflects the fact that on very long slopes Q_s does not increase indefinitely. Rather, on gentle lower (depositional slopes) infiltration is high and surface water infiltrates into the ground (leaving its load on the surface and further contributing to the depositional material on the slope).

Holmes (1955) has distinguished two types of slopes based upon the basic types of processes operative. These two types, best seen in arid regions, are *gravity* or *derivation slopes* and *wash slopes*. Gravity slopes are generally steep (greater than 6° and often steeper than 30°) and are controlled by rate of weathering as well as by rate of action of gravity-controlled processes (mass movements). Wash slopes are gentle (always less than 30° and often less than 6°). Wash slopes are controlled by the amount and the nature of load carried by sheet flow and rills. Between 6 and 30°, both gravity and wash slopes may occur. In arid areas, the two extremes are readily seen, whereas in humid climates intermediate slopes (partly protected by vegetation) are common.

(F) Influence of Climate

Much has been made of the influence of climate upon slope form and development. According to Davisian precepts the following is generally true: (1) Slopes in humid climates are smooth, relatively gentle, mantled with soil and vegetation, and consist of convex-concave profiles which decline with time. (2) Slopes in arid climates are rough, relatively steep, barren of soil and vegetation, and consist primarily of straight slopes which retreat with time to produce pediments. (3) Slopes in glacial and periglacial climates have specialized forms and development.

In contrast to such statements, King (1957) has strongly contended that slopes develop similarly in virtually all climates, with climate accounting only for minor and superficial aspects of slope morphology.

Lawson (1915) described hillslopes in arid climates as having two main characteristics: (1) The angle of slope is related to the nature of the bedrock, with steeper slopes occurring upon lithologies which produce coarse detritus. (2) Slopes undergo *parallel retreat* until the rock-controlled slopes disappear. Bryan (1940) supported these observations and noted that parallel retreat is demonstrated by the existence of residual masses (*inselbergs, bornhardts*, q.v.) of all sizes (and in virtually all climates). However, bornhardts may be the product of deep weathering and subsequent regolith stripping [see section (G)]. Bryan also noted that there is nothing in the nature of humid climate processes to induce slope decline, i.e., processes should act with equal intensity over the entire slope and hence each part of the slope would wear back at the same rate. Davis (1930) admitted that humid and arid slope might be analogous (similar in form) although he did not admit homology (similar origin). Melton

(1965) presented data which indicate that slope angle is not necessarily dependent on coarseness of surficial debris, but may reflect the frictional properties of the rock and fragments.

There is general agreement that arid climates produce erosional slopes with relatively little soil and vegetation (the soil cover is often absent), with the result that factors of structure and lithology are of more importance in controlling the landscape than in humid climates. Many slopes in the arid areas of today may be the product of earlier more humid climatic regimes.

Slope development in the tropics has been described by numerous authors (e.g., references in Bryan, 1940). In mountainous terrain, slopes tend to be steep (30–40°) and straight (see *Selva*). Chemical weathering is intense, and mass movements are frequent. Freise (1938) found that there is an intimate relation between the process of retreat of tropical slopes and the vegetation. From his observations, Freise proposed the following characteristic cycle: (1) Bare rock slopes (35–52°, depending on rock type) are weathered producing (2), soil which further develops beneath thick vegetation and often attains a profile depth of 10 meters. (3) Underground earth flows occur beneath crusts which form in the upper soil by silicification and deposition of ferruginous minerals, following deterioration of the forest (see *Duricrust*). (4) The exposed soil dries and becomes vulnerable to rainwash and mass movements. (5) Landslides and rainwash ultimately expose bare rock and the cycle begins again.

In humid temperate climates, detailed field studies such as those of Hack and Goodlett (1960) and Schumm (1956) have confirmed many of the Davisian precepts listed above. However, it has been found that valley side slopes are often straight and fairly steep (25–30°). Studies made in areas of low relief have found convex-concave profiles (Mabbutt and Scott, 1966; also Rougerie, 1960).

Slopes in periglacial climates have been the subject of much study but represent a rather special case which will not be covered here. References include: Twidale (1959), Hopkins and Wahrhaftig (a bibliography, 1960), Jahn (1960) and Rapp (1960) (see also *Cryopedology; Frost Action; Periglacial Landscapes*).

Despite the claims of King and others, most geomorphologists seem to believe that slope forms and processes (or process intensities) do vary with climate (see *Morphogenetic Classification*). However, there are many other factors which control slopes; moreover, there are some slopes whose origin reflects past climatic conditions. As demonstrated by Mabbutt and Scott (1966), only detailed field observations of slope form and cover can ascertain the exact relationships between slope and climate.

Valleyside hillslopes often show *asymmetric profiles* due to having different exposure to solar radiation and hence different microclimates (see *Asymmetric Valleys*). Asymmetry may also be due to factors such as structural control, Coriolis effect or stream meandering.

Many studies have been concerned with seasonal or altitudinal variation of climate, as manifested in slope processes and form. Schumm and Lusby (1963) described the following sequence for some slopes in the western United States. (1) During winter the soil surface is loosened by frost action. (2) Then during spring and summer, the process of rainbeat compacts the soil and creep occurs. (3) Compaction of soil decreases infiltration capacity and increases runoff (and erosion). (4) Winter frost action destroys the summer rills and increases infiltration capacity. Erosion is thus higher in summer and autumn than in winter and spring.

Dollfus (1964) described slope variation with altitude in the Andes. Different climatic zones occur in direct relation to altitude and orientation to solar radiation. Each zone produces characteristic slope processes and slope forms. Bik (1967) made a similar study; he emphasized the inheritance of some landscape features formed under different climates during the Quaternary.

(G) Nature and Influence of Regolith

Slopes are frequently covered with *regolith* (either transported debris or residual *saprolite*), especially in humid and periglacial climates. The nature of the regolith reflects the nature of the slope processes and, in turn, the regolith influences slope development by partly controlling infiltration, weathering and mass movements.

At least one theory of slope development is largely dependent upon the nature of regolith development and removal. This theory, called *etchplanation*, is thought by many to explain a large number of the major plains on the earth's surface. Etchplanation involves deep weathering (generally on a surface of moderate to low relief) which produces a very deep residual regolith (saprolite) over an irregular bedrock surface. Eventually (due to uplift, climate change, etc.), the regolith is stripped away and the formerly buried bedrock surface becomes the new surficial landscape. Etchplanation may well account for many landscapes in low latitudes, although there is considerable argument as to its validity and extent.

Baulig (1940) and Birot (1949) both regarded regolith as being the key element in control of slope form and development. Baulig conceived of graded slopes as being covered by a "current" of material; slopes were, therefore, mobile and changeable. Youthful slopes may be irregular and steep, but with time the slopes become smooth and gentle. Convex slopes occur because debris at summits and ridge tops is relatively thin, coarse and permeable; hence, runoff is limited and creep dominates. Lower down, the runoff crosses thicker, finer, impermeable debris; slopewash is concentrated and converted to rill wash, resulting in concave slope elements. The entire slope is one of degradation. As time goes on, the slopes decline, debris becomes increasingly finer (due to gentler slopes, more weathering), and the concave portion of the profile becomes increasingly more important.

Birot adopted Baulig's ideas but put greater emphasis on the importance of the relative impermeability of debris on footslopes. He believed that concavities are maintained on footslopes of low angle, because of the fine-textured, impermeable debris produced by weathering.

Several observers have arrived at results which contradict the conclusions of Baulig and Birot. For example, Hack and Goodlett (1960) found that for some small basins in Virginia, regolith is coarser on footslopes than on crests. However, their observations were made in an area of few concave slopes. Culling (1965) proposed the following theoretical deductions: (1) In arid climates, or where there are slopes with impermeable debris (e.g., clays), runoff will exceed weathering with the result that most material is removed overland. Regolith is absent, and slopes are steep, straight in profile and undergo parallel retreat. (2) In humid climates, and/or where there is permeable debris, weathering will produce more material than is removed by runoff. In this circumstance, groundwater removal of material will be the most important erosional process. Regolith will accumulate and slopes should be gentle, convex-concave in profile, and may undergo slope decline. Field observations by Schumm (1956) support these deductions to a considerable extent.

Young (1963) also proposed certain theoretical slope-regolith relationships. He deduced (by means of computer models) that for slopes on which removal of material is mainly by means of creep and slope wash, the prevalent form will be smoothly convex-concave and development will be slope decline. Conversely, removal of debris by groundwater will result in parallel retreat of slopes. Note that these conclusions are opposite to those of Culling.

As with other aspects of slope study, regolith-slope relationships are complex and not clearly understood at present.

(H) Lithology, Structure and Slopes

In the preceding sections the influence of rock type and bedrock structure upon slopes has not been considered. A great many observations have been made on this subject, but without many simple generalizable conclusions. As usual, the problem is that rocks and structures act in combination with climate, tectonism and other factors to produce complex landscapes.

Rock type *per se* is known to control various slope parameters, including slope angle. Resistant lithologies produce slopes which are steeper than those formed on weaker rock types, especially when bare rock is exposed. On the other hand, weak rock types which are highly cohesive, such as many clays, may also form steep slopes. Rock type may also influence slopes by determining regolith characteristics (e.g., texture, infiltration capacity).

As mentioned above, slopes developed upon chalk are typically convex, due to the high permeability of this rock type. However, as a rule it is difficult to relate lithology and profile characteristics, except locally (see study by Macar and Forneau, 1960). Dumanowski (1960) showed that for certain arid zone slopes in Egypt, rock type controls both the slope angle and the relative lengths of concave and convex portions of the slope profile.

The dynamics and mechanics of rock control on slopes have been discussed by many authors (e.g., Ostermann, 1960). Terzaghi (1962) related slopes on bedrock to several mechanical factors, including the cohesion of the rock, its angle of shearing resistance, seepage pressure in joints and pores, and the relation of joints to slope angle.

It is a matter of common observation that the dip of layered rock has a pronounced topographic effect—hence, the existence of mesas, cuestas, hogbacks and flatirons. As dips become steeper, slopes become increasingly more regular; dip slopes increase in angle in direct proportion to increase of dip (Miller, 1953).

Quite commonly, layered rock produces slopes with a relatively steep portion, or *escarpment*, separating two relatively level areas. Such scarped slopes are fairly simple; hence, they are better understood than other slope types. Lehmann (1933) considered escarpments mathematically (Fig. 9); the mathematical approach has been expanded upon by Bakker and Le Heux (see references in Bakker and Strahler, 1956). This approach has resulted in equations relating angle of retreating walls, angle of adjacent talus slopes and type of recession. Bakker *et al.* have shown that under conditions of rectilinear retreat of slopes, and in the absence of deposition of a large volume of talus, the ultimate slope of a rock wall will be a rock surface with a straight profile sloping at an angle equal to the angle of repose of the rock debris. Where the slope retreat is parallel and waste material is

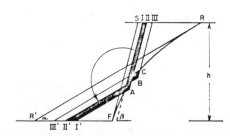

FIG. 9. Parallel weathering of a steep slope with scree piling up at the bottom (after Lehmann, 1933).

allowed to accumulate slowly at the base of the slope (e.g., there is no stream removal), the talus will lie upon and protect a bedrock surface which has a convex profile (Fig. 9). Field observations are not yet sufficient to determine the validity of this model.

Wood (1942) accepted Lehmann's theories for arid areas only and substituted his own ideas as to the nature of humid slope development (Fig. 10). Wood assumed that vertical slopes were due to stream downcutting and were not related to lithology. However, it is clear from photographs (e.g., Wood, 1942, Plate 5) that his observations pertained to rock-controlled slopes. King (1957) adopted Wood's terminology in relation to slope profiles such as illustrated in Fig. 7. King postulated that such profiles are ubiquitous except under extraordinary climatic or tectonic conditions. He felt that these profiles are the inevitable result of the action of slope wash, mass movement and other slope processes. Many authors have objected to King's conclusions (e.g., Frye, 1959). Twidale (1960) stated that the complex interaction of structure, vegetation, climate, paleoclimates and time forbid one simple explanation for all slopes. This view is supported by Ollier and Tuddenham (1961) whose studies of

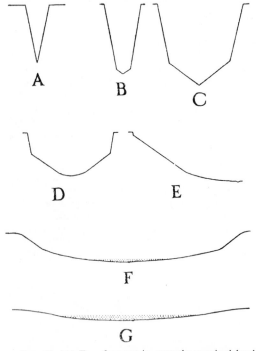

Fig. 10. (A) Free face cut in recently upraised land surface. (B and C) Constant slopes form. (D and E) Waning slope (pediment of King) forms. (F) Waxing slope forms. Alluvial fill (dots) begins. (G) Fill deepens, slopes gradually flatten, and approach a peneplain (or pediplain, depending on interpretation). (From Wood, 1942.)

monoliths (inselbergs) in central Australia show clearly that conditions controlling slope form and development are highly variable and not subject to sweeping generalizations.

Where layered rocks (horizontal or dipping) exercise strong topographic control, one may certainly expect to find slopes of the type described by Wood and King (e.g., Fig. 8); examples are provided from studies by Koons (1955) and Schumm and Chorley (1966). Koons found that the intersection between free face and debris slopes (Fig. 7) does not always coincide with the stratigraphic boundary between resistant cap rock and underlying weak rock (usually shale). Rather the intersection oscillates as follows: (1) Weathering and removal of material on debris slopes results in a steepening of the debris slope and a lowering of the level of the break in slope. (2) This exposes the underlying shale to weathering and erosion and ultimately results in the undermining of the cap rock. (3) This in turn results in a rock fall which produces a gentler debris slope which raises the break in slope to above the hard rock/soft rock contact. The cycle continues until all cap rock is destroyed.

Schumm and Chorley (1966) have shown that the actual form of the scarp depends upon four variables: (1) rock resistance, as controlled by cementation and porosity, (2) the orientation and spacing of joints and bedding planes, (3) the directions of dip, and (4) the proportion of the scarp face composed of cap rock. As rock resistance increases so does the relative size of the vertical cliff component of the scarp (free face). Wide spacing of joints and bedding planes prevents accumulation of large amounts of talus (on debris slopes) while closely spaced joints allow breakup of resistant rocks (e.g., sandstone) and subsequent talus accumulation.

Direction of dip often controls location of *drainage divides*. Along a simple scarp, a belt of *badlands* (q.v.) may develop on shales, while on more resistant rock rounding of the crest may occur. If the layers dip away from the scarp (Fig. 11) there will be eventual destruction of the scarp (assuming no overall lowering of the regional erosional surface). Dip toward the scarp has the effect of adding strength to relatively weak (thin bedded and jointed) cap rock.

Thin cap rock (or underlying shale) promotes rapid retreat of the scarp and the development of badlands; conversely, an increase in the effective thickness of cap rock produces compound scarps in which both cap rock and underlying shale are important in profile development. Figure 11 shows the change in form of a scarp during down-dip retreat; note that the cap rock becomes an increasingly important component of the slope.

There can be little doubt that when structurally controlled escarpments form, parallel retreat is the dominant method of slope evolution. Whether such is the case for slopes of other forms (e.g., slopes

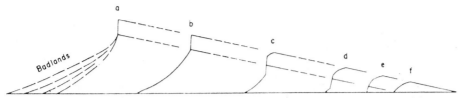

FIG. 11. Sketch showing change in form of a scarp, as during downdip retreat the caprock becomes an increasingly important component of the scarp face.

developed on isotropic bedrock) remains to be established. One attempt to describe mathematically the possible relationships between slope form and development and various conditions of lithologic control is by Scheidegger (1963). He derived several hypothetical profiles based on various assumptions and computer models (Fig. 12). As pointed out by Schumm (1966), this system (like the earlier models of Davis and Penck) is not based on an appreciation of the processes and rates of erosion. While the resultant profiles resemble many which can be observed in the field, their origin may be quite different from that which is assumed as a basis for the theoretical development.

(I) Relationships between Slope, Relief, Tectonism and the Drainage Net

Little study has been directed toward the important problem of the exact nature of slopes within drainage basins. One study, that of Hack and Goodlett (1960), has been cited previously (Fig. 5). It is not known whether the slope pattern of Fig. 5 is widespread. Probably this pattern is common in areas of humid climates possessing moderate to strong relief and subject to relatively little structural control. The configuration of slopes within basins of second (and higher) order is not known in detail.

An example of the problems remaining to be solved is given by Sparks (1960). It is evident that

creep and runoff (among other processes) should have differing effects on slope which vary in plan. On the end of interfluves, for example, slopes are convex in plan. The slope orthogonals thus diverge, and creep and runoff should be more diffuse downslope. If creep is responsible for convex *profiles*, then the convexity in profile should not be as pronounced on a slope which is convex in *plan* (i.e., where creep becomes less concentrated downslope) as on a slope which is straight (or concave) in *plan*. Conversely, slope orthogonals will converge at valley heads and other areas which are concave in plan. This should result in concentration of creep downslope, and thus valley heads should be areas of the greatest convexities in profile. Similarly, if slope wash is responsible for concave slopes, then concentrations of wash (as in valley heads) should produce greater concavities than where wash is diffuse.

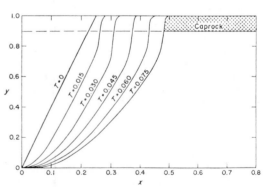

FIG. 12(b). Slope evolution where slope is controlled by resistant cap rock.

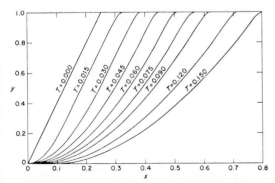

FIG. 12(a). Mathematical models of slope evolution under lithologic control by Scheidegger (1963). T represents an arbitrary value of time elapsed. See Scheidegger (1961) for discussion of models of slope evolution in absence of lithologic control. This figure shows slope evolution in homogeneous material.

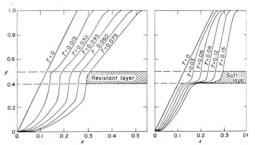

FIG. 12(c). Slope controlled by resistant layer.

FIG. 12(d). Slope controlled by soft layer.

There are few field observations which confirm or deny Spark's conclusions. It has been suggested by many authors that it is the relative concentration of wash which controls the length and the magnitude of convex, straight and concave profiles. This would mean that the specific conclusions cited above are only partly valid. In any case, it is clear that plan geometry of drainage basins is an important factor in determining the nature of slope profiles.

A major concept of modern geomorphology is that drainage basins (and other landform assemblages) are open systems which tend to achieve an equilibrium state. Graded streams are a fundamental part of such basins, as are *graded slopes* (Strahler, 1950). It is impossible to consider slopes and streams as separate entities for, as members of the same open system, they must continuously interact. Slope form and angle will adjust to supply the amount of load which the stream can transport. Similarly, the hydraulic parameters of the stream will adjust to transport the amount of load which the slope supplies. When the slope-stream system is in equilibrium, then the entire drainage basin can be considered graded.

Over a period of time, equilibrium drainage basins undergo progressive changes or *allometric growth* (see *Open Systems—Allometric Growth*). If all the environmental conditions which affect the basin are constant, including base level, then basin relief must decrease with time. This loss of relief (negative allometric growth) is a natural consequence of the constraint of the open system by a base level (see *General Systems Theory*). The entire drainage basin undergoes changes in form, according to the simple laws of allometric growth. Among other parameters, stream load and gradient decline with time, in general accordance with Davisian principles. To maintain the long-term equilibrium of the drainage basin, slopes must also *decline* with time. Such decline will occur by erosion, deposition or both, unless there are strong structural, tectonic or climatic factors which oppose this change.

Control of slopes by layered rock may result in parallel retreat of individual slope elements; nonetheless, slopes within drainage basins must ultimately decline, if base level is constant. This conclusion is supported by Strahler (1950) who showed that a strong correlation exists between slope and channel gradients (Fig. 13). In an ideal cycle, as time passes and relief decreases, slope and channel gradients will decrease (as along the regression line of Fig. 13).

There are other relationships between slopes, streams and/or relief. Stream deposition significantly flattens lower hillslopes (as on flood plains), while undercutting steepens slopes and often leads to mass movements (see below). Both slope angle and sediment loss (hence rate of change of slope) are greatest where relief is at a maximum.

High relief is often associated with areas of

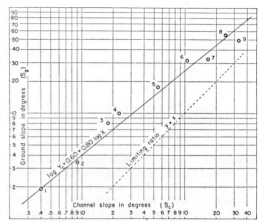

FIG. 13. Slope ratio s_c/s_g for nine maturely dissected regions. (1 and 2) Grant, La. (3) Rappahannock Academy, Va. (4) Belmont, Va. (5) Allen's Creek, Ind. (6) Hunter-Shandaken, N.Y. (7) Mt. Gleason, Calif. (8) Petrified Forest, Ariz. (9) Perth Amboy (clay fill), N.J. All data from U.S.G.S., A.M.S. or special field maps (from Strahler, 1950).

tectonic activity. Strahler (1950) showed that for certain slopes in tectonically active southern California in a uniform bedrock slopes are relatively steep (generally more than 30°) and straight. Many observers have noted that areas of lower relief and areas of tectonic stability seem to be characterized by relatively gentle convex-concave slopes. It is possible, but by no means certain, that as an ideal Davisian cycle progresses and relief gradually decreases, slope profiles will change from being steep and straight during early maturity to being convex-concave by late maturity.

Penck (English translation, 1953) considered at length the relationships between slopes and tectonism. He challenged the Davisian assumption that during an erosion cycle, uplift is essentially complete before erosion begins (see discussion in Schumm, 1963). Penck felt that where uplift was more rapid than erosion, streams would be downcutting and slopes would be convex. Where rate of uplift equaled erosion, the streams would cut down only as fast as the land rose; in this case, slopes would be straight. Where rate of uplift was slow, streams could grade to base level (as in the Davisian

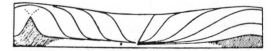

FIG. 14. Contrasted slope profiles. Widening of valleys and change in slope profile during the cycle. Right, youth to old age, according to W. M. Davis. Left, with parallel scarp retreat, according to W. Penck (from Davis, 1930).

cycle); this would result in concave slopes. Penck made further deductions, which have not been widely accepted. However, the theoretical development outlined above may be correct, at least in part. Undercutting by streams commonly steepens adjacent valley side slopes, often resulting in local convexities. As noted above, straight slopes are associated with high relief, which in turn may result locally from rate of uplift being approximately equal to rate of erosion.

(J) Theories of Slope Development and Evolution

Many aspects of slope genesis, development and evolution have been mentioned in preceding sections of this article. The most controversy has centered around the origin of various slope forms (concave, straight, convex profile elements) and the nature of slope change with time (e.g., parallel retreat versus slope decline). Although Davis, in his earlier works, did not discuss slopes directly, it is clear that he envisaged slopes as declining with time, at least in humid climates. Penck (1953) and Lawson (1915) considered slope replacement and parallel retreat (Fig. 2) to occur on some slopes. Davis (1930) recognized that parallel retreat occurs in arid climates, but he maintained that slope decline pre-

vails in humid regions (Fig. 14). Bryan (1940) saw no reason why slope processes should not act with equal effectiveness on all slope elements and hence considered it possible that parallel retreat occurs in all climates. Wood (1942) and King (1957) postulated slope profiles differing from those envisaged by most earlier workers, but also considered parallel retreat and slope replacement to be the primary modes of change.

Many recent studies have used mathematical models involving both parallel retreat and slope decline; these studies are as yet inconclusive. Analysis of valley side slopes as members of drainage basin open systems shows that if base level is constant the slope should decline (or undergo replacement) with time. This implies that Bryan's conclusions were incorrect: i.e., that some processes act with greater effectiveness on certain slope elements. For example, deposition by colluvial material (by slope wash, for example) is most important on footslopes.

The nature of slope change is a critical factor in the controversy over the dominant form of landscape evolution. Parallel retreat gives rise to *pediments* and *pediplains* while slope decline produces *peneplains*, although as numerous observers have

TABLE 2. CHART SHOWING POSSIBLE FACTORS THAT MAY RESULT IN THE DEVELOPMENT OF VARIOUS ASPECTS OF SLOPES. NO EFFORT HAS BEEN MADE TO BE COMPLETE OR TO BE MORE OBJECTIVE THAN THE AVAILABLE INFORMATION WARRANTS. SOURCES INCLUDE REFERENCES IN BIBLIOGRAPHY, BUT REFLECT THE AUTHOR'S OWN PREJUDICES

Slope Type, Process, Mode of Change	Occurrence	Important Factors in Genesis	Other Possibly Important Factors
(A) Convex slope profiles	Crests, waxing slopes	Creep, diverging slope wash	Slope plan often also convex
	Chalk and some other rocks	Creep, rainbeat	High infiltration prohibits slope wash
	Valley bottoms	Oversteepening due to downcutting or lateral cutting of adjacent streams	
	Valley sides	Structural control (layered rock)	
(B) Straight slope profiles	Valley sides	Unconcentrated slope wash and/or groundwater removal of clays	Equilibrium between slope wash and gullying or between erosion and deposition
	Escarpments	Resistant bedrock	Faulting
	Debris slopes	Angle of repose of talus	
(C) Concave slope profiles	Valley bottoms, valley heads	Rill wash, gullying and/or deposition	Slope plan often also concave
	Interfluves (long profiles)	In grade with parallel channels	
	Pediments	Slope wash, mudflows, lateral planation	Depositional veneer, exhumation
	Footslopes of some residual hills	Deposition;'or rill and wash erosion	Subsurface piping

TABLE 2 (CONTINUED)

Slope Type, Process, Mode of Change	Occurrence	Important Factors	Other Possibly Important Factors
(D) Steep slopes (25–30° or more)	High relief areas	Rapid erosion, little deposition	Basal removal of debris by streams; slope profile often straight
	Dry climates	Relatively high erosion little soil	Protection by vegetation is minimal
	Escarpments	Resistant bedrock	Jointing, rock falls
(E) Gentle slopes (20–30° or less)	Areas of low relief	Deposition on footslopes; runoff filters into permeable regolith	Slope profiles often convex-concave
	Humid climates (except where there is high relief)	As above	As above; protection by vegetation
(F) Parallel retreat	Areas of high relief	High erosion rates, lowering of base level	Ultimately decline occurs when base level becomes constant
	Mountain fronts; residual hills	Processes debated: slope wash, lateral planation, weathering	Original slope often tectonic or structural
	Areas of layered bedrock	Lithologic control is key factor	Retreat controlled by cap-rock (e.g., jointing)
(G) Slope decline	Graded drainage basins	Adjustment to loss of relief	Erosion on crests, deposition on footslopes
	Footslopes	Deposition of colluvial material	Masks steeper slope on underlying bedrock

pointed out, peneplains and pediplains are in many ways analogous. Two other forms of landscape evolution are no doubt locally important in slope development. These are *etchplanation* (removal of deeply weathered regolith) and *panplanation* (q.v.) (erosion by lateral corrasion of streams).

Numerous localized studies have attempted to evaluate the relative importance of parallel retreat versus slope decline. Until more investigations are made, it will not be possible to make many generalizations about slopes with any degree of confidence.

Similarly, many studies have been concerned with the rate of change of slopes and the controls of rates of slope processes. Here too, no certain conclusions have been reached. Rates of processes and slope change may be controlled by slope angle, or slope angle may be controlled by rates of processes.

No single theory of hillslope evolution can now be demonstrated. Table 2 is an attempt to summarize ideas concerning slopes; it also indicates the areas of uncertainty that remain.

LEE WILSON

References

Bakker, J. P., and Strahler, A. N., 1956, "Bibliography of quantitative investigations of slopes," *Premier Rapport de la Commission pour l'Etude des Versants, International Geographical Congress, Rio de Janeiro,* 33–41.

Baulig, H., 1940, "Le profil d'equilibre des versants," *Ann. Geograph.,* **49,** 81–97.

Baver, L. D., 1956, "Soil Physics," Third ed., New York, John Wiley & Sons, 489 pp.

Bik, M. J. J., 1967, "Structural Geomorphology and Morphoclimatic Zonation in the Central Highlands. Australian New Guinea," in (Jennings and Mabbutt, editors) "Landform Studies from Australia and New Guinea," 26–47, Austral. Nat. Univ. Press.

Birot, P., 1949, "Essai sur quelques problèmes de morphologie générale," Lisbon, Instituto para Alta Cultura, Centro de Estudos Geograficos, 176pp.

Birot, P., 1956, "Essai de bibliographie sur l'étude expérimentale de la désagrégation des roches," *Premier Rapport de la Commission pour l'Etude des Versants, International Geographical Congress, Rio de Janeiro,* 25–29.

Bryan, Kirk, 1940, "The retreat of slopes," *Ann. Assoc. Am. Geog.,* **30,** 254–268.

Chorley, R. J., 1966, "The Application of Statistical Methods to Geomorphology" in (Dury, G. H., editor), "Essays in Geomorphology," 275–387, New York, Amer. Elsevier Publ. Co.

Chorley, R. J., Dunn, A. J., and Beckinsale, R. P., 1964, "The History of the Study of Landforms," London, Methuen & Co.; New York, John Wiley & Sons, 677pp.

Churska, Z., Galon, R. and Roszko, L., 1967, "Degradation of moraine plateau and slope processes along the lower Vistula valley and neighbouring valleys," *L'Évolution des Versants Sympos. Internat. Géomorph., Liège-Louvain, 1966,* 75–88.

Culling, W. E. H., 1965, "Theory of erosion on soil-covered slopes," *J. Geol.,* **73,** 230–254.

Davis, W. M., 1930, "Rock floors in arid and in humid climates," *J. Geol.,* **38,** 1–27, 136–158.

de la Noë, G. D., and de Margerie, E., 1888, "Les Formes du Terrain," Paris, 205pp.

Dollfus, O., 1964, "L'influence de l'exposition dans le modelé des versants des Andes Centrales Peruviennes," *Zeit. Geomorphol.* Supplementband, **5,** 131–135.

Dumanowski, B., 1960, "Notes on the evolution of slopes in an arid climate." *Zeit. Geomorphol. Supplementband.* **1,** 178–189.

Fenneman, N. M., 1908, "Some features of erosion by unconcentrated wash," *J. Geol.,* **16,** 746–754.

Freise, F. W., 1938, "Inselberge und Inselberg-Landschaften in Granit und Gneissgebiete Brasiliens," *Zeit. Geomorphol.,* **10,** 137–168.

Frye, John C., 1959, "Climate and Lester King's 'Uniformitarian nature of hillslopes'," *J. Geol.,* **67,** 111–113.

Gibbs, H. S., 1945, "Tunnel gulley erosion on the Wither Hills, Marlborough," *New Zealand J. Sci. Technol.,* **27** (sec. A), 135–146.

Gilbert, G. K., 1877, "Report on the Geology of the Henry Mountains," Washington, 160pp.

Gilbert, G. K., 1909, "The convexity of hill tops," *J. Geol.,* **17,** 344–350.

Hack, J. T., and Goodlett, J. C., 1960, "Geomorphology and forest ecology of a mountain region in the central Appalachians," *U.S. Geol. Survey Profess. Paper* **347,** 66pp.

Holmes, C., 1955, "Geomorphic development in humid and arid regions: a synthesis," *Am. J. Sci.,* **253,** 377–390.

Hopkins, D. M., and Wahrhaftig, C., 1960, "Annotated bibliography of English-language papers on the evolution of slopes under periglacial climates," *Zeit. Geomorphol., Supplementband* 1, 1–8.

Horton, Robert, E., 1945, "Erosional development of streams and their drainage basins; hydrophysical approach to quantitative morphology," *Bull. Geol. Soc. Am.,* **56,** 275–370.

Jahn, A., 1960, "Some remarks on the evolution of slopes in Spitsbergen," *Zeit. Geomorphol. Supplementband* 1, 49–58.

Jahn, A., 1964, "Slopes morphological features resulting from gravitation," *Zeit. Geomorphol., Supplementband* 5. 59–72.

Kellogg, C. E., 1941, "The Soils that Support Us," New York, The Macmillan Co., 370pp.

King, L. C., 1957, "The uniformitarian nature of hillslopes," *Trans. Edinburgh Geol. Soc.,* **17,** Pt. 1, 81–102.

Koons, D., 1955, "Cliff retreat in the southwestern United States." *Am. J. Sci.,* **253,** 44–52.

Lawson, A. C., 1915, "Epigene profiles of the desert," *Calif. Univ. Dept. Geol. Bull.,* **9,** 23–48.

Lawson, A. C., 1932, "Rain-wash erosion in humid regions," *Bull. Geol. Soc. Am.,* **43,** 703–724.

Lehmann, O., 1933, "Morphologische Theorie der Verwitterung von Steinschlagwänden," *Vierteljahresschr. Schwiez. Natf. Gesellsch., Zürich,* **78,** 83–126.

Leopold, L. B., Emmett, W. W., and Myrick, R. M., 1966, "Channel and hillslope processes in a semiarid area, New Mexico," *U.S. Geol. Surv. Profess. Paper* **352-G,** 60pp.

Leopold, L. B., Wolman, M. G., and Miller, J. P., 1964, "Fluvial Processes in Geomorphology," San Francisco, W. H. Freeman and Co., 522pp.

Linton, D. T., 1956, "Bibliography of field studies in rock weathering," *Premier Rapport de la Commission pour l'Etude des Versants, Int. Geogr. Congress, Rio de Janiero,* 16–24.

Mabbutt, J. A., and Scott, R. M., 1966, "Periodicity of morphogenesis and soil formation in a savanna landscape near Port Moresby, Papua," *Zeit. Geomorphol.,* **10,** 69–89.

Macar, P., and Forneau, R., 1960, "Relations entre versants et nature du substratum en Belgique," *Zeit. Geomorphol., Supplementband* 1, 124–128.

Melton, M., 1965, "Debris covered hillslopes of the southern Arizona desert—a consideration of their stability and sediment contribution," *J. Geol.,* **73,** 715–729.

Miller, O. M., and Summerson, C. H., 1960, "Slope-zone maps," *Geogr. Rev.,* **50,** 194.

Miller, V. C., 1953, "A quantitative geomorphic study of drainage basin characteristics in the Clinch Mountain area, Virginia and Tennessee," *Project NR* 389–042, *Tech. Rept.* 3, Department of Geology, Columbia University, New York.

Ollier, C. D., and Tuddenham, W. G., 1961, "Inselbergs of Central Australia," *Zeit. Geomorphol.,* **5,** 257–276.

Osterman, J., 1960, "Views on the stability of clay slopes," *Geol. Foren. Stockholm Forh.,* **82,** 346.

Penck, Walther, 1953, "Morphological Analysis of Landforms," English translation, London, Macmillan & Co. Ltd., 429pp.

Rapp, A., 1960, "Recent developments of mountain slopes in Kärkevagge and surroundings, northern Scandinavia," *Geog. Ann.,* **42,** No. 2–3.

Rapp, A., 1967, "Pleistocene activity and Holocene stability of hillslopes, with examples from Scandinavia and Pennsylvania," *L'Évolution des Versants Sympos. Internat. Géomorph., Liège-Louvain, 1966,* 229–244.

Rougerie, G., 1960, "Sur les versants en milieux tropicaux humides," *Zeit. Geomorphol., Supplementband* 1, 12–18.

Ruxton, B. P., 1958, "Weathering and subsurface erosion in granite at the Piedmont angle, Balos, Sudan," *Geol. Mag.,* **95,** 353–377.

Ruxton, B. P., and Berry, L., 1961, "Weathering profiles and geomorphic position on granite in two tropical regions," *Rev. Géomorphol. Dynamique,* **12,** 16–31.

Sabarís, L. S., 1956, "Rapport bibliographique pour l'étude de l'évolution des versants sous le climat méditerrannean," *Premier Rapport de la Commission pour l'Etude des Versants, International Geographical Congress, Rio de Janeiro,* 107–122.

Savigear, R. A. G., 1956, "Technique and terminology in the investigation of slope forms," *Premier Rapport de la Commission pour l'Etude des Versants, International Geographical Congress, Rio de Janeiro,* 66–75.

Savigear, R. A. G., 1960, "Slopes and hills in West Africa," *Zeit. Geomorphol., Supplementband* 1, 156–171.

Scheidegger, A. E., 1961, "Mathematical models of slope development," *Bull. Geol. Soc. Am.,* **72,** 37–50.

Scheidegger, A. E., 1963, "Lithologic variations in slope development theory," *U.S. Geol. Surv. Circ.,* **485,** 8pp.

Schumm, S. A., 1956, "The role of creep and rainwash

on the retreat of badland slopes," *Am. J. Sci.*, **254,** 693–706.

Schumm, S. A., 1963, "The disparity between present rates of denudation and orogeny," *U.S. Geol. Surv. Profess. Paper* **454-H,** 1–13.

Schumm, S. A., 1966, "The development and evolution of hillslopes," *J. Geol. Education,* **14,** 98–104.

Schumm, S. A., and Chorley, R. J., 1966, "Talus weathering and scarp recession in the Colorado Plateaus," *Zeit. Geomorphol.,* **10,** 11–36.

Schumm, S. A., and Lusby, G. C., 1963, "Seasonal variation of infiltration capacity and runoff on hillslopes in western Colorado," *J. Geophys. Res.,* **68,** 3655–3666.

Seret, G., 1963, "Essai de classification des pentes en Famenne," *Zeit. Geomorphol.,* **7,** 71–85.

Smith, D. D. and Wischmeier, W., 1962, "Rainfall erosion," *Advances in Agronomy,* **14,** 109–148.

Sparks, B. W., 1960, "Geomorphology," New York, John Wiley & Sons, 371pp.

Strahler, A. N., 1950, "Equilibrium theory of erosional slopes approached by frequency distribution analysis," *Am. J. Sci.,* **248,** 673–696, 800–814.

Strahler, A. N., 1952, "Hyposmetric (area-altitude) analysis of erosional topography," *Bull. Geol. Soc. Am.,* **63,** 1117–1142.

Strahler, A. N., 1956, "Quantitative slope analysis," *Bull. Geol. Soc. Am.,* **67,** 571–596.

Strahler, A. N., 1964, "Quantitative Geomorphology," in (Chow, V. T., ed.) "Handbook of Applied Hydrology," pp. 4–39 to 4–76, New York, McGraw-Hill Book Co.

Terzaghi, K., 1962, "Stability of steep slopes on hard unweathered rock," *Géotechnique,* **12,** 251–271.

Troeh, F. R., 1965, "Landform equations fitted to contour maps," *Am. J. Sci.,* **263,** 616–627.

Twidale, C. R., 1959, "Slope evolution in central Labrador and Quebec," *Ann. Geograph.,* **365,** 54–70.

Twidale, C. R., 1960, "Some problems of slope development," *J. Geol. Soc. Australia,* **6,** 131–147.

White, J. F., 1966, "Convex-concave landscapes: a geometrical study," *Ohio J. Sci.,* **66,** 592–608.

Wood, A., 1942, "The development of hillside slopes," *Proc. Geol. Assoc.,* **53,** 128–138.

Young, A., 1960, "Soil movement by denudational processes on slopes," *Nature,* **188** (4745), 120–122.

Young, H., 1963, "Deductive models of slope evolution," *Nachr. Akad. Wiss. Goettingen, II. Math. Physik. Kl.,* **5,** 45–66.

Young, A., 1964, "Slope profile analysis," *Zeit. Geomorphol., Supplementband* 5, 17–27.

Cross-references: *Aggradation; Alluvium; Asymmetric Valleys; Badlands; Baer-Babinet Law; Base Level; Bornhardt; Climatic Geomorphology; Colluvium; Cryopedology; Cuesta; Degradation; Denudation; Drainage Basin; Duricrust; Endogenic Dynamics; Erosion; Escarpments; Etchplain; Exogenic Dynamics; Frost Action; General Systems Theory in Geomorphology; Geomorphology—Expanded Theory; Gradation; Grade, Graded Stream; Gully Erosion; Haldenhang or Wash Slope; Head; Hogback and Flatiron; Hypsometric Analysis; Inselberg; Interfluve; Karst; Landscape Analysis; Landscape Types—Genetic; Landslides; Littoral Processes; Mass Movement; Mass Wasting; Mesa and Butte; Monadnock; Morphogenetic Classification; Open Systems—Allometric Growth; Pan-*

planation; Pediments; Peneplain; Periglacial Landscape; Process—Structure—Stage; Quantitative Geomorphology; Quaternary; Regolith and Saprolite; Rivers; Sand Dunes; Sediment Transport; Selva Landscape; Sheet Erosion, Sheetwash, etc.; *Slope Analysis; Soil Creep; Solifluction; Stream Channel Characteristics; Stream Orders; Structural Control in Geomorphology; Talus Fan or Cone; Terraces; Valley Evolution; Watershed; Weathering; Wind Action.* Vol. I/II: *Coriolis Force.* Vol. II: *Arid Climate; Astroblemes and Meteorite Craters; Climate and Geomorphology; Fluid Mechanics; Insolation; Laminar Flow; Mid-latitude Climate; Solar Radiation.* Vol. V: *Epeirogeny; Gravity; Orogenesis; Taphrogeny; Volcanoes and Vulcanology.* Vol. VI: *Deposition; Groundwater; Soil Erosion; Vegetation Markers and Landscapes; Weathering—Chemical; Weathering—Organic.*

SLUICEWAY—*See* GLACIAL SPILLWAYS AND PROGLACIAL LAKES

SLUMP—*See* MASS MOVEMENT

SNOW AVALANCHES

Introduction

Snow avalanches are active geological agents of erosion and have been a source of natural disasters as long as man has dwelled in the mountains. They are common features of mountainous terrain throughout the temperate and arctic regions of the earth, and they may fall wherever snow is deposited on slopes steeper than about 30°. Small avalanches, or *sluffs*, run in uncounted numbers each winter, while the larger avalanches, which may encompass slopes a mile or more wide and millions of tons of snow, fall infrequently but inflict most of the destruction. The *avalanche hazard* arises whenever man and his works are exposed to sliding snow. Such hazard has been familiar to inhabitants of the Alps and Scandinavia for many centuries, while it is a more recent development in other parts of the world.

Avalanches run in the same *paths* year after year, the danger zones often being well known in normal circumstances. Exceptional weather at intervals of many years may produce exceptional avalanches which overrun their normal paths and even break new ones where none existed for centuries. Unwise timber removal in alpine terrain can also create avalanches where none existed before. Given exceptional snow conditions, even short slopes like the walls of a ravine can become dangerous. Snow avalanche may fall wherever enough snow is deposited in the right circumstances on an inclined surface.

These right circumstances sometimes consist of abnormally large snowfalls, but not always so. Avalanches find their genesis in snow cover structural weaknesses which are often induced by internal changes. A large overburden of snow alone may not result in avalanching if it is anchored to a solid underlayer. On the other hand, even a shallow snow layer can slide from the mountainside if poorly bonded. The snow avalanche is a complex problem in mechanical stability which can best be understood in terms of the physical processes taking place in the changeable winter snow and the dependence of these on temperature (see *Snow: Winter Cover*, pr Vol. VI).

Types of Avalanches and Their Characteristics

The wide variety of snow avalanche origin, nature of motion and size reflects the highly changeable nature of snow. The fundamental classification of avalanches is based on conditions prevailing at the point of origin, or the *release zone*. There are two basic types, *loose snow* and *slab* avalanches. Each is subdivided according to whether the snow involved is dry, damp or wet; whether the slide originates in a surface layer or involves the whole snow cover (slides to the ground); and whether the motion is on the ground, in the air, or mixed.

Loose snow avalanches form in snow with little internal cohesion among individual snow crystals. When such snow lies in a state of unstable equilibrium on a slope steeper than its natural angle of repose, a slight disturbance sets progressively more and more snow in downhill motion. If enough momentum is generated, the sliding snow may run out onto level ground, or even ascend an opposite valley wall. Such an avalanche originates at a point, growing wider as it sweeps up more snow in its descent. The demarcation between sliding and undisturbed snow is diffuse, especially in dry snow.

Three processes commonly leave snow on a slope steeper than its natural angle of repose: (1) deposition of stellar or dendritic crystals with little or no wind, (2) reduction of internal cohesion among crystals by metamorphism, and (3) reduction of internal cohesion by intrusion of liquid water. Though very numerous, most dry loose snow avalanches are small, and few achieve sufficient size to cause damage. With advent of spring melting, wet loose snow avalanches also are common. Most of the latter, too, are small, but they are more likely to develop occasional destructive size, especially when confined to gulleys.

Slab avalanches originate in snow with sufficient internal cohesion to enable a snow layer, or layers, to react mechanically as a single entity. The degree of this required cohesion may range from very slight in fresh, new snow (*soft slab*) to very high in hard, wind-drifted snow (*hard slab*), according to circumstances of layer attachment to the external environment. A slab avalanche breaks free along a characteristic *fracture line*, a sharp division of sliding from stable snow whose face stands perpendicular to the slope. The entire surface of unstable snow is set in motion at the same time. A slab release may take place across an entire mountainside, with the fracture racing from slope to slope to release adjacent or even distant slide paths. The mechanical conditions leading to slab avalanche formation are found in a wide variety of snow types, both new and old, dry and wet. They may be induced by the nature of snow deposition (wind drifting is the prime agent of slab formation) or by internal metamorphism. Slab avalanches are often dangerous and unpredictable in behavior. Providing most of the winter avalanche hazard, they are the primary object of avalanche defense and control measures.

Avalanches composed of dry snow usually generate a *dust cloud* as part of the sliding snow is whirled into the air. Such slides, called *powder snow avalanches*, most frequently originate as soft slabs. Under favorable circumstances, enough snow crystals are mixed with the air to form an aerosol which behaves as a sharply bounded body of dense gas rushing down the slope ahead of the sliding snow. This *wind-blast* can achieve high velocities which inflict heavy and capricious destruction well beyond the normal bounds of the avalanche path.

Wet snow avalanches move more slowly than dry ones and are seldom accompanied by dust clouds. Their higher snow density can lend them enormous destructive force in spite of lower velocities. As wet slides reach their deposition zones, the interaction of sliding and stagnated snow produces characteristic *channeling*.

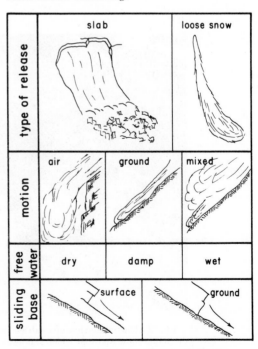

Fig. 1. The classification of snow avalanches.

Direct action avalanches fall as the immediate result of a single snow-storm. They usually involve only the fresh snow. *Climax* avalanches are caused by a series of snowstorms or a culmination of weather influences. Their fall is not necessarily associated with a given current storm or weather situation.

The Mechanism of Avalanche Release

Most avalanches of dangerous size originate on slope angles between 30 and 45°. They seldom occur below 30° and hardly ever below 25°. Above 45–50°, sluffs and small avalanches are common, but snow seldom accumulates to sufficient depths to generate large slides.

Though internal metamorphism or stress development may sometimes initiate snow rupture, avalanches are often dislodged by external *triggers*. An overload of new snow may dislodge an existing slab. Falling cornices or chunks of snow from trees are common natural triggers, similar in action to the *sunballs* or snow wheels which frequently initiate wet slides. In the absence of external triggers, unstable snow may revert to stability with passage of time, and no avalanche occurs. Artificial triggers in the form of mechanical disturbance may be intentionally introduced for control purposes (see below). Unintentional triggers are a major cause of accidents; most skiers who fall victim to an avalanche trigger the slide which traps them.

Slab avalanches fall when a well-defined snow layer breaks free and slides away. The sliding surface is usually the interface between distinguish-able layers of snow which have been formed by variations in weather or snow deposition. In some cases, the sliding surface may be the ground (entire snow cover avalanches). There often exists a *lubricating layer* of low shear strength which allows the slab to break free from the sliding surface. This lubricating layer may be generated by deposition of fragile crystal forms (e.g., surface hoar), internal metamorphism, or the intrusion of meltwater. In some cases, the lubricating layer is absent, instability being provided simply by a poor bond between snow slab and the sliding surface.

The primary instability develops when the component of force parallel to the slope due to the weight of the slab exceeds the shear strength of the bond to the underlayer (sliding surface). The situation is mechanically complex due to irregular attachment of the slab to stable snow or other anchorages at the head, toe and sides. In general, slab avalanche release occurs when one of these attachments is broken by a trigger; redistributed stresses then exceed the strength of the other bonds and an avalanche falls. One part of the slab attachments may be weak, while others are strong. In this case, a trigger will initiate fracturing in the snow, but the slab remains in place and no avalanche falls.

Snow settles as destructive metamorphism proceeds, and on an inclined surface, it also creeps downhill under the influence of gravity by internal plastic deformation and slip on the ground. Creep velocity varies with temperature, snow type, snow depth, slope inclination and profile, and ground

FIG. 2. The fracture line of a slab avalanche, showing the sharp boundary between the stable snow and that which slid away to the left. Note blocks of the hard slab resting on the sliding surface.

cover. These variations from one zone of the snow cover to another develop *creep stresses*. The zones of *creep tension* are favorable locations for slab avalanche fracture lines; these commonly occur on convex profiles or at the head of open slopes where the snow cover first finds anchorage (trees, ridge top, etc.). A snow slab under tension may not only break free when triggered but may shatter into blocks as well when the stress is relieved. In hard snow of high tensile strength, this release may achieve almost explosive violence. Creep stresses are in large measure responsible for the dangerous and unpredictable character of slab avalanches.

Forecasting Snow Avalanches

Although the general features of snow instability are known, many details of avalanche formation are not clearly understood. Forecasting snow avalanches is therefore largely an empirical art based on accumulated experience. Known physical and mechanical principles of snow behavior provide a qualitative understanding of avalanche origin, but quantitative extension of these principles to specific situations is difficult, for nature presents too many variables to allow exact calculation of snow stress and strength variations with time. The precise time a given slope will avalanche cannot be predicted, but the general degrees of instability in a given area can be estimated with reasonable accuracy.

There are two basic methods of anticipating avalanche hazard. One is the examination of snow cover structure for patterns of weakness, particularly those leading to slab avalanches. This method finds its greatest success in forecasting climax slab avalanches caused by structural weaknesses which may be evolved over a period of time and by a variety of weather conditions. The second method is analysis of meteorological factors affecting snow deposition. The latter is now successful in forecasting direct-action soft slab avalanches which run in fresh surface snow layers when structure is poorly differentiated. In practice, the two methods overlap and both are used. Emphasis on one or the other depends on local climate, snow type and avalanche characteristics. Both apply principally to winter avalanches in dry snow; forecasting wet spring avalanches depends on a knowledge of the heat input to the snow surface as well as elements of the foregoing methods.

Snow cover structure is investigated directly by digging pits and examining the exposed stratigraphy. Snow temperature, density, strength properties and crystal type are all important for determining stability. Time variations in these properties are examined by a succession of pits in a given study area, the result being plotted in a time profile. Indirect evidence on snow structure can be gathered by instruments probing from the surface. The most useful of these is the *ram penetrometer* which measures snow strength variations with depth by means of a pointed rod driven by a falling weight. Periodic observations at representative study plots (usually on level ground) are compared with snow profiles from actual avalanche fracture lines to determine and anticipate stability trends.

The basic structure leading to slab avalanche formation is a cohesive snow layer resting on a weak substratum which offers poor support or attachment. Actual combinations of slab layer and substratum strength vary widely. A heavy, hard slab of great thickness may exert enough shear stress at its base to rupture a relatively strong supporting layer which would provide adequate anchorage for a lesser overburden. On the other hand, even shallow layers of soft, weak snow may break free as a slab avalanche if the substratum is sufficiently fragile. A common source of weakness is *depth hoar* formed in the early winter snow cover. This provides very poor support for subsequent snowfalls, which often slide off fully developed depth hoar regardless of their individual character. Thin layers of depth hoar, surface hoar or graupel can also provide a fragile bond (good lubricating layer) when sandwiched between stronger layers. The general process of constructive metamorphism always weakens snow layer strength and bonds; it may precipitate an avalanche long before recognizable depth hoar crystals actually appear. An-

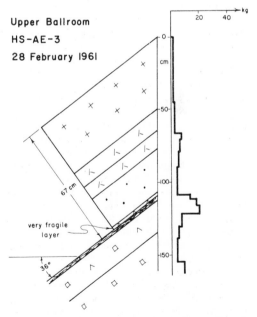

FIG. 3. Typical snow structure at the fracture line of a slab avalanche. Layers of new, partly metamorphosed and old snow are separated from an icy crust by a thin layer of very fragile depth hoar crystals. The profile of ram resistance at right indicates low strength in the slab layer which slid away. (Alta, Utah. The code HS-AE-3 designates a hard slab of medium size artificially released by explosives.)

other frequent cause of slab avalanching is an ice layer or crust which provides a smooth sliding surface. Crusts formed by refreezing following a rain storm offer especially poor anchorage to subsequently deposited snow layers. The bond between slab layer and a crust can be poor at low temperatures, while it rapidly gains strength if the interface is near the freezing point. Other patterns of snow stratigraphy also lead to slab avalanche formation in dry snow though these are the most important.

Soft slab avalanches usually run during or immediately after a storm. In motion, they are similar to dry loose snow avalanches and sometimes are confused with the latter when they fall during poor visibility. The characteristic fracture line and the initial motion as a cohesive layer are nevertheless present, identifying them as true slab avalanches. Observation of contributory weather factors before and during a snow storm provides the basis for forecasting this hazard situation. The *depth and surface character of the existing snow base*, established by previous storms, must be known. A deep snow cover favors avalanching by smoothing the terrain, while certain surface conditions such as a crust (see pr Vol. VI) offer a good sliding surface. The *new snow depth*, *type* and *density* also offer clues to stability. New snow layers more than 25–30 cm thick most frequently lead to soft slabs, with graupel and intermediate stages of rimed crystals the most favorable crystal type and new snow densities above about 0.12 g/cm^3 a warning sign. (Very low new snow densities, 0.05 g/cm^3 or less, are usually associated with dry loose snow avalanches.) *Settlement* in the new snow is a stabilizing factor. Rising *temperature* during a storm accompanied by rising new snow density tends to cause avalanching, while falling temperatures have the opposite effect. New snow *precipitation intensity* is a significant factor, for it represents the rate at which the slopes are being overloaded. Values above 2.5 mm of water per hour warn of impending hazard. In practice, this factor may not be measured directly; instead, new snow density and *snowfall intensity* are observed. The *wind* is also critically important, for soft slab avalanches seldom occur unless sustained average wind velocity exceeds 6–7 m/sec. The most reliable indicator of developing avalanche hazard is a sustained period of coincident high wind and high precipitation intensity.

Wet snow avalanches are generated by intrusion of percolating liquid water (rain or snow melt) in the snow cover. The rapid temperature rise quickly alters snow behavior, while the water itself reduces snow strength. Liquid water accumulating at an impervious crust provides an especially good lubricating layer for slab release. The most extensive wet snow avalanching occurs during winter rains or the first prolonged melt period in spring, when liquid water intrudes into previously subfreezing snow. Snow melt by solar radiation is the com-monest source of wet snow avalanching, and this is amenable to quantitative prediction. It is essential, though, that the total snow surface energy balance be considered in estimating amount of melt, for long-wave radiation, vapor exchange and sensible heat from the air all play an important part. A warm, windy, overcast day may produce more melting (and avalanche activity) than sunshine and cloudless skies.

Accuracy of formal forecasting procedures is enhanced by frequent field checks of snow stability. For this purpose, small, accessible avalanche paths are sometimes chosen as sites for *test skiing*, where snow conditions are checked by actually trying to set the snow in motion. This technique is particularly useful in detecting incipient soft slab formation during storms. It is less effective (and more dangerous) on hard slabs formed by heavy wind drifting. Tests of the latter are usually restricted to blasting with high explosives.

Avalanche Control Techniques

Avalanche hazard can be mitigated or eliminated by the application of operational and engineering techniques. There are two fundamental methods of avalanche control: modification of terrain and modification of the snow cover.

Terrain modification may deflect the sliding snow away from fixed facilities to be protected, or it may actually prevent the avalanche release. Examples of deflecting structures are *snowsheds* used to protect railways and highways. These must be strong enough to support the dynamic load of sliding snow; hence, most modern snowsheds are built of reinforced concrete. Where sheds are impractical, the sliding snow can be diverted laterally by *wedges*, *pylons* or *diversion walls*. In favorable terrain, the snow may be arrested by *snow dams* or *catchment basins*. Avalanches are also arrested in the outrun, or *transition zone*, of their paths by *braking mounds*—conical, earthen or masonry mounds, 4 meters or more high, which are arranged in a pattern to break up the flowing snow into crosscurrents which internally dissipate its kinetic energy. All of the passive deflection structures act principally on snow sliding on the ground which may exert impact forces up to 100 tons/m^2. They have less effect on the dust cloud accompanying a powder snow avalanche.

Active avalanche defense by terrain modification is achieved with *supporting structures* in the avalanche release zone. These are large walls, fences or nets arranged to retain snow and prevent avalanches from falling. Their size and spacing are designed to (1) terrace the mountainside into discrete zones, each of which has snow deposited to a surface slope less than the mean, (2) break up the continuity of the snow surface and prevent slab formation, and (3) support snow on the mountainside in small, manageable sections. These supporting structures, mostly massive fences in modern design, must be strong enough to support creep pressures reaching tons per square meter, while at the same time being light enough to be economically transported and erected high on a mountainside. Another type of defense used in the release zone is the *wind baffle*, a wall or panel arranged to induce irregular wind drifting which breaks the continuity of snow slabs. They are not designed to withstand large creep pressures and are less effective than supporting structures.

Avalanche control by snow modification does not give the high degree of protection afforded by terrain modification but is much cheaper. It is commonly used to reduce the hazard to mobile entities, such as skiers or highway traffic, which may be removed during periods of danger. The most common technique is *artificial release*, which brings down avalanches at a chosen safe time and inhibits formation of large avalanches by relieving slopes of their snow burden piecemeal in small ones. Slides on small paths are sometimes intentionally released by skiing, but the preferred method is the detonation of a brisant high explosive on the snow surface close to the expected fracture line; 1 kg of TNT, or its equivalent, is considered the minimum reliable charge. The charge may be placed by hand, but this can be difficult and is sometimes dangerous. Artillery shells, armed with superquick point-detonating fuses, are much more efficient, for a number of targets can quickly and safely be engaged from a single gun emplacement. Principal disadvantages of artillery are limitations to military or government use and possible damage from shrapnel dispersion. Mortars, light howitzers and recoilless rifles have all been successfully used for avalanche control; the 75-mm recoilless rifle is the most practical weapon for this purpose. Where frequent artificial release is undertaken to protect a ski area or highway, a fixed artillery emplacement permits increased efficiency by blind-firing during storms or at night. Artificial release cannot be effectively employed at random. It must be based on accurate appraisal of snow and weather conditions and on careful selection of targets.

Another snow modification technique is the application of mechanical disturbance to break up slab formation (especially soft slabs) and induce stabilization through age-hardening. Skier traffic is the most common available disturbance, while deliberate packing of the snow by foot or ski is sometimes used. Depth hoar can be satisfactorily stabilized only by intensive foot packing. Mechanical aids, such as oversnow vehicles, can seldom be used at the slope angles existing in avalanche release zones.

E. LaChapelle

References

Bucher, E., 1948, "Beitrag zu den theoretischen Grundlagen des Lawinenverbaus," *Beitr. Geol. Schweiz, Geotech. Ser., Hydrologie*, Lief. G, Bern. (In English as "Contribution to the theoretical foundations of avalanche defense construction," *U.S. Army Corps of Engineers*, *S.I.P.R.E., Translation No. 18.*).

de Quervain, M., Salm, B., and Haefeli, R., 1961, "Lawinenverbau im Anbruchgebiet," *Eidg. Inspektion fur Forstwesen*, Bern. (In English as "Avalanche control in the starting zone," *U.S. Dept. Agr. Forest Serv. Rocky Mt. Forest Range Expt. Sta., Sta. Paper, 71.*)

Roch, A., 1955, "Le mécanisme du declenchement des avalanches. Les Alpes," (In English as "The mechanism of avalanche release," *U.S. Army Corps of Engineers*, *S.I.P.R.E., Translation No. 52.*)

U. S. Dept. of Agriculture, 1961, "Snow Avalanches," Handbook no. 194.

Seligman, G., 1962, "Snow Structure and Ski Fields," reprinted edition, London, Macmillan & Co., 1936.

Cross-references: *Avalanche; Cirque; Frost Action; Mass Wasting; Snow: Metamorphism of Deposited Snow; Talus Fan or Cone*, etc. Vol. VI: *Snow: Winter Cover.*

SNOW AND ICE FORMS—*See* pr Vol. VI

SNOW LINE—*See* FJELL; *also* pr Vol. VI

SNOW: METAMORPHISM OF DEPOSITED SNOW

Many of the unique properties of snow are due to the fact that ice, unlike most other solid materials, is normally encountered at temperatures very close to its melting point. Water molecules are, therefore, comparatively free to migrate within the ice lattice by volume diffusion, over the surface of the crystals by surface diffusion, and to evaporate readily into the vapor phase. As a result of this molecular mobility, water molecules will always be redistributed in a given volume of snow in such a way as to decrease the total surface area of the crystals and hence reduce the free energy of the system. Therefore, following the deposition of fresh snow on the ground, the snowflakes, which initially form a loose cover of density from 0.01–0.25 g/cm^3, gradually change their shapes and join together to form a

Designation	Age	Density (g.cm.$^{-3}$)	Ram resistance to Penetration (kg.)
new snow	—	0.01–0.25	1–10
powder snow	weeks	0.05–0.20	5–20
old snow	months	0.1–0.4	5–100
firn	years	0.55–0.85	20–500
glacier ice	100's of years	0.8–0.9	—

FIG. 1. Changes in the density and mechanical strength of snow with time.

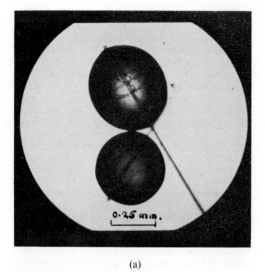

(a)

(b)

FIG. 2. The growth of a neck between two spheres of ice at a temperature of $-5°C$ (a) at contact and (b) 320 minutes after contact.

stronger and more dense compact. The final equilibrium condition of snow is represented by the large single crystals of ice found in glaciers; however, conditions such as this may not be reached even after hundreds of years.

The various stages in the metamorphism of snow are listed in Fig. 1. In the initial stage, the variously shaped snow crystals are converted into spherical particles (*powder snow*). In the absence of other effects, such as melting or strong winds, which can accelerate this process, the transformation to powder snow is generally accomplished in a matter of weeks. The snow then consists of spherical particles in contact at a number of points, but this system is still not one of minimum force energy for

the total surface area may be reduced further by the transfer of material to the points of contact between the particles. This will result in the development of necks of ice, or *ice bonds*, between the particles.

The driving force for the transfer of material to the points of contact between the particles is provided by the gradient in chemical potential existing between the highly stressed regions adjacent to the concave necks and points elsewhere in the system. Under the influence of this driving force, molecules can move to the points of contact by four possible mechanisms: transfer through the vapor phase, volume diffusion through the ice lattice, surface diffusion over the particles, and plastic or viscous flow. Hobbs and Mason (1964) have recently shown that the first of these four mechanisms is the dominant one in the transfer of material to the necks. Water molecules diffuse through the air to the regions of low vapor pressure immediately above the surfaces of the necks, and the latter therefore increase in size as a result of continuous condensation upon their surfaces. These workers have shown that the rate of growth of the neck between two ice spheres of equal radii r by this mechanism is:

$$\left(\frac{x}{r}\right)^5 = \frac{20\gamma\delta^3}{kTr^3}F(T)t \tag{1}$$

where x is the radius of the neck at time t, γ is the surface energy of ice ($\simeq 90$ erg/cm^2), δ is the intermolecular spacing ($\simeq 3 \times 10^{-8}$cm), k is Boltzmann's constant (1.381×10^{-16} erg/°K), T is the temperature, and $F(T)$ is a temperature-dependent function. [$F(T) = 1.0 \times 10^{-7}$ cm^2/sec at $-3°C$, $F(T) = 9.0 \times 10^{-9}$ cm^2/sec at $-40°C$]. Two stages in the growth of the neck between two spheres of ice held at a temperature of $-5°C$ are shown in Fig. 2.

Now as the bonding between the particles in deposited snow increases so does the strength of the compact, a process which is referred to as *age hardening*. It is clear, moreover, that the mechanical strength of the snow at any instant of time must be directly proportional to the total area of contact between the particles and this, in turn, is proportional to x^2. Hence, it can be seen from Eq. (1) that the mechanical strength of the snow should increase with time according to the power law $t^{2/5}$. Therefore, if the strength of a sample of snow held at a constant temperature is plotted against time on a log-log plot, the results should lie on a straight line of slope 0.4.

Measurements have been made on the mechanical strength of snow as a function of time by Jellinek, Bender, Wuori and Nakaya (see references in Hobbs, 1965) and these results are shown in Figs. 3 and 4. The fact that the experimental results lie on fairly well-defined straight lines supports the conclusion that the strength of the snow is

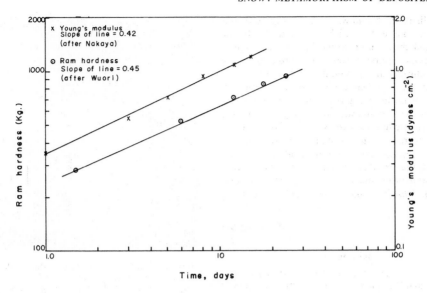

FIG. 3. Experimental results for the age hardening of snow, expressed in terms of Young's modulus and ram hardness.

related to time by a simple power law. Also, the slopes of the lines (0.42, 0.3, 0.42 and 0.45) are in good agreement with the theoretical value of 0.4 predicted by Eq. (1).

Due to the fact that the function $F(T)$ decreases by more than an order of magnitude when the temperature falls from -3 to $-40°C$, the rate of age hardening decreases with decreasing temperature. However, over a long period of time a deposit of snow may attain a greater ultimate strength if it hardens at low temperatures due to the fact that

the tensile strength of ice increases with decreasing temperature. It can also be seen from Eq. (1) that small particles (small r) will age harden more quickly than large particles. This fact is put to practical application in the preparation of roads and runways from snow in arctic regions where it is common practice to disintegrate (or mill) freshly fallen snow.

The metamorphic processes described above can all take place at temperatures below the melting point of ice and in the absence of tempera-

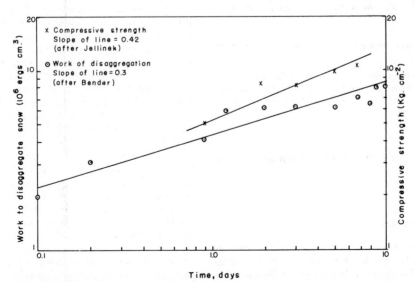

FIG. 4. Experimental results for the age hardening of snow, expressed in terms of compressive strength and work of disaggregation.

ture gradients in the snow. If the temperature rises above 0°C, meltwater will be introduced into the system and this can, on refreezing, cause a significant increase in the density and strength of the snow. Temperature gradients within the snow cover, on the other hand, give rise to a reduction in the mechanical strength of the snow, for water molecules will evaporate from regions in the snow where the temperature is high, diffuse through the air, and recondense in regions of low temperature. This process can therefore lead to a partial return to the isolated crystals which are poorly bonded and mechanically weak (see *Snow: Metamorphism into Ice*; *Snow: Winter Cover*, both in Vol. VI).

P. V. HOBBS

References

Anderson, D. L., and Benson, C. S., 1963, "The Densification and Diagenesis of Snow," in "Ice and Snow," p. 391, Cambridge, Mass., Massachusetts Institute of Technology Press.

Bader, H., Haefeli, R., Bucher, E., *et al.*, 1939, "Der Schnee und scine Metamorphase" (Snow and its Metamorphism), *Beitr. Geol. Schweiz, Geotech. Ser., Hydrologie,* **3**; USA SIPRE *Corps of Engineers, Translation No. 14* (1954).

de Quervain, M., 1963, "On the Metamorphism of Snow," in "Ice and Snow," p. 377, Cambridge, Mass., Massachusetts Institute of Technology Press.

Hobbs, P. V., 1965, "The effect of time on the physical properties of deposited snow," *J. Geophys. Res.,* **70**, 3903–3906.

Hobbs, P. V., and Mason, B. J., 1964, "The sintering and adhesion of ice," *Phil. Mag.,* **9**, 181–197.

*Yosida, Z., *et al.*, 1955, "Physical Studies on Deposited Snow," Institute of Low Temperature Science, Hokkaido University, Sapporo, Japan (reprinted by University Microfilms, Inc., Ann Arbor, Michigan, 1965).

* Additional bibliographic references may be found in this work.

Cross-references: Vol. II: *Ice Phase in the Atmosphere*; *Precipitation*; *Snowflakes*. Vol. VI: *Ice—Structure and Properties*; *Snow: Metamorphism into Ice*; *Snow: Winter Cover*.

SOIL—*See* REGOLITH AND SAPROLITE; *also* pr Vol. VI

SOIL CRACKS—GIANT

Giant soil cracks, king-size soil cracks, giant soil polygons, etc., are a system of fissures measuring from 1–150 meters in length, generally enclosing polygonal surfaces, which by shape analogy might be compared with *ice-wedge polygons* in perma-

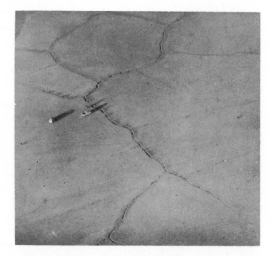

FIG. 1. Giant soil cracking within a playa of the Mojave Desert, USA, as seen at a 200-meter elevation. (Photographed by R. J. Chico, U.S. Air Force, Cambridge Research Laboratories "Operation Waterhole," 1963).

frost, patterns of gigantic *mud cracks* or *earthquake soil fissures*. *Giant soil cracks* geometrically are similar to vernacularly named "*pimpled plains*" (Oklahoma), "*prairie mounds*," "*hog-wallows*" (California), "*Mima mounds*" (Washington), and "*puffs*" (Australia). Geographically *giant soil cracks* are encountered in several non-permafrost areas. Consequently, genetically (Black, 1952; Knechtel, 1952; Chico, 1963) they might have been formed by a process or processes other than the classical one known for *ice-wedge polygons* in *permafrost* (Leffingwell, 1915; Lachenbruch, 1962).

There is meager information on *giant soil cracks*; however, most authors associate their formation to subsurface conditions, primarily the water table, as follows. In subarctic zones, *giant soil cracks* are due to seasonal freezing of a shallow water table (Black, 1952; Arnaud and Whiteside, 1961); in tropical *alluvial plains*, earth fissures might be caused by a lowering of the water table (Robinson and Peterson, 1962). Giant polygonal cracking on *playas* has been also assigned to water table drop (Wilden and Mabey, 1961).

There is more than one example, however, of large soil cracking produced because of *hydrostatic* and *thermal gradients* of a *hot spring* action. It has been determined locally that the decrease of soil polygon sizes away from the hot spring outlet correlates with the drops of soil moisture content and isothermic convective fronts caused by the rise of *thermal waters* (Chico, 1963).

Although giant soil cracking polygon systems might be preserved during *diagenesis*, no positive identification in the geological record has been reported with the exception of some fissures in the eastern part of the *Russian platform* (Novikova, 1951).

Raymundo J. Chico

References

Arnaud, R. J. St., and Whiteside, E. P., 1961, "Physical breakdown in relation to soil development," *J. Soil Sci.*, **14**(2), 267–281.

Black, R. F., 1952, "Polygonal patterns and ground conditions from aerial photographs," *Photogrammetric Eng.*, **8**(1), 123–134.

Chico, R., 1963, "Playa mud cracks: Regular and king size." *Geol. Soc. Am., Special Paper No. 76*, p. 306.

Knechtel, M., 1952, "Pimpled plains of Oklahoma," *Bull. Geol. Soc. Am.*, **63**, 689–700.

Lachenbruch, A., 1962, "Mechanics of thermal contraction cracks and ice-wedge polygons in permafrost," *Geol. Soc. Am., Special Paper No. 70.*

Leffingwell, E. de K., 1915, "Ground-ice wedges; the dominant form of ground ice on the north coast of Alaska," *J. Geol.*, **23**, 635–654.

Neal, J. T., Langer, A. M., and Kerr, P. F., 1968, "Giant desiccation polygons of Great Basin playas," *Bull. Geol. Soc. Am.*, **79**, 69–90.

Novikova, A. S., 1951, "O treshchinovatosti osadochnykh porod vostochnoi Russkoi platformy," *Akad. Nauk SSSR, Iz. Serv. Geol.*, No. 5, 68–85.

Robinson, G. M., and Peterson, D. E., 1962, "Notes on earth fissures in southern Arizona," *U.S. Geol. Surv. Circ.*, **466**, 7pp.

Wilden, C. R., and Mabey, D. R., 1961, "Giant desiccation fissures on the Black Rock and Smoke Creek Deserts, Nevada," *Science*, **133**(3461), 1359–1360.

Cross-references: *Mud Cracks*; *Patterned Ground*; *Permafrost*; *Playa*; *Prairie Mounds.*

SOIL CREEP

This is the slow movement of soil materials down slopes under the influence of gravity. The soil is normally lubricated by a good deal of moisture or aided by *frost heaving* (q.v.). Four kinds of creep were identified by Sharpe (1938): *soil creep, talus creep, rock-glacier creep,* and *rock creep.* The first concerns only fine-grained particles; the others involve rock debris. Soil creep in subpolar latitudes and at high altitude grades im-

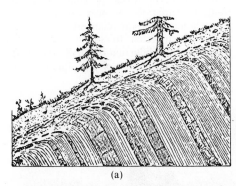 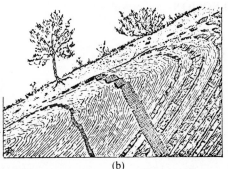

FIG. 1. (a) Soil creep over steeply dipping strata. (b) A completely overturned case. Note how dip readings on a steep slope could be completely false. (Sketches by R. Kettner.)

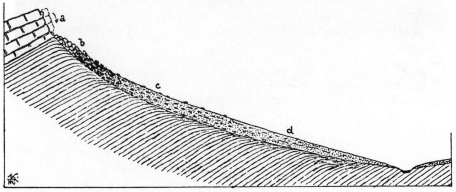

FIG. 2. Transition from rock fall (a) to rock talus (b), to rock creep (c), to soil creep (d). (Sketch by R. Kettner).

perceptibly into *solifluction* (q.v.) phenomena and into *earthflow* in temperate latitudes.

Parizek and Woodruff (1957) stress that "creep" implies *imperceptible* motion, and this distinguishes it from earthflow, slumps, etc. They urge that the term creep may be applied, therefore, as a general category for all imperceptible superficial earth motions, regardless of genesis.

RHODES W. FAIRBRIDGE

References

Parizek, E. J., and Woodruff, J. F., 1957, "A clarification of the definition and classification of soil creep," *J. Geol.*, **65**, 653–656.

Schumm, S. A., 1956, "The role of creep and rainwash on the retreat of badland slopes," *Am. J. Sci.*, **254**, 693–706.

Sharpe, C. F. S., 1938, "Landslides and Related Phenomena," New York, Columbia University Press.

Sharpe, C. F. S., and Dosch, E. F., 1942, "Relation of soil-creep to earthflow in the Appalachian plateau," *J. Geomorphol.*, **5**, 312–324.

Cross-references: *Frost Heaving; Mass Movement; Mass Wasting; Periglacial Landscape; Solifluction; Talus.*

SOIL EROSION—*See pr Vol. VI*

SOIL MECHANICS—*See pr Vol. VI*

SOLIFLUCTION

This term was first used by the Swede J. G. Anderson in 1906 to describe naturally occurring downslope movement of soil material resulting from frost action; it is occasionally incorrectly used to describe movements where frost action is not a cause (Stamp *et al.*, 1961). The term "congelifluction" is preferred by Dylik and others, to avoid this confusion.

Distribution and Surface Characteristics. Innumerable descriptions exist in the geological literature, of solifluction observed in tundra and colder regions throughout the world; solifluction is largely absent from cold, forested regions as the presence of tree roots substantially stabilizes the soil.

Solifluction may appear as small ripples in a bryophyte-covered surface, as staircase-like "terracettes" or as large terraces with steep fronts 2–3 meters high, and in a wide variety of somewhat similar forms (Fig. 1). Movement can often be confirmed by the presence of buried vegetation remains. Sometimes the phenomenon occurs with little surface indication. Some forms are restricted to geographical regions of particular climatic, pedological or topographic conditions. Different forms may occur in near proximity, however, as a result of variations in near surface conditions. Many hundreds of square meters of a slope may be uniformly subjected to solifluction. Conversely, some form of solifluction is usually found within a few square kilometers of any tundra or colder

FIG. 1. Solifluction terrace at Dovrefjell, Norway. (Photo: P. J. Williams).

FIG. 2. Solifluction terraces at Trollheimen, Norway. (Photo: P. J. Williams).

region with sufficient soil cover. Solifluction influences the composition of the vegetation cover, but there is an absence of vegetation generally only in the case of especially rapid or sudden movements.

Rates of Movement. Movement varies greatly according to the type of solifluction. Repeated measurements of stakes or painted boulders have shown surface movements of a few mm to 5–15 cm/yr; the latter may occur where the slope is only 10–20° and possibly less (see references in Rapp, 1960). Landslide or mudflow features resulting from freeze-thaw processes give rise to sporadic and localized movements which are far larger; such features however are sometimes not considered as solifluction.

Movements may be confined to a few cm depth. Experimental investigations have also shown movements to approximately 75-cm depth, the rate of movement increasing towards the surface. Indirect evidence suggests movements to greater depth in certain features. The depth reached by annual freezing and thawing is a limiting factor, reducing maximum depth of movement in the coldest regions. In middle latitude, continental regions, with cold winters and relatively deep frost penetration, thawing from below with consequent possibility of drainage downward, apparently prevents the phenomenon from occurring (see below).

Causes of Solifluction Movements. Little research

has been carried out on the deformation processes by which the soil displacement occurs. Frost-heaving soils (which have an excess of water, in the form of discrete ice lenses when frozen) occur in most solifluction features. On thawing, such soils may settle with a resultant downslope displacement. Areas of coarse, sandy or gravelly soils (which are not susceptible to frost heaving) show relatively little solifluction, and this is restricted to a few types occurring under particular, local conditions.

During the spring thaw, the disturbed, oversaturated, and weakened state of the soil (especially if frost heaving has occurred), when drainage is hindered by an underlying still-frozen layer (not necessarily permafrost), is also an important cause.

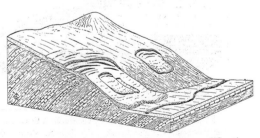

FIG. 3. Block diagram illustrating solifluction-generated earth flow and terracette formation (jointly prepared by Q. Zaruba and R. Kettner).

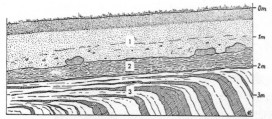

FIG. 4. Old solifluction structures underlying a loess cover (1) which indicates that it is older than the corresponding cold stage of the Pleistocene when the loess was laid down. Example at Šafranka, near Prague (Q. Zaruba). The slumped material (2) consists largely of Cretaceous clays with blocks of sandstone. The underlying Ordovician shales (3) are affected by creep deformation.

Solifluction occurs frequently in association with late-lying snow accumulations where large amounts of meltwater enter the soil. Most solifluction is a form of flowage, without development of well-defined slip surfaces.

Recent laboratory studies on creep of frozen ground suggest that some movement in natural slopes may take place in the frozen state. This may occur, in permafrost regions, at a greater depth than that affected by annual freezing and thawing.

Fossil Solifluction Deposits. In present-day temperate regions, sedimentary deposits resembling tills are found, which are believed to have been subject to solifluction during the colder climates of the ice ages (see Flint, 1957, and references). These are called flow earth, head, solifluction mantle and cryoturbation deposits, and are often widespread up to 200 miles beyond the limits reached by the former glacier ice cover. In mountainous areas they are found all the way to the equator and as much as 2000 meters below the limits of present activity.

Significance of Solifluction. Solifluction prevents the development of typical soil profiles. It may cause accumulations of boulders, stones, and par-

ticular particle sizes. It affects the conditions for plant growth. Highways, railroads and other engineering constructions may be damaged by the soil movements. These movements are not always predictable by conventional engineering analysis of slope stability.

Geomorphologically, solifluction is a potent agent of mass movement, more effective than those generally operating in temperate regions. When occurring uniformly over large areas, it is believed to produce characteristic, smooth slopes.

P. J. WILLIAMS

References

Charlesworth, J. K., 1957, "The Quaternary Era," pp. 566–569, London, Arnold.

Dziewanski, J., and Starkel, L., 1963, "Relationship between fluvial and solifluction accumulation as a criterion for dating of Quaternary terraces in the Carpathians," *Rept. VI INQUA (Int. Congr. Quaternary, Warsaw, 1961)*, **3**, 89–94.

Flint, R. F., 1957, "Glacial and Pleistocene Geology," pp. 197–199, New York, John Wiley & Sons.

Rapp, A., 1960, "Recent development of mountain slopes in Kärkevagge and surroundings, northern Scandinavia," *Geogr. Ann.* **42**, Nos. 2–3, 179–183.

Rathjens, C., 1965, "Ein Beitrag zur Frage der Solifluctionsgrenze in den Gebirgen Vorderasiens," *Zeitschr. f. Geomorph.*, **9**, 35–49.

Stamp, L. D., 1961, "A Glossary of Geographical Terms," London, Longmans, 539pp.

Troll, C., 1947, "Die Formen der Solifluktion und die periglaziale Bodenabtragung," *Erdkunde*, **1**, 162–175.

Williams, P. J., 1957, "Some investigations into solifluction features in Norway," *Geogr. J.*, **123**, 42–58.

No single book or large work exists summarizing knowledge of the subject but other valuable sources of reference are:

Biuletyn Preyglacjalny, Lodz, Poland (periodical devoted to periglacial research).

Cross-references: *Cryopedology, Cryonivation*, etc.; *Frost Action*; *Landslides*; *Mass Movement*; *Permafrost*; *Slopes*; *Soil Creep*; *Terraces, Fluvial—Environmental Control*; *Terracettes.* Vol. VI: *Quickclay*; *Snowline*.

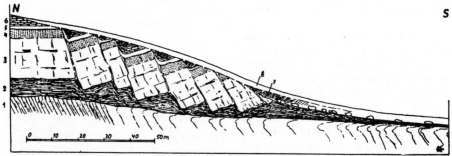

FIG. 5. Landslips caused by solifluction during cold stages of the Pleistocene: sketch of an example near Prague, Czechoslovakia (Q. Zaruba, sketched by R. Kettner). 1. Weathered Ordovician shales, with distinct creep near the surface; 2. Perucer Clays of the Cretaceous (Cenomanian); 3. Kaolinic sandstones (Cenomanian); 4. Glauconitic sandstones (Cenomanian); 5. Semicer Clays (Upper Cretaceous); 6. Weisser Berg-Pläner Limestones (Upper Cretaceous); 7. Older Loess; 8. Younger Loess.

SOLUSPHERE—*See pr Vol. VI*

SOLUTION PITS AND PANS

Solution pits and pans are small-scale, surface weathering features found in many parts of the world and in most climatic belts in such diverse rock types as granite, basalt, limestone and quartzitic sandstone. The pits are small pockmarks, from a few millimeters to some centimeters in diameter and depth; the pans develop from pits by lateral extension in all directions but for the most part maintain a perfectly flat floor. The larger pans (50 cm to 2 meters diameter) usually have undercut rims, reaching a few centimeters under the lip of the pan. The floor of each pan is usually indurated and smooth, while the undercut is hackly in texture and shows every sign of chemical etching. Joint planes are further etched out, showing the solvent effects also of overflow waters.

The pits and pans are thus evidently related to solution in standing water. The edges of the pans are often blackened by a layer of dead algae, and little rolls of algal mats may sometimes be seen on the floor. When water-filled, the pan may appear green and thin sections of the walls disclose a penetration by the algae to depths of 1–2 mm.

It should be stressed that these pits and pans are not in any way related to the alveolar weathering or *tafoni* (q.v.) that commonly affects granites and certain sandstones; this honeycomb structure involves vertical or overhanging surfaces, not the horizontal areas. Salt crystallization and fretting, acting jointly with chemical induration, are the principal agencies in tafoni, while biochemical solution (also accompanied by induration) seems to be the essential agency in pan development.

What makes the precise nature of pan solution rather puzzling is the astonishing range of environments where pans are observed. Matthes (1930, p. 64) described them as *"weather pits"* affecting granitic rocks high in the Sierra Nevada, and thus had to present careful arguments to show that they had nothing to do with glaciation; indeed they pockmark the older glaciated surfaces in places. Matthes (1930) remarks:

"The development of cavities of this type is promoted as a rule by the presence in the rock of local aggregates of readily soluble minerals. A small initial hollow having been formed by the decomposition of such an aggregate of minerals, it becomes a receptacle for water from rains or melting snow and is enlarged gradually by both chemical and mechanical processes. Acids produced by decomposing pine needles, lichens, or other vegetal matter attack the weaker minerals, and in freezing weather the ice, expanding with force as it crystallizes, pries off flakes and grains of rock from the walls. Thus weather pits may expand from an initial diameter of about an inch to diameters of 2 or 3 feet, and those situated close together may eventually coalesce as their

Fig. 1. Solution pan in the slightly calcareous, quartz sandstone of Permian age at Canyon de Chelly, Arizona. Note blackened rim from dead algae and little rolls of organic mat in the middle. (Photo: Rhodes W. Fairbridge)

FIG. 2. Similar solution pan at Canyon de Chelly. Note the bedding of the sandstone is but little affected by the solution of the pan. (Photo: Rhodes W. Fairbridge)

rims intersect. Their growth in depth, on the other hand, seldom keeps pace with their lateral expansion, for the less-soluble particles of rock detached from the rims collect at the bottom and, although the finer particles are blown out by the wind in dry weather, usually enough of the coarser ones remain to form a protective pad that tends to retard downward excavation.

"It is a significant fact that weather pits do not occur on freshly glaciated rock surfaces. Not a single one is to be found within the area that was covered by the later glaciers. Evidently they develop at an extremely slow rate, and not enough time even for their initiation has elapsed since the glacial epoch. On the other hand, weather pits do occur on rock surfaces that were over-ridden by the earlier glaciers, as well as on such surfaces as have remained wholly unglaciated, these two kinds being indistinguishable, so far as effects of weathering are concerned. Particularly fine examples of weather pits that have developed since the passage of the earlier ice are to be seen on the summit of North Dome; examples of weather pits that have developed in un-glaciated localities are to be seen on the summits of Sentinel Dome and Illilouette Ridge.

"The presence of weather pits on Glacier Point thus clearly affords no proof of the glaciation of that prom-ontory but attests its long exposure to the weather since it was glaciated."

The writer first noticed solution pans in the Pre-cambrian granite gneiss of Australia (near Southern Cross), as remarkable a contrast from the Sierra Nevada as one might wish. Later they were found on the south coast of Western Australia, subject to salt spray filling. Referring to the Bohemian granites of Czechoslovakia, Demek (1964a and b) mentions

FIG. 3. Deep etching of an intertidal limestone surface (a quartz-rich calcarenite) with spray-filled pools. Note etching along joint planes and overflow channel. Site: on coast south of Geraldton, Western Australia. (Photo: Rhodes W. Fairbridge)

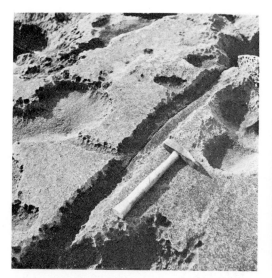

FIG. 4. Detail of etched surfaces, as illustrated in Fig. 3. Note semicircular "eating" of walls, yet relatively smooth surfaces of pit and channel floors. (Photo: Rhodes W. Fairbridge)

FIG. 5. Solution pool in a mid-Holocene beach rock, filled with seawater; note very sharply bounded "scallops." Site: Murchison River, Western Australia. (Photo: Rhodes W. Fairbridge)

dew holes, rock niches and *pseudo-lapiés,* in addition to honeycomb erosion and weather pits. In central Australia, deep natural water cisterns (wider at the bottom than at the neck) develop in the granite gneiss that are known as *gnamma holes* (Jutson, 1934). They play an important role in the survival economy of the aboriginal australoids on "walkabout." Their origin is related to the evolution of solution pits, and additional deepening has been aided by ablation of fine insoluble debris. Gnamma holes have also been reported in quartzites (Driscoll, 1964). In Brazil they are found under almost analogous conditions in granite gneiss, and known there as *oriçangas.*

We illustrate here examples of pits and pans observed in a quartz sandstone at Canyon de Chelly, Arizona (Figs. 1 and 2). The solubility of silica in groundwater is normally very low, except when the pH is above 9. Most igneous rocks, however, are most soluble in acid waters (pH 2–5). Birot (1964) has recently noted some experiments in this field. *Pseudo-karst caves* with *siliceous stalactites* have even been reported, from the Sahara, by Renault (1953). The walls and slopes of Ayers Rock, a gigantic monolithic inselberg of quartzite in central Australia, are fluted and channeled by solution (as well as locally affected by tafoni), and it is evident that running water may have the necessary solvent power; no evidence of such extreme, high pH levels is found in rainwater (Carroll, 1962). High alkalinity is obtained by evaporation of water already charged by salts obtained by solution under acid conditions. The role of so-called humic acids was discussed many years ago (Senft, 1871; Julien, 1880), but little

attention has been given to them. Bremer (1965) has suggested that much of this corrosion is left over from times of tropical climate (Tertiary or interglacial).

The solution pits and pans in limestone are found mostly at the coast, in the spray zone, and were described from La Jolla, California by Emery (1946), where the rock is a somewhat calcareous sandstone. Examples in coral limestones were

FIG. 6. Jagged surface of spray-etched beachrock (as in Fig. 5) interrupted by flat-floored pans. (Photo: Rhodes W. Fairbridge)

described from Bikini by Revelle and Emery (1957), and the general problem of intertidal calcareous erosion has been discussed by Revelle and Fairbridge (1957). Both Emery and the writer carried out numerous pH studies and other tests to determine the chemical processes operative in these pools. It was established that marked diurnal oscillations of pH did indeed occur, extremes ranging from 6.5–10. With atmospheric cooling and production of CO_2 (respiration and bacterial activity) in the pools at night, the pH drops, while in daylight algal photosynthesis, warming and evaporation all tend to raise the pH. Thus the oscillation of alternately "acid" and "alkaline" conditions first favors etching and then induration through every 24-hour period (Figs. 3–6). Slow complexing of the bicarbonate ion plays an important role.

It is curious that the process is operative in both sea-water in one region and rainwater in another, and, furthermore, over such a wide range of lithology. A chemical explanation appropriate only to $CaCO_3$ is thus certainly inadequate, and it would seem that there is room for further interesting studies of these phenomena.

RHODES W. FAIRBRIDGE

References

Birot, P., 1964, "Expériences sur la désagrégation des roches en mileu acidi et oxydant," *Z. Geomorphol., Suppl.*, **5**, 28–29.

Bremer, H., 1965, "Ayers Rock ein Beispiel für klimagenetische Morphologie," *Z. Geomorphol.*, **9**(3), 249–284.

Carroll, D., 1962, "Rainwater as a chemical agent of geologic processes—a review," *U.S. Geol. Surv. Water Supply Paper* **1535-B**, 18pp.

Demek, J., 1964a, "Slope development in granite areas of Bohemian Massif," *Z. Geomorphol., Suppl.*, **5**, 82–106.

Demek, J., 1964b, "Castle koppies and tors in the Bohemian Highland (Czechoslovakia)," *Biul. Peryglac.*, **14**, 195–216.

Driscoll, E. M., 1964, "Landforms in the Northern Territory of Australia," in (Steel, R. W., and Prothero, R. M., editors) "Geographers and the Tropics: Liverpool Essays," pp. 57–80, London, Longmans, Green & Co.

Emergy, K. O., 1946, "Marine solution basins," *J. Geol.*, **54**, 209–228.

Gavrilović, D., 1968, "Kamenice im magmatischen Gestein Jugoslawiens," *Zeit. Geomorph.*, **12**, 43–59.

Julien, A. A., 1880, "On the geological action of the humus acids," *Proc. Am. Assoc.*, **28**, 311–410.

Jutson, J. T., 1934, "The physiography (Geomorphology) of Western Australia," *Bull. Western Australia Geol. Surv.*, **95**, 366pp.

Matthes, F. E., 1930, "Geologic History of Yosemite Valley," *U.S. Geol. Surv. Profess. Paper* **160**, 1–119.

Renault, P., 1953, "Caractères généraux des grottes gréseuses du Sahara méridional," *1st Congrès Inter. Spéléologie, Paris*, 275–289.

Revelle, R., and Emergy, K. O., 1957, "Chemical erosion of beach rock and exposed reef rock," *U.S. Geol. Surv. Profess. Papers*, **260-T**, 699–709.

Revelle, R., and Fairbridge, R. W., 1957, "Carbonates and carbon dioxide," in "Treatise on marine ecology and paleoecology," *Geol. Soc. Am. Mem. 67*, **1**, 239–296.

Senft, F., 1871, "Vorläufige Mittheilungen über die Humussubstanzen und ihr Verhalten zu den Mineralien," *Z. Deut. Geol. Ges.*, **23**, 665–669; also 1874, **26**, 954–955.

Cross-references: *Biological Erosion*; *Corrosion*; *Granite Landforms*; *Lapiés*; *Limestone Coastal Weathering*; *Salt Weathering*; *Tafoni*.

SOLUTION (WEATHERING)—*See* KARST; GRANITE LANDFORMS; LIMESTONE COASTAL WEATHERING: SPHEROIDAL WEATHERING

SPELEOLOGY

(1) General Background

Speleology is an interdisciplinary field which pertains to knowledge of caves. Speleogenesis is the formation of caves. Topics generally included under the heading of speleology include cave discovery, exploration and surveying; the biology of cave life (mainly taxonomy and ecology); vertebrate paleontology and prehistory of those finds which occur in caves; and, of course, the geological relations of caves themselves. Of these, cave geology is the least well-developed as a science.

Most research on caves is conducted by amateurs and semiprofessionals, and the results are published in a large number of specialty journals. In the United States, the journal is the *Bulletin of the National Speleological Society* (Arlington, Va.). Some of the principal foreign journals include the *International Journal of Speleology* (Germany), *Studies in Speleology* (England), *Annales de Spéléologie* (France), *Rassegna Speleologia Italiana* (Italy), *Die Höhle* (Austria), and *Československy Kras* (Czechoslovakia). The speleological membership organization in the United States is The National Speleological Society. In addition, the Cave Research Foundation (Yellow Springs, Ohio), the Cave Research Associates (Berkeley, California) and the Institute of Speleology (University of Kentucky) support fundamental research in the cave-related sciences.

(2) Caves and Their Distribution

Caves, being natural voids beneath the earth's surface, are more difficult to define than externally measured objects. Normally only those openings accessible by human beings are considered caves, although it is obvious that when reconstructing a limestone drainage net or studying the migration of a microfauna, much smaller openings and tunnels must be considered.

Cave	Location	Length	
		Miles	*Kilometers*
Hölloch Cave	Muotatal, Switzerland	48.7	78.0
Mammoth Cave	Kentucky, USA	44.5	71.2
Flint Ridge Cave System	Kentucky, USA	40.5	64.8
Eisriesenwelt Cave	Salzburg, Austria	26.3	42.0
Greenbrier Caverns	West Virginia, USA	15.2	24.3
Domica Cave	Hungary and Yugoslavia	13.7	22.0
Jewel Cave	South Dakota, USA	13.1	21.0
Anvil Cave	Alabama, USA	12.0	19.2
Dent de Crolles System	Isere, France	11.2	18.0
Tantalhöhle	Salzburg, Austria	10.0	16.0
Postojnska Cave	Yugoslavia	9.4	15.0
Agen Allwedd Cave	South Wales, United Kingdom	9.0	14.4
Demänova Cave	Czechoslovakia	8.7	14.0
Dachstein Mammuthöhle	Austria	8.7	14.0
Sullivan Cave	Indiana, USA	8.5	13.6
Carroll Cave	Missouri, USA	8.3	13.3
d'En Gorner Cave	France	8.2	13.2
Powell's Cave	Texas, USA	8.2	13.2
Cueva Palomera	Burgos Province, Spain	7.5	12.0
Carlsbad Caverns	New Mexico, USA	7.4	11.8

Genetically, caves may be classified into *solution caves*, opened by underground water; *sea caves* cut by wave action; *glacial caves* opened by meltwater; *ice caves*, those in which dripping water freezes to form icicles like stalactites and ice-covered lakes; *eolian caves* scoured by wind action, found generally in deserts or in regions of thick loess deposits; *talus caves*, crevices between unconsolidated blocks; and *tectonic caves*, opened by earth movements. Of these, only the solution caves occurring in limestone or, more rarely, in dolomite or gypsum, are generally large enough to deserve special study (cf. also *Tafoni*).

Caves occur wherever soluble rocks are exposed at the surface. They are found in high alpine regions, particularly the Austrian and French Alps, the Pyrenees, and the Caucasus. They occur in regions of intermediate and low relief, in the tropics and in the Arctic. Caves tend to be larger in temperate and tropic climates, but the longest cave in the world occurs in an alpine environment. Table 1 gives a list of 16 of the longest caves known.

In the United States, extensive cavern development occurs in localized areas (Fig. 1). By far, the most extensive is the Appalachian region. In the folded Appalachians, caves are relatively small; they often have simple patterns and have a tendency to be oriented along the strike of the folded Ordovician and Devonian rocks. Many typical descriptions are found in Davies (1958). In the Appalachian Plateaus which extend westward into Kentucky and Tennessee are some of the largest caves known. These tend to be complex arrange-ments of tubular passages developed in nearly flat-lying Mississippian rocks. The Dougherty Plain of Georgia and the Ocala region of Florida contain many small caves in Oligocene and Eocene limestones. These are usually of irregular pattern and many have been reflooded by post-Pleistocene sea-level rise. The Driftless Area of Wisconsin includes numerous small caves, many of which have been mineralized with lead and zinc deposits. In the Interior Province, most caves occur near the valley of the Mississippi River. They tend to be small with simple patterns. The Ozark Dome of Missouri and Arkansas is one of the principal cave areas of the United States: 1100 caves are known in Missouri alone. The caves are often very large and tend to have tubular patterns. Many have sizable underground streams (Bretz, 1956). The caves are formed mainly in the flat-lying rocks of Ordovician and Mississippian age. The Edwards Plateau of Texas and the Pecos Lowlands of New Mexico are the best examples of semi-arid karst. Caves of the Edwards Plateau are very numerous, generally small, and located mostly in the Balcones Fault Zone. The Cretaceous Edwards limestone is one of the most important limestone aquifers, carrying water from a recharge area to a series of large springs near San Antonio. The Pecos area has some very large caves, mainly in the Permian Capitan limestone. Although now in an arid climate, the caves are often profusely decorated with dripstone deposits suggesting a record of an earlier wet period. In the Kaibab region of northern Arizona, there are many caves in the Pennsylvanian Redwall limestone

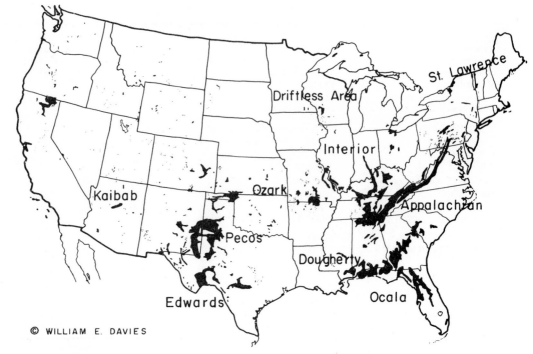

FIG. 1. Distribution of karst regions in the United States (compiled by William E. Davies and reproduced with permission of copyright owner).

and the underlying Muav formation. Many of these are active stream systems draining the Kaibab Plateau into the Grand Canyon. There are many other minor cave areas shown on the map in Fig. 1. Of greatest importance are the limestones in the Rocky Mountains of Colorado and Wyoming and in the Wasatch mountains of Utah which provide the best U.S. examples of alpine cave systems. The 1186-foot-deep Neff Canyon Cave in Utah is the deepest in the United States. In all, the Cave Files Committee of the National Speleological Society now has records of more than 11,000 caves in the United States alone.

(3) Cavern Features

In their grossest outlines, caverns are composed of passageways of basically two types; horizontal and vertical. Passages sloping at steep angles are quite uncommon except in alpine caves. Passage width and height vary from perhaps 100 feet or more to the smallest penetrable dimensions. Passage cross sections, where not modified by collapse, have tubular or rectangular shapes in many caves where well-defined flow paths can be traced; irregular cross sections occur in other caves. Cave passages are rarely observed as continuous conduits but have been modified by collapse or fill into truncated segments. Thus a cave, as observed, is only a fragment of the original drainage path and must be interpreted as such.

The vertical openings are the active recharge points of groundwater into the limestone aquifer. In areas in which the limestone is capped with impervious beds, the vertical openings appear as vertical shafts located at the edge of the caprock. The vertical shaft is a roughly cylindrical void with smooth vertical walls and heights up to several hundred feet. Its most characteristic feature is the near-perfect verticality of the walls regardless of variations in the dip of beds and joints. Other types of vertical openings exist, particularly in areas without capping beds. These tend to be irregular chimneys and are more controlled by rock structure.

Small caves, less than perhaps 2000 feet in length, can often be classified by the pattern of their ground plan. Network caves have a grid of intersecting passageways. Branchwork caves (genuine branchworks are quite rare) have a dendritic, branching pattern of increasingly smaller passages. Angulate caves consist of essentially one tube with numerous twists and turns. A subclass of the angulate caves is the linear cave, usually found in limestones of high dip, which tends to be strike oriented. For the cave pattern to have genetic significance, it is necessary that the pattern represent only one drainage line. In larger caves, there are usually several and perhaps many drainage lines represented, and the total cave pattern is a composite of these with the pattern varying from place to place in the same cave.

In addition to the overall pattern, caves contain a variety of solutional sculpturing which, if interpreted with some care, can help deduce the past history of the drainage system. Scallops, asymmetric cusps cut in the bedrock walls, give past flow directions and at least a rough measure of the flow velocity. Ceiling and wall pockets, spongework, and bedding- and joint-plane anastomoses are evidence of flow at lower velocities under saturated conditions. Evidence of flow of free-surface streams is obtained from incised meanders in the floor, horizontal grooves crossing the bedding in the walls, and pendants and channels in the ceilings.

(4) The Solution Process

Caves are generated by the solvent action of underground water moving in well-localized flow paths. A maturely developed limestone aquifer offers very little resistance to groundwater flow and cannot support a large hydrostatic head. The karst water table as a result is very flat with gradients of 10-30 ft/mile being quite common. There has been much discussion in the American literature of the relationship between the zone of maximum cavern development and the position of the water table. A summary of this discussion may be found in any geomorphology text book. Multicycle evolution and stream piracy are widely advocated (Woodward, 1961).

Movement of groundwater in a maturely developed karst aquifer takes place mainly by localized flow in either open channels or closed conduits. In either case, the flow is turbulent and D'Arcy's Law cannot be used to describe the flow. In D'Arcy flow the flow velocity varies linearly with the hydrostatic head. In either channel or conduit flow, the velocity and hence the discharge vary as the square root of the hydrostatic head. Open channel flow in limestone is very similar to flow of surface streams and is described by an appropriate Froude number. Closed conduit flow in limestone is analogous to flow in pipes and is described by a Reynolds number (Burdon and Papakis, 1963).

Recharge of water into the aquifer is of two types. Concentrated recharge takes place when sinking streams enter the aquifer at a localized swallow hole. Diffuse recharge is provided by the precipitation which falls on the limestone area and enters through sinkholes and fissures. Most discharge from the limestone aquifer is concentrated in big springs although some diffuse discharge probably takes place.

In regions of moderate and low relief, flow takes place at or just below the regional base level, yielding cave passages of low gradient and a nearly flat water table. Such flow usually trends from the highest available recharge point to the lowest possible discharge point and may completely ignore minor surface valleys and surface drainage divides. In regions of high relief and high recharge, the flows do not move horizontally close to base level, and cave systems of high relief are developed. In all cases, seasonal variations in the flow play an important role.

In regions of folded rocks, artesian conditions often obtain. Cave development follows the artesian flow lines. Under these conditions, cavern development may take place considerably below the regional base level. The complex caves of the Black Hills of South Dakota may be examples of this type.

An exact understanding of the rate of limestone solution and thus of the rate of cavern development and the age of caves is still very much lacking. Weyl (1958) found that the rate of solution by laminar flow was controlled by the diffusion of ions across the laminar streamlines. The rate of solution is faster in turbulent flow and increases as the velocity increases. It may be that diffusion of ions across the laminar sublayer is the rate-controlling factor. It is certain, both from laboratory experiments and from measured discharge of dissolved material from limestone springs, that the solution of limestone is quite rapid and that the active development of a cavern passage is a very rapid process of any geological time scale.

WILLIAM B. WHITE

References

Baker, G., and Frostick, A. C., 1947, "Pisoliths and ooliths from some Australian Caves and Mines," *J. Sed. Petrol.*, **17**, 39–67.

Bretz, J H., 1956, "Caves of Missouri," *Missouri Dept. Business Admin. Div. Geol. Surv. Water Resources*, **39**, 490pp.

Burdon, D. J., and Papakis, N., 1963, "Handbook of Karst Hydrogeology," U.N. Food and Agricultural Organization, Institute for Geology and Subsurface Research, Athens, Greece.

Chico, R. J., 1964, "Detection of caves by gravimetry," *Internat. J. Speleology*, **1**, 101–108.

Cullingford, C. H. D., 1962, "British Caving," Second ed., London, Routledge and Kegan-Paul.

Davies, W. E., 1958, "Caverns of West Virginia," *West Va. Geol. Econ. Surv.*, **19A**, 330pp.

Hess, F. L., 1929, "Oolites or cave pearls in the Carlsbad Caverns," *Proc. U.S. National Museum*, **76**, Art. 16, 1–8.

Trombe, F., 1952, "Traité de Spéléologie," Paris, Payot, 376pp.

Weyl, P. K., 1958, "The solution kinetics of calcite," *J. Geol.*, **66**, 163–176.

Woodward, H. P., 1961, "A stream piracy theory of cave formation," *Bull. Natl. Speleol. Soc.*, **23**, 39–58.

Cross-references: *Dolina; Driftless Area; Incised Meanders; Karst; Limestone Caves; Limestone Coastal Weathering; Polje; Sink, Sink-hole, Swallow Hole; Speleothems; Tafoni; Thermokarst.* Vol. II: *Reynolds, Froude and Other Dimensionless Numbers.* Vol. VI: *Groundwater; Porosity and Permeability.*

SPELEOTHEMS

Crystalline deposits that develop in a limestone cave after the formation of the cave itself are called *speleothems*. The most common of these are *stalactites*, which hang downward from the ceiling, and *stalagmites*, which grow upward from the floor. Most speleothems are composed of the mineral calcite ($CaCO_3$), the same mineral that makes up the limestone wallrock of the cave. They are formed by a loss of carbon dioxide from the dripping water rather than by evaporation of the water itself—a process that cannot take place because of the 100% relative humidity in most caves. Surface water seeping into the soil acquires a high carbon dioxide content from decaying humus (Fig. 1). This carbonated water moves down through the limestone, reacts with it, and dissolves some of it. When the water reaches the ceiling of a well-ventilated cave, it encounters cave air that contains very little carbon dioxide. The air therefore takes some of the carbon dioxide out of the water, which consequently becomes less capable of holding calcite in solution; in other words, it becomes supersaturated with calcite, some of which is deposited according to the following reaction:

$$Ca^{+2} + 2HCO_3^{-1} \rightarrow CO_2 \uparrow + CaCO_3 + H_2O$$

| calcium bicarbonate solution | carbon dioxide | calcite | water |

A tiny ring of calcite forms on the ceiling (Fig. 2). In time, the ring grows downward into a tubular stalactite, which in turn may become the core of a huge conical stalactite like those that decorate so many limestone caves.

The rate of growth of stalactites depends upon the rate of flow of the water and its degree of supersaturation with respect to calcite. It is always variable, and at certain times of the year some stalactites stop growing entirely and are partly dis-

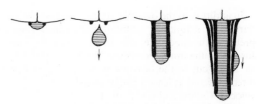

FIG. 2. A stalactite begins growing as a small ring of calcite where the surface of a water drop intersects the ceiling of a cave. This ring grows into a tube, which often acquires a tapering shape when water flows down its outer surface.

solved away by water that is undersaturated because of seasonal variations in the flow rate, the limestone-dissolving rate, and the carbon dioxide content of the water and cave air. However, repeated micrometer measurements of many tubular stalactites indicates that their net rate of elongation averages about 0.2 mm/yr.

After the water has left a stalactite, *stalagmites* form where it drips on the floor and *flowstone* where it runs down the wall. Small unattached spheres of calcite, known as *cave pearls*, are also occasionally formed in small basins of water. All these deposits build outward as parallel layers in which the individual calcite crystals are perpendicular to the surfaces of deposition.

Water seeping from cracks in the walls of caves may form still other speleothems, some of which are curiously shaped. Among the more common of these are the spirally curved objects known as *helictites*, the petal-like structures called *cave flowers*, and the nodular encrustations known as *cave coral*. Most of these deposits are as hard as stalactites, but one kind, *moonmilk*, is soft and resembles white clay. When moonmilk is dissolved in a weak acid, a slime of bacteria and other microorganisms remains behind, and these have evidently played a part in the deposition of this curious substance.

About 70 mineral species are known to form speleothems in caves. Some of these, in addition to the dominant mineral calcite, are gypsum ($CaSO_4 \cdot 2H_2O$), ice (H_2O), aragonite ($CaCO_3$), dolomite [$CaMg(CO_3)_2$], carbonate-apatite [$Ca_{10}(PO_4)_6CO_3 \cdot H_2O$], goethite ($HFeO_2$), and birnessite [$(Ca, Mg, K)Mn_7O_{14} \cdot 2H_2O$]. As most of these minerals grow very slowly at low temperatures, their actual mode of formation cannot often be observed under ordinary laboratory conditions, but all stages of their growth can be observed in caves, where their environment has remained almost stable for thousands of years.

GEORGE W. MOORE

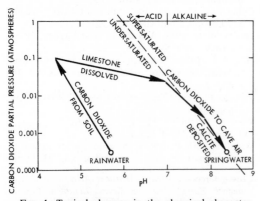

FIG. 1. Typical changes in the chemical characteristics of rainwater as it moves through the soil, through the limestone, into a cave, and finally back to the surface from a limestone spring.

References

Moore, G. W., and Nicholas, G., 1964, "Speleology," Boston, D. C. Heath and Co., 120 pp.

Warwick, G. T., 1962, "Cave formations and deposits," in (Cullingford, C. H. D., editor) "British Caving, an Introduction to Speleology," Second ed., pp. 83–119, London, Routledge and Kegan Paul Ltd.

Cross-references: *Limestone Caves; Speleology; Stalactite and Stalagmite.* Vol. IV: Individual Mineral Articles.

SPHEROIDAL WEATHERING

A characteristic weathering form in massive rocks, granite, dolerite, basalt, and even some sedimentary types such as silicified sandstones, results in the production of *spheroidal boulders* of unweathered rock, around which are to be observed layers or flakes of disintegrated material. The process is closely related to that of *exfoliation* (q.v.), except that the latter refers usually to large-scale sheeting on the scale of a hill, or whole igneous dome, while "spheroidal weathering" is restricted to boulder-sized phenomena. Concentric layering or spalling is often called *onion-weathering*, but this is not always present.

The difference between spheroidal weathering and exfoliation is more than just a matter of scale. The large sheets of massive exfoliating rocks are primarily related to *mechanical joints*, and stress release is therefore the basic criterion of exfoliation (the theory of G. K. Gilbert). Fine flaking in spheroidal weathering is associated with onion-skin peeling and is demonstrably marked by *chemical*

alteration (Figs. 1–3) as pointed out also in the last century by Merrill and Dana (see review by Blackwelder, 1925); it is a characteristic feature of *saprolite* (see *Regolith and Saprolite*). Spheroidal weathering is sometimes identified as "non-hypogene exfoliation" to distinguish it from the sheeting related primarily to deep-seated joints (Barton, 1938).

What many observers have failed to appreciate in the past is that the landscape of today is largely inherited or even exhumed, and that in many of the cool humid regions of today, there were subtropical humid climates during the late Tertiary. Thus deep chemical weathering established a massive saprolite, leaving "*corestones*" of relatively unweathered rock. These were liberated by mechanical slope wash and fluvial stripping during the semiarid periods of the Quaternary cold stages (both by periglacial solifluction as well as by strictly desertic processes). Spheroidally weathered boulders and *tors* (q.v.) thus remain today largely as witnesses of a long polycyclic weathering history under extreme oscillations of climate (Fig. 2). *Bornhardts* (q.v.) and *inselbergs* (q.v.) are large-scale examples of this and related problems (see, for example, *Etchplain*).

The parent rock is necessarily jointed; those with well-spaced joints (say 1–10 meters) produce large boulders, as seen strikingly in the granite "kopjes" of South Africa, while closely spaced joints, as in basalt, lead to "cannon-ball" boulders. Systematic large-scale weathering leads to "tors" (see *Granite Landforms*).

Fig. 1. Spheroidal weathering of granite (at Palmer, South Australia). Note fresh corestone and crumbly disintegration layers. (Photo: C. R. Twidale).

FIG. 2. Spheroidal weathering, particularly of "onion" type, in diorite (at Tooma Dam, Snowy Mts., New South Wales). Note relative freshness of onion layers. (Photo: C. R. Twidale)

It was believed by Walther on the basis of extensive observation in Egypt, that the principal agent was thermal, solar heating and nighttime cooling. Experiments by Blackwelder (1933) tended to discount this "insolation theory." Field measurements by Gentilli (1950) showed that maximum spalling occurred on the shady side of the boulders, that side affected mainly by prevailing winds (with rain).

Barton (1938, p. 111) remarked: "If non-hypogene exfoliation can take place to a depth of 5–8 mm in a period of 2000–5000 years in Egypt as an effect of moisture, much of the disintegration and exfoliation of granite in moist temperate regions of the world is not the result of unloading of rocks but an effect of moisture, presumably hydration and incipient further alteration." Salt crystallization (see *Etched Pebbles*; *Salt Weathering*) also plays an important role in the fretting of Egyptian monuments that have lain for some time on the water-saturated flood plain (Knetch, 1960; Winkler, 1965). Mineral studies by Chapman and Greenfield (1949) showed that the spalled rock fragments were rich in secondary minerals such as kaolinite, sericite, serpentine, montmorillonite and chlorite; there was thus no doubt that chemical weathering

FIG. 3. Onion-skin weathering in diorite, Tooma Dam, Snowy Mountains, N.S.W., Australia. There is a deep saprolite, in which the chemical weathering seems to be guided in part by flowage planes in the diorite. Near the surface, the fine-grained weather material has been differentially removed. (Photo: C. R. Twidale)

FIG. 4. Spheroidal weathering of granite boulders in the American southwest, where the present climate is semi-arid. The boulders were probably liberated by chemical weathering in the late-Tertiary subtropical humid regime. (Photo: R. W. Fairbridge)

(the hydration and oxidation of silicate minerals) played an important role.

Petrographic and X-ray studies by Simpson (1964) on the weathering flakes of the Upper Pocahontas Sandstone in West Virginia showed that the swelling was due to the formation and expansion of dioctahedral vermiculite.

Active saprolitic profiles marked by spheroidal weathering today, usually in the humid tropics but sometimes in humid temperate regions, are often stripped of vegetation (by man or by landslides) and then disclose chemical geomorphic solution forms, such as *solution pits and pans* (q.v.), fluting and "pseudokarren" (see, for example, Hsi-Lin Tschang, 1961).

Consideration of many different rock types and climatic conditions suggests that the causes are multiple and progressive: (a) geodynamic stress release in igneous masses favors jointing, which permits penetration of groundwater; (b) thermal expansion and contraction favor omnidirectional scaling; (c) chemical erosion leads to increased expansion and eventual disintegration.

RHODES W. FAIRBRIDGE

References

Barton, D. C., 1938, "Discussion: The disintegration and exfoliation of granite in Egypt," *J. Geol.*, **46,** 109–111.

Blackwelder, E., 1925, "Exfoliation as a phase of rock weathering," *J. Geol.*, **33,** 793–806.

Blackwelder, E., 1933, "The insolation theory of rock weathering," *Am. J. Sci.*, *Ser. 5*, **26,** 97–113.

Chapman, R. W., and Greenfield, M. A., 1949, "Spheroidal weathering of igneous rocks," *Am. J. Sci.*, **247,** 407–427.

Gentilli, J., 1950, "Rainfall as a factor in the weathering of granite," *C. R. Congr. Int. Géographie* (*Lisbonne, 1949*), **2,** 263–269.

Knetsch, G., 1960, "Arid weathering with special refer-

FIG. 5. Solution microrelief and spheroidal weathering, picking out joint planes and bedding surfaces of Carboniferous sandstone, in region of seasonal precipitation. Grampian Mountains, Victoria (Australia).

FIG. 6. Spheroidal weathering in a Tertiary dolerite dike, intrusive into Triassic sandstones, Isle of Arran, Scotland. (Photo: Geological Survey, Great Britain)

ence to both natural and artificial walls in Egypt," *Z. Geomorphol., Suppl.*, **1**, 190–205.

Simpson, D. R., 1964, "Exfoliation in the Upper Pocahontas Sandstone, Mercer County, West Virginia," *Am. J. Sci.*, **262**, 545–551.

Tschang, Hsi-Lin, 1961, "The pseudokarren and exfoliation forms of granite on Pulau Ubin, Singapore," *Z. Geomorphol.*, **5**, 302–312.

Walther, J., 1924, "Das Gesetz der Wüstenbildung in Gegenwart und Vorzeit," Fourth ed., Leipzig, Verlag Quelle & Meyer, 421pp.

Winkler, E. M., 1965, "Weathering rates as exemplified by Cleopatra's Needle in New York City," *J. Geol. Educ.*, **13**(2), 50–52.

Cross-references: *Bornhardt*; *Etched Pebbles*; *Etchplain*; *Exfoliation*; *Exhumed Landscape*; *Granite Landforms*; *Inselberg*; *Quaternary*; *Regolith and Saprolite*; *Salt Weathering*; *Solution Pits and Pans*; *Tor*. Vol. IV: *Hypogene*.

SPILLWAYS—*See* GLACIAL SPILLWAYS AND PROGLACIAL LAKES

SPITS—*See* BARRIERS; BARS

SPONGE REEFS—*See* pr Vol. VII

SPRINGS—*See* pr Vol. VI

STABILITY OF COASTS—*See* COASTAL STABILITY

STACK

This is an isolated pinnacle of rock, standing up in the sea, generally from a platform of marine abrasion, where the cliff has retreated, leaving remnants offshore. The sides of the stacks are generally steep to vertical, evidence that the erosion has been at wave height, and not subaerial.

The term "stack" comes from *stakkur* in the Scandinavian dialect of the Faeroe Islands, where they are rather common. Typical examples are seen off most high, cliffed coasts. They are sometimes referred to as pillars, chimney rocks, columns, skerries, needles, etc. There is a classic example of three stacks in the white Cretaceous chalk at the

FIG. 1. Typical stacks in flat-lying Miocene limestones; the Twelve Apostles, Port Campbell (Victoria), Australia.

west end of the Isle of Wight (England) known as "The Needles," where the dip is nearly vertical. Stacks occur generally in sedimentary rocks, but the dips may vary from horizontal to vertical. Thornbury (1954, p. 437) illustrates an interesting example of former stacks rising above an uplifted marine terrace at Port Harford, California.

RHODES W. FAIRBRIDGE

References

Stamp, L. D., (editor), 1961, "A Glossary of Geographical Terms," London, Longmans, Green and Co., 539pp.

Steers, J. A., 1964, "The Coastline of England and Wales," Second ed., Cambridge, The University Press, 750pp.

Thornbury, W. D., 1954, "Principles of Geomorphology," New York, John Wiley & Sons, 618pp.

Cross-references: *Beach Erosion; Beachrock; Limestone Coastal Weathering; Littoral Processes; Platforms—Wave-Cut.*

STAGNANT ICE MELTING

A variety of landforms have been interpreted as evidence that ice stagnated and melted over large areas during its retreat from various parts of Europe and North America. However, only some of the more basic landforms can be discussed here; further information on variations in landforms, terminology and interpretation can be found in Hoppe (1952), Gravenor and Kupsch (1959), Stalker (1960) and Clayton (1964), as well as in the bibliography within these publications.

Basic Landforms

Among the most significant features are ridges and plateaus which vary in size, shape, locale and other characteristics. Stalker states that the ridges rarely are more than 80 feet above the surrounding country, and range from a few to several hundred feet in width. They generally are long ridges, in a few instances straight but generally curved or circular. The ridges are often associated with basins or hollows and also with roughly flat to saucer-topped plateaus.

Stalker subsumes various types of plateaus under the general name "dead-ice" plateaus and, within this term, distinguishes two sub-types, the "plains plateaus" and the "moraine plateaus" (Hoppe, 1952). He states that the plains plateaus are normally smaller and more numerous than the moraine plateaus, and also that they occur typically on relatively gentle ground moraine. The moraine plateaus, on the other hand, are said to occur typically in hummocky moraine, "and commonly in the highest parts and areas of strongest development of such moraines." They vary greatly in size, the biggest, in the areas familiar to Stalker, being about 7 miles long and covering about 12 square miles. They range downward in size to those a few hundred feet, or less, in diameter (Figs. 1 and 2). Commonly, part or all of the margins or edges of the plateaus rise above their central portions. This marginal rise forms what is called the "rim ridge."

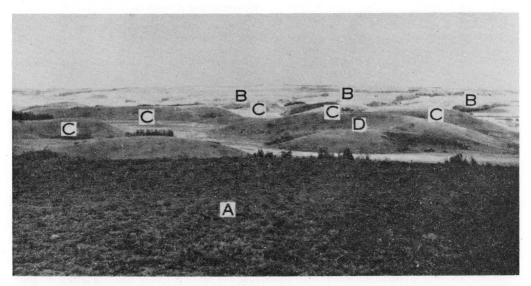

FIG. 1. Moraine plateaus. View from surface of a moraine plateau (A) across small plateaus (C) toward large, flat-topped plateau (B). Notice rim ridge encircling small plateau (D). Looking northeastward from the southwest ¼, sec. 30, tp. 35, rge. 20, W. 4th mer (Alberta, Canada, from Stalker, 1960).

FIG. 2. Plains plateau, about 15 feet high and 300 feet in diameter. Notice person standing on left slope of plateau. S.W. ¼, sec. 5, tp. 18, rge. 27, W. 4th mer (Stalker, 1960).

"From their summits, these ridges slope towards the centres of the plateaux at generally low angles (between about 5° and 15°) and disappear beneath the flat, central parts of the plateaux . . . . The water-deposited sediments of the central parts . . . generally consist of clay, silt, sand and gravel, with included lenses and thin beds of till" (Stalker, 1960, p. 7) (Fig. 3).

Some Landform Patterns

Gravenor and Kupsch prefer the term "ice disintegration" to describe "the process of breaking up of ice into numerous small blocks, which finally comes about in a stagnant and thus wasting glacier." They note that disintegration may produce a variety of landforms, depending on such factors as the amount of debris carried by the ice, the amount of meltwater and so forth. Gravenor and Kupsch also discuss patterns of features which develop over a relatively large area as a result of ice disintegration or the melting of stagnant ice. Thus:

"When the forces that operate to break up an ice-sheet are equal in all directions, the disintegration may be said to be uncontrolled, and the result is a field of round, oval, rudely hexagonal, or polygonal features, and a general lack of dominant linear elements."

On the other hand:

"Where the ice separated along fractures or other lines of weakness, the disintegration may be said to be controlled, and the result is a field of linear or lobate landforms" (Gravenor and Kupsch, 1959, p. 49) (Figs. 4 and 5).

Origin

The processes involved in the origin of stagnant ice landforms are a subject of some discussion. According to Gravenor and Kupsch:

"All studies made by the writers on ice disintegration features suggest that the features were formed late in the existence of a glacier. The features resulted from the letting-down of till due to ablation, from the squeezing-up of till into openings at the base of the ice, or from a combination of both causes" (Gravenor and Kupsch, 1959, p. 56).

Ablation

In discussing these various modes of origin, Gravenor and Kupsch go on to say:

"Although there are many indications that ablation moraine was being deposited during disintegration of an ice sheet, the hypothesis that all material of a dead-ice origin was let down from above fails to explain certain

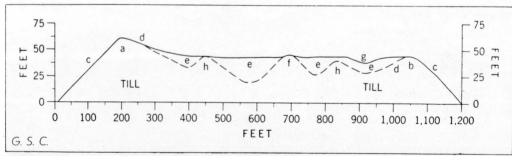

FIG. 3. General hypothetical cross section through a moraine plateau; (a) till rim ridge rising above plateau surface; (b) till rim ridge rising to plateau surface; (c) steep outward slope of rim ridge toward adjoining kettles; (d) gentle inward slope of rim ridge to beneath central sediments; (e) flat central area of water-deposited sediments; (f) till knob rising above plateau surface; (g) shallow kettle-hole; (h) buried till knobs (drawn mostly from examples seen in sec. 32, tp. 35, rge. 20, W. 4th mer Alberta; from Stalker, 1960).

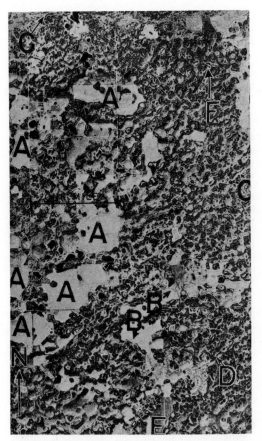

FIG. 4. High relief disintegration moraine. Location: T 46. R.12. W. 4th mer.. Alberta. (Air photograph reproduced by permission of government of Alberta, Dept. of Lands and Forests) (A) Moraine plateau. (B) Closed till disintegration ridge on Moraine plateau (rim ridge). (C) Linear till disintegration ridge, sinuous. (D) Linear ridge, beaded. (E) Moraine plateau which forms the headwater region of an ice-walled channel leading off to the south. (F) Closed till disintegration ridges, surrounding depressions (rimmed Kettles) (from Gravenor and Kupsch. 1959).

observed relationships. Ablation material is characteristically loose, non-compact, and non-fissile, and contains abundant gravel and larger stones .... In western Canada, however, many features that apparently resulted from disintegration are composed of till which may be very compact ..." (Gravenor and Kupsch, 1959, p. 58).

Although not excluding an ice-pressed origin, Clayton has observed and described ablation processes on a contemporary glacier in southeastern Alaska, and has linked these processes with dead-ice features of the northern Great Plains. Clayton studied karst-like features such as sink-holes, tunnels, caves, and residual soils or ablation till, on stagnant, drift-covered sections of the Martin Glacier. He notes that in some areas, the ablation

till was unstable and "constantly sliding down the sides of the numerous sink-holes." Such observations lead him to conclude that:

"Funnel-shaped sink-holes were also very abundant on some parts of the stagnant glaciers in the northern Great Plains ... in late Wisconsin time. Where the ablation till was thick and had a high silt and clay content, it flowed into the sink-holes and, when the glacial topography was inverted, formed ... 'circular disintegration ridges' that are common there today ..." (Clayton, 1964, p. 110).

Squeezing or Pressing

Hoppe (1952) and Stalker (1960) are proponents of the idea of origin by squeezing or ice-pressing. Hoppe visualizes the dead-ice features as forming from basal till squeezed into openings, closed to the sky, under the ice. His supporting arguments have

FIG. 5. Linear disintegration ridges. Locations: T. 48, R. 1, W. 4th mer., Alberta (Air photograph reproduced by permission of government of Alberta, Dept. of Lands and Forests). The ice movement in this area was slightly east of south, which is at right angles to the curvilinear or lobate ridges. On the eastern side of the photograph the intersecting ridges form a box pattern (from Gravenor and Kupsch, 1959).

been summarized as follows:

(1) The till does not show evidence of washing, as would be the case with super-glacial material that had fallen from the ice surface, or from the side walls into an open crevasse.

(2) The till is compact and has all the characteristics of basal till.

(3) The till contains pebbles and cobbles that show a distinct fabric, with their long axes oriented at right angles to the long dimension of the ridge. This fabric is regarded as a primary characteristic of the till, induced by the lateral pressure of the ice blocks which squeeze the till up into the crevasse (Gravenor and Kupsch, 1959, p. 59).

Combined Origin

Gravenor and Kupsch (1959, p. 61) also state that the hypotheses of ablation and squeezing are not mutually exclusive, and they hold that in the formation of many dead-ice features, both processes may have operated to varying degrees. Thus:

"Material squeezed into sub-glacial crevasses and other openings may, in addition, receive material from above during ablation. Some disintegration features appear to be composed of cores of clayey till, squeezed upward and overlain by a covering of loose materials dropped from above."

Other Origins

Finally, Gravenor and Kupsch make the important point that the features so often attributed to the melting of stagnant ice can be formed by other processes; for example, "landforms created by thawing ground ice may be very similar to those formed by melting and evaporation of dead glacier ice buried by debris." Thus, certain rimmed depressions, located in the Netherlands and previously interpreted as kettles, have been reinterpreted as pingo remnants.

Significance

The application and amplification of the ideas of Hoppe and his Scandinavian-European predecessors, by Gravenor, Kupsch, and Stalker, has resulted in the reinterpretation of the origin of morainal deposits and so of the glacial history of parts of western Canada and the United States. Such interpretations have involved difficult and perhaps somewhat tenuous distinctions between various kinds of moraines of high relief. Thus, the extent and width of morainal landforms, the overall trend of the deposit, the pattern or trend of the ridges, or other features within a morainal area have all been used to separate an end or recessional moraine thought to be representative of essentially active ice, from the hummocky moraine envisioned as forming during melt of stagnant ice. As an example, the Moose Mountain upland in southeastern Saskatchewan was interpreted as a northwest-trending end moraine. Recently, however, the area has been found devoid

of "any trends and shows no visible traces of live-ice deposition" and has been reinterpreted as due to the melt of stagnant ice.

Stalker has advanced some dramatic and challenging ideas on the significance of dead-ice concepts to the interpretation of glacial history. According to Stalker (1960, p. 33):

"The large moraines of central and southern Alberta that were thus built within stagnant ice, and generally on high ground, do not necessarily represent former margins of the ice-sheet, though they could have formed in marginal positions. They may have been constructed during halts in the down-melting, during rejuvenation and subsequent thickenings in the ice-sheet, or even during normal lowering of the ice-surface. Thus, for example, a Cary re-advance of the Wisconsin stage may be represented in these moraines by hummocky moraine at a certain elevation, rather than by a moraine marking the ice-margin of the maximum of this re-advance period. If this is so, correlation between such moraines in any broad region should not be made solely by locations of the moraines, but chiefly by altitudes. Thus, a certain sub-stage of glacier advance or retreat would be represented by moraines at a certain altitude. A moraine lying a short distance to the southwest of another on the prairies and in the direction from which the ice retreated, but at a lower altitude, may be younger than the other".

J. G. NELSON

References

Clayton, L., 1964, "Karst topography on stagnant glaciers," *J. Glaciol.*, **5**, 107–112.

Embleton, C. and King, C. A. M., 1968, "Glacial and Periglacial Geomorphology," London, E. Arnold Ltd., 608pp.

Gravenor, C., and Kupsch, W. O., 1959, "Ice-disintegration features in western Canada," *J. Geol.*, **67**, 48–64.

Hoppe, G., 1952, "Hummocky moraine regions, with special reference to the interior of Norbotton," *Geografiska Annaler*, **34**, 1–71.

Nelson, J. G., 1963, "The origin and geomorphological significance of the Morley Flats, Alberta," *Bull. Canadian Petrol. Geol.*, **11**, 169–177.

Stalker, A. MacS., 1960, "Ice-pressed drift forms and associated deposits in Alberta," *Bull. Can. Geol. Surv.*, **57**, 38pp.

Tricart, J. and Cailleux, A., 1962, "Traité de Géomorphologie, **3**, Le modélé glaciaire et nival," Paris, Soc. Ed. Sns. Sup., 508pp.

Cross-references: *Ablation Moraine*; *Glacial Geology*; *Kettle*; *Moraine*; *Outwash Plain*; *Pingo*; *Thermokarst*. Vol. VI: *Ablation*; *Glaciology*.

STALACTITE AND STALAGMITE

"Stalactite" and "stalagmite" are the familiar names of columnar concretions or chemically deposited formations found in natural caverns in "*karst*" (q.v.) country. The term "speleothem" is now widely adopted to describe all crystalline deposits in caves, including stalactites and stalagmites. European archaeologists sometimes use

FIG. 1. Delicate drape type of stalactite, "the Indian Canopy," Jenolan Caves, N.S.W., Australia (Photo: N.S.W. Government).

FIG. 2. Stalactite and stalagmite. "The Minaret," a stalagmite from Jenolan Caves, New South Wales, Australia. This highly ornamented type of cave formation is considered by Corbel (1954) to be characteristic of deposition in a warm climate. Extended cone stalactites and some straws can be seen in the background.

"stalagmite" for the deposits defined below as a synonym for "flowstone."

Occurrence

Speleothems are known in caves in calcareous rocks throughout the world. Stalactites may also grow from wetted overhangs on open cliffs faces, from cement beneath bridges and in damp cellars. Flowstone and rimstone are deposited at many springs.

Mineralogy

Speleothems are reported formed of barytes, chalcedony, gypsum, iron pyrites, limonite and rock salt. Ice faithfully reproduces many of the forms and some occur in mud. However, calcium carbonate (as calcite or aragonite) is overwhelmingly the most common and abundant compound, creating speleothems of the greatest size and variety. Calcite is the common precipitate, but aragonite (which is less stable in the cave environment) is more widespread than was formerly believed.

Calcite or aragonite is precipitated when CO_2 is lost from groundwater supersaturated with calcium bicarbonate, forming a dense, layered and concentrically banded rock "*travertine*." It is sometimes called "calc sinter." The rise in pH is critical. In a majority of cave atmospheres, relative humidity exceeds 90% so that precipitation by simple evaporation and rise of alkalinity is usually negligible. Where evaporation *is* important (at cave entrances, springs, etc.), a more or less cellular deposit known as "calc tufa" or "soft stalagmite" is formed. It has a dull appearance and is easily crumbled, in contrast to the gleaming, hard, travertine deposits of the cave interior.

The crystal habit of calcite is prismatic, rhombohedral or scalenohedral; that of aragonite, pris-

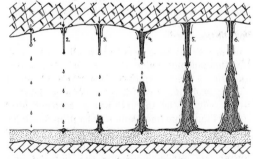

FIG. 3. Sketch showing idealized evolution of soda-straw (1), to one fed internally and externally (2), to thickening of walls (3), and rapid upgrowth of stalagmite (4), to blocking of central tube (5), eventually (6) to the complete roof-to-floor column (R. Kettner).

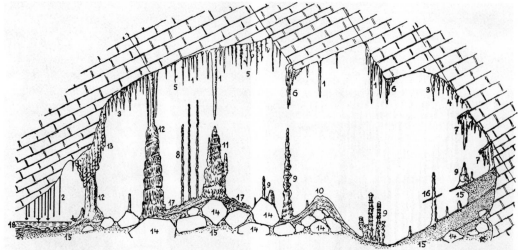

FIG. 4. Idealized polycyclic karst cave with stalactites, stalagmites and related speleothems (R. Kettner). (1) Simple stalactites; (2) soda-straws or "quills," in places reaching into water pool 18, forming travertine sinter collars; (3) radish stalactites; (4) onion stalactites; (5) stalactites with lateral pipes; (6) travertine pendants; (7) travertine drum-heads; (8) rod stalagmites; (9) stalagmites-various; (10) cone stalagmite with cup at the top (sometimes site of "cave pearls," i.e., pisoliths); (11) compound stalagmites, due to intergrowth; (12) flowstone pillars ("stalagnates"); (13) flowstone (travertine) curtain or drape; (14) limestone blocks, fallen from roof (such blocks are often correlated in time from a periglacial phase; the cave was excavated in a moderately warm-wet cycle, affected by a freeze-thaw cycle and then affected by present mild cycle; in Central Europe many of the cave falls are associated with Paleolithic Man remains, and associated foodstuff mammal bones); (15) soil deposits (paleosols) on the cave floor alternating with travertine layers (again often climatic indicators with dateable fossil records; the "soil" is often loess); (16) Stalagmite with overgrowth of travertine sheet in places covering loess; (17) Travertine (sinter terrace) dams with small pools; (18) lake in a travertine-lined basin with spiney outgrowths and moldings or ledges, marking various water levels of the pool.

matic and orthorhombic. Crystals in speleothems commonly occur in irregular layers. Adjacent layers may be separated by a very thin deposit of impurities. In growth, randomly oriented seed crystals are deposited upon the impurities. Those having "c" axes normal to the plane of the impurities then grow preferentially, cannibalizing the others.

Calcite and aragonite speleothems of great purity are white or translucent. Impurities give a great variety of colors and shades. Most common is the range yellow-buff-red or pink, attributable to iron.

Speleothem Forms

(a) *Stalactites* hang vertically from a cave roof. The fundamental initial form is the *soda straw-stalactite*, a tube composed of a single sheath of crystals enclosing a central groundwater canal. It grows only at the tip and has a diameter little greater than 5 mm (the diameter of a drop of water). Where groundwater is available to flow down the outer surface of the formation, further layers of crystals are added, increasing the diameter and creating an extended cone form.

(b) *Stalagmites* grow upward from a cave floor toward the drip source in the roof. Forms range from slender pillars to broad bosses. They may be intricately ornamented with corbelling and other shapes in half-relief, a feature uncommon on stalactites. Where stalactite and stalagmite are joined the form is known as a *column*.

(c) *Drapes* or *curtains*: Where a rivulet of groundwater flows down an inclined cave roof, precipitation may occur throughout its length, creating a drape-like form, growing vertically downward. The drape may be delicately folded, reflecting the sinuous course of the original rivulet. Drapes are often banded with impurities to give the appearance of a "rasher of bacon."

(d) *Helictites*, *heligmites*, and *globulites* are known collectively as "erratic speleothems." They grow outward into cave space, rather than up or down, and are unsupported beneath. *Helictites* are the most common, being soda straw tubes which extend outward from a normal stalactite or vertical cave wall. *Heligmites* grow upward from the floor, branching outward. In detail, there is a great variety of forms, hooks and spirals being most frequent. *Globulites* are botryoidal helictites, particularly associated with desert caves (e.g., Carlsbad Caverns). Erratic speleothems are smaller than others, rarely exceeding 12 inches in length.

(e) *Flowstone* is a general floor or wall deposit of low relief, any irregularities reflecting those in the

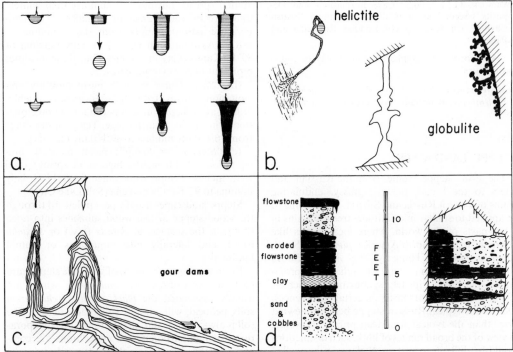

FIG. 5. (a) The growth of soda straw and extended cone stalactites (after Warwick) (b) Helictite and erratic column from British caves, profile of a globulite deposit from a desert cave in California. (c) Section through stalagmites and layered flowstone; lamination is simplified (after a group at Javoříčko Cave, Czechoslovakia). (d) Alternating stream deposition (clastics), flowstone deposition and stream erosion illustrated by two sections from St. Cuthbert's Swallet, England.

underlying rock or fill. The formative groundwater may derive from stalagmites, widespread seepage or regular cave streams.

(f) *Rimstone* or *gour dams*: Groundwater ponded by irregularities on a flowstone or other cave floor tends to deposit preferentially along the overspill rim, raising a barrier which is self-perpetuating (see *Waterfalls*, "autoconsequent"). Successions of stepped pools are formed, as in some hydrothermal areas ("sinter terraces"). Rimstone dams greater than 40 feet in height are known while micro-forms only a few millimeters high abound on stalagmites and flowstone.

Rate of Growth

Variation in rates of growth are extreme. Neighboring speleothems may differ widely and the rate of extension of an individual may change with time. Soda straw stalactites and helictites elongate faster than the larger forms: a mean rate of 0.25 mm/yr is determined from some commercially exploited caves in the United States, while 3 mm/yr has been measured in a Czechoslovakian cave. Only 1–2 mm of flowstone was found on some artifacts dated at 30,000 B.P. in Grotte Riusec, France, but it is evident that calcite deposition had been discontinuous there.

Climatic Zones and Climatic Change

In arctic and subarctic Europe, speleothems tend to be small and plain, and are dominated by pendant varieties. In mediterranean regions and the tropics, forms are massive (particularly stalagmites) and intricately ornamented. Cool, temperate speleothems are intermediate (Corbel, 1957).

Abundant evidence in temperate Europe indicates that speleothem deposition is delicately adjusted to climate. In southern England, many larger speleothems are today being destroyed by drips from the original formative source ("re-solution"). Several previous cycles of deposition and destruction are recorded. Modern deposits may have obtained their maximum growth during the hypsithermal phase of postglacial time.

DEREK C. FORD

References

Corbel, J., 1954, "Les phénomènes karstiques dans les grands Causses," *Rev. Géog. Lyon*, **29**(4), 287-315.
Corbel, J., 1957, "Les karsts du nord-ouest de l'Europe," Université de Lyon.
*Curl, R. L., 1962, "The aragonite-calcite problem," *National Speleological Soc. Am., Bull.*, **24**(2), 57-73.
Kettner, R., 1959, "Allgemeine Geologie," Berlin, Deutscher Verlag Wissensch., 460pp.

*Warwick, G. T., 1962, "Cave Formations and Deposits," Second ed., in (Cullingford, editor) "British Caving," Ch. 4, pp. 83–119, London, Routledge and Paul.

* Additional bibliographic references may be found in this work.

Cross-references: *Karst*; *Limestone Caves*; *Speleology*; *Speleothems*; *Waterfalls*. Vol. VI: *Groundwater*.

STEPPE LANDSCAPE

The term "steppe" comes from the Russian, and refers to the broad, treeless, grassy, undulating plains of eastern Russia and Siberia. It has come to be applied to similar mid-latitude, treeless plains in other parts of the world, where local names like *prairie* in western North America, *pampas* in South America, *puszta* in Hungary, *High Veld* in South Africa and *downs* in eastern Australia are approximately but not completely synonymous (Küchler, 1947). Certain authors insist on certain differences, such as the typical Russian steppe being somewhat drier than the typical American prairie; however, in view of the broad ranges of both, such distinctions would be difficult to sustain. Stefansson has called the tundra an "Arctic prairie," but this ignores the usefulness of the accepted international term and is an extension of the steppe-prairie concept that is impossible to defend.

Steppe is a typical landscape term; it therefore carries an integrated definition based on relief-climate-vegetation; no inherited or morphogenetic history is involved or implied, although it may be noted that the steppes and prairies of Eurasia and the Americas are large accumulation plains ("sed-plains" of Mescherikov; see *Plains*), while the High Veld and downs of South Africa and Australia are largely destructional pediplains. Steppes were generally deserts during the last glacial period and consequently here and there show inherited landforms such as vegetated ("fixed") dunes and ablation hollows ("blowouts"). Old periglacial belts still show soil polygons. It is generally believed that steppe grasses helped to fix *loess* accumulations in the periglacial regions of Eurasia and North America during the cold maxima of the Ice Ages. Inter-loess paleosols contain the roots, pollen and characteristic fauna (rodents, tiny snails) of steppe grasslands. The *relief* characteristic of the steppe simply requires a flat-to-rolling plainland.

The *climatic* criteria are broad and usually labeled in terms of the characteristic vegetation (see below); thus, for example, the three classes given by S. R. Eyre (1963) are:

(a) "*Long Grass Steppe*": mean monthly precipitation ranges from 0.5 (Akmolinsk in January) to 4.9 (Kansas City in May) inches with fairly even annual spread, but more in summer than winter; total precipitation range 10–40 inches. The temperature pattern ranges from daily minima of −8°F (Akmolinsk in winter) to daily maxima of 89°F (Kansas City in summer), but these localities represent rather extreme cases.

(b) "*Short Grass Steppe*": mean monthly precipitation ranges from 0.2–2.0 inches (Pueblo, N.M.), again higher in summer, but total precipitation is in the 10–15 inch range. Temperature range from 16°F daily minima to 89°F daily maxima.

(c) "*Semi-desert Scrub*": mean monthly precipitation 0.1–2.0 inches, highest in spring; total 5–15 inches. Temperature range from 17°F daily minima to 92°F daily maxima (Salt Lake City).

Steppe landscapes usually pass poleward through the wood-steppe or leaf-wood subzones into *taiga* (q.v.), in the tropics, to *deserts* (q.v.) or *savanna* (q.v.), and laterally into mountains or humid landscapes.

From the *vegetation* point of view, the steppes are part of the world's *grasslands*, with which are usually associated the *black earth* or *chernozem* soils, pedocals with about 10% organic matter. The soil is always basic and, thanks to the high evaporation, calcium carbonate soil concretions are common. In the drier areas, the soils grade into the brown, dark-brown or *chestnut-brown soils*. In the wetter areas there is a transition to the slightly acid pedalfer soils (see Vol. VI, *Pedology*). Often the boundary between forest and steppe or prairie is quite abrupt, and the presence of trees has a profound effect upon the soil regime. In the marginal steppe areas, the role of man in setting alight prairie fires (to stimulate grass-growth or for game stampedes) may play an important role in keeping down potential tree growth. In certain regions, e.g., eastern Australia and the Bushveld of South Africa, there are genuine transitional zones into *Savanna landscapes* (q.v.). In the North German Plain, the sandy outwash plains favor a heathland that has been called Steppe-heath ("*Steppenheide*" in German); the "Steppenheide Theory" of Gradmann postulated that late Stone Age Man settled these open spaces in preference to the forested areas after the continental ice retreat. In a previous era, the general increasing continentality of the earth during the Tertiary (from nearly 70 million to about 3 million years ago) favored the evolution of grasses and grasslands. These, in turn, offered the "open range" habitat that led to the development of long-legged ruminants (horses, antelope) and their feline predators.

A work on plant ecology by Conrad (1951) contains a translation from the German of "The Plant Life of the Danube Basin" by Anton Kerner of 1863 which provides the following interesting passage (pp. 5–6): "Whereas Humbolt considers the north German heather-covered coastal plains as steppes, and Koch applied that name to a formation composed of high sod-forming grasses and tall herbs, and Willkomm restricts the term to formations on saline soils of both highlands and lowlands, Grisebach, whose usage of the word steppe we shall follow, conceives of a steppe as a region in which, because of extreme heat, sterility and drought of summer, no tree can survive, and in which the most diverse other formations composed of grasses, herbs, etc., may develop."

RHODES W. FAIRBRIDGE

References

Allan, H. H., 1946, "Tussock grassland or steppe?," *N.Z. Geogr.*, **2**, 223–234.

Berg, L., 1950, in (Morrison, T. A., and Nikiforoff, editors) "Natural Regions of USSR," New York, The Macmillan Co., 436pp. (translated by G. A. Titelbaum from Second Russian ed., 1938).

Conrad, H. S., 1951, "The Background of Plant Ecology," Iowa State College Press, 238pp.

Dansereau, P., 1957, "Biogeography: An Ecological Perspective," New York, Ronald Press Co., 394pp.

Eyre, S. R., 1963, "Vegetation and Soils," Chicago, Aldine, 324pp.

Küchler, A. W., 1947, "Localizing vegetation terms," *Ann. Am. Assoc., Geogr.*, **37.**

Stamp, L. D. (editor), 1961, "A Glossary of Geographical Terms," London, Longmans, 539pp.

Cross-references: *Deserts and Desert Landforms*; *Loess*; *Plains*; *Savanna Landscape*; *Taiga Landscape*; *Tundra Landscape*. Vol. II: *Vegetation Classification*. Vol. VI: *Pedology*.

STEREOSCOPY—*See pr* Vol. VI

STONE NETS, POLYGONS—*See* PATTERNED GROUND; PERIGLACIAL LANDSCAPE

STONE STRIPES, RINGS, POLYGONS—*See* FROST ACTION; PATTERNED GROUND

STRAND-FLAT—*See* PLATFORMS—WAVE-CUT

STRANDLINE

Used in its literal sense, strandline is synonymous with shore line, so that, following Johnson (1919), it would mean the water line along the shore at any particular time. However, possibly due to its similarity with the Norwegian term *strandflat* (which refers to a coastal platform raised above high tide level on the Norwegian coast: Nansen, 1922), *strandline* has become generally reserved for "ancient shore lines" (shore lines out of reach of present wave action) by most geomorphologists (e.g., Charlesworth, 1957), though many still prefer "emergent" or some other appropriate adjective

with "strandline" or "terrace" to achieve this meaning (e.g., Flint, 1957). The spelling "strandline" in a single word is adopted by many writers, following the Germanic root, *Strandlinie*.

As an ancient shore line, *strandline* refers collectively to the assemblage of various features characteristic of the former coastal area. Strandlines, in this sense, may be either above or below the actual water level. Strandlines need not necessarily refer to marine features; ancient lake shore lines are occasionally called strandlines (e.g., around ancient Lake Bonneville).

The formation of a strandline (ancient shore line) requires that land and water remain stable, or else that their movements be equal and in the same sense, long enough for features characteristic of the shore area to be created before displacement takes place. Displacement may be due to many causes. Among these may be numbered, for sea areas: changes in the volume of the oceans due to alterations in the size of the ice sheets ("*glacio-eustasy*"), isostatic movements of areas burdened by ice masses or loads of sediment, tectonic disturbances, and changes in temperature of the seawater ("steric changes"). For lake areas: changes in lake volume due to changes in the flow of influent streams in addition to isostatic movements consequent upon changes in volume (and therefore loading) of the lake.

DAVID E. SMITH

References

Charlesworth, J. K., 1957, "The Quaternary Era," London, Edward Arnold, 2 vols.

Embleton, C. and King, C. A. M., 1968, "Glacial and Periglacial Geomorphology," London, E. Arnold Ltd., 608pp.

Evers, W., 1962, "The problem of coastal genesis, with special reference to the 'strandflat,' the 'banks,' or 'grounds,' and 'deep channels' of the Norwegian and Greenland coasts," with a discussion by H. Holtedahl, *J. Geol.*, **70**(5), 621–633.

Flint, R. F., 1957, "Glacial and Pleistocene Geology," New York, John Wiley & Sons, 553pp.

Johnson, D. W., 1919, "Shore Processes and Shoreline Development," New York, John Wiley & Sons, 583pp.

Nansen, F., 1922, "The strandflat and isostasy," *Kristiania* (Videnskapsselskapets Skrifter, 1. Math-Naturv. Klasse, 1921, No. 11).

Cross-references: *Eustasy*; *Postglacial Isostatic Rebound*; *Warping*; *Water Loading and Crustal Response*.

STRATH, STRATH TERRACE

The Scottish (Gaelic) word *strath* means any wide, flat-floored valley. It has some special modifications in geomorphology. Fluvial terraces may be either degradational or aggradational. To distinguish the former, W. Bucher (1932) suggested the employment of the word *strath*, "where the flat valley bottom is the result of degradation first by lateral stream cutting and later by whatever processes of degradation may be involved." The *thalweg* (q.v.) or bed of the stream would be running on a bedrock floor in this case, though ephemeral flood-level alluvial deposits may form its banks. Lateral cutting during the meander process will progressively rework and shift this material downstream.

A revival of the stream's cutting energy, by increased precipitation, crustal uplift, or drop of sea level (see *Terraces—Thalassostatic*), will lead to the abandonment of *strath terraces*, which are liable to have little residual fluvial sediment left on them. The truncated valley slope is known as a *berm*. Von Engeln (1942) refers to the remnant of the original valley floor as the *strath*, which is not in accord with Bucher's definition. Major rivers crossing the Appalachians, like the Susquehanna River, are evidently straths in the Bucher sense (see Johnson, 1931). It has been claimed that straths could expand and coalesce into partial peneplains.

Howard (1959) has proposed that straths affecting only valley fill material should be called *fill-straths*.

RHODES W. FAIRBRIDGE

References

Bucher, W. H., 1932, "Strath as a geomorphic term," *Science*, **75**, 130–131.

Howard, A. D., 1959, "Numerical systems of terrace nomenclature: A critique," *J. Geol.*, **67**, No. 2, 239–243.

Johnson, D. W., 1931, "Stream Sculpture on the Atlantic Slope," New York, Columbia University Press, 142pp.

Stamp, L. D. (editor), 1961, "A Glossary of Geographical Terms," London, Longmans, 539pp.

Von Engeln, O. D., 1942, "Geomorphology," pp.357–364, New York, The Macmillan Co.

Cross-references: *Aggradation*; *Degradation*; *Etchplain*; *Floodplain*; *Peneplain*; *Rivers*; *Terraces—Fluvial*; *Terraces—Thalassostatic*; *Thalweg*.

STREAM CAPTURE, PIRACY

Stream capture occurs when an actively eroding low level stream encroaches on the drainage of a nearby stream flowing at a higher level and diverts part of the water of the higher stream. It may be caused by *abstraction* (Gilbert, 1877), *headward erosion*, *lateral planation*, or *subterranean diversion*. A minor distinction is sometimes made between capture and piracy, but is rarely recognized today. Usually they are synonymous. The "winning"

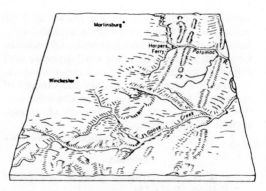

FIG. 1. Stages in the formation of Snickers, Ashby, and Manassas gaps through progressive stream piracy. Above: initial stage; below: final stage (drawing by William J. Wayne; from Thornbury, 1957). (By permission of John Wiley & Sons, N.Y.)

stream may be called the *captor*, *diverter* or *predatory stream*.

Abstraction occurs at an early stage in the cycle of stream erosion when insequent streams form a fine-textured drainage pattern. Some streams cut down more rapidly than others, and the divides shift laterally to engulf adjacent streams. In this way, master streams are developed and the texture of the drainage is coarsened. Such lateral shifting of divides is well-displayed on the unconsolidated material in mine dumps where erosion by small insequent streams is rapid.

Capture by *headward erosion* occurs when two adjacent streams are at different levels and the tributaries of the lower stream are working back toward the upper stream. Eventually the lower stream will gnaw back the valley head until it has cut through the divide.

Headward erosion is the probable cause of most easily recognizable stream captures. It usually takes place in the young or early mature stage of development of a drainage pattern, and may occur because the pirate stream is cutting its valley in softer rock, or because it has a steeper gradient. In the early stages of capture, surface valley-head erosion

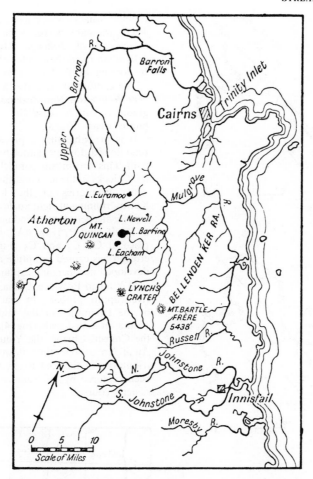

FIG. 2. The rectangular nested pattern of the rivers draining the
Atherton Tableland, Queensland, Australia (after F. Jardine).

is active, but as the divide is reduced and the capture pending, subterranean seepage from the higher to the lower stream may hasten capture.

In the Appalachian region of the eastern United States, there are many captures which are controlled by differences in rock hardness. A few streams have courses transverse to the geologic structure, but most streams flow in strike valleys parallel to the structure. The transverse streams are limited in the rate at which they can deepen their valleys by their ability to erode the more resistant rocks across their courses, whereas the longitudinal streams are usually flowing upon belts of weak rock and are able to erode their valleys more rapidly. Well-known examples in the Appalachian area of Virginia are the captures which resulted in the formation of Snickers, Ashby and Manassas gaps (Fig. 1). The gaps are now *wind* or *air gaps* (q.v.), a term applied to *water gaps* (q.v.) through which streams no longer flow, but formerly a stream flowed eastward through the Blue Ridge in each of

them. A tributary of the Potomac, the Shenandoah River, cut headward along a belt of weak rock, to the west of Blue Ridge, and successively captured the headwaters of streams flowing through Snickers, Ashby and Manassas gaps. The Shenandoah River was able to do this for two reasons: (1) it was eroding its valley in weak rock, whereas the three transverse streams were retarded in down-cutting by the harder rock of the Blue Ridge; (2) the Shenandoah was at a lower level than the three other streams because the Potomac, of which it is a tributary, is a larger river and hence able to cut more rapidly downward through the Blue Ridge than lesser streams.

The point at which the capture is effected is known as the *elbow of capture* since it is commonly marked by a right angle turn into the pirate stream. In some cases the captured tributary may be at an acute angle to the main stream and flow in the opposite direction to it. This is a *barbed tributary* (Fig. 2).

FIG. 3. Capture of the Silver Stream by the Karori, near Wellington, New Zealand (Lauder, 1962).

Funnel, Isaacs, Mackenzie and Dawson rivers. There are many barbed tributaries resulting from a reversal of drainage. However the eastern Australian rivers have often suffered derangement by doming, or blocking by lava flows.

The capture of the Silver Stream by the Karori near Wellington, New Zealand, shows how unequal gradients can increase the eroding power of a pirate stream (Fig. 3).

It is probable that a precedent stream at one time flowed down a shatter belt of the Wellington fault. This stream was parallel to the axis of tilt of fault blocks in the area and thus maintained grade, while tributaries of the Kaiwharawhara and Karori, running at right angles to the tilt axis, were rapidly steepened and pending captures developed at P_1, P_2 and P_3 [Fig. 3(A)]. Finally capture took place at C_1, C_2 and C_3 [Fig. 3(B)] and further erosion has caused recapture at R [Fig. 3(C)], and developed new pending captures at P_4, P_5 and P_6.

In Yunnan Province, China, and adjacent areas, river capture, probably by headward erosion of one of the tributaries of the middle Yangtze basin, occurs on a vast scale (Fig. 4). It is probable that the Chinsha-Chiang, the Yalung-Chiang, and the Anningho at one time flowed to the south as tributaries of the Red River, but they have since been captured by the Yangtze and diverted to an easterly course.

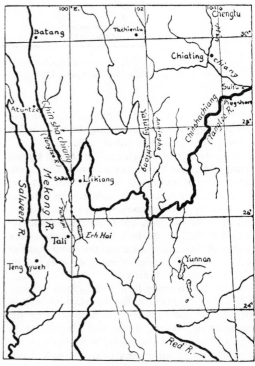

FIG. 4. Present drainage system of northern Yunnan and adjacent areas (Barbour, 1935).

In eastern Australia capture by headward erosion is common (Taylor, 1911). In the Fitzroy basin, Queensland, the Fitzroy River has breached an old divide at the Connors Range and captured the

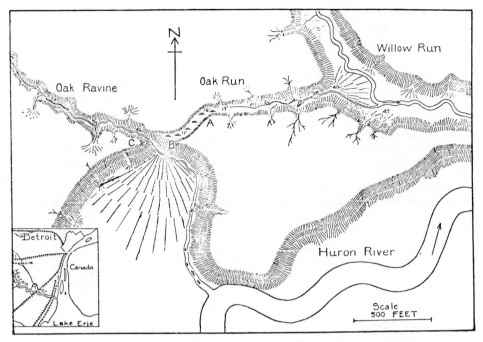

Fig. 5. Map of beheaded Oak Run, west of Detroit, Michigan (Bowman, 1904).

If a tributary stream flows more or less parallel to the course of a major river, and at no great distance from it, then there may be capture by *lateral planation* (Fig. 5). Near Ann Arbor, Michigan, a swinging meander of the Huron River has beheaded the Oak Run Stream at C leaving a swampy dry valley between A and B at the head of the much reduced remnant of the Oak Run Stream. The term *beheading* is commonly used for such events.

Subterranean capture occurs where the rocks are soluble in, or pervious to, water. Water from a stream flowing at high level percolates underground eventually forming a tunnel to a stream at lower level through which the higher stream is diverted.

In Scott County, Virginia, Stock Creek originally followed a wide, open channel past Horton Summit to enter the north fork of the Clinch River. The lower portion of the course of Stock Creek (i.e., that below Natural Tunnel) was at that time occupied by a small but vigorous tributary of Clinch River. Back-cutting by this tributary stream and seepage through the limestone that occurs here caused the formation of a tunnel which today averages 75 feet in height over its 900 feet of length and has an average width of 130 feet (see *Natural Bridge*). The headwaters of the north fork of Clinch River were diverted through this tunnel and now form part of Stock Creek.

W. R. LAUDER

References

Barbour, G. B., 1935, "Physiographic history of the Yangtze," *Mem. Geol. Surv. China, Ser. A*, No. 14, 1–112.

Bowman, I., 1904. "A typical case of stream capture in Michigan," *J. Geol.*, **12**, 326–334.

Campbell, M. R., 1904, "Drainage modifications and their interpretation," *J. Geol.*, **4**, 567–581, 657–678.

Crosby, I. B., 1937, "Methods of stream piracy," *J. Geol.*, **45**, 465–486.

Gilbert, G. K., 1877, "Report on the geology of the Henry Mountains," p. 141, Washington, *U.S. Geograph. and Geol. Surv. of the Rocky Mountains Region.*

Johnson, D. W., 1939. "Drainage modifications," *J. Geomorphol.*, **2**, 87–91.

Lauder, W. R., 1962, "The Kaiwharawhara Capture," *New Zealand J. Geol. Geophys.*, **5**, 141–142.

Taylor, Griffith, 1911, "Physiography of eastern Australia," *Commonwealth Bureau of Meteorology, Melbourne, Bull. No. 8*, 1–18.

Thornbury, W. D., 1957, "Principles of Geomorphology," pp. 152–154. New York, John Wiley & Sons.

Woodward, H. P., 1936, "Natural Bridge and Natural Tunnel, Virginia," *J. Geol.*, **44**, 604–616.

Cross-references: *Drainage Patterns; Lava-displaced Drainage; Natural Bridge; Rivers; Water Gap; Wind Gap.*

STREAM CHANNEL CHARACTERISTICS

Channels can be characterized by measurements of width (w), depth (d), and velocity (v) which make up discharge (Q), flow resistance (n) and slope (s). The most useful parameter for describing channel shape is probably the width-depth ratio, w/d.

Stream channels vary widely in appearance and character, from those with both bed and banks of bedrock to those with bed and banks of stream-deposited materials. Most streams have reaches with both types of materials in bed and banks. There is much current research in the field of fluvial morphology. Leliavsky (1955) and Leopold, Wolman, and Miller (1964) have extensive bibliographies on the study of channel characteristics.

Bedrock channel characteristics are determined by the discharge of water, the discharge and size of sediment, and by the resistance of the bedrock to abrasion, solution, hydraulic removal of joint blocks and loosening of surface material caused by wetting and drying and by freezing and thawing.

Where stream velocities are very high, cavitation also may have an effect. Large rivers like the Colorado River of the West, which transport sand and gravel, may remove obstacles such as falls and rapids from their courses more rapidly than do rivers such as the St. Lawrence and St. Clair which have deposited their abrasive tools in the lakes upstream. The fluted surfaces and potholes in most bedrock channels give clear evidence of the effectiveness of abrasion.

Resistant bedrock channels are eroded much more slowly than alluvial channels in which bed and bank resistance to erosion is quite limited. Large local variations in channel cross section and slope are common in bedrock channels. Slope

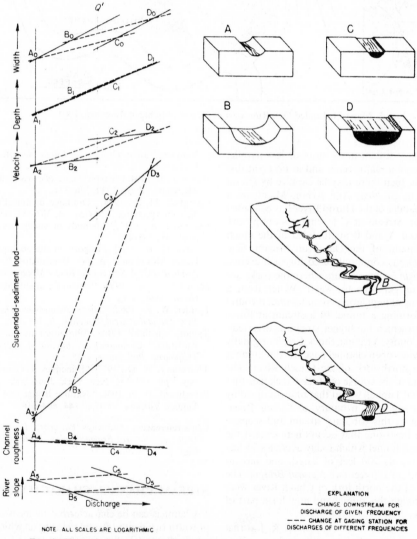

NOTE ALL SCALES ARE LOGARITHMIC

EXPLANATION
—— CHANGE DOWNSTREAM FOR DISCHARGE OF GIVEN FREQUENCY
– – – CHANGE AT GAGING STATION FOR DISCHARGES OF DIFFERENT FREQUENCIES

FIG. 1. Channel characteristics. Average hydraulic geometry of river channels expressed by relations of width, depth, velocity, suspended-sediment load, roughness, and slope to discharge at a station and downstream (from Leopold and Maddock, 1953).

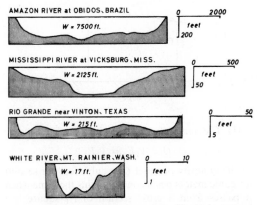

AMAZON RIVER at OBIDOS, BRAZIL

W = 7500 ft.

0   2000
feet
200

MISSISSIPPI RIVER at VICKSBURG, MISS.

W = 2125 ft.

0   500
feet
50

RIO GRANDE near VINTON, TEXAS

W = 215 ft.

0   50
feet
5

WHITE RIVER, MT. RAINIER, WASH.

W = 17 ft.

0   10
feet
1

FIG. 2. River channel cross sections. Vertical exaggeration 5X.

can vary from nearly vertical to almost horizontal, from waterfalls in resistant rock to less than 1 ft/mile in areas of weak rock and low relief.

Channel characteristics in alluvium vary systematically with changes in discharge, bed and bank materials, and sediment transport. Leopold and Maddock (1953) and Wolman (1955) demonstrated a systematic variation in the characteristics of channels with change in discharge at a cross section of the stream and with the normal increase in discharge in a downstream direction (Fig. 1).

Channel widths, depths, and velocities vary with discharge as simple power functions at a cross section and from point to point along the stream provided that different points along the stream are compared at discharges that occur with equal frequency. For example: width, depth, velocity and suspended load all increase with increasing discharge (Fig. 1). Width increases more rapidly than depth in the downstream case which means that the larger rivers have higher width/depth ratios than the smaller channels (Fig. 2).

The velocity for discharges of equal frequency also increases downstream (Fig. 1). When, as Mackin (1963) suggests, one considers only those velocities capable of moving the materials of the bed and banks and thus forming or modifying the channel, one finds that extraordinary flood discharges are necessary to form or modify the smaller channels with bed and banks of coarse materials, whereas lower discharges which occur with greater frequency may be capable of gradually modifying downstream reaches with bed and banks of finer materials.

It must be noted that for most streams at a given cross section, the relations between the descriptive parameters are primarily hydraulic in nature (Wolman, 1955) representing the manner in which increasing discharge is accommodated by a channel which was developed in large part by earlier flows. An exception to this is the manner in which steep

channels in coarse, noncohesive gravels appear to adjust to changes in discharge and maintain approximately the same shape over a wide range of flows (Fahnestock, 1963). In contrast, the changes in parameters between cross sections along a stream reflect the increase in size of the channel due to the larger flows that occur as the area contributing to the drainage increases.

Schumm (1963) found that narrower and more sinuous streams had higher silt and clay content in bed and banks than did wider and straighter streams. The silts and clays would appear to give the banks the resistance necessary for the development of a more sinuous channel. Streams with bed and bank materials chiefly of sand depend on vegetation for stability of banks and vary considerably in width depending on the effectiveness of the vegetation. Such sand channel streams often have their deepest portions adjacent to the banks, while the midstream depths are much shallower with bars exposed at lower flows (Fig. 2) (Fahnestock and Maddock, 1964).

Channel alignment plays an important part in determining local channel shape. Curved channels tend to be deeper on the outside of beds and shallower on the inside with a greater asymmetry of the cross section as the curvature is more pronounced. The greatest asymmetry occurs where large changes in current direction take place against especially resistant or artificially stabilized banks.

Velocities and velocity distributions vary with changes in discharge, bed form, and location within the channel. The Manning equation

$$V = \frac{1.5R^{2/3}S^{1/2}}{n}$$

(where V is the velocity, n is the flow resistance coefficient, R is the hydraulic radius which is approximately equal to depth in most natural streams, and S is the slope of energy gradient usually taken as the slope of the water surface) is often used to predict velocities in river channels; Manning's n indicates the frictional resistance that the river channel offers to the flow. As seen in the equation, velocity increases with depth and slope and decreases with increasing resistance to flow or bed roughness. This roughness can be caused by resistance to the flow as it passes over individual irregularities, or particles of the bed in the case of a sand bed; this occurs as the flow passes over the individual bed forms created by the interaction of the flow with the bed.

Channel characteristics are determined in part by the amount and size of debris transported by a stream. Coarse debris is often conveyed in wide shallow channels, and it has been suggested that this cross section is the most efficient for this purpose (Leopold and Maddock, 1953). Narrow channels also transport large quantities of coarse debris, usually without the bar formation, multiple channels and bank erosion characteristics of the wider reaches. Wide shallow channels may develop because the high velocities necessary to transport coarse debris overcome erosion resistance of the bank rather than because the wider section is more efficient.

Streams may have one or more channels separated by alluvial islands. Individual channels of both single and multiple channel reaches are usually sinuous; straight reaches are relatively uncommon (Leopold and Wolman, 1957). Multiple channel reaches are usually associated with relatively erodible banks, often with large loads of sand or larger materials.

R. K. FAHNESTOCK

References

Fahnestock, R. K., 1963, "Morphology and hydrology of a glacial stream, White River, Mount Rainier, Wash.," *U.S. Geol. Surv. Profess. Paper* **422A,** 70pp.

Fahnestock, R. K., and Maddock, Thomas, Jr., 1964, "Preliminary report on bed forms and flow phenomena in the Rio Grande near El Paso, Texas," *U.S. Geol. Surv. Profess. Paper* **501-B,** B140–142.

Kondratev, N. E. (editor), 1962, "River Flow and River Channel Formation," Israel Program for Sci. Trans. (available from Office of Tech. Services, U.S. Dept. of Commerce, Washington, D.C.)

Leliavsky, Serge, 1955, "An Introduction to Fluvial Hydraulics," London, Constable & Co., 257pp.

Leopold. L. B., and Maddock, Thomas, Jr., 1953, "The hydraulic geometry of stream channels and some physiographic implications," *U.S. Geol. Surv. Profess. Paper* **252,** 57pp.

Leopold, L. B., and Wolman, M. G., 1957, "River channel patterns, braided, meandering, and straight," *U.S. Geol. Surv. Profess. Paper* **282B,** 85pp.

Leopold, L. B., Wolman, M. G., and Miller, J. P., 1964, "Fluvial Processes in Geomorphology," San Francisco, William Freeman and Co., 522pp.

Mackin, J. H., 1963, "Rational and Empirical Methods in Geology," in "The Fabric of Geology," pp. 135–163, Reading, Mass., Addison Wesley & Co.

Schumm, S. A., 1960, "The shape of alluvial channels in relation to sediment type," *U.S. Geol. Surv. Profess. Paper* **352B,** 30pp.

Schumm, S. A., 1963, "Sinuosity of alluvial rivers on the Great Plains," *Bull. Geol. Soc. Am.,* **74**(9), 1089–1099.

Wolman, M. G., 1955, "The natural channel of Brandywine Creek Pa.," *U.S. Geol. Surv. Profess. Paper* **271,** 56pp.

Cross-references: *Abrasian*; *Alluvia*; *Floodplain*; *Pothole*; *Rivers*; *Rivers—Meandering and Braiding*; *Sediment Transport*; *Stream Flow*; *Thalweg*; *Waterfalls.* Vol. II: *Fluid Mechanics.* Vol. VI: *Bedforms in Alluvial Channels*; *Fluvial Sediment Transport.*

STREAM FLOW

The following basic equations are valid for stream flow:

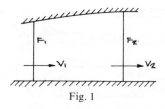

Fig. 1

(1) *The continuity equation* which (see Fig. 1) says:

$$Q = V_1 F_1 = V_2 F_2$$

or the quantity of water Q in cubic feet per second (or cubic meters per second) remains the same when it passes from a cross section of F_1 square feet (square meters) with velocity V_1 feet per second (meters per second) to a cross section of F_2 square feet (square meters) with velocity V_2 feet per second (meters per second).

(2) *The energy equation* which (see Fig. 2) says:

$$z_1 + p_{1/\gamma} + \frac{V_1^2}{2g} = z_2 + p_{2/\gamma} + \frac{V_2^2}{2g} + \frac{dAi + dAu}{\gamma \, dQ} \quad (1)$$

When z_1 and z_2 are the geometrical heights over a certain level, p_1 and p_2 are the corresponding pressures, V_1 and V_2 are the corresponding velocities between parallel streamlines (lines which indicate direction of the flow at any time), dAi is the energy lost by interior friction and dAu is the energy lost by exterior friction, γ is the specific gravity of the fluid, and Q the quantity of flow per second passing through the cross section considered located between parallel streamlines.

This is the classical Bernoulli equation (Daniel Bernoulli, 1738) expanded to include energy losses by interior friction, turbulence and surface shear stresses. The single elements in the equation have the dimension feet (meters). p/γ is the pressure in feet (or in meters) of liquid, and $V^2/2g$ is the velocity head.

Simply, the energy equation says that the sum of

(a) geometrical head,
(b) pressure head,
(c) velocity head,
(d) head losses,

always equals the sum of (a), (b) and (c) in initial cross section upstream.

(3) *The equation of momentum* which says:

$$\frac{d\overline{B}}{dt} = \frac{d}{dt} \int_V \overline{V} \, dm = \int_V d\overline{K} \quad (2)$$

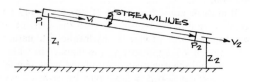

Fig. 2

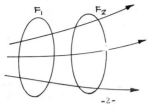

Fig. 3

or that the change in momentum ($\int_V \overline{V} \, dm$ = mass times velocity vector) per second in magnitude and direction equals the resultant force ($\int_V d\overline{K}$) acting on the volume of fluid V. The resultant force equals the momentum per second because momentum is defined as the integral of force with respect to time.

Consider stationary movement of a fluid which means a movement when the direction and magnitude of velocity in a fixed point is independent of time. Figure 3 shows streamlines which indicate the direction of flow in each particular point. After the time interval dt, a certain volume described by F_1 in Fig. 3 has moved and changed to F_2 which may have a different geometrical shape than F_1 but the volume is still the same. Therefore, no change in momentum has taken place from F_1 to F_2.

Various types of flow exist. If the velocity vector does not change in either magnitude or direction with passage of time at any fixed point in a moving fluid, such flow is called steady. In unsteady flow, either the magnitude or the direction of the velocity, or both, will vary with time. Under such conditions, the pattern of streamlines may generally be expected to change in form from instant to instant; only if the velocity changes in magnitude but not direction will the streamlines remain the same as time passes.

Whereas steadiness refers to lack of variation of the velocity vector with time at a given point, uniformity refers to lack of variation of the velocity vector with distance along a streamline at a given instant, with both the magnitude and the velocity vector being considered. In uniform flow, the streamlines must obviously be straight and parallel. In nonuniform flow in which the velocity varies in direction only, the streamlines must be concentric circles. In nonuniform flow in which the velocity vector varies in magnitude only, the streamlines must be straight lines which either converge or diverge. In normal nonuniform flow, all streamlines will be curved and either divergent or convergent in various zones.

The actual shape of any one of the patterns of streamlines is described by what is known as the stream function and customarily given the symbol ψ. The quantity ψ can only vary with coordinate location, and along any particular streamline the quantity ψ has a constant magnitude and its form thus represents a graph of x against y and z for a particular numerical value of the function. A surface containing all streamlines characterized by the same magnitude of ψ is called a stream surface. A stream surface is merely the boundary of a particular stream tube of finite size. A family of such stream surfaces, each encased by the next and having a progressively greater magnitude of ψ, will include between each successive pair a finite increment of the total flow. If a mathematical equation or a graphical representation of the stream function (i.e., the flow pattern) is available for given boundary conditions, it is possible to determine the magnitude and the direction of the relative velocity at all points in the flow.

If "irrational flow" (the single fluid elements do not rotate) is assumed, a related function called "velocity potential" (usually given the symbol φ) is commonly used. In addition to the family of stream surfaces of constant ψ, there will also exist a family of potential surfaces of constant φ which are normal to the stream surfaces at every point. If the increment $\Delta\varphi$ between all successive potential surfaces (distance Δs) is made the same, the spacing of these surfaces will be inversely proportional to the velocity magnitude at every point, that is $V = \Delta\varphi/\Delta s$.

The velocity component in any direction will then generally be given by the derivative of the velocity potential in that direction, e.g., for flow around a sphere:

$$V = \frac{\partial\varphi}{\partial s}, \quad Vx = \frac{\partial\varphi}{\partial x}, \quad Vy = \frac{\partial\varphi}{\partial y}, \quad V = \frac{d\psi}{\partial n},$$

$$Vx = \frac{\partial\psi}{\partial y}, \quad Vy = -\frac{\partial\psi}{\partial x} \tag{3}$$

Two important parameters in any kind of flow are viscosity and fluid turbulence. Viscosity is that property of a liquid which gives rise to an internal stress opposing deformation of the fluid during flow. The dynamic viscosity, usually called μ, of any fluid is defined simply as the ratio of the stress intensity to the accompanying rate of fluid deformation. With reference to Fig. 4, as the element A travels at the mean velocity v in the direction x, it will become deformed at an angular rate equal to dv/dy, whence the intensity of shear along plane a–a will be as first expressed by Newton.

$$T = \mu\frac{dv}{dy}, \qquad \mu = \rho v \tag{4}$$

When ρ is the density and v the kinematic viscosity, the Reynolds number $R = vL/v$ (where v is the characteristic relative velocity between the fluid and the boundary and L is a typical dimension, e.g.,

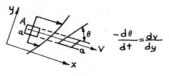

Fig. 4

depth of flow) is used to characterize laminar flow. Laminar flow is bounded on one side by a stationary solid at zero velocity. Velocities are very small and there is no lateral mixing. The smaller the Reynolds number, the more important is the viscous influence and vice versa. As the Reynolds number for any state of laminar flow is continuously increased, a stage will eventually be reached at which the flow becomes unstable to disturbances of a particular magnitude. The higher the Reynolds number, as a general rule, the smaller is the disturbance for which the flow remains stable. With increasing velocity, the laminar layer which is clinging to the boundary becomes thinner and thinner. Eddies generated in the initial zone of instability spread rapidly through the fluid, and the additional disturbances eventually cause a disruption of the entire flow pattern resulting in fluid turbulence. The major distinction between turbulent and laminar flow thus lies in the existence of a complex secondary motion superimposed upon the primary motion of translation. A sensitive velocity meter immersed at any point of a turbulent stream would show continual deviations from the mean velocity due to the effect of eddies carried with the flow.

The total shear stress between fluid and boundary caused by viscosity and turbulence may be written as

$$T = (\mu + \eta)\frac{dv}{dy} \tag{5}$$

when $\eta/\rho = \varepsilon$ is a kinematic eddy viscosity. Laminar flow occurs in low-viscosity liquids and with very low velocities in water. The common case is turbulent flow.

Interaction between Flow and Boundary

In a steady, uniform, open-channel flow, the average shear stress τ_0 (tractive force) at the stream bed is found from a simple equilibrium condition to be

$$\tau_0 = \gamma DI \tag{6}$$

in which γ is the specific gravity of the water, D is the mean depth and I is the energy gradient (slope). The friction velocity U_f is then defined as

$$U_f = \sqrt{\tau_0/\rho} = \sqrt{gDI} \tag{7}$$

The friction factor f is expressed by the relation

$$I = f\frac{V^2}{2g}\frac{1}{D} \tag{8}$$

where V is the mean velocity and g the acceleration of gravity. From this we find the following simple expression

$$V = U_f\sqrt{\frac{2}{f}} \tag{9}$$

A non-dimensional parameter of basic importance is the Froude number, F,

$$F = \frac{V}{\sqrt{gD}} \tag{10}$$

When $F < 1$ the flow is said to be subcritical, while $F > 1$ corresponds to supercritical flow. Critical flow occurs when $F = 1$, so that $V = \sqrt{gD}$. The physical interpretation of this situation is that the flow velocity V is equal to the celerity

$$c = \sqrt{gD} \tag{11}$$

of a surge wave traveling over the bottom.

When the Froude number is introduced, Eq. (8) is rewritten as

$$I = \tfrac{1}{2}fF^2 \tag{12}$$

The stream bed is called hydraulic smooth if a viscous sublayer is formed. The average thickness δ of the sublayer is usually calculated from the expression

$$\delta = \frac{11.6v}{U_f} \tag{13}$$

in which v is the kinematic viscosity of the fluid. Hence, for increasing velocity, δ is decreasing. When δ becomes of a magnitude comparable to that of the roughness elements of the bed, the sublayer is "broken." When the quantity calculated by Eq. (13) is smaller than the equivalent sand roughness k of the bed, no viscous sublayer will occur, and the bed is said to be hydraulic rough. The transition between smooth and rough conditions depends on the detailed structure and distribution of the roughness elements.

In fully turbulent flow, the shear is transferred by the exchange of momentum caused by the turbulent fluctuations. Near a smooth boundary, the turbulence ceases and the shear is transferred to the wall through the sublayer essentially by viscous forces.

At a rough wall, conditions are different since no viscous sublayer is present. In this case, the shear stress is transferred to the wall as drag (and shear) on the individual roughness elements. The distribution of the velocity U of the mean motion is given by

$$\frac{U}{U_f} = 8.5 + 2.5\ln\frac{y}{k} \tag{14}$$

in which k denotes the sand roughness and y the distance from the wall. The average velocity V along the vertical is

$$\frac{V}{U_f} = 6 + 2.5\ln\frac{D}{k} \tag{15}$$

The energy dissipation is defined as the part of the total mechanical energy that is transferred into heat. Per unit length of a uniform channel flow it amounts to

$$\tau_0 V = \gamma(DV)I = \gamma qI \qquad (16)$$

The energy gradient is

$$I = \tau_0 V/\gamma q \qquad (17)$$

Most natural streams are shallow in the sense that the mean depth D is small compared with the surface width B. If the local depth is y (see Fig. 5), the bed shear stress is

$$\tau_0 = \gamma yI \qquad (18)$$

if the shear forces in vertical sections are neglected. By integration all over the wetted parameter P, one obtains:

$$\int_P \tau_0 \, dP \simeq \tau_m P \simeq \tau_m B = \gamma IA \qquad (19)$$

so that the mean shear stress τ_m becomes

$$\tau_m = \gamma IA/B = \gamma DI \qquad (20)$$

It is obvious that the geometry of the cross section is a factor of some importance. The shear stress varies in linear proportion to the depth which means that the bed configuration may change considerably in a given cross section (see article by Kennedy, *Bed Forms in Alluvial channels*, pr Vol. VI). For instance, it may happen that plane bed and standing waves occur in the middle part of the streams, while dunes or ripples are formed near the banks.

Secondary (crosswise) currents occur in natural streams as well as in flumes, particularly in relation to bends. The secondary currents induced by meandering of the streams may have a pronounced influence on the shape of the cross section, making it shallow on the inner side of the bend and deep on the outer side.

From a geological point of view, no rivers can be considered to be in exact equilibrium. For practical engineering purposes, however, it is often realistic to accept streams as being in equilibrium if they have not changed their characteristics notably in a number of years, seasonal changes being disregarded.

There are several sources of the sediment transported in alluvial streams. For "equilibrium" streams, however, that resulting from sheet erosion as a result of surface runoff is usually the most important.

Thus it follows that the sediment discharge of a

river is primarily determined by the nature of the drainage area. From hydrology, the same is known to be true for the water discharge. Or, stated in another way: Both sediment and water discharge are factors essentially independent of the river itself and almost exclusively determined by the hydrology, geology and topography of the drainage area.

For a given water and sediment discharge, the river itself will tend to create the geometry of its stream channel in a specific manner. This means that if the river is left alone for sufficiently long time, with fixed values of the water and sediment discharge, it will adjust itself with a definite slope, depth, width and meander pattern.

For a given river, the water and sediment discharges generally increase in the downstream direction. The same is found to be true for the depth and width of the stream. The slope and the grain size usually decrease gradually from source to estuary. The grain size decreases approximately exponentially in the downstream direction.

These observations make it natural to look for *empirical relations for the variation of the depth, width and slope as functions of the discharge*, which appears to be the most important independent parameter. Many "regime" relations have been suggested by various researchers. Contributions to these relations include those given by T. Blench:

$$B \sim Q^{1/2} \qquad (21)$$

$$D \sim Q^{1/3} \qquad (22)$$

$$I \sim Q^{-1/6} \qquad (23)$$

where B denotes the width, D the depth, I the slope and Q the water discharge. In the present edition of Blench's formulas, all variations with sediment discharge and grain size have been omitted for the sake of simplicity.

According to Blench, rivers with erodible banks always tend to meander or at least create alternate shoals in apparently straight-looking reaches. These observations agree excellently with theoretical results.

An empirical relationship expressing the observations of meander "wavelengths" has been suggested by C. C. Inglis,

$$L \sim Q^{1/2} \qquad (24)$$

Comparison of equations indicates a direct proportionality between the width of the stream and the meander length. This was investigated empirically by L. B. Leopold and M. G. Wolman for a large number of American and Indian rivers as well as for several small-scale model tests. From their data, the following relation is found to be valid over several decades of the widths:

$$L = 10B \qquad (25)$$

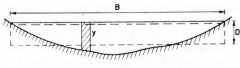

FIG. 5.

If one considers the subjectiveness of assessment of meander lengths and stream width as well as the disturbing influence of local geological formations, the observed deviations from Eq. (25) are surprisingly small.

PER BRUUN

References

Bretting, A. E., 1958, "Stable channels," *Acta Polytech. Scand. 245*, **12**, No. 7, 115pp.

Blench, T., 1966, "Mobile-Bed Fluviology," Edmonton, Canada, 300pp.

Bruun, Per, 1962, "Engineering Aspects of Sediment Transport," in "Reviews in Engineering Geology," Vol. 1, pp. 39–103, *The Geological Society of America.*

Chow, Ven Te, 1959, "Open-channel Hydraulics," New York, McGraw-Hill Book Co., Civil Engineering Series, 680pp.

Einstein, H. A., and Barbarossa, N. L., 1952, "River channel roughness," *Trans. Am. Soc. Civil Engrs.*, **117.**

Engelund, F., 1966, "Hydraulic resistance of alluvial streams," *J. Hydraulics Div. Am. Soc. Civil Engrs.*, **92,** HY 2.

Engelund, F., and Hansen, E., 1966, "Investigations of flow in alluvial streams," *Acta Polytech. Scand.*, Civil Engineering and Building Construction Series No. 35.

Engelund, F., and Hansen, E., 1967, "A Monograph on Sediment Transport in Alluvial Streams," Copenhagen, Danish Technical Press, 62pp.

Hansen, E., 1967, "On the Formation of Meanders as a Stability Problem," Basic Research-Progress Report No. 13. Hydraulic Laboratory. Techn., University of Denmark.

Kennedy, J. F., 1961, "Stationary Waves and Antidunes in Alluvial Channels," Rep. No. KH-R-2, W. M. Keck Laboratory of Hydraulics and Water Resources, California Institute of Technology.

Kennedy, J. F., and Alam, A. M. Z., 1967, discussion of "Hydraulic resistance of alluvial streams," *J. Hydraulics Div. Am. Soc. Civil Engrs.*, **93,** HY 1.

Leopold, L. B., Wolman, M. G., and Miller, J. P., 1964, "Fluvial Processes in Geomorphology," San Francisco, W. H. Freeman and Co., 522pp.

Leviavsky, S., 1955, "An Introduction to Fluvial Hydraulics," London, Constable and Company Ltd.

Nikuradse, J., 1933, "Strömungsgesetze in rauben Rohren," *Forsch.-Arbeiten Ing.-Wesen*, No. 361.

Nordin, C. F., Jr., 1964, "Aspects of flow resistance and sediment transport, Rio Grande near Bernalillo, New Mexico," *U.S. Geol. Surv. Water Supply Paper*, **1498H.**

Prandtl, L., 1927, Über die ausgebildete Turbulenz," *Verh. Intern. Kongr. Techn. Mech., Zürich (1926).*

Prandtl, L., 1949, "Strömungslehre," Braunschweig, Friedr. Vieweg und Sohn, 407pp.

Cross-references: *Rivers; Rivers—Meandering and Braiding; Sediment Transport—Fluvial and Marine; Stream Channel Characteristics.* Vol. II: *Bernoulli's Theorem; Fluid Mechanics; Friction and Viscosity; Laminar Flow, Boundary Layer; Reynolds, Froude and Other Dimensionless Numbers; Streamlines, Streamline Annalysis; Turbulence; Viscosity.* pr Vol. VI: *Bedforms in Alluvial Channels.*

STREAM GRADATION—*See* GRADE, GRADED STREAM

STREAM ORDERS

The streams in a drainage basin can be assigned orders (e.g., see Leopold *et al.*, 1964). This can be done in several ways.

(a) *Horton orders:* Horton (1945) originally developed the notion of stream orders. First-order streams are those which have no tributaries, second-order streams are those which receive as tributaries only streams of the first order, etc. However, the main stream is denoted by the same order number all the way to its headwaters, and hence one of the first-order streams (normally either the longest or the one which seems the most direct upstream continuation of the main stream) has to be renumbered as second order. The renumbering procedure is repeated with higher-order streams, so that the *N*th order stream extends headward to the beginning of the longest tributary. Thus, as a stream-order map is prepared, one of the lower-order streams is renumbered every time two channels of equal order join one another.

(b) *Strahler orders.* Strahler (1952, 1957) modified the Horton system by eliminating the concept that the main stream must be followed back to its headwaters. Thus all unbranched tributaries are first order streams; when two channel segments of order *N* join they form a channel of order *N* + 1. Assuming that all unbranched tributaries in a regular river system have virtually identical geometric and hydraulic characteristics, the Strahler system is the more accurate of the two systems. Despite this, many workers remain unaware of the differences between the two systems (see Leopold, *et al.*, 1964). Both Horton and Strahler ignored the junction of an Nth-order channel with lower-order channels in assigning order numbers. Figure 1 illustrates the application of these stream-ordering systems to a hypothetical drainage basin. Excellent correlations between stream order and various drainage basin geometric and hydrologic parameters have been established (see *Quantitative Geomorphology*).

(c) *Consistent orders:* The Horton and Strahler schemes assume that the stream order increases by 1 if a stream is joined by another of the same order. This assumption is meaningful in an idealized river system which is very regular, such as an idealized river network which consists only of the confluence of streams of the same order, combining to form a stream of the next higher order. However, real streams are more complex; many of them receive numerous tributaries of lower order. What, then, should be the order of a combined stream? Scheidegger (1965) has recently shown how a consistent algebra for stream-order numbers, where the junctions with lower-order streams are no

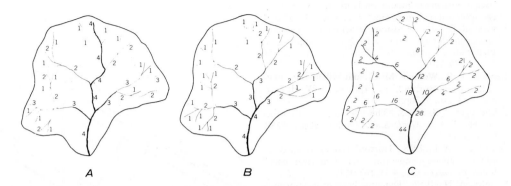

FIG. 1. Stream-ordering systems of Horton (A), Strahler (B), and "consistent ordering" (C), as applied to a hypothetical stream (in part after Bowden and Wallis, 1964; Scheidegger, 1965). In C, the italic numbers $= 2^N$ where $N =$ stream order.

longer ignored, can be devised. The basic property of stream-order numbers is that if two "orders" N are combined [operation denoted by an asterisk (*)], the resulting stream is of order $N + 1$. Hence

$$N*N = N + 1$$

This relates algebraically the operation of combination and the operation of addition [denoted as usual by plus $(+)$], with respect to channels of the same order. Assuming that one of the N-order streams is the combination of two $N - 1$ order streams, one must postulate

$$N*(N - 1)*(N - 1) = N + 1$$

Furthermore, in order that the distributive law be valid (i.e., that the order in which the rivers join is immaterial), it is postulated that

$$[N*(N - 1)]*(N - 1) = N*[(N - 1)*(N - 1)]$$

So that the commutative law can be satisfied (since the result must be the same whether an M-order river joins an N-order one, or vice versa) it is postulated that

$$N*M = M*N$$

The above postulates define completely the algebra of combination of stream-order numbers.

Any integral N can be expressed in terms of smaller orders:

$$N = (N - 1)*(N - 1)$$
$$= (N - 2)*(N - 2)*(N - 2)*(N - 2)$$
$$= M*M*M* \ldots *M$$

where the number of "factors" M is equal to 2^{N-M}. Thus we may write

$$N = M*2^{N-M}$$

where the asterisk in the "exponent" indicates that the "multiplications" (i.e., combinations de-

noted by *) refer to confluences of streams of the indicated order.

Continuing the algebraic analysis to include hypothetical zero-order streams (which do not exist in nature), one has

$$N = 0*2^N$$

and

$$N*M = 0*2^N 0*2^M = 0*(2^N + 2^M)$$

Also,

$$N*M = 0*2^{(N*M)}$$

Hence, setting

$$X = N*M$$

we have, from a combination of the three previous equations:

$$2^X = 2^N + 2^M$$

or

$$M*N = X = \frac{\log(2^N + 2^M)}{\log 2} \equiv \log_2(2^N + 2^M)$$

This is the general law for the composition of stream-order numbers, derived from the fundamental postulates for integer values of N and M; by analytic continuation, it may be extended to noninteger values.

The scheme of stream ordering engendered by the last formula is also shown in Fig. 1, which compares the various systems of ordering of the same basin with each other.

[The above article is largely abstracted from one by the author, 1965, quoted below.]

A. E. SCHEIDEGGER

References

Bowden, K. L., and Wallis, J. R., 1964, "Effect of

stream-ordering technique on Horton's law of drainage composition," *Bull. Geol. Soc. Am.*, **75**, 767–774.

Horton, R. E., 1945, "Erosional development of streams and their drainage basins; hydrophysical approach to quantitative morphology," *Bull. Geol. Soc. Am.*, **56**, No. 3, 275–370.

Leopold, L. B., Wolman, M. G., and Miller, J. P., 1964, "Fluvial Processes in Geomorphology," W. H. Freeman and Co., 522pp.

Scheidegger, A. E., 1965, "The algebra of stream-order numbers," *U.S. Geol. Surv. Profess. Paper* **525B**, B187–B189.

Scheidegger, A. E., 1968, "Horton's Law of stream order numbers and a temperature-analog in river nets," *Water Resources Res.*, **4**(1), 167–171.

Strahler, A. N., 1952, "Dynamic basis of geomorphology," *Bull. Geol. Soc. Am.*, **63**, 923–938.

Strahler, A. N., 1957, "Quantitative analysis of watershed geomorphology," *Trans. Am. Geophys. Union*, **38**, No. 6, 913–920.

Cross-references: *Drainage Patterns*; *Open Systems—Allometric Growth*; *Quantitative Geomorphology*; *Rivers*.

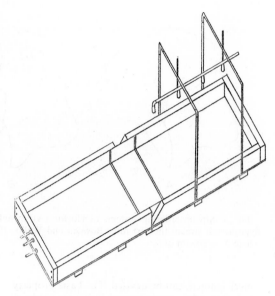

FIG. 1. Sketch of Schwartz stream table.

STREAM PATTERN—*See* DRAINAGE PATTERNS

STREAM TABLE CONSTRUCTION AND OPERATION

A stream table is a trough-like structure in which sand, water and accessory materials dynamically simulate geologic processes and their resultant landforms. It can be used for classroom demonstrations or as a research tool. The construction and operation of an inexpensive stream table are here described.

Construction

Assemble the following components:

Metal Lining. Fold an 8-inch panel at a 90° angle on two long sides and one end of each of two sheets (4 × 5 feet and 4 × 6 feet) of 20-gauge galvanized iron sheet metal. Shaping may be done by machinery at a sheet metal shop or by hand, using mallets and wooden blocks. Construct wooden supporting frames around each of the metal liners. Fold the excess of the metal side panels over and down the sides of the wooden frames. Remove the metal liners, solder the corners and test for leaks. Replace the liners in the frames and secure them in place with screws along the outside overlap. Prepare the metal for a protective coating by etching the surface with diluted acetic or muriatic acid. Apply two coats of epoxy resin paint.

Wooden Frame. Use Douglas fir throughout. As noted, construct wooden supporting frames around the metal liners after their sides are shaped, being careful to obtain a close fit. Leave one end open on each frame, corresponding to the open ends of the liners, for subsequent hinged joining. Use $\frac{1}{2}$-inch plywood for the bottom, securely nailed to the sides consisting of 2 × 6 inch timbers on edge. Bevel the sides at the open end of the larger frame to permit raising when hinged. Secure cross braces of 2 × 4 inch timbers under the frames with 2 × 6 inch timber under the open ends, and insert heavy lag bolts at each corner, to strengthen the frames. Apply three coats of high-grade wood preservative.

Hinge Assembly. Join the open ends of the two sections with a heavy, wide piano hinge. Over this, cement a 9-inch-wide heavy rubber strip across the bottom and up the sides. Secure the rubber in place with a metal bracket along each edge, screwed to the bottom and sides of each section of the table. Further waterproof the joint by caulking the outer edges of the rubber strip with ceramic tile cement.

Spray System. Construct a tubular aluminum frame to support four spray heads in tandem, in an adjustable overhead position. Attach a spring clamp to the upper end of the table where a hose may be secured when a single water source is needed.

Water Level Drains. Drill three $\frac{9}{16}$-inch holes through the end of the smaller section at evenly spaced levels. Through these insert $\frac{1}{2}$ × 3 inch pipe nipples that have had their threads extended on the outer end. Place rubber gaskets, made of rubber left over from the hinge assembly, over the nipples on the inside of the table. Using floor flanges that have been back-tapped to permit insertion of the nipples from behind, tighten up on both sides of the table end until the hardware is locked tightly in place. Connect gate valves to the outer ends of the nipples.

Wave Generator. Obtain a small piston-type aquarium aerator motor which uses a leather diaphragm as the piston within the cylinder. Dismantle the cylinder, piston and connecting rod.

A 5-inch metal rod, threaded at each end, may now be inserted in the end of the connecting rod to replace the screw that formerly held the leather diaphragm in place. Reassemble the unit, passing the metal rod through a hole drilled in the bottom of the cylinder. To the free end of the rod, attach a 3 × 6 inch panel of rubber (the wave paddle). Mount the wave generator on a platform clamped to the side of the stream table, with the wave paddle inserted in the water.

In the absence of a wave generator, satisfactory results may be attained by rhythmically paddling the water by hand with a block of wood.

Maintenance. Remove the sand, scrape and repaint the metal lining, and recaulk the rubber hinge at least once a year.

Operation

To set up the stream table, elevate it by placing two flat 2 × 4 inch timbers under upper end of the small (drain) section, and four flat 2 × 4 inch timbers under upper end of the large (spray) section. Always support hinged end of large section with wooden blocks to compensate for elevation changes. Connect spray system to water source and pipe water level controls to drain. Approximately 500 pounds of fine sand are required to fill the stream table. Place half of the sand in the larger section, extending slightly past the hinge into the lower section. Cover the sand with plastic sheeting with the edges turned up 1 inch on all sides. Place the balance of the sand in the stream table covering the plastic sheet and extending well down into the smaller section. Provide an automobile jack to raise and lower the large section.

Prior to each demonstration, open water level control valves above desired water level as a precaution against possible flooding. Test water supply and spray heads. Wet sand thoroughly and shape basic topography required by demonstration.

Oceanic Density Currents. To create a turbidity current, shape a steep shoreline and remove all sand from the sloping basin floor. Fill the basin to the top drain level. Mix one quarter cup of soil with three quarters cup of water. Pour mixture slowly into the basin at the steeply sloping shore line. Note current flow of dense mud slurry under the clear body of water in the basin and deposition of fine (mud) sediment over wide area on basin bottom.

A temperature current may be induced by repeating the demonstration substantially as outlined above. Fill the basin, however, with warm water and mix food dye in a cup of ice cold water, then proceed as before. Note current flow of cool (dense) water beneath body of warm (less dense) water.

A salinity current will result if the demonstration is repeated with food dye mixed in a cup of saturated salt solution at the same temperature as the basin

water. Observe current flow of saline (dense) water beneath body of fresh (less dense) water.

A control demonstration may be run by taking a cup of water from the basin and tinting it lightly with food dye. Pour it into the basin as before and watch slow dilution and absence of current flow.

Shorelines. Shape shoreline with inland topography of moderate relief and steeply sloping beach. Fill basin to half of beach height. This will establish base line from which to relate submergence and emergence. Raise water level until stream valleys and other low areas are inundated. Note estuaries, bays, peninsulas, and numerous islands characteristic of shorelines of submergence.

For a shoreline of emergence, generate waves briefly, open drain valve and allow water level to recede to lowest possible level, exposing the sand transported from upland area and deposited in ocean basin. Note gently sloping coastal plain of low relief.

Beach Formation. Form a steeply sloped beach. Raise the water level to about half the height of the beach. Generate waves until equilibrium is reached between land and sea. Watch the progressive development of nip stage, wave-cut notch, abrasion platform, shoreline terrace, and finally the beach. Careful observation during the beach formation will reveal particle sorting and beach drifting of individual sand grains.

To form an elevated beach, lower water level halfway down newly formed beach. Generate waves until a new beach is developed at lower level. Observe repetition of process at lower level, and elevated shoreline indicating change of relative level between land and sea.

Spits. Shape a cliffed headland projecting onto a shallow offshore shelf. Generate waves in basin so that waves approach headland normal to shoreline. Observe erosion of headland cliff, longshore drift of individual particles and development of spits on both sides of headland.

Tombolo. Shape an island on a shallow offshore shelf. Generate waves in basin so that waves approach the island in an oblique direction. Continue wave generation until transport of sediment from island beach along spit, via longshore drift, forms a tombolo connecting the island to the mainland.

Bay-mouth Bar. Shape a shallow bay, flanked by a high, steep shore line, opening onto a shallow offshore shelf. Generate waves in basin so that waves approach the bay mouth normal to the shoreline. Continue wave generation until development of spits progressing simultaneously from both sides closes off the bay with a bay-mouth bar. Observe the effect this transition has in simplifying the coastline.

Submarine Sand Dunes. Position lower section of the stream table in level attitude and form a sloping beach in the vicinity of the hinge. Fill the basin thus formed to the bottom of the lowest drain outlet, leaving all drains open. Gently sweep any sand on the basin up to the beach. Pour sand to form three small conical mounds on the otherwise bare basin bottom. Induce a swift current around the perimeter of the basin by discharging a flow of water along one side with the supply hose or by substituting an off-centered soft rubber panel for the regular wave generator paddle.

As the current flows, subaqueous transverse ridges will form near the shore line where sand is plentiful, and subaqueous barchans will develop on the basin bottom where sand is scarce. In both cases, note the asymmetrical profile and the direction of movement caused by sand grains being eroded from the low sloping side and deposited on the steep lee side.

Sedimentation. Shape a stream bed from a single water source down to a steeply sloping shore line. Place a strip of glass (approximately 6 × 20 inches) on edge alongside of stream mouth, with one end embedded in the sand and the other jutting well out into the basin area. Initiate a gentle stream flow until a thin layer of sand is transported to basin and deposited on the bottom. Stop stream flow. Place half a cup of wet, colored sand across stream bed just above stream mouth. Continue stream flow until the colored sand is transported to the basin and deposited in a layer on top of the previous sediments. Repeat process several times, alternating the colors of the sand. When the process has been repeated the desired number of times, drain basin completely and clean outer side of the glass. The view through the glass will reveal bedding of the various sediments, and the development of facies and pinchouts.

Stream Types. The effect of a rising ridge is obtained by lowering the upper section, thus shifting the relative elevation of the ridge upward.

Antecedent Stream. Raise the upper section of the stream table to an intermediate level. Construct a ridge across the width of the stream table. Shape a shallow depression in the center of the ridge, turn on the sprays and fill the basin formed by the ridge. As the lake thus formed overflows through the gap, start to lower the stream table section slowly. Pace the lowering of the stream table to a slower rate than the down-cutting of the stream channel as it passes through the ridge, thus maintaining the original course.

Subsequent Stream. Raise the upper section of the stream table near to its maximum elevation. Construct a curved ridge across the width of the stream table. Shape a shallow depression in the center of the ridge, and a deep gap at the upper side of the ridge. Turn on the sprays, and fill the basin formed by the ridge. As the lake thus formed overflows through the shallow gap, start to lower the stream table section quickly to its normal position. Note that the rising ridge precludes further flow through the original gap, thus trapping the stream. As the basin

fills, the lower gap is reached, and a new stream channel, breaching the ridge, is formed. A wind gap, elevated on ridge, marks the old stream course.

Superimposed Stream. Raise upper stream table section to intermediate level. Construct a ridge of compacted moist sand across the width of the stream table. Fill area on both sides of the ridge with loose, unconsolidated dry sand to level slightly above ridge top. Turn on sprays, allowing a gentle stream flow over loose sand and ridge. The stream quickly establishes a channel in the unconsolidated, dry sand, and as downcutting of this established channel continues, it cuts through the ridge without being diverted or trapped.

Stream Capture. Raise upper table section to intermediate level. Construct a curved ridge across the width of the stream table so that it is directly under the most downgrade spray head. Shape a deep gap in the upper side of the ridge. Start moderate stream flow and observe progress. (It may be necessary to concentrate spray flow to facilitate headward erosion at the ridge.) As basin fills up, stream flow proceeds through the side gap. As the ridge is breached however, by headward erosion of the stream formed by the end spray head, the main flow is diverted into a new course leaving the old channel abandoned.

Stream Erosion Cycle. Shape slight center depression down entire length of sand in stream table. Elevate large section to maximum gradient. Use a single water source, and turn water on for a heavy flow of short duration. Stop stream flow when a gorge-like stream course is developed. At this stage, the youthful stream has a straight course, steeply sloping valley walls and depth equal to or exceeding width (no flood plain). Now lower large section to intermediate gradient, and resume moderate stream flow until above-noted features are moderated. Typical of early maturity is the slight deviation from a straight course, lessened steepness of valley walls, and width beginning to exceed depth (slight flood plain). For full maturity, lower large section of table to lowest gradient. Turn on water slightly allowing continual, gentle stream flow. Note meandering course, recession and diminution of valley walls, and extreme width compared to shallow depth (extensive flood plain). Observe development of meanders, terraces, bluffs, bars and spits, cutoffs, chutes, oxbow lakes, braided streams, and downgrade progression of a meander.

Peneplain and Monadnock. On site of greatest spray concentration, loosely shape sand into semblance of mountain chains with an occasional high peak. If desired, a block of granite may be buried under the sand to simulate a magmatic intrusion. Turn on sprays and wait until area is almost leveled and granite is exposed. Note that processes of erosion have reduced the former rugged terrain to one of low relief with a monadnock exposed where underlain by resistant rock.

Alluvial Fan. Form a stream bed on the upper section, terminated by a bluff or cliff near the middle of the stream table. Shape a flat plain at the foot of the bluff. Allow a slight stream flow over the cliff until a satisfactory alluvial fan is developed. Note the fan-shaped outline, constant slope and changing course of the stream bed.

Delta. Form a central valley down to a steeply sloping shoreline. Fill basin to slightly below level of the valley mouth. Allow a moderate stream flow and follow the progressive development of the delta, particularly the bottom-set, foreset and top-set beds, and the changing course of the distributaries.

Groundwater. Proceeding from the upper end of the stream table, form a lake bed, lowland, hilltop, hillside and small basin. Control single water source to keep lake level full until water flows at bottom of demonstration area. Sink a well hole in the hillside. Consider the water level of each of the following in relation to the surface and the underlying plastic sheet: lake, swamp, well, pond, spring and stream.

Slump. Thoroughly wet all the sand in the table. Construct a ridge across the stream table, fronted by a steep slope. Turn on sprays and allow water to accumulate behind the ridge. As earth flow progresses, there will be characteristic slumping of saturated material, step-like terraces, scarps and a bulging "toe." To create a slump block, repeat the above with a brick buried in the ridge face. Watch the rotary backward motion on a horizontal axis, curved slip plane and bulging "toe."

Rockslide. Slope a valley down the center of the table. Construct a steep hill adjacent to the valley. Place a piece of glass on the hillside, with one edge in the stream bed, and build up a hillside on the glass surface. Allow a gentle stream flow and pour water onto the upper exposed surface of the glass above the reconstructed hillside. Continue stream flow and glass wetting until rockslide occurs. The hillside will start movement as a whole, with sliding motion over flat plane (wet glass). Observe damming of stream, formation of lake and subsequent cutting of new stream channel when lake rises to sufficient level.

Talus Cone. Form a cliff with flat terrain at the base. Notch the edge of the cliff at one point. Mix a few small pebbles in a pile of dry, fine sand. Slowly push or pour the mixture into the notched cliff edge. Proceed until a satisfactory cone is formed. Note fan-shaped plan of the cone and sorting as pebbles roll to the bottom during cone development. Slope angle closely approximates 35°.

Faults. Start with the table in standard position. Construct a broad plateau of hard packed, semi-moist sand across the width of the table, centered above the hinge. Raise the stream table to its maximum elevation. This will generate a thrust fault with overriding of one section upon the other as a result of crustal compression.

For a normal fault, start with stream table at maximum elevation. Construct a plateau of hard packed, semi-moist sand across the width of the table, with one edge above the hinge. Shape balance of broad plateau of loosely assembled dry sand. Lower stream table to standard position. Note difference in elevation and outward displacement of sections, as a result of crustal extension.

Starting with the stream table at maximum elevation, a graben or rift valley will result by constructing a plateau of hard packed, semi-moist sand across the width of the table, with a trough centered above the hinge. Fill the trough with loosely assembled dry sand and lower stream table to standard position. Observe drop of central block, leaving a flat-bottomed valley with parallel fault-scarped side walls.

M. King Hubbert's classic experimental faulting in sand may be reproduced on the stream table. Stand a strip of glass on edge, longitudinally, in the center of the stream table basin, with one end propped against a drain outlet and the other end embedded in sand. Stand a plywood panel on edge in back of the glass, perpendicular to it. Place alternate layers of light and dark sand in back of the glass on both sides of the plywood. Tamp each layer down firmly. Move the plywood firmly toward the end of the stream table until normal faulting develops on one side with a dip of about 63°; then continue to move the plywood until thrust faulting develops on the other side with a dip of about 28°.

Glacial Landforms. Freeze a pan of water in which a curved metal strip has been placed. Remove and separate the two blocks of ice. Place ice blocks in U-shaped valley with their corresponding curves slightly separated and the outer edges almost touching the valley walls. Cover blocks of ice with layer of sand. Use a localized water source to wash sand into the space between the blocks of ice, between the ice and the valley walls, and over the lower ends of the ice. Wait until ice melts away leaving the transported sand exposed as free-standing forms. Observe course and symmetrical cross section of crevasse filling, kame terraces along both valley walls, and delta kame elevated above the valley floor.

To produce an esker, freeze a pan of water in which a rubber hose has been submerged lengthwise on the bottom in a curved position. Form a U-shaped valley on the stream table. Remove the rubber hose from the block of ice and place the ice in the valley, with the tunnel thus formed at the bottom. Allow a light flow of ice water to proceed down the valley and through the tunnel under the ice. Continue flow until sand is aggraded along the length of the ice tunnel. Allow ice to melt and reveal sinuous ridge composed of aggraded sediments along course of stream which flowed in ice tunnel.

Next form a broad U-shaped valley, with the bottom close to the level of the plastic sheeting.

Place a ridge of gravel (fine sand and pebbles) across valley mouth. Pile mixture of gravel and crushed ice in valley behind gravel ridge (use considerably more ice than gravel). Partially bury pieces of ice in flat area downgrade from valley. Allow all of the ice to melt and note debris-covered ground moraine or till plain, unsorted terminal moraine, and low relief outwash plain pitted here and there with kettles.

Pillow Lava. Construct a steeply sloping beach. Fill basin until water level is halfway up beach slope. Melt lead or solder in a plumber's ladle and quickly pour onto sloping beach, just above the shore line. Note rounded, stacked appearance of forms created by melt as it is rapidly cooled by the water. Observe that the spaces between the pillow structures are filled with sediment during the violent agitation accompanying their formation.

MAURICE L. SCHWARTZ

References

Balchin, W. V. G., 1952, "Practical and Experimental Geography," p. 48, New York, John Wiley & Sons.

Brown, W. C., 1960, "Classroom stream table," *J. Geol. Educ.*, **8**, No. 2, 63–64.

Dzulynski, St., and Walton, E. K., 1963, "Experimental production of sole markings," *Trans. Edinburgh Geol. Soc.*, **19**, 279–305.

Hubbert, M. K., 1951, "Mechanical basis for certain familiar geologic structures, "*Bull. Geol. Soc. Am.*, **62**, 355–372.

Schwartz, M. L., 1963, "Stream table development of glacial landforms," *J. Geol. Educ.*, **11**, No. 1, 29–30.

Strong, C. L., 1963, "How to construct a stream table to simulate geological processes," in "The amateur Scientist," *Sci. Am.* **208**, No. 4, 168–179.

STREAMS—*See* RIVERS

STREAMS—UNDERFIT

Underfit streams are streams which have undergone drastic reduction of discharge and which are now too small for the valleys (or, less usually, the channels) which they occupy. Reduction should be

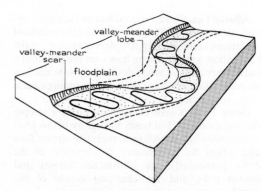

FIG. 1. Manifestly underfit stream.

understood to refer to channel-forming discharge, which is discharge at or near the bankfull stage; more precisely, the reduction refers to that discharge frequency which corresponds to channel-forming discharge.

(1) Field Characteristics

(a) Change of Channel Trace. Underfit streams were first recognized and named by Davis (see references in Dury, 1964a), who confined himself to those which combine stream meanders with valley meanders (Fig. 1). Underfit streams of this type are now classed as *manifestly underfit*. Stream shrinkage is indicated by the known relationship between meander wavelength and channel-forming discharge; the largeness of the valley meanders shows that this discharge was formerly greater than it is now. On some other streams which flow in meandering valleys, meanders are absent from the present channel, but the spacing of pools and riffles shows that if stream meanders did occur, they would be smaller than the valley meanders (Fig. 2). Streams of this, the Osage, type are also underfit.

(b) Change of Channel Cross Section. The floodplains of many underfit streams are known to be underlain by large channels (Dury, 1964b). These channels were cut by the same large former streams which cut valley meanders. Numbers of

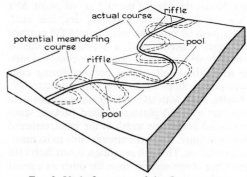

FIG. 2. Underfit stream of the Osage type.

the channels, consequent on reduction of discharge, have been infilled both laterally and vertically.

(2) Degree of Reduction

(a) **Reduction of Dimensions.** On some streams (or reaches), the wavelengths of valley meanders are ten times those of stream meanders, but a ratio of five to one is more common. Corresponding reductions have occurred in channel width.

(b) **Reduction of Discharge.** The dimensional changes indicate reduction in channel-forming discharge to as little as one-fiftieth of its former value, but more commonly to about one-twentieth (Dury, 1965).

(3) Causes of Reduction

(a) **Special.** The shrinkage of some streams is due, in whole or in part, to river capture, glacial diversion, the cessation of meltwater discharge, or some other type of derangement.

(b) **General.** The regionally operating cause of underfitness is climatic change, which has affected streams in the northern hemisphere, at least in the range from $66\frac{1}{2}$ to $18\frac{1}{2}°$ latitude. Less is known about the southern hemisphere, but it seems likely that similar conditions obtain there also. Climatic change may have included increase in temperature (with accompanying increase in evapotranspiration) or decrease in precipitation; in practice, these factors appear to have operated in combination.

(4) Chronology of Reduction

The last episode of shrinkage, which caused the large former streams to dwindle so that they no longer maintained large meanders or kept their large channels clear, occurred in the range 9000–12,000 years ago (Dury, 1964b). That is, the last major change was associated with the rapid waning of the continental ice caps. Since then, lesser fluctuations involving spans of centuries have alternately favored channeling and filling. The most pronounced of these, an episode of channel clearance, occurred about 5000–6000 years ago. Areas which were still covered by land ice at a later time can nevertheless have underfit streams; these areas have been affected by climatic change subsequent to ice recession.

Ice recession and climatic change associated with glacials earlier than the last are also likely to have reduced streams to an underfit condition. However, less is known of this matter than of cutting of valley meanders, which on some rivers began very early in the Pleistocene.

(5) Degree of Climatic Change

Reconstruction of climate at the last glacial maximum involved low-level air temperatures as much as 15°C lower than present temperatures, for places near the former limits of the ice. But since the large former meanders were still in use when the ice was receding, underfit streams have been affected by a lesser change—perhaps something in the range 5–10°C. In addition, they have been affected by decrease in precipitation, to about one-half or two-thirds of its former value (Dury, 1965). Climatic changes of this order, occurring on a continent-wide scale, explain the continent-wide distribution of underfit streams between the Arctic Circle and the Tropic of Cancer.

G. H. DURY

References

Davis, W. H., 1913, "Meandering valleys and underfit rivers," *Am. Assoc. Geog. Ann.,* **3,** 150–152.

Dury, G. H., 1964a, "Principles of underfit streams," *U.S. Geol. Surv. Profess. Paper* **452-A.**

Dury, G. H., 1964b, "Subsurface exploration and chronology of underfit streams," *U.S. Geol. Surv. Profess. Paper* **452-B.**

Dury, G. H., 1965, "Theoretical implications of underfit streams," *U.S. Geol. Surv. Profess. Paper* **452-C.**

Cross-references: *Floodplain*; *Glacial Geology*; *Glacial Spillways*; *Morphogenetic Classification*; *Relict Landforms*; *River Capture, Piracy*; *Rivers—Meandering and Braiding*; *Stream Channel Characteristics.* Vol. II: *Climatic Variations—Historical Record.*

STRENGTH OF SEDIMENTS—*See* pr Vol. VI

STRIAE, STRIATED PAVEMENT

The expression *striae* (always plural) or *striation* is generally applied to scratches, scourings or furrows gouged on a rock surface by the boulders and smaller debris caught up in the sole of a moving glacier. Characteristic *chattermarks* often show the direction of motion (Chamberlin, 1888). Considerable glacial abrasion (frictional scour) is obtained in this way. Striation may also be found on the larger pebbles and boulders that "arm" the glacier; in this case, however, one should speak of "attrition" since the process will gradually lead to the reduction of the boulders in question. *Pseudoglacial striae* (Kayser, 1912) and *faceted surfaces* (Popescu-Voitesti, 1925) may occur on boulders carried by salt or gypsum in diapirs. Mudflows and soil creep may also produce some striae. Therefore, if there is any possibility of confusion, where the ice-scratched examples are involved, they may be called "*glacial striae.*"

A *striated pavement* that has long, uniform gouges or short, parallel scratches is regarded almost as proof positive of a trace of former glacial activity. Most of the harder rocks of the Canadian Shield (over 1 million square miles), those of the Fennoscandian Shield and many

FIG. 1. Fine glacial striations (of Pleistocene age) cutting across slate, at Kilchiaran, Islay, Scotland. (Photo: Geol. Survey, Great Britain).

mountainous areas in Central Asia, bear these marks of the Pleistocene glacial stages. Similar striated pavements (largely covered by younger sediments) are found over the entire southern hemisphere on the surfaces of the rocks that were exposed in late Carboniferous and Permian times, although, of course, many have now been destroyed or are still covered by younger sediments. The same is true for several stages of the Precambrian though for these very old rocks, the evidence is much more scattered (Schwarzbach, 1963).

In glaciated valleys, the former level of the ice may be measured precisely by the so-called *scoring* or *scouring limit* (German, *Schliffkehle*) on the valley sides (Penck 1905). Where striated surfaces occur high up on cirque headwalls, it is probably evidence of a former more extensive ice cap or carapace (Dort, 1957).

RHODES W. FAIRBRIDGE

References

Chamberlin, T. C., 1888, "The rock scourings of the great ice invasions," *U.S. Geol. Surv., Ann. Rept.*, **7**, 147–248.

Dort, W., Jr., 1957, "Striated surfaces on the upper parts of cirque headwalls," *J. Geol.*, **65**, No. 5.

Kayser, E., 1912, "Lehrbuch der Geologie," Fourth ed., Vol. 1, Stuttgart, Enke.

Penck, A., 1905, "Glacial features in the surface of the Alps," *J. Geol.*, **13**, 1–19.

Popescu–Voitesti, I., 1925, "Galettes à facettes, dans la brèche tectonique des massifs de sel de Roumanie," *Compt. Rend. Acad. Sci., Paris*, **180**, 1113.

FIG. 2. Pleistocene striations and grooves with abrupt terminations, and with "disruptive gouges" convex in the direction of ice movement, on sandstone at Amherst, Ohio (Chamberlin, 1888).

FIG. 3. Highly polished and lightly striated pavement of Permo-Carboniferous age, on Precambrian mudstone. Hallett Cove, South Australia.

FIG. 4. Deeply grooved pavement of Permo-Carboniferous age in the Inman Valley, South Australia. Note secondary abrasion by modern glacial scour. (Photo: Rhodes W. Fairbridge)

Schwarzbach, M., 1963, "Climates of the Past" (Das Klima der Vorzeit), London and Princeton, D. van Nostrand Co. (translated from German, 1961 ed., by R. O. Muir).

Cross-references: *Glacial Geology*; *Glacial Scour*; *Mudflow*; *Quaternary Period*; *Soil Creep*. Vol. V: *Diapirism*; *Halokinesis*; *Salt Domes*. Vol. VI: *Attrition*; *Icecap*.

STRUCTURAL CONTROL IN GEOMORPHOLOGY

By structural control in geomorphology is here meant the influence of geologic structures on the development and appearance of landscapes. The influence of geologic structures ranges from large features which exert a dominant influence on the form of an entire landscape, to small features which affect an individual landform and the geomorphic processes operating on it. For example, the physiography of the Black Hills of South Dakota is controlled by the great domal structure on which these hills are developed (see *Dome Mountains*), whereas the shape of a ridge crest in the Ridge and Valley of the Folded Appalachians may be determined locally by the direction and intensity of joints in the Tuscarora Quartzite (see *Ridge and Valley Topography*).

For purposes of this discussion, structural control in geomorphology is separated into two basic types:

(1) Active structures whose form is directly impressed on the modern landscape.

(2) Ancient structural features whose influence on a modern landscape is due primarily to differential erosion.

Active Structures

Structures which have undergone movement in Quaternary time are commonly visible directly in the present landscape (see *Neotectonics*). Because such movement is most generally small, these features are most easily recognized in areas of low relief and recent deposition. Such areas as coastal plains, alluvial fans, and interior plains show the effect of recent local structural deformation which includes "draping" of sedimentary rocks over buried structures or topography. The aerial photograph, which gives a three-dimensional, bird's-eye view of the landscape is an important tool in such studies.

In the Gulf Coastal Plain of the southern United States, the gentle uplift of the surface over rising salt domes commonly causes radial and concentric drainage patterns (see below) to develop. The subtle topographic highs associated with such uplifts are obvious in the better internal drainage of the soil and often in a more dense drainage pattern. In the western United States where modern fault movement is found, alluvial fans of recent origin are sometimes cut by small fault scarps ("scarplets") which break

the otherwise smooth longitudinal profile of the fan. Recent movements along the San Andreas Fault in California, as well as similar faults in New Zealand, Japan and elsewhere, have resulted in lateral offsets of fences and roads. Across these faults streams of various sizes have also been offset laterally by former movements.

Several major oil companies have used the geomorphic expression of geologic structures in low relief areas ("flatlands") as a method of reconnaissance oil exploration in the search for possibly petroliferous structures. All told, however, the study of the influence of active structures in geomorphology has received less study than the influence of old structures in erosional topography. To correct this state of affairs, the International Union of Geodesy and Geophysics has established a *Commission on Neotectonics and Recent Movements of the Earth's Crust*, and several symposia have been organized.

Ancient Structural Features

Nearly all landscapes whose form and pattern is due primarily to erosion rather than deposition show the influence of geologic structures to a greater or lesser extent. The structures herein to be considered are assumed to have undergone all or most of their deformation in pre-Quaternary time.

As these landscapes are due primarily to erosion and the structures are inactive today, the basic concept underlying any discussion of the role of such structural influence in geomorphology may be simply stated as follows:

"The influence of inactive geologic structures in erosional landscapes is due to the differential or selective nature of the weathering and erosional processes."

Stated in more expanded form, this concept holds that such structural influence is manifest in an erosional landscape because (1) weathering and erosion attack different types of rocks at different rates under various climates, and (2) structural deformation causes a variety of rock types to be present at the topographic surface. It must be borne in mind that such structural deformation may range from simple tilting to complex folding.

The differential nature of the weathering and erosional processes operates at all scales. Thus the Appalachian Ridges stand topographically above the intervening valleys because they are composed of more resistant rock. At the same time, in the slopes of these ridges, thinner formations of more and less resistant rocks (i.e., a thin layer of sandstone in a section of shale) will make a small break in slope. Or again, on the microrelief scale, in a granite boss the individual feldspar grains may be weathered more rapidly than the quartz grains, giving the rock a pitted appearance (see *Corrosion* and *Granite Landforms*).

A corollary of the basic concept holds that no

matter how intense the deformation of the rocks is, if the rocks possess uniform resistance to erosion, the structure will not be manifested in the topography. Large areas of uniform rock resistance are not common, but crystalline rocks may approach this condition, and their joint patterns become the dominant controls in differential weathering. In the Appalachian Piedmont, the structural deformation in the uniformly complex crystalline metamorphics (deeply cloaked by saprolite) is poorly expressed in the topography and in many cases is not expressed at all. Similarly, in the Appalachian Valley intense deformations of thick shale sequences are not expressed unless thin beds of siltstone or limestone are present. Conversely, if the rock resistance to weathering and erosion ranges widely, as in the Appalachian Ridge and Valley Section, the gross structural deformation is clearly apparent in the topography. The greatest range in rock resistance to erosion is usually found in sedimentary terranes; therefore, geologic structures are most clearly expressed in such areas.

Climate, as it directly effects weathering and erosion, plays an important role in the geomorphic expression of structure. For example, limestone, which weathers primarily by solution, is often a "weak" rock in humid regions but a "resistant" rock in arid regions. The terms "weak" and "resistant" are, of course, relative and, therefore, dependent on climate. In many humid areas, limestone is "weak" relative to siltstone, but in dry areas it may be "resistant" relative to the same siltstone.

Climate also influences the clarity or "sharpness" of the topographic expression of structure. In humid areas (non-glaciated), a thick weathered mantle (*Saprolite*; also *Head*) commonly develops and tends to mask the small variations in rock resistance. In arid areas, however, the weathered mantle tends to be thinner and less continuous, resulting in topographic expression of even minor differences in erosion. Finally, microclimatic differences, or differences in the degree of exposure to weathering, also affect the expression of various

rock units. For example, in southern California it is common to see a clear expression of different rock layers in the profile of western slopes of hills and ridges but a smoother profile (masking of rock differences) on the eastern slopes.

In addition to the structural control in geomorphology due to the differences in rock resistance to erosion which are expressed in the landforms themselves, the development of the regional stream or drainage pattern is similarly affected. Particular *drainage patterns* (q.v.) are associated with certain types of structural deformation as discussed below.

For the sake of simplicity the following discussion will deal first with the geomorphic influence of large and "simple" structures and will conclude with some smaller and more indirect structural influences. For the reasons given above, most of the examples will be drawn from sedimentary rock terranes within which the rocks have a markedly different resistance to erosion.

Simple Regional Tilting

Simple, uniform regional tilting (*homoclinal structure*) is expressed very directly in the physiography. The expression is a function, among other things, of the amount of tilt which is here considered to be recorded in the dip of the rocks (i.e., initial dip is assumed equal to zero). As the regional tilting may be any amount, it is obvious that a complete gradation exists among the various geomorphic expressions affected by the amount of dip. The breakdown that follows, therefore, is artificial and for the sake of clarity.

(*a*) *Zero Tilt*. The case of absolutely horizontal surfaces is very rare in present landscapes, being perhaps most closely approximated by the floors of former lakes such as glacial lakes. Since the surface and the sedimentary bedding are horizontal, only one type of lithology is theoretically exposed at the surface and differential erosion is not effective. Such a condition, one of literally no structural control, is manifested by an insequent drainage pattern [Fig. 1(a)] which is believed to be possible only in areas

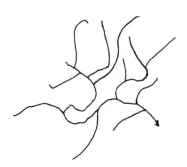

(a)   (b)

FIG. 1. (a) Insequent drainage. (b) Dendritic drainage.

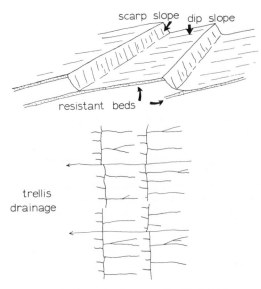

FIG. 2. Cuesta landscape and trellis drainage.

where no regional structural control is apparent.

(b) *Gentle Tilt and No Differential Erosion.* An area which has undergone very gentle tilting so that only a single rock type underlies the surface, or an area of steeper tilt but underlain by a single, homogeneous rock type, will also exhibit no differential erosion effects. The geomorphic expression of such a structural condition is believed to be the dendritic drainage pattern—the familiar branching, tree-like pattern [Fig. 1(b)].

(c) *Gentle Tilt and Differential Erosion.* If an area is tilted up to about 6 or 7°, i.e., the dip is up to about 7° (depending on climate), and layers of different rock types are exposed to erosion, the cuesta landform (Fig. 2) will develop. Such landforms give rise to a "belted" topography such as the belted coastal plains of the eastern and southern United States.

The gentle dip slope (Fig. 2) of the cuesta is controlled approximately by the direction and amount of dip. The valleys follow the strike of weaker beds, and the cuesta crest follows the outcrop of the more resistant beds. Such cuesta forms may extend for many miles as in the case of the Niagara Escarpment in the Great Lakes region, the Cotswold Hills in England, or the Schwabische Alb in Bavaria.

The main consequent drainage cuts across the cuestas, the subsequent drainage follows the strike valleys, long tributaries to the subsequent drainage flow down the dip slopes of the cuestas (flowing in the dip direction), and short, steep tributaries flow down the scarp face. The result is the classic trellis drainage pattern (Fig. 2).

(d) *Moderate Tilt and Differential Erosion.* As the tilting (dip) becomes steeper, up to about 20–25°, the cuestas are made narrower and become asymmetrical ridges [Fig. 3(a)]. Such asymmetrical ridges are very common in the Jura Mountains, in the Appalachians and throughout the western United States.

(e) *Steep Tilt and Differential Erosion.* If the tilting (dip) becomes steeper than about 20–25° (higher in arid areas, lower in humid areas), symmetrical ridges are developed. As shown in Fig. 3(b), talus and soil coming from the ridge achieve an angle of repose which is less than the dip of the resistant layer or layers forming the ridge. The ridge is symmetrical because the slopes on both sides are the same and equal to the angle of the repose of the weathered material. At the eastern "front" of the Rocky Mountains in Colorado, for example, such ridges developed on the Dakota sandstone and other formations extend for miles and are called "*hogbacks*" (q.v.), a term applied to such features usually in semiarid and arid regions. Dipslopes along the east-facing side are termed "*flat-irons*".

Folding

Folding, as anticlines, synclines, domes, and

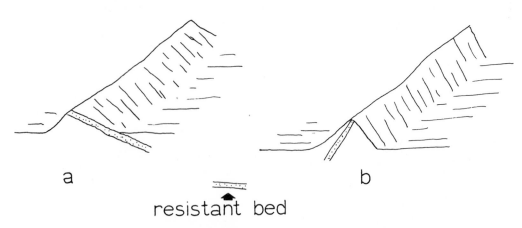

FIG. 3. (a) Asymmetrical ridge, (b) Symmetrical ridge ("hogback").

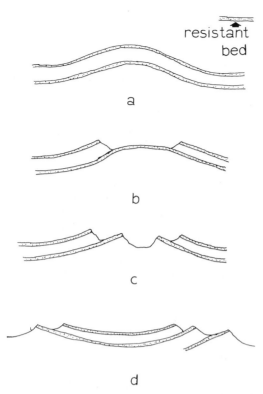

FIG. 4. Cross sections of: (a) unbreached dome, (b) partially breached dome, (c) breached dome, (d) basin.

the topographic surface [Fig. 4(a)]. Partial breaching may also occur as in Fig. 4(b), or the structure may be breached [Fig. 4(c)].

(*a*) *Unbreached Dome or Anticline.* In the case of an unbreached uplift, differential erosion is not, of course, effective, and the structure is shown directly in the topography and perhaps by the drainage pattern. The radial drainage pattern [Fig. 5(a)] is commonly developed, particularly on domes.

(*b*) *Partially Breached Dome or Anticline.* The partially breached uplift exhibits, around the unbreached center, more or less concentric ridges which, depending on the amount of dip, may be cuestas, asymmetrical or symmetrical ridges. The strike valleys developed on the weaker rocks cause the subsequent drainage to be concentric to the structure, and a common drainage pattern is, therefore, the radial and concentric pattern [Fig. 5(b)]. Although the center is crystalline rock, the Black Hills approximate a partially breached dome.

(*c*) *Breached Dome or Anticline.* In a breached uplift, the center is developed on weaker rock and, therefore, is topographically lower than the surrounding ridges. Again, depending on amount of dip, these ridges may be any of the types listed in the previous section. The Appalachian Ridges and Valleys are a typical example of a topography strongly affected by breached anticlines.

(*d*) *Basins and Synclines.* Basins and synclines are not affected by breaching, but concentric ridges may surround these structures [Fig. 4(d)]. These ridges may be any of the three basic types discussed previously.

Faulting and Fracturing

Active faulting was discussed at the beginning of this article, and the discussion here is limited to faulting which is no longer active. Faulting and fracturing (which may or may not be associated with

basins, is expressed geomorphologically mostly as one, or a combination, of the features discussed under regional tilting. The additional factor of breaching or lack of breaching enters the consideration of domes and anticlines (see *Dome Mountains*). An unbreached fold is an anticline or dome in which a resistant bed is continuous across the structure at

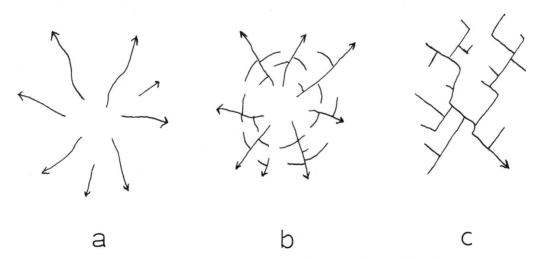

FIG. 5. (a) Radial drainage. (b) Radial and concentric drainage. (c) Rectangular drainage.

faulting) have not to date received as much study as the geomorphic expression of tilting and folding.

Faulting and fracturing have a unique geomorphic property—they may render an otherwise uniform rock (i.e., one possessing a uniform resistance to erosion) subject to differential erosion. Faulting and fracturing (including jointing and "shear zones") usually weaken an otherwise resistant rock, but if mineralization or intrusion follows these faults or fracture zones, a more resistant belt may develop. Consequently, most zones of faulting or fracturing may result in topographic "lows" but some cause ridges.

The geomorphic expression of fracturing and faulting depends on the steepness of dip of the zone. In general, the steeper the dip, i.e., the more nearly vertical, the more obvious is the topographic influence.

The topographic effect of inactive faults or fracture zones may be divided into several categories.

(a) Faults. One of the most obvious geomorphic effects of faulting is topographic offset (see *Fault Scarps*). Here again the effect can usually best be seen where differential erosion has occurred. For example, a ridge following the outcrop of a resistant bed may be offset at a fault because the resistant bed on which it is developed had been offset by the fault sometime in the past. Similarly a series of ridges surrounding a fold may be offset by a fault crossing the strike of the beds which form the ridges.

Generally, if the topography is not offset, as in the case of a fault which parallels the strike of the bedding, the fault cannot be detected from the physiography.

(b) *Faults and Fracture Zones*. Even if no offset is apparent along a fault, or in the case of a fracture zone within which the rocks are broken but along which no stratigraphic offset has occurred, these features may be expressed in the topography. The rocks are generally weakened along these zones and hence are "etched out" by differential erosion. Linear valleys not related to strike of the bedrock may follow such zones which are particularly obvious if they trend at a high angle to the strike of the rocks. A system of well-developed joints, fracture zones or small faults may give rise to a rectangular drainage pattern with many straight stream segments and sharp, angular changes in stream direction [Fig. 5(c)].

Experience has indicated, as expected, that faults, fracture zones and jointing have a more obvious topographic manifestation in arid areas than in moist areas. The aerial photograph is a uniquely powerful tool, particularly in arid areas, for studying the geomorphic influence of such rock breakage.

Special Cases

(a) *Crystalline Rocks*. Structural patterns in igneous and metamorphic rocks are usually not as apparent as those in sedimentary rocks because the differences in the resistance to erosion of the various crystalline rocks are not so marked as those of the sedimentary rocks. The crystalline rock structures are frequently of small scale and quite complicated, which further diminishes their obvious structural expression.

Nevertheless, broad "swirling" patterns in metamorphic terranes are visible on high-altitude, small-scale, aerial photographs, and the recent use of satellite photography and radar imagery has disclosed such patterns in Scotland and Canada. These broad patterns, covering hundreds of square miles, are a topographic reflection of different crystalline lithologies, but this topographic expression is too subtle and of too large a scale to be seen by the ground observer.

If, of course, adjacent crystalline rocks have considerable difference in resistance to weathering and erosion, this difference will be "etched out" and expressed in the topography.

(b) *Carbonate Rocks*. Since limestone and dolomite weather primarily by solution, the topographic expression of structure in carbonate terrane is primarily due to differential solution. The differences in solubility are usually not great; therefore, the topographic expression of structures in carbonate terrane, e.g., the Appalachian Valley, is not pronounced. Sometimes the outcrop of a particularly soluble bed is marked by concentrations of sinkholes or the alignment of oriented sinkholes along the outcrop belt. Faults and fracture zones may also be expressed in a similar manner by sinkholes. The joints may well be etched out in *lapiés* (q.v.). Because of the relatively poor topographic expression of structure in carbonate terrane, the aerial photograph is a particularly useful tool in such studies. Generally, structures in carbonate rocks are more obvious in humid than in arid regions.

Summary

In general, the expression of structure in the geomorphology or physiography of a region is due to the different rock types that the structural deformation causes to be exposed to weathering and erosion, or to a weakening or strengthening of the resistance of the rock along the structure (faults and fracture zones). The differential attack of weathering and erosion on these various lithologies "etches" the structural effect into the landscape. Obviously, therefore, the degree of such structural expression depends on the degree of difference in resistance of adjacent rock layers, the selectivity of the weathering attack which is affected by climate and exposure, and to a lesser extent, the thickness of a masking weathered mantle.

All geologists are aware of this structural expression, and the field geologist makes conscious or unconscious use of large and small-scale topographic features in tracing bedding to produce a geologic map.

LAURENCE LATTMAN

References

Cotton, C. A., 1952, "Geomorphology," Sixth ed., New York, John Wiley & Sons, 505pp.

Davis, W. M., 1909, "Geographical Essays," New York (Dover reprint 1954), 777pp.

Hinds, N. E., 1943, "Geomorphology; The Evolution of Landscape," Englewood Cliffs, N.J., Prentice-Hall, 894pp.

Hobbs, W. H., 1931, "Earth Features and Their Meaning," Second ed., pp. 433–445, New York, The Macmillan Co.

Lobeck, A. K., 1939, "Geomorphology, An Introduction to the Study of Landscapes," New York, McGraw-Hill Book Co., 731pp.

Thornbury, W. D., 1954, "Principles of Geomorphology," New York, John Wiley & Sons, 618pp.

Cross-references: *Alluvial Fan; Basin and Range Landscape; Block Mountain; Caldera; Climatic Geomorphology; Coastal Plain; Corrosion; Crater; Crustal Movements; Cuesta; Dome Mountain; Drainage Patterns; Endogenic Dynamics; Erosion; Escarpments; Fault Scarp; Glacial Lakes; Graben; Granite Landforms; Head; Hogback; Horst; International Organizations for Geomorphology; Lapiés; Mountain Types; Neotectonics; Plateau; Quaternary Period; Regolith and Saprolite; Relict Landforms; Ridge and Valley Landscape; Sink, Sinkhole; Talus Fan or Cone; Tectonic Landscape; Terrain; Volcanic Landscapes; Weathering. Vol. II: Climate and Geomorphology; Microclimate. Vol. V: Structural Geology. Vol. VI: Photogeology; Photo Interpretation; Radar Scanning in Geosciences. pr Vol. VIII: Appalachian Province.*

SUBMARINE GEOMORPHOLOGY

Submarine topography, like its terrestrial counterpart, can be interpreted in classical geomorphological terms: *structure, process* and *time* (or stage). The division of the sea floor into physiographic provinces is based largely upon structure. The actively evolving *Mid-Oceanic Ridge* stands above the *ocean basin floors*, which in turn border the *continental margins*. Within these provinces there is a great variety in form. The most fundamental variations reflect the amount of time over which submarine *sedimentation* has acted. As time proceeds there is a general smoothing of the original structural terrain.

Sedimentation is controlled by sediment supply from continents, ocean bottom contour currents, the growth of organisms (hence temperature, salinity), and many other factors. Turbidity currents, glacial action, wave action and slumping are important agents of erosion and deposition. Submarine topography and sediments frequently reflect Pleistocene climatic changes and changes of sea level. Sedimentation covers oceanic structures, of which fracture zones, rifts, trenches, ridges, plateaus, and volcanoes are the most important.

Techniques

Submarine geomorphology is made especially challenging because of the difficulty of observing submarine processes and topography at first hand. In general, submarine topographic data is obtained by echo-sounding devices while surface mapping is based on samples collected by sediment coring devices and dredges. Subsurface information is obtained by seismic methods and by analysis of gravity, magnetic and heat flow data. Additional useful geomorphic information comes from measurement of bottom currents and from visual exploration of the sea floor, as by underwater cameras and submersible vehicles.

Classification of Submarine Topography

Heezen *et al.* (1959) presented an outline classification of submarine topographic features (Fig. 1). The basic division in global geology and geomorphology is between *oceans* and *continents*. However, an appreciable part (about 15%) of the continental crust is submerged, forming the *continental margin* (especially the continental shelf and marginal plateaus). The truly oceanic crust characterizes two provinces, a broad fractured arch called the *Mid-Oceanic Ridge*, and the remaining areas, collectively termed the *ocean basin floor*. The type area for this tripartite division of submarine physiography is the North Atlantic Ocean. However these three divisions are found in all the world's major oceans. Figure 2 gives a map and profile illustrating the distribution and topography of the provinces in the North Atlantic. Figure 3 provides a graphical basis for judging slopes on exaggerated profiles.

Continental Margin. The continental margin includes those provinces associated with the transition from continent to ocean floor. Figure 4 illustrates the type profile of the continental margin provinces. This profile is generally representative of most of the Atlantic and Indian Oceans, but is not typical of the Pacific. The continental margin can be divided into three categories of provinces, which are generally parallel to the coastline (Fig. 5). Category I includes the continental shelf, marginal plateaus and epicontinental seas. Table 1 summarizes dimensional characteristics of these physiographic divisions.

The *continental shelf* is shallow and gently sloping. *Marginal plateaus* are shelflike, but lie at greater depths than normal shelves (Table 1), and are separated from the shelf by an appreciable slope. They are subsided relic shelves.

Category II subdivisions include all the steep slopes which border the continental block. Most common of these is the continental slope, but also

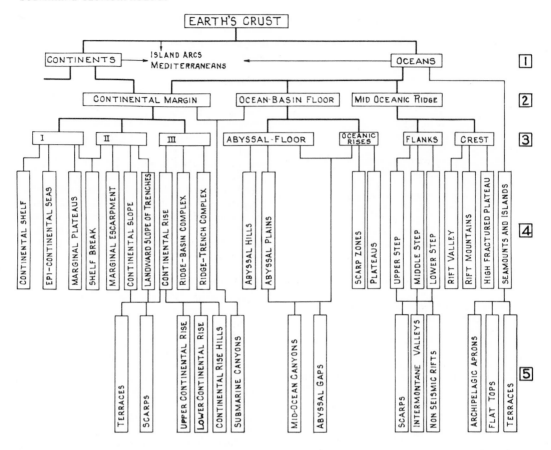

FIG. 1. Outline of submarine topography (Heezen and Menard, 1963; based on Heezen *et al.*, 1959): (1) first-order features of the crust; (2) major oceanic topographic features; (3) superprovinces; (4) provinces; (5) subprovinces and other important features. (By permission of John Wiley & Sons, N.Y.)

included are marginal escarpments and the landward slopes of marginal trenches. The *continental slope* (Figs. 3 and 4) is that relatively steep (3–6°) portion of the sea floor which lies at the seaward border of the continental shelf. The top and bottom of the slope are generally abrupt; the top break in slope is called the *shelf break* (see Table 1 for typical depths, gradients).

Marginal escarpments are precipitous scarps forming the seaward edge of marginal plateaus. *Landward slopes of marginal trenches* are morphologically similar (Table 1).

Category III provinces occur between the continental slope and the ocean basin floor. The simplest case (Fig. 3), that of a more or less continuous, gentle gradient from slope to abyssal floor, is termed the *continental rise*. Less simple is the *marginal basin-outer ridge* complex which consists of a basin at the foot of the continental slope (or marginal escarpment) which is bounded on its seaward side by a broad ridge. A third common province is the *marginal trench-outer ridge complex*. Narrow, steep-sided marginal trenches commonly parallel the trend of the continental margin and are separated from the ocean floor by a low outer ridge.

Figure 5 gives several profiles of continental margins. Figure 6 shows four typical combinations of the provinces of the margin and in addition contains crustal structure information obtained by geophysical methods. The two basic margin types are (1) shelf, slope, rise and (2) broken shelf, landward slope of trench, trench, outer ridge. Another margin type, found locally along parts of the Pacific coast of the United States is the *continental borderland*, which is characterized by numerous depressions and rises. *Submarine canyons* are commonly associated with the continental margins; these are deep gorges cutting nearly all the continental slopes. Other commonly observed features are submerged sand bars and shorelines, terraces and scarps of many kinds, deep sea fans and cones, and others. Of particular significance are *island arcs*, which are a part of the marginal trench-outer ridge complex.

Ocean Basin Floor. The broad floors of the ocean

TABLE 1. TYPICAL DIMENSIONS OF MAJOR FEATURES OF SUBMARINE TOPOGRAPHY (BASED ON HEEZEN *et al.*, 1959, HEEZEN AND MENARD, 1963, AND OTHER SOURCES). MORE EXTREME DIMENSIONS OCCUR

Feature	Typical Dimensions	Comments	Example
Continental shelf	Width: few to >300 km Relief: <20 m Depth: <200 m Gradient: <1:1000	Seaward boundary, or shelf break occurs where gradient changes to >1:40	Northeastern United States (Fig. 4)
Marginal plateau	Similar to shelf except depth: between 200–1200 m	No seaward barrier or sill	Blake Plateau (Fig. 5)
Epicontinental sea	Similar to shelf except depth: between 100–1500 m Relief: often >40 meters	Seaward barrier or sill	Gulf of Maine
Continental slope	Width: few to 150 km Relief: locally >2000 m Depth: drops from 100+ to 2000+ m Gradient: >1:40 (3–6°)	Upper boundary is shelf break; high relief is associated with canyons	Northeastern United States (Fig. 4)
Marginal escarpment	Width: few km Height: 2000–4000 m Depth: begin at 1000–3000 m Gradient: >1:10	Precipitous slope	Blake Escarpment (Fig. 5)
Landward slope of trench	Height: several thousand meters Depth: drop from 500–5000 m Gradient: >1:40	Always associated with trench	North of Puerto Rico (Fig. 5)
Continental rise	Width: few to >300 km Relief: <40 m Depth: 1500–5000 m Gradient: 1:1000 to 1:700	Seaward limit is change to <1:1000, although 1:2500 (and 1:50) can occur	Northeastern United States (Fig. 4)
Outer ridge	Width: >150 km Height: 200–2000 m	Lies seaward of a basin or trench	North of Puerto Rico (Fig. 5)
Marginal basin	Variable dimensions Depth: <5000 m Gradient: often <1:1000	Defined by position *re* outer ridge, continental slope	Blake Plateau area (Fig. 5)
Marginal trench	Width: 30–100 km Length: 300–5000 km Depth: 3000–10,000 m Relief: >2000 m	Narrow, steep sided	Puerto Rico Trench (Fig. 5)
Continental borderland	Similar to shelf except relief: 100–1000 m Depth: up to 2000 m Gradient: 1:1000–1:40	Rises and depressions are common	Off Southern California
Submarine canyon	Width: 1–15 km Relief: 20–2000 m Depth: 20–2000 m Gradient: <1:40	Most commonly cut continental rise; length to 500 km	Hudson Canyon, off New York
Abyssal hills	Width: 100 m–100 km Height: few to 1500 m	Found seaward of abyssal plains, usually in belts	Western Atlantic Abyssal Hills Province (Fig. 7)
Abyssal plains	Width: few to 1000 km Depth: usually >3000 km Gradient: <1:1000 (to 1:10,000) Relief: Nil	Small plains occur in trench bottoms; plains are very flat, gentle	Nares and Sohm Plains, North Atlantic
Oceanic rises	Width: 300–500 km Height: up to 5000 m	Aseismic features with highly variable relief (smooth slopes-rough scarps)	Bermuda Rise

TABLE 1. (continued)

Feature	Typical Dimensions	Comments	Example
Aseismic ridges	Width: to 150 km Length: to 4000 km Height: up to 4000 m	Strongly asymmetrical	Walvis Ridge (Fig. 8)
Seamounts	Width: 2–100 km Height: >1000 m Depth: 0–2000 m (top surface)	Submerged volcanoes; often wave truncated and sub- merged (guyots); may have atolls	East Pacific (Fig. 19)
Oceanic plateaus	Dimensions similar to oceanic rises Gradient: <1:1000 on top; >1:40 on sides	Also termed "Microcontinents"	Mascarene Plateau Indian Ocean
Mid-Oceanic Ridge	Width: 2000–4000 km Length: 35,000–40,000 miles Height: 1–3 km Depth: 0–5000 m	Includes flank and crest regions. Worlds greatest mountain range	Mid-Atlantic Ridge (Fig. 9)
Ridge flank	Width: 500–1500 km Relief: up to 1000 m Depth: >3000 m	Includes fractured plateau, and steps on flank	Mid-Atlantic Ridge (Fig. 9)
Ridge crest	Width: 500–1000 km Relief: 2000 m Depth: 2000–4000 m	Includes rift zone, which may be 20–50 km wide	Mid-Atlantic Ridge (Fig. 9)

basins make up the second of the three basic divisions of oceanic physiography. Approximately one-third of the Atlantic and Indian Oceans and three-fourths of the Pacific Ocean fall in this division. Two categories of provinces are recognized (Heezen and Menard, 1963, p. 253): (1) abyssal floor; (2) oceanic rises and aseismic ridges.

The abyssal floor includes flat, low-gradient *abyssal plains,* which typically occur at the foot of the continental rise, and *abyssal hills,* representing terrain of moderate relief (see Table 1) and characteristically occurring at the seaward edge of the abyssal plains. Figure 7 gives some typical profiles of the abyssal floor in the North Atlantic.

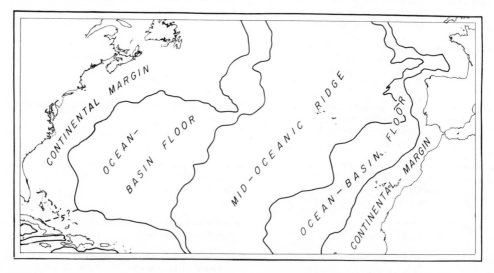

FIG. 2. Major morphologic divisions: North Atlantic Ocean (Heezen *et al.,* 1959). The profile is at 40:1 vertical exaggeration (see Fig. 3) and is representative of a profile from New England to the Sahara Coast.

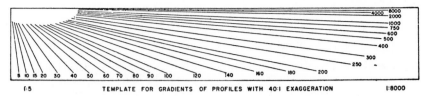

Fɪɢ. 3. Gradients from 1:5 to 1:8000 shown at a 40:1 vertical exaggeration (Heezen *et al.*, 1959). Most profiles reproduced in this paper are at 40:1 vertical exaggeration.

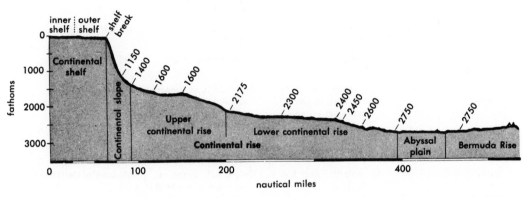

Fɪɢ. 4. Continental margin provinces: type profile off northeastern United States (after Heezen *et al.*, 1959).

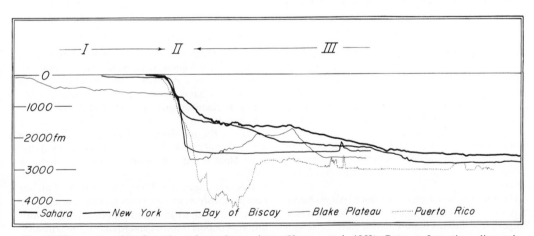

Fɪɢ. 5. Three categories of continental margin provinces (Heezen *et al.*, 1959). Category I provinces lie on the continental block. Category II provinces form the side of the continental block. Category III provinces are the upturned or depressed margins of the ocean basin, or the downfaulted, downwarped edge of the continental block.

Tᴀʙʟᴇ 2. Lᴀʏᴇʀs ᴏf ᴛʜᴇ Oᴄᴇᴀɴɪᴄ Cʀᴜsᴛ

Layer Number	Average Thickness (km)	Typical Seismic Velocity (km/sec)	Character of Layer
Seawater	4.5	1.5	Sea water
1	0.5 or less	2	Surficial sediment
2	1.75 (variable)	5	Uncertain: basalt? gabbro? lithified sediment?
3	4.7	6.7	Basalt? gabbro?
4	—	8.1	Mantle: eclogite? peridotite?

TABLE 3. CLASSIFICATION OF CONTINENTAL SHELVES BY SHEPARD (1963)[a]

	Shelf Type	Morphology	Genesis	Example
1	Shelves off glaciated land masses	Irregular, deep basins and troughs (to 500–2000 m); banks along outer portions	Glacial excavation of troughs, deposition on banks	Grand Bank, Newfoundland
2	Shelves with parallel ridges and troughs	Relatively smooth, with low linear features (10 m high, or less), sand covered	Ridges are drowned barrier islands formed during low stands of sea level	Atlantic Ocean, off Virginia, New Jersey
3	Smooth shelves in high latitudes	Very smooth, flat	Planed by shore and floating ice	Off northern Alaska
4	Shelves with strong currents	Narrow, with megaripples	Current scoured	Off Miami, Florida
5	Shelves in clear tropical seas	Large reefs or no reefs and sandy terraces, fossil river systems	Reef growth or subaerial erosion during low stands of sea level	Off Queensland or Western Australia
6	Shelves with rocky banks along the outside	Irregular, often with islands	Block faulted, with some island erosion and basin filling	Off southern California
7	Shelves bordering large deltas	Variable size, variable sediment	Deltaic sedimentation, subsidence; sea level variation	Mississippi Delta region

[a] Note: This table is based on text material in Shepard, 1963.

Rising above the abyssal floor are *oceanic rises* and *plateaus*, which are large features of considerable variety, and *aseismic ridges* (Fig. 8), which are high, long, strongly asymmetrical features (see Table 1). Among the other features which occur prominently on the ocean basin floor are fracture zones, seamounts (submerged volcanoes) and linear archipelagos such as the Hawaiian Islands. Minor features on the abyssal floor include gaps connecting distinct but adjacent abyssal plains and mid-ocean canyons.

The Mid-Oceanic Ridge. The third basic subdivision of oceanic topography is the Mid-Oceanic Ridge, a continuous feature which runs the length of the Atlantic, Indian and South Pacific Oceans for nearly 40,000 miles. The ridge is essentially a broad fractured swell bounded at the axes of maximum depth at each side and by a distinct change in the gradient between the abyssal hills and the ridge flanks. The typical ridge profile can be subdivided into: (1) a central main range or *crest*, within which occurs a *rift valley* (sometimes absent) and a high fractured plateau, and (2) a terraced *flank zone*. Typical profiles are given in Fig. 9; morphometry is summarized in Table 1.

Submarine Structures and Crust

The major features of the sea floor are structural in origin. Folds are relatively minor and occur in

connection with slumping and other sliding mechanisms. Minor folding may occur also in trenches. However, there is evidently little compression in the oceans, or what compression exists is compensated for by mechanisms other than folding. Jointing is no doubt common (probably ubiquitous) in lithified rocks on the sea floor. But jointing patterns are generally too closely knit to effect topography on the scale which is normally observed on echo-sounding records.

Fracture zones are long, thin bands that are conspicuously more mountainous than the sea floor in general and which often separate regions with different depths (Heezen and Menard, 1963, p. 260). These features are remarkably straight, can be up to 100 km wide and some are over 2000 km long. Within the zones are asymmetrical ridges and narrow troughs parallel to the general trend (Fig. 10). Seamounts are common along the zones, and there relief can be as much as 4000 meters. Fracture zones are only active features where they offset the crest of the Mid-Oceanic Ridge. Since the ridge continuously widens through the addition of mantle material in the Mid-Oceanic Rift Valley, the fracture zones steadily grow longer at the center line of the Ridge. The motion along the active fracture zone is therefore opposite to that deduced from the displaced crests. The term transcurrent faulting formerly included both types of motion but the type of

TABLE 4. DOMINANT GEOLOGIC AND GEOPHYSICAL CHARACTERISTICS OF MAJOR SUBMARINE PHYSIOGRAPHIC PROVINCES (NO ATTEMPT IS MADE TO BE COMPLETE; NOTE THAT MANY MINOR FEATURES (e.g., ASEISMIC RIDGES) ARE NOT DISCUSSED)

Province	Surface Geology	Geophysical Characteristics (*N.B.* all areas are isostatically compensated, except trenches)	Probable Genesis
Continental shelf	Unconsolidated terrigenous sediments of all sizes	Aseismic, with magnetic anomalies over buried volcanoes, structures	Represents filled-in ridges and troughs
Continental slope	Unconsolidated terrigenous silts and clays; in places lithified and truncated	Aseismic, with major magnetic anomaly associated with abrupt edge of continent	Represents structural edge of continent
Continental rise	Unconsolidated silts and clays often deposited by turbidity currents and reworked by contour currents	Aseismic, with smooth magnetics (modern trench areas are seismic and iso-statically uncompensated)	Sedimentary prism, perhaps filling in old trenches
Abyssal plains	Unconsolidated silts and sands of turbidity current and pelagic origin	Aseismic with magnetic anomalies revealing linear patterns unrelated to obvious surficial structures	Sedimentary plain overlying abyssal hill terrain
Abyssal hills	Alkali basalt and gabbro	Similar to abyssal plains	Older Mid-Oceanic Ridge crust (see below)
Mid-Oceanic Ridge flanks	Similar to abyssal hills	Aseismic; minor linear magnetic anomalies paralleling boundaries	Older Mid-Oceanic Ridge crust, brought to surface in crest area and moved from crest with time
Mid-Oceanic Ridge crest	Alkali basalt and gabbro (serpentine)	Highly seismic with large magnetic anomaly over rift. High heat flow	Zone of introduction of mantle material which becomes oceanic crust and moves away from ridge crest

strike slip fault which occurs at fracture zones has recently been called *transform* and since about 1966 the term transcurrent excluded this notion.

A number of fracture zones have open rifts or deep trenches (Fig. 11). Others border aseismic ridges or coastal blocks. Island arcs and adjacent deep-sea trenches are zones of faulting resulting in rift-like forms. Many continental shelves show evidence of block faulting.

Submarine *volcanoes* may or may not rise above sea level. They often occur along fracture zones but can occur singly or in small groups. Submerged volcanoes are called *seamounts*; flat-topped seamounts are termed *guyots*.

The oceanic crust differs radically from the continental crust in composition and thickness. Seismic data have revealed a general layering of oceanic crust. Table 2 summarizes the character of the oceanic crustal layers. Nonoceanic (continental) crust occurs beneath the continental margins and at least some of the microcontinents (Mascarene Plateau, etc.) tend to be "granite," in contrast to the "basaltic" material beneath the deep-sea floor.

Continental Margins. Figures 6 and 12 illustrate typical crustal structures of the continental margins. These sections make it clear that although surficial

sedimentation may smooth out the profile of the continental margins in many places, the underlying profiles are nearly everywhere irregular. In many cases, the irregularities are directly related to faulting. It is possible to delineate two basic types of continental margin. One type occurs where sediment has filled in the rises and depressions of the crust (as off the eastern United States); subtypes are based on the detailed nature of the erosional and depositional processes acting (now or in the past) on the shelf.

The second type occurs where sediment has not filled in the rises and depressions of the crust, although partial filling may have occurred. These margins can be subdivided according to structure and degree of filling. The continental shelves are developed on "granitic" crust, as a rule, and hence are geologically part of the continents, although geographically a part of the oceans.

Continental slopes and analogous provinces (marginal escarpments, landward slopes of trenches) seem generally to be related to large-scale crustal structures (e.g., Fig. 6) and in particular a dramatic thinning of the earth's crust, from tens of kilometers to less than 10 km. Many continental margins show faulting and fault scarps at the continental slope

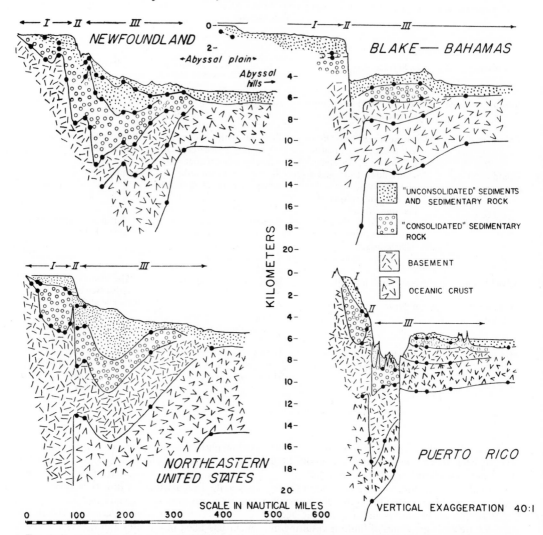

FIG. 6. Crustal structure and continental margin provinces (after Heezen *et al.*, 1959). The four profiles represent typical areas of the continental margin of eastern North America. They may represent a genetic sequence, starting with an unfilled trench, such as that of Puerto Rico (bottom right) and ending with a filled marginal trench, as illustrated by the Newfoundland profile (top left). Note the association of category II provinces with major structures; note also basement rock beneath category III provinces, but not beneath abyssal floor.

(e.g., Fig. 6, third section). As more geophysical data comes in, it is becoming apparent that the continental slope generally represents the major zone in which continental crust pinches out, and the crust becomes oceanic in nature.

The origin of this tremendous change is a speculative point in many theories. To those who favor continental displacements, the fault margin represents the ruptured edge of the formerly continuous continental crust. Exponents of convection currents would have this be a zone of downward convection, causing the sharp oceanic-continent transition, and

would also generally relate the continental slopes to the original faulting along which continents have split. Non-drifters generally explain the slope as either the seaward margin of the continental crust (which "floats" on the oceanic layer) or as simply a depositional feature, somewhat like the seaward edge of a delta. However, the continental slope often truncates shelf sediments, unlike a delta margin.

The continental rise was once thought to consist simply of modified fans or aprons of sediment derived from the adjacent shelf and land. The rise is

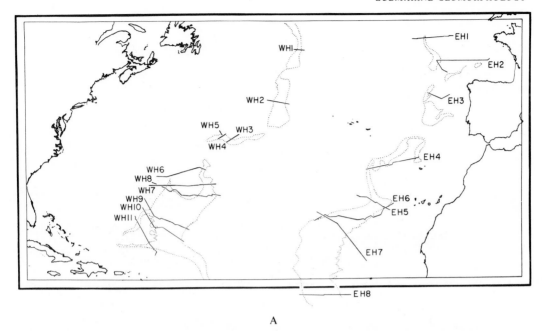

A

FIG. 7. Profiles of the abyssal floor in the North Atlantic Ocean, vertical exaggeration 40:1 (from Heezen *et al.*, 1959). (A) Index chart, location of profiles of (B) and (C). Limits of abyssal hills provinces shown by dotted lines. (B) (below) Eleven profiles, Western Atlantic Abyssal Hills Province. (C) (see p. 1088) Eight profiles, Eastern Atlantic Abyssal Hills Province.

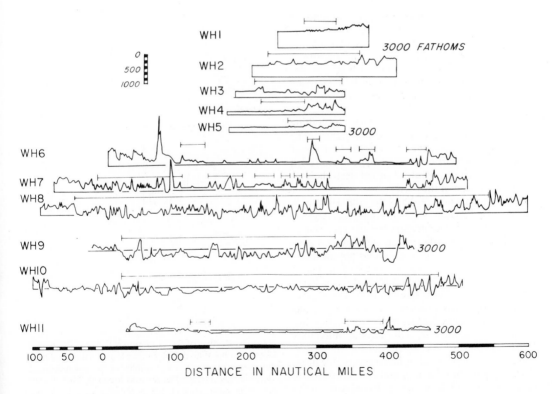

7B

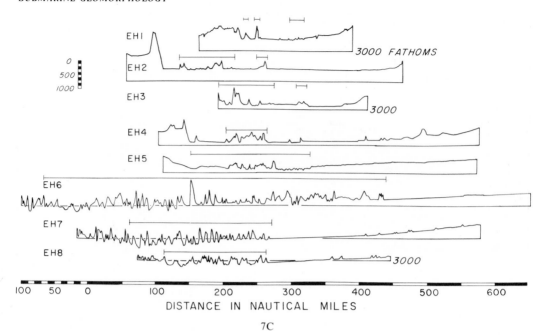

7C

a sedimentary prism as has been demonstrated by seismic work. The commonly observed terracing of the rise is not structurally controlled but is the result of dynamic processes of sedimentation.

In summary, the gross shape of continental margins strongly reflects underlying crustal structure, although minor structures are usually obscured by accumulations of sediment. The resultant form is controlled by geomorphic processes where sediment cover is extensive, but is controlled by underlying structure in the absence of a cover. The shelf structures may be block faults or trench-like. The continental slope appears to be localized by faulting associated with the continent-ocean transition. The continental rise is a sedimentary wedge, usually of geosynclinal proportions whose shape is controlled by contour currents involved in the deep thermohaline circulation of the oceans.

Ocean Basin Floor. Table 2 (p. 1083) shows a typical crustal section of the abyssal floor. Abyssal plains appear to be sedimentary features exclusively. The relatively thin sediment blanket covers a sub-surface topography which resembles abyssal hills. Since abyssal hills are always seaward of the plains (i.e., further from sediment sources), it seems likely that the plains represent filled in hills. The abyssal hills generally consist of volcanic rock similar to that of the Mid-Oceanic Ridge, with which they are topographically aligned. The abyssal hills thus probably represent older ridge rocks.

Widely distributed minor lineations on the deep-sea floor frequently lie in pinnate patterns relative to the major lineations such as island arcs, archipelagos and fracture zones (Heezen and Menard,

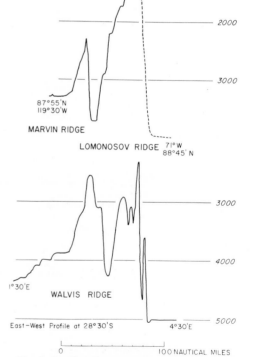

FIG. 8. Profiles of the Lomonosov Ridge in the Arctic Ocean and the Walvis Ridge in the South Atlantic. These two ridges are excellent examples of the asymmetrical aseismic ridges (from Heezen and Menard, 1963; based on earlier publications). (By permission of John Wiley & Sons, N.Y.)

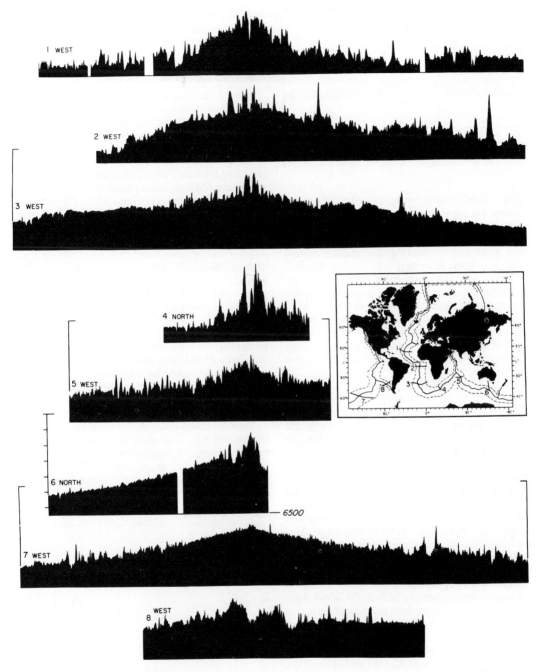

FIG. 9. Eight typical profiles of the Mid-Oceanic Ridge. The smooth relief across the crest of the ridge in the South Pacific contrasts markedly with the rougher topography of the other oceans. Vertical exaggeration of profiles is 100:1 (based on previously published profiles of Heezen).

1963). These lineations, which may be up to 200 km long, consist of volcanoes with or without atolls, or asymmetrical ridges and/or narrow troughs.

Oceanic plateaus or microcontinents are fault-bounded areas raised above the ocean basin floor and generally bearing a thin sedimentary cover.

Aseismic ridges also occur in the ocean basins. The Walvis Ridge, a type example, has a smooth surface with a condensed sedimentary section dating from Upper Cretaceous. Continuous current scour and periodic slumping probably removes sediment from the crest of the steep ridge sides.

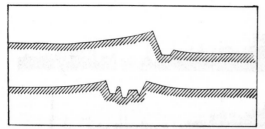

FIG. 10. Profiles of idealized types of topography of fracture zones in the northeastern Pacific (from Menard, 1964). (By permission McGraw-Hill Book Co., N.Y.)

Seamounts, while occurring throughout the ocean bottom, are most important on the ocean basin floor, especially in the Pacific. Seamounts most often lie in linear rows; many are surrounded by a moat, which may be due to the effect of either current scour or isostatic downwarp.

In summary, the ocean basin floor is a tectonically quiet area (at present), dominated by irregular topography on abyssal hills (older example of Mid-Oceanic Ridge flanks) and smooth topography on abyssal plains (filled in abyssal hills). Rising above the floor are numerous seamounts and a few large plateaus, ridges and rises. Inactive fracture zones are common.

The Mid-Oceanic Ridge. The Mid-Oceanic Ridge system (Figs. 9, 14, 15 and 16) is largely a structural feature. The crest of the ridge in many places consists of a rift zone, bordered symmetrically by rift mountains and high, fractured plateaus. Vulcanism is extremely important. Sedimentation is of minor importance in determining its form. The rift valley is highly seismic and is an area of high heat flow. A large positive magnetic anomaly characteristically coincides with the rift valley, gravity data indicate isostatic equilibrium, and seismic evidence indicates the existence of relatively light mantle material. Also the age of crustal rocks appears to increase away from the rift valley and the topography becomes more subdued (Fig. 14). This suggests a gradual introduction of upper mantle derivatives along the rift and a displacement or drift of the ocean floor and the continents away from the ridge. This is also suggested by the symmetry of the Atlantic Ocean and the median location of the ridge, which roughly parallels the continental outlines (Fig. 15).

It is interesting to note that the mid-oceanic rift valley is topographically similar and continuous with the African rift valleys (Fig. 16) and the central graben of Iceland. The ridge crest also passes directly beneath the North American continent in the Basin and Range Province. Thus, major continental areas of active tension faulting are associated with oceanic areas undergoing expansion of the sea floor.

The ridge flanks would seem to be older oceanic crust which originated in the rift valley and has moved laterally. The topography is smoothed by

infilling with sediment, by weathering and erosion and redeposition by bottom currents. The ridge contains many active volcanoes, seamounts and all the active fracture zones, as discussed above.

Submarine Geomorphic Processes

Among the processes which are important in the evolution of submarine topography are: particle by particle vertical sedimentation, contour currents, turbidity currents, and other bottom currents, mass-wasting, weathering, reef building and wave action.

Little is known about the nature of weathering reactions (or *halmyrolysis*) in submarine rocks and sediments. Most chemical changes in sediments are diagenetic and are closely related to the internal sedimentary environment; such changes are not weathering in the generally accepted sense. Dredge samples clearly show that hard rocks (e.g., basalt) do weather on the ocean floor; most reactions seem to involve change of water content of the rocks involved.

Although direct evidence is scarce, it is generally assumed that submarine mass-wasting, via *slumping* and *landsliding*, is quite common. The mechanisms for these processes are similar to those on land except that the water-saturated nature of submarine sediments should favor mass movement. The resultant scarps and depositional lobes are not sufficiently large to appear on any but the best echo-sounding records; hence, their morphology is not well known but is probably similar to that on land (as in Fig. 17).

Turbidity currents supply the sediment which fills the abyssal hills to produce the abyssal plains. At the lower end of submarine canyons, turbidity currents build low-angle fans which gradually merge into abyssal plains, the slopes decreasing

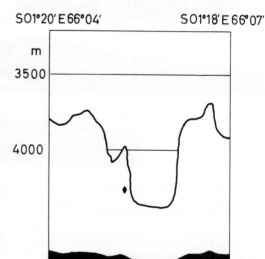

FIG. 11. A fracture zone in the Carlsberg Ridge, Indian Ocean. Below (in black), a true scale profile (from Koczy, F. F., 1954, *Deep-Sea Res.*, 1, 180).

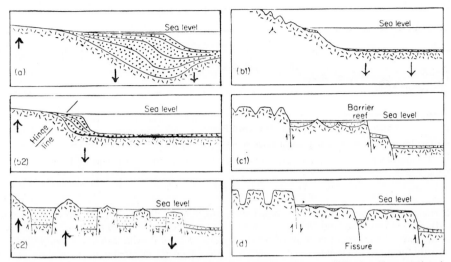

FIG. 12. Types of continental margins (from Guilcher, 1963, p. 300): (a) Constructional, subsiding type with wide shelf, wide and thick sedimentary basin (e.g., eastern North America, northwest Europe. (b1) Flexured type with no significant sedimentation (e.g., near Nice). (b2) Flexured type with narrow shelf and sedimentary wedge (e.g., west and south of Africa). (c1) Faulted type, irregularities filled (e.g., Queensland). (c2) Faulted type, partial infilling (e.g., Southern California). (d) Fissured type, due to glacial overdeepening (e.g., Norway, Labrador). (By permission of John Wiley & Sons, N.Y.)

from 1 to .1° and less. Turbidity currents flush out and erode submarine canyons and build up the flank with natural levees.

Contour currents are geostrophically controlled. They are especially important geomorphic agents. Evidence for bottom current action includes bottom photographs of ripples, scour and bending or organisms in currents of velocities commonly reaching 5–15 cm/sec and higher. Ocean bottom currents rework turbidites and other deposits and produce finer-grained, better-sorted sediment, called contourite. Contour currents control the shape of the major deep sea sediment bodies and are one of the most important processes of deposition in the deeper parts of the continental margin.

Deep-sea *sediments* are transported by the currents mentioned above and by glaciers, ice rafts and wind (including volcanic and meteoritic dust). Most important in the open ocean is pelagic sediment, either as a biogenic rain of tests of foraminif-

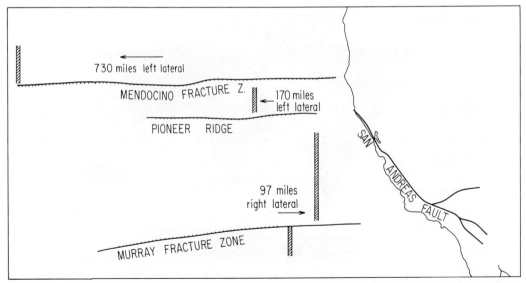

FIG. 13. Three of the major fracture zones of the northeastern Pacific Ocean. Displacement of a prominent magnetic anomaly (in statute miles) is shown (after Vacquier *et al.*, 1961, *Bull. Geol. Soc. Am.*, **72**, 1251).

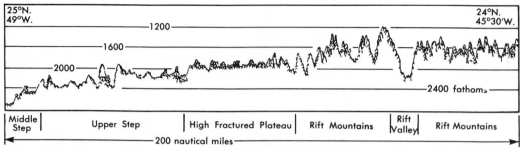

FIG. 14. Tracing of a precision depth recorder record showing crest and western flank of the Mid-Atlantic Ridge (Heezen *et al.*, 1959).

era and similar organisms, or as very fine clay (often red), carried from the land to mid-ocean by suspension. Clay composition and rate of deposition are partly functions of climate.

Reef growth is a relatively minor aspect of marine topography, but it is of supreme importance along some tropical coasts of the Pacific, where the water is shallow and warm and there is a constant supply of food, nutrient salts and dissolved gases. *Wave action* is important along all coasts and results in erosion, longshore drift of sediment and buildup of beaches and bars. Wave action can result in actual removal of beach material and partial transport toward the open ocean. Sedimentation on the inner shelf is dominated by this process. Yet another coastal feature is the *delta*, a sedimentary accumulation built out by rivers entering the sea.

Numerous minor processes are active on the ocean floor. *Tsunamis* are waves of sufficient length to stir up bottom material, as are the tides. Along the margins of glacial regions, scour by *ice* is important and generally produces depressions and gouges bordered to seaward by ridges. Spectacular examples of flowing sand and *sand falls* have been described as occurring in submarine canyons in response to seaward flow of water following exceptionally large storm swells.

Continental Margins. The basic topography of many continental margins is structural in origin. Continental shelves, representing filled-in borderlands, and continental rises, representing filled-in trenches and basins, are sedimentary in origin, and hence reflect the action of submarine processes.

Shepard (1963) recognizes seven basic shelf types, based on geomorphic criteria. These are summarized in Table 3. It is clear that the general morphology of a shelf depends on whether or not sediment has filled in the underlying structure. If it has, then the shelf morphology reflects the action of various submarine and coastal erosional and depositional processes, particularly scour by ice and currents, and deposition by wave action, rivers and reefs.

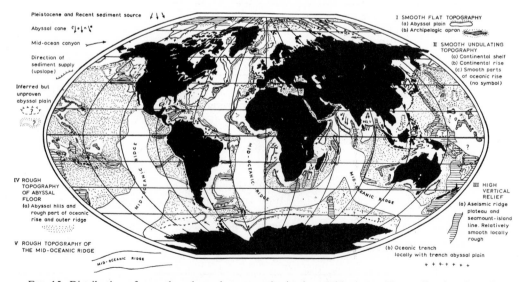

FIG. 15. Distribution of smooth and rough topography in the world oceans. The median location of the Mid-Atlantic Ridge is clearly seen (from Heezen and Tharp, 1965, *Phil. Trans. Roy. Soc.*, **258**, 99).

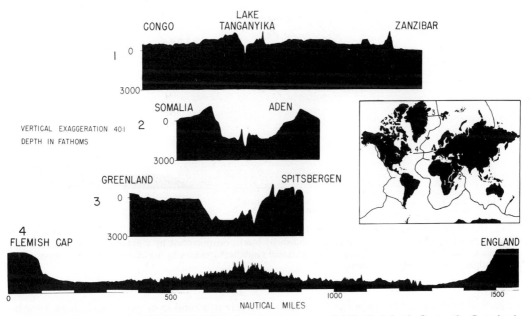

FIG. 16. Profiles across the Mid-Oceanic Ridge, from bottom to top, the North Atlantic Ocean, the Greenland Sea, the Red Sea graben and a typical African Rift zone, showing broad similarities in form.

The continental rise is a sedimentary prism constructed at the foot of the continental slope in part by a series of coalescing deep-sea fans or cones, in part by downslope transport at the mouths of submarine canyons, and in part by the seaward diffusion of very fine sediment. However, the uniformity in morphology, sediment type, stratification and structure of the rise is not explained by the mechanism of coalescing fans, nor does this explain the abrupt boundaries of the rise.

Heezen *et al.* (1966) explain the uniformity of the rise and the abrupt boundaries as being caused by shaping by bottom currents following the contours of the continental slope and rise (Fig. 18). Deep currents are deflected by the Coriolis force against the sides of the ocean basins.

Ocean Basin Floor. *Oceanic rises* may be of structural origin, but at least some appear to be partly sedimentary features. For example, the Bermuda Rise is an oval symmetrical arch, 500 by 1000 km, somewhat irregular in form, although much smoother than the Mid-Oceanic Ridge. On the east, it is bounded by scarps 500–1700 meters high, and it is partially capped by a broad plateau from which rise a number of seamounts. However seismic data show that the rise is in large part a sedimentary accumulation. Certainly contour currents have played a part in shaping the Bermuda Rise.

Among the lesser features of the ocean basin floor are *abyssal gaps* and *mid-ocean canyons*. The former are passages connecting two adjacent but distinct abyssal plains and are probably cut by turbidity currents transporting material from one plain to another. Mid-ocean canyons are found in the middle of the ocean basin floor, and may cross regional slopes and cut through topographical barriers. Their origin is not known, although turbidity and bottom currents both must play a part.

Ocean basin seamounts often have reefs developed on their tops or sides, producing *atolls*. Of particular interest is the existence of guyots, or seamounts which have a comparatively smooth top (Figs. 19 and 20). Many of these guyots are capped by drowned reefs, indicating a former existence at

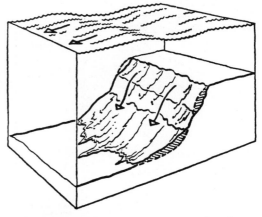

FIG. 17. Submarine mass-wasting. A landslide of loose sediment accumulated on the brow of a steep submarine slope is set in motion, perhaps by an earthquake, perhaps due to undercutting by a contour current (from Bascom, 1964, p. 104).

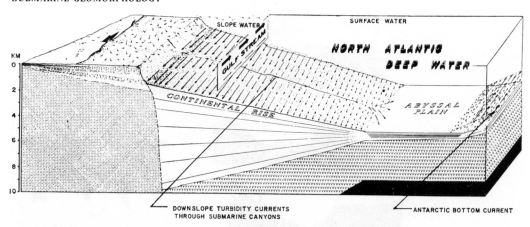

FIG. 18. Shaping of the continental rise by bottom contour currents, as off eastern North America. Arrows indicate prevailing bottom currents. Mantle is shown by black; oceanic crust by v pattern; continental crust by dash-blocks. Sedimentary rock is shown by conventional symbols; turbidites by horizontal ruling; rise deposits by open wedges (from Heezen, *et al.*, 1966).

sea level and subsequent submergence. Evidence is strong for a wave truncation origin of the flat top. The guyots occupy an area in the central Pacific (Fig. 21). Subsidence apparently began in the late Mesozoic or early Tertiary. Reefs developed on top of the guyots, but were drowned where subsidence was rapid.

The Mid-Oceanic Ridge. The mid-oceanic ridge is largely structural in origin. Modifications by sedimentation and erosion have occurred on the flank regions and on some associated aseismic ridges. Sedimentation is the principal smoothing process; pelagic sediments, slumps and current action are all probably important. As elsewhere, a smooth slope indicates sedimentation, while rough topography indicates tectonic-structural control.

Microtopography

Small topographic features, known as microtopography, are known mainly from bottom photographs and from high-resolution echo sounding. These features include: bedrock outcrops; pebbles and cobbles, including glacial erratics and manganese nodules; ripples and scour marks; organic features (e.g., small "reefs"); subaqueous sand dunes. In general, microtopographic features are related to surface geology (outcrops, sedimentation, nodules), currents (ripples, dunes), or organisms (e.g., Fig. 22).

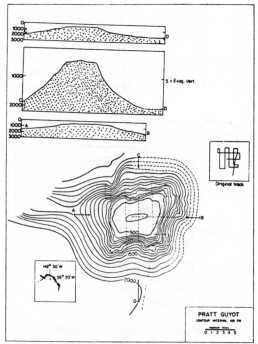

FIG. 19. Pratt Guyot in the North Pacific (Menard and Ladd, 1963, p. 373). (By permission of John Wiley & Sons, N.Y.)

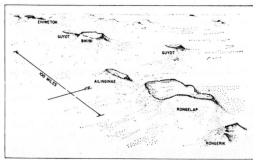

FIG. 20. Atolls and guyots in the Marshall Islands; perspective sketch as they might appear were the water removed (from Menard and Ladd, 1963, p. 379). (By permission of John Wiley & Sons, N.Y.)

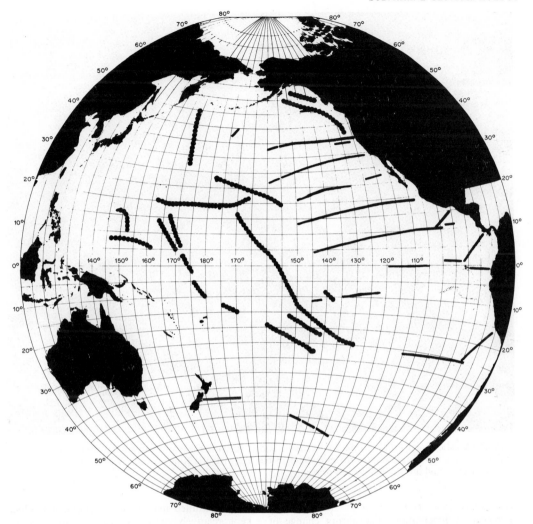

FIG. 21. Fracture zones of the eastern Pacific compared with trends of guyots and archipelagos of the western Pacific. Fracture zones are shown by solid lines; archipelagos, many of which are atoll-capped guyots, are shown by chains of dots (from Heezen and Menard, 1963, p. 1959). (By permission of John Wiley & Sons, N.Y.)

The Role of Time

With time, submarine topography evolves from an original rough surface, due to structural and tectonic controls, to a relatively smooth surface, due to erosion and especially to deposition. A second influence of time is that during the Quaternary the intensity and location of many processes has varied because of climatic change, shift of oceanic circulation patterns and fluctuations in sea level.

Both influences are seen on the continental margins. The margins have evolved in some places from an original rough borderland to a smooth continental shelf; on younger margins, filling of original structures is as yet incomplete and the borderland (block faulted) topography still dominates. Similarly, older trenches and basins have been filled to

produce the continental rise. Many shelves in high latitudes show the effect of glacial scour and deposition during cold periods, while others show the effects of varying sea level, as by the presence of submerged coastal features.

On the ocean basin floor, the originally rough abyssal hill topography has been smoothed with time, due to infilling by turbidity currents and other modes of sedimentation. Sedimentation rates and current patterns have varied with Quaternary climatic changes.

The Mid-Oceanic Ridge shows an evolutionary history. The present rift area is the locus of introduction of new crust from the mantle; the crust gets older away from the ridge crest. As a result of this age gradient, there is a progressive smoothing of

FIG. 22A. Microtopography on the Mid-Oceanic Ridge. Basaltic rocks outcrop amid a thin cover of pelagic sediment at the top of the western rift mountains of the Mid-Atlantic Ridge; depth—2800 meters. A branching gorgonian coral and several sponges can be seen.

topography away from the ridge crests, due to increasing sedimentation. The abrupt change of texture and sediment thickness between the crust and the flanks of the Mid-Oceanic Ridge has been interpreted as evidence of a pause in crustal growth which ended some 10 million years ago. But this is also the point where current effects are seen to diminish markedly.

Table 4 (p. 1085) summarizes some of the geological and geophysical aspects of the major submarine geomorphic features.

Summary

The continental margins consist of a continental shelf (locally a structural plateau), a continental slope (of several types) and a continental rise (locally a trench and ridge complex). The continental shelf areas represent the structurally irregular margin of the continental block. As time passes, sediment fills in the margin, creating the relatively smooth shelf which is then acted upon by many processes, including subaerial and subglacial mechanisms. The continental slope usually represents the original faulted margin of the continental block, kept relatively steep by mass movements and currents. The continental rise represents sediment accumulated in a basin or trench, shaped and smoothed by contour currents. Submarine canyons, steep valley-like gorges cutting the continental slope, probably result from the combined action of subaerial river erosion, cutting by turbidity currents, sand flows and slumps; locally faulting is important. Submarine abyssal fans and cones are formed at canyon mouths, due to supply of sediment by turbidity currents.

The ocean basin floor consists of the old oceanic crust. Turbidity current-derived sediment has filled in between the irregular abyssal hills in many places, resulting in smooth abyssal plains. Elsewhere inactive fracture zones, volcanic lineations and aseismic ridges occur. The mid-Pacific contains many flat-topped seamounts or guyots, which were wave truncated at sea level and subsequently submerged.

The Mid-Oceanic Ridge represents a structural feature along which new crust is introduced from the mantle. The youngest ridge areas are moun-

FIG. 22B. Microtopography: current lineations made by the southerly flowing Western Boundary Undercurrent east of the crest of the outer ridge, near the base of the continental slope, off the eastern United States; Depth—3183 meters. (Photo: Heezen and Hollister, Lamont Geological Observatory).

tainous and are cut by longitudinal rifts and transverse fracture zones. The ridge plateau and flanks represent increasingly older crust which has been smoothed by erosion and sedimentary infilling.

BRUCE C. HEEZEN
LEE WILSON

References

Bascom, W., 1964, "Waves and Beaches," Garden City, N.Y., Doubleday & Co., 267pp.

Emery, K. O., 1960, "The Sea off Southern California," New York, John Wiley & Sons, 366pp.

Guilcher, A., 1963, "Continental Shelf and Slope," in (Hill, M. N., editor) "The Sea," Vol. III, pp. 281–311. New York, John Wiley & Son.

Heezen, B. C., Hollister, C. D., and Ruddiman, W. F., 1966, "Shaping of the continental rise by deep geostrophic contour currents," *Science*, **152**, 502–508.

Heezen, B. C., and Menard, H. W., 1963, "Topography of the Deep Sea Floor," in (Hill, M. N., editor), "The Sea," Vol. III, pp. 233–280, New York, John Wiley & Sons.

Heezen, B. C., Tharp, M., and Ewing, M., 1959, "The floors of the oceans, I. The North Atlantic," *Geol. Soc. Am. Spec. Paper* **65**, 122pp.

Laughton, A. S., 1963, "Microtopography," in (Hill, M. N., editor) "The Sea," Vol. III, pp. 437–472, New York, John Wiley & Sons.

Menard, H. W., 1964, "Marine Geology of the Pacific," New York, McGraw-Hill Book Co., 271pp.

Menard, H. W., and Ladd, H. S., 1963, "Oceanic Islands, Seamounts, Guyots and Atolls," in (Hill, M. N., editor) "The Sea," Vol. III, pp. 365–387. New York, John Wiley & Sons.

Shepard, F. P., 1963, "Submarine Geology," New York, Harper and Row, 557pp.

Cross-references: *Atolls; Beach; Coral Reefs; Delta; Glacial Scour; Island Arcs; Littoral Processes; Mass Movement; Process—Structure—Stage; Quaternary Period; Rift Valley; Sediment Transport—Fluvial and Marine.* Vol. I: *Abyssal Hills; Abyssal Plains; Aseismic Ridge; Bathymetry; Continental Borderland; Continental Rise; Continental Shelf; Continental Slope; Mid-Oceanic Ridge; Ocean Bottom Currents; Ocean Bottom Features; Oceanographic Surveys; Seamounts; Seismic Reflection Profiling at Sea; Sounding; Subaqueous Sand Dunes; Submarine Canyons; Submarine Cones or Fans; Submarine Plateaus; Trenches; Tsunami; Turbidity Currents; Underwater Photography.* pr Vol. VI: *Halmyrolysis; Pelagic Sediments.*

SUBMERGED SHORELINES

(1) Introduction

Most submerged shorelines have been discovered by study of conventional charts, or by special echo-sounding surveys. Most are found at depths less than 150 m, though Heezen (1959) reports terraces at 260 m. The shallower terraces are thought to be of Pleistocene age (caused by glacial eustasy, but possibly modified by crustal movements) and only these will be considered in this article.

The North American and Pacific literature, including the work of Veatch and Smith, Yabe and Tayama, Komukai, Shepard and Wrath, Carrigy and Fairbridge, Dietz and Menard, and Houboldt, and others, has been discussed by Emery (1958). Early European papers, including the work of Boule, Deperet, Doumergue, de Marchi, and Zeuner, are discussed by Blanc (1942). Later European work, including that of van Giffen, Hurtig, Godwin, Köster, Blanc, Woldstedt, Zeuner, and Hafemann, is discussed by Jelgersma (1961), together with recent American work by Fisk, Fairbridge, Shepard, and Curray.

(2) Detection and measurement

(a) Since ambiguity has been caused by description of shorelines in terms of "flat areas" or "breaks of slope," an attempt should be made to classify field observations in terms of the sea level which caused the features. This requires very detailed observation.

(b) Echo sounding is best carried out on a recording machine with fast paper speed so that position fixes are accurate and gradients easily measured. Profiles must be run close enough together to enable unambiguous correlation and assessment of horizontal continuity of features. Spacing may range from 200 m to 1 km in any one area, depending on the variability encountered.

(c) The profiles can be supported by extensive bottom sampling by grabs or corers, and sometimes with detailed topographic and physiographic observations by free divers.

(d) Field data can be considered in terms of erosional or depositional forms.

(3) Erosional Forms and Associated Sea Levels

(a) The rock which best preserves erosion traces is massive, partially metamorphosed limestone, at least in Mediterranean and temperate conditions. It is eroded by the sea into easily identifiable shoreline features which preserve their form through subaerial weathering and subsequent variations of sea level. The ideal feature is a submerged cliff joining a relatively flat terrace, thinly covered with, or free of, sediment and with a row of caves and stacks along the foot of the cliff. Such features have been surveyed by the author at Gibraltar, Marseille, and Palinuro (southern Italy), and from them it is possible to deduce the original sea level to within 2 m.

(b) The cliff-terrace junctions are often covered with sediment of unknown depth, or one may have only an echo-sounding profile with no details of the nature of the bottom. In such a case, the outer edge of the terrace and its slope allow the sea level to be calculated to within about 5 m.

(c) When the sea rests against a vertical limestone cliff cut by an earlier low sea level and is more than about 5 m above the cliff-terrace junction, no wave erosion takes place, but a solution notch is formed. This feature often allows the determination of the causing sea level to within 1 m by diving observation.

(4) Depositional Forms

(a) These forms may be found in the sea or beneath present terrestrial deposits. Shepard and Curray have derived the course of the last marine transgression in the northwestern Gulf of Mexico from physiographic and mineralogical analysis of submerged bar, spit, and shore formations to a depth of 100 m. The last transgression has also been studied by borings in land or deltaic deposits by Fisk, Jelgersma, and others. This approach depends on tracing the marine-subaerial boundary by study of flora, pollen, and C^{14} dating.

(b) Depositional studies have occasionally revealed alternating marine and terrestrial conditions, but the bulk of the data on actual sea levels and shorelines refers only to the last transgression. Erosional study seems capable of revealing data on exact depths throughout the Pleistocene, but as yet provides no dating system. The two approaches might profitably be combined in one area.

(5) Very Recent Changes

Variations in sea level in the last 8000 years can be checked by study of coastal archeological sites. Indian middens have been found at depths of 30 m off the California coast and Neolithic artifacts have been recovered from the North Sea. Some 12% of the classical Roman and Greek cities are submerged in the western Mediterranean, but these are situated in part around volcanoes, deltas, and seismic centers; probably there has been less than 2 m net eustatic change in the last 2000 years.

(6) Complicating Factors

(a) Initial land slope affects the form which subsequent marine erosion will produce. On a vertical cliff well above its foot there will be no erosion; if the slope is greater than 1/4, erosion is slow since much energy is reflected; if the slope is 1/4–1/10, erosion is at a maximum; if the slope is less than 1/50, erosion is extremely slow and a protective beach is probably formed. This variability, even on uniform rock, underlines the necessity to calculate the sea level for each feature independently before correlation is attempted.

(b) Continuous tectonic or isostatic depression of the land while a sequence of eustatic terraces is being formed will expand the spacing of the series if it is formed in order lowest first, highest last, and compression of the spacing if formed in the reverse order.

(c) Continuous uplift of the land will compress the spacing of a series formed lowest first, highest last, and will expand a series formed in the reverse order.

(d) Tilting along the line of the coast will result in expansion of the spacing of the uplift end of a series formed highest first, and compression of the uplift end of a series formed lowest first. This factor can sometimes be a help to discover the order of formation of a series, but if the terraces cross it becomes too complex.

(7) Conclusions

The most general and wide-ranging synthesis of the factors involved, including variations of land and sea level, climatic causes, and glacial/eustatic chronology, is given by Fairbridge (1961).

The present author's estimates of the depths of Pleistocene low sea levels agree broadly with those of Fairbridge and other authors and are as follows: −5–10 m, −27 m, −55 m, and −96 m. No features below 100 m were studied by the author, but it is possible that at some time in the Pleistocene the level dropped below this depth. Correlations of sea levels with specific glacial maxima are still very tentative. [Work by Soviet scientists suggests that the Riss glaciation was markedly greater than the Würm.]

Principal oscillations of the last transgression were probably about 79–91 m (16,000–14,000 B.P.); 20–24 m (12,000–10,000 B.P.); and 4–10 m (9000–8000 B.P.); with a halt in the rise at about 15 m, and probably many smaller oscillations at other levels.

N. C. FLEMMING

References

*Blanc, A. C., 1942, "Variazone climatiche ed oscillazioni della linea rivea nel Mediterraneo," *Geol. Meere Binnengewässer,* **5**(2), 137–219.

*Emery, K. O., 1958, "Shallow water submerged marine terraces of South California," *Bull. Geol. Soc. Am.,* **69,** 39–60.

*Fairbridge, R. W., 1961, "Eustatic changes in sea level," in "Physics and Chemistry of the Earth," vol. 4, pp. 99–185, London, Pergamon.

Heezen, B. C., 1959, "Submerged ancient beaches of the Atlantic," *Intern. Oceanog. Congress. Preprints, Am. Assoc. Adv. Science,* 622–623.

*Jelgersma, S., 1961, "Holocene sea level changes in the Netherlands," *Mededl. Geol. Sticht., Ser. C-VI,* 101pp.

* Additional bibliographic references may be found in this work.

Cross-references: *Eustasy; Holocene; Platforms—Wavecut; Postglacial Isostatic Rebound; Terraces.* Vol. I: *Mean Sea Level; SCUBA as a Scientific Tool; Sounding.* Vol. II: *Climatic Variations.* Vol. V: *Isostasy.*

SUBSEQUENT VALLEY, STREAM—*See* RIVERS; *also* DRAINAGE PATTERNS

SUFFOSION AND TUNDRA CRATERS

Suffosion (a word of classical origin, like "suffusion," suggesting erosion from below) has been used by Nikoroff (1928) for certain periglacial phenomena observed in the tundra of Siberia. Paterson (1940, p. 125) gave the following explanation:

"The rapidity of soil thaw depends on the texture and character of vegetation, so that the upper surface of the permanently frozen ground is very uneven during the summer. Between this surface and the earth above, which dries hard, water accumulates during the late stages of thaw, and, finding its way to lower levels, there exerts pressure on the dry crust and pours out, carrying with it silt and mud. If there is much mud present small convex mounds are formed. The result, on low ground, is the sporadic separation of blocks of bedded material by irregular masses of mud, seemingly without relation to any neighboring deposit."

Paterson spoke of "suffosion bursts," which appear in the manner of mud volcanoes, found in the oil-bearing orogenic belts. Experimental models (by the writer), employing differential loading of water-saturated clays and sands, produced self-sustaining mud volcanoes without gas drive, where only diapiric processes were involved.

Under tundra conditions, it is evident that partial melting of ground ice in irregular lithology (e.g., morainic sands, gravels and boulder clay) leads to marked differences in density and intergranular mobility. Paterson (1940) reported:

"A most striking example of this phenomenon on a large scale was observed at Keel Bay, East Baffin Land. A fairly steep slope of outwash conglomerate and glacial deposit was clothed with a thick *Cassiope* vegetation. Near the base of the slope, completely isolated, stood a large conical mound of mud, boulders and gravel, almost 10 feet high and about 20 feet in diameter, already somewhat weathered and entirely free from vegetation. Presumably, under the influence of gravity, a stream of mud and boulders beneath a hard dried upper skin of earth had burst through this skin at one small point towards the base of the hill slope, so forming the conical mound. 'Fossil' forms of this nature can be seen in the Gannicox pit, at Stroud, in the Severn valley" (England).

On a large scale and under freezing conditions, it seems probable that suffosion leads ultimately to the *pingo* (q.v.) or pseudo-volcanic hydrolaccolith; it should be understood, however, that the latter is essentially a dynamic ground ice phenomenon, while suffosion operates under groundwater alone, though certainly patches of ground ice may remain; it is therefore more related to *thermokarst* (q.v.) phenomena, i.e., melting processes rather than freezing.

Suffosion is also involved on a smaller scale in the production of "*tundra craters*" which are occasionally evident in soil polygon or stone ring formation (see *Frost Action; Patterned Ground; Periglacial Landscape*). Jahn (1948, p. 52) writes:

"By the name of '*tundra craters*' I mean the forms of circular or shapeless silt islands, sporadically met with on the tundras. Convex surfaces of silt without vegetation are clearly distinguished from the plant-covered spaces of tundra. The name of 'crater' is justified by the transformation which takes place in the form of the island, especially during the period of thawing in the tundra. At this time the silt rises to the surface and pours like lava from a miniature volcano.

"On the 9th July we dug a cutting across one of the craters on the Base peninsula. After removing a dry layer of silt (25 cm thick), we found a damp, semifluid silt, which rushed forth with violence towards the surface. This example proves that a 'crater' can be 'active' even in the summer, and its activity is checked merely by the upper, crusted layer of dried-up silt."

Jahn (1948, p. 57) continues:

"An exact analysis of the situation of the tundra craters allows us to assume that these forms are to be found in places where the accumulation terraces are composed of silts, covered with a layer of sand or rock debris. If this cover of gravel is not too thick, the underlying silts force their way through the cover and appear in the form of pillars. This process is due to the difference between the gravity and the mass of the upper layer, composed of gravel and sand, and the nether layer, composed of silt. The difference is caused not only by the difference of the specific gravity of the two masses, but also by the unequal soaking of both layers. The silts, which lie immediately on the impervious surface of frozen ground, are usually soaked with water up to a fluid state. This causes a diminution of the specific gravity of the mass, taken as a whole. The contrary occurs with the upper layer, composed of gravel, which does not retain water and easily becomes dry.

"Under the pressure of a heavy layer of gravel the silt is thrust out towards the surface. If, however, the current of silt encounters a hindrance, such as a dry, hardened crust of silt mass—and this is generally the case in the summer—the crater cannot continue to be 'active.' The period of 'activity' (the exudation of silt on the surface of the tundra) occurs only at the moment when the consistency of the upper layer changes from the solid state into the liquid or plastic one. This happens generally in the autumn. Observations made by Grigoriew (1925) confirm this opinion on the subject."

Tundra craters appear to have been described by de Quervain (1920) in Greenland under the name of *Erdquelle* ("mud springs"); in Lapland they have been referred to by Bergström (1912) as *Krater-rutmark*, and by Frödin (1912) as *Gärlehm*. Brainerd Mears (personal communication) mentions similar effects in the high tundra areas of Wyoming and has called our attention to the problematic *mima mounds* (see discussion in *Prairie Mounds*). Little attention has been paid to this phenomenon, and no mention of any of these terms is found in the standard international glossaries. In conversation, I have heard "*piping*" (q.v.) compared with suffosion, but the process of piping involves disaggregation of clastics and sometimes solution (see *Thermokarst* and *Salt Karst*) which is just the opposite of suffosion.

RHODES W. FAIRBRIDGE

References

Bergström, E., 1912, "En märkling form av rutmark fran barrskonsregionen i Lappland," *Geol. Foren. Stockholm Forh.* **34**, 335–342.

Frödin, G., 1912, "Beobachtungen über den Einfluss der Pflanzendecke auf die Bodentemperatur," *Lunds. Univ. Arsskr.*, **8**.

Grigoriew, A., 1925, "Typen des Tundra-Mikroreliefs von Polar-Eurasien, ihre geografische Verbreitung und Genesis," *Geogr. Z.*, **31**.

Jahn, A., 1948, "Research on the structure and temperature of the soils in western Greenland," *Bull. Acad. Polon. Sci. Lettres, Krakow*, 50–59.

Nikoroff, C., 1928, "The perpetually frozen subsoil of Siberia," *Soil Sci.*, **36**, 61.

Paterson, T. T., 1940, "The effects of frost action and solifluxion around Baffin Bay and in the Cambridge District," *Quart. J. Geol. Soc. London*, **96**, Pt. 1, 99–130.

Quervain, A. de, 1920, "Ergebnisse der Schweizerische Grönland expedition 1912–1913," Zurich.

Cross-references: *Cryopedology, Cryoplanation, Cryoturbation; Frost Action; Patterned Ground; Periglacial Landscape; Pingos; Piping; Prairie Mound; Salt Karst; Thermokarst; Tundra Landscape.*

SUPERPOSED VALLEY, STREAM—*See* DRAINAGE PATTERNS; RIVERS

SURELL'S LAWS OF FLUVIAL EROSION

Alexandre Surell was a French civil engineer who in 1841 published a classic work *Étude sur les torrents des Hautes-Alpes*, the first close study of mountain rivers, their hydrodynamics and control. He followed the Italian specialists but was probably independent in recognizing that (a) erosion in the headwater area is more vigorous than it is downstream, and (b) the erosive channel of a stream was concave up. He established the important concept of the *pente-limite* (limit slope) or steady-state equilibrium between the sediment load and the stream bedform, while the *thalweg* (q.v.) becomes increasingly concave upstream. These tendencies toward regression erosion and a concave equilibrium profile are sometimes known as *Surell's Laws* (Haug, 1907; Mougin, 1914; Baulig, 1925). Surell pointed out that it was not only mountain torrents that followed these rules but rivers of all sizes and gradients.

Expressed by Haug (1907, pp. 408–412), and translated in Termier and Termier (1963, p. 106), these two basic laws of fluvial erosion are:

Law 1; "The deepening process of a river by the flow of water takes place from its mouth upstream, leaving a fixed point at the base of the slope, which is base level. Its movement is thus regressive" (i.e., erosion is headward and downward, but there is no erosion at base level (Fig. 1), the principle of *headwards regression*).

Law 2; "The longitudinal profile leaves base level in a regular curve. This curve is concave toward the top and tangential to the horizontal in its lower section; and upstream it trends sharply upward so that it becomes tangential to the vertical."

These two statements should be compared with Gilbert's *law of declivities* (q.v.), which expresses the dynamic cause.

Surell also observed how tributary streams joining a main stream grade to the latter, which in his own words "acts as a sort of stable datum level, although upstream the bed of the tributary stream is subject to continual variations" (p. 28). This is

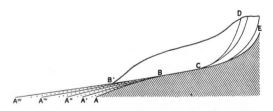

FIG. 1. Profile along a simplified fluvial thalweg, "approaching its state of equilibrium" (Haug, 1907, Fig. 161). Surell's first law is illustrated by the evolution of the rock-cut stream bed from D–B' to ECB. His second law is partly shown by the trace ECB but downstream the accumulating alluvial fan ("*cone de dejection*") is not shown flattening to base level, which may be far removed from the mountain.

what Powell (1875) later called the "local base level."

The youth-maturity-old age evolutionary concept of W. M. Davis was clearly foreshadowed by Surell, who wrote: "One may divide streams into three stages corresponding to age, all having a common origin, but different characteristics. The first period corresponds to the creation of the longitudinal profile of the stream bed. In the second period, the curve evolves but is not fixed, being controlled by the slope equilibrium, though at the same time it can meander. Finally, a third period corresponds to the development of a stable regime."

RHODES W. FAIRBRIDGE

References

Baulig, H., 1925, "La notion de profil d'équilibre: histoire et critique," *Compt. Rend. Congr. Intern. Geogr.* (Cairo), **3**, 51–63 (reprinted with extensive notes in "Essais de Géomorphologie," 1950, *Publ. Fac. Let. Univ. Strasbourg*, **114**, 43–86).

Gilbert, G. K., 1877, "Report on the geology of the Henry Mountains," *U.S. Geol. Surv. Rocky Mt. Reg.*, 160pp.

Haug, E., 1907, "Traité de Géologie," Vol. 1, p. 408, Paris, A. Colin, 2 vols.

Mougin, P., 1914, "Les torrents de la Savoie," Grenoble.

Powell, J. W., 1875, "Exploration of the Colorado River of the West and Its Tributaries," Washington, 291pp.

Surell, Alexandre, 1841, "Étude sur les torrents des Hautes-Alpes," Paris (Second ed., with additions by E. Cézanne, 1872, 2 vols, 321 and 386pp.).

Termier, H., and Termier, G., 1963, "Erosion and Sedimentation," London and Princeton, N.J., D. Van Nostrand, 433pp. (translated by D. W. and E. E. Humphries).

Cross-references: *Base Level*; *Equilibrium*; *Law of Declivities, Law of Structure, etc.*; *Profile of Equilibrium*; *Rivers*; *Thalweg*; *Youth-Maturity-Old Age.* pr Vol. VI: *Bedforms in Alluvial Channels.*

SURVEYING—*See* pr Vol. VI

SURVEYS—*See* pr Vol. VI, **EARTH SCIENCE INFORMATION AND SOURCE**

SWALE—*See* **BEACH RIDGES**

SWAMP, MARSH AND BOG—*See* pr Vol. VI

SWASH, SWASH MARK

Swash is the motion of water up a beach, after the breaking of a wave. *Swash mark* is a miniature arcuate ridge 1–2 millimeters high, representing the upper limit of swash after each wave break. With a falling tide, numerous swash traces leave an intersecting arcuate pattern. In fossil beach deposits, these delicate traceries are often faithfully recorded.

FIG. 1. Swash marks and beach cusps on the north coast, Puerto Rico. (Courtesy of A. K. Lobeck.)

The swash tends to carry a thin layer of sand up the beach. In calm weather, the *backwash* of the returning water has little energy, creating a diamond pattern of small rills; in any case, some of this water is dissipated, soaking into the beach and moving through the porous sand to emerge once more at the foot of the beach. During heavy weather, wave frequency and height increase, thereby increasing backwash energy, and erosion ensues.

Where waves approach the beach diagonally, refraction reduces the angle of impact, though the swash is not quite normal to the slope of the beach, but the backwash is. The result is a zigzag motion of sand up and down the beach, leading to mass transport of sand in a longitudinal sense, the *beach drifting* of Johnson (1919).

On wide beaches with a well-developed longshore bar or bars, and on coasts of large tidal range, at a mid-stage of a rising tide, the swash may sweep over the innermost bar, bringing a thin sheet of water to run over the inner face of the bar. Since the bar surface undulates slightly in a longitudinal sense, the swash comes over the depressed sectors and pairs of swash sheets intersect, setting up small interference ripples, in diamond patterns, so-called *rhomboid ripples*. For these to be preserved, quiet, prograding littoral conditions are required.

RHODES W. FAIRBRIDGE

References

Bascom, W., 1964, "Waves and Beaches," New York, Doubleday & Co., 267pp.

Inman, D. L., 1949, "Sorting of sediments in the light of fluid mechanics," *J. Sediment. Petrol.,* **19,** 51–70.

Johnson, D. W., 1919, "Shore Processes and Shoreline Development," New York, John Wiley & Sons, 583pp.

Kuenen, P. H., 1950, "Marine Geology," New York, John Wiley & Sons, 568pp.

Cross-references: *Bars; Beach; Littoral Processes.* Vol. I: *Waves.*

SYMMETRY INDEX—*See* ASYMMETRIC VALLEYS

SYNCLINAL RIDGES, VALLEYS—*See* STRUCTURAL CONTROL IN GEOMORPHOLOGY

SYSTEMS—*See* GENERAL SYSTEMS THEORY IN GEOMORPHOLOGY; OPEN SYSTEMS—ALLOMETRIC GROWTH

T

TAFONI

Tafoni (Italian; sing. *tafone*; spelled *taffoni* in French, from Corsica) was established as a generic term in geomorphology by A. Penck (1894) on the basis of Corsican examples so named. They are forms of cavernous weathering, chiefly found in medium- and coarse-grained, acid to intermediate, crystalline rocks, but also occurring in other rocks such as sandstone, limestone, and schist. These hollows range in diameter and depth from a decimeter or so to several meters, though those smaller than a football are sometimes distinguished as miniature tafoni. In shape, they tend to be ellipsoidal or spherical, enlarging inside the opening. The larger ones frequently exhibit thin, canopy-like overhangs on their upper margins, whereas their lower margins are smoothed over. Smaller rounded depressions may diversify the larger tafoni, especially in the roof. Side-tafoni, breaching the steep sides of boulders and of pillars and domes of bedrock, have been distinguished from basal-tafoni, which develop on the undersides of boulders and exfoliation sheets (Fig. 1).

Tafoni surfaces often show scaling and flaking, with plates of rock a few millimeters thick and a few centimeters in length; this has been termed negative exfoliation. Other inner surfaces suffer granular disintegration, the rock minerals lacking the original cohesion of fresh rock. In some areas, tafoni face in all directions, whereas in others, preference occurs for the lee sides in terms of prevalent winds and for shaded sides where the midday sun falls low enough for this to be significant.

Related forms are weather pits and pans (gnammas, Australian) on the upper surfaces of similar rock features, and pedestal rocks may some-

FIG. 2. Tafoni, of small-scale "honeycomb" weathering style, developed in Jurassic sandstones under spray influence near high-tide level on the Otway coast, Victoria, Australia. (Photo: R. W. Fairbridge). Note: a synonym for honeycomb weathering is "alveolar weathering."

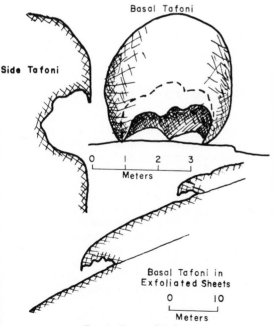

Fig. 1. Types of Tafoni.

1103

times be partly due to the merging of tafoni. Even more closely allied is honeycomb-weathering or stone-lattice, which develops in a greater variety of rocks and in a wider range of circumstances; in this feature, arrays of small hollows, often less rounded than miniature tafoni, are strongly controlled by structure.

Tafoni are regarded as being most characteristic of tropical and subtropical, semiarid to moderately arid climates. The southwest of the United States, the Peruvian and western Argentinian deserts, the Namib of South Africa, parts of Tanganyika, the Sudan near Kordofan, and western Australia can be cited in this connection. However, they are also found in the colder deserts of the continental interior of Asia and of polar regions, where the forms tend to be small. They are also found in subhumid and even humid climates such as northern Portugal, Corsica, Elba, Aruba and Hong Kong, where the occurrences are mainly coastal. Here, exposure to strong and persistent sea winds can cause microclimatic aridity. Not all the more humid localities are of this type, as in interior Uruguay, where variability of rain may induce frequent drought at the rock surface. Under certain circumstances, tafoni may be used as paleoclimatic indicators.

The comparative absence of tafoni from extreme deserts is one of the reasons which has led to the rejection of marked temperature changes and wind erosion as causes of their formation, though wind may help by removing the products of rock breakup. The Saharan Hoggar has tafoni, but these are thought to be inherited from a former pluvial period, since degraded by wind abrasion. Within any locality, the preference for more persistently moist places —shaded and lee sides, basal situations—has favored the idea that water is critical to the weathering involved. It has been maintained that the proces-

ses involved are physical—the penetration of water during temperature fluctuations causing expansion and loss of cohesion in a surface layer—since some tafoni are apparently developed in undecomposed rock. But chemical weathering, particularly kaolinization of feldspars and removal of iron from biotite, may be necessary. In the macro- and microclimates concerned, it is thought that strong evaporation draws salt solutions by capillary action to the surface, where depositions of silica, iron and manganese oxides cause resistant rind to develop over rotted interior. At more persistently moist points, the rind is breached or never develops, and from these points the weakened interior is excavated.

J. N. JENNINGS

References

Bremer, H., 1965, "Ayers Rock, ein Beispiel für klimagenetische Morphologie," *Zeit. Geomorphol.*, **3**, 249–284.

Calkin, P., and Cailleux, A., 1962, "A quantitative study of cavernous weathering (taffonis) and its application to glacial chronology in Victoria Valley, Antarctica," *Zeit. Geomorphol.*, *N.F.*, **6**, 317–324.

Klaer, W., 1956, "Verwitterungsformen im Granit auf Korsika," *Pet. Geogr. Mitt.*, **261**.

Kvelberg, I., and Popov, B., 1937, "Die Tafoni-Verwitterungserscheinung," *Acta. Univ. Latviensis Fac. Chem. Ser.*, **4**(6), 129–370.

Ottmann, F., 1956, "Sur l'âge de quelques "taffoni" en Corse," *C.R. Somm. Soc. Géol. France,* 62–64.

Penck, A., 1894, "Morphologie der Erdoberfläche," **1**, 214, Stuttgart.

Wilhelmy, H., 1958, "Klimamorphologie der Massengesteine," pp. 139–179, Braunschweig, G. Westermann.

Cross-references: *Exfoliation; Exudation; Granite Landforms; Weathering.*

FIG. 3. Tafoni, weathered out of quartz sandstone, leaving tubular supports in horizontal rocks, which may represent cemented worm tubes or some other diagenetic phenomenon; from Tumblagooda Sandstone, Murchison River, W. Australia. (Photo: R. W. Fairbridge.)

TAIGA LANDSCAPE

A taiga (from Russian or Yakut *taïga*, clumps or patches of woodland) is the open *subpolar* or *Arctic* or *boreal woodland* of coniferous trees that represents the northern part of the *boreal forest* province. The ground is largely covered by moss and lichen ("reindeer moss," "caribou moss": *Cladonia rangiferina*) or tussocks, and is wet. In Canada, those swampy areas are called "*muskeg*" (Küchler, 1947).

The climate of the taiga is cold-temperate. The mean temperatures of the warmest month are in the range 12–20°C with a high humidity, while in the coldest month they are down to minus 40°C, with continuous snow cover. Precipitation involves 300–700 mm a year, and is related to the westerly storm tracks.

Since the thaw in the northern continents (Canada, Siberia) occurs while the lower reaches of

FIG. 1. Taiga landscape in the Siberian platform, with scattered conifers (larch) and moss-covered ground. Air view of vegetation and rapids where the Moyero River crosses a Paleozoic dolerite sill. (Photo: S. A. Strelkov)

north-flowing rivers are still frozen, there is commonly widespread flooding in the middle reaches, contributing to the wet nature of the taiga. Because the subsoil is largely within the *permafrost* zone (q.v.), there is no downward drainage. To the north of the taiga region is the belt of *tundra* (q.v.). Taiga and tundra are largely limited to the northern hemisphere, because their corresponding climatic latitudes, 50–70°N, in the south are occupied by the Southern Ocean, and only a few scattered islands or small regions of South America fall into this belt (see *Taiga Climate*, Vol. II).

The coniferous evergreens of the boreal woodlands show an extraordinary adaptation to the short summer growing periods and intensely cold, long winters. The "cold pole" of the northern hemisphere lies in the Siberian taiga. On the one hand, the needle-shaped leaves of the conifers reduce transpiration, for the belt is one of very low precipitation, and on the other, the multiple needles permit adequate photosynthesis during the growing season. In North America and in Asia, the variety of the flora increases in each case from west to east, while northernmost Europe is quite limited (mainly *Pinus sylvestris*). The more varied forests include fir (*Abies*) and spruce (*Picea*). In the light needle taiga (larch, pine), characteristic of more continental climates,

there are also shrubs of birch, willow, rhododendron, etc. In the dark needle taiga (fir, spruce and cedar) there are few shrubs and more wet ground with moss cover. This second category is found in the wetter and milder situations particularly on the western sides of the continents and mountain ranges.

Curiously enough, in the more marginal areas, where the "tree line" is marked as a rule by a break-up of the forest into scattered clumps and valley groves, there is a reappearance of certain deciduous trees, which survive for the very fact that they do lose all their leaves in winter. In northern Siberia, the dominant form is the dahurian larch (*Larix*), the shallow roots of which are able to spread out above the permafrost; dwarf and stunted forms of birch (*Betula*) and aspen (*Populus*) also have their place. Growth rates are extremely slow. Excessive leaching leads to podzolization, and the remaining surface soil often consists of little more than a pure quartz sand, the poorness of which for plant growth is obvious. Human settlement is accordingly very restricted. In mountain taiga (see Sokolova, 1964), soils are less acid because of better drainage, but more humic.

The taiga association evolved as a mountain flora in early and middle Tertiary and became widespread during the Pliocene and Quaternary. The taiga is

FIG. 2. First (postglacial) fluvial terrace with young larch forest in the Siberian taiga (67°30′N, 104°E) on the Moyero River, a tributary of the Kotuy-Khatanga. (Photo: S. A. Strelkov).

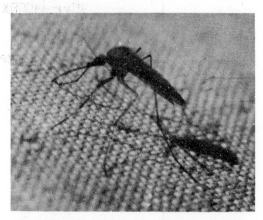

FIG. 3. Representative member of the summer swamp fauna; mosquitoes are very abundant for a brief period. (Photo: S. A. Strelkov).

one of the world's great sources of timber, particularly in northern Canada, Alaska, the USSR and Finland. Fauna in the taiga, apart from insects (see Fig. 3!), consists typically of elk, bear, squirrel, wood-grouse (capercailie), hazel grouse, and crossbill.

RHODES W. FAIRBRIDGE
SERGE A. STRELKOV

References

Baird, P. D., 1964, "The Polar World," London, Longmans, 328pp.

Dansereau, P., 1957, "Biogeography: An Ecological Perspective," New York, Ronald Press Co., 394pp.

Eyre, S. R., 1963, "Vegetation and Soils," Chicago, Aldine Publishing Co., 324pp.

Küchler, A. W., 1947, "Localizing vegetation terms," *Ann. Am. Assoc. Geogr.*, **37**, 197–208.

Lavrenko, E. M. (ed.), 1947, "Geobotanicheskoze Raionirovanie S.S.R.", Moscow (in Russian).

Marr, J. W., 1948, "Ecology of the forest-tundra ecotome of the east coast of Hudson Bay," *Ecol. Monogr.*, **18**, 117–144.

Mayer, H., 1890, "Die Wandlung von Nordamerika," München.

Putnam, D. F., 1952, "Canadian Regions," Toronto, Dent.

Sokolova, T. A., 1964, "Effect of rocks on podzol formation," *Soviet Soil Sci. (English Transl.)*, **3**, 233–240.

Cross-references: *Frost Action*; *Periglacial Landscape*; *Permafrost*; *Quaternary*; *Tundra Landscape.* Vol. II: *Arctic Climate*; *Cold Pole*; *Taiga Climate*; *Vegetation Classification and Description.* pr. Vol. VI: *Podzolization.*

TALUS FAN OR CONE; SCREE AND CLIFF DEBRIS

The rock fragments found on slopes or at the foot of steep slopes and cliffs under conditions of subpolar or arid subtropical climates are variously referred to as talus, scree or rock debris. The term *talus* is of French origin ("slope") but is employed in a special sense in geomorphology; its broad use in French, meaning an embankment, is often a source of confusion, e.g., the French term for the continental slope is the "talus continental."

The term talus is most commonly used in the United States, while *scree* is somewhat more favored in Britain; they are used in a synonymous way as a rule, but some authors prefer to use scree to mean any loose rock fragment covered surfaces, such as one often sees in steep slatey rock slopes, while talus would be restricted to strictly cliff debris (which may be stabilized at the foot of the cliff).

The following categories of talus may be generally recognized (Sidney White, 1968):

Rockfall talus—produced mainly by rockfall (individual blocks falling, shattering, rolling, bounc-

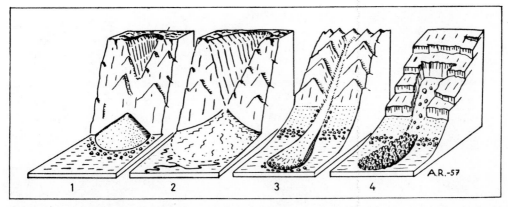

FIG. 1. Sketch of four types of debris accumulations. 1:1 Talus cone, 1::2 Alluvial cone, 1:3 Avalanche boulder tongue, 1:4 Rockslide tongue (Rapp, 1959). For further description, see text.

ing); there is a high percentage of coarse blocks, with fine sizes in the minority; larger sizes occur at the bottom of 37°–40° slopes; freeze-thaw and heavy rain releases the blocks; rarely associated with vegetation.

Alluvial talus—produced mainly by water transportation; all particle sizes occur, with the fines washed down into the interstices, and a crude bedding is possible; the larger sizes tend to stop at the top; the upper slopes are 35°–38°, while the lower slopes are 35°–30° and less; this alluvial talus accumulates during and after heavy rains or melting snow, by rainwash, during storm flow, and by miniature mudflows with mudflow levees; vegetation is often found, but may be gouged out or covered by mudflows.

Avalanche talus—this is predominantly carried down by both clean and dirty avalanches; particles are of all sizes, with the fines washed into interstices, the accumulation being nonsorted and nonbedded; there is an absence of any discernible size distribution; slopes are 35°–30°, or less; it accumulates when dirty avalanches occur, with boulder-protected debris tails and debris scattered haphazardly on the slope; vegetation is found in stripes where not removed by avalanching, rainwash and mudflow.

Talus creep is the slow, downhill shifting of talus that may merge into *rock streams or rock glaciers* (q.v.). Its motion is greatly aided by snow, and by freeze and thaw (*nivation*, q.v.). The relative uniformity of active talus or scree slopes is a function of the rock fragment sizes and sorting, corresponding to the critical angle of repose plus a small factor relating gravitational acceleration to friction (Jeffreys, 1932).

In some cirques, the talus material slides down over the firn bank, névé or compacted snowbank, coming to rest near its foot in a semicircular ridge, 1–6 meters high and up to 300 meters long (first noted by Daly, 1912, p. 593; named *protalus ramparts* by Bryan, 1934).

A less advanced type is the *protalus lobe,* a tongue of rock rubble or debris that is the product of creep or solifluction at the toe of a talus slope (Richmond, 1962, p. 20). An essentially *in situ* talus is the *frost rubble sheet*, a talus developed on a slope, but lacking a cliff or rockwall as a source area; it consists of a thin layer of angular blocks and rubble with few fines, resulting from freeze-thaw action and downslope creep.

Relict talus or scree of Pleistocene origin is found in many areas not affected by periglacial frost action today. Where the debris or country rock consists of limestone, the talus is liable to cementation and thus may be preserved for extended periods. In Cyrenaica, North Africa, Hey (1963) has reported two sets of such material, the older, well-cemented series, probably 50,000–43,000 B.P., and the second uncemented, probably 32,000–12,000 B.P. The famous Hötting breccia of Innsbruck is a similar, well-cemented example dating from an early interglacial.

A number of related features have been more closely defined by Rapp (1959, etc.). Figure 1 shows talus and related debris accumulations which are formed on mountain slopes by various types of mass movement:

Talus cone (1:1): An accumulation of rock debris, formed close to a mountain wall, mainly through many small rockfalls. In mountains of middle and high latitudes, the rockfalls are most frequent in late spring when the walls are thawing after the winter freeze. Rockfalls are also triggered by earthquake shocks. For example, in the Chugach mountains, Alaska, large talus cones were formed by continuous rockfalls from shear zones in a high trough valley side near Eklutna Lake. The shear zones were apparently activated during and following the Good Friday earthquake in 1964 (Karlstrom, 1965, p. 133). The rockfalls continued for more than one year. The slope profile of the talus is straight or very slightly curved, and the inclination is 30–40°.

FIG. 2. Talus cones, 250 meters high, in Permocarboniferous cherts and sandstones, Mt. Templet, Spitsbergen. Raised beaches in the foreground. Cone No. 3 from the left is slightly eroded by snow avalanches, the others are pure gravity cones. (Photo: A. Rapp).

The material is angular rock debris, with the big boulders at the talus base (fall sorting), where they form a so-called *base fringe*. The latter can extend out a little on ground that is less steep than about 30°, but if the finer material of the talus (gravel, cobbles, pebbles) covers the slope down to about 25° or a lower inclination, the base fringe is formed by some type of mass movement other than small rockfalls.

The particles of the talus generally show a slight imbrication and rough orientation of the long axis downslope, probably due to secondary talus creep. According to measurements, the rate of creep movements in active talus cones can be about 10 cm/yr or more in the surface layer on the upper part of the cone, decreasing toward zero below the surface and on the lower portion of the talus (Rapp, 1961, p. 173.)

If the rockwall is weathering uniformly over its entire free surface, a simple talus slope is formed instead of a series of cones. In formerly glaciated mountains, the volume of debris in talus cones with no removal of material (e.g., by running water, waves, glaciers or solifluction) can give a measure of the total, postglacial weathering of the parent bedrock wall.

Steep alluvial cone (1:2): An accumulation of rock debris formed by torrents and *mudflows* (q.v.). The profile line is generally concave from top to base.

The surface of steep *alluvial fans* (q.v.) is uneven with gullies and mudflow levees (Sharp, 1942, p. 222). The material is generally subangular. Alluvial cones can be formed through the transformation of talus cones by mudflows and water transport. Because of this, the sorting of the debris is the reverse of that of a talus cone; i.e., there is coarse debris at the apex and fine debris at the base of an alluvial cone. (*Note:* Alluvial cone and fan are often taken as synonyms; here we take cone to be steeper than fan. "Apron" may be used for "fan.")

Avalanche boulder tongue (1:3): An accumulation of rock debris, eroded and deposited by *snow avalanches* (q.v.). All transition forms from true talus cones to true avalanche tongues occur. These forms are best developed in mountains with strong influence of winds and snow drifting (e.g., northern Scandinavia, northern Rockies). The slope profile is markedly concave. The distal part of the tongue may reach far out on flat ground in the valley floor and sometimes it may continue upslope on the opposite valley side. The surface of the accumulation is flattened out like a roadbank. The broad, straight avalanche track has a smooth surface, sometimes vegetation covered and often with very characteristic detail forms, *inter alia*, the so-called avalanche debris tails (Rapp, 1957, p. 183).

Many avalanche boulder tongues have an asymmetrical transverse profile with a more distinct limit on the leeward side, due to a protecting accumulation of snow. The rock debris in the tongue is generally angular and   not strictly sorted according to size.

Rock-slide tongue (1:4): A tongue-like accumulation of rock debris gene ally with concave profile and small inclination in the distal part. In this it resembles the avalanche boulder tongues but can easily be distinguished because of its larger size and rough or hummocky surface, which consists of very large, angular boulders without any sorting or detailed forms (Heim, 1932, p. 99; Sharpe, 1938, Pl. IB and VIIIB).

This type of accumulation has not been formed by more or less continuous debris supply in portions as have the three earlier types, but it has been formed in one single catastrophic movement.

ANDERS RAPP
RHODES W. FAIRBRIDGE

References

Behre, C. H., Jr., 1933, "Talus behavior above timberline in the Rocky Mountains," *J. Geol.*, **41**, 622–635.

Bryan, K., 1934, "Protalus moraine—Talus," *Geogr. Rev.*, **24**, 655.

Daly, R. A., 1912, "Geology of the North American Cordillera at the forty-ninth parallel," *Geol. Surv. Canada Mem.*, **38**, 857pp.

Davison, C., 1888, "Note on the movement of scree material," *Quart. J. Geol. Soc., London*, **44**, 232–238, 826–827.

Heim, A., 1932, "Bergsturz und Menschenleben," *Vierteljahrsschr. Naturforsch. Ges. Zuerich*, **77**.

Hey, R. W., 1963, "Pleistocene screes in Cyrenaica (Libya)," *Eiszeitalter Gegenwart*, **14**, 77–84.

Jeffreys, H., 1932, "Scree slopes," *Geol. Mag.*, **69**, 383–384.

Karlstrom, T., 1965, "Upper Cook Inlet area and Matanuska River valley," *INQUA, VII Congr., Guidebook Field Conf. F*, 114–141.

Rapp, A., 1957, "Studien über Schutthalden in Lappland und auf Spitzbergen," *Zeit. Geomorphol.*, **1**, 179–200 (in German, English summary).

Rapp, A., 1959, "Avalanche boulder tongues in Lappland," *Geogr. Ånn.*, **41**, 34–48.

Rapp, A., 1961, "Recent development of mountain slopes in Kärkevagge and surroundings, northern Scandinavia," *Geografiska Ann.*, **42**, 71–200.

Rapp, A., 1963, "The debris slides at Ulvådal, western Norway: An example of catastrophic slope processes in Scandinavia," *Akad. Wissen. Göttingen*, No. 13, 195–210.

Richmond, G. M., 1962, "Quaternary stratigraphy of the La Sal Mountains, Utah," *U.S. Geol. Surv. Profess. Paper* **324**.

Sharp, R. P., 1942, "Mudflow levees," *J. Geomorphol.*, **5**(3), 222–227.

Sharpe, C. F. S., 1938, "Landslides and Related Phenomena," New York, Columbia University Press, 137pp.

Varnes, D. J., 1958, "Landslide types and processes," in (Eckel, E. B., editor), "Landslides and Engineering Practice," *Natl. Acad. Sci. Natl. Res. Council Publ.*, **544**, 20–47.

White, S. E., 1968, "Rockfall, alluvial, and avalanche talus in the Colorado Front Range," *Geol. Soc. Am. Special Paper* (abs. for 1967).

Cross-references: *Alluvial Fan, Cone; Avalanche; Frost Action; Haldenhang; Landslide; Mass Movement; Mudflow; Nivation; Rock Streams; Slopes; Snow Avalanche.*

TARN

A word used frequently in northern England to indicate a small mountain lake, tarn has been used by some geomorphologists in a more specific sense. In formerly glaciated mountainous areas, the head of a valley is usually occupied by a rock basin set in a steep-walled amphitheatre in the mountainside. Such basins were probably the product of erosion by cirque glaciers, while the amphitheatre was largely due to freeze-thaw action (Lewis, 1960). The word "tarn" has been adopted by many (e.g., Charlesworth, 1957; Thornbury, 1954) to refer to the lakes which frequently occupy such rock-cut basins, and in this sense, it is synonymous with cirque-lake, corrie-lake, or cwm.

DAVID E. SMITH

References

Charlesworth, J. K., 1957, "The Quaternary Era," London, Edward Arnold, 2 vols.

Lewis, W. V., 1960, "The Problem of Cirque Erosion," in (Lewis, W. V., editor), "Norwegian Cirque Glaciers," (Vol. 4), Royal Geographical Society Res. Ser., London, John Murray.

Thornbury, W. D., 1954, "Principles of Geomorphology," New York, John Wiley & Sons, 618pp.

Cross-references: *Cirque; Cirque Glacier; Frost Action; Glacial Lakes.*

TECTONIC LANDSCAPES

According to accepted usage, landforms that result from crustal movements are described as tectonic. Though many geologists have used "structural" in the same sense, a convention among geomorphologists restricts "structural" to the description of forms that have been developed by erosion under the control of the internal structure of the terrain.

Since sculpture by erosion must be preceded by

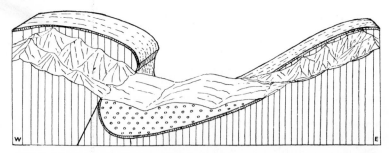

Fig. 1. Paparoa Range (west) and Victoria Range (east), composed of old folded rocks but carved by erosion from arches upheaved in the Pleistocene (shown uneroded at rear), Reefton district, New Zealand [data from R. P. Suggate, *N.Z. Geol. Surv. Bull.* **56,** (1957)].

upheaval, all mountains and mountain ranges except volcanoes (mountains of accumulation) might strictly be included in the tectonic category. This would then include "fold" mountains—those composed internally of folded rocks—even if the upheaval that has led to the sculpture by erosion of present-day mountains could be dated as contemporaneous with the folding of their rocks. In few such ranges, if any, however, can this be assumed to be the case. The welt of folded strata may have remained low-lying during, and for a long time after, its folding, or if it was simultaneously upheaved this upheaval has commonly taken place so long ago that the initial relief due to it must long since have been destroyed by mature dissection followed by planation.

There are many ranges that consist internally of folded rocks but obviously owe their mountainous relief to a relatively recent (e.g., Pleistocene) renewal of anticlinal upheaval; the majority of these are now maturely dissected. Examples of such are the Paparoa and Victoria Ranges, with relief of 4000–5000 feet, in the northwest of the South Island of New Zealand (Fig. 1), and indeed the Southern Alps of New Zealand as a whole could be so described, as well as many other ranges in Alpine belts throughout the world.

It is convenient, however, to exclude from the tectonic category mountains such as these that are so thoroughly dissected that the initial form of the upheaved mass can be restored only by guesswork. Even "block" mountains (isolated by faults) can no longer be recognized as such on geomorphic evi-

dence when they are worn down to the "old stage" (Davis, 1954, Fig. 115) or even dissected to late maturity. The description tectonic is best reserved, therefore, for those landscape forms on which sufficiently large areas of an upheaved surface have escaped erosion to allow the shapes of the crustal blocks, arches, or domes that were produced by deformation accompanying upheaval to be at least roughly restored.

Mountain ranges are separated from one another by major valleys and lowlands that commonly also have resulted from deformation, and the tectonic origin of these may be more obvious than in the case of the mountains associated with them, for, having less available relief, they have generally been less dissected. In valleys and lowlands, however, especially in those of regions with considerable rainfall, the erosive activity of major rivers has commonly destroyed the infantile forms or disguised them beyond recognition. For this reason, primarily, examples of tectonic relief have been drawn for the most part not from humid but from semiarid regions, where river erosion has been less destructive, e.g., the North American Great Basin and Central Otago, New Zealand.

Live Anticlines

Tectonic forms produced by differential upheaval of surfaces composed of soft sediments are so rapidly dissected and destroyed that their survival is very unusual. Initial or infantile (i.e., uneroded) forms of mountains composed of such materials have indeed had no real existence, because they have been de-

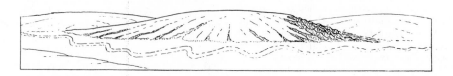

Fig. 2. Diagrammatic representation of undulations produced by anticlinal upheavals deforming a coastal plain that has emerged from the sea very recently in northwestern Wellington, New Zealand.

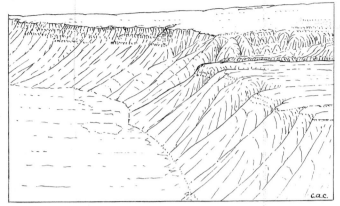

FIG. 3. Table-topped fault blocks, western side of Steens Mountain, Oregon.

stroyed while relatively slow or intermittent upheaval has been in progress. They can only be imaginary forms which it may be convenient to deduce to help explain present-day erosional reliefs and river courses.

There are, however, some relatively small anticlinal upheavals of recent origin that diversify the otherwise flat surfaces of unconsolidated marine sediments. Such forms, which seem to be still rising, are present on the recently emerged (end-Pleistocene) coastal plain of northwestern Wellington, New Zealand, throughout an area of several hundred square miles (Te Punga, 1957). Of elongated-dome shape, these are of various heights from a few hundred up to 1000 feet, and the surface inclination on their flanks is generally less than 10°. Where locally the slope is steeper, dissection is mature, but the gentler slopes are incised only by shallow consequent valleys between which infantile forms of the anticlinal slopes survive (Fig. 2).

Block Mountains

The shape of tectonic mountains is preserved where the tectonic forms (blocks, arches, or domes) have surfaces of very resistant rock, either flat-lying lava sheets, as in the case of the well-known faulted blocks of Oregon or, as is more commonly the case, surfaces planed by ancient erosion that bevel or truncate the folded structure of terrains of resistant rocks. However, should hard-rock surfaces such as these be present beneath layers, even thick piles of layers, of much softer materials, erosion may strip them bare—"as mud is washed from a board"—and reveal the tectonic shapes of mountains.

Some of the best-known examples of tectonic landforms are the "block" mountains that have been produced by uplift along faults. Uplifted blocks may have the table-like form of horsts, bounded on the longer sides by more or less parallel faults, but tilted blocks are also common, one long

side being the scarp of a fault and the other an inclined back slope.

Davis (1954, p. 726) regarded the lava blocks of Oregon "as types of the youngest, most elementary mountain forms..." and "the ranges of the Great Basin in Utah and Nevada as the types of ... more maturely sculptured ranges." These latter are composed of folded ancient rocks that have been beveled long ago by an erosion surface.

Because of the simplicity of their structure, the Oregon blocks preserve particularly well the broad outlines (and in places some details) of the tectonic initial form (Fig. 3). These lava mountains are not so young, however, that the actual subaerial surface of the last deposited layer survives on the tops of the blocks (Fuller, 1931). Yet it seems that only the softer materials have been washed away so as to expose everywhere practically the same horizon of hard lava, and the forms of the uplifted blocks are nearly the same as would have resulted from dislocation of an uneroded pile of lava sheets. The preservation of the block form is due to (a) resistance of the cap rock to erosion, whether it be a subaerial surface or a stripped one; (b) the nearly horizontal attitude of the lavas, which has indefinitely delayed dissection; and (c) simplicity of scarp development, for on this type of structure the scarp tends to retreat parallel to itself like a structural escarpment.

The Basin Ranges

Davis's second group, "the ranges of the Great Basin in Utah and Nevada," affords the type of block mountains of major dimensions whose original shapes are recognizable because an ancient erosion surface has been dislocated. Apart from the fault scarps that bound the ranges laterally, there are recognizable forms that indicate the initial shapes of generally tilted blocks now more or less thoroughly dissected.

FIG. 4. A block mountain of the Basin Range type. Part of the fault scarp forming the western face of the Wasatch Range, Utah. Sharp-edged facets on the spur ends indicate recent renewal of uplift of the range.

Where deep dissection since block uplift has destroyed the peneplain or late-mature surface forming the initial table tops and back slopes, the origin of blocks can be inferred only by analogy with better-preserved blocks or by the contrast of mountain relief with that of wide valleys, lowlands, and lake basins which are negative forms complementary to the tectonic mountains. Under the semiarid climate of the Great Basin, the floors of such forms are generally undissected; instead they are considerably aggraded. Some tectonic lowlands have also increased in area at the expense of mountain blocks that have been partially destroyed by pedimentation, but this is a condition that indicates approach to the "old" stage of evolution of the landscape, and is not found in association with features that indicate recent tectonic development.

The fault-scarp fronts of young Basin Range blocks are characteristically dissected and have been accepted as the type of high scarps that border fault blocks of mountainous dimensions. Similar development takes place also on the scarps of smaller blocks where, perhaps because of arching of the upland surface, streams that run down the infantile slope of the fault scarp head initially far back on the upland or are extended back by headward erosion. Thus, being of considerable volume, they cut deep ravines across the scarp. When scarps are thus deeply dissected, facets may be preserved on the ends of the spurs between dissecting ravines. Where such facets are well marked, as at the base of the Wasatch scarp (Fig. 4), it can generally be assumed, as Davis has pointed out, that scarp-making fault movement has recently been renewed. Without such scarp rejuvenation, the spurs taper to blunt ends or even to points. Their ends are, however, in line, indicating the trace of the fault, until in old age even this characteristic is lost.

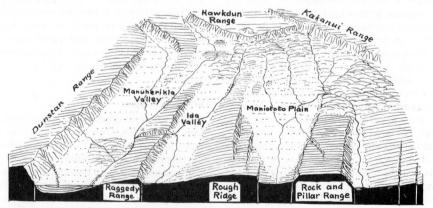

FIG. 5. New Zealand tectonic relief. Diagrammatic sketch of block mountains and tectonic basins in semiarid Central Otago, New Zealand.

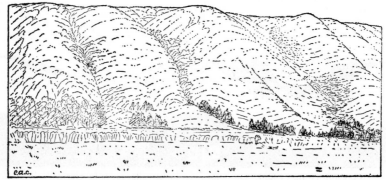

FIG. 6. Undissected fault scarp (or tectonic fault-line scarp) of Hunters Hills tilted block, South Island, New Zealand.

New Zealand Block Mountains

The New Zealand type of block-mountain landscape (Fig. 5) has features in common with the Basin Range type, but individual blocks are smaller, which makes it possible to see the tectonic units almost as a whole from the air and from some viewpoints on the ground. There is strong development of block tilting, so that major valleys are for the most part in well-marked fault angles, though some of these are broad and in part synclinal. There are also more warped surfaces in evidence, so that quite commonly the block form passes into an arched form, while the scarps are in part monoclinal. Some hard-rock plateau surfaces are arched, warped, faulted, and monoclinally flexed into a multitude of minor tectonic forms that resemble block mountains in miniature.

The planed surface that has been warped and dislocated both on a large and on a small scale is for the most part a resurrected fossil peneplain that cuts across schist and folded greywacke formations.* The covering beds under which this planed surface is buried are preserved in tectonic lowlands, where they are sculptured into erosional forms of relatively small relief and are traversed by rivers.

Antecedent and Anteconsequent Gorges

While the rivers of a tectonic landscape are largely consequent, following courses through relatively downthrown basins and fault angles,

---

* In parts of southern New Zealand, including Central Otago, as interpreted by some authors, this surface was retouched and beveled by erosion after preliminary block-forming movements had taken place and the cover had been stripped from upraised parts of the terrain. Renewed and stronger movements of dislocation followed, and the younger erosion plain thus forms some block surfaces. According to W. N. Benson, this is a peneplain of late Miocene age; according to B. L. Wood, it is an early to middle Pleistocene surface of cryoplanation.

there are usually some that have cut gorges across upheaved blocks (a gorge, for example, through Raggedy Range, Fig. 5). Though such courses may have been first taken on covering strata and are then, strictly speaking, superposed where they are cut down into underlying rocks, gorges across mountain blocks are in the main of antecedent origin. Simple antecedence is probably the correct explanation of a few rivers that have maintained courses in gorges through block mountains of the Basin Range type, e.g., one through the Canyon Range, Utah.

However, some such gorges, notably many through ranges of recent tectonic origin in various parts of New Zealand, seem to have originated in two stages. In an early stage of deformation of the terrain, they were consequent on the range-and-basin pattern as it was then developed, but as deformation proceeded or was renewed after a pause, this pattern changed and some ranges that were earlier nonexistent or discontinuous rose and became continuous across rivers, which maintained antecedent courses through them. The well-known gorge of the Manawatu River, New Zealand, originated in this way when the main axial range, formerly discontinuous, rose and became continuous across the course of the river. Through this gorge, the drainage of a large area east of the axial range is carried westward to the sea.

Fault Scarps

A great many low fault scarps escape dissection such as characterizes the Basin Range type (already described). They thus remain wall-like. This is true of the Oregon lava type, which retreats like a structural escarpment (Fig. 3), but it is true also of innumerable scarps in other rocks with complex structure, especially where block surfaces are tilted back from the crest lines. Dissection of these scarps is confined to the formation of shallow erosional furrows separated by rounded spurs, with little difference of gradient between furrows and spurs (Fig. 6). The slope assumed by such a scarp

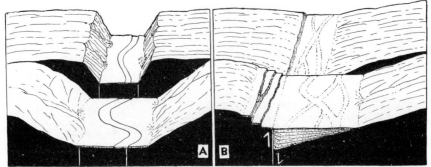

FIG. 7. Transformation of fault scarps into erosional valley-sides by rivers. A: A narrow graben (at rear) becomes a cryptotectonic valley (front). B: Development of a river-trimmed and terraced fault scarp as a result of intermittent fault movement, exemplified by the Hope fault scarp, bordering the Hanmer basin plain, New Zealand. Hypothetical early stage at rear.

as a whole (or by spur-end facets on dissected scarps) is governed by the local conditions of erosional slope development and gives no indication of the inclination of the theoretical initial (or infantile) scarp form or of the fault surface underground, which is commonly steep, even vertical or overhanging.

Monoclinal scarps, if steep, are indistinguishable from fault scarps when maturely dissected, but on monoclinal scarps that are of gentle inclination facets of the original surface (of hard rocks) may be preserved, and in the case of some very low scarps —in Otago, New Zealand, for example—the flexed surface, even though steep, is entirely undissected.

The foregoing applies to scarps that are not undercut by rivers. Where a river has taken its course through a broad down-faulted trough or fault-angle depression, two cases must be distinguished. In semiarid regions, e.g., the American Great Basin, dissection of the scarp bounding a mountain block commonly supplies sufficient waste to build a fringe of confluent alluvial fans along the base, which pushes back the rather inefficient rivers

of the adjacent lowland. To this protection from attack by river erosion Basin Range scarps owe their characteristic form, with spur ends aligned on the fault. Where, however, a river flowing initially along or parallel to the base of a scarp is vigorous enough to carry away rock debris as it is supplied by scarp dissection—the Awatere type, common in humid districts of New Zealand (Cotton, 1950)— the features that distinguish a conventional (Basin Range) fault scarp may be destroyed by lateral river erosion, and the scarp may thus come to resemble a valley side of erosional origin. The only geomorphic evidence that it is a fault scarp may be valley dissymmetry—the absence, especially in the case of fault-angle structure, of a similar or complementary valley side facing the scarp across a river.

Fault scarps bounding narrow tectonic trenches that are followed by rivers rapidly become unrecognizable as such [Fig. 7(A)] unless rejuvenated by renewed faulting.

In some cases of trimming by rivers—that, for example, of the Hope Fault scarp, which descends

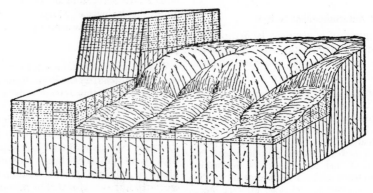

FIG. 8. A tectonic scarp consisting of a fault scarp (in the strict sense) above and a fault-line scarp (stripped by erosion) below. Initial form at right.

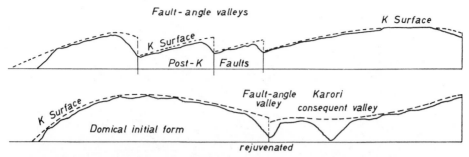

FIG. 9. Tectonic features defined by dislocation and warping of a peneplain. West-to-east profiles (5 miles long) across the Wellington Peninsula, New Zealand.

to the Hanmer basin plain, New Zealand, where repeated movements on the fault have taken place in recent times—scarps may become terraced, the terraces being "unilateral," i.e., they may have no counterparts across the rivers [Fig. 7(B)].

Many Tectonic Scarps Have Become Fault-line Scarps

In addition to fault scarps and the closely related monoclinal scarps, many of the boundaries between positive and negative tectonic features might be defined strictly as "fault-line" erosional scarps. This is necessarily the case in a region (like New Zealand) with compound structure, where a basement of resistant rocks has been overlaid by weak covering strata. When such a terrain is deformed or dislocated, not only is the cover soon washed by erosion from higher standing blocks, but along many fault boundaries cover that has lain against the fault surface on the downthrown side is also stripped away. At this stage, a tectonic scarp that dislocates the landscape is composite, partly a fault scarp and partly a fault-line scarp (Fig. 8). It is obvious that with greater thickness of cover, as compared with the throw of the fault, the whole of the scarp can become a fault-line scarp. Thus scarps cannot be excluded from the tectonic category because it is possible to class them by strict definition as fault-line scarps. Blackwelder (1928), however, quite properly excluded as non-tectonic such scarps as are revealed by erosion on old fault structures— these being the only forms he recognized as fault-line scarps. They are structural, not tectonic.

Tectonic Valley Forms

Some regions of tectonic relief are better described in terms of the valleys than of the salient forms associated with them, these being perhaps maturely dissected. A common tectonic form is the fault-angle valley, which may separate two tilted block mountains. Such a valley is bounded on one side by a fault scarp and on the other by the back slope of a block; it is thus strongly asymmetrical. Contrasting with this is the more symmetrical "rift

valley" of East African type, which is downthrown as a graben between parallel faults (Johnson, 1929). The basins of some large and very deep lakes have originated in this way. Bordering rift valleys, there may be plateaus of vast extent.

Many of the fault scarps that border tectonic valleys are still clearly recognizable as such; but narrow rift valleys are among the many tectonic forms that are readily disguised by erosion so as to become indistinguishable from purely erosional forms [Fig. 7(A)].

Minor Tectonic Features in the Mobile Belts

In mountainous parts of the mobile belts—notably in New Zealand—it is unsafe to assume an erosional origin for valleys large or small. Even where development from tectonic forms is not obvious, the possibility of remote tectonic origin must be kept in mind. Thus, throughout the ranges of Wellington, New Zealand, alignment of many valleys in a general way parallel to the strike of folded rocks, instead of being due to subsequent erosion, is largely if not wholly consequent, for streams cutting the valleys have been guided by fault angles between elongate tilted blocks, a sheaf of which forms each range. Modification of such small blocks by erosion can obscure their tectonic origin—relegating them and the valleys between them to a cryptotectonic category. Where, however, the minor horsts and tilted-block ridges of the relief can still be identified, the problem is simplified. Near and northeast of the city of Wellington (Fig. 9), some such blocks are recognizable because of partial preservation on them of remnants of a peneplain isolated by dislocation and erosion—the "K Surface" (Cotton, 1957).

Seismic Scarplets

Regions where most of the landscape features are tectonic or cryptotectonic are commonly seismic. In such regions—notably in parts of New Zealand—numerous low scarps ("fault scarplets") break the ground surface on the traces of faults that have recently been active, fault movements coin-

FIG. 10. The end of a broad spur (foreground) descending from a dissected fault scarp (at rear) has been shifted to the left along a transcurrent fault TF. East side of Tararua Range, New Zealand. (Drawn from a photograph taken by C. C. Rich).

ciding with earthquakes. Some scarplets are traceable for many miles as more or less well-preserved and more or less continuous walls up to 10 feet (or more) in height, crossing both level and uneven ground. Some of the faults thus indicated seem to have moved only once, but other scarplets are due to renewal of older fault movements. They follow the axes of valleys or are aligned closely along the bases of scarps some of which might not otherwise be recognized with certainty as tectonic.

Transcurrent Faulting

Many seismic scarplets are on the traces of transcurrent faults. Where the aggregate of fairly recent horizontal movements is considerable, these have deflected stream courses and, in some cases, have cut off and shifted the ends of spurs so as partly or wholly to block small valleys, forming "shutter ridges" (Fig. 10).

In general however, such fault movements produce less obvious changes in the landscape than do those with a large vertical component. Though some valleys have apparently been opened by transcurrent fault movement (some parts, for example, of the trace of the San Andreas fault, California) this is perhaps the result of down-buckling of one or other of the laterally moving blocks. Some upheaval of blocks appears also to be due to such buckling of the terrain, but though the effects of recent subsidence and upheaval on the landscape may be readily seen, the relation of vertical to

horizontal movements is generally a matter of inference.

Whereas some fault traces are strongly curved, faults that have, or have formerly had, strong horizontal components of movement commonly trace nearly straight lines for long distances.

C. A. COTTON

References

Blackwelder, E., 1928, "The recognition of fault scarps," *J. Geol.,* **36,** 289–321.

Cotton, C. A., 1948, "Landscape," Second ed., Ch. 20–22, Cambridge, The University Press; New York, John Wiley & Sons.

Cotton, C. A., 1950, "Tectonic scarps and fault valleys," *Bull. Geol. Soc. Am.,* **61,** 717–758.

Cotton, C. A., 1957, "Tectonic features in a coastal setting at Wellington," *Trans. Roy. Soc. New Zealand,* **86,** 761–790.

Davis, W. M., 1954, "The mountain ranges of the Great Basin," *Bull. Museum Comp. Zool.,* **42,** 129–177 (1903); reprinted in (Johnson, D. W., editor) "Geographical Essays," 725–772, New York, Dover Publ.

Fuller, R. E., 1931, "The Geomorphology and Volcanic Sequence of Steens Mountain in Southeastern Oregon," Seattle, University of Washington Press.

Johnson, D. W., 1929, "Geomorphologic aspects of rift valleys," *C.R. 15th Intern. Geol. Congr. S. Africa,* **2,** 354–373.

Te Punga, M. T., 1957, "Live anticlines in western Wellington," *New Zealand J. Sci. Technol.,* **B38,** 433–446.

Cross-references: *Asymmetric Valleys*; *Basin and Range Landscape*; *Block Mountain*; *Dome Mountain*; *Fault Scarp*; *Graben*; *Horst*; *Mountain Types*; *Neotectonics*; *Plateau*; *Rift Valley*; *Rivers*; *Warping*.

TERMITARIA, TERMITE MOUNDS—See ORGANISMS AS GEOMORPHIC AGENTS

TERRACES, FLUVIAL—INTRODUCTION

Fluvial terraces are topographic "platforms," "benches," "treads," "flats" or "steps" in river valleys that usually represent former levels of the valley floor or flood plain. Consideration of the heights and internal composition of terraces contributes significantly to a fundamental understanding of the geologic history of many valleys and the climatic evolution of the regions in which the valleys are cut (Cotton, 1940; Peltier, 1949).

Terraces may be located at more or less constant heights above the present flood plain or valley flat. The individual terraces are usually separated by low bluffs, rises or scarps. In places, the lower terraces may be long, continuous strips for hundreds of kilometers, but the higher levels are for the most part so dismembered that only isolated patches remain. From this progressive dismemberment, it may be deduced that the highest terraces are the oldest, but, as will appear below, this is not always so; in some places there are older buried terraces, and these may be exhumed.

The flood plain of a given epoch is related to *base level* (q.v.). Terraces reflect variations in base level and stream energy, two parameters which may change independently or together (Culling, 1957). Toward the ocean, base level is in turn related approximately to the height of mean sea level today, but it should be remembered that this level has changed eustatically over a range of more than 200 meters through the course of the Quaternary (see *Eustasy*; *Terraces—Thalassostatic*), and in the coastal sector the approximate parallelism between the terraces and flood plain breaks down (see *Terraces, Fluvial—Environmental Controls*). Toward the mountains, the stream energies have been more variable from time to time and the relief has periodically been rejuvenated, so that again the parallelism is not strictly maintained. In some valleys, as in the middle course of the Rhine, tectonic revival has arched up a given sector, and here the older terraces are progressively higher than up or downstream. In another region, e.g., where the Danube crosses the Little Hungarian Plain, the older terraces are progressively downwarped and can only be identified by drilling and geophysical work (Rónai, 1965).

Erosional and Depositional Terraces

Two fundamental categories of fluvial terraces exist: erosional and depositional. The former are eroded out of preexisting formations, and the latter result directly from accumulation of stream deposits; in the words of McGee (1891, p. 256), there are "terraces of destruction" and "construction."

The *erosional terrace* may be eroded in bedrock or in a former sedimentary valley fill. An erosional terrace in bedrock is often called a rock-cut terrace. Erosional terraces are formed when a river meanders from one side of its flood plain to the other, eroding laterally into the bedrock valley slopes or into the remains of an earlier valley fill. Long-continued lateral cutting suggests that the stream is in equilibrium, that it has no excess energy for downcutting. This generally implies tectonic or climatic stability: A lowered base level, for example, would cause vertical trenching and incised meanders until a new equilibrium was reached and lateral cutting could resume at the lower level (Fig. 1).

The *depositional terrace* is a result of upbuilding of the valley floor by deposition of alluvium. Alluviation in any one gross cycle is likely to pass through a coarse, medium and fine gradation from bottom to top. In detail, the valley fill includes as a rule many small lenses, each cross-bedded and graded from bottom to top, as in the case of either a *meandering stream* or a *braided stream* condition (see *Rivers—Meandering and Braiding*): on the other hand, in the case of overbank discharge and some sluice-type *proglacial* valley fill parallel bedding may appear (see *Fluvioglacial Processes*).

Dynamically, permanent alluvial deposition calls for diminution of transporting power, i.e., a rise of load or a fall in discharge. It is a disequilibrium condition, often brought about by a change toward aridity (with loss of vegetation) and accompanied by an unusual loading due to accelerated mass-wasting, such as slope wash, mudflows or solifluction (with or without a drop in runoff). Temporary alluviation may occur, of course, under any condition. An erosional terrace remnant is often found to include a veneer of contemporaneous terrace alluvium, clearly indicating varied components of an erosional cycle, the alluvial remnant being the last "temporary" deposit that was isolated by the incidence of a new cycle of down-cutting.

Rock-cut and Fill-cut Terraces

Two distinctive types of erosional terrace are recognized, those carved out of the country rock and those notched in a preceding valley fill of alluvium (Fig. 2). For rock-cut terraces the term *bench* is often appropriate.

In fluvial evolution under changing energy conditions due to changes in climate, tectonism, etc., it is inevitable that both cut and fill occur. The *Commission of Terraces and Erosion Surfaces* of the International Geographical Union has stressed that the simple term *terrace* applies to the landform and not to the material. Its genesis, however, cannot be

FIG. 1. Fill terraces on the Rakaia River, in the South Island of New Zealand; Mt. Hutt Range in the distance, with alluvial fans. Note the characteristic braided channel system in the river, indicative of high load/volume ratio and variable flow. (Photo: V. C. Browne, by permission).

determined on geometry alone; a geological approach is therefore essential. The distinction between the geomorphic feature and the stratigraphy of the deposits has been discussed by Hare (1947). The deposits are best referred to as *alluvial terrace deposits, terrace alluvium, terrace gravel,* etc. (see

Alluvium). A fill-cut terrace (also called a "*scour terrace*" for obvious reasons) often carries a "*lag gravel*" or layer of coarse debris and boulders, from which the fine components were removed during the scouring.

A *strath* is a Scottish term for a long, open valley

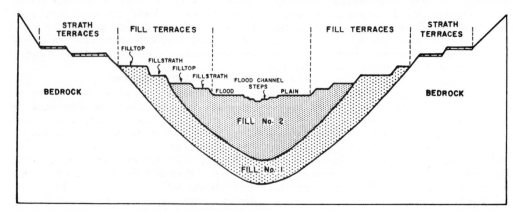

FIG. 2. Generalized diagram of rock-cut (strath) and fill terraces and flood-channel steps. These relationships may be complicated by burial of terraces under later fills, by subsequent lateral planation across successive fills and into the confining bedrock, and by the development of unpaired, as well as paired, terraces (Howard, 1959).

(in contrast to a narrow *glen*) often with a flat, rock-cut floor. The term *strath terrace* has been applied by Bucher (1932) to a mature valley, which is incised by the present stream (see also *Streams—Underfit*); the two constitute a "two-cycle" valley. The strath terrace in many places has a thin veneer of alluvium, unless "stripped." Where the strath is cut in a preceding alluvial fill, Howard (1959) suggests it be called a *fillstrath*. In many valleys multiple strath terraces and fill terraces occur.

Some of the world's great river valleys have been evolving for periods of the order of 10^7–10^8 years, but most of the early valley fills were scoured out during the last high-energy phases, and most of the present vast alluvial fills date from less than 1×10^5 years ago.

It is important to recognize the relative resistance of the rocks, saprolite, or sediment in the bed of a stream (the *thalweg*, q.v.). If the thalweg is cut in a resistant rock, the rate of down-cutting, regardless of stream energy, will be extremely slow; thus, an increase in the stream discharge will be expressed by higher flood levels, and accordingly an accumulation of terrace deposits will take place immediately after peak flow, but much of it is only temporary. In contrast, if the discharge decreases in a rock-lined gorge, there will be accumulation ("fill") (Fig. 3).

On the other hand, if the thalweg is in soft alluvium or saprolite, an increased flow (other than in that part of the valley close to base level) will lead to deeper dissection and therefore to erosional terraces at progressively lower elevations. After any given flood, the bed load will be partly redeposited but, of course, always farther downstream. A severe discharge decrease in a thalweg of alluvial sands and gravels causes siltation and may often lead to the total disappearance of the running streams, except immediately after periodical rains, and the water flow remains entirely out of sight in the alluvial gravels. The "unseen flow" of such valley gravels is a common source of domestic and irrigation water in parts of Australia and Africa, as well as in the southwestern United States.

Two directions of cutting are thus recognized, *down-cutting* and *sideways cutting* (lateral planation). The first represents a lowering of the thalweg, related to higher stream energy in a sector above its base level; the second a very slow broadening of the flood plain with *side-wall retreat* as the stream approaches its base level. It should be emphasized that although ultimate base level for rivers is mean sea level, a resistant rock barrier or a lake may constitute intermediate base levels. The latter exist therefore for any given energy/gradient sector, usually separated by *nickpoints* (q.v.).

Nearly a century ago, Gilbert pointed out that

FIG. 3. A rock-cut gorge near Chinle, Arizona (a small tributary of the Colorado River system), showing fill-top terraces of yellow-red silts that were formed during the semiarid alluviation of this valley during the last glacial phase. High precipitation during several stages of the early Holocene caused dissection in this semiarid landscape. (Photo: R. W. Fairbridge).

most terraces are erosional rather than depositional. The step from one level to the next lower one implies a rise in energy level. "River terraces imply surges of erosion" in the words of Cotton (1940). This surge may be brought about either by a drop of local or absolute base level where these result in an increase in stream slope and *velocity* or by an increase in velocity due to increase in discharge or some other factor. As mentioned above, however, if a hard rock-cut valley is involved, a brief rise in discharge will not lead immediately to terrace cutting but to higher flood levels, and after the seasonal flood high terrace alluvium will be left behind; this is a temporary disequilibrium condition (see *Terraces, Fluvial—Environmental Controls*). It is proper to emphasize that *most* terraces are cut in earlier fill, and thus *lateral planation,* as Cotton says, is the main factor in terrace formation.

Paired, Unpaired and Structural Terraces

Terraces that match in level on opposite sides of the valley are said to be "paired," while those that occur at staggered levels are "unpaired" or single. Paired terraces reflect mature lateral planation followed by sudden rejuvenation, with rapid incision the immediate result. Unpaired ones indicate slower and more continuous rejuvenation with lateral erosion still important [Figs. 4(A) and 4(B)]. While "terrace" refers to the geomorphic feature,

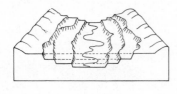

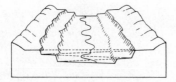

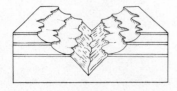

FIG. 4. (A) Paired terraces (due to intermittent rejuvenation caused by climatic changes or uplifts). (B) Unpaired terraces (due to continuous rejuvenation). (C) Structural terraces (due to differential erosion). (Sketches: A. D. Howard).

"terrace level" describes the reconstructed former flood plain surface between any terrace pair. Paired terraces very commonly have a cyclic significance, corresponding for example, to the climatic cycles of the Quaternary. Unpaired terraces are normally noncyclic. They are, respectively, referred to sometimes as *cyclic and noncyclic terraces.*

A special type of paired terrace [Fig. 4(C)], beautifully displayed for example in the Grand Canyon of the Colorado River, owes its origin to the presence of horizontal layers of hard rock in the valley walls. These layers retard down-cutting by the main stream during which time the valley sides recede in steps as a result of differential weathering and sidestream erosion. Such terraces are known as *structural terraces.* Unlike the paired terraces previously discussed, they provide no evidence in themselves of changes in level of land or sea, or of climatic changes.

In an incised winding valley of moderate gradient, the lateral planation is directed always into the outside curves, leading to cliff development, while the inside curves may preserve traces of older higher terraces. This inside band is a kind of dynamic *slip-off slope* (q.v.). Unpaired terraces are at progressively lower elevations going downstream, so that at any one cross section, the terraces on opposite sides of the valley are not at equivalent elevations.

Unpaired terraces suggest that rejuvenation took place continuously. Thus, in Fig. 4(B), there is no evidence of stillstands of the stream during deepening of the valley. The staggered elevations of the terraces below the original valley floor suggest that lateral abrasion was accompanied by down-cutting as the stream wandered from one valley side to the other. Such continuous incision or rejuvenation commonly results from secular tectonic uplift, gradual tilting, climatic change or change in load-volume relation of stream.

Cut-and-fill Terraces

Both paired and unpaired terraces may be produced by repeated episodes of alluviation and entrenchment in deep stream valleys. Waste from upstream or from unprotected valley sides clogs and aggrades valley floors at times when there is insufficient precipitation to maintain adequate vegetation and perennial streams (Moss, 1963, p. 317). Channeling with lateral planation across the valley is resumed with return to sufficient rainfall to restore plant cover and perennial streams [Figs. 5(A) and 5(B)]. A following cycle of alluviation and entrenchment in the secondary valley thus formed may provide a lower set of benches [Fig. 5(C)] if the older valleys are not completely filled. With each episode of alluviation terrace benches are formed (Fig. 5, T-1 and T-2) and prior channels are obliterated so that the stream formed at the beginning of a new cycle of entrenchment develops a randomly oriented channel with respect to valley walls. The terraces

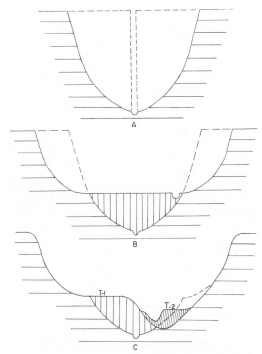

FIG. 5. Development of cut and fill terraces. (A) Valley formed by stream entrenchment (between dashed lines) and mass-wasting of valley walls. (B) Valley bottom alluviated by waste from valley walls. Subsequently a stream channel is randomly developed on alluvial floor, shown here displaced to the right of center. (C) Inner valley has been formed by entrenchment and mass-wasting followed by partial filling and a stream channel forming on the new alluvial surface, to the left of center of the inner valley. A second inner valley is thus formed, providing two nonpaired terrace levels T-1 and T-2. These terraces are of successively younger age and differ in this respect from paired terraces.

thus produced may or may not be symmetrically developed. They are called *cut-and-fill terraces* (Quinn, 1957, p. 152; Leopold, Wolman and Miller, 1964, p. 458–468, Figs. 11–11, 11–12). Such terraces are commonly the products of sudden changes in the climatic regime.

Fill-cut terraces in rocky gorges, e.g., in Afghanistan, have been described as having their bases protected by the hard-rock floor. As the stream has cut lower and swung laterally a remnant of fill has been left up on the slope, as a "*rock-defended terrace*" (see, for example, Zeigler, 1958).

For the major rivers it is important to recognize that their source regions may enjoy totally different climatic conditions from the mid-courses. Thus, for example, after a generous supply of mountain meltwater, the river may flow through an almost arid region where slopes and tributary streams contribute almost nothing to the alluvium. In another example, the mid-course may lie in a more humid

but still semiarid belt which lacks continuous vegetation and thus furnishes a considerable supply of slope colluvium to interfinger and mix with the alluvium.

Paired Terraces and Back-wasting

Paired fluvial terraces [Fig. 4(A)], those at matching elevations but not structural features, are most commonly formed by intermittent cycles of alluviation of progressively shorter duration. These result in the obliteration of the earlier stream channels (Fig. 6) and permit random stream entrenchment on valley floors. Under humid conditions, valley sides are protected from rapid erosion by plant cover. The "traction carpet" (Moss, 1963) is eliminated and entrenchment may initially be rapid. Perennial youthful streams will tend to entrench their channels. During less humid or semiarid times, detritus from upstream or valley sides clogs channel floors, thereby preventing entrenchment (Quinn, 1959, p. 1659). Provided that streams remain more or less perennial and carry away sediments, valley sides become escarpments which waste parallel with stream channels, widening valleys and forming slopes or pediments of similar magnitude on either side of the stream channel.

Increased precipitation provides for return of plant cover, reduced erosion of valley sides and renewed entrenchment. The escarpments earlier formed retain their identity, and renewed semiarid conditions permit renewed back-wasting not only of the new channel walls but also of the older escarpments. Thus a pair of escarpments is formed with each episode of entrenchment, and a pair of terraces is formed at the foot of each pair of escarpments during each semiarid episode. The process is similar in effect to methods of open pit mining where any desired number of levels can be initiated consecutively and mined simultaneously by blasting back the walls and removing the waste. Thus while paired terraces may be successively initiated, the surfaces are often rejuvenated. Fluvial terraces of this sort are most abundant and maturely formed in areas distributed along the 25–50 cm (10–12 inch) rainfall belts. It should be stressed that back-wasting of the early terraces will usually be at a slower rate than lateral planation by an active stream. As mentioned earlier, both back-wasting and planation are largely inhibited (retarded) in a hard rock-cut gorge.

Associated Features

So far we have only referred to the terraces themselves. The existence of a former base level at the elevation of any given terrace would lead to a number of associated landform features, the study of which may be helpful in elucidating the age and climatic environment of terrace formation and its dissection.

In a *karst* region for example, horizontal cavern systems may debouch at the old terrace level be-

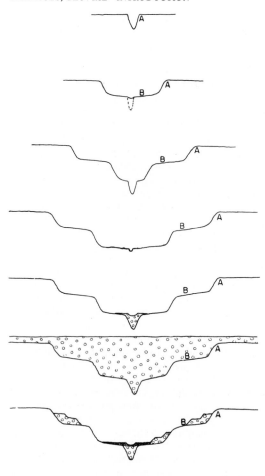

FIG. 6. Development of paired terraces, diagrammatic cross section of a typical valley on the Texas Coastal Plain near the Balcones fault escarpment (Quinn, 1957, p. 150, Fig. 1).

(1) A represents a valley side formed by stream entrenchment and mass-wasting.

(2) B represents a pediment slope produced by back-wasting of A. Dashed line in center indicates ensuing entrenchment.

(3) A second escarpment and terrace has been added. Simultaneous back-wasting of both escarpments has displaced terrace B to the right (and on opposite side of stream to the left).

(4) Continued back-wasting and subsequent entrenchment has provided additional, potential escarpments.

(5a) Valley partially filled with alluvium north of Balcones escarpment.

(5b) Valley completely filled with alluvium on Coastal Plain south of Balcones escarpment. (This total filling reflects siltation and blocking due to extreme aridity.)

(6) Alluvium incompletely removed by stream at later time providing the appearance of "bedrock" benches or terraces coated with sand and gravel (in this case all gravels contain the same fossil assemblage including that in the bed of the stream); redrawn from Quinn, 1957, p. 159, Fig. 4.

cause this was the former water table when part of a higher flood plain. Thus a given series of karst caves and tunnels (sometimes with associated fossils or artifacts) can be correlated to a certain terrace level. Examples have recently been documented from Buchan, Victoria, Australia (Sweeting, 1960) and from the Ardennes, Belgium (C. Ek, 1961).

In a region that was periglacial during the Quaternary cold epochs, the colluvial slope deposits of *solifluction* material fan out onto terrace surfaces and establish relative age relations. The slope deposit may wedge into the valley fill and establish contemporaneity.

In certain areas as diverse as Nebraska, Poland and the Nile valley, there may be a lateral association with *eolian sands*, which wedge into the valley fill and suggest that semiarid conditions (at least locally) were contemporaneous with valley alluviation, although not all such eolian activity is limited to strictly arid climates. The relationship of loess, with its fossiliferous interstadial soils, to the terraces in central Europe (especially in Hungary, Austria, Czechoslovakia and Poland) have played a key role in permitting the dating of the terraces.

In other regions there may be a chance fall of volcanic ash that provides a "silver thread" through all the alluvial deposits of that particular date. In the Rhine terraces of Germany, volcanic eruptions in the Eifel district provide these invaluable markers and have been subjected to K/A dating (Frechen and Lippolt, 1965). Heavy minerals provide additional data (Zonneveld, 1956). In the midwestern United States for example, the Pearlette volcanic ash provides an analogous marker, having fallen during the late Kansan glacial episode.

Terrace formations that are contemporary with glaciation may carry ice-rafted boulders. Pitted terrace surfaces or small *kettles* (q.v.) may indicate grounded ice. The terrace deposits formed earlier in the glacial episode often show appropriate evidence of periglacial conditions, with ice wedge structures, convolution and patterned ground effects.

Nomenclature of Terraces

Multiple terraces occur in many valleys, and a system of labels is needed for easy identification. Since the terraces are not always in the same order, a system of numbers such as Terrace I, II, III or descriptors such as "lower," "middle," "main," "upper," "uppermost" in the long run is liable to cause misunderstanding or confusion. Furthermore, terraces identified by labels in terms of elevation above the flood plain are useful only within limited distances; one often hears a lame apology such as: "This is the 10-meter terrace, only here it is actually about 15 meters."

Like stratigraphic and structural features, terraces should receive geographic names appropriate to a certain region. Beyond that region or beyond reasonable limits of correlation, a new series of names should be established (Howard, 1959). A binomial system is urged by Howard (Fig. 1), involving a geographic name and a terminological descriptor, e.g., *fill-terrace, fill-top terrace, fill-strath terrace, strath terrace*, etc. Local mean elevation above the flood plain, in addition to the geographic name, might help readers to follow the descriptions.

With paleontological and absolute dating methods it is now possible in many cases to identify terraces by their ages: "Mid-Holocene Terrace," "Alleröd Terrace," etc., but vague terms like "Mid-Pleistocene terrace" should only be used with a lower-case "t" to indicate a loose genetic term rather than a precise name, implied by the upper-case "T". There is an element of danger in using time-stratigraphic labels, because of the possibility of mistaking the time indicators. The latter themselves are in some places mixed in fluvial deposits, e.g., the bones or teeth of large beasts like mammoths can be carried down from periglacial colluvium into a warm interglacial alluvium that may not have other fossils, and thus a false date is obtained; likewise human artifacts (of flint) are extremely durable and are easily transported from one horizon to another, with misleading implications.

Terrace Stratigraphy

In mapping terraces it is important to recognize that the *geomorphic terrace* is a landform surface and must be mapped as a physiographic type, while the *terrace alluvium* is to be mapped as a stratigraphic unit, i.e., a lithologic formation (Frye and Leonard, 1954). Specific rules of stratigraphic nomenclature apply. Some of the pitfalls in terrace mapping are illustrated by Frye and Leonard. Such pitfalls include differential erosion between a terrace cover (often soft) and its bedrock material (often hard), the mantling or hiding of an alluvial terrace fill by loess, the lateral merging of a terrace deposit into a pediment veneer (i.e., a slope deposit) where boundary is difficult to determine, the narrowing of a valley and thinning of the terrace deposits upstream from a resistant formation that causes a nick point. Altitude matching is altogether fraught with difficulties (Johnson, 1944); especially if there are lateral fans obscuring the "heel" of the terrace deposits, it is difficult to determine the mean terrace height, while the scarp on the flood plain side may be abrupt or severely degraded.

Concerning the general methodology of terrace studies, it is evident that both geomorphic and sedimentary petrographic procedures are essential. Altimetric analyses, as recommended by Tricart (1948), should be related to absolute elevation, rather than merely to the present flood plain or river bed.

ARTHUR D. HOWARD
RHODES W. FAIRBRIDGE
JAMES H. QUINN

References

Bucher, W. H., 1932, "'Strath'" as a geomorphic term," *Science*, **75**, 130–131.

Cotton, C. A., 1940, "Classification and correlation of river terraces," *J. Geomorphol.*, **3**(1), 26–37.

Culling, W. E. H., 1957, "Equilibrium states in multicyclic streams and the analysis of river-terrace profiles," *J. Geol.*, **65**(5), 451–467.

Ek, C., 1961, "Conduits souterrains en relation avec les terraces fluviales," *Ann. Soc. Géol. Belg.*, **84**, 313–340.

Frechen, J., and Lippolt, H. J., 1965, "Kalium-Argon-Daten zum Alter des Laacher Vulkanismus, der Rheinterrassen und der Eiszeiten," *Eiszeitalter Gegenwart*, **16**, 5–30.

Frye, J. C., and Leonard, A. R., 1954, "Some problems of alluvial terrace mapping," *Am. J. Sci.*, **252**, 242–251.

Frye, J. C., Swineford, A., and Leonard, A. B., 1948, "Correlation of Pleistocene deposits of the central Great Plains with the glacial section," *J. Geol.*, **56**, 501–525.

Hare, F. K., 1947, "The geomorphology of a part of the middle Thames," *Proc. Geologists Assoc. (London)*, **58**, 294–339.

Howard, A. D., 1959, "Numerical systems of terrace nomenclature: A critique." *J. Geol.*, **67**(2), 239–243.

Johnson, D., 1944, "Problems of terrace correlation," *Bull. Geol. Soc. Am.*, **55**, 793–818.

Leopold, L. B., Wolman, M. G., and Miller, J. P., 1964, "Fluvial Processes in Geomorphology," San Francisco, W. H. Freeman & Co., 522 pp.

McGee, W J, 1891, "The Pleistocene history of northeastern Iowa," *U.S. Geol. Surv. Ann. Rept.*, **11**, 189–577.

Moss, A. J., 1963, "The physical nature of common sandy and pebbly deposits," *Am. J. Sci.*, **261**, 297–343.

Peltier, L. C., 1949, "Pleistocene terraces of the Susquehanna River, Pennsylvania," *Bull. Penn. Geol. Surv.* G, **23**, 158pp.

Quinn, J. H., 1957, "Paired river terraces and Pleistocene glaciation," *J. Geol.*, **65**, 149–166.

Quinn, J. H., 1959, "Bed load and stream entrenchment," *Bull. Geol. Soc. Am.*, **70**, 1659 (abs.).

Rónai, A., 1965, "Neotectonic subsidences in the Hungarian Basin," in (Wright and Frey, editors) "International studies on the Quaternary," *Geol. Soc. Am. Spec. Paper* **84**, 219–232.

Smith, H. T. U., 1949, "Physical effects of Pleistocene climate changes in non-glaciated areas: eolian phenomena, frost action and stream terracing," *Bull. Geol. Soc. Am.*, **60**, 1485–1516.

Sweeting, M. M., 1960, "The caves of the Buchan area, Victoria, Australia," *Z. Geomorphol., Suppl.*, **2**, 81–91.

Tricart, J., 1948, "Methode d'étude des terrasses," *Bull. Soc. Géol. France* (for 1947), Series 5, No. 17, 47–49, 559–575.

Zeigler, J. M., 1958, "Geological study of Shamshir Ghar Cave, southern Afghanistan, and report of terraces along Panjshir valley near Kabul," *J. Geol.*, **66**, 16–27.

Zonneveld, J., 1956, "The use of heavy minerals for stratigraphic purposes," *Actes IV Congr. Quat.*, Rome-Pise, 1953, **I**, 268–277.

Cross-references: *Alluvium; Altimetric Frequency Curve; Base Level; Eustasy; Exhumed Landscape; Fluvio-*

TERRACES, FLUVIAL—ENVIRONMENTAL CONTROLS

It is possible to generate theoretically a few simple explanations to account for most fluvial terraces and their characteristics. In fact, however, the environmental controls of terrace genesis are widely divergent. Terraces of seemingly identical morphology may have completely different origins. Moreover, few terraces reflect the simple (monogenetic) control of a few constant variables. More commonly the environmental controls have varied through time (i.e., have been polygenetic), thus producing terraces of a complex and/or compound nature. Indeed, the repeated shifting of climatic belts over the past few million years, coupled with tectonic instability in many places, and the world-wide oscillation of sea level, has resulted in the production of landforms (including terraces) and entire landscapes of a multiple origin, reflecting both the present and many past environments (see Figs. 1 and 2).

When viewing fluvial terraces on a world, long-term basis, it is apparent that the literature is packed with contradictory statements, which might well be resolved if one were to consider the dynamics of fluvial regimes in terms of the following variables:

(a) *Climatic controls:* In simple terms one may recognize a few general types—fluvioglacial, periglacial, humid temperate, mediterranean, arid, monsoonal, equatorial (humid tropical); these belts possess climatic characteristics defined by such parameters as: precipitation—annual; precipitation —per rainstorm; snow melt (if any). Further, there are related geomorphic characteristics, such as precipitation–runoff ratio; weathering of saprolite and other regolith; colluvium supply with or without solifluction; vegetation density, etc. (Fig. 3). One may also add monocyclic or polycyclic controls which would involve inherited soils and similar problems.

(b) *Relief and slope characteristics:* In the broad picture, one may distinguish mountains and plains as end members, though in detail there are many transitions as well as mixed regions, e.g., basin and range provinces.

Fig. 1. Poorly developed fluvial terraces in a low energy, tectonically highly stable region of central Australia (Macdonnell Ranges). A fundamental erosion surface of Mesozoic age truncates all Paleozoic and Precambrian folded structures on which the main drainage channels are superimposed. The present streams are braided, while their rock floors are buried below thick gravels. This is a dry savanna, characteristic of the hot arid phase, i.e., valley-filling, under a rainfall regime of 5-10 inches, and a mean January temperature of nearly 90°F.

FIG. 2. Multiple fill terraces, developed in a high energy, tectonically active region of New Zealand Rangitikei Valley, North Island (photo: S. N. Beatus, N.Z. Geological Survey)]. In the distance is a fine-textured, highly dissected terrain, furnishing plentiful sediment load. The climate is humid temperate.

(c) *Tectonic activity or "relative stability"* may be considered mainly in terms of vertical movement, positive or negative, and stated in terms of rate, fast or slow, such as millimeters per year or millimeters per millenium and less. Over the short run, slow movement approximates tectonic stability. Over a longer time range, variable movement is the rule, be it fast or slow.

(d) *Thalassostatic controls* concern the sector of the stream channel or thalweg that is affected by the eustatic rise and fall of sea level; there are major differences between these effects on steep, mountainous coasts and on low relief coasts which may involve belts 100–1000 km in width in the plainland regions. To simplify the picture of eustatic trend, these controls may often be taken as broadly positive or negative, rising or sinking, since eustatic oscillations of less than about 500 years have little effect on fluvial regimes.

An integration of these four basic categories, reduced to rather broad generalizations, in order to keep the possibilities down to manageable propor-

tions, would supply the following variation potentials:
  (i) Climatic Belts—7,
  (ii) Relief—2,
  (iii) Tectonic—4,
  (iv) Thalassostatic—2.
This extreme simplification provides 112 potential terrace situations (Fig. 4). No systematic world treatment of fluvial terraces on such a basis has ever been attempted, but some day, with increased computer availability, no doubt it will be.

Climatic Controls

The broad patterns of terrace morphology and composition are introduced in the previous article (*Terraces, Fluvial—Introduction*); arising therefrom are two basic environmental principles that must be clearly established:

(1) Huntington's Principle (Huntington, 1907; Cotton, 1963; etc.). This states that valley *degradation* (erosion) takes place in *wet* climates and *aggradation* (sedimentation) takes place in *dry* climates. It should be stressed that these are *relative* terms, and refer to disturbance of the equilibrium in either direction. It must also be evident that this principle applies to a given sector of a stream system, usually in a mature stage, because upstream of an aggradation sector there must be an erosion sector (normally a youthful stage); by the same token, downstream of a "mature" degradation sector there will be sedimentation (often, in the ocean, Fig. 5).

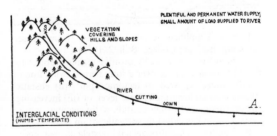

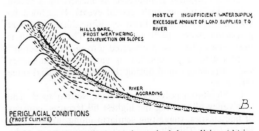

FIG. 3. Contrast between interglacial condition (A) in a middle latitude hilly terrain and the periglacial condition (B). Note the protection of hill slopes by vegetation in the first case, and stripping under solifluction in the second, although the actual precipitation is much less in the latter than the former (from Zeuner, 1945).

(2) Langbein-Schumm Rule (Langbein and Schumm, 1958; Schumm, 1965; see also *Continental Erosion*). This is a supplement to Huntington's Principle, establishing that, in a high-relief (humid) region, with a decrease in discharge (headwater precipitation), there is an increase in erosion on the slopes, down to a limit of about 250–600 mm (10–24 inches), because of the discontinuous vegetation coverage (see Fig. 6). Below this limit further decrease in precipitation results in decreasing erosion until both variables reach zero. Downstream of the headwater area, beyond a certain "neutral point" there will be an inverse rule: in a humid regime sedimentation rises with decreasing precipitation (down to the 250–600 mm limit). In regions of extreme aridity (less than 250 mm precipitation), a rise of precipitation increases the erosion at that point, but still increases the sedimentation downstream, unless the stream enters a high rainfall belt; thus the general validity of Huntington's principle still holds. The critical point is not ideally expressed in precipitation figures, but depends actually on the continuity of the vegetational ground-cover.

Selected Examples of Terrace Systems

(1) Terraces of the Alpine and German Valleys (in general). In the headwaters of the Danube, Rhine and other Alpine rivers, it was first demonstrated by Penck that the Alpine moraines passed outward into the terrace-fill gravels. These moraines were identified as *Günz, Mindel, Riss* and *Würm*, and are now

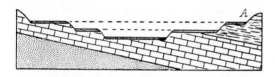
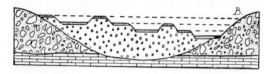
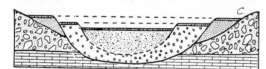

Fig. 4. Simplified terrace examples (from Ansel Gooding, Earlham College, Bull. 2, 1957).
A. Signifies a tectonically positive setting, subject to fluvial erosion at grade over a long period (wide floodplain), under repeated (i) tectonic uplift, (ii) eustatic (thalassostatic) lowering of base level, or (iii) increasing stream energy under high rainfall, well-vegetated conditions. Cotton has called these "valley-train terraces."
B. Signifies a glacial/periglacial/postglacial sequence. A glacial till-sheet is indicated as incised by a broad valley (probably an early glacial event). It is filled by gravels, an event most likely to occur during the next glaciation under solifluction energy. The gravel-fill is then seen to have been dissected into multiple "scour" or fill-cut terraces, representing variable stream energy with increasing runoff during the early postglacial stage (Holocene).
C. Signifies a polycyclic sequence, similar to B. The first valley-fill, leaving the highest fill terraces, consists of fine clastics, suggesting semiarid filling farther from the ice front. This fill was largely scoured out too, to be replaced by gravels, suggesting vigorous periglacial solifluction. The gravels in turn were incised (but less extensively) and again filled. This polycyclic succession could develop with interstadial oscillations near the beginning and end of a cold cycle.

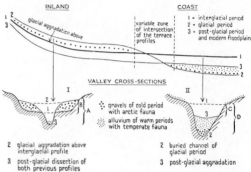

Fig. 5. River Terraces and eustatic movements of sealevel (Stephens and Synge, 1966).
Valley Cross Sections
IA. Post-glacial valley incision has dissected the glacial and interglacial deposits laid down formerly in the wider pre-glacial valley.
IB. The gravels of the cold period rest upon the alluvium of the previous warm period, the section indicating two different periods of contrasting aggradation. The glacial terrace (profile 2) is the dominant morphological feature and the interglacial alluvium may not be readily seen. Where both glacial and interglacial deposits are composed of gravels there may be extreme difficulty of interpretation.
IIC. Post-glacial incision has been sufficient to lower the present profile *below* the interglacial profile, but postglacial aggradation has been considerable, and the lower part of the valley may be drowned.
IID. During glacial times with a lower sea-level there was sufficient time for the river to erode a deeply incised valley in rock, in the base of which glacial gravels are found. Post-glacial alluvium may cover these glacial gravels to a considerable depth. In contrast to IA, the depth of the valley in rock, IID, does not represent the total amount of post-glacial incision.
Considerable difficulties of interpretation occur where some of the deposits may be missing or concealed, or where in the variable zone of intersection of terrace profiles the three different stages of valley development are compressed into a small height range. Tectonic movements or coastal flexuring may be additional factors which have to be considered when interpretation is made. (By permission of Heinemann Educ. Books, London, and American Elsevier Publ. Co., N.Y.)

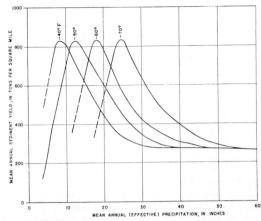

FIG. 6. While 12 inches, or 300 mm., is often taken as an average precipitation to provide maximal sediment yield (for a mean annual temperature of 50°F), this value varies greatly with temperature because of the evaporation factors. In a hot savanna (mean temperature 70°F) however, increasing precipitation will bring increased slope erosion and valley sedimentation up to a critical limit (25 inches). That critical point drops with temperature, and in a tundra would be passed at 8 inches. Nevertheless with increasingly humid conditions, over 25 inches or so, there will always be a decreasing sediment yield (slightly modified from Schumm, 1965).

believed to be equivalent, respectively, to the North American Nebraskan, Kansan, Illinoian and Wisconsin (see *Quaternary*). Penck concluded that the terrace accumulations were therefore glacial equivalents, and many followed this lead (e.g., Soergel, 1919).

By 1924, Soergel determined that there were no less than ten aggradation stages along the river Ilm in Thuringia. With increasing precision, subsequent field studies in the periglacial regions have suggested that there is no simple correlation, e.g. glacial = sedimentation and interglacial = erosion. The sedimentation phase correlated better with the increasing coldness, and thus with decreasing vegetation and frost action at the interglacial/glacial transition stage (Udluft, 1934; Zeuner, 1959). In contrast, the principal erosive phase was recognized as corresponding to warming, revegetation, deglaciation, the great melting and scouring.

During the warm interglacials, most of the landscape would be covered with vegetation and therefore one would expect an equilibrium condition, without major erosion or sedimentation. In view of the confinement then of the mature streams within meandering beds and vegetated banks, occasional surges in discharge would lead to overbank floods and higher accumulation of fine-grained loams (silts) over the coarse glacial stage deposits. On the other hand, in the headwaters there is erosion. This interglacial form of accumulation is quite different from the glacial, when, broadly speaking, the rela-

tions were reversed (sedimentation in the mountains and middle courses, erosion in the lower courses due to eustatic lowering of base level). Soil formation would proceed only during warm interglacials, and where pockets of snails are found in those soils (brown earths, typically), they indicate deciduous forests (oak and beech woods, for the most part) with vigorous earthworm populations feeding on the leaf mold (humus). In places there are travertine or tufa spring deposits that correlate with these interglacials, and here there are often a great variety of fossil remains (leaves, snails, bones), always with warm indications. During the cold arid epochs, the carbonate-rich spring waters dwindled or froze up, so that in central Europe these limestone deposits are exceptionally useful as climate and environment indicators.

As a general terminology to assist description of the two transition stages, Trévisan (1949) proposed the following:

(a) *Anaglacial*: transition from interglacial to glacial;

(b) *Kataglacial*: transition from glacial to interglacial.

Though useful, the terms tend to suggest oversimplification, because each of the transitions is accompanied by several marked subcycles or oscillations (*interstadials*, the warmer subphases, and *stadials*, the cooler subphases: Lüttig, 1965).

We know now, therefore, that not all of the terrace deposits are glacial, as proposed by Penck. Some of the mid-course terrace sedimentation is now stratigraphically fixed as belonging also to the postglacial climatic epochs (Brunnacker, Graul, and others; see discussion in German, 1965; C^{14} dates, Groschopf, 1961). Evidently, the high gravel supply in the piedmont areas was provided in part by vigorous solifluction of pre-existing gravels during cold-humid early glacial stages and in part by the seasonal meltwaters of the advancing ice (and increased meltwaters through the early interstadials) which permitted the transport of enormous bed loads of gravel ("Schotter"). Isostatic uplift of the mountains during late glacial retreat stages and early interstadials and interglacials would also tend to provide energy for the further (fluvial) transportation of vast boulder and gravel banks left in front of the moraines (Troll, 1926). In places this mechanism, therefore, furnishes a second phase of gravel transport within the same cycle.

It is sometimes possible to distinguish the maximal cold epoch gravels from the presence of diagnostic boulders. For example, on the upper Danube, Graul (1953) pointed out that the "cold" gravels contained fresh granites from the Schwarzwald (Black Forest), but these are absent from the Recent or interglacial gravels. Floating ice was also capable of moving large boulders in some rivers, e.g., the River Seine in France, where there are never any large ice floes today.

The cold character of the early glacial gravels is also confirmed by the covering of fine alluvium, grading up into loess without any unconformity or weathered zone (soil). The molluscan association (snails) in the transition zone is characteristic of maximum glaciation, extremely cold and dry (Brunnacker, Ložek, and others). In view of Soergel's pioneering recognition of ten aggradation (cold) cycles in Thuringia, it is interesting that Kukla *et al.* (1961) have now demonstrated ten loess stages in Moravia. The number may just be coincidence, but there are certainly far more than merely the oversimplified four great glacial episodes. Structural profiles show that the gravels were, for the most part, laid down in braided streams by seasonal runoff (see *Fluvioglacial Processes*).

In the northern Alpine foothills, the two oldest gravel terraces are called the *Deckenschotter* (*Decken* = sheet) because they covered broad areas of a relatively undissected landscape; in other words, they were like the *piedmont* (q.v.) gravels at the foot of the Rocky Mountains. The older Deckenschotter covers the Tertiary peneplain, and the younger Deckenschotter veneered the first major rock-cut terrace levels, 100 meters or so below the older level (Fig. 1). The younger gravel terraces are called the *Terrassenschotter*, the two major ones, respectively, "upper" and "lower"; minor levels are identified (as N_1, N_2, and so on).

(2) Middle Danube Terraces. Very generally, in eastern Europe, e.g., on the Great Hungarian Plain, semiarid climatic conditions existed at the same time as the Alpine glaciers and were reflected by dune-building and the development of vast loess plains. The loess is contemporary with the glacial maxima and retreat stages. It is found to spill over and blanket the gravel terraces of the braided valley gravel train that began to form in the early stages of a given glacial event. The loess in such places may reach a thickness of 20 meters or so. The warm interglacials or mild interstadials are marked by paleosols (Brunnacker, 1956; Fink, 1956). The latter often contain bones of mammoth,

woolly rhinoceros, etc., as well as human artifacts and various small mollusca, snails, etc., that serve the useful paleoecologic purpose of indicating the climatic type. At Paks, for example south of Budapest, several such interglacial or interstadial interruptions are indicated (Scherf, 1938; Krivan, 1955; Pécsi, 1964). From the climatic point of view, it is interesting that the glacial periods here were essentially arid deserts (though without glaciers) and the interglacials were warm, mild and rather moist (as shown by the snails and paleosols). Continuous occupation by man was only possible in some of the foothill and valley areas, e.g., along major watercourses like the Danube or in foothill areas like Lower Austria. It was in the latter region at Willendorf where the interstadial Göttweiger soil is overlain by alluvium (Würm II) and loess with reindeer bones and middle Aurignacian tools (about 28,000 yr. B.P.); the so-called Willendorf Venus was found here, the oldest known example of plastic art—probably a fertility symbol.

A complicating factor in the sector between Bratislava and Győr (Raab) is the progressive subsidence of all terraces beneath the Little Hungarian Plain (Fig. 7).

(3) Bohemian/Moravian Terraces. In the central parts of Czechoslovakia an interesting climatic setting existed during the glacial periods. Mountain and icecap glaciers lay across the Alps, in the Krkenoše or Giant Mountains (Sudeten) and in the Tatras (Carpathians), while Scandinavian continental ice came right across to the foothills in Silesia. But the inner plateaus and uplands of Bohemia and Moravia remained free from ice, so that their valleys preserve complete undisturbed records of the entire Quaternary. The mountains are long-stable crystalline masses, but the relatively high relief insured repeated down-cutting, whenever the precipitation permitted, so that the younger sequences are almost always lower than the older. Careful fossil studies, particularly on the mollusca in the interglacials and in interstadial loess soils and so on, provide paleoecologic indications of climate,

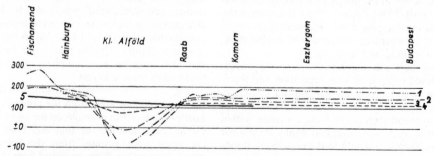

FIG. 7. Progressive tectonic subsidence of the Danube terraces below the Little Hungarian Plain (Kl. Alfölf) between Hainburg (near Bratislava) and Győr (Raab). 1. Laaerberg Terrace; 2. Arsenal Terrace; 3 and 4. Middle and Younger Pleistocene terraces; 5. Present floodplain (from Woldstedt, 1958; after Szadecky–Kardoss, 1938). (By permission of Enke Verlag, Stuttgart.)

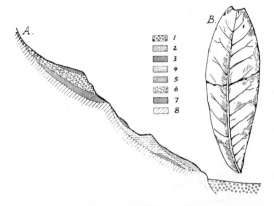

FIG. 8. Profile, illustrating (A) the relationships of the Höttinger Breccia to the Inn Valley [from Woldstedt, 1958; after Penck (1921) and Klebelsberg (1929)]. (By permission of Enke Verlag, Stuttgart.) With an inset (B), a fossil leaf of *Rhododendron ponticum* (after R. von Wettstein, 1892). Explanation: 1. Inn Alluvium and talus; 2. "Scherbenschotter" (Holocene); 3. "Hangendmoräne" (Würm); 4. Inn Valley Terrace filling; 5. "Sockelmoräne" (?Riss); 6. Höttinger Breccia; 7. "Liegendmoräne (?Mindel); 8. Basement (Triassic).

and C^{14} datings confirm the dates of the last two cycles (Zaruba, 1942, 1961; Prošek and Ložek, 1957; Kukla *et al.*, 1961; Ložek, 1965).

In the remarkable profiles near Prague (Sedlec Clay Pits), along the valleys of the Moldau (Vltava) and upper Elbe, and near Brno in Moravia, the loesses were positively identified as glacial equivalents on account of the characteristic cool steppe-type snails *Pupilla* (Zaruba-Pfeffermann, 1942), whereas the interglacial soils contain mollusca of the so-called Banatica Fauna, characteristic today of warm, southern latitudes, 500 km or more to the south. The surfaces of the glacial fill terraces are strewn with ventifacts, illustrating the cold, arid climates which marked the successive glacial stages before they were buried by the loess. The valley cutting (the future fill-cut and rock-cut terraces) was evidently achieved in relatively brief, early interglacial periods during which time there was considerable precipitation in the mountains, but dense vegetative cover prevented the development of a heavy bed load of gravels; the latter were largely provided by periglacial frost action and solifluction in the mountains, and only locally added to by cirque glaciation. The warm interglacial climate (shown also by the "brown earth" soils) was thus marked by appreciable runoff, but it was halted during each ensuing glacial aridity when only braided streams could be maintained; after seasonal meltwater floods the gravel load came to a rest, except for a narrow main channel. These important Bohemian and Moravian sections (without major glaciers in their headwaters) are significant because they show that the gravels were not the product of

postglacial meltwater (as some might deduce to be the case in the Alps) but the result of the periglacial stripping of the earlier regolith from non-glacial uplands.

(4) High Alpine Terraces. Perhaps the best-preserved and best-known Alpine terraces are those of the upper Inn valley in the Austrian Tyrol, around Innsbruck. This is a region of rapid tectonic uplift (averaging 2 mm/yr or more for some millions of years and still in progress). The valleys have been deeply incised, and the older terraces, where preserved, are perched high up on the mountainsides. One may take a cable car up from Innsbruck to see one of the most important discovery sites (Fig. 8). A probable Riss (Mindel according to Penck) moraine is there overlapped by a carbonate-cemented talus deposit (the Höttinger Breccia), which contains the fossil leaves of *Rhododendron ponticum* L., which today grows only in the moist, warm foothills around the southern Black Sea and in Spain (Sierra Nevada). Furthermore, the flora contains *Abies alba*, *Corylus*, *Fagus* and *Vitis silvestris*, which confirms the outstandingly interglacial nature of the breccia. Discovered more than 70 years ago, this deposit was really the first proof that there was more than one glaciation, and not surprisingly, a great controversy raged over it.

(5) The Somme Terraces and Others of Western Europe and Algeria. Human artifacts, and eventually human skeletal remains, made famous by Boucher de Perthes and the Abbé Breuil, have been dug out of the Somme terraces in northern France (Picardy) for over a century (see Table 1). These too provided a source of controversy, partly because, if interpreted as Pleistocene, the terrace deposits would imply the great antiquity of early man and during the religious controversies of the last century this was anathema to the conservative theologians.

The most important feature of the Somme terraces is that with their rich human artifact contents, they are easily dated (at least in sequence), and it is evident that in this region, situated entirely outside the limits of continental ice, thus a non-glacial setting, an almost uninterrupted succession of glacial-interglacial fluvial deposits have accumulated on the rock-cut terraces. Because of eustatic oscillations near the mouth of the river, there are old deposits of the glacial stages at lower elevations than the younger deposits of the later interglacials (Breuil, 1939). The terraces are excavated in Cretaceous chalk, in which there are very durable black flints, and the terraces are veneered by "lag gravels" of these flints. Loess cappings date the glacial maxima, as well as solifluction deposits at the foot of slopes (further details can be found in *Terraces—Thalassostatic*).

Curiously enough, it was a general of artillery in the Seventh Army of France who played a key role in the matter, General Leon de Lamothe, who noticed the remarkable parallelism of terraces, both

TABLE 1. CHRONOLOGY OF THE ALLUVIAL SHEETS OF THE SOMME (ALIMEN, 1967)

Glacial Chronology	Alluvial Deposits	Prehistoric Cultures	Faunas
Post-Würm and end of Würm	Alluvial deposits below the present-day alluvial plain	Neolithic Aurignacian	
Würm I–II	Lower lower terrace (5 m)	Levalloisian	Cold-climate fauna with *Elephas primigenius, Rhinoceros tichorhinus* and *Rangifer tarandus*
Riss	Upper lower terrace (10 m)	Upper Acheulian VI–VII and Levalloisian	Cold-climate fauna with *Elephas primigenius* Warm-climate fauna with *Elephas antiquus* and *Hippopotamus*
Mindel II	Middle terrace of Cagny (17 m) and Saint-Acheul	Acheulian III (Cagny Workshop) Acheulian II and Clactonian	*Elephas primigenius* (archaic) *Elephas antiquus* (archaic) *Elephas trogontherii*
Mindel I	Upper Montières terrace (40 m) and terrace of the Champ de Mars stage at Abbeville	Acheulian Chellean	*Elephas trogontherii* (archaic) *Elephas meridionalis* *Hippopotamus major* *Machairodus, Equus stenonis* *Trogontherium*
Günz	Upper terraces Lower Grâce terrace (40–45 m) Upper Grâce terrace (50 m)	Burnt flints	*Equus stenonis*
Donau	Montières Forest alluvial deposits (65–70 m)		

fluvial (in the upper Moselle of eastern France) and marine (in Algeria); the marine terraces he interpreted, with Suess, as eustatic, which would necessarily be high in interglacials, but he discovered (for the first time, at the mouth of the Isser River in Algeria) that they merge with the high fluvial terraces, which, as we have seen above, were identified by Penck as glacial. De Lamothe extended his surveys over about half a century (roughly 1880–

1930) to take in the Rhine valley, the Rhone and other major rivers in western Europe. He claimed a general correlation with the Algerian sea level data, with absolute altimetric identity, namely, at 15–16, 30–35, 100, 130 and 150 meters. No allowance was made for stream energy and little for tectonics. The remarkable thing is how nearly right he was, although it was achieved by quite unsatisfactory methods.

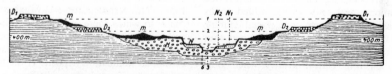

FIG. 9. Idealized profile through the Upper Rhine Valley in Switzerland (Albert Heim, 1919). D_1 = Older Deckenschotter (1 = its original floor); D_2 = Younger Deckenschotter (2 = its original floor); H = High Terrace Gravels (3 = previous downcutting; 4 = original extent of surface); N = Lower (Nieder-) Terrace Gravels (N_1 = upper, N_2 = lower stage, 5 = original floor); M = Moraines of the "greatest glaciation"; 6 = Present Floodplain.

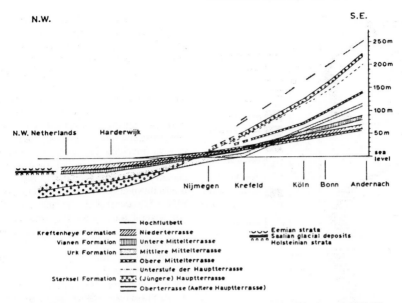

N.W.

S.E.

N.W. Netherlands   Harderwijk

Nijmegen   Krefeld   Köln   Bonn   Andernach

— Hochflutbett

Kreftenheye Formation ▨ Niederterrasse
Vianen Formation ▦ Untere Mittelterrasse
Urk Formation ▨ Mittlere Mittelterrasse
▨ Obere Mittelterrasse
- - - Unterstufe der Hauptterrasse
Sterksel Formation ▨ (Jüngere) Hauptterrasse
▨ Oberterrasse (Aeltere Hauptterrasse)

◡◡◡ Eemian strata
≈≈≈ Saalian glacial deposits
∩∩∩ Holsteinian strata

Fig. 10. Relationships between the terraces in the area of uplift along the Middle Rhine in Germany and the lithostratigraphical units in the area of subsidence in the Netherlands [modified from J. I. S. Zonneveld, 1963, by de Jong (1967)]. For correlation and dating of the terrace names, see article *Quaternary*. Note that the highest (oldest) terraces in Germany (on the right) correspond to the most deeply buried formations in the Netherlands (left). (By permission of John Wiley & Sons, N.Y.)

On the River Seine, in France, the lower terrace gravels range from about the level of the present floodplain up to some 15 meters. The lowest section always contains a warm fauna (with *Elephas antiquus*, *Rhinoceros merckii*, *Hippopotamus*, etc.), while the upper parts contain cold indicators (*Elephas primigenius*, *Rhinoceros tichorhinus*, etc., together with a Levallois industry). In the lower valley, near the sea, this terrace is cut through by a deep erosion phase, which can be traced in bores to at least −30 meters (below mean sea level), and is filled by postglacial Flandrian facies. It may be concluded, therefore, that the terrace building, here at any rate, probably began about the very end of the last interglacial, when frosts were beginning to furnish periglacial debris, but the sea level was still high and warm faunas were still surviving; increasing aridity and terrace accumulation continued until close to the glacial maximum, at which time the buildup of ice caused eustatic lowering to bring about steepening of the stream gradients and deep dissection of the valley fill. This dissection stage of late glacial time would not call for increased discharge, but a simple decrease in load would be sufficient. Similar records around other major streams in western Europe show that this is not an isolated example (Woldstedt, 1958–65; Zeuner, 1959; Beckinsale and Richardson, 1964). We thus see that modest down-cutting is normal for inter-

glacials, but in thalassostatic areas it must also have occurred during the glacials. During deglaciation, increasing precipitation and vegetation might raise discharge but decrease loading; this would initially accelerate incision but eventually develop a new equilibrium with gentler gradients.

(6) The Rhine Terraces. An added complication is provided in the lower Rhine valley, because the delta area, along with the western Netherlands, is in the subsiding basin of the North Sea (an active paraliageosyncline). According to tide gauge data from Amsterdam (kept since A.D. 1682), the mean subsidence rate here today is about 0.7 mm/yr, and the basal Pleistocene there is downwarped to about −600 meters. Thus the high fluvial terraces of the middle and upper Rhine cross over (roughly about the German border) and in western Holland the oldest river deposits are far below sea level (Figs. 9–11). As emphasized particularly by Brouwer (1956), Woldstedt (1960), Kaiser (1961) and Zonneveld (1963), the erosional stages upstream often correspond to depositional stages in the delta and vice versa. The regime is not merely controlled by a simple climatic alternation as in the middle Danube or Moldau, or by the climate and eustatic interplay of the Somme terraces, but is complicated by a third great variable, the *differential tectonics* related to uplifts (not uniform, either) in the middle Rhine and subsidence in the lower course and the

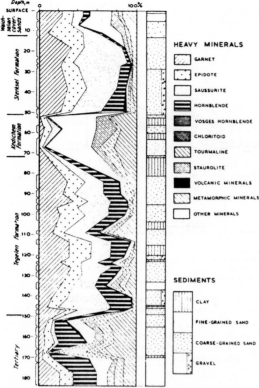

Fig. 11. Distribution of heavy minerals in the Vessem boring, southern Noordbrabant, in the Netherlands (de Jong, 1967). This bore penetrates the deepest Pleistocene deposits, corresponding to the highest Rhine terraces of Germany. Note how the Tegelen Formation, the first cool-climate fluviatile facies (with Rhineland material) represents a striking change in mineral content from the Tertiary. It contains cool-type flora and fauna, as well as cryoturbation structures. The overlying Kedichem Formation shows a reversion in part to warmer (non-Rhine) mineral assemblages. The Sterksel Formation is a gravelly facies equivalent to the glacial "Younger Main Terrace" of the Rhine. Mineral species are thus very helpful in contributing to the identification of terrace environments. (By permission of John Wiley & Sons, N.Y.)

North Sea basin. The tectonics involve both broad differential warping and horst-and-graben movements (i.e., positive and negative blocks). A further complication was the damming back of the (?) Riss glacial drainage (which would elsewhere have been rejuvenated by glacio-eustasy) by the formation of a glacially dammed lake in the southern North Sea due to the extension of the Scandinavian ice to join the British ice; its eventual overflow to the southeast and the cutting of the "Channel River" through the Straits of Dover during the late Riss and Würm stage permitted renewed dissection.

The lower Rhine during Riss and Würm times was a braided stream, i.e., characterized by little water, low energy and heavy loading (due to solifluction plus lack of vegetation). In the interglacials, with high sea levels and thalassostatic damming, the lower course became marked by levees and backswamp and oxbow lake deposits (black organic clays, peat, etc.) The middle Rhine sector, in contrast, was more like the Moldau in Bohemia, and it seems reasonable to correlate the terrace cutting with evolution during repeated early interglacial stages. The erosional terraces were capped by early glacial gravels (marking the drop in vegetation and precipitation), while these in turn were topped by glacial loesses (the glacial arid indicators). According to numbers of German workers (see Woldstedt, 1958–65), several of the terraces are still regarded as late glacial (i.e., meltwater products) despite the common discoveries of bones of large warm-type mammals.

Unusual but quite serendipitous events were the ash eruptions at the Laacher See, a volcanic area on the middle Rhine. The principal ash and pumice are incorporated as pebbles in a specific terrace, the "Untere Niederterrasse" (or "Bimterrasse"), the youngest deposits of which extend up to about 9500 B.P. (this terrace belongs to the Valders readvance or "Young Tundra" cold stage) and rest discordantly on an older or "Obere Niederterrasse" (Würm). Another helpful event for an earlier Rhine terrace dating is the occurrence of augite and other distinctive minerals in the middle "Mittelterrasse," also derived from Eifel eruptions. K/Ar dates have been made by Frechen and Lippolt (1965). The last important change in the middle Rhine regime was the switch from the periglacial situation of the late Würm to the slight down-cutting of the Holocene (warm climate, high precipitation condition), which has left a slightly higher "flood plain" between Bonn and Nijmegen and has produced an enormous sediment fill in the thalassostatic sector below this point. These last events may, indeed, be used as the Lyellian indicators for interpreting the earlier sequences.

(7) **The Mississippi Terraces.** Just as in Europe, the Mississippi terraces have long been a bone of contention between those working in the middle course (Midwest) and those working in the delta region of Louisiana (Woldstedt, 1960). Great similarities exist with the Rhine, though in the case of the Mississippi, there was less contemporary tectonism, and furthermore the Great Lakes postglacial spillway supplied discharge that vastly exceeded anything in the Rhine.

The highest of the easily mapped erosion surfaces in the Mississippi basin in general is the Mio-Pliocene surface which has a capping of lag gravels, loosely known as the *Lafayette Gravels* (Potter, 1955) with scattered relict patches—the Lancaster Plain, Smithland Plain, etc. They may be equivalent to the Citronelle of the coastal belt (Doering, 1958). The Mississippi delta itself represents pro-

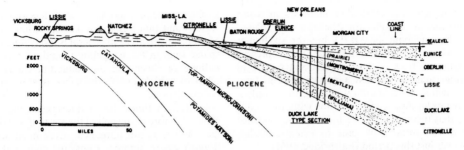

FIG. 12. Profile correlating the fluvial terraces of the lower Mississippi valley, from Vicksburg to Baton Rouge, with the subsurface Quaternary formations of the progressively downwarped Mississippi delta, as disclosed by oil-well drilling (Doering, 1958). The earliest Pleistocene consists of the Citronelle (Williama) gravels, comparable in some ways with the Rhine "Deckenschotter" (see Figs. 9–10). It is followed in the delta by the Duck Lake (Bentley), Lissie (Montgomery), Oberlin (Prairie) and Eunice formations, which seem to correspond to the four principal glacial stages (each with high sediment discharge characteristics). Well wooded landscapes in the interglacials would have greatly reduced the sediment discharge.

gressive Quaternary downwarping to over 1800 meters (thus three times that of the Rhine delta) and as much as 140 meters in the Holocene alone. Around the delta region it is clear that the high terraces are interglacial, but as one goes upstream most authorities would call them glacial. Trowbridge (1954) has spelled out the problem.

Fisk (1951) approached the question from the delta stratigraphy. Clearly each successive postglacial sea level rise would dam back the river flow and cause thalassostatic sedimentation. He deduced that the gravel terraces were therefore all related to the deglacial stages. Correspondingly, each stage of incision should match a glacial advance. This interpretation displays a total disregard for the fluvial dynamics. The Mississippi was a heavily loaded braided stream during glacials, furnishing up to 40 meters of loess during the classical Wisconsin (by radiocarbon dates) to the eastern bluffs. The gravels must have been furnished largely by solifluction during glacial advances. Retreat stages were marked by finer-grained material (Fig. 12). There was a fluvial theory of loess due to Russell (1940) that is equally ill-founded.

With advancing vegetational cover since Alleröd times, there has been a marked drop in bed load, the braided "flood plain" has become forested, the river has become incised and has assumed a meandering regime. Thalassostatic effects are really limited to the delta and shelf areas. Since 6000 B.P. there have been several interesting displacements of the principal delta outlets (Fisk and McFarlan, 1955). In the writer's opinion, each of these shifts, dated by C^{14}, corresponds to a small worldwide rise of sea level, the subsequent drop permitting a new (random) delta fan to build out. The clear eustatic picture, however, is difficult to perceive at first sight owing to the strong subsidence tendency of the delta (see *Platforms—Wave-cut*).

The apparent passage of eustatic terraces into the river terraces is illusory; the latter can be traced by drilling to dip down progressively under the delta. In a case like de Lamothe's Mediterranean terraces in Algeria or Morocco, a warming trend with rising sea level corresponds to desiccation in the hills, so that alluviation and eustatic rise go hand in hand. There it is proper to correlate the two. In the Mississippi, which receives its main runoff in more northerly latitudes, the major alluviation is precisely out of phase with eustatic rise.

(8) Swedish Holocene Terraces. The deglaciation of the continental ice in Scandinavia was accompanied by two phenomena that went on more or less hand-in-hand: isostatic rise of the land surface and eustatic rise of sea level. If the two had progressed at exactly the same rate, there would be no terraces. As the rate of uplift has been maximal in north-central Sweden, the streams in this region are more rejuvenated and entrenched than the others. Furthermore, many valleys show complex terracing.

As an example, the River Viskan has some nine large terraces over a distance of 20 km above the point where it issues into Lake Vesselangen, now about 8 meters above mean sea level. Precise mapping by Wenner (1950) shows that the river probably came into existence at about 7000 years B.P. when this sector of southern Sweden emerged above sea level. There was next a brief negative eustatic oscillation and the first rock-cut terrace was cut, followed by a marine transgression, damming back the river and causing the top alluvial terrace to fill in. It would normally be impossible to decide if these terrace cutting and filling stages were due to temporary increases in discharge or in brief swings of sea level (Wenner, 1950, p. 79), but Wenner had regional evidence in favor of the latter; besides, the coastal terraces related to such oscillations are extremely well dated across southern Sweden, by paleontology, varves and C^{14} dates. The three lowest terraces are related to increases in water volume and are not eustatic (the lake was isolated from the sea about 4400 B.P.), but the six higher terraces are each thalassostatic; i.e., they represent the damming back of the river and sharp drop in carrying capacity through a eustatic rise in base level. Each such oscillation was quite small, only a few meters in amplitude. It is not without significance that there seems to be independent evidence from marine terraces of some six eustatic oscillations over just this period (Fairbridge, 1961).

(9) Mediterranean Holocene Terraces. The present Mediterranean climate is for the most part marked by a long, dry summer and a short, wet winter; interglacial conditions were similar. During the Pleistocene glacial periods, the region suffered successively extreme aridity at the cold maxima, when the glacial anticyclonic center of northern Europe forced cool, dry air over the surrounding countries. When there was partial ice retreat, or in early advance stages, this dry regime alternated with year-round wetness and strong westerly storms passed over the Mediterranean (Butzer, 1964). Since the climate data and terrace history are fairly well known for the historical era, it is helpful to establish

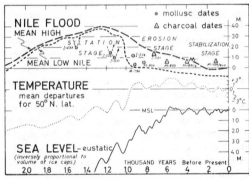

FIG. 13. Record of Nile terraces over the last 20,000 years, compared with mean temperature record (for midlatitudes) and with mean sea level, glacio-eustatically controlled (Fairbridge, 1962). Three gross stages are recognized in the Nile terraces: (a) "*Siltation Stage*" (*ca*. 25,000–13,000 yr. B.P.), when the middle Nile was reduced to a sluggish braided stream and almost dried up, the sediment fill reaching 40 meters above the present flood level, and extending from rock wall to rock wall, completely blocking the present rock-cut gorge. (b) "*Erosion Stage*" (*ca*. 13,000–7500 yr. B.P.), a time of violently oscillating conditions, sometimes with very heavy rains from the tropical monsoons in Ethiopia and central Africa, alternating with brief dry cycles (compare with record of Lake Bonneville: see article *Pluvial Lakes*). (c) "*Stabilization Stage*" when the river had cut down to its old bedrock floor and during when the Nile floods grew progressively weaker, as much of North Africa became desiccated. Note that the entire record is marked by strong oscillations, which are omitted for sake of clarity; only a few dozen C[14] dates are shown.

Lyellian principles here as a guide to less well-known regions and times. Because the vegetation cover in Mediterranean areas in general is today much more sparse than in the temperate humid countries, the volume of sheetwash and alluvium transport is often of a high order; discharge is seasonal, but ordinarily low.

In Roman times the Mediterranean region lay generally more in the belt of the westerlies and summer rains were not infrequent. Even in Alexandria (Egypt) where summer rains are quite unknown now, there are records by Ptolemy of rains for every month except August. Indeed, North Africa was the granary of the Roman Empire, as indicated by extant documents and corroborated by the evidence of great cities (Carthage, Leptis Magna, Sabratha, now largely engulfed in sand). About A.D. 400, however, longer and longer summer droughts were experienced and the underbrush on the hillsides must have died off. Goats are recognized as contributing to the destruction of vegetation, but they could hardly have been the only cause, since they were equally plentiful in earlier centuries. In any case, it is now becoming recognized that from A.D. 400–900 heavy siltation occurred along all the river valleys, while extensive soil erosion occurred on the hillsides. Short, thunderstorm-type rains contribute to this type of violent soil erosion, in contrast to the cool, soaking rains associated with westerly low-pressure systems. The main westerly systems were evidently retreating to the north.

In Morocco, the post-Roman period alluvial fills are known as the Rharbian (Choubert, 1962); they have been described by Judson near Rome itself and in Sicily; the fill has been extensively excavated in a number of places to uncover buried cities—Banasa (Morocco), Tubusuctu (Algeria), Olympia (Greece). At the latter site, the earthquake that destroyed much of the city fixes the time rather nicely, and Büdel (1963a) describes siltation for over 4 meters on the flood plain of the River Alpheos on which the city was built. Vita-Finzi (1964) describes the post-Roman water courses as seasonal, sluggish, braided streams. There were several oscillations in siltation, but it continued on and off till medieval times, when cool conditions returned generally in Europe, and valley incision began once more. In many cases these post-Roman silts now underlie terraces that stand 2–3 meters above the present stream beds.

To generalize: Outside of thalassostatic influences in a region of strongly seasonal rainfall of Mediterranean type (up to about 500 mm), a drop in rainfall causes sedimentation in the middle courses; this is for two reasons: (1) the vegetative cover is reduced and rainfall type is restricted to brief thunderstorms, and (2) the volume of precipitation and total runoff is inadequate to carry the silt away to the ocean, so it backs up and chokes the valleys; V-shaped or U-shaped meandering channels revert to braided patterns. The date of abandonment of the resultant terrace surface marks the end of the dry period or, just as well, the beginning of the next wet phase. The fossils *in* the terrace building silt date the dry period; fossils found *on* the terrace (e.g., human artifacts) may very well date the succeeding wet period. Beneath the silt, there is the terrace-cut surface of the preceding wet period. During such wet periods, the silts are carried seaward under an appropriate equilibrium regime.

(10) The Middle Nile Terraces. The Nile has no corresponding equivalent in the Americas, since it rises in regions of equatorial and monsoonal rains (central Africa and Ethiopia) and debouches in a Mediterranean area, while the middle section is totally arid. During the last few years it has been discovered that a vast siltation stage occurred here during the last glacial stage (thoroughly dated by C^{14}: Fairbridge, 1962, 1965; Büdel, 1963b; and others). During the succeeding Alleröd and early Holocene, heavy rains in the equatorial regions led to progressive down-cutting, with oscillating stages, leaving multiple terraces, which became progressively lower from 13,000 to about 7500 B.P.

At this stage, in the rock-cut sectors of the Middle Nile an interesting change in the erosional sequence occurred. At first, the increased energy had been expressed by progressive down-cutting, but now the old rock floor was reached and the regime changed to lateral planation. At the same time, there was a cyclic but progressive drop in the total discharge, so that the present stream is distinctly underfit. After the change to the hard-rock floor stage began, any increase in discharge would result in a higher flood level, so that alluvium would be dropped on top of much older terrace surfaces. A complex stratigraphy is therefore set up which must be unraveled in order to understand the nature of the terrace formation.

The development of an arid valley-filling stage in the Nile during the last glaciation was matched by similar events in all the great rivers of tropical and equatorial Africa—the Senegal, Niger, Congo, etc. Almost the whole Congo basin was invaded by dune sands from the Kalahari during the period 50,000–10,000 B.P. (de Ploey, 1965), though in the north the sand invasion came from the Sudan (Fairbridge, 1964, 1965). These ancient dunes cover the older terraces, and are vegetated and "fixed" today.

The tropical river terraces are essentially free from glaciation effects and only locally disturbed by tectonics, and so contribute the following paleoclimatic generalization to the general terrace problem: (a) in a deep, precut valley a long arid phase causes general alluviation to a sluggish, braided

FIG. 14. Traces of a late Pleistocene alluvial fill, occupying a rock-cut gorge near Chinle, Arizona. It is interpreted as having been formed during the late glacial aridity and to have been incised by higher energy runoff during the early Holocene. This interpretation represents a small scale analog to the record of the Nile terraces (cf. Fig. 13). (Photo: R. W. Fairbridge.)

ephemeral stream condition; (b) a rise in precipitation and runoff then results in deep dissection, with climatic oscillations producing terracing; an overall secular reduction of rainfall is essential during this sequence or else the alluvial fill will be scoured out completely; (c) when the rock floor is reached, a high-discharge phase causes a new high terrace accumulation with more lateral corrasion, whereas in (b) a high-discharge cycle causes deeper incision.

There is also a general paleoclimatic deduction to be drawn from the African data, namely, that a "pluvial" (rainy) stage in the Mediterranean latitudes (due to an equatorward shift of westerly wind belts during ice advances) is likely to be matched in the equatorial and tropical latitudes by aridity. Widespread low- and mid-latitude deserts thus coincide with glacial maxima, a conclusion corresponding to meteorological theory which indicates that during the low solar radiation epochs of glacial epochs, the evaporation from the oceans would be reduced by 20–30%, resulting in worldwide droughts.

(11) Terraces in the American Southwest. The semiarid country of Arizona, New Mexico and neighboring states presents a complex problem to the student of terraces, because of its (1) relatively high relief, (2) tectonic youth and (3) mixed climatic influences. The first point means that the highest mountains were glaciated in cold epochs, so that periglacial denudation and solifluction materials were fed into the creeks; further, the high relative relief means that constant lowering of base level occurs in the main valleys. Point two is relatively unimportant, but faulting and volcanic activity cause local complications. The third point is particularly confusing: a southerly shift of westerlies during a cold epoch means an incidence of gentle winter rainfall and extension of sagebrush (*Artemisia*), whereas a northerly shift of the weather during a warm phase brings in a heavier incidence of tropical or summer monsoonal rains with cactus-type vegetation (air masses either from the Gulf of Mexico, or from the Gulf of California, or both); furthermore, there is the trend toward general aridity during the cold maxima. In pollen profiles, the sage brush or mountain forest pollens are well represented, but a subtropical phase is marked by almost no pollen because cacti are not contributors.

Using the Lyellian principle, Kirk Bryan and Antevs have pointed out that during the last half century, because of warming and drying, accompanied by overgrazing of cattle, there has been a general increase in arroyo cutting. Therefore it was concluded that the entrenchment was to be equated quite generally with drought or overgrazing; the loss of vegetation and incidence of rare summer thunderstorm rains were quite evident. There was a fallacy however—the area affected by any single rainstorm of this sort is small and the sediment load furnished by the arroyo cutting is high in relation

to runoff. Accordingly, sedimentation recurs a short distance downstream and the *net effect* of drier conditions is an alluvial filling of all the valleys. Conversely, during epochs of cool winter rains there must be a general vegetative cover (forest on higher slopes, sagebrush in the plains), resulting in lower E:P ratios with reduced bed loads, so that continuous through-running erosion was possible. According to Antevs (1952) and others following the Bryan model, the siltation was caused by a moderate increase in precipitation. This deduction is unfortunately false, as may be seen (a) from the historical record in the post-Roman Mediterranean region and (b) from the C^{14}-dated record in the African valleys. Following the Langbein-Schumm Rule, above 300 mm precipitation, the increasing precipitation leads to increasing vegetation, which decreases slope wash and the relative loading; in addition the silts are not dropped in mid-course but carried down to the sea (or lake basin).

Considering the overall picture in the American Southwest, the Tertiary landscape was one of deep saprolite resulting from chemical weathering over an era of warm/wet subtropical conditions. Repeated tectonic uplift led to progressively greater relative and absolute relief as the Quaternary was approached. At the same time, a secular worldwide chilling added to the cooling effects of the higher altitudes and so by Blancan time (the continental Plio-Pleistocene, i.e., Villafranchian) a new regime was introduced. It is hard to say, as yet, which factor was most important: the higher relief, the loss of semi-tropical vegetation, the drier climates in the plains and rainshadow areas; all were operative and valleys like the Rio Grande and Gila were at first scoured out (depths up to 2 km) due to the increasing relief and then with increasing aridity they filled up with silt. The volume of the siltation in the middle and lower Rio Grande valley was colossal. It is important to recognize that as the Quaternary progressed, the amount of Tertiary saprolite and soil (representing perhaps 5×10^8 years of weathering) could not be replaced in the relatively brief interglacial periods of warm/wet conditions (each about 5×10^4 years duration). The mountains, once stripped, remained relatively bare. Thus the vast Blancan sedimentation is not repeated for each climatic cycle, but only on a smaller scale.

Through the Pleistocene there was a cyclic succession of deep dissection of the Blancan and younger fills during the wet stages, leaving paired alluvial terraces, stepping down progressively in elevation, and alternating with refilling episodes during the dry stages. In many valleys the earlier fills would be swept away completely during the flood phases, so that only the fill of the last major cycle is present. The question arises: Were the arid phases the glacial equivalents as in tropical Africa, or were they interglacial equivalents as in the Mediterranean? Is it possible that there were two sorts of wet stage, a cold-wet pluvial with a strong westerly regime (in early and late glacial times), and a warm-wet, strong monsoonal rain regime (in the warmest interglacials), with arid phases at intermediate times? For the two types of pluvial there is mixed evidence: there are discoveries of fossil Capybara, a giant rodent at present living only in equatorial forests of Central America. Pollen data show certainly records of cool/wet winter rains (the sage brush, *Artemisia*) alternating with low pollen stages (cactus-rich, Sonora type, semiarid conditions). The "pluvial" lake record largely corresponds to the cool periods, but it should not be forgotten too that in Africa and in Mexico (in spite of abundant errors in the earlier literature) the evidence now shows that lake growth occurred in the warm interstadials and interglacials, as meteorologic theory would suggest, and that desiccation occurred in the glacial stages.

The history of late Quaternary terrace formations and alluvial fills in the Southwest has been fairly well worked out, but its interpretation is still subject to considerable discussion (Hester and Schoenwetter, 1964).

RHODES W. FAIRBRIDGE

References

Alimen, M.-H., 1967, "The Quaternary of France," in (Rankama, K., editor), "The Quaternary," Vol. 2, pp. 89–2385, New York, Interscience, Publishers.

Antevs, E., 1952, "Arroyo-cutting and filling," *J. Geol.,* **60,** 375–385.

Beckinsale, R. P., and Richardson, L., 1964, "Recent findings on the physical development of the lower Severn Valley," *Geogr. J.,* **130,** Pt. 1, 87–105.

Breuil, H., 1939, "The Pleistocene succession in the Somme Valley," *Proc. Prehist. Soc. London,* **5,** 33–38.

Brouwer, A., 1956, "Thalassostatic terraces and Pleistocene chronology," *Leidse Geol. Mededel.,* **20,** 22–23.

Brunnacker, K., 1956, "Regionale Bodendifferenzierungen während der Würmeiszeit," *Eiszitalter Gegenwart,* **7.**

Büdel, J., 1963a, "Aufbau und Verschüttung von Olympia," *Erdkunde,* **17.**

Büdel, J., 1963b, "Die pliozänen und quartären Pluvialzeiten der Sahara," *Eiszitalter Gegenwart,* **14,** 161–187.

Butzer, K. W., 1964, "Environment and Archeology," Chicago, Aldine Publ. Co., 524pp.

Choubert, G., 1962, "Réflexions sur les parallélismes probables des formations quaternaires atlantiques du Maroc avec celles de la Méditerranée," *Quaternaria,* **6,** 137–175.

Cotton, C. A., 1963, "Did the Murrumbidgee aggradations take place in glacial ages?", *Australian J. Sci.,* **26,** 54.

de Jong, J. D., 1967, "The Quaternary of the Netherlands," in (Rankama, K., editor), "The Quaternary," Vol. 2, pp. 301–426, New York, Interscience Publishers.

de Ploey, J., 1965, "Position géomorphologique, génèse et chronologie de certains dépôts superficiels au Congo occidental," *Quaternaria,* **7,** 131–154.

Doering, J. A., 1958, "Citronelle age problem," *Bull. Am. Assoc. Petrol. Geologists,* **42,** 764–786.

Fairbridge, R. W., 1961, "Eustatic Changes in Sea Level," in "Physics and Chemistry of the Earth," London, Pergamon Press, **4,** 99–185.

Fairbridge, R. W., 1962, "New radiocarbon dates of Nile sediments," *Nature,* **195,** 108–110.

Fairbridge, R. W., 1964, "African Ice-Age Aridity," in (Nairn, A.E.M., editor), "Problems in Palaeoclimatology," pp. 356–363, Interscience Publishers.

Fairbridge, R. W., 1965, "Eiszeitklima in Nordafrika," *Geol. Rundschau,* **54**(1), 399–414.

Fink, J., 1956, "Zur Korrelation der Terrassen und Lösse in Österreich," *Eiszeitalter Gegenwart,* **7.**

Fisk, H. N., 1951, "Loess and Quaternary geology of the lower Mississippi Valley," *J. Geol.,* **59,** 333–356.

Fisk, H. N., and McFarlan, E., Jr., 1955, "Late Quaternary deltaic deposits of the Mississippi River," *Geol. Soc. Am. Spec. Paper,* **62,** 279–302.

Flint, R. F., and Brandtner, F., 1961, "Climatic changes since the last interglacial," *Am. J. Sci.,* **259,** 321–328.

Frechen, J., and Lippolt, H. J., 1965, "Kalium-Argon, Daten zum Alter des Laacher Vulkanismus, der Rheinterrassen und der Eiszeiten," *Eiszitalter Gegenwart,* **16,** 5–30.

German, R., 1965, "Glazial oder interglazial?", *Mitt. Oesterr. Geogr. Ges.,* **107,** 1–19.

Graul, H., 1953, "Ueber die quartären Geröllfazien im deutschen Alpenvorlande," *Geol. Bavarica,* **19.**

Groschopf, P., 1961, "Beiträge zur Holozänstratigraphie Südwestdeutschlands nach C^{14} Bestimmungen," *Jahresh. Geol. Landesamtes Baden-Wuerttemberg,* **4,** 137–143.

Heim, A., 1919, "Geologie der Schweiz," Leipzig, Tauchnitz, 1, 704pp.

Hester, J. J., and Schoenwetter, J. (editors), 1964, "The reconstruction of past environments," *Fort Burgwin Res. Center Publ.,* No. 3, 89pp.

Hjulström, F., 1949, "Climatic changes and river patterns," *Geogr. Ann. (Stockholm),* **31,** 83–89.

Huntington, E., 1907, "Some characteristics of the glacial period in non-glaciated regions," *Bull. Geol. Soc. Am.,* **18,** 351–388.

Jovanovic, P. S., 1940, "Les Profile Fluviatiles en Long, Leurs Formes et Leur Génèse," Paris, Armand Colin, 192pp.

Judson, S., 1963, "Erosion and deposition of Italian stream valleys during historic time," *Science,* **140,** 898–899.

Kaiser, K., 1961, "Gliederung und Formenschatz des Pliozäns und Quartärs am Mittel- und Niederrhein . . . ," in "Köln und die Rheinlände," Wiesbaden, pp. 236–278, F. Steiner Verl.

Krivan, P., 1955, "La division climatologique du pleistocène en Europe Centrale et le profile de loess de Paks," *Ann. Inst. Geol. Public. Hung.,* **43,** 363–512.

Kukla, J., Ložek, V., and Záruba, Q., 1961, "Zur Stratigraphie der Lösse in der Tschechoslowakei," *Quartär (Bonn),* **13,** 1–29.

Lamothe, L. de, 1918, "Les anciennes nappes alluviales et lignes de rivage du bassin de la Somme et leurs rapports avec celles de la Méditerranée occidentale," *Bull. Soc. Géol. France,* **18**(4).

Langbein, W. B., and Schumm, S. A., 1958, "Yield of sediment in relation to mean annual precipitation," *Trans. Am. Geophys. Union,* **39,** 1076–1084.

Lewis, W. V., 1944, "Stream trough experiments and terrace formation," *Geol. Mag.*, **81**, 241–258.

Ložek, V., 1965, "The relationship between the development of soils and faunas in the warm Quaternary phases," *Anthropozoikum (Prague)*, **3**, 7–51.

Lüttig, G., 1965, "Interglacial and interstadial periods," *J. Geol.*, **73**(4), 579–591.

Pécsi, M., 1964, "Ten Years of Physico-geographic Research in Hungary," Budapest, Akad. Kiadó, 132pp.

Penck, A., and Brückner, E., 1909, "Die Alpen im Eiszeitalter," Leipzig, Tauchnitz, 3 vols., 1199pp.

Potter, P. E., 1955, "Petrology and origin of the Lafayette gravel," *J. Geol.*, **63**, 1–38.

Prošek, F. and Ložek, V., 1957, "Stratigraphische Übersicht des tschechoslowakischen Quartärs," *Eiszeitalter Gegenwart*, **8**, 37–90.

Russell, R. J., 1940, "Quaternary history of Louisiana," *Bull. Geol. Soc. Am.*, **51**, 1199–1234.

Scherf, E., 1938, "Versuch einer Einteilung des ungarischen Pleistozäns auf moderner polyglazialistischer Grundlage," *Verh. INQUA III, Wien.*

Schultz, C. B., and Stout, T. M., 1948, "Pleistocene mammals and terraces in the Great Plains," *Bull. Geol. Soc. Am.*, **59**, 553–588.

Schumm, S. A., 1965, "Quaternary Paleohydrology," in (Wright and Frey, editors), "The Quaternary of the United States," pp. 783–794, Princeton N.J., Princeton University Press.

Smith, H. T. U., 1949, "Physical effects of Pleistocene climate changes in non-glaciated areas: eolian phenomena, frost action, and stream terracing," *Bull. Geol. Soc. Am.*, **60**, 1485–1516.

Soergel, W., 1919, "Lösse, Eiszeiten und paläolithische Kulturen, Eine Gliederung und Altersbestimmung der Lösse," Jena, G. Fischer, 177pp.

Soergel, W., 1924, "Die diluvialen Terrassen der Ilm und ihre Bedeutung für die Gliederung des Eiszeitalters," Jena, G. Fischer, 79pp.

Stephens, N. and Synge, F. M., 1966, "Pleistocene Shorelines," in (Dury, G. H., editor), "Essays in Geomorphology," New York, Amer. Elsevier, 1–51.

Trévisan, L., 1949, "Genèse de terrasses fluviatiles en relation avec les cycles climatiques," *Compt. Rend. Intern. Géogr. (Lisbon)*, 2.

Troll, C., 1926, "Die jungglazialen Schotterfluren im Umkreis der deutschen Alpen," *Forsch. Deutsch. L. u. V. Kde*, **24**, 157–256.

Trowbridge, A. C., 1954, "Mississippi River and Gulf Coast terraces and sediments as related to Pleistocene history—a problem," *Bull. Geol. Soc. Am.*, **65**, 793–812.

Udluft, H., 1934, "Bemerkungen zur Frage der Terrassen-Aufschotterung und der Diluvialchronologie," *Jahrb. Preuss. Geol. Landes-Anst. (Berlin)*, **54**.

Vita-Finzi, C., 1964, "Synchronous stream deposition throughout the Mediterranean area in historical times," *Nature*, **202**, 1324.

Wenner, C.-G., 1950, "The deltas and terraces of the River Viskan between Berghem and Horred," *Geogr. Ann. (Stockholm)*, **32**, 60–81.

Woldstedt, P., 1958–65, "Das Eiszeitalter," Second ed., Stuttgart, Enke Verlag, (Vol. 1, 1961; Vol. 2, 1958; Vol. 3, 1965).

Woldstedt, P., 1960, "Mississippi und Rhein," *Eiszeitalter Gegenwart*, **11**, 31–38.

Zaruba-Pfeffermann, Q., 1942, "Längsprofil durch die Moldauterrassen zwischen Kamaik und Weltrus," *Mitt. Tschech. Akad. Wiss.*, **52**(9).

Zaruba, Q., 1961, "River terraces in the Bohemian Massif," *Prace Inst. Geol.*, Warszawa (Czwar, Europ. Srod. Wsch. pt. I), **4**, 65–70.

Zeuner, F. E., 1959, "The Pleistocene Period: Its Climate, Chronology and Faunal Successions," London, Hutchinson & Co., 447pp. (Second revised ed. of 1945 work).

Zonneveld, J., 1956, "The use of heavy minerals for stratigraphic purposes," *Actes IV Congr. Quat. (Rome-Pise, 1953)*, **1**, 268–277.

Zonneveld, J., 1963, "Accumulation and erosion in the Lower Rhine area," *Rept. VI Int. Congr. Quat.*, *Warsaw, 1961*, **3**, 403–410.

Cross-references: *Base Level; Continental Erosion; Eustasy; Fluvioglacial Processes; Glacial Geology; Holocene; Loess; Morphogenetic Classification; Periglacial Landscapes; Piedmont Landforms; Platforms—Wavecut; Pluvial Lakes; Postglacial Isostatic Rebound; Quaternary Period; Rivers—Meandering and Braiding; Terraces, Fluvial—Introduction; Terraces—Thalassostatic. Vol. II: Climatic Variations; Ice Age Meteorology.* pr Vol. VII: *Paleontology; Palynology; Varve Chronology; Volcanic Ash Chronology (Tephrochronology).*

TERRACES—LACUSTRINE

Dynamically, a lake terrace, erosional or constructional, is essentially the same as a marine terrace. It reflects the intersection of a horizontal water plane with the land surface. Terrace building or erosion is thus achieved by wave action and longshore currents, just as in the ocean, although the energy available may be some orders of magnitude less, since many lakes are quite small and lack the necessary "fetch" to develop an appreciable swell. Furthermore, lakes tend to be relatively short lived, even ephemeral, features of the earth's surface. If the lake surface is above present mean sea level, then headward erosion of the draining stream is liable to lower the lake outlet progressively or even catastrophically, thereby changing the local base level (lake datum) and thus the water plane that controls the terrace level.

Lakes with an outlet are less sensitive to climate change than closed basins, for the threshold and outlet channel will eventually adapt to changes in input; hardrock thresholds, however, may require extremely long adjustment periods, during which time such lakes may act as effective natural "gauging stations" for measuring runoff within the drainage basin concerned. Lakes in closed basins reflect runoff variability rather closely, although in large shallow lakes (especially in mid- and low latitudes) mean temperature, and thus evaporation, become progressively more important with the rise in temperature of air and lake waters. Thus measurement and dating of terrace developments in closed-basin lakes is of extraordinary interest to paleoclimatology.

Lake terraces most likely to reflect climatic variations include the following—going from high to low latitudes:

(1) *Ice-dammed lakes*, relatively short-lived, terraces usually marking ice maxima and retreat stages; classic example—the "Parallel Roads of Glenroy", Scotland (see *Glacial Spillways and Proglacial Lakes*). A special subclass of fluvioglacial terrace forms in ice-dammed lakes of small size. The terrace deposits are often varved, even in tributary valleys which merge into the principal proglacial valleys. These tributary streams were evidently dammed by the rapid alluviation of the main valleys during catastrophic deglaciation (Shaw, 1911; Fidlar, 1948; Gooding, 1957).

(2) *Ice-scoured, morainic and related glacial lakes*, usually longer lived than (1), but often small and thus tending to fill with sediment. In the cool, humid climatic belts, most of these depressions overflow, so that terracing is unusual unless the rock threshold is gradually lowered. The *Great Lakes of North America* (q.v.) provide a classic record of post-Wisconsin deglaciation (Hough, 1958). Tilting of the water planes during glacial retreat provides critical data for the isostatic rebound question (see *Postglacial Isostatic Rebound*; *Water Loading and Crustal Response*). Numbers of proglacial meltwater lakes disappeared almost immediately after the ice withdrew so that often only a single terrace developed. One of the extensive areas where the lakes remain is the historic Masurian Lakes of eastern Poland and White Russia that began to develop during the Alleröd (*ca.* 11,000 B.P.). Stasiak (1963) finds that the changes of level are controlled mainly by temperature, rather than by precipitation; at first, the rise of temperature leads to rise of meltwaters, but after ice retreat, the rise of temperature means evaporation and drop of lake level in this essentially continental climate.

(3) *Mid-latitude pluvial lakes* are those that filled with water in response to rise in precipitation coupled with shifts in the main westerly storm belts (or both). The best-known examples are *Lakes Bonneville* and *Lahontan* in Utah and Nevada, which reached their peaks at 12,000 B.P. (early Alleröd) and 9500 B.P. (Preboreal/Yoldia), (Broecker and Kaufman, 1965). The description of their terraces by Gilbert (1890) is one of the classics of geology. Tilting of these terraces following the removal of the water load has provided critical data on the strength of the earth's crust (see *Water Loading and Crustal Response*). Recent work traces earlier Kansan and Illinoian stages (Morrison, 1965; Morrison and Frye, 1965), and it seems clear that interglacials were represented by soil formation but low lake levels; however, the radiocarbon dates suggest that the lakes were only high during deglaciation and that they may have been low also at the glacial maxima when there was worldwide aridity due to the lowered ocean water temperatures. Immense numbers of pluvial lakes developed in the periglacial regions in the postglacial retreat stage of the late Wisconsin, and their terrace dating represents a valuable correlation potential (see *Pluvial Lakes*). Most of the lakes themselves are now no longer in existence, due to renewed aridity, to filling or to natural drainage.

The *Dead Sea* (q.v.) is an example that is still fed by winter snows (from the Lebanon), but the terracing may be complicated by renewed tectonic activity. The terraces of the great seas and lakes of Asia, the *Caspian* (q.v.), the *Aral Sea* (q.v.) and *Lake Balkhash* (q.v.), represent useful gauges of precipitation and runoff in their respective catchment areas. Australia's *Lake Eyre* (q.v.) is in an analogous position.

(4) *Low-latitude pluvial lakes* are divisible into two sorts, so that the datings of their terraces are mutually out of phase. The middle- and low-elevation pluvial lakes [e.g., *Lake Chad* (q.v.); the *East African Lakes* (q.v.), such as Tanganyika, Victoria, Nyassa (Malawi), etc.] appear to rise and fall with the strength of solar radiation and the energetics of the monsoon systems (Dixey, 1964); they would have thus been highest in the interglacial phases of the Quaternary. Significant is a C^{14} dating of the 8–9 foot terrace on Lake Victoria (3720 B.P.: Bishop, 1965) which corresponds to the late Peron stage of the mid-Holocene "climatic optimum." Tectonic tilting, however, complicates the interpretation of the higher terraces of Lake Victoria. During the late Wisconsin period, Lake Victoria was shallower and its shores were marked by savanna and not by jungle as today (Kendall, 1965). The shallower lakes, e.g., Chad, probably dried out altogether during the last glacial advance (late Wisconsin) but expanded to immense size in the interstadials or postglacial warmup (10,000–8,000 B.P.) according to C^{14} material collected by Faure (1965). There is even evidence that the enormous water body of the Red Sea was cut off from the ocean during the last glaciation and, being converted into an evaporating salt lake, dried out almost completely; its terraces have partly been traced by submarine sounding and sampling (Olausson, personal communication).

In contrast, very high-altitude lakes in the tropics, as well as those of rainshadow deserts (e.g., Peru), were affected by the lowering of the snow line during the cold, glacial stages of the Quaternary (e.g., at 18,000 B.P. on Mt. Kenya the mean temperature dropped 5°C (Coetzee, 1964). They became shallower or dried out completely during the warm phases.

RHODES W. FAIRBRIDGE

References

Bishop, W., 1965, "Quaternary geology and geomorphology in the Albertine Rift Valley, Uganda," *Geol. Soc. Am., Spec. Paper* **84**, 293–321.

Broecker, W., and Kaufman, A., 1965, "Radiocarbon chronology of Lake Lahontan and Lake Bonneville II, Great Basin," *Bull. Geol. Soc. Am.,* **76**, 537–566.

Coetzee, J. A., 1964, "Evidence for a considerable depression of the vegetation belts during the Upper Pleistocene on the East African mountains," *Nature*, **204**, 564–566.

Dixey, F., 1964, "Cyclic phenomena in hydrology and solar activity," *J. Hydrol.*, **2**(1), 15–18.

Faure, H., 1965, "Great Saharian lakes evolution during Holocene," *INQUA, Abstracts (Denver)*, **7**, 138.

Fidlar, M. M., 1948, "Physiography of the Lower Wabash valley," *Bull. Indiana Dept. Conserv., Div. Geol.*, **2**, 112pp.

Gilbert, G. K., 1890, "Lake Bonneville," *U.S. Geol. Surv., Mon.*, **1**, 438pp.

Gooding, A. M., 1957, "Pleistocene terraces in the upper Whitewater drainage basin, Southeastern Indiana," *Bull. Earlham College, Sci.*, **2**.

Hough, J. L., 1958, "Geology of the Great Lakes," Urbana, Univ. of Illinois Press, 313pp.

Kendall, R. L., 1965, "Climatic change in East Africa: the evidence from Lake Victoria," *INQUA, Abstracts (Denver)*, **7**, 264.

Morrison, R. B., 1965, "New evidence on Lake Bonneville stratigraphy and history from southern Promontory Point, Utah," *U.S. Geol. Surv. Profess. Paper* **525-C**, C110–C119.

Morrison, R. B., and Frye, J. C., 1965, "Correlation of the Middle and Late Quaternary successions of the Lake Lahontan, Lake Bonneville, Rocky Mountain (Wasatch Range), Southern Great Plains and Eastern Midwest areas", *Nevada Bur. Mines, Rept.*, **9**, 45pp.

Shaw, E. W., 1911, "Preliminary statement concerning a new system of Quaternary lakes in the Mississippi basin," *J. Geol.*, **19**, 481–491.

Stasiak, J., 1963, "Historia jeziora Kruklin ...," *Polska Akad. Nauk, Pr. Geogr.*, **42**, 93pp.

Cross-references: *Aral Sea; Caspian Sea; Cryptodepressions; Dead Sea; Deglaciation; East African Lakes; Glacial Lakes; Glacial Spillways and Proglacial Lakes; Great Lakes (North America); Lake Balkhash; Lake Chad; Lake Eyre; Pluvial Lakes; Postglacial Isostatic Rebound; Quaternary Period; Terraces, Fluvial—Environmental Controls; Water Loading and Crustal Response.* Vol. I: *Fetch.* Vol. II: *Climatic Optimum; Paleoclimatology.*

TERRACES—MARINE (Introductory Concepts)

The continued attack of the waves on the land develops a characteristic coastal profile consisting of a sea cliff and a submarine terrace, often a wave-cut platform. In Fig. 1, the original slope of the land is indicated by the broken line between A and B. Under wave attack, the sea cliff started as a low feature which increased in height as it was driven inland. In its wake, there was left a submarine platform (BC) trimmed across bedrock. This is the surface of the wave-cut terrace (EBC).

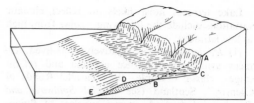

FIG. 1. Ideal shore profile showing cliff (AC), wave-cut platform (BC), and wave-built terrace (BDE).

The material eroded from the cliff is carried seaward by bottom currents and deposited beyond the edge of the rock terrace. The sedimentary surface (BD) is part of the wave-built terrace (BDE). Along some coasts, the longshore currents are so strong that the sediment eroded from the land is carried away and the wave-cut platform is the only feature present (for further discussion, see *Platforms* and *Wave Base*).

If sea level was to remain essentially stable for a long period of time or, according to a second hypothesis, was to rise extremely slowly, the sea cliff would be driven far inland and the wave-cut terrace would be very broad. If the period of time involved was short, however, the wave-cut terrace would be very narrow.

During the last million years or so, sea level has risen and fallen relatively rapidly a number of times, primarily in response to episodes of glaciation and deglaciation (see *Eustasy*). During times of glaciation, when considerable volumes of water were locked up as ice on the lands, sea level stood low; during interglacial times, when much of the ice melted away, returning the waters to the sea, sea level stood high. During some of the interglacial episodes, the climate was even warmer than now and less ice was locked up in Greenland, Antarctica, and the high mountains of the earth than at present. The seas were then especially full and the shore lines rested high on the coastal slopes.

Changes in the volume of ocean water, however, are not the only causes of shifting shore lines. Many coasts, like that of California, are unstable and have been subject to both uplift and subsidence during recent geologic times. These vertical shifts of the land have brought the sea into contact with the coast at different relative levels. In places where both land and the sea have changed position

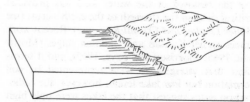

FIG. 2. Terraced coast, produced by intermittent emergence.

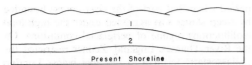

FIG. 3. Generalized section along a warped coast, showing greater warping of shoreline 1 than 2.

repeatedly, the record of the ancient shore lines is difficult indeed to decipher. Hereafter, when referring to rises and falls in sea level, the terms will be used in a relative sense without any implication as to whether it was the sea, land, or both that changed level. De Martonne recommended use of the noncommittal terms "emergence" and "submergence".

If sea level rises to a new level and remains stationary there for some time, a new sea cliff and platform is developed. Thus, each stillstand of the sea is recorded by a sea cliff and platform. Should sea level drop again, its former levels will be indicated by a succession of steps or terraces etched into the coastal slopes (Fig. 2). The highest ones, having been exposed longest to weathering and erosion, tend to be obscure, often being represented by nothing more than steepenings of the slope where the old sea cliffs used to be.

Terraces abandoned when sea level dropped to levels lower than now, were of course submerged as sea level rose to its present position. As the rising sea overrode the terraces, they were subject to considerable erosion by waves and partly buried by sediment, hence submerged terraces are generally much subdued.

In some places it is possible to demonstrate that land movements contributed to the succession of terraces. The demonstration is based on the reasonable assumption that in the absence of differential warping of the land, ancient shore lines should appear horizontal. Locally, however, the situation is as shown in Fig. 3. Shore line 1, now several hundred feet above sea level, was presumably horizontal when formed, just as is the present shore line. If it had been abandoned by a drop in sea level alone, it should still be horizontal. Instead, it is bowed upward. Part of the bowing apparently took place prior to development of shore line 2. Shore line 2 is also warped, however, indicating a continuation of the warping. That the warping is local is indicated by the fact that elsewhere the shore lines are horizontal, due either to worldwide drops of sea level, broad vertical uplifts of the land, or combinations of these. A coast showing typical youthful emergence is seen in Fig. 4.

A powerful new tool has recently been brought to bear on the problem of past fluctuations of sea level. This tool is C^{14} age determination, involving measurement of the amount of decay of a weakly radioactive form of carbon found in $CaCO_3$ shells and organic material of ancient shoreline deposits; it permits fairly precise dating as far back as 50,000 years. Thus, careful field study of terraces and their related deposits, supplemented by modern laboratory studies, are slowly clarifying the complex record of our unstable shores.

ARTHUR D. HOWARD

References

Guilcher, A., 1958, "Coastal and Submarine Morphology," London, Methuen (translated by B. W. Sparks and R. H. W. Kneese).

FIG. 4. Wave-cut terraces, San Clemente Island, California. (U.S. Navy photograph by R. S. Dietz).

Johnson, D. W., 1944, "Problems of terrace correlation," *Bull. Geol. Soc. Am.*, **55,** 793–818.

Kuenen, Ph. H., 1950, "Marine Geology, pp. 221–229, New York, John Wiley & Sons.

Thornbury, W. D., 1954, "Principles of Geomorphology," pp. 433–443, New York, John Wiley & Sons.

Cross-references: *Coastal Geomorphology*; *Eustasy*; *Littoral Processes*; *Platforms—Wave-cut*; *Prograding Shoreline*; *Retrograding Shoreline*; *Strandline*; *Warping*; *Wave Base*. Vol. I: *Mean Sea Level Changes*.

TERRACES, PLUVIAL—*See* PLUVIAL LAKES

TERRACES, THALASSOSTATIC

Definition

Writing in 1931, Wilhelm Ramsay suggested that "the terraces on the lower courses of the rivers running to the sea seem to illustrate the eustatic changes of sea level during the glacial and interglacial epochs in a plainer manner than do the raised shores." In 1945, F. E. Zeuner coined the term *thalassostatic* to identify those river terraces formed by aggradation during the high sea levels of the Pleistocene. He envisaged the infilling of an estuary produced by drowning, perhaps with some related extension of the aggradation upstream as the estuarine delta extended seaward. However, most of the upper course would be unaffected, and downcutting would occur there.

Zeuner also emphasized the contrast between these high sea-level (and, therefore, interglacial) terraces and the terraces formed during a glacial period when that part of the river course bounded by steep slopes was aggraded under the high-load (solifluction) regime of periglacial conditions. On the River Thames, England, Zeuner restricted the thalassostatic terraces to the area below London (the present tidal limit), implying that the terraces above London represented cold-period aggradation. His refusal to envisage high sea-level aggradation extending far upstream is supported by modern American work on aggradation behind dams.

Earlier workers have correlated terraces over the length of a valley and ascribed them to high interglacial sea levels. This applies to the classic work of de Lamothe (1918) on the Somme, France, where the concept of eustatic terraces really originated (Fig. 1). Brouwer (1956) regarded eustatic aggradation throughout a valley as a theoretical possibility, but recognized the advantages in practice of restricting the term thalassostatic to "terraces formed in the lowermost river course." Rigorously restricted to *quasi-horizontal dissected estuarine fills of interglacial age*, thalassostatic terraces are of very limited extent and by no means easy to identify. In many places where they may have been deposited during the earlier Pleistocene stages, they have been completely removed by later erosion since this is inevitably most severe in estuarine areas.

Occurrence and Correlation

Aggradations caused by the rising sea levels experienced during each interglacial have been most widely recognized in deltas such as the Rhine and the Mississippi. In both regions, unfortunately, they tend to be found at low levels due to later subsidence. Thalassostatic terraces that

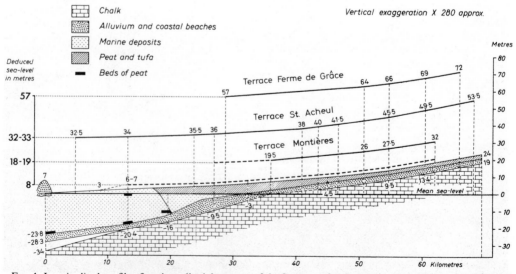

FIG. 1. Longitudinal profile of ancient alluvial terraces of the Somme (after Lamothe, 1918, Fig. 1, p. 7). Most of the peat (in the "modern" floodplain alluvium) is dated early Holocene to Neolithic.

TABLE 1 (ALL HEIGHTS ARE IN METERS)

Interglacial Terminology (after Zeuner)	Somme	Thames	Loire	Sea-level Terminology (after Zeuner)
First Interglacial	57	?60	55–60	Milazzian
Great Interglacial	32–33	32	33	Tyrrhenian
Last Interglacial	18–19	17	15–20	Main Monastirian
	8	7.5	—	Late Monastirian

give a direct indication of the interglacial sea level are restricted to the smaller, stable estuarine river mouths, and the only successful correlations are limited to northwest Europe, where they are at times supported by independent dating of the aggraded deposit. Long-range correlations are few and insecure; typical is the attempt by Smit Sibinga (1953) to establish a Pleistocene chronology of Indonesia using the eustatic approach. Within northwest Europe, the heights originally established by de Lamothe for the Somme have been matched in other rivers, notably the Thames, as shown in Table 1.

In practice, many of the heights in this Table are not derived solely from thalassostatic terraces but also from terraces that occur for the full length of the river valley. Sea level is then estimated from the height difference between the terrace remnants and the present floodplain. It may be questioned why thalassostatic terraces have not been described from other areas. In part, this reflects limited knowledge: the Somme and Thames sequences are based on numerous sections and the combined efforts of many researchers. Terraces cannot be identified as thalassostatic on surface morphology alone. They may also require a combination of rapid sedimentation with local structural stability, and it could be that these conditions are restricted to those few areas comparable with northwest Europe in these respects.

KEITH M. CLAYTON

References

Bourcart, J., 1950, "Les variations du *"niveau de base"* et dégagement des terrasses alluviales," *Rev. Géomorph. Dyn.*, No. 6, 277–284.

Brouwer, A., 1956, "Thalassostatic terraces and Pleistocene chronology," *Leidse Geol. Mededel.*, 20, 22–33.

Lamothe, Gen. de, 1918, "Les anciennes nappes alluviales et lignes de Rivage du bassin de la Somme et leurs rapports avec celles de la Méditerranée occidentale," *Bull. Soc. Géol. France, Paris*, 18(4), 3–58.

Ramsay, Wilhelm, 1931, "Changes of sea-level resulting from the increase and decrease of glaciation," *Fennia*, 52, No. 5, 1–62.

Sibinga, G. L. Smit, 1953, "Pleistocene eustasy and glacial chronology in Borneo," *Geol. Mijnbouw*, 15, 365–383.

Zeuner, F. E., 1945, "The Pleistocene Period," Ray Society (Second ed. 1959, London, Hutchinson & Co., 447pp.).

Cross-references: *Aggradation*; *Delta*; *Estuary*; *Eustasy*; *Holocene*; *Periglacial Landscape*; *Quaternary*; *Ria, Rias Coast*; *Terraces, Fluvial—Environmental Controls.* Vol. I: *Mean Sea Level Changes.*

TERRACETTES, LYNCHETS AND "CATTLE TRACKS"

On moderate to steep slopes in cool humid terrain, usually with soil and grass, there can often be found one or another variety of relatively narrow

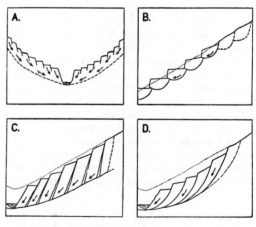

FIG. 1. Origin of landslip terracettes. (A) Conditions particularly favorable for the formation of terracettes; valley in unconsolidated material, fairly steep sides with toes of slopes actively undercut by deeply trenched stream. (B) Terracettes formed by rotation of superficial blocks as pictured by Ødum. (C) Terracettes caused by slippage of blocks on major slip plane or partially fluent zone. (D) Terracettes caused by typical slump movements resulting from slippage on deep-seated curved surfaces (Sharpe, 1938). (By permission of Columbia University Press, N.Y.)

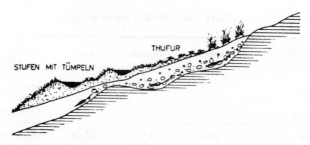

FIG. 2. Development of terracettes on a high subalpine solifluction surface (in Basutoland, South Africa, elevation 3100 meters), with horizontal fill and puddles (*Stufen mit Tümpeln*), and higher upslope, isolated tussocks or thufur (Van Zinderen Bakker, 1965).

terraces, discontinuous flat shoulders, or anastomosing lines of steps that collectively are known as "terracettes." They are sometimes called "pseudo-terraces" or "false terraces." These features should not be confused with "structural terraces" (litho-logic) described elsewhere (see *Terrace, Fluvial*). They have been explained in a remarkable number of ways: as tectonic, as ablation products, as fluvial terraces, as landslip effects, as solifluction and altiplanation products, as vegetation "accidents", as man-made, as produced by sheep or by cattle. Often they are simply referred to as "sheep tracks" or "cattle tracks." Similar terms appear in French and German literature (*Sentiers de vaches, Viehtreppen*).

Consideration of the problem by the writer, over some years, has convinced him that all of the explanations are correct in one place or another, but that the right answers have not always been applied to each particular case. Criteria should be closely studied for each agency. To summarize, those characteristics and agencies are:

(1) Tectonic Terracettes. These may be observed locally in Nevada, Japan, New Zealand and elsewhere, usually along recently active fault lines, where the main fracture has split up near the surface into masses of smaller wedges. They are easy to recognize, but, on the whole, rather scarce.

(2) Landslip Terracettes. Gravitational sliding is most frequently observed on slopes where the lithology consists of poorly consolidated materials and the slopes are maintained in a steep condition by

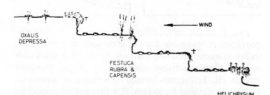

FIG. 3. Ablation terracettes, so-called cattle tracks from the subalpine meadows of Basutoland, South Africa (Van Zinderen Bakker, 1965). Note how varied sorts of vegetation protect an exposed slope from wind erosion.

rapid downcutting of the streams, as is common in periglacial and some recently deglaciated regions (Fig. 1), as well as in some of the humid tropics. Examples are given by Ødum (1922) and by Sharpe (1938). There are also transitions into type 3 (below).

(3) Solifluction or Altiplanation Terracettes. Small-scale gravitational action common in high mountain areas under periglacial action may result in creep and series of small slumps which then form swampy troughs that fill gradually with slope wash and vegetation, forming discontinuous platforms, 1–5 meters in width and flat or gently sloping in their lengthwise sense (Fig. 2). Vegetation clumps tend to retain small tussocks or earth mounds here; the *hummocks* are commonly known in literature as *thufur* (an Icelandic name). These terracettes are often sites of névé accumulation today (e.g. in Alaska); Pleistocene ones are well developed in Wales.

(4) Ablation Terracettes. Under cold, dry conditions, solifluction steps lose their fine soil components, leaving a sort of subalpine "miniature hamada" of residual boulders, the steep sections being protected by resistant plants (Van Zinderen Bakker, 1965; see Fig. 3).

(5) Ice-thrust Terracettes. An unexpected step or pseudo-terrace is often observed on the sides of drumlins, eskers and end moraines. In each case, the lithology indicates that the feature was once at the ice margin and is an ice-thrust phenomenon. The evidence has been extensively illustrated and documented by Krause (1929).

(6) Lynchets (Linchs). An old Anglo-Saxon name for a terrace of soil fill is "lynchet" or "linch." It forms on the uphill side of a stone wall or a thickset hedge due to cultivation and accelerated slope wash. In view of the fact that the fence or hedge was man-made, these features are artificial (Stamp, 1961). Some of them, in northern France and southern England, go back to the Neolithic period, *circa* 5000–7000 B.P. Traces of the old hedgerows may have disappeared almost completely. In France they are known as *rideaux*.

(7) Cattle Tracks and Sheep Tracks. In soft wet turf on steep slopes, the sharp hooves of both cattle and sheep can cut the surface mat of grass. Constant trampling along the same tracks gradually establishes well-marked walkways, sometimes parallel to the slopes, sometimes anastomosing, sometimes sloping gently. These tracks are usually quite narrow and not to be confused with most of the solifluction and landslip terracettes. The essential criterion is that they are tracks, i.e., they are continuous, and not random. Some slopes that would be dangerously steep for the animals in this way become gradually trampled down to a condition favoring simple accessibility (Rahm, 1962).

RHODES W. FAIRBRIDGE

References

Bennet, H. H., 1939, "Soil Conservation" (Terracettes, pp. 295–296), New York and London, McGraw-Hill Book Co.

Krause, P. G., 1929, "Über pseudoterrassen und Geländestufen im norddeutschen Glazialdiluvium," *Jahrb. Preuss. Geol. L.A.*, **50**, 135–147.

Meynier, A., 1951. "Pieds de vaches et terrassettes," *Rev. Géomorphol. Dynamique*, No. 1, 81–83.

Ødum, H., 1922, "Om faarestiernes natur," *Dansk. Geol. Fören, Medd.*, **6**(7), 29.

Rahm, D. A., 1962, "The terracette problem," *Northwest Sci.*, **36**, 65–80.

Robert, P., 1964, "Quelques problèmes géomorphologiques dans la région de Nessonvaux: Étude des terrassettes," *Ann. Soc. Geol. Belg.*, **87**(9).

Sharpe, C. F. S., 1938, "Landslides and Related Phenomena—A Study of Mass-movements of Soil and Rock," New York, Columbia University Press, 137pp.

Stamp, L. D., 1961, "A Glossary of Geographical Terms," London, Longmans, Green, 539pp.

Troll, C., 1944, "Strukturböden, Solifluktion und Frostklimate der Erde," *Geol. Rund.*, **34**, 545–694.

Van Zinderen Bakker, E. M., 1965, "Über Moorvegetation und den Aufbau der Moore in Süd- und Ostafrika," *Bot. Jb.*, **84**, 215–231.

Cross-references: *Altiplanation*; *Landslides*; *Mass Wasting*; *Solifluction*; *Terraces, Fluvial*.

TERRAIN ANALYSIS—*See* pr Vol. VI.

TERRAIN, TERRANE

Terrain (alternatively spelled "terrane") refers to any tract or region of the earth's surface, considered as a purely physical feature, an ecologic environment, a geologic setting or as a site of some applied activity of man—an engineering location, an architectural setting, or a landscape analyzed in terms of military science. "Terrain studies" for military geology or engineering generally call for regional analysis of *relief, bedrock, soil, vegetation, drainage* and *culture* (man-made aspects). This would be synonymous with the early use of the term *topography*, but modern use of the latter is restricted to *relief*.

Terrain analysis in its strict sense is purely descriptive, an analytic science treating with topography, i.e., relief, with no consideration being given to genesis, history or dynamics. It is a vital part of any regional work in geomorphology, but it is restricted to the collecting, mapping and organization of the raw data. It must therefore be clearly differentiated from *landscape analysis* (q.v.) and *land-form studies*, i.e., *morphogenetic regions* (q.v.). The scope of terrain analysis has been broadened in recent decades to take in much of modern military terrain science, which will not be considered here.

There is an out-of-date convention in geology, still used sometimes in France, which employed "terrain" in the sense of the rocks of a certain age, particularly of a system, thus "Silurian terrain." Nevertheless, it is quite usual in geology to use the term to designate the surface area of outcrop of certain rocks (lithologies) or sequences of certain ages, thus "granite terrain," "volcanic terrain," "glacial terrain," "Silurian terrain."

Basis of Terrain Analysis

Terrain can be broken down into relief, roughness (microrelief form) and surface material. Relief can be analyzed in terms of absolute and relative or local elevation, e.g., a plain landform may exist at high or low elevation, the relief by definition being low; while quite modest mountains may rise 1000 m above a high plain of 4000 m, their absolute relief is quite appreciable.

Roughness or microrelief is an important aspect of military or engineering terrain study, since upon it rest many questions of traversibility for men, animals and machines. Steepness of *slopes* (q.v.) is similarly critical. The valleys and divides (*interfluves*, q.v.) may be measured for a characteristic cross-sectional form, such as U-shaped, V-shaped, box canyons and an infinity of transitional forms.

Material of the ground surface may involve both bedrock and soil, though in certain areas either one or the other may be hardly represented at all. Rock hardness and degree of weathering ("saprolite"), presence or absence of permafrost or periglacial cover, as well as soil types, duricrust, and so forth, constitute in themselves major fields of investigation.

World Terrain Types

Finch, *et al.* (1957) recognized eight major terrain categories on a worldwide basis (Table 1), although notable differences in the percentages exist from continent to continent, as might be expected, in view of their climatic zonation and varied geologic histories. Australia is the continent with minimal relief and is only about 20% covered by hills and mountains, against the world mean figure of 36%, or North America with about 33% and Asia with over 50%. The two great icecaps of Antarctica and

TABLE 1. AREAS OF WORLD TERRAIN TYPES
(MODIFIED AFTER FINCH, *et al.*, 1957)

(a) *Flat plains*, nearly level country, little relief	6%
(b) *Rolling and irregular plains*, mostly gentle slopes, low relief	30%
(c) *Tablelands and Plateaus*, upland plains, dissected by valleys and canyons	5%
(d) *Hilly plains* surmounted by scattered hills or mountains, locally moderate relief	13%
(e) *Hill country*, moderate to steep slopes, and low to moderate relief	8%
(f) *Low mountains*, mostly steep sloping, moderate to high relief	14%
(g) *High mountains*, steep slopes, high absolute and relative relief	14%
(h) *Ice sheets*, continental glacial ice plateaus, with scattered nunataks and mountains	10%
	100%

Greenland introduce quite exceptional terrain types. Long cordillera-type mountains (see *Mountain Types*; *Mountain Systems*) exist extensively only in the Americas and Eurasia; they are quite small in Africa and only present in an interrupted way (on islands) in Australasia. The great plains underlain by youthful flat-lying sediments are most widely developed in North America and Eurasia, while plains in Africa–Brazil–India–Australia (the genetically related "Gondwanaland" countries) have a great deal in common, being largely degraded uplands and dissected plateau lands (see *Plains*; *Plateau*).

RHODES W. FAIRBRIDGE

References

Baraniecki, L., 1963, "The application of aerial photographs to the preliminary analysis of the terrain," *Acta Univ. Wratislaviensis, Studia Geogr.*, **I**, 15–26 (in Polish with English summary).

Beckett, P. H. T., and Webster, R., 1962, "The storage and collation of information on terrain," *Military Eng. Exptl. Establ. Rept.*, 40pp.

Common, R., 1961, "A suggestion for terrain profiles, based upon the thalweg and watershed lines," *Irish Geogr.*, **4**(3), 209–212.

Finch, V. C., *et al.*, 1957, "Elements of Geography," Fifth edition, New York, McGraw-Hill Book Co., 693 pp.

Pressman, A. E., 1963, "Comparison of aerial photographic terrain analysis with investigation in Arctic Canada," *Photogram. Engineering*, **29**(2), 245–252.

Radforth, N. W., 1962, "Organic terrain and geomorphology," *Canadian Geogr.*, **6**(3–4), 166–171.

Stamp, L. D., 1961, "A Glossary of Geographical Terms," London, Longmans, Green and Co., 539pp.

Stone, R. O. and Dugundji, J., 1965, "A study of microrelief—its mapping, classification, and quantification by means of a Fourier analysis," *Engin. Geol.*, **1**(2), 89–187.

Thrower, N. J. W., 1960, "Cyprus—a landform study," *Ann. Assoc. Am. Geogr.*, **50**(1), Map Supplement No. 1.

U.S. Dept. of Army, 1952, "Geology and its military applications," *Tech. Manual*, 5–545.

U.S. Dept. of Army, 1953, "Dictionary of U.S. Army Terms," p. 298, S.R. 320–5–1.

Van Lopik, J. R., and Kolb, C. R., 1959, "A technique for preparing desert terrain analogs," *U.S. Army Engineer Waterways Exptl. Sta., Tech. Rept.* 3-506, 70pp.

Wood, W. F., and Snell, J. B., 1960, "A quantitative system for classifying landforms," *Quartermaster Res. and Engin. Command, U.S. Army, Tech. Rept. EP-124*, 20pp.

Zakrzewska, B., 1963, "An analysis of landforms in a part of the central Great Plains," *Ann. Assoc. Am. Geogr.*, **53**(4), 536–658.

Cross-references: *Interfluve*; *Landscape Analysis*; *Microrelief*; *Morphogenetic Regions*; *Mountain and Hilly Terrain*; *Mountain Systems*; *Mountain Types*; *Plains*; *Plateau*; *Regolith and Saprolite*; *Slopes*. pr Vol. VI: *Terrain Analysis*.

TEXTURE—TOPOGRAPHIC

Texture is defined as the disposition or manner of union of the particles or smaller constituent parts of a body or substance. This may apply to rocks or soil (see, respectively, Vols. V and VI), but in geomorphology it applies to topography or terrain relief. Expressed simply, topographic texture refers to the frequency of the changes in the ups and downs of the landscape. A *badlands* (q.v.) has an extremely *fine texture*; a mature undulating plain may have a very *coarse texture*. It is thus an expression of slope change or relative *dissection*.

Texture may also be represented by the relative closeness of the drainage network, i.e., *drainage density*. Thus a high drainage density results in fine texture and a low density in coarse texture.

Texture lends itself ideally to *hypsometric analysis* (q.v.), morphometry and *quantitative geomorphology* (q.v.; Strahler, 1957, 1958, 1960). Simplified it may be treated thus:

Drainage Density

$$= \frac{\text{Total Length of Streams (km or miles)}}{\text{Total Area (km}^2 \text{ or square miles)}}$$

The controls of topographic texture are multiple and not always easy to interrelate in their relative importance. It is a subject on which there has been extremely little research. The principal factors are:

(1) Climate. Following the Langbein–Schumm rule (see *Continental Erosion; Terraces, Fluvial—Environmental Controls*), it is clear that erosion is maximal at about 300 mm (12 inches) rainfall at a mean annual temperature of 10°C or 50°F (Schumm, 1965), but varies somewhat according to temperature, because of vegetation sparsity and so on. An important aspect of this precipitation is season-

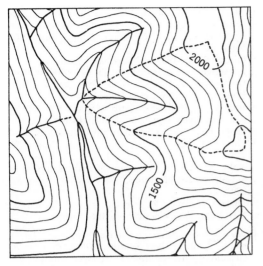

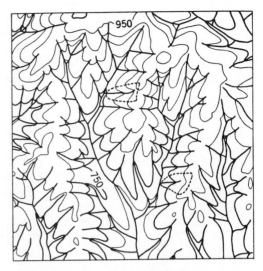

A. Low drainage density or coarse texture, Driftwood, Pennsylvania, Quadrangle.

B. Medium drainage density or medium texture, Nashville, Indiana, Quadrangle.

C. High drainage density or fine texture, Little Tujunga, California, Quadrangle.

D. Extremely high drainage density or ultrafine texture, Cuny Table West, South Dakota, Quadrangle.

FIG. 1. Four areas of 1 square mile each serve as representative examples of the natural range in drainage density. A dashed line shows the perimeter of a representative drainage basin of the first order. In diagram D, streams are omitted for clarity (from maps of the U.S. Geological Survey, Strahler, 1960). (By permission of John Wiley & Sons, N.Y.)

ality; if it all falls at once during summer thunderstorms it will be much more erosive than if it is spread out in gentle winter rains. On the other hand, after *heavy* soaking precipitation, erosion will be more effective than after short, sharp rains (Hack and Goodlett, 1960).

(2) Lithology. Homogeneous unconsolidated sediment or soft rocks favor the finest textural development. Finest texture is seen in badlands, the

intertidal channels on mud flats, fresh volcanic ash cones and so on. Consolidated and massive rocks resist erosion and tend to produce coarser textures.

(3) Permeability. A coarse granular material, such as detrital sand and silt, an ash or tuff, has a high permeability and permits rapid infiltration of rainwater. On the other hand, a finer-grained material such as clay resists infiltration and some clays actually swell or compact so as to become

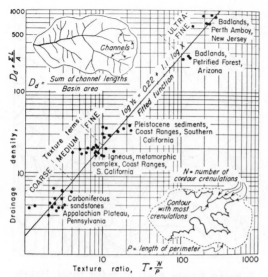

FIG. 2. Definitions of drainage density and texture ratio (Strahler, 1957).

rapidly impervious. Hence, the coarser materials absorb much of the precipitation and the finer ones shed it; thus a fine drainage network and texture develop better with the latter than with the former.

(4) Joints and Related Structures. A hard, massive igneous rock or well-indurated sedimentary rock is invariably jointed, and possibly faulted. Precipitation is largely shed from the massive sectors, and sinks in along the joints and bedding planes. The resultant topographic texture thus tends to be moderate to coarse.

(5) Relief and History. In regions of low or moderate relief, particularly where other factors (named above) favor coarse texture, a maturing drainage system tends toward a simplification and coarsening of the texture. However, if the landscape is youthfully emerged or rejuvenated, it seems likely that a fine texture will develop (or become "overprinted" on the old), although quantitative studies are lacking. The steeper the slopes, the finer is the texture. The youthful overprint is often seen where a thick mature soil (saprolite) has developed over an earlier (and simple) texture and is now being actively eroded due to rejuvenation. One might say that the stages youth—maturity—old age would be expressed by the textures fine, medium and coarse, respectively, but the overriding controls of lithology, etc., would make this a dangerous generalization.

RHODES W. FAIRBRIDGE

References

Cotton, C. A., 1963, "Development of fine-textured landscape relief in temperate pluvial climates," *N.Z. J. Geol. Geophys.*, **6**(4), 528–533.

Hack, J. and Goodlett, J., 1960, "Geomorphology and forest ecology of a mountain region in the central Appalachians," *U.S. Geol. Surv. Profess. Paper* **347**, 66pp.

Schumm, S. A., 1965, "Quaternary Paleohydrology," in (Wright, H. E. and Frey, D. G., editors) "The Quaternary of the United States," pp. 783–794, Princeton, N.J., Princeton Univ. Press.

Smith, K. G., 1950, "Standards of grading texture of erosional topography," *Am. J. Sci.*, **248**, 655–668.

Strahler, A. N., 1957, "Quantitative analysis of watershed geomorphology," *Trans. Am. Geophys. Union*, **38**, 913–920.

Strahler, A. N., 1958, "Dimensional analysis applied to fluvially eroded landforms," *Bull. Geol. Soc. Am.*, **69**, 279–300.

Strahler, A. N., 1960, "Physical Geography," Second ed., New York, John Wiley & Sons, Inc., 534pp.

Cross-references: *Badlands; Continental Erosion; Hypsometric Analysis; Open Systems—Allometric Growth; Quantitative Geomorphology; Terraces, Fluvial—Environmental Controls; Terrain.*

THALASSOSTATIC TERRACES—*See* TERRACES, THALASSOSTATIC

THALWEG or TALWEG

A term of German origin meaning originally the way (*weg*) of the valley (*tal*), the word *Thalweg* was spelt with an "h" before the 1902 German orthographic reform. Since it was adopted into geomorphologic literature before 1902, the older spelling is still sometimes preferred. For instance, L. Dudley Stamp (1961) writes: "Talweg (German), Thalweg (older spelling)," whereas C. A. Cotton (1948) uses an "h". In France, the *Annales de Géographie* spell it, as a rule, "th," but the *Revue de Géographie Alpine* writes "t".

The first meaning of the term is *navigable channel* in a stream. H. Baulig (1956) writes (article 116: thalweg): "The *talweg* in the language of boatmen is the '*fil de l'eau'/chenal navigable/ navigable channel/Fahrwasser, Stromrinne*, that is to say the line of the greatest depths, which is also that of the greatest speeds." According to that significance, the talweg joins the bottoms of the deeps (or pools) cutting from one to the next through the shoals (or fords, or crossings). It is a winding line.

That first meaning of the word is useful only for hydrodynamics. The elevation of the bottom of the navigable channel in a river is no base level for the sculpture of hillslopes. The term has, however, taken on a meaning that is of a broader use in geomorphology.

From the significance "navigable channel," a derived one is, as Baulig (1956; article 116) writes "the axis of the valley bottom," i.e. "die mittlere Richtung des Tales" (A. Penck). Baulig writes elsewhere in his "Vocabulary" (article 39, footnote 3), saying the word "has taken in morphology the meaning of *Tallinie, Talgrund/ fond de vallée/valley bottom.*" In this sense, talweg is the line joining all low points of a valley. If there is no river in the valley, it is properly a line; if there is a river, the talweg has a definite breadth. However, on a small-scale map, it can without any difficulty be confused with a line. The level of the talweg is then taken as the height of the surface of the water. Let the valley be dry or not, the talweg, in this meaning, is the base level for the sculpture of the hillslopes.

As a talweg is not a mere abstract line but a part of the landscape, it may be analyzed by considering both its long profile and its cross profile. The long profile may or may not be graded; cross profile may be an angle, a flat floor or a concave rounded form. A dry valley (as in karst country) has generally a flat or rounded bottom, not a V-shaped one, as R. Clozier pointed out (1940, p. 98) for "it is necessarily a mature valley, because the evolution of the valley sides is the only process going on." The former talweg of such a dry valley is then filled in little by little by the waste coming from the sides; the only possible transportation of debris is through solution or wind action, but it is generally much smaller than the aggradation. In other words, a talweg is the result of an entrenching agent and tends to be obscured or attenuated as soon as the cutting force is checked.

The down-cutting agent is generally a permanent stream, but it can be a temporary one, as happens in arid lands, in karst areas, including fairly pervious regions such as chalk country. In some cases, the agent may be a paleoclimatic one; in temperate latitudes, the water table was generally higher during the cold periods of the Quaternary era so that many valleys had at that time a stream and have none at present. Many dry valleys have such an origin. Non-fluviatile erosion may, in some cases, be responsible for the modification and entrenching of a former talweg: along a fault, gelifraction may cause a gully as is usual, for example, in Labrador; wind may also, although it has been disputed, excavate valleys or depressions (for instance in Spanish Sahara, or along the eastern foot of the Rocky Mts., in Wyoming), even in rather resistant rocks. Of course, in loose material, wind very easily carves out depressions, but their forms are basins that cannot be confused with talwegs.

On the whole, talwegs develop wherever entrenching agents give rise to long depressed areas; on the other hand, we cannot speak of talweg if the low parts of the topography are mere isolated points, funnels or depressions (karst "dolinas" or "sink holes" for instance). A swale or interdune depression is also a linear depression, produced by aggradation, but it is not genetically related to the fluvial talweg.

A talweg may be defined in contradistinction to an *interfluve*, which is all of what in a landscape is not talweg. But the opposite of the talweg itself is a *divide*, i.e., the lines joining all high points in topography.

The distinction of talwegs and interfluves (with their divides) is easy in certain types of landscapes, but not in all. It is easy in mountains, in gently rolling landscapes, as frequently found in temperate countries and equatorial ones (*mar de mauros* of Atlantic Brazil). On the other hand, the concept lacks precision in such topographies as deltas or pediments. In deltas, depressions are formed between the arms where the natural levees are generally higher than the surrounding land (because aggradation takes place along the banks). Even in an alluvial valley, the river may flow higher than the floodplain (the Mississippi valley is a classical example of this feature). On pediments, the numerous rills flow at the same level as the space between them, so that the whole topography is an inclined plane, not a regular succession of talwegs and interfluves. African pediplains which are nearly horizontal planes, also show no difference between anything like talweg and interfluve. In short, where lateral erosion, sapping, river deflection or areal degradation are the main processes of landscape making, the concept of talweg has little application.

MAX DERRUAU

References

Baulig, H., 1956, "Vocabulaire Franco-Anglo-Allemand de Géomorphologie," Paris, Publ. Fac. Lettres Univ. Strasbourg, No. 130, 230pp.
Bull, A. J., Gossling, F., Green, J. F. N., Hayward, H. A., Turner, E. A., and Wooldridge, S. W., 1934, "The River Mole," *Proc. Geol. Assoc.,* **45,** 35–69.
Clozier, R., 1940, "Les Causses de Quercy," Paris, Bailliere, 183pp.
Cotton, C. A., 1948, "Landscape, as Developed by Processes of Normal Erosion," Second ed., London, Australia and New Zealand, Whitcombe and Tombs.
Stamp, L. D., 1961, "A Glossary of Geographical Terms," London, Longmans, Green, 539pp.
Wooldridge, S. W., and Morgan, R. S., 1959, "An Outline of Geomorphology," Second ed., London, Longmans, Green, 409pp.

Cross-references: *Blind Valley*; *Dell*; *Dry Valley*; *Grade, Graded Stream*; *Interfluve*; *Karst*; *Rivers*; *Slopes*; *Quaternary*; *Watershed*.

THERMOKARST

Definition

In the permafrost areas of North America and Siberia, there is often a peculiar topography of pits, dry gullies and valleys, small hummocks and closed depressions, frequently with lakes. This karst-like topography is due to the melting of ground ice, and for it the Russian geologist Ermolaev coined the term *thermokarst*. Kachurin, referring to the appearance of thermokarst topography, says: "the term thermokarst applies to all the forms produced by settling or caving of the ground surface as a result of such thermal changes within the ground, such as may ultimately lead to melting of ice in the upper part of permafrost."

Later, however, it became clearly understood that thermokarst topography must be regarded only as manifestation of a process. Thermokarst is, basically, a thermal process that leads to the melting of ground ice and therefore causes subsidence or caving of the soil and the underlying sediments. Thermokarst characterizes only permafrost areas with an appreciable content of ground ice. The primary aspect of thermokarst, the basic one, is indubitably the melting phenomenon itself, whereas the thermokarst topography is only its secondary, and not always persistent, effect. If thermokarst processes operate below a lake bottom, they may cause the underlying permafrost to melt completely away, and the processes may fail to produce any visible surface forms.

Just as "normal" karst is produced by chemical properties of rocks consisting of calcium carbonate, thermokarst results from certain physical properties of permafrost (soil and ice), which may be regarded as a peculiar kind of rock formation. Hence, the thermokarst is confined exclusively to permafrost areas, and therefore the forms due to the melting of glacier ice, like stagnant, dead-ice hollows, cannot be regarded as thermokarst features.

Types of Thermokarst Development

There are two types of thermokarst development: (a) general or regional, which develops over broad areas as a result of climatic change toward increasing temperatures, and (b) local or topographic development occurring under severe climatic conditions and accompanied by progressive aggradation of permafrost.

Essential for the general development of thermokarst is more or less uniform degradation of permafrost resulting from warmer climatic conditions. The waning of the permafrost occurs over a broad front, progressing down from the earth's surface. Thermokarst processes are not very efficient in ground-ice masses. In fact, they are quite contrary to the effect on permafrost because of the greater thermal conductivity of mineral particles in the latter, where the melting attacks mainly interstitial segregations of ice. Hence, melting of the other ground-ice categories appearing in the mass (e.g., fissure ice) is later than in permafrost. This type of thermokarst development tends to obliterate the contrast of the relief because of very intensive flow of soil masses saturated with water derived from melting of the segregation ice. The same process leads to the effacement of the deformation structures resulting from ground-ice formation.

Local development of thermokarst acts in cold climates in a way that is essentially opposed to melting processes, but restricted to places where there exists some particularly favorable topographic condition. Such conditions may be caused by human activity such as deforestation, agriculture, movement of heavy vehicles, etc., or by natural conditions. Among natural causes, such as tension fissures and forest fires ignited by lightning, the most important is the presence of surficial water because of its latent heat capacity which is five times greater than thermal capacity of the mineral material.

The operating efficiency of thermokarst processes depends largely on the ratio between the thickness of the seasonally thawed layer and that of seasonal refreezing. The value of this ratio and, consequently, the possibility of thermokarst development depend equally on both macro- and microclimatic conditions, especially on the microclimate of the soil and of the underlying sediments. Extreme continental climates provide the most suitable conditions for thermokarst development because the winter freeze may not be able to balance the deep summer thaw. Even a shallow water layer, if it freezes down to the bottom in winter, as in water pools in low centered polygons, induces thermokarst development. The amount of heat absorbed in summer raises the temperature of the bottom sediments, thereby inducing local permafrost degradation.

Thermokarst Topography

Among various forms of thermokarst topography, small pits and hollows, funnels, gullies, minor valleys and small basins are the best known and most frequently mentioned. However, the traditional procedure of giving a descriptive classification to land forms failed in the case of thermokarst because of convergency of forms which,

FIG. 1. Thermokarst pit in loess, Fairbanks, Alaska. The semi-circular dark area at the base of the wall at the far side of the pit is an opening to an underground passageway extending from the pit. (Photo by T. L. Péwé, June 23, 1948).

despite their external resemblance, could be different in origin.

The melting of ground ice in permafrost causes a mass deficiency. An essential aspect in the formation of thermokarst topography is this mass loss although there are other contributing factors such as thermal and mechanical erosion and different mass movements. Hence, the forms of thermokarst topography depend on the nature of ground ice; consequently, the various types of ground ice are the only logical basis for a genetic classification of the thermokarst land forms. Fissure ice or ice veins, injection and segregation ice create particular relief forms and determine their various ways of evolution. Besides the corresponding ground-ice type, the mode and stage of ground-ice degradation must be taken into consideration. Formation and evolution of the thermokarst land forms are controlled by the waning development of particular ground-ice structures.

Large masses of injection ice, as in the cores of *hydrolaccoliths* or *pingos*, when melting, lead to the formation of small basins. More complicated is the problem of the waning development of polygonal fissure ice bodies. If the melting starts from the fissures, as is usual in the high centered polygons, the resulting forms are gullies and even a complex polygonal relief, especially if deep trenches separate accumulations that are sometimes conical in shape, called *baydjarakh* (or *baijerach*) in Siberia. However, when the thermokarst process acts below the water pools in low centered polygons, the waning evolution results in lakes and basins. In Antarctica, good examples are found around Bunger Oasis in the marginal moraines (Grigorev, 1965).

Paleogeographic Importance

Traces of thermokarst found in the Pleistocene deposits of ancient periglacial areas give clear evidence of the former existence of permafrost. One should also remember that all "fossil" periglacial features due to ground-ice formation in permafrost were ultimately formed by thermokarst processes; this, no doubt, is the case in the so-called *ice-wedge casts*.

The sequence of thermokarst structures in vertical sections of deposits characteristic of a cold stage could provide valuable paleogeographic information. In a given stratigraphic column, the lowest structures of the type in question may help us to estimate the beginning of permafrost formation. Other indications, situated at higher horizons, when examined in the light of thermokarst phenomena, local or general, offer the evidences of climatic fluctuations and provide the data for reconstruction of permafrost history.

JAN DYLIK

References

Baranov, Y., 1962, "Cryometamorphism of rocks and its influence on the paleogeography of the Quaternary" (in Russian), *Vopr. Kryolog. Izuch. Chetvert. Otlojeniy, Akad. Nauk SSSR*.

Dylik, J., 1963, "Traces of thermokarst in the Pleistocene sediments of Poland," *Bull. Soc. Sci. Lettres Łódź*, **14**, 2.

Grigorev, N. F., 1965, "Thermokarst phenomena in East Antarctica," in "Soviet Antarctic Expedition," Vol. 3, pp. 174–177, Amsterdam, Elsevier (English translation).

Halicki, B., 1951, "The role of ground-ice in shaping Pleistocene periglacial forms," *Acta Geol. Polon.*, **2**.

Hopkins, D. M., 1949, "Thaw lakes and thaw sinks in the Imuruk Lake area, Seward Peninsula, Alaska," *J. Geol.*, **57**, 119–131.

Hopkins, D. M., Karlstrom, T. N. V., *et al.*, 1955, "Permafrost and ground water in Alaska," *U.S. Geol. Surv. Profess. Paper* **264-F**.

Kachurin, S. P., 1959, "Thermokarst within the territory of the USSR" (in Russian) *Materialy po obshchemu merzlotovedeniyu VII mejduvedomstvennogo Soveshchaniya po merzlotovedeniyu*, **1956**.

Péwé, T. L., 1954, "Effect of permafrost on cultivated fields Fairbanks Area, Alaska," *Bull. U.S. Geol. Surv.*, **989-F**.

Popov, A. I., 1956, "Le thermokarst," *Biul. Peryglacjalny*, No. 4.

Cross-references: *Frost Action*; *Periglacial Landscapes*; *Permafrost*; *Pingos*; *Quaternary*; *Tundra Landscape*.

THUFUR—*See* TERRACETTES, LYNCHETS AND "CATTLE TRACKS"

TIDAL DELTA

This is a 90–180° fan of coarse-grained sediment extending out from either end of a *tidal inlet* (q.v.) and cut by its channel fans. It may reach up to 7 miles out from either entrance. The inner of a pair of tidal deltas is usually the larger, but the reverse is sometimes true (Fig. 1). Either delta may be laterally asymmetrical. A tidal delta connects the severed ends of a barrier below water and around the terminal channel shoals. The surface of the delta is composed of shifting bars and shoals and of low, usually marshy, islands bordered by low tidal levees or beach ridges. Progradational cuspate forelands on barrier ends are common emergent parts of the deltas. The forelands are composed of parallel to nested beach ridges, cheniers, dune chains or inwardly recurved spits.

Developmental factors of tidal deltas are largely those of the inlet, the deltas in turn influencing the pattern of the channels. Stabilizing vegetation of shoals, delta islands and the adjacent barrier ends are factors in delta development. Inlet migration modifies the shapes and areas of the associated deltas (Price, 1952, 1954, 1963).

Some of the following statements may have less

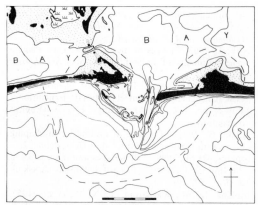

FIG. 1. Large asymmetrical outer tidal delta, with smaller, divided inner delta. Entrance to Mobile Bay, Alabama from Gulf of Mexico. Scale bar, 5 miles. Complex progradational tidal deltas, with major sand accumulation at Gulf side of barrier in coastal sector of medium wave energy. Channel dredging without jetties has altered delta little. Land areas, black; shoals stippled, shallower shoals heavily stippled. Depth contours: 6, 10, 20, 30, 40, 50, 60 and 70 feet. Elongate channel holes, 0–4 feet deeper than deepest associated contour (from Coast and Geodetic Survey Navigation Chart 1266, 1950).

than general applications, but most are usually applicable. Coarse-grained sediments are thought to be deposited chiefly by the longshore drift and the tidal jet, deposition by the latter being prominent where the jet bifurcates and otherwise loses velocity (see figures in *Tidal Inlet*). At bifurcations, some channel holes may be associated with nearby bar and island deposits. The drain and jet sets of channels of the inlet are separated by shifting bars and shoals, over which the water flows with decreased speed (Bates, 1953).

Some sand from the longshore drift may bypass the inlet during in-and-out transport or by shifts in the channel fans (Bruun and Gerritsen, 1959). Sands in lagoonal areas of and near the delta may be finer than sands on the outer beaches (Watts, 1956). Delta sediment finer than sand is restricted mainly to the inner parts of the inner delta. A migrating inlet will plow up and rework delta and barrier deposits through which the channels and their holes migrate (Johnson, 1919). The holes may penetrate underlying, pre-barrier materials, some being reworked into the delta.

W. ARMSTRONG PRICE

References

Bates, C. C., 1953, "Rational theory of delta formation," *Bull. Am. Assoc. Petrol. Geologists*, **37**, 2119–2162.

Bruun, Per, and Gerritsen, F., 1959, "Natural by-passing of sand at coastal inlets," *J. Waterways Harbors Div., Proc. Am. Soc. Civil Engrs.*, **WW4**, Paper 2301, 75–107.

El-Ashry, M. T. and Wanless, H. R., 1965, "Birth and early growth of a tidal delta," *J. Geol.*, **73**, 404–406.

Johnson, D. W., 1919, "Shore Processes and Shoreline Development," pp. 376, 377, New York, John Wiley & Sons, 584pp.

Price, W. A., 1952, "Reduction of maintenance by proper orientation of ship channels through tidal inlets," Proc. 2nd Conf. Coastal Engineering, Houston, Texas (1951), Council on Wave Research, Berkeley, California, pp. 243–255.

Price, W. A., 1954, "Dynamic environments—reconnaissance mapping, geologic and geomorphic, of continental shelf of Gulf of Mexico," *Trans. Gulf Coast Assoc. Geol. Soc.*, **4**, 75–107.

Price, W. A., 1963, "Patterns of flow and channeling in tidal inlets," *J. Sediment. Petrol.*, **33**, 279–290.

Watts, G. M., 1956, "Behavior of beach fill at Ocean City, New Jersey," *Beach Erosion Board, U.S. Army Corps of Engineers, Tech. Mem. No. 77*, 35 pp. (see pp. 6, 31).

Cross-references: *Barriers—Beaches and Islands; Bars; Beach Ridges; Cuspate Foreland or Spit; Delta; Estuary; Lagoon; Littoral Processes; Tidal Inlet.*

TIDAL INLET

A tidal inlet is a short, narrow waterway, with 90–180° terminal channel fans, connecting a bay, lagoon or similar body of water with a large parent water body, usually oceanic, and maintained wholly

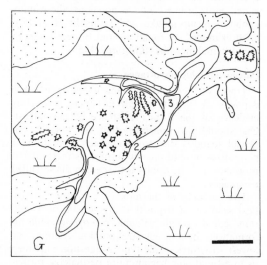

Fig. 1. Tidal inlet through clayey marsh peninsula, Southwest Pass, Louisiana. Gulf of Mexico to Vermilion Bay. Scale bar, 1 mile. North at top when reading. Mapping indicates inlet non-migratory, channels erosional, no tidal deltas, no dredging. Areas shallower than −6 feet MLW, stippled. Star-shaped and jagged bodies, oyster reefs and beds. Depth contours, 6, 20, 30, 40 feet MLW. Elongate channel holes *1*, 149; *2*, 93; *3*, 97 ft.; hole ½ mi. W of 3, 54 feet (from Coast and Geodetic Survey navigation chart 1277, 1937).

FIG. 2. Tidal inlet through reentrant sector of sandy barrier chain, with paired tidal deltas, Ocracoke Inlet, North Carolina. From Atlantic Ocean to Pamlico Sound. Scale bar, 3 miles. Mapping indicates inlet only slightly migratory, no jetties, no dredging. Portsmouth Island sector of barrier, at southwest, partially rebuilt after overwash of 1944 hurricane. Tidal deltas enclosed by dashed lines, slightly asymmetrical laterally. Islands, black. Shallower bottoms stippled. Depth contours, full line, 6, 20, 30, 40, 50 and 60 feet; broken line, 12 feet. Bottoms of elongate channel holes 1–11 feet below deepest associated closed contours. Deepest hole, 51 feet (from Coast and Geodetic Survey navigation shart 419, 1946).

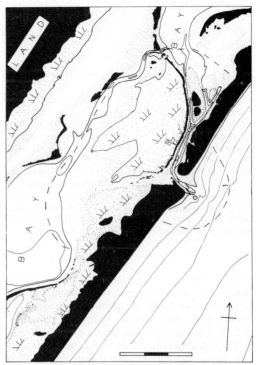

FIG. 3. Cyclicly migratory inlet through sandy barrier chain, with paired tidal deltas, Aransas Pass, Texas. From Gulf of Mexico to Aransas (north) and Corpus Christi (southwest) bays. See Figs. 4 and 5. Scale bar, 3 miles. Before artificial stabilization, strong longshore drift to southwest lengthened narrow up-drift barrier end and eroded broad down-drift end as inlet gorge migrated while remaining perpendicular to barrier. Down-drift end prograded, up-drift end did not. Southwest end protruded seaward, no overlap. Inner delta and channels, asymmetrical laterally. Deltas enclosed by dashed lines. Land, black. Denser stippling indicates the shallower shoals. Marshy areas flooded at higher tide levels. Depth contours: 6, 10, 20, 30, 40, 50 and 60 feet. Elongate channel holes, 4–9 feet deeper than deepest associated depth contours (from Coast and Geodetic Survey navigation chart 210, 1887).

or in part by tidal flow (Price, 1963). The relatively deep axial channel ("gorge") is straight or curved, has elongate holes 30–150 feet deep at constrictions and confluences, is flanked by shallow shoulders, and cuts through a shoal or emergent barrier of sand, gravel, clay, rock or organic reef. All channels are slot-shaped in cross section (1:20 to 1:200). Either or both fans may be erosional (Fig. 1), or may pass through a *tidal delta* (q.v.) with shifting channels, shoals and bars and more or less fixed islands (Figs. 2, 3, 7).

A tidal inlet may be wholly natural, or it may have been stabilized by seawalls, deepened by dredging, and prolonged seaward between jetties to deep water (Fig. 4). Only the natural condition is considered here. Factors controlling inlets include: tidal range and regime, inlet flow volume, land runoff, currents, channel turbulence, wind-driven sheets of water and other marine floods, great waves, long-period wave energy, local precipitation and evaporation, seasonal ice, bottom sediment drift, and the lithology of bottoms, shores and transported sediments, as well as the volume of these sediments.

An established inlet is in *dynamic equilibrium*, or partly so. Modifying factors and conditions from outside the equilibrium include changes in the size and depth of the interior body of water (Lucke, 1934), changes in nearby river deltas and

non-deltaic streams, volcanic eruptions, crustal instability and relation to other inlets. Figures 1–8 show some variations in inlet type and conditions.

Flow through the "gorge" produces a local maximum of energy and velocity. During both rising (flood) and falling (ebb) tides, water enters the gorge laterally at its then high-water end— the *tidal drain*—and emerges centrally from the low end—*the (plane) tidal jet*. The drain is erosive, the jet partly depositional. Deposition is prominent at the turn of the tide. Jet and drain channels are partly separated by bars and shoals (Fig. 7). The jet current flares typically at 20° (Albertson *et al.*, 1950), characteristically bifurcating several diameters off the mouth at a crescentic bar (Bates, 1953) or at an island.

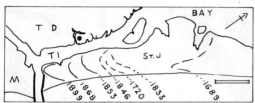

FIG. 4. Cyclic migration of Aransas Pass tidal inlet, Texas. See Figs. 3 and 5. Scale bar, 1 mile. Dates show approximate positions of up-drift end of barrier behind migration inlet referred to in 1951 mapping. Broken lines, less sure positions. Dotted lines indicate dates. Migration cycles, 1689–1720 and 1833–1884, with slight growth by 1899. Stabilization 1886–1910, sea walls and jetties, heavy line. M, Mustang Island; St. J, St. Joseph Is.; T. I, tidal inlet with branches, T D, Harbor Is. tidal delta. Solid circle, Aransas Pass light (1855–), now unused (from a study of 1961 by W. A. Price).

Tidal inlets may originate as barrier overwash channels deepened as flood waters return to the parent body of water. Some inlets are essentially stable, with only minor reversing variations (Fig. 2). A net excess of longshore bottom-sediment drift in one direction, chiefly along the outer shore face, makes the inlet migrate down drift. The up drift barrier end may elongate as a recurved spit, the current being thrown against the opposite end, which is eroded and retreats (Fig. 3), or migration may be caused by progressive overlap of one barrier end in front of the other (Fig. 6), the gorge then lying wholly outside the barrier in the

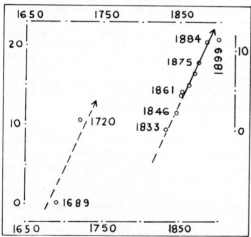

FIG. 5. Migration rates, Aransas Pass, Texas; two cycles. See Figs. 3 and 4. Horizontal axis, years; vertical axis, thousands of feet beyond initial points. Cycle of 1833–1884 accurate 1861–1884; stabilization 1886–1909. Migration rates, 1861–1884, average 235 ft. per yr.; inaccurate mapping of 1689–1720 suggests similar average rate. Interval 1720–1833 may have had other cycles of migration (from a study of 1961 by W. A. Price).

FIG. 6. Down-drift overlap of extending barrier ends. Sandy barrier chain (black) of southwestern coast of Long Island, New York. Inlets connect Atlantic Ocean with coastal lagoon. North arrow points to New York harbor mouth. Scale bar, 15 miles. Maximum overlap shown, 3.5 miles (from Coast and Geodetic Survey navigation chart 1108, 1960).

outer tidal delta. Migration may carry the gorge to a stable or to an inefficient position (Bruun and Gerritsen, 1959, 1961), in the latter case usually closing when a more efficient inlet forms updrift. If migration is resumed, this history is cyclicly repeated (Figs. 4 and 5).

A channel through a zone of bars across the broad mouth of a large, embayed estuary, as Chesapeake and Delaware bays, may have tidal inlet characteristics (Fig. 8). Straits of continental

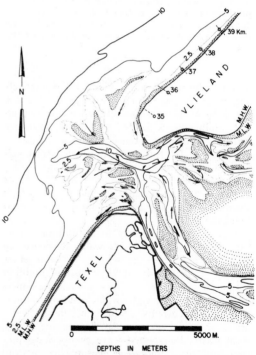

FIG. 7. Entering (drain) and discharging (jet) channels of terminal fans through sandy barrier, Eyerlandse Inlet, West Frisian Islands, Netherlands. Between North Sea and Ijsel Meer. Scale bar, 5000 meters. Depth contours, 2.5, 5 and 10 meters. Depth contours and vector arrows of sand movement show jet (central) and drain (lateral) channels separated terminally by bars and shoals (stippled) (after Bruun and Gerritsen, 1959, Fig. 17).

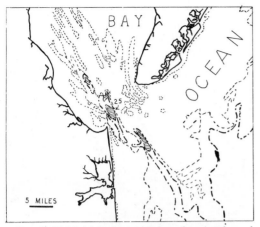

FIG. 8. Tidal inlet characteristics of main channel through bars and shoals of mouth of large embayed estuary between Delaware Bay and Atlantic Ocean, Delaware and New Jersey. Scale bar, 5 miles. North at top when reading. Shoals lie inside dotted lines. Depth contours: 10 fathoms, dashed; 15 fathoms, heavy dot-dash. Elongate channel holes, cross-lined, deepest, 25 feet (from Coast and Geodetic Survey navigation chart 1109, 1945).

shelves (Shepard, 1948), but not deep oceanic straits, are inlet-like and might be so designated.

W. ARMSTRONG PRICE

References

Albertson, N. L., Dai, Y. B., Jensen, R. A., and Rouse, H., 1950, "Diffusion of submerged jets," *Trans. Am. Soc. Civil Engrs.*, **115**, 639–697.
Bates, C. C., 1953, "Rational theory of delta formation," *Am. Assoc. Petrol. Geol. Bull.*, **37**, 2119–2162.

Bruun, Per, and Gerritsen, F., 1959, "Natural bypassing of sand at coastal inlets," *J. Waterways Harbors Div., Proc. Am. Soc. Civil Engrs.*, **WW4**, No. 2301, 75–107.
Bruun, Per, and Gerritsen, F., 1961, "Stability of coastal inlets," *Proc. 7th Conf. on Coastal Engineering*, Berkeley, Calif., **23**, 386–417.
Price, W. A., 1963, "Patterns of flow and channeling in tidal inlets," *J. Sediment. Petrol.*, **33**, 279–290.
Lucke, J. B., 1934, "A theory of evolution of lagoon deposits on shorelines of emergence," *J. Geol.*, **42**, 561–584.
Shepard, F. P., 1948, "Submarine Geology," New York, Harper and Bros., 348pp.

Cross-references: *Barriers—Beaches and Islands; Bars; Coral Reefs; Cuspate Foreland or Spit; Delta; Drowned Valley, Coast, Reef; Estuary; Lagoon; Sediment Transport; Tidal Delta.*

TIDAL POWER—*See* pr Vol. VI

TILL—*See* MORAINE; also pr Vol. VI, TILL AND TILLITE

TJAELE—*See* CRYOPEDOLOGY; FROST ACTION; PERMAFROST

TOMBOLO

This term comes originally from Italy and is applied to one or more sand spits connecting an island to the mainland (see for example Stamp, 1961, p. 454). It is a fairly common feature along "coastlines of submergence" which are presently

FIG. 1. Tombolo at Double Head, Emu Park, Queensland (Australia).

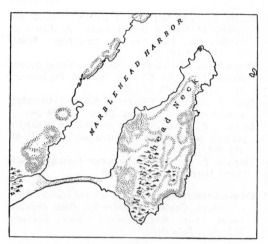

FIG. 2. Single tombolo connecting former island of Marblehead, Massachusetts, with the mainland (Johnson, 1919). (By permission of John Wiley & Sons, N.Y.)

FIG. 4. Monte Argentario, Italy, tied to the mainland by a double tombolo (Johnson, 1919). (By permission of John Wiley & Sons, N.Y.)

in a youthful or early mature stage of development. A single tombolo is necessarily associated with a *tied island*; examples include Portland Bill in southern England, tied by the Chesil Beach to the mainland, and Chester, Nova Scotia. In the case of Portland Bill, the island consists of an erosional remnant of the rocks making up the mainland, while Chester consists of a partly submerged drumlin; several of the latter type occur also in New England.

In a double tombolo, a lagoon is formed between the two tombolos and gradually becomes filled with sediment to produce a broad flat bar (von Engeln, 1942). An example of such a double tombolo is Gibraltar. Multiple tombolos also occur, e.g., on north shore of Long Island, N.Y. Perhaps the world's biggest tombolo was that which formerly connected Ceylon with India, across Palk Strait, the so-called Adams Bridge; apparently it was destroyed during a small change of sea level several

thousand years ago and all that is left today is a row of islets (Walther, 1891).

STUART A. HARRIS

References

Guilcher, A., 1965, "Drumlin and spit structures in the Kenmare River," *Irish Geogr.* **5**(2), 7–19.

Guilcher, A. and King, C. A. M., 1961, "Spits, tombolos

FIG. 3. A Y-shaped tombolo at Morro del Puerto Santo, Venezuela (Johnson, 1919). (By permission of John Wiley & Sons, N.Y.)

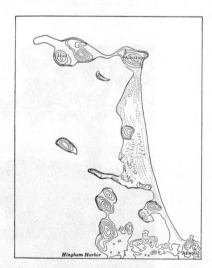

FIG. 5. Present form of the Nantasket Beach complex tombolo, connecting a series of drowned glacial drumlins with the mainland of Massachusetts (Johnson and Reed, 1910).

and tidal marshes in Connemara and West Kerry, Ireland," *Proc. Roy. Irish Acad.* **61B,** (17), 283–338.

Johnson, D. W., 1919, "Shore Processes and Shoreline Development," New York, John Wiley & Sons, 584pp.

Johnson, D. W. and Reed, W. G., 1910, "The form of Nantasket Beach," *J. Geol.*, **18,** 162–189.

Stamp, L. D. (editor), 1961, "A Glossary of Geographical Terms," London, Longmans, Green & Co. Ltd. 539pp.

von Engeln, O. D., 1942, "Geomorphology," New York, The Macmillan Co., 655pp.

Walther, J., 1891, "Die Adamsbrücke und die Korallenriffe der Palkstrasse," *Peterm. Geogr. Mitt.*, **102,** 1–40.

Cross-references: *Coastal Stability*; *Cuspate Foreland or Spit*; *Drumlin*; *Littoral Processes*.

TOPOGRAPHIC INVERSION—*See* INVERSION (OF TOPOGRAPHY, RELIEF)

TOPOGRAPHIC MAPPING AND SURVEY— *See* pr Vol. VI

TOR

Tor is an English term used to describe, "a bare rock mass surmounted and surrounded by blocks and boulders" (Linton, 1955, p. 470), particularly on Dartmoor, the granite massif in the southwest of England (Fig. 1). The term has acquired a much wider connotation embracing similar outcrops in a variety of rock types and climatic environments. Definitions are varied and the origin of tors has been disputed. In Africa, the term *Kopje* or *Koppie* (Afrikaans) is widely used for similar landforms, but it is given a separate connotation by certain authors (Thomas, 1965).

FIG. 2. Tor with characteristic morphology defined by rectilinear jointing in a hornblende-biotite granite of Jurassic age, Jos Plateau, Northern Nigeria.

Tors seldom exceed 50 feet in height and may be very much less; Waters (1955) claimed that a relation exists between the vertical extent of tors and the horizontal dimensions of their constituent blocks. They display marked structural control and are delineated by joint planes, which are commonly near-vertical and quasi-horizontal. The latter often correspond with sheeting (exfoliation) fractures in crystalline rocks, and many tors surmount *bornhardt* summits. According to Linton (1955) and Thomas (1965), tors are characterized by *spheroidal weathering* of constituent joint blocks, distinguishing them from outcrops resulting from frost shattering or subaerial collapse; some authors would not admit this distinction. Tors are underlain by unaltered bedrock, and the joint blocks remain *in situ*; detached and spheroidally weathered boulders within the regolith or on the surface are designated *core stones* (Linton, 1955) (Figs. 2, 3). Tors occupy a considerable variety of topographic sites: they crown summits and divides, rise from gentle slopes leading to summits, occur frequently at the break

FIG. 1. Characteristic tor in the Hercynian granites of southwest England (Rough Tor on Bodmin Moor). Note the sub-horizontal jointing probably representing sheeting (exfoliation) fractures.

FIG. 3. Corestones in a granite weathering profile (artificially exposed). Biotite granite of Precambrian age, Jos Plateau, Northern Nigeria.

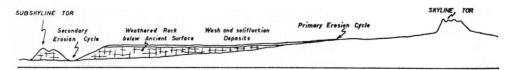

SUBSKYLINE TOR · SKYLINE TOR · Secondary Erosion Cycle · Weathered Rock below Ancient Surface · Wash and solifluction Deposits · Primary Erosion Cycle

FIG. 4. Section showing the relation between skyline tors (relicts of an older denudation cycle) and sub-skyline tors (youthful features of a new cycle) (King, 1962). (By permission of Oliver & Boyd, Edinburgh.)

of slope above valley sides and at spur ends, and are sometimes found in valley bottoms. King (1958) distinguished between *skyline tors* "occupying the highest points in the landscape" and *sub-skyline tors* "on valley sides and in depressions" (Fig. 4); both Handley (1952) and King (1958, 1962) have found skyline tors associated with old planation surfaces, and sub-skyline tors with zones of recent dissection. Tors are characteristic of coarse porphyritic granites, but jointing characteristics of rocks appear more important than detailed mineralogy, and they are known in most granitic rocks (though rarely in schists) and have been recorded in sedimentary rocks such as quartzites and feldspathic grits (Palmer and Radley, 1961).

Origin

No general agreement exists as to the origin of tors. Four principal theories are advanced: (1) that atmospheric weathering can cause spheroidal modi-

fication to the morphology of outcrops produced by differential erosion of *bedrock*; (2) that exposure of tors is due to a two-stage process: a period of prolonged subsurface groundwater weathering brings about the decay of closely jointed rock and the spheroidal modification of larger blocks, followed by a period of erosional stripping leading to the exposure of the tor; (3) that skyline tors in

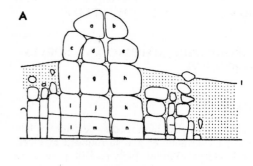

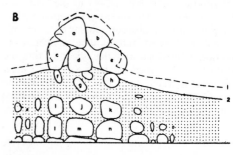

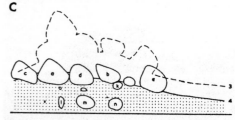

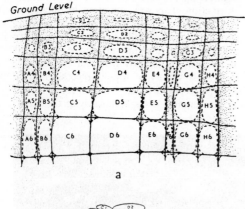

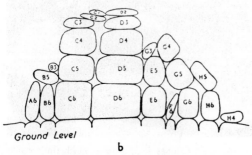

FIG. 5. Stages in the evolution of a tor by sub-surface rock rotting (Linton, 1955).

FIG. 6. Stages in the outward collapse of a domical tor group. (*Top*) The effects of continued groundwater weathering beneath the exposed tor group. (*Middle and lower*) The progressive collapse of the tor group as a result of the washing out of the weathered material from below, during several phases (1–4) of lowering of the surrounding surface (M. F. Thomas, 1965).

1158

FIG. 7. Castle kopje. Collapsed bornhardt or kopje. Precambrian granite, near Zaria, Northern Nigeria. The collapse of a former dome has resulted in the survival of a keystone or monolith surmounting a cone of talus. (Photo: M. F. Thomas).

hypothesis (4) has come from Palmer and Radley (1961) and Palmer and Neilson (1962).

A choice has to be made between genetic and descriptive definitions of tors. Thomas (1965), accepting theory (2), made spheroidal modifications of the cuboid joint blocks a criterion for tor morphology; he attempted to distinguish tors from *castle-koppies* (Fig. 7; see also *Bornhardts*). Tors resulted, in his view, from subaerial collapse of angular blocks and from frost-shattered forms in cold climates. Temperate and cold climate tors, however, even if formed by exhumation from a deep regolith, subsequently undergo subaerial modification including frost shattering and no final descriptive definition is without ambiguity.

MICHAEL F. THOMAS

References

Embleton, C. and King, C. A. M., 1968, "Glacial and Periglacial Geomorphology," London, E. Arnold Ltd., 608pp.

Falconer, J. D., 1912, "The origin of kopjes and inselbergs," *Brit. Assoc. Adv. Sci. Trans. Section C*, 476.

Handley, J. R. F., 1952, "The geomorphology of the Nzega area of Tanganyika with special reference to the formation of granite tors," *Congr. Géol. Intern. Compt. Rend. Algiers*, **21**, 201.

King, L. C., 1958, Correspondence—"The problem of tors," *Geograph. J.*, **124**, 289–291.

King, L. C., 1962, "The Morphology of the Earth." Edinburgh, Oliver and Boyd, 699pp. (2nd ed., 1967.)

Linton, D. L., 1955, "The problem of tors," *Geograph. J.*, **121**, 470.

Palmer, J. and Neilson, R. A., 1962, "The origin of granite tors on Dartmoor, Devonshire," *Proc. Yorkshire Geol. Soc.*, **33**, 315–340.

Palmer, J. and Radley, J., 1961, "Gritstone tors of the English Pennines," *Zeit. Geomorph.*, NF **5**, 37–52.

Thomas, M. F., 1965, "Some aspects of the geomorphology of domes and tors in Nigeria," *Zeit. Geomorph.*, NF **9**, 63–81.

Waters, R. S., 1955, see discussion of Linton, D. L. *op. cit.*

Cross-references: *Bornhardt; Exfoliation; Inselberg; Granite Landforms; Regolith and Saprolite; Spheroidal Weathering.*

particular result from the reduction in area of larger inselbergs by scarp retreat and the formation of pediments; (4) that tors are isolated, especially along scarp edges, as a result of freeze-thaw weathering, followed by solifluction over permafrost in a periglacial climate.

It is clear that while authors of all these theories call the resultant landforms tors, forms of different origins have been classified under this term. Tors in the type location have become generally associated with theory (2) following an analysis by Linton (1955) who invoked antecedent (possibly Tertiary) deep weathering followed by stripping due to accelerated mass movement during periglacial phases of the Pleistocene (Figs. 5, 6). He defined tors genetically, thus: "a tor is a residual mass of bedrock produced below the surface level by a phase of profound rock rotting effected by groundwater and guided by joint systems, followed by a phase of mechanical stripping of the incoherent products of chemical action" (Linton, 1955, p. 476). In general form, this hypothesis has been current for over 50 years; Falconer (1912) used it to explain Nigerian examples, and it was elaborated more recently in East Africa (Tanzania) by Handley (1952). While King (1962) broadly accepts exhumation for subskyline tors, he is the principal advocate of theory (3) and states that "skyline tors are . . . the final unconsumed remnants (of once larger rock masses) upon a surface of extremely advanced pediplanation and must carefully be distinguished from the sub-skyline tors which are developing now within the broad valleys as *youthful* features in a newer cycle of erosion" (p. 388). He thus equates skyline tors with *koppies*. However Handley (1952) stated: "rock platforms occupy less than 1 % of the area between tor and valley bottom," and he did not regard summit tors as pedimented residuals. Interpretation of British tors according to the last

TOREVA BLOCKS

Toreva blocks are a special type of landslide product, first described by Parry Reiche (1937), from the vicinity of Toreva in the Black Mesa region of the Hopi Indian Reservation of northeastern Arizona.

What makes the toreva blocks of particular interest is their position as "end members" of the landslide type, for large individual blocks of "unjostled material" have "undergone a backward rotation toward the parent cliff about a horizontal axis which roughly parallels it." In the type area sandstones of the basal Mesaverde Formation (Upper Cretaceous) cap the prominent buttes and mesas with gentle to horizontal dips. They rest on the soft, silty Mancos Shale, which is rich in the expanding lattice clay mineral, montmorillonite, notoriously liable to cause landslips. Numerous blocks up to 600 meters in length have slipped distances as great as 300 meters from their sources, along extremely low angles and always marked by backward rotation reaching angles of 40–80°. This rotational motion has been extensively studied by engineers and geologists, and is a well-recognized feature of *landslides* (q.v.).

Most of the blocks are not now in active development and evidently date from a stage of different climatic conditions, possibly more humid periods in the late Pleistocene. They have moved in places across the surfaces of two ancient pediments and in other places override some wind-blown sand accumulations. A few small slides have occurred during historical times. On the other hand, many of the toreva blocks are partially buried by the late Pleistocene Jeddito Formation (of Hack), an alluvial valley fill that presumably corresponds to the cool-dry (winter rain) conditions of the last cold epoch, when grasses would decrease the runoff and favor general alluviation. The humid conditions that favored slippage could have been either during a strong southward displacement of the westerly storm tracks in an early stage of the glacial event, or during heavy summer rainfall of an interglacial; the deep, soaking effect of the former seems to be most likely.

RHODES W. FAIRBRIDGE

References

Reiche, P., 1937, "The toreva-block, a distinctive landslide type," *J. Geol.,* **45,** 538–548.

Cross-references: *Landslides; Quaternary.* Vol. II: *Climatic Variation—Historical Records.*

TRACTION—*See* SEDIMENT TRANSPORT; WIND ACTION; *also* pr Vol. VI, BEDFORMS IN ALLUVIAL CHANNELS

TRANSPORT—*See* EOLIAN TRANSPORT: SEDIMENT TRANSPORT

TRANSVERSE VALLEYS, STREAMS—*See* DRAINAGE PATTERNS

TREPPEN CONCEPT (PENCK)

This was the concept used by Penck to explain the *piedmont benchlands* or *piedmonttreppen* that surround the Black Forest in Germany (Thornbury, 1954, pp. 203–205). These geomorphic features are

numerous broad terraces or steps which he regarded as being the result of continuous uplift of an enlarging dome mountain complex undergoing accelerated uplift. The rocks are homogeneous and he regarded the highest surface as being a *primärrumpf* (q.v.). The landscape undergoing uplift of this sort was supposed to exhibit more youthful land forms as the rate of uplift increased, i.e., the reverse sequence to that expected in the Geographical Cycle of Davis.

The biggest problem with the concept is to find a mechanism for producing the nick points along the thalwegs of the radiating streams. Once the nick points were formed, parallel retreat could produce the steps. Penck assumed that the streams flowed radially out from the center of the dome and that the uplift would be greatest along the outer margins. In this way, the greater volume and erosive power of streams would coincide with the zone of steepest gradient. He therefore assumed that the upper segment would produce a gentle concave thalweg, while the lower segment would erode a steep concave section. In between there would be a convex section that he assumed would gradually be eliminated by upstream movement of the lower nick point. Subsequently further movements would produce more nick points, though the mechanism for this was not explained.

This concept has been severely attacked by many authors. It is an alternative explanation to the much simpler one based on the Geographical Cycle of Davis. On this second interpretation the benches would merely be regarded as terraces marking incomplete erosion cycles interrupted by sudden periods of uplift. On this interpretation the nick points are explained as being the result of the change in base level. Penck's critics point out that it is somewhat doubtful whether the convex part of the profile will be destroyed, Baulig (1939) considering that it should expand with time. Wager (1937), in studying the thalweg of the river Arun, where it crosses the zone of maximum uplift in the Himalayas, found no nick points but he did find a large convex zone. Thus subsequent work does not support the Treppen Concept, and the evidence for the alternative, simpler, and more orthodox interpretation appears to be reasonably satisfactory.

STUART A. HARRIS

References

Baulig, H., 1939, "Sur les 'Gradin de Piedmont'," *J. Geomorphol.,* **2,** 281–304.
Penck, W., 1927, "Die Morphologische Analyse," Stuttgart, Engelhorns, 283pp.
Thornbury, W. D., 1954, "Principles of Geomorphology," New York, J. Wiley & Sons, 618pp.
Wager, L. R., 1937, "The Arun river drainage pattern and the rise of the Himalaya," *Geograph. J.,* **89,** 239–249.

TROPICAL KARST—*See* KARST

TROPICAL WEATHERING AND RELIEF

Technically, the tropics extend $23\frac{1}{2}°$ of latitude either side of the equator to the parallels of Cancer on the north and Capricorn on the south. Actually, this is a geographer's convention based on earth-sun relations. The phenomena that are geologically more or less characteristic of the tropical zone are found at least 30° to either side of the equator. These are the geologic and geomorphic low latitudes. And it is therein that we find some of the world's highest mountains, most extensive and driest deserts, densest jungles, highest plateaus and flattest plains in a wealth of topographic and climatic diversity.

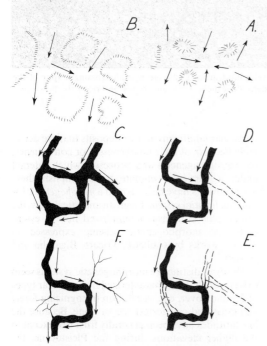

FIG. 1. Development of channeled drainage from arid (A) through humid (B–F) conditions as typified by the Rio Caroni, Venezuela. Initial expression (A) is of ephemeral arid sheetfloods on an alluvial terrain of low relief and undrained depressions. Runoff modifications of (A) are expressed (B) by perennial sheetflood transmission of runoff essentially unconfined with ill-defined flow directions, (C) anastomosing channels developed by deepening of sheetflood flow routes, (D) network channel piracy due to selective deepening of channels, (E) further piracy, local drainage reversals and development of a trunk channel, and (F) systematic, directed incision by a river.

In spite of the aforementioned variation, for many if not most people, the term "tropics" evokes visions of a steaming rain forest. And for more than a century the classic geomorphic approach to tropical landscape-making processes and their results has involved the seemingly inevitable marriage of the words "hot," "wet" and "permanent." The highly specialized and adapted, low-latitude, broad-leafed forest floras and faunas have been taken to exemplify all three words. In turn, this seemed to bear out the implication of the general permanence of climates (apart from "glacial accidents") that was the keystone of W. M. Davis (1899) "normal erosion cycle."

Davis' "normal" cycle was theoretically achieved in what has come to be known as a humid or "rain and rivers" environment, presumably without serious interruption of any kind, certainly not by climate change. In fact, Davis' predecessors, notably Lyell, Geikie, Ramsay, Powell and Gilbert (see references in Cailleux and Tricart, 1955; Jaudel and Tricart, 1958), had laid much of the groundwork for his attitude toward climate as an unchanging factor in landscape genesis.

Apart from glacial changes, the majority of later researchers followed the passive climatic scheme for weathering and erosion in both higher and lower latitudes, as shown by studies by Penck, Passarge and de Martonne (Cailleux and Tricart, 1955). Penck eventually recognized that climate belts near glaciers (periglacial) shifted equatorward with the ice. This, and the idea of slight shifts in low-latitude climate belts, constitituted an important step. Nevertheless many workers (e.g., Büdel, 1951) believed that tropical humidity was accentuated during glacial times. For most specialists, this hypothesis included a moistening (or "pluvial" condition) in the low-latitude deserts. Though climates were conceded to have changed somewhat, the jungles stayed the same.

Followed to its logical conclusion in the tropics, the concept of low-latitude climatic stability relates sugarloaf-shaped hills and mountains (*inselbergs*, q.v.), broad savanna plains and indeed all commonly observed tropical landforms and deposits to a single environment in a "monogenetic" climate theory of landform origin. For the first half of the twentieth century, geomorphologists were seriously misled by geographic association. What a particular climate was thought to be able to accomplish was established by what was found within that climatic area. Also there has been a great tendency to equate the chronologic duration of an environment with its geographic permanence. Only recently have researchers begun to discuss landscapes without giving essentially complete genetic dominance to the now-prevailing climate, e.g., Tricart, Cailleux, Büdel, Cotton, Quinn (see references in Garner, 1966).

In 1955, Cailleux and Tricart suggested that extensive semiaridity had affected parts of humid,

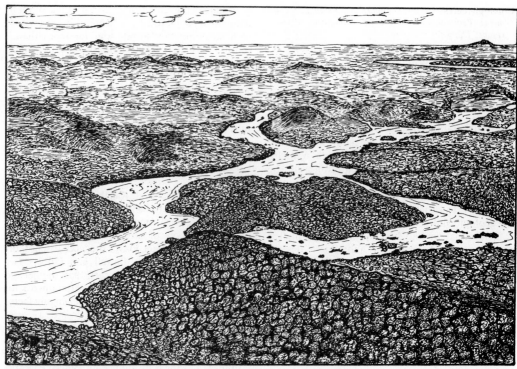

FIG. 2. Multiple channel network in a reach of the developing Caroni Drainage System crossing a spur of the Imataca Mountains and forming high hill islands in southern Venezuela. Falls and rapids interrupt the flow every few hundred feet and the current is very swift.

tropical lands, and the writer (1959) suggested that aridity had alternated with humidity in parts of the humid tropics during the Pleistocene; in many areas glacial epochs were the driest. Support for these views has since been voiced by Fairbridge (1964), Büdel (1963), Bigarella and co-workers (1965), and Garner (1966, 1967a and b). Thus emerged the concept of large-scale, secular changes of climate that materially affected landscapes in low latitudes. These ideas comprise a "polygenetic" theory of landform genesis. If the tropics with their vast climatic and topographic diversity were a realm of geographically and chronologically static environments, it would be appropriate here to discuss weathering and relief-making processes and their products as they occur in each isolated environment. Such does not appear to be the case. In most instances, when we look at a desert or a jungle, a large measure of what we see looks the way it does or does what it does because the desert used to be wet and vegetated and the forested area used to be barren. With this in mind, tropical weathering and relief is further discussed with the polygenetic climate theory of landscape in mind.

Geomorphic Effects of Climatic Origin

From a geomorphic standpoint, climates are only significant to the extent that they separately evoke particular landforms and/or deposits that are detectable because of their uniqueness. For convenience, the various agencies and processes which interact unde. a particular climate to accomplish these unique results have been termed a *morphogenetic* (or *morphoclimatic*) *system*. From an analytical view, the geomorphic consensus summarized here is essentially the morphogenetic scheme expressed in various works by Cailleux, Tricart, Bigarella and Garner.

The most distinctive morphogenetic systems seem to be those that are characterized by particular types of ground cover, e.g., vegetation (recognizing forest and grassland categories), ice, or none. Because the low latitudes have been generally frost free except in the higher elevations during the Pleistocene, the categories of continuous ground cover (vegetation) versus discontinuous ground cover (effectively barren) are of main concern.

It is of particular significance to this discussion that (in the tropics) vegetated and nonvegetated conditions correspond, respectively, to rock decomposition processes that are effectively chemical (under humidity) or effectively mechanical (under aridity). In high latitudes and high elevations where moist conditions are also accompanied by frost action, soil and regolith composition, as well as derivative stream sediment load (principally quartz

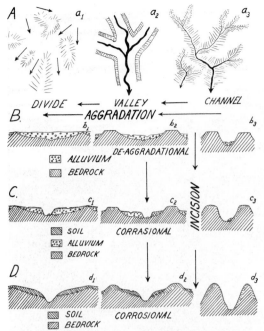

FIG. 3. Diagram of erosional relief development and destruction under alternating arid-humid conditions. Adjacent elements of A and B (reading from right to left) are respectively channel, valley and divide aggradation stages (a_3b_3–a_1b_1). Incisional stages (read top to bottom) portray humid modifications starting with a mild arid channel aggradation (a_3–d_3), with a moderate arid valley aggradation (a_2–d_2), and with a severe arid divide aggradation (a_1–d_1). Dominantly arid relief relations (a_1b_1) contrast with dominantly humid relief relations (a_3d_3). Note that incisional erosion modes under humidity change from alluvial removal (de-aggradation), to bedrock abrasion by particles (corrasion), to solutional channeling (corrosion) as mantle constituents are chemically altered from coarse solids to fine solids and solutes.

sand, with or without gravel), reflects the general absence of intense silica leaching, prevalent elsewhere in the humid tropics and displays more effective mechanical rock fragmentation. On the contrary, only deserts having mainly mechanical rock breakdown on a large scale can produce widespread, coarse, commonly metastable gravels in low-elevation tropical areas (see *Hamada; Gibbers*). High-intensity chemical decomposition of bedrock in humid tropical settings, if prolonged, can even eliminate quartz sand fractions entirely from weathered saprolite and derivative stream loads.

Low relief land surfaces that are due to aridity, glaciation, volcanism, marine emergence or other non-humid geomorphic processes, on becoming humid also require drainage and in response to the runoff of surplus water become channeled, randomly at first in sheetfloods and anastomosing channel systems (*deranged drainages*: Fig. 1) and then

systematically in rivers. Early channel network obstructions are represented by bedrock hills and islands that could not have been deposited by water or cut by headward erosion and therefore call for an accentuated upstream water supply (Fig. 2). In contrast, arid regions generally develop no external drainage but may evolve some internal drainage (often of centripetal pattern) which is generally limited in scope to flow from uplands to lowlands. A lack of vegetal cover permits upland rilling and channeling during sediment load acquisition by sporadic runoff. Both evaporation and infiltration often combine to cause almost immediate deposition downslope so that existing depressions are alluviated. Eventually valleys may become so deeply buried with floors rising to progressively higher elevations that in extreme cases (prolonged accumulation) the divides between old drainage basins become covered (Fig. 3, A–B).

Within the limits established by overall elevation, the long-term effect of humid fluvial processes is an accentuation of relief (Fig. 3, a_3–d_3), whereas under aridity, valleys are leveled by aggradation and slopes affected by scarp retreat. (On the microrelief scale, aridity may lead to close-textured badlands and thus a short-term accentuation.) Thus, in the broad view, those steep slopes and scarps which are not specifically related to rock type or structure are generally caused by vertical stream incision under humid conditions. In the same context, flats, pediments and plains in the tropics, whether subaerially erosional or depositional, may be generally regarded as having been formed under conditions of arid gradation. Where one or the other environment has been maintained or has dominated to the point of attainment of dynamic equilibrium, aridity produces a vegetationless aggradational plain (Fig. 3, b_1) such as observed in the *bajadas* (q.v.) of the Southwest. On the other hand, humidity produces a densely incised forested land consisting almost entirely of slopes with knife-edged interfluves, characteristic of *selva* (q.v.; Fig. 3, d_3), often termed a *feral topography*. In the more common situations where neither climate type has dominated for long periods, each environment in turn lends its own particular attributes to the other's relicts to produce a stairstep ("stepped") topography (Fig. 3, a_2–d_2).

In the characteristic frost-free conditions of the humid tropics, wherever there is abundant moisture and plant cover, chemical weathering effects cause the development of deeply leached, clay-rich saprolites on bedrock (particularly uplands—Fig. 4) or on relict alluvium (Fig. 5). These soils are generally profiled (zoned), are often high in iron (laterite) or aluminum (bauxite), and are usually more or less deficient in silica and humic matter. Many of these soils are highly acidic, and where drainage is good the weathering depths may attain several hundred feet (Fig. 4). In late stages of humidity where slopes are almost stable, such weathered profiles can supply

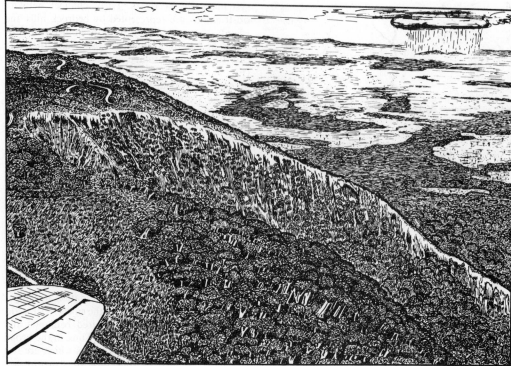

Fig. 4. East slope and crest of the "iron mountain" Cerro Bolivar in southern Venezuela. This bornhardt rises about 1000 feet above the alluviated savannas some 50 miles south of the Orinoco River, and its deeply decomposed, iron-rich crest indicates continued chemical decomposition under plant cover at present and in the past when the surrounding lowlands were arid. Many lower, rounded inselbergs in this same shield region have little plant cover and no appreciable weathered interval.

rivers with very little abrasive material, and stream incision then necessarily occurs largely by solution and is relatively slow (Fig. 3, d_1-d_3). The fine-grained material in the humid weathered zones is readily attacked by water and wind if plant cover is lost through climate change. This soil cover may be retained on higher, more moist uplands and on mountain flanks during low-level aridity (cf. Figs. 4 and 5). Wind erosion and sheetwash during subsequent aridity may strip fine-grained weathered material from the deforested hills to expose rounded bedrock highs (*inselbergs; tors; bornhardts*, q.v.) locally topped or fringed by undecomposed, rounded blocks of rock (core stones) formerly bounded by joints in the bedrock and later enclosed by spheroidal, concentric zones of decomposition within the weathered material (saprolite).

In those latitudes where there is little moisture and plant cover is consequently discontinuous or absent, fine-grained material is subject to eolian deflation and is usually blown away as it is exposed to the air. Where the bedrock contains quartz and there was incomplete silica leaching in the preceding humid times, the relict, sand-rich soils and sandy alluvium become a major source for later desert wash and dune sands. Desert sands are not products

of abrasion, but of previous chemical loosening and fluvial sorting. In these same deserts, bedrock tends to disintegrate mechanically (to hamada, gibbers, etc.), in part from temperature-induced stresses, but to a larger degree from dew-moistened, intergranular chemical activity (e.g., incipient clay formation around feldspar crystals) that ceases when grains are exposed to dry air. This produces rock and mineral fragments, generally too large to blow away, that show little chemical alteration.

Arid weathering products comprise a sedimentologically immature and dominantly coarse regolith that can only optimistically be called a soil (Fig. 5). Much of this material has undergone some sporadic fluvial and slope wash transport across barren terrain with little reduction of particle size. Even so, coarseness of arid alluvium generally diminishes with distance from source (local escarpments and uplands). With progressive burial of low areas and reduction of divides, most such deposits also show upward particle size reduction.

Coarse arid weathering detritus is the prime source for fluvial abrasive material during subsequent humid eposodes in the tropics (Fig. 3, c_1-c_2). In fact, effective fluvial incision during humid phases in the broad tropical lowlands, to be really efficient,

FIG. 5. Rainforest on soil on alluvium reflects opposing weathering equilibria. These gravels near Socopo Wells. Venezuela demonstrate former mechanical fragmentation of rock under aridity on the northeast lowlands of South America. The dense forest cover typifies plant response to present humidity and (inset) is environmentally related to the surficial fine-grained soil which exemplifies contemporary chemical rock decomposition. Similar soils developed to much greater depths on bedrock occur on nearby uplands (cf. Fig. 4).

FIG. 6. Mountain valley on the heavily vegetated, dominantly humid north slope of the Sierra del Norte on the coast of Venezuela. Weathered valley sides incline directly to channel banks, and bare rock channel floor slopes about 15° away from viewer. Heavy rains in this and similar regions occasionally cause weathered, vegetated tracts to tear loose in gravity slides which introduce weathered rock, soil and plant debris into drainage lines.

requires the corrasional erosive debris provided by periodic aridity. In the dominantly humid uplands and mountains, continued incision into bedrock without appreciable lateral corrasion causes valley walls to steepen to the channel banks (Fig. 6). In the high mountains of the low latitudes there can be high elevation aridity or occasionally frost action which can provide debris that tends to perpetuate corrasional valley deepening downslope in the main streams of humid areas. Deep gorges of most low-latitude mountains and high plateaus are thus formed; either they are cut rapidly by corrasion with

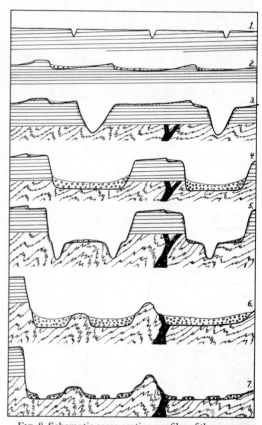

FIG. 7A. Angel Falls (the world's highest) drop some 3300 feet from a high mesa in southern Venezuela as part of a tributary to the Rio Caroni (cf. Fig. 13). In this long-humid headwaters area, the stream flows through V-shaped valleys of dendritic pattern incised into old arid planation surfaces. The top of this and many similar elevations in eastern South America remained humid during most lower-level Pleistocene arid periods.

FIG. 8. Schematic cross-section profiles of the sequence of geomorphic development in the northeastern South American lowlands. The events depicted are: (1) Humid incision of relatively undeformed Roraima Series (Pre-cambrian) to a depth of about 200 feet. (2) Arid planation-aggradation stage develops cuestas and scarps of which remnants are preserved on the high plateaus. (3) Humid incision into elevated plateau surface. (4) Aridity (valley stage of aggradation) with scarp retreat. (5) Humid incision into lower surfaces ranging from about 500 feet in the north to more than 1000 feet in the south. (6) Drainage system destruction (derangement) under aridity (valley and local divide aggradation stage); cumulative local aggradation thickness from this phase and older mantle relics totals 0–400 feet: 2000–3000 feet in Andes Mountain valleys to the northwest. (7) Recent perennial drainage system development extending to present. The prevailing fluvial incision phase appears to have been briefly interrupted by arid releveling of drainage networks. The erosional events depicted here compare in kind and general magnitude with those outlined in the southeastern Peruvian Andes (Garner, 1959, Fig. 12).

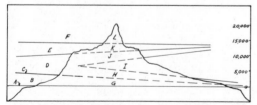

FIG. 7B. Continental atmospheric moisture zonation and most common climate belts. (A) sea level—evaporation surface, (B) adiabatic gap—undersaturated air, (C) minimum precipitation elevation, (D) near-saturated air—triggered precipitation, (E) moisture-depleted air, (F) frost zone, (G) coastal deserts, (H) semiarid steppes, (I) humid uplands, (J) semiarid transition, (K) desert plateaus. (L) frigid peaks (elevations are in feet). In this relation, the sea surface at left is assumed to be cold, that to the right warm.

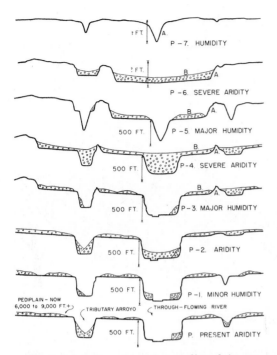

FIG. 9. Schematic cross-section profiles of the geomorphic sequence and development in the Cordillera Occidental, Peru. In chronological sequence from oldest to youngest the events are as follows: (P − 7) Humid dissection of a surface of volcanic deposition; incision develops scarp A. (P − 6) Arid pedimentation and scarp retreat, aggradation of surfaces, and the formation of surface B. (P − 5) Relatively strong humid incision of stream channels to a maximum depth of 400 feet at an elevation of 7500 feet. (P − 4) Severe arid aggradation of all channels and interfluves, coincident destruction and retreat of scarps. (P − 3) Thorough humid erosion of channel deposits leaving only remnants. (P − 2) Minor arid aggradation of channels to a depth not exceeding 80 feet, essentially complete destruction of scarp A, development of a pediplain. (P − 1) Incision of channel alluvium, local development of alluvial terraces. (P) Present arid aggradation of perched dry tributary arroyos; through-flowing streams and eroding at high elevations, at grade at intermediate levels, and aggrading at low elevations, through volume loss downslope.

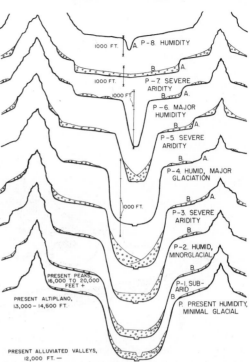

FIG. 10. Schematic cross-section profiles of the geomorphic sequence and development in the Cordillera Oriental, Peru. In chronological sequence from oldest to youngest the events are: (P − 8) Humid dissection of an elevated surface of erosion having local topographic highs of considerable magnitude; development of scarp A. (P − 7) High-elevation arid pedimentation with aggradation of surfaces and retreat of scarp A surface B. (P − 6) Major humid period; valley incision to depths exceeding 2000 feet, partial removal of alluvial residuals. (P − 5) Severe arid period, scarp retreat, valley widening, and aggradation. (P − 4) Major humid glaciation, erosion of arid residuals and development of U-shaped valley profiles to relatively low elevations. (P − 3) Severe and widespread period of aridity and subaridity, high-level scarp retreat, mergence of scarp A with slopes of upland peaks and formation of talus cones and confluent alluvial fans in valleys. (P − 2) Minor humidity, high-level glacial removal of valley fills and minor lower-level erosion of arid residuals. (P − 1) Minor subaridity, local formation of small talus cones. (P) Present-day humid incision of valley residuals, glaciers confined to high peaks.

little interruption throughout the year where snow meltwater maintains flow, or they evolve more slowly under continuous humidity and solution during downslope dry periods [Fig. 7(A)].

Tropical mountain glaciers are local, of sporadic development and limited water storage capacity. Thus the alternations of major arid and humid climatic episodes of a broad region are reflected more in the principal flat lands and scarps, respectively. Each minor period of cut or fill may not produce its own distinctive break in slope. But most episodes will at least give rise to a soil, alluvial deposit or paleopavement. Truly regional breaks in slope such as at piedmont heads and at the margins of high-elevation plateaus are probably localized by the long-term mean climatic boundaries [Fig. 7(B)]. It is therefore instructive to compare examples of climate-relief evolution and expression in tropical lowlands (Fig. 8) with those of high mountains in the same latitudes (Figs. 9 and 10).

Climate Zone Effects in Time and Space

During the Pleistocene epoch, low-latitude landscapes developed largely in response to conditions

FIG. 11. Schematic block diagram of the western slopes of the Cordillera Occidental southeast of Guayaquil, Ecuador. Illustrated as of particular importance are the Gulf of Guayaquil, left foreground; mouth of the Guayas River, left background: thick alluvial valley fills occupying steep, modified V-shaped mountain valleys on the western slopes of the Cordillera Occidental; rather thick, generally flat-topped coarse alluvial remnants on the coastal lowland which resemble the valley-fill alluvium; meandering channels of coastal plain streams which drain mountain front; the relations show certain striking contrasts and similarities to the Cordillera Occidental of Peru (cf. Fig. 12). Vertical exaggeration 8 × .

FIG. 12. Schematic block diagram of the Cordillera Occidental and Coastal Desert, Peru. Illustrated in relative positions within the regional setting are the Pacific Ocean, lower coastal desert of residual gravels and "blind," double-ended arroyos which carry water only rarely and then to local base levels, large valleys of through-flowing rivers which have sources in summit region, contemporary talus accumulations at scarp bases, beveled bedrock pediment surfaces which have alluvial veneers, remnant pediment surfaces or buttes, and summit mountains—including volcanoes—moderate seasonal rainfall, weak or extinct glacial development, and waste-clad lower slopes. Vertical exaggeration 10 × .

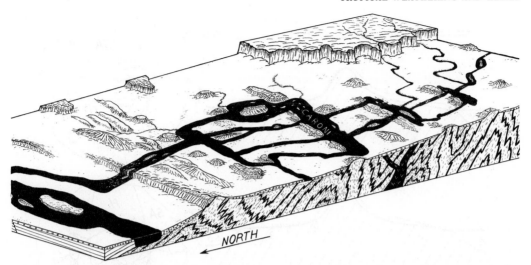

Fɪɢ. 13. Schematic block diagram view to southeast showing the anastomosing channel complex of the Caroni drainage area, Venezuela, in the course of development into a river with a trunk stream and tributaries. The flow on these eastern South American lowlands proceeds through several small, formerly arid drainage basins and across divides obscured by alluviation. The larger channel to the left is that of the Orinoco.

imposed by alternating arid and humid climates. The resultant expressions in present-day climate zones are therefore typical of neither vegetated nor barren morphogenetic systems as a rule. Most zones express attributes of both. In various orographic and meteorologic settings, either arid or humid effects usually seem to have dominated the landscape. In western Ecuador (Fig. 11) humidity has dominated, whereas in western Peru (Fig. 12) aridity has clearly had the upper hand. But in neither place are the present and the immediately preceding climates the same.

In most tropical regions, the erosive processes of the prevailing climate are today modifying the geo-

Fɪɢ. 14. Intermediate-level alluvial fill along the Urubamba River, Cordillera Oriental, southeastern Peru. Urubamba River Valley near 9000-feet elevation. Channel is incised to depths of 50–175 feet into coarse alluvial valley fill from confluent alluvial fans and cones (cf. with Fig. 17).

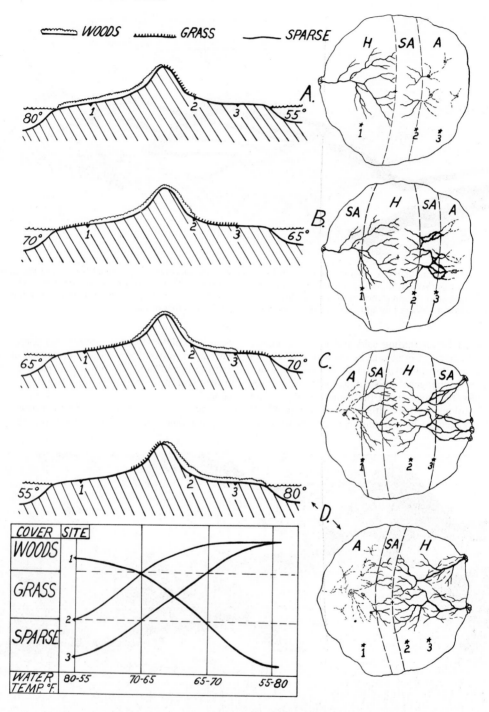

FIG. 15. Change of climate over thousands of years alters the patterns of drainage and vegetation of a hypothetical land mass that is just north or south of the equator. The region is shown in plan views (right) and in corresponding sections (left). The alternations of climate reflect changes in the surface temperatures of the oceans adjoining the continent in response to glaciation. At top, the land near the warm ocean receives ample rain and forests begin at the water's edge; the opposite ocean is cold, so that air masses have to rise before rain can fall, and there is a coastal desert. As the temperature of one ocean falls and that of the other rises, the situation is slowly reversed. In a graph at the bottom, three random localities (1–3) record differing climatic and geomorphic histories during the same time span.

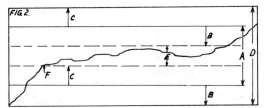

FIG. 16. High-level arid atmospheric zonation and gradation datum acting in lieu of base level: (A) Mean position of moisture depleted air zone [cf. Fig 7(B)]. (B) Maximum zonal depression. (C) Maximum zonal elevation. (D) Vertical scope of long-term zonal oscillation. (E) Residual, permanently or dominantly arid zone of protracted planation and aggradation. (F) Regional slope change from arid plateaus to humid mountain slopes—keyed to long-term climate zone boundary position as periodically modified by tectonism.

morphic relics created under an earlier environment. Thus, in a humid zone in southern Venezuela today, one may observe fine-grained soils developing in place by chemical action under heavy vegetation on coarse gravel of arid origin (Fig. 5). In the same general region and farther south in the Amazonas province of Brazil, the extremely humid areas of today lack well-integrated, systematic, external drainage channel systems and meandering rivers are only just developing (Fig. 13). In the eastern Peruvian Andes, rivers today are eroding coarse gravel from their channels although essentially none is presently being formed there by weathering (Fig. 14). Throughout many tropical regions, high, rounded, dome-like inselbergs and mountains rise above vast plains. The origins of these bornhardts or tors have been variously explained. Many of them surrounded by dense jungle are barely vegetated and have no soil because of vegetal loss and stripping under prior aridity which has not yet been overcome in moister times. In these and similar relations, a polygenetic climatic origin of tropical landscapes is particularly striking.

A climate zone functions as a space-time continuum, and a climate's chronological duration should not be confused with its geographical permanence, i.e., fixedness in space (Fig. 15). Thus, the very specialized biota of the tropical rain forest merely signifies the long-term persistence of warm, wet conditions (in *some place*); to survive, it must have persisted in areas geographically proximate to those of the present but not necessarily coextensive. The biological (ecologic) attributes of a climate can shift with the climate zone if it is displaced geographically, and for the successive generations of organisms the climate has not changed—both have gone through similar relative migrations. Often, in areas of high relief, the climates continue to exist only when atmospheric zones that give rise to them can shift up- or downslope (Figs. 4 and 7B). However, at latitude zero in Ecuador the usual coastal

desert is pinched out between the rain forest and the sea. And in southern Peru, on the same coast, the usual upland moisture belt has been pushed off the mountain crests by a widening coastal desert.

In contrast to mobile climatic agents, landforms and deposits created under a particular climate can increase their degree of adjustment to that climate (toward dynamic equilibrium) only so long as the climate remains geographically fixed. Drainage systems, for example, are developed and refined under humidity, but are either deteriorating where they are abandoned in deserts, or forming anew where humid zones replace former deserts (Fig. 15). The relative motions of a climate zone and its related landforms can be quite distinct. But in the long run, the mean position occupied by a given climate zone should enclose its most pronounced effects (Fig. 16). Occasionally, meteorologically and/or physiographically favored sites may cause local retention of a particular type of ground cover and its allied landforms and deposits (Fig. 4). Both of these situations provide geomorphic analogs for the related climate, and in many cases they serve a double role for climax biologic refuges, at least where highly specialized plant and animal types have survived (Garner, 1967a and b).

The phenomenon of simultaneous polar glaciation may lead one to conclude that equatorial rain belts simply widened or narrowed at the expense of adjacent deserts during Pleistocene time as suggested by Penck half a century ago. Studies by Forbes, Grove, Tricart, Prescott and White, Dresch, and Bigarella indicate that the two hemispheres are not quite symmetrical. On theoretical grounds, this was deduced also by Bernard (1962; see *Paleoclimatology*, Vol. II). For example (see references in Garner, 1966, 1967b), in the north-eastern Andes, about 7° north of the equator (in Venezuela) a coarse alluvial valley fill 2000–3000 feet thick is today thoroughly incised by the Rio Motatan (Fig. 17). The area is now semiarid, the stream discharges there are small and incision is weak. To the south of the equator a similar distance and at comparable elevations (6000–9000 feet) in the very humid southeastern Peruvian Andes, large, torrential, strongly eroding rivers including the Urubamba and Ucayali have not yet completed incision of valley alluvium only 300–600 feet thick (Fig. 14). It is thus clear that east Andean valley incision and alluviation is not perfectly synchronous on either side of the equator. The northern alluviation and incision in the eastern Andes was apparently earlier than that in the south. Similarly, in the moist lowlands north of the equator, gravel veneers of arid origin are surficially weathered to some depth (Fig. 5). But a similar distance to the south of the equator in the Brazilian state of Minas Geraes, similar deposits at or on the surface in a humid, vegetated setting have not yet developed a soil cover.

These and similar relations in Africa, India and

FIG. 17. The Mesa de Jajo dissected valley fill in the Rio Motatan valley, Sierra de Merida, Estado Barinas, Venezuela. View from main highway looking east. Estimated fill thickness is 2500–3000 feet. House in lower right at end of trail provides scale.

Australia indicate that the equatorial rain belt has intermittently shifted north and south and thereby affected landscapes. The implied hemispheric inequalities of past climates find parallels in the differing physical geography at each pole and the current concentration of continental ice in the south. East–west transcontinental climatic variations related to ocean current temperature differences are also apparent.

H. F. GARNER

References

Bernard, E., 1962, "Interpretation astronomique des pluviaux et interpluviaux du Quaternaire africain," *Actes IV Congr. Panafricain Prehist. Quat.*, **1,** 67–95 (*Ann. Mus. Roy. Afr. Cent., Tervuren. Sci. Hum.* 40).

Bigarella, J. J., and de Andrade, G. O., 1965, "Contributions to the study of the Brazilian Quaternary," *Geol. Soc. Am. Spec. Paper* **84,** 433–451.

Bigarella, J. J., Mousinho, M. R., and DaSilva, J. X., 1965, "Processes and Environments of the Brazilian Quaternary," Curitiba, Univ. Paraña Press, 71pp.

Büdel, J., 1951, "Die Klimazonen des Eiszeitalters," *Eiszeitalter Gegenwart,* **1,** 16–20.

Büdel, J., 1963, "Die pliozänen und quartären Pluvial zeiten der Sahara," *Eiszeitalter Gegenwart,* **14,** 161–187.

Cailleux, A., and Tricart, J., 1955, "Cours de Géomor-phologie," Paris, Centre Documentation Univ., 229pp.

Davis, W. M., 1899, "The geographical cycle," *Geogr. J.,* **14,** 481–504 (reproduced in "Geographical Essays," 1909, pp. 249–278. Boston, Ginn and Co., Dover reprint).

Fairbridge, R. W., 1964, "African Ice-Age Aridity," in (Nairn, editor) "Problems of Palaeoclimatology," pp. 356–360, New York, Interscience Publishers.

Galon, R., 1966, "Klimamorphologische Probleme der Tropen am Beispiel von Venezuela," *Wissen. Veröf., New Ser.* 23/24, 259–267.

Garner, H. F., 1959. "Stratigraphic-sedimentary significance of contemporary climate and relief in four regions of the Andes Mountains," *Bull. Geol. Soc. Am.,* **70,** 1327–1368.

Garner, H. F., 1966, "Derangement of the Rio Caroni, Venezuela," *Rev. Géomorphol. Dyn.,* **16,** 54–83.

Garner, H. F., 1967a, "Rivers in the making," *Sci. Am.,* **216,** 83–94.

Garner, H. F., 1967b, "Geomorphic analogs and climax morphogenesis," *Proc. Ark. Acad. Sci.,* **21,** 82–95.

Jaudel, L., and Tricart, J., 1958, "Les précurseurs Anglo-Saxons de la notion Davisienne de cycle d'érosion," *Rev. Gen. Sci. Paris,* **65,** 237–247.

Cross references: *Arid Cycle; Bajada; Bornhardt; Braided Channels; Climatic Geomorphology; Cycles, Geomorphic; Deflation; Drainage Patterns; Erosion; Equilibrium in Geomorphology; Exfoliation; Frost Action; Geomorphology—General; Gibbers; Glacial Refuge; Hamada; Holocene; Humid Cycle; Inselberg; Mass*

TROTTOIR

The term "trottoir" designates a narrow organic intertidal reef construction composed of either a solid mass or a simple crust covering a rocky substratum. Situated close to the mean tide mark in seas of small tidal amplitude, the marine "trottoir" separates the shore line from the sea in the same way that a sidewalk separates the street from the adjoining houses. (This explains the use of the term "trottoir" which is the French word for sidewalk; "ledge" is the nearest English term for it, *Felsbühne* in German.)

In the Mediterranean, two different types of "trottoir" have been described.

(1) The "trottoir" constructed by *Lithophyllum tortuosum* (*Tenarea tortuosa*). This "trottoir", more appropriately called "corniche", is represented by a sideward growing belt, constructed by calcareous algae and formed on a vertical or extremely inclined rock surface. The resulting formation is located in the lower horizon of the Mediolittoral Zone (see *Benthos*, Vol. I). The mass of these calcareous algae is perforated by numerous crevices.

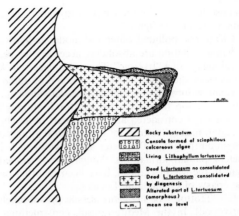

FIG. 1. "Trottoir" constructed by *Lithophyllum tortuosum*.

Only the outermost algae are living, while the inner mass, having undergone diagenesis, is transformed into a true rock (see Guilcher, 1958, Fig. 3E).

The various organisms characteristic of this formation present a mixture of: (a) typical marine mediolittoral forms (*Lithophyllum tortuosum*, the bivalves *Lasaea rubra* and *Brachydontes*, the gastropod *Oncidiella*, etc.), or those of terrestrial origin (Myriapods, Collembols, mites, the spider *Desidiopsis*, etc.); (b) those forms which belong to the superficial fringe of the Infralittoral Zone (the polychaete worm *Syllidae*, nematodes, polyplacophors, etc.), which find a refuge in the cavities

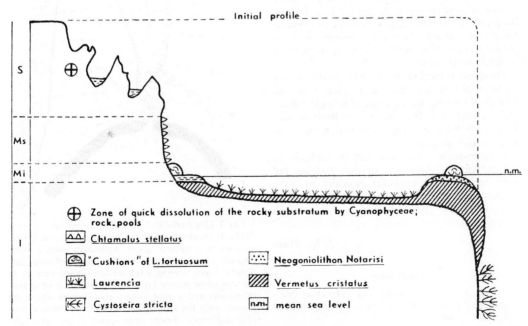

FIG. 2. "Trottoir" of *Vermetus*.

against desiccation, too much hydrodynamic agitation, or too much light.

Clean, non-polluted water and moderate hydrodynamic agitation are absolutely necessary for the development of a "trottoir". The assemblage, which appears in the shade of the "trottoir" of *Lithophyllum*, is formed of sciaphilous calcareous algae which develop thanks to the "trottoir", although they are not considered an integral part of it. The Mediterranean "trottoir" of *Lithophyllum* attains a maximum height of 0.8 meter and a width of 1–2 meters. Similar formations, though less developed than in the Mediterranean, have been reported on the coasts of Ghana and Tasmania.

(2) "Trottoir" of *Vermetus* (sessile prosobranch gastropod). In the Mediterranean, constructional formations of *Vermetus*, especially *Vermetus cristatus*, exist on vertical or steep cliffs, but these forms are rare. The true *Vermetus* "trottoir" is found only on rocky coasts in the rather warm regions of the western Mediterranean (Sicily, Algeria), in the Persian Gulf, etc. This is a simple crust on the rock, up to several centimeters thick. The *Vermetus* and the *Lithophyllum* are each found in a different zone. The *Vermetus* are associated with the red algae Corallinacea (notably *Jania*), a part of the superficial fringe of the Infralittoral Zone.

For the formation of a *Vermetus* "trottoir", the shore line must consist of a calcareous substratum, which is subject to a physicochemical subaerial erosion. The rapid erosion of the emerged rocks, more or less aided by spray, leads to a regression of the shore line, but the portions of the rocks below sea level are soon covered by the shells of the *Vermetus* which protect the substratum against further marine erosion. A platform is formed, bordered on the outer edge by a ledge of *Vermetus* toward the exterior. Permanent immersion of the platform is an indispensable factor for the survival of infralittoral animals.

These infralittoral vermetid reef formations seem to be relatively abundant in tropical seas: the Islands of Cap Verde, the coast of Senegal, Ghana and the Barbados. The "Boilers" in Bermuda and Florida are of the same type of formation, but in the form of *microatolls* (q.v.).

Sometimes the *Vermetidae* can be replaced by the polychaetes *Serpulidae* or *Sabellariidae*, but these formations constructed basically by polychaetes never seem to form a "trottoir" on which one could walk. They only form a crust or small lumps.

J. M. PERES

References

Guilcher, A., 1958, "Coastal and Submarine Morphology," London, Methuen (transl. by Sparks and Kneese), 274pp.

Peres, J. M., 1958, "Océanographie Biologique et Biologie Marine," in "La Vie Benthique," Paris, Presses Univ. France, 541pp.

Peres, J. M., and Picard, J., 1964, "Manuel de Bionomie Benthique de la Mer Mediterranée," *Rec. Trav. St. Mar. Endoume, Marseille,* Second ed., 122pp.

Cross-references: *Algal Reefs; Atoll; Coral Reefs; Limestone Coastal Weathering; Littoral Processes; Microatoll; Platforms—Wave-cut.* Vol. I: *Benthos.*

TRUMPET VALLEYS

In the moraine landscape of former piedmont glaciers, the central part of each lobe is usually

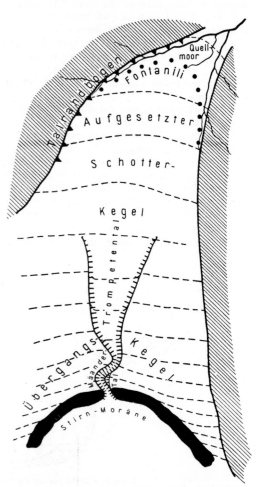

FIG. 1. Idealized sketch map of a trumpet valley (Troll, 1957). It breaks through the terminal moraine (*Stirnmorain*) in a narrow gorge, sometimes with a short meander and then funnels out over the gravel cone (fan; *Schotterkegel*) leaving a further fan-shaped veneer. At the foot of the porous fan there is a semicircle of springs (*Fontanili*) and a peat swamp (*Quellmoor*) where the gravels abut the restraining walls of the country rock (*Talrandbogen*). Form lines indicate the gradually flattening gradient of the gravel fan.

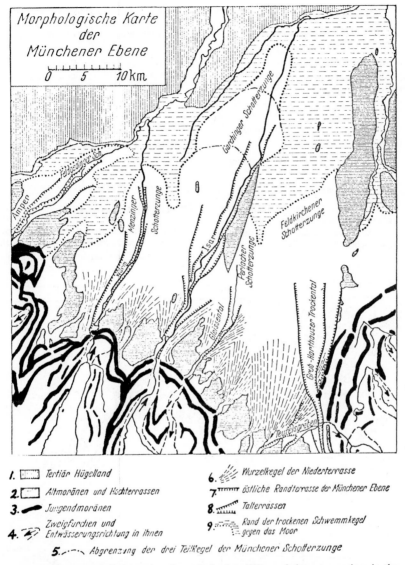

Fig. 2. Trumpet valleys cutting through the late Würm piedmont moraines in the Munich Plain (Bavaria) according to Troll (1926, p. 172). Although numbers of such valleys are shown (*Talterrassen*), note that there are blockage, river capture and drainage reversal in many of them. Key: 1. tertiary hills; 2. older moraines and higher terraces; 3. young moraines; 4. drainage directions; 5. boundaries of three fans of the Munich gravel tongue; 6. main fan of lower terrace; 7, eastern border terrace of Munich Plain; 8. trumpet valley terraces; 9. border of dry gravel fan and swamp.

found to be cut through by a narrow valley or gorge, which opens out into a broad funnel as it reaches the fluvioglacial sand and gravel cone or fan of the lower piedmont. Such valleys are very distinctive and were named *Trompetental* or in diminutive form, *Trompetentälchen* by Carl Troll (1924; 1926, p. 172; 1957).

They are particularly prevalent along the northern Alpine foothills in Bavaria, where the Pleistocene glacier tongues came down to the plain, leaving multiple semicircular end moraines, which in the retreat stages, dammed up numerous proglacial lakes. Overflow channels cutting through the morainal wall, cut deeply into the poorly consolidated till and widened out, gradually shallowing into a braided stream bed across the alluvial cone. The result was this characteristic funnel-shape "trumpet valley" landform.

With continued advance and retreat cycles, the trumpet valleys of the Alpine foothills became progressively "nested" leaving older terraces on the valleys. The streams with most energetic downcutting later captured the less vigorous trumpet valley streams, and numbers of reversed drainage directions are now mapped.

The trumpet valleys are similar to outwash channels from continental terminal moraine areas in having deep cuts through the outer moraines, but they differ in their steeper gradients and rapid flaring out of the funnel-shaped distal ends with diminution of height of channel sides.

Rhodes W. Fairbridge

References

Troll, C., 1924, "Der Diluviale Inn-Chiemsee Gletscher," *Forsch. Deutsch. L. u. V. Kde.,* **23**(1), 121pp.
Troll, C., 1926, "Die Jungglazialen Schotterfluren im Umkreis der deutschen Alpen," *Forsch. Deutsch. L. u. V. Kde.,* **24**.
Troll, C., 1957, "Tiefenerosion, Seitenerosion und Akkumulation der Flüsse im fluvioglazialen und periglazialen Bereich," *Peterm. Mitt.,* **262** (Machatschek Festschrift), 213–226.

Cross-references: *Alluvial Fan, Cone; Fluvioglacial Processes; Glacial Lakes; Glacial Spillways and Proglacial Lakes; Lobes, Lobation; Moraine; Piedmont; Stream Capture; Terraces, Fluvial.*

TUNDRA CRATERS—*See* SUFFOSION AND TUNDRA CRATERS

TUNDRA LANDSCAPE

The tundra zone is a cool forestless landscape type, developed almost exclusively in the northern hemisphere. The tundra vegetation consists of moss

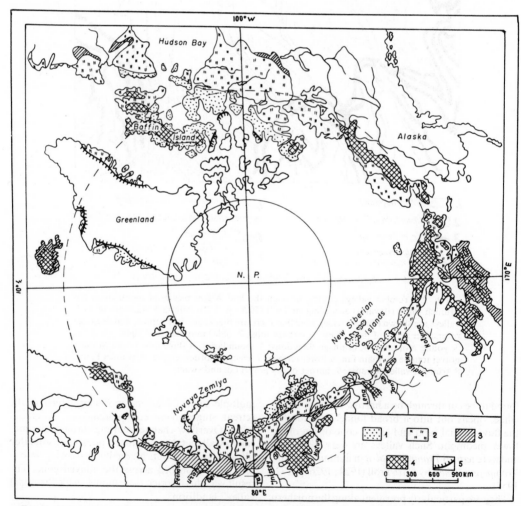

Fig. 1. Sketch map of the Tundra zone of the northern hemisphere (S.A. Strelkov). (1) Arctic tundra subzone. (2) Typical tundra subzone. (3) Shrub tundra subzone. (4) Mountain tundra. (5) Boundary of arctic desert zone.

FIG. 2. Coastal tundra at the Lena delta; the grave of the American explorer G. W. De Long, who perished here of starvation with eleven crew members of the ill-fated *Jeanette* expedition in 1881. (Photo: S. A. Strelkov).

FIG. 4. Relief of little domes ("baiyerachs") due to the melting out of ice wedges; the coastal plain, 25 m high, in the Lena delta, 73°N, 125°E. (Photo: S. A. Strelkov)

and lichen formations with various grasses, dwarf shrubs and, sometimes, large shrubs. Its southern boundary approximately coincides with the warmest monthly isotherm 10–12°C and to a certain extent follows the configuration of northern borders of the circum-Arctic continents. The northern boundary, dividing it from the *Arctic desert zone*, coincides with the warmest monthly isotherm +5°C. Essentially it occupies nearly all the northern coasts of Eurasia and America and the coasts of Greenland except for the northern parts of Taimyr and Boothia peninsulas which belong to the Arctic desert zone. Only the southern parts of the Canadian Arctic Archipelago, however, belong to the tundra zone. In Labrador, it penetrates southward as far as 55°N latitude.

The low temperatures of the short vegetative growing period (less than 100 days), the excessive swampiness (lack of drainage), and conditions of physiological dryness are the reasons for the lack of forests.

On the basis of its vegetation, the tundra zone is subdivided into three subzones (Fig. 1). The *Arctic subzone* is characterized by an interrupted cover of sparse vegetation of moss-lichens-sedges. The typical *tundra subzone* contains various types of moss-lichens-sedge vegetational associations with rare shrubs in river valleys. In the *shrub tundra subzone*, dwarf birch and willow shrubs are usual, together with mosses, sedges and grasses. Along the mountain summits, the tundra extends well to the south, being enriched by Alpine flora elements. This kind is called *mountain tundra*.

The tundra type of vegetation evolved during the Pliocene and Quaternary under conditions of general cooling and the displacement of vegetation zones under the influence of glaciation.

The *topography* of the tundra zone is determined by geological features, neotectonic movements, the Quaternary history and recent climatic conditions. Mountain areas, embracing folded systems of different ages, were very generally revived in Neogene–Quaternary time by the neotectonic crustal movements. This happened, for example, in Scan-

FIG. 3. A pingo ("bulgunyach") or hydrolaccolith 22 meters high formed by recurrent freezing of water-saturated ground of drained lake hollows in permafrost area; Gydan Peninsula, 70°N, 80°E. (Feature standing on left summit is a survey marker. (Photo: S. A. Strelkov)

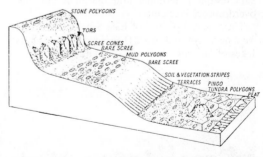

FIG. 5. Tundra phenomena; diagramatic sketch of varied land forms, according to slope (Baird, 1964). On the steep slope (top left) stone polygons pass to stone stripes (known as "dellies" in Siberia). Pingos are often surrounded by traces of former lake depressions (with ancient beaches). On river banks the polygons pass into tetragons, parallel and perpendicular to the bank. (By permission of Longmans, Green & Co., London.)

FIG. 6. Soil polygons in the "spotted tundra"; Gydan Peninsula, U.S.S.R. (Photo: S. A. Strelkov)

dinavia, the Urals, and Byrranga; these three areas are up to 1000–3000 meters high and have rather subdued topography, while the Mesozoic orogenic belts of the Verkhoyansk–Kolyma mountain system and Brooks Range, together with the Koryak and Coastal Ranges, have more rugged topography. The platform areas are characterized either by rocky gently undulating relief (Canadian Shield, Arctic Archipelago, Greenland, Scandinavia) or by flat or hilly sedimentary plains (Russian Plain, West and North Siberian Lowlands, Alaska and East Siberian Coastal Plains). In central Siberia, mountain tundra occupies the upper part of the great basalt plateau up to 1700 meters, and in the northern part of the Anabar Shield, up to about 500–800 meters.

In the marine coastal plains the Gydan and the northern part of the Yamal Peninsula, the surface appearance of the tundra zone shows traces of Quaternary marine transgressions and of the Wisconsin (Würm, or Zyrjanian) glaciation. There are very many lakes lying among the morainic hills on the plains. In mountains, one can see glacial troughs, kars (cirques), terminal and marginal moraines, overdeepened lakes, etc.

The "coastal plains" of East Siberia and Alaska were never covered by ice (Fig. 1). They have many lakes of *thermokarst* origin (q.v.) and drained lake hollows. Pingos ("bulgunyachs" in Siberia) are usual in wet places and drained lake basins (Fig. 3). The fluvio-lacustrine areas contain many traces of ice (wedges, veins, etc.), so that thermokarst is well developed. There are sometimes rows of little lakes or pools of water in the polygons between the ice wedges (see *Oriented Lakes*). In Siberia, the little soil domes (polygon relics) are called "baiyerachs" (Fig. 4). Sometimes the destroying of vegetative cover by human activity may lead to the renewing of the process of thermokarst.

The modern climatic conditions of the tundra zone, the particularly long winters with temperatures for three months from -5 down to $-35°C$, and the small amount of precipitation (usually 200–400 mm/yr) permit the existence of permafrost of up to 500 meters in thickness. The *permafrost* (q.v.) has a great influence on the river regimes, on recent geomorphological processes, and on fauna and flora. The most striking effect of permafrost is the phenomenon of the so-called spotted tundra or *patterned ground* (q.v.), formed by mostly horizontal moving of silt and the pushing up of boulders during freezing and melting (Figs. 5 and 6). Since the runoff coefficient is up to 90 %, the drainage network is rather fine.

Animal life, because of the hard ecological conditions, is represented by few species but, as a rule, has many individuals. The typical animals of the tundra are: reindeer in Eurasia (Fig. 7), caribou in America, ovibos (arctic ox) in Greenland, polar fox, some species of lemmings, polar bear along the seacoast, and among the birds ptarmigan and white arctic owl. In the nesting period, there are many waterfowl (duck, geese). Relicts of warm-dry period of the mid-Holocene time include the marmot and snow sheep (in the Verkhoyansk Mountains).

In the southern hemisphere, only some islands belong to the tundra zone (e.g., South Georgia, parts of Falkland Islands, Kerguelen, Macquarie).

SERGE A. STRELKOV

References

Akad. Nauk. SSSR, 1964, "Fisiko-geographicheskiy

FIG. 7. Wild reindeer in the arctic tundra subzone; Taimyr Peninsula. (Photo: S. A. Strelkov)

Atlas Mira," Glavn. Upr. Geodez. i. Kartogr., Moscow.

Alechin, W. W., 1951, "Rastitelnost' SSSR w osnownich zonach," Moscow.

Antipova, A. B., 1965, "Kanada," Moscow.

Baird, P. D., 1964, "The Polar World," London, Longmans, Green & Co., 328pp.

Berg, L., 1950, in (Morrison, T. A., and Nikiforoff, C. C., editors) "Natural Regions of USSR," New York. The Macmillan Co., 436pp. (translated by G. A. Titelbaum from Second Russian ed., 1938).

Berg, L. S., 1955, "Priroda SSSR," Moscow.

Bolshaia Sovjetskaia Encyclopedia, Second ed., "Tundra Zone."

Canada, Dept. of Mines and Techn. Surv., Geogr. Branch. 1957. "Atlas of Canada," Ottawa.

Dagon, R. R., 1966, "Tundra—A definition and structural description," *Polar Notes*, Dartmouth College Library, no. 6, 22–35.

Dunbar, M., and Greenway, K. R., 1956, "Arctic Canada from the Air," Ottawa, Canada Defence Res. Bd., 541pp.

Eyre, S. R., 1963, "Vegetation and Soils," Chicago, Aldine Publishing Co., 324pp.

Grigorjev, A. A., 1946, "Subarctica," Moscow.

Ives, R. L., 1941, "Tundra ponds," *J. Geomorphol.*, **4**, 285–296.

Tikhomirov, B. A., 1962, "The treelessness of the Tundra." *Polar Record*. **11**(70), 24–30.

Washburn, A. L., 1956, "Classification of patterned ground and review of suggested origins," *Bull. Geol. Soc. Am.*, **67**(7), 823–865.

Cross-references: *Cirque; Coastal Plain; Crustal Movements; Frost Action; Holocene; Neotectonics; Oriented Lakes; Periglacial Landscape; Plains; Patterned Ground; Permafrost; Pingo; Quaternary; Savanna Landscape; Suffosion and Tundra Craters; Taiga Landscape; Thermokarst. Vol. II: Arctic Climate; Arctic Meteorology; Tundra Climate; Vegetation Classification and Description. Vol. VI: Snowline.*

TYRRELL SEA

Tyrrell Sea is the name given to an inland sea that existed during and following deglaciation of Hudson Bay basin. It reached its maximum extent 7000 or 8000 years ago. Hudson Bay is a relict of the Tyrrell Sea. The sea was named after the Canadian explorer and geologist, Joseph Burr Tyrrell (1858–1957), who carried out early studies on this submergence, followed by Bell, Stanley, Manning, Cooke, Shaw, Bird, Fyles and Lee (see references in Bird, 1954; Lee, 1962).

The sea extended from latitude 50–66°N, excluding Foxe Channel, and arbitrarily ended at the boundary between the districts of Keewatin and Franklin. Longitude is from 75–97°W. The sea covered all of Hudson Bay and surrounding lands in Quebec, Ontario, Manitoba, and Keewatin, extending northward to, and including, Wager Bay and the islands of Southampton, Coats and Mansel.

History

This region lies within the central zone of the maximum Wisconsin Laurentide ice sheet; it was greatly downwarped during the period of ice occupation, was flooded during ice recession, and later was partly emerged as upwarping progressed. The Tyrrell Sea came into being when Atlantic water penetrated through Hudson Strait into the Hudson Bay Area. The marine waters soon divided the shrunken Wisconsin Laurentide ice sheet into two, or more, separate major icecaps, one to the west and one to the east of Hudson Bay. The then deep water being in contact with the icecaps controlled the manner of their recession and gave an unusually distinctive record to the transgressive phase of the sea.

The limit of the Tyrrell Sea is found at an elevation of about 120–180 meters (400–600 feet) above present sea level west of Hudson Bay, compared with about 250–275 meters (800–900 feet) east of the bay. A probable cause for this difference was a thinner remnant icecap on adjacent land west of Hudson Bay when the strandlines were formed.

Upwarping of the land began upon removal of the ice load and caused a regression of the sea. Radiocarbon dates on shells, wood and bones collected from the marine deposits around Hudson Bay indicate that land emergence was at first very rapid, then decreased exponentially to the present, except for a probable stillstand which resulted in a low continuous terrace about 9 miles inland from the west coast of the bay. The emergence curve is similar to that given for the Gulf of Bothnia region in Sweden by Magnusson, G. Lundqvist and Granlund and by J. Lundqvist (see references in Lundqvist, 1965).

Sediments

Sediments of the Tyrrell Sea are time transgressive. An unusually clear story is given for the transgressive phase of the sea by the "*De Geer moraines.*" These distinctive drift ridges were formed by ice calving into the sea and have been studied by De Geer and Hoppe in the Baltic region of Sweden, and by Mawdsley, Norman, Shaw and Lee in Canada (see references in Shaw, 1944; Lee, 1962). Lithology of a De Geer moraine in the Tyrrell Sea is till in some places, and sand and gravel with boulders in others. The material forms low narrow ridges about 5 meters (15 feet) high, and about 35 meters (100 feet) wide. Regional trend of the ridges is remarkably linear, typical for ice calving into water. The trend is northerly on both the west and the east sides of Hudson Bay, and it shows the orientation of the transgressive strandlines of the Tyrrell Sea. Transgression inland of the Tyrrell Sea was relatively uniform as shown by spacing of the De Geer moraines at about 250-meter (800-foot) intervals, with extremes of 35- and 300-meter (100- and

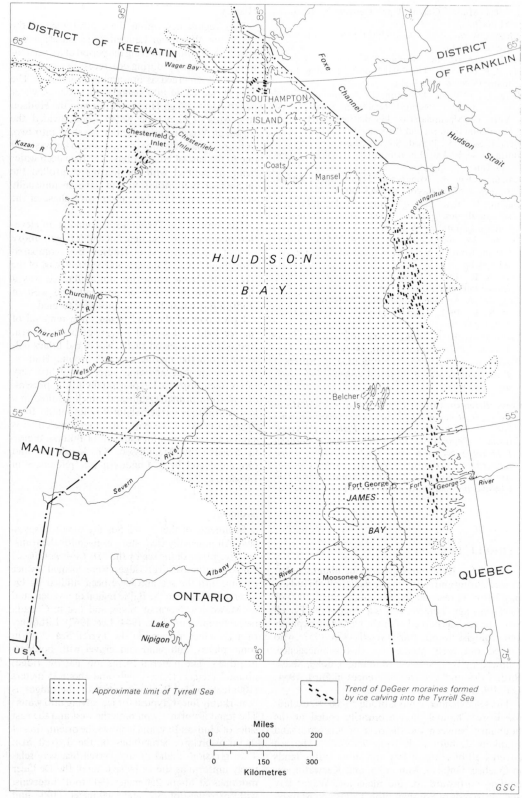

FIG. 1. Map showing limits of Tyrrell Sea about 7000 years ago.

1000-foot) intervals, assuming that the moraines are annual.

Silt and clay were deposited in the Tyrrell Sea during both its transgressive and its regressive phases. Typical exposures are on the east side of Hudson Bay along banks of the Fort George River. The maximum recorded thickness is 56 meters (185 feet) measured in a drill hole section at Fort George where the silt and clay unit lies between alluvial sand at the top and bedrock at the base. Environments of deposition for the silt and clay include a basin of restricted circulation giving a black, odoriferous clay, in places with wood and shells, and a basin with good circulation giving silts containing numerous ice-rafted stones and a few shells.

Gravel, sand and boulder facies were formed during the regression of the Tyrrell Sea by wave action on hill slopes. The resulting forms are depositional terraces, beach ridges and spits. Large areas of the former sea floor however are not covered by sediments but are bare bedrock.

Dating

The Tyrrell Sea reached its maximum extent 7000–8000 years ago, as indicated by radiocarbon dates on shells collected from near the highest strandlines south and west of the bay. Ages of 7875 ± 200 and 7280 ± 50 years were obtained on shells south of Hudson Bay (Hughes, 1965), and an age of 6975 ± 250 years was obtained on shells from west of Hudson Bay. Dates are not yet available for the east coast of Hudson Bay.

HULBERT A. LEE

References

*Bird, J. B., 1954, "Postglacial marine submergence in Central Arctic Canada," *Bull. Geol. Soc. Am.,* **65,** 457–464.

Hughes, O. L., 1965, "Surficial geology of part of the Cochrane District, Ontario, Canada," *Geol. Soc. Am., Spec. Paper* **84,** 535–565.

*Lee, H. A., 1962, "Method of deglaciation, age of submergence, and rate of uplift west and east of Hudson Bay, Canada," *Biul. Peryglacjalny,* II, Lodz, 239–245.

*Lundqvist, J., 1965, "The Quaternary of Sweden," in (Rankama, K., editor) "The Quaternary," Vol. 1, pp. 139–198, New York, Interscience Publishers.

Shaw, G., 1944, "Moraines of late Pleistocene ice fronts near James Bay, Quebec," *Trans. Roy. Soc. Can. Sec. IV,* **38,** 79–85.

* Additional bibliographic references may be found in this work.

Cross-references: *Glacial Lakes; Holocene; Moraine; Quaternary; Strandline; Warping; Water Loading and Crustal Response.* Vol. VI: *Icecap.*

U

UNDERFIT STREAMS—*See* **STREAMS–UNDERFIT**

UNICLINAL SHIFTING—*See* **SLIPOFF SLOPE**

UNIFORMITARIANISM—*See* pr Vol. VI

UNION OF GEOLOGICAL SCIENCES—*See* pr Vol. VI, **INTERNATIONAL UNION OF GEOLOGICAL SCIENCES**

UNITS, NUMBERS, CONSTANTS, SYMBOLS —*See* Vol. II

URSTROMTÄLER—*See* **GLACIAL SPILLWAYS AND PROGLACIAL LAKES**

UVALA

A word in Serbo–Croat from the classic Yugoslavian Karst region, the uvala comprises a series of joined or coalescent dolinas, often elongate and marking a former subterranean stream channel or series of collapsed sinkholes. It does not necessarily contain a stream at the present time. An uvala is generally of the order of 1 km in length; it is thus intermediate in size between a *dolina* (q.v.) and a *polje* (q.v.). When there is an active stream, entering at one side and leaving at the other, Malott (1932) has referred to it as a "*karst window*."

RHODES W. FAIRBRIDGE

References

Cvijić, J., 1924, "The evolution of lapiès. A study in karst physiography," *Geograph. Rev.,* **14,** 26–49.
Malott, C. A., 1932, "Lost River at Wesley Chapel Gulf, Orange County, Indiana," *Proc. Indiana Acad. Sci.,* **41,** 285–316.
Sanders, E. W., 1921, "The cycle of erosion in a karst region (after Cvijić)," *Geograph. Rev.,* **11,** 593–604.

Cross-references: *Blind Valley; Dolina; Dry Valley; Karst; Polje; Sink, Sinkhole.*

V

VALLEY ASYMMETRY—*See* **ASYMMETRIC VALLEYS**

VALLEY EVOLUTION

There is hardly any phenomenon on the earth's surface whose origin has been discussed and explained in as many different ways as valleys have. Even the ancient philosophers made a start on the difficult problem of gradational processes, and erosion in general, as can be seen from Strabo's *Geographia*, Seneca's *Quaestiones*, and other sources. Herodotus hints at the watergap of the River Isker in the Heimos Range and also at the analogous gorge of the Greek River Peneios.

After these comparatively promising beginnings, there was no further progress till the Renaissance when Leonardo Da Vinci displayed his remarkable insight into uplift and subsequent erosion, concepts that were added to by Varenius and Kircher, who first distinguished undercut and slip-off slopes. In the eighteenth century, the gradational activity of running water was emphasized by many scientists, especially by Hutton in his "Theory of the Earth". Strangely enough, it was this same time that gave rise to a strong opposition against the concept of fluviatile incision since part of the geologists then regarded the valleys as tectonic features, gigantic chasms. The dawn of modern geography and geology in the past century brought the definite victory of the erosional theory. Lyell with his paper "On the Gradual Excavation of the Valleys in which the Meuse, the Moselle, and Some Other Rivers Flow"; Rütimeyer in the article "Über Thal- und See-bildung", Heim, and Rubidge are some of its foremost advocates. A little later, Powell and Gilbert deduced specific laws of fluviatile erosion, and with this, the concept of valley evolution due to stream action eventually made its way. It became an integral part of the systematic geomorphology whose first textbooks appeared by that time.

(1) The Interaction of Incision and Slope Denudation

The long profile of a stream is not identical with that of its valley since the former depends on the loops of the stream but the latter on the gradient of the flood plain. The stream in its thalweg controls all the valley-forming processes although a direct influence is limited to the bed and the flood plain. But by swinging against the valley walls, cutting at their bases, and pushing them apart by undercutting, the stream constantly renews the slope processes. Among them, rain wash, creep, and—under periglacial conditions—solifluction are the most important ones, whereas quicker mass movements such as rockfalls, landslides, and mudflows are generally exceptions. Thus a valley is the result of both incision (I) and slope denudation (D), and its transverse profile depends essentially on the ratio I/D.

(2) Classification of Valleys according to their Transverse Profile

(*i*) Streams with steep gradients are swift and, given tools to scour or abrade their beds, are able to cut downward much more vigorously than laterally. If the above-mentioned ratio $I/D \rightarrow \infty$, i.e., if there is practically no widening of the valley at the top due to denudation in comparison to incision, which is often accomplished by the downward boring of potholes, the walls are $\pm$ perpendicular or even overhanging. This type of valley is called saw-cut valley, slot or gash (*Klamm* in German). Well-known examples are the Partnach-Klamm near Garmisch-Partenkirchen (Bavarian Alps, Germany) or the Watkins Glen, New York.

(*ii*) A valley that is a little open at the top, its transverse profile resembling a very narrow V, is called a gorge. Gorges can only originate in resistant rocks. In regions of high elevation, they may be hundreds or even thousands of feet deep, while in regions of low elevation or great distance from the respective local base level of erosion, they may be only a few feet deep, although their shapes are similar. Both are young in terms of stage of development, but there may be a vast difference in their absolute ages measured in terms of years.

(*iii*) If the ratio $I/D \approx 1$, i.e., if widening keeps pace with the downward cutting, a V-shaped valley *sensu stricto* originates. In loose material, which washes or slides easily, the V is likely to be broad and open, while in hard, resistant rocks, it will be narrow and gorge-like.

(*iv*) A V-shaped valley cut into nearly horizontal strata of unequal resistance is characterized by a

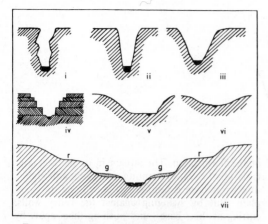

FIG. 1. Transverse profiles of valleys. (i) = saw-cut valley, (ii) = gorge, (iii) = V-shaped valley, (iv) = canyon, (v) = flat-floored valley, (vi) = shallow, trough-shaped valley with sides flaring out, (vii) = river terraces (r = rock t., g = gravel t.). Modified after Neef, 1956.)

step-like profile, where the exposed edges of the more-resistant strata form the sheer rises and some of the benches; those of the less-resistant strata form the intervening slopes. This special variant of the gorge type is called a canyon; it is developed best in arid, shortly dissected plateaus. Its often fantastic shaping is the normal result of several conditions. Orographic precipitation in bordering mountains furnishes water for streams able to cross the dry plateau surface, which is high above its base level. Thus the exotic streams have high gradients and are able to erode deeply. Most high plateaus are comprised of solid rocks able to stand in steep slopes when dissected by stream erosion. The slow rate of weathering and the small amount of slope wash normal to dry climates tend to preserve the steepness of the valley walls. Canyons of great length and depth are those of the Colorado and Snake Rivers in the United States, that of the middle course of the Zambezi River in South Africa, and the Tibetan courses of the Brahmaputra and other rivers that leave the great Asiatic plateau region. The most magnificent of its kind is the Grand Canyon in Arizona, cut through more than 4000 feet of nearly horizontal sedimentary strata and more than 1000 feet into the underlying crystalline rocks. The width of this canyon amounts to about 16 miles at the top.

(v) When the incision decreases, the morphogenous activity of a stream is more and more characterized by undercutting (with $I \to 0$ in the ratio I/D). A flat-floored valley originates, whose bottom borders on the valley walls in often marked knick lines. The transverse profile is generally chest-like with a varying inclination of the slopes. Where denudational processes could be active for

a longer time, it assumes a convex shape at the top. In this connection, it must be emphasized that there are still two other possible modes of formation of flat-floored valleys. In one case, they are due to fluvial aggradation in a V-shaped valley ($I < 0$); in the other, they come into existence in the course of a very vigorous incision under the climatic conditions of the almost vegetationless high-arctic tundra [see Section (5) of this article].

(vi) If the stream, e.g., in a still more advanced stage of development, is no longer able to transport the material sliding or falling from the sides or carried in by rain wash, the transverse profile becomes trough shaped. The valley bottom merges insensibly in the walls, the lower parts of which are frequently concave, whereas the upper parts have a convex shape.

W. M. Davis, in his widely accepted, mostly deductive explanation of landforms, regarded these valley types as subsequent stages of a developmental series beginning with young and ending with old-age forms, having as intermediate stage that of mature valleys. The modern climatogenetic geomorphology, however, has taught us to see the Davisian concept with a little more reservedness. Here, only a few fundamental facts are to be hinted at. First of all, it is an apriori fact that all these transverse profiles can originate from one another. Furthermore, one must object to a form of "youth" which is, on the one hand, the result of only short-time application of process and, on the other hand, an expression of marked structural resistance to degradational action. Finally, it must be taken into account that, generally speaking, valley evolution is much more controlled by climate than by any other factor. Thus "old-age" valley forms can in fact be the first developmental stage, where there is an appropriate savanna climate (see section 6).

(vii) River terraces—often a characteristic feature of valley cross profiles—originate when lateral corrasion of the river alternates with incision. Terraces may be cut into the solid rock or consist of a rock bench veneered with a comparatively small thickness of alluvium (rock terrace). Another group of river terraces is due to the dissection of $\pm$ deep aggradations (gravel terraces), which either result from a tectonically or eustatically conditioned decrease of gradient or from climatic variations which causes changes in the discharge of the streams and in the nature of the destruction of the valley sides. The latter may well cause the amount and the caliber of the load to alter. Thus in the periglacial areas of the Pleistocene, the tundra conditions resulted in the rapid weathering of large quantities of material so that the load was increased in both amount and caliber. This load could not be transported over the preexisting gradients, as these were not sufficiently steep. Hence aggradation took place. The surfaces of these aggradations, now dissected by later erosion, remain in the form of terraces.

A very conspicuous terrace sequence is that of the River Rhine, which comprises some 13 alluvial terraces, two of which are of Pliocene age, whereas 10 are due (mainly) to interglacial dissection of periglacial aggradations.

(*viii*) Asymmetrical valleys. Downcutting in beds of considerable dip develops asymmetrical slopes which are due to monoclinal shifting. It results from the fact that an inclined layer of durable rock maintains a steep escarpment slope at its outcrop edge and a gently inclined dip slope on its upper surface. Another group of systematically asymmetrical transverse profiles, namely those of large lowland rivers (Volga, Yenissei, Lena, Danube, Yukon, Mississippi) with the right bank characteristically steeper than the left, results from the right-hand rotational deflection of the river current (von Baer's law).

Asymmetry can furthermore be lithologically caused by unequal resistance to degradational processes, but in most cases it is climatically conditioned and a characteristic feature of the Pleistocene and present-day permafrost regions. In them, the south- to west-facing slopes thaw earlier and more deeply than the opposite ones, where the pergelisol remains near the surface. Wherever solifluction as the most important periglacial degradational process becomes active alone, it predominates on these thermally favored slopes, which are flattened. On the contrary, these less-resistant south- to west-facing valley sides become steepened if melting waters for selective undercutting are available. Their activity during the Pleistocene was often sponsored by the long-lasting solifluction on the ubac which helped to push the stream off toward the more deeply thawed slope.

(*ix*) Trough valleys are shaped by valley glaciers and characterized by a cross section likened to the letter U, if they are eroded out of resistant rocks. Their bottom is usually broad and flat, and it may

possess enclosed basins, steps and *roches moutonnées*. The walls of a typically developed trough are oversteepened with the valley side spurs truncated and often remarkably straight. Above the walls, the average slope usually decreases but ice erosion is still visible. Its influence ends at the ice-scour limit, which is often a groove. Above it, the rock is only liable to supraglacial weathering. Typical valley side shoulders (s in Fig. 2) with a trough end are found only when a terrace valley has been modeled by glacial scour. In addition to these comparatively common trough forms of the Alps, there are trough-in-trough valleys with several shoulders or benches, and also very deep troughs without any sign of a shoulder in the Caucasus, Altai, Himalayas, and Karakoram; finally there are shallow troughs in some arid regions of the United States (Anaconda Range, Montana; Big Horn Mts., Wyoming).

A typical feature of all sorts of trough valleys are tributary valleys that often hang markedly above the main valleys.

The very mechanism of the conversion of a stream valley into a U-shape during a glaciation is illustrated in Fig. 2, which needs no additional explanation if it is duly realized that (*ceteris paribus*) the amount of ice erosion is a function of the ice thickness. With regard to the difficult problem of explaining in an exact quantitative way the manifold steps in the long profile of a trough valley, see Louis (1952).

Finally it must be emphasized that the U-shaped cross section is a feature not confined to glaciated valleys; it is also found in limestone regions (e.g., Meseta in the Spanish province of Soria and cuesta landscapes of Southwestern Germany).

(3) The Long Profile of Streams

The general form of the profile is concave upward, but the degree of concavity generally varies considerably. The regularity of the curve may also vary between different streams, and many are concave only if the irregularities are ignored. A separation of regular concave sections by convex ones is the rule. The latter can be due to differential uplift or to the outcrop of resistant rocks.

A study of the beds of streams shows that material is eroded from some sections of the course, while in others it is deposited. A genetic understanding of these processes implies an insight into the energy balance of the streams.

The energy of any stream varies with the gradient of the stream surface and with the volume of the stream, but only a comparatively small part of this energy is available for the erosion and transport of material from the bed and the banks. The greater portion is transformed into heat in overcoming the external friction (between the stream and its wetted perimeter) and the internal one (shearing between turbulent currents). The losses through internal

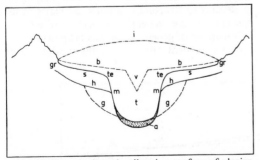

FIG. 2. Trough-shaped valley. i = surface of glacier, b = preglacial valley, V = V-shaped valley, intrenched into b, gr = groove, s = valley side shoulders, te = trough end, h = hanging valley, m = mouth of h, t = trough, g = gorge, a = aggradation.

friction are hardly separable from those caused by external friction, as an increase in the roughness of the bed will cause a greater retardation of the bottom layers and those above, and hence a more powerful turbulence.

Since the turbulence is responsible for setting particles into motion, the stream energy required to overcome friction cannot strictly be separated from the energy used in transporting material, as is sometimes rather arbitrarily done.

The sections where the gradient of the stream surface is above normal are sections of increased frictional activity. This causes a more vigorous incision tending to remove the irregularities, which recede upstream while being worn down. This fact is known since the classical studies of Greenwood and Gilbert and is called the law of regressive incision. Ultimately, the steeper sections will be so lowered that the whole profile of the stream is smooth from source to mouth.

In addition to the effect of regressive incision, there are two other factors under the influence of base level, both of which tend to the production of the concavity usually observed. They are the downstream increases in discharge and—conditions of a humid climate provided—comminution of the load. The increase in discharge as effected by tributaries and springs may transport the combined load over decreasing gradients, provided that the cross-sectional form of the channel does not change. Similarly, because of the variation in competence with the sixth power of bed velocity, the comminution of debris downstream allows the stream to flow over ever-decreasing gradients.

A stream is at grade when it has developed a slope delicately adjusted to provide, with available discharge and prevailing channel characteristics, just the velocity required for the transportation of the load supplied from the drainage basin. Such a graded stream is a system in equilibrium, whose profile is known as a graded profile. Its diagnostic characteristic is that any change in one of its controlling factors will cause a displacement of the equilibrium in a direction that will tend to absorb the effect of the change.

These ideas (conceived by Davis and Hettner, and further defined by Baulig, Mackin, von Wissmann, Birot, and Louis) imply the following facts:

the profile of the stream is organized to transport the debris; erosion will not cease definitely, although it may well proceed very slowly; a change in any factor in any part of the stream transmits an effect through the whole profile. In practical conformity with this profile of equilibrium is the so-called smoothing profile (*Glättungsprofil* in German) as defined by Louis (1960).

If the actual long profile of a stream is beneath the graded profile, the latter is approximated by aggradation; if the stream flows above grade, incision takes place. In nature, a deviation of the actual profile from grade is the rule, although there may well be concavity from source to mouth.

The upper course of such streams is predominantly shaped by degradation, while the lower course is mostly characterized by aggradation. These two sections of opposite gradational activity are separated by a section of (an unstable) equilibrium, i.e., balance between power and load. If short time intervals are involved, subcision is the only factor at work. It is not limited to this part of the stream, however, but is usually active in the upper and lower courses, too: in the first case, as a component in the modeling of entrenched meanders and, in the second, as combined with aggradation. If channel characteristics are equal, the gradient of this equilibrium profile depends mainly on the ratio of load (l) to discharge (d), which von Wissmann (1951) called *Belastungsverhältnis*. The greater this ratio, the steeper is the gradient, and vice versa. The changes which the long profile of a stream undergoes when the quotient l/d increases and the sea level (= base level) is lowered (e.g., during the anaglacial phase of a glacial period) are shown in Fig. 3.

(4) Structurally and Tectonically Controlled Valley Evolution

In addition to the classification of valleys according to the transverse and longitudinal profiles as listed above, the relation to structure and crustal movements can also form the basis of a classification. The first case to be described is the adaptation of streams to structure as studied by Davis in his concept of the geographical cycle, where the following set of genetic terms was proposed.

(*i*) Consequent streams are those which have

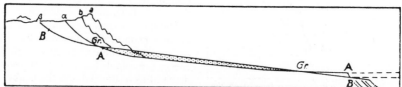

Fig. 3. Changes in the long profile of a stream owing to an increase of the ratio load: discharge and a lowering of the base level. A-A = interglacial long profile, B-B = glacial long profile, Gr = limit of aggradation, α, β = divides shifted by regressive vertical erosion, - - - - = respective base level (from von Wissman, 1951).

their courses determined by the initial slope of the land. They often flow in the same direction as the dip of the beds, especially in the well-known example of scarpland drainage, but rarely at the same angle as the dip. However, they need not flow with the dip. Johnson, who has contributed appreciably to the discussion of stream terminology, cited the drainage of a gently tilted fault block, where the streams draining both the gentle back slope and the fault face are equally consequents, since their direction depends on the nature of the initial surface.

(*ii*) Subsequent streams are "developed by headward erosion under the guidance of weak substructures" (Davis, 1909). From this definition, it can be seen that there are two classes of subsequent streams: those eroding in an area of soft rocks between two areas of harder ones and those which are guided by faults and shatter belts. The majority of subsequent valleys follow the outcrop of weak strata and hence correspond in direction with the strike of the beds. Often, they constitute broad lowlands that are bounded downdip by escarpment slopes, capped by the more resistant strata. The escarpment and the back slope together form a cuesta.

(*iii*) Resequent streams are those which appear to be consequent in direction but of later origin. As tributaries of class (*ii*) streams they have sometimes been called secondary consequents, but it is better not to apply this term.

(*iv*) Obsequents were originally defined as streams having a direction opposite to that of the consequent streams in their vicinity. Usually, however, the term is interpreted to mean merely a stream flowing against the direction of dip. Valleys of obsequent streams are often deeply entrenched gorges dissecting an escarpment slope. Headwater erosion is very effective. Therefore, capture and diversions of higher level subsequents and beheading of consequents are frequent phenomena; wind gaps where the underfit beheaded consequents have their (new) sources, are characteristic landscape features (for well-studied examples of all the classes listed up to this point, see G. Wagner on Swabia).

(*v*) Finally the last class of streams is termed insequent: either they owe their courses completely to chance, or they are guided by lithological differences too small to be detected by man.

It must be noted that these terms—by virtue of their definition—carry considerable implications as to the history of erosion of their respective region. When the history of the drainage pattern is unknown, it is convenient to apply a set of descriptive terms, usually relating the streams and their valleys to some structural feature. Longitudinal and transverse would specify relationships with fold trends; anticlinal, synclinal, strike and dip are further terms making the position of the valley with regard to structure immediately obvious.

Antecedence and superimposition (Fig. 4): If an oldland is uplifted by slow folding or faulting with the axes of the folds or the fault line athwart the courses of existing drainage, it may be possible for the larger streams to maintain their paths against the uplift. On the downstream axis of uplift, the gradient of the antecedent stream is increased, hence its downcutting is more vigorous. On the upstream side, there will be aggradation and probably a temporary ponding. Antecedence frequently accounts for the evolution of deep, narrow gorges, e.g., those of the Columbia River across the Cascade Mts. and the River Rhine across the Rhine block. The latter example is also important from the historical point of view, since here conclusive evidence of the verity of the antecedence concept was presented. A well-developed sequence of gravel terraces flanking the river is found to be warped upward over an anticlinal axis near Bingen, which runs athwart the river's course. The higher the terraces, the more arched they are. Warping reached its maximum amount in the Cromer interglacial; hence, the picturesque gorge between Bingen and Bonn dates mostly from that time.

Superimposed (= epigenetic) drainage is a common phenomenon. It results from the transection of an unconformable cover of younger strata on which the drainage is initiated. As the valley walls of these trenched strata hold the stream to its previously established course, the undermass will be dissected in the same way, no matter what erosional difficulties or structures are encountered. Often the deposits of the surface of initiation have disappeared. Smaller examples of superimposition may be explicable by climatic change, e.g., between

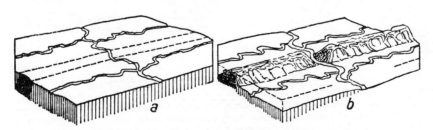

FIG. 4. Development of a superimposed valley (from Neef, 1956).

cold and warm periods of the Pleistocene. Epigenetic processes on a large scale, however, bringing about gaps of several hundred feet of depth, imply the interaction of upwarping.

Fine examples of epigenetic valley formation are the water gaps of the River Danube in the Swabian and Franconian Alps, and the numerous sharply defined water gaps of the Middle Atlantic States section of the Folded Appalachian Mountains.

(5) Meander Valleys

Meander valleys with their regular windings show a sequence of spurs and coves. Their cross-profile often possesses an asymmetry proving that the meanders developed during the incision: steep undercut slopes and gentle slip-off slopes, often covered by aggradations.

Whereas research work in the last decades has made a great advance toward the genetic understanding of free meanders (cf. the experiments of the U.S. Waterways Experimental Station and those carried out by Hjulström), the explanation of valley meanders is still much under the influence of Davis's cycle theory. According to this, incised meanders are derived as "inherited meanders" from free meanders on plateaus.

Modern studies on valley meanders formed during the Pleistocene (Troll, 1954), have shown, however, that they originate only during the phase of most intensive incision without any free meanders preceding them and that their evolution can only be understood in relation to climatic changes and tectonics. Troll could prove with the River Inn that the dissection of the uniform Würm outwash plain

commenced with the ingrowing of meanders which, farther downstream, change into a comparatively straight, sharp-edged and flat-floored valley section whose ground plan is likened to a trumpet ("Trompetental"). The classic valley meanders of the River Moselle were formed when the extensive aggradation of the Günz period, produced by a braided—not a meandering!—river system had come to an end. The climatically conditioned ingrowing was subsequently intensified by the uplift in the Günz/Mindel interglacial period. The following glaciations interrupted the normal development of these incised meanders by aggradations that were partly eroded later.

(6) Climatic Zones

In the preceding paragraphs valley evolution has been dealt with mainly in an analytical way; hence, a final explanatory view of the distribution of typical valley forms is necessary to provide a synthetic complement. It will be based on the concept of climatogenetic geomorphology since climate is the predominant morphogenic factor, although landforms are also due to a number of other ("aclimatic") factors of more local character (petro-variance, epeiro-variance, distance from base level, etc.). The influence of the latter varies also in a systematic way according to the respective climate, thus including the primarily haphazard changes into the general climatic (and hence morphogenetic) zonation of the earth.

According to the climatically controlled kind of interaction, i.e., the complex of morphogenic processes, the continents may be subdivided into

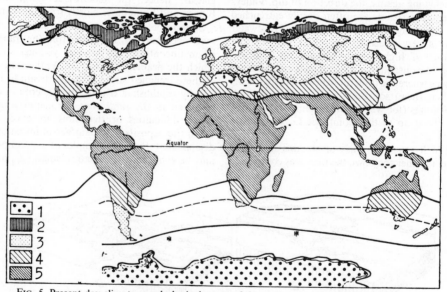

FIG. 5. Present-day climatomorphological zones of the earth (after Büdel, 1963). Explanation: 1. Glaciated regions; 2. Permafrost and periglacial belt; 3. Cool humid and subhumid belt; 4. Subtropical and mediterranean belt; 5. Tropical zone (see text).

the following present-day climatomorphological zones (Büdel, 1963). Five such zones are delineated on Figure 5, as follows:

1 = Glaciated regions with formation of U-shaped valleys.

2 = Zone of excessive valley formation, i.e., nonglaciated polar regions (frost-debris belt and tundras) and especially those with permafrost. Today, this zone comprises an area of $\approx 3 \times 10^6$ square miles ($= 8 \times 10^6$ km^2), but during the glacial periods of the Pleistocene it was extended to about double that area. Flat-floored broad valleys with steep walls, slip-off terraces and a regular long profile are the characteristic erosional features of this zone, where the destruction reaches its maximum in the world. This is due to a high discharge efficiency (permafrost impedes seepage and evapotranspiration almost completely) in the melting period, which makes much coarse gravel available as tools of abrasion. The high load of tundra streams is the combined effect of lateral drainage, solifluction and loosening of the subsurface rock by ground ice (Taber ice). The latter process is also active in the bed itself; consequently the polar stream need not cut into the solid rock but merely has the task of transporting this loosened material together with its other load. Thus incision can take place over the entire width of the valley floor while a regular long profile is maintained. Owing to the interaction of the processes listed above, the total amount of cutting down is several times higher in the frost-debris belt than in any other climatomorphological zone.

3 = Extratropical zone of valley formation. Here the intensity of wearing down is considerably reduced in comparison to zone 2, but morphogenetic influences from fossil polar climates are usually very pronounced. V-shaped valleys, alluvial river terraces, and flat-floored valleys with meandering streams are characteristic relief features of this zone.

4 = Subtropical zone of pediment and valley formation. As a whole, the intensity of downcutting (V-shaped and entrenching flat-floored valleys, i.e., torrenti in southern Italy) is still more reduced than in the preceding zones, whereas undercutting (pediments) becomes very important.

5 = Tropical zone with predominance of erosion surfaces. As in zone 2, weathering reaches deeply beneath the surface of erosion. Here, it is the most intensive chemical weathering that produces the thick, easily erodible, kaolinitic clays of the plastosol group. The lower boundary surface of this soil cover is irregularly shaped according to the unequal progress of weathering. The upper one is really modeled by the combined vertical erosion of overflowing rivers and the rill- and sheet-wash of the numerous interlacing streamlets; it is an erosion surface (peneplain) with broad gently convex swells between shallow valleys with sides flaring out.

In marked contrast to these extremely smooth valley forms of the erosion surfaces are the V-shaped, often gorge-like valleys of the tropical high mountains, especially in the zone of equatorial rain forests. Their walls always have a comparatively thick soil cover, although the gradient may exceed 45°; only the thalweg is cut into solid rock. The longitudinal profiles of such streams are rather irregular with numerous knick points and waterfalls, especially at the mouth of tributaries.

OTTO FRÄNZLE

References

Birot, P., 1952, "Sur le mécanisme des transports solides dans les cours d'eau," *Rev. Géomorph. Dyn.*, **3**(3), 105–141.

Büdel, J., 1963, "Klima-genetische Geomorphologie," *Geogr. Rundschau*, **7**, 269–286.

Davis, W. M., 1909, "Geographical Essays," New York, Dover Publications, Inc., reprint, 1954.

Davis, W. M., and Rühl, A., 1912, "Die erklärende Beschreibung der Landformen," Leipzig, Teubner, 565 pp.

Louis, H., 1952, "Zur Theorie der Gletschererosion in Tälern," *Eiszeit. Gegenwart*, **2**, 12–24.

Louis, H., 1960, "Allgemeine Geomorphologie," Berlin, de Gruyter, 355pp. (2nd ed., 1967.)

Neef, E. (editor), 1956, "Das Gesicht der Erde," Leipzig, Brockhaus, 980 pp.

Thornbury, W. D., 1954, "Principles of Geomorphology," New York and London, John Wiley & Sons, 618 pp.

Troll, C., 1954, "Uber Alter und Bildung von Talmäandern," *Erdkunde*, **8**, 286–302.

Wagner, G., 1950, "Einführung in die Erd- und Landschaftsgeschichte," Öhringen.

Wissmann, H. v., 1951, "Über seitliche Erosion," *Colloq. Geograph.*, **1**, 71 pp.

Cross-references: *Abrasion; Aggradation; Asymmetric Valleys; Baer–Babinet Law; Base Level; Canyon Cutting; Corrasion; Degradation; Denudation; Drainage Patterns; Erosion; Eustasy; Floodplain; Glacial Geology; Glacial Scour; Gradation; Grade, Graded Stream; Hanging Valley; Incised Meander; Landslides; Mass Movement; Morphogenetic Classification; Morphogenetic Regions; Mudflows; Nickpoint; Pediment; Peneplain; Permafrost; Pothole; Profile of Equilibrium; Quaternary; Rivers; Rivers—Meandering and Braiding; Roche Moutonnée; Savanna Landscape; Slipoff Slope; Solifluction; Stream Capture; Stream Channel Characteristics; Structural Control in Geomorphology; Terraces, Fluvial; Thalweg; Trumpet Valley; Tundra Landscape; Valley (Mountain) Glaciers; Waterfalls; Water Gap; Youth–Maturity–Old Age.* Vol. II: *Climatic Classification; Climatic Variations; Vegetation Classification and Description.* Vol. VI: *Fluvial Sediment Transport; Weathering—Chemical.*

VALLEY AND RIDGE LANDSCAPE—*See* RIDGE AND VALLEY TOPOGRAPHY

VALLEY (MOUNTAIN) GLACIERS*

Valley glaciers comprise one of the two general classifications of glaciers. The other is ice sheets or icecaps. Valley glaciers are also referred to as mountain glaciers, ice streams, or Alpine glaciers (Matthes, 1942, p. 151; Flint, 1957, p. 11).

Valley glaciers originate in cirques at the head of high mountain valleys and flow downward much as a stream of water follows an existing channel. In general, they are rather narrow in relation to length. The length of a mountain glacier may vary from a fraction of a mile to tens of miles; widths from a few hundred feet to several miles. Altitudes may range from near the summit of lofty mountains to sea level. Some of the Alaskan and Canadian glaciers have an altitude range of over 15,000 feet.

Hobbs preferred "mountain glacier," and evidently included within this term the nunatak-studded margins of an ice sheet such as Greenland. Cotton spoke of "mountain-and-valley glaciers" and subdivided them into "valley glaciers" *sensu stricto* and "hanging glaciers" (*Cirque* or *corrie*

* Publication authorized by Director, U.S. Geological Survey.

glaciers q.v.). Baulig gives four subdivisions for "valley glacier": (a) *normal* or *alpine type*; (b) *rudimentary type*, "Pyreneean," cirque or corrie type; (c) *hypertrophic type*, the "transection glacier" of Ahlmann, where several valley glaciers are welded together, crossing over the cols; (d) *piedmont, Alaskan type* or *Malaspina type* or "intermontane glaciers" which debouch onto plains or into open valleys. A number of other special, local types of valley glacier are known, e.g., the *Turkestan type*, which is not fed by névé but exclusively by snow avalanches; the *Mustag type*, also without a névé basin, but a central Asiatic form, occupying a snow-filled valley, evidently recently elevated to the snow line, the "firnketeltype" of Visser. The valley glacier with many tributaries is sometimes called the *dendritic glacier* or *trunk type*, the *Himalayan type* or *polysynthetic glacier*.

Distribution

Glaciers are found on all continents except Australia, which nevertheless suffered fairly localized Pleistocene glaciation. Most are located in the higher latitudes but there are high-mountain glaciers along or near the equator in Africa and South

FIG. 1. Barnard Glacier, St. Elias Mountains, Alaska. Note multiple medial moraines, one corresponding to each tributary glacier. (Photo: Bradford Washburn, by permission).

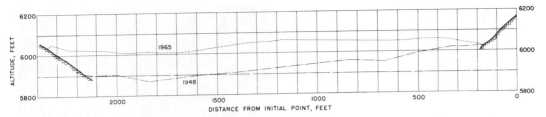

FIG. 2. Nisqually Glacier, Mt. Rainier National Park, Washington, cross profiles.

America, and in the mid-latitudes of central Asia. The area bordering the Gulf of Alaska is particularly notable for the number and size of the valley glaciers. According to Dyson (1962, p. 55) they include some of the longest and largest valley glaciers in the world. Particularly notable are the Hubbard and Logan Glaciers which originate at or near the summit of Mt. Logan, elevation 19,850 feet, in Yukon Territory (Canada). The Hubbard Glacier, as shown on the St. Elias quadrangle (1964) has a length of 65 miles, with its terminus at tidewater in Disenchantment Bay. The Logan Glacier has a length of about 60 miles.

The glaciers in the conterminous United States are small in comparison with those in Alaska and parts of Canada. Most are located in the State of Washington along the northern Cascades and on the high peaks, namely, Mt. Baker, Glacier Peak, Mt. Rainier, Mt. Adams, and Mt. St. Helens. The principal glaciers in Oregon are on Mt. Hood and in California on Mt. Shasta.

The largest valley glacier in this Pacific Northwest region is the Emmons Glacier which originates at the summit of Mt. Rainier, elevation 14,408 feet. It has a length of about 5 miles, with the terminus at an elevation of about 5200 feet. Probably the best known glacier in this region is the Nisqually Glacier. It also originates at the summit of Mt. Rainier and, in a length of slightly over 4 miles, descends to a terminal elevation of 4700 feet (1961).

Valley glaciers are usually enclosed between steeply rising, ice-eroded mountain slopes and frequently have prominent lateral moraines along their borders. This is particularly true where the glaciers have been at an appreciably higher stage during some previous period. Glaciers that have experienced a pronounced recession may or may not have a terminal moraine. Terminal moraines that have been formed may be obliterated by sudden floods originating on the glacier. These are usually of short duration and the actual volume of water may not be large, but the sudden release of a comparatively small volume of water can be very destructive. There are no conspicuous terminal moraines downvalley from the Nisqually Glacier, the terminus of which has receded over a mile since first observed in 1857 by Lt. Kautz. The Emmons Glacier, on the other hand, has a very prominent

terminal moraine as shown on the topographic map of Mt. Rainier National Park by the U.S. Geological Survey.

A valley glacier may be a single ice stream or it may consist of a main stream and several tributaries, similar to a river system. The Barnard Glacier in the St. Elias Mountains in Alaska (Fig. 1) is an example of a glacier with several tributaries (Dyson, 1962, Plate XIX). Unlike streams of water, the tributaries do not mix with the main stream but maintain their identity, separated by medial moraines, as the glacier moves downvalley. This is well illustrated in Fig. 1. It will be noted from the separate moraines on the tributary glaciers that they in turn have been formed by smaller tributaries.

Glacier Flow

A glacier moves downvalley due to the pull of gravity and also due to plastic flow (see *Glacier Geophysics*, Vol. VI). Plastic flow will occur when an ice body attains a thickness of 100–150 feet (Matthes, 1942, p. 154). Like a stream of water, the greatest velocity is in the central portion with lesser velocities toward the edges. This results in the central portion of a glacier being somewhat higher than at the edges. The flow of water is generally expressed in feet per second whereas the flow of a glacier is expressed in inches or feet per day or per year. There is considerable variation in the rate of movement between different glaciers and even for the same glacier, depending on whether it is in a state of equilibrium, is shrinking, or is increasing in thickness. For example, measurements on the Nisqually Glacier, near a cross-profile at an altitude of 6000 feet (Fig. 2), during the period 1943–1947 when the glacier surface altitude was gradually decreasing, show the maximum movement as 50–60 ft/yr. There was a pronounced increase in surface altitude from 1948–58. The maximum movement from 1957–58 was somewhat over 400 feet (Johnson, 1960, p. 59). Subsequent observations (unpublished data) indicate annual movement in this area of as much as 500 feet.

The surface of a glacier is seldom smooth but is cut by crevasses. These result from tensional forces set up by glacier motion. Crevasses vary in width from a few feet to as much as 50 feet or more, and they attain depths of as much as 100 feet. Flint

(1957, p. 15) defines five varieties, namely, transverse, longitudinal, radial, marginal and *bergschrund* (q.v.).

ARTHUR JOHNSON

References

Canada, Department of Mines and Technical Surveys, Surveys and Mapping Branch, 1964, St. Elias Quadrangle, scale 1:500,000.

Dyson, James L., 1962, "The World of Ice," New York, Alfred A. Knopf, 292pp.

Flint, Richard Foster, 1957, "Glacial and Pleistocene Geology," New York, John Wiley & Sons, 553pp.

Johnson, Arthur, 1960, "Variation in surface elevation of the Nisqually Glacier, Mt. Rainier, Washington," *Intern. Assoc. Scientific Hydrology*, Bull., **19.**

Matthes, F. E., 1942, "Glaciers in Hydrology," in "Physics of the Earth," Vol. 9, New York, McGraw-Hill Book Co.

U.S. Geological Survey, 1963, Nisqually Glacier, 1951, 1956, and 1961, Mt. Rainier National Park, Washington, scale 1:12,000.

Cross-references: *Bergschrund*; *Cirque Glacier*; *Crevasse*. Vol. VI: *Glacier Geophysics*; *Glaciology*.

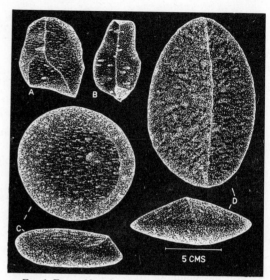

FIG. 1. Faceted basalt pebbles. Heard Island, Southern Indian Ocean. From a conglomerate in which the surface pebbles are being faceted. (Collector, P. J. Stephenson.)

VALLEY TRAIN—*See* **OUTWASH PLAIN, FAN, TERRACE, SANDUR**

VARVES—*See* pr Vol. VI

VEGETATION CLASSIFICATION AND DESCRIPTION—*See* Vol. II

VEGETATION MARKERS AND LANDSCAPES—*See* pr Vol. VI

VEGETATIVE ZONATION—*See* pr. Vol. VI **ZONATION OF TERRESTRIAL ECOLOGIC BELTS**

VENTIFACTS

A ventifact is a stone which has been shaped to some extent by the abrasion of wind-driven sand. Such abrasion produces characteristic features, the most striking being that rather flat faces, termed "facets," are commonly developed. These meet one another and the remaining unabraded surface of the stone, if any, at sharp angles (Fig. 1). There may be from one to perhaps eight or more facets. These, though generally well polished, ordinarily have surface irregularities and sometimes show marked fluting or grooving, which in a reasonably homogeneous rock is aligned with the wind direction.

The term "dreikanter" has been widely applied to ventifacts having three pronounced edges, but

unfortunately the word has had inconsistent usage (Bryan, 1931). "Zweikanter" has two facets.

Distribution. Ventifacts occur almost exclusively in desert sediments, but they are occasionally found elsewhere where there is great eolian sand movement (e.g., near Marlborough, New Zealand; King, 1936). Ventifacts of recent origin are fairly common in the great torrid deserts, as in North Africa, but the most spectacular occurrences are in cold deserts, such as in Iceland, where winds of exceptional force and duration are experienced.

Ventifacts are known in various ancient desert sediments dating back to the Precambrian. There are many Pleistocene (periglacial) examples in places where deserts formerly bordered retreating ice sheets (Cailleux, 1942).

Manner of Facet Formation. Early contention concerning the manner in which facets are formed (Bryan, 1931, for summary and bibliography) has now been largely resolved, and current interpretation may be summarized as follows.

It has been observed (Sharp, 1949, and others) that where large boulders, unmoved for long intervals, become deeply cut by the sand blast of a wind which varies little in direction, a single, rather flat, upward and windward facing surface is developed on each stone. Smaller stones associated with such large, single-faced boulders commonly have several abrasion faces. Such stones have been moved at intervals during the long process of abrasion, either by rare floods or by being undermined by wind erosion, so that different sides of the stones have faced the wind at different periods, and a succession of facets has been developed.

Abrasion close to the ground is slight, but it

becomes stronger upward to a height of as much as a foot or more, depending on wind strength. In consequence, the upper part of an abrasion face recedes more rapidly than the lower part, and ultimately the face approaches the horizontal. Unless the texture or mineralogy of the stone being cut imparts very variable abrasion resistance, the abrasion face flattens as it is formed. Where a stone is of reasonably homogeneous material and dense texture, a fairly sharp angle develops between the upper edge of the receding face and the lee surface of the stone [Fig. 1(C) and (D)].

It is generally possible to determine the abrasion direction for well-developed facets by reference to the direction of fluting or grooving and the position of the sharpest bounding edge of the facet. Other features also may betray the wind direction. Thus, where a ventifact is of decidedly heterogeneous material, e.g., having sizable quartz grains among soft minerals, the hard grains will stand out from the facet surface and will have slightly upstanding "tails" of softer material on their protected lee sides. Again, empty vesicles become cut out most strongly on their downwind sides as abrasion exposes them, and downwind extended depressions result [Fig. 1(B)]. Any mineralogical soft spot in a rock can create a similar feature.

It has been assumed above that the simplest possible circumstances apply, i.e., that the stones are more or less rounded to begin with and the direction of sand blast varies little. However, these conditions do not always apply, and it can then become very difficult to interpret the origin of individual facets. Thus, the wind can vary in direction, and it has been shown by experiment (Schoewe, 1932) that stones of suitable original shapes may be cut away, even in these circumstances, so that they come to resemble closely those which are formed by unidirectional blasting.

Even more important, stones may have fracture "facets" before becoming abraded, or they may become fractured during the period of sand abrasion. In the latter case, the origins of the fractures are normally ancient cracks or cleavages which become opened by thermal expansion and contraction of the pebbles themselves or by repeated freezing of water in the cracks. Where such fractures exist, and subsequently become sand blasted, it can be very difficult to distinguish them from facets cut entirely by abrasion (Sugden, 1964).

There is scarcely any doubt that the stones shown in Fig. 1(C) and (D) had their facets developed entirely by the abrasion of originally almost ellipsoidal pebbles. Figure 1(C) shows top and side views of a pebble which lay with its major axes horizontal during sand blasting. The blast was from the left, the sharp edge of the single, slightly fluted facet being to the right. The stone in Fig. 1(D) has had two faces developed in consequence

of its being turned horizontally through approximately 180° at some stage during abrasion. The pebbles A and B, however, from the same site, have pocked and fluted faces which are so arranged relative to one another that the faceting evidently could not have been produced by sand blast alone, and fracture face formation either before or during the process of abrasion is the only possible explanation.

W. Sugden

References

Bryan, K., 1931, "Wind worn stones or ventifacts; a discussion and bibliography," Rept. Comm. Sedimentation 1929–1930; *Natl. Res. Council Circ.*, **98,** 29–50.

Cailleux, A., 1942, "Les actions éoliennes périglaciaires en Europe," *Mém. Soc. Géol. France*, **46,** 176pp.

King, L. C., 1936, "Wind faceted stones from Marlborough, New Zealand," *J. Geol.*, **44,** 201–213.

Schoewe, W. H., 1932, "Experiments on the formation of wind-faceted pebbles," *Am. J. Sci.*, **24,** 111–134.

Sharp, R. P., 1949, "Pleistocene ventifacts east of the Big Horn Mountains, Wyoming," *J. Geol.*, **57,** 175–195.

Sugden, W., 1964, "Origin of faceted pebbles in some Recent desert sediments of southern Iraq," *Sedimentology*, **3,** 65–74.

Walther, J., 1924, "Das Gesetz der Wüstenbildung," Leipzig, Quelle & Meyer, 421pp.

Cross-references: *Abrasion; Arid Cycle; Deserts and Desert Landforms; Desert Varnish; Eolian Transport; Periglacial Eolian Effects; Wind Action.*

VOLCANIC AVALANCHE—*See* pr Vol. V

VOLCANIC LANDSCAPES

Volcanic landscapes consist for the most part of accumulations of solidified lava and of fragmentary volcanic products. Assemblages of landforms so built, though in some cases themselves partly dissected by erosion, contrast strongly with most other landscapes which are largely shaped by erosional sculpture of the land.

The constructional features fall broadly into two categories: (a) cones and fields of cones, domes, and related salient forms, and (b) plateaus and plains. There are, however, volcanic complexes consisting partly of extruded domes of lava and partly of volcanic plateaus. These are, moreover, diversified by negative features—explosively blown-out rifts and hollows, the largest of which are calderas. Lakes associated with these in part occupy explosion-made depressions but also occupy valleys dammed by solidified lava or warped by differential subsidence caused by volcanicity.

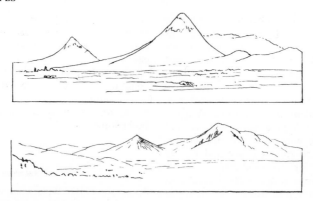

FIG. 1. Ararat and its twin volcano, from Erivan, as sketched (above) by A. K. Lobeck, with exaggerated steepness; (below) by George Barbour, in correct proportions.

Andesitic Volcanic Fields

Many of the largest volcanic mountains are cones consisting of materials of andesitic, or intermediate, composition (with medium-silica content). Most such lavas are explosive when they reach the surface, and 50–90 % of their product consists of fragmentary (pyroclastic) material, much of which is built into cones. Cones consist either entirely of pyroclastic material heaped around a localized (central) vent, the crater or orifice of a volcanic pipe ("ash" cones), or of alternating layers of pyroclastics and of lava, the latter having overflowed either from the lip of the crater or from high on the flank of the volcano. With an increasing proportion of lava layers, there is a transition to lava cones. The layered structure of cones, especially of those with alternating ash and lava, has led to their description as "stratovolcanoes."

In general, it may be said that ash cones are both the steepest and the most symmetrical, for on their slopes material has come to rest at the angle of repose. When sketching volcanic mountains, artists tend to exaggerate the steepness of their slopes, and thus cones are often drawn chimney-like with slopes averaging about 45° and even steeper towards the summit (Fig. 1, above). Rarely, however, is any part of the slope much steeper than 30° (Fig. 1, below).

When the steepness of a lava cone or stratovolcano approaches the angle of repose of fine pyroclastic material (Fig. 2), it may be assumed that the ash-cone form has dominated its shape. Even if the outer layer consists entirely of lava, this must be a thin sheath resting on ash slopes. It has solidified not as a continuous sheet but as many lava tongues that have flowed down successively and overlap at their edges.

The feeding pipe that leads up through the center of a cone to the crater at the summit, where cone-building eruptive ejection is concentrated, does not change appreciably in diameter during growth of the cone. Thus large cones seem sharp at the apex (Fig. 1), while smaller ones are bluntly truncated (Fig. 4), so that when quite small they are more accurately described as mounds than as cones.

Seen at close quarters, the ash slopes of rapidly growing cones are not smooth but are generally fluted with radial furrows due to a sliding of hot ash, and the slopes of cones may also be dissected to some extent by ravines cut by erosion between eruptions.

The symmetry of even the most perfectly conical volcanoes is commonly marred to some extent by upgrowth of at least one "parasitic" cone on the flank—as in the case of Fuji, in Japan, and Egmont, in New Zealand (Fig. 3).

Large cones like Fuji and Egmont, which from a distance seem almost perfectly symmetrical, are venerated as objects of great beauty, but they are not common. Though the popular idea of a volcano envisages a perfect cone, clustering of vents with production of multiple volcanoes is quite usual, and so volcanic mountains of rather irregular form are the rule rather than the exception. Examples of multiple volcanoes are Ruapehu and Tongariro, in the center of the North Island of New Zealand, but on the flank of the latter, there is a single symmetrical cone, Ngauruhoe (Fig. 4).

FIG. 2. Profile of an andesite lava cone "at the most only a few thousand years old" (Healy, 1962), Mount Edgecumbe, Bay of Plenty, New Zealand. Height of cone, about 2500 feet.

FIG. 3. Nearly perfect cone of a stratovolcano, Mount Egmont, New Zealand, with a parasitic cone on its flank.

Around and among clustered andesitic volcanoes are fields of widespread ash (and with it, some coarse debris) that may form plains of almost regional extent. Volcanic explosion must be understood to mean a rending of lava into fragments which will yield dust, sand, and large pumiceous blocks and bombs. It is brought about by exsolution of gases (largely steam) throughout a considerable body of still liquid lava, generally in the throat of a volcano. A succession of such explosions supplies the layers of "ash" of which cones are largely built, but much fine material and even some coarse fragments also are ejected with such force that they fall beyond the steep slopes of the cones. The finest material is carried away by winds and is deposited far and wide. Thus, the surrounding country is veneered and gradually built up by debris that falls as "showers" and accumulates over the nearer parts of the landscape to a considerable depth; this debris will partly or wholly blanket erosional forms whether these are older than the volcanicity or have been developed by dissection of the volcanic landscape.

As a result of explosive ejection that carries pyroclastic materials to a distance beyond the upper slopes, and partly as a result of the washing down of ash and its deposition as alluvial fans and of the avalanching of newly deposited hot, mobile, gas-rich ash, the lower slopes of a cone are gentler than its upper slopes. The profile as a whole is thus concave.

In addition to showers, most andesitic volcanoes supply much material by ejection as "nuées ardentes" and/or as "lahars," both of which may cause the accumulation of large quantities of debris on lower slopes and the surrounding country. Nuées ardentes (glowing clouds) are very mobile, hot gaseous emulsions derived from exploding lava and containing glowing particles and fragments which may be still giving off gas. The "clouds," which either overflow a crater rim or are shot out laterally by explosion from viscous protruding domes of lava, portions of which disintegrate, are heavy enough to flow down slopes with velocities of up to 70 m.p.h., and thus spread widely. Such an outburst of very hot and largely gaseous material from a volcano in Martinique passed through the town of St. Pierre in 1902, killing the inhabitants. Material carried by such nuées ardentes contributes to the building up of plains between and around volcanic mountains with sandy debris.

Lahars (volcanic mudflows) also supply aprons of rocky debris—for example, that which forms an extensive plain west of the central volcanic mountains of the North Island of New Zealand (Ruapehu and Tongariro). A mixture of fine debris and water, derived generally from a lake in the crater of a

FIG. 4. Growing cone of Ngauruhoe, New Zealand, with behind it the multiple volcano Tongariro, as seen from Mount Ruapehu.

FIG. 5. Submaturely dissected (and drowned) northeast slope of the Akaroa basalt dome, Banks Peninsula, New Zealand.

dormant volcano, bursts out when eruption is resumed, forming mud that rushes down the mountain side. The ratio of debris to water is commonly so high that the density of the mixture is great enough to buoy up and carry along a great quantity of boulders. During the slow growth of some andesitic volcanoes, innumerable lahars have distributed, far and wide, both fine debris and lava blocks derived from near the mountain tops. The surface of a recently formed accumulation of lahar-carried material is usually a field of boulder mounds—a topography developed very widely, for example, over the lower western slopes of Egmont volcano, New Zealand. These have been mistaken for cones built by minor eruptions, while others, on the northern lower slope of Ruapehu volcano, have been mistaken for glacial moraines.

Basaltic Lava Forms

Lava of basic composition is less viscous, and thus less explosive, than andesite; hence, it supplies a much smaller proportion of pyroclastic material. It commonly yields very voluminous lava flows, which because of their low viscosity spread out thinly. Such outflows of basalt build large lava domes, shield volcanoes, and also lava plains and some volcanic plateaus. Shield volcanoes and basalt domes are built up to some extent like andesitic cones as a result of emission from localized vents, but in other respects they have more in common

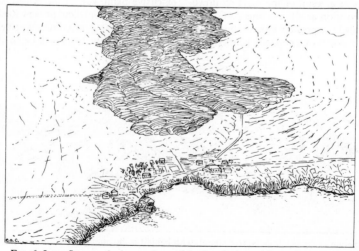

FIG. 6. Lava flow on the lower slope of the basalt dome Mauna Loa, Hawaii.

FIG. 7. The high Mauna Kea basalt dome, Hawaii, with scoria-built cones and mounds on its flanks.

with lava plains and basalt plateaus. Basalt emerges from fissures rather than from pipe-like conduits, though the distinction between these is somewhat arbitrary, pipes developing where emission, primarily through fissures, has been localized, perhaps where feeding fissures intersect.

"Shield" volcanoes, typically developed in Iceland, are very flat cones of moderate size with summit craters usually so small as not to interfere appreciably with the conical shape (Rittmann, 1962, pp. 117–118). They have grown very rapidly. The Rangitoto Island volcano, at Auckland, New Zealand, 750 feet high, is an example. Though extinct, it is of very recent origin and seems to have been built by a single eruption.

Basaltic domes of the type described in the Hawaiian Islands, but occurring also in Samoa and other volcanic islands in the Pacific and Indian Oceans, have domical form (analogous to the conical form of andesitic and shield volcanoes) because of a concentration of feeding fissures beneath the volcano, not so much at points as in zones ("rift" zones, of T. A. Jaggar). The domes are, therefore, generally elongated. Such domes (as well as shield volcanoes) also differ from andesitic cones in being composed almost entirely of flows of lava and having gentle surface slopes. Both of these characteristics are attributable to the mobility (lower viscosity) of basaltic lava as compared with andesitic—due to its basic chemical composition, i.e., low content of silica—and the related property of emitting gas quietly, without explosion.

The largest of all volcanic mountains are basalt domes such as Etna, in Sicily, and Pacific and Indian Ocean island volcanoes—two large and three smaller domes, for example, forming the large island of Hawaii. Among islands of the Pacific Ocean, there are basalt domes in all stages of dissection and destruction by erosion. Two domes, maturely dissected, form the island of Tahiti, and

twin overlapping domes, dissected submaturely and partly submerged, form Banks Peninsula, New Zealand (Fig. 5).

The large size of such domes can be appreciated when it is realized that much of their bulk is below sea level; the two largest in Hawaii, Mauna Kea and Mauna Loa, have been built up to a height of $5\frac{1}{2}$ miles from the ocean floor.

The dome form is not perfect. A large central area on the active volcano Mauna Loa, for example, is not far from level because of its tendency to subside with the formation of steep-walled fracture-bounded sinks, which become filled with horizontally bedded lava flows that issue from fissures within the sinks. Outflow from radial fissures that open on the flanks of the mountain at the same time supplies other flows that run down, solidify on, and continually build out, the gentle slopes of the flanks (Fig. 6). Similar outbuilding takes place on Etna.

With waning of activity, the lava emitted from a basalt dome is generally of less basic composition and higher viscosity, so that eruption becomes more explosive, supplying pyroclastic material. Thus, the active central vent on the lava dome of Etna has recently built a summit cone, and a similar cone surmounts the Mauna Kea dome, Hawaii, while both of these great domes are peppered over with small (adventive) cones (Fig. 7). These, however, do not obscure the domical form of the mountains as seen from a distance (Fig. 8). The shield volcano of Rangitoto Island is also surmounted by a scoria mound.

Apparently related closely in origin to basalt domes, more especially to dome complexes such as that of the island of Hawaii, are basalt plateaus. To build these, however, lava has risen through fissures not grouped in rift zones but sporadically distributed, so that flows from a multitude of sources have spread out and interfingered to make a pile of sheets thousands of feet thick, thus form-

FIG. 8. Domes of Hawaii Island. Mauna Kea (left) and Mauna Loa (right) each over 13,000 feet in altitude.

Fig. 9. Lava spur, Egmont volcano, New Zealand, showing inversion of relief developed by erosion.

ing a plateau. A recently built and as yet little dissected example is the Snake River basalt "plain," 20,000 square miles in extent, in Idaho. Ancient basalt plateaus are known in various parts of the world, the most extensive in the Deccan, India, and the Columbia River region of western North America (over 100,000 square miles in area). These are now in various stages of destruction by erosion, and the landscapes so produced are, like other structural plateaus, characterized by stepped escarpments, mesas, and buttes.

Other (non-basaltic) volcanic plateaus—those consisting of ignimbrite—will be described later, as they are emplaced by a process very different from the piling up of lava sheets that builds basalt plateaus.

Basalt *plains* are, as it were, embryonic forms of basalt plateaus. Consisting of much thinner and less extensive piles of lava sheets, they are common throughout the world; they are, indeed, with associated accumulations of coarse scoriaceous material forming mounds and cones, the most prevalent of volcanic landscapes. Consisting of single layers, or at most a few superposed layers, of lava, they have solidified on gentle land slopes or after running down on to the floors of valleys and are thus approximately plane and nearly level. They may be hundreds of square miles in extent. Some valleys are thus blocked, impounding lakes.

When plain-forming lava sheets are partly destroyed by erosion, the surviving remnants assume distinctive forms. As the margins are undercut and steepened by erosion, they become escarpments, for the basalt is commonly much more resistant than the underlying rocks. Gorges develop, and where ponded rivers overflow across lava dams spectacular waterfalls (miniature Niagaras) are formed. Of these, there are good examples in the North Auckland district of New Zealand.

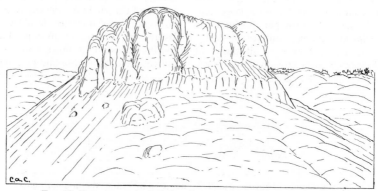

Fig. 10. Butte on an ignimbrite plateau at Mamaku, New Zealand.

FIG. 11. A large multiple rhyolite dome of recent origin, Mount Tarawera, New Zealand.

Because of the hardness of lava that buries a valley floor or plain, inversion of relief commonly develops as general lowering of the land surface by erosion proceeds. Thus, a flow that has followed a valley becomes in its turn a ridge. Similar inversion takes place on the flanks of conical volcanoes, where radial ravines cut in dormant periods have been occupied by tongues of lava, and later, with continued erosion of the cone, have become spurs (Fig. 9).

Though the lavas that build plains are sometimes regarded as flowing from the flanks of volcanoes, cones and mounds associated with them are as a rule subsidiary to the lava flows, which have been emitted from fissures or from vents localized on fissures by pipe-forming enlargement. Cones, better termed mounds when small, because of their blunt truncation, are built around the vents; they consist of scoria, i.e., vesicular lumps of lava generally supplied by fire-fountaining (lava-fountaining), a phenomenon caused by vertical escape of powerful jets of gas from the lava vents, carrying up with it spray and clots of liquid lava, brilliantly glowing, to solidify in the air and fall around the vent, where the scoria accumulates at the angle of repose.

Basaltic scoria mounds and cones are conspicuous forms, though of less than mountainous dimensions (up to several hundred feet in height). As a rule, each mound or cone is the product of a single eruption, as is the lava flow associated with it, but several such flows may coalesce to form a lava plain, parts of which may be of different ages. Scoria mounds are built also at points on the radial fissures from which lava flows on the flanks of basalt domes.

A finer grade of pyroclastic debris is produced in considerable quantity by explosion of basalt lava in contact with water—generally seawater—and "tuff" rings are sometimes built of this violently ejected material. These are steep on the inner side and slope gently outward. An example is that forming Diamond Head, near Honolulu.

The Rhyolitic Landscape Complex

Just as andesitic landscapes are characterized by great cones and cone clusters with surrounding plains built up by deposits of shower, lahar and nuée-ardente origin, and basaltic lava plains with associated mounds and cones constitute another very common type of volcanic landscape, so also the acid-volcanic landscape complex is a distinctive type. This is exemplified in the North Island of New Zealand by the features of the Taupo-Rotorua volcanic field. The most striking landforms of this region are great plateaus of ignimbrite southeast and northwest of the elongated sunken area of the Taupo Volcanic Zone as strictly defined. Plateau-forming ignimbrites are emplaced by a different mechanism from that building basalt plateaus (see above). The ignimbrite is an acid (high-silica) rock composed of agglutinated (or "welded") particles that have settled from "glowing clouds" of a special kind, derived from magma with high gas content and emitted not like ordinary nuées ardentes but in much greater volume from fissures.

"A turbulent suspension of magma particles in a continuous gas phase boils over the rim of the fissure as a fluidized system of pumice, glass shards, [and crystals], all surrounded by very hot and highly compressed gases, which reduce the internal friction.... This mixture reaches the surface in great quantities per time unit.... The bulk of the material spreads sidewards from the eruption fissure as a pyroclastic ash flow of very low viscosity, flooding and burying the topography.... Successive eruptions may rapidly follow.... Thick sheets can accumulate" (R. W. van Bemmelen).

"The outpouring ... must take place uninterruptedly, so that it takes on more the character of a vigorous overflow than of an explosive ejection.... Owing to their high mobility [overflowing glowing clouds] spread out extremely quickly and cover enormous surfaces with their still hot deposits, which weld with their own weight.... The volumes of solid and glassy materials produced ... often amount to hundreds of cubic kilometres" (Rittmann, 1962, p. 227).

One of the several sheets now recognized in the Taupo-Rotorua region "had a volume of at least 50 cubic miles and flowed for more than 40 miles from its source   .   . .. Any craters or vents from which [the ignimbrites] issued were probably buried and obliterated" (Healy, 1962).

In plateaus of such origin, naturally some of the features of basalt plateaus are duplicated, but because of the thickness of the sheets, stepped structural escarpments and related forms are not usually developed. Where plateau margins are steepened by erosion, however, the ignimbrite forms vertical-faced escarpments, generally fluted by large-scale columnar jointing.

A plateau surface may be far from smooth because of incomplete agglutination of particles toward the top of the ignimbrite sheet. When first emplaced, this must have been a sandy plain resembling that formed by the great "sand flow" of the Valley of Ten Thousand Smokes, Alaska, where in 1912 a broad valley was infilled by glowing clouds emitted from fissures. The "smokes" were fumaroles of steam from the cooling mass or underlying fissures. Such gaseous emanations at many points introduce mineral matter that locally indurates the sand layer. Where the loose sand has been removed by erosion from an ignimbrite plateau (as, for example, at Mamaku, near Rotorua, New Zealand), buttes of locally indurated rock may diversify the surface (Fig. 10).

Another feature of "acid" volcanicity illustrated in the Taupo-Rotorua volcanic field is a grouping in some localities of steep-sided domes and short flows of rhyolite lava. In general, extrusion of rhyolite has followed ignimbrite eruption. Acid lava is extremely viscous when emitted, and when it disintegrates explosively the resulting pyroclastic materials are generally ejected too violently to build typical cones around vents. Thus, a rhyolite volcano usually grows as a protruded mass of lava that assumes a roughly domical shape (sometimes spinous). Because of their irregular form these domes may not at first sight be recognizable as volcanic accumulations. The largest of such edifices in the Taupo-Rotorua region is Mount Tarawera (Fig. 11), which is a multiple dome only about 900 years old (Healy, 1962) and thus untouched by erosion. (The mountain is crossed, however, by a long rift blown out along a fissure in 1886; this eruption, strangely enough, emitted pyroclastic material of basic composition.)

Sheets of ejected rhyolitic pumiceous ash and pumice breccia also mantle the surface. In the Taupo Volcanic Zone, much of this was ejected from vents within Lake Taupo about 1700 years ago. The pumice that recently accumulated on slopes is dissected by closely spaced consequent ravines. Around Lake Taupo, many streams that earlier cut winding valleys now flow under pumice that partly infills these, and so have ceased to erode.

In regions of large-scale acid volcanicity, the emission of large volumes of material to form sheets of ignimbrite, the protrusion of rhyolite domes, and the ejection of much airborne pumice lead to subsidence of the roof over the underlying magma. In the Taupo-Rotorua region, this has let down the land surface over an area of fully a thousand square miles. There is much normal faulting, and the Taupo Volcanic Zone, in the restricted sense, is separated by fault scarps from surviving ignimbrite plateaus northwest and southeast of it, the total area of which is some thousands of square miles. Within the subsided zone, some faulted blocks of ignimbrite also stand up.

Numerous lakes of volcanic origin are associated with such volcanic fields. Within the Taupo Volcanic Zone, some of these are in valley systems drowned by warping within the area of general subsidence. The basin, 10 miles in diameter, that contains Lake Rotorua is, however, described as a caldera partly bounded by "ring" faults (Healy, 1962) and is probably one of the sources of ignimbrite eruption.

Lake Taupo, the largest lake in this region, partly occupies an area of subsidence bounded by faults, having ignimbrite plateaus east and west of it, but the northwestern part of the lake basin is bounded by sheer cliffs of ignimbrite and rhyolite and must be a caldera (Healy, 1962). It was probably produced by a series of explosions accompanied by collapse. It is thought that this part of the lake covers centers of eruption that have produced both ignimbrite-forming clouds and voluminous emissions of pumice.

C. A. COTTON

References

Cotton, C. A., 1952, "Volcanoes as Landscape Forms," Second ed., New York, John Wiley; Christchurch, Whitcombe and Tombs, 416pp.

Healy, J., 1962, "Structure and volcanism in the Taupo Volcanic Zone, New Zealand," in "Crust of the Pacific Basin," *Geophys. Monogr.*, **6**, 151–157.

Rittmann, A., 1962, "Volcanoes and their Activity," New York, John Wiley & Sons, 305pp.

Williams, H., 1932, "The history and character of volcanic domes," *Univ. Calif. Publ. Geol. Sci.*, **21**(5), 47–146.

Williams, H., 1941, "Calderas and their origin," *Univ. Calif. Publ. Geol. Sci.*, **25**(6), 239–346.

Cross-references: *Alluvial Fan, Cone*; *Caldera*; *Crater*; *Crater Lakes*; *Dome Mountain*; *Erosion*; *Inversion (of Topography, Relief)*; *Lava-displaced Drainage*; *Mesa and Butte*; *Mudflow*; *Plains*; *Plateau*; *Volcanic Necks and Diatremes*; *Warping*. Vol. V: *Andesite*; *Basalt*; *Magma*; *Nuées Ardente*; *Rhyolite*; *Volcanoes*. Vol. VI: *Tuff*; *Volcanic Ash Deposits*.

VOLCANIC NECKS AND DIATREMES

Products of igneous volcanic activity, volcanic necks and diatremes (gas pipes) are both pipe-like masses of lava, agglomerates and breccias that occupy former conduits for lavas and other ejectamenta to reach the earth's surface, and today form geomorphic features reflecting the differential erosion of the various materials. In most cases, the volcanic neck or "plug" stands up like a stump, crag or tower (Figs. 1 and 2). In others, the resistant, fine-grained rock in the chill zone of the extrusion, or the adjacent baked or silicified zone of the country rock, is more resistant to weathering than the middle of the pipe; in this case, the latter is eroded out as a

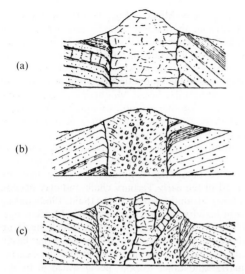

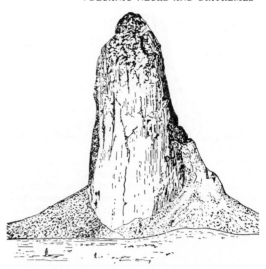

FIG. 1. Examples of deeply eroded volcanic necks from Scotland (Geikie, 1897): (a) "Neck," or funnel of old volcano, plugged up with basalt; (b) "Neck" filled up with agglomerate; (c) "Neck" occupied by agglomerate and basalt.

FIG. 4. Spine of "Aiguille" of Mont Pelée, Martinique, which rose bodily to reach over 300 meters in height in the eruption of 1902. (Sketch: Lobeck, 1939). (By permission of McGraw-Hill Book Co., N.Y.)

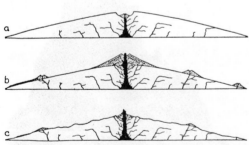

FIG. 2. The structure of Largo Law (Scotland) and a suggested restoration of the profile of the original volcano (Geikie, 1897).

shallow basin and the altered wall rocks act as a barrier all around or on one side (Allen and Balk, 1954; Barrington and Kerr, 1961). A special case is the *Kimberlite pipe* (see Vol. V).

The neck may sometimes crown a shield-shaped volcano, as is commonly observed in the Pacific Northwest (Washington, Oregon) Cascade Mountains (Fig. 3). In a somewhat exceptional case (certain felsic volcanoes), the neck may be forced bodily up during an eruption revival (Williams, 1932), as in the celebrated example of the "spine" of

FIG. 3. Evolution of a typical High Cascade volcano. (a) Shield-shaped cone of olivine basalt and olivine-bearing basaltic andesite built almost wholly by quiet effusions. Cone of fragmental ejecta beginning to grow in the summit crater. (b) The fragmental cone continues to grow. Thin flows contribute to its rise. A central plug and a swarm of dikes, usually a radial swarm invade the cone. Parasitic cinder cones develop on the lower flanks of the lava shield. (c) Glacial erosion reduces the volcano to its present condition. These simplified diagrams apply to such High Cascade cones as North Sister, Husband, Broken Top, Mt. Washington, Mt. Thielsen, and Union Peak (Williams, 1932).

A VOLCANIC NECK CONSISTING OF VOLCANIC BRECCIA

FIG. 5. The "Rocher" (Rock) of Saint Michael, at Le Puy (Velay) in the Auvergne, central France. (Sketch: Lobeck, 1939). (By permission of McGraw-Hill Book Co., N.Y.)

FIG. 6. Devil's Tower, Wyoming. Regarded as a degraded laccolith by Darton, but as a volcanic neck by Johnson. Note that the lava of a crater filling will develop vertical columnar joints, while lower down there will be a transition to radial joints in the pipe, which is suggested at the base of the "tower." (Sketch: Lobeck, 1939). (By permission of McGraw-Hill Book Co., N.Y.)

Mont Pelée on Martinique in the West Indies, which rose 300 meters in the 1902 eruption (Fig. 4).

Perhaps the most famous volcanic neck is that of Arthur's Seat, the site of Edinburgh Castle, Scotland, where it has been so recognized since the days of Hutton and Playfair (see Black, 1966). Also very well-known are the impressive "puys" of the Auvergne in France (Scrope, 1858; Glangeaud, 1923; also Fig. 5). Columnar jointing bears witness to the cooling patterns of the lava, curving in and downward from the wall of the neck or the floor of the crater. A classic problem in this respect is Devil's Tower, Wyoming; its columnar jointing is largely vertical (Fig. 6). Is it a volcanic plug? In this case there would be radial jointing beneath the surface (the interpretation of Johnson, 1907). Or is it part of a laccolith? (Laccoliths do occur in the area, the suggestion of Darton and O'Harra, 1907.)

Some of the most striking necks and diatremes are those of the southern part of the Colorado Plateau, e.g., the Hopi Buttes in northeastern Arizona. Here they are scattered across a broad plateau landscape and under semiarid conditions are extremely well displayed (Fig. 7). Both the stumps of old volcanoes and the pipes of diatremes are present; the difference between them is not obvious at first sight but requires close petrographic study (Gregory, 1917; Williams, 1936; Hack, 1942).

Volcanic necks that appear in mature landscapes of low relief are naturally all the more striking because one is not so accustomed to seeing volcanoes in stable areas. The lavas of these rather rare volcanoes (and diatremes also) are sometimes the curious rocks of the leucitite group, e.g., in the Kaiserstuhl of Germany, the Leucite Hills of Wyoming (Kemp and Knight, 1903) and the Noonkambah area of the Fitzroy Valley, Kimberley Div., Western Australia (Prider, 1940; Fig. 8).

Radial dikes are often laid bare by deep erosion of a volcanic neck, a classic example being that of Ship-

rock in New Mexico (Fig. 9). On the island of Moorea in the Society Islands, just northwest of Tahiti, a narrow radial dike forms a high ridge, but lower down a rectangular block has fallen out of it, giving one the odd view of sky and clouds on the other side of the mountain. Radiating dikes are also seen in the Glasshouse Mountains of Queensland (Fig. 10). Another example of a radial dike ridge is seen in the Auvergne at the Dent de Rancune on the Puy de Sancy (Rittmann, 1962, Fig. 74).

Another type of neck involves *breccia pipes* and *collapse features*, where the volcanic connection may be somewhat tenuous, e.g., some that are found in the early Tertiary chalk and clay plateau country around Cairo in Egypt (Said, 1962), dating from activity of late Oligocene-early Miocene age. These are diatremes of quartzite which stand up above the desert as towers. It is believed that basalt injections caused the groundwater in water-bearing quartz sandstones to boil. Being sealed in by impervious chalks and clays, steam built up a high pressure that was only released by upward boring in *phreatic diatremes*. These sand-filled pipes were later silicified by hydrothermal circulation (Rittmann, 1962, p. 241).

FIG. 7. Agathla Peak, in Monument Valley, Southern Utah; a volcanic neck of black lamprophyric rock that rises 1400 feet above the valley floor. (Photo: Lee Wilson).

FIG. 8. Machell's Pyramid, a leucitite volcanic neck, forming a residual hill above a "discordant plain" in a tropical region, where folded Permian sediments directly underlay a surface marked by laterite soil (note termite "hills," red in color). Noonkanbah Station, Kimberley, N.W. Australia. (Photo: R. W. Fairbridge).

Similar physiographic features are formed by the *silica plugs* and *sandstone pipes* which are analogous to diatremes but were emplaced by ascending hypo-gene siliceous solutions (Barrington and Kerr, 1963; Megrue and Kerr, 1965). On the Colorado Plateau, near Cameron (Arizona) the same hydrothermal

FIG. 9. Shiprock, a volcanic neck with prominent radiating dikes, in northeastern New Mexico, looking northeast. (Oblique air photo: Lee Wilson).

FIG. 10. Trachyte volcanic necks of Tertiary age, the Glasshouse Mountains, north of Brisbane, Australia. First seen from the sea by Capt. Cook, they were named the "Glasshouses." The highest is 556 meters above sea level. (Photo: Queensland Railways).

liquids have led to local solution of limestone horizons resulting in quaquaversal collapse basins (Figs. 11 and 12).

RHODES W. FAIRBRIDGE

References

Allen, J. E., and Balk, R., 1954, "Mineral resources of Fort Defiance and Tohatchi quadrangles, Arizona and New Mexico," *New Mexico Bur. Mines Mineral Resources Bull.*, **36**.

Barrington, J., and Kerr, P. F., 1961, "Breccia pipe near Cameron, Arizona," *Bull. Geol. Soc. Am.*, **72**, 1661–1674.

Barrington, J., and Kerr, P. F., 1963, "Collapse features and silica plugs near Cameron, Arizona," *Bull. Geol. Soc. Am.*, **74**, 1237–1258.

Black, G. P., 1966, "Arthur's Seat," Edinburgh, Oliver & Boyd, 226pp.

Cloos, H., 1941, "Bau und Tätigkeit von Tuffschloten. Untersuchungen an dem Schwabischen Vulkan," *Geol. Rundschau*, **32**, 709–800.

Craig, G. (editor), 1965, "The Geology of Scotland," Edinburgh, Oliver & Boyd, 556pp.

Darton, N. H., and O'Harra, C. C., 1907, "Description of the Devil's Tower quadrangle, Wyoming," *U.S. Geol. Surv. Folio*, **150**, 9pp.

Geikie, A., 1897, "The Ancient Volcanoes of Great Britain," London, 2 vols, 478 and 492pp.

Glangeaud, P., 1923, "La chaine des Puys," *Bull. Serv. Carte Géol. France*, **135**, 256pp.

Gregory, H. E., 1917, "Geology of the Navajo country," *U.S. Geol. Surv. Profess Paper* **93**.

Hack, J. T., 1942, "Sedimentation and volcanism in the Hopi buttes, Arizona," *Bull. Geol. Soc. Am.*, **53**, 335–372.

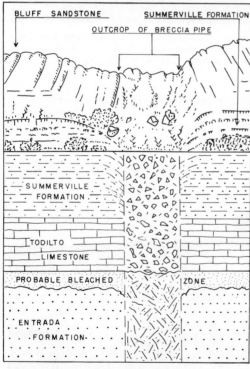

FIG. 11. Interpretation of a south Laguna breccia-pipe structure, New Mexico. The pipe is about 10 meters in diameter (Megrue and Kerr, 1965).

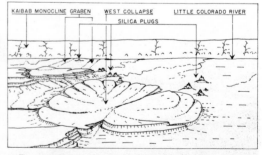

FIG. 12. West collapse, looking south (Cameron, Arizona). The central group of silica plugs lies along the southern rim of the collapse feature. The Little Colorado River gorge and the East Kaibab monocline lie in the distance. Diameter is about 600 meters (Barrington and Kerr, 1963).

Johnson, D. W., 1907, "Volcanic necks of the Mount Taylor region, New Mexico," *Bull. Geol. Soc. Am.,* **18,** 303–324.

Kemp, J. F., and Knight, W. C., 1903, "Leucite hills of Wyoming," *Bull. Geol. Soc. Am.,* **14,** 305–336.

Lobeck, A. K., 1939, "Geomorphology," New York, McGraw-Hill Book Co., 731pp.

Megrue, G. H., and Kerr, P. F., 1965, "Alteration of sandstone pipes, Laguna, New Mexico," *Bull. Geol. Soc. Am.,* **76,** 1347–1360.

Mitchell, G. H., Walton, E. K., and Grant, D., (editors), 1960, "Edinburgh Geology," Edinburgh, Oliver & Boyd, 222pp.

Perry, V. D., 1961, "The significance of mineralized breccia pipes," *Mining Engr.,* **13,** 367–376.

Prider, R. T., and Wade, A., 1940, "Leucite-bearing rocks of the West Kimberley areas, Western Australia," *Quart. J. Geol. Soc. London,* **96,** 39–98.

Rittmann, A., 1962, "Volcanoes and Their Activity," New York, Interscience Publishers, 305pp.

Russell, I. C., 1897, "Volcanoes of North America," New York, 346pp.

Said, R., 1962, "The Geology of Egypt," Amsterdam-New York, Elsevier, 377pp.

Scrope, G. P., 1858, "The Geology and Extinct Volcanos of Central France," Second ed., London, John Murray, 258pp.

Scrope, G. P., 1872, "Volcanos, the Character of their Phenomena," Second ed., London, Longmans, Green and Co., 490 pp. (First ed., 1825).

Shoemaker, E. M., and Moore, H. J., II, 1956, "Diatremes on the Navajo and Hopi reservations," *U.S. Geol. Surv. Trace Elem. Inv. Rept.,* **640,** 197–203.

Williams, H., 1932, "The history and character of volcanic domes," *Univ. Calif. (Berkeley) Publ. Geol. Sci.,* **21,** 51–146.

Williams, H., 1936, "Pliocene volcanoes of the Navajo–Hopi country," *Bull. Geol. Soc. Am.,* **47,** 111–171.

Cross-references: *Crater Lakes; Craters; Volcanic Landscapes.* Vol. V: *Kimberlite.*

VOLCANO—*See* **CRATER;** *also* Vol. V.

VOLCANO–KARST

Freshly erupted volcanic materials, especially pyroclastics such as certain tuffs and agglomerates that contain unstable minerals, are highly susceptible to corrosion by rainwater and a variety of karst-type microrelief forms develop, just as in a limestone *karst* (q.v.). Cliffs of similar rocks often permit the development of broad platforms of marine erosion, and sometimes the cliffs are undercut by a deep notch that is usually characteristic only of limestones (see *Limestone Coastal Weathering*); these marine examples are common in central Queensland, New Caledonia, Fiji, Samoa, New Zealand (North Island) and elsewhere.

The term *volcano–karst* was first proposed by Naum *et al.* (1962) in a Rumanian publication and thus may not have attracted much attention, but it is a useful term for microrelief forms that are often observed. In the Caliman Massif of the Eastern Carpathians, these volcano–karst features include alveolae (tafoni), lapiés, pits and pans, dolinas and sinkholes. Stalactites and flowstone are developed in *limonite*. The volcanic formations consist of pyroxene andesites, corrosion being largely achieved by the kaolinization of the feldspars, under high rainfall and mild temperature conditions. The rocks are well-jointed, which aids the penetration of rainwater. Marked solution occurs on horizontal structural surfaces where rainwater will stand.

The role of *salt crystallization* also plays a role in many volcano–karsts, facilitating the evolution of pits, pans, alveolae (honeycomb weathering) and *tafoni* (q.v.). The salts are derived partly from cyclic salts (i.e., of marine origin, carried in by rain clouds) and partly as by-products of the weathering itself. Among the tuffaceous products most commonly corroded are also the zeolites and feldspathoids.

In regions of contrasting seasonal rains and strong evaporation, well-developed crusts are associated with solution phenomena. This combination makes for naturally "cemented" walls and soft interior rock. Certain tribes of ancient men have utilized

Fig. 1. Pinnacles left by the cliff retreat in the volcano-karst of the Bandelier Rhyolite Tuff, Bandelier Canyon, New Mexico.

FIG. 3. Detail of alveolar weathering in the volcano-karst of the Bandelier Tuff. Note induration of external surfaces in contrast to flaking and fretting of the soft interior surfaces. (Photo: R. W. Fairbridge).

FIG. 2. Solution fluting of canyon walls in Bandelier Tuff.

FIG. 4. Fluting and pyramidal weathering forms in Bandelier Tuff.

them for digging out cave dwellings, granaries, etc. Remarkable examples are known in Anatolia (Turkey) and in north central New Mexico. In the latter, in the region of the Valle (Jemez) caldera (one of the largest such volcano-tectonic complexes in the world: Smith and Bailey, 1966) there are tuff formations that range from Miocene, the Abiquiu Tuff, to the early Quaternary Bandelier Rhyolite Tuff (Smith, 1938), which in places display remarkable volcano–karst effects. The Pearlette ash of late Kansan age that extends over several states to Iowa is probably from this source. In the Bandelier National Monument, situated along the Frijoles Canyon, a branch of the Rio Grande, the Bandelier Tuff shows remarkable fluting, tafoni and case hardening (see *Induration*); in addition, a former population of Pueblo Indians took advantage of the soft interior of the tuff for excavating living caves and storage vaults. A parallel use of similar tuffs may be observed in Anatolia (Turkey), but by a completely distinct racial group.

The Anatolian troglodyte dwellings, forts and churches are really among the "wonders of the world." Situated in the ancient province of Cappadocia, in the valleys of the Kizilirmak and Göreme, some of the settlements are traceable back to 3000 B.C. Some of the honeycombs of rooms extend to

FIG. 5. Volcano-karst weathering on a youthful tuff cone. Note the induration of the original surfaces and the etching and dissection of the drainage rills. Mt. Banko, Indonesia.

seven floors underground. Towns still occupied today include Nevşehir, Kaymakli, Derinkuyu,

FIG. 6. Volcano-karst cones with perched boulders in tuff, Göreme Valley, Anatolia. (Photo: courtesy of Turkish Ministry of Tourism and Information.)

FIG. 7. Tuff cones in the Göreme Valley, Anatolia, honeycombed with troglodyte dwellings. (Photo: courtesy of Turkish Ministry of Tourism and Information.)

Ürgüp, Orta Hisar, Uçhisar, Avcilar (Maçan), Çavuşin. The tuff erupted from Mt. Erciyes and erosion has produced immense conical pillars, chimneys, pedestal rocks with perched boulders.

In some pyroclastic eruptions, the initial heat of the dust clouds (*nuées ardentes*) produces a welding of the particles to ignimbrite ("autopneumatolysis," Rittmann, 1962, p. 142). Such welded tuffs may develop columnar jointing just like a lava, but in other deposits of lower-temperature origin, there is subaerial diagenesis which may be quite superficial. And when this crust is penetrated by erosional streams, a deep corrosion begins. A pumice-type trachytic ash, known as *trass*, is so reactive that it is commonly used as a natural seawater-resistant cement. It functions alone as a hydraulic mortar but is usually added to lime or portland cement. Its traditional source is the Eifel district of Germany (formerly worked in the Brohl valley, more recently in the Nette valley). In Italy its equivalent is *puzzolana*. It is also worked in Java.

RHODES W. FAIRBRIDGE

References

Henderson, J., 1913, "Geology and topography of the Rio Grande region in New Mexico," *Bur. Am. Ethnology Bull.*, **54**, 23–29.

Naum, T., *et al.*, 1962, "Vulcanokarstul din Masivul Calimanuliu (Carpatii Orientali)," *Anal. Univ. Bucuresti. Ser. Stiint. Nat. Geol. Geogr.*, **32**, 143–179.

Rittmann, A., 1962, "Volcanoes and their Activity," New York, Interscience Publishers, 305pp. (translated by E. A. Vincent).

Ségalien, P., 1957, "Étude des sols dérivés de roches volcaniques basiques à Madagascar," *Mém. Inst. Sci. Madagascar, Ser. D*, **8**.

Smith, H. T. U., 1938, "Tertiary geology of the Abiquiu quadrangle, New Mexico," *J. Geol.*, **46**, 933–965.

Smith, R. L. and Bailey, R. A., 1966, "The Bandelier Tuff," *Bull. Volcan.*, **29**, 83–104.

Wilcox, R. E., 1965, "Volcanic-ash chronology," in (Wright, H. E., Jr., and Frey, D. G., editors), "The Quaternary of the United States," pp. 807–816, Princeton, N.J., Princeton University Press.

Cross-references: *Earth Pillars*; *Induration*; *Karst*; *Limestone Coastal Weathering*; *Salt Karst*; *Tafoni*; *Thermokarst*.

W

WARPING

This is a term used by geologists to indicate deformations of the land surface over large areas due to differential movement within the crust, probably in response to subcrustal flow of magmatic material (see *Crustal Movements—Contemporary*). Crustal movements may be of two kinds: the first, termed isostatic, occurs in response to loading or unloading of the crustal surface, such as in the growth and decay of ice masses. The second, termed endogenic, is caused by subcrustal movements of an indeterminate or problematic character.

Isostatic Warping

The degree of flexibility of the crust has always been a source of argument. It is undoubtedly true, however, that the surface of the earth responds quickly to changes in the load placed upon it. Nansen (1905) reported that during high tides in the Bay of Biscay the land surface was depressed, and observations have since confirmed this for various parts of the world. On a larger scale, depressions in the crust have been observed in areas where sediments are being deposited, as at the mouths of rivers (King, 1955), and crustal uplift has been measured in regions undergoing excessive erosion. Probably the most notable examples of isostatic movement, however, occur where the growth and decay of great ice sheets have caused crustal loading and unloading.

Glacial isostasy was first proposed by Jamieson in 1865. He was concerned with explaining the altitude and stratigraphical position of certain ancient marine beds in Scotland. He theorized that a great mass of ice placed upon the earth's surface would depress the land and that when the ice melted away the land would respond by recovering its former altitude. It was implied (Jamieson, 1882) that variations in height of an ancient shoreline reflected variations in the thickness of the original ice sheet and consequently in the measure of the recovery of the crust. Isostatic movement was envisaged as being a slow but continuous process, and the formation of shore lines was believed to have been accomplished when the rate of the rising sea level (due to melting ice) matched the rate of the rising land (the *Isokinetic Theory* of Wright, 1937).

Areas deformed by ice loading and unloading appear to have smooth outlines in plan, and local

areas of very d p   ery shallow ice cover do not stand out in either   te or amount of recovery. The response of the land to unloading, however, first thought to be very slow, is now believed to be surprisingly rapid (Sissons and Smith, 1965). The typical curve of rate of rise of the land during and after deglaciation is initially steep, then flattening off exponentially.

The greatest areas known to have suffered vertical deformation as a result of glaciation are North America and Scandinavia. In North America the greatest depressions of the land occurred south of Hudson Bay, where the rate of rise is still about

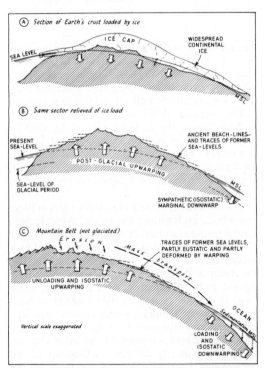

FIG. 1. Warping of several types: (A) ice loading; (B) postglacial upwarping, showing elevated beach lines (strandlines), with sympathetic marginal downwarp; (C) upwarping of a mountain belt due partially to endogenic causes, aided by unloading due to erosion. Near the coast (C) there is "continental flexure" due to transport of material from the subaerial sector to the submarine area with its sediment loading (R. W. Fairbridge).

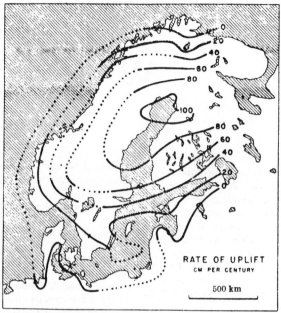

FIG. 2. Present-day rate of upwarping in Scandinavia (Gutenberg, 1954, p. 247).

2 m/century (Gutenberg, 1941). It is calculated that here a further rise of 250 meters is needed before the land regains its pre-Wisconsin elevation. However, 1000 miles to the south at the glacial limit, near New York City, relatively little crustal warping appears to have occurred (Fairbridge and Newman, 1968). In Scandinavia, the northern part of the Gulf of Bothnia, center of the former ice sheet, is still rising at a rate of 1 m/century, and it is calculated that the ice depressed the land some 720 meters. Of the latter figure, 200 meters have still to be recovered (Gutenberg, 1941).

In cross section, the field of isostatic uplift in these and other areas is a nearly flat-topped dome. Irregularities in its surface have been postulated by Wright (1925) who suggests that uplift is accomplished by a succession of concentric waves emanating at either the center or the periphery and passing outward or inward. In North America and Scandinavia, variations in the dome surface, called hinge lines, have been observed: Peripheral areas recover their former elevations progressively as the ice recedes, and further movement is restricted to an inner area, resulting in markedly different inclinations of the ancient shorelines. Such features may be due to the irregular nature of retreat of the ice sheet, interrupted by readvances. In Scandinavia, a radial pattern of fault lines is noticeable around the former ice center (Härme, 1961). There was a general synchroneity and parallelism on both sides of the Atlantic (Fig. 3).

Isostatic movement and its concomitant effects have never been studied more closely than in the glaciated areas. Depression and elevation of the crust consequent upon deposition and erosion was first suggested by Jamieson in 1908. Jamieson had earlier attributed the differential elevation of raised shorelines in Scotland to glacial isostasy, but he later believed there were other isostatic movements at work. Certain areas of Scotland appeared to be more greatly eroded by both glacial and other agencies than others; when Jamieson saw that postglacial raised shorelines were generally higher in these areas, he attributed part of the higher elevation to the effects of greater erosion.

More recently, King (1955) has ascribed the warping of cyclic erosional surfaces in South Africa to the effects of isostatic uplift consequent upon denudation, while in the United States the deltaic deposits of the Mississippi are believed to be depressing the continental shelf at a rate of 1–5 mm/yr.

Non-isostatic Warping (Endogenic Warping)

Glacial isostasy is an exogenic phenomenon, as are isostatic reactions to the unloading of mountains by denudation and the loading of basins by deltas. There is, however, a quite distinct type of warping due to endogenic forces; in this case the cause lies deep within the mantle. We do not know the nature of these causes, but it is suspected that subcrustal flowage and phase changes occur in what seismologists term the "low-velocity layer." This appears to consist of several layers of decoupling, notably between 100 and 400 km, but varies somewhat beneath continents and beneath oceans. The slowing down of

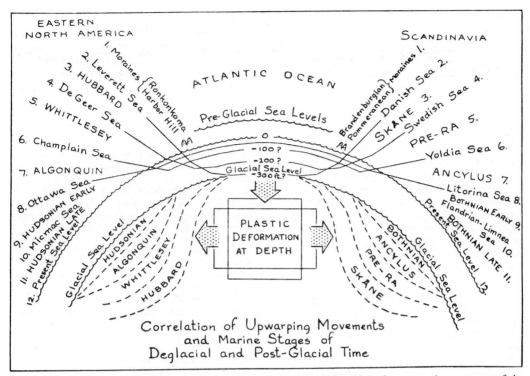

FIG. 3. Transatlantic parallelism of postglacial upwarp (Lougee, 1956). Note the progressive crossover of the lowest and earliest strandlines, which become the most elevated, and the later strandlines (e.g., Litorinna, about 5000 B.P.) that are much less elevated.

seismic waves within this region suggests that it is mantle material close to its melting point. The seismic shocks themselves and the transmission of the resultant energy show that the material behaves as a solid to a sudden shock, but in response to long-term thermal disequilibrium it is likely to flow plastically in a sort of sluggish convection current.

Whatever the causes of these deep endogenic forces, it is observed from the geomorphology and structure of many continental regions that there are broad warpings of the crust, utterly removed from glaciation and from the coastal regions where the continental flexure may be operative. The presence of such broad interior warpings was first brought to general attention (on the basis of geologic and geomorphic observations) by Berkey and Morris (1927) after their celebrated expedition to the great plains of eastern Asia on behalf of the New York Museum of Natural History (Fig. 4). Differential warping of this sort also leads to differential erosion and deposition, so that a minor isostatic factor is added to the endogenic trigger. It may be possible that this very subtle trigger eventually sets in motion a progressive isostatically maintained differential warping that produces large interior uplifts and depressions.

Such uplifts and depressions over platform regions (with foundations of long-consolidated shield-type crystalline rocks) have long been known to

stratigraphers, and the paleogeographic history of the continental interior of North America is characterized by the evolutions of these broad domes and basins ("autogeosynclines" in Kay's terminology). The geomorphic expression of such warping is beautifully brought out by Lobeck's "Physiographic Diagram of Kentucky" and its accompanying profile (Fig. 5). In Asia, the Russians have recognized the importance of analogous structures and given them the formal terms "anteclise" and "syneclise" (see also Vol. V). The continent that best displays them is Africa, where the broad basins of Chad, Congo, Kalahari, and so on, alternate with broad arches and

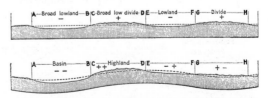

FIG. 4. Endogenic warping of a relatively stable shield region under semiarid conditions (Mongolia; from Berkey and Morris, 1927, p. 369). *Above*: A maturely dissected region of low relief, showing a first cycle of warping. *Below*: The same region after a second cycle of warping, of longer "wavelength." (Courtesy of the American Museum of Natural History.)

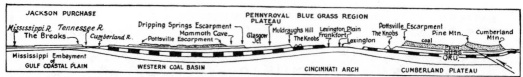

JACKSON PURCHASE
PENNYROYAL BLUE GRASS REGION
PLATEAU
Mississippi R. Tennessee R. Dripping Springs Escarpment Pottsville Escarpment
The Breaks Cumberland R. Mammoth Cave Muldraughs Hill Lexington Plain The Knobs Pine Mtn. Cumberland
Pottsville Escarpment Glasgow Frankfort coal Mtn.
The Knobs Jct. Lexington
Mississippi Embayment
of
GULF COASTAL PLAIN WESTERN COAL BASIN CINCINNATI ARCH CUMBERLAND PLATEAU

FIG. 5. Effect of long-continued warping in a humid region. Geological section across Kentucky (redrawn by A. K. Lobeck from Kentucky Geological Survey).

plateaus. Cloos (1937) called these "felder" (fields), recognizing that they were great geotectonic features, hitherto not recognized in the complex jigsaw puzzle of western European geology. Hills (1947) has recognized them further in Australia.

It was not realized at all until quite recently that warping across the continents outside of glaciated regions was an active, measurable phenomenon of the present day. Repeated survey levels by the cadastral surveyors of different regions were rarely coordinated or systematically reoccupied. This was first done in the U.S.S.R. on the Russian Platform, and the astonishing fact emerged that wave-like oscillations with vertical amplitudes of 1–10 mm/yr are going on at the present time, right across the so-called stable shield and platform areas (Mescherikov, 1959).

In orogenic belts like those of Japan, New Zealand and California, broad epeirogenic uplifts, as well as minor oscillations, are well-known. Such structures postdate the main orogeny in every case. Even in some of the less seismic mountains like the Alps, the geodetic releveling shows very active differential uplift today (1–5 mm/yr). The geomorphic evidence suggests that individual blocks are being warped, but over much smaller "wavelengths" than in the platform regions. Figure 6 by Kober (1928) shows the subdivision of the Austrian Alps into longitudinal warps ("Grossfalten" of Abendanon) and faulted synclinal valleys. In some cases these undulations parallel the older structures, but in others they are discordant and independent. Van Bemmelen (1936) developed a geotectonic theory based on such large-scale warping of the earth's crust, which he called the "Undation Theory" (see further in Vol. V).

DAVID E. SMITH
RHODES W. FAIRBRIDGE

References

Berkey, C. P., and Morris, F. K., 1927, "The Geology of Mongolia," New York, American Museum of Natural History.

Bourcart, J., 1950, "La theorie de la flexure continentale," *Congr. Intern. Géogr.* (*Lisbonne*, 1949), **2**, 167–190.

Cloos, H., 1937, "Zur Grosstektonik Hochafrikas und seine Ungebung," *Geol. Rundschau*, **28**, 334–348.

Fairbridge, R. W., and Newman, W. S., 1968, "Postglacial crustal subsidence of the New York area," *Z. Geomorphol. N.F.*, **11**.

Gutenberg, B., 1941, "Changes in sea level, post-glacial uplift, and the mobility of the earth's interior," *Bull. Geol. Soc. Am.*, **52**, 721–772.

Gutenberg, B., 1954, "Postglacial uplift in the Great Lakes region," *Arch. Meteorol. Geophys. Bioklimatol. Ser. A*, **7**, 243–251.

Härme, M., 1961, "On the fault lines of Finland," *Bull. Comm. Geol. Finlande*, **196**, 437–444.

Hills, E. S., 1947, "Tectonic patterns in the earth's crust," *Rept. Aust. and New Zealand Assoc. Adv. Sci.* (*Perth*), **26**, 290–302.

Jamieson, R. F., 1865, "On the history of the last geological changes in Scotland," *Quart. J. Geol. Soc. London*, **21**, 161–203.

Jamieson, R. F., 1882, "On the cause of the depression and re-elevation of the land during the glacial period," *Geol. Mag.*, **9**, 400–407.

Jamieson, R. F., 1908, "On changes of level and the production of raised beaches," *Geol. Mag.*, **5**, 206–209.

King, P. B., 1955, "Orogeny and epeirogeny through time," in (Poldervaart, A., editor), "Crust of the earth," *Geol. Soc. Am. Spec. Paper* **62**, 723–739.

King, P. B., 1965, "Tectonics of Quaternary Time in Middle North America," in (Wright, H. E. and Frey, D. G., editors), "The Quaternary of the United States," pp. 831–870, Princeton, N.J., Princeton Univ. Press.

Kober, L., 1928, "Der Bau der Erde," Second ed., Berlin, Borntraeger, 499pp.

Lougee, 1956, *I.G.U. Rept. Erosion Surfaces*, **8**, 53.

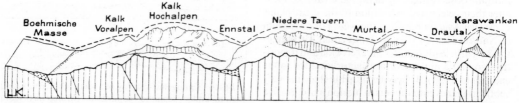

Boehmische Kalk Kalk Niedere Tauern Karawanken
Masse Voralpen Hochalpen Ennstal Murtal Drautal
L.K.

FIG. 6. Major warps in a profile through the Austrian Alps, from the borders of the Bohemian Mass (Czechoslovakia, extreme left), through the Limestone Alps, Tauern to Karawanken (right, on the borders of Yugoslavia). Length of profile: 280 km. Note the faulting corresponding to the major synclinal, longitudinal valleys (Danube, Enns, Mur, Drau), each associated with young overthrust sedimentary fill (from Kober, 1928, Fig. 38). (By permission of Gebrüder Borntraeger, Stuttgart.)

Mescherikov, Y. A., 1959, "Contemporary movements in the earth's crust," *Intern. Geol. Rev.*, **18**, 40–51.

Miller, A. A., 1939, "Attainable standards of accuracy in the determination of preglacial sea levels," *J. Geomorphol.*, **2**, 95.

Nansen, F., 1905, "Oscillations of shorelines," *Geogr. J.*, **26**, 604–616.

Sissons, J. B., and Smith, D. E., 1965, "Raised shorelines associated with the Perth Readvance in the Forth Valley and their relation to glacial isostasy," *Trans. Roy. Soc. Edinburgh*, **66**, 143–168.

Van Bemmelen, R. W., 1936, "The undation theory of the development of the earth's crust," *Intern. Geol. Congr. Rept.*, **2**, 965–982.

Vening Meinesz, C. A., 1954, "Crustal warping in the Netherlands," *Geol. Mijnbouw N.S.*, **16**(6), 206.

Wright, W. B., 1925, "Three short papers on isostasy," *Geol. Mag.*, **62**, 227–234.

Wright, W. B., 1937, "The Quaternary Ice Age," Second ed., London, Macmillan and Co., 478pp.

Cross-references: *Continental Flexure; Crustal Movements—Contemporary; Endogenic Dynamics; Exogenic Dynamics; Isobase; Neotectonics; Postglacial Isostatic Rebound; Strandline; Water Loading and Crustal Response.* Vol. V: *Anteclise; Geosynclines; Isostasy; Mantle; Seismic Waves; Syneclise; Undation Theory.*

WASHBOARD MORAINES AND OTHER MINOR MORAINE TYPES

The term "washboard moraines" was used by Mawdsley (1936) to describe small, parallel, regularly spaced moraine ridges in northwestern Quebec which were later identified as De Geer's "annual moraines" by Norman (1938). In 1913, H. L. Fairchild used the word "washboard" to describe a type of drumlin landscape in western New York. Later, following Mawdsley, the term "washboard moraines" was used to describe regularly spaced parallel ridges transverse to the ice movement in a general sense by Elson (1953), and it has been so used by many geologists on the Great Plains of Canada and the United States since then.

Five types of minor moraine ridges are described in Table 1, and are illustrated in Figs. 1 and 2.

Type A, De Geer Moraines. These are the straight-ridged minor moraines of Lee (1959) and are probably also the cross-valley moraines of Andrews (1963). A patch of these moraine ridges was referred to as a "mora" by De Geer. Their pattern resembles that of crevasses in the Ross Ice Shelf of Antarctica. These ridges are most abundant north of the Baltic Sea, in northwestern Quebec, northern Ontario, and west of Hudson Bay in Canada.

De Geer thought that these moraines were ridges pushed up by an ice margin advancing during winter months; small intermediate ridges formed during the summer, and there were some extra stony moraines which he thought resulted from earthquakes, making available more shattered rock for glacial transport ("seismic moraines"). He found that the spacing of moraines corresponded to the annual areal extension of varved clays, a view supported by Sauramo (1929) in Finland, and Norman (1938) in Canada, though not supported by recent studies in middle Sweden (Strömberg, 1965).

More recent hypotheses (Hoppe, 1959) involve seasonal fluctuations of glacial lake levels which cause crevasses to form near the ice margin. Debris either melted out of the ice and fell into the crevasses or else was squeezed up into crevasses from below while in a saturated condition (Andrews, 1963).

Type B, Minor Moraines. These resemble a washboard more than do any of the other ridge patterns. They are abundant in the north central United States and in the western plains of Canada.

Gwynne suggested that these ridges formed by lodgment of till underneath an ice margin, but that some small moraines resulted from a pushing process. Elson (1957) suggested that they formed by lodgment of till in a zone of thrusting behind an apron of stagnant ice at the margin of a thin glacier. Emplacement of the ridges resulted either from bottom melting lowering the englacial debris without disturbing the tectonic fabric imposed on it in the ice, or else from a lodgment process where the active ice ended. The spacing of the ridges depended upon the supply of englacial sediment and on the geometry of the thinning ice edge. The spacing is compatible with the amount of surface melting that would take place in a year, but annual deposition is not proved.

Type C, Small Moraines. Some of Gwynne's "minor moraines" are in this category. These seem to occur in the more distal parts of the glaciated areas; some are within lake basins and some are not. Those not in lake basins are thought to have been the result of ice push at the glacier margin. Those within the lake basins are thought by Løken and Leahy (1964) to have resulted from the squeezing up of previously deposited lacustrine sediment into the open bottoms of crevasses formed in a glacier whose margin was being buoyed up by a glacial lake (cf. Henderson, 1967).

Type D, Ribbed Moraine. This type has also been called "ridged ablation moraine" and "dead ice landscape." These ridges are most common in the central parts of the areas covered by the continental ice sheets and are the dominant type of minor moraine ridge found in the Arctic and close to ice divides. Probably several different phenomena are included in this category and there is a complete gradation from transverse ridges to aligned drumlinoid features. The ridges are abundant in Sweden, Finland, Ireland, and in northern Canada.

Early investigators suggested that the ridges were

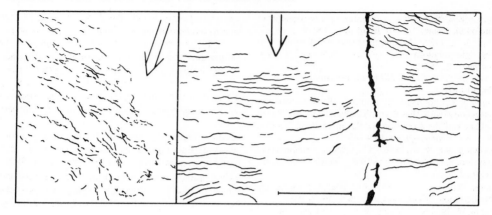

FIG. 1(a).

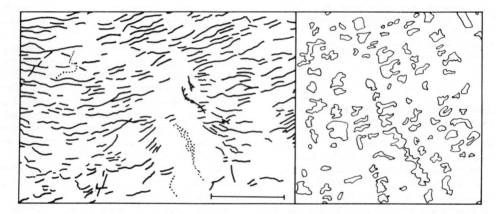

FIG. 1(b).

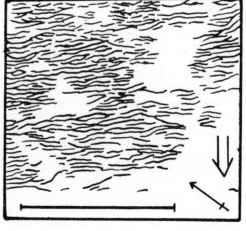

FIG. 1(c).

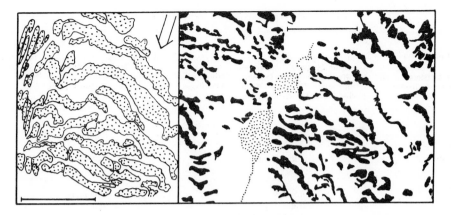

Fig. 1(d).

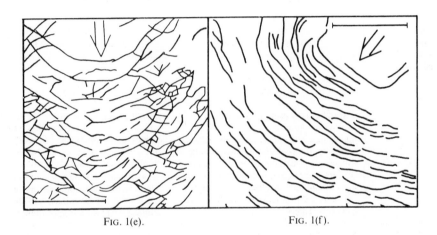

Fig. 1(e).   Fig. 1(f).

Fig. 1. Maps showing minor moraine patterns at approximately the same scale. North is at the top unless otherwise shown. The bars are 1 mile long; broad arrows indicate the direction of the last glacier movement. Letter designations correspond to columns in Table 1 except for 1(f) (ice-thrust ridges).

(a) *Left*: "Annual moraines" at Bromma, Sweden, the type locality after De Geer (1940, Plate 59). *Right*, De Geer moraines. "Washboard" moraines east of Wapikaimaski Lake, Northern Ontario, Canada (after RCAF Airphoto No. A13906-130). The ridges curve up-glacier as the esker (irregular line trending south) is approached. Most blank areas are occupied by lakes; both figures are at the same scale.

(b) *Left*: Minor moraines northeast of Cartwright, Manitoba, Canada. The lines represent only the ridge crests. Stippled area and dotted lines are eskers. *Right*: Moraine area north of Holmfield, Manitoba, showing pattern of depressions (slough-chains) gradational into minor moraines; both figures are after Elson (1953) and are at the same scale.

(c) Small end moraines west of Red Deer, Alberta, Canada, similar to those described by Gwynne (1942) and Løken and Leahy (1964); interpreted from Gravenor, Green and Godfrey (1960, p. 12, photograph 160-5205: 1555-15). Small arrow indicates north.

(d) Ribbed moraine. *Left*: Ridge pattern west of Cow Lake, Quebec. Stippled areas are ridges in fluted ribbed moraine that grades into drumlinoid ridges in the left (west); interpreted from Hughes (1964, Plate 1). *Right*: Ribbed minor moraines and part of an esker system (stippled), south of Ennadai, District of Keewatin, Canada; interpreted from Lee (1959, Plate IX).

(e) Rectilinear till ridges south of Lloydminster, Alberta, Canada; traced from Gravenor, Green and Godfrey (1960, p. 13).

(f) Ice-thrust ridges, Neutral Hills, Alberta, Canada. Ridge crests traced from Gravenor, Green and Godfrey (1960, p. 12, photograph 160-5203: 1501-38).

TABLE 1. CHARACTERISTICS OF MINOR MORAINE TYPES

Moraine type[a] Characteristics (all dimensions are given in ft)	A De Geer Moraines (Hoppe, 1959; Norrbotten, Sweden); Washboard Moraines (Mawdsley, 1936; Opawica–Chibougamau area, Quebec); Annual Moraines (De Geer, 1889: Bromma, Sweden)	B Minor Moraines (Gwynne, 1951: Davison County, South Dakota); Washboard Moraines (Elson, 1953; Cartwright Area, Manitoba, Canada)

Height:
  range:
  "mean"[b]
  uniformness[c]
	2–30
	15
	Fairly uniform
		2–30
		15
		Fairly uniform

Width:
  range
  "mean"[b]
  uniformness[c]
	15–130
	100
	Fairly constant
		100–400
		300
		Fairly constant

Profile	Asymmetric, distal side (down-glacier) steepest; crests rounded; ridges rest on a planar surface.	Rounded, usually symmetrical; may rest on flat surface or form sinusoidal curve with adjacent depressions.
Length: range	100 to more than 6000	300 to more than 10,000

Spacing, crest to crest:
  range
  "mean"[c]
	400–1000
	600
		300–700
		500

Pattern	Parallel ridges, straight or gently curved, commonly sinuous in detail, and a few have minor branches; arcuate pattern concave down-glacier in broad valleys suggesting a calving ice front; trend is straight across plains including drumlins and other relief features as high as 40 feet; pattern curves up-glacier adjacent to eskers.	Parallel ridges, straight or arcuate; arcuate pattern is convex down-glacier; ridges curve up-glacier adjacent to eskers. Ridges may cross lower, more widely-spaced ridges parallel to ice flow, forming a series of shallow depressions with each depression elongate parallel to the moraines, and the series aligned in the direction of ice flow.
Constitution (material, fabric if studied)	Stony sandy till; stone orientation is transverse to the ridge in the proximal side, parallel to it in the distal side.	Sandy silty till, compact, stone orientation is parallel to the direction of glacier movement, may be transverse or oblique to the trend of the ridge.
Situation	In glacial lake basins and areas of marine submergence.	Plains, flat or sloping slightly up-glacier; uplands rather than lowlands; not in glacial lake basins.

[a] A name that is preferred because it eliminates confusion is given first.
[b] Not a statistical value, but a general impression given by authors.
[c] Refers to the characteristic of a single ridge, rather than a group of ridges.

formed of material dumped into crevasses from above as stagnant ice melted. More recent theories take into account the till stone orientations. Some ridges are thought to have been molded by the actively moving ice which became overloaded with debris in areas of easily plucked and abraded bedrock (Henderson, 1959). Hoppe (1959) suggests that the till was squeezed out from under the margin of the ice sheet to form ridges while it was in a fluid condition. Some of the ridges are grouped close to

deltaic expansions of eskers which suggest that proglacial lakes may be involved in the formation of the ridges (Hughes, 1964), though there is commonly little or no other evidence of glacial lakes. Goldthwait (1951) saw moraines being deposited on an icecap margin in Baffin Island where debris melted out from the dirty ice of thrust plains to form ice-cored ridges and was gradually lowered to the ground so that a series of subparallel ridges resembling ribbed moraine resulted.

C	D	E
Swell and Swale Topography (Gwynne, 1942: Story County, Iowa); Small Moraines (Løken and Leahy, 1964: Little Cataraqui Creek near Kingston, Ontario)	Ribbed Moraine (Hughes, 1964: West of Cow Lake, Quebec, Latitude 52°32′N, Longitude 70°29′W); Rogen Moraine (Hoppe, 1957: Sweden); Rippled Till (Ives, 1956: Esker Lake, Labrador)	Rectilinear Till Ridges; Linear Disintegration Ridges (Gravenor and Kupsch, 1959; Vermilion Area, Alberta); Ice-crack Moraines (Colton, 1958: Oswego, Montana)
2–20 8 Irregular	20–90 30 Very irregular	3–35 15 Uniform
5–130 100 Pinch and swell 30–70%	50–1000 700 Very irregular	25–300 200 Uniform
Rounded, usually symmetrical; ridges and depressions form a sinusoidal curve but in some areas a rounded ridge rests on a plain.	Generally smoothly rounded but irregular in detail; locally drumlinoid.	Rounded, resting on a generally flat or undulating surface.
200–2000	300–1200	100 to more than 40,000
0–330 170	300–1200 1000	Parallel ridges 500–1500, varies greatly.
Subparallel to parallel; some ridges are forked, some are crooked; locally linear depressions occur in the ridge crests forming short double ridges.	Irregularly subparallel, locally branching, usually arcuate, convex down-glacier; may be irregularly sinuous; ridges curve up-glacier adjacent to eskers.	Generally two or more sets of parallel ridges; one set is more continuous than the others and may be straight or arcuate, convex down-glacier. Intersecting ridges form trapezoids, parallelograms and triangles.
Silt (reworked lake sediment) or silty till.	Mostly compact sandy till; some stratified drift near eskers; stone orientations are parallel to the direction of ice flow.	Sandy and silty till with distorted inclusions of stratified drift.
In basins of extinct glacial lakes (southern Ontario); till plains, uplands rather than basins (Iowa).	Plains, gently sloping upland areas; in some short-lived, relatively shallow extinct glacial lake basins.	Plains, uplands rather than basins; plain commonly slopes gently away from the glacier.

Type E, Rectilinear Till Ridges. These ridges are known mainly on the plains of Manitoba, Saskatchewan, Alberta, Montana, and North Dakota. Gravenor and Kupsch (1959) think that they formed as a result of material either entering crevasses from above or by saturated drift being squeezed up from below. In some areas, these ridges are gradational into minor moraines (Type B). Rectilinear till ridges are usually on surfaces sloping away from the glacier where extending flow must have occurred, whereas the minor moraines are on flat surfaces or surfaces sloping slightly toward the glacier where glacier flow was of the compressive type.

Ice-thrust Ridges (Kupsch, 1962). These are not listed in Table 1 but are shown in Figs. 1(f) and 2(F); they are occasionally included with minor moraines (Type B). They are common on the Great Plains of North America and occur on the sides of escarpments formed of relatively incompetent rocks that face the direction from which the ice sheet moved. Ice-pushed ridges (Rutten, 1960) are common in Holland and northwestern Germany. They are sometimes called "push moraines."

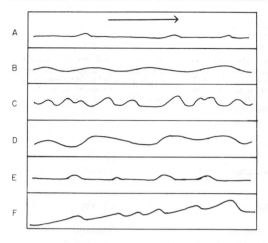

FIG. 2. Characteristic profiles across minor moraine ridges. Letter designations correspond to columns in Table 1. In all cases, the direction of ice movement [arrow in (A)] was from left to right. (A) De Geer moraines, (B) minor moraines, (C) swell and swale topography, (D) ribbed moraine, (E) rectilinear till ridges, (F) ice-thrust ridges. Schematic, not to scale, vertically exaggerated.

These ridges are typically 30–200 feet high, about 500–1000 feet in width and as long as 3 miles. They are asymmetrical and are generally much steeper on the distal side than on the proximal side. They occur in groups of parallel to subparallel ridges and a group is commonly arcuate in plan. The material consists of either deformed bedrock with some drift incorporated into it, or drift. In some regions, the structure of the ridges is that of an isoclinal fold system (Fuller, 1914).

These ridges formed as a result of deformation by the shearing action of moving glacier. From 200–500 feet of subjacent material is incorporated into some of these features, and one school of thought believes that this ground was in a frozen condition when the thrusting occurred. Others feel that the frozen condition is incompatible with drainage conditions (toward the ice margin) which tended to cause accumulations of water in lakes where the thrusting occurred. Ridges are being formed now of frozen outwash by thrusting in front of Thompson Glacier in northern Canada.

Conclusion

It is likely that features of several origins have been included within some categories of moraines given in this article. Most theories of origin consider the ridges to have been formed behind the margin of the ice sheet so that the ridges are not individual moraines in the sense that they represent a position of equilibrium of the ice margin, however brief. Hence many areas containing the ridges should be regarded as a special type of ground moraine with

a strongly developed transverse element rather than as groups of end moraines clustered together.

The regular spacing of minor moraine ridges is compatible with estimated amounts of marginal retreat resulting from thinning of the ice sheet by annual melting. There is a strong temptation to give the ridges some chronological significance, especially since varved clay studies have supported this theory in some places. However, the regular spacing may be the result of a "searching" process tending to maintain a uniform dissipation of the glacier's energy (increase in entropy) toward the ice margin. This is accomplished in rivers by the alternation of local sites of energy dissipation (by skin and spill resistance and internal distortion) with local sites of energy accumulation (pools). The mechanisms by which a glacier would achieve this have not been suggested in this context as yet, but they may prove to be capable of damping out the annual effects of snow accumulation and melting.

J. A. ELSON

References

Andrews, J. T., 1963, "The cross-valley moraines of north-central Baffin Island: a quantitative analysis," *Geographical Bull.*, No. 20, 82–129.

Colton, R. B., 1958, "Ice-crack moraines in northwestern North Dakota and northeastern Montana," in Guidebook, Ninth Annual Conference, Midwestern Friends of the Pleistocene, May 17–18, 1958, *N. Dakota Geol. Surv., Misc. Ser. No. 10*, 99–107.

De Geer, Gerard, 1940, "Geochronologica Suecica Principles," *K. Svensk Vetenskaps Akad., Handl., Ser. 3*, **18**, No. 6, 96–130.

Elson, J. A., 1953, "Periodicity of deglaciation in North America since the Late Wisconsin maximum, Part II Late Wisconsin recession," *Geograf. Ann.*, **35**, 95–104.

Elson, J. A., 1957, "Origin of washboard moraines," *Bull. Geol. Soc. Am.*, **68**, 1721.

Fuller, M. L., 1914, "The geology of Long Island, New York," *U.S. Geol. Surv. Profess. Paper* **82**, 201–207.

Goldthwait, R. P., 1951, "Development of end moraines in east-central Baffin Island," *J. Geol.* **52**, 567–577.

Gravenor, C. P., Green, R., and Godfrey, J. D., 1960, "Air photographs of Alberta," *Res. Council Alberta Bull.*, **5**, 12, 13.

Gravenor, C. P., and Kupsch, W. O., 1959, "Ice-disintegration features in western Canada," *J. Geol.*, **67**, 48–64.

Gwynne, C. S., 1942, "Swell and swale pattern of the Mankato lobe of the Wisconsin drift plain in Iowa," *J. Geol.*, **50**, 200–208.

Gwynne, C. S., 1951, "Minor moraines in South Dakota and Minnesota," *Bull. Geol. Soc. Am.*, **62**, 233–250 (*Note:* some of the Minnesota features are streamlined forms).

Henderson, E. P., 1959, "A glacial study of central Quebec–Labrador," *Bull. Can. Geol. Surv.*, **50**, 18–23.

Henderson, E. P., 1967, in "Guidebook, Geology of Parts of Eastern Ontario and Western Quebec," Kingston, 203–204.

Hoppe, G., 1957, "Problems of glacial morphology and the ice age," *Geograf. Ann.*, **39**, 1–18.

Hoppe, Gunnar, 1959, "Glacial morphology and inland ice recession in northern Sweden," *Geograf. Ann.*, **41**, 193–212.

Hughes, O. L., 1964, "Surficial geology, Nichicun–Kaniapiskau maparea, Quebec," *Bull. Can. Geol. Surv.*, **106**, 3–9.

Ives, J. D., 1956, "Till patterns in central Labrador," *Canadian Geographer*, No. 8, 25–33.

Kupsch, W. O., 1962, "Ice-thrust ridges in western Canada," *J. Geol.*, **70**, 582–594.

Lee, H. A., 1959, "Surficial geology of southern District of Keewatin and the Keewatin ice divide, Northwest Territories," *Bull. Can. Geol. Surv.*, **51**, 12–13.

Løken, O. H., and Leahy, E. J., 1964, "Small moraines in southeastern Ontario," *Canadian Geographer*, **8**, 10–21.

Mawdsley, J. B., 1936, "Wash-board moraines of the Opawica–Chibougamau area, Quebec," *Trans. Roy. Soc. Can. Ser. 3, Sec. IV*, **30**, 9–12.

Norman, G. W. H., 1938, "Last Pleistocene ice-front in Chibougamau district, Quebec," *Trans. Roy. Soc. Can. Ser. 3, Sec. IV*, **32**, 69–86.

Rutten, M. G., 1960, "Ice-pushed ridges, permafrost and drainage," *Am. J. Sci.*, **258**, 293–297.

Sauramo, Matti, 1929, "The Quaternary geology of Finland," *Geol. Comm. Finland Bull.*, **86**, 19.

Strömberg, Bo, 1965, "Mappings and geochronological investigations in some moraine areas of south-central Sweden," *Geograf. Ann.*, **47A**, 73–82.

Cross-references: *Ablation Moraine*; *Crevasse*; *Deglaciation*; *Drumlin*; *Esker*; *Glacial Lakes*; *Glacial Moulin*; *Glacial Spillways and Proglacial Lakes*; *Holocene*; *Ice Thrusting*; *Moraine*; *Stagnant Ice Melting*. Vol. VI: *Glacier Geophysics*; *Till and Tillite*.

WASHED DRIFT—*See* DRIFT, GLACIAL: DRIFT THEORY

WASH SLOPE—*See* HALDENHANG OR WASH SLOPE; SHEET EROSION; SLOPES

WATERFALLS

A waterfall is a very steep (commonly vertical) fall of some magnitude in a river course. "*Cataract*" is a synonym; "*cascade*" describes a fall of only a few feet, or a succession of such falls. "*Rapids*" are less steep but sufficient to accelerate noticeably the rate of flow and maintain white water at all stages of discharge. Large falls regularly develop a considerably overdeepened "*plunge pool*" at their foot and this becomes progressively enlarged during recession of the fall.

Waterfalls and rapids are sites of discordance in the longitudinal profile of a river which elsewhere may possess a slope that is in broad equilibrium with discharge. In the "normal cycle of erosion" (see *Cycles, Geomorphic*) of temperate latitudes, they correspond to *nickpoints* (q.v.) and are considered to be transitory phenomena of the earliest stage, *youth*; the exceptional erosive capability generated by the bedload of pebbles and boulders at falls ensures their comparatively rapid modification. In tropical climates, the high level of chemical erosion tends to reduce rock to solutions and clay-size particles, so that their mechanical erosion potential is greatly reduced; many tropical rivers, therefore, lack graded profiles and show step-like sectors, separated by falls and cataracts, e.g., Nile, Congo, Niger.

The highest reported waterfall is Angel Falls, Venezuela, with a single drop of 3212 feet (986 meters). Yosemite Falls, California, have a drop of 2600 feet (800 meters), in three sections. Many other falls exceed 1000 feet but, like those named above, have only a modest volume of flow. Victoria Falls, Rhodesia (400 feet or 123 meters), Iguazu Falls, Brazil–Argentina (230 feet or 70 meters) and Niagara Falls (200 feet or 62 meters) have the greatest known discharges: by weighted multiplication of height and volume, each has been acclaimed "the world's greatest waterfall" by different authors.

Classification of Waterfalls

On genetic grounds, three classes of waterfalls may be distinguished:

(1) Erosional waterfalls simply attributable to the differential erosion potential of the country rock. Such waterfalls are created during the entrenchment of a river channel. Sub-types are:

(a) Waterfalls over horizontal or gently dipping strata. *Caprock falls* are the most common. A resistant capping formation is underlain by weaker rocks. Rapid erosion at the base undermines the cap: the fall retreats upstream, maintaining a vertical or undercut face. The Horseshoe Falls at Niagara are the most famous example: the massive Silurian Lockport Dolomite forms the cap, which is undermined in lower shale formations.

Von Engeln (1942) mentions a special case of the caprock fall where the undermined and fallen blocks are too large to be readily cleared and thus accumulate as a debris pile which may smother the undercutting, reducing the fall to a lengthy series of cascades.

Step Falls develop in strata of more uniform erodibility where the undermining occurs along individual bedding planes.

(b) Waterfalls over vertical rock bars. A dike, vertically-dipping beds, etc., may juxtapose rocks of greatly differing erodibility along a vertically oriented contact; this becomes the site of the falls. The Great Falls of the Yellowstone River are an example where ash and lavas decomposed by local hotspring waters have been removed, leaving the lip of the falls upstanding in durable lava beds. By their nature, vertical barrier falls will not recede upstream, as falls in horizontal strata do, but will be reduced *in situ*.

(2) Erosional waterfalls where the discordance

is primarily attributable to causes other than differing erodibility, though the latter may enhance the development. Examples are: waterfalls down fresh fault scarps, falls from tributary valleys into main valleys overdeepened by glacial erosion (see *Hanging Valleys*), and falls over rapidly receding sea cliffs. Other falls of this class may be due to the sudden emplacement of a barrier across the river course, such as a tongue of lava.

(3) Constructional or auto-consequent waterfalls are created by the deposition of calcite (precipitated from solution in groundwater), as a continuous rim across the lip of a pool in a limestone cave or spring (see *Stalactite and Stalagmite*). Given a sustained supply of saturated groundwater, growth in height of the rim is self-perpetuating and creates a waterfall on the downstream side. Such falls are commonly small and occur in a succession of cascades. Individual rimstone falls as great as 40 feet (12 meters) are reported.

Rate of Recession of Falls

Caprock waterfalls will tend to erode (mainly by recession) more rapidly than the other types. The Niagara Falls have been particularly carefully studied in this respect. Gilbert (1907) reported on the changes revealed by five triangulated surveys of the crestlines of the Falls made between 1842 and 1905. During the first half of this period, the main falls (Horseshoe or Canadian Falls) receded at an average rate of 4.0 ft/yr. This increased to 6.6 ft/yr (mean) after 1875. The change of rate was attributed to local variations in the jointing of the caprock or to survey errors. At the lesser American Falls, the mean rate of recession for the whole period was estimated to be only 3 in./yr.

Recent C^{14} datings (Goldthwait *et al.*, 1965) show that the modern Falls originated 12,000 ± 500 years ago. The mean rate of recession since that time has been 3.07 ft/yr.

In the case of a subtropical river like the Nile, however, the rate of recession can scarcely be detected. Flood marks and other inscriptions cut into the granite walls of the cataracts by the Pharoahs show little sign of wear after nearly 4000 years (editor's note: R.W.F.).

DEREK C. FORD

References

Flint, R. F., 1965, "Introduction: Historical Perspectives," in (Wright, H. E. and Frey, D. G., editors), "The Quaternary of the United States," pp. 3–11, Princeton, N.J., Princeton Univ. Press.
Gilbert, G. K., 1907, "Rate of recession of Niagara Falls," *U.S. Geol. Surv. Bull.*, **306**, 31pp.
Goldthwait, R. P., Dreimanis, A., Forsyth, Jane L., Karrow, P. F., and White, G. W., 1965, "Pleistocene Deposits of the Erie lobe," in (Wright, H. E., Jr., and Frey, D. G., editors), "The Quaternary of the United States," pp. 92–95, Princeton, N.J., Princeton University Press.
Schwarzbach, M., 1967, "Isländische Wasserfälle und eine genetische Systematik der Wasserfälle überhaupt," *Zeit. Geomorph.*, **11**(4), 377–417.
Von Engeln, O. D., 1942, "Geomorphology," New York, Macmillan (see especially pp. 179–196).

Cross-references: *Cycles, Geomorphic*; *Glacial Moulin*; *Hanging Valley*; *Karst*; *Nickpoint*; *Rivers*; *Stalactite and Stalagmite*.

WATER GAP

A water gap is a geomorphic term for a short gorge or valley cut by a river through a resistant ridge or mountain range. The usual setting for water gaps is in a region of antecedent drainage (see *Drainage Patterns*; *Rivers*), where a river course established over a preexisting erosion surface has maintained itself while base level has been slowly lowered or broad regional upwarping has occurred. As a result, where the underlying structure is folded or of contrasting components, the resistant ridges now stand out as a structural framework of relatively high relief, while major rivers cut directly across them in narrow transverse valleys or gorges. An essential feature is that the gorges are short, connecting one low relief area with another. A long gorge or canyon is to be interpreted in terms of general antecedence or upwarping affecting flat-lying rocks or rocks of little erosional contrast.

A water gap may also be generated by the evolution of a superposed (or superimposed) stream, i.e., one that has maintained itself during the uplift of a single fold; however, examples of this sort are extremely rare except in such regions as Japan and New Zealand, since such rigorous contemporary folding tectonics are not experiences in the more stable regions.

Classic examples of water gaps are to be seen in the Chalk downs of southeastern England where they connect the low-lying parts of the Weald with the London Basin in the north and with the coast to the south. Even more impressive gaps are observed in the folded Appalachians, particularly in Pennsylvania where rivers like the Delaware, Lehigh and Susquehanna have cut most impressive gorges, through the Kittatinny and Blue Ridge Mountains, today marked also by the major transportation routes.

RHODES W. FAIRBRIDGE

References

Cotton, C. A., 1952, "Geomorphology," Sixth ed., New York, John Wiley & Sons, 505pp.
Davis, W. M., 1889, "The rivers and valleys of Pennsylvania," *Natl. Geogr. Mag.*, **1**, 183–253 (also in

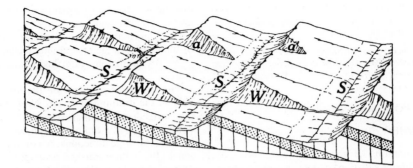

Fig. 1. Subsequent lowlands, water gaps, and wind gaps. *S*, subsequent lowlands; *W*, water gaps; *a, a'*, wind gaps (air gaps) (Cotton, 1952). (By permission of John Wiley & Sons, N.Y.)

"Geographical Essays," New York, Dover reprint, 1954).

Lobeck, A. K., 1939, "Geomorphology," New York, McGraw-Hill Book Co., 731pp.

Meyerhoff, H. A., and Olmsted, E. W., 1934, "Wind gaps and water gaps in Pennsylvania," *Am. J. Sci., Ser. 5,* **27**, 410–416.

Meyerhoff, M. A., and Olmstead, E. W., 1936, "The origins of Appalachian drainage," *Am. J. Sci.,* **32**, 21–42.

Ver Steeg, K., 1930, "Wind gaps and water gaps of the northern Appalachians," *Ann. N.Y. Acad. Sci.,* **32**, 87–220.

Ver Steeg, K., 1940, "The formation of water gaps by solution and piracy," *Am. J. Sci.,* **238**, 32–41.

Wooldridge, S. W., and Morgan, R. S., 1959, "An Outline of Geomorphology," Second ed., London, Longmans, Green & Co., 409pp.

Cross-references: *Base Level; Drainage Patterns; Gipfelflur; Rivers; Valley Evolution; Warping; Wind Gap.*

WATER LOADING AND CRUSTAL RESPONSE

Transient loads of water, like those of ice, elicit both an elastic (recoverable-compressional) and a plastic response (nonrecoverable deformation due to flow) in the solid Earth. The elastic deformation takes place within a few years, and in the best documented example, Lake Mead, Nevada, the deflection asymptotically approached 25 cm over a period of twenty years—about the value predicted by theory (Raphael, 1954). For loads of greater horizontal extent (100 km or more in diameter), the magnitude of the deflection should approach the theoretical limit and be on the order of 1 meter for each 150 meters of water. Loads of considerably greater extent involve deformation of the earth as a whole, as demonstrated by Slichter and Caputo (1960). No geologic example of a complete cycle of loading and unloading has been documented, but

there is every reason to expect that recovery from elastic deformation will be complete.

The plastic (isostatic) response of the earth occurs more slowly, the time required for the anomaly to be reduced to $1/e$ of its initial value generally ranging from 1000–5000 years. The best documented example, Lake Bonneville, Utah (Crittenden, 1963) involves cyclic loading and unloading of about 300 meters of water. The final emptying (unloading) resulted in a 64-meter domical arching of the once-level shorelines. Similar deformation must be expected to result from any load exceeding 100 km in diameter.

It has recently been suggested (Bloom, 1963; Higgins, 1965) that the Earth may yield plastically to water loads of other kinds, e.g., the encroaching wedges of sea-water rising over gently shelving coastlines as a result of eustatic sea level change. The main postglacial rise of sea level ($\sim$ 100 meters) 6000 years ago should have resulted in a depression of the shelf on the order of 10 meters. This would be essentially complete now assuming a time constant ($1/e$) of 1000 years, or would be about 70% complete assuming a time constant of 4000 years.

Max D. Crittenden, Jr.

References

Bloom, A. L., 1963, "Late-Pleistocene fluctuations of sea level and postglacial rebound in coastal Maine," *Am. J. Sci.,* **261**, 862–879.

Bloom, A. L., 1967, "Pleistocene shorelines: a new test of isostasy," *Geol. Soc. Am. Bull.,* **78**, 1477–1493.

Crittenden, M. D., Jr., 1963, "Effective viscosity of the earth derived from isostatic loading of Pleistocene Lake Bonneville," *J. Geophys. Res.,* **68**, No. 19, 5517–5530.

Higgins, C. G., 1965, "Causes of relative sea-level changes," *Am. Scientist,* **53**, 464–476.

Raphael, J. M., 1954, "Crustal disturbances in the Lake Mead area (Nevada-Arizona)," *U.S. Bur. Reclam. Eng. Monograph,* **21**, 14pp.

Slichter, L. B., and Caputo, Michele, 1960, "Deformation of an earth model by surface pressures," *J. Geophys. Res.*, **65**, 4151–4156.

Cross-references: *Coastal Stability; Eustasy; Holocene; Pluvial Lakes; Postglacial Isostatic Rebound; Terraces —Lacustrine; Terraces—Marine; Warping.* Vol. I: *Mean Sea Level Changes.*

WATER POWER—*See* pr Vol. VI

WATERSHED

The definitions of the term "watershed" are varied. Webster's dictionary defines watershed as:

(1) "Waterparting. The boundary line between one drainage and others is rightly termed watershed, but it is better to call it a water parting, or, as in America, a divide."

(2) "The whole region or area contributing to the supply of a river or lake; catchment or basin."

The *Encyclopedia Britannica* gives a similar definition.

The A.G.I. "Glossary of Geology and Related Sciences" considers three explanations of the term:

(1) "The area contained within a drainage divide above a specified point on a stream (Leopold, L. B., and Maddock, T., 1954, "The Flood Control Controversy," p. 251)."

(2) "The height of land or divide from which the natural drainage of a district flows in opposite directions (Roy. Com.)."

(3) "A term used loosely to mean both drainage basin and drainage divide. It is considered undesirable (after Meinzer, (1923). USGS-WSP 494, p. 15)."

Stamp (1961), following the Mill Dictionary, defines it as the "same as *water parting* or *divide*. The line from which surface streams flow in two different directions, the line, separating two contiguous areas." He distinguishes:

(1) A normal watershed running along the crest of the highest range of a mountain chain (Fig. 1).

(2) An anomalous watershed not following such a crest.

The European authors use the term watershed only in the meaning of divide. Neef (1956) defines the watershed (German *Wasserscheide*) as 'the boundary line of a drainage basin, separating areas of different slope directions. According to Machatschek (1927), the watershed develops by intersection of two opposite gradient directions of the drainage.

Characteristics

Following the original definition, i.e., as a divide, and *not* as a catchment or drainage basin, the features of the watersheds are still rather varied: (a) The original watershed may develop along geanticlines and follow the highest ridges or crests of a mountain chain. (b) If the latter is deeply dissected, the drainage areas on both sides of the watershed can progressively interfinger, and drainage directions may periodically alternate. (c) The watershed may be located in a cross-valley or a valley sequence (e.g., Toblacher Feld between Drau-Rienz, Italy). (d) In flat areas, as in many parts of North America, the watershed can be crossed easily by canals or portages; the "continental divide" in central New Mexico is a flat plain. (e) In a bog or fan it is quite indistinct and vaguely developed. (f) In arid areas, in permeable sandstone, or calcareous karst areas, the surface watershed often differs from the subterranean water parting and is difficult to define. There may be subterranean communication of rivers, as is the case at the Danube percolation in Germany. (g) Sometimes in lowland watersheds two river systems may be joined together by a "bifurcation." The best-known example occurs between the Orinoco and Rio Negro, connected by the Casiquiare. The headwaters of the Rio Negro have captured part of the Orinoco system. (h) If lakes or bogs are drained in different directions a water divide is represented. Examples include the Rokitno Bog which drains partly to the Dniepr and partly to the Vistula (Weichsel); the Lesjakogenvand in Norway goes to both the Rauma and the Lågen; the Tuburi Swamp in southwestern Chad drains partly to the Benuë-Niger and partly to the Logone-Shari during the wet season, giving an example for a vague watershed between an area with drainage to the sea and one with interior drainage. (i) River divides occur also on deltas and alluvial fans. For example, the Two Ocean Creek drains over its alluvial fan sometimes into the Missouri and the Atlantic and sometimes into the Columbia River and the Pacific.

Categories of Watershed

There exist several grades or classes of watersheds:

FIG. 1. The main crest of the Hohe Tauern (Austrian Alps) as watershed between the Salzach and the Drau.

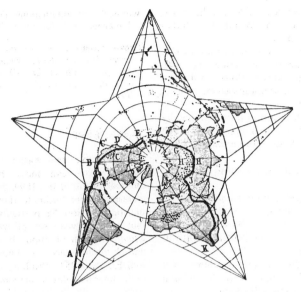

Fig. 2. The principal watersheds of the earth (according to von Tillo, 1887).

(1) The *main watershed of the world* separates the drainage areas of the Atlantic, Pacific and Indian Ocean. In the New World it follows the Cordilleran Belt, in Asia the east Siberian and central Asian mountain ranges, in Africa the East African Rifts (Fig. 2).

(2) The *continental divides* separate the drainage areas of rivers flowing to different oceans.

(3) Watersheds of progressively lower categories exist, down to the level of *interfluve* (q.v.).

Migration

The migration of watersheds is a frequently observed process due to differential erosion of a steeper slope where erosion is more effective; the divide shifts toward the gentler slope (Fig. 3). By the recession of valley heads toward the crest, the evolving watershed grows progressively more sinuous (Fig. 4), and on a given mountain range notches and summits eventually develop. When two valley heads meet at the watershed a gap or *col* (q.v.) may be formed. Thornbury (1954) classifies several kinds of divide migration:

(I) Slow divide migration occurs:

(1) With gently dipping, alternating soft and resistant beds the watershed shifts progressively down from the steep cuesta toward the gentler backslope.

(2) With unequal rainfall on the two sides of a divide when winds prevail from one direction, as, for example, on the Hawaiian Islands.

(II) Rapid divide migration is caused:

(1) By stream diversion due to *piracy* (see *Stream Capture*):

(a) By headward erosion caused by change in rock resistance (e.g., Snickers Gap in the Appalachians).

(b) By an asymmetric gradient along two opposite, competing rivers at cuestas, plateaus or tilted fault blocks (e.g., Front of Catskill Mts.).

(c) By the activity of subterranean streams

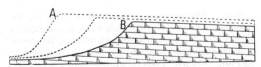

Fig. 3. Section to show the recession of a watershed from A to B as a result of the effect of unequal slopes on erosion (Holmes, 1945, p. 175, Fig. 82). (By permission of T. Nelson & Sons, London.)

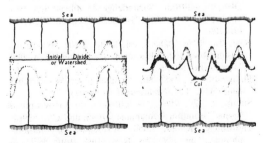

Fig. 4. Development of a zigzag watershed by headward erosion (Holmes, 1945, p. 176, Fig. 83). (By permission of T. Nelson & Sons, London.)

in areas where soluble rock lies above the base level of erosion (e.g., Indian Creek, Indiana).

(d) By lateral erosion or planation of a master stream dissecting the ridge which separates it from a tributary, diverting the sector above the point of dissection.

(2) By stream diversion without piracy by rapid aggradation of a valley from which the river overflows into another valley at a lower level.

(III) Stream derangement due to factors other than rivers:

(1) By glaciation, when the advancing ice front deflected the preglacial route of a river. For example, the upper Missouri was deflected in this way from the Hudson Bay to the Mississippi.

(2) By wind sedimentation of dunes. For example, the Calumet River in Indiana was diverted from its direct course to Lake Michigan by dune building.

(3) By diastrophism, e.g., subsidence. The drainage of the Nyanza area in East Africa formerly flowed to the Congo, but by subsidence and tilting produced a lake (Lake Victoria), draining to the Nile.

(IV) By volcanic eruptions:

Lava flows frequently block drainage channels and cause stream displacement, either laterally or into completely different drainage basins, e.g. in eastern Australia, in Massif Central of France, in Columbia River area of northwestern United States.

THERESE PIPPAN

References

Encyclopedia Britannica, 1955 ed., "Watershed," pp. 430–431.

Holmes, A., 1945, "Principles of Physical Geology," pp. 173–178, London, Nelson. (Second ed., 1965.)

Howell, J. V., and Weller, J. M., (editors), 1960, "Glossary of Geology and Related Sciences," p. 319, Washington, Amer. Geol. Inst.

Machatschek, F., 1927, "Die Flüsse," in (Supan, A., and Obst, E., editors), "Grundzüge der physischen Erdkunde, Vol. 1, pp. 371–374, Berlin-Leipzig, Walter de Gruyter.

Neef, E., 1956, "Das Gesicht der Erde. Brockhaus Taschenbuch der physischen Geographie," p. 944, Leipzig, Brockhaus.

Philippson, A., 1885–86, "Studien über Wasserscheiden," *Mitt. Ver. Landeskunde* (*Leipzig*).

Stamp, L. D., 1961, "A Glossary of Geographical Terms," London, Longmans, Green and Co., 539pp.

Thornbury, W. D., 1954, "Principles of Geomorphology," pp. 151–156, New York, John Wiley & Sons.

Tillo, A. v., 1887, "Ein Wort über die Hauptwasserscheide der Erde," *Petermanns Mitt.*, **33**, 101.

Webster's New International Dictionary of the English Language, 1953, Second ed., Vol. II, p. 2886.

Cross-references: *Col*; *Crustal Movements—Contemporary*; *Drainage Basin*; *Drainage Patterns*; *Glaciation*; *Interfluve*; *Karst*; *Lava-Displaced Drainage*; *Neotectonics*; *Planation Surface*; *Slopes*; *Stream Capture, Piracy*.

WAVE BASE

In principle, wave base is the downward limit to which waves can move bottom particles. As defined by Gulliver (1899, pp. 76–77), wave base determines the ultimate depth of a platform of marine abrasion. No particular depth was specified, but in recent years several workers have placed its *effective* depth at about 10 meters, perhaps ultimately about twice this (Dietz and Menard, 1951; Fairbridge, 1952; Bradley, 1958). It is observed that unconsolidated clay-size particles may be stirred up by heavy swell down to nearly 200 meters, and this is *ultimate* wave base, but in no sense is this vigorous abrasion.

Marine abrasion of consolidated rock is largely conditioned by the pre-rotting or loosening of the coastal rocks by the subaerial chemical weathering action of ground water (Bartrum, 1926). The role of waves is thus primarily a mechanical one, to remove the debris (Fig. 1). Additional marine erosional forces are (a) mechanical abrasion, sand and boulders being propelled by wave action at the cliff foot, (b) hydraulic action (air compression in joints, etc.), and (c) biologic agencies (borers, algal buoyancy, etc.).

The principal locus of attack by all the above agencies is the intertidal belt. In exposed areas offshore, strong abrasion extends to the depth where waves begin to peak and, under storm conditions, break. More than 95% of wave energy is dissipated in this zone between about 10 meters and

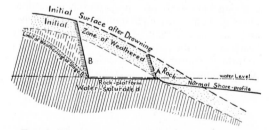

FIG. 1. The site of marine abrasion, involving the removal of subaerially rotted rock waste as visualized by Bartrum (1926). Wave action easily removes the "initial zone of weathered rock" to the point A, producing a cliff and "normal" offshore profile. Backwasting from point A favors further chemical weathering down to, but not below, the level of sea-water saturation. Marine abrasion thus tends to develop a horizontal platform, terminating at cliff **B**.

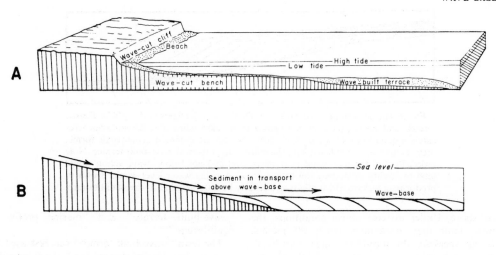

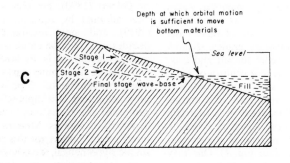

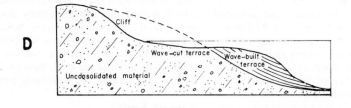

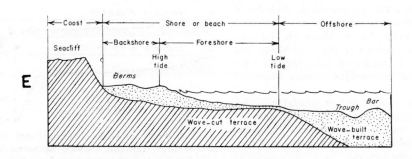

FIG. 2. Various views concerning the origin of the wave-cut and wave-built terraces, all of which imply a controlling effect of wave base. (A) After Longwell, Knopf, and Flint (1948); (B) after Clark and Stearn (1960); (C) after Garrels (1951); (D) after Von Engeln (1942); and (E) after Leet and Judson (1958).

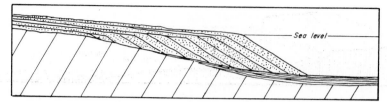

FIG. 3. The delta terrace redrawn from Dunbar and Rodgers (1957, p. 47). Topset, foreset, and bottomset beds are shown to develop when a sediment-laden river enters a quiet body of water. Such delta terraces are common geomorphic forms; they should not be confused with the entirely hypothetical wave-built terrace. Note especially that the nick-point is at water level and not below; wave action would tend to modify or destroy the delta terrace. A rising water level would drown it, producing a feature which might erroneously be interpreted as a wave-built terrace.

the shore. Under extreme storm conditions, the outer limit may sometimes reach 20 meters. Strictly speaking, this should be called "surf base" or "surge base" as it is related to surf action rather than the depth of stirring by open-sea waves (Dietz, 1963). As Moore and Curray (1964) have pointed out, there is really a *zone* of wave base, effective for various sedimentary grades, shallow for boulders and gravel, deeper for silt and clay, that is activated in cycles up to a century or so.

Historically, there has been much confusion about the lower limit of wave base and marine abrasion. The traditional tendency was to relate the depth of the shelf edge, which is normally situated at about 100–200 meters, to the bottom friction of open-sea waves (see Fig. 1). One may certainly speak of a "feeling the bottom" by open sea waves, but this is unimportant as compared to the surf action, especially over long periods when it is combined with the large Quaternary oscillations of sea level. Several authors have remarked on the widespread evidence of late Pleistocene shore lines and undisturbed relic sediments on the outer shelf. Evidently this means that since the time that sea level has been at its approximate (modern) level (a matter of about 6000 years), there has been no large-scale abrasion on the outer shelf. In regions of little accumulation, clear, rock-cut terraces may be followed in steps right across the shelf (Carrigy and Fairbridge, 1954). In certain other areas, a considerable thickness of post glacial fine-grained sediments has accumulated here, strictly speaking an unconformable Holocene stratigraphic formation (see Fig. 1 of Moore and Curray, 1964). In neither of these regional types could there be any serious erosion below 10 meters.

"Wave base" when used in stratigraphic discussions essentially refers to the upper limits of medium- or fine-grained sediments that lack evidence of littoral action, beach facies, sand bars, boulder conglomerates, etc.

Wave-built Terrace

Related to wave base are two other concepts,

"wave-built terrace" and "marine profile of equilibrium."

The term "wave-built terrace" was first used for a prograding littoral deposit (on Lake Bonneville) by Gilbert (1890), but this was not in the sense later adopted by Johnson and others. Johnson (1919), and most text-book writers in recent decades, consider the entire continental shelf to be a wave-cut terrace in its inner part and a wave-built terrace in its outer part (see Fig. 2). Accordingly, the continental slope would always be the prograding face of a dipping series of clastic beds composed of detritus swept out from the shore and deposited as a talus. Modern survey work at sea rarely offers support for this model and, in fact, a simple hypothetical wave-built terrace of this sort seems to be fictitious. Shepard (1948, 1963) especially has shown that *continental shelves* (q.v. Vol. I) are of great diversity and complexity, but none of them seem to correspond to Johnson's concept. It is important that this fallacy should be corrected, for it appears in almost every basic textbook.

The nearest equivalent to a wave-built terrace seems to be the *delta terrace* (see Fig. 3). When drowned by a rise of sea level, these are quite liable to false interpretation as wave-built terraces.

Wave-cut Terrace

From the evidence for the lower limit of effective

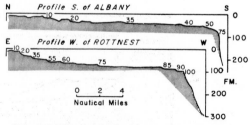

FIG. 4. Profile across the continental shelf off semi-arid Western Australia, showing abrasional notches corresponding to former eustatic sea levels (Carrigy and Fairbridge, 1954). Contemporary "wave-base" erosion, if effective down to − 100 meters, would destroy such features.

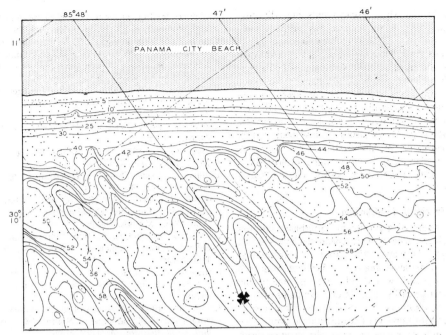

Fig. 5. Detailed topographic form of the inner shelf off Panama City, Florida, a region of clastic deposition (depths given in feet). A smooth-sloping gradient extends to a depth of 40 feet; presumably this is a near-shore marine profile of equilibrium. But greater depths are marked by a rough relict topography. A submerged forest is located at the point marked X having a radiocarbon date indicating an age in excess of 40,000 B.P. (after Dietz, 1963).

marine abrasion, noted above, it is clear that the continental shelf sediments cannot be underlain by a wave-cut terrace that was formed under the present sea-level regime.

However, sub-bottom acoustic profiling (Moore, 1960) has demonstrated many wave-cut terraces partly hidden beneath a thin veneer of late Holocene sediments. These terraces are separated from

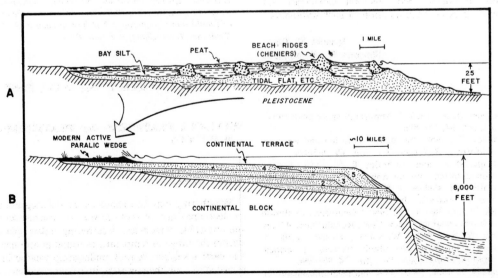

Fig. 6. Paralic wedge building up the continental terrace today off Louisiana (Dietz, 1963). (A) Detail of complex Holocene segment. No appreciable Holocene sediments are recorded beyond 25 feet (8 meters). (B) Progressive effect under eustatic control with steady subsidence.

one another by short escarpments and dip uniformly seaward. Along tectonically active coasts, such as that off southern California, these wave-cut terraces have evidently been warped and tilted seaward. On more stable coasts, e.g., off Western Australia (Carrigy and Fairbridge, 1954), such terraces are almost horizontal and seem to represent marine stillstands during the late and postglacial eustatic changes of sea level (Fairbridge, 1961) (see Fig. 4). In areas of low sedimentary supply, especially on island shelves, the veneer of Holocene cover may be very slight, or longshore currents may keep them swept clear ("hard-grounds").

Marine Profile of Equilibrium

The concept of a profile of equilibrium applies well to rivers, where MSL (mean sea level) is the base level. However, the slope of continental shelves is in no sense analogous. Wave motion falls off asymptotically with depth, and a marine profile of equilibrium in loose sediments develops only to a depth of about 20 meters (Fig. 5). This paralic (i.e., nearshore) profile of equilibrium is created by the tendency of waves to push the tractive sand load onshore. A concave sand lens results which is balanced against the leveling effect of gravity.

The surface of the outer shelf is not a profile of equilibrium but rather a relict surface reflecting especially the effect of recently lower sea levels. A deep-water profile of equilibrium, as supposed by Johnson, simply does not exist.

A constructional continental terrace builds up from an active *paralic wedge* (Fig. 6) the locus of which shifts successively inward and outward across the continental margin as sea level rises and falls eustatically. Slow tectonic subsidence aids the progressive accumulation of such sediments.

Robert S. Dietz
Rhodes W. Fairbridge

References

Bartrum, J. A., 1926, "'Abnormal' shore platforms," *J. Geol.,* **34,** 793–806.

Bradley, W., 1958, "Submarine abrasion and wave-cut platforms," *Bull. Geol. Soc. Am.,* **69,** 967–974.

Carrigy, M. A., and Fairbridge, R. W., 1954, "Recent sedimentation, physiography, and structure of the continental shelves of Western Australia," *J. Roy. Soc. W. Australia,* **38,** 65–95.

Clark, T. and Stearn, C., 1960, "Geological Evolution of North America," New York, Ronald Press, 434pp.

Dietz, R. S., 1963, "Wave-base, marine profile of equilibrium, and wave-built terraces: a critical appraisal," *Bull. Geol. Soc. Am.,* **74,** 971–990.

Dietz, R. S., 1964, "Wave-base, marine profile of equilibrium, and wave-built terraces: reply," *Bull. Geol. Soc. Am.,* **75,** 1275–1282.

Dietz, R., and Menard, H., 1951, "Origin of abrupt changes in slope at continental shelf margins," *Bull. Am. Assoc. Petrol. Geologists,* **35,** 1994–2016.

Dunbar, C., and Rodgers, J., 1957, "Principles of Stratigraphy," New York, John Wiley & Sons, 356pp.

Fairbridge, R., 1952, "Marine erosion," *Proc. Pacific Sci. Congr. Pacific Sci. Assoc. 7th,* **3,** 347–358.

Fairbridge, R. W., 1961, "Eustatic Changes of Sea Level," in "Physics and Chemistry," Vol. 4, pp. 99–185, Pergamon Press.

Garrels, R., 1951, "Textbook of Geology," New York, Harper, 511pp.

Gilbert, G. K., 1890, "Lake Bonneville," *U.S. Geol. Surv. Monograph,* **1,** 438pp.

Gulliver, F., 1899. "Shoreline topography," *Proc. Am. Acad. Arts Sci.,* **34,** 151–258.

Johnson, D., 1919 (1938, Second ed.), "Shore Processes and Shoreline Development," New York, John Wiley & Sons, 584pp.

Leet, L. D., and Judson, S., 1958, "Physical Geology," Second edition, Englewood Cliffs, N.J., Prentice Hall, 502pp.

Longwell, C., Knopf, A. K., and Flint, R., 1948, "Physical Geology," New York, John Wiley & Sons, 543pp.

Moore, D., 1960, "Acoustic-reflection studies of the continental shelf and slope off Southern California," *Bull. Geol. Soc. Am.,* **71,** 1121–1136.

Moore, D. G., and Curray, J. R., 1964, "Wave-base . . . discussion" (of Dietz, 1963), *Bull. Geol. Soc. Am.,* **75,** 1267–1273 (Reply, pp. 1275–1281).

Shepard, F. P., 1948, "Submarine Geology," New York, Harper & Bros., 348pp.

Shepard, F. P., 1963, "Thirty-five Thousand Years of Sea Level," in (Stevenson, R. E., editor), "Essays in Marine Geology in Honor of K. O. Emery," pp. 1–10, Los Angeles, Univ. South California Press.

Von Engeln, O., 1942, "Geomorphology," New York, MacMillan Co., 665pp.

Cross-references: *Abrasion; Base Level; Delta; Eustasy; Holocene; Littoral Processes; Nickpoint; Organisms as Geomorphic Agents; Platforms—Wave-cut; Profile of Equilibrium; Quaternary.* Vol. I: *Continental Shelf; Mean Sea Level Changes; Ocean Waves.*

WAVE-BUILT TERRACE—*See* WAVE BASE

WAVE-CUT PLATFORM—*See* PLATFORMS —WAVE-CUT

WEATHERING

Weathering may be defined as the disintegration or decomposition of rocks *in situ.* In contrast with metamorphic processes, weathering takes place within the range of temperatures found at and near the earth's surface. A rock undergoing weathering is not static; on the contrary, in certain weathering processes some minerals and elements are lost, others gained, and yet others redeposited at another level at the same site. There is considerable movement of material beneath the ground surface. But the main mass of the rock remains *in situ* and is not transported.

Many weathering processes are known in outline and in theory, but in many instances what actually takes place in nature is obscure. It is in any case rather unreal to define and explain most weathering processes in isolation, for several processes commonly combine to cause rock weathering, of which two general types are recognized. Physical (or mechanical) weathering involves rock disintegration, without any alteration of the constituent minerals. In chemical weathering, on the other hand, some or all of the rock-forming minerals suffer decay or alteration; some of these changes involve an increase in volume, thereby causing the rock to crumble or rupture; some entail loss of material and the formation of cavities, which promotes further weathering; and some actually toughen the rock, as by the addition of silica or iron.

Physical Weathering

Factors responsible for physical weathering are thermal expansion, pressure release, crystal growth and living organisms.

Thermal expansion has long been cited as a cause of disintegration (see *Spheroidal Weathering*). Both granular disintegration and the formation of flakes, shells and massive sheets have been attributed to unequal expansion and contraction due to diurnal and annual changes in insolation. Rocks are poor conductors of heat, and it is obvious that the surfaces exposed to the sun's rays are heated and should therefore expand to a far greater extent than the rocks a few inches or feet below the surface. Due to its expansion, the outer mass becomes detached from the main body of the rock, forming a shell or thin sheet. This type of weathering was once referred to as exfoliation, but the term has now been applied to so many varieties of laminae, flakes, shells and sheets, of different origins, that it is best avoided.

Another argument, following roughly the same lines, is that since rock-forming minerals are of different colors, they therefore absorb heat at different rates, expand differentially in consequence, and thus disintegrate into the constituent mineral grains.

Many travelers in the arid tropics where diurnal temperatures are greatest, and where insolation should on this account be most effective, have reported hearing, in the evening or night, loud reports which they attribute to the cracking of rocks as they contract and rupture. And it is true that intense heat, such as is generated in bushfires, promotes flaking and splitting of rocks. For thousands of years, fires have been used as a quarrying tool in ancient Egypt and India. Fires are lit on a rock surface cleared of soil, and the intense local heat causes the arching of a sheet several inches thick, which is easily broken into blocks with a hammer. But such heating is local and far beyond the range of normal diurnal temperature fluctuations, even in the deserts. Moreover, there is clear evidence that even in conditions of extreme aridity, and intense insolational heating, it is chemical, not physical, weathering that is predominant. The Egyptian desert near Cairo experiences very low average rainfall and searing heat. Granite columns that have fallen on their sides are partly exposed to the full blast of the sun's rays, partly shaded, and partly buried by the desert sands. Contrary to expectation, it is not the surfaces exposed to the sun that are weathered, but the shaded areas and especially the areas that are or were buried in the sands. Even here, there is some moisture in the surface sand, and it has effectively promoted decay and disintegration. Similarly in northwestern Eyre Peninsula (South Australia), in a 13-inch rainfall zone, many granite surfaces exposed to the powerful summer sun are quite smooth, but beneath even a thin veneer of soil and debris, the rock surface is intensely pitted due to chemical alteration of some of the rock-forming minerals.

Experimental work has also indicated that heating and cooling do not of themselves produce detectable weathering. Such laboratory work is always open to the charge that the great expanses of geological time cannot be simulated. If cycles of heating and cooling within the natural range were continued over a period of thousands of years, would they gradually cause fatigue and weakening of the bonds holding minerals together? The experimental evidence suggests not, but the question remains open because of the time problem. However, it is equally clear that in many instances the insolation hypothesis has provided a too facile and ready explanation of weathering: it is difficult to prove and is to be used as a last resort.

The insolation hypothesis nevertheless seems so logical and rings so true that, in spite of the evidence to the contrary, it dies hard. And because there are features difficult to explain in terms other than insolation, there are periodic and insistent revivals of the hypothesis. Recently, for instance, it has been cogently argued that no other explanation is feasible for the boulders of the Olgas conglomerate, in the southern part of the Northern Territory, which are split off in the same plane as the hillslope in which they occur.

It has been shown in the laboratory that temperature changes can cause minerals to fissure in the presence of moisture, and since there is occasional moisture in the soil surface even in desert regions, this fact is important. There is also some evidence that water can contribute to disintegration (without significant alteration). In clays which are most rapidly affected, there is dispersion, a phenomenon known to drillers as "slacking"—a solid core of clays will, after immersion in water, quickly disintegrate to a pile of clay particles. Presumably, surface tension phenomena and colloidal and dilation behavior, as well as fatigue, are involved. The ionic bonding of juxtaposed minerals may be weakened by water. This may be an instance of slight physical activity opening the way for chemical weathering. In other rocks, the addition of water to crystal lattices or to solutions, without chemical alteration—a process known as *hydration*—takes place. Again, the increase in the so-called water of crystallization may involve volume increase and the shattering of a rock. This process is probably significant, for the chemical changes involved in spheroidally weathered rocks, for example, are very slight and appear unlikely to cause disintegration by virtue of volume change. The alternate wetting and drying of rocks is believed by some workers, particularly those engaged in coastal studies, to cause fatigue and eventual disintegration.

Many types of rock, but especially granites, are subdivided into a series of massive sheets or shells by arched fractures which transgress normal sedimentary, metamorphic and igneous structures. Such fractures are commonly attributed to the *release of pressure* consequent upon erosion of superincumbent strata; this is known as offloading. Granites, for example, originate deep in the earth's crust under very high-pressure conditions. As erosion strips off the superincumbent strata, pressures are diminished and the granite tends to expand, which is manifested in the development of massive arches. Many sediments have been deeply buried, and similar arguments apply. The hypothesis seems reasonable and is widely cited; but it does not explain the field evidence and particularly the field relations of arched structures in some areas, and it has been suggested that the arching is a result of strong lateral pressures of tectonic origin. Whatever its origin, however, the arched fractures are yet another form of rock weathering.

As crystals develop or grow, they exert a pressure sufficient to shatter some rocks. The best-known example is that of *ice crystal growth*. In subarctic regions or at high elevations, temperatures frequently oscillate about the freezing point. Water in rock cracks and crevices suffers alternations of freezing and thawing and, in consequence, oscillates between its solid and liquid forms. Changes in volume are involved, and the pressures exerted, though not as great as often assumed because of incomplete confinement, are nevertheless sufficiently powerful to disrupt many rocks, especially those that are fissile (finely bedded or well cleaved). Rapid disintegration of such rocks is achieved, and many shale and phyllite outcrops in the subarctic are covered by a chaotic mass of frost-shattered plates.

The *crystallization of salt* also causes disintegra-

tion of rocks under certain conditions, though there is doubt concerning its effectiveness on fresh crystalline rocks. Some authors have made great claims for the process in arid lands, but there is a dearth of basic knowledge concerning the pressures exerted by growing crystals. In weakly consolidated clays, in rocks that are already partly weathered, and in soft materials, salt crystallization causes rocks to be shattered. There is good evidence in Egypt, and in some coastal regions, that salt crystallization can at least contribute to the shattering of certain rocks such as sandstones and shales. However there is no conclusive evidence that fresh tough rocks can be disrupted by this means, though early workers such as Jutson attributed much weathering and planation at the margins of salinas to the process termed *exudation*. As is the case with many other weathering processes, it is difficult to differentiate between the possible influence of salt crystallization and that of other mechanisms. In the early years of the century, for instance, it was reported that igneous and other crystalline rocks in Manitoba had been "chemically disintegrated" due to the action of salts in brine drawn over the rock surfaces by surface tension. Large boulders had been reduced to half their original size. But it was also acknowledged that hydration was important, and the relative significance of each process is hard to assess.

Tree roots can occasionally be shown to have forced apart adjacent joint blocks, though again it is necessary to be quite sure that the roots are not merely growing in preexisting cracks. Worms, rabbits and other burrowing creatures create avenues for other weathering agencies, and there is a suggestion that soil colloids may pluck off or loosen rock fragments, thus contributing to disintegration. There is some laboratory and field evidence in support of this contention.

Chemical Weathering

The decomposition or chemical weathering of rocks is accomplished in a variety of ways. No rock-forming mineral is absolutely chemically inert, but some minerals are far more readily altered than others. Thus, of the common rock-forming minerals, olivine is the least stable, followed in order by lime plagioclase, augite, lime soda plagioclase, hornblende and soda lime plagioclase, soda plagioclase, biotite, orthoclase, muscovite and quartz. But even quartz (SiO_2), which is reckoned the most stable of minerals, is very slightly soluble in water, and as with many other minerals, it is more soluble in saline waters.

A few minerals such as rock salt are significantly *soluble in water*. Others, such as anhydrite which readily takes up water to form gypsum, are susceptible to hydration. Many more combine with OH radicals; iron, for instance, readily unites with both oxygen and water to form various hydrolized iron oxides ranging in color from yellow to reddish brown.

Many minerals are *soluble in weak acids*. Limestone, for instance, is insoluble in water but reacts with weak carbonic acid to form the bicarbonate which is soluble in water:

$$CaCO_3 + H_2O + CO_2 \rightarrow Ca(HCO_3)_2$$

Likewise, waters containing humic acids effect some solution. It is rather typical that the products of other chemical weathering processes are transported as carbonates, sulfates or chlorides in solution in groundwaters and rivers. The Mississippi, for instance, carries an average of 136 million tons of material to the sea each year in this way alone.

By reacting with water, oxygen, iron or carbon dioxide, minerals are wholly or partially altered. In some cases, the structure of the rock is weakened; in others, the volume is changed. Reactions are commonly complex. For instance, the feldspar orthoclase, subjected to both hydration and carbonation, produces a colloidal clay, soluble salt and silica:

$$2KAlSi_3O_8 + 2H_2O + CO_2 \rightarrow H_4Al_2Si_2O_9$$
$$+ K_2O_3 + 4SiO_2$$

Outside the humid tropics, the typical end products of chemical weathering are sand and clay, but in the humid tropics, both are unstable, and compounds rich in Al, FeO and H_2O form the mantle of waste—hence, the development in such regions of laterite and bauxite, deposits rich in iron and alumina, respectively. The course of weathering in these lands varies considerably, but the sort of sequence of changes that are suffered is detailed by considering a pervious volcanic ash. First, soluble salts of Ca, K, Na and some SiO_2, for example, are leached. FeO is oxidized to Fe_2O_3, and MnO to MnO_2. Where drainage is good, kaolinite is formed, but montmorillonite is found where it is poor. The leaching of bases continues, and the depth of weathering increases. Because of this leaching, there is a relative concentration of Fe_2O_3 and Al_2O_3 in the near-surface horizons, while silica is precipitated in a layer close to the parent rock. The iron- and alumina-rich layer near the surface develops in nodular form and may form a thick carapace: this is laterite or bauxite depending on the relative predominance of Fe and Al in the crust. Fe- and Al-rich layers also form in "monsoonal" lands: at Weipa, in north Queensland, the bauxite has formed by the intense leaching of a sandstone. The ore was formed in the Tertiary, but formation is alleged to be proceeding. Pedogenic lime is called "kunkar" in the Middle East and "caliche" in the American Southwest, or more generally "calcrete" (cf. iron rich or lateritic layers or ferricrete). It forms massive lenses or beds.

Travertine is morphologically indistinguishable from kunkar but forms in stream beds and near springs. In arid lands, and possibly also in certain lacustrine conditions, horizons rich in silica may form; they are known as "silcrete" or, in Australia, "billy" (possibly because after spheroidal weathering, they lie out on the plains like billy goats?).

The *role of organisms* in chemical weathering is an important one. The effects of humic acids have already been mentioned, and the extraction of soluble nutrients is also significant. On granite and other rock surfaces, for example, lichens can be shown to disintegrate rocks with their hyphae and also to extract iron from minerals and concentrate it at, and immediately beneath, the rock surface.

Climate and mineralogy obviously have a great influence on the type and course of weathering. In the humid tropics, temperatures are consistently high, and moisture and humic acids are everywhere abundant. The rate of most chemical reactions increases with rise in temperature and in moisture. Silicate weathering, for instance, involving ionic exchange of cations from the crystal lattice and hydrogen ions from water, increases in humid tropical conditions, though even there it is very slow by any but geological standards. The subarctic lands are most prone to frost shattering; the hot deserts, to the effects—direct or indirect—of insolation.

The effects of mineral composition have already been suggested by the order of weathering listed above. Obviously basic rocks such as basalt, containing much olivine, augite and the calcium-rich plagioclase feldspar, weather more rapidly than, say, granite. Structure and texture are also important influences—the first because the number of joints, for example, determines how many avenues are open to weathering agencies. The size of constituent fragments or crystals and the perfection, or otherwise, of their interlocking has a bearing on the rate of weathering. The rate of erosion or evacuation of weathered debris is also significant for, if erosion is negligible, the weathered mantle may come to form a protective veneer on the land surface. On the other hand, where there is strong erosion, the products of weathering are rapidly evacuated, and fresh rocks are brought within the range of weathering processes, there is said to be renewal of weathering.

Weathering is a very important complex of processes. Its chief significance is that it prepares rocks for transportation and erosion. Without preliminary weathering, rivers and wind—and probably glacier ice too—can accomplish little erosion. The development of resistant crusts, pans and horizons in soils also has its effect on the landscape: they render a surface impenetrable, with significant consequences for runoff and erosion; they may also, after dissection, come to form resistant cappings to plateaus. Weathering is both selective and differential, and sometimes remarkable minor landforms such as caverns and *tafoni* (q.v.) develop on this account. In the humid tropics, the transportation of the products of weathering in solution may contribute significantly to the lowering of the land surface, but the most important work of weathering is in the preparation of rocks for transportation.

C. R. TWIDALE

References

Blackwelder, E., 1933, "The insolation hypothesis of rock weathering," *Am. J. Sci.*, **26,** 97–113.
Chapman, R. W., Greenfield, M. A., 1949, "Spheroidal weathering of igneous rocks," *Am. J. Sci.*, **247,** 407–429.
Goldich, S. S., 1938, "A study of rock weathering," *J. Geol.*, **46,** 17–58.
Griggs, D. T., 1936, "The factor of fatigue in rock exfoliation," *J. Geol.*, **44,** 783–796.
Keller, W. D., 1955, "Principles of Chemical Weathering," Columbia, Mo., Lucas Bros., 88pp.
Linton, D. L., 1955, "The problem of tors," *Geograph. J.*, **121,** 470–487.
Merrill, G. P., 1921, "Rocks, Rock-weathering and Soils," New York, London, Macmillan Co., 411pp.
Ollier, C. D., 1963, "Insolation weathering: examples from central Australia," *Am. J. Sci.*, **261,** 376–381.
Reiche, P., 1950, "A Survey of Weathering Processes and Products," Revised ed., University of New Mexico Press, 95pp.
Rougerie, G., 1959, "Latéritisation et pédogénés intertropicales," *L'inf. Géogr.*, 199–205.
Trendall, A. F., 1962, "The formation of 'apparent peneplains' by a process of combined lateritisation and surface wash," *Zeit. Geomorphol.*, **6,** (N.S.), 183–197.
Wilhelmy, H., 1958, "Der Klimamorphologie der Massengesteine," Braunschweig, G. Westerman, 238pp.
Williams, J. E., 1949, "Chemical weathering at low temperatures," *Geograph. Rev.*, **39,** 129–135.

Cross-references: *Duricrust*; *Erosion*; *Etchplain*; *Exfoliation*; *Exudation*; *Frost Action*; *Limestone Caves*; *Limestone Coastal Weathering*; *Organisms as Geomorphic Agents*; *Salt Weathering or Fretting*; *Spheroidal Weathering*; *Tafoni*; *Tor*; *Tropical Weathering and Relief*. Vol. II: *Insolation*. Vol. IV: *Bauxite*; *Kaolinite*; *Montmorillonite*. Vol. VI: *Caliche*; *Laterite*; *Leaching*; *Silcrete*; *Travertine*; *Weathering—Chemical*; *Weathering—Organic*.

WEATHERING UNIT

Where weathering occurs in unconsolidated rocks such as clays or sands, it commences at the surface and works its way downward. As a result, the sequence of layers below any one point on the surface will be typical of the whole area. Accordingly, description of the *weathering profile* lying vertically below a point will adequately describe the sequence in the area.

A sharp boundary called a *weathering front* or

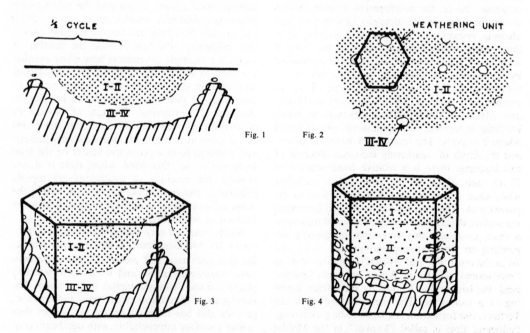

FIGS. 1–4. Cross-section (Fig. 1), detailed map (Fig. 2), and weathering unit (Fig. 3) of a common type of weathering pattern developed on consolidated rocks. Figure 4 shows another weathering unit from a different pattern of weathering. Roman numerals refer to the weathering zones of Berry and Ruxton (1959) (after Harris, 1963).

basal surface separates the weathered zone above from the unweathered material underneath. The weathered zone may be several hundred feet thick in the humid tropics and has been subdivided into a series of four zones by Berry and Ruxton (1959). These zones are based on the degree of oxidation or color, and on the presence of rounded blocks of unweathered rock in varying proportions.

Over unconsolidated materials, only the zones due to varying degrees of oxidation occur, whereas the full sequence is found over consolidated rocks. In these, the weathering processes work on the exposed rock surfaces, i.e., the surfaces of the joints, bedding planes and any other fractures. As weathering proceeds, the weathering products increase at the expense of the unweathered rock. The joints are spaced unevenly and divide the rocks into blocks of different sizes. Consequently, the smaller blocks will be destroyed long before the larger ones, and differences in distribution of joint pattern produce markedly different results, greatly affecting the distribution of weathering zones. A severely fractured part of the rock will be weathered very deeply at a stage when portions with few fractures will consist mainly of *corestones* (Figs. 1 and 4). The relatively unweathered or weathered pockets may be found scattered at random across the countryside as in Fig. 2. No single weathering profile below a point will be typical of the entire area, and thus the question arises of how to describe this relationship.

This can be overcome by using a three-dimensional body called a *weathering unit*, with its lower limit coinciding with the surface of fresh rock. It must have three dimensions and be large enough laterally to permit the study of the nature of any horizons present, i.e., its area ranges from 1–10 square meters, depending on the variability of the parent materials.

The sequence in Figs. 1 and 2 can be divided into cycles with unweathered "hills" of rock at each end. Only half a cycle is needed to describe the nature of the weathered material using a three-dimensional approach as in Figs. 3 and 4. If half a cycle is greater than 7 meters, the "hills" are far enough apart to be mapped individually. In this case, or where the weathering material shows only minor variations, a hexagonal block about 1 square meter in surface area will provide an adequate description.

STUART A. HARRIS

References

Berry, L., and Ruxton, B. P., 1959, "Notes on weathering zones and soils on granitic rocks in two tropical regions," *J. Soil Sci.*, **10**, 54–63.

Harris, S. A., 1963, "Weathering units and weathering catenas," *Proc. Geol. Assoc. London*, **74**, 441–443.

Cross-references: *Etchplain*; *Tor*; *Tropical Weathering and Relief*; *Weathering*. Vol. VI: *Soil Profile*; *Weathering—Chemical*.

WIND ACTION

Although wind action is less important than water for the whole earth, it is a major force in altering landscapes. Wind action erodes, transports, and deposits soil, sand, dust and soluble compounds (e.g., NaCl) over long periods of time. Our knowledge of the physics of wind action owes much to R. A. Bagnold's wind tunnel studies and field experiments in the mid and late 1930's. His book *The Physics of Blown Sand and Desert Dunes*, though published in 1941, still represents the clearest and most definitive statement in this area. As in so many aspects of natural processes, there are numerous logarithmic relations to be found in the subject.

Erosion

Wind erodes primarily by *deflation*, a process of lifting loose particles of sand size or finer materials from the land surface. The largest size normally moved by wind is about 1 mm.

Using sand particles picked up by deflation, wind may then scour a surface to extreme smoothness by the process of *corrasion* or *abrasion*. One of the major products of corrasion is the *ventifact*. These are pebbles or small rocks which have been faceted as illustrated in Fig. 1. Another product is *rock*

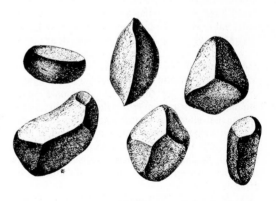

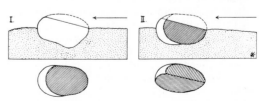

FIG. 1. Various forms of ventifacts arise from complex winds and disturbance of lag gravels (after Kettner, 1960).

FIG. 2. Approach of a dust storm over an Australian farming community (Walther, 1924, p. 84).

tanks which Bryan (1923) attributes to the gouging of areas of slightly less resistant rock on a scoured rock plain. These are common features of arid regions, as are *yardangs* (Blackwelder, 1934), alternating rib-like projections and deflation tongues.

The depth to which deflation may proceed may be hundreds of meters in favored spots in deserts (Butzer, 1965), until particles too large or too fine to be lifted by the wind are encountered, or the water table is reached. Many elongate marshes in coastal regions, tanks and other depressions on the high plains of Texas, Colorado, and western Kansas and in comparable semiarid landscapes in North Africa, Australia, and elsewhere either are elongated in the direction of the present dominant sand-moving wind, or may mirror paleo-wind directions.

Unusual effects of wind in governing snow deposition, cirque location, and development of level flats at high altitudes are described by Löve (1965 in INQUA). The term coined to cover such effects is "anemo-orographic system," introduced by Jenik in 1962.

As recently as 1920 many geologists attributed much of the broad-scale modeling of desert landscapes to wind erosion. We now know this view to be seriously in error. Many features thought clearly to indicate the abrasive action of wind-driven sand particles are becoming increasingly suspect. Bagnold's (1941) studies indicating that the relative density of sand flow falls off sharply above a few centimeters over a sand surface, and less than 10 cm over a pebble-strewn surface, has eliminated many pedestal rocks with notches from 30–150 cm above the ground as possible wind

erosion features. The coincidence of notching with lithology and, in selected areas, the discovery of clear crystalline selenite (a variety of gypsum, a mineral easily frosted by wind blast) as a surface litter near pedestal rocks and the preservation of Paleolithic rock pictures above the abrasion zone are further evidence of restricted wind cutting even in desert areas. The preservation of ancient surfaces composed of fine-textured materials not subject to wind action is also widely reported in arid regions.

Transportation

The transportation of particles by wind action involves three processes: *suspension, saltation,* and *creep* (Bagnold, 1941). Almost all air movement is turbulent and contains eddies which give vertical motions equal to about one-sixth of the horizontal velocity. These vertical motions define the limiting terminal velocity of fall for a given wind speed. This in turn governs the maximum size of particles which may be held in suspension, for those with a terminal velocity of fall less than the lift of air turbulence enter suspension. These particles may form dust clouds like the one shown in Fig. 2. Most loess was transported by this means, and ranges in size from 0.02–0.07 mm.

Saltating particles progress by intermittent bounces or leaps of varying lengths depending upon grain size and weight and wind velocity. The path length of a single jump of a saltating sand grain increases with wind speed as buoyancy is approached in turbulent air. In the movement of sands, Chepil (1945) has shown that saltation is overwhelmingly the most important process. Most

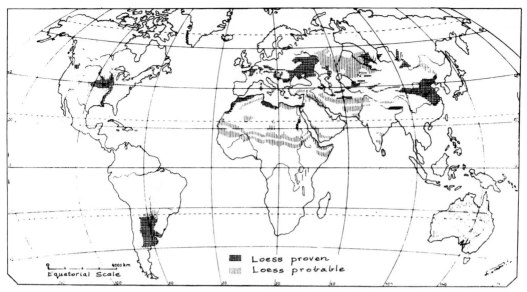

FIG. 3. Distribution of loess deposits over the surface of the earth (Woldstedt, 1954, p. 172). (By permission of Enke Verlag, Stuttgart.)

dune sands have mean diameters in the range of 0.15–0.3 mm.

Surface creep is induced by saltating grains striking particles and knocking them forward. Bagnold (1941) notes that "a high-speed grain in saltation can by impact move a surface grain six times its diameter, or more than 200 times its own weight." Since these creeping particles are large and travel slowly, surface creep contributes to the coarse size-grading of sand deposits.

Deposition

Bagnold (1941) describes three types of deposition of wind-transported materials. *Sedimentation* occurs when particles drop, usually from suspension, with insufficient force to induce either saltation or surface creep. Most dust, because of its low terminal velocity of fall, settles in this fashion. *Accretion* results when grains moving by saltation strike the surface with insufficient force to move as much material by surface creep so that deposition exceeds removal. *Encroachment* takes place when a barrier obstructs the movement of some particles. Encroachment occurs on dunes where particles roll to rest in the lee of the dune crest. Two principal types of wind deposits are formed, loess and sand dunes. These are discussed elsewhere in this volume.

Loess (q.v.) is a fine silty material found in extensive deposits in many parts of the world (Fig. 3). Notable deposits include those in the north China plain, much of the north European plain, and extensive areas in the central United States and the Argentine. Loess is commonly associated with glacial phenomena ("cold" loess), since glacial action produces a very fine powder (glacial flour) which lends itself admirably to wind movement along the glacial front. Other prime sources of loess are from wind reworking of weathered materials in desert areas ("hot" loess) (Yaalon in INQUA, 1965), semiarid and sub-humid sand dune fields (Lugn in INQUA, 1965), and from wholesale loss of soil stability during the Pleistocene climatic changes, as documented in Australia by Crocker (1946). In the Murray River basin, Australia, eolian clays were termed *parna* by Butler (1956), to differentiate them from loess.

Over recent years it has become increasingly evident that deposition of fine dust (obvious in the case of thick loess) has occurred in very thin mantles, normally undetected, over broad areas. The latter is a vastly underrated factor in the maintenance of soil fertility in wide regions. Wind-carried volcanic ash is also of great importance, forming soils of distinctive character and marking stratigraphic episodes (bentonite). The role of wind-carried "cyclic" salts (sodium chloride, gypsum, calcium carbonate) in influencing soil formation is now widely recognized in several continents, especially in Australia and Africa. In the former, solonization of utterly unlike soils arising from accessions of cyclic salt is widespread in the southern half of the continent, and there has been extensive transportation and deposition of dust high in calcium carbonate which many authors have regarded as a major factor in the building of soil travertines (caliche or calcrete) in northwest Africa, the southwestern United States and in

1235

much of the Mallee district of Victoria and South Australia.

DAVID S. SIMONETT

References

Bagnold, R. A., 1941, "The Physics of Blown Sand and Desert Dunes," London, Methuen and Co. Ltd., 265pp. (Second ed. 1954).

Blackwelder, Eliot, 1934, "Yardangs," *Bull. Geol. Soc. Am.*, **45**, 159–166.

Bryan, Kirk, 1923, "Wind erosion near Lees Ferry, Arizona," *Am. J. Sci.*, **206**, 291–307.

Butler, B. E., 1956, "Parna—An aeolian clay," *Australian J. Sci.*, **18**(5), 145–151.

Butzer, K. W., 1965, "Environment and Archeology," Chicago, Aldine, 524pp.

Chepil, W. S., 1945, "Dynamics of wind erosion: III. The transport capacity of the wind," *Soil Sci.* **60**, 475–480.

Crocker, R. L., 1946, "Post-Miocene climatic and geologic history and its significance in relation to the genesis of the major soil types of South Australia," *CSIRO Bull. 193*, Australia, Melbourne.

INQUA (International Association for Quaternary Research), 1965. *Abstracts*, VII International Congress, Aug.–Sept. 1965, Boulder, Colorado.

Kettner, Radim, 1960, "Allgemeine Geologie," Vol. IV, Berlin, Verlag der Wissenschaften.

Walther, Johannes, 1924, "Das Gesetz der Wustenbildung in Gegenwart und Vorzeit," Fourth ed., Leipzig, Verlag Quelle und Meyer, 421pp.

Williams, G., 1964, "Some aspects of the eolian saltation load," *Sedimentology*, **3**(4), 257–287.

Woldstedt, Paul, 1954, "Das Eiszeitalter," Vol. 1, Stuttgart, Ferdinand Enke Verlag.

Cross-references: *Abrasion; Arid Cycle; Clay Dunes; Corrasion; Deflation; Deserts and Desert Landforms; Eolian Transport; Erosion; Loess; Sand Dunes; Ventifacts; Yardang.* Vol. II: *Tornadoes; Whirlwinds;*

Wind—Principles; Wind Measurement; Winds—Local. Vol. VI: *Caliche; Parna; Salts—Cyclic; Volcanic Ash Deposits.*

WIND GAP

A wind gap (or air gap) in geomorphology is a notch or col in a ridge or mountain range that is not occupied by a stream. By implication it is a former *water gap* (q.v.) that has been abandoned due to stream capture (piracy), during the evolution of an antecedent drainage system.

Classical wind gaps are found in the North and South Downs of England and in the Kittatinny, Blue Ridge and other ridges of the folded Appalachians. The township of Wind Gap is situated at the foot of the latter in eastern Pennsylvania, not far from the Delaware Water Gap.

RHODES W. FAIRBRIDGE

References

Cotton, C. A., 1952, "Geomorphology," Sixth ed., New York, John Wiley & Sons, 505pp.

Sparks, B. W., 1960, "Geomorphology," London, Longmans, Green & Co; New York, John Wiley & Sons, 371pp.

Ver Steeg, K., 1930, "Wind gaps and water gaps of the northern Appalachians," *Ann. N.Y. Acad. Sci.*, **32**, 87–220.

Wooldridge, S. W., and Morgan, R. S., 1959, "An Outline of Geomorphology," Second ed., London, Longmans, Green & Co., 409pp.

Cross-references: *Col; Drainage Patterns; Stream Capture, Piracy; Water Gap.*

WINDOW (FENSTER)—See STRUCTURAL CONTROL IN GEOMORPHOLOGY

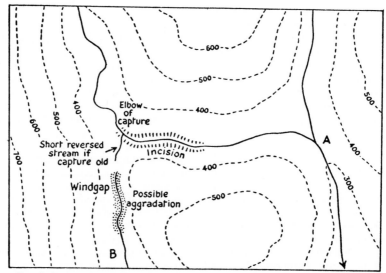

FIG. 1. A wind gap and other signs of river capture (Sparks, 1960). (By permission of John Wiley & Sons, N.Y., Longmans, Green & Co., London.)

X Y Z

XEROPHILE, XEROPHYTE, XEROSERE

These words, based on the Greek *xeros* for dry, are generally applicable to desert regions, usually to the *vegetation* (see *Vegetation Markers and Landscapes*, Vol. VI). Xerophile or xerophilous (adj.) means dry-loving or drought-loving organisms, such plants being characterized by various ecologic adaptations to desert life, such as excessively long roots, fleshy stems (cacti) or thin leaves (acacia). A xerophyte (xerophytic, adj.) is a xerophylous plant of any sort.

A vegetational community that commonly inhabits a particular environment such as soil, e.g., a pervious sandy soil that has very poor water-retaining capacity, is called a *xerosere*. In a similar climatic zone a clayey soil may well retain moisture, but excess *evapotranspiration* (q.v., Vol. II) causes capillary return to the atmosphere, resulting in the accumulation of salts (salts from weathering solution brought in by ephemeral streams and "cyclic salts" from the ocean); the resultant vegetation displaying corresponding salt adaptations is then called *halophytic*.

The term *xerothermic index* refers to a measure or index of the intensity of biological *drought* (q.v., Vol. II), with *xerothermic* climates marked by long, dry days, and *xerochimenic* climates marked by short, dry days (Bagnouls and Gaussen, 1957).

Finally, in soil science, the term *xerorendsina* has sometimes been applied to an ashy, grey rendsina, characteristic of dry steppe lands, although more usually the classification serosem (sierozem) would be applied to such soils (Kubiena, 1953).

RHODES W. FAIRBRIDGE

References

Bagnouls, F., and Gaussen, H., 1957, "Les climats biologiques et leur classification," *Ann. Géogr.* (*Paris*), **66**, 193–220.

Beadle, N. C. W., 1968, "Some aspects of the ecology and physiology of Australian xeromorphic plants," *Australian J. Sci.*, **30**(9), 348–355.

Dansereau, P., 1957, "Biogeography," New York, The Ronald Press Company.

Kubiena, W. L., 1953, *Soil Science.*

Sears, P. B., 1942, "Xerothermic theory," *Botan. Rev.*, **8**, 708–736.

Stamp, L. D., 1961, "A Glossary of Geographical Terms," London, Longmans, Green and Co., 539pp.

Cross-references: *Desert*; *Holocene*; *Playa*. Vol. II: *Climatic Optimum*; *Drought*; *Evapotranspiration*; *Vegetation Classification*. Vol. VI: *Hydrology in Semiarid Regions*; *Pedology*; *Vegetation Markers and Landscapes*.

YARDANG

In arid regions where soft poorly consolidated rocks are exposed at the surface, there may be wind erosion which is both spectacular and distinctive. One of the most notable features, first described by Sven Hedin from Turkestan, and adopted by Eliot Blackwelder, the *yardang*, consists of an elongated ridge aligned parallel to the strongest prevalent wind direction. Yardangs commonly occur in groups or fields. In the southern Lut of Iran, for instance, there is an area 150 km by 70 km underlain by unconsolidated silts that has been thoroughly scoured by the wind. The most prominent result is the development of vast yardangs, long streamlined whalebacks separating deep depressions. Their crests stand as much as 200 meters above the troughs and which run SSE–NNW, parallel to the prevailing wind. In the Mojave Desert of the western United States the yardangs or fins are undercut, and slightly overhanging. Blackwelder argues that this maximum scour within a few inches of the base of the ridges indicates that it is small gravel picked up by the funnelled winds which achieves greatest erosion.

In the Mojave, the yardangs have been explained as eolian modifications of preexisting systems of ravines and ridges, some of which run parallel to the prevalent local wind and thus suffer retouching. But elsewhere there is no evidence of preliminary preparation by stream activity, and it seems likely that turbulent eddies of wind cause differential erosion of soft rocks, thus initiating the development of elongate depressions which are subsequently enlarged and deepened. In the Lut of Iran the features do not appear to have been formed by other than the wind, and near Lake Eyre, in South Australia, where the locally developed wind drift dunes display elongate cores of lacustrine clays which have been eroded by wind scour, there is likewise no evidence of preliminary stream preparation.

Climatic changes in central Asia have resulted in some anomalous relationships, such as temporarily inundated yardangs (Hörner and Chen, 1935).

FIG. 1. Yardangs from wind erosion, Libyan Desert, Africa (after J. Walther).

Thus the yardang is one of the few landforms which is due wholly, or to a significant extent, to the abrasive action of the wind-borne sand and fine gravel.

Blackwelder (1930) compared yardangs with the *zastruga* (pl. *zastrugi*, also spelled with an "s") of snowfields that suffer deflation, but melt-processes are also involved in this case.

C. R. TWIDALE

References

Blackwelder, E., 1930, "Yardang and Zastruga," *Science*, **72**, 396–397.
Blackwelder, E., 1934, "Yardangs," *Geog. Soc. Amer. Bull.*, **45**, 159–166.
Bobek, H., 1963, "Nature and Implications of Quaternary Climate Changes in Iran," in "Changes of Climate," pp. 403–413, UNESCO Symposium, Proceedings, 488pp.
Hedin, S., 1903, "Central Asia and Tibet," Vol. 1, p. 350, 608pp, London.
Hörner, N. G. and Chen, P. C., 1935, "Alternating lakes," *Geogr. Ann.*, **17** (S. Hedin vol.), 145–166.
King, D., 1956, "The Quaternary stratigraphic record at Lake Eyre North and the evolution of existing topographic forms," *Trans. Royal Soc. S. Australia*, **79**, 93–103.
Walther, J., 1924, "Das Gesetz der Wüstenbildung," Fourth ed., Leipzig, Quelle & Meyer, 421pp.

Cross-references: *Arid Cycle*; *Deflation*; *Hamada*; *Holocene*; *Lake Eyre*; *Ventifacts*; *Wind Action*. Vol. II: *Climatic Variations (Historical Record)*.

"When streams raise their courses above the level of their flood plains, their tributaries cannot join the main stream. In some cases such tributaries become blocked to form lakes but usually the tributaries flow along the side of the flood plain until they reach some point farther downstream where the main stream swings against the valley wall. Many of the tributaries of the Mississippi behave in this manner. Because the Yazoo River is a good case, it is taken as the type example."

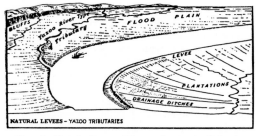

FIG. 1. Sketch (from oblique air view) of the type Yazoo River in the Mississippi Valley (from Lobeck, 1939). (By permission of McGraw-Hill Book Co., N.Y.)

A necessary condition appears to be the "old-age" stage in stream development when natural levees are building up the river banks above the mean level of the flood plain, which in turn is bounded by bluffs. In this way, tributary streams become systematically shifted downstream.

RHODES W. FAIRBRIDGE

YAZOO RIVERS OR STREAMS

A term proposed by Lobeck (1939), a Yazoo river or stream is one that flows on the flood plain of a larger river, running subparallel to it, and eventually joining it. As explained by Lobeck:

References

Lobeck, A. K., 1939, "Geomorphology," New York, McGraw-Hill Book Co., 731pp.

Cross-references: *Flood Plain*; *Levee*; *Oxbow Lake*.

YOUTH—MATURITY—OLD AGE

In any theoretical cycle of landform development, some method must be used to signify the stage reached by a given landscape. *Youth, maturity* and *old age* were the three stages used by W. M. Davis (1899) when he devised the first of these cycles, the so called "Geographic Cycles" (see *Cycles, Geomorphic*: also *Process—Structure—Stage*). All the cyclical landform models suggested since then have followed his lead, though the third stage may be omitted where unnecessary, and there may be subdivision of a stage by adding the prefix "early" or "late."

Even though the concept of three stages would appear to be very easy to apply, it can still cause difficulties. The original cycle of Davis is actually three cycles combined into one. (1) There is the cycle of drainage development; (2) the cycle of landscape development, and (3) the cycle of slope development. It is most unlikely that any two of these cycles will reach maturity at once (see Sparks, 1960). Thus the plains of southern Russia exhibit an early stage in landscape development, an early mature stage in slope development, and a mature stage in river development. On the other hand, the Himalayas exhibit a mature stage of landscape

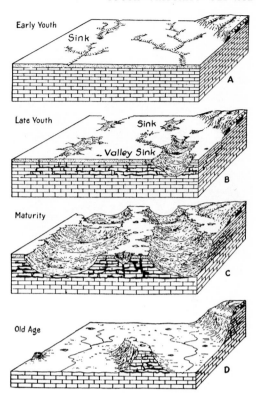

FIG. 2. Four stages in the life cycle of a limestone plateau having cryptorheic or underground drainage (from Lobeck). It should be stressed that the "stages" are really quite arbitrary, and simply convenient terms for expressing a relative degree of denudation to a given base level. (By permission of McGraw-Hill Book Co., N.Y.)

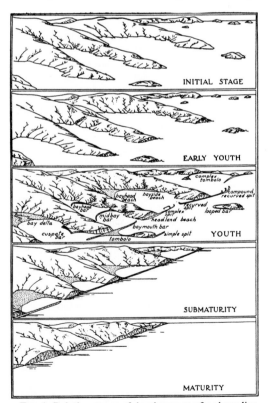

FIG. 1. Relative stages of development of a shore line of submergence (assuming soft, easily eroded formations). (After Johnson, from Lobeck, 1939; by permission of McGraw-Hill Book Co., N.Y.)

FIG. 3. Youthful relief. Initial drainage of dendritic pattern developed over a late Pleistocene loess landscape in Nebraska. Note that the gullies do not yet reach the interfluves. Age of relief: about 15,000 years. (Photo: John Moore).

FIG. 4. Mature relief. Dissected Pliocene-Pleistocene sediments, Wanganui-Rangitikei area, North Island, New Zealand. Ruahine Range, of Mesozoic greywacke, in background. (Photo: S. N. Beatus, New Zealand Geological Survey).

FIG. 5. Old-age relief. Ancient peneplain on Precambrian metasediments. Note traces of earlier drainage systems partly engulfed by drifting sand. (Air photo over Saudi Arabia, location 22°35′N, 44°30′E).

development with a youthful stage in river development. The slopes vary from a mature stage on soft materials to an early youthful stage on very resistant rocks.

More recently Hack and Goodlett (1960) have shown that any study of landform development should integrate the various morphologic components into a unified system. Thus, when studying a drainage basin, it is necessary to evaluate both slopes *and* channels, and to establish their interaction, in order to create a coherent picture of landscape evolution.

A second problem arises when two authors independently decide that a new cycle is needed for the same group of landscape features, and they choose different positions for the various stage boundaries. This happened in the case of the karst cycle of erosion (see Thornbury, 1954, Ch. 13). Beede in 1911 published a cycle divided into youth, maturity and old age. In youth, there are the beginnings of underground drainage with the development of *dolines* (q.v.). Maturity is characterized by the karst plain phase with a maximum development of sinkholes and underground drainage. Only major entrenched streams crossing the area maintain their courses. His stage of old age corresponded to the decline of karst features and the reappearance of the drainage.

Then in 1918, Cvijić published independently a cycle which agreed on the youth-maturity boundary but which used late maturity for all the old-age stage of Beede except that in which the drainage is

entirely exposed at the surface and only a few hums remain. Since Cvijić published in a less obscure journal, his views are commonly followed in the later literature, often without reference to the clash in interpretation.

Such clashes in interpretation obscure the more fundamental idea behind the series of stages youth—maturity—old age, namely that landforms undergo *sequential development*, or evolution; terms such as youth are therefore relative, somewhat arbitrary, and useful primarily as conceptual aids.

STUART A. HARRIS

References

Davis, W. M., 1899, "The geographical cycle," *Geograph. J.*, **14**, 481–504.

Hack, J. T., and Goodlett, J. C., 1960, "Geomorphology and forest ecology of a mountain region in the central Appalachians," *U.S. Geol. Surv. Profess. Paper* **347**, 66pp.

Lobeck, A. K., 1939, "Geomorphology," New York, McGraw-Hill Book Co., 731pp.

Sparks, B. W., 1960, "Geomorphology," London, Longmans Green & Co., 371pp.

Thornbury, W. D., 1954, "Principles of Geomorphology," New York, John Wiley & Sons, 618pp.

Cross-references: *Base Level*; *Cycles, Geomorphic*; *Dolina*; *Equilibrium in Geomorphology*; *Grade, Graded Stream*; *Land Mass and Major Landform Classification*; *Process—Structure—Stage*; *Rivers*; *Surell's Law*.

ZONATION OF TERRESTRIAL ECOLOGIC BELTS—*See* pr Vol. VI.

INDEX*

Abandoned meander channel, 798
Abers, 943
Abies, 1105
Ablation, 1047, 1145. *See also* pr Vol. VI
Ablation drift, 1
ABLATION MORAINE, ABLATION TILL, **1**, 392, 396,
    397, 437, 443, 547, 711, 1047
ABRASION, **1**, 31, 40, 246, 262, 279, 299, 321, 431,
    434, 444, 457, 655, 664, 667, 860, 964, 1192,
    1224, 1233
Abrasion plain, 850
Abrolhos Islands, 6, 39
Abrolhos Submergence, 192, 533
Absolute Age of Quaternary deposits Commission
    (of INQUA), 562
Absolute relief, 745
Absorption, 283, 313
Abspülung, 991
Abstraction, 1054
Abyssal gap, 1093
Abyssal hills, 1082. *See also* Vol. I
Abyssal plain, 526, 614, 1082. *See also* Vol. I
Abyssinian Plateau, 878
Acacia aneura, 297, 979, 1237
Acadian phase, 748
Accelerated denudation, erosion, 262, 517
Acceleration erosion. *See* GULLY EROSION
Accidental aspects, 633
"Accidents," 414
Accordance-type morphostructure, 854
Accretion, 1235
Accretion of fold belts, 738
Accumulation, mountain of, 751
Accumulation rate, 269, 664
Accumulation sector, 893
Acer, 528
Acheulian culture, 1130
Acid action, acidity, 204, 211
Acquifer, 608, 649
Active layer, 230, 371, 833, 845
Actualism, 262. *See also* pr Vol. VI
Adams Bridge, 1156
Adelaide-Flinder-Macdonnell System, 750
Adélie Island, 575
Adhémar, J. F., 475
Adirondack Dome, 282
Adirondack Mountains, 449, 460
Adji- Darya, 579
Adjustment to structure, 286, 316
Adobe, 676
Advancing coast, 139, 154, 659, 894
Adventive cones, 1197
Aeolian, (aeolianite). *See* Eolian, Eolianite

Aeolian processes. *See* ARID CYCLE; SAND DUNES,
    WIND ACTION
Aerial photograph, 84, 415. *See also* Air photography
Aestus, 325
Afghanistan, 994. *See also* pr Vol. VIII
Äfja, 602
Africa, 483, 734, 936, 1171, 1192, 1235. *See also* pr
    Vol. VIII
    statistics, 179
African Rift Valley, 243, 303
African River Systems, 261
Aftonian Stage, 919
Agassiz Lake, 451, 453. *See also* GLACIAL LAKE
    AGASSIZ
Agassiz, Jean, 411
Agassiz, Louis, 476. *See also* pr Vol. VIII
Age, 919
Age of Man, 912
Age of Metals, 525
Agents of erosion, 318, 891
Agglomerates, 1200, 1205
AGGRADATION, **2**, 49, 64, 129, 312, 456, 485, 519,
    1002, 1125, 1142, 1184, 1224
Aggradation plains, 130
Aggradation stages, 1127
Aggrade, 894
Agricultural terracing, 399
Agulhas Shelf, 182
Aiguilles, 747
Ailsa Crag, 551
Air gap, 1055, 1236
Air photography, 287, 628, 641, 664
Akchagyl Sea, 112
Alabama, 1152
Alaska, 22, 1107, 1150, 1178, 1191
Alaskan arctic coastal plain, 792
Alaskan Arctic Slope, 835
Alaskan Rockies, 748
Alaskan type glacier, 1190
Alaskides, 748
Albany, Lake, 451. *See also* GLACIAL LAKE ALBANY
Albe, 752
Albedo, 1, 914. *See also* Vol. II
Alberta, 1048
Aleutian Arc, 566
Aleutian Arc—Alaskan Range, 748
Alewife, 502
Algae, 4, 19, 36, 127, 204, 245, 513, 580, 767, 1173
Algal Biscuits, 4
Algal limestone, 779
Algal mats, 4
Algal pavement, 5
ALGAL REEFS, **3**

* Words listed in small capital letters represent titles of articles; boldface numbers refer to pages on which
articles begin.